DICTIONARY OF ORGANIC COMPOUNDS

Volume III

DICTIONARY OF ORGANIC COMPOUNDS

THE CONSTITUTION AND PHYSICAL AND CHEMICAL PROPERTIES OF THE PRINCIPAL CARBON COMPOUNDS AND THEIR DERIVATIVES, TOGETHER WITH THE RELEVANT LITERATURE REFERENCES

VOLUME THREE

NAPHTHACARBAZOLE — ZYGADENINE

Edited by

I. M. HEILBRON, D.S.O., D.Sc., LL.D., F.I.C., F.R.S.

Professor of Organic Chemistry at the Imperial College of Science and Technology, London

AND

H. M. BUNBURY, M.Sc., F.I.C. *Barrister-at-Law*

Imperial Chemical Industries Ltd.

Assistant Editor

W. E. JONES, Ph.D., B.Sc., A.I.C.

Authors

J. H. BEYNON, Ph.D., M.Sc., D. H. COFFEY, M.Sc., W. DORAN, M.Sc., A.I.C., D. H. HEY, D.Sc., Ph.D., F.I.C., E. R. H. JONES, Ph.D., B.Sc., A. LOWE, Ph.D., M.Sc., A.I.C., A. McGOOKIN, Ph.D., B.Sc., A.I.C.

Assistant Authors

T. BARR, B.Sc., A.I.C., P. G. CARTER, Ph.D., B.Sc., J. L. GRIEVE, Ph.D., B.Sc., A. S. HAIGH, Ph.D., B.Sc., A.I.C., S. H. HARPER, Ph.D., B.Sc., A.R.C.S.

Readers

J. W. BATTY, B.Sc., E. C. BUTTERWORTH, M.Sc., E. HAWORTH, M.Sc., T. KENNEDY, M.Sc., R. WILKINSON, M.Sc., H. R. WRIGHT, Ph.D., B.Sc., A.I.C.

1943

NEW YORK: OXFORD UNIVERSITY PRESS

PRINTED IN GREAT BRITAIN

TABLE OF ABBREVIATIONS

A	Acid (A_2, two mols of acid).
A°	Angstrom unit. (10^{-8} cm.).
Abs. EtOH	Absolute alcohol.
AcOH	Acetic acid.
Ac_2O	Acetic anhydride.
AcOEt	Ethyl acetate.
Add.	Additive.
Addn.	Addition.
A.G.F.A.	Aktien-Gesellschaft für Anilinfabrikation.
Alc.	Alcohol, alcoholic.
Alc. NH_3	Alcoholic ammonia.
Alk.	Alkali, alkaline.
[α]	Specific rotation.
Amorph.	Amorphous.
Anhyd.	Anhydrous.
Aq.	Aqueous.
Atm.	Atmosphere(s), atmospheric.
B	Base (B_2, two mols of base).
Badische	Badische Anilin und Sodafabrik.
Belg. P.	Belgian Patent.
B.D.C.	British Dyestuffs Corporation.
Bibl.	Bibliography.
B.p.	Boiling point.
C_p	Constant pressure.
C_v	Constant volume.
Cal.	Calories.
Can. P.	Canadian Patent.
Col.	Colour, coloration.
Comb.	Combustion.
Comp.	Compound.
Conc.	Concentrated.
Corr.	Corrected.
Crit.	Critical.
Cryst.	Crystals, crystalline, crystallise.
$(COOH)_2$	Oxalic acid.
$(CH_2COOH)_2$	Succinic acid.
D	Density.
d	Dextrorotatory.
dl	Racemic. Optically inactive by external compensation.
Decomp.	Decomposed, decomposition.
Deriv.	Derivative.
Dil.	Dilute, dilution.
Diss.	Dissolves, dissolved.
Dist.	Distil, distillation.
D.R.P.	German Patent.
E.P.	English (British) Patent.
Et	Ethyl.
Et_2O	Ether (diethyl ether).
EtOH	Ethyl alcohol.
Fluor.	Fluoresces, fluorescence.
F.p.	Freezing point.
F.P.	French Patent.
Form.	Formation.
γ	10^{-6} gm. or 10^{-3} mgm. (microgrammes).
gm.	Gramme(s).
Hyd.	Hydrolyses, hydrolysed, hydrolysis.
i	Optically inactive by internal compensation.
I.C.I.	Imperial Chemical Industries.
I.G.	Interessen Gemeinschaft Farbenindustrie Aktien-Gesellschaft.
Insol.	Insoluble.

I.U.	International Unit.
Jap. P.	Japanese Patent.
k	Dissociation constant.
l	Lævorotatory.
Liq.	Liquid.
m	Meta (position).
Max.	Maximum.
Me	Methyl.
MeOH	Methyl alcohol.
Me_2CO	Acetone.
Min.	Mineral (inorganic).
Misc.	Miscible.
M.L.B.	Meister, Lucius, & Brüning.
mm.	Millimetres.
Mod.	Moderately.
Mol.	Molecule, molecular, molar.
M.p.	Melting point.
ms	Meso (position).
MW	Molecular weight (formula weight).
mgm.	Milligramme(s).
mμ	Millimicron. (10^{-7} cm.).
n	Normal (chain).
n_D	Refractive index (D line, etc.).
NaHg	Sodium amalgam.
NH_3	Ammonia, aqueous ammonia.
$NH_3.AgNO_3$	Ammoniacal silver nitrate.
o	Ortho (position).
Ord.	Ordinary.
Org.	Organic.
Ox.	Oxidise, oxidation.
p	Para (position).
P	Patent.
Part.	Partly, partial.
Pet. ether	Petroleum ether.
$PhNO_2$	Nitrobenzene.
PhOH	Phenol.
Ppd.	Precipitated.
Ppt.	Precipitate.
Pptn.	Precipitation.
Prac.	Practically.
Press.	Pressure(s).
ψ	Pseudo.
Py	Pyridine.
r	Racemic.
Red.	Reduce, reduction.
Ref.	Reference.
Russ.P.	Russian Patent.
S.C.I.	Societé pour l'industrie chimique à Basle.
Sec.	Secondary.
Sol.	Soluble, solution.
Spar.	Sparingly.
Sp. gr.	Specific gravity.
Sp. heat	Specific heat.
Suppl.	Supplement.
Sym.	Symmetrical.
Temp.	Temperature(s).
Tert.	Tertiary.
Undecomp.	Undecomposed.
Unsym.	Unsymmetrical.
UV.	Ultraviolet.
Vac.	Vacuum.
Vap.	Vaporisation.
Vol.	Volume.

JOURNAL ABBREVIATIONS

Journals not listed here are given their full titles in the text.

Acta Phytochim.	Acta Phytochimica (Japan).
Am. Chem. J.	American Chemical Journal.
Am. J. Pharm.	American Journal of Pharmacy.
Am. J. Sci.	American Journal of Science.
Anales soc. españ fís. quím.	Anales de la sociedad española de física y química.
Angew. Chem.	Angewandte Chemie.
Ann.	Annalen der Chemie.
Ann. chim.	Annales de chimie.
Ann. chim. applicata	Annali di chimica applicata.
Ann. chim. phys.	Annales de chimie et de physique.
Ann. phys.	Annales de physique.
Ann. Physik	Annalen der Physik.
Ann. Rev. Biochem.	Annual Review of Biochemistry.
Arch. Pharm.	Archiv der Pharmazie (und Berichte der deutschen pharmazeutischen Gesellschaft).
Arkiv Kemi, Mineral. Geol.	Arkiv för Kemi, Mineralogi och Geologi.
Atti accad. Lincei	Atti della reale accademia nazionale dei Lincei.
Ber.	Berichte der deutschen chemischen Gesellschaft.
Ber. deut. pharm. Ges.	Berichte der deutschen pharmazeutischen Gesellschaft.
Ber. ges. Physiol. exptl. Pharmakol.	Berichte über die gesamte Physiologie und experimentelle Pharmakologie.
Biochem. J.	Biochemical Journal.
Biochem. Z.	Biochemische Zeitschrift.
Biol. Zentr.	Biologisches Zentralblatt.
Brit. Chem. Abstracts	British Chemical Abstracts.
Bull. Chem. Soc. Japan	Bulletin of the Chemical Society of Japan.
Bull. Imp. Inst.	Bulletin of the Imperial Institute.
Bull. Inst. Phys. Chem. Research (Tokyo).	Bulletin of the Institute of Physical and Chemical Research, Toyko.
Bull. sci. acad. roy. Belg.	Bulletin de la classe des sciences, academie royale de Belgique.
Bull. sci. pharmacol.	Bulletin des sciences pharmacologiques.
Bull. soc. chim.	Bulletin de la société chimique de France.
Bull. soc. chim. Belg.	Bulletin de la société chimique de Belgique.
Bull. soc. chim. biol.	Bulletin de la société de chimie biologique.
Can. Chem. Met.	Canadian Chemistry and Metallurgy.
Can. J. Research	Canadian Journal of Research.
Chem. Abstracts	Chemical Abstracts (of the American Chemical Society).
Chem. Ind.	Die Chemische Industrie.
Chem. Met. Eng.	Chemical and Metallurgical Engineering.
J. Indian Chem. Soc.	Journal of the Indian Chemical Society.
J. Indian Inst. Sci.	Journal of the Indian Institute of Science.
Chem. News	Chemical News (and Journal of Industrial Science).
Chem.-Tech. Rundschau	Chemische-Technische Rundschau.
Chem. Trade J.	Chemical Trade Journal (and Chemical Engineer).
Chem. Umschau	Chemische Umschau (auf dem Gebiete der Fette, Oele, Wachse, und Harze). Now Fettchemische Umschau.
Chem. Weekblad	Chemisch Weekblad.
Chem. Zentr.	Chemisches Zentralblatt.
Chem.-Ztg.	Chemiker-Zeitung.
Compt. rend.	Comptes rendus (hebdomadaires des séances de l'académie des sciences).
Compt. rend. acad. sci. U.R.S.S.	Comptes rendus de l'Académie des Sciences de l'U.R.S.S.
Compt. rend. soc. biol.	Comptes rendus des séances de la société de biologie.
Dinglers polytech. J.	Dinglers polytechnisches Journal.
Fettchem. Umschau	Fettchemische Umschau.
Gazz. chim. ital.	Gazzetta chimica italiana.
Giorn. chim. applicata	Giornale di chimica applicata.
Giorn. chim. ind.	Giornale di chimica industriale.
Giorn. chim. ind. applicata	Giornale di chimica industriale ed applicata.
Helv. Chim. Acta	Helvetica Chimica Acta.
Ind. Eng. Chem.	Industrial and Engineering Chemistry.
Jahresber. Fortschr. Chem.	Jahresbericht über die Fortschritte der Chemie.
J. Am. Chem. Soc.	Journal of the American Chemical Society.
J. Am. Pharm. Assocn.	Journal of the American Pharmaceutical Association.
J. Applied Chem., U.S.S.R.	Journal of Applied Chemistry, U.S.S.R.
Japan. J. Chem.	Japanese Journal of Chemistry.
J. Bact.	Journal of Bacteriology.
J. Biochem. Japan.	Journal of Biochemistry of Japan.
J. Biol. Chem.	Journal of Biological Chemistry.
J. Chem. Education	Journal of Chemical Education.
J. Chem. Ind. Japan	Journal of Chemical Industry (Japan). Now J. Soc. Chem. Ind. Japan.
J. Chem. Physics	Journal of Chemical Physics.
J. Chem. Soc.	Journal of the Chemical Society (London).
J. Chem. Soc. Abstracts	Abstracts of the Chemical Society (London).
J. Chem. Soc. Japan	Journal of the Chemical Society of Japan.
J. chim. phys.	Journal de chimie physique.
J. Chinese Chem. Soc.	Journal of the Chinese Chemical Society.
J. Gen. Chem. U.S.S.R.	Journal of General Chemistry, U.S.S.R.
Proc. Chem. Soc.	Proceedings of the Chemical Society (London).
Proc. Roy. Soc.	Proceedings of the Royal Society (London).

J. Org. Chem.	Journal of Organic Chemistry.
J. Pharmacol.	Journal of Pharmacology and Experimental Therapeutics.
J. pharm. Belg.	Journal de pharmacie de Belgique.
J. pharm. chim.	Journal de pharmacie et de chimie.
J. Pharm. Soc. Japan	Journal of the Pharmaceutical Society (Japan).
J. Phys. Chem.	Journal of Physical Chemistry.
J. prakt. Chem.	Journal für praktische Chemie.
J. Proc. Roy. Soc. N.S. Wales	Journal and Proceedings of the Royal Society of New South Wales.
J. Russ. Phys.-Chem. Soc.	Journal of the Russian Physical-Chemical Society.
J. Soc. Chem. Ind.	Journal of the Society of Chemical Industry.
J. Soc. Chem. Ind. Japan	Journal of the Society of Chemical Industry (Japan).
J. Soc. Dyers Colourists	Journal of the Society of Dyers and Colourists.
Monatsh.	Monatshefte für Chemie und verwandte Teile anderer Wissenschaften.
Mem. Coll. Sci., Kyoto Imp. Univ.	Memoirs of the College of Science, Kyoto Imperial University.
Naturwiss.	Naturwissenschaften.
Org. Chem. Ind. U.S.S.R.	Promischlennosti Organitscheskoi Chimii, U.S.S.R.
Pharm. J.	Pharmaceutical Journal and Pharmacist.
Pharm. Ztg.	Die deutsche Pharmazeutische Zeitung.
Pharm. Zentralhalle.	Pharmazeutische Zentralhalle.
Phil. Mag.	Philosophical Magazine and Journal of Science.
Proc. Acad. Sci., Amsterdam	Proceedings of the Royal Academy of Sciences of Amsterdam.
Proc. Imper. Acad., Tokyo	Proceedings of the Imperial Academy, Tokyo.
Quart. J. Indian Chem. Soc.	Quarterly Journal of the Indian Chemical Society.
Quart. J. Pharm. Pharmacol.	Quarterly Journal of Pharmacy and Pharmacology.
Rec. trav. chim.	Recueil des travaux chimiques des Pays-Bas.
Rev. chim. ind.	Revue de chimie industrielle.
Rev. prod. chim.	Revue des produits chimiques.
Sci. Papers Inst. Phys. Chem. Research, Tokyo	Scientific Papers of the Institute of Physical and Chemical Research (Tokyo).
Sci. reps. Natl. Tsinghua Univ.	Science Reports of the National Tsinghua University.
Sci. reps. Natl. Univ. Peking	Science Reports of the National University of Peking.
Sitzb. Akad. Wiss. Wien	Sitzungsberichte Akademie der Wissenschaften in Wien.
Trans. Faraday Soc.	Transactions of the Faraday Society.
Trans. Roy. Soc.	Transactions of the Royal Society (London).
Trans. Roy. Soc. Canada.	Transactions of the Royal Society of Canada.
Z. anal. Chem.	Zeitschrift für analytische Chemie.
Z. angew. Chem.	Zeitschrift für angewandte Chemie. Now Angewandte Chemie.
Z. anorg. allgem. Chem.	Zeitschrift für anorganische und allgemeine Chemie.
Z. Chem.	Zeitschrift für Chemie.
Z. Elektrochem.	Zeitschrift für Elektrochemie und angewandte physikalische Chemie.
Z. ges Naturwiss.	Zeitschrift für die gesamte Naturwissenschaft.
Z. physik. Chem.	Zeitschrift für physikalische Chemie.
Z. physiol. Chem.	Zeitschrift für physiologische Chemie (Hoppe-Seyler).

LIST OF SUBSTITUENTS

In the following table is given a list of the principal substituent groups as they are used in the dictionary.

1	—F	Fluoro
2	—Cl	Chloro
3	—Br	Bromo
4	—I	Iodo
5	—NO	Nitroso
6	$—NO_2$	Nitro
7	$—N{=}N{\rightleftarrows}N$	Azido, Triazo
8	—OH	Hydroxy (*followed by* $—OCH_3$ Methoxy, $—OC_2H_5$ Ethoxy, $—O{\cdot}CH_2{\cdot}O—$ methylenedioxy, $—OC_6H_5$ Phenoxy, $—O{\cdot}CO{\cdot}CH_3$, Acetoxy, *etc. in the order of the group attached to the oxygen*)
9	—SH	Mercapto
10	—SO	Thionyl
11	$—SO_2$	Sulphonyl
12	—SCN	Thiocyano
13	═O (in C—CO—C)	Keto
14	>NH	Imino
15	═N·OH	Isonitroso, Oximino
16	—S—	Thio
17	$—SO_3H$	Sulpho
18	$—NH_2$	Amino
19	$—NH{\cdot}C_6H_5$	Anilino, Phenylimino
20	$—NH{\cdot}C_6H_4{\cdot}CH_3$	Toluidino
21	$—NH{\cdot}CO{\cdot}NH_2$	Ureido
22	$—NH{\cdot}C({:}NH){\cdot}NH_2$	Guanidino
23	—NH·OH	Hydroxylamino
24	$—NH{\cdot}NH_2$	Hydrazino
25	—NH·NH—	Hydrazo
26	—N:N—	Azo
27	·N⋮N]·X	Diazonium, Diazo (X = OH, Cl, etc.)
28	$—\underset{\ddot{O}}{N}{=}N—\ \left(—\underset{\downarrow O}{N}{=}N—\right)$	Azoxy
29	—As:As—	Arseno
30	—NH·N:N— (*open*)	Diazoamino
31	—NH·N:N— (*cyclic*)	Azimino
32	$—CH_3$	Methyl
33	$—CH_2OH$	Hydroxymethyl, Methylol
34	$—C_2H_5$	Ethyl

35	$—CH_2·CH_2·CH_3$	*n*-Propyl
36	$—CH(CH_3)_2$	Isopropyl
37	$—CH_2·CH_2·CH_2·CH_3$	*n*-Butyl
38	$—CH_2·CH(CH_3)_2$	Isobutyl
39	$—C(CH_3)_3$	*ert.*-Butyl
40	$—CH_2·[CH_2]_3·CH_3$	*n*-Amyl
41	$—CH(C_2H_5)_2$	*sec.-n*-Amyl
42	$—CH_2·CH_2·CH(CH_3)_2$	Isoamyl
43	$—CH_2·CH<^{CH_3}_{C_2H_5}$	*active* Amyl
44	$—C(CH_3)(C_2H_5)(CH_3)$	*tert.*-Amyl
45	$—CH_2·[CH_2]_4·CH_3$	*n*-Hexyl
46	$—CH_2·[CH_2]_2·CH(CH_3)_2$	Isohexyl
47	$—CH_2·[CH_2]_5·CH_3$	*n*-Heptyl, Oenanthyl
48	$—CH_2·[CH_2]_3·CH(CH_3)_2$	Isoheptyl
49	$—CH_2·[CH_2]_6·CH_3$	Octyl, Capryl
50	$—CH_2·[CH_2]_7·CH_3$	Nonyl
51	$—CH_2·[CH_2]_8·CH_3$	Decyl
52	$—CH_2·[CH_2]_9·CH_3$	Undecyl
53	$—CH_2·[CH_2]_{10}·CH_3$	Dodecyl
54	$—CH_2·[CH_2]_{11}·CH_3$	Tridecyl
55	$—CH_2·[CH_2]_{12}·CH_3$	Tetradecyl
56	$—CH_2·[CH_2]_{13}·CH_3$	Pentadecyl
57	$—CH_2·[CH_2]_{14}·CH_3$	Cetyl, Hexadecyl
58	$—CH_2·[CH_2]_{15}·CH_3$	Heptadecyl
59	$—CH_2·[CH_2]_{16}·CH_3$	Octadecyl
60	$—CH_2·[CH_2]_{18}·CH_3$	Eicosyl
61	$—CH_2·[CH_2]_{24}·CH_3$	Ceryl
62	$—CH_2·[CH_2]_{28}·CH_3$	Myricyl, Melissyl
63	$—CH<^{CH_2}_{CH_2}$	Cyclopropyl (*followed by* Cyclobutyl, Cyclopentyl, Cyclohexyl, Cycloheptyl (Suberyl) *in that order*)
64	$—CH:CH_2$	Vinyl
65	$—CH:CH·CH_3$	Propenyl
66	$—C(:CH_2)·CH_3$	Isopropenyl
67	$—CH_2·CH:CH_2$	Allyl
68	$—CH:CH·CH_2·CH_3$	α-Butenyl
69	$—CH_2·CH:CH·CH_3$	β-Butenyl, Crotyl
70	$—CH_2·CH_2·CH:CH_2$	γ-Butenyl, Allylomethyl
71	$—CH_2·[CH_2]_7·CH:CH·[CH_2]_7·CH_3$	Octadecenyl
72	$—C⋮CH$	Acetylenyl, Ethinyl
73	$—CH_2·C⋮CH$	Propargyl
74	$—C_6H_5$	Phenyl
75	$—C_6H_4·CH_3$	Tolyl
76	$—CH_2·C_6H_5$	Benzyl
77	$—CH_2·C_6H_4·OH$ (*-o*)	Salicyl
78	$—CH_2·C_6H_4·OCH_3$ (*-p*)	Anisyl
79	$—CH_2·CH_2·C_6H_5$	Phenylethyl
80	$—CH_2·C_6H_4·CH_3$	Xylyl
81	$—C_6H_4·CH(CH_3)_2$	Cumyl
82	$—C_6H_2(CH_3)_3$ (1 : 2 : 4)	ψ-Cumyl
83	$—C_6H_2(CH_3)_3$ (1 : 3 : 5)	Mesityl
84	$—CH:CH·C_6H_5$	Styryl
85	$—CH_2·CH:CH·C_6H_5$	Cinnamyl
86	$—C_{10}H_7$	Naphthyl
87	$—C_6H_4·C_6H_5$	Diphenylyl, Xenyl
88	$—CH(C_6H_5)_2$	Benzhydryl, Diphenylmethyl
89	$—C_{14}H_9$	Anthryl, anthranyl
90	$—C_{14}H_9$	Phenanthryl
91	$—C(C_6H_5)_3$	Triphenylmethyl
92	$—CH_2·CH_2—$	Ethylene, Dimethylene
93	$—CH(CH_3)·CH_2—$	Propylene
94	$—CH_2·CH_2·CH_2—$	Trimethylene
95	$—CH_2·CH_2·CH_2·CH_2—$	Tetramethylene
96	$—C(CH_3)_2·CH_2—$	Isobutylene
97	$—CH_2·[CH_2]_3·CH_2—$	Pentamethylene
98	$—CH_2[·CH_2]_4·CH_2—$	Hexamethylene
99	$—CH_2·[CH_2]_5·CH_2—$	Heptamethylene
100	$—CH_2·[CH_2]_6·CH_2—$	Octamethylene
101	$—CH:CH—$	Vinylene
102	$—C_6H_4—$	Phenylene
103	$—C_6H_3(CH_3)—$	Tolylene
104	$—CH_2—$	Methylene
105	$=CH·CH_3$	Ethylidene
106	$=CH·CH_2·CH_3$	Propylidene
107	$=C(CH_3)_2$	Isopropylidene
108	$=CH·CH_2·CH_2·CH_3$	Butylidene
109	$=CH·CH(CH_3)_2$	Isobutylidene
110	$H_2C<^{CH_2—CH_2}_{CH_2—CH_2}>C=$	Cyclohexylidene
111	$=C:CH_2$	Vinylidene
112	$=CH·CH:CH_2$	Allylidene
113	$CH_3·CH:CH·CH=$	Crotylidene
114	$=CH·C_6H_5$	Benzylidene
115	$=CH·C_6H_4·OH$ (*-o*)	Salicylidene
116	$=CH·C_6H_4·OCH_3$ (*-p*)	Anisylidene
117	$=CH·C_6H_4·CH(CH_3)_2$ (*-p*)	Cuminylidene
118	$=CH·CH:CH·C_6H_5$	Cinnamylidene
119	$—CH_2·CO·CH_3$	Acetonyl
120	$—CH_2·CO·C_6H_5$	Phenacyl
121	$—CH_2·CO·C_6H_4·CH_3$	Tolacyl
122	$C_6H_5·\underset{\vert}{C}H·CO·C_6H_5$	Desyl
123	$—CHO$	Aldehydo, Formyl
124	$\equiv CH$	Methinyl
125	$—CO·CH_3$	Acetyl, Aceto
126	$—CO·CH_2·CH_3$,	Propionyl
127	$—CO·CH_2·CH_2·CH_3$	Butyryl
128	$—CO·CH(CH_3)_2$	Isobutyryl
129	$—CO·CH_2·[CH_2]_2·CH_3$	Valeryl
130	$—CO·CH_2·CH(CH_3)_2$	Isovaleryl
131	$—CO·CH_2·[CH_2]_3·CH_3$	Caproyl
132	$—CO·CH_2·[CH_2]_{13}·CH_3$	Palmityl
133	$—CO·CH_2·[CH_2]_{15}·CH_3$	Stearyl
134	$—CO·[CH_2]_7·CH:CH·[CH_2]_7·CH_3$	Oleyl
135	$—CO·C_6H_5$	Benzoyl
136	$—CO·C_6H_4·OH$ (*-o*)	Salicyloyl
137	$—CO·C_6H_4·OCH_3$ (*-p*)	Anisoyl
138	$—CO·CH_2·C_6H_5$	Phenylacetyl
139	$—CO·C_6H_4·CH_3$	Toluyl
140	$—CO·CH:CH·C_6H_5$	Cinnamoyl
141	$—CO·C_{10}H_7$	Naphthoyl
142	$—CO·CO—$	Oxalyl
143	$—CO·CH_2·CO—$	Malonyl
144	$—CO·CH_2·CH_2·CO—$	Succinyl
145	$—CO·C_6H_4·CO—$	Phthaloyl, Isophthaloyl, Terephthaloyl
146	$—COOH$ ($—CO·OCH_3$, $—CO·OC_2H_5$, etc.)	Carboxy, (Carbomethoxy, Carbethoxy, etc.)
147	$—CO·NH_2$	Carbamyl
148	$>CO$	Carbonyl
149	$—C(:NH)·NH_2$	Guanyl
150	$—CN$	Cyano
151	$—CO·CH_2NH_2$	Glycyl
152	$—CO·CH(NH_2)·CH_3$	α-Alanyl
153	$—CO·CH_2·CH_2NH_2$	β-Alanyl
154	$—CO·CH(NH_2)·CH(CH_3)_2$	Valyl
155	$—CO·CH(NH_2)·CH_2·CH(CH_3)_2$	Leucyl
156	$—CO·CH_2·NH·CO·C_6H_5$	Hippuryl
157	$—C_4H_3O$	Furyl
158	$—C_4H_3S$	Thienyl
159	$—CH_2·C_4H_3O$	Furfuryl
160	$=CH·C_4H_3O$	Furfurylidene
161	$—CO·C_4H_3O$	Furoyl, Pyromucyl
162	$—C_4H_3NH$	Pyrryl
163	$—C_5H_4N$	Pyridyl

DICTIONARY OF ORGANIC COMPOUNDS

N

2 : 3-Naphthacarbazole

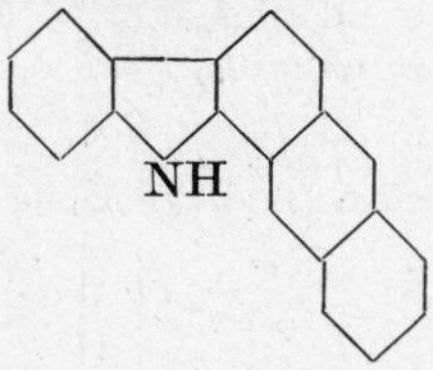

$C_{20}H_{13}N$ MW, 267

Yellow leaflets with greenish fluor. M.p. 325°. Very spar. sol. org. solvents. Conc. H_2SO_4 ⟶ deep blue col.

Braun, Bayer, *Ann.*, 1929, **472**, 97, 101.

Naphthacene (2 : 3-*Benzanthracene*)

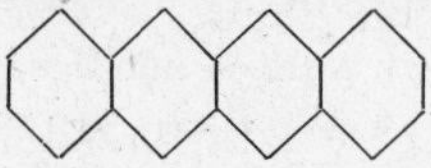

$C_{18}H_{12}$ MW, 228

Orange-red leaflets from xylene. M.p. 341° (335–6°, 331°). Sublimes ⟶ greenish-yellow vapour. Sol. conc. H_2SO_4 ⟶ dull green col. Insol. C_6H_6. Fuming HNO_3 ⟶ naphthacenequinone.

Clar, *Ber.*, 1932, **65**, 517.
Dziewoński, Ritt, *Chem. Abstracts*, 1928, **22**, 2561.
Deichler, Weizmann, *Ber.*, 1903, **36**, 552.

Naphthacenequinone (2 : 3-*Benzanthraquinone*, lin-*benzanthraquinone*, 2 : 3-*phthaloylnaphthalene*)

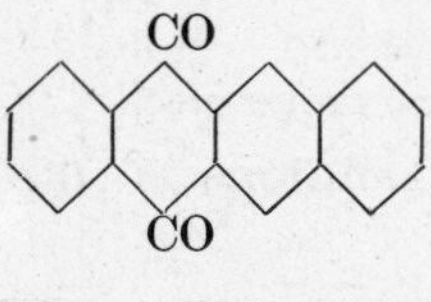

$C_{18}H_{10}O_2$ MW, 258

Cryst. from $PhNO_2$ in yellow needles. M.p. 294° (285°). Sublimes. Sol. conc. H_2SO_4 ⟶ red-violet col. Spar. sol. hot C_6H_6, hot Me_2CO. Very spar. sol. AcOH. Sn + AcOH ⟶ yellow needles of the anthrone, m.p. 196°, sol. conc. H_2SO_4 to bright red sol. Sn + Ac_2O + AcONa ⟶ orange needles of naphthacenehydroquinone-diacetate, m.p. 269°.

Fieser, *J. Am. Chem. Soc.*, 1931, **53**, 2336.
Waldmann, Mathiowetz, *Ber.*, 1931, **64**, 1713.

Naphthacetin.
See under 4-Amino-1-naphthol.

Naphthacetol.
See under 4-Amino-1-naphthol.

α:β-Naphthacoumarin (5:6-*Benzcoumarin*)

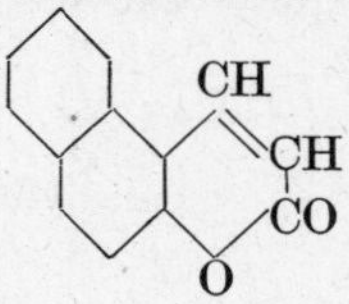

$C_{13}H_8O_2$ MW, 196

Bright yellow needles from EtOH.Aq. M.p. 118°. Sol. EtOH, Et_2O, $CHCl_3$, AcOH. Spar. sol. hot H_2O ⟶ bluish fluor.

Dey, Rao, Sankaranarayanan, *J. Indian Chem. Soc.*, 1932, **9**, 71.

β:β-Naphthacoumarin (6:7-*Benzcoumarin*)

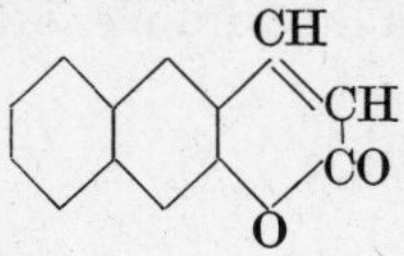

$C_{13}H_8O_2$ MW, 196

Pale yellowish cryst. from $CHCl_3$–pet. ether. M.p. 163–4°.

Boehm, Profft, *Arch. Pharm.*, 1931, **269**, 25 (*Chem. Zentr.*, 1931, I, 1922).

β:α-Naphthacoumarin (7:8-*Benzcoumarin*

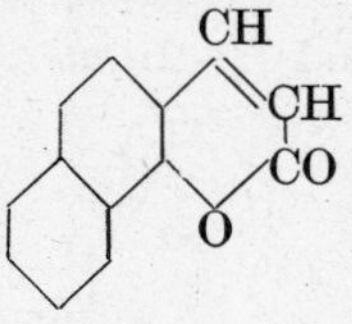

$C_{13}H_8O_2$ MW, 196

Pale yellow needles from EtOH. M.p. 141–2° (138°). Sol. Me_2CO, $CHCl_3$, C_6H_6, AcOH. Spar. sol. Et_2O. Insol. H_2O. Greenish-yellow sol. in conc. $H_2SO_4 \longrightarrow$ blue fluor.

Dey, Rao, Sankaranarayanan, *J. Indian Chem. Soc.*, 1932, **9**, 71.
Bezdzik, Friedländer, *Monatsh.*, 1909, **30**, 280.
See also previous reference.

Naphthacridine.
See Chrysidine.

2′ : 1′-Naphtha-1 : 2-fluorene

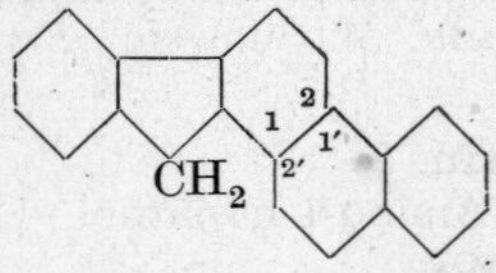

$C_{21}H_{14}$ MW, 266

Colourless leaflets from xylene. M.p. 327–8°. Forms add. comp., m.p. 249–51°, with 2 : 7-dinitroanthraquinone.

Cook *et al.*, *J. Chem. Soc.*, 1934, 1737.

1′ : 2′-Naphtha-2 : 3-fluorene

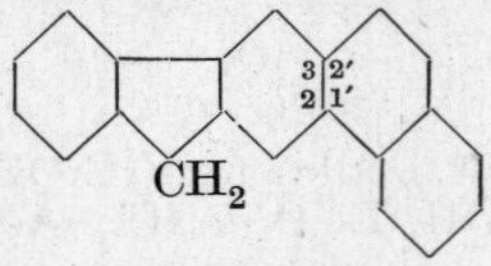

$C_{21}H_{14}$ MW, 266

Colourless leaflets from C_6H_6–EtOH. M.p. 226°.

Cook *et al.*, *J. Chem. Soc.*, 1935, 1323.

2′ : 3′-Naphtha-2 : 3-fluorene (lin-*Naphthafluorene*)

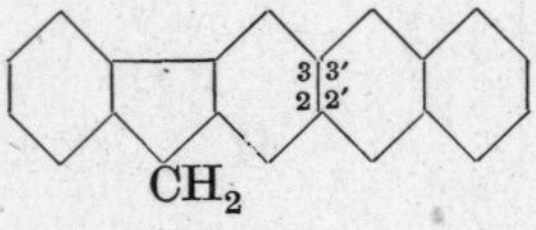

$C_{21}H_{14}$ MW, 266

Cryst. from toluene. M.p. 317°. Sol. $C_6H_6 \longrightarrow$ bright blue fluor. Sol. conc. $H_2SO_4 \longrightarrow$ bright green fluor.

Barnett, Goodway, Watson, *Ber.*, 1933, **66**, 1890.

2′ : 1′-Naphtha-1 : 2-fluorenone

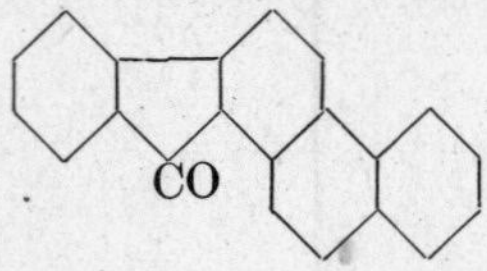

$C_{21}H_{12}O$ MW, 280

Reddish-orange needles from AcOH. M.p. 207–8°.

Cook *et al.*, *J. Chem. Soc.*, 1934, 1737.

1′ : 2′-Naphtha-2 : 3-fluorenone

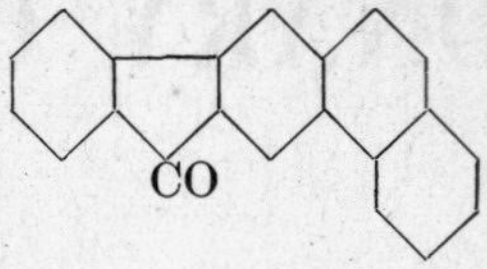

$C_{21}H_{12}O$ MW, 280

Reddish-brown needles. M.p. 215°. Sol. in conc. $H_2SO_4 \longrightarrow$ magenta col.

Cook *et al.*, *J. Chem. Soc.*, 1935, 1323.

α-Naphthafuran (6 : 7-*Benzcoumarone*)

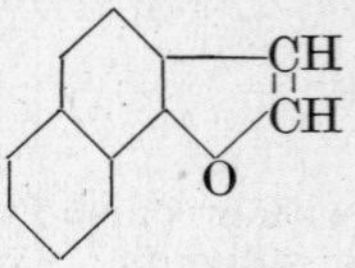

$C_{12}H_8O$ MW, 168

Pale yellow oil. M.p. – 7°. B.p. 282–4°/755 mm. D^{14} 1·1504. n_D^{16} 1·634. Sol. conc. $H_2SO_4 \longrightarrow$ yellowish-green col., on warming $\longrightarrow$ blue $\longrightarrow$ violet fluor

Picrate: reddish-yellow needles. M.p. 113°.

Stoermer, *Ann.*, 1900, **312**, 310.
Boes, *Chem. Zentr.*, 1902, I, 1356.

β-Naphthafuran (4 : 5-*Benzcoumarone*)

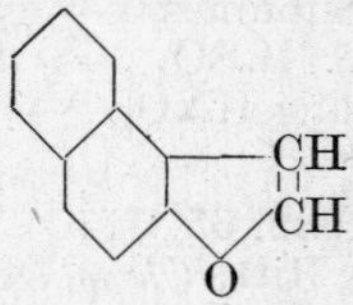

$C_{12}H_8O$ MW, 168

Needles. M.p. 60–1° (65°). B.p. 284–6° (280°). Sol. conc. $H_2SO_4 \longrightarrow$ yellowish-green col., on warming $\longrightarrow$ pale violet $\longrightarrow$ dirty bluish-green $\longrightarrow$ brownish-violet fluor.

Picrate: red needles. M.p. 141°.

See previous references.

β-Naphthafurandione (4 : 5-*Benzcoumarandione*)

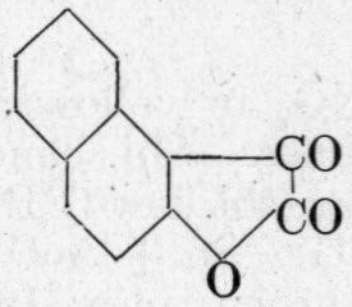

$C_{12}H_6O_3$ MW, 198

Orange-yellow needles from AcOH or C_6H_6.

M.p. 182° decomp. Sol. EtOH. Spar. sol. H_2O, pet. ether. The blood-red sol. in conc. H_2SO_4 turns colourless on warming.
2-*Anil* : m.p. 126–7°.
2 : 3-*Phenazine* : m.p. 286–7°.
3-*Phenylhydrazone* : m.p. 226–7°.
3-*Semicarbazone* : m.p. 240–1°.
Picrate : m.p. 109°.

Giua, Franciscis, *Gazz. chim. ital.*, 1924, **54**, 509.
Passerini, *ibid.*, 184.
Staudinger, Swiss Ps., 92,688, 93,486, (*Chem. Abstracts*, 1924, **18**, 989).

α-Naphthafuranone-3 (6 : 7-*Benzcoumaranone*-3)

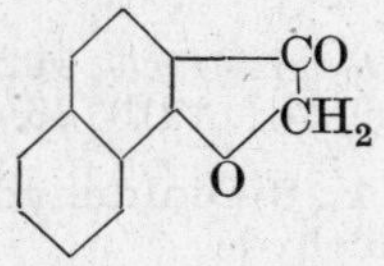

$C_{12}H_8O_2$ MW, 184

Pale yellow needles. M.p. 119°. Yellow sol. in conc. $H_2SO_4 \longrightarrow$ green fluor. Fehling's $\longrightarrow$ deep purple col.
2-*Benzylidene deriv.* : m.p. 130°.

Ingham, Stephen, Timpe, *J. Chem. Soc.*, 1931, 895.

β - Naphthafuranone - 2 (2 - *Hydroxy* - 1 - *naphthylacetic lactone*, 4 : 5-*benzisocoumaranone*)

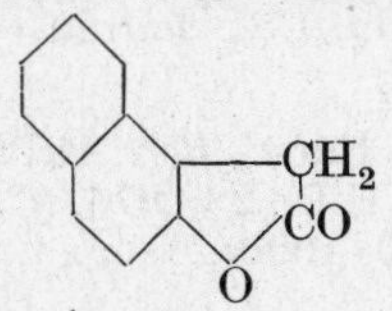

$C_{12}H_8O_2$ MW, 184

Leaflets. M.p. 107° (104°). Very spar. sol. H_2O. Sol. conc. $H_2SO_4 \longrightarrow$ green fluor.

I.G., D.R.P., 562,391 ; E.P., 330,916, (*Chem. Abstracts*, 1933, **27**, 735 ; 1930, **24**, 6031).
Mayer, Schäfer, Rosenbach, *Chem. Zentr.*, 1929, II, 3009.

β-Naphthafuranone-3 (4 : 5-*Benzcoumaranone*)

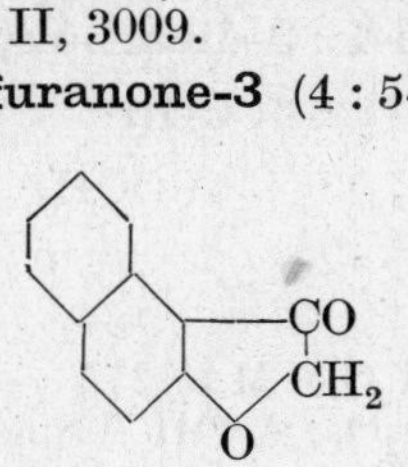

$C_{12}H_8O_2$ MW, 184

Colourless needles from pet. ether, EtOH, or AcOH. M.p. 133°. Sol. Et_2O, C_6H_6. Sol. conc. H_2SO_4 with pale yellow col. Sol. alc. NaOH with bluish-red col. $HNO_3 \longrightarrow$ 2-nitro-deriv., m.p. 190° decomp.
2-p-*Nitrobenzylidene deriv.* : m.p. 270°.

Dziewoński, Duzyk, *Chem. Abstracts*, 1934, **28**, 4415.
Fries, Frellstedt, *Ber.*, 1921, **54**, 715.

Naphthalaldehyde (*Naphthalene* 1 : 8-*dialdehyde*, 1 : 8-*dialdehydonaphthalene*)

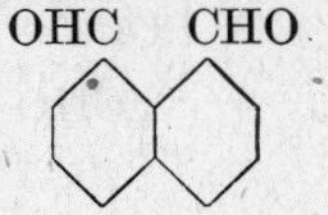

$C_{12}H_8O_2$ MW, 184

Hydrate : $C_{12}H_8O_2,H_2O$. Colourless needles from C_6H_6. M.p. 130°. Reduces $NH_3.AgNO_3$.
Di-p-nitrophenylhydrazone : reddish needles. M.p. 229°.

Criegee, Kraft, Rank, *Ann.*, 1933, **507**, 194.

1-Naphthaldehyde (*Naphthalene α-aldehyde*)

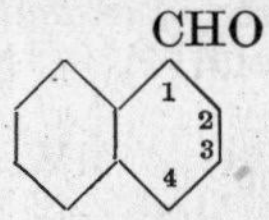

$C_{11}H_8O$ MW, 156

M.p. 33–4°. B.p. 292°, 156°/19 mm., 150°/9 mm. Forms bisulphite comp. Ox. in air $\longrightarrow$ 1-naphthoic acid.
Anil : m.p. 71°.
Azine : m.p. 152°.
Oxime : m.p. 98° (39°).
Phenylhydrazone : m.p. 80°.
p-*Nitrophenylhydrazone* : m.p. 234°.
Semicarbazone : m.p. 221°.
Picrate : m.p. 94°.

Shoppee, *J. Chem. Soc.*, 1933, 42.
Wuyts *et al.*, *Bull. soc. chim. Belg.*, 1932, **41**, 196 ; 1931, **40**, 665.
I.G., E.P., 250,955, (*Chem. Abstracts*, 1927, **21**, 1272).
Stephen, *J. Chem. Soc.*, 1925, **127**, 1877.
Weil, Ostermeier, *Ber.*, 1921, **54**, 3217.
Gattermann, *Ann.*, 1912, **393**, 227.

2-Naphthaldehyde (*Naphthalene β-aldehyde*).

Leaflets from boiling H_2O. M.p. 61° (59°). Sol. EtOH, Et_2O. Volatile in steam. Gives bisulphite comp. $KMnO_4 \longrightarrow$ 2-naphthoic acid.
Anil : m.p. 113°.
Azine : m.p. 232°.
Phenylhydrazone : m.p. 217–18° (205–6°).

p-*Nitrophenylhydrazone* : m.p. 230°.
Semicarbazone : m.p. 245°.

See first two and last two references above.

Naphthaldehyde-carboxylic Acid.
See Naphthaldehydic Acid.

1 : 2-Naphthaldehydic Acid (2-*Formyl*-1-*naphthoic acid, naphthalene*-2-*aldehyde*-1-*carboxylic acid,* 2-*aldehydo*-1-*naphthoic acid,* 2-*naphthaldehyde*-1-*carboxylic acid*)

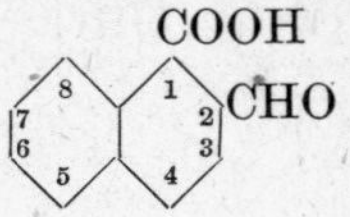

$C_{12}H_8O_3$ MW, 200

M.p. 176°.
Oxime : m.p. 215°.

Mayer, Schäfer, Rosenbach, *Chem. Abstracts*, 1930, **24**, 839.

1 : 8-Naphthaldehydic Acid (8-*Formyl*-1-*naphthoic acid, naphthalene*-8-*aldehyde*-1-*carboxylic acid,* 8-*aldehydo*-1-*naphthoic acid,* 1-*naphthaldehyde*-8-*carboxylic acid*).

Leaflets from EtOH.Aq. M.p. 167–8° decomp. (rapid heat.).

Me ester : $C_{13}H_{10}O_3$. MW, 214. Rhombic cryst. M.p. 105°. Mod. sol. hot H_2O. Sol. EtOH, Et_2O, C_6H_6.

Acetyl deriv. of lactone form : $C_{14}H_{10}O_4$. MW, 242. M.p. 140°.

Graebe, Gfeller, *Ann.*, 1893, **276**, 13.
Zink, *Monatsh.*, 1901, **22**, 988.
Winterstein, Maxim, *Helv. Chim. Acta*, 1919, **2**, 202.

Naphthalene

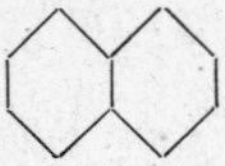

$C_{10}H_8$ MW, 128

Colourless plates from EtOH. M.p. 80·3°. B.p. 218°. Sublimes at 50°/760 mm., 22°/7 mm. Volatile in steam. D^{19} 1·1517, D_4^{100} 0·9625. n_D^{99} 1·58232. Heat of comb. C_p and C_v 1242 Cal. (9605 cal./gm.). Very sol. Et_2O, C_6H_6, toluene, xylene, chlorobenzene, tetralin, hot EtOH, $CHCl_3$. Mod. sol. MeOH, cold EtOH. Spar. sol. cold pet. ether. Insol. H_2O. Forms add. comps. with 1 : 3-dinitrobenzene, m.p. 52° ; 2 : 4-dinitrophenol, m.p. 95° ; 2 : 4-dinitrotoluene, m.p. 61° ; 2 : 4 : 6-trinitrotoluene, m.p. 97°. Passed through red-hot tube $\longrightarrow$ 2:2′-dinaphthyl. H_2SO_4 + $HgSO_4$, or air + (vanadium comps.) $\longrightarrow$ phthalic acid. $KMnO_4$.Aq. $\longrightarrow$ phthalonic acid. HNO_3 or CrO_3.Aq. $\longrightarrow$ phthalic acid. CrO_3 + AcOH $\longrightarrow$ 1 : 4-naphthoquinone + phthalic acid.

Picrate : m.p. 149·5°.
Styphnate : m.p. 168–9°.

Ward, *J. Phys. Chem.*, 1934, **38**, 761.
Hill, U.S.P., 1,819,680, (*Chem. Abstracts*, 1931, **25**, 5759).
Schroeter, U.S.P., 1,763,410, (*Chem. Abstracts*, 1930, **24**, 3803).
Salont, *Dyer and Calico Printer*, 1928, **60**, 208 (*Review*).
Weissenberger, *Z. angew. Chem.*, 1927, **40**, 776.
Veselý, Jakes, *Bull. soc. chim.*, 1923, **33**, 955.
Davy, *Chem. Abstracts*, 1920, **14**, 618.
Bamberger, *Ber.*, 1913, **46**, 1899 (*Bibl.*).

Naphthalene 1 : 8-Dialdehyde.
See Naphthalaldehyde.

Naphthalene-1-diazonium chloride (α-*Diazonaphthalene chloride*)

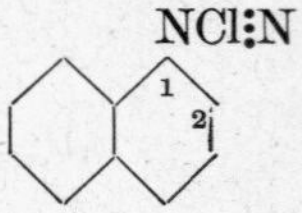

$C_{10}H_7N_2Cl$ MW, 190·5

Pale yellow needles. M.p. 96° decomp. Sol. H_2O, AcOH, MeOH. Spar. sol. EtOH, Me_2CO. Insol. Et_2O, C_6H_6, CS_2, ligroin. Forms stable comp. with $ZnCl_2$.

Baudisch, Fürst, *Ber.*, 1912, **45**, 3428.
Badische, E.P., 238,676, (*Chem. Abstracts*, 1926, **20**, 1996).

Naphthalene-2-diazonium chloride (β-*Diazonaphthalene chloride*).

Yellow needles. Explodes on heating. Sol. H_2O. Insol. Et_2O, C_6H_6, CS_2. Forms stable comp. with $ZnCl_2$.

Knoevenagel, *Ber.*, 1895, **28**, 2052, 2057.
See also second reference above.

Naphthalene-1 : 2-dicarboxylic Acid

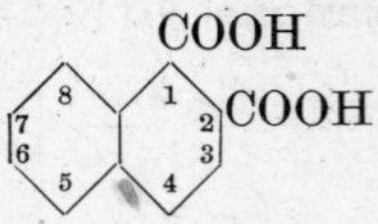

$C_{12}H_8O_4$ MW, 216

Cryst. from H_2O. M.p. 175° $\longrightarrow$ anhydride. Sol. EtOH, Et_2O, AcOH. Spar. sol. C_6H_6, ligroin, $CHCl_3$, CS_2.

Di-Me ester : $C_{14}H_{12}O_4$. MW, 244. Cryst. from MeOH. M.p. 80°. Spar. sol. pet. ether.

Diamide : $C_{12}H_{10}O_2N_2$. MW, 214. Plates. M.p. 265° ⟶ imide.

Dinitrile: 1 : 2-dicyanonaphthalene. $C_{12}H_6N_2$. MW, 178. Needles from C_6H_6. M.p. 190°. Sublimes. Spar. sol. EtOH.

Anhydride : $C_{12}H_6O_3$. MW, 198. Needles from EtOH. M.p. 168–9°. Sublimes. Sol. Et_2O.

Imide : $C_{12}H_7O_2N$. MW, 197. M.p. 224°.

Waldmann, Weiss, *J. prakt. Chem.*, 1930, **127**, 195.
Noto, *Gazz. chim. ital.*, 1915, **45**, ii, 126, 427.
Freund, Fleischer, *Ann.*, 1913, **399**, 212.

Naphthalene-1 : 4-dicarboxylic Acid.

Rodlets from AcOH. M.p. 309° (288°). Sol. EtOH ⟶ blue fluor. Insol. boiling H_2O.

Di-Me ester : cryst. from AcOH. M.p. 64°. B.p. 195–7°/12 mm.

Dichloride : $C_{12}H_6O_2Cl_2$. MW, 253. Needles from pet. ether. M.p. 80°.

Dinitrile : 1 : 4-dicyanonaphthalene. Needles from AcOH. M.p. 206°. Spar. sol. EtOH, Et_2O.

I.G., D.R.P., 558,471, (*Chem. Abstracts*, 1933, **27**, 310).
Mayer *et al.*, *Ber.*, 1922, **55**, 1841.
Scholl, Neumann, *ibid.*, 120.

Naphthalene-1 : 5-dicarboxylic Acid.

Colourless needles from $PhNO_2$. M.p. 315–20° decomp. Insol. ord. solvents.

Di-Me ester : leaflets from MeOH. M.p. 114–15°.

Di-Et ester : $C_{16}H_{16}O_4$. MW, 272. Needles. M.p. 123–4°.

Diphenyl ester : $C_{24}H_{16}O_4$. MW, 368. Cryst. from C_6H_6. M.p. 198–9°.

Dichloride : needles from $CHCl_3$. M.p. 155–6°.

Dinitrile : 1 : 5-dicyanonaphthalene. Needles from EtOH. M.p. 260° (267°). Sublimes.

Salkind, *Ber.*, 1934, **67**, 1031.
See also third reference above.

Naphthalene-1 : 6-dicarboxylic Acid.

Needles from AcOH. M.p. 310°. Sol. hot EtOH, hot AcOH.

Di-Me ester : needles from EtOH. M.p. 99°.

Dinitrile : 1 : 6-dicyanonaphthalene. Needles from EtOH. M.p. 208–10°.

Weissgerber, Kruber, *Ber.*, 1919, **52**, 354.

Naphthalene-1 : 7-dicarboxylic Acid.

Micro-cryst. powder from EtOH.Aq. M.p. 294–6° decomp. Sol. ord. org. solvents.

Di-Me ester : cryst. from EtOH. M.p. 86–7°.

Ruzicka, Melsen, *Helv. Chim. Acta*, 1931, **14**, 397.

Naphthalene-1 : 8-dicarboxylic Acid.

See Naphthalic Acid.

Naphthalene-2 : 3-dicarboxylic Acid.

Prisms from AcOH. M.p. 239–41° (246° after sublimation). Sol. hot EtOH. Spar. sol. Et_2O, hot AcOH. Very spar. sol. ligroin, $CHCl_3$, C_6H_6, CS_2, cold H_2O. Heat + aniline ⟶ phenylimide. $SOCl_2$ or PCl_5 ⟶ anhydride. The NH_4 salt at 270° ⟶ imide.

Anhydride : rectangular plates from AcOH. M.p. 246°.

Mono-nitrile : 3-cyano-2-naphthoic acid. $C_{12}H_7O_2N$. MW, 197. Yellow cryst. M.p. 273–4°.

Imide : micro-needles from $CHCl_3$–EtOH. M.p. 275° (softens at 250°).

Phenylimide : $C_{18}H_{11}O_2N$. MW, 273. Rectangular silvery plates from $CHCl_3$–EtOH. M.p. 277–8°.

Waldmann, Mathiowetz, *Ber.*, 1931, **64**, 1713.
I.G., F.P., 682,474, (*Chem. Abstracts*, 1930, **24**, 4306).
Freund, Fleischer, *Ann.*, 1913, **402**, 68.

Naphthalene-2 : 6-dicarboxylic Acid.

Needles from EtOH.Aq. M.p. above 300° decomp. Insol. boiling C_6H_6, toluene, AcOH.

Di-Me ester : cryst. from MeOH. M.p. 191°. Sol. Et_2O, $CHCl_3$, toluene, hot ligroin. Spar. sol. pet. ether.

Mono-nitrile : 6-cyano-2-naphthoic acid. M.p. above 300° decomp. Very spar. sol. org. solvents.

Dinitrile : 2 : 6-dicyanonaphthalene. Needles from AcOH. M.p. 296–7°. Insol. boiling EtOH, Et_2O, C_6H_6.

Dianilide : leaflets from aniline. Does not melt below 320°.

Kaufler, Thien, *Ber.*, 1907, **40**, 3257.

Naphthalene-2 : 7-dicarboxylic Acid.

Needles from EtOH. M.p. above 300° decomp. Very spar. sol. boiling C_6H_6, toluene, AcOH.

Di-Me ester : cryst. from MeOH. M.p. 135–6° (141°). Sol. hot ligroin. Spar. sol. pet. ether.

Di-Et ester : m.p. 238°.

Diphenyl ester : $C_{24}H_{16}O_4$. MW, 368. M.p. 162°.

Mono-nitrile : 7-cyano-2-naphthoic acid. M.p. above 300° decomp.

Dinitrile : 2 : 7-dicyanonaphthalene. Needles from AcOH. M.p. 267–8°. Sol. hot EtOH.

Dianilide : scales from aniline. M.p. 297–8°.

Purgotti, *Chem. Abstracts*, 1926, **20, 1618.**
See also previous reference.

Naphthalene-dihydride.
See Dihydronaphthalene.

Naphthalene-1 : 5-disulphinic Acid

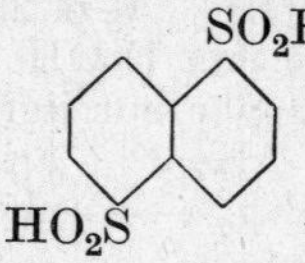

$C_{10}H_8O_4S_2$ MW, 256

Glittering leaflets from HCl.Aq. M.p. 166–7° (174–5° decomp.). Sol. hot H_2O, hot EtOH. Spar. sol. Et_2O, cold EtOH, cold H_2O. Reduces cold alk. $KMnO_4$. Reacts with *p*-benzoquinone (2 mols.) $\longrightarrow$ comp., m.p. 294°.

Di-NH$_4$ salt : prisms from EtOH. M.p. 194°.

Curtius, Tüxen, *J. prakt. Chem.*, 1930, **125**, 406.
Corbellini, Albenga, *Gazz. chim. ital.*, 1931, **61**, 111.

Naphthalene-1 : 2-disulphonic Acid

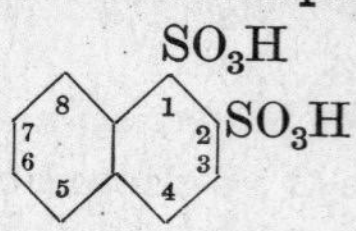

$C_{10}H_8O_6S_2$ MW, 288

Anhydride : $C_{10}H_6O_5S_2$. MW, 270. M.p. 198–9°.

Gattermann, *Ber.*, 1899, **32**, 1156.

Naphthalene-1 : 3-disulphonic Acid.

Dichloride : $C_{10}H_6O_4Cl_2S_2$. MW, 325. Prisms from C_6H_6. M.p. 138°.

Dressel, Kothe, *Ber.*, 1894, **27**, 1197.
Armstrong, Wynne, *Chem. News*, 1890, **62**, 163.

Naphthalene-1 : 4-disulphonic Acid.

Dichloride : plates. M.p. 160°. Sol. C_6H_6.
Diamide : $C_{10}H_{10}O_4N_2S_2$. MW, 286. Needles from EtOH.Aq. M.p. 273°.
Dianilide : pearly leaflets. M.p. 179°.

Gattermann, *Ber.*, 1899, **32**, 1156.

Naphthalene-1 : 5-disulphonic Acid ("γ-" *Naphthalenedisulphonic acid*).

Plates + $4H_2O$ from HCl.Aq. M.p. anhyd. 240–5°. Sol. 0·98 part H_2O at 20°. Aq. sol. tastes bitter-astringent. Forms series of arylamine salts of definite m.ps.

Di-Me ester : $C_{12}H_{12}O_6S_2$. MW, 316. Cryst. from $CHCl_3$. M.p. 205°.
Mono-Et ester : $C_{12}H_{12}O_6S_2$. MW, 316. Cryst. from EtOH. M.p. 147°.
Difluoride : $C_{10}H_6O_4F_2S_2$. MW, 292. M.p. 203°.
Dichloride : prisms from C_6H_6. M.p. 183°.
Diamide : does not melt below 340°.
Dianilide : m.p. 248–9°.
Diazide : $C_{10}H_6O_4N_6S_2$. MW, 338. Cryst. from AcOH or $CHCl_3$. M.p. 177°.
Dihydrazide : $C_{10}H_{12}O_4N_4S_2$. MW, 316. Micro-needles from H_2O. Does not melt (blackens at 240°).
Benzyl-ψ-thiourea salt : m.p. 251° decomp.

Corbellini, Albenga, *Gazz. chim. ital.*, 1931, **61**, 111.
Curtius, Tüxen, *J. prakt. Chem.*, 1930, **125**, 401.
Steinkopf *et al.*, *ibid.*, 1927, **117**, 1.
Lynch, Scanlan, *Ind. Eng. Chem.*, 1927, **19**, 1010.
Fierz-David, Hasler, *Helv. Chim. Acta*, 1923, **6**, 1133.
Forster, Hishiyama, *J. Soc. Chem. Ind.*, 1932, **51**, 297T.
Hann, Keenan, *J. Phys. Chem.*, 1927, **31**, 1086.

Naphthalene-1 : 6-disulphonic Acid ("δ"-*Naphthalenedisulphonic acid*).

Prisms + $4H_2O$ from H_2O. M.p. anhyd. 125° decomp. Sol. 0·61 part H_2O at 18–20°. Forms α-naphthylamine salt, m.p. 265–7° decomp.

Dichloride : leaflets from C_6H_6. M.p. 129°. Very sol. C_6H_6.
Diamide : m.p. 297–8°.
Benzyl-ψ-thiourea salt : decomp. at 81°.

Ufimzew, Kriwoschlükowa, *J. prakt. Chem.*, 1934, **140**, 172.
Ambler, *Ind. Eng. Chem.*, 1927, **19**, 417; 1920, **12**, 1080.
See also last three references above.

Naphthalene-1 : 7-disulphonic Acid.

Dichloride : prisms from C_6H_6. M.p. 123°. Sol. 7% in C_6H_6.

See first reference above.

Naphthalene-1 : 8-disulphonic Acid.

Anhydride : plates. M.p. 227°. Sol. hot AcOH, hot xylene. Spar. sol. C_6H_6.

Armstrong, Wynne, *Chem. News*, 1893, **67**, 299.

Naphthalene-2 : 6-disulphonic Acid ("β"-*Naphthalenedisulphonic acid*).

Leaflets. Deliquesces very slowly in air. Forms series of arylamine salts of definite m.ps.

Dichloride : flat needles. M.p. 225°. Spar. sol. C_6H_6. Insol. Et_2O.

Benzyl-ψ-thiourea salt : m.p. 256°.

Hann, Keenan, *J. Phys. Chem.*, 1927, **31**, 1086.
Heid, *J. Am. Chem. Soc.*, 1927, **49**, 844.
Forster, Keyworth, *J. Soc. Chem. Ind.*, 1924. **43**, 165T.
Fierz-David, Hasler, *Helv. Chim. Acta*, 1923, **6**, 1133.
Armstrong, Wynne, *Chem. News*, 1890, **62**, 163.

Naphthalene-2 : 7-disulphonic Acid ("α"-*Naphthalenedisulphonic acid*).

Very hygroscopic needles. Spar. sol. cold conc. HCl. Forms series of arylamine salts of definite m.ps.

Dichloride : four-sided plates from C_6H_6. M.p. 159°. Mod. sol. Et_2O.

Dibromide : $C_{10}H_6O_4Br_2S_2$. MW, 414. Prisms from C_6H_6. M.p. 137°.

Diamide : needles. M.p. 242–3°.

Benzyl-ψ-thiourea salt : m.p. 211–12° decomp.

Ufimzew, Kriwoschlükowa, *J. prakt. Chem.*, 1934, **140**, 172.
Ambler, *Ind. Eng. Chem.*, 1920, **12**, 1194.
See also first four references above.

Naphthalene-1-sulphinic Acid (*α-Naphthalenesulphinic acid*)

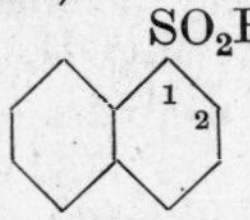

$C_{10}H_8O_2S$ MW, 192

Needles from H_2O. M.p. 98–9° (84–5°). Sol. H_2O. Mod. sol. EtOH. Spar. sol. HCl.Aq., Et_2O. Dil. HCl at 180° ⟶ naphthalene + SO_2.

Höchst, D.R.P., 224,019, (*Chem. Zentr.*, 1910, II, 513).
Knoevenagel, Kenner, *Ber.*, 1908, **41**, 3319.
Rosenheim, Singer, *Ber.*, 1904, **37**, 2154.
Otto, Rössing, Troeger, *J. prakt. Chem.*, 1893, **47**, 95.
Thomas, *J. Chem. Soc.*, 1909, **95**, 342.

Naphthalene-2-sulphinic Acid (*β-Naphthalenesulphinic acid*).

Needles from H_2O. M.p. 105°. Sol. H_2O, EtOH, Et_2O. Sol. in conc. H_2SO_4 gradually turns green. Dil. HCl at 150° ⟶ naphthalene + SO_2.

Me ester : $C_{11}H_{10}O_2S$. MW, 206. Leaflets from pet. ether. M.p. 44°. Sol. ord. org. solvents. Decomp. on standing. Hyd. by H_2O.

See last two references above.

Naphthalene-1-sulphonic Acid (*Naphthalene-α-sulphonic acid*)

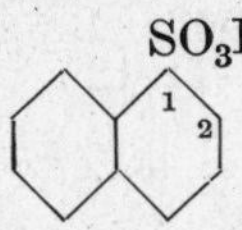

$C_{10}H_8O_3S$ MW, 208

Prisms + $2H_2O$ from HCl.Aq. M.p. 90°. Sol. H_2O, EtOH. Spar. sol. Et_2O. $k = 0{\cdot}18 \times 10^{-3}$ at 25°. Forms series of arylamine salts of definite m.ps. Acid $KMnO_4$ ⟶ phthalic acid.

Me ester : $C_{11}H_{10}O_3S$. MW, 222. M.p. 78° (72–3°). B.p. 214°/15 mm.

Et ester : $C_{12}H_{12}O_3S$. MW, 236. Liq. Decomp. on dist.

Phenyl ester : $C_{16}H_{12}O_3S$. MW, 284. M.p. 75°.

Fluoride : $C_{10}H_7O_2FS$. MW, 210. M.p. 56°.

Chloride : $C_{10}H_7O_2ClS$. MW, 226·5. Leaflets from Et_2O. M.p. 68°. B.p. 194–5°/13 mm., 147·5°/0·9 mm.

Bromide : $C_{10}H_7O_2BrS$. MW, 271. M.p. 88–9°.

Amide : $C_{10}H_9O_2NS$. MW, 207. M.p. 150°.

Anilide : m.p. 152°.

Azide : cryst. from EtOH. M.p. 53°, decomp. at 133°.

Hydrazide : needles from EtOH.Aq. M.p. 123° decomp. *HCl salt* : m.p. 142°.

Piperidide : m.p. 133–4°.

Benzyl-ψ-thiourea salt : m.p. 138°.

2-*Naphthylamine salt* : m.p. 276–9° decomp.

Geigy F.P., 765,771, (*Chem. Abstracts*, 1934, **28**, 6726).
Cumming, Muir, *Chem. Abstracts*, 1934, **28**, 4409.
Masters, U.S.P., 1,922,813, (*Chem Abstracts*, 1933, **27**, 5085).
Radcliffe, Short, *J. Chem. Soc.* 1931, 220.
Curtius, Bottler, Hasse, *J. prakt. Chem.*, 1930, **125**, 366.
Fierz-David, Weissenbach, *Helv. Chim. Acta*, 1920, **3**, 310, 315.
Rodionow, *Bull. soc. chim.*, 1929, **45**, 117.
Hann, Keenan, *J. Phys. Chem.*, 1927, **31**, 1084.
Forster, Keyworth, *J. Soc. Chem. Ind.*, 1924, **43**, 299T.

Naphthalene-2-sulphonic Acid (*Naphthalene-β-sulphonic acid*).

Very hygroscopic cryst. M.p. 91°. On standing in air, or cryst. from HCl.Aq. ⟶ trihydrate, m.p. 83°. Kept over $CaCl_2$ or conc. H_2SO_4 ⟶ monohydrate, m.p. 124°. $k = 0{\cdot}25 \times 10^{-3}$ at 25°. Very sol. ord. org. solvents. Forms series of arylamine salts of definite m.ps.

With 1 mol. glycine ⟶ cryst. comp., m.p. 193°. Neutral or acid $KMnO_4$ ⟶ phthalic acid.

Me ester: m.p. 56°. B.p. 224–5°/15 mm.

Et ester: m.p. 11–12°. B.p. 134°/vac. of cathode light.

Phenyl ester: m.p. 98–9°.

Fluoride: m.p. 87–8°.

Chloride: m.p. 79° (66°). B.p. 201°/13 mm., 148°/0·6 mm.

Bromide: m.p. 96–7°.

Amide: m.p. 217° (212°).

Azide: needles from ligroin. M.p. 44–6° slight decomp.

Hydrazide: m.p. 137–9°. *HCl salt*: m.p. 148–50°.

Disulphonimide: $(C_{10}H_7SO_2)_2NH$. Cryst. from C_6H_6. M.p. 180–1°. Sol. H_2O.

Benzyl-ψ-thiourea salt: m.p. 193°.

2-*Naphthylamine salt*: m.p. 211° (brown at 202°).

I.G., D.R.P., 574,836; E.P., 384,722, (*Chem. Abstracts*, 1933, **27**, 4543, 4251).

Dennis, U.S.P., 1,332,203, (*Chem. Abstracts*, 1920, **14**, 1123).

See also last three references above.

Naphthalene-1 : 4 : 5 : 8-tetracarboxylic Acid

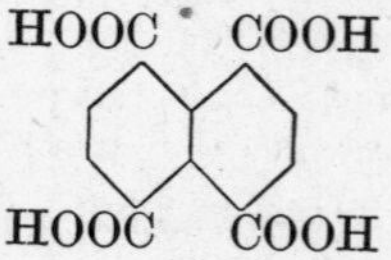

$C_{14}H_8O_8$ MW, 304

Leaflets or needles from HCl.Aq. No characteristic m.p. Rapid heat at 200–50° ⟶ decomp., slow heat at 140–50° or cryst. from AcOH ⟶ anhydride. Sol. Me_2CO.Aq. Mod. sol. H_2O, hot AcOH. Very spar. sol. C_6H_6, $CHCl_3$, CS_2, EtOH.

Di-anhydride: $C_{14}H_4O_6$. MW, 268. Needles from AcOH. Sublimes above 300°. Heat + NH_3 ⟶ di-imide.

Di-imide: $C_{14}H_6O_4N_2$. MW, 266. Yellowish needles from H_2O. Sublimes above 270°. Very spar. sol. ord. org. solvents.

Greune, Eckert, U.S.P., 1,970,651, (*Chem. Abstracts*, 1934, **28**, 6159).

I.G., D.R.P., 601,104; F.P., 756,156, (*Chem. Abstracts*, 1934, **28**, 7267, 2018). F.P., 721,339, (*Chem. Abstracts*, 1932, **26**, 4184). E.P., 364,116, (*Chem. Abstracts*, 1933, **27**, 2457). E.P., 363,044, (*Chem. Abstracts*, 1933, **27**, 1642).

Freund, Fleischer, *Ann.*, 1913, **402**, 74.

Bamberger, Philip, *Ann.*, 1887, **240**, 182.

Naphthalene- : 3 : 5 : 7-tetrasulphonic Acid

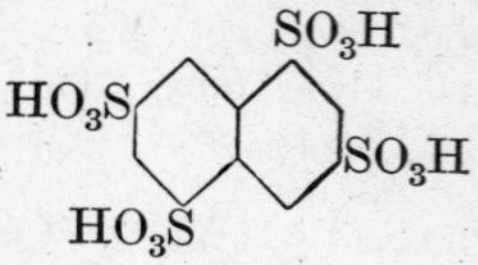

$C_{10}H_8O_{12}S_4$ MW, 448

Ba salt: $C_{10}H_4(SO_3)_4Ba_2$. Dimorphous. Blunt prisms + $14H_2O$ at 15° (efflorescent). Cryst. + $8H_2O$ at 35° (stable in air).

Tetrachloride: $C_{10}H_4O_8Cl_4S_4$. MW, 522. Tetrahedral cryst. M.p. 261–2°. Spar. sol. C_6H_6, Me_2CO.

Schmid, *Chem. Abstracts*, 1922, **16**, 2141.

Fierz-David, *J. Soc. Chem. Ind.*, 1923, **42**, 421T.

Cf. Ufimzew, Kriwoschlükowa, *J. prakt. Chem.*, 1934, **140**, 172.

Naphthalene-1 : 2 : 5-tricarboxylic Acid

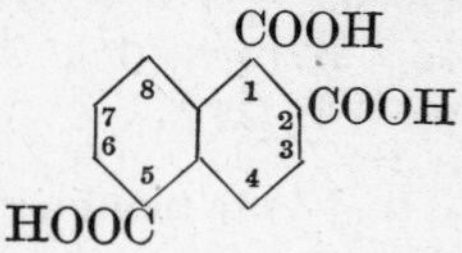

$C_{13}H_8O_6$ MW, 260

Colourless feathery needles. M.p. (vac. sublimed) 270–2°. Sol. MeOH.

Tri-Me ester: $C_{16}H_{14}O_6$. MW, 302. Cryst. M.p. 91–2°.

Heilbron, Wilkinson, *J. Chem. Soc.*, 1930, 2546.

Ruzicka, Hosking, *Helv. Chim. Acta*, 1930, **13**, 1405, 1411.

Naphthalene-1 : 4 : 5-tricarboxylic Acid.

Cryst. from conc. HCl. Does not melt, but at 100–20° forms the anhydride.

Anhydride: $C_{13}H_6O_5$. MW, 242. Cryst. from EtOH.Aq. M.p. 274° (243°).

Anhydride Me ester: $C_{14}H_8O_5$. MW, 256. Needles from AcOH. M.p. 222°.

Fieser Peters, *J. Am. Chem. Soc.*, 1932, **54**, 4352.

Graebe, Haas, *Ann.*, 1903, **327**, 95.

Naphthalene-1 : 3 : 5-trisulphonic Acid

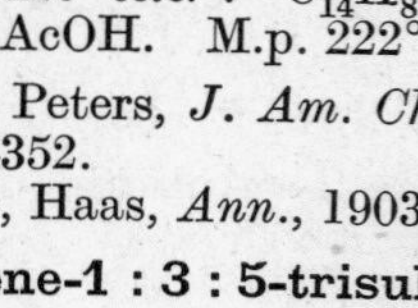

$C_{10}H_8O_9S_3$ MW, 368

Amorph. mass. Readily takes up H_2O ⟶

oily liq. which carbonises cellulose and decomposes NaCl.

Trichloride: $C_{10}H_5O_6Cl_3S_3$. MW, 423·5. Cryst. from C_6H_6–ligroin. M.p. 146°.

Erdmann, *Ber.*, 1899, **32**, 3188.
Gattermann, *ibid.*, 1158.

Naphthalene-1 : 3 : 6-trisulphonic Acid.

Pb salt: very sol. H_2O.

Trichloride: prisms from C_6H_6–pet. ether. M.p. 194°.

Armstrong, Wynne, *Chem. News*, 1888, **57**, 9; 1890, **62**, 162.
Cf. Ufimzew, Kriwoschlükowa, *J. prakt. Chem.*, 1934, **140**, 172.
See also first reference above.

Naphthalene-1 : 4 : 5-trisulphonic Acid.

Na salt: cryst. Effloresces in air. Very sol. H_2O.

Trichloride: needles. M.p. 156–7°.

Gattermann, *Ber.*, 1899, **32**, 1139, 1158.

Naphthalene-2 : 3 : 6-trisulphonic Acid.

Na salt: spar. sol. H_2O.

Trichloride: plates from C_6H_6. M.p. 200°.

Armstrong, Wynne, *Chem. News*, 1893, **67**, 299.

Naphthalic Acid (*Naphthalene*-1 : 8-*dicarboxylic acid*)

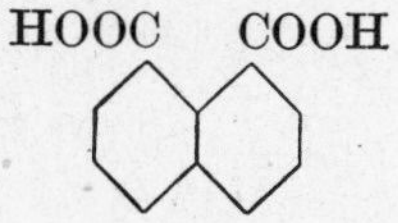

$C_{12}H_8O_4$ MW, 216

Needles from EtOH. Sol. warm EtOH. Spar. sol. Et_2O. Insol. H_2O.

Di-Me ester: $C_{14}H_{12}O_4$. MW, 244. Prisms from MeOH.Aq. M.p. 102–3°.

Di-Et ester: $C_{16}H_{16}O_4$. MW, 272. Leaflets from EtOH.Aq. M.p. 59–60°. B.p. 238–9°/19 mm. Sol. in conc. $H_2SO_4 \longrightarrow$ blue fluor.

Dibutyl ester: $C_{20}H_{24}O_4$. MW, 328. Cryst. from MeOH.Aq. M.p. 52–3°.

Dichloride: naphthalyl chloride. $C_{12}H_6O_2Cl_2$. MW, 253. Prisms from CS_2. M.p. 84–6°. B.p. 195–200°/0·2 mm.

Mono-nitrile: 8-cyano-1-naphthoic acid. $C_{12}H_7O_2N$. MW, 197. M.p. 210–50° decomp.

Anhydride: $C_{12}H_6O_3$. MW, 198. Needles from EtOH. M.p. 274°.

Imide: $C_{12}H_7O_2N$. MW, 197. M.p. 300° (290–1°).

N-*Me imide*: $C_{13}H_9O_2N$. MW, 211. M.p. 205°.

N-*Et imide*: $C_{14}H_{11}O_2N$. MW, 225. M.p. 148°.

N-*Phenyl imide*: $C_{18}H_{11}O_2N$. MW, 273. M.p. 202°.

Dianilide: m.p. 250–82° decomp.

Di-Me anilide: m.p. 245–6°.

Duckert, *Chem. Abstracts*, 1934, **28**, 1255 (*Bibl.*).
Jaeger, Canadian P., 321,683, (*Chem. Abstracts*, 1932, **26**, 3263).
Davies, Leeper, *J. Chem. Soc.*, 1927, 1124.
Mason, *J. Chem. Soc.*, 1924, **125**, 2116.
Wislicenus, Penndorf, *Ber.*, 1912, **45**, 410.
Graebe, Gfeller, *Ber.*, 1892, **25**, 653; *Ann.*, 1893, **276**, 6.

Naphthamide.

See under Naphthoic Acid.

Naphthane.

See Decahydronaphthalene.

β-Naphthanene.

See 1 : 2 : 3 : 4 : 5 : 8 : 9 : 10-Octahydronaphthalene.

Naphthanol.

See Decahydronaphthol.

α-Naphthanone (1-*Ketodecahydronaphthalene*)

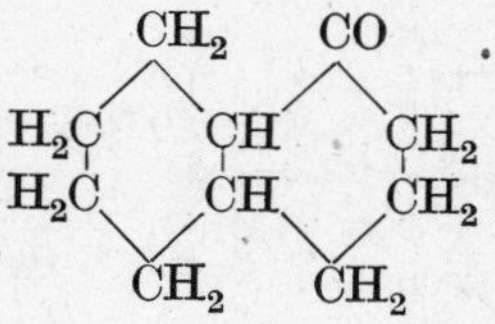

$C_{10}H_{16}O$ MW, 152

Prismatic plates with pronounced menthol-like odour. M.p. 32°. Sol. ord. org. solvents. Spar. sol. H_2O. Gives unstable comp. with $NaHSO_3$.

Oxime: cryst. from EtOH. M.p. 165°. Sublimes in needles at 100°.

Semicarbazone: needles. M.p. about 230°.

Leroux, *Ann. chim. phys.*, 1910, **21**, 522.

β-Naphthanone (2-*Ketodecahydronaphthalene*).

Colourless liq. with strong unpleasant odour. B.p. 240°, 110°/15 mm. D^{16} 0·979. n_D^{16} 1·4834. Sol. EtOH, Et_2O, AcOH. Spar. sol. H_2O. Reduces Fehling's and $NH_3.AgNO_3$.

Oxime: prisms from pet. ether. M.p. 76°. Sol. EtOH, Et_2O. Spar. sol. pet. ether.

Semicarbazone: needles from EtOH. M.p. 195°.

See previous reference.

Naphthanthracene (1 : 2-*Benzanthracene*)

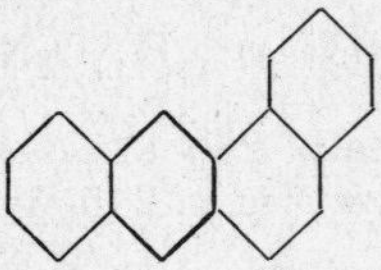

$C_{18}H_{12}$ MW, 228

Leaflets from EtOH–AcOH. M.p. 158–9° (141°). Sublimes. Sols. fluor. intense yellowish-green. $Na_2Cr_2O_7$ + AcOH ⟶ naphthanthraquinone.

Picrate : red needles. M.p. 133°.

Barnett, Matthews, *Chem. News*, 1925, **130**, 339.
Gabriel, Colman, *Ber.*, 1900, **33**, 447.
Graebe, *Ann.*, 1905, **340**, 258.

Naphthanthraquinone (ang-*Benzanthraquinone*, 1 : 2-*benzanthraquinone*, 1 : 2-*phthaloylnaphthalene*)

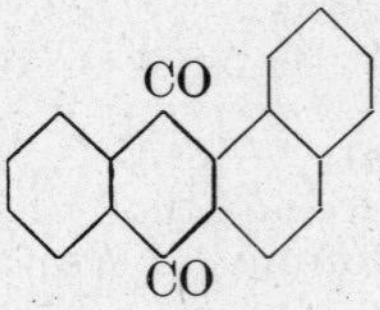

$C_{18}H_{10}O_2$ MW, 258

Yellow cryst. from hot xylene or $PhNO_2$. M.p. 168°. Sol. C_6H_6, $CHCl_3$, toluene. Spar. sol. most other solvents. Conc. H_2SO_4 ⟶ olive-green sol. $KMnO_4$ ⟶ anthraquinone-1 : 2-dicarboxylic acid. Zn + NH_3 ⟶ naphthanthracene.

Dziewoński, Ritt, *Chem. Abstracts*, 1928, **22**, 2561.
See also second reference above.

***ang*-Naphthaphenazine** ("α"-*Benzophenazine*)

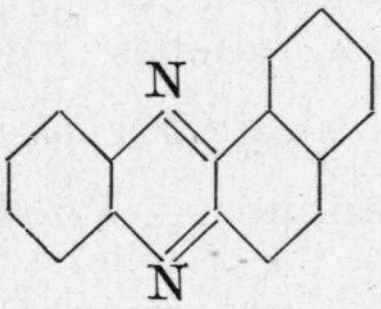

$C_{16}H_{10}N_2$ MW, 230

Bright yellow needles. M.p. 142°. Dist. undecomp. above 360°. Sol. EtOH, Et_2O, AcOH. Insol. H_2O. Sol. conc. H_2SO_4 ⟶ reddish-brown; on dilution ⟶ golden-yellow col. + cryst. ppt. of the azine.

Ethiodide : $C_{18}H_{15}N_2I$. MW, 386. Black needles with violet reflex. M.p. 150° decomp.

N-*Oxide* : $C_{16}H_{10}ON_2$. MW, 246. Green cryst. M.p. 182°.

Kehrmann, Mermod, *Helv. Chim. Acta*, 1927, **10**, 64.
Fischer, Hepp, *Ber.*, 1897, **30**, 393.

***lin*-Naphthaphenazine** ("β"-*Benzophenazine*)

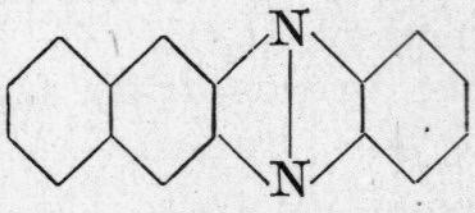

$C_{16}H_{10}N_2$ MW, 230

Red leaflets from C_6H_6. M.p. 233° (darkens). Sol. $CHCl_3$, C_6H_6, hot AcOH. Spar. sol. EtOH. Conc. H_2SO_4 ⟶ yellow sol.

Hinsberg, *Ann.*, 1901, **319**, 261.

Naphthapyrene

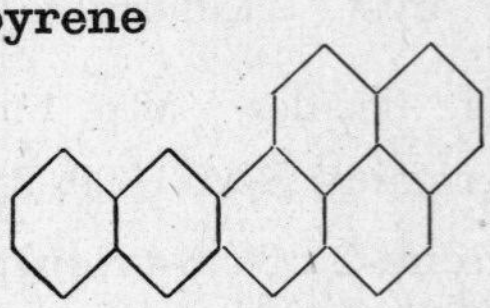

$C_{24}H_{14}$ MW, 302

Deep orange leaflets from C_6H_6. M.p. 273°.

Cook, Hewett, *J. Chem. Soc.*, 1933, 403.

α : β-Naphthapyrone (7 : 8-*Benzchromone*, "α-*naphthochromone*")

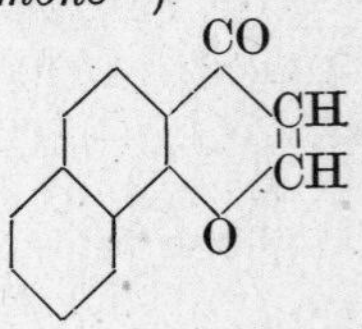

$C_{13}H_8O_2$ MW, 19

Needles from EtOH.Aq. M.p. 125°. Yellow sol. in conc. H_2SO_4 ⟶ intense bluish-green fluor.

Semicarbazone : m.p. 256° decomp.

Pfeiffer, Grimmer, *Ber.*, 1917, **50**, 922.

β : α-Naphthapyrone (5 : 6-*Benzchromone* "β-*naphthochromone*")

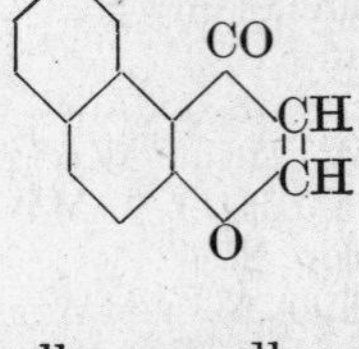

$C_{13}H_8O_2$ MW, 19

Stout pale yellow needles from pet. ether M.p. 103°. Sol. EtOH, C_6H_6, AcOH. Spar sol. cold pet. ether. The colourless sol. in boiling AcOH + 1 drop conc. $H_2SO_4 \longrightarrow$ blue fluor.

Menon, Venkataraman, *J. Chem. Soc.*, 1931, 2593.

α-Naphthaquinoline (7 : 8-*Benzquinoline, naphtha*-1′ : 2′ : 2 : 3-*pyridine*)

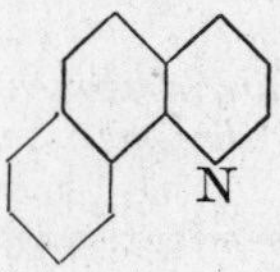

$C_{13}H_9N$ MW, 179

Plates from pet. ether. M.p. 52°. B.p. 338°/719 mm., 223°/47 mm. Sol. ord. org. solvents. Insol. H_2O. Volatile with superheated steam.

B,HCl : yellowish needles. M.p. 213°.

B_2,H_2PtCl_6 : bright yellow prisms. M.p. 224°. Very spar. sol. H_2O.

Methiodide : $C_{14}H_{12}NI$. MW, 321. M.p. 179°.

Picrate : m.p. 191–2°.

Stewart, *J. Chem. Soc.*, 1925, **127**, 1332.
Haid, *Monatsh.*, 1906, **27**, 318.
Claus, Imhoff, *J. prakt. Chem.*, 1898, **57**, 68.

β-Naphthaquinoline (5 : 6-*Benzquinoline, naphtha*-2′ : 1′ : 2 : 3-*pyridine*)

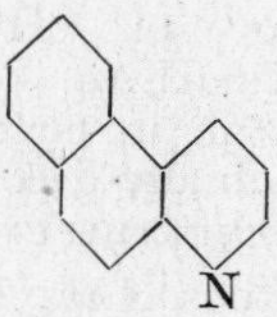

$C_{13}H_9N$ MW, 179

Leaflets from H_2O or pet. ether. M.p. 94°. B.p. 350°/721 mm., 210–15°/22 mm. Difficultly volatile in steam. Sol. ord. org. solvents. Very spar. sol. H_2O. Sol. dil. HCl with fluor.

B,H_2SO_4 : yellow needles. M.p. 90°.

Methiodide : $C_{14}H_{12}NI, 2H_2O$. M.p. 200–5° decomp. (186°).

Ethiodide : $C_{15}H_{14}NI$. MW, 335. M.p. 206° decomp.

Benzyl chloride quaternary salt : $C_{20}H_{16}NCl, 2H_2O$. M.p. anhyd. 196°.

Picrate : m.p. 259° (251–2°).

Bamberger, Müller, *Ber.*, 1891, **24**, 2643.
Knueppel, *Ber.*, 1896, **29**, 708.
Braun, Gruber, *Ber.*, 1922, **55**, 1714.

Naphthastyril (8-*Amino*-1-*naphtholactam*, peri-*naphthazolone*)

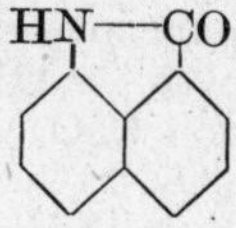

$C_{11}H_7ON$ MW, 169

Fine needles from EtOH. M.p. 180–1°. Sublimes in yellow needles. Sol. EtOH $\longrightarrow$ green fluor. Mod. sol. boiling H_2O. Spar. sol. Et_2O. Sol. warm $H_2SO_4 \longrightarrow$ yellow col.; pptd. unchanged on dilution.

N-*Acetyl* : needles. M.p. 125°.

N-*Benzoyl* : needles. M.p. 170°.

N-1-*Naphthoyl* : needles. M.p. 150°.

N-2-*Naphthoyl* : needles. M.p. 197–8°.

N-p-*Toluenesulphonyl* : m.p. 174°.

Rule, Brown, *J. Chem. Soc.*, 1934, 137.
Corbellini, Barbaro, *Giorn. chim. ind. applicata*, 1933, **15**, 335.
I.G., D.R.P., 531,889, 511,212, (*Chem. Abstracts*, 1932, **26**, 155; 1931, **25**, 1266).
Pisovschi, *Bull. soc. chim.*, 1911, **9**, 86.

1 : 8-Naphthasultam

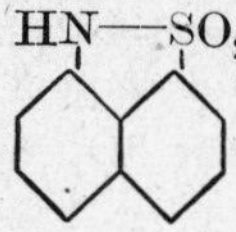

$C_{10}H_7O_2NS$ MW, 205

Needles from C_6H_6. M.p. 177–8°. Sol. Et_2O, hot H_2O. Spar. sol. EtOH, $CHCl_3$, AcOH, C_6H_6. Sols. fluor. green. Alc. $FeCl_3 \longrightarrow$ dark blue ppt.

N-*Me* : $C_{11}H_9O_2NS$. MW, 219. Yellowish needles from MeOH. M.p. 125°.

N-*Et* : $C_{12}H_{11}O_2NS$. MW, 233. M.p. 85°.

N-*Phenyl* : m.p. 158°.

N-p-*Tolyl* : m.p. 152°.

N-*Acetyl* : cryst. from EtOH. M.p. 188°. Sol. $CHCl_3$, AcOH, C_6H_6.

König, Wagner, *Ber.*, 1924, **57**, 1056.
König, Köhler, *Ber.*, 1922, **55**, 2146.
Dannerth, *J. Am. Chem. Soc.*, 1907, **29**, 1319.
Zincke, Jülicher, *Ann.*, 1916, **411**, 202.

1 : 8-Naphthasultam-4-sulphonic Acid

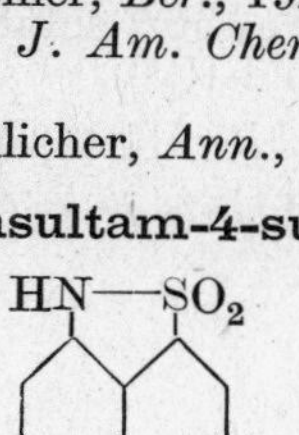

$C_{10}H_7O_5NS_2$ MW, 285

Faintly pink needles. Very sol. H_2O.

Mono-K salt: prisms + $1\frac{1}{2}H_2O$. Decomp. at 300°. Sol. hot, spar. sol. cold H_2O.

Di-K salt: cryst. + $1H_2O$. Fluor. green. Stable at 300°. Sol. H_2O. Spar. sol. EtOH.

Chloride: $C_{10}H_6O_4NS_2Cl$. MW, 303·5. Leaflets. Decomp. above 185°. Sol. C_6H_6, toluene.

Anilide: colourless plates. Decomp. above 230°.

α-*Naphthalide*: leaflets. M.p. 240° decomp.

König, Keil, *Ber.*, 1922, **55**, 2149.

Naphthasultone (1-*Naphthol*-8-*sulphonolactone*)

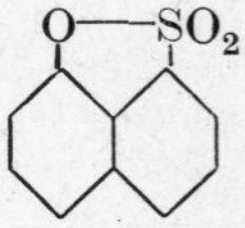

$C_{10}H_6O_3S$ MW, 206

Stout glassy prisms from C_6H_6. M.p. 156°. Dist. undecomp. above 360°. Very sol. $CHCl_3$. Sol. hot C_6H_6. Spar. sol. EtOH. Very spar. sol. CS_2. Insol. H_2O. Stable to cold alkalis.

Erdmann, *Ann.*, 1888, **247**, 344.
Cumming, Muir, *Chem. Abstracts*, 1934, **28**, 4410.

Naphthasultone-3-sulphonic Acid (1-*Naphthol*-8-*sulphonolactone*-3-*sulphonic acid*)

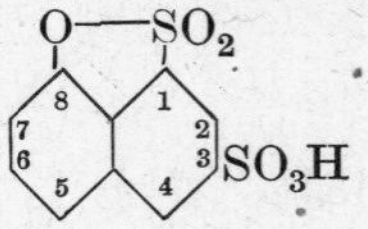

$C_{10}H_6O_6S_2$ MW, 286

Long needles from H_2O. M.p. 241°.

Na salt: needles + $3H_2O$ from H_2O. Sol. 93 parts H_2O at 15°.

Ba salt: needles. Insol. cold H_2O.

Bernthsen, *Ber.*, 1889, **22**, 3331.
B.D.C., E.P., 296,458 (derivs.).

Naphthasultone-4-sulphonic Acid (1-*Naphthol*-8-*sulphonolactone*-4-*sulphonic acid*).

Na salt: leaflets or plates + $3H_2O$ from H_2O. More sol. H_2O than the 3-sulphonate (cf. above).

Ba salt: sol. cold H_2O.

Bernthsen, *Ber.*, 1890, **23**, 3090.

Naphthazarin (5-8-*Dihydroxy*-1 : 4-*naphthoquinone*)

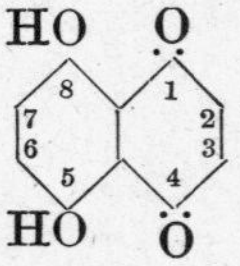

$C_{10}H_6O_4$ MW, 190

Reddish-brown needles with green reflex from EtOH. Sublimes in vac./2–10 mm. Decomp. on heating at ord. press. Mod. sol. AcOH. Spar. sol. H_2O, EtOH, Et_2O. Sol. alkalis ⟶ cornflower blue col. Gives coloured lakes with polyvalent metal hydroxides. Sol. conc. H_2SO_4 with magenta col. Heat with NaOH.Aq. ⟶ naphthapurpurin.

Diacetate: golden-yellow prisms from $CHCl_3$. M.p. 192–3°.

Mono-phenylsemicarbazone: m.p. 218° decomp.

Di-phenylsemicarbazone: m.p. 285–7° decomp. (darkens at 280°).

p-*Bromophenylsemicarbazone*: decomp. at 223°.

p-*Nitrophenylsemicarbazone*: decomp. at 234°.

Ellis, Olpin, Kirk, U.S.P., 1,911,945, (*Chem. Abstracts*, 1933, **27**, 3952).
Dreyfus, F.P., 667,917, (*Chem. Abstracts*, 1930, **24**, 1393).
Zahn, Ochwat, *Ann.*, 1928, **462**, 72.
Pfeiffer, *Ber.*, 1927, **60**, 111.
Charrier, Tocco, *Gazz. chim. ital.*, 1923, **53**, 431.
Wheeler, Edwards, *J. Am. Chem. Soc.*, 1916, **38**, 387.
Friedländer, Silberstern, *Monatsh.*, 1902, **23**, 518.

***o*-Naphthazarin** (5 : 6-*Dihydroxy*-1 : 4-*naphthoquinone*).

Dark red needles with green metallic reflex from H_2O. M.p. 201–2°. Very sol. Me_2CO. Sol. EtOH. Spar. sol. $CHCl_3$, C_6H_6. Insol. ligroin. Sol. in NaOH.Aq. ⟶ cornflower-blue ⟶ green col. Sol. in conc. H_2SO_4 ⟶ dull violet col. and gradually decomp.

Mono-Py salt: glittering green cryst. from Py.

Dimroth, Roos, *Ann.*, 1927, **456**, 177, 186.

Naphthazole.

See α-Naphthindole.

Naphthenes.

Cyclic (5- and 6-membered) saturated hydrocarbons of polymethylene type comprising about one-fourth of the total vol. of the world's crude petroleum oil. They include monocyclic hydrocarbons of from 4 up to 12 carbon atoms and polycyclic of 13 to 26 carbon atoms. They are comparatively stable, not reacting readily with conc. H_2SO_4, nitrating mixture, or halogens. Under the influence of heat or certain chemical reagents, or both combined, they may undergo according to circumstances such reactions as carbon–carbon scission, hydrogenation or dehydrogenation, polymerisation or depolymerisation, isomerisation. Their sulphonic acids are strongly capillary active. Among the simpler naphthenes identified in crude oil are cyclobutane, cyclopentane, methylcyclopentane, cyclohexane, mono-, di- and tri-methylcyclohexanes, cycloheptane, cyclo-octane.

Sakhanow *et al.*, *Chem. Abstracts*, 1934, **28**, 295–9.
Dijk, *ibid.*, 886.
Naphthali, *Fettchem. Umschau*, 1933, **40**, 149, 176, 219 (*Review*).
Egloff, Bollmann, Levinson, *J. Phys. Chem.*, 1931, **35**, 3489 (*Bibl.*, *Review*).
Petrov, *Chem. Abstracts*, 1930, **24**, 4415.
Komppa, *Ber.*, 1929, **62**, 1562.

Naphthenic Acids.

Naphthenecarboxylic acids found in petroleum; one of the simplest has been shown to be 1-methylcyclopentane-carboxylic acid. Members of this series containing 9 and 10 carbon atoms in a monocyclic structure have been made artificially by the cracking of oleic acid in the presence of H_2O and alumina at 380–90°, or by air-oxidation of petroleum at 90–100°. Salts of naphthenic acids have wetting and emulsifying properties. They have also been used as disinfectants and in the resin and lacquer industries.

Malyatskii, Margolis, *Chem. Abstracts*, 1933, **27**, 4153.
Petrov, Ivanov, *J. Am. Chem. Soc.*, 1932, **54**, 239.
Braun *et al.*, *Ann.*, 1931, **490**, 100–79.
Carpenter, *Journal of the Institute of Petroleum Technology*, 1930, **16**, 284 (*Review*).
Komppa, *Ber.*, 1929, **62**, 1562.
Tiutiunnikov, *Chem. Abstracts*, 1927, **21**, 4055.
Augustin, *Seifensieder Zeitung*, 1927, **54**, 899.
Zernik, *Chem. Zentr.*, 1925, II, 1403.
Tanaka, Nagai, *Chem. Abstracts*, 1926, **20**, 2744.

Naphthidine.

See 4 : 4′-Diamino-1 : 1′-dinaphthyl.

α-Naphthil (1 : 1′-*Dinaphthoyl*)

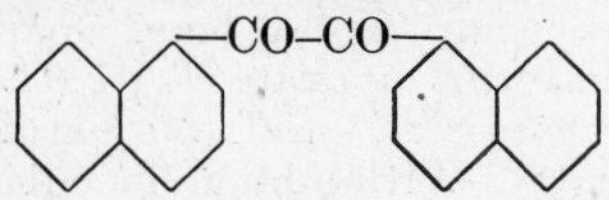

$C_{22}H_{14}O_2$ MW, 310

Yellow prisms from C_6H_6. M.p. 189–90°.
Quinoxaline deriv.: m.p. 203–4°. Conc. H_2SO_4 ⟶ deep indigo-blue col.

Gomberg, Bachmann, *J. Am. Chem. Soc.*, 1930, **52**, 4972.

β-Naphthil (2 : 2′-*Dinaphthoyl*)

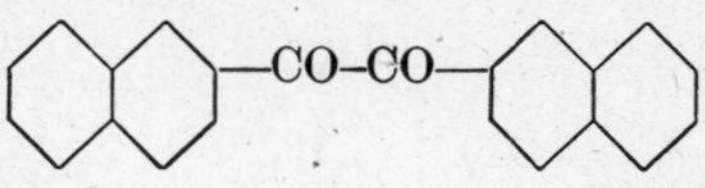

$C_{22}H_{14}O_2$ MW, 310

Cream-coloured needles from hot C_6H_6. M.p. 157–8°.

Gomberg, Bachmann, *J. Am. Chem. Soc.*, 1928, **50**, 2767.

α : **β-Naphthiminazole**

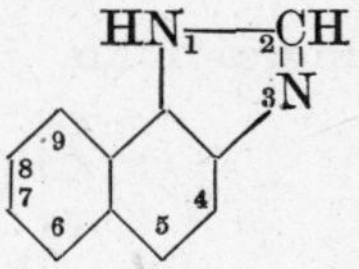

$C_{11}H_8N_2$ MW, 168

Leaflets from C_6H_6. M.p. 178°. Sol. EtOH, Et_2O. Spar. sol. C_6H_6, $CHCl_3$, ligroin.
1-N-*Acetyl*: needles from C_6H_6. M.p. 153°.
1-N-*Benzoyl*: needles from EtOH. M.p. 120°.
1-N-*Me*: $C_{12}H_{10}N_2$. MW, 182. Needles from Et_2O or EtOH.Aq. M.p. 88°.
1-N-*Et*: $C_{13}H_{12}N_2$. MW, 196. Prisms from Et_2O. M.p. 129–30°. Et_2O sols. fluor. blue.
3-N-*Et*: yellow oil. *$HgCl_2$ double salt*: m.p. 182°.

Fischer, Dietrich, Weiss, *J. prakt. Chem.*, 1920, **100**, 171.
Fischer, Reindl, Fezer, *Ber.*, 1901, **34**, 933.

***peri*-Naphthiminazole.**

See Perimidine.

α-Naphthindane (4 : 5-*Benzhydrindene*, 2 : 3-*dihydronaphthindene*)

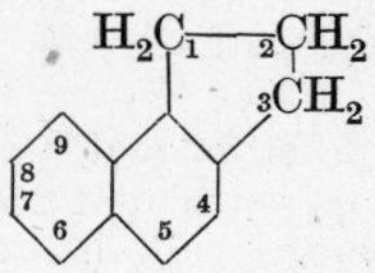

$C_{13}H_{12}$ MW, 168

Colourless oil with faint aromatic odour. B.p. 294–5°/757 mm. D_4^{20} 1·066. n_D^{20} 1·6290. Tends to resinify on exposure to light. $Na_2Cr_2O_7$ + AcOH ⟶ α-naphthindanone-3. Alk. $K_3Fe(CN)_6$ ⟶ naphthalene-1 : 3-dicarboxylic acid.
Picrate: m.p. 110°.

Kruber, *Ber.*, 1932, **65**, 1383.

peri-Naphthindane (peri-*Trimethylenenaphthalene*)

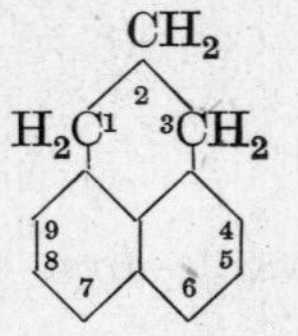

$C_{13}H_{12}$ MW, 168

Silky leaflets from dil. EtOH. M.p. 68–9°.
Picrate : m.p. 134–5°.

Fleischer, Retze, *Ber.*, 1922, **55**, 3280.

α : β-Naphthindandione (4 : 5-*Benzdiketohydrindene*)

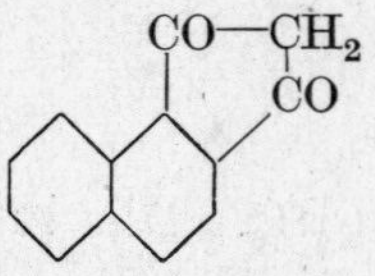

$C_{13}H_8O_2$ MW, 196

Yellow needles from EtOH. M.p. 180°. Sol. AcOH. Very spar. sol. Et_2O, C_6H_6. Easily sol. alkalis with red col.
Benzylidene deriv. : m.p. 190°. Hyd. by hot alkalis into its components.
Di-phenylhydrazone : m.p. 220° decomp.

Noto, *Gazz. chim. ital.*, 1915, **45**, ii, 127, **427**.

peri-Naphthindandione (1 : 8-*Malonylnaphthalene*)

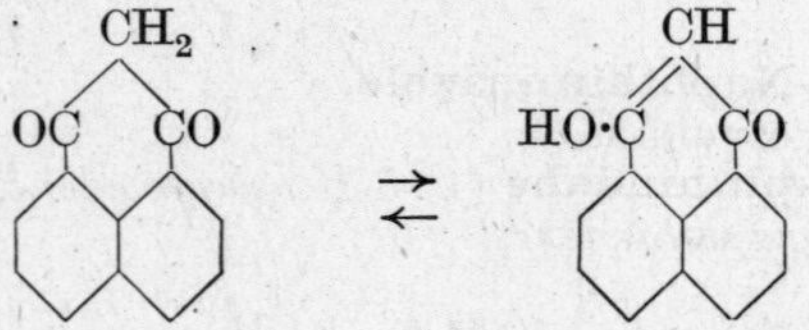

$C_{13}H_8O_2$ MW, 196

Yellow or reddish-brown cryst. from AcOH. M.p. 265° decomp. (brown at 250°). Sol. EtOH, AcOH, weak bases, alkali carbonates. Very spar. sol. H_2O, xylene, pet. ether.
1-*Me enol-ether* : $C_{14}H_{10}O_2$. MW, 210. Yellowish plates. M.p. 144°.
1-*Et enol-ether* : $C_{15}H_{12}O_2$. MW, 224. Yellowish brown cryst. M.p. 148°.

Badische, D.R.P., 283,365, (*Chem. Zentr.*, 1915, I, 965).
Fleischer, Retze, *Ber.*, 1922, **55**, 3280.

α-Naphthindanone (4 : 5-*Benzhydrindone*)

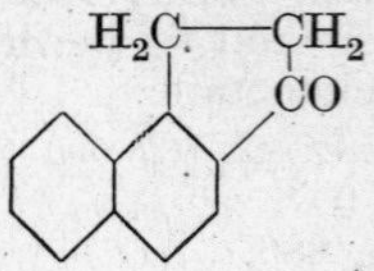

$C_{13}H_{10}O$ MW, 182

Colourless needles from MeOH or ligroin. M.p. 103°. Yellow sol. in conc. H_2SO_4 with blue fluor.

I.G., D.R.P., 512,717, (*Chem. Abstracts*, 1931, **25**, 1260).
Mayer, Müller, *Ber.*, 1927, **60**, 2283.

peri-Naphthindanone (7 : 8-*Dihydrophenalone*-9)

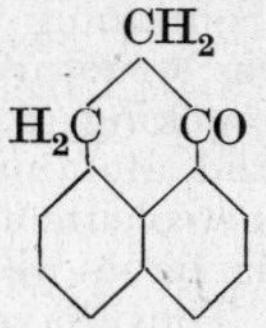

$C_{13}H_{10}O$ MW, 182

Yellow leaflets. M.p. 85–6°. Unstable.
Oxime : needles from EtOH. M.p. 124–5°.
Benzylidene deriv. : yellow cryst. from MeOH. M.p. 163°.

Mayer, Sieglitz, *Ber.*, 1922, **55**, 1844.
Braun, Manz, Reinsch, *Ann.*, 1929, **468**, 301.
Cf. Cook, Hewitt, *J. Chem. Soc.*, 1934, 369, 373.

peri-Naphthindantrione

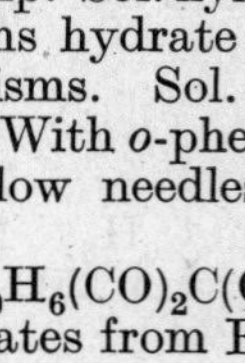

$C_{13}H_6O_3$ MW, 210

M.p. 273° decomp. Sol. xylene. Spar. sol. C_6H_6. In moist air forms hydrate $C_{10}H_6(CO)_2C(OH)_2$, golden-yellow prisms. Sol. 50 parts hot, 500 parts cold H_2O. With *o*-phenylenediamine ⟶ a phenazine, yellow needles from C_6H_6, m.p. 255–6°.
Alcoholate : $C_{10}H_6(CO)_2C(OH)(OC_2H_5)$. MW, 256. Triclinic plates from EtOH. Decomp. at 140°.

Errera, *Gazz. chim. ital.*, 1913, **43**, i, 583.

α-Naphthindazole

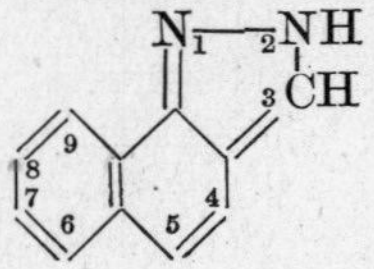

$C_{11}H_8N_2$ MW, 168

M.p. 158°.
2-N-*Acetyl* : m.p. 108–9°.
Picrate : m.p. 193°.

Veselý, Medvedeva, Müller, *J. Chem. Soc. Abstracts*, 1935, 991.

β-Naphthindazole

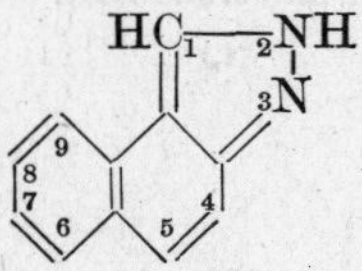

$C_{11}H_8N_2$ MW, 168

M.p. 231°.
2-N-*Acetyl* : m.p. 116·5°.
Picrate : m.p. 217–18°.

See previous reference.

Naphthindenone.
See Phenalone.

α-Naphthindole (*Naphthazole*)

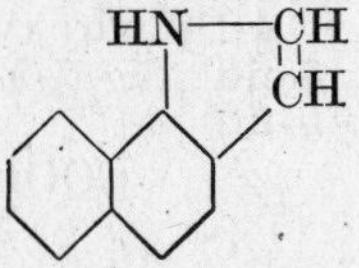

$C_{12}H_9N$ MW, 167

Cryst. from MeOH. M.p. 173°.

Mayer, Oppenheimer, *Ber.*, 1918, **51**, 1240.

2 : 3-Naphthindole

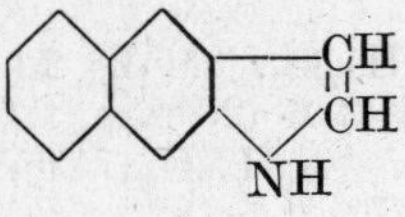

$C_{12}H_9N$ MW, 167

Cryst. M.p. 68–70°. Sol. ord. org. solvents. Pine-chip reaction ⟶ violet col.

I.G., D.R.P., 516,675, (*Chem. Zentr.*, 1931, I, 1832).

***peri*-Naphthindone.**
See Phenalone.

Naphthionic Acid (1-*Naphthylamine-4-sulphonic acid*)

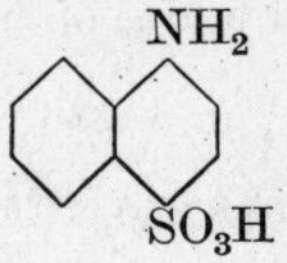

$C_{10}H_9O_3NS$ MW, 223

Needles + $\frac{1}{2}H_2O$ from H_2O. Very spar. sol. H_2O. Sols. of the acid and its salts fluor. strongly blue. $k = 2{\cdot}1 \times 10^{-3}$ at 25°. NaHg ⟶ 1-naphthylamine + SO_2. The Na salt + SO_2 in H_2O at 95° ⟶ 1-naphthol-4-sulphonic acid. Important intermediate for azo dyestuffs, *e.g.* Congo Red, Benzopurpurins, and Fast Reds.

N-*Acetyl* : needles. Sol. H_2O, EtOH. Forms series of arylamine salts of definite m.ps. *Et ester* : m.p. 148°. *Amide* : m.p. 241°. *Anilide* : m.p. 231°.

N-*Me* : $C_{11}H_{11}O_3NS$. MW, 237. Needles. Sol. H_2O. *Na salt* : needles. Very sol. H_2O.

N-*Di-Me* : $C_{12}H_{13}O_3NS$. MW, 251. Prisms + $1H_2O$ from H_2O.

Amide : $C_{10}H_{10}O_2N_2S$. MW, 222. Needles from EtOH. M.p. 206°.

Langguth, *Chimie et Industrie*, 1930, **24**, 31, (*Chem. Abstracts*, 1930, **24**, 5035).
I.G., E.P., 326,022, (*Ibid.*, 4170).
Wahl, Vermeylen, *Bull. soc. chim.*, 1927, **41**, 522 ; *Compt. rend.*, 1927, **184**, 334.
Forster, Watson, *J. Soc. Chem. Ind.*, 1927, **46**, 225T.
Ehrhardt, Hereward, E.P., 254,402, (*Chem. Abstracts*, 1927, **21**, 2479).
Rupe, Metzger, *Helv. Chim. Acta*, 1925, **8**, 842.
Bayer, D.R.P., 255,724, (*Chem. Zentr.*, 1913, I, 478).
Füssganger, *Ber.*, 1902, **35**, 977.
Badische, D.R.P., 117,471, (*Chem. Zentr.*, 1901, I, 349).
Bretscheider, *J. prakt. Chem.*, 1897, **55**, 299.
Paul, *Z. angew. Chem.*, 1896, **9**, 685.

1 : 2-Naphthisatin (α-*Naphthisatin*)

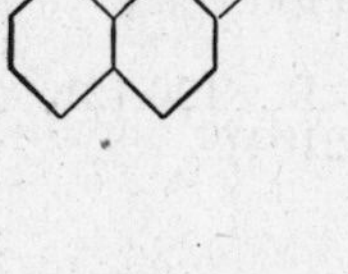

$C_{12}H_7O_2N$ MW, 197

Red needles from EtOH. M.p. 255°. Spar. sol. EtOH. Very spar. sol. H_2O. Green sol. in conc. H_2SO_4, on addn. of trace of thiophene ⟶ blue col.

Phenylhydrazone : m.p. 286° (262°).

I.G., E.P., 308,980, (*Chem. Zentr.*, 1930, I, 287).
I.G., E.P., 286,358, (*Chem. Abstracts*, 1929, **23**, 156).
Stollé, *J. prakt. Chem.*, 1922, **105**, 144.
Martinet, *Ann. chim.*, 1919, **11**, 94, 118; *Compt. rend.*, 1918, **166**, 851; cf. *Chem. Zentr.*, 1919, III, 711.
Mayer, Oppenheimer, *Ber.*, 1918, **51**, 1241, 1245.

2 : 1-Naphthisatin (β-*Naphthisatin*)

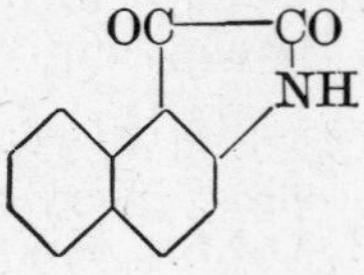

$C_{12}H_7O_2N$ MW, 197

Red needles from EtOH. M.p. 253° (248°). Insol. H_2O. Alc. KOH ⟶ dark violet col. Sol. in conc. H_2SO_4 ⟶ intense reddish-brown col.

Phenylhydrazone : m.p. 225°.

N-*Et* : m.p. 173°. *Phenylhydrazone* : m.p. 180°.

Kränzlein, Wolfram, Hausdörfer, U.S.P., 1,792,170, (*Chem. Abstracts*, 1931, **25**, 1845).
Wahl, Lobeck, *Ann. chim.*, 1929, **12**, 156.
See also second and third references above.

1 : 8-Naphthisatin (peri-*Naphthisatin*)

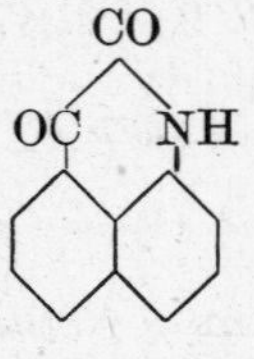

$C_{12}H_7O_2N$ MW, 197

Cryst. from $PhNO_2$. M.p. above 300°. Sol. in conc. H_2SO_4 with reddish-yellow col. Sol. alkalis with intense red col.

I.G., Swiss P., 126,721, (*Chem. Zentr.*, 1929, II, 2104).

***meso*-Naphthodianthrene**

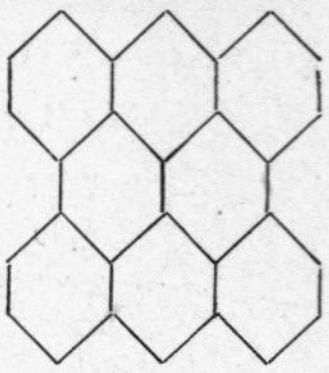

$C_{28}H_{14}$ MW, 350

Stout dark blue needles with violet cast from $PhNO_2$. Sublimes. Very spar. sol. ord. org. solvents ⟶ blue sols. Conc. H_2SO_4 ⟶ green-blue-violet col.

Scholl, Meyer, *Ber.*, 1934, **67**, 1237.

***meso*-Naphthodianthrone**

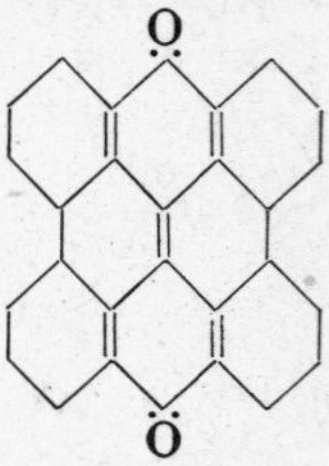

$C_{28}H_{12}O_2$ MW, 380

Glittering brown micro-leaflets from quinoline. Does not melt, but slowly decomp. at 550°.

Scholl, *Ber.*, 1919, **52**, 1835.

Naphthohydroquinone.

See 1 : 2- and 1 : 4-Dihydroxynaphthalenes.

1-Naphthoic Acid (*Naphthalene*-1-*carboxylic acid*, α-*naphthoic acid*)

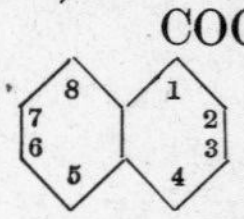

$C_{11}H_8O_2$ MW, 172

Needles from AcOH.Aq. M.p. 161°. Sol. EtOH. Spar. sol. H_2O. Heat of comb. C_p 1232·6 Cal., C_v 1232·0 Cal. $k = 2{\cdot}04 \times 10^{-4}$ at 25°.

Et ester : $C_{13}H_{12}O_2$. MW, 200. B.p. 309°, 220·5°/74 mm., 183–6°/20 mm. D_{15}^{15} 1·1274.

d-*Amyl ester* : $C_{16}H_{18}O_2$. MW, 242. B.p. 222°/25 mm. $[\alpha]_D^{20}$ + 5·28°.

Bornyl ester : $C_{21}H_{24}O_2$. MW, 308. M.p. 69–70°. $[\alpha]_D^{20}$ − 33·5° in EtOH.

l-*Menthyl ester* : $C_{21}H_{26}O_2$. MW, 310. B.p. 215°/20 mm. D_{15}^{15} 1·0557. $[\alpha]_D^{20}$ − 79·5° in EtOH.

Chloride : $C_{11}H_7OCl$. MW, 190·5. M.p. 20°. B.p. 297·5°, 172–3°/15 mm., 163°/10 mm.

Amide : $C_{11}H_9ON$. MW, 171. M.p. 202°.

Anhydride : $C_{22}H_{14}O_3$. MW, 326. M.p. 145°.
Nitrile : *see* 1-Naphthonitrile.
Piperidide : m.p. 85–7°.

Gilman, McCorkle, Calloway, *J. Am. Chem. Soc.*, 1934, **56**, 745.
Salkind, *Ber.*, 1934, **67**, 1033.
Gilman, St. John, Schulze, *Organic Syntheses*, 1931, XI, 80.
McMaster, Langreck, *J. Am. Chem. Soc.*, 1917, **39**, 106.
Whitmore, Fox, *J. Am. Chem. Soc.*, 1929, **51**, 3363.
Loder, Whitmore, *J. Am. Chem. Soc.*, 1935, **57**, 2727.

2-Naphthoic Acid (*Naphthalene-2-carboxylic acid, β-naphthoic acid*).

Needles from ligroin, plates from Me_2CO. M.p. 184° (185·5°). Sol. EtOH, Et_2O, $CHCl_3$. Spar. sol. ligroin, hot H_2O. Heat of comb. C_p 1228·4 Cal., C_v 1227·8 Cal. $k = 6{\cdot}78 \times 10^{-5}$ ($5{\cdot}23 \times 10^{-5}$) at 25°.
Me ester : $C_{12}H_{10}O_2$. MW, 186. M.p. 77°. B.p. 290°.
Et ester : f.p. 32°. B.p. 308–9°, 224°/74 mm. D_{15}^{15} 1·1212.
d-*Amyl ester* : b.p. 265°/about 100 mm. D_4^{20} 1·0531. $[\alpha]_D^{20} + 9{\cdot}34°$.
Bornyl ester : m.p. 88–90°. $[\alpha]_D^{20} - 34{\cdot}5°$ in EtOH.
l-*Menthyl ester* : m.p. 77–77·5°. $[\alpha]_D^{20} - 98{\cdot}5°$ in C_6H_6.
dl-*Menthyl ester* : m.p. 70°.
Neomenthyl ester : m.p. 98°.
Chloride : m.p. 43°. B.p. 304–6°.
Amide : m.p. 192° (195°).
Anhydride : m.p. 133–4°.
Nitrile : *see* 2-Naphthonitrile.
Piperidide : m.p. 88–90°.

Gilman, St. John, *Rec. trav. chim.*, 1929, **48**, 743.
Salkind, *Ber.*, 1934, **67**, 1033.

1-Naphthol (1-*Hydroxynaphthalene, α-naphthol*)

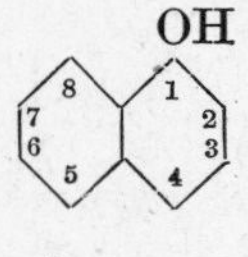

$C_{10}H_8O$ MW, 144

F.p. 96·1° (94·2°). M.p. 94°. B.p. 278–80°. Sol. EtOH, Et_2O, $CHCl_3$, C_6H_6. Spar. sol. H_2O. $D_4^{98\cdot7}$ 1·09539. $n_D^{98\cdot7}$ 1·62064. Sublimes. Heat of comb. C_p 1188·5 Cal. Volatile in steam. Reduces Tollen's. $FeCl_3 \longrightarrow$ α-dinaphthol. CrO_3 in AcOH $\longrightarrow$ α-naphthoquinone. Na + amyl alcohol $\longrightarrow$ *ar*-tetrahydro-1-naphthol.
Chloroformyl : b.p. 132°/5 mm.
Acetyl : m.p. 48–9°.
Chloroacetyl : m.p. 48°.
Oxalyl : m.p. 161–2°.
Succinyl : m.p. 155°.
Benzoyl : m.p. 56°.
3 : 5-*Dinitrobenzoyl* : m.p. 217·4°.
Salicyloyl : alphol. M.p. 83°.
Sulphite : m.p. 92–3°.
Acid sulphate : m.p. 182°.
Di-acid phosphate : m.p. 142°.
Phosphate : m.p. 145° (148–9°).
Picrate : m.p. 189°.
Me ether : *see* Methyl 1-naphthyl Ether.
Et ether : *see* Ethyl 1-naphthyl Ether.
Propyl ether : $C_{13}H_{14}O$. MW, 186. B.p. 298°/762 mm. $D_4^{18\cdot4}$ 1·04471. $n_D^{18\cdot4}$ 1·59277.
Isoamyl ether : $C_{15}H_{18}O$. MW, 214. B.p. 317–19°/741·9 mm. $D_4^{14\cdot2}$ 1·00689. $n_D^{14\cdot2}$ 1·57049.
α-*Glyceryl ether* : $C_{13}H_{14}O_3$. MW, 218. M.p. 95°.
α : α-*Diglyceryl ether* : $C_{23}H_{20}O_3$. MW, 344. M.p. 116°.
Phenyl ether : $C_{16}H_{12}O$. MW, 220. M.p. 55–6°. B.p. 349·5°/753 mm.
p-*Nitrobenzyl ether* : $C_{17}H_{13}O_3N$. MW, 267. M.p. 140°.
1-*Naphthyl ether* : *see* 1 : 1′-Dinaphthyl Ether.

Cotton, U.S.P., 1,962,137, (*Chem. Abstracts*, 1934, **28**, 4748).
Vendelshtein, Shpinel, *Chem. Abstracts*, 1933, **27**, 5320.
Franzen, Kempf, *Ber.*, 1917, **50**, 103.

2-Naphthol (2-*Hydroxynaphthalene, β-naphthol*).

Plates. M.p. 123°. B.p. 285–6°. Sol. EtOH, Et_2O, $CHCl_3$, C_6H_6. Spar. sol. H_2O, pet. ether. Sublimes. Volatile in steam. Heat of comb. C_p 1190·3. Cal. Reduces Tollen's. $FeCl_3 \longrightarrow$ β-dinaphthol. Na + AcOH $\longrightarrow$ *ac*-tetrahydro-1-naphthol + *ar*-tetrahydro-2-naphthol.
Formyl : b.p. 117°/1·5 mm. D^{23} 1·1554. n_D^{20} 1·60932.
Acetyl : m.p. 70°.
Propionyl : m.p. 51°.
Isobutyryl : m.p. 43°.
Isovaleryl : b.p. 180–4°/20 mm.
Oxalyl : m.p. 191° (188–9°).
Malonyl : m.p. 146–7°.
Succinyl : m.p. 163°.
Benzoyl : m.p. 107°.
o-*Nitrobenzoyl* : m.p. 112°.

m-*Nitrobenzoyl* : m.p. 134°.
p-*Nitrobenzoyl* : m.p. 169°.
3 : 5-*Dinitrobenzoyl* : m.p. 210·2°.
Salicyloyl : betol. M.p. 95°.
Di-acid phosphate : m.p. 167°.
Acid phosphate : m.p. 147–8°.
Phosphate : m.p. 111°.
Picrate : m.p. 157°.
Me ether : *see* Methyl 2-naphthyl Ether.
Et ether : *see* Ethyl 2-naphthyl Ether.
Propyl ether : $C_{13}H_{14}O$. MW, 186. M.p. 39·5–40°. *Picrate* : m.p. 75°.
Isopropyl ether : m.p. 41°. *Picrate* : m.p. 92°.
Isobutyl ether : $C_{14}H_{16}O$. MW, 200. M.p. 33°. *Picrate* : m.p. 80–80·5°.
Isoamyl ether : $C_{15}H_{18}O$. MW, 214. M.p. 26°. B.p. 323–6°/759·3 mm. decomp. D_4^{12} 1·01555. n_D^{12} 1·57679. *Picrate* : m.p. 90·5–100°.
α-*Glyceryl ether* : $C_{13}H_{14}O_3$. MW, 218. M.p. 109–10°.
Phenyl ether : $C_{16}H_{12}O$. MW, 220. M.p. 46°. B.p. 335·5°/753 mm.
o-*Nitrophenyl ether* : $C_{16}H_{11}O_3N$. MW, 265. Prisms from MeOH. M.p. 58°.
2 : 4-*Dinitrophenyl ether* : $C_{16}H_{10}O_5N_2$. MW, 310. M.p. 95°.
p-*Tolyl ether* : $C_{17}H_{14}O$. MW, 234. M.p. 135°.
Benzyl ether : $C_{17}H_{14}O$. MW, 234. M.p. 99°.
p-*Nitrobenzyl ether* : $C_{17}H_{13}O_3N$. MW, 279. M.p. 106·5°.
1-*Naphthyl ether* : *see* 1 : 2′-Dinaphthyl Ether.
2-*Naphthyl ether* : *see* 2 : 2′-Dinaphthyl Ether.

Vorozhtov, Krasova, *Chem. Abstracts*, 1933, **27**, 5321.
Franzen, Kempf, *Ber.*, 1917, **50**, 104.

Naphtholactone.
See under 8-Hydroxy-1-naphthoic Acid.

Naphthol-carboxylic Acid.
See Hydroxynaphthoic Acid.

1-Naphthol-2 : 4-dicarboxylic Acid

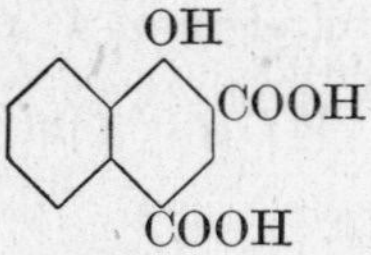

$C_{12}H_8O_5$ MW, 232

Cryst. from EtOH. M.p. 304° decomp. Blue fluor. in EtOH. $FeCl_3 \longrightarrow$ green col.
Di-Me ester : $C_{14}H_{12}O_5$. MW, 260. M.p. 144°.
Di-Et ester : $C_{16}H_{16}O_5$. MW, 288. M.p. 98°.
Me ether : $C_{13}H_{10}O_5$. MW, 246. M.p. 252° decomp. *Diamide* : $C_{13}H_{12}O_3N_2$. MW, 244. M.p. 198° decomp. *Dianilide* : m.p. 262° decomp.

Soc. anon. pour l'ind. chim. à Bâle, D.R.P., 373,736, (*Chem. Abstracts*, 1924, **18**, 2174).
Montmollin, Spieler, U.S.P., 1,474,928, (*Chem. Abstracts*, 1924, **18**, 693).
Menon, *J. Chem. Soc.*, 1935, 1061.

1-Naphthol-2 : 4-disulphonic Acid

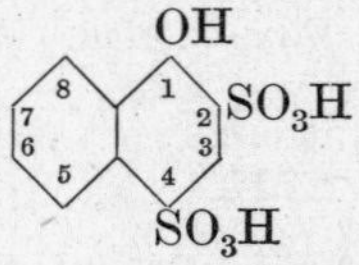

$C_{10}H_8O_7S_2$ MW, 304

K salt sol. gives with $FeCl_3$, a blue col., with $CH_3{\cdot}COOK$, a red col. Heat with acids $\longrightarrow$ 1-naphthol-2- and -4-sulphonic acids.
Dichloride : $C_{10}H_6O_5S_2Cl_2$. MW, 341. M.p. 149°.
Dianilide : m.p. 228°.

Bayer, D.R.P., 255,724, (*Chem. Zentr.*, 1913, I, 478).
Pollak, Gebauer-Fülnegg, Blumenstock-Halward, *Monatsh.*, 1928, **49**, 193.
Conrad, Fischer, *Ann.*, 1893, **273**, 105.

1-Naphthol-2 : 5-disulphonic Acid.
NaOH fusion $\longrightarrow$ 1 : 5-dihydroxynaphthalene-2-sulphonic acid.

Bayer, D.R.P., 68,344.

1-Naphthol-2 : 7-disulphonic Acid.
Zn salt sol. H_2O. $HNO_3 \longrightarrow$ 2 : 4-dinitro-1-naphthol-7-sulphonic acid.

Vignon, D.R.P., 32,291.
Friedländer, Taussig, *Ber.*, 1897, **30**, 1463.

1-Naphthol-3 : 6-disulphonic Acid

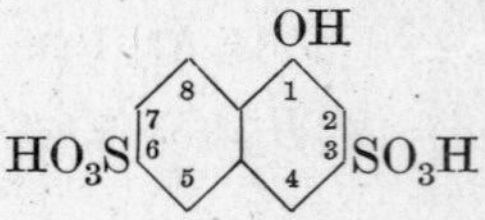

$C_{10}H_8O_7S_2$ MW, 304

Sol. H_2O. $FeCl_3 \longrightarrow$ blue col. Alkali salt sols. have green fluor.
Dichloride : *carbethoxyl deriv.*, m.p. 95°.

Gebauer-Fuelnegg, Haemmerle, *J. Am. Chem. Soc.*, 1931, **53**, 2653.
Gürke, Rudolph, D.R.P., 38,281.

1-Naphthol-3 : 7-disulphonic Acid.
Heat with $NH_3 + NH_4Cl \longrightarrow$ 3-amino-1-

naphthol-7-sulphonic acid + 1 : 3-naphthalenediamine-7-sulphonic acid.

Freund, D.R.P., 27,346.
Kalle, D.R.P., 233,934, (*Chem. Zentr.*, 1911, I, 1468).

1-Naphthol-3 : 8-disulphonic Acid (ε-*Acid, epsilon acid*).

K salt sol. ⟶ blue col. with $FeCl_3$.
Na salt : prisms + $6H_2O$. Sol. H_2O.
Dichloride : *carbethoxyl deriv.*, m.p. 180–1°.
8-*Amide* : $C_{10}H_9O_6S_2N$. MW, 303. Cryst. Sol. H_2O.

B.D.C., F.P., 653,595, (*Chem. Abstracts*, 1929, **23**, 3816) ; E.P., 296, 458.
Gebauer-Fuelnegg, Haemmerle, *J. Am. Chem. Soc.*, 1931, **53**, 2653.
Kalle, D.R.P., 64,979.

1-Naphthol-4 : 7-disulphonic Acid.

Dichloride : *carbethoxyl deriv.*, m.p. 120°.

Friedländer, Taussig, *Ber.*, 1897, **30**, 1460.
Gebauer-Fuelnegg, Haemmerle, *J. Am. Chem. Soc.*, 1931, **53**, 2652.
Oehler, D.R.P., 74,744.

1-Naphthol-4 : 8-disulphonic Acid (α-*Naphthol-disulphonic acid-S, Schöllkopf's Acid*).

HNO_3 ⟶ 2 : 4 - dinitro - 1 - naphthol - 8 - sulphonic acid. NaOH fusion ⟶ 1 : 8-dihydroxynaphthalene-4-sulphonic acid.
Dichloride : *carbethoxyl deriv.*, m.p. 177–9°.

Gebauer-Fuelnegg, Haemmerle, *J. Am. Chem. Soc.*, 1931, **53**, 2653.
Bernthsen, *Ber.*, 1890, **23**, 3092.
Bucherer, *J. prakt. Chem.*, 1904, **69**, 80; 1904, **70**, 347.

1-Naphthol-5 : 8-disulphonic Acid.

Alk. fusion ⟶ 1 : 8-dihydroxynaphthalene-4-sulphonic acid.

Bayer, D.R.P., 70,857.

1-Naphthol-6 : 8-disulphonic Acid.

$FeCl_3$ ⟶ green col. Alk. fusion ⟶ 1 : 8-dihydroxynaphthalene-3-sulphonic acid.

Kalle, D.R.P., 82,563.
Bucherer, *J. prakt. Chem.*, 1904, **70**, 347.

2-Naphthol-1 : 5-disulphonic Acid

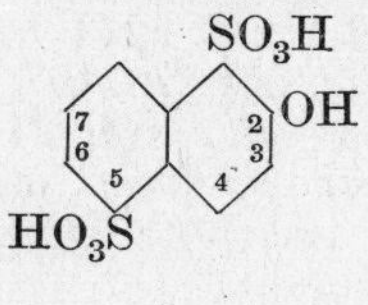

$C_{10}H_8O_7S_2$ MW, 304

Dichloride : $C_{10}H_6O_5S_2Cl_2$. MW, 341. M.p. 177°.
Dianilide : m.p. 231°.

Pollak, Gebauer-Fülnegg, Blumenstock-Halward, *Monatsh.*, 1929, **53** & **54**, 83.

2-Naphthol-1 : 6-disulphonic Acid.

Cryst. + $1H_2O$ from H_2O. $FeCl_3$ ⟶ red col. Acids at 90° ⟶ 2-naphthol-6-sulphonic acid.
Dichloride : m.p. 111°.
Dianilide : m.p. 191°.
Et ether : *diamide*, $C_{12}H_{14}O_5N_2S_2$. MW, 330. M.p. 253–4°.

Engel, *J. Am. Chem. Soc.*, 1930, **52**, 2842.
Lapworth, *Chem. News*, 1895, **71**, 206.

2-Naphthol-1 : 7-disulphonic Acid.

Salt sols. show blue fluor. Ba salt sol. H_2O. Heat with dil. HCl ⟶ 2-naphthol-7-sulphonic acid.
p-*Toluidine salt* : m.p. 219°.
Dichloride : m.p. 169°.
Dianilide : m.p. 233°.

Bayer, D.R.P., 77,596.
Pollak, Gebauer-Fülnegg, Blumenstock-Halward, *Monatsh.*, 1929, **53** & **54**, 83.
Forster, Keyworth, *J. Soc. Chem. Ind.*, 1927, **46**, 28T.

2-Naphthol-3 : 6-disulphonic Acid (*R-Acid*).

Needles. Sol. H_2O, EtOH. Insol. Et_2O. Salt sols. show bluish-green fluor. Alk. fusion ⟶ 2:3-dihydroxynaphthalene-6-sulphonic acid. The disodium salt (R Salt) is used extensively in the manufacture of azo dyestuffs.
Ba salt : spar. sol. H_2O. Insol. EtOH.
Aniline salt : m.p. 254°.
p-*Chloroaniline salt* : m.p. 254°.
m-*Nitroaniline salt* : m.p. 299°.
o-*Toluidine salt* : m.p. 257°.
m-*Toluidine salt* : m.p. 242°.
p-*Toluidine salt* : m.p. 250°.
m-*Xylidine salt* : m.p. 196°.
ψ-*Cumidine salt* : m.p. 301°.
1-*Naphthylamine salt* : m.p. 292°.
2-*Naphthylamine salt* : m.p. 304°.
p-*Anisidine salt* : m.p. 267°.
Dianisidine salt : m.p. 317–18°.
p-*Phenetidine salt* : m.p. 244°.
Dichloride : $C_{10}H_6O_5S_2Cl_2$. MW, 341. *Carbethoxyl deriv.*, m.p. 125°.
Anilide : m.p. 202°.

Et ether: *dichloride*, $C_{12}H_{10}O_5Cl_2S_2$. MW, 369. M.p. 121°.

Pollak, Blumenstock-Halward, *Monatsh.*, 1928, **49**, 209.
Forster, Keyworth, *J. Soc. Chem. Ind.*, 1927, **46**, 27T.
Kawaguchi, *Chem. Abstracts*, 1924, **18**, 2891.
Vorontzov, Sokolova, *Chem. Abstracts*, 1934, **28**, 3730.
Shcherbachev, Bashkirova, *ibid.*, 5370.
Masters, E.P., 210,120, (*Chem. Abstracts*, 1924, **18**, 1673).

2-Naphthol-3 : 7-disulphonic Acid.
Salt sols. show green fluor. Alk. fusion ⟶ 2 : 7-dihydroxynaphthalene-3-sulphonic acid.
Ba salt: spar. sol. H_2O.

Bayer, D.R.P., 78,569.
Shcherbachev, Bashkirova, *Chem. Abstracts*, 1934, **28**, 5370.
Forster, Keyworth, *J. Soc. Chem. Ind.*, 1927, **46**, 28T.

2-Naphthol-4 : 7-disulphonic Acid.
Heated with aniline and aniline hydrochloride ⟶ N:N′-diphenyl-1 : 3-naphthylenediamine-6-sulphonic acid.

Bayer, D.R.P., 77,860.

2-Naphthol-4 : 8-disulphonic Acid (β-*Naphtholdisulphonic acid-C*).
Sol. H_2O. Salt sols. show blue fluor.

Cassella, D.R.P., 65,997.

2-Naphthol-6 : 8-disulphonic Acid (*G-Acid*, β-*naphthol-γ-disulphonic acid*).
The disodium salt (G Salt) is used as intermediate in the manufacture of azo dyestuffs.
o-*Chloroaniline salt*: m.p. 255°.
p-*Chloroaniline salt*: m.p. 242°.
o-*Toluidine salt*: m.p. 270–1°.
p-*Toluidine salt*: m.p. 294°.
ψ-*Cumidine salt*: m.p. 300–3°.
p-*Phenetidine salt*: m.p. 214–15°.
Dianisidine salt: m.p. 317°.
1-*Naphthylamine salt*: m.p. 302°.
2-*Naphthylamine salt*: m.p. 254°.
Dichloride: m.p. 161–2°. *Carbethoxyl deriv.*, m.p. 131°.
Dianilide: m.p. 195°. *Carbethoxyl deriv.*, m.p. 178°.
Et ether: *dichloride*, $C_{12}H_{10}O_5Cl_2S_2$. MW, 369. M.p. 158°.

Masters, E.P., 210,120, (*Chem. Abstracts*, 1924, **18**, 1673).

Pollak, Blumenstock-Halward, *Monatsh.*, 1928, **49**, 208.
Forster, Keyworth, *J. Soc. Chem. Ind.*, 1927, **46**, 27T.
Kawaguchi, *Chem. Abstracts*, 1924, **18**, 2891.

1-Naphthol-2-sulphonic Acid

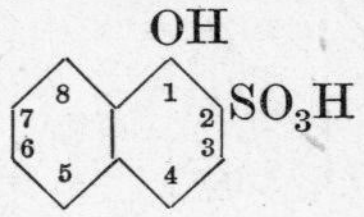

$C_{10}H_8O_4S$ MW, 224

Plates from H_2O. Does not melt below 250°. Sol. hot H_2O. Insol. Et_2O. K salt ⟶ blue col. with $FeCl_3$.
Chloride: *acetyl deriv.*, m.p. 87·5°. *Carbethoxyl deriv.*, m.p. 130°.
Anilide: *acetyl deriv.*, m.p. 157·5°.
p-*Toluidide*: *acetyl deriv.*, m.p. 135·5°.

Anschutz, *Ann.*, 1918, **415**, 64.
Bayer, F.P., 429,999, (*Chem. Abstracts*, 1912, **6**, 2536).
Gebauer-Fülnegg, Gluckmann, *Monatsh.*, 1929, **53** & **54**, 104.

1-Naphthol-3-sulphonic Acid.
Chloride: *carbethoxyl deriv.*, m.p. 140°.
Anilide: m.p. 236°. *Carbethoxyl deriv.*, m.p. 153°.

Bayer, D.R.P., 255,724, (*Chem. Zentr.*, 1913, I, 478).
Gebauer-Fülnegg, Gluckmann, *Monatsh.*, 1929, **53** & **54**, 105.

1-Naphthol-4-sulphonic Acid (*Nevile and Winthers' acid*, *NW-Acid*).
Plates from H_2O. M.p. 170° decomp. (rapid heat). Sol. H_2O. Salt sols. ⟶ blue col. with $FeCl_3$. $K_2Cr_2O_7$ ⟶ α-naphthoquinone. Intermediate for azo dyestuffs.
Aniline salt: m.p. 186–7°.
p-*Chloroaniline salt*: m.p. 184–5°.
o-*Toluidine salt*: m.p. 203–4°.
p-*Toluidine salt*: m.p. 196°.
p-*Nitro-o-toluidine salt*: m.p. 249°.
m-*Xylidine salt*: m.p. 228–9°.
ψ-*Cumidine salt*: m.p. 227–8°.
Tolidine salt: m.p. 214–15°.
o-*Anisidine salt*: m.p. 202–3°.
p-*Anisidine salt*: m.p. 224°.
Dianisidine salt: m.p. 207–9°.
1-*Naphthylamine salt*: m.p. 216–17°.
Chloride: *carbethoxyl deriv.*, m.p. 84°.
Anilide: m.p. 199–200°. *Carbethoxyl deriv.*, m.p. 149°.

Diphenylamide : m.p. 176°.
2-*Naphthalide* : m.p. 204°.
Et ether : *Me ester* : $C_{13}H_{14}O_4S$. MW, 266. M.p. 105–6°. *Et ester* : $C_{14}H_{16}O_4S$. MW, 280. M.p. 102–3°. *Chloride* : $C_{12}H_{11}O_3ClS$. MW, 270·5. M.p. 101°. *Amide* : $C_{12}H_{13}O_3NS$. MW, 251. M.p. 167°.

Major, E.P., 328,220, (*Chem. Abstracts*, 1930, **24**, 5509).
Binns, Lurie, U.S.P., 1,880,701, (*Chem. Abstracts*, 1933, **27**, 515).
Gebauer-Fülnegg, Schlesinger, *Ber.*, 1928, **61**, 781.
Baddeley, Payman, Bainbridge, U.S.P., 1,452,481, (*Chem. Abstracts*, 1923, **17**, 1969) ; E.P. 186,515.
Rowe, *J. Soc. Dyers Colourists*, 1919, **35**, 128.
Zincke, Ruppersberg, *Ber.*, 1915, **48**, 122.
Vorojzoff, Karlasch, *Revue des matières colorantes, teinture, impression, blanchiment, apprêts*, 1935, **39**, 373.

1-Naphthol-5-sulphonic Acid.
Cryst. M.p. 110–12°.
Chloride : *acetyl deriv.*, m.p. 129°. *Carbethoxyl deriv.*, m.p. 174°.
Anilide : m.p. 201°. *Carbethoxyl deriv.*, m.p. 127°.

Gebauer-Fülnegg, Gluckmann, *Monatsh.*, 1929, **53** & **54**, 105.
Heller, *J. prakt. Chem.*, 1929, **121**, 196.

1-Naphthol-6-sulphonic Acid.
Chloride : *carbethoxyl deriv.*, m.p. 112°.
Anilide : m.p. 181°. *Carbethoxyl deriv.*, m.p. 140°.

Bayer, D.R.P., 109,122, (*Chem. Zentr.*, 1900, II, 359).
Gebauer-Fülnegg, Gluckmann, *Monatsh.*, 1929, **53** & **54**, 105.

1-Naphthol-7-sulphonic Acid.
Hygroscopic cryst. Sol. H_2O, EtOH. $FeCl_3$ ⟶ brownish-violet col.
Chloride : *carbethoxyl deriv.*, m.p. 105°.
Anilide : m.p. 155°.

Gebauer-Fülnegg, Gluckmann, *Monatsh.*, 1929, **53** & **54**, 105.
See also first reference above.

1-Naphthol-8-sulphonic Acid (α-*Naphthol-sulphonic acid-S*).
Cryst. + $1H_2O$. M.p. 106–7°. Mod. sol. H_2O. $FeCl_3$ ⟶ green col.

Amide : m.p. 222° decomp.

Straub, Schneider, U.S.P., 1,503,172, (*Chem. Abstracts*, 1924, **18**, 2967).
Soc. anon. pour l'ind. chim. à Bâle, E.P., 207,162, (*Chem. Abstracts*, 1924, **18**, 1206).

2-Naphthol-1-sulphonic Acid (*Oxy-Tobias acid, Stebbin's acid*)

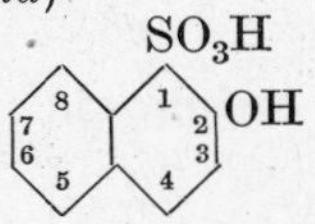

$C_{10}H_8O_4S$ MW, 224

Sol. H_2O. $FeCl_3$ ⟶ red col. (blue with salt sols.).
Aniline salt : m.p. 182°.
o-*Toluidine salt* : m.p. 178–9°.
p-*Toluidine salt* : m.p. 162°.
Chloride : $C_{10}H_7O_3ClS$. MW, 242·5. M.p. 124°. *Acetyl deriv.* : m.p. 115·5°.
Et ether : *chloride*, $C_{12}H_{11}O_3ClS$. MW, 270·5. M.p. 115–16°. *Amide* : $C_{12}H_{13}O_3NS$. MW, 251. M.p. 158°.

Engel, *J. Am. Chem. Soc.*, 1930, **52**, 2841.
Tinker, Hanson, U.S.P., 1,934,216, (*Chem. Abstracts*, 1934, **28**, 495).
Anschutz, *Ann.*, 1918, **415**, 89.
Cotton, U.S.P., 1,913,748, (*Chem. Abstracts*, 1933, **27**, 4248).
Parmelee, U.S.P., 1,716,082, (*Chem. Abstracts*, 1929, **23**, 3716).
Forster, Keyworth, *J. Soc. Chem. Ind.*, 1927, **46**, 29T.

2-Naphthol-3-sulphonic Acid.
Cryst. + $1H_2O$. Salt sols. show blue fluor. $FeCl_3$ ⟶ deep blue col.
Na salt : cryst. + $1H_2O$ from EtOH.
Aniline salt : m.p. 241–2°.
1-*Naphthylamine salt* : m.p. 247–8°.
Amide : $C_{10}H_9O_3NS$. MW, 223. M.p. 110°.
Anilide : m.p. 112°.
Me ether : *chloride*, $C_{11}H_9O_3ClS$. MW, 256·5. M.p. 137–8°. *Amide* : $C_{11}H_{11}O_3NS$. MW, 237. M.p. 113°. *Anilide* : m.p. 173–4°.

Holt, Mason, *J. Soc. Dyers Colourists*, 1930, **46**, 270.

2-Naphthol-4-sulphonic Acid.
Sol. H_2O with bluish-violet fluor. PCl_5 ⟶ 1 : 3-dichloronaphthalene.
Ba salt : sol. H_2O.

Morgan, Jones, *J. Soc. Chem. Ind.*, 1923, **42**, 97T.
Bogdanov, Levkoev, Durmashkina, *Chem. Abstracts*, 1934, **28**, 4728.

2-Naphthol-5-sulphonic Acid (β-*Naphthol-γ-sulphonic acid*).

Na salt sol. shows greenish-blue fluor. ⟶ violet-red col. with $FeCl_3$. KOH fusion ⟶ 1 : 6-dihydroxynaphthalene.

Armstrong, Wynne, *Chem. News*, 1889, **59**, 141.
Claus, *J. prakt. Chem.*, 1889, **39**, 315.
Dahl, D.R.P., 29,084.

2-Naphthol-6-sulphonic Acid (*Schäffer Acid*, β-*naphtholsulphonic acid-S*).

Cryst. + $1H_2O$. from H_2O., m.p. 129°; + $2H_2O$, m.p. 118°. M.p. 167° anhyd. Sol. H_2O, EtOH. Na salt sol. ⟶ green col. with $FeCl_3$. Intermediate for azo dyestuffs.

Aniline salt : m.p. 264°.
o-*Chloroaniline salt* : m.p. 225°.
p-*Chloroaniline salt* : m.p. 234°.
o-*Toluidine salt* : m.p. 208°.
p-*Toluidine salt* : m.p. 248°.
m-*Xylidine salt* : m.p. 220°.
ψ-*Cumidine salt* : m.p. 226–7°.
p-*Anisidine salt* : m.p. 230–1°.
p-*Phenetidine salt* : m.p. 255°.
Dianisidine salt : m.p. 282°.
1-*Naphthylamine salt* : m.p. 254°.
2-*Naphthylamine salt* : m.p. 268°.
Phenyl ester : $C_{16}H_{12}O_4S$. MW, 300. M.p. 131°.
Chloride : *acetyl deriv.*, m.p. 107° (95°). *Carbethoxyl deriv.*, m.p. 118°.
Amide : $C_{10}H_9O_3NS$. MW, 223. M.p. 237–9°.
Di-Me amide : $C_{12}H_{13}O_3NS$. MW, 251. M.p. 125°.
Anilide : m.p. 161°. *Carbethoxyl deriv.*, m.p. 130°.
Me ether : *chloride*, $C_{11}H_9O_3ClS$. MW, 256·5. M.p. 93°. *Amide* : $C_{11}H_{11}O_3NS$. MW, 237. M.p. 199°.
Et ether : *chloride*, $C_{12}H_{11}O_3ClS$. MW, 270·5. M.p. 107·5°. *Amide* : $C_{12}H_{13}O_3NS$. MW, 251. M.p. 185°.

Heller, *J. prakt. Chem.*, 1929, **121**, 196.
Forster, Keyworth, *J. Soc. Chem. Ind.*, 1927, **46**, 29T.
Wend, *Zeitschrift für Farbenindustrie*, 1929, **20**, 272.
Engel, *J. Am. Chem. Soc.*, 1930, **52**, 211, 2841.
Vorontzov, Sokolova, *Chem. Abstracts*, 1934, **28**, 3730.
Vorontzov, *Chem. Abstracts*, 1931, **25**, 5515.

2-Naphthol-7-sulphonic Acid (*F Acid*, β-*naphthol-δ-sulphonic acid*).

Cryst. + $1H_2O$, m.p. 108–9°; + $2H_2O$, m.p. 95°; + $4H_2O$, m.p. 67°; anhyd. m.p. 115–16°. Sol. H_2O, EtOH. Insol. Et_2O, C_6H_6. Na salt sol. shows blue fluor. ⟶ blue col. with $FeCl_3$.

Aniline salt : m.p. 249°.
p-*Toluidine salt* : m.p. 237°.
Et ether : *chloride*, m.p. 103°. *Amide* : m.p. 172°.

Harland, Forrester, Pain, *J. Soc. Chem. Ind.*, 1931, **50**, 100T.
Kogan, *Chem. Abstracts*, 1933, **27**, 978.
Forster, Keyworth, *J. Soc. Chem. Ind.*, 1927, **46**, 29T.

2-Naphthol-8-sulphonic Acid (*Crocein acid, Bayer acid*, β-*naphthol-α-sulphonic acid*).

Intermediate for azo dyestuffs.

Aniline salt : m.p. 240°.
o-*Toluidine salt* : m.p. 242°.
p-*Toluidine salt* : m.p. 232°.
1-*Naphthylamine salt* : m.p. 241°.
2-*Naphthylamine salt* : m.p. 247–8°.
Benzidine salt : m.p. 293–4° decomp.
Chloride : *acetyl deriv.*, m.p. 129°. *Carbethoxyl deriv.*, m.p. 118°.
Anilide : m.p. 195°.
Me ether : *chloride*, $C_{11}H_9O_3ClS$. MW, 256·5. M.p. 137°. *Amide* : $C_{11}H_{11}O_3NS$. MW, 237. M.p. 153°.
Et ether : *chloride*, $C_{12}H_{11}O_3ClS$. MW, 270·5. M.p. 93°. *Amide* : $C_{12}H_{13}O_3NS$. MW, 251. M.p. 165°.

Engel, *J. Am. Chem. Soc.*, 1930, **52**, 2841.
Gebauer-Fülnegg, Schlesinger, *Ber.*, 1928, **61**, 784.
Forster, Keyworth, *J. Soc. Chem. Ind.*, 1927, **46**, 29T.

2-Naphthol-1 : 3 : 6 : 7-tetrasulphonic Acid

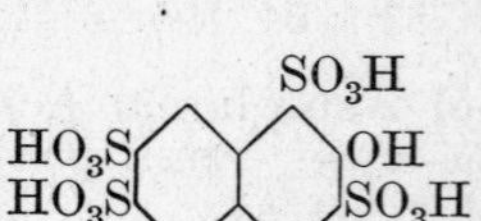

$C_{10}H_8O_{13}S_4$ MW, 464

Alk. salt sols. show bluish-green fluor. Heat with NH_3 ⟶ 2-naphthylamine-1 : 3 : 6 : 7-tetrasulphonic acid. Hot dil. HCl ⟶ 2-naphthol-3 : 6 : 7-trisulphonic acid.

Na salt : sol. H_2O.
Ba salt : spar. sol. H_2O.

Anschutz, *Ann.*, 1918, **415**, 95.

1-Naphthol-2 : 4 : 7-trisulphonic Acid

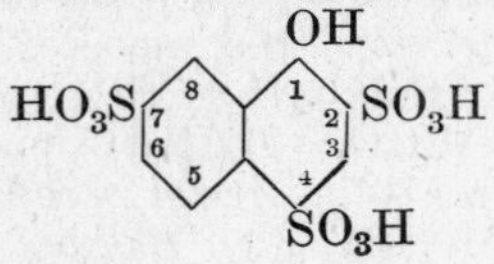

$C_{10}H_8O_{10}S_3$ MW, 384

Needles. Na salt sol. ⟶ blue col. with $FeCl_3$. Ox. ⟶ phthalic acid. Red. with sodium amalgam + acid ⟶ 1-naphthol-2 : 7-disulphonic acid.

Chloride: $C_{10}H_5O_7Cl_3S_3$. MW, 439·5. M.p. 174°.

Anilide: m.p. 227° (240° decomp.).

Friedländer, Taussig, *Ber.*, 1897, **30**, 1463.
Badische, D.R.P., 10,785.
Gebauer-Fülnegg, Gluckmann, *Monatsh.*, 1929, **53** & **54**, 108.
Bender, *Ber.*, 1889, **22**, 993.
Gebauer-Fuelnegg, Haemmerle, *J. Am. Chem. Soc.*, 1931, **53**, 2651.

1-Naphthol-2 : 4 : 8-trisulphonic Acid.

Na salt sol. ⟶ deep blue col. with $FeCl_3$. NaOH fusion ⟶ 1 : 8-dihydroxynaphthalene-2 : 4-disulphonic acid.

Dressel, Kothe, *Ber.*, 1894, **27**, 2144.

1-Naphthol-3 : 6 : 8-trisulphonic Acid (*Oxy-Koch Acid*).

KOH fusion at 200° ⟶ 1 : 8-dihydroxynaphthalene-3 : 6-disulphonic acid.

M.L.B., D.R.P., 71,495.

1-Naphthol-4 : 6 : 8-trisulphonic Acid.

Trichloride: $C_{10}H_5O_7Cl_3S_3$. MW, 439·5. M.p. 217°.

Gebauer-Fuelnegg, Haemmerle, *J. Am. Chem. Soc.*, 1931, **53**, 2651.

2-Naphthol-1 : 3 : 7-trisulphonic Acid

$C_{10}H_8O_{10}S_3$ MW, 384

Alk. salt sols. show bluish-green fluor., and give violet col. with $FeCl_3$. $NH_3 + NH_4Cl$ on heating ⟶ 2-naphthylamine-1 : 3 : 7-trisulphonic acid.

Na salt: sol. H_2O. Insol. EtOH.

Ba salt: sol. H_2O.

Dressel, Kothe, *Ber.*, 1894, **27**, 1207.

2-Naphthol-3 : 6 : 7-trisulphonic Acid.

Alk. salt sols. show bluish-green fluor., and with $FeCl_3$ ⟶ violet col. Alk. fusion ⟶ 2 : 7-dihydroxynaphthalene-3 : 6-disulphonic acid. Heat with NH_3 ⟶ 2-naphthylamine-3 : 6 : 7-trisulphonic acid.

Na salt: spar. sol. H_2O.

Ba salt: spar. sol. H_2O.

Dressel, Kothe, *Ber.*, 1894, **27**, 1209.
Bayer, D.R.P., 78,569.

2-Naphthol-3 : 6 : 8-trisulphonic Acid.

Na salt sol. shows green fluor. ⟶ deep violet col. with $FeCl_3$. Heat with NH_3 ⟶ 2-naphthylamine-3 : 6 : 8-trisulphonic acid.

Trifluoride: $C_{10}H_5O_7F_3S_3$. MW, 390. M.p. 153–9°.

Trichloride: $C_{10}H_5O_7Cl_3S_3$. MW, 439·5. M.p. 196°.

Trianilide: m.p. 152–5°.

Levinstein, *Ber.*, 1883, **16**, 462.
M.L.B., D.R.P., 22,038.
Blumenstock-Halward, Jusa, *Monatsh.*, 1928, **50**, 128.
Pollak, Gebauer-Fülnegg, Blumenstock-Halward, *Monatsh.*, 1928, **49**, 200.

Naphthol Yellow S.

See Flavianic Acid.

1-Naphthonitrile (1-*Cyanonaphthalene*)

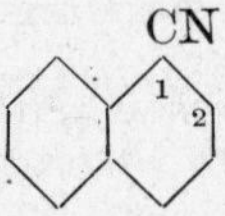

$C_{11}H_7N$ MW, 153

Needles from ligroin. M.p. 37·5° (35–6°, 33·5°). B.p. 299° (297·8°, 296·5°). Sol. EtOH. D_{15}^{15} 1·1167. $n_D^{17\cdot8}$ 1·6298. Heat of comb. C_p 1333·2 Cal.

Maihle, *Bull. soc. chim.*, 1918, **23**, 237.
Merck, D.R.P., 168,728, (*Chem. Zentr.*, 1906, I, 1469).
McRae, *J. Am. Chem. Soc.*, 1930, **52**, 4550.
Rule, Barnett, *J. Chem. Soc.*, 1932, 177.

2-Naphthonitrile (2-*Cyanonaphthalene*).

Leaflets from ligroin. M.p. 66° (63°, 60–1°). B.p. 306–5° (304–5°, 303°). Sol. EtOH, Et_2O, hot ligroin. Spar. sol. H_2O. D_{60}^{60} 1·0939. Heat of comb. C_p 1327·3 Cal.

See first reference above.

Naphthopicric Acid.
See 2 : 4 : 5-Trinitro-1-naphthol.

Naphthopurpurin (5 : 6 : 8-*Trihydroxy*-1 : 4-*naphthoquinone*)

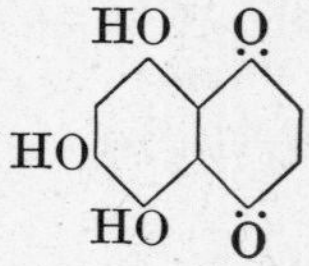

$C_{10}H_6O_5$ MW, 206

Red needles from C_6H_6. Sol. hot H_2O, EtOH, AcOH. Spar. sol. cold H_2O. NaOH sol. is purple-red. Conc. $H_2SO_4 \longrightarrow$ red sol. Colours wool orange-red in AcOH.

Jaubert, *Compt. rend.*, 1899, **129**, 684.
Badische, D.R.P., 167,641, (*Chem. Zentr.*, 1906, I, 1126).

Naphthopyrogallol.
See 1 : 2 : 3-Trihydroxynaphthalene.

1 : 2-Naphthoquinone (β-*Naphthoquinone*)

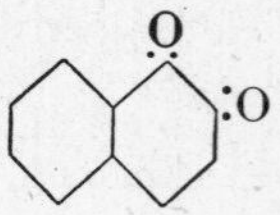

$C_{10}H_6O_2$ MW, 158

Red needles from Et_2O, orange leaflets from C_6H_6. M.p. 115–20° decomp. Conc. $H_2SO_4 \longrightarrow$ green sol. Non-volatile in steam. Turns bluish-black on standing. $SO_2 \longrightarrow$ 1 : 2-dihydroxynaphthalene.

Oxime: *see* Nitrosonaphthol.

Imide-oxime: *see* Nitrosonaphthylamine.

Phenylhydrazone: *see* Benzeneazonaphthol.

Tolylhydrazone: *see* Tolueneazonaphthol.

1-o-*Nitrophenylhydrazone*: 1-*o*-nitrobenzene-azo-2-naphthol. $C_{16}H_{11}O_3N_3$. MW, 293. Orange-red needles from AcOH. M.p. 209°. Spar. sol. EtOH. Insol. aq. alkalis. *Me ether*: $C_{17}H_{13}O_3N_3$. MW, 307. Red leaflets from EtOH. M.p. 136–7°. Sol. C_6H_6, $CHCl_3$. Spar. sol. EtOH, Et_2O, ligroin. Conc. $H_2SO_4 \longrightarrow$ red sol. *B,2HNO*$_3$: red cryst. M.p. 103°. Spar. sol. Et_2O, C_6H_6, $CHCl_3$. *Et ether*: $C_{18}H_{15}O_3N_3$. MW, 321. Red plates from EtOH. M.p. 111°. Sol. C_6H_6, $CHCl_3$, toluene. Spar. sol. EtOH, Et_2O. Conc. $H_2SO_4 \longrightarrow$ red sol. *B,2HNO*$_3$: red plates. M.p. 105° decomp.

1-m-*Nitrophenylhydrazone*: 1-*m*-nitrobenzene-azo-2-naphthol. Orange cryst. from toluene. M.p. 193–4°. Sol. alc. KOH with orange-red col. Insol. aq. alkalis. *Me ether*: red needles from EtOH. M.p. 94–5°. Sol. C_6H_6, $CHCl_3$. Spar. sol. EtOH, Et_2O, ligroin. *B,2HNO*$_3$: golden-yellow leaflets. M.p. 66–8°. Sol. EtOH, $CHCl_3$. *Et ether*: red needles from EtOH. M.p. 106–7°. Sol. C_6H_6, $CHCl_3$, toluene. Spar. sol. EtOH, Et_2O. *B,2HNO*$_3$: golden-yellow leaflets. M.p. 70°. *Acetyl*: red needles from EtOH. M.p. 161–2°. *Benzoyl*: orange-red needles from EtOH. M.p. 171°. Spar. sol. hot EtOH.

1-p-*Nitrophenylhydrazone*: 1-*p*-nitrobenzene-azo-2-naphthol. Paranitraniline Red, Para Red. Orange-brown plates from toluene. M.p. 250–1° (246°). Mod. sol. hot AcOH. Insol. EtOH. aq. alkalis. *Me ether*: red leaflets. M.p. 128–9°. Sol. $CHCl_3$, C_6H_6. Mod. sol. EtOH. Spar. sol. Et_2O. *B,2HNO*$_3$: green leaflets. M.p. 75° decomp. Sol. $CHCl_3$. Spar. sol. Et_2O, C_6H_6, ligroin. *Et ether*: red leaflets from EtOH. M.p. about 186°. Sol. C_6H_6, $CHCl_3$, toluene. Mod. sol. EtOH, Et_2O. Conc. $H_2SO_4 \longrightarrow$ red sol. *B,2HNO*$_3$: green leaflets. M.p. 95–7° decomp. *Acetyl*: orange needles from EtOH. M.p. 192–3°. Spar. sol. EtOH.

2-o-*Nitrophenylhydrazone*: 2-*o*-nitrobenzene-azo-1-naphthol. Brownish-red needles with green fluor. from isoamyl alcohol. M.p. 218°. Sol. hot xylene, Me_2CO. Spar. sol. EtOH, Et_2O, C_6H_6. Conc. $H_2SO_4 \longrightarrow$ green sol.

2-p-*Nitrophenylhydrazone*: 2-*p*-nitrobenzene-azo-1-naphthol. Deep red needles with green lustre. M.p. 234–5°. Sol. xylene, boiling iso-amyl alcohol. Spar. sol. EtOH, Et_2O, Me_2CO, C_6H_6, $CHCl_3$, AcOH. Conc. $H_2SO_4 \longrightarrow$ red sol. *Acetyl*: red needles from AcOH. M.p. 179·5°.

Dioxime: yellow needles from EtOH. M.p. 169°. 1-*Me ether*: pale yellow cryst. M.p. 161°. 1-*Et ether*: greenish-yellow needles from EtOH.Aq. M.p. 153°. Mod. sol. EtOH, C_6H_6, AcOH. Insol. H_2O. Conc. $H_2SO_4 \longrightarrow$ red sol. 1-*Benzyl ether*: yellow prisms from Me_2CO–$CHCl_3$. M.p. 168°.

Diphenylhydrazone: yellow cryst. M.p. 211–12°.

1-*Semicarbazone*: golden-yellow leaflets from EtOH. Decomp. at 184°.

2-*Phenylsemicarbazone*: red needles from Py. M.p. 250–1°. Sol. $CHCl_3$, Py. Insol. other solvents.

1-*Anil*: green needles from EtOH. M.p. 99–100°. Sol. EtOH, Et_2O, C_6H_6.

1-*Chloroimide*: yellow needles from C_6H_6–pet. ether. M.p. 86–7°. Sol. Et_2O, C_6H_6. Spar. sol. cold EtOH, AcOH, pet ether.

2-*Chloroimide*: brownish-yellow needles from C_6H_6–pet. ether. Decomp. at 98°.

Dichloroimide: yellow needles from C_6H_6–pet. ether. M.p. 105°.

Hantzsch, Glover, *Ber.*, 1906, **39**, 4171.
Lagodzinski, Hardine, *Ber.*, 1894, **27**, 3076.
Friedländer, Reinhardt, *Ber.*, 1894, **27**, 240.
Charrier, Ferreri, *gazz. chim. ital.*, 1913, **43**, ii, 236; i, 557; i, 239.
Bamberger, *Ber.*, 1897, **30**, 515; 1895, **28**, 849.

1 : 4-Naphthoquinone (*α-Naphthoquinone*)

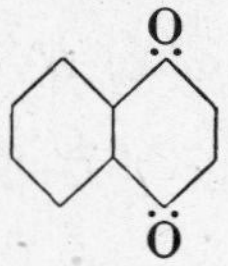

$C_{10}H_6O_2$ MW, 158

Yellow needles from EtOH or pet. ether. M.p. 125°. Sol. Et_2O, C_6H_6, $CHCl_3$, CS_2. Mod. sol. EtOH, AcOH. Spar. sol. H_2O, pet. ether. Volatile in steam. Alkalis ⟶ reddish-brown sol.

Oxime: *see* Nitrosonaphthol.

Imide-oxime: *see* Nitrosonaphthylamine.

Phenylhydrazone: *see* Benzeneazonaphthol.

Tolylhydrazone: *see* Tolueneazonaphthol.

o-*Nitrophenylhydrazone*: 4-*o*-nitrobenzeneazo-1-naphthol. $C_{16}H_{11}O_3N_3$. MW, 293. Dark red needles with bronze reflex from hot xylene. M.p. 244–5°. Sol. xylene, amyl alcohol. Spar. sol. EtOH, Et_2O, C_6H_6, Me_2CO, $CHCl_3$.

m-*Nitrophenylhydrazone*: 4-*m*-nitrobenzene-azo-1-naphthol. Cryst. from EtOH. M.p. 288° decomp. *Et ether*: m.p. 145–6°. Sol. usual solvents.

p-*Nitrophenylhydrazone*: 4-*p*-nitrobenzene-azo-1-naphthol. Brown needles with blue reflex from $PhNO_2$. M.p. 277–9°. Spar. sol. most solvents. Reagent for magnesium. *Me ether*: red needles from EtOH. M.p. 169°. Sol. C_6H_6, AcOH. Less sol. EtOH. *Acetyl*: red needles from AcOH. M.p. 165–6°.

Dioxime: needles from EtOH.Aq. M.p. 207° decomp.

Semicarbazone: greenish-yellow cryst. from AcOH. M.p. 247° decomp. Insol. H_2O, EtOH.

Chloroimide: yellow needles from EtOH. M.p. 109·5°, decomp. at 130–3°. Sol. hot EtOH, Et_2O, C_6H_6, ligroin.

Dichloroimide: yellow needles from EtOH or C_6H_6. M.p. 142–3°. Sol. EtOH, Et_2O, C_6H_6. Insol. H_2O.

Anil: red cryst. from Et_2O. M.p. 103°. Sol. EtOH, Et_2O, C_6H_6.

Dianil: golden-yellow leaflets. M.p. 187°. Spar. sol. EtOH.

Jaeger, U.S.P., 1,692,126, (*Chem. Abstracts*, 1929, **23**, 612).
Conant, Freeman, *Organic Syntheses*, Collective Vol. I, 375.
Bamberger, Meimberg, *Ber.*, 1895, **28**, 1888.
Meyer, Irschick, Schlösser, *Ber.*, 1914, **47**, 1749.
Bamberger, *Ber.*, 1895, **28**, 848.

Naphthoresorcinol.
See 1 : 3-Dihydroxynaphthalene.

α-Naphthoxazole

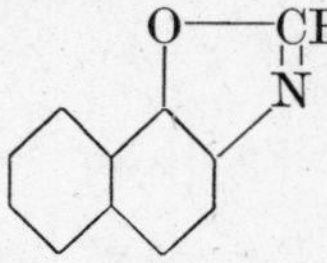

$C_{11}H_7ON$ MW, 169

Needles from ligroin. M.p. 79°. Sol. EtOH, Et_2O.

Fischer, *J. prakt. Chem.*, 1906, **73**, 440.

β-Naphthoxazole

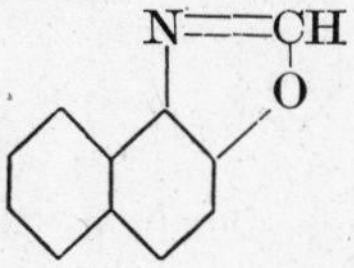

$C_{11}H_7ON$ MW, 169

Leaflets from ligroin. M.p. 63·5–64°. Sol. EtOH, $CHCl_3$. Spar. sol. ligroin.

B,HgCl₂: needles from EtOH. M.p. 183–4°.

Picrate: m.p. 133–4°.

See previous reference.

α-Naphthoxdiazole

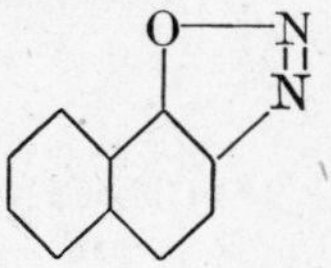

$C_{10}H_6ON_2$ MW, 170

Yellow leaflets from pet. ether. M.p. 76°. Explodes at 112°. Sol. org. solvents.

Veselý, Dvořák, *Bull. soc. chim.*, 1923, **33**, 319.
Bamberger, *Ber.*, 1894, **27**, 680.
Geigy, D.R.P., 172,446, (*Chem. Zentr.*, 1906, II, 476).

β-Naphthoxdiazole

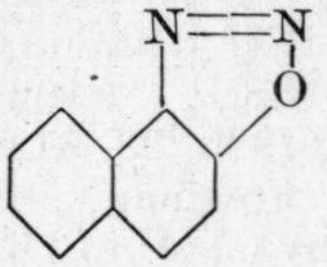

$C_{10}H_6ON_2$ MW, 170

Yellow plates. M.p. 95°.

See last two references above.

α-Naphthoxindole

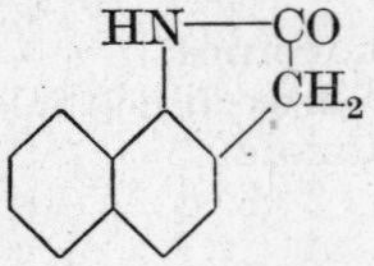

$C_{12}H_9ON$ MW, 183

Needles from EtOH.Aq. or AcOH. M.p. 247°.

Hinsberg, *Ber.*, 1888, **21**, 116.
Mayer, Oppenheimer, *Ber.*, 1918, **51**, 1245.

β-Naphthoxindole

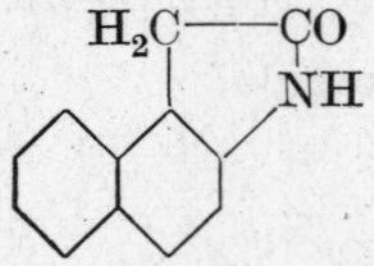

$C_{12}H_9ON$ MW, 183

Pale greenish needles from EtOH. M.p. 234°. Mod. sol. EtOH, Et_2O, AcOH. Spar. sol. H_2O.

Hinsberg, *Ber.*, 1888, **21**, 114.
M.L.B., D.R.P., 216,639, (*Chem. Zentr.*, 1910, I, 130).

α-Naphthoxyacetaldehyde (*Glycollic aldehyde* 1-*naphthyl ether*)

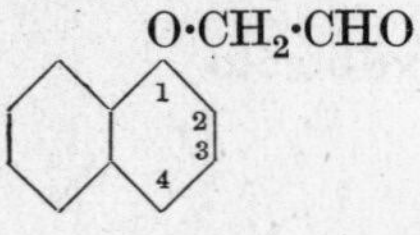

$C_{12}H_{10}O_2$ MW, 186

Hydrate : $C_{10}H_7 \cdot O \cdot CH_2 \cdot CH(OH)_2$. MW, 204. Cryst. from H_2O. M.p. 86°.

Di-Et acetal : b.p. 207–8°/18 mm. D^{14} 1·0698. n_D^{16} 1·5610. $ZnCl_2$ in hot AcOH ⟶ α-naphthafuran.

Oxime : m.p. 108°.

Semicarbazone : m.p. 149–50°.

Stoermer, *Ber.*, 1897, **30**, 1703.

β-Naphthoxyacetaldehyde (*Glycollic aldehyde* 2-*naphthyl ether*).

Hydrate : needles from H_2O. M.p. 87°. Spar. sol. H_2O. Reduces Fehling's and $NH_3.AgNO_3$.

Di-Et acetal : yellow oil. B.p. 240°/60 mm., 206–7°/17 mm. D^{14} 1·0654. n_D^{16} 1·557. Very spar. volatile in steam. $ZnCl_2$ in hot AcOH ⟶ β-naphthafuran.

Oxime : cryst. M.p. 123·5°.

Semicarbazone : white cryst. with blue fluor. M.p. 182°.

Phenylhydrazone : cryst. M.p. 145°. Turns brown in air.

See previous reference and also
Hesse, *Ber.*, 1897, **30**, 1439.

α-Naphthoxyacetic Acid (*Glycollic acid* 1-*naphthyl ether*)

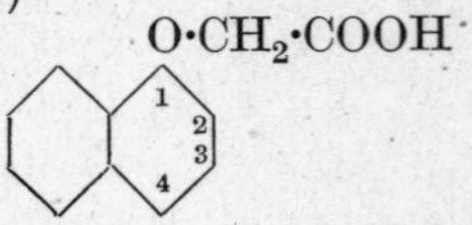

$C_{12}H_{10}O_3$ MW, 202

Prisms. M.p. 190°. Very sol. EtOH, Et_2O. Spar. sol. H_2O.

NH_4 salt : needles. M.p. 119–20°.

Et ester : $C_{14}H_{14}O_3$. MW, 230. Cryst. M.p. 173–4°. Sol. EtOH, Et_2O.

Amide : $C_{12}H_{11}O_2N$. MW, 201. Leaflets or needles from EtOH.Aq. M.p. 155°. Sol. EtOH. Spar. sol. H_2O.

Chloride : $C_{12}H_9O_2Cl$. MW, 220·5. Oil. B.p. 194°/10 mm.

Anilide : needles from EtOH. M.p. 144°.

p-*Phenetidide* : needles. M.p. 145–6°. Mod. sol. EtOH.

Spica, *Gazz. chim. ital.*, 1886, **16**, 438.
Ingham, Stephen, Timpe, *J. Chem. Soc.*, 1931, 897.

β-Naphthoxyacetic Acid (*Glycollic acid* 2-*naphthyl ether*).

Prisms from H_2O. M.p. 156°. Sol. EtOH, Et_2O, AcOH. Mod. sol. hot H_2O.

NH_4 salt : cryst. M.p. 180°. Spar. sol. cold H_2O.

Et ester : plates. M.p. 48–9°. Triboluminescent.

m-*Tolyl ester* : $C_{19}H_{16}O_3$. MW, 292. Needles from pet. ether. M.p. 91–2°.

Amide : needles or plates. M.p. 147°. Sol. EtOH, Et_2O. Spar. sol. H_2O.

Chloride : needles from C_6H_6. M.p. 54°. B.p. 207°/10 mm.

Nitrile : $C_{12}H_9ON$. MW, 183. Leaflets. M.p. 72°. Sol. EtOH, Et_2O.

Anilide : needles from EtOH. M.p. 145°.

p-*Phenetidide* : needles. M.p. 164 5°. Spar. sol. hot EtOH.

See previous references and also
Lees, Shedden, *J. Chem. Soc.*, 1903, **83**, 758.
Spitzer, *Ber.*, 1901, **34**, 3192.
Stoermer, *Ber.*, 1897, **30**, 1702.

α-Naphthoxyacetone (*Hydroxyacetone 1-naphthyl ether*)

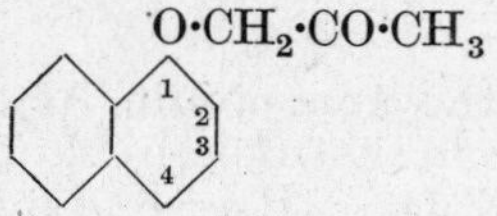

$C_{13}H_{12}O_2$ MW, 200

Liq. B.p. 205–8°/14 mm.
Semicarbazone : m.p. 103°.

Stoermer, *Ann.*, 1900, **312**, 313.

β-Naphthoxyacetone (*Hydroxyacetone 2-naphthyl ether*).
Plates. M.p. 78°. Spar. volatile in steam.
Oxime : leaflets. M.p. 123°.
Semicarbazone : m.p. 203°.
Phenylhydrazone : leaflets. M.p. 154°.

See previous reference.

***o*-1-Naphthoylbenzoic Acid**

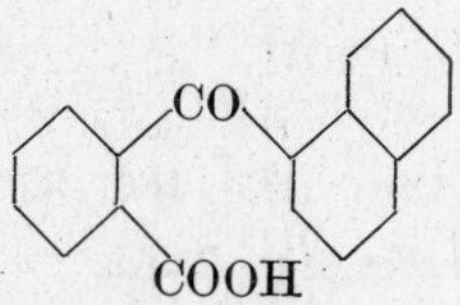

$C_{18}H_{12}O_3$ MW, 276

Prisms from EtOH.Aq. M.p. 176·4°. Sol. 12 parts $CHCl_3$. Insol. H_2O. Sol. conc. H_2SO_4 with violet col. Heat at 275° ⟶ naphthanthraquinone. KOH fusion ⟶ 1-naphthoic and benzoic acids.
Me ester : $C_{19}H_{14}O_3$. MW, 290. Yellow cryst. from MeOH. M.p. 120°. Conc. H_2SO_4 ⟶ yellow sol. ⟶ red on standing.
Et ester : $C_{20}H_{16}O_3$. MW, 304. M.p. 123–4°
Amide : $C_{18}H_{13}O_2N$. MW, 275. Needles from. EtOH. M.p. 215°. Sol. C_6H_6. Spar. sol. H_2O, EtOH.

Heller, Schulke, *Ber.*, 1908, **41**, 3633.
Graebe, *Ann.*, 1889, **340**, 251.
Groggins, Newton, *Ind. Eng. Chem.*, 1930, **22**, 157.

***o*-2-Naphthoylbenzoic Acid**

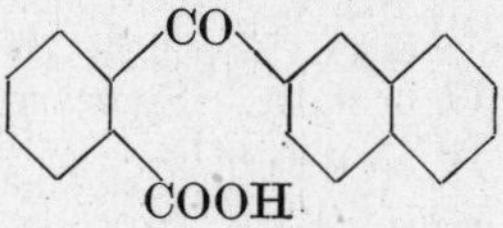

$C_{18}H_{12}O_3$ MW, 276

Needles from toluene. M.p. 165°.
Acetyl : cryst. from Ac_2O. M.p. 140°. Sol. Et_2O, Me_2CO, C_6H_6, $CHCl_3$. Insol. EtOH.

McMullen, *J. Am. Chem. Soc.*, 1922, **44**, 2058.

1-Naphthoylformic Acid (*1-Naphthylglyoxylic acid*)

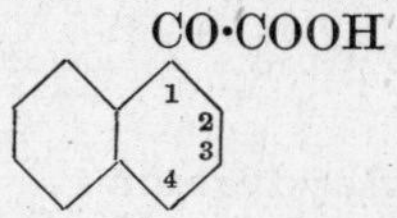

$C_{12}H_8O_3$ MW, 200

Needles. M.p. 107–8° decomp. Sol. H_2O, EtOH, Et_2O, C_6H_6. Spar. sol. CS_2, pet. ether. NaHg ⟶ 1-naphthylglycollic acid. $KMnO_4$ ⟶ 1-naphthoic acid.
Et ester : $C_{14}H_{12}O_3$. MW, 228. Liq. B.p. 213–15°/23 mm. D^0 1·19. *Picrate* : yellow needles. M.p. 77°.
Amide : $C_{12}H_9O_2N$. MW, 199. Needles from EtOH. M.p. 151°.
Nitrile : $C_{12}H_7ON$. MW, 181. Yellow needles from Et_2O. M.p. 101°. B.p. 230°/85 mm. Decomp. by boiling H_2O.
Oxime : m.p. 193–5°.

Rousset, *Bull. soc. chim.*, 1897, **17**, 301.
Boessneck, *Ber.*, 1882, **15**, 3065; 1883, **16**, 640.

2-Naphthoylformic Acid (*2-Naphthylglyoxylic acid*).
Cryst. from C_6H_6. M.p. 171°. Sol. H_2O.
Semicarbazone : cryst. from EtOH. M.p. 230°.
Thiosemicarbazone : yellowish cryst. from EtOH. M.p. 226°. Spar. sol. other solvents.

Popovici, *Compt. rend.*, 1930, **191**, 210.

1-*N*-Naphthoylglycine (*α-Naphthoylaminoacetic acid*)

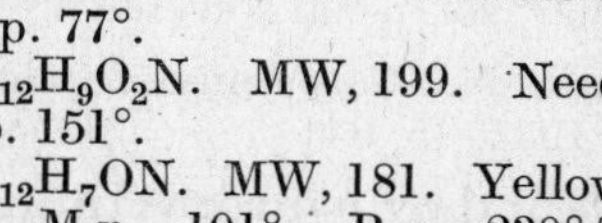

$C_{13}H_{11}O_3N$ MW, 229

Needles from H_2O. M.p. 153°.

Cohn, *Ber.*, 1894, **27**, 2911.

2-*N*-Naphthoylglycine (β-*Naphthoylamino-acetic acid*).

Needles from H_2O. M.p. 169–70°. Sol. MeOH, EtOH, Me_2CO, AcOEt. Spar. sol. H_2O, Et_2O, C_6H_6, CS_2, $CHCl_3$, pet. ether.

Friedmann, Türk, *Biochem. Z.*, 1913, **55**, 466.

1-Naphthoylhydrazine

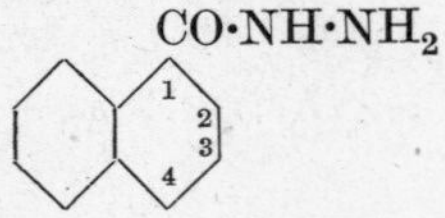

$C_{11}H_{10}ON_2$ MW, 186

Needles from EtOH. M.p. 166°.

Stollé, Zinsser, *J. prakt. Chem.*, 1906, **74**, 19.

2-Naphthoylhydrazine.

Needles from 50% EtOH. M.p. 147·5°. Sol. boiling H_2O, EtOH, C_6H_6, $CHCl_3$, AcOH. Sol. HCl. Spar. sol. AcOH.Aq. Reduces $NH_3.AgNO_3$.

N′-*Acetyl*: cryst. from 50% EtOH. M.p. 138°. Sol. boiling H_2O, EtOH, $CHCl_3$, AcOH.

N′-*Naphthoyl*: plates from AcOH. M.p. 241°. Spar. sol. usual solvents.

Goldstein, Cornamusaz, *Helv. Chim. Acta*, 1932, **15**, 941.

1-*N*-Naphthoylhydroxylamine (α-*Napht-hydroxamic acid*)

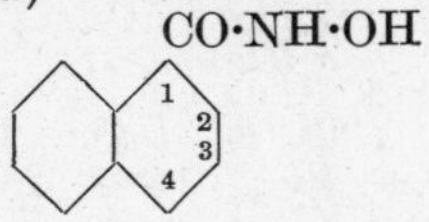

$C_{11}H_9O_2N$ MW, 187

Plates from EtOH. M.p. 186–7° decomp. Sol. hot EtOH. Spar. sol. Et_2O, C_6H_6. Boiling aq. sol. gives deep wine-red col. with $FeCl_3$.

O-1-*Naphthoyl*: needles from EtOH, prisms from C_6H_6. M.p. 150°. Sol. Et_2O, C_6H_6. No col. with $FeCl_3$.

Ekstrand, *Ber.*, 1887, **20**, 1355.

2-*N*-Naphthoylhydroxylamine (β-*Napht-hydroxamic acid*).

Plates from EtOH. M.p. 168°. Sol. EtOH. Spar. sol. H_2O, Et_2O, C_6H_6. $FeCl_3 \longrightarrow$ wine-red col.

O-1-*Naphthoyl*: needles from EtOH. M.p. 160°. Mod. sol. EtOH.

O-2-*Naphthoyl*: needles from EtOH. M.p. 171°. Spar. sol. EtOH.

See previous reference.

2-α-Naphthoylpropionic Acid

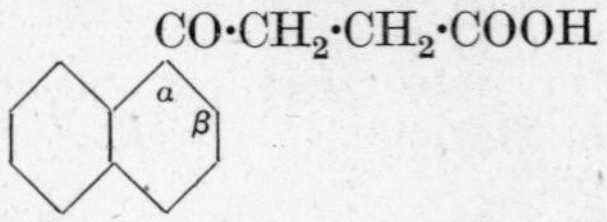

$C_{14}H_{12}O_3$ MW, 228

Cryst. from C_6H_6. M.p. 131–2° (118°).

Giua, *Ber.*, 1914, **47**, 2115.
Schroeter, Mullen, Huang, *Ber.*, 1929, **62**, 656.

2-β-Naphthoylpropionic Acid.

Needles from EtOH.Aq. M.p. 174° (165°). Spar. sol. Et_2O, C_6H_6. KOH fusion $\longrightarrow$ 2-naphthoic acid + naphthalene.

Me ester: $C_{15}H_{14}O_3$. MW, 242. Prisms. M.p. 74°. Very sol. most org. solvents. Conc. $H_2SO_4 \longrightarrow$ yellow sol.

Et ester: $C_{16}H_{16}O_3$. MW, 256. Cryst. from EtOH. M.p. 47–8°.

Oxime: cryst. from EtOH.Aq. M.p. 135–6°.

See previous references and also
Borsche, Sauernheimer, *Ber.*, 1914, **47**, 1645.

***N*-2-Naphthoylurea**

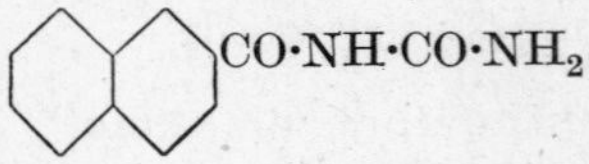

$C_{12}H_{10}O_2N_2$ MW, 214

Needles from EtOH. M.p. 215°. Mod. sol. EtOH. Spar. sol. Et_2O, C_6H_6, $CHCl_3$.

Vieth, *Ann.*, 1876, **180**, 322.

Naphthydroxamic Acid.

See N-Naphthoylhydroxylamine.

1-Naphthylacetaldehyde

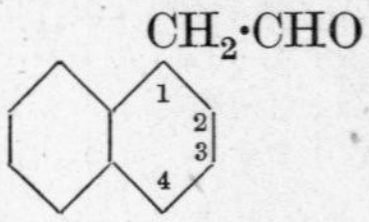

$C_{12}H_{10}O$ MW, 170

Liq. B.p. 163–6°/13 mm. Alk. $Ag_2O \longrightarrow$ 1-naphthylacetic acid. Forms bisulphite comp.

Semicarbazone: m.p. 208°.

Oxime: needles from CCl_4. M.p. 118°.

Tiffeneau, Daudel, *Compt. rend.*, 1908, **147**, 679.

2-Naphthylacetaldehyde.

Oxime: needles from CCl_4. M.p. 120°.

Mayer, Sieglitz, *Ber.*, 1922, **55**, 1858.

1-Naphthylacetic Acid

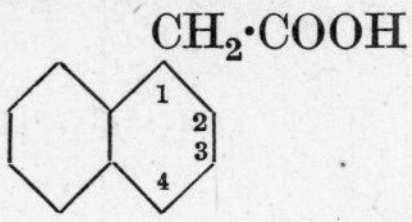

$C_{12}H_{10}O_2$ MW, 186

Needles from H_2O. M.p. 131° (129°). Sol. hot H_2O, EtOH, Et_2O, AcOH, C_6H_6. Heat with lime ⟶ 1-methylnaphthalene.

Et ester: $C_{14}H_{14}O_2$. MW, 214. Oil. B.p. 177–9°/13 mm.

Chloride: $C_{12}H_9OCl$. MW, 204·5. Yellowish oil. B.p. 188°/23 mm., 148–55°/0·05 mm.

Amide: $C_{12}H_{11}ON$. MW, 185. Needles from EtOH. M.p. 180–1° (154°). Sol. hot H_2O, Et_2O, CS_2, C_6H_6, AcOH. Difficult to hydrolyse.

Nitrile: $C_{12}H_9N$. MW, 167. Oil. F.p. 5°. B.p. 183–7°/13 mm.

Mayer, Oppenheimer, *Ber.*, 1916, **49**, 2139.
Wislicenus, Elvert, *ibid.*, 2822.
Weitzenböck, Lieb, *Monatsh.*, 1912, **33**, 556.
Willegerodt, Scholz, *J. prakt. Chem.*, 1910, **81**, 387.
Keach, *J. Am. Chem. Soc.*, 1933, **55**, 2974.
I.G., D.R.P., 562,391, (*Chem. Abstracts*, 1933, **27**, 734).
Gen. Aniline Works, U.S.P., 1,951,686, (*Chem. Abstracts*, 1934, **28**, 3423).

2-Naphthylacetic Acid.

Leaflets from H_2O, cryst. from C_6H_6. M.p. 142°. Sol. Et_2O, $CHCl_3$, AcOEt, ligroin. Dist. ⟶ 2-methylnaphthalene.

Et ester: cryst. from pet. ether. M.p. 31–2°. B.p. 186–7°/14 mm.

Amide: leaflets from H_2O. M.p. 200°. Sol. EtOH, Et_2O. Less sol. hot H_2O.

Nitrile: needles and leaflets from 50% EtOH. M.p. 86° (79–81°). Very sol. Et_2O, C_6H_6, $CHCl_3$, CS_2, AcOEt. Spar. sol. EtOH, warm H_2O. Insol. pet. ether.

Kikkoji, *Biochem. Z.*, 1911, **35**, 77.
Wislicenus, Elvert, *Ber.*, 1916, **49**, 2828.
Willegerodt, *J. prakt. Chem.*, 1909, **80**, 188.
Blank, *Ber.*, 1896, **29**, 2374.
Mayer, Oppenheimer, *Ber.*, 1916, **49**, 2140.

1-Naphthylacetylene

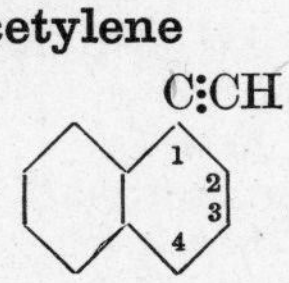

$C_{12}H_8$ MW, 152

Liq. B.p. 143–4°/25 mm. H_2SO_4 → methyl 1-naphthyl ketone.

Leroy, *Bull. soc. chim.*, 1891, **6**, 386.

2-Naphthylacetylene.

Cryst. M.p. 36°. Sol. EtOH, Et_2O, CS_2. H_2SO_4 ⟶ methyl 2-naphthyl ketone.

Leroy, *Bull. soc. chim.*, 1892, **7**, 648.

2-α-Naphthylacrolein

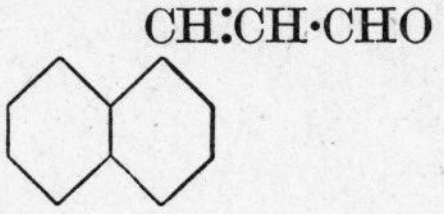

$C_{13}H_{10}O$ MW, 182

Pale yellow needles from pet. ether. M.p. 48°. B.p. 160–70°/0·4 mm.

Oxime: m.p. 152°.

Semicarbazone: light yellow. M.p. 228°.

v. Braun, Nelles, *Ber.*, 1933, **66**, 1470.

1-α-Naphthylacrylic Acid

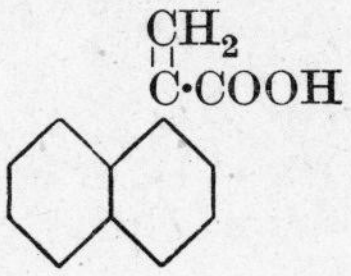

$C_{13}H_{10}O_2$ MW, 198

Plates from C_6H_6. M.p. 152–4°. Sol. Et_2O. Mod. sol. warm C_6H_6, hot H_2O. Spar. sol. pet. ether.

Wislicenus, Butterfass, Koken, *Ann.*, 1924, **436**, 77.

2-α-Naphthylacrylic Acid

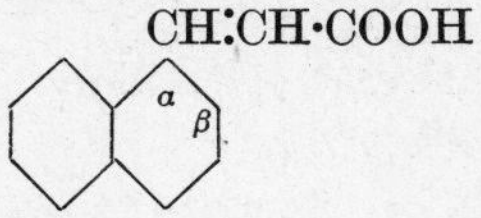

$C_{13}H_{10}O_2$ MW, 198

Needles from EtOH. M.p. 211–12° (205°). Sol. 2000 parts boiling H_2O. Sol. Et_2O. $KMnO_4$ ⟶ 1-naphthaldehyde.

Chloride: $C_{13}H_9OCl$. MW, 216·5. Liq. B.p. 180°/0·4 mm.

Anilide: cryst. from C_6H_6. M.p. 212°.

Brandis, *Ber.*, 1889, **22**, 2153.
v. Braun, Nelles, *Ber.*, 1933, **66**, 1470.
West, *J. Am. Chem. Soc.*, 1920, **42**, 1664.

2-β-Naphthylacrylic Acid.

Needles. M.p. 203° (196°). Mod. sol. hot H_2O.

Monier-Williams, *J. Chem. Soc.*, 1906, **89**, 277.

N-1-Naphthylalanine (1-α-*Naphthylaminopropionic acid*)

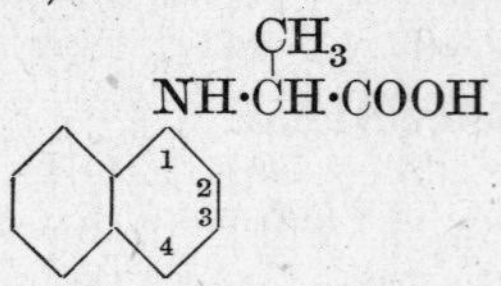

$C_{13}H_{13}O_2N$ MW, 215

Cryst. from C_6H_6. M.p. 161°. Sol. EtOH, Et_2O, $CHCl_3$, dil. HCl, Na_2CO_3.

Et ester: $C_{15}H_{17}O_2N$. MW, 243. Cryst. from EtOH. M.p. 65·5°. Sol. Et_2O, C_6H_6, $CHCl_3$, Me_2CO, AcOH, CS_2. Spar. sol. cold EtOH, ligroin.

Nitrile: $C_{13}H_{12}N_2$. MW, 196. Prisms from EtOH.Aq. M.p. 104–5°. Sol. C_6H_6, toluene. Mod. sol. EtOH.

Bischoff, Hausdörfer, *Ber.*, 1892, **25**, 2309.
Maron, D.R.P., 144,536, (*Chem. Zentr.*, 1903, II, 779).

N-2-Naphthylalanine (1-β-*Naphthylaminopropionic acid*).

Cryst. from EtOH. M.p. 170–1°. Spar. sol. EtOH, Et_2O, AcOH, C_6H_6. Insol. CS_2, ligroin.

Et ester: prisms from EtOH. M.p. 84°. Sol. most org. solvents.

N-*Acetyl*: prisms from $CHCl_3$–ligroin. M.p. 199–200°. Sol. EtOH, Me_2CO, AcOH, $CHCl_3$. Spar. sol. cold C_6H_6. Insol. CS_2, ligroin.

Bischoff, Hausdörfer, *Ber.*, 1892, **25**, 2311.

1-α-Naphthylallyl Alcohol.

See Vinyl-1-naphthylcarbinol.

3-α-Naphthylallyl Alcohol (1-γ-*Hydroxypropenylnaphthalene*)

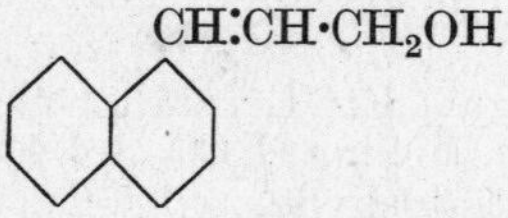

$C_{13}H_{12}O$ MW, 184

Cryst. M.p. 39–40°. B.p. 209–10°/18 mm.

Acetyl: b.p. 210–11°/9 mm.

p-*Nitrobenzoyl*: needles from AcOH. M.p. 138–9°.

Phenylurethane: needles from C_6H_6–pet. ether. M.p. 120°.

Burton, *J. Chem. Soc.*, 1931, 761.

1-β-Naphthylallyl Alcohol.

See Vinyl-2-naphthylcarbinol.

3-β-Naphthylallyl Alcohol (2-γ-*Hydroxypropenylnaphthalene*)

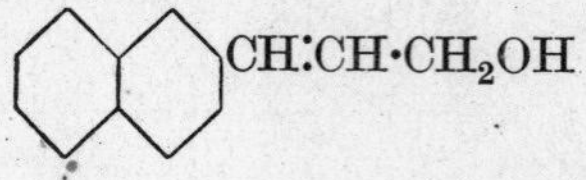

$C_{13}H_{12}O$ MW, 184

Needles from C_6H_6. M.p. 116°.

p-*Nitrobenzoyl*: plates from EtOH. M.p. 148°. Spar. sol. EtOH.

Burton, *J. Chem. Soc.*, 1931, 761.

1-Naphthylamine (α-*Naphthylamine*)

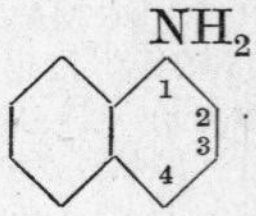

$C_{10}H_9N$ MW, 143

Needles from EtOH.Aq. or Et_2O. M.p. 50°. B.p. 300·8°/760 mm. Very sol. EtOH, Et_2O. Sol. to 0·167% in H_2O at 25°. D_{25}^{25} 1·1229, D_{50}^{50} 1·1144. n_D^{51} 1·67034. Heat of comb. C_p 1268 Cal. $k = 9{\cdot}9 \times 10^{-11}$ at 25°. Sublimes. Bitter taste. Volatile in steam. Reduces warm $NH_3.AgNO_3$.

Chloroacetic acid salt: m.p. 93–4°.

m-*Nitrobenzoic acid salt*: needles from C_6H_6. M.p. 105–6°.

2 : 4 : 6-*Trinitrobenzoic acid salt*: needles. M.p. 197°.

Benzenesulphonic acid salt: needles. M.p. 225°.

p-*Toluenesulphonic acid salt*: prisms. M.p. 239°.

$C_{10}H_9N,C_6H_3(NO_2)_3$-1 : 3 : 5 : red prisms. M.p. 214°. Sol. EtOH, AcOH. Spar. sol. ligroin.

Picrate: greenish-yellow prisms from EtOH. M.p. 181–2° decomp.

Styphnate: cryst. from EtOH. M.p. 181–2°.

N-*Me*: *see* *N*-Methyl-1-naphthylamine.

N-*Di-Me*: *see* Dimethyl-1-naphthylamine.

N-*Et*: *see* *N*-Ethyl-1-naphthylamine.

N-*Di-Et*: *see* Diethyl-1-naphthylamine.

N-*Propyl*: $C_{13}H_{15}N$. MW, 185. Yellow oil. B.p. 316–18°/771 mm. N-*Acetyl*: leaflets from EtOH.Aq. M.p. 94°.

N-*Dipropyl*: $C_{16}H_{21}N$. MW, 227. Oil. B.p. above 300°. B_2,H_2PtCl_6: decomp. at 212°.

N-*Pentadecyl*: needles from EtOH. M.p. 47–8°. Sol. Et_2O, C_6H_6, $CHCl_3$, Me_2CO. *B,HCl*: needles from pet. ether. M.p. 92–4°. Sol. $CHCl_3$. Spar. sol. Et_2O.

N-*Heptadecyl*: cryst. from EtOH. M.p. 53–5°. Sol. Et_2O, C_6H_6, $CHCl_3$, pet. ether. Insol. H_2O. Sol. conc. H_2SO_4. *B,HCl*: plates from pet.

ether. M.p. 96–7°. Sol. $CHCl_3$. Insol. Me_2CO, Et_2O, cold pet. ether.

N-*Phenyl*: *see* *N*-Phenyl-1-naphthylamine.

N-m-*Chlorophenyl*: cryst. from EtOH. M.p. 73°. B.p. 238–41°/12 mm. Conc. $H_2SO_4 \longrightarrow$ yellow sol.

N-p-*Chlorophenyl*: yellowish prisms from EtOH.Aq. M.p. 102–3°. Conc. $H_2SO_4 + HNO_2 \longrightarrow$ blood-red col.

N-2 : 4-*Dinitrophenyl*: orange-red needles from EtOH. M.p. 190·5°. Very sol. C_6H_6, Me_2CO, $CHCl_3$. Spar. sol. EtOH, AcOH. Insol. H_2O.

N-2 : 4 : 6-*Trinitrophenyl*: *see* *N*-Picryl-1-naphthylamine.

N-*Diphenyl*: *see* Diphenyl-1-naphthylamine.

N-o-*Tolyl*: needles from ligroin. M.p. 94–5°. B.p. 198–202°/9 mm. Sol. EtOH, Et_2O, C_6H_6.

N-m-*Tolyl*: solid. B.p. 234–5°/11 mm.

N-p-*Tolyl*: prisms from EtOH. M.p. 79°. B.p. 230°/10 mm. Sol. Et_2O, C_6H_6. Spar. sol. cold EtOH. Sols. show blue fluor. Conc. $H_2SO_4 \longrightarrow$ yellow sol. turning blue and then yellowish-brown on adding HNO_2. *Acetyl*: cryst. from AcOEt. M.p. 124°. Sol. usual solvents.

N-*Benzyl*: *see* *N*-Benzyl-1-naphthylamine.

N-o-*Nitrobenzyl*: golden-yellow needles from EtOH. M.p. 97°. Sol. Et_2O, C_6H_6, $CHCl_3$, AcOH. Spar. sol. cold EtOH, ligroin. *Acetyl*: leaflets from EtOH. M.p. 130°. Sol. Et_2O, C_6H_6.

N-m-*Nitrobenzyl*: orange-yellow prisms from EtOH. M.p. 94°. Mod. sol. C_6H_6. Spar. sol. EtOH, Et_2O, ligroin.

N-p-*Nitrobenzyl*: orange-yellow leaflets from EtOH. M.p. 126–7°. Sol. Et_2O, C_6H_6. Spar. sol. EtOH, ligroin. *Acetyl*: needles from EtOH. M.p. 112–13°.

N-*Dibenzyl*: *see* Dibenzyl-1-naphthylamine.

N-*Naphthyl*: *see* Dinaphthylamine.

N-*Benzylidene*: *see* Benzylidene-1-naphthylamine.

N-o-*Nitrobenzylidene*: yellow. M.p. 118°.

N-m-*Nitrobenzylidene*: yellow plates from ligroin. M.p. 102–3°.

N-*Cinnamylidene*: plates and needles from EtOH. M.p. 65°.

N-*Salicylidene*: orange prisms from MeOH. M.p. 45·5°.

N-*Anisylidene*: plates from EtOH. M.p. 100–1°.

Formyl: needles from C_6H_6–pet. ether. M.p. 138·5°. Sol. boiling H_2O.

Acetyl: 1-acetnaphthalide. Cryst. from EtOH. M.p. 160°. Very sol. EtOH. Mod. sol. boiling H_2O. *B*,$C_6H_3(NO_2)_3$-1 : 3 : 5 : yellow needles. M.p. 140·5°.

Chloroacetyl: needles from EtOH. M.p. 161°.
Propionyl: cryst. from EtOH. M.p. 116°.
Butyryl: cryst. from EtOH. M.p. 120°.
Valeryl: cryst. from EtOH. M.p. 111°.
Caproyl: m.p. 112°.
Heptylyl: m.p. 106°.
Caprylyl: m.p. 95°.
Pelargonyl: m.p. 91°.
Lauryl: m.p. 100°.
Myristyl: needles. M.p. 110° (105°). B.p. 162·5°/10 mm.

Palmityl: needles. M.p. 112·8°. B.p. 182°/10 mm.

Stearyl: needles. M.p. 110·8°. B.p. 205°/10 mm.

Benzoyl: 1-benznaphthalide. Needles from EtOH or AcOH. M.p. 161–2°. Sol. AcOH, EtOH.Aq. Spar. sol. EtOH. *B*,$C_6H_3(NO_2)_3$-1:3:5: yellow needles from CCl_4. M.p. 131–2°. *Benzenesulphonyl*: cryst. from C_6H_6–ligroin. M.p. 193–4°.

1-*Naphthoyl*: cryst. M.p. 244°. Spar. sol. EtOH. Insol. C_6H_6.

2-*Naphthoyl*: needles or prisms from EtOH. M.p. 160°. Mod. sol. EtOH, C_6H_6, $CHCl_3$.

Benzenesulphonyl: needles from EtOH. M.p. 168–9°.

p-*Toluenesulphonyl*: prisms from EtOH. M.p. 147°.

Knoll, D.R.P., 241,853, (*Chem. Zentr.*, 1912, I, 178).
Knoevenagel, *J. prakt. Chem.*, 1914, **89**, 17, 22.
Liebermann, Jacobsen, *Ann.*, 1882, **211**, 42.
Mailhe, Murat, *Bull. soc. chim.*, 1910, **7**, 955.
Dehn, *J. Am. Chem. Soc.*, 1912, **34**, 1405.
De'Conno, *Gazz. chim. ital.*, 1917, **47**, i, 98, 122.
Robertson, *J. Chem. Soc.*, 1908, **93**, 1037.
Jacobs, Heidelberger, *J. Am. Chem. Soc.*, 1917, **39**, 1446.
Le Sueur, *J. Chem. Soc.*, 1911, **99**, 831.
West, *J. Chem. Soc.*, 1925, **127**, 494.
Popov, *Chem. Abstracts*, 1934, **28**, 1671.

2-Naphthylamine (β-*Naphthylamine*).

Leaflets from H_2O. M.p. 113°. B.p. 294°. Sol. H_2O. D_4^{98} 1·0614. Heat of comb. C_p 1267·5 Cal. n_D^{98} 1·64927. $k = 2{\cdot}0 \times 10^{-10}$ at 25°. Volatile in steam. Heat at 230° with trace of I $\longrightarrow$ 2 : 2′-dinaphthylamine. S + I at 230° $\longrightarrow$ thio-2 : 2′-dinaphthylamine. Reduces warm $NH_3.AgNO_3$.

m-*Nitrobenzoic acid salt*: pale yellow needles. M.p. 119°.

2 : 4 : 6-*Trinitrobenzoic acid salt*: m.p. 156°.

$C_{10}H_9N,C_6H_3(NO_2)_3$-1 : 3 : 5 : red needles. M.p. 162°. Sol. most org. solvents.

Picrate: yellow needles from H_2O. M.p. 195° decomp.

Styphate: cryst. from EtOH. M.p. 194–5°.

B,HCl: leaflets. M.p. 254°.

N-*Me*: *see* *N*-Methyl-2-naphthylamine.

N-*Di-Me*: *see* Dimethyl-2-naphthylamine.

N-*Et*: *see* *N*-Ethyl-2-naphthylamine.

N-*Di-Et*: *see* Diethyl-2-naphthylamine.

N-*Propyl*: oil. B.p. 322–4°/761 mm.

N-*Butyl*: oil with characteristic odour. B.p. 348–50°. $D_4^{16\cdot5}$ 1·02. Insol. H_2O. Shows faint violet fluor. *B,HCl*: m.p. 176–8°. p-*Bromobenzoyl*: prisms from EtOH. M.p. 125°.

N-*Pentadecyl*: plates from EtOH. M.p. 53–4°. Sol. Et_2O, C_6H_6, pet. ether. Insol. H_2O. Sol. conc. H_2SO_4. *B,HCl*: needles from $CHCl_3$–pet. ether. M.p. 176–7°. Sol. hot $CHCl_3$. Insol. EtOH, Et_2O, pet. ether.

N-*Heptadecyl*: plates from EtOH. M.p. 59–61°. Sol. Et_2O, C_6H_6, $CHCl_3$. Spar. sol. Me_2CO, pet. ether. Insol. H_2O. Sol. conc. H_2SO_4. *B,HCl*: needles from $CHCl_3$–pet. ether. M.p. 170–1°. Sol. boiling $CHCl_3$. Insol. EtOH, Et_2O, pet. ether.

N-*Phenyl*: *see* *N*-Phenyl-2-naphthylamine.

N-o-*Chlorophenyl*: cryst. from EtOH. M.p. 89°. B.p. 236–8°/13·5 mm. Conc. H_2SO_4 ⟶ yellow sol. ⟶ red on adding HNO_2.

N-m-*Chlorophenyl*: cryst. from EtOH. M.p. 101°. B.p. 250–3°/11 mm. Conc. H_2SO_4 ⟶ yellow sol. ⟶ brown on adding HNO_2.

N-p-*Chlorophenyl*: cryst. from EtOH. M.p. 101°. B.p. 251·5°/13 mm. Conc. H_2SO_4 ⟶ yellowish sol. ⟶ orange-red on adding HNO_2.

N-o-*Nitrophenyl*: orange needles from EtOH. M.p. 110°.

N-p-*Nitrophenyl*: yellow cryst. from C_6H_6. M.p. 283–4°. Spar. sol. cold EtOH, Et_2O. Sol. C_6H_6.

N-2 : 4-*Dinitrophenyl*: red cryst. M.p. 183° (169°). Sol. hot AcOH, Me_2CO. Mod. sol. Et_2O, C_6H_6. Spar. sol. EtOH.

N-2 : 4 : 6 -*Trinitrophenyl*: *see* *N*-Picryl-2-naphthylamine.

N-o-*Tolyl*: cryst. from ligroin. M.p. 95° (105°). B.p. 400–5°, 235–7°/14 mm. Sol. C_6H_6, EtOH, Et_2O, Me_2CO, $CHCl_3$, ligroin. *Benzoyl*: leaflets from EtOH. M.p. 117–18°.

N-m-*Tolyl*: cryst. from EtOH. M.p. 68–9°. B.p. 243–6°/15 mm. Sol. hot EtOH with blue fluor., C_6H_6, Et_2O, Me_2CO, ligroin.

N-p-*Tolyl*: leaflets from hot EtOH. M.p. 102–3°. Sol. Et_2O, C_6H_6. Spar. sol. cold EtOH, ligroin. Sols. show blue fluor. *Acetyl*: needles. M.p. 85°. Mod. sol. EtOH, Et_2O, C_6H_6. *Benzoyl*: needles from EtOH. M.p. 139°.

N-*Benzyl*: *see* *N*-Benzyl-2-naphthylamine.

N-o-*Nitrobenzyl*: red leaflets from EtOH or AcOH. M.p. 162°. Sol. C_6H_6, $CHCl_3$, CS_2. Spar. other solvents. *Acetyl*: prisms from EtOH. M.p. 117–18°.

N - m - *Nitrobenzyl*: yellow needles from EtOH.Aq. M.p. 80°.

N - p - *Nitrobenzyl*: yellow leaflets from EtOH.Aq. M.p. 121·5°. Sol. C_6H_6, Et_2O. Spar. sol. cold EtOH.

N-*Naphthyl*: *see* Dinaphthylamine.

N-*Benzylidene*: *see* Benzylidene-2-naphthylamine.

N - o - *Nitrobenzylidene*: yellow leaflets from EtOH. M.p. 91°. Sol. org. most solvents.

N-m-*Nitrobenzylidene*: yellow plates from EtOH. M.p. 90°. Sol. Et_2O, C_6H_6, $CHCl_3$. Spar. sol. EtOH.

N-p-*Nitrobenzylidene*: golden-yellow needles. M.p. 120–1°. Very sol. Et_2O, Me_2CO.

N-*Cinnamylidene*: yellow cryst. from EtOH. M.p. 125°. Very sol. $CHCl_3$. Sol. MeOH, C_6H_6, Et_2O. Mod. sol. Me_2CO, AcOEt, toluene.

N-*Salicylidene*: reddish-yellow needles from EtOH. M.p. 126°.

N-*Furfurylidene*: leaflets from EtOH. M.p. 85°. Mod. sol. cold EtOH.Aq. Insol. H_2O.

Formyl: leaflets. M.p. 129°. Sol. EtOH, C_6H_6, $CHCl_3$. Less sol. Et_2O. Spar. sol. hot H_2O.

Acetyl: 2-acetnaphthalide. Leaflets from H_2O or EtOH. M.p. 134°. *B,HCl*: needles. M.p. 152°.

Diacetyl: plates from ligroin. M.p. 66·5°. Sol. most org. solvents.

Chloroacetyl: needles from EtOH.Aq. M.p. 117–18°. Sol. EtOH. Spar. sol. C_6H_6. Insol. H_2O.

Butyryl: cryst. from pet. ether. M.p. 125°.

Valeryl: m.p. 112°.

Caproyl: m.p. 107°.

Heptylyl: m.p. 101°.

Caprylyl: m.p. 103°.

Pelargonyl: m.p. 103°.

Capryl: m.p. 104°.

Lauryl: m.p. 106°.

Myristyl: needles from EtOH. M.p. 108°. B.p. 179°/10 mm. Very sol. Et_2O, $CHCl_3$, C_6H_6. Sol. Me_2CO.

Palmityl: cryst. from EtOH. M.p. 109°. B.p. 198·5°/10 mm. Sol. Et_2O, C_6H_6, $CHCl_3$.

Stearyl : needles from EtOH. M.p. 112° (109°). B.p. 220·5°/10 mm. Very sol. Et_2O, C_6H_6, $CHCl_3$.

Benzoyl : 2-benznaphthalide. Needles from C_6H_6 or AcOH. M.p. 162–3°. Sol. Et_2O, $CHCl_3$, hot EtOH. *Benzenesulphonyl* : needles. M.p. 161–2°.

Benzenesulphonyl : needles or prisms from EtOH. M.p. 102–3°.

p-*Toluenesulphonyl* : needles and leaflets from EtOH. M.p. 133°.

Knoll, D.R.P., 241,853, (*Chem. Zentr.*, 1912, I, 178).
Knoevenagel, *J. prakt. Chem.*, 1914, **89**, 17, *et seq.*
De'Conno, *Gazz. chim. ital.*, 1917, **47**, i, 98.
Robertson, *J. Chem. Soc.*, 1919, **115**, 1221.
Le Sueur, *J. Chem. Soc.*, 1911, **99**, 830.
Pawlewski, *Ber.*, 1902, **35**, 112.
Cosiner, *Ber.*, 1881, **14**, 59.
Badische, D.R.P., 117,471, (*Chem. Zentr.*, 1901, I, 349).
Campbell, *Chem. Abstracts*, 1922, **16**, 3400.
A.G.F.A., D.R.P., 164,130, (*Chem. Zentr.*, 1905, II, 1476).
Reilly, Drumm, O'Sullivan, *J. Soc. Chem. Ind.*, 1927, **46**, 437T.
Kym, *J. prakt. Chem.*, 1895, **51**, 328, 332.
Warren, Smiles, *J. Chem. Soc.*, 1932, 2778.
Ryan, Drumm, *Chem. Abstracts*, 1919, **13**, 563.

1-Naphthylamine-2 : 4-disulphonic Acid

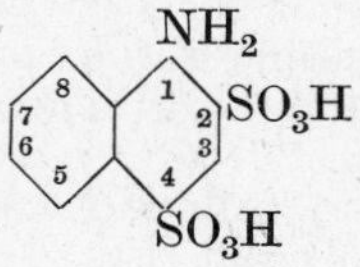

$C_{10}H_9O_6NS_2$ MW, 303

NaOH fusion ⟶ 1-amino-2-naphthol-4-sulphonic acid. Diazo-comp. warmed + dil. HNO_3 ⟶ 2 : 4-dinitronaphthol. Di-Na salt : easily sol. H_2O.

Gulinov, *Chem. Abstracts*, 1933, **27**, 3929.
Hunter, Sprung, *J. Am. Chem. Soc.*, 1931, **53**, 1437.

1-Naphthylamine-2 : 5-disulphonic Acid.

Needles. Very sol. H_2O. Spar. sol. dil. min. acids. Alkali salts very spar. sol. H_2O. Sols. of acid and salts fluor. bluish-green. Part. hyd. by dil. H_2SO_4 at 160° ⟶ 1-naphthylamine-5-sulphonic acid. 50% NaOH.Aq. at 240–70° ⟶ 5-amino-1-naphthol-6-sulphonic acid. Sulphonation by 40% anhydro-acid at 120° ⟶ 1-naphthylamine-2 : 5 : 7-trisulphonic acid.

Badische, D.R.P., 160,536, (*Chem. Zentr.*, 1905, I, 1678).
Tobias, *Ber.*, 1890, **23**, 1631.

1-Naphthylamine-2 : 7-disulphonic Acid (*Kalle's Acid*).

Needles. Sols. of alkali salts show weak blue fluor. Heat with dil. H_2SO_4 or H_2O under press. ⟶ 1-naphthylamine-7-sulphonic acid. Na salt : prisms from dil. EtOH. Ba salt : very spar. sol. H_2O.

Bayer, D.R.P., 255,724, (*Chem. Zentr.*, 1913, I, 478).

1-Naphthylamine-2 : 8-disulphonic Acid.

Felted needles. Mod. sol. H_2O. Sols. of alkali salts show green fluor. Does not give reactive diazo-comp., but couples with diazotised bases ⟶ azo-dyestuffs. Fused with NaOH ⟶ 8-amino-1-naphthol-7-sulphonic acid.

Dressel, Kothe, *Ber.*, 1894, **27**, 2139.

1-Naphthylamine-3 : 5-disulphonic Acid.

Mono-K salt : needles + $2H_2O$.

Armstrong, Wynne, *Proc. Chem. Soc.*, 1895, **11**, 240.

1-Naphthylamine-3 : 6-disulphonic Acid (*Freund's Acid*).

Needles. Very sol. H_2O, EtOH. H_2O at 180° ⟶ 1-naphthol-3 : 6-disulphonic acid. Heat with 75% NaOH.Aq. ⟶ 4-amino-2-naphthol-7-sulphonic acid + 5-amino-2-naphthol-7-sulphonic acid. NH_3 at 180° ⟶ 1 : 3-naphthylenediamine-6-sulphonic acid. NaHg ⟶ 1-naphthylamine. Mono-Na and K salts : cryst. + $3H_2O$. Very sol. H_2O. Ca salt : cryst. + $5H_2O$. Sol. H_2O. Ba salt : cryst. + $4H_2O$. Sol. H_2O.

Kalle, D.R.P., 233,934, (*Chem. Zentr.*, 1911, I, 1468).
Friedländer, Taussig, *Ber.*, 1897, **30**, 1462.
Armstrong, Wynne, *Proc. Chem. Soc.*, 1895, **11**, 82.
Alén, *Ber.*, 1884, **17** (Referate), 436.

1-Naphthylamine-3 : 7-disulphonic Acid.

Needles. Very sol. H_2O. Sols. of the acid and its salts show blue fluor. H_2O at 180° ⟶ 1-naphthol-3 : 7-disulphonic acid. 40% NaOH.Aq. at 200° ⟶ 8-amino-2-naphthol-6-sulphonic acid + an isomeric acid. NH_3 at 180° ⟶ 1 : 3-naphthylenediamine-7-sulphonic acid. Mono-K salt : needles. Mod. sol. hot H_2O. Ca salt : needles + $2H_2O$. Insol. cold, sol. hot H_2O. Ba salt : needles + $1H_2O$. Spar. sol. H_2O.

See first and fourth references above.

1-Naphthylamine-3 : 8-disulphonic Acid. Flakes + $3H_2O$. Very sol. hot H_2O. The diazo-comp. + dil. H_2SO_4 on warming ⟶ naphthasultone-3-sulphonic acid. Couples with diazotised *m*- or *p*-nitroaniline but not with diazotised aniline. H_2O at 180° or prolonged boiling + dil. H_2SO_4 ⟶ 1-naphthol-3 : 8-disulphonic acid. Boiled with 75% H_2SO_4, or with Zn dust + NaOH.Aq., or with NaHg in cold ⟶ 1-naphthylamine-3-sulphonic acid. Fused with NaOH below 210° ⟶ 1-amino-8-naphthol--sulphonic acid. Heat with 9% NaOH.Aq. at 250° ⟶ 1 : 8-dihydroxynaphthalene-3-sulphonic acid. NH_3 at 180° ⟶ 1 : 3-naphthylenediamine-8-sulphonic acid. Mono-Na salt : cryst. + $2H_2O$. Sol. 30 parts H_2O. Di-Na salt : cryst. + $6H_2O$. Very sol. H_2O. Ba salt : needles + $4H_2O$. Spar. sol. H_2O.

Stanier, E.P., 161,859, (*Chem. Abstracts*, 1921, **15**, 2445).
Bayer, D.R.P., 255,724, (*Chem. Zentr.*, 1913, I, 478).
Paul, *Z. angew, Chem.*, 1896, **9**, 562.
Friedländer, Lucht, *Ber.*, 1893, **26**, 3032.
Schultz, *Ber.*, 1890, **23**, 77.

1-Naphthylamine-4 : 6-disulphonic Acid (*Dahl's Acid II*).

Needles. Sol. to 17% in H_2O at 20°, very sol. hot H_2O. Sol. hot 85% EtOH. Sols. of acid and salts fluor. blue. Couples with diazo-comps. Fused with NaOH at 180–200° ⟶ 1-amino-6-naphthol-4-sulphonic acid; at 200–20° ⟶ 1 : 6-dihydroxynaphthalene-4-sulphonic acid. Sulphonated with 35% anhydro-acid at 80–90° ⟶ 1-naphthylamine-2 : 4 : 6-trisulphonic acid. Mono-Na salt : sol. 6 parts H_2O at 20°. Di-Na and K salts : very sol. H_2O. Ca salt : needles + $5H_2O$.

Kalle, D.R.P., 233,934, (*Chem. Zentr.*, 1911, I, 1468).
Erdmann, *Ann.*, 1893, **275**, 218.
Armstrong, Wynne, *Proc. Chem. Soc.*, 1890, **6**, 126.

1-Naphthylamine-4 : 7-disulphonic Acid (*Dahl's Acid III*).

Needles from H_2O. Sol. to 0·7% H_2O at 20°, to 5% at 100°. Insol. 85% EtOH. Sols. of acid and its salts show blue fluor. Couples with diazo-comps. Sulphonated with 35% anhydro-acid at 80–90° ⟶ 1-naphthylamine-2 : 4 : 7-trisulphonic acid. Mono-Na salt : needles, Sol. 140 parts H_2O at 20°, 20 parts at b.p. Insol. 85% EtOH. Di-K salt : cryst. + $2\frac{1}{2}H_2O$. Spar. sol. H_2O. Ca salt : spar. sol. cold H_2O.

Bucherer, Barsch, *J. prakt. Chem.*, 1925, **111**, 322.
M.L.B., D.R.P., 215,338, (*Chem. Zentr.*, 1909, II, 1710).
See also second reference above.

1-Naphthylamine-4 : 8-disulphonic Acid. Couples with diazo-comps. Fused with NaOH at 200° ⟶ 1-amino-8-naphthol-4-sulphonic acid. 60% NaOH.Aq. at 250° ⟶ 1 : 8-dihydroxynaphthalene-4-sulphonic acid. Sulphonated with 40% anhydro-acid ⟶ naphthasultam-2 : 4-disulphonic acid. Mono-Na salt : flakes. Spar. sol. cold H_2O. Di-Na salt : needles + $2H_2O$. Sol. H_2O.

König, Keil, *Ber.*, 1922, **55**, 2149.
Stanier, E.P., 161,859, (*Chem. Abstracts*, 1921, **15**, 2445).
Kalle, D.R.P., 283,727, (*Chem. Zentr.*, 1915, I, 1238).
Bayer, D.R.P., 255,724, (*Chem. Zentr.*, 1913, I, 478).
Bucherer, *J. prakt. Chem.*, 1907, **75**, 258; 1904, **70**, 347.

1-Naphthylamine-5 : 8-disulphonic Acid. Needles. Very spar. sol. H_2O. Sols. of alkali salts show intense greenish-yellow col. Couples with diazo-comps. 75% NaOH.Aq. at 150–60° ⟶ 1-amino-8-naphthol-5-sulphonic acid; 60% NaOH.Aq. at 250° ⟶ 1 : 8-dihydroxynaphthalene-4-sulphonic acid. NaHg ⟶ 1-naphthylamine. Sulphonation with 40% anhydro-acid at 80–90° ⟶ naphthasultam-disulphonic acid-D. Mono-Na salt : needles + $1\frac{1}{2}H_2O$. Spar. sol. cold H_2O.

Gattermann, *Ber.*, 1899, **32**, 1156.

2-Naphthylamine-1 : 5-disulphonic Acid

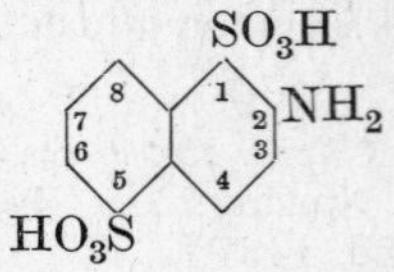

$C_{10}H_9O_6NS_2$ MW, 303

The diazo-comp. + alk. NaOCl or + Na_2CO_3 at 50–60° ⟶ diazo-oxide of 2-amino-1-naphthol-5-sulphonic acid. Fused with NaOH at 210–30° ⟶ 2-amino-5-naphthol-1-sulphonic acid. Sulphonation with 40% anhydro-acid at 100° ⟶ 2-naphthylamine 1 : 5 : 7-trisulphonic acid.

Di-K salt : cryst. Mod. sol. H_2O.

Bucherer, Wahl, *J. prakt. Chem.*, 1921, **103**, 129.

Kalle, D.R.P., 233,105, (*Chem. Zentr.*, 1911, I, 1263).

Armstrong, Wynne, *Proc. Chem. Soc.*, 1896, **12**, 238; 1890, **6**, 129.

2-Naphthylamine-1 : 6-disulphonic Acid.

Needles. Very sol. H_2O. Spar. sol. EtOH. Dil. sols. show weak blue fluor. The cryst. diazo-comp. + Na_2CO_3.Aq. ⟶ diazo-oxide of 2-amino-1-naphthol-6-sulphonic acid. Mono-Na salt : long needles + $2H_2O$. Very sol. H_2O. Mono-K salt : needles + $1H_2O$. Spar. sol. H_2O. Di-NH_4 salt : red prisms + $1H_2O$. Sol. H_2O. Di-Na salt : long needles. Very sol. H_2O. Di-K salt : large yellow cryst. + $2H_2O$. Very sol. H_2O.

Badische, D.R.P., 148,882, (*Chem. Zentr.*, 1904, I, 619).

Armstrong, Wynne, *Proc. Chem. Soc.*, 1890, **6**, 130.

Forsling, *Ber.*, 1888, **21**, 3495.

2-Naphthylamine-1 : 7-disulphonic Acid.

Sols. of salts show violet-blue fluor. In AcOH does not couple with diazobenzene. Long boiling with 20% HCl ⟶ 2-naphthylamine-7-sulphonic acid. The diazo-comp. + Na_2CO_3.Aq. ⟶ diazo-oxide of 2-amino-1-naphthol-7-sulphonic acid. Mono-K salt : needles. Spar. sol. cold H_2O. Di-K salt : large cryst. + $3H_2O$. Ba salt : needles. Mod. sol. H_2O.

Dressel, Kothe, *Ber.*, 1894, **27**, 1194.

Armstrong, Wynne, *Chem. News*, 1890, **62**, 164.

2-Naphthylamine-3 : 6-disulphonic Acid (*Amido-R-acid*).

Plates or amorph. powder. Sol. H_2O with violet-blue fluor. Couples with diazo-comps. 75% NaOH.Aq. at 230–50° ⟶ 2-amino-3-naphthol-6-sulphonic acid.

Kalle, D.R.P., 233,934, (*Chem. Zentr.*, 1911, I, 1468).

Griesheim-Elektron Fabrik, D.R.P., 217,277, (*Chem. Zentr.*, 1910, I, 395).

Armstrong, Wynne, *Proc. Chem. Soc.*, 1890, **6**, 12.

Pfitzinger, Duisberg, *Ber.*, 1889, **22**, 398.

2-Naphthylamine-3 : 7-disulphonic Acid.

Cryst. Sol. hot, spar. sol. cold H_2O. Couples with diazo-comps. Dil. sols. of alkali salts show blue fluor. Sulphonation with 40% anhydro-acid at 80–90° ⟶ 2-naphthylamine-1 : 3 : 7-trisulphonic acid. Mono-Na salt : sol. 50 parts H_2O at 20°, 12·5 parts at b.p. Mono-K salt : flakes. Spar. sol. H_2O. Acid Ba salt : microscopic flakes. Very spar. sol. H_2O.

Dressel, Kothe, *Ber.*, 1894, **27**, 1199.

Armstrong, Wynne, *Proc. Chem. Soc.*, 1890, **6**, 127.

2-Naphthylamine-4 : 7-disulphonic Acid (*Andresen's Acid*).

Dil. sols. of alkali salts fluor. strongly blue. The diazo-comp. boiled with H_2O ⟶ 2-naphthol-4 : 7-disulphonic acid. 35% KOH.Aq. at 180–200° ⟶ 2-amino-4-naphthol-7-sulphonic acid. Mono-Na salt : needles + $1H_2O$ from boiling H_2O. Ba salt : prisms from boiling H_2O. Spar. sol. cold H_2O.

Armstrong, Wynne, *Proc. Chem. Soc.*, 1891, **7**, 27.

Schultz, *Ber.*, 1890, **23**, 77.

See also first reference above.

2-Naphthylamine-4 : 8-disulphonic Acid.

Prisms. The alkali salts in aq. sol. show deep blue fluor. Does not couple with diazo-comps. H_2O or 10% H_2SO_4 at 180° ⟶ 2-naphthol-4-sulphonic acid. Fused with KOH at 215° ⟶ 2-amino-4-naphthol-8-sulphonic acid. The acetyl deriv. + HNO_3 ⟶ 6-nitro-deriv. Boiled with Zn dust + NaOH.Aq. ⟶ 2-naphthylamine-4-sulphonic acid + 2-naphthylamine-8-sulphonic acid. NaHg in cold ⟶ 2-naphthylamine-8-sulphonic acid + 2-naphthylamine. Na salt : needles. Sol. hot H_2O. Acid Ba salt : minute needles. Sol. H_2O.

Bayer, D.R.P., 255,724, (*Chem. Zentr.*, 1913, I, 478).

Kalle, D.R.P., 233,934, (*Chem. Zentr.*, 1911, I, 1468).

Friedländer, Fischer, *Chem. Zentr.*, 1899, I, 289.

Friedländer, Lucht, *Ber.*, 1893, **26**, 3033.

2-Naphthylamine-5 : 7-disulphonic Acid.

Rhombic needles + $5H_2O$ from H_2O. Sol. to 23% in H_2O at 20°. Sols. of salts show green fluor. 50% NaOH.Aq. at 190° ⟶ 2-amino-5-naphthol-7-sulphonic acid. NaHg in cold ⟶ 2-naphthylamine-7-sulphonic acid. Sulphonation with 40% anhydro-acid at 100° ⟶ 2-naphthylamine-1 : 5 : 7-trisulphonic acid. Mono-Na salt : needles + $4H_2O$. Sol. to 8% in H_2O at 20°. Mono-K salt : prisms + $4H_2O$. Sol. to 2·6% in H_2O at 20°. Di-Na salt : needles + $6H_2O$. Sol. to 72% in H_2O at 20°. Di-K salt : needles + $2H_2O$. Sol. to 64% in H_2O at 20°. Ca salt : hexagonal cryst. + $4H_2O$. Sol. to 40% in H_2O at 20°. Ba salt : cryst. + $3H_2O$.

Sol. to 23% in H_2O at 20°. Mg salt: needles or prisms + $8H_2O$. Sol. to 21% in H_2O at 20°.

Ofitzerov, *Chem. Abstracts*, 1935, **29**, 2530, 1086.
Fierz-David, Braunschweig, *Helv. Chim. Acta*, 1923, **6**, 1146.
Bayer, D.R.P., 255,724, (*Chem. Zentr.*, 1913, I, 478).
Dressel, Kothe, *Ber.*, 1894, **27**, 1197.
Armstrong, Wynne, *Proc. Chem. Soc.*, 1890, **6**, 129.

2-Naphthylamine-6 : 8-disulphonic Acid (*Amido-G-Acid*).

Needles + $4H_2O$ from H_2O. Sol. to 9% in H_2O at 20°. Sols. of salts show blue fluor. Does not couple with diazo-comps. 75% NaOH.Aq. at 230–50° ⟶ 2-amino-8-naphthol-6-sulphonic acid ("Gamma-acid"). Sulphonation with 40% anhydro-acid at 120–30° ⟶ 2-naphthylamine-3 : 6 : 8-trisulphonic acid. Mono-K salt: rhombic cryst. + $2H_2O$. Sol. to 2·5% in H_2O at 20°. Di-Na salt: prisms + $3H_2O$. Sol. to 59% in H_2O at 20°. Di-K salt: prisms + $2H_2O$. Sol. to 52% in H_2O at 20°. Ca salt: plates + $3H_2O$. Sol. to 29% in H_2O at 20°. Ba salt: plates + $3H_2O$. Sol. to 12% in H_2O at 20°. Mg salt: cryst. + $8H_2O$. Sol. to 9% in H_2O at 20°.

Veinberg, *Chem. Abstracts*, 1935, **29**, 8336.
Bucherer, *J. prakt. Chem.*, 1904, **70**, 358.
Dressel, Kothe, *Ber.*, 1894, **27**, 2152.
Armstrong, Wynne, *Proc. Chem. Soc.*, 1890, **6**, 128.
See also first two references above.

1-Naphthylamine-2-sulphonic Acid

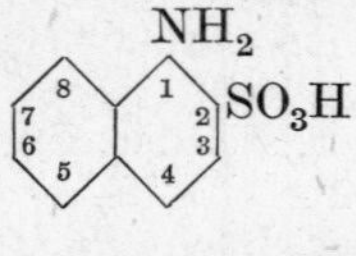

$C_{10}H_9O_3NS$ MW, 223

Needles from H_2O. M.p. 272° decomp. Sol. 244 parts H_2O at 20°; 31·3 parts at 100°. Heat of comb. C_p 1258·1 Cal. HNO_3 ⟶ 5-nitro-deriv. Sulphonation with 10% anhydro-acid in cold ⟶ 1-naphthylamine-2 : 5-disulphonic acid. Na salt: flakes. Sol. 10 parts boiling H_2O, 60 parts cold H_2O. K salt: needles. Spar. sol. cold H_2O. Ca salt: flakes. Spar. sol. H_2O.

N-*Acetyl*: needles + $1H_2O$ from H_2O.

N-*Et*: needles from H_2O. M.p. 207–8°. Spar. sol. H_2O. Insol. C_6H_6.

Bayer, D.R.P., 293,184, (*Chem. Zentr.*, 1916, II, 291).
Wildt, *Rec. trav. chim.*, 1904, **23**, 185.
Erdmann, *Ann.*, 1893, **275**, 225.

1 - Naphthylamine - 3 - sulphonic Acid (*Cleve's γ-Acid*).

Needles. Spar. sol. H_2O. Couples with diazo-comps. Fused with KOH at 250–60° ⟶ 1-amino-3-naphthol. 60% NaOH.Aq. at 250–80° ⟶ *o*-toluic acid. NH_3.Aq. at 180° ⟶ 1 : 3-naphthylenediamine. Sulphonation with 20% anhydro-acid in cold ⟶ 1-naphthylamine-3 : 5-disulphonic acid. Na, K, Ca and Ba salts: very sol. H_2O.

N-*Phenyl*: $C_{16}H_{13}O_3NS$. MW, 299. Cryst. Mod. sol. H_2O. *Na salt*: mod. sol. H_2O.

Amide: $C_{10}H_{10}O_2N_2S$. MW, 222. Needles + $1H_2O$. M.p. 131°. 1-N-*Acetyl*: m.p. 220–1°.

Bayer, D.R.P., 255,724; 251,099, (*Chem. Zentr.*, 1913, I, 478; 1912, II, 1243); 70, 349.
Kalle, D.R.P., 233,934, (*Chem. Zentr.*, 1911, I, 1468).
Gattermann, Schulze, *Ber.*, 1897, **30**, 54.
Friedländer, Lucht, *Ber.*, 1893, **26**, 3032.

1-Naphthylamine-4-sulphonic Acid.
See Naphthionic Acid.

1 - Naphthylamine - 5 - sulphonic Acid (*Laurent's Acid*).

Needles + $1H_2O$. Sol. 940 parts cold H_2O. Heat of comb. C_p 1255·2 Cal. $k = 2{\cdot}4 \times 10^{-4}$ at 25°. Dil. aq. sols. of the acid and its salts show greenish fluor. Diazo-comp. forms first component of many azo-dyestuffs. Conc. NaOH.Aq. at 250° ⟶ 1-amino-5-naphthol. Sulphonation with 35% anhydro-acid at 90–120° ⟶ 1-naphthylamine-2 : 5 : 7-trisulphonic acid. The acetyl deriv. + 30% anhydro-acid in cold ⟶ the 5 : 7-disulphonic acid. Na salt: needles. Sol. H_2O. K salt: needles + $1H_2O$. Sol. H_2O. Ca salt: plates + $9H_2O$. Sol. H_2O.

N-*Phenyl*: cryst. Spar. sol. H_2O. *Na salt*: spar. sol. H_2O.

N-*Acetyl*: aniline salt, decomp. at 344°.

Amide: m.p. 259–60°. 1-N-*Acetyl*: m.p. 231–2°. 1 : 1-N-*Diacetyl*: m.p. 200°.

Anilide: m.p. 171°.

Vendelshtein, Shpinel, *Chem. Abstracts*, 1933, **27**, 5320.
Newport Chem. Co., D.R.P., 562,513, (*Chem. Abstracts*, 1933, **27**, 1010).
Heller, Sturm, *J. prakt. Chem.*, 1929, **121**, 193.
Forster *et al.*, *J. Soc. Chem. Ind.*, 1928, **47**, 155, 157T.
Fierz, *Helv. Chim. Acta*, 1920, **3**, 318.
Erdmann, *Ann.*, 1893, **275**, 193, 264.
Bayer, D.R.P., 70,349.

1 - Naphthylamine - 6 - sulphonic Acid (*Cleve's Acid*).

Needles + $2H_2O$. Sol. 1000 parts H_2O at 16°. Heat of comb. C_p 1258·4 Cal. $k = 1{\cdot}95 \times 10^{-4}$ at 25°. Couples with diazo-comps. Fused with KOH ⟶ 1-amino-6-naphthol. Sulphonation with 10% anhydro-acid ⟶ 1-naphthylamine-4 : 6-disulphonic acid. Na salt : plates + $4\frac{1}{2}H_2O$. Sol. H_2O. K salt : flakes + $1H_2O$. Sol. H_2O. Ba salt : needles + $1H_2O$. Spar. sol. H_2O. Ca salt : plates + $7H_2O$. Sol. H_2O.

N-*Phenyl* : cryst. Spar. sol. H_2O. *Na salt* : spar. sol. H_2O.

Amide : m.p. 218–19° decomp. 1-N-*Acetyl* : m.p. 238–9°.

Anilide : m.p. 127–8°.

See last five references above.

1 - Naphthylamine - 7 - sulphonic Acid (*Cleve's-θ-Acid*).

Flakes + $1H_2O$. Sol. 220 parts H_2O at 25°. Couples with diazo-comps. Heat of comb. C_p 1259·5 Cal. $k = 2{\cdot}27 \times 10^{-4}$ at 25°. $FeCl_3$ ⟶ blue col. 60% NaOH.Aq. at 250° ⟶ 1-amino-7-naphthol. Sulphonated with 25% anhydro-acid at 50° ⟶ 1-naphthylamine-4 : 7-disulphonic acid. Na salt : needles + $\frac{1}{2}H_2O$. Sol. H_2O. K salt : flakes. Sol. H_2O. Ba salt : needles. Spar. sol. H_2O. Ca salt : cryst. + $2H_2O$. Sol. H_2O.

N-*Phenyl* : cryst. Spar. sol. H_2O. *Na salt* : mod. sol. H_2O.

Amide : needles + $1\frac{1}{2}H_2O$. M.p. 181°. 1-N-*Acetyl* : m.p. 213°.

Anilide : m.p. 146–7°.

Friedländer, Zinberg, *Ber.*, 1896, **29**, 41.
Cleve, *Ber.*, 1888, **21**, 3264.
Bayer, D.R.P., 70,349.
A.G.F.A., D.R.P., 159,353, (*Chem. Zentr.*, 1905, I, 975).
See also previous references.

1-Naphthylamine-8-sulphonic Acid (*Peri Acid, Schöllkopf Acid*).

Needles + $1H_2O$. Sol. 4800 parts H_2O at 21°, 238 parts boiling H_2O. Heat of comb. C_p 1254·4 Cal. $k = 1{\cdot}02 \times 10^{-5}$ at 25°. Couples with diazo-comps. H_2O at 200° ⟶ 1-naphthol-8-sulphonic acid. 9% NaOH.Aq. at 220–60° ⟶ 1 : 8-dihydroxynaphthalene. Fused with KOH at 200° ⟶ 1-amino-8-naphthol. $POCl_3$ at 130° ⟶ naphthasultam. 40% anhydro-acid at 80–90° ⟶ naphthasultam-2 : 4-disulphonic acid; 10% anhydro-acid in cold ⟶ 1-naphthylamine-4 : 8-disulphonic acid.

N-*Acetyl* : aniline salt, m.p. 273°.

Anilide : m.p. 139–40°.

Chuksanova, Bilik, *Chem. Abstracts*, 1935, **29**, 1085.
Mow, U.S.P., 1,996, 822, (*Chem. Abstracts*, 1935, **29**, 3353).
Tinker, E.P., 389,098, (*Chem. Abstracts*, 1933, **27**, 4545).
Martin, *Chem. Abstracts*, 1928, **22**, 2665.
Forster, Hanson, Watson, *J. Soc. Chem. Ind.*, 1928, **47**, 155T.
Wahl, Vermeylen, *Bull. soc. chim.*, 1927, **41**, 514.
Finzi, *Ann. chim. applicata*, 1925, **14**, 50.

2 - Naphthylamine - 1 - sulphonic Acid (*Tobias' Acid*)

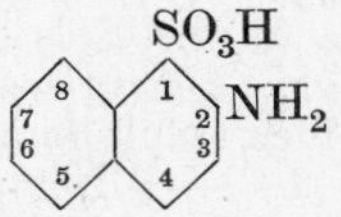

$C_{10}H_9O_3NS$ MW, 223

Anhyd. flakes from hot, or hydrated needles from cold H_2O. Used as first component in many azo-dyestuffs. Diazo-comp. readily forms 2-naphthol-1-sulphonic acid. Na salt heated in dry atm. at 230° ⟶ Na β-naphthylsulphamate. Sulphonation with 20% anhydro-acid ⟶ 2-naphthylamine-1 : 5-disulphonic acid.

Green, Vakil, *J. Chem. Soc.*, 1918, **113**, 40.
Bucherer, *J. prakt. Chem.*, 1904, **70**, 357.
Dressel, Kothe, *Ber.*, 1894, **27**, 2140.
Erdmann, *Ann.*, 1893, **275**, 274.

2-Naphthylamine-4-sulphonic Acid.

Long needles + $1H_2O$. Couples with diazo-comps. 60% NaOH.Aq. at 230–80° ⟶ *o*-toluic acid. Na salt : flakes + $4H_2O$. Aq. sols. show violet fluor. K salt : needles + $1\frac{1}{2}H_2O$.

Kalle, D.R.P., 233,934, (*Chem. Zentr.*, 1911, I, 1468).
Friedländer, Rüdt, *Ber.*, 1896, **29**, 1611.

2-Naphthylamine-5-sulphonic Acid.

Needles from H_2O. Sol. 0·033 in 100 parts H_2O at 20°, 1 in 260 parts boiling H_2O. $k = 9{\cdot}4 \times 10^{-5}$ at 25°. The acid and its salts in dil. aq. sol. show reddish-blue fluor. KOH at 260–70° ⟶ 2-amino-5-naphthol. NaHg ⟶ 2-naphthylamine + SO_2. Sulphonation with 20% anhydro-acid in cold ⟶ 2-naphthylamine-5 : 7-disulphonic acid (mainly) + 2-naphthylamine-1 : 5-disulphonic acid. Na salt : prisms + $5H_2O$. Sol. 10 parts boiling 95% EtOH. The aq. sol. + $CuSO_4$ ⟶ deep red col. Ca salt : needles + $11H_2O$. Sol. 11 parts cold H_2O.

N-*Phenyl* : $C_{16}H_{13}O_3NS$. MW, 299. Cryst.

Very spar. sol. H_2O. *Na*, *K*, and *NH_4* salts mod. sol. H_2O.

Amide : $C_{10}H_{10}O_2N_2S$. MW, 222. Needles. M.p. 165°.

Waterman, Groot, *Chem. Zentr.*, 1928, I, 1288.
Green, Vakil, *J. Chem. Soc.*, 1918, **113**, 38.
Kappeler, *Ber.*, 1912, **45**, 635.
Erdmann, *Ann.*, 1893, **275**, 277.
Friedländer, Lucht, *Ber.*, 1893, **26**, 3032.
Lesser, *Ber.*, 1894, **27**, 2364.
Clayton Aniline, D.R.P., 53,649.

2-Naphthylamine-6-sulphonic Acid (*Brönner Acid*).

Leaflets + $1H_2O$. Sol. 7790 parts H_2O at 20°, 630 parts boiling H_2O. Sols of acid or its salts show bluish fluor. Diazotises and couples with phenols and amines. Sulphonated with 20% anhydro-acid at 20° ⟶ 2-naphthylamine-1 : 6-disulphonic acid + 2-naphthylamine-6 : 8-disulphonic acid. NH_4 salt : plates + $1H_2O$. Very spar. sol. H_2O. Na salt : cryst. + $2H_2O$. Sol. 40 parts cold H_2O. Aq. sol. + $CuSO_4$ ⟶ yellow ppt. $K_3Fe(CN)_6$ in alk. sol. ⟶ dinaphthazine-disulphonic acid. K salt : cryst. + $2H_2O$. Sol. 45 parts cold H_2O. Ca salt, Ba salt : each + $6H_2O$. Spar. sol. H_2O.

N-*Phenyl* : plates. Sol. 15 parts hot, 60 parts cold H_2O. *Na salt* : sol. 22 parts hot H_2O.

N-*Acetyl* : aniline salt, m.p. 256°.

Forster, Hanson, Watson, *J. Soc. Chem. Ind.*, 1928, **47**, 155T.
Reitzenstein, Fitzgerald, *J. prakt. Chem.*, 1914, **89**, 288.
Bucherer, *J. prakt. Chem.*, 1904, **70**, 357.
Bischoff, *Ber.*, 1890, **23**, 1914.
Green, *J. Chem. Soc.*, 1889, **55**, 37 ; 1918, **113**, 35.
Bucherer, Stohmann, *J. prakt. Chem.*, 1905, **71**, 435, 449.
Badische, D.R.P., 122,570, (*Chem. Zentr.*, 1901, II, 670).
See also first reference above.

2-Naphthylamine-7-sulphonic Acid (*Bayer's Acid*, *Amido-F Acid*, *δ-Acid*).

Needles + $1H_2O$. Sol. 5040 parts H_2O at 20°, 350 parts boiling H_2O. $k = 1{\cdot}02 \times 10^{-4}$ at 25°. Sols. of acid and its salts show reddish-violet fluor. Couples with diazo-comps. 50% NaOH.Aq. at 260–80° ⟶ 2-amino-7-naphthol. The Na salt + 20% $NaHSO_3$ at 90–100° for 24 hours ⟶ Na 2 : 2′-dinaphthylamine-7 : 7′-disulphonate. Sulphonation with 20–25% anhydro-acid at ord. temp. ⟶ 1 : 7-, 4 : 7-, and 5 : 7-β-naphthylaminedisulphonic acids. Na salt : needles + $4H_2O$. Sol. 70 parts cold H_2O. Aq. sol. + $CuSO_4$ ⟶ orange-yellow ppt.

N-*Phenyl* : cryst. Spar. sol. H_2O. *Na salt* : spar. sol. H_2O.

Bayer, D.R.P., 255,724, (*Chem. Zentr.*, 1913, I, 478) ; 70, 349.
Erdmann, *Ber.*, 1888, **21**, 637.
Weinberg, *Ber.*, 1887, **20**, 2908.
Bayer, Duisberg, *ibid.*, 1432.
See also third, fourth, and fifth references above.

2-Naphthylamine-8-sulphonic Acid (*Badische Acid*).

Prisms or needles from H_2O. Sol. 1680 parts H_2O at 20°, 200 parts boiling H_2O. $k = 1{\cdot}22 \times 10^{-4}$ at 25°. Dil. aq. sols. of the acid and its salts show blue fluor. Aq. sol. + $CuSO_4$ ⟶ orange-red ppt. With diazo-comps. ⟶ sol. yellow diazoamino-comps. Fused with KOH at 260–70° ⟶ 2-amino-8-naphthol. NaHg ⟶ 2-naphthylamine + SO_2. Sulphonation with 20% anhydro-acid in cold ⟶ 2-naphthylamine-6 : 8-disulphonic acid. K salt : six-sided plates + $\frac{1}{2}H_2O$. Ca salt : plates + $6H_2O$. Sol. 11 parts cold H_2O.

N-*Phenyl* : *Na*, *NH_4*, and *Ca salts* sol. H_2O.

Green, *J. Soc. Chem.*, 1918, **113**, 41 ; 1889, **55**, 36.
Kappeler, *Ber.*, 1912, **45**, 635.
Bucherer, *J. prakt. Chem.*, 1904, **70**, 358.
Erdmann, *Ann.*, 1893, **275**, 281.
Friedländer, Lucht, *Ber.*, 1893, **26**, 3033.
Pfitzinger, Duisberg, *Ber.*, 1889, **22**, 397.
Clayton Aniline, D.R.P., 53, 649.
Bayer, D.R.P., 70,349.
Bucherer, Stohmann, *J. prakt. Chem.*, 1905, **71**, 451.
See also first reference above.

2-Naphthylamine-1 : 3 : 6 : 7-tetrasulphonic Acid

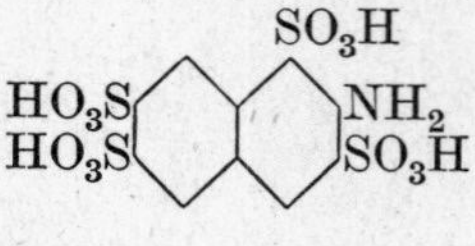

$C_{10}H_9O_{12}NS_4$ MW, 463

Acid sols. part. hyd. by boiling ⟶ 2-naphthylamine-3 : 6 : 7-trisulphonic acid. Salts in aq. sol. show violet-blue fluor. Na salt : cryst. Easily sol. H_2O. Ba salt : micro-cryst. + $6H_2O$. Spar. sol. H_2O.

Dressel, Kothe, *Ber.*, 1894, **27**, 1203.

1 - Naphthylamine - 2 : 4 : 6 - trisulphonic Acid

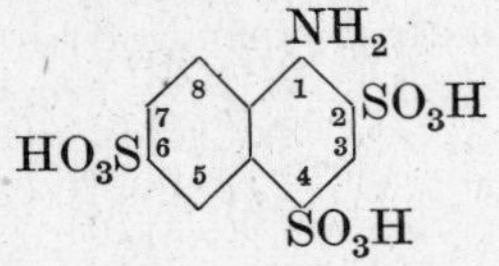

$C_{10}H_9O_9NS_3$ MW, 383

Does not couple with diazo-comps. Heat with min. acids ⟶ 1-naphthylamine-2 : 6-disulphonic acid. NaHg in cold ⟶ 1-naphthylamine-2 : 4-disulphonic acid. Mono-Na salt : needles. Aq. sols. show blue fluor.

Bayer, D.R.P., 255,724, (*Chem. Zentr.*, 1913, I, 478).

1 - Naphthylamine - 2 : 4 : 7 - trisulphonic Acid.

Sol. 18·4 in 100 parts H_2O at 20°, 31·5 in 100 parts H_2O at 80°. Salts + H_2O under press. at 230° ⟶ 1-naphthylamine-2 : 7-disulphonic acid. Di-Na salt : cryst. + $1\frac{1}{2}H_2O$. Sol. 18·5 in 100 parts H_2O at 20°, 27·1 in 100 parts at 80°. Di-K salt : cryst. + $1\frac{1}{2}H_2O$. Sol. 29·3 in 100 parts H_2O at 20°, 66·3 in 100 parts at 80°. Ba salt : cryst. + $3H_2O$. Sol. 2·5 in 100 parts H_2O at 20°, 25·7 in 100 parts at 80°. Ca salt : cryst. + $2H_2O$. Sol. 16·9 in 100 parts H_2O at 20°, 32·0 in 100 parts at 80°. Mg salt : cryst. + $1\frac{1}{2}H_2O$. Sol. 19·3 in 100 parts H_2O at 20°, 23·5 in 100 parts at 80°.

Frisch, *Helv. Chim. Acta*, 1930, **13**, 768.
M.L.B., D.R.P., 215,338, (*Chem. Zentr.*, 1909, II, 1710).

1 - Naphthylamine - 2 : 5 : 7 - trisulphonic Acid.

The acid and its Na salt in aq. sol. show green fluor. 50% KOH.Aq. at 180–200° ⟶ 1-amino-5-naphthol-2 : 7-disulphonic acid. NaHg (cold) or Zn dust + boiling NaOH.Aq. ⟶ 1-naphthylamine-2 : 7-disulphonic acid. Mono-Na salt : needles. Easily sol. H_2O.

Bayer, D.R.P., 255,724, (*Chem. Zentr.*, 1913, I, 478).
Cassella, D.R.P., 188,505, (*Chem. Zentr.*, 1907, II, 1467).

1 - Naphthylamine - 3 : 5 : 7 - trisulphonic Acid.

Salts sol. H_2O with green fluor. Fused with NaOH at 160–70° ⟶ 1-amino-5-naphthol-3 : 7-disulphonic acid. NaHg (cold) or Zn dust + boiling NaOH.Aq. ⟶ 1-naphthylamine-3 : 7-disulphonic acid.

See first reference above.

1 - Naphthylamine - 3 : 6 : 8 - trisulphonic Acid (*Koch Acid*).

Hair-like needles + $6H_2O$ from H_2O. Sol. 1 in 0·5 parts H_2O at 18°, 1 in 8 parts EtOH at 18°. H_2O at 180–250° ⟶ 1-naphthol-3 : 6 : 8-trisulphonic acid. 30–40% NaOH.Aq. at 210° ⟶ 1-amino-8-naphthol-3 : 6-disulphonic acid. NH_3 at 160–80° ⟶ 1 : 3-naphthylenediamine-6 : 8-disulphonic acid. Zn dust + boiling NaOH.Aq. ⟶ 1-naphthylamine-3 : 6-disulphonic acid. Sulphonation with 25% anhydro-acid at 70–80° ⟶ naphthasultam-3 : 4 : 6-trisulphonic acid. Di-Na salt : cryst. + $4H_2O$. Sol. 1 in 15 parts H_2O at 18°. Spar. sol. brine, dil. HCl. Tri-Na salt : cryst. + $3H_2O$. Sol. 1 in 3 parts H_2O at 18°. Tri-K salt : cryst. + $1H_2O$. Sol. 1 in 4 parts H_2O at 18°. Ca salt : sol. 1 in 3 parts H_2O at 15°. Aniline salt : m.p. 312° decomp.

Kurochkin, *Chem. Abstracts*, 1932, **26**, 4326.
Forster, Hanson, Watson, *J. Soc. Chem. Ind.*, 1928, **47**, 157.
Kalle, D.R.P., 233,934, (*Chem. Zentr.*, 1911, I, 1468).
Dressel, Kothe, *Ber.*, 1894, **27**, 2147.

1 - Naphthylamine - 4 : 6 : 8 - trisulphonic Acid.

Does not couple with diazo-comps. Boiled with 75% H_2SO_4 ⟶ 1-naphthylamine-6 : 8-disulphonic acid. H_2O at 160–220° ⟶ 1-naphthol-6 : 8-disulphonic acid. 70% NaOH.Aq. at 175° ⟶ 1-amino-8-naphthol-4 : 6-disulphonic acid. Sulphonation with 25% anhydro-acid ⟶ naphthasultam-2 : 4 : 6-trisulphonic acid.

Kalle, D.R.P., 275,449 ; 233,934, (*Chem. Zentr.*, 1914, II, 281 ; 1911, I, 1468).

2 - Naphthylamine - 1 : 3 : 7 - trisulphonic Acid

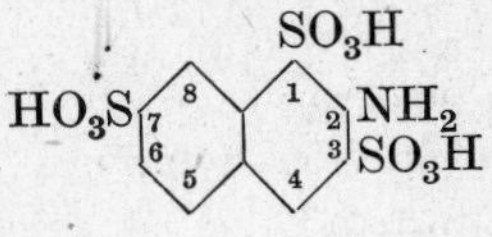

$C_{10}H_9O_9NS_3$ MW, 383

Boiled with dil. min. acids ⟶ 2-naphthylamine-3 : 7-disulphonic acid. Sulphonation with 40% anhydro-acid at 130° ⟶ the 3 : 5 : 7- and 3 : 6 : 7-trisulphonic acids + 1 : 3 : 6 : 7-tetrasulphonic acid. Di-Na salt : leaflets + $4H_2O$. Easily sol. H_2O with violet-blue fluor.

Dressel, Kothe, *Ber.*, 1894, **27**, 1199.

2-Naphthylamine-1 : 5 : 7-trisulphonic Acid.

Salts easily sol. H_2O with blue fluor. Does not couple with diazo-comps. The diazo-comp. + Na_2CO_3.Aq. ⟶ diazo-oxide of 2-amino-1-naphthol-5 : 7-disulphonic acid. 60% NaOH.Aq. at 160–220° ⟶ 2-amino-5-naphthol-1 : 7-disulphonic acid. Part hyd. by boiling dil. min. acids ⟶ 2-naphthylamine-5 : 7-disulphonic acid. Heat with 30% anhydro-acid at 140–60° ⟶ 2-naphthylamine-3 : 5 : 7-trisulphonic acid.

Ofitzerov, *Chem. Abstracts*, 1935, **29**, 1086.

2-Naphthylamine-3 : 5 : 7-trisulphonic Acid.

Salts very sol. H_2O with intense green fluor. 30% NaOH.Aq. at 190° ⟶ 2-amino-5-naphthol-3 : 7-disulphonic acid. Tri-Na salt : needles + $5\frac{1}{2}H_2O$ from EtOH.Aq.

Dressel, Kothe, *Ber.*, 1894, **27**, 1202.

2-Naphthylamine-3 : 6 : 7-trisulphonic Acid.

Dil. aq. sols of salts show intense blue fluor. 55% NaOH.Aq. at 180–240° ⟶ 2-amino-7-naphthol-3 : 6-disulphonic acid. Sulphonation with 40% anhydro-acid at 100–30° ⟶ 2-naphthylamine-1 : 3 : 6 : 7-tetrasulphonic acid. Di-Na salt : needles + $3H_2O$. Spar. sol. cold H_2O. Very spar. sol. cold HCl. Tri-Na salt : easily sol. H_2O.

See previous reference.

2-Naphthylamine-3 : 6 : 8-trisulphonic Acid.

Salts in aq. sol. show intense sky-blue fluor. 80% NaOH.Aq. at 220–60° ⟶ 2-amino-8-naphthol-3 : 6-disulphonic acid. Zn dust + boiling NaOH.Aq. ⟶ 2-naphthylamine-3 : 6-disulphonic acid. Di-K salt : needles + $1\frac{1}{2}H_2O$. Sol. 40 parts H_2O at 20°, 13 parts at 100°.

Kalle, D.R.P., 176,621, (*Chem. Zentr.*, 1906, II, 1746).
See also previous reference.

2-Naphthylamine-4 : 6 : 8-trisulphonic Acid.

60% NaOH.Aq. at 170–80° ⟶ 2-amino-4-naphthol-6 : 8-disulphonic acid. Di-Na salt : micro-needles. Aq. sol. ⟶ brilliant blue fluor.

Morgan, Mitchell, *J. Chem. Soc.*, 1932, 1910.

1-Naphthylaminopropionic Acid.
See Naphthylalanine.

***N*-α-Naphthylanthranilic Acid** (2-[1-*Naphthylamino-*]-*benzoic acid,* N-*phenyl-*1-*naphthylamine-*2′-*carboxylic acid,* 2-*carboxyphenyl-*α-*naphthylamine*)

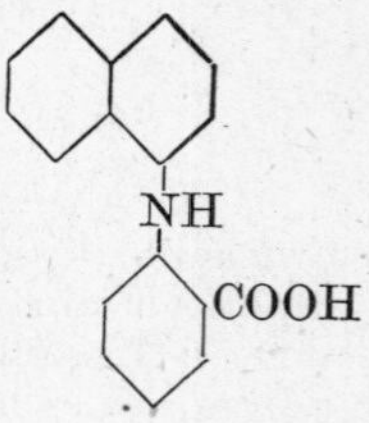

$C_{17}H_{13}O_2N$ MW, 263

Leaflets or needles from C_6H_6–ligroin or EtOH. M.p. 208° (204–6°). Sol. C_6H_6, EtOH, AcOH. Spar. sol. hot H_2O, ligroin. Insol. cold H_2O. Sol. in conc. H_2SO_4 on warming ⟶ yellow col. + bluish-green fluor.

Ullmann, Rasetti, *Ann.*, 1907, **355**, 348.
Houben, Brassert, *Ber.*, 1906, **39**, 3239.

***N*-β-Naphthylanthranilic Acid** (2-[2-*Naphthylamino-*]-*benzoic acid,* N-*phenyl-*2-*naphthylamine-*2′-*carboxylic acid,* 2-*carboxyphenyl-*β-*naphthylamine*)

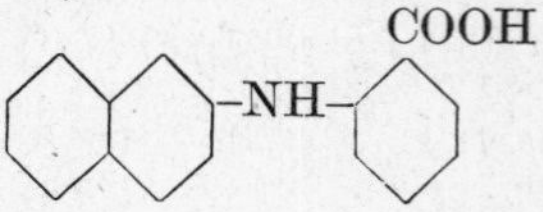

$C_{17}H_{13}O_2N$ MW, 263

Needles from EtOH or Me_2CO. M.p. 212° (208–9°). Sol. hot C_6H_6, EtOH, Me_2CO. Very spar. sol. ligroin. Insol. H_2O.

Bucherer, Seyde, *J. prakt. Chem.*, 1907, **75**, 279.
See also first reference above.

1-Naphthyl azide (1-*Azidonaphthalene*)

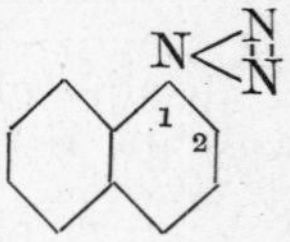

$C_{10}H_7N_3$ MW, 169

Prisms. M.p. 12°. Decomp. by heat or by conc. H_2SO_4. Sol. EtOH, Et_2O, Me_2CO.

Forster, Fierz, *J. Chem. Soc.*, 1907, **91**, 1945.

2-Naphthyl azide (2-*Azidonaphthalene*). Needles or prisms. M.p. 33°. Sol. ord. org. solvents. Very spar. sol. boiling H_2O. Decomp. by 66% H_2SO_4. Turns yellow on exposure to light.

See previous reference.

o-1-Naphthylbenzoic Acid (α-o-*Carboxyphenylnaphthalene*)

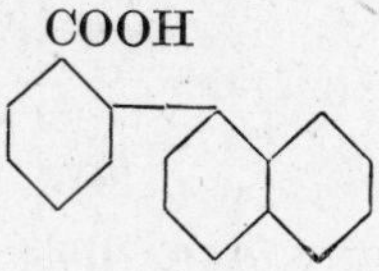

$C_{17}H_{12}O_2$ MW, 248

Cryst. from AcOH. M.p. 229°.
Nitrile : $C_{17}H_{11}N$. MW, 229. M.p. 73–7°. B.p. 230–40°/14 mm.

Braun, Anton, *Ber.*, 1934, **67**, 1056.

p-1-Naphthylbenzoic Acid (α-p-*Carboxyphenylnaphthalene*)

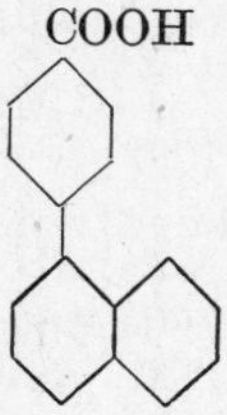

$C_{17}H_{12}O_2$ MW, 248

Rhombic cryst. from MeOH. M.p. 161·5°.

Schaarschmidt, Georgeacopol, *Ber.*, 1918, **51**, 1083.

o-2-Naphthylbenzoic Acid.
See α-Chrysenic Acid.

Naphthylbenzylamine.
See Benzylnaphthylamine.

1-Naphthylbiuret (α-*Naphthylallophanamide*)

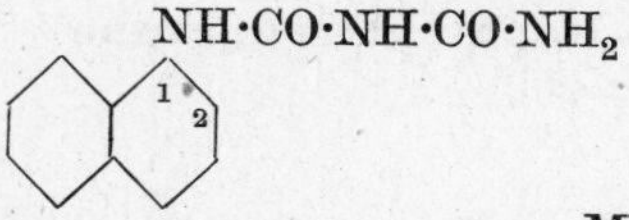

$C_{12}H_{11}O_2N_3$ MW, 229

Needles from EtOH.Aq. M.p. 259° (211°, 217°). Decomp. above m.p. ⟶ 1-naphthylurea. Spar. sol. H_2O, Et_2O. Does not give biuret test.

Bougault, Leboucq, *Bull. soc. chim.*, 1930, **47**, 600.
Davis, Blanchard, *J. Am. Chem. Soc.*, 1929, **51**, 1805.

2-Naphthylbiuret (β-*Naphthylallophanamide*).

Needles. M.p. 230° (203°). Decomp. above m.p. ⟶ 2-naphthylurea.

See first reference above.

3-α-Naphthylbutyric Acid

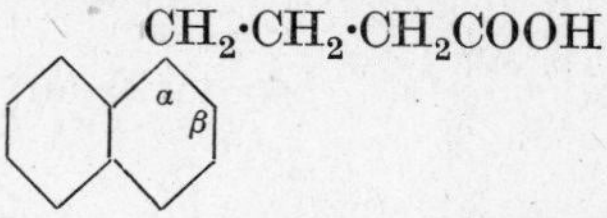

$C_{14}H_{14}O_2$ MW, 214

Cryst. M.p. 106–7°. B.p. 217°/15 mm.
Amide : $C_{14}H_{15}ON$. MW, 213. M.p. 160°.

Willgerodt, *J. prakt. Chem.*, 1909, **80**, 183.
Schroeter, Müller, Huang, *Ber.*, 1929, **62**, 656.

3-β-Naphthylbutyric Acid.

Leaflets from pet. ether or EtOH.Aq. M.p. 100° (94–5°).
Et ester : $C_{16}H_{18}O_2$. MW, 242. Oil. B.p. 216–18°/20 mm.

Borsche, *Ber.*, 1919, **52**, 2083.
Schroeter, Müller, Huang, *Ber.*, 1929, **62**, 657.

1 : 2-Naphthylenediamine (α : β-*Diaminonaphthalene*)

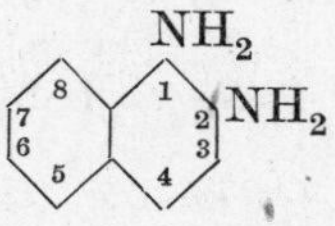

$C_{10}H_{10}N_2$ MW, 158

Leaflets from hot H_2O. M.p. 98°. B.p. 150–1°/0·5 mm. Sol. EtOH, Et_2O, $CHCl_3$. Spar. sol. H_2O. $FeCl_3$ on HCl sol. ⟶ green col. Forms add. comps.: with catechol, m.p. 104·5°; with *sym.*-trinitrobenzene, m.p. 203–4°.
1-N-*Benzenesulphonyl* : m.p. 215° decomp.
1 : 2-N-*Diacetyl* : needles. M.p. 234°.
1 : 2-N-*Dibenzoyl* : leaflets. M.p. 291°.
1-N-*Phenyl* : $C_{16}H_{14}N_2$. MW, 234. M.p. 170° (161°). *Benzoyl deriv.* : m.p. 215°.
2-N-*Phenyl* : m.p. 136–7° (138–40°). 1-N-*Me* : m.p. 85°.

Reilly, Drumm, O'Sullivan, *J. Soc. Chem. Ind.*, 1927, **46**, 437T.
Fischer, Kracker, *J. prakt. Chem.*, 1922, **104**, 118.
Erdmann, *Ber.*, 1903, **36**, 3461.
Gattermann, Schulze, *Ber.*, 1897, **30**, 53.
Bamberger, Schieffelin, *Ber.*, 1889, **22**, 1376.
Harden, *Ann.*, 1889, **255**, 161.
Noelting, Grandmougin, Freimann, *Ber.*, 1909, **42**, 1380.
Zincke, Lawson, *Ber.*, 1887, **20**, 1170.
Witt, *ibid.*, 573, 1184.

1 : 3-Naphthylenediamine (1 : 3-*Diaminonaphthalene*).

Plates from H_2O. M.p. 96°.

1 : 3-N-*Diacetyl* : needles from AcOH. M.p. 263–5°.

Atkinson, Thorpe, *J. Chem. Soc.*, 1906, **89**, 1922.

1 : 4-Naphthylenediamine (1 : 4-*Diaminonaphthalene*).

Bright yellow needles. M.p. 120°. Unstable in moist air. Forms add. comp. with *sym.*-trinitrobenzene, m.p. 208° decomp.

1 : 4-N-*Diacetyl* : m.p. 303–4°.

1 : 4-N-*Dibenzoyl* : m.p. 280·5°.

1-N-p-*Toluenesulphonyl* : m.p. 187–8°. 1-N-*Benzoyl* : m.p. 186°.

1 : 4-N-*Tetra-Et* : $C_{18}H_{26}N_2$. MW, 270. M.p. 47–8°.

N-*Phenyl* : plates from C_6H_6. M.p. 148°. *Diacetyl deriv.* : needles from AcOH. M.p. 278°.

Kuhn, Wassermann, *Helv. Chim. Acta*, 1928, **11**, 79.
Krollpfeiffer, *Ann.*, 1923, **430**, 199.
Morgan, U.S.P., 1,442,818 ; E.P., 160,853, (*Chem. Abstracts*, 1923, **17**, 1242 ; 1921, **15**, 2445).
Cobenzyl, *Chem.-Ztg.*, 1915, **39**, 860.
Casale-Sacchi, *Gazz. chim. ital.*, 1914, **44**, ii, 398.
Fischer, *Ann.*, 1895, **286**, 183.
Weiss, Woidich, *Monatsh.*, 1925, **46**, 458.

1 : 5-Naphthylenediamine (1 : 5-*Diaminonaphthalene*).

Prisms from H_2O. M.p. 190°. Sol. EtOH, Et_2O, $CHCl_3$. Mod. sol. hot. H_2O. Sublimes. $FeCl_3$ on aq. suspension ⟶ bluish-violet col. Forms add. comps. : with *m*-dinitrobenzene, m.p. 78–9° ; with *sym.*-trinitrobenzene, m.p. 245° ; with 1 : 3 : 5-trinitronaphthalene, black needles, decomp. at 243°.

1 : 5-N-*Diacetyl* : m.p. 360°.

1 : 5-N-*Tetra-Et* : m.p. 41°.

Lenkhold, *Chem. Abstracts*, 1933, **27**, 5279.
Kunckell, Schneider, *Chem.-Ztg.*, 1912, **36**, 1021.
Bucherer, Ullmann, *J. prakt. Chem.*, 1909, **80**, 212.
Möller, *Elektrochemische Zeitschrift*, 1904, **10**, 201.
Meyer, Müller, *Ber.*, 1897, **30**, 774.
See also first and second references above.

1 : 6-Naphthylenediamine (1 : 6-*Diaminonaphthalene*).

Needles. M.p. 85–6° (77·5°). Sol. EtOH, C_6H_6, hot H_2O. Spar. sol. Et_2O, cold H_2O. H_2O sol. shows blue fluor.

1 : 6-N-*Diacetyl* : m.p. 257° (263·5°).

1: 6-N-*Dibenzoyl* : m.p. 265°.

Krollpfeiffer, *Ann.*, 1923, **430**, 199.
Sachs, *Ber.*, 1906, **39**, 3022.
Bucherer, Wahl, *J. prakt. Chem.*, 1922, **103**, 253.

1 : 7-Naphthylenediamine (1 : 7-*Diaminonaphthalene*).

Leaflets from C_6H_6. M.p. 117·5°. Sol. EtOH, C_6H_6. Mod. sol. hot H_2O. Spar. sol. Et_2O, ligroin.

1 : 7-N-*Diacetyl* : m.p. 213°.

Friedländer *et al.*, *Ber.*, 1896, **29**, 41 ; 1892, **25**, 2082.

1 : 8-Naphthylenediamine (1 : 8-*Diaminonaphthalene*).

Needles from EtOH.Aq. M.p. 66·5°. Sol. EtOH, Et_2O, hot H_2O. Sublimes. $FeCl_3$ ⟶ brown ppt. Forms add. comp. with *sym.*-trinitrobenzene, m.p. 225°.

1 : 8-N-*Dibenzoyl* : needles. M.p. 311–12°.

1 : 8-N-*Tetra-Et* : m.p. 31–2°.

Kuhn, Wassermann, *Helv. Chim. Acta*, 1928, **11**, 79.
Krollpfeiffer, *Ann.*, 1923, **430**, 199.
Möller, *Elektrochemische Zeitschrift*, 1904, **10**, 222.
Ullmann, Consonno, *Ber.*, 1902, **35**, 2801.
Meyer, Müller, *Ber.*, 1897, **30**, 775.

2 : 3-Naphthylenediamine (2 : 3-*Diaminonaphthalene*)

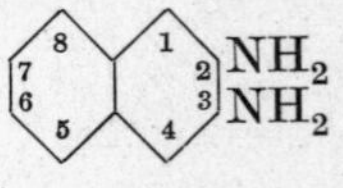

$C_{10}H_{10}N_2$ MW, 158

Leaflets from H_2O. M.p. 196°. Sol. EtOH, Et_2O.

2 : 3-N-*Diacetyl* : m.p. 247°.

2 : 3-N-*Tetra-Et* : $C_{18}H_{26}N_2$. MW, 270. M.p. 75–6°.

Morgan, Godden, *J. Chem. Soc.*, 1910, **97**, 1718.
Sachs, *Ber.*, 1906, **39**, 3021.
See also first two references above.

2 : 6-Naphthylenediamine (2 : 6-*Diaminonaphthalene*).

Needles or leaflets from H_2O. M.p. 216–17°. Spar. sol. EtOH, Et_2O, hot H_2O.

2 : 6-N-*Tetra-Et* : m.p. 69–70°.

Kuhn, Wassermann, *Helv. Chim. Acta*, 1928, **11**, 79.
Krollpfeiffer, *Ann.*, 1923, **430**, 199.
Jacchia, *Ann.*, 1902, **323**, 132.
Friedländer, Lucht, *Ber.*, 1893, **26**, 3033.

2 : 7-Naphthylenediamine (2 : 7-*Diaminonaphthalene*).

Leaflets from H_2O. M.p. 166° (159°).
2 : 7-N-*Diacetyl* : m.p. 261°.
2 : 7-N-*Dibenzoyl* : m.p. 267°.
2 : 7-N-*Tetra-Et* : b.p. 234–6°/13 mm.
Dipicrate : m.p. 210°.

Kuhn, Jacob, Furter, *Ann.*, 1927, **455**, 270.
Windaus, *Ber.*, 1924, **57**, 1737.
Kaufler, Karrer, *Ber.*, 1907, **40**, 3262.
See also first two references above.

1 : 8 - Naphthylenediamine - 3 : 6 - disulphonic Acid

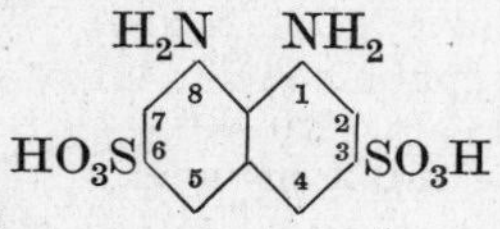

$C_{10}H_{10}O_6N_2S_2$ MW, 318

Sols. of salts fluor. green. Heat with dil. acids at 100–20°, or with NaOH.Aq. at 200–10° ⟶ 8-amino-1-naphthol-3 : 6-disulphonic acid. Heat with dil. acids at 150–60° or with NaOH.Aq. at 260–80° ⟶ 1 : 8-dihydroxynaphthalene-3 : 6-disulphonic acid. Condenses with 1 mol. Me_2CO in presence of min. acids. Mono-K salt : needles + $3H_2O$. Sol. hot H_2O. Ba salt : needles + $6H_2O$. Sol. hot. H_2O.

Alén, *Ber.*, 1884, **17** (Referate), 437.
Badische, D.R.P., 121,228, (*Chem. Zentr.*, 1901, I, 1395) ; D.R.P., 122,475, (*Chem. Zentr.*, 1901, II, 447).

1 : 8 - Naphthylenediamine - 4 : 5 - disulphonic Acid.

Leaflets. Sol. H_2O. Couples rapidly with 1 mol., less rapidly with 2 mols. diazo-comps. HNO_2 ⟶ azimino-comp. Heat with min. acids ⟶ 1-amino-8-naphthol-4 : 5-disulphonic acid. Na salt : sol. H_2O.

Bucherer, Barsch, *J. prakt. Chem.*, 1925, **111**, 313, 336.

1 : 2 - Naphthylenediamine - 3 - sulphonic Acid

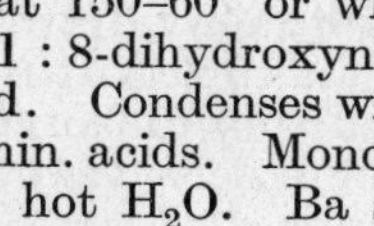

$C_{10}H_{10}O_3N_2S$ MW, 238

Needles. Aq. sol. + $FeCl_3$ ⟶ intense emerald-green col. NaHg ⟶ 1 : 2-naphthylenediamine.

Gattermann, Liebermann, *Ann.*, 1912, **393**, 209.

1 : 2 - Naphthylenediamine - 4 - sulphonic Acid.

Needles from hot H_2O. NaHg ⟶ 1 : 2-naphthylenediamine.

Friedländer, Kielbasinski, *Ber.*, 1896, **29**, 1978.

1 : 2 - Naphthylenediamine - 5 - sulphonic Acid.

Light brown glittering leaflets. Spar. sol. H_2O. Aq. sol. + $FeCl_3$ ⟶ emerald-green col. NaHg ⟶ 1 : 2-naphthylenediamine.

Gattermann, Liebermann, *Ann.*, 1912, **393**, 205.

1 : 2 - Naphthylenediamine - 6 - sulphonic Acid.

Needles. Very spar. sol. pure H_2O. Aq. sol. + $FeCl_3$ ⟶ dirty green ppt. With Ac_2O ⟶ an iminazole. With phenanthraquinone ⟶ an azine.

Witt, *Ber.*, 1888, **21**, 3484.

1 : 2 - Naphthylenediamine - 7 - sulphonic Acid.

Grey powder. Spar. sol. H_2O. Aq. sol. + $FeCl_3$ ⟶ dirty green ppt.

See previous reference.

1 : 3 - Naphthylenediamine - 5 - sulphonic Acid

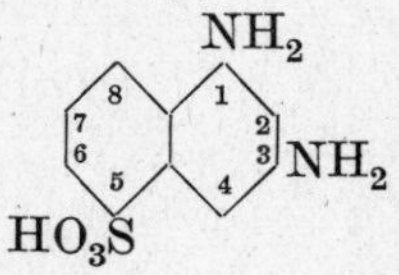

$C_{10}H_{10}O_3N_2S$ MW, 238

Needles. Sol. H_2O.

Dannerth, *J. Am. Chem. Soc.*, 1907, **29**, 1327.

1 : 3 - Naphthylenediamine - 6 - sulphonic Acid.

Needles. Spar. sol. cold H_2O. Alkali salts easily sol. H_2O.

Friedländer, Taussig, *Ber.*, 1897, **30**, 1462.

1 : 4 - Naphthylenediamine - 2 - sulphonic Acid

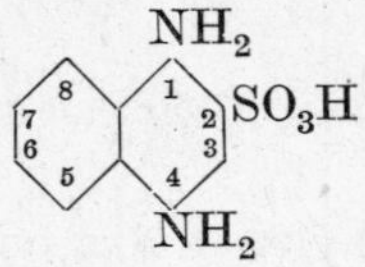

$C_{10}H_{10}O_3N_2S$ MW, 238

Reddish needles. Very spar. sol. boiling H_2O. The yellow sol. in AcONa.Aq. shows green fluor. NaHg ⟶ 1 : 4-naphthylenediamine.

Gattermann, Liebermann, *Ann.*, 1912, **393**, 209.

1 : 4 - Naphthylenediamine - 5 - sulphonic Acid.

Steel-blue leaflets. NaHg ⟶ 1 : 4-naphthylenediamine.

See previous reference.

1 : 4 - Naphthylenediamine - 6 - sulphonic Acid.

Needles. Stable when dry. Sol. 223 parts H_2O. Sol. inorganic acids.

1-N-*Acetyl* : needles. Very spar. sol. hot H_2O.

4-N-*Acetyl* : needles. Spar. sol. H_2O. Aq. sol. + $FeCl_3$ or CrO_3 ⟶ blue col. The product of ox. by alk. $KMnO_4$ when fused with KOH at 200–20° ⟶ 4-hydroxyphthalic acid.

Fabriowicz, Lesnianski, *Chem. Abstracts*, 1932, **26**, 3791.
Gaess, D.R.P., 138,030, (*Chem. Zentr.*, 1903, I, 109).
Ammelburg, *J. prakt. Chem.*, 1893, **48**, 286.

1 : 5 - Naphthylenediamine - 2 - sulphonic Acid

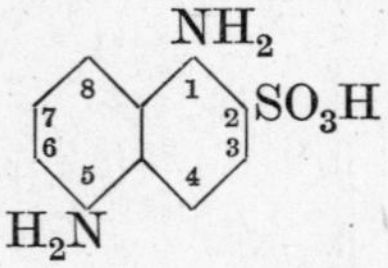

$C_{10}H_{10}O_3N_2S$ MW, 238

Cryst. + $3H_2O$. Spar. sol. H_2O. Heat with dil. min. acids ⟶ 1 : 5-naphthylenediamine.

Hydrochloride : spar. sol. cold H_2O.

Sulphate : insol. H_2O.

Bucherer, Ullmann, *J. prakt. Chem.*, 1909, **80**, 213.
Friedländer, Kielbasinski, *Ber.*, 1896, **29**, 1983.

1 : 5 - Naphthylenediamine - 4 - sulphonic Acid.

Bluish-grey leaflets.

N-*Acetyl* : spar. sol. H_2O.

See first reference above.

1 : 6 - Naphthylenediamine - 4 - sulphonic Acid.

Needles from hot H_2O. Very spar. sol. cold H_2O. Sols. of salts fluor. strongly bluish-violet.

Friedländer, Kielbasinski, *Ber.*, 1896, **29**, 1979.

1 : 8 - Naphthylenediamine - 4 - sulphonic Acid

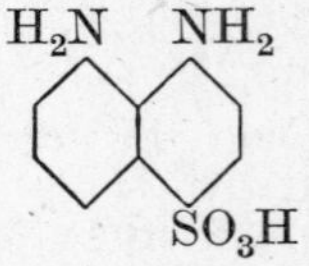

$C_{10}H_{10}O_3N_2S$ MW, 238

Leaflets. Very spar. sol. H_2O. The alkali salts are very sol. H_2O. Couples with 1 mol. or 2 mols. diazo-comps. HNO_2 ⟶ azimino-comp. Na salt heated with Na_2SO_3 ⟶ 8-amino-1-naphthol-4-sulphonic acid. Heat with milk of lime under press. at 220–40° ⟶ 1 : 8-dihydroxynaphthalene-4-sulphonic acid.

Bayer, D.R.P., 216,075, (*Chem. Zentr.*, 1909, II, 1950).
Badische, D.R.P., 120,690, (*Chem. Zentr.*, 1901, I, 1395).

Naphthylenediphenyldiamine.

See Diphenylnaphthylenediamine.

Naphthyleneditolyldiamine.

See Ditolylnaphthylenediamine.

Naphthylethane.

See Ethylnaphthalene.

2-α-Naphthylethyl Alcohol (1-β-*Hydroxyethylnaphthalene*)

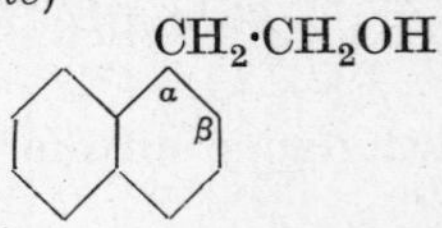

$C_{12}H_{12}O$ MW, 172

Cryst. M.p. 62°. B.p. 174–8°/13 mm., 125°/0·2 mm. Heat with KOH under reduced press. ⟶ 1-naphthylethylene.

Haworth, Mavin, *J. Chem. Soc.*, 1933, 1014.
Sontag, *Ann. chim.*, 1934, **1**, 399.
Shoruigin, Shoruigina, *Chem. Abstracts*, 1935, **29**, 6886.

2-β-Naphthylethyl Alcohol (2-β-*Hydroxyethylnaphthalene*).

Needles from ligroin. M.p. 68°. B.p. 178–88°/15 mm. Sol. Et_2O, EtOH. Orange-like odour. Heat with KOH ⟶ 2-naphthylethylene.

See second reference above.

1-α-Naphthylethylamine (1-α-*Aminoethylnaphthalene*, 1-*methyl*-α-*naphthylmethylamine*)

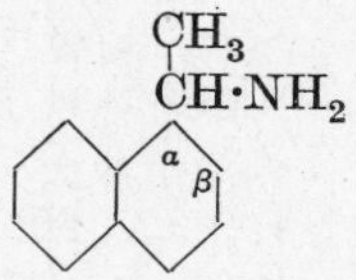

$C_{12}H_{13}N$ MW, 171

d-.

B.p. 153°/11 mm. D^{25} 1·055. $[\alpha]_D^{17}$ + 82·8°, $[\alpha]_D^{19}$ + 61·6° in EtOH.

B,HCl : cryst. + $1H_2O$. $[\alpha]_D^{18}$ + 3·9° in H_2O.

l-.

Liq. $[\alpha]_D^{25}$ − 80·8°, $[\alpha]_D^{25}$ − 60·8° in EtOH.

B,HCl : $[\alpha]_D^{18}$ − 3·9° in H_2O.

B_2,H_2SO_4 : needles + $4H_2O$. M.p. 230–2°.

Oxalate : prisms. M.p. 232° decomp.

α-*Camphorate* : needles. M.p. 212–13° decomp.

Acid-α-*camphorate* : needles. M.p. 196°.

Acid-d-*tartrate* : needles + H_2O. M.p. 186°.

Urea deriv. : m.p. 186°.

dl-.

Liq. B.p. 156°/15 mm., 153°/11 mm.

B,HCl : needles or prisms. Decomp. at 240–5°.

B_2,H_2SO_4 : cryst. + $1H_2O$. M.p. 233°.

Oxalate : needles. M.p. 221° decomp.

Urea deriv. : m.p. 181–2°.

Benzoyl : m.p. 166–166·5°.

Picrate : m.p. 212–13° decomp.

Samuelsson, *Chem. Abstracts*, 1924, **18**, 1833.

1-β-Naphthylethylamine (2-α-*Aminoethylnaphthalene*, 1-*methyl*-β-*naphthylmethylamine*).

d-.

M.p. 53°. $[\alpha]_D^{19}$ + 19·4° in EtOH.

B,HCl : needles. M.p. 219°. $[\alpha]_D^{17}$ + 5·4° in H_2O.

B_2,H_2SO_4 : needles + $2H_2O$. M.p. 262–3°.

Oxalate : m.p. 240°.

Acid-d-*tartrate* : needles + H_2O. M.p. 199–200°.

Urea deriv. : m.p. 182°. $[\alpha]_D^{17}$ + 67·9° in EtOH.

l-.

M.p. 53°. $[\alpha]_D^{20}$ − 18·9° in EtOH.

B,HCl : m.p. 219°. $[\alpha]_D^{17}$ − 6·0° in H_2O.

Urea deriv. : m.p. 182°. $[\alpha]_D^{17}$ − 66·8° in EtOH.

dl-.

M.p. 23°. B.p. 142–3°/6–7 mm. D^{20} 1·047.

B,HCl : needles. M.p. 199–200°.

B_2,H_2SO_4 : needles. M.p. 243–4°.

Oxalate : needles. M.p. 232–3°.

Urea deriv. : m.p. 198°.

See previous reference.

2-α-Naphthylethylamine (1-β-*Aminoethylnaphthalene*)

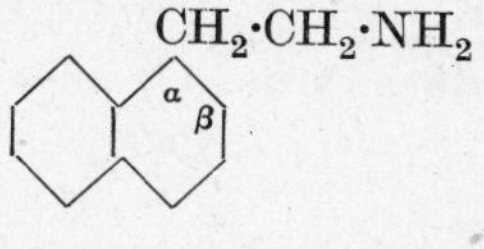

$C_{12}H_{13}N$ MW, 171

B.p. 182–3°/18 mm. (170–3°/16 mm.).

B,HCl : m.p. 243–8°.

N-*Acetyl* : m.p. 91°.

N-*Benzoyl* : needles from ligroin. M.p. 97° (softens at 87°).

Picrate : m.p. 201–2°.

Mayer *et al.*, *Ber.*, 1923, **56**, 1413; 1922, **55**, 1847.

2-β-Naphthylethylamine (2-β-*Aminoethylnaphthalene*).

Cryst. below room temp. B.p. 174–5°/25 mm. (160–5°/15 mm.).

B,HCl : m.p. 250° decomp.

N-*Acetyl* : m.p. 110°.

N-*Benzoyl* : prisms from C_6H_6. M.p. 140–1°.

Picrate : m.p. 196°.

Mayer *et al.*, *Ber.*, 1923, **56**, 1411; 1922, **55**, 1858.

2-α-Naphthylethyl bromide (1-β-*Bromoethylnaphthalene*)

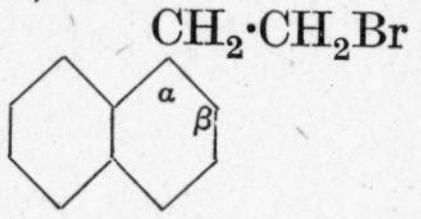

$C_{12}H_{11}Br$ MW, 235

B.p. 172°/20 mm., 145–8°/0·3 mm., 114° 0·15 mm.

Kon, *J. Chem. Soc.*, 1933, 1085.
Ruzicka, Bossard, Schmid, *Helv. Chim. Acta*, 1933, **16**, 836.
Haworth, Mavin, *J. Chem. Soc.*, 1933, 1014.

2-β-Naphthylethyl bromide (2-β-*Bromoethylnaphthalene*).

M.p. 59°. B.p. 146–7°/18 mm.

Sontag, *Ann. chim.*, 1934, **1**, 405.

2-α-Naphthylethyl chloride (1-β-*Chloroethylnaphthalene*)

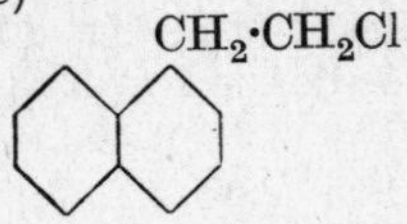

$C_{12}H_{11}Cl$ MW, 190·5

Yellowish liq. B.p. 167–8°/17 mm.
Picrate: m.p. 67–8°.

Cook, Hewett, *J. Chem. Soc.*, 1933, 1107.

1-Naphthylethylene (1-*Vinylnaphthalene*

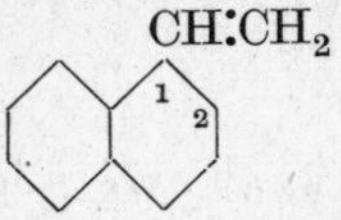

$C_{12}H_{10}$ MW, 154

B.p. 124–5°/15 mm., 115–16°/3–4 mm. D_4^{18} 1·036. n_D^{20} 1·644. Readily polymerises.
Picrate: m.p. 101–2° decomp.
Styphnate: m.p. 96–7°.

Sontag, *Ann. chim.*, 1934, **1**, 400.
I.G., U.S.P., 1,985,844, (*Chem. Abstracts*, 1935, **29**, 1099).
Shoruigin, Shoruigina, *Chem. Abstracts*, 1935, **29**, 6866.

2-Naphthylethylene (2-*Vinylnaphthalene*).
Cryst. from EtOH.Aq. M.p. 66°. B.p. 135–7°/18 mm. Intense thyme-like odour. More stable than the 1-isomer.

See first and second references above.

1-Naphthylglycollic Acid (α-*Naphthylglycollic acid*)

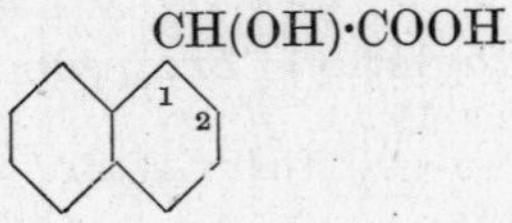

$C_{12}H_{10}O_3$ MW, 202

d-.
Leaflets from C_6H_6. M.p. 124–5°. $[\alpha]_{5461}^{13}$ + 230° in EtOH. Conc. H_2SO_4 ⟶ blue col.
Me ester: $C_{13}H_{12}O_3$. MW, 216. Liq. B.p. 230–2°/36 mm. $[\alpha]_{5461}^{16}$ + 175° in Me_2CO.
l-*Menthyl ester*: cryst. from pet. ether. M.p. 71–2°. $[\alpha]_{5461}^{20}$ + 27·6° in Me_2CO.

l-.
Leaflets from C_6H_6. M.p. 124–5°. $[\alpha]_{5461}^{16}$ − 228° in EtOH.
l-*Menthyl ester*: needles from pet. ether. M.p. 62–3°. B.p. 220°/24 mm. $[\alpha]_{5461}^{20}$ − 148·7° in Me_2CO.

dl-.
Needles from H_2O. M.p. 98–9° (91°). Sol. EtOH, Et_2O. Mod. sol. H_2O. Conc. H_2SO_4 ⟶ blue col.
Me ester: needles from pet. ether. M.p. 79°.
Et ester: $C_{14}H_{14}O_3$. MW, 230. Needles from pet. ether. M.p. 69°.
l-*Menthyl ester*: m.p. 38·5–39·5°. $[\alpha]_{5461}^{21}$ − 61·4° in Me_2CO.
Amide: $C_{12}H_{11}O_2N$. MW, 201. Plates from Me_2CO–pet. ether. M.p. 134–5°.

McKenzie, Dennler, *J. Chem. Soc.*, 1926, 1599; *Ber.*, 1927, **60**, 221.
McKenzie, Gow, *J. Chem. Soc.*, 1933, 35.
Roger, Gow, *J. Chem. Soc.*, 1934, 130.

2-Naphthylglycollic Acid (β-*Naphthylglycollic acid*).
Cryst. from ligroin. M.p. 158°. Sol. hot EtOH, AcOH. Less sol. hot H_2O. Spar. sol. Et_2O, ligroin.
Me ester: needles from EtOH. M.p. 75°.
Et ester: needles from ligroin. M.p. 87°.
Amide: leaflets from EtOH. M.p. 227–8°.
Nitrile: *benzoyl*: cryst. from $PhNO_2$. M.p. 239°.
Acetyl: cryst. from AcOH. M.p. 150°.

Schweitzer, *Ber.*, 1891, **24**, 549.
Madelung, Oberwegner, *Ber.*, 1932, **65**, 940.

β-Naphthylglyoxal

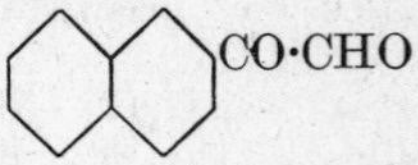

$C_{12}H_8O_2$ MW, 184

Intensely yellow oil. B.p. 183°/20 mm. part decomp.
Diacetate: $C_{10}H_7\cdot CO\cdot CH(O\cdot CO\cdot CH_3)_2$. Prisms from C_6H_6–pet. ether. M.p. 150°.
Di-Me acetal: $C_{10}H_7\cdot CO\cdot CH(O\cdot CH_3)_2$. B.p. 194°/16 mm.
Hydrate: $C_{10}H_7\cdot CO\cdot CH(OH)_2$. Leaflets from H_2O. M.p. 98°.

Madelung, Oberwegner, *Ber.*, 1932, **65**, 939.

Naphthylglyoxylic Acid.
See Naphthoylformic Acid.

N-Naphthylheptadecylamine.
See Heptadecylnaphthylamine.

1-Naphthylhydrazine

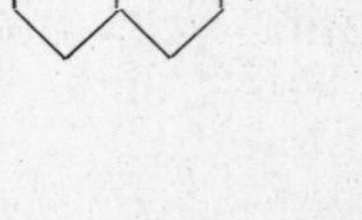

$C_{10}H_{10}N_2$ MW, 158

Plates from H_2O. M.p. 116–17°. B.p. 203°/20 mm. Very sol. hot EtOH, C_6H_6, $CHCl_3$. Spar. sol. cold H_2O. Mild ox. agents give naphthalene + N_2.

Acetyl deriv.: needles from EtOH.Aq. M.p. 143°. Sol. EtOH, Et_2O, C_6H_6.

N′-*Phenyl*: leaflets. M.p. 124°. N : N′-*Diacetyl*: m.p. 264°.

N′-o-*Tolyl*: m.p. 107°. N : N′-*Diacetyl*: m.p. 252°.

Fischer, *Ann.*, 1886, **232**, 237.

2-Naphthylhydrazine.

Leaflets from H_2O. M.p. 124–5°. Sol. hot EtOH, C_6H_6, $CHCl_3$. Spar. sol. Et_2O. $FeCl_3$ ⟶ naphthalene + N_2. HCl in sealed tube at 200° ⟶ 2-naphthylamine + NH_3.

See previous reference.

1-Naphthylhydroxylamine

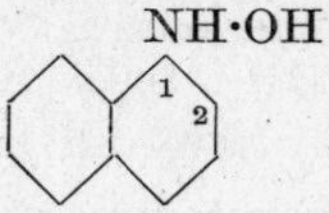

$C_{10}H_9ON$ MW, 159

Cryst. + H_2O. M.p. anhyd. 79°. Sol. org. solvents. Mod. sol. H_2O. Reduces $NH_3.AgNO_3$ and Fehling's. Ag_2O ⟶ 1-nitrosonaphthalene.

Willstätter, Kubli, *Ber.*, 1908, **41**, 1937.

2-Naphthylhydroxylamine.

Leaflets from $CHCl_3$. M.p. 126°.

Baudisch, Furst, *Ber.*, 1917, **50**, 324.

1-Naphthyl isocyanate

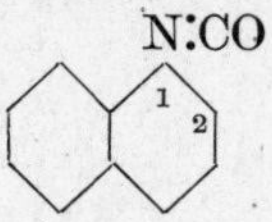

$C_{11}H_7ON$ MW, 169

Liq. B.p. 269–70°.

Vittenet, *Bull. soc. chim.*, 1899, **21**, 957.

2-Naphthyl isocyanate.

Leaflets. M.p. 55–6°. Sol. Et_2O, C_6H_6.

See previous reference.

1-Naphthylmalonic Acid

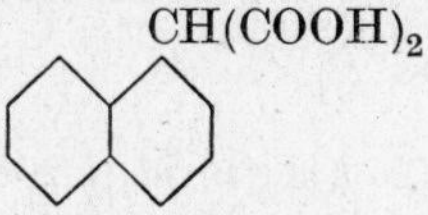

$C_{13}H_{10}O_4$ MW, 230

Di-Me ester: $C_{15}H_{14}O_4$. MW, 258. Needles from 50% EtOH. M.p. 104°.

Di-Et ester: $C_{17}H_{18}O_4$. MW, 286. Prisms or plates from pet. ether. M.p. 59–60°. Very sol. $CHCl_3$. Sol. EtOH, C_6H_6.

Keach, *J. Am. Chem. Soc.*, 1933, **55**, 3440.

Wislicenus, Butterfass, Koken, *Ann.*, 1924, **436**, 81.

Naphthyl Mercaptan.

See Thionaphthol.

1-Naphthylmethylamine (α-*Menaphthylamine*, 1-α-*aminomethylnaphthalene*)

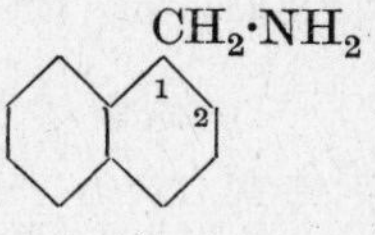

$C_{11}H_{10}N$ MW, 156

Liq. B.p. 155°/12 mm.

B,HCl: m.p. 262–4°. Mod. sol. H_2O, EtOH.

Acetyl: needles from ligroin. M.p. 134°.

Benzenesulphonyl: m.p. 148°. Spar. sol. cold EtOH.

Picrate: m.p. 223°. Mod. sol. EtOH.

Methiodide: leaflets from EtOH. M.p. 213°.

Phenylurea deriv.: m.p. 216°. Spar. sol. EtOH.

v. Braun, Blessing, Zobel, *Ber.*, 1923, **56**, 1996.

I.G., U.S.P., 1,873,402, (*Chem. Abstracts*, 1932, **26**, 5965).

2-Naphthylmethylamine (β-*Menaphthylamine*, 2-α-*aminomethylnaphthalene*).

Cryst. M.p. 60°. B.p. 148–9°/12 mm.

B,HCl: m.p. 269°.

Acetyl: m.p. 126°.

Picrate: m.p. 226°. Spar. sol. EtOH.

Methiodide: prisms from EtOH. M.p. 168°.

See first reference above.

2-β-Naphthyl-1-naphthoic Acid.

See Picenic Acid.

Naphthylnitromethane.

See ω-Nitromethylnaphthalene.

Naphthylphenylenediamine.

See under Phenylenediamine.

1-Naphthylpropiolic Acid

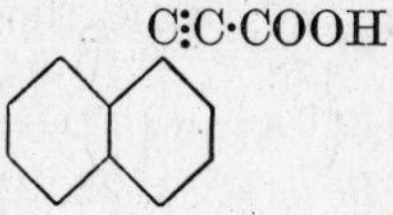

$C_{13}H_8O_2$ MW, 196

Needles from H_2O or CS_2. M.p. 138–9° decomp. Sol. EtOH, Et_2O, CS_2. Spar. sol. H_2O, cold CCl_4. Turns yellow in air. H_2O is sealed tube at 125° ⟶ 1-naphthylacetylene.

Leroy, *Bull. soc. chim.*, 1892, **7**, 645.
West, *J. Am. Chem. Soc.*, 1920, **42**, 1666.

1-α-Naphthylpropionaldehyde

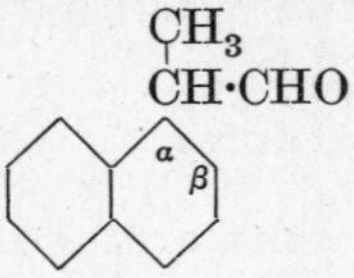

$C_{13}H_{12}O$ MW, 184

Liq. B.p. 170°/14 mm., 131–2°/4 mm. D^0 1·118.
Semicarbazone: m.p. 209–10°.

Darzens, *Compt. rend.*, 1907, **145**, 1342.
Tiffeneau, Daudel, *Compt. rend.*, 1908, **147**, 679.

1-β-Naphthylpropionaldehyde.
Cryst. M.p. 53°.
Semicarbazone: m.p. 134–5°.

See first reference above.

1-α-Naphthylpropionic Acid

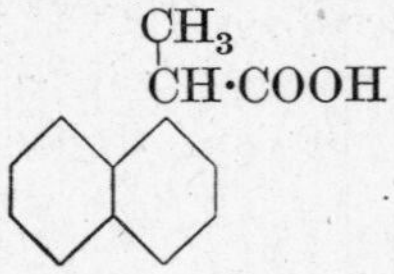

$C_{13}H_{12}O_2$ MW, 200

Cryst. M.p. 145°.

Tiffeneau, Daudel, *Compt. rend.*, 1908, **147**, 679.

2-α-Naphthylpropionic Acid (α-*Menaphthylacetic acid*)

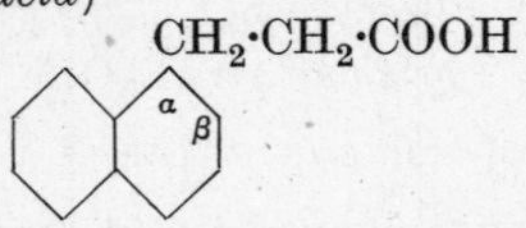

$C_{13}H_{12}O_2$ MW, 200

Needles from EtOH. M.p. 156° (148°). B.p. 179°/11 mm.
Me ester: $C_{14}H_{14}O_2$. MW, 214. B.p. 162°/2 mm.
Chloride: $C_{13}H_{11}OCl$. MW, 218·5. M.p. 26°. B.p. 179–80°/12 mm.
Amide: $C_{13}H_{13}ON$. MW, 199. Needles from H_2O. M.p. 140° (133°).
Hydrazide: needles from EtOH. M.p. 125–6°.

Brandis, *Ber.*, 1889, **22**, 2156.
Willgerodt, *J. prakt. Chem.*, 1909, **80**, 183.
Darzens, Lévy, *Compt. rend.*, 1935, **201**, 902.

2-β-Naphthylpropionic Acid (β-*Menaphthylacetic acid*).
Leaflets from H_2O. M.p. 135° (129–30°).
Et ester: $C_{15}H_{16}O_2$. MW, 228. Leaflets. M.p. 28°. B.p. 195–8°/25 mm.
Amide: leaflets from H_2O. M.p. 168°.
Hydrazide: needles. M.p. 156°.

See last reference above and also
Monier-Williams, *J. Chem. Soc.*, 1906, **89**, 277.
Willgerodt, *J. prakt. Chem.*, 1909, **80**, 188.
Mayer, Schnecko, *Ber.*, 1923, **56**, 1411.

1-α-Naphthylsemicarbazide

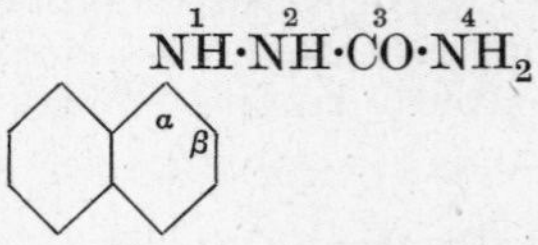

$C_{11}H_{11}ON_3$ MW, 201

Leaflets from hot amyl alcohol. M.p. 231°. Spar. sol. cold EtOH. Insol. H_2O, Et_2O.

Pinner, *Ber.*, 1888, **21**, 1222.

1-β-Naphthylsemicarbazide.
Leaflets from H_2O. M.p. 225°. Sol. hot EtOH, AcOH. Spar. sol. Et_2O, C_6H_6, $CHCl_3$, CS_2. Insol. cold H_2O. Reduces warm Fehling's.
4-o-*Tolyl*: needles from AcOH. M.p. 215°. Spar. sol. EtOH.
4-p-*Tolyl*: needles from EtOH. M.p. 187°.

Pinner, *Ber.*, 1888, **21**, 1223.

4-β-Naphthylsemicarbazide

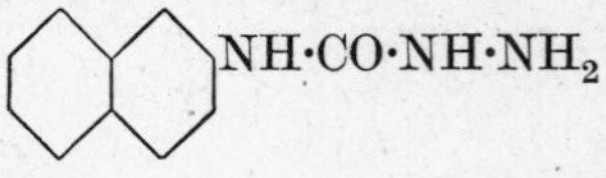

$C_{11}H_{11}ON_3$ MW, 201

Cryst. powder. M.p. 258–9°. Stable.
B,HCl: needles from H_2O. M.p. about 260° decomp.

Borsche, *Ber.*, 1901, **34**, 4302; 1905, **38**, 836.

1-Naphthylsuccinic Acid

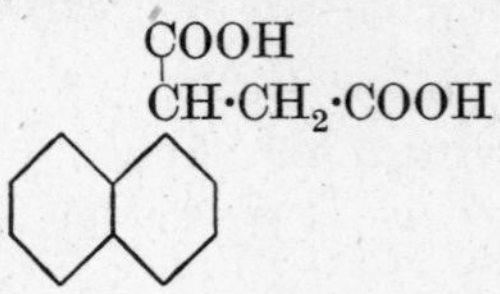

$C_{14}H_{12}O_4$ MW, 244

Leaflets from hot H_2O. M.p. 206°. Sol. EtOH, Et_2O, AcOH. Spar. sol. pet. ether.

Wislicenus, Butterfass, Koken, *Ann.*, 1924, **436**, 81.

1-α-Naphthylthiosemicarbazide

$$\overset{1}{N}H\cdot\overset{2}{N}H\cdot\overset{3}{C}S\cdot\overset{4}{N}H_2$$

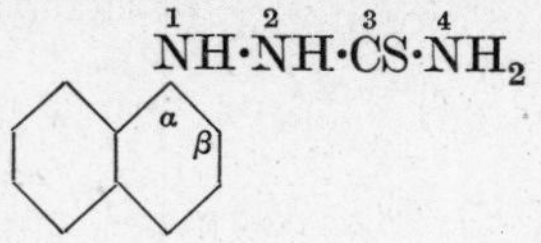

$C_{11}H_{11}N_3S$ MW, 217

Leaflets from EtOH. M.p. 209° decomp. Spar. sol. EtOH, C_6H_6, CS_2. Insol. Et_2O, $CHCl_3$.
4-*Me* : m.p. 195°.
4-*Et* : m.p. 149°.
4-p-*Tolyl* : m.p. 169°.
4-α-*Naphthyl* : m.p. 192°.
4-β-*Naphthyl* : m.p. 179°.

Freund, Schuftan, *Ber.*, 1891, **24**, 4190.
Marckwald, *Ber.*, 1899, **32**, 1087.

1-β-Naphthylthiosemicarbazide.

Cryst. from EtOH. M.p. 204° (201–2°). Sol. hot EtOH, hot aniline. Spar. sol. C_6H_6, CS_2, ligroin. Insol. H_2O, Et_2O.
4-*Me* : m.p. 212° (209°).
4-*Et* : m.p. 169°.
4-*Allyl* : m.p. 155°.
4-*Phenyl* : leaflets from EtOH. M.p. 202°.
4-o-*Tolyl* : m.p. 192°.
4-p-*Tolyl* : m.p. 195°.
4-α-*Naphthyl* : m.p. 207°.
4-β-*Naphthyl* : m.p. 187°.

See last reference above and also
Hauff, *Ann.*, 1889, **253**, 30.

4-α-Naphthylthiosemicarbazide

$$NH\cdot CS\cdot NH\cdot NH_2$$

$C_{11}H_{11}N_3S$ MW, 217

Needles from EtOH, leaflets from C_6H_6. M.p. 138–9°. Mod. sol. most solvents. Spar. sol. ligroin.

Busch, Ulmer, *Ber.*, 1902, **35**, 1715.

α-Naphthylthiourea

$$NH\cdot CS\cdot NH_2$$

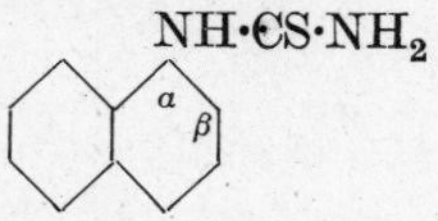

$C_{11}H_{10}N_2S$ MW, 202

Prisms from EtOH. M.p. 198°. Spar. sol. H_2O, cold EtOH, Et_2O.
N′-*Me* : m.p. 196°.
N′-*Allyl* : m.p. 145°.
N′-*Phenyl* : plates. M.p. 162–3°. Spar. sol. EtOH, Et_2O. N′-*Me* : m.p. 135–6°. N′-*Et* : m.p. 129–129·5°.

N′-o-*Tolyl* : needles from EtOH. M.p. 167°.
N′-p-*Tolyl* : needles from EtOH. M.p. 168°.
N′-*Benzyl* : m.p. 172–3°.
N′-*Naphthyl* : see sym.-Di-1-naphthylthiourea.
N′-*Acetyl* : needles from EtOH. M.p. 198°. Sol. 40 parts boiling EtOH. Spar. sol. Et_2O.
N′-*Benzoyl* : yellow prisms from EtOH. M.p. 172–3°. Sol. 50 parts hot EtOH.

Heller, Bauer, *J. prakt. Chem.*, 1902, **65**, 380.
de Clermont, Wehrlin, *Bull. soc. chim.*, 1876, **26**, 126.
Dyson, Hunter, *Chem. News*, 1927, **134**, 4.

β-Naphthylthiourea.

Leaflets from EtOH. M.p. 186° (180°). Spar. sol. usual solvents.
N′-*Phenyl* : leaflets from EtOH. M.p. 182–3° (165°). N′-*Me* : m.p. 124·5–125°. N′-*Et* : plates. M.p. 128·5–129°.
N′-o-*Tolyl* : m.p. 193–4°.
N′-p-*Tolyl* : m.p. 163–4°.
N′-*Benzyl* : plates from EtOH. M.p. 165–6°. Sol. Et_2O, C_6H_6, $CHCl_3$. Spar. sol. boiling EtOH.
N′-*Naphthyl* : see sym.-Di-2-naphthylthiourea.
N′-*Acetyl* : prisms from EtOH. M.p. 158°.

See first reference above and also
Cosiner, *Ber.*, 1881, **14**, 61.

α-Naphthylurea

$$NH\cdot CO\cdot NH_2$$

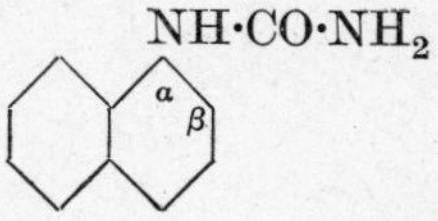

$C_{11}H_{10}ON_2$ MW, 186

Needles from EtOH. M.p. 215–20°. Very sol. EtOH. Sol. Et_2O. Spar. sol. H_2O. Above m.p. ⟶ sym.-di-1-naphthylurea.
N′-*Phenyl* : m.p. 222–3°.
N′-p-*Tolyl* : needles. M.p. 234°.
N′-*Benzyl* : leaflets from EtOH. M.p. 203°.
N′-*Acetyl* : needles. M.p. 214–15°. Mod. sol. EtOH, C_6H_6.
N′-*Benzoyl* : exists in two forms. (i) Needles. M.p. 243–243·5°. (ii) Prisms. M.p. 165–6°.
N′-*Carboethoxyl* : needles from EtOH or C_6H_6. M.p. 170–170·5°.
N′-α-*Naphthyl* : see sym.-Di-1-naphthylurea.

Young, Clark, *J. Chem. Soc.*, 1897, **71**, 1200.
Walther, Wlodkowski, *J. prakt. Chem.*, 1899, **59**, 277.
Sah, *Chem. Abstracts*, 1934, **28**, 6122.

β-Naphthylurea.

Needles from EtOH. M.p. 219–20° (213–14°). Sol. hot EtOH. Insol. cold H_2O. Above m.p. ⟶ *sym.*-di-2-naphthylurea.

N′-*Phenyl*: prisms from EtOH. M.p. 220–1°.

N′-*Acetyl*: needles. M.p. 202–202·5°. Sol. boiling EtOH, C_6H_6. Spar. sol. boiling H_2O.

N′-*Benzoyl*: needles from EtOH. M.p. 219–20°.

N′-*Carboethoxyl*: needles from EtOH. M.p. 140°.

N′-*Naphthyl*: *see* Di-2-naphthylurea.

See previous references.

α-Naphthylurethane

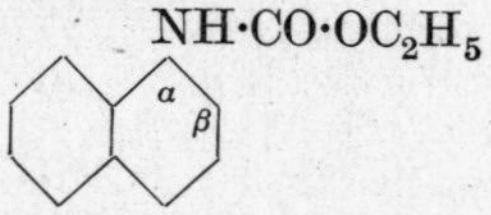

$C_{13}H_{13}O_2N$ MW, 215

Needles from EtOH. M.p. 79°.

Hofmann, *Ber.*, 1870, **3**, 657.

β-Naphthylurethane.

Needles. M.p. 73°. Sol. boiling H_2O, EtOH, Et_2O, C_6H_6, $CHCl_3$.

Cosiner, *Ber.*, 1881, **14**, 60.
Groeneveld, *Rec. trav. chim.*, 1932, **51**, 783.

1 : 5-Naphthyridine (1 : 5-*Pyridopyridine, isonaphthyridine*)

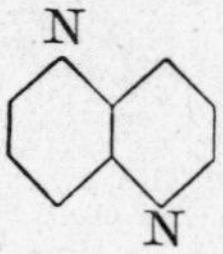

$C_8H_6N_2$ MW, 130

Yellowish needles from pet. ether. M.p. 75°. B.p. 112°/15 mm. Very sol. all solvents. Aq. sol. has bitter taste and reacts neutral. Sublimes very readily. Volatile in steam.

B,H₂SO₄: m.p. about 218° decomp. Sol. H_2O, EtOH.

Picrate: m.p. 200°. Sol. H_2O, EtOH.

Schering-Kahlbaum, D.R.P., 507,637, (*Chem. Abstracts*, 1931, **25**, 716).
Bobrański, Sucharda, *Ber.*, 1927, **60**, 1081.

1 : 8-Naphthyridine (1 : 8-*Pyridopyridine*)

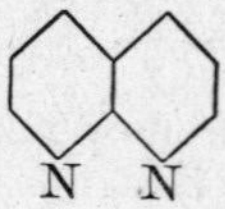

$C_8H_6N_2$ MW, 130

Needles. M.p. 98–9°. Sublimes at 80°/13 mm. Very hygroscopic. Bitter taste. Reacts with dil. $KMnO_4$.

Picrate: yellow needles from EtOH. M.p. 207–8°.

Methiodide: orange-yellow needles from EtOH. M.p. 180–1°. Sol. H_2O. Less sol. EtOH.

Koller, *Ber.*, 1927, **60**, 1918.

Narceine (3 : 4 : 6′-*Trimethoxy*-4′ : 5′-*methylenedioxy*-2′-[β-*dimethylaminoethyl*]*deoxybenzoin*-2-*carboxylic acid*)

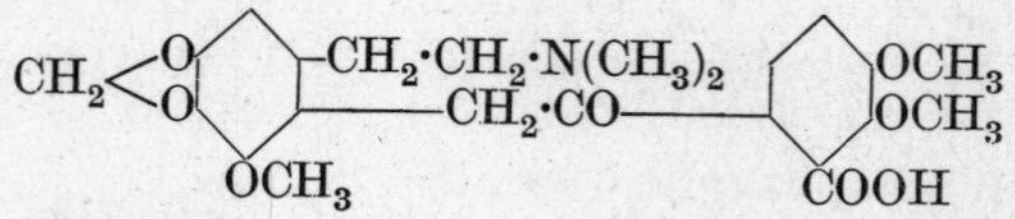

$C_{23}H_{27}O_8N$ MW, 445

Needles or prisms + $3H_2O$ from boiling H_2O. M.p. 171° (176–7°), anhyd. 145·2°. Sol. 769 parts H_2O at 25°, 1285 parts H_2O at 13°, 945 parts 80% EtOH at 13°. Insol. Et_2O, C_6H_6, $CHCl_3$, pet. ether. Sol. NH_3.Aq., dil. alkalis. Weak base. NaOH + Me_2SO_4 ⟶ narceonic acid. Dil. iodine sol. gives blue col. Dil. H_2SO_4 + resorcinol ⟶ red col. on heating. Tannin + H_2SO_4 on heating ⟶ green col. ⟶ yellowish-brown on cooling.

B,HCl: m.p. 192°.

B,HAuCl₄: yellow needles from EtOH. M.p. 130°.

B₂,H₂PtCl₆: golden-yellow needles. M.p. 195–6°.

B,HgCl₂: m.p. 120–3°.

Picrate: m.p. 195°.

Methochloride: cryst. from EtOH. M.p. 243°. Sol. H_2O, EtOH. Insol. Et_2O.

Methiodide: needles. M.p. 207°.

Methochloroplatinate: yellow leaflets from EtOH.Aq. M.p. 209–10°.

Methylbetaine: m.p. 266° decomp. Very sol. H_2O. Spar. sol. EtOH, Et_2O.

Ethochloride: m.p. 231°. Very sol. H_2O. Sol. EtOH. Insol. Et_2O.

Ethochloroplatinate: m.p. 181–2°.

Ethylbetaine: m.p. 175–7°.

Me ester: $C_{24}H_{29}O_8N$. MW, 459. *B,HCl*: plates from H_2O. M.p. 151–2°. *B,HBr*: prisms from H_2O. M.p. 153–4°. *B,HI*: m.p. 181–2°. *B₂,H₂PtCl₆*: m.p. 205–6°. *Methiodide*: needles. M.p. 211°. *Methosulphate*: m.p. 213–14°.

Et ester: $C_{25}H_{31}O_8N$. MW, 473. *B,HCl*: prisms. M.p. 208–10°. Sol. EtOH, $CHCl_3$. Sol. 120 parts cold H_2O. *B,HBr*: prisms from

H_2O. M.p. 215–16°. *B,HI*: prisms. M.p. 212–13°. *B_2,H_2PtCl_6*: m.p. 194–5°. *Methochloride*: m.p. 214–16°. Sol. H_2O, EtOH. *Methiodide*: m.p. 209–10°. *Methochloroplatinate*: m.p. 220°. *Ethochloride*: m.p. 218–19°. Sol. H_2O. *Ethiodide*: cryst. + H_2O from H_2O. M.p. 141°. *Ethochloroplatinate*: m.p. 220°.

Isopropyl ester: *B,HI*, m.p. 224–5°.

Butyl ester: *B,HI*, m.p. 185–6°.

Diethylaminoethyl ester: $C_{29}H_{40}O_8N_2$. MW, 544. Prisms from MeOH. M.p. 203°.

Amide: $C_{23}H_{28}O_7N_2$. MW, 444. Cryst. + H_2O from EtOH.Aq. M.p. 178°. Sol. EtOH, C_6H_6, $CHCl_3$. Insol. H_2O. *B,HCl*: plates. M.p. 236–7°. Sol. hot H_2O. *B,HI*: prisms. M.p. 216–18°.

Oxime: prisms + H_2O from 80% EtOH. Decomp. at 167°. Very sol. alkalis. *Me ether*: cryst. from MeOH. M.p. 190°.

Addinall, Major, *J. Am. Chem. Soc.*, 1933, **55**, 1202, 2153.
Freund, Frankforter, *Ann.*, 1893, **277**, 25.
Freund, *Ber.*, 1907, **40**, 194.
Freund, Michaelis, *Ann.*, 1895, **286**, 250.
Tambach, Jäger, *Ann.*, 1906, **349**, 191.

Narceol.
See under p-Cresol.

Narceonic Acid (*3 : 4 : 6′-Trimethoxy-4′ : 5′-methylenedioxy-2′-vinyldeoxybenzoin-2-carboxylic acid*)

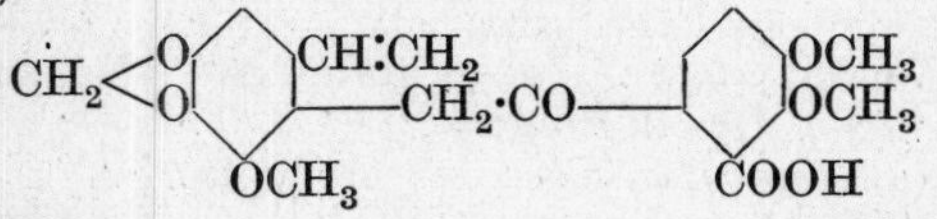

$C_{21}H_{20}O_8$ MW, 400

Plates from EtOH–$CHCl_3$. M.p. 217°. Sol. $CHCl_3$. Less sol. EtOH, AcOH. Insol. H_2O.

Me ester: $C_{22}H_{22}O_8$. MW, 414. Cryst. from MeOH. M.p. 155°.

Et ester: $C_{23}H_{24}O_8$. MW, 428. Cryst. from EtOH. M.p. 139–40°.

Addinall, Major, *J. Am. Chem. Soc.*, 1933, **55**, 1207.
Freund, *Ann.*, 1893, **277**, 56.

Narcindonine

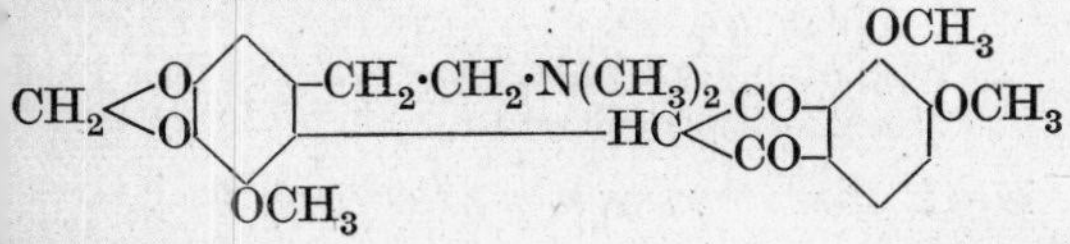

$C_{23}H_{25}O_7N$ MW, 427

Red cryst. + $1\frac{1}{2}H_2O$ from H_2O. M.p. 174°. Sol. hot H_2O, EtOH, MeOH, warm $CHCl_3$, AcOH. Insol. Et_2O, C_6H_6, ligroin.

B,HCl: cryst. M.p. 255°. Mod. sol. H_2O. Spar. sol. EtOH.

B,HI: cryst. M.p. 246°.

Methiodide: leaflets from EtOH. M.p. 217°. Mod. sol. EtOH, AcOH. Less sol. H_2O. Sol. alkalis with red col. Warm saturated NaOEt sol. ⟶ narcindone. *Me ether*: yellowish-red platelets from EtOH. M.p. 207°. Sol. MeOH, EtOH. Mod. sol. H_2O. Insol. Et_2O.

Freund, Oppenheim, *Ber.*, 1909, **42**, 1092.

Narcindone

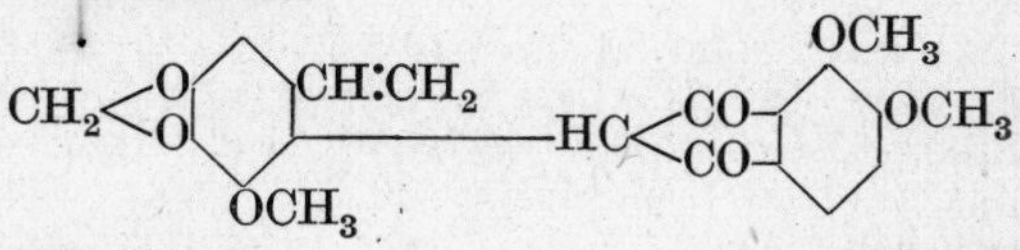

$C_{21}H_{18}O_7$ MW, 382

Leaflets from AcOH. M.p. 136–7°. Very sol. MeOH, EtOH, AcOH. Sol. alkalis with red col. Insol. NH_3.Aq., Na_2CO_3.

Freund, Oppenheim, *Ber.*, 1909, **42**, 1094.

Narcipoetine

$C_{18}H_{22}O_4N$ MW, 316

Alkaloid from *Narcissus poeticus*, Linn. Silky needles from EtOH.Aq. M.p. 172°. $[\alpha]_D$ + 84·4° in 96% EtOH.

B,HCl: cryst. + H_2O. M.p. 271° decomp. $[\alpha]_D$ + 111·2° in 96% EtOH.

B,HAuCl₄: yellow cryst. M.p. 131–2° decomp.

Picrate: yellow cryst. from EtOH. M.p. 261° decomp.

Kolle, Gloppe, *Chem. Zentr.*, 1934, II, 261.

Narcissine.
See Lycorine.

α-Narcotine

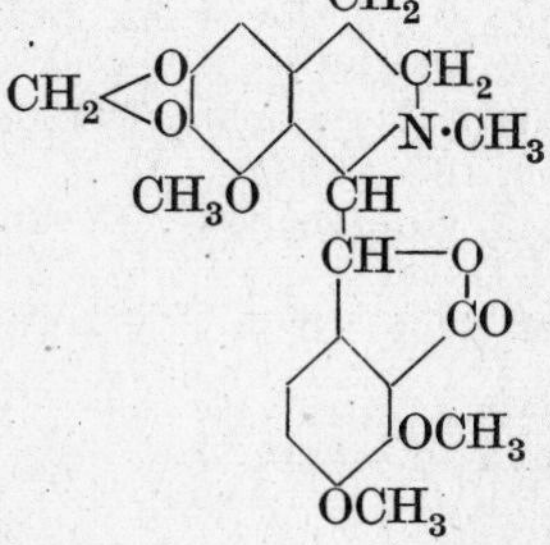

$C_{22}H_{23}O_7N$ MW, 413

l-,

One of the opium alkaloids. Needles from hot EtOH. M.p. 176°. Sol. $CHCl_3$. Sol. 166 parts

Et_2O, 100 parts 80% EtOH, 24 parts Me_2CO, 31 parts AcOEt, 22 parts C_6H_6, 25 parts aniline, 2·3 parts Py, 1·7 parts piperidine, 0·4 parts diethylamine, at 16° C. Insol. H_2O, alkalis. $[\alpha]_D$ −198·0° in $CHCl_3$, + 50° in 1% HCl. Salts easily decomp. by H_2O. Heat of comb. C_p 2645 Cal. $k = 1{\cdot}5 \times 10^{-8}$ at 25°. Conc. $H_2SO_4 \longrightarrow$ pale yellow $\longrightarrow$ yellowish-red col. $HNO_3 \longrightarrow$ yellowish-red col. $\longrightarrow$ colourless on standing. Dil. H_2SO_4 or $Ba(OH)_2 \longrightarrow$ hydrocotarnine + opianic acid. $HNO_3 \longrightarrow$ opianic acid + cotarnine.

N-*Oxide*: solid. $[\alpha]_D$ +135° in $CHCl_3$. Very sol. H_2O, EtOH, $CHCl_3$. Hygroscopic. Unstable to heat. $SO_2 \longrightarrow$ narcotine. Gives red col. with acetic anhydride. *B,HCl*: m.p. 193°. Very sol. H_2O. $[\alpha]_D$ + 100°. *Picrate*: m.p. 130°. *Chloroplatinate*: m.p. 175°.

Picrate: m.p. 174°.

d-*Bromocamphorsulphonate*: needles from EtOH or AcOEt. M.p. 110–20°. $[\alpha]_D$ +100·7° in $CHCl_3$.

l-*Bromocamphorsulphonate*: prisms from AcOEt. M.p. 180–5°. $[\alpha]_D$ + 29° in $CHCl_3$.

d-.

Needles from EtOH. M.p. 175°. $[\alpha]_D$ + 199·9° in $CHCl_3$.

d-*Bromocamphorsulphonate*: prisms from AcOEt. M.p. 170–85°.

l-*Bromocamphorsulphonate*: m.p. 80–90°. $[\alpha]_D$ − 97·2° in $CHCl_3$.

dl-. α-Gnoscopine.

Needles from EtOH. M.p. 232–3°. Sol. hot $CHCl_3$. Spar. sol. C_6H_6. Very spar. sol. EtOH. Much less sol. than active forms.

Picrate: yellow prisms from MeOH. M.p. 188–9°.

Methiodide: prisms + $2H_2O$. M.p. 210–12°.

dl-*Bromocamphorsulphonate*: prisms from AcOEt. M.p. 189°.

Polonovski, Polonovski, *Bull. soc. chim.*, 1930, **47**, 361.
Marshall, Pyman, Robinson, *J. Chem. Soc.*, 1934, 1317.
Perkin, Robinson, *J. Chem. Soc.*, 1911, **99**, 775.
Hesse, *Ann.*, 1872, **8**, 284 (Suppl.).

β-Narcotine.

Stereoisomer of α-narcotine.

d-.

Plates from EtOH. M.p. 176°. $[\alpha]^{18}_{546}$ + 103° in $CHCl_3$.

l-.

Leaflets or plates from EtOH, prisms from Me_2CO. M.p. 176°. $[\alpha]^{18}_{546}$ − 101° in $CHCl_3$, − 60° in 1% HCl. Much less readily racemised than α-form.

Picrate: yellow needles from EtOH. M.p. 118°.

Methiodide: prisms from hot H_2O. M.p. 208°.

dl-.

See β-Gnoscopine.

See second reference above.

Naringenin (*Naringetol, salipurol*, 5 : 7 : 4′-*Trihydroxyflavanone*)

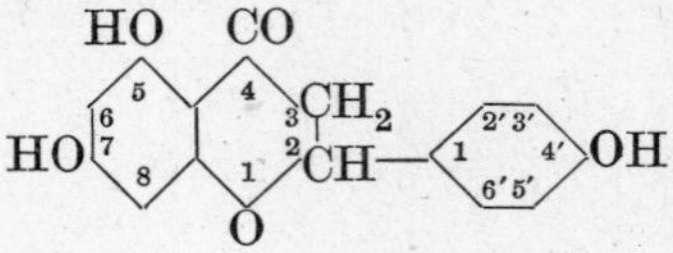

$C_{15}H_{12}O_5$ MW, 272

Needles or leaflets from EtOH.Aq. M.p. 251°. Sol. EtOH, Et_2O, C_6H_6. Insol. H_2O. Alkalis $\longrightarrow$ yellow sols. which are decomp. by CO_2. Conc. $H_2SO_4 \longrightarrow$ yellow sol. changing to red on standing. Alc. $FeCl_3 \longrightarrow$ deep reddish-brown col. Mg + alc. HCl $\longrightarrow$ reddish-violet col. Heat with conc. KOH $\longrightarrow$ phloroglucinol + *p*-coumaric acid.

4′-*Me ether*: *see* Isosakuranetin.

7-*Me ether*: *see* Sakuranetin.

7 : 4′-*Di-Me ether*: isosakuranetin Me ether. *See under* Isosakuranetin.

Tri-Me ether: isosakuranetin di-Me ether. *See under* Isosakuranetin.

5-*Rhamnoglucoside*: *see* Naringin.

Oxime: needles from EtOH.Aq. M.p. 233°.

Triacetyl: cryst. from AcOH. M.p. 53–5°. No col. with $FeCl_3$. Mg + alc. HCl $\longrightarrow$ deep red col. Acetic anhydride + Na acetate $\longrightarrow$ 4 : 2′ : 4′ : 6′-tetracetoxychalkone.

Tetra-acetyl: cryst. from EtOH. M.p. 133–6°.

Shibata, Nagai, *Acta Phytochim.*, 1924, **2**, 37.
Shinoda, Uyeda, *Chem. Zentr.*, 1929, II, 1547.
Asahina, Shinoda, Inubuse, *Chem. Zentr.*, 1928, II, 49.
Asahina, Inubuse, *Ber.*, 1928, **61**, 1514.
Rosenmund, Rosenmund, *ibid.*, 2608.

Naringin (*Naringenin-5-rhamnoglucoside*)

$C_{27}H_{32}O_{14}$ MW, 580

Found in fruits of *Citrus decumana*. Needles + $8H_2O$ from H_2O. M.p. 82°. After drying at 110° contains $2H_2O$ and has m.p. 171°. Very sol.

ıot EtOH. Sol. hot H_2O, AcOH. Sol. 8000 parts H_2O at 20°. Insol. Et_2O, C_6H_6, $CHCl_3$. $[\alpha]_D^{19}$ − 82·11° in EtOH. Bitter taste. Gives intense yellowish-red col. with alkalis. Alc. $FeCl_3 \longrightarrow$ brownish-red col. Hyd. $\longrightarrow$ naringenin + glucose + rhamnose.

Asahina, Inubuse, *Chem. Zentr.*, 1929, I, 2429; *Ber.*, 1928, **61**, 1514.
Zoller, *Chem. Zentr.*, 1918, II, 635.

Nataloin

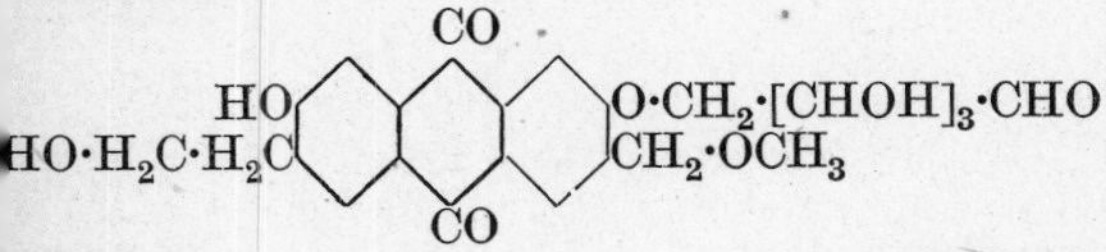

$C_{23}H_{24}O_{10}$ MW, 460

l-.

Pale yellow plates from MeOH. $[\alpha]_D^{18}$ −145°. Sol. AcOEt, Py. Mod. sol. MeOH. Insol. H_2O, Et_2O. Sol. HCl, HNO_3. Alk. sols. decomp. by CO_2. Conc. H_2SO_4 + fuming $HNO_3 \longrightarrow$ green col. NaOH + ammonium persulphate $\longrightarrow$ violet col.

α-Penta-acetyl: m.p. 198°. $[\alpha]_D^{20}$ − 53° in EtOH, − 50° in AcOH. Hyd. $\longrightarrow$ *l*-nataloin.

β-Penta-acetyl: $[\alpha]_D$ − 44°. Hyd. $\longrightarrow$ *l*-nataloin.

dl-.

Penta-acetyl: m.p. 245° decomp. Hyd. $\longrightarrow$ *l*-nataloin + mixture of *d*- and *l*-nataloin, $[\alpha]_D$ + 63°.

Léger, *J. pharm. chim.*, 1903, **17**, 13.

Neobornylamine

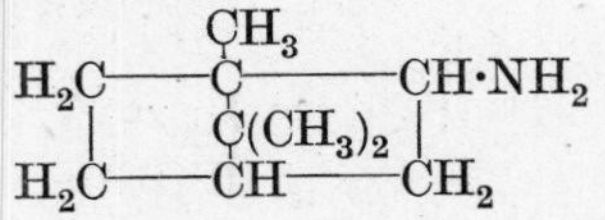

$C_{10}H_{19}N$ MW, 153

d-.

Powder. M.p. 184°. Very sol. all org. solvents. Insol. H_2O. $[\alpha]_D$ − 43·7° in EtOH, − 27° in C_6H_6.

B,HCl: needles from H_2O. Does not melt below 320°. Very sol. H_2O, EtOH. Sol. Et_2O, $CHCl_3$. $[\alpha]_D$ − 44·2° in EtOH.

B_2,H_2PtCl_6: orange leaflets from EtOH. M.p. 303° decomp. Very sol. hot EtOH. Sol. hot H_2O.

Picrate: yellow prisms from EtOH. M.p. 248° decomp. Sol. hot EtOH.

Formyl: leaflets from EtOH.Aq. M.p. 72–3°. $[\alpha]_D^{20}$ − 19·4° in EtOH. Very sol. EtOH, pet. ether.

Acetyl: needles from pet. ether. M.p. 144°. $[\alpha]_D$ − 19·5° in EtOH. Sol. EtOH. Spar. sol. pet. ether.

Benzoyl: leaflets from EtOH.Aq. M.p. 130°. Sol. EtOH. Spar. sol. cold pet. ether.

Urethane: cryst. M.p. 36°. $[\alpha]_D$ − 9·63° in C_6H_6. Sol. org. solvents. Spar. sol. H_2O.

Forster, *J. Chem. Soc.*, 1898, **73**, 394.
Forster, Hart-Smith, *J. Chem. Soc.*, 1900, **77**, 1152.

Neocinchophene.

See under 6-Methyl-2-phenylquinoline-4-carboxylic Acid.

Neodorme (1-*Bromo*-1-*isopropylbutyramide*)

$CH_3·CH_2·CBr·CONH_2$
$CH(CH_3)_2$

$C_7H_{14}ONBr$ MW, 208

Cryst. M.p. 50–1°. Odour resembling menthol. Sol. 150 parts cold H_2O. Readily sol. most org. solvents. Sublimes in needles. Aq. sols. react acid. Decomp. by boiling H_2O and hot aq. alkalis. Hypnotic and sedative.

Kuhlmann, *Pharm. Ztg.*, 1931, **76**, 113.
Knoll, U.S.P., 1,780,131, (*Chem. Abstracts*, 1931, **25**, 1038).

Neoergosterol

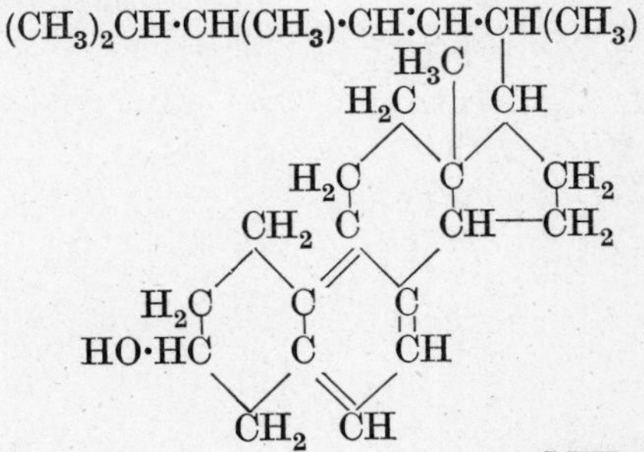

$C_{27}H_{42}O$ MW, 382

Prisms from EtOH. M.p. 151–2°. $[\alpha]_D$ − 12° in $CHCl_3$. Does not give Salkowski or Liebermann-Burchard colour reactions.

Acetyl: needles from Me_2CO. M.p. 122–3°.

Dibromide: cryst. from MeOH–Me_2CO. M.p. 183°.

3 : 5-*Dinitrobenzoyl*: cryst. from C_6H_6–EtOH. M.p. 218–20°. $[\alpha]_D^{16}$ − 13° in $CHCl_3$.

Dibromide: m.p. 212° decomp.

Windaus, Borgeaud, *Ann.*, 1928, **460**, 235.
Bonstedt, *Z. physiol. Chem.*, 1929, **185**, 165.
Inhoffen, *Ann.*, 1932, **497**, 130.

Neoisomenthol (3-*Methyl*-6-*isopropylcyclohexanol*, p-*menthanol*-3)

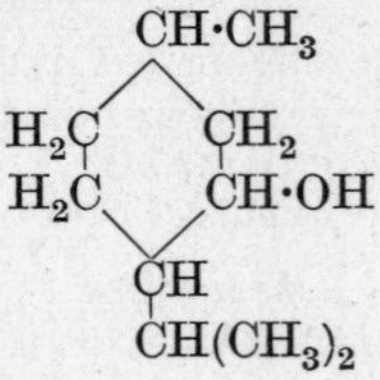

$C_{10}H_{20}O$ MW, 156

d-.

F.p. −8°. B.p. 214·6°/760 mm., 84·2°/7·5 mm. D_4^{18} 0·9131. $[\alpha]_D^{15}$ + 2·2° in EtOH. n_D^{18} 1·4674. Easily oxidised to *d*-isomenthone.

p-*Nitrobenzoyl*: pale yellow prisms from EtOH. M.p. 72·5–73°. $[\alpha]_D^{15}$ − 5·3° in $CHCl_3$.

3 : 5-*Dinitrobenzoyl*: needles from EtOH–AcOEt. M.p. 100·5–101°. $[\alpha]_D^{15}$ − 9·5° in $CHCl_3$.

d-*Camphor*-10-*sulphonate*: prisms from pet. ether. M.p. 69–70°. $[\alpha]_D^{16}$ + 17·3° in $CHCl_3$.

l-*Camphor*-10-*sulphonate*: needles from pet. ether. M.p. 84–6°. $[\alpha]_D^{16}$ − 41·0° in $CHCl_3$.

B,H₃PO₄: m.p. 60°.

dl-.

F.p. 14°. B.p. 81°/6 mm. n_D^{17} 1·4676.

p-*Nitrobenzoyl*: yellow needles from EtOH. M.p. 63–4°.

3 : 5-*Dinitrobenzoyl*: leaflets from EtOH. M.p. 73–73·5°.

Read, Grubb, *J. Chem. Soc.*, 1934, 315.

Neoisomenthylamine (3-*Methyl*-6-*isopropylcyclohexylamine*)

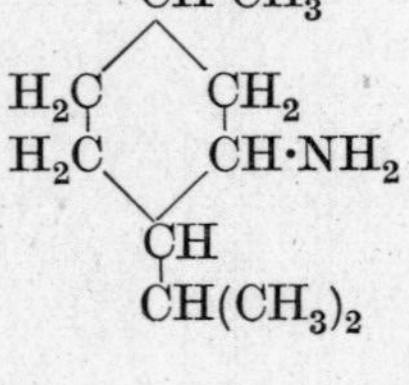

$C_{10}H_{21}N$ MW, 155

d-.

Liq. $[\alpha]_D^{15}$ + 9° in $CHCl_3$.

B,HCl: needles from Me_2CO–MeOH. Does not melt below 250°. $[\alpha]_D^{15}$ + 20·9° in H_2O.

Formyl: oil. $[\alpha]_D$ − 3·9° in $CHCl_3$.

Acetyl: needles from pet. ether. M.p. 99–100°. $[\alpha]_D^{15}$ − 2·6° in $CHCl_3$. Very sol. org. solvents.

Benzoyl: needles from EtOH. M.p. 151°. $[\alpha]_D^{15}$ − 10·4° in $CHCl_3$.

2-*Naphthalenesulphonyl*: cryst. from EtOH. M.p. 120°. $[\alpha]_D^{15}$ − 10·7° in $CHCl_3$.

Benzylidene: needles from MeOH. M.p. 68–9°. $[\alpha]_D^{15}$ − 34·2° in $CHCl_3$.

Salicylidene: yellow needles from Et_2O–pet. ether. M.p. 99–100°. $[\alpha]_D^{15}$ − 17·9° in $CHCl_3$.

Carbamide: needles from Et_2O–pet. ether. M.p. 115–16°. $[\alpha]_D^{15}$ − 3·1° in $CHCl_3$.

Phenylcarbamide: needles from Et_2O–pet. ether. M.p. 149–50°. $[\alpha]_D^{15}$ − 12·1° in $CHCl_3$.

Phenylthiocarbamide: prisms from Et_2O–pet. ether. M.p. 99°. $[\alpha]_D^{15}$ − 6·7° in $CHCl_3$.

Read, Robertson, *J. Chem. Soc.*, 1927, 2168.

Neolactose

$C_{12}H_{22}O_{11}$ MW, 342

Constitution unknown. Prisms from MeOH. M.p. 190° decomp. $[\alpha]_D^{20}$ + 34·6° ⟶ + 35·5° in H_2O. Hyd. ⟶ *d*-galactose + *d*-altrose. Br water ⟶ neolactobionic acid. HNO_3 ⟶ mucic acid.

Phenylosazone: yellow cryst. from H_2O. M.p. 195° decomp.

β-*Hepta-acetyl*: prisms. M.p. 135–6°. $[\alpha]_D$ + 10·0° ⟶ + 21·0° in $CHCl_3$.

α-*Octa-acetyl*: laminæ from EtOH. M.p. 178°. $[\alpha]_D^{24}$ + 53·4° in $CHCl_3$. Reduces hot Fehling's.

β-*Octa-acetyl*: plates from EtOH. M.p. 148°. $[\alpha]_D^{23}$ − 7·04° in $CHCl_3$.

α-*Chlorohepta-acetyl*: m.p. 182° decomp. $[\alpha]_D^{25}$ + 71·2° in $CHCl_3$.

Kunz, Hudson, *J. Am. Chem. Soc.*, 1926, **48**, 1978, 2435.
Richtmyer, Hudson, *J. Am. Chem. Soc.*, 1935, **57**, 1716.

Neomenthol (β-*Pulegomenthol*, 3-*methyl*-6-*isopropylcyclohexanol*, p-*menthanol*-3)

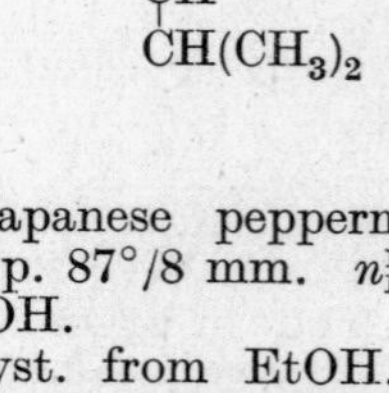

$C_{10}H_{20}O$ MW, 156

d-.

Found in Japanese peppermint oil. Liq. F.p. − 22°. B.p. 87°/8 mm. n_D^{17} 1·4617. $[\alpha]_D^{15}$ + 17·80° in EtOH.

Benzoyl: cryst. from EtOH. M.p. 68–9°. B.p. 181°/16 mm. $[\alpha]_{546}$ + 32·3° in $CHCl_3$.

p-*Nitrobenzoyl*: cryst. from EtOH.Aq. M.p. 94·5–95°. $[\alpha]_D^{15}$ + 17·8° in $CHCl_3$.

l-*Menthoxyacetate*: m.p. 28·5°. $[\alpha]_D^{18}$ − 31·5° in $CHCl_3$.

d-*Menthoxyacetate*: m.p. 64°. $[\alpha]_D^{16}$ + 80·9° in $CHCl_3$.

Acid phthalate: cryst. from AcOH. M.p. 142–4°. $[\alpha]_D$ + 68·7° in $CHCl_3$. *Brucine salt*: cryst. from Me_2CO. M.p. 125–7° decomp.

l-.

Liq. B.p. 97·6°/10 mm. n_D^{12} 1·4638. $[\alpha]_D^{17}$ − 20·7° in EtOH.

p-*Nitrobenzoyl*: yellow needles from EtOH. Aq. M.p. 95°. $[\alpha]_D^{13}$ − 17·9° in $CHCl_3$.

3 : 5-*Dinitrobenzoyl*: yellow needles from AcOEt–EtOH. M.p. 153°. $[\alpha]_D^{13}$ − 23·9° in $CHCl_3$.

Phenylurethane: m.p. 107–8°. $[\alpha]_D$ − 26·77° in $CHCl_3$.

l-*Menthoxyacetate*: needles from MeOH. M.p. 64°. $[\alpha]_D^{19}$ − 81·1° in $CHCl_3$.

d-*Menthoxyacetate*: needles. M.p. 28·5°. $[\alpha]_D^{19}$ + 32·0° in $CHCl_3$.

d-*Camphor*-10-*sulphonate*: long needles from pet. ether. M.p. 116° decomp. $[\alpha]_D^{18}$ + 8·9° in $CHCl_3$.

l-*Camphor*-10-*sulphonate*: cryst. from pet. ether. M.p. 92° decomp. $[\alpha]_D^{18}$ − 50·3° in $CHCl_3$.

dl-.

Plates from pet. ether. M.p. 51°. B.p. 212·1°/163 mm., 103–5°/16 mm. Sol. org. solvents. Insol. H_2O. $CrO_3 \longrightarrow$ *dl*-menthone.

p-*Nitrobenzoyl*: needles from warm EtOH. M.p. 78·5°.

3 : 5-*Dinitrobenzoyl*: yellow needles from EtOH–AcOEt. M.p. 130°. Mod. sol. hot EtOH.

2-*Naphthoyl*: prisms from EtOH. M.p. 98°.

Phenylurethane: m.p. 114°.

Acid phthalate: prisms from AcOH. M.p. 175–7°.

Pickard, Littlebury, *J. Chem. Soc.*, 1912, **101**, 110.
Read, Grubb, *J. Chem. Soc.*, 1933, 167.
Read, Grubb, *J. Soc. Chem. Ind.*, 1934, **53**, 52T.

Neomenthylamine (3-*Methyl*-6-*isopropylcyclohexylamine*)

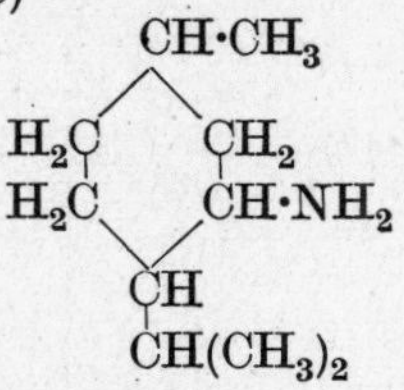

$C_{10}H_{21}N$ MW, 155

d-.

Liq. $[\alpha]_D^{20}$ +15·73° in $CHCl_3$.

B,HCl: prisms from pet. ether. M.p. 189°. $[\alpha]_D^{15}$ +21·5° in H_2O.

Formyl: cryst. from MeOH. M.p. 117–18°. $[\alpha]_D^{15}$ + 53·8° in $CHCl_3$, + 62·4° in EtOH. Mod. sol. Et_2O, pet. ether.

Acetyl: m.p. 169–70°. $[\alpha]_D^{15}$ +53·0° in $CHCl_3$.

Benzoyl: m.p. 121·5°. $[\alpha]_D^{15}$ +22·7° in $CHCl_3$.

2-*Naphthalenesulphonyl*: leaflets from EtOH–$CHCl_3$. M.p. 208°. $[\alpha]_D^{15}$ + 43·7° in $CHCl_3$.

Benzylidene: m.p. 45–6°. $[\alpha]_D^{15}$ + 61·7° in $CHCl_3$.

Salicylidene: m.p. 99–100°. $[\alpha]_D^{15}$ +30·0° in $CHCl_3$.

l-.

Formyl: cryst. from EtOH. M.p. 116–17°. $[\alpha]_D^{15}$ − 53·6° in $CHCl_3$.

dl-.

B,HCl: cryst. from pet. ether. M.p. 184–5°. Sol. most org. solvents.

B,HBr: prisms from EtOH. Does not melt below 220°. Spar. sol. Et_2O. Insol. pet. ether.

B_2,H_2PtCl_6: orange prisms from H_2O. M.p. 206–7° decomp.

Picrate: yellow needles or orange prisms from EtOH. M.p. 183–4°.

Formyl: prisms from Et_2O–pet. ether. M.p. 86°. Sol. most org. solvents. More sol. than *d*-form.

Acetyl: needles from Et_2O–pet. ether. M.p. 160–1°.

Benzoyl: needles from pet. ether. M.p. 101–2°.

2-*Naphthalenesulphonyl*: plates from boiling MeOH. M.p. 209–10°. Spar. sol. MeOH.

Salicylidene: yellow needles from MeOH. M.p. 69·5°.

Carbamide: prisms from Me_2CO. M.p. 162–3°.

Phenylcarbamide: prisms from MeOH. M.p. 183–4°.

Phenylthiocarbamide: prisms from MeOH. M.p. 169–70°.

Read, Robertson, *J. Chem. Soc.*, 1926, 2218.
Read, Cook, Shannon, *ibid.*, 2227.
See also Tutin, Kipping, *J. Chem. Soc.*, 1904, **85**, 68.

Neo-2-methyl-1-hydrindamine (*Neo*-2-*methyl*-1-*indanamine*)

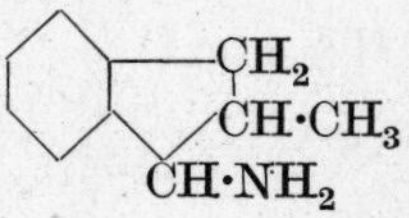

$C_{10}H_{13}N$ MW, 147

d-.

B,HCl: $[\alpha]_D$ + 3·1° in H_2O.

Acid-d-*tartrate*: prisms + H_2O from H_2O.

M.p. 166–7°. Very sol. H_2O. $[\alpha]_D + 16{\cdot}2°$ in H_2O.

d-*Camphorsulphonate*: needles from H_2O. Decomp. at 195–205°. $[\alpha]_D + 14{\cdot}8°$.

3-*Bromo*-d-*camphor*-8-*sulphonate*: needles + H_2O from H_2O. M.p. 229–30°. Sol. EtOH. Mod. sol. H_2O, Me_2CO, AcOEt. Insol. Et_2O, CCl_4.

l-.

B,HCl: needles from H_2O. Decomp. at 235°. Very sol. H_2O, EtOH. Sol. $CHCl_3$, AcOEt. Almost insol. Et_2O, CCl_4. $[\alpha]_D - 3{\cdot}1°$ in H_2O.

Acid-d-*tartrate*: prisms + H_2O from EtOH or H_2O. M.p. 173°. Sol. H_2O. Less sol. EtOH. Almost insol. Me_2CO, C_6H_6, $CHCl_3$, AcOEt. $[\alpha]_D + 11{\cdot}4°$ in H_2O.

d-*Camphorsulphonate*: prisms from H_2O. M.p. 220°. Very sol. H_2O. Sol. $CHCl_3$. Spar. sol. EtOH, Me_2CO. Insol. Et_2O, AcOEt. $[\alpha]_D + 11{\cdot}6°$ in H_2O.

3-*Bromo*-d-*camphor*-8-*sulphonate*: needles from H_2O. M.p. 214°. Sol. EtOH, AcOEt, Me_2CO, $CHCl_3$. Mod. sol. H_2O. Insol. Et_2O. $[\alpha]_D + 57{\cdot}1°$ in H_2O.

Benzoyl: needles from EtOH.Aq. M.p. 171°.

dl-.

B,HCl: needles from H_2O. Decomp. at 235°.

B_2,H_2SO_4: plates from H_2O. M.p. about 220° decomp.

Acid oxalate: prisms + $2H_2O$ from EtOH.Aq. M.p. anhyd. 173–5°. *Benzoyl*: m.p. 169°.

3-*Bromo*-d-*camphor*-8-*sulphonate*: prisms from EtOH or H_2O. M.p. 194°. Sol. hot H_2O, EtOH, Me_2CO, $CHCl_2$. Almost insol. Et_2O, C_6H_6, pet. ether. $[\alpha]_D + 58{\cdot}8°$ in H_2O, $+ 50{\cdot}3°$ in $CHCl_3$, $+ 72{\cdot}3°$ in MeOH.

Benzoyl: needles from EtOH. M.p. 169°. Sol. Me_2CO, $CHCl_3$. Mod. sol. EtOH, C_6H_6. Spar. sol. H_2O, Et_2O, pet. ether.

Picrate: yellow plates from EtOH. M.p. 195–6°. Spar. sol. H_2O.

Harris, *J. Chem. Soc.*, 1919, **115**, 61.
Tattersall, Kipping, *J. Chem. Soc.*, 1903, **83**, 825.

Neonal (*Soneryl*, 5-*ethyl*-5-n-*butylbarbituric acid*)

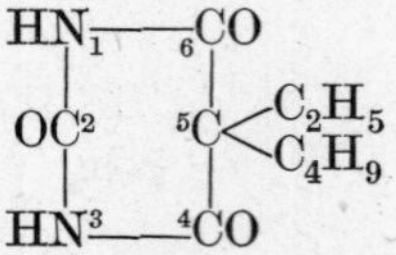

$C_{10}H_{16}O_3N_2$ MW, 212

Cryst. from EtOH.Aq. M.p. 127–8°. Sol. EtOH, dil. alkalis. Spar. sol. H_2O.

N-p-*Nitrobenzyl*: m.p. 146°.

Hargreaves, Nixon, *Chem. Zentr.*, 1934, I, 2324.
Dox, Yoder, *J. Am. Chem. Soc.*, 1922, **44**, 1580.
Poulenc, D.R.P., 481,129, (*Chem. Abstracts*, 1929, **23**, 4950).

Neonicotine.
See under Anabasine.

Neopentane.
See Tetramethylmethane.

Neopentyl Alcohol.
tert.-Butylcarbinol, *q.v.*

Neopilocarpine (*Methylpilocarpidine*)

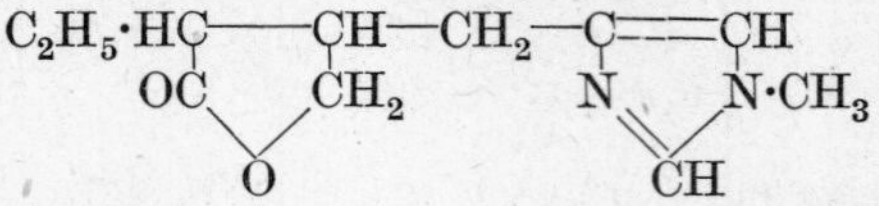

$C_{11}H_{16}O_2N_2$ MW, 208

Cryst. M.p. 39–40°. Sol. H_2O, most org. solvents. Insol. ligroin.

B,HCl: prisms from EtOH–Me_2CO. M.p. 177°. Sol. H_2O, EtOH. $[\alpha]_D + 66{\cdot}4°$. Deliquescent.

B,HNO₃: needles from EtOH. M.p. 94–5°.

Picrate: needles from EtOH. M.p. 117–19°.

Burtles, Lee, Pyman, *J. Chem. Soc.*, 1925, **127**, 581.

Neopine (β-*Codeine*)

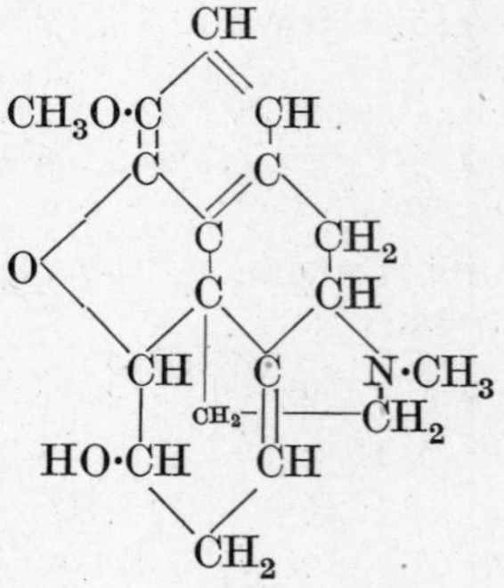

$C_{18}H_{21}O_3N$ MW, 299

Alkaloid of opium. Colourless needles from pet. ether. M.p. 127–127·5°. Sol. H_2O, EtOH, Et_2O, C_6H_6, $CHCl_3$. $[\alpha]_D^{23} - 28{\cdot}10°$ in $CHCl_3$. Optically inactive in H_2O. Hydrogenation ⟶ dihydrocodeine.

B,HBr: m.p. 282–3° decomp. $[\alpha]_D^{23} + 17{\cdot}32°$ in H_2O.

Acetyl: pale yellow varnish. *Methiodide*: long needles from MeOH. M.p. 256–7°.

Dobbie, Lauder, *J. Chem. Soc.*, 1911, **99**, 34.
v. Duin, Robinson, Smith, *J. Chem. Soc.*, 1926, 903.
Gulland, Robinson, *J. Chem. Soc.*, 1923, **123**, 980, 998.

Neopiperitol (Δ^1-p-*Menthenol*-3)

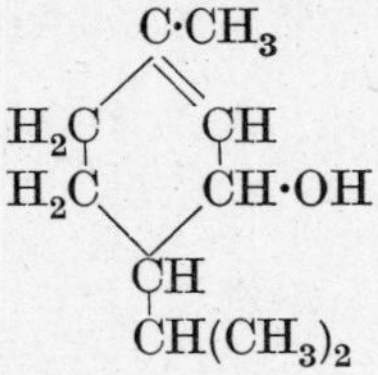

$C_{10}H_{18}O$ MW, 154

d-.

Liq. B.p. 96·5–98·5°/15·5 mm. D_4^{25} 0·9119. n_D^{17} 1·4976, n_D^{25} 1·4729. $[\alpha]_D^{16}$ + 21·22°.

dl-.

Viscous liq. with characteristic odour. B.p. 94–6°/15·5 mm. $n_D^{19\cdot5}$ 1·4740.

Read, Storey, *J. Chem. Soc.*, 1930, 2779.

Neosalvarsan (*914*, *Novarsenobenzene*)

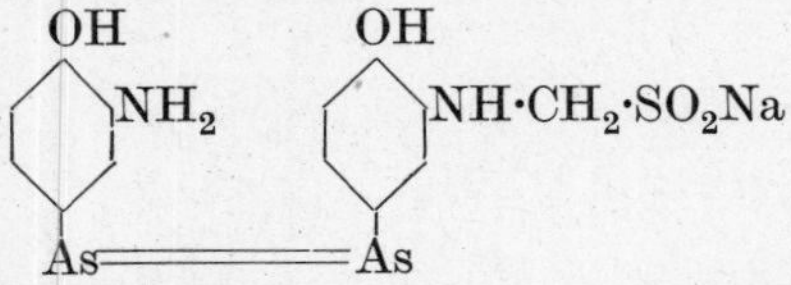

$C_{13}H_{13}O_4N_2SAs_2Na$ MW, 466

Yellow solid. Sol. $H_2O \longrightarrow$ a neutral solution. Solutions decomp. easily by heat, light or exposure to air. Employed in treatment of protozoal diseases.

M.L.B., D.R.P., 245,746, (*Chem. Zentr.*, 1912, I, 1522); D.R.P., 260,235, (*Chem. Zentr.*, 1913, II, 105).
Dyke, King, *J. Chem. Soc.*, 1934, 1707.

Neotropine (2 : 6-*Diamino*-6′-*butyloxy*-3 : 3′-*azopyridine*)

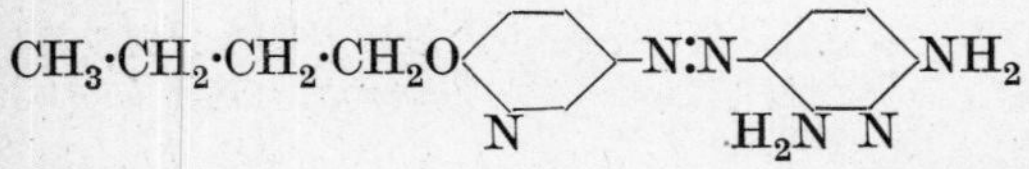

$C_{14}H_{18}ON_6$ MW, 286

Orange cryst. M.p. 129°. Used as antiseptic.
Hydrochloride: m.p. 227°.
Picrate: m.p. 240° decomp.
Picrolonate: m.p. 204° decomp.

Zernik, *Pharm. Ztg.*, 1930, **75**, 1204, (*Chem. Zentr.*, 1930, II, 3812).
Schering-Kahlbaum, E.P., 341,598, (*Chem. Zentr.*, 1931, I, 2678).

Neotruxinic Acid

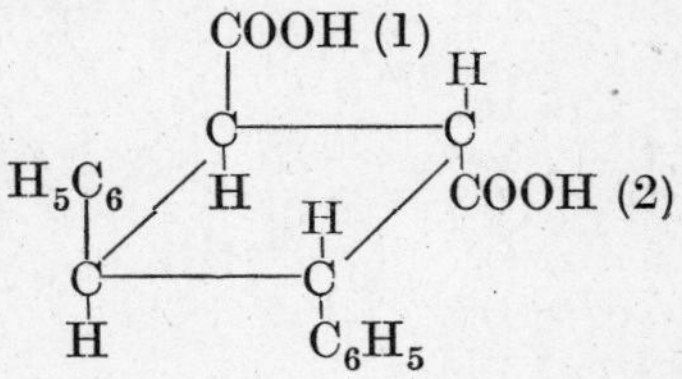

$C_{18}H_{16}O_4$ MW, 296

d-.

Fine needles from EtOH.Aq. M.p. 236–7°. $[\alpha]_D^{18}$ + 52·63° in Me_2CO.
Cinchonine salt: cryst. from EtOH. M.p. 216–17°.
Di-Me ester: $C_{20}H_{20}O_4$. MW, 324. Cryst. from MeOH. M.p. 100°. $[\alpha]_D^{20}$ + 48·11° in Me_2CO.
Di-Et ester: $C_{22}H_{24}O_4$. MW, 352. Needles from EtOH. M.p. 53°. $[\alpha]_D^{20}$ + 18·33° in Me_2CO.
Dichloride: $C_{18}H_{14}O_2Cl_2$. MW, 333. Cryst. from C_6H_6–pet. ether. M.p. 103–4°. $[\alpha]_D$ − 15·98° in Me_2CO.
Diamide: $C_{18}H_{18}O_2N_2$. MW, 294. Cryst. from EtOH. M.p. 260–1°. Spar. sol. most solvents.
Dianilide: cryst. from hot AcOH. M.p. 226–7°. $[\alpha]_D^{17}$ − 52·23° in Me_2CO. Spar. sol. most solvents.

l-.

Cryst. from EtOH. M.p. 236–7°. $[\alpha]_D^{1}$ − 53·95° in Me_2CO.
Quinine salt: felted cryst. from EtOH. M.p. 138°.
Di-Me ester: cryst. from EtOH. M.p. 100–1°. $[\alpha]_D^{20}$ − 51·99° in Me_2CO.
Methylamide: needles from MeOH.Aq. M.p. 126–7°.
Ethylamide: needles from EtOH.Aq. M.p. 175°. $[\alpha]_D^{16}$ + 30·30° in Me_2CO.

dl-.

Fine needles from C_6H_6–AcOH. M.p. 209–209·5°. Sol. EtOH, Et_2O, AcOH. Spar. sol. C_6H_6. KOH fusion $\longrightarrow$ δ-truxinic acid. Ac_2O at 160° $\longrightarrow$ β-truxinic acid.
NH_4 salt: cryst. powder. M.p. 235°. Sol. H_2O. Insol. EtOH. Above m.p. $\longrightarrow$ β-truxinic imide.

1-*Me ester*: cryst. + H_2O. M.p. anhyd. 139°.

2-*Me ester*: cryst. from MeOH. M.p. 234°.

Di-Me ester: needles from MeOH.Aq. M.p. 126–7°.

1-*Et ester*: $C_{20}H_{20}O_4$. MW, 324. Needles. M.p. 163·5°.

2-*Et ester*: m.p. 123°.

1-*Amide*: $C_{18}H_{17}O_3N$. MW, 295. Needles from Me_2CO.Aq. M.p. 214°. *Me ester*: $C_{19}H_{19}O_3N$. MW, 309. M.p. 213·5°. *Et ester*: $C_{20}H_{21}O_3N$. MW, 323. M.p. 139°.

2-*Amide*: cryst. from EtOH.Aq. M.p. 213°. *Me ester*: needles. M.p. 153·5°. *Et ester*: m.p. 142·5°.

Diamide: $C_{18}H_{18}O_2N_2$. MW, 294. Plates from EtOH. M.p. 249° (239°).

Stoermer, Laage, *Ber.*, 1921, **54**, 96.
Stoermer, Bachér, *Ber.*, 1922, **55**, 1874.
Stoermer, Asbrand, *Ber.*, 1931, **64**, 2801.

Nepaline.

See ψ-Aconitine.

Neral.

See Citral.

Nerol (2 : 6-*Dimethyl*-2 : 6-*octadienol*-8)

$$(CH_3)_2C{:}CH{\cdot}CH_2{\cdot}CH_2{\cdot}\overset{CH_3}{\overset{|}{C}}{:}CH{\cdot}CH_2OH$$

$C_{10}H_{18}O$ MW, 154

Constituent of many essential oils. B.p. 224–7°, 125°/25 mm. D^{15} 0·8813. Optically inactive. Dil. CrO_3 ⟶ neral. $KMnO_4$ ⟶ Me_2CO + lævulinic acid.

Formyl: neryl formate. Liq. B.p. 119–21°/25 mm. D^{15} 0·9166. n_D^{20} 1·4568.

Acetyl: neryl acetate. B.p. 134°/25 mm., 93–4°/3 mm. D^{15} 0·905. n_D^{20} 1·452.

Propionyl: neryl propionate. D^{15} 0·9044. n_D^{30} 1·4550.

Butyryl: neryl butyrate. D^{15} 0·8968. n_D^{20} 1·4538.

Isobutyrate: neryl isobutyrate. D^{15} 0·8925. n_D^{20} 1·4518.

Tetrabromide: needles from EtOH. M.p. 118–19°.

Allophanate: cryst. from Me_2CO. M.p. 101·5°.

Diphenylurethane: cryst. from C_6H_6. M.p. 52–3°.

v. Soden, Zeitschel, *Ber.*, 1903, **36**, 267.
Reclaire, *Chem. Abstracts*, 1930, **24**, 2424.
Verley, E.P., 127,575, (*Chem. Abstracts*, 1919, **13**, 2376).
Sornet, *Rev. chim. Ind.*, 1930, **39**, 98 (*Bibl.*).

Nerolidol (*Peruviol, methylvinylhomogeranylcarbinol*)

$$(CH_3)_2C{:}CH{\cdot}CH_2{\cdot}CH_2{\cdot}\overset{CH_3}{\overset{|}{C}}{:}CH{\cdot}CH_2{\cdot}CH_2{\cdot}\underset{OH}{\overset{CH_3}{C}}{\cdot}CH{:}CH_2$$

$C_{15}H_{26}O$ MW, 222

d-.

Found in orange-blossom and Peru balsam. B.p. 276°, 128–9°/6 mm., 97°/0·2 mm. D^{15} 0·8987. D_4^{20} 0·8778. n_D^{20} 1·48982. $[\alpha]_D$ + 15·5°. CrO_3 ⟶ farnesal.

Phenylurethane: cryst. M.p. 37–8°.

dl-.

Liq. B.p. 145–6°/12 mm., 98–100°/0·3 mm. D_4^{16} 0·8788. n_D^{16} 1·4801.

Ruzicka, U.S.P., 1,644,546, (*Chem. Abstracts*, 1927, **21**, 3908).
Grosjean, Martinet, *Chimie et industrie*, 1925, **14**, 363 (*Bibl.*).
Schimmel, *Chem. Zentr.*, 1914, I, 1654.
Ruzicka, *Helv. Chim. Acta*, 1923, **6**, 483, 492.
Naef, E.P., 213,250, (*Chem. Abstracts*, 1924, **18**, 2225).

Nerolin.

See Methyl 2-naphthyl Ether *and* Ethyl 2-naphthyl Ether.

Nervone

$CH_3{\cdot}[CH_2]_7{\cdot}CH{:}CH{\cdot}[CH_2]_{13}{\cdot}CO$
NH
$CH_3{\cdot}[CH_2]_{12}{\cdot}CH{:}CH{\cdot}CH{\cdot}CH{\cdot}CH_2OH$
O
$HO{\cdot}CH_2{\cdot}CH{\cdot}[CHOH]_3{\cdot}CH$
└——O——┘

$C_{48}H_{91}O_8N$ MW, 809

A cerebroside. Needles from EtOH. M.p. 180°. Sol. warm Py, EtOH, C_6H_6, AcOH, Me_2CO, $CHCl_3$, AcOEt in hot. Insol. H_2O, Et_2O, pet. ether. $[\alpha]_D^{16}$ − 4·33° in Py. H_2SO_4 in MeOH ⟶ nervonic acid + sphingosin + galactose. Conc. H_2SO_4 ⟶ yellow col. ⟶ purple on standing.

Klenk, *Z. physiol. Chem.*, 1925, **145**, 244.
Klenk, Härle, *Z. physiol. Chem.*, 1930, **189**, 243.

Nervonic Acid (*Selacholeic acid*, cis-14-*tetracosenic acid*)

$$CH_3{\cdot}[CH_2]_7{\cdot}CH{:}CH{\cdot}[CH_2]_{13}{\cdot}COOH$$

$C_{24}H_{46}O_2$ MW, 366

Cryst. powder from EtOH. M.p. 42·5–43° (40–1°). Sol. EtOH, Et_2O, Me_2CO. Melt over HNO_3 ⟶ *trans*-14-tetracosenic acid.
Na salt: sol. hot EtOH.
Pb salt: spar. sol. cold EtOH.

Klenk, *Z. physiol. Chem.*, 1926, **157**, 283.
Tsujimoto, *J. Soc. Chem. Ind. Japan*, 1927, **30**, 868.
Hale, Lycan, Adams, *J. Am. Chem. Soc.*, 1930, **52**, 4536.

Netoric Acid

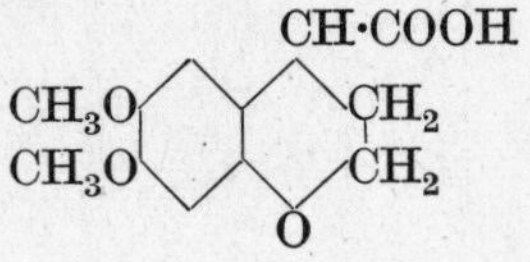

$C_{12}H_{14}O_5$ MW, 238

Cryst. + H_2O from H_2O. M.p. 91–2°, anhyd. 134°. Does not reduce Fehling's.
Me ester: $C_{13}H_{16}O_5$. MW, 252. Needles. M.p. 60°.

Robertson, Rusby, *J. Chem. Soc.*, 1936, 212.
Smith, La Forge, *J. Am. Chem. Soc.*, 1930, **52**, 4596.
Clark, *J. Am. Chem. Soc.*, 1932, **54**, 2538.
Takei, Miyajima, Ono, *Ber.*, 1932, **65**, 289.

Neuridine.
See Spermine.

Neurine (*Trimethylvinylammonium hydroxide*)

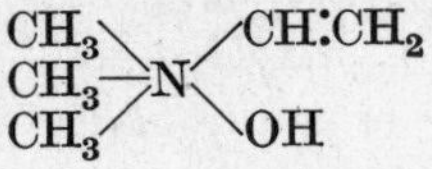

$C_5H_{13}ON$ MW, 103

Occurs free and combined in many animal and vegetable products, *e.g.* bile, brain, yolk of egg, etc.

Liq. Forms cryst. hydrate with 3 mols. H_2O. Easily decomp. ⟶ $(CH_3)_3N$. Dist. ⟶ $(CH_3)_3N$ + CH⁚CH_2OH. Very poisonous.
Bromide: plates from EtOH–Et_2O. M.p. 194° decomp. Sol. H_2O, EtOH. Insol. Et_2O.
Iodide: needles. M.p. 196°. Sol. H_2O, EtOH.
Aurichloride: long yellow needles. M.p. 248° decomp.
Chloroplatinate: m.p. 213–14° (195·5–198°) decomp.
Picrate: golden-yellow needles from H_2O. M.p. 246°. Sol. H_2O, hot EtOH. Spar. sol. $CHCl_3$, cold EtOH.

Hofmann, *Compt. rend.*, 1858, **47**, 559.
Meyer, Hopff, *Ber.*, 1921, **54**, 2277.
Renshaw, Ware, *J. Am. Chem. Soc.*, 1925, **47**, 2992.

Neuronal (1-*Bromodiethylacetamide*)

$(C_2H_5)_2CBr·CONH_2$

$C_6H_{12}ONBr$ MW, 194

Cryst. M.p. 66–7°. Sol. hot H_2O, EtOH, Et_2O, C_6H_6. Less sol. pet. ether. Sol. 115 parts cold H_2O. Hypnotic and sedative.

Kalle, D.R.P., 170,629, (*Chem. Zentr.*, 1906, I, 1807); D.R.P., 158,220, (*Chem. Zentr.*, 1905, I, 635).

Nevile and Winthers' Acid.
See 1-Naphthol-4-sulphonic Acid.

Ngaiol

$C_{15}H_{24}O_3$ MW 252

Constituent of ngaio tree. Exists in two isomeric forms. (i) B.p. 191–2°/29 mm. D_{20}^{20} 1·0163. n_D^{20} 1·4784. $[\alpha]_D$ − 25·00°. (ii) B.p. 188–90°/29 mm. D_{20}^{20} 1·013. n_D^{20} 1·4794.
Me ether: $C_{16}H_{26}O_3$. MW, 266. B.p. 178–9°/29 mm. D_{20}^{20} 0·9913. n_D^{20} 1·4701. $[\alpha]_D$ − 16·82°.
Acetyl deriv.: yellow oil. B.p. 190–2°/29 mm. D_{20}^{20} 1·0337. n_D^{20} 1·4720.

McDowall, *J. Chem. Soc.*, 1925, **127**, 2205; 1928, 1324.

Ngaione

$C_{15}H_{22}O_3$ MW, 250

Liq. B.p. 183°/27 mm.
Semicarbazone: m.p. 120–2° decomp.
p-*Nitrophenylhydrazone*: m.p. 103°.

McDowall, *J. Chem. Soc.*, 1925, **127**, 2200.

Nickel carbonyl (*Nickel tetracarbonyl*)

$Ni(CO)_4$

C_4O_4Ni MW, 170·5

Yellow liq. B.p. 43·2–43·33°/769 mm. Crit. temp. 200°. Crit. press. 30 atmospheres. Vapour explodes at 60° but not in presence of an inert gas. Halogens ⟶ nickel halides. H_2S ⟶ NiS. C_6H_6 + $AlCl_3$ ⟶ anthracene. Used as antidetonant in motor fuels.

v. Duin, *Rec. trav. chim.*, 1927, **46**, 381.
I.G., E.P., 394,906, (*Chem. Abstracts*, 1934, **28**, 267).
Manchot, Gall, *Ber.*, 1929, **62**, 678.
Dewar, Jones, *Proc. Roy. Soc.*, 1903, **71**, 427; *J. Chem. Soc.*, 1904, **85**, 203, 212.

Nickel tetracarbonyl.
See Nickel carbonyl.

Nicoteine.
Recent work has shown this substance to be a mixture of *l*-anabasine and nornicotine, *q.v.*

Nicotidine (3-[3-*Pyridyl*]-*piperidine*, 3-[3-*piperidyl*]-*pyridine*)

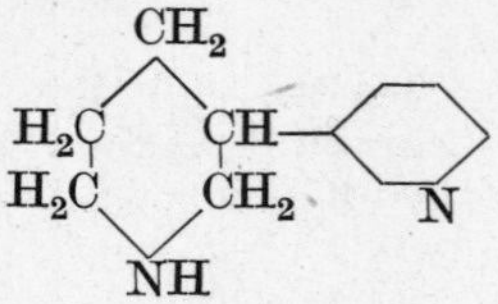

$C_{10}H_{14}N_2$ MW, 162

Viscous, pale yellow oil. B.p. 287–9° (284–5°). Very sol. H_2O, EtOH. Spar. sol. Et_2O. Poisonous.

Picrate : cryst. from H_2O. M.p. 206°.

Smith, *J. Am. Chem. Soc.*, 1931, **53**, 282.
Skraup, Vortmann, *Monatsh.*, 1883, **4**, 597.

Nicotimine

$C_{10}H_{14}N_2$ MW, 162

Alkaloid found in *Nicotiana tabacum*. Oil. B.p. 250–5°. Misc. with H_2O, org. solvents in all proportions. Reacts alkaline.

Hydrochloride : cryst. Very deliquescent.

Chloroplatinate : bright yellow cryst. Decomp. at 270°.

Aurichloride : bright yellow leaflets. M.p. 182–5° decomp.

Mercurichloride : needles. Decomp. at 190°.

Picrate : yellow prisms. M.p. 163°.

Pictet, Rotschy, *Ber.*, 1904, **37**, 1225.
Pictet, *Arch. Pharm.*, 1906, **244**, 388.
Ehrenstein, *Arch. Pharm.*, 1931, **269**, 627.
Cf. Smith, *J. Am. Chem. Soc.*, 1931, **53**, 278.

Nicotinamide (*Nicotinic acid amide*)

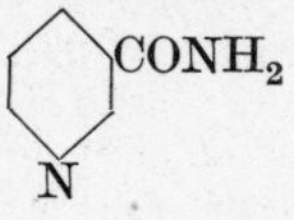

$C_6H_6ON_2$ MW, 122

Needles from C_6H_6. M.p. 122°. Dist. with P_2O_5 at 25 mm. press., or $SOCl_2$ at 100° ⟶ 3-cyanopyridine.

N-*Me* : $C_7H_8ON_2$. MW, 136. Needles from C_6H_6 or $CHCl_3$–ligroin. M.p. 104–5°.

N-*Di-Et* : coramine. $C_{10}H_{14}ON_2$. MW, 178. Yellowish oil. B.p. 280°, 175°/25 mm. Sol. H_2O, org. solvents. Used as an analeptic.

N-*Dipropyl* : $C_{12}H_{18}ON_2$. MW, 206. Yellowish oil. B.p. 184°/17 mm.

N-*Isoamyl* : $C_{11}H_{16}ON_2$. MW, 192. Thick liq. B.p. 191°/8 mm. Sol. Et_2O. Easily decomp.

Chloroaurate : m.p. 205°.

Pollak, *Monatsh.*, 1895, **16**, 53.
Camps, *Arch. Pharm.*, 1902, **240**, 354.
Pictet, Sussdorff, *Chem. Zentr.*, 1898, **I**, 677.
Hartmann, Seiberth, U.S.P., 1,403,117, (*Chem. Abstracts*, 1922, **16**, 935).
La Forge, *J. Am. Chem. Soc.*, 1928, **50**, 2480.

Nicotine (1-*Methyl*-2-[3-*pyridyl*]-*pyrrolidine*)

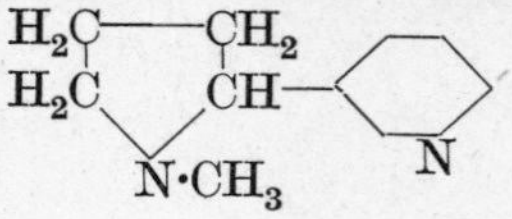

$C_{10}H_{14}N_2$ MW, 162

l-.

Alkaloid from *Nicotiana tabacum*. Liq. with odour of Py. B.p. 246·1°/730·5 mm. D_4^{20} 1·0097. n_D^{20} 1·5280. $[\alpha]_D^{20}$ − 166·39° to − 168·5°. Very sol. EtOH, Et_2O, pet. ether. Misc. with H_2O below 60° and above 210°. Volatile in steam. Readily turns brown in air. $HgCl_2$ gives white cryst. ppt. Aq. K_2PtI_6 ⟶ black ppt.

B,HCl : $[\alpha]_D$ + 102·2°.

B_2,H_2SO_4 : $[\alpha]_D$ + 84·8°.

B_2,H_2PtCl_6 : decomp. at 275°.

Acetate : $[\alpha]_D$ + 110·29°.

d-*Acid tartrate* : cryst. + $2H_2O$ from EtOH–Et_2O. M.p. 88–9°. $[\alpha]_D^{27}$ + 26·60° in H_2O.

d-*Ditartrate* : cryst. + $2H_2O$ from EtOH–Et_2O. M.p. 68·5°. $[\alpha]_D^{29\cdot5}$ + 25·99° in H_2O.

Picrate : prisms from EtOH. M.p. 218°.

Picrolonate : cryst. from EtOH. M.p. 238° (213°).

Tetrachloroiodide : orange cryst. M.p. 150°. Very stable.

d-.

Liq. B.p. 245·5–246·5°/729 mm. D_4^{10} 1·0171. D_4^{20} 1·0094. $[\alpha]_D^{20}$ + 163·17°.

l-*Ditartrate* : cryst. from H_2O. M.p. 88–9°. $[\alpha]_D^{15}$ − 25·58° in H_2O.

dl-.

Tetrahydronicotyrine. Liq. B.p. 242·3°. D_4^{20} 1·0082.

B_2,H_2PtCl_6 : decomp. about 280°.

Picrate : long yellow needles from H_2O. M.p. 218°.

Methiodide : cryst. from MeOH. M.p. 219°.

Laiblin, *Ann.*, 1879, **196**, 130.
Pictet, Rotschy, *Ber.*, 1901, **34**, 696; 1904, **37**, 1226.
Späth, Bretschneider, *Ber.*, 1928, **61**, 327.
Craig, *J. Am. Chem. Soc.*, 1933, **55**, 2856.
Späth, Kuffner, *Ber.*, 1935, **68**, 494.

α-Nicotine.
See under 2-[2-Pyridyl]-pyrrolidine.

Nicotinic Acid (*Pyridine-3-carboxylic acid*)

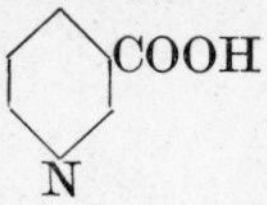

$C_6H_5O_2N$ MW, 123

Needles from H_2O or EtOH. M.p. 232°. Sol. hot H_2O, EtOH. Spar. sol. Et_2O. Sublimes. $k = 1{\cdot}4 \times 10^{-5}$ at 25°.

B,HCl: prisms or plates from H_2O. M.p. 274°.

B,HBr : plates. M.p. 275°. Sublimes.

B,HNO_3 : plates or prisms + H_2O. M.p. 190–2° (185°).

B,$HAuCl_4$: yellow leaflets. M.p. 207°.

Piperidine salt : needles. M.p. 122°.

Tetrachloroiodide : yellow. M.p. 137°.

Ethochloroplatinate : light yellow needles from EtOH–HCl. M.p. 205° decomp. Spar. sol. H_2O.

Me ester : $C_7H_7O_2N$. MW, 137. Cryst. M.p. 38°. B.p. 204°. Sol. H_2O, EtOH, C_6H_6.

Et ester : $C_8H_9O_2N$. MW, 151. Liq. B.p. 223–4°, 107–8°/17 mm., 103°/5 mm. Sol. H_2O, EtOH, Et_2O, C_6H_6, ligroin. *B,HCl*, needles. M.p. 126–7°. *B,HNO_3* : m.p. 185°. *B,$HAuCl_4$* : pale yellow leaflets from EtOH–HCl. M.p. 117°. *B_2,H_2PtCl_6* : yellow needles from EtOH. M.p. 161°. *Ethochloroplatinate* : yellow plates from EtOH–HCl. M.p. 176°. Spar. sol. H_2O. *Ethochloroaurate* : leaflets from EtOH.Aq. M.p. 59°.

Propyl ester : $C_9H_{11}O_2N$. MW, 165. Liq. B.p. 232°.

Isoamyl ester : $C_{11}H_{15}O_2N$. MW, 193. Liq. B.p. 259°.

Phenyl ester : $C_{12}H_9O_2N$. MW, 199. Cryst. from EtOH. M.p. 71°.

Chloride : *see* Nicotinyl chloride.

Amide : *see* Nicotinamide.

Nitrile : *see* 3-Cyanopyridine.

Anilide : needles + $2H_2O$ from H_2O, m.p. 85° : needles from C_6H_6–ligroin or $CHCl_3$–ligroin, m.p. 132°. Sol. hot H_2O, EtOH, $CHCl_3$, C_6H_6. Insol. H_2O, ligroin.

p-*Toluidide* : needles from boiling H_2O. M.p. 150°.

Methylbetaine : *see* Trigonelline.

Ethylbetaine : plates. M.p. 84–6°. Sol. H_2O. Less sol. EtOH. Insol. Et_2O, usual solvents.

Anhydride : cryst. from C_6H_6. M.p. 122–4°. Hygroscopic.

Hydrazide : needles from EtOH or C_6H_6. M.p. 158–9°. Sol. H_2O, EtOH. Less sol. C_6H_6. *B,2HCl* : needles from alc. HCl + Et_2O. M.p. 227°. *Benzylidene* : cryst. from C_6H_6. M.p. 149–52°.

Azide : cryst. M.p. 47–8°.

Phenylhydrazide : m.p. 185°.

Graf, *Biochem. Z.*, 1930, **229**, 166.
Engler, *Ber.*, 1894, **27**, 1787.
Pictet, Sussdorff, *Chem. Zentr.*, 1898, I, 677.
Camps, *Arch. Pharm.*, 1902, **240**, 353.
Pollak, *Monatsh.*, 1895, **16**, 46.
McElvain, *Organic Syntheses*, Collective Vol. I, 378.

Nicotinyl chloride (*Nicotinic acid chloride*)

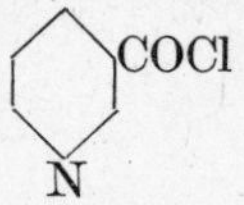

C_6H_4ONCl MW, 141·5

Cryst. M.p. 15–16°. B.p. 85°/12 mm.

B,HCl : needles. M.p. 155·5–156·5°. Sol. H_2O. Insol. Et_2O, C_6H_6, $CHCl_3$, pet. ether. Sublimes.

Meyer, Graf, *Ber.*, 1928, **61**, 2205.
Späth, Spitzer, *Ber.*, 1926, **59**, 1479.

2 : 2′-Nicotyrine (*α-Nicotyrine*, N-*methyl*-2-[2-*pyridyl*]-*pyrrole*)

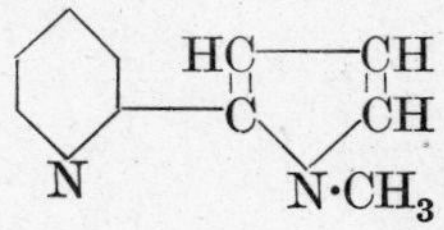

$C_{10}H_{10}N_2$ MW, 158

Exists in two forms.

(i) Liq. F.p. − 28°. B.p. 273°/764 mm., 149–50°/22 mm. Turns red on standing. Gives blue col. with pine splint + HCl. HCl + dimethylaminobenzaldehyde ⟶ intense reddish-violet col. ⟶ brownish-red on standing.

Picrate : yellow leaflets from EtOH. M.p. 143° (138–9°).

Methiodide : yellowish-brown cryst. from H_2O. M.p. 188°.

(ii) Cryst. M.p. 43·5–44·5°. Turns brown on standing. Sol. EtOH, C_6H_6, dil. HCl. Mod. sol. Et_2O. Insol. cold H_2O. HCl + dimethylaminobenzaldehyde ⟶ intense reddish-violet col. ⟶ bluish-violet on standing.

Picrate : m.p. 193–4°.

Methiodide : needles from EtOH. M.p. 146·2–146·6°. Sol. H_2O, EtOH. Insol. Et_2O.

Tschitschibabin, Bylinkin, *Ber.*, 1923, **56**, 1748.
Wibaut, Dingemanse, *Rec. trav. chim.*, 1923, **42**, 1033.
Wibaut, Coppens, *Rec. trav. chim.*, 1924, **43**, 526.

3 : 2′-Nicotyrine (N-*Methyl*-2-[3-*pyridyl*]-*pyrrole*)

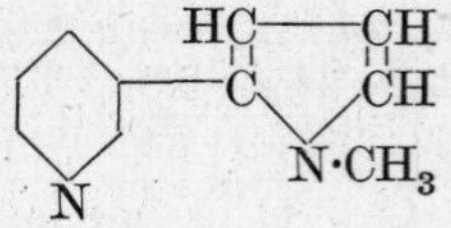

$C_{10}H_{10}N_2$ MW, 158

Liq. B.p. 280–1°/744 mm., 150°/15 mm. D^{13} 1·124. Sol. EtOH. Spar. sol. H_2O.

B_2,H_2PtCl_6 : reddish-brown plates + $2H_2O$ from H_2O. M.p. 158–60°.

Picrate : m.p. 168–9° (163–4°).

Wibaut, Overhoff, *Rec. trav. chim.*, 1928, **47**, 925.
Blau, *Ber.*, 1894, **27**, 2537.

Nipecotic Acid.
See Hexahydronicotinic Acid.

Niperyt.
See under Pentaerythritol.

Nirvanol (5-*Ethyl*-5-*phenylhydantoin*)

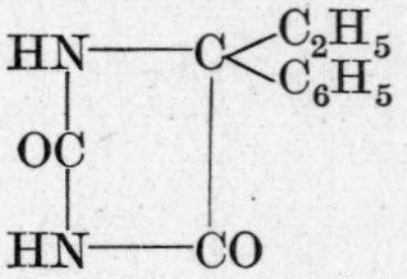

$C_{11}H_{12}O_2N_2$ MW, 204

d-.

Flaky platelets from 10% EtOH. M.p. 237°. $[\alpha]_D$ + 123° in EtOH, + 169° in aq. alkalis. Slightly less effective than *dl*-, but only one third as toxic.

l-.

Cryst. from EtOH.Aq. M.p. 235–7°. $[\alpha]_D$ − 121° in EtOH, − 167° in aq. alkalis.

dl-.

Prisms from EtOH.Aq. M.p. 199–200° (197°). Sol. warm Me_2CO, EtOH, AcOH. Sol. 1650 parts cold, 110 parts hot H_2O. Insol. C_6H_6. Used as hypnotic.

Sobotka, Holzman, Kahn, *J. Am. Chem. Soc.*, 1932, **54**, 4698.
M.L.B., Swiss P., 72,561, (*Chem. Abstracts*, 1917, **11**, 186); 73,891, (*Chem. Abstracts*, 1917, **11**, 1259).
Hermanns, U.S.P., 1,285,703, (*Chem. Abstracts*, 1919, **13**, 248).
v. Heyden, D.R.P., 335,993, (*Chem. Abstracts*, 1923, **17**, 1802).
Bergs, D.R.P., 566,094, (*Chem. Abstracts*, 1933, **27**, 1001).

Nitraldin (o-*Nitrophenylethylene oxide*)

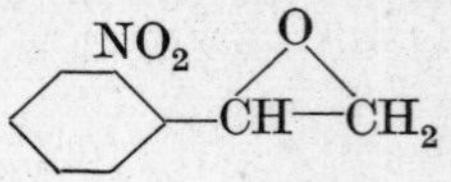

$C_8H_7O_3N$ MW, 165

Pale yellow plates from MeOH. M.p. 65°. B.p. 150°/15 mm., 144°/10 mm. Sol. Et_2O, C_6H_6. Less sol. MeOH. Mod. sol. hot pet. ether. Spar. sol. hot H_2O. Decomp. vigorously above 200°. Deflagrates violently on contact with conc. H_2SO_4.

Arndt, Partale, *Ber.*, 1927, **60**, 451.
Arndt, Eistert, Partale, *Ber.*, 1928, **61**, 1107.

Nitranilic Acid (3 : 6-*Dinitro*-2 : 5-*dihydroxy*-p-*benzoquinone*)

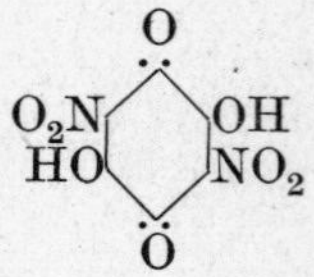

$C_6H_2O_8N_2$ MW, 230

Golden-yellow plates + H_2O. M.p. 86–7° (100°) decomp. Very sol. H_2O, EtOH. Insol. Et_2O. Explodes on heating in sealed tube.

Meyer, *Ber.*, 1924, **57**, 326.

Nitroacetaldoxime.
See Methazonic Acid.

3-Nitroacenaphthene

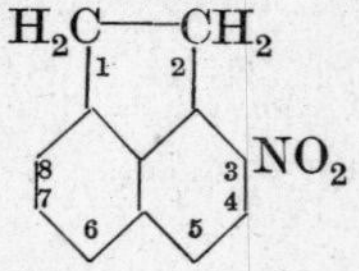

$C_{12}H_9O_2N$ MW, 199

Yellow needles from AcOH. M.p. 151·5°.

Morgan, Harrison, *J. Soc. Chem. Ind.*, 1930, **49**, 413T.

5-Nitroacenaphthene.

Yellow needles from ligroin. M.p. 106° (101°). Sol. hot H_2O, EtOH, Et_2O, ligroin. Conc. H_2SO_4 $\longrightarrow$ bluish-violet col.

Sachs, Mosebach, *Ber.*, 1911, **44**, 2854.

5-Nitroacenaphthenequinone

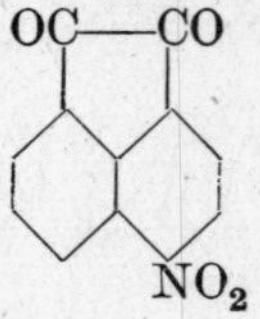

$C_{12}H_5O_4N$ MW, 227

Yellow needles from AcOH. M.p. 218° (199°).
Monophenylhydrazone: reddish-brown needles from Py. M.p. 234–5° (186°).
Diphenylhydrazone: m.p. 148°.

Rowe, Davies, *J. Chem. Soc.*, 1920, **117**, 1349.
Mayer, Kauffmann, *Ber.*, 1920, **53**, 296.

6-Nitroacenaphthene-3-sulphonic Acid

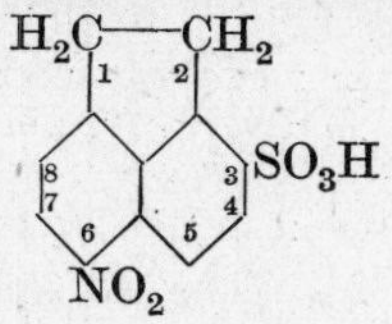

$C_{12}H_9O_5NS$ MW, 279

Yellow amorph. powder.
Me ester: $C_{13}H_{11}O_5NS$. MW, 293. Needles from ligroin. M.p. 143–4°.
Chloride: $C_{12}H_8O_4NClS$. MW, 297·5. Reddish-brown amorph. powder. Sol. C_6H_6. Spar. sol. ligroin.

Dziewoński, Orzelski, *Chem. Zentr.*, 1927, I, 1461.

6-Nitroacenaphthene-4-sulphonic Acid.
Yellow needles.
Me ester: yellow needles from ligroin. M.p. 146°.
Chloride: yellow cryst. from AcOH. Very sol. C_6H_6.

See previous reference.

***o*-Nitroacetanilide**

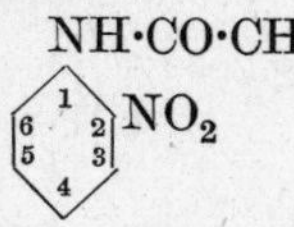

$C_8H_8O_3N_2$ MW, 180

Yellow plates or prisms from ligroin. M.p. 94°. Sol. hot H_2O, EtOH, $CHCl_3$. D^{15} 1·419.
N-*Me*: *see under* 2-Nitro-*N*-methylaniline.

Böeseken, *Rec. trav. chim.*, 1912, **31**, 351.
Menke, E.P., 235,698, (*Chem. Abstracts*, 1926, **20**, 916).

***m*-Nitroacetanilide.**
Leaflets from EtOH. M.p. 154–6°. Sol. $PhNO_2$. Mod. sol. $CHCl_3$.
N-*Me*: *see under* 3-Nitro-*N*-methylaniline.
N-*Et*: *see under* 3-Nitro-*N*-ethylaniline.

Kaufmann, *Ber.*, 1909, **42**, 3482.
Pawlewski, *Ber.*, 1898, **31**, 661.

***p*-Nitroacetanilide.**
Prisms. M.p. 215–16° (207°). Heat of comb. C_p 969 Cal. Sol. cold KOH with orange col. Spar. sol. H_2O, Et_2O, $CHCl_3$, ligroin.
N-*Me*: *see under* 4-Nitro-*N*-methylaniline.
N-*Et*: *see under* 4-Nitro-*N*-ethylaniline.
N-*Benzoyl*: plates from AcOEt. M.p. 180°.

See first reference above and also
Witt, Utermann, *Ber.*, 1906, **39**, 3903.

ω-Nitroacetanilide

$$C_6H_5{\cdot}NH{\cdot}CO{\cdot}CH_2{\cdot}NO_2$$

$C_8H_8O_3N_2$ MW, 180

Yellow plates from H_2O. M.p. 138–9°. Sol. EtOH, Et_2O, C_6H_6, $CHCl_3$, AcOEt. Spar. sol. cold H_2O. Sol. Na_2CO_3. Red. ⟶ glycine.

Steinkopf, Daege, *Ber.*, 1911, **44**, 499.

Nitroacetanisidide.
See under Nitroanisidine.

Nitroacetic Acid

$$NO_2{\cdot}CH_2{\cdot}COOH$$

$C_2H_3O_4N$ MW, 105

Needles from $CHCl_3$. M.p. 87–9° decomp. Very sol. EtOH, Et_2O. Sol. C_6H_6, toluene, hot $CHCl_3$. Insol. pet. ether. Heated with H_2O ⟶ nitromethane.
Me ester: $C_3H_5O_4N$. MW, 119. Liq. B.p. 107°/28 mm., 94–5°/16 mm. D_4^0 1·320. Spar. sol. H_2O.
Et ester: $C_4H_7O_4N$. MW, 133. Liq. B.p. 105–7°/25 mm., 93–5°/10 mm. Misc. with EtOH. Spar. sol. H_2O. D_0^0 1·226, D_4^{20} 1·992. $k = 1{\cdot}4 \times 10^{-6}$ at 25°. Aq. sol. reacts acid to litmus. *NH_4 salt*: needles from EtOH. M.p. 124°.
Propyl ester: $C_5H_9O_4N$. MW, 147. B.p. 105°/18 mm.
Isopropyl ester: b.p. 92–3°/12 mm. *NH_4 salt*: m.p. 107–9°.
Isobutyl ester: $C_6H_{11}O_4N$. MW, 161. B.p. 111·5–112·5°/15 mm., 102°/8 mm. *NH_4 salt*: m.p. 110–12°.
Isoamyl ester: $C_7H_{13}O_4N$. MW, 175. B.p. 122–3°/16 mm. *NH_4 salt*: m.p. 112–15°.
Amide: $C_2H_4O_3N_2$. MW, 104. Needles from C_6H_6. M.p. 106–7°. Sol. H_2O, EtOH, Me_2CO. Spar. sol. C_6H_6. Insol. ligroin.
Nitrile: $C_2H_2O_2N_2$. MW, 86. Yellow oil. Decomp. on heating. D^{18} 1·36. Sol. H_2O, EtOH, Et_2O, C_6H_6.

Bouveault, Wahl, *Bull. soc. chim.*, 1904, **31**, 851.
Steinkopf, *Ber.*, 1909, **42**, 619, 3925.
Steinkopf, Haugen, Schkade, *Ann.*, 1923, **434**, 26.

Nitroacetnaphthalide.
See under Nitronaphthylamine.

2′-Nitro-4-acetodiphenyl

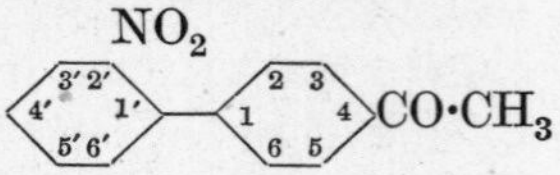

$C_{14}H_{11}O_3N$ MW, 241

Prisms from EtOH. M.p. 110°. $KMnO_4$ ⟶ 2′-nitrodiphenyl-4-carboxylic acid.

Grieve, Hey, *J. Chem. Soc.*, 1933, 970.

4′-Nitro-4-acetodiphenyl.

Yellow prisms or needles from EtOH or C_6H_6. M.p. 152–3°. $KMnO_4$ ⟶ 4′-nitrodiphenyl-4-carboxylic acid.

See previous reference and also
Dilthey, Neuhaus, Reis, Schommer, *J. prakt. Chem.*, 1930, **124**, 124.
I.G., F.P., 735,846, (*Chem. Abstracts*, 1933, **27**, 1001).

4′-Nitro-4-acetodiphenyl Ether

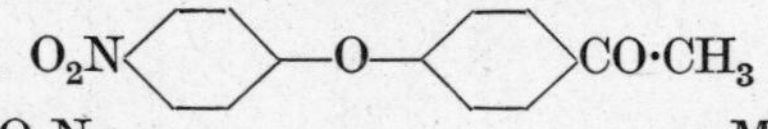

$C_{14}H_{11}O_4N$ MW, 257

Needles from 95% EtOH. M.p. 82–3° (80–1°). Conc. H_2SO_4 ⟶ greenish-yellow col.

Suker, Oberg, *J. Am. Chem. Soc.*, 1931, **53**, 1567.
Dilthey, Bach, Grütering, Hausdörfer, *J. prakt. Chem.*, 1927, **117**, 361.

Nitroacetone

$CH_3 \cdot CO \cdot CH_2 \cdot NO_2$

$C_3H_5O_3N$ MW, 103

Plates or needles from Et_2O or C_6H_6. M.p. 49–50°. B.p. 103–4°/24 mm. Very sol. C_6H_6. Sol. EtOH, Et_2O. Mod. sol. H_2O. Reacts acid. Gives no col. with $FeCl_3$.

Oxime: oil. Sol. H_2O.

Semicarbazone: needles from EtOH. M.p. 163–4°.

Anil: yellow needles from EtOH or ligroin. M.p. 87°.

Harries, *Ann.*, 1901, **319**, 251.

***o*-Nitroacetophenone**

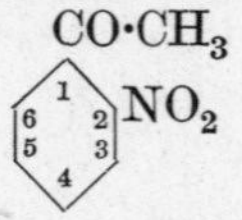

$C_8H_7O_3N$ MW, 165

Oil. B.p. 178–9°/32 mm., 159°/16 mm. Sol. EtOH, Et_2O, $CHCl_3$. Insol. H_2O.

Kermack, Smith, *J. Chem. Soc.*, 1929, 814.

***m*-Nitroacetophenone.**

Needles from EtOH. M.p. 81°. B.p. 202°, 167°/18 mm. Volatile in steam. Easily reduced.

Oxime: needles from boiling H_2O. M.p. 131–2°. Sol. EtOH, Et_2O, $CHCl_3$, AcOH. Mod. sol. C_6H_6. Spar. sol. CS_2, pet. ether. *Me ether*: needles. M.p. 63–4°. Sol. Et_2O, C_6H_6, $CHCl_3$, AcOH, CS_2. Mod. sol. EtOH, pet. ether. Volatile in steam.

Phenylhydrazone: orange needles from EtOH. M.p. 128°. Sol. EtOH, Et_2O, C_6H_6. Insol. ligroin.

o-*Tolylhydrazone*: m.p. 135–6°.

Gabriel, *Ber.*, 1882, **15**, 3063.
Corson, Hazen, *Organic Syntheses*, 1930, **10**, 74.
Morgan, Watson, *J. Soc. Chem. Ind.*, 1936, **55**, 29T.

***p*-Nitroacetophenone.**

Yellow prisms. M.p. 80–1°.

Phenylhydrazone: cryst. from EtOH. M.p. 132°.

Engler, Zielke, *Ber.*, 1889, **22**, 203.
Barkenbus, Clements, *J. Am. Chem. Soc.*, 1934, **56**, 1369.

ω-Nitroacetophenone.
See Benzoylnitromethane.

3-Nitroacetophenone-4-carboxylic Acid
(2-*Nitro*-4-*acetobenzoic acid*)

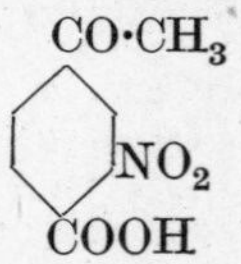

$C_9H_7O_5N$ MW, 209

Pale yellow cryst. M.p. 178–9°.

Me ester: $C_{10}H_9O_5N$. MW, 223. Needles. M.p. 58°. B.p. 211–14°/22 mm.

Mayer, Stark, Schön, *Ber.*, 1932, **65**, 1335.

ω-Nitroacetophenone-2-carboxylic Acid
(2-*Nitroacetobenzoic acid*, o-*carboxybenzoylnitromethane*)

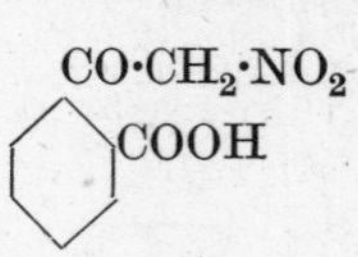

$C_9H_7O_5N$ MW, 209

Plates from H_2O at 80°. M.p. 121·5°. Alkalis ⟶ yellow sols. Conc. H_2SO_4 ⟶ greenish-blue col. ⟶ indigo blue on standing.

Gabriel, *Ber.*, 1903, **36**, 574.

4-Nitro-2-acetothienone (*4-Nitro-2-acetylthiophene*)

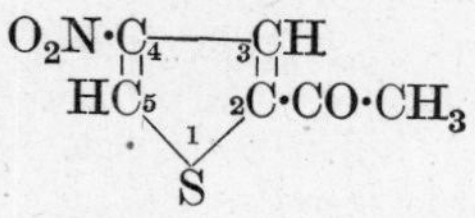

$C_6H_5O_3NS$ MW, 171

Needles from EtOH. M.p. 127°. Sol. EtOH, Et_2O. Spar. sol. H_2O.

Oxime: needles from H_2O. M.p. 129° (127°).

Rinkes, *Rec. trav. chim.*, 1933, **52**, 538.
Steinkopf, Jaffé, *Ann.*, 1917, **413**, 336.

5-Nitro-2-acetothienone (*5-Nitro-2-acetylthiophene*).

Platelets from EtOH. M.p. 106–7°.

Oxime: light yellow leaflets from EtOH. M.p. 189°.

See previous references.

Nitroacet-toluidide.
See under Nitrotoluidine.

4-Nitroacetylcatechol.
See ω-Nitro-3 : 4-dihydroxyacetophenone.

1-Nitroacridine

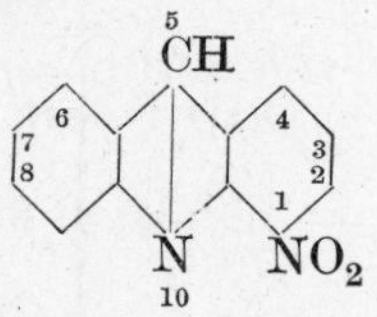

$C_{13}H_8O_2N_2$ MW, 224

Plates from MeOH. M.p. 172° (167°). Sol. EtOH. Insol. H_2O.

Jensen, Friedrich, *J. Am. Chem. Soc.*, 1927, **49**, 1051.
Lehmstedt, *Ber.*, 1927, **60**, 1371.

3-Nitroacridine.

Yellow plates from EtOH. M.p. 216°. Sublimes. Very sol. EtOH, Et_2O. Mod. sol. $CHCl_3$. Insol. H_2O.

Jensen, Friedrich, *J. Am. Chem. Soc.*, 1927, **49**, 1049.
Lehmstedt, *Ber.*, 1927, **60**, 1370.
I.G., D.R.P., 545,265, (*Chem. Zentr.*, 1932, I, 2513).

1-Nitroacridone

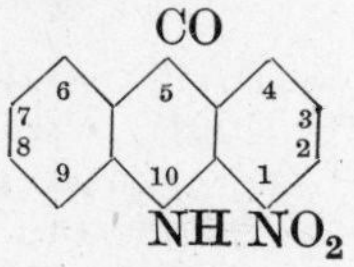

$C_{13}H_8O_3N_2$ MW, 240

Orange needles from toluene. M.p. 262°. Sol. EtOH, AcOH, toluene, $PhNO_2$.

N-Me: $C_{14}H_{10}O_3N_2$. MW, 254. Cryst. from EtOH. M.p. 168°. Mod. sol. EtOH, $CHCl_3$, C_6H_6. Insol. Et_2O.

Ullmann, *Ann.*, 1907, **355**, 328.
Lehmstedt, *Ber.*, 1931, **64**, 2381.
Lehmstedt, Hundertmark, *ibid.*, 2386.

2-Nitroacridone.

Yellow needles. Does not melt below 350°. Sol. $PhNO_2$, aniline, Py. Spar. sol. EtOH, AcOH, toluene. Insol. Et_2O, ligroin. $C_6H_5N(CH_3)_2$ $\longrightarrow$ 2-nitro-5-*p*-dimethylaminophenylacridine, m.p. 255°.

Ullmann, Wagner, *Ann.*, 1907, **355**, 364.
Lehmstedt, *Ber.*, 1932, **65**, 999.

3-Nitroacridone.

Yellow needles from $PhNO_2$. Does not melt below 350°. $C_6H_5N(CH_3)_2 \longrightarrow$ 3-nitro-5-*p*-dimethylaminophenylacridine, m.p. 225°.

N-Me: cryst. from AcOH. M.p. 276°. Mod. sol. common org. solvents. Insol. Et_2O.

Ullmann, Bader, Labhardt, *Ber.*, 1907, **40**, 4797.
Lehmstedt, *Ber.*, 1927, **60**, 1371; 1931, **64**, 2381.
Lehmstedt, Hundertmark, *Ber.*, 1931, **64**, 2386.

4-Nitroacridone.

Yellow needles from $PhNO_2$. Does not melt below 350°. Sol. $PhNO_2$, aniline. Spar. sol. EtOH, Et_2O, AcOH, C_6H_6. Insol. ligroin. $C_6H_5N(CH_3)_2$ $\longrightarrow$ 4-nitro-5-*p*-dimethylaminophenylacridine, m.p. 235°.

Ullmann, *Ann.*, 1907, **355**, 332.

5-Nitro-2-aldehydobenzoic Acid (*5-Nitro-o-phthalaldehydic acid*)

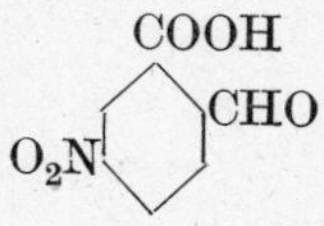

$C_8H_5O_5N$ MW, 195

Cryst. M.p. 162°.

Phenylhydrazone: bright red cryst. from MeOH or AcOH $\longrightarrow$ pyridazone deriv., m.p. 171°, on heating.

2 : 4-*Dinitrophenylhydrazone*: yellow cryst. M.p. 292°. Sol. MeOH, $CHCl_3$, AcOH, AcOEt.

Borsche, Diacont, Hanau, *Ber.*, 1934, **67**, 680.

2′-Nitro-4-aldehydodiphenyl

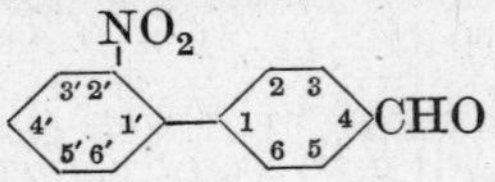

$C_{13}H_9O_3N$ MW, 227

Yellow needles from EtOH. M.p. 101°. $KMnO_4 \longrightarrow$ 2′-nitrodiphenyl-4-carboxylic acid.

Grieve, Hey, *J. Chem. Soc.*, 1935, 114; 1933, 971.

4′-Nitro-4-aldehydodiphenyl.

Yellow needles from EtOH. M.p. 127–8°. $KMnO_4 \longrightarrow$ 4′-nitrodiphenyl-4-carboxylic acid.

See previous references.

2′-Nitro-2-aldehydodiphenyl Ether

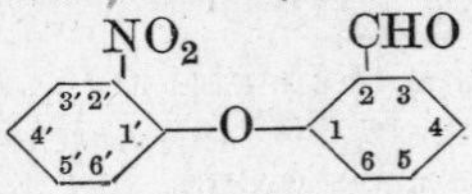

$C_{13}H_9O_4N$ MW, 243

Cryst. from ligroin. M.p. 77°.

Brewster, Strain, *J. Am. Chem. Soc.*, 1934, **56**, 118.

4′-Nitro-2-aldehydodiphenyl Ether.

Cryst. from EtOH. M.p. 112°.

See previous reference.

2′-Nitro-4-aldehydodiphenyl Ether.

White powder. M.p. 84–5°.

Suter, Oberg, *J. Am. Chem. Soc.*, 1931, **53**, 1567.

4′-Nitro-4-aldehydodiphenyl Ether.

Needles from dil. AcOH. M.p. 104–5°.

See previous reference.

3-Nitroalizarin

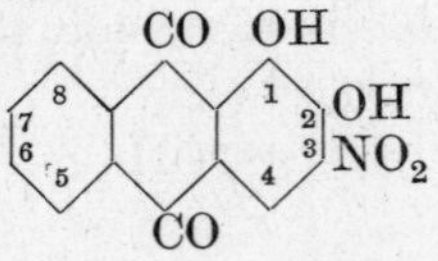

$C_{14}H_7O_6N$ MW, 285

Orange-yellow needles from C_6H_6 or yellow plates from EtOH. M.p. 244°. Sol. EtOH, C_6H_6, $CHCl_3$, AcOH. Mod. sol. H_2O. Sol. conc. H_2SO_4 with orange-yellow col.

Diacetyl: yellow needles from C_6H_6. M.p. 218°.

Schunck, Roemer, *Ber.*, 1879, **12**, 584.

4-Nitroalizarin.

Golden-yellow needles from EtOH or AcOH. M.p. 289° decomp. Mod. sol. EtOH, AcOH. Spar. sol. H_2O. Conc. $H_2SO_4 \longrightarrow$ deep yellow col.

2-*Me ether*: $C_{15}H_9O_6N$. MW, 299. Yellow plates from AcOH. M.p. 280–2°. Sol. Py, $PhNO_2$. Mod. sol. EtOH, Et_2O, C_6H_6. Conc. $H_2SO_4 \longrightarrow$ orange-red sol.

Di-Me ether: $C_{16}H_{11}O_6N$. MW, 313. Yellow needles from AcOH. M.p. 209–10°. Sol. Me_2CO, $CHCl_3$, AcOH, $PhNO_2$. Spar. sol. EtOH, Et_2O, CS_2. Conc. $H_2SO_4 \longrightarrow$ red sol.

Diacetyl: golden-yellow needles from AcOH. M.p. 194–195·5°.

M.L.B., D.R.P., 150,322, (*Chem. Zentr.*, 1904, I, 1043).

Brasch, *Ber.*, 1891, **24**, 1611.

4-Nitro-5-aminoacenaphthene

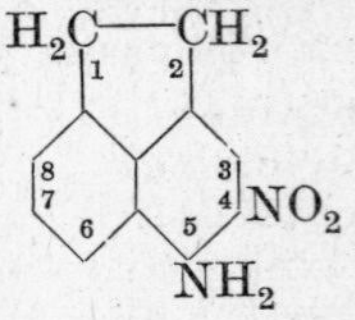

$C_{12}H_{10}O_2N_2$ MW, 214

Red prisms from EtOH. M.p. 222–4° (219°). Sol. 80 parts hot EtOH with greenish fluor. Sol. AcOH.

Formyl: yellow needles from AcOH. M.p. 227°. Sol. EtOH, $CHCl_3$.

Acetyl: golden-yellow needles from AcOH. M.p. 253° (251°). Sol. 60 parts hot EtOH. Spar. sol. other solvents. Conc. $H_2SO_4 \longrightarrow$ greenish-brown sol.

Benzoyl: pale yellow needles from AcOH. M.p. 233°.

Sachs, Mosebach, *Ber.*, 1911, **44**, 2857.

Morgan, Stanley, *J. Soc. Chem. Ind.*, 1924, **43**, 343T.

Nitroaminoacetanilide.

See under Nitrophenylenediamine.

3-Nitro-o-aminoacetophenone

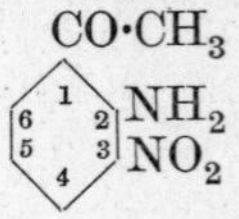

$C_8H_8O_3N_2$ MW, 180

Yellow needles from EtOH. M.p. 92·5°. Very sol. boiling EtOH. Sol. Et_2O, AcOEt. Spar. sol. cold H_2O. Volatile in steam. Conc. $H_2SO_4 + HCl \longrightarrow$ yellow sol.

Semicarbazone: golden-yellow prisms from AcOH. M.p. 223°.

Bamberger, *Ber.*, 1915, **48**, 562.

5-Nitro-*o*-aminoacetophenone.
Yellow needles from H_2O. M.p. 150–1 Very sol. boiling EtOH. Mod. sol. Et_2O. Spar. sol. H_2O. Non-volatile in steam.

See previous reference.

5-Nitro-*m*-aminoacetophenone

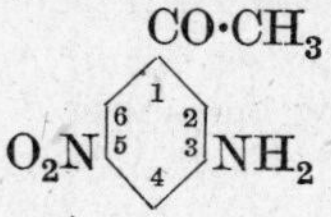

$C_8H_8O_3N_2$ MW, 180

Yellow needles from H_2O. M.p. 156–8°.

Berend, Heymann, *J. prakt. Chem.*, 1904, **69**, 471.

6-Nitro-*m*-aminoacetophenone.
N-*Di-Me*: $C_{10}H_{12}O_3N_2$. MW, 208. Yellow needles with steel-blue reflex from EtOH.Aq. M.p. 149–50°. Mod. sol. EtOH. Less sol. H_2O.

Rupe, Braun, v. Zembrzuski, *Ber.*, 1901, **34**, 3525.

3-Nitro-*p*-aminoacetophenone

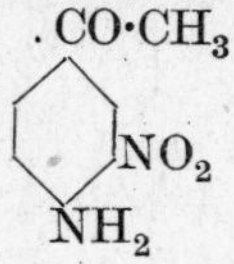

$C_8H_8O_3N_2$ MW, 180

Yellow needles from EtOH.Aq., reddish-brown cryst. from toluene. M.p. 153–4° (148–9°).
N-*Acetyl*: yellow needles from EtOH. M.p. 140–1° (137°).

Mayer, Stark, Schön, *Ber.*, 1932, **65**, 1335.
Gibson, Levin, *J. Chem. Soc.*, 1931, 2403.

2-Nitro-5-aminoacridine

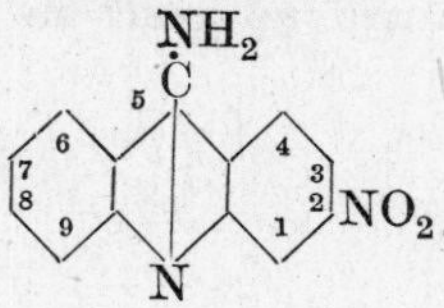

$C_{13}H_9O_2N_3$ MW, 239

Cryst. M.p. above 300° decomp.

M.L.B., D.R.P., 364,037, (*Chem. Zentr.*, 1923, II, 1251).
I.G., D.R.P., 304,280, (*Chem. Zentr.*, 1930, II, 626).

6-Nitro-3-aminoanisic Acid.
See under 6-Nitro-4-hydroxy-*m*-aminobenzoic Acid.

Nitroaminoanisole.
See Nitroanisidine.

2-Nitro-1-aminoanthraquinone

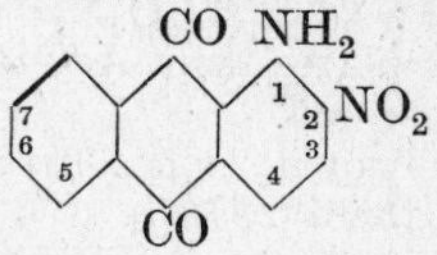

$C_{14}H_8O_4N_2$ MW, 268

Orange-red cryst. Sol. Py. Conc. $H_2SO_4 \longrightarrow$ yellow sol. $\longrightarrow$ violet-red on adding boric acid.
Urethane: cryst. Conc. $H_2SO_4 \longrightarrow$ yellow sol.

Drescher, Thomas, U.S.P., 1,528,470, (*Chem. Abstracts*, 1926, **20**, 425).
Bayer, D.R.P., 167,410, (*Chem. Zentr.*, 1906, I, 1065).

3-Nitro-1-aminoanthraquinone.
Dark red needles from EtOH. M.p. 265°.

Dhar, *J. Chem. Soc.*, 1920, **117**, 1003.

4-Nitro-1-aminoanthraquinone.
Yellowish-red needles from $PhNO_2$. M.p. 296°. Spar. sol. EtOH. Insol. H_2O. Conc. $H_2SO_4 \longrightarrow$ yellow sol.
N-*Me*: $C_{15}H_{10}O_4N_2$. MW, 282. Reddish-brown cryst. M.p. 250°. Sol. Me_2CO, Py. Spar. sol. EtOH, AcOH. N-*Acetyl*: orange prisms. Conc. $H_2SO_4 \longrightarrow$ yellow sol.
N-*Acetyl*: golden-yellow cryst. from AcOH or Py. M.p. 256–8°. Sol. AcOH, Py, aniline. Spar. sol. EtOH, Et_2O, ligroin. Insol. H_2O. Conc. $H_2SO_4 \longrightarrow$ yellow sol.
Urethane: cryst. from AcOH.

Bayer, D.R.P., 125,391, (*Chem. Zentr.*, 1901, II, 1219).
Noelting, Wortmann, *Ber.*, 1906, **39**, 643.

5-Nitro-1-aminoanthraquinone.
Red cryst. from EtOH. M.p. 293° decomp. Sol. AcOH, boiling toluene. Insol. Et_2O, ligroin.
N-*Me*: $C_{15}H_{10}O_4N_2$. MW, 282. Violet-black needles from AcOH. M.p. 250–2°. Very sol. $PhNO_2$. Sol. AcOH. Spar. sol. C_6H_6, EtOH.
N-*Acetyl*: yellow cryst. from chlorobenzene. M.p. 275°. Very sol. $PhNO_2$. Sol. hot $CHCl_3$. Spar. sol. C_6H_6, EtOH. Conc. $H_2SO_4 \longrightarrow$ yellow sol.
N-*Et*: $C_{16}H_{12}O_4N_2$. MW, 296. Black needles from AcOH. M.p. 238°. Very sol. $PhNO_2$. Sol. chlorobenzene. Spar. sol. EtOH, AcOH. N-*Acetyl*: orange-yellow plates from chlorobenzene. M.p. 242°. Very sol. $PhNO_2$. Sol. chlorobenzene. Spar. sol. EtOH, AcOH.

N-p-*Tolyl*: $C_{21}H_{14}O_4N_2$. MW, 358. Brownish-violet plates from AcOH. Cold conc. H_2SO_4 ⟶ yellowish-brown sol.

N-α-*Naphthyl*: $C_{24}H_{16}O_4N_2$. MW, 396. Brownish-violet plates from AcOH. Cold conc. H_2SO_4 ⟶ green col.

N-*Benzoyl*: brown cryst. from *o*-dichlorobenzene. M.p. 236·5–237°.

N-o-*Chlorobenzoyl*: yellowish-brown prisms. M.p. 265–6°.

N-m-*Methoxybenzoyl*: yellowish prisms. M.p. 199–200°.

N-*Anisoyl*: yellow needles. M.p. 255–6°.

Ullmann, Kertész, *Ber.*, 1919, **52,** 556.
M.L.B., D.R.P., 292,395, (*Chem. Zentr.*, 1916, II, 41).
Hefti, *Helv. Chim. Acta*, 1931, **14,** 1409.

7-Nitro-1-aminoanthraquinone.

N-p-*Tolyl*: $C_{21}H_{14}O_4N_2$. MW, 358. Violet-black needles from Me_2CO. Cold conc. H_2SO_4 ⟶ brownish-yellow sol. ⟶ reddish-brown on heating.

Bayer, D.R.P., 126,542, (*Chem. Zentr.*, 1901, II, 1373).

8-Nitro-1-aminoanthraquinone.

Red cryst. Fuming sulphuric acid (40% SO_3) ⟶ yellow sol.

N-*Me*: $C_{15}H_{10}O_4N_2$. MW, 282. Red needles from Py.

N-*Di-Me*: $C_{16}H_{12}O_4N_2$. MW, 296. Cryst. from Py. $CHCl_3$ ⟶ bluish-red sol. Conc. H_2SO_4 ⟶ colourless sol.

N-*Et*: $C_{16}H_{12}O_4N_2$. MW, 296. Brown needles with green reflex.

N-*Di-Et*: $C_{18}H_{16}O_4N_2$. MW, 324. Needles. $CHCl_3$ ⟶ bluish-red sol. Conc. H_2SO_4 ⟶ yellow sol. ⟶ violet on heating with boric acid.

N-*Phenyl*: 8-nitro-1-anilinoanthraquinone. $C_{20}H_{12}O_4N_2$. MW, 344. Bluish-violet needles from AcOH.

N-p-*Tolyl*: $C_{21}H_{14}O_4N_2$. MW, 358. Cryst. from AcOH. Sol. Me_2CO. Conc. H_2SO_4 ⟶ brown sol. ⟶ violet-blue on heating.

N-*Benzoyl*: brownish-green needles from *o*-dichlorobenzene. M.p. 266·5–267·5°.

N-o-*Chlorobenzoyl*: brownish-green prisms. M.p. 253–4°.

N-*Anisoyl*: brown prisms. M.p. 246·5–247·5°.

Bayer, D.R.P., 144,634, (*Chem. Zentr.*, 1903, II, 750); D.R.P., 147,851, (*Chem. Zentr.*, 1904, I, 132).
Hefti, *Helv. Chim. Acta*, 1931, **14,** 1410.

1-Nitro-2-aminoanthraquinone

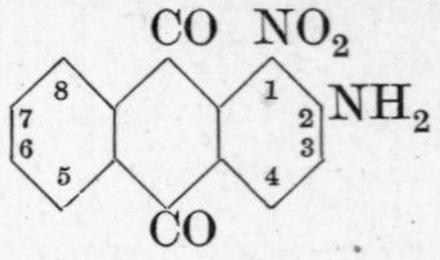

$C_{14}H_8O_4N_2$ MW, 268

Light green plates from AcOH or $PhNO_2$. M.p. 310°. Sol. Py, quinoline. Mod. sol. Me_2CO. Spar. sol. EtOH, Et_2O. Sol. 20 parts boiling $PhNO_2$. Conc. H_2SO_4 ⟶ yellow sol.

N-*Acetyl*: needles from AcOH. M.p. 277–8°. Sol. $PhNO_2$. Spar. sol. EtOH, AcOH. Insol. Et_2O. Conc. H_2SO_4 ⟶ green sol.

Urethane: cryst. from Me_2CO. M.p. 205°. Sol. boiling AcOH, toluene. Spar. sol. EtOH. Almost insol. Et_2O.

Ullmann, Medenwald, *Ber.*, 1913, **46,** 1806.
Chem. Fabr. Griesheim-Elektron, D.R.P., 259,432, (*Chem. Zentr.*, 1913, I, 1742).

3-Nitro-2-aminoanthraquinone.

Yellowish-brown cryst. from $PhNO_2$. M.p. 316–17° (305–6°). Sol. $PhNO_2$. Spar. sol. EtOH, C_6H_6, Py, xylene. Conc. H_2SO_4 ⟶ orange sol.

Urethane: cryst. from toluene. M.p. 225°. Sol. boiling AcOH, toluene. Spar. sol. EtOH. Insol. Et_2O.

See first reference above and also
Badische, D.R.P., 148,109, (*Chem. Zentr.*, 1904, I, 230).

5-Nitro-2-aminoanthraquinone.

Orange-red cryst. from $PhNO_2$. M.p. 274°. Mod. sol. $PhNO_2$, chlorobenzene. Less sol. AcOH.

Eckert, *Monatsh.*, 1914, **35,** 296.

3′-Nitro-4-aminoazobenzene

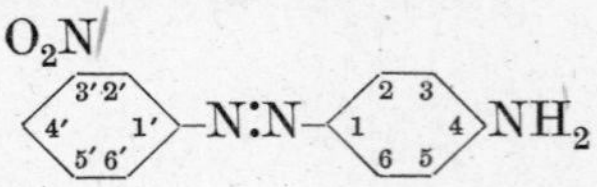

$C_{12}H_{10}O_2N_4$ MW, 242

Orange leaflets from EtOH.Aq. M.p. 212–13°. Sol. EtOH, Me_2CO, C_6H_6.

B_2,H_2PtCl_6: brick-red ppt. M.p. about 210° decomp.

Meldola, *J. Chem. Soc.*, 1884, **45,** 112.

4′-Nitro-4-aminoazobenzene.

Cryst. from toluene. M.p. 216° (203–5°). Spar. sol. cold EtOH.

N-*Me*: $C_{13}H_{12}O_2N_4$. MW, 256. Blue prisms

and needles from C_6H_6, plates from EtOH or AcOH. M.p. 206–7°. Boiling dil. HCl ⟶ red sol. Dichroic. N-*Acetyl*: orange-red needles. M.p. 194–5°.

N-*Acetyl*: orange-red needles. M.p. 245–6°.

Witt, Kopetschni, *Ber.*, 1912, **45**, 1148.

4-Nitro-*o*-aminobenzaldehyde

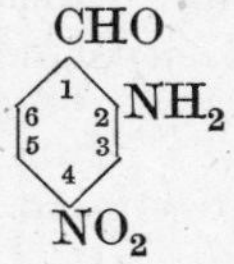

$C_7H_6O_3N_2$ MW, 166

Needles from hot H_2O. M.p. 124°. Slowly reduces $NH_3.AgNO_3$.

Oxime: light yellow cryst. from Me_2CO.Aq. M.p. 193°.

Semicarbazone: light yellow cryst. from AcOH. Decomp. at 390°.

Anil: red cryst. from hot EtOH. M.p. 147°.

Sachs, Sichel, *Ber.*, 1904, **37**, 1862.

5-Nitro-*o*-aminobenzaldehyde.

Yellow prisms from EtOH. M.p. 200·5°. Sol. hot H_2O.

N-*Di-Me*: $C_9H_{10}O_3N_2$. MW, 194. Yellow needles from ligroin. M.p. 105°. *Oxime*: m.p. 125°.

Oxime: yellow cryst. from EtOH. M.p. 203°.

N-*Acetyl*: needles from H_2O. M.p. 160–1°. Sol. H_2O, EtOH. *Oxime*: needles from EtOH. M.p. 239°.

N-p-*Toluenesulphonyl*: m.p. 181–2°.

Cohn, Springer, *Monatsh.*, 1903, **24**, 98.
General Aniline Works, U.S.P., 1,876,955, (*Chem. Abstracts*, 1933, **27**, 993).

6-Nitro-*m*-aminobenzaldehyde

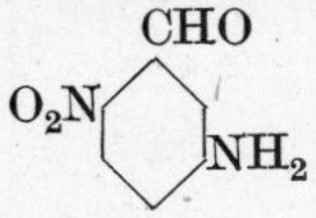

$C_7H_6O_3N_2$ MW, 166

Yellow needles from H_2O.

N-*Acetyl*: yellow needles from H_2O, EtOH.Aq., or xylene. M.p. 161°. *Oxime*: reddish-yellow needles. M.p. 189°. Sol. EtOH. *Phenylhydrazone*: red cryst. from Me_2CO. M.p. 247°. Sol. EtOH. Spar. sol. C_6H_6. Insol. H_2O.

Phenylhydrazone: red needles from EtOH.Aq. M.p. 212°.

Friedländer, Fritsch, *Monatsh.*, 1903, **24**, 8.

2-Nitro-*p*-aminobenzaldehyde

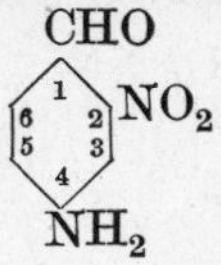

$C_7H_6O_3N_2$ MW, 166

Oxime: orange-yellow needles from 50% EtOH. M.p. 177–8°.

Semicarbazone: red cryst. from H_2O. Decomp. at 330°.

Phenylhydrazone: light red needles from EtOH. M.p. 163°.

Sachs, Kempf, *Ber.*, 1902, **35**, 1234, 2705.

3-Nitro-*p*-aminobenzaldehyde.

Yellow needles from H_2O. M.p. 190·5–191°. Sol. EtOH. Spar. sol. H_2O. Insol. Et_2O.

N-*Di-Me*: $C_9H_{10}O_3N_2$. MW, 194. Yellow needles from EtOH. M.p. 105°. Sol. EtOH, Et_2O, C_6H_6. Mod. sol. hot ligroin. Conc. H_2SO_4 ⟶ yellow sol. *Oxime*: orange prisms. M.p. 132°.

N-*Acetyl*: yellow needles from H_2O. M.p. 155°. Sol. warm EtOH, hot H_2O. Spar. sol. Et_2O. *Oxime*: yellow needles from EtOH. M.p. 206°. *Phenylhydrazone*: red cryst. from AcOH. M.p. 209°. p-*Nitrophenylhydrazone*: orange needles from EtOH. M.p. 289–90°.

Phenylhydrazone: reddish-brown plates. M.p. 202°.

Oxime: orange needles from EtOH.Aq. M.p. 207°. Dil. NaOH ⟶ deep red sol.

p-*Nitrophenylhydrazone*: dark maroon needles from AcOH. M.p. 270–2°.

Cohn, Springer, *Monatsh.*, 1903, **24**, 92.
Hodgson, Beard, *J. Chem. Soc.*, 1927, 23.

3′-Nitro-4-aminobenzhydrol

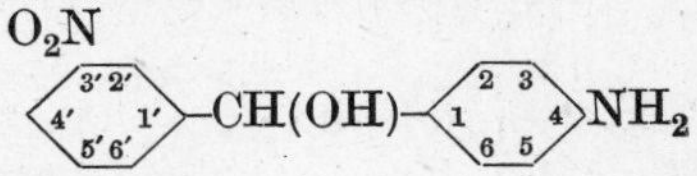

$C_{13}H_{12}O_3N_2$ MW, 244

N-*Di-Me*: $C_{15}H_{16}O_3N_2$. MW, 272. Yellow cryst. M.p. 74°. Sol. EtOH. Insol. H_2O.

N-*Di-Et*: $C_{17}H_{20}O_3N_2$. MW, 300. Yellow cryst. M.p. 65°. Sol. EtOH. Insol. H_2O.

Kalle, D.R.P., 45,806.

4′-Nitro-4-aminobenzhydrol.

Only known as polymer. M.p. about 240°. Sol. AcOH–HCl. Insol. EtOH, Et_2O, C_6H_6, AcOH.

N-*Me*: $C_{14}H_{14}O_3N_2$. MW, 258. Yellow

needles from 25% EtOH. M.p. 113° (108°). Sol. EtOH.

N-*Di-Me*: $C_{15}H_{16}O_3N_2$. MW, 272. Yellow needles from EtOH.Aq. M.p. 96°. Sol. most solvents. Insol. H_2O, ligroin. *Methiodide*: cryst. M.p. 175° decomp.

N-*Et*: $C_{15}H_{16}O_3N_2$. MW, 272. Yellow cryst. M.p. 99°. Sol. EtOH. Insol. H_2O.

N-*Di-Et*: $C_{17}H_{20}O_3N_2$. MW, 300. Yellow cryst. M.p. 92°. Sol. EtOH. Insol. H_2O.

Esselen, Clarke, *J. Am. Chem. Soc.*, 1914, **36**, 314.
Albrecht, *Ber.*, 1888, **21**, 3294.
Kalle, D.R.P., 119,461, (*Chem. Zentr.*, 1901, I, 866).
See also previous reference.

Nitro-*o*-aminobenzoic Acid.

See Nitroanthranilic Acid.

2-Nitro-*m*-aminobenzoic Acid

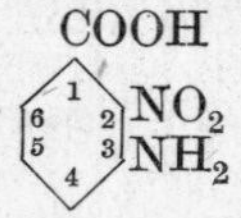

$C_7H_6O_4N_2$ MW, 182

Golden-yellow needles from H_2O or EtOH.Aq. M.p. 156–7°. Sol. hot H_2O, EtOH, Et_2O, AcOH. Insol. ligroin.

N-*Acetyl*: needles or plates. M.p. 240–1° decomp. Sol. EtOH, Me_2CO, AcOH.

Kaiser, *Ber.*, 1885, **18**, 2950.

4-Nitro-*m*-aminobenzoic Acid.

Red plates or needles from EtOH. M.p. 298° decomp. Sol. EtOH, Et_2O. Spar. sol. H_2O.

Et ester: $C_9H_{10}O_4N_2$. MW, 210. Red needles from EtOH or AcOH. M.p. 139°. Sol. EtOH, Et_2O, Me_2CO, $CHCl_3$, AcOH.

Amide: $C_7H_7O_3N_3$. MW, 181. Reddish-yellow needles from boiling H_2O. M.p. 231–2°. Sol. hot H_2O, EtOH, AcOH.

N-*Me*: $C_8H_8O_4N_2$. MW, 196. Red leaflets from EtOH. M.p. 268° decomp. *Methylamide*: $C_9H_{11}O_3N_3$. MW, 209. Needles from hot H_2O. M.p. 194°. Sol. hot H_2O, EtOH, AcOH. Spar. sol. Et_2O, C_6H_6.

N-*Acetyl*: yellow plates. M.p. 205–6°. Sol. boiling EtOH, Me_2CO, AcOH. Spar. sol. cold H_2O.

Thieme, *J. prakt. Chem.*, 1891, **43**, 464.
See also previous reference.

5-Nitro-*m*-aminobenzoic Acid.

Golden-yellow prisms from H_2O. M.p. 209–10° (208°). Very sol. hot AcOH. Sol. EtOH. Less sol. Et_2O, C_6H_6, CS_2. $k = 2{\cdot}1 \times 10^{-4}$ at 25°.

Me ester: $C_8H_8O_4N_2$. MW, 196. Yellow needles from H_2O, prisms from EtOH. M.p. 160°. Very sol. EtOH, Et_2O. Less sol. C_6H_6. N-*Acetyl*: cryst. M.p. 165–7°. N-*Benzoyl*: m.p. 178°.

Et ester: $C_9H_{10}O_4N_2$. MW, 210. Yellow needles from EtOH. M.p. 155°. Sol. EtOH. Spar. sol. H_2O. N-*Acetyl*: cryst. from EtOH.Aq. M.p. 168°. Very sol. pet. ether.

Hydrazide: reddish-yellow plates from H_2O. M.p. 221°. Sol. AcOH. Spar. sol. hot EtOH. Insol. Et_2O, C_6H_6, $CHCl_3$, ligroin. Reduces warm Fehling's and $NH_3.AgNO_3$.

N-*Et*: $C_9H_{10}O_4N_2$. MW, 210. Yellow needles from H_2O. M.p. 208°. Almost insol. H_2O.

Hübner, *Ann.*, 1884, **222**, 81.
Curtius, Riedel, *J. prakt. Chem.*, 1907, **76**, 255.
Cohen, McCandlish, *J. Chem. Soc.*, 1905, **87**, 1267.

6-Nitro-*m*-aminobenzoic Acid.

Yellow needles or prisms from H_2O. M.p. 235° decomp. Sol. EtOH. Spar. sol. hot H_2O, Et_2O.

Et ester: $C_9H_{10}O_4N_2$. MW, 210. Yellow cryst. from EtOH.Aq. M.p. 107·5°.

N-*Acetyl*: brownish-red cryst. from H_2O, needles from AcOH. M.p. 225°. Sol. most org. solvents.

Hydrazide: yellow prisms from EtOH. Sol. H_2O, AcOH. Mod. sol. EtOH. Almost insol. Et_2O.

Hewitt, Mitchell, *J. Chem. Soc.*, 1907, **91**, 1258.
Kalb, Gross, *Ber.*, 1926, **59**, 736.

2-Nitro-*p*-aminobenzoic Acid

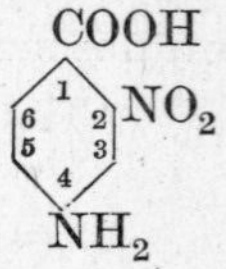

$C_7H_6O_4N_2$ MW, 182

Red needles from hot H_2O. M.p. 255° (234–5°). Sol. EtOH, AcOH. Spar. sol. cold H_2O. Sweet taste.

Me ester: $C_8H_8O_4N_2$. MW, 196. Light brown prisms from EtOH.Aq. M.p. 157–159·5°. N-*Acetyl*: needles from H_2O. M.p. 76°. N-*Benzoyl*: needles from C_6H_6. M.p. 93–4°.

Et ester: $C_9H_{10}O_4N_2$. MW, 210. Pale yellow needles from hot H_2O. M.p. 130°. Sol. EtOH, Et_2O.

Anilide: needles from hot H_2O. M.p. 226°.

Spar. sol. H_2O, EtOH, Et_2O. N-*Acetyl*: yellow needles from H_2O. M.p. 238°.

Hydrazide: golden-yellow plates from hot H_2O. M.p. 212°. Sol. EtOH. Spar. sol. AcOH. Insol. C_6H_6, $CHCl_3$, Et_2O, ligroin. Reduces warm Fehling's and $NH_3.AgNO_3$.

N-*Acetyl*: light yellow needles from EtOH. M.p. 219°.

Bogert, Kropff, *J. Am. Chem. Soc.*, 1909, **31**, 847.
Curtius, Bollenbach, *J. prakt. Chem.*, 1907, **76**, 288.
Cohen, McCandlish, *J. Chem. Soc.*, 1905, **87**, 1268.
Höchst, D.R.P., 204,884, (*Chem. Zentr.*, 1909, I, 474).

3-Nitro-*p*-aminobenzoic Acid.

Reddish-yellow needles from EtOH. M.p. 284°. Spar. sol. hot EtOH.

Me ester: $C_8H_8O_4N_2$. MW, 196. Yellow cryst. from Me_2CO.Aq. M.p. 199·5–200°.

Et ester: $C_9H_{10}O_4N_2$. MW, 210. Yellow needles from EtOH. M.p. 145°. Sol. usual org. solvents. N-*Acetyl*: m.p. 96–7°. N-*Chloroacetyl*: yellow needles from EtOH or C_6H_6–pet. ether. M.p. 102°.

Amide: $C_7H_7O_3N_3$. MW, 181. Yellow needles from EtOH. M.p. 227°. Sol. Me_2CO. Spar. sol. hot EtOH. Insol. C_6H_6, $CHCl_3$, pet. ether. N-*Acetyl*: yellow needles from EtOH. M.p. 239·5° (sealed tube). Sol. boiling H_2O, EtOH. Spar. sol. $CHCl_3$. Insol. Et_2O, C_6H_6. Sublimes.

Nitrile: $C_7H_5O_2N_3$. MW, 163. Yellow needles. M.p. 159–60°. Sol. hot H_2O, EtOH. Less sol. Me_2CO, C_6H_6. N-*Acetyl*: light yellow needles from EtOH. M.p. 131·5°. Sol. H_2O, EtOH. Less sol. C_6H_6. Insol. CCl_4.

Anilide: red needles from EtOH. M.p. 215–16°. Sol. EtOH, Me_2CO, C_6H_6, $CHCl_3$, AcOH. Insol. pet. ether.

N-*Me*: *see* 3-Nitro-*p*-methylaminobenzoic Acid.

N-*Di-Me*: *see* 3-Nitro-*p*-dimethylaminobenzoic Acid.

N-*Et*: $C_9H_{10}O_4N_2$. MW, 210. Golden-yellow needles from H_2O, EtOH or ligroin. M.p. 239–40°. *Et ester*: $C_{11}H_{14}O_4N_2$. MW, 238. Yellow needles. M.p. 92°. Sol. EtOH, AcOH. Insol. H_2O.

N-*Di-Et*: $C_{11}H_{14}O_4N_2$. MW, 238. Reddish-yellow needles from ligroin. M.p. 117°.

N-*Phenyl*: *see* 2-Nitrodiphenylamine-4-carboxylic acid.

N-o-*Tolyl*: *see* 2-Nitro-2′-methyldiphenylamine-4-carboxylic acid.

N-p-*Tolyl*: *see* 2-Nitro-4′-methyldiphenylamine-4-carboxylic acid.

N-α-*Naphthyl*: $C_{17}H_{12}O_4N_2$. MW, 308. Reddish-brown powder. Sol. usual solvents. *Et ester*: $C_{19}H_{16}O_4N_2$. MW, 336. Reddish-brown plates from EtOH.Aq. M.p. 109°. Sol. EtOH, C_6H_6, $CHCl_3$, AcOH.

N-β-*Naphthyl*: $C_{17}H_{12}O_4N_2$. MW, 308. Dark red powder. Sol. EtOH, Me_2CO, AcOH. Less sol. C_6H_6, $CHCl_3$. *Et ester*: $C_{19}H_{16}O_4N_2$. MW, 336. Light yellow needles from EtOH. M.p. 127·5°. Sol. EtOH, Me_2CO, AcOH, $CHCl_3$.

N-*Formyl*: needles from EtOH. M.p. 221° decomp. Mod. sol. EtOH. Insol. H_2O.

N-*Acetyl*: yellow plates. M.p. 220–1°. Sol. boiling EtOH, Me_2CO, AcOH. Spar. sol. cold H_2O.

Borsche, Stackmann, Makaroff-Semljanski, *Ber.*, 1916, **49**, 2232.
Bogert, Wise, *J. Am. Chem. Soc.*, 1910, **32**, 1497.
Thieme, *J. prakt. Chem.*, 1891, **43**, 456.
Reverdin, de Luc, *Ber.*, 1909, **42**, 1726.

5-Nitro-2-aminobenzophenone

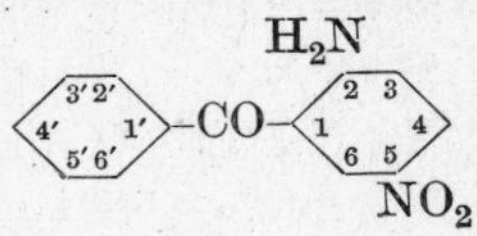

$C_{13}H_{10}O_3N_2$ MW, 242

Yellowish-red prisms with blue reflex. M.p. 161·5°. Sol. EtOH, AcOH.

N-*Phenyl*: $C_{19}H_{14}O_3N_2$. MW, 318. Yellow leaflets from EtOH. M.p. 155°. Sol. EtOH, Et_2O, C_6H_6. Spar. sol. ligroin.

N-o-*Methoxyphenyl*: $C_{20}H_{16}O_4N_2$. MW, 348. Pale yellow needles or greenish-yellow leaflets from EtOH. M.p. 139°.

Ullmann, Mallet, *Ber.*, 1898, **31**, 1695.
Ullmann, Ernst, *Ber.*, 1906, **39**, 300.

2′-Nitro-2-aminobenzophenone.

Brownish-yellow needles from EtOH. M.p. 149–50°.

Heyl, *Ber.*, 1898, **31**, 3033.

5-Nitro-3-aminobenzophenone.

Exists in two forms.

(i) Orange needles from EtOH.Aq., plates from C_6H_6. M.p. 130°.

(ii) Cryst. from EtOH. M.p. 146°.

Diacetyl: pale yellow needles from EtOH.Aq. M.p. 191°.

Waters, *J. Chem. Soc.*, 1929, 2110.

3-Nitro-4-aminobenzophenone.

Yellow needles from EtOH. M.p. 140·5°. (135°). Sol. AcOH, $CHCl_3$, Py. Spar. sol. EtOH, Me_2CO, C_6H_6. Insol. H_2O, Et_2O, CS_2.

N-*Di-Me*: $C_{15}H_{14}O_3N_2$. MW, 270. Golden-yellow cryst. from EtOH. M.p. 116°. Spar. sol. ligroin.

N-*Et*: $C_{15}H_{14}O_3N_2$. MW, 270. Yellow needles. M.p. 99–100°.

N-*Phenyl*: $C_{19}H_{14}O_3N_2$. MW, 318. Orange needles. M.p. 157°.

N-*Acetyl*: pale yellow needles from EtOH. Spar. sol. EtOH, Et_2O. Mod. sol. C_6H_6.

N-*Benzoyl*: plates from Me_2CO. M.p. 154–5°. Sol. C_6H_6, CS_2. Mod. sol. Me_2CO. Spar. sol. EtOH, ligroin. Insol. H_2O.

Schöpff, *Ber.*, 1891, **24**, 3772.
Maron, Fox, *Ber.*, 1914, **47**, 2778.

3′-Nitro-4-aminobenzophenone.

N-*Di-Me*: $C_{15}H_{14}O_3N_2$. MW, 270. Yellow cryst. M.p. 173°. Spar. sol. EtOH.

Höchst, D.R.P., 42,853.

4-Nitro-2-aminobenzthiazole (3-*Nitro*-1-*aminobenzthiazole*)

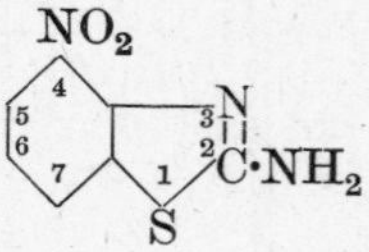

$C_7H_5O_2N_3S$ MW, 195

Yellow plates from EtOH–AcOEt. M.p. 233° decomp.

Dyson, Hunter, Morris, *J. Chem. Soc.*, 1927, 1192.

6-Nitro-2-aminobenzthiazole (5-*Nitro*-1-*aminobenzthiazole*).

Orange, microcryst. powder from AcOEt. M.p. 243°.

Acetyl: pale yellow cryst. powder. M.p. 292°.

Hunter, Jones, *J. Chem. Soc.*, 1930, 2203.

2-(or 4)-Nitro-3-aminocarbazole

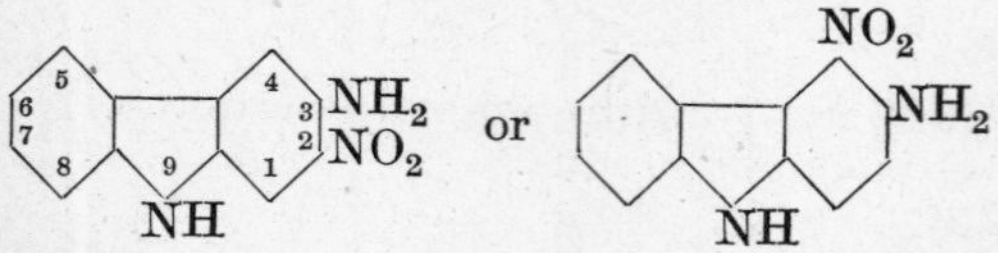

$C_{12}H_9O_2N_3$ MW, 227

Dark violet needles from EtOH. M.p. 233°. Sol. EtOH, Et_2O, C_6H_6, AcOH.

3-N-*Acetyl*: red needles from EtOH. M.p. 274°. Sol. hot EtOH. Insol. H_2O.

Diacetyl: greenish-yellow cryst. from AcOH. M.p. 226°. Sol. hot AcOH, C_6H_6. Insol. H_2O.

Kehrmann, Zweifel, *Helv. Chim. Acta*, 1928, **11**, 1213.

4-(or 2)-Nitro-3-aminocarbazole.

Dark reddish-brown needles from EtOH. M.p. 177°. Sol. hot EtOH, C_6H_6. Insol. H_2O.

3-N-*Acetyl*: reddish-brown needles. M.p. 198°. Sol. EtOH, AcOH, Et_2O, C_6H_6. Insol. H_2O.

See previous reference.

3-Nitro-5-aminocarvacrol

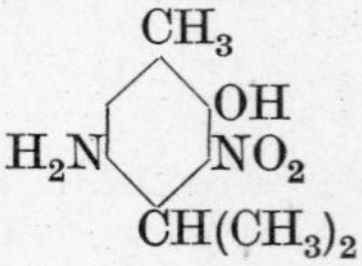

$C_{10}H_{14}O_3N_2$ MW, 210

Yellow cryst. from EtOH. M.p. 134–5°.

O-*Benzoyl*: cryst. M.p. about 280–3°.

O : N-*Diacetyl*: needles from C_6H_6. M.p. 222–5°.

Soderi, *Gazz. chim. ital.*, 1895, **25**, ii, 406.

5-Nitro-3-aminocatechol

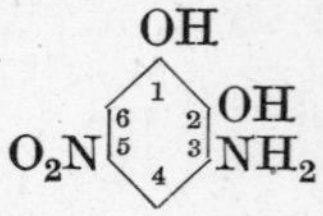

$C_6H_6O_4N_2$ MW, 170

1 - *Me ether*: 5 - nitro - 3 - aminoguaiacol. $C_7H_8O_4N_2$. MW, 184. Brown needles from H_2O. M.p. 182° decomp. N-*Acetyl*: needles + H_2O from H_2O. M.p. 224–6° decomp. O : N-*Diacetyl*: needles from H_2O. M.p. 204° decomp.

1 : 2-*Di-Me ether*: 5-nitro-3-aminoveratrol. $C_8H_{10}O_4N_2$. MW, 198. Brown needles from MeOH.Aq. M.p. 105–6°. Sol. most org. solvents. Spar. sol. cold H_2O. N-*Acetyl*: yellowish plates from EtOH. M.p. 172–3°. N-*Benzoyl*: needles from AcOH. M.p. 145–6°.

Meldola, Woolcott, Wray, *J. Chem. Soc.*, 1896, **69**, 1331.
Gibson, Simonsen, Rau, *J. Chem. Soc.*, 1917, **111**, 75.

3-Nitro-4-aminocatechol.

2 - *Me ether*: 6 - nitro - 5 - aminoguaiacol. $C_7H_8O_4N_2$. MW, 184. Light red needles from C_6H_6 or H_2O. M.p. 169–71°. N-*Acetyl*: orange-red cryst. from EtOH. M.p. 223°. O : N-*Diacetyl*: yellow plates or needles from H_2O or EtOH. M.p. 158°. O : N-*Dibenzoyl*: yellow needles from EtOH. M.p. 177°.

1 : 2-*Di-Me ether*: 3-nitro-4-aminoveratrol.

$C_8H_{10}O_4N_2$. MW, 198. Red needles from EtOH.Aq. M.p. 74°. Spar. sol. pet. ether. Dichroic.

Fichter, Schwab, *Ber.*, 1906, **39**, 3340.
Pisovschi, *Ber.*, 1910, **43**, 2142.

5-Nitro-4-aminocatechol.

1 : 2-*Di-Me ether* : 5-nitro-4-aminoveratrol. $C_8H_{10}O_4N_2$. MW, 198. Orange prisms or needles from EtOH. M.p. 175° (171°). Sol. hot EtOH, Me_2CO, hot AcOEt. Spar. sol. C_6H_6, $CHCl_3$. Sol. conc. min. acids. N-*Acetyl* : yellow needles from EtOH. M.p. 199° (196°). Spar. sol. EtOH, AcOH. Insol. H_2O. N-*Benzoyl*: yellow needles from EtOH. M.p. 153–4°.

Simonsen, Rau, *J. Chem. Soc.*, 1918, **113**, 27.
Jones, Robinson, *J. Chem. Soc.*, 1917, **111**, 914.

6-Nitro-4-aminocatechol.

Yellowish-orange needles from H_2O. M.p. 228°. Sol. EtOH.

O : O : N-*Triacetyl* : needles from AcOH. M.p. 207°. Sol. EtOH, AcOEt. Spar. sol. C_6H_6.

Meldola, Woolcott, Wray, *J. Chem. Soc.*, 1896, **69**, 1334.
Heller, Lindner, Georgi, *Ber.*, 1923, **56**, 1872.

3-Nitro-*o*-aminocinnamic Acid

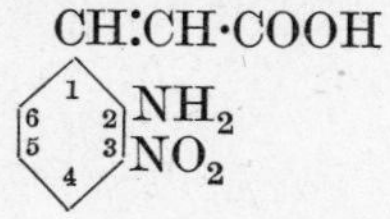

$C_9H_8O_4N_2$ MW, 208

Amide : $C_9H_9O_3N_3$. MW, 207. Cryst. in plates. Heat with HCl in sealed tube to 140° ⟶ 8-nitrocarbostyril.

v. Miller, Kinkeln, *Ber.*, 1889, **22**, 1711.

4-Nitro-*o*-aminocinnamic Acid.

Light reddish-brown needles. M.p. 240°. Sol. EtOH, Me_2CO. Spar. sol. H_2O. Insol. Et_2O, C_6H_6, ligroin. With HCl in sealed tube at 150° ⟶ 7-nitrocarbostyril.

Et ester : $C_{11}H_{12}O_4N_2$. MW, 236. Dark reddish-brown needles. M.p. 158–60°.

Friedländer, Lazarus, *Ann.*, 1885, **229**, 242.

3-Nitro-*p*-aminocinnamic Acid

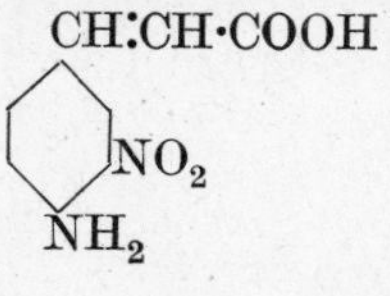

$C_9H_8O_4N_2$ MW, 208

Red needles from H_2O. M.p. 224·5° (218°). Sol. EtOH, AcOH. Mod. sol. H_2O. Prac. insol. C_6H_6, ligroin.

N-*Acetyl* : yellow cryst. M.p. 261–6°.

Gabriel, Herzberg, *Ber.*, 1883, **16**, 2042.
Cohn, Springer, *Monatsh.*, 1903, **24**, 94.

4-Nitro-3-amino-*o*-cresol

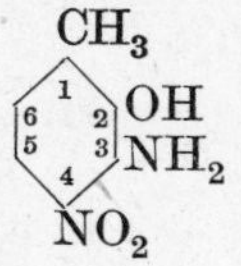

$C_7H_8O_3N_2$ MW, 168

Me ether : $C_8H_{10}O_3N_2$. MW, 182. Needles from MeOH. M.p. 72°. Sol. most org. solvents. Volatile in steam. N-*Acetyl* : prisms from H_2O. M.p. 170–1°. Sol. H_2O.

Simonsen, Nayak, *J. Chem. Soc.*, 1915, **107**, 831.

5-Nitro-3-amino-*o*-cresol.

Reddish-brown needles from C_6H_6. M.p. 165° decomp.

Me ether : yellow needles from MeOH. M.p. 113°. N-*Acetyl* : needles + H_2O. M.p. anhyd. 141–2°.

Cazeneuve, *Bull. soc. chim.*, 1897, **17**, 206.
Bovini, *Chem. Abstracts*, 1928, **22**, 1578.
See also previous reference.

6-Nitro-3-amino-*o*-cresol.

Me ether : yellowish cryst. from MeOH. M.p. 103°. Sol. most org. solvents. N-*Acetyl* : needles from EtOH.Aq. M.p. 119–20°.

Simonsen, Nayak, *J. Chem. Soc.*, 1915, **107**, 830.

3-Nitro-5-amino-*o*-cresol.

Reddish-brown needles from EtOH. M.p. 118°.

N-*Acetyl* : yellow needles from EtOH. M.p. 217°.

Nietzki, Ruppert, *Ber.*, 1890, **23**, 3477.

2-Nitro-6-amino-*m*-cresol

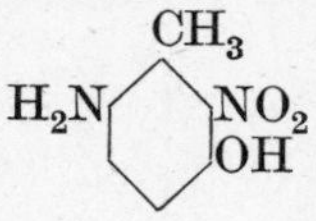

$C_7H_8O_3N_2$ MW, 168

Reddish-brown needles from EtOH. M.p. 201°. Sol. dil. acids and alkalis.

O : N-*Diacetyl* : needles. M.p. 127–8°.

Cohen, Marshall, *J. Chem. Soc.*, 1904, **85**, 527.
Brand, Zöller, *Ber.*, 1907, **40**, 3332.

5-Nitro-3-amino-*p*-cresol

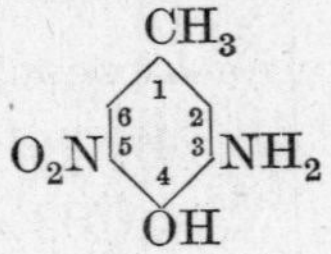

$C_7H_8O_3N_2$ MW, 168

Reddish-brown cryst. from EtOH. M.p. 119° (110°).

N-*Acetyl* : yellow cryst. from EtOH. M.p. 143°.

Kehrmann, Winkelmann, *Ber.*, 1907, **40**, 618.
Lindemann, Romanoff, *J. prakt. Chem.*, 1929, **122**, 229.

6-Nitro-3-amino-*p*-cresol.

Yellow cryst. from EtOH. M.p. 199–200° decomp.

Me ether : 6-nitrocresidine. $C_8H_{10}O_3N_2$. MW, 182. Yellow needles. M.p. 132°. N-*Acetyl* : needles from EtOH.Aq. M.p. 156°.

N-*Acetyl* : needles from AcOH. M.p. 242°.

Baranger, *Bull. soc. chim.*, 1931, **49**, 1215.
Limpach, *Ber.*, 1889, **22**, 790.
Bloxam, E.P., 168,681, (*Chem. Abstracts*, 1922, **16**, 500).

Nitroamino-*N*-diethylaniline.

See under Nitrophenylenediamine.

Nitroamino-*N*-dimethylaniline.

See under Nitrophenylenediamine.

3-Nitro-5-amino-2 : 4-dimethylbenzoic Acid

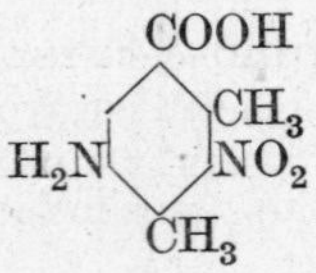

$C_9H_{10}O_4N_2$ MW, 210

Pale yellow prisms from EtOH. M.p. 251° decomp. Spar. sol. H_2O.

B,HCl : prisms. M.p. 250° decomp.

Acetyl : needles. M.p. 247°. Sol. hot EtOH. Mod. sol. H_2O.

Wheeler, Hoffmann, *Am. Chem. J.*, 1911, **45**, 440.

Nitroamino-3 : 5-dimethylbenzoic Acid.

See Nitroaminomesitylenic Acid.

4-Nitro-6-amino-2 : 3-dimethyldiphenylamine.

See under 5-Nitro-2 : 3-diamino-*p*-xylene.

3-Nitro-2-aminodiphenyl

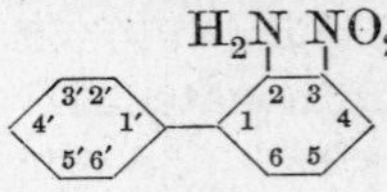

$C_{12}H_{10}O_2N_2$ MW, 214

M.p. 44–5°.

N-*Acetyl* : m.p. 188°.

Sako, *Bull. Chem. Soc. Japan*, 1934, **9**, 55

5-Nitro-2-aminodiphenyl.

Yellow needles from EtOH. M.p. 125°.

N-*Acetyl* : orange needles from EtOH. M.p. 133°.

N-p-*Toluenesulphonyl* : pale yellow needles from AcOH. M.p. 169°.

See previous reference and also
Bell, *J. Chem. Soc.*, 1928, 2774.

2′-Nitro-2-aminodiphenyl.

Free base not obtained pure.

N-*Acetyl* : cryst. from C_6H_6, m.p. 158° cryst. from EtOH.Aq., m.p. 151–2°.

N-*Diacetyl* : yellow needles. M.p. 120–1 (125°).

Picrate : m.p. 167·5°.

Mascarelli, Gatti, Pirona, *Gazz. chim. ital* 1931, **61**, 786.
Mascarelli, Gatti, *Atti accad. Lincei*, 1929 **10**, 441 ; *Gazz. chim. ital.*, 1929, **59**, 861

4′-Nitro-2-aminodiphenyl.

Orange-red needles from EtOH. M.p. 159°.

N-*Acetyl* : yellow needles from EtOH. M.p 199°.

N-p-*Toluenesulphonyl* : pale yellow needle from AcOH. M.p. 163°.

Finzi, Bellavito, *Gazz. chim. ital.*, 1934 **64**, 343.
Scarborough, Waters, *J. Chem. Soc* 1927, 96.
Bell, *J. Chem. Soc.*, 1928, 2775.

4-Nitro-3-aminodiphenyl

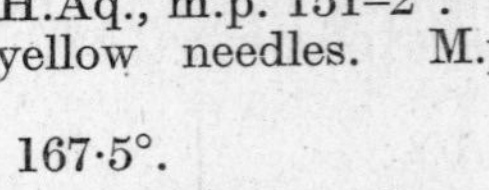

$C_{12}H_{10}O_2N_2$ MW, 21

Orange needles from dil. EtOH. M.p. 116°.

N-*Acetyl* : yellow needles from EtOH. M.p 115°.

Blakey, Scarborough, *J. Chem. Soc.*, 192 3008.

3′-Nitro-3-aminodiphenyl.

Not obtained pure. M.p. 115–40°.

B,HCl : m.p. 275–6° decomp.

N-*Acetyl* : m.p. 156–7°.

Mascarelli, Gatti, *Gazz. chim. ital.*, 1929, **59**, 863; 1931, **61**, 322.

4′-Nitro-3-aminodiphenyl.

Orange needles from EtOH. M.p. 137°. $CrO_3 \longrightarrow$ *p*-nitrobenzoic acid.

N-*Acetyl* : yellow needles from EtOH. M.p. 192°.

Blakey, Scarborough, *J. Chem. Soc.*, 1927, 3009.

3-Nitro-4-aminodiphenyl (3-*Nitroxenylamine*)

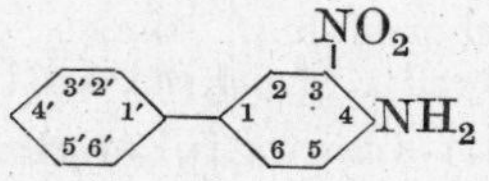

$C_{12}H_{10}O_2N_2$ MW, 214

Red needles from EtOH. M.p. 167° (168–70°).

N-*Acetyl* : yellow needles from EtOH. M.p. 132°.

N-*Benzoyl* : needles from AcOH. M.p. 143°.

N-*Me* : red cryst. M.p. 112–13°.

Fichter, Sulzberger, *Ber.*, 1904, **37**, 881.
Banús, Tomás, *Anales soc. españ fís. quím.*, 1921, **19**, 293.

2′-Nitro-4-aminodiphenyl (2′-*Nitroxenylamine*).

Red prisms from EtOH. M.p. 99°. Sol. EtOH. Prac. insol. H_2O.

Finzi, Bellavito, *Gazz. chim. ital.*, 1934, **64**, 342.
Schultz, *Ann.*, 1874, **174**, 225.
Schultz, Schmidt, Strasser, *Ann.*, 1881, **207**, 350.

3′-Nitro-4-aminodiphenyl (3′-*Nitroxenylamine*).

Red prisms. M.p. 127°.

Finzi, Mangini, *Gazz. chim. ital.*, 1932, **62**, 676.

4′-Nitro-4-aminodiphenyl (4′-*Nitroxenylamine*).

Red needles from EtOH. M.p. 200–1° (198°). Sol. hot EtOH. Prac. insol. hot H_2O. $CrO_3 \longrightarrow$ *p*-nitrobenzoic acid.

N-*Acetyl* : yellow needles. M.p. 264° (240°).

N-*Benzenesulphonyl* : yellow plates from dil. EtOH. M.p. 174°.

Willstätter, Kalb, *Ber.*, 1906, **39**, 3479.
Schmidt, Schultz, *Ann.*, 1881, **207**, 347.
Codolosa, *Chem. Abstracts*, 1934, **28**, 3068.
Guglialmelli, Franco, *Chem. Abstracts*, 1931, **25**, 4252.

4-Nitro-2-aminodiphenylamine

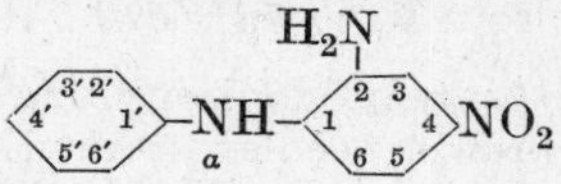

$C_{12}H_{11}O_2N_3$ MW, 229

Red needles + H_2O from H_2O. M.p. 134° (125°). Sol. EtOH, AcOH. Mod. sol. C_6H_6.

α-N-*Me deriv.* : $C_{13}H_{11}O_2N_3$. MW, 243. Red cryst. M.p. 76°. Sol. usual org. solvents.

Ullmann, *Ann.*, 1904, **332**, 98.
Nietzki, Almenräder, *Ber.*, 1895, **28**, 2971.
Lindemann, *Ber.*, 1924, **57**, 559.

6-Nitro-2-aminodiphenylamine.

Dark red cryst. from EtOH. M.p. 101°.

Borsche, Rantscheff, *Ann.*, 1911, **379**, 168.

2′-Nitro-2-aminodiphenylamine.

Yellowish-red needles from H_2O. M.p. 103°.

Kehrmann, Steiner, *Ber.*, 1901, **34**, 3091.

4′-Nitro-2-aminodiphenylamine.

Reddish-brown needles with blue lustre from EtOH.Aq. M.p. 144°. Sol. EtOH. Spar. sol. C_6H_6, Et_2O.

Ullmann, Dahmen, *Ber.*, 1908, **41**, 3755.

2′-Nitro-3-aminodiphenylamine

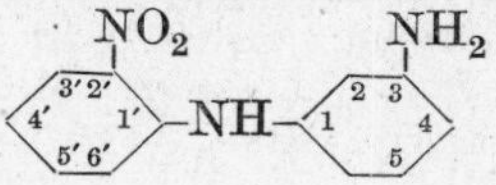

$C_{12}H_{11}O_2N_3$ MW, 229

Reddish needles from EtOH. M.p. 112°. Sol. EtOH, Et_2O, C_6H_6, AcOH. Spar. sol. H_2O.

Kehrmann, Steiner, *Ber.*, 1901, **34**, 3090.

4′-Nitro-3-aminodiphenylamine.

Yellowish-brown plates from EtOH.Aq. M.p. 156°. Sol. EtOH, Me_2CO. Spar. sol. C_6H_6. Insol. ligroin.

Ullmann, Dahmen, *Ber.*, 1908, **41**, 3754.

2-Nitro-4-aminodiphenylamine

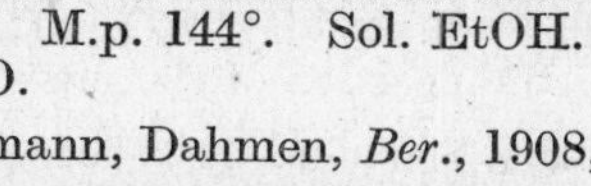

$C_{12}H_{11}O_2N_3$ MW, 229

α-N-*Et deriv.*: $C_{14}H_{15}O_2N_3$. MW, 257. Cryst. M.p. 86°. *B,HCl*: orange leaflets from EtOH. M.p. 183–5° decomp.

Storrie, Tucker, *J. Chem. Soc.*, 1931, 2258.

2′-Nitro-4-aminodiphenylamine.
Cryst. M.p. 105–6°. Sol. hot EtOH.

Bandrowski, *Chem. Zentr.*, 1900, II, 852.

4′-Nitro-4-aminodiphenylamine.
Reddish-brown needles from EtOH. M.p. 211–12° (205°). Sol. EtOH, Me_2CO. Spar. sol. C_6H_6, Et_2O. Insol. ligroin.

Morgan, Micklethwait, *J. Chem. Soc.*, 1908, **93**, 611.
Ullmann, Dahmen, *Ber.*, 1908, **41**, 3753.
Ullmann, D.R.P., 193,448, (*Chem. Zentr.*, 1908, I, 1003).

3-(?)-Nitro-2-aminodiphenylene oxide

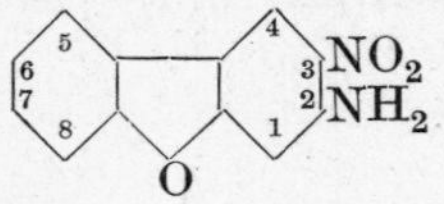

$C_{12}H_8O_3N_2$ MW, 228

Orange-red needles with green reflex from $PhNO_2$ or toluene. M.p. 222°. Conc. H_2SO_4 ⟶ light yellow sol. Mod. sol. Me_2CO, C_6H_6, AcOH. Spar. sol. EtOH, Et_2O. There is some doubt as to the position of the nitro group.

Borsche, Schacke, *Ber.*, 1923, **56**, 2504.

6-Nitro-2-aminodiphenylene oxide.
Yellowish-orange needles from Me_2CO–EtOH. M.p. 268°. Sol. hot AcOH, Me_2CO. Slightly sol. EtOH, C_6H_6, $CHCl_3$.

Cullinane, *J. Chem. Soc.*, 1932, 2367.

4-Nitro-2-aminodiphenyl Ether

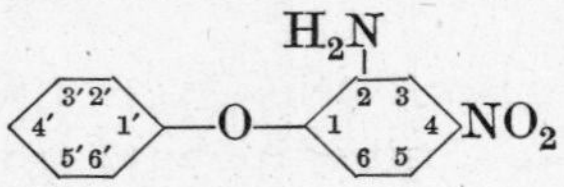

$C_{12}H_{10}O_3N_2$ MW, 230

Red cryst. from EtOH. M.p. 107°.
N-*Acetyl*: m.p. 118°.

Brewster, Strain, *J. Am. Chem. Soc.*, 1934, **56**, 118.
Ryan, Keane, M'Gahon, *Chem. Abstracts*, 1928, **22**, 70.

5-Nitro-2-aminodiphenyl Ether.
Yellow plates from dil. MeOH. M.p. 116°.
N-*Acetyl*: yellow cryst. from MeOH. M.p. 180°.

McCombie, Macmillan, Scarborough, *J. Chem. Soc.*, 1931, 531.
Bayer, D.R.P., 228,763, (*Chem. Zentr.*, 1911, I, 105).

2′-Nitro-2-aminodiphenyl Ether.
Yellow needles from EtOH. M.p. 56°.

Cullinane, Davey, Padfield, *J. Chem. Soc.*, 1934, 719.

3-Nitro-4-aminodiphenyl Ether.
Red prisms from dil. MeOH. M.p. 82°.
N-*Acetyl*: yellow needles from EtOH. M.p. 104° (100°).

Brewster, Strain, *J. Am. Chem. Soc.*, 1934, **56**, 118.
Scarborough, *J. Chem. Soc.*, 1929, 2366.
Oesterlin, *Monatsh.*, 1931, **57**, 38.

3-Nitro-4-aminodiphenylmethane

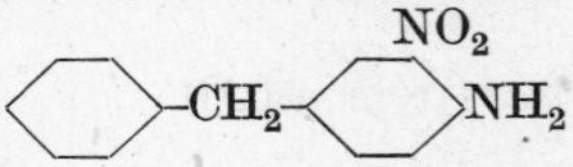

$C_{13}H_{12}O_2N_2$ MW, 228

Orange plates from MeOH, needles from dil. MeOH. M.p. 78°. Br in AcOH ⟶ 5-bromo-3-nitro-4-aminodiphenylmethane.
N-*Acetyl*: yellow plates from dil. MeOH. M.p. 99°.

Waters, *J. Chem. Soc.*, 1935, 1875.

4′-Nitro-4-aminodiphenyl sulphide

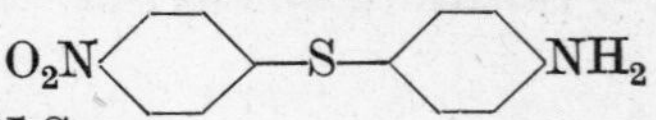

$C_{12}H_{10}O_2N_2S$ MW, 246

Orange prisms with blue reflex from C_6H_6. M.p. 143°. Sol. usual org. solvents. Insol. H_2O.

Kehrmann, Bauer, *Ber.*, 1896, **29**, 2362.
Fromm, Wittmann, *Ber.*, 1908, **41**, 2264.

6′-Nitro-6-amino-2 : 2′-ditolyl (6′-*Nitro-6-amino-*2 : 2′-*dimethyldiphenyl*)

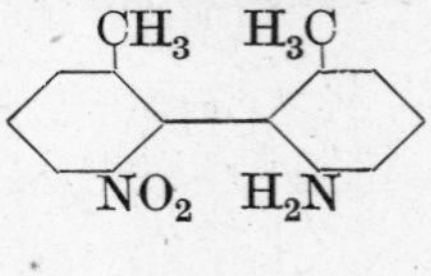

$C_{14}H_{14}O_2N_2$ MW, 242

d-.
M.p. 122–3°. $[\alpha]_D^{20}$ + 40°.
d-*Tartrate*: m.p. 141°.

l-.
Yellowish leaflets. M.p. 122–3°. $[\alpha]_D^{20}$ − 40°
d-*Tartrate*: m.p. 151°.

dl.-
Yellow prisms or leaflets. M.p. 129–30°.

Angeletti, *Gazz. chim. ital.*, 1931, **61**, 651.

4′-Nitro-4-amino-3 : 3′-ditolyl (4′-*Nitro-*-*amino*-3 : 3′-*dimethyldiphenyl*)

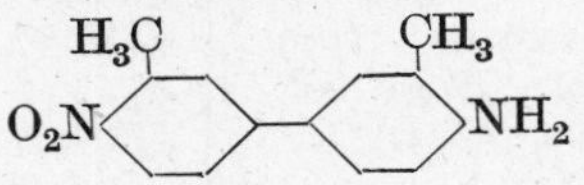

$C_{14}H_{14}O_2N_2$ MW, 242

Yellow needles from EtOH. M.p. 142–3°.

Schultz, Rohde, Vicari, *Ann.*, 1907, **352**, 121.

2′-Nitro-2-amino-4 : 4′-ditolyl (2′-*Nitro-*2-*amino*-4 : 4′-*dimethyldiphenyl*)

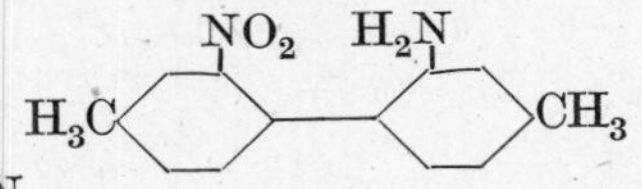

$C_{14}H_{14}O_2N_2$ MW, 242

B,HCl: cryst. from EtOH–Et_2O. M.p. 129–30°.

N-*Acetyl*: light yellow cryst. from C_6H_6. M.p. 145–6°.

N-*Diacetyl*: yellow cryst. from pet. ether. M.p. 116–17°.

Mascarelli, Gatti, *Gazz. chim. ital.*, 1929, **59**, 858.

3-Nitro-2-aminofluorene (3-*Nitro-2-fluorylamine*)

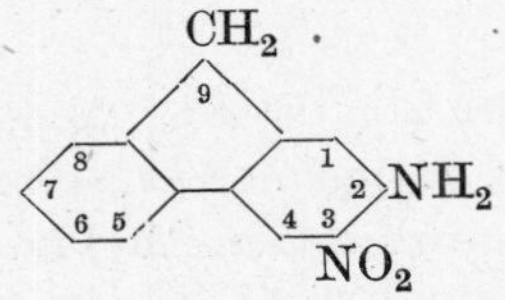

$C_{13}H_{10}O_2N_2$ MW, 226

Brownish-red needles from AcOH. M.p. 206°. Mod. sol. AcOH. Spar. sol. hot EtOH, Et_2O, C_6H_6.

B,HCl: bronze cryst. from AcOH + conc. HCl.

Diels, Schill, Tolson, *Ber.*, 1902, **35**, 3286.

7-Nitro-2-aminofluorene (7-*Nitro-2-fluorylamine*).

Orange-red prisms. M.p. 232°. Sol. EtOH, AcOH.

See previous reference.

3-Nitro-2-aminofluorenone

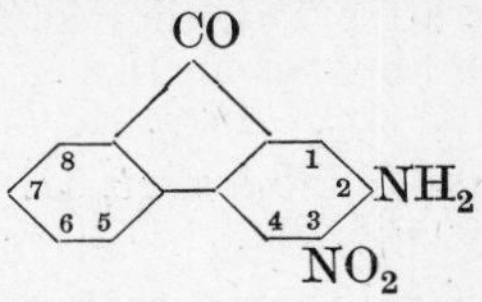

$C_{13}H_8O_3N_2$ MW, 240

Violet-red cryst. from $PhNO_2$. M.p. 269°.

N-*Acetyl*: red cryst. from chlorobenzene. M.p. 245–6°.

N-*Carboethoxyl*: reddish-yellow cryst. from chlorobenzene. M.p. 204°.

Eckert, Langecker, *J. prakt. Chem.*, 1928, **118**, 263.

7-Nitro-2-aminofluorenone.

Needles from chlorobenzene. M.p. 279°.

N-*Acetyl*: red cryst. from $PhNO_2$. Does not melt below 300°.

See previous reference.

7-Nitro-4-aminofluorenone.

Scarlet micro-needles from Py. M.p. 292–3°. Sol. hot AcOEt, Py, aniline, dimethylaniline, chlorobenzene. Insol. C_6H_6, ligroin, CCl_4.

Moore, Huntress, *J. Am. Chem. Soc.*, 1927, **49**, 1331.

Nitroaminoguaiacol.

See under Nitroaminocatechol.

2-Nitro-4-aminohydrocinnamic Acid

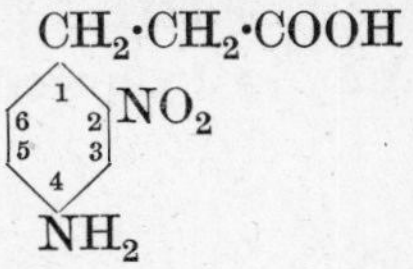

$C_9H_{10}O_4N_2$ MW, 210

Red plates or needles from H_2O. M.p. 137–9°. Sol. EtOH, Et_2O, AcOH. Insol. CS_2.

Gabriel, Zimmermann, *Ber.*, 1879, **12**, 601.

3-Nitro-4-aminohydrocinnamic Acid.

Orange cryst. M.p. 145°. Sol. H_2O, EtOH, Et_2O, AcOH. Spar. sol. C_6H_6. Insol. CS_2.

N-*Acetyl*: yellow needles. M.p. 174°. Sol. EtOH, AcOH, C_6H_6. Spar. sol. Et_2O, H_2O. Insol. CS_2.

Gabriel, Steudemann, *Ber.*, 1882, **15**, 844.

***p*-Nitro-α-aminohydrocinnamic Acid**

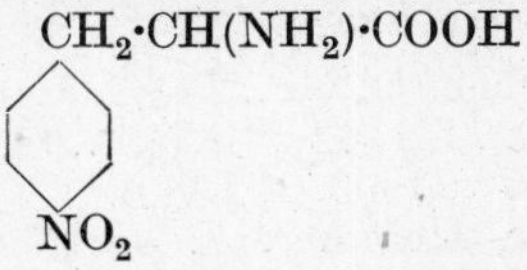

$C_9H_{10}O_4N_2$ MW, 210

Prisms + $1\frac{1}{2}H_2O$ from H_2O or NH_4OH. M.p. 245° decomp. after darkening at 220°.

B,HCl : needles from H_2O. M.p. 220° decomp. Sol. EtOH. Insol. Et_2O.

Curtius, Mühlhäusser, *J. prakt. Chem.*, 1930, **125**, 298.

o-Nitro-β-aminohydrocinnamic Acid

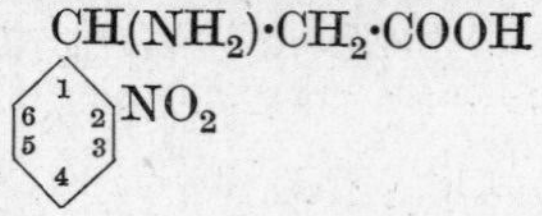

$C_9H_{10}O_4N_2$ MW, 210

Yellow plates from H_2O. M.p. 222° decomp. Sol. dil. acids and alkalis. Spar. sol. cold H_2O, EtOH.

Posner, *Ann.*, 1912, **389**, 40.

***m*-Nitro-β-aminohydrocinnamic Acid.** Yellow needles from H_2O. M.p. 236° decomp. Sol. dil. acids and alkalis. Spar. sol. cold H_2O, EtOH.

B,HCl : m.p. 210–211·5°.

Rodionow, Malewinskaja, *Ber.*, 1926, **59**, 2952.

See also previous reference.

***p*-Nitro-β-aminohydrocinnamic Acid.** Yellow cryst. powder. M.p. 226–7° decomp. Sol. dil. acids and alkalis. Spar. sol. cold H_2O, EtOH.

See previous references.

5-Nitro-2-aminohydroquinone

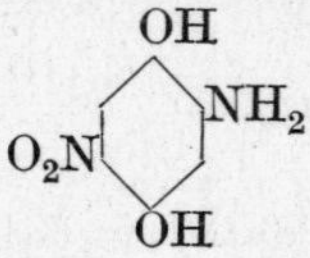

$C_6H_6O_4N_2$ MW, 170

Red cryst. from C_6H_6. M.p. 154° decomp. Dil. alkalis ⟶ blue sol. ⟶ green, then yellow on standing.

Di-Me ether : $C_8H_{10}O_4N_2$. MW, 198. Yellow prisms from C_6H_6. M.p. 158°. N-*Acetyl* : yellow needles. M.p. 164°. Sol. EtOH, C_6H_6.

1-*Me*-4-*Et ether* : $C_9H_{12}O_4N_2$. MW, 212. Yellowish-brown cryst. from C_6H_6. M.p. 148°.

Acetyl deriv. : red needles from EtOH. M.p. 226° decomp.

Diacetyl deriv. : m.p. 183–4°.

Badische, D.R.P., 141,398, (*Chem. Zentr.*, 1903, I, 1163); D.R.P., 141,975, (*Chem. Zentr.*, 1903, I, 1380).

Heller, Hemmer, *J. prakt. Chem.*, 1931, **129**, 207.

6-Nitro-4-aminoisophthalic Acid

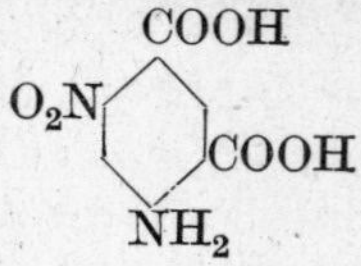

$C_8H_6O_6N_2$ MW, 226

Yellow prisms from AcOH–EtOH. M.p. 280° decomp. Spar. sol. H_2O.

Di-Me ester : $C_{10}H_{10}O_6N_2$. MW, 254. Yellowish-brown cryst. M.p. 153°. Sol. EtOH.

N-*Acetyl* : cryst. from EtOH or AcOH. M.p. 264° decomp. Sol. EtOH. Spar. sol. H_2O.

Errera, Maltese, *Gazz. chim. ital.*, 1903, **33**, ii, 287.

Bogert, Kropff, *J. Am. Chem. Soc.*, 1909, **31**, 846.

6-Nitro-2-aminomesitylenic Acid (6-*Nitro-2-amino-3 : 5-dimethylbenzoic acid*)

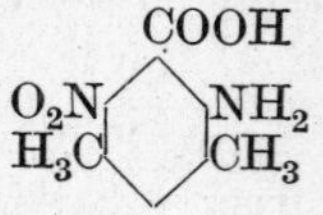

$C_9H_{10}O_4N_2$ MW, 210

Yellow needles from H_2O or xylene, plates from EtOH. M.p. 190°. Easily sol. EtOH. Sol. Et_2O, hot H_2O, hot xylene.

Bamberger, Demuth, *Ber.*, 1901, **34**, 31.

2′-Nitro-4-amino-2-methylazobenzene

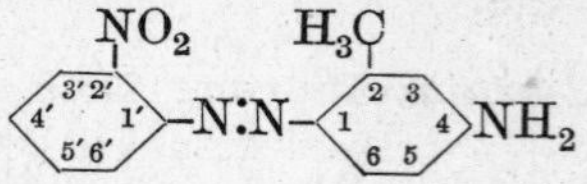

$C_{13}H_{12}O_2N_4$ MW, 256

Violet needles from EtOH. M.p. 119–21°.

Mehner, *J. prakt. Chem.*, 1902, **65**, 461.

3′-Nitro-4-amino-2-methylazobenzene. Orange needles from EtOH. M.p. 172°.

Mehner, *J. prakt. Chem.*, 1902, **65**, 459.

4′-Nitro-4-amino-2-methylazobenzene. Deep reddish-violet needles from EtOH. M.p. 152–3°.

Mehner, *J. prakt. Chem.*, 1902, **65**, 457.

2′-Nitro-4-amino-3-methylazobenzene

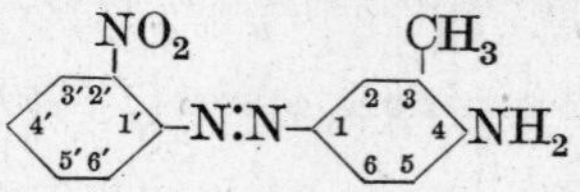

$C_{13}H_{12}O_2N_4$ MW, 256

Red needles from ligroin. M.p. 99°.

Mehner, *J. prakt. Chem.*, 1902, **65**, 468.

3′-Nitro-4-amino-3-methylazobenzene.
Red plates from EtOH or C_6H_6. M.p. 151–2°.

Mehner, *J. prakt. Chem.*, 1902, **65**, 467.

4′-Nitro-4-amino-3-methylazobenzene.
Reddish-brown cryst. from EtOH. M.p. 200–1° (195–7°).

Mehner, *J. prakt. Chem.*, 1902, **65**, 464.
A.G.F.A., D.R.P., 131,860, (*Chem. Zentr.*, 1902, II, 83).

Nitroaminomethylnaphthalene.
See Nitromethylnaphthylamine.

2-Nitro-4-amino-1-naphthol

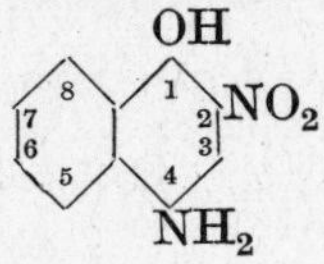

$C_{10}H_8O_3N_2$ MW, 204

Maroon needles from EtOH. M.p. 160° decomp.

B,HCl: pale yellow needles from HCl–EtOH. M.p. 175° decomp.

Me ether: $C_{11}H_{10}O_3N_2$. MW, 218. N-*Acetyl*: needles. M.p. 214°.

N-*Acetyl*: yellow-orange needles from AcOH. M.p. 250° (238°) decomp.

N-*Benzoyl*: orange needles from EtOH. M.p. 330°.

Hodgson, Smith, *J. Chem. Soc.*, 1935, 673.

5-Nitro-8-amino-1-naphthol.
Me ether: $C_{11}H_{10}O_3N_2$. MW, 218. Reddish-brown cryst. from EtOH. M.p. 193°. Spar. sol. H_2O.

N-*Acetyl*: red needles from EtOH.Aq. M.p. 240°. Sol. EtOH. Spar. sol. Et_2O, C_6H_6, $CHCl_3$.

O : N-*Diacetyl*: needles from EtOH. M.p. 224°.

Fichter, Kühnel, *Ber.*, 1909, **42**, 4751.
Fichter, Gageur, *Ber.*, 1906, **39**, 3335.

8-Nitro-7-amino-2-naphthol

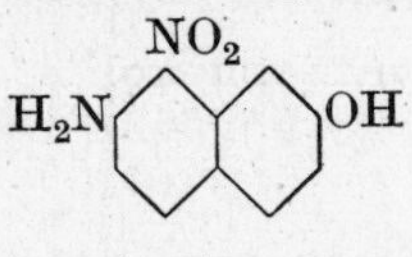

$C_{10}H_8O_3N_2$ MW, 204

Me ether: $C_{11}H_{10}O_3N_2$. MW, 218. Reddish-yellow needles from H_2O or ligroin. M.p. 115–16°. Sol. EtOH, Et_2O, C_6H_6, $CHCl_3$, AcOH. Spar. sol. hot H_2O. *B,HBr*: yellow plates. M.p. 159–60°. *Picrate*: red needles from MeOH. M.p. 125°. N-*Acetyl*: yellow needles from EtOH. M.p. 149–50°. N-*Benzoyl*: yellowish needles from AcOH. M.p. 203–4°. N-*Benzylidene*: reddish cryst. from Et_2O–pet. ether. M.p. 126–7°. N-*Salicylidene*: light brown needles from ligroin. M.p. 202°.

O : N-*Di-Me*: $C_{12}H_{12}O_3N_2$. MW, 232. Yellowish-red needles from ligroin. M.p. 149–50°. Sol. MeOH, EtOH, Et_2O. Spar. sol. ligroin. Almost insol. H_2O. HCl ⟶ dark yellow sol.

Fischer, Kern, *J. prakt. Chem.*, 1916, **94**, 38.

4-Nitro-2-amino-1-naphthol-7-sulphonic Acid

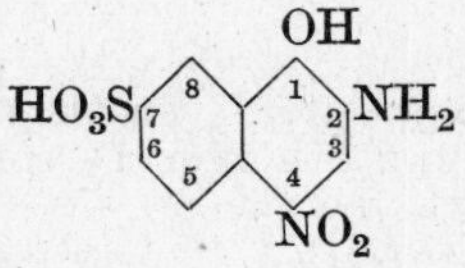

$C_{10}H_8O_6N_2S$ MW, 284

Yellow cryst. Spar. sol. cold H_2O.

Ges. für. chem. Ind., D.R.P., 189,513, (*Chem. Zentr.*, 1907, II, 2006).

2-Nitro-4-amino-1-naphthol-7-sulphonic Acid.
Golden-yellow leaflets from H_2O. Mod. sol. hot H_2O. Alkalis ⟶ intense blood-red sols.

Lauterbach, *Ber.*, 1881, **14**, 2029.
See also previous reference.

5-Nitro-3-amino-2-naphthol-7-sulphonic Acid

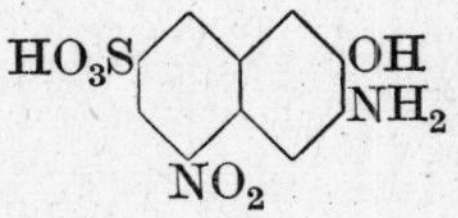

$C_{10}H_8O_6N_2S$ MW, 284

Yellow needles. Mod. sol. H_2O.

Cassella, D.R.P., 110,369, (*Chem. Zentr.*, 1900, II, 548).

5-Nitro-2-aminonicotinic Acid (5-*Nitro-2-aminopyridine-3-carboxylic acid*)

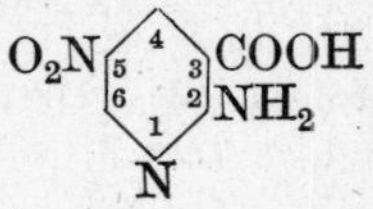

$C_6H_5O_4N_3$ MW, 183

Golden-yellow needles from H_2O or C_6H_6. M.p. 233°. Sol. H_2O, EtOH, Et_2O, C_6H_6.

Räth, *Ann.*, 1931, **486**, 294.

5-Nitro-6-aminonicotinic Acid (5-*Nitro-6-aminopyridine-3-carboxylic acid*).
Yellow needles from H_2O. M.p. 300–1° (280°) decomp. Sol. hot H_2O, EtOH. Spar. sol. usual

org. solvents. Mod. sol. acids. Sublimes with part. decomp.

Marckwald, *Ber.*, 1893, **26**, 2189; 1894, **27**, 1334.
Räth, Prange, *Ann.*, 1928, **467**, 8.

5-Nitro-2-aminophenanthraquinone

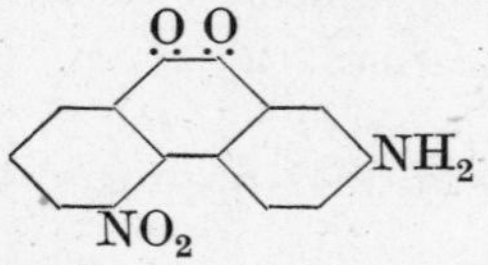

$C_{14}H_8O_4N_2$ MW, 268

Dark brown powder. Decomp. on heating. Spar. sol. H_2O and common org. solvents. With $H_2SO_4 \longrightarrow$ dark brown sol. With NaOH.Aq. $\longrightarrow$ yellowish-green sol. Constitution given as 4-nitro-5-aminophenanthraquinone until 1926.

N-*Diacetyl*: brown needles. M.p. 280°.

Schmidt, Leipprand, *Ber.*, 1905, **38**, 3735.
Christie, Holderness, Kenner, *J. Chem. Soc.*, 1926, 671.

Nitroaminophenetole.
See Nitrophenetidine.

3-Nitro-*o*-aminophenol

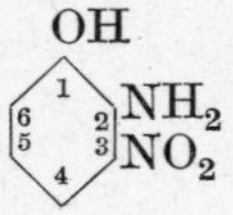

$C_6H_6O_3N_2$ MW, 154

Red needles from H_2O. M.p. 216–17° (212°). Sol. 100 parts boiling H_2O.

Me ether: *see* 3-Nitro-*o*-anisidine.

Et ether: *see* 3-Nitro-*o*-phenetidine.

N-*Acetyl*: 6-nitro-2-hydroxyacetanilide. Yellow cryst. M.p. 172°. O-p-*Toluenesulphonyl*: m.p. 120°.

O-p-*Toluenesulphonyl*: pale yellow cryst. M.p. 136°.

King, *J. Chem. Soc.*, 1927, 1058.
Fourneau, Tréfouel, Tréfouel, *Bull. soc. chim.*, 1927, **41**, 448.

4-Nitro-*o*-aminophenol.

Orange prisms + H_2O. M.p. 80–90°, anhyd. 142–3°. Sol. EtOH, Et_2O. Spar. sol. H_2O. $k = 0{\cdot}26 \times 10^{-6}$ at 25°.

Me ether: *see* 4-Nitro-*o*-anisidine.

Et ether: *see* 4-Nitro-*o*-phenetidine.

N-*Benzoyl*: needles from aniline. Decomp. above 200°. Spar. sol. EtOH, AcOH.

O-p-*Toluenesulphonyl*: yellowish needles from AcOH or EtOH. M.p. 122°.

Post, Stuckenberg, *Ann.*, 1880, **205**, 72.
Hofer, Jakob, *Ber.*, 1908, **41**, 3196.

5-Nitro-*o*-aminophenol.

Light brown needles from H_2O. M.p. 201–2°.

Me ether: *see* 5-Nitro-*o*-anisidine.

Et ether: *see* 5-Nitro-*o*-phenetidine.

O:N-*Diacetyl*: needles from H_2O. M.p. 187°.

N-*Anisylidene*: yellow plates from C_6H_6. M.p. 160–1°. Sol. C_6H_6. Insol. ligroin.

O-p-*Toluenesulphonyl*: light yellow cryst. from EtOH or AcOH. M.p. 188° (185°). N-*Acetyl*: m.p. 189°.

Meldola, Woolcott, Wray, *J. Chem. Soc.*, 1896, **69**, 1325.
A.G.F.A., D.R.P., 165,650, (*Chem. Zentr.*, 1906, I, 516).

6-Nitro-*o*-aminophenol.

Red needles from EtOH.Aq. M.p. 111–12°. Very sol. Et_2O, C_6H_6, $CHCl_3$, AcOH. Sol. EtOH. Spar. sol. H_2O.

Me ether: *see* 6-Nitro-*o*-anisidine.

Benda, *Ber.*, 1914, **47**, 1010.
Post, Stuckenberg, *Ann.*, 1880, **205**, 85.

4-Nitro-*m*-aminophenol

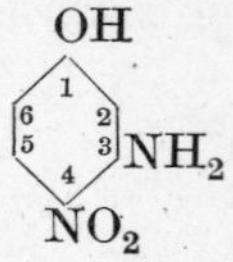

$C_6H_6O_3N_2$ MW, 154

Orange needles from H_2O. M.p. 185–6°.

Me ether: *see* 4-Nitro-*m*-anisidine.

Et ether: *see* 4-Nitro-*m*-phenetidine.

N-*Acetyl*: 6-nitro-3-hydroxyacetanilide. Needles from AcOH. M.p. 266°.

N-*Phenyl*: *see* 6-Nitro-3-hydroxydiphenylamine.

Meldola, Stephens, *J. Chem. Soc.*, 1906, **89**, 924.

5-Nitro-*m*-aminophenol.

Yellow cryst. M.p. 165°. Very sol. EtOH, Et_2O, AcOH, Me_2CO. Spar. sol. C_6H_6, $CHCl_3$, ligroin.

Me-ether: *see* 5-Nitro-*m*-anisidine.

Et ether: *see* 5-Nitro-*m*-phenetidine.

N-*Acetyl*: 5-nitro-3-hydroxyacetanilide. Dark yellow prisms from AcOEt or 50% AcOH. M.p. 260–70° decomp. Sol. EtOH, Me_2CO, AcOH. Spar. sol. C_6H_6, Et_2O, $CHCl_3$, ligroin.

Heller, *Ber.*, 1909, **42**, 2193.

6-Nitro-*m*-aminophenol.

Orange-yellow needles from H_2O. M.p. 162° (158°).

Me ether: *see* 6-Nitro-*m*-anisidine.

Et ether: *see* 6-Nitro-*m*-phenetidine.

N-*Acetyl*: 4-nitro-3-hydroxyacetanilide. Yellow prisms or needles from AcOH. M.p. 221°.

O : N-*Diacetyl*: needles from H_2O or AcOH. M.p. 149°. Sol. EtOH.

M.L.B., D.R.P., 285,638, (*Chem. Zentr.*, 1915, II, 511).
Meldola, Stephens, *J. Chem. Soc.*, 1906, **89**, 925.

2-Nitro-*p*-aminophenol

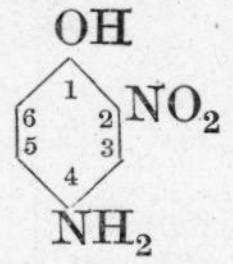

$C_6H_6O_3N_2$ MW, 154

Dark red plates or needles. M.p. 131° (127°).

Me ether: *see* 2-Nitro-*p*-anisidine.

Et ether: *see* 2-Nitro-*p*-phenetidine.

N-*Me*: $C_7H_8O_3N_2$. MW, 168. Reddish-brown cryst. from EtOH. M.p. 113–14°.

N-*Acetyl*: 3-nitro-4-hydroxyacetanilide. Yellow needles. M.p. 157–8°.

Bart, D.R.P., 258,059, (*Chem. Zentr.*, 1913, I, 1374).
Friedländer, Zeitlin, *Ber.*, 1894, **27**, 196.
Girard, *Bull. soc. chim.*, 1924, **35**, 772.

3-Nitro-*p*-aminophenol.

Dark red prisms with green reflex from Et_2O. M.p. 154°. Sol. Et_2O, $CHCl_3$.

Me ether: *see* 3-Nitro-*p*-anisidine.

Et ether: *see* 3-Nitro-*p*-phenetidine.

N-*Acetyl*: 2-nitro-4-hydroxyacetanilide. Brownish-yellow needles from H_2O. M.p. 218°.

O-m-*Nitrobenzoyl*: yellow needles. M.p. 184°.

O-p-*Toluenesulphonyl*: yellow plates from EtOH. M.p. 134°.

O : N-*Diacetyl*: yellow prisms from EtOH.Aq. M.p. 146–7°.

Reverdin, *Ber.*, 1906, **39**, 3796.
Hähle, *J. prakt. Chem.*, 1891, **43**, 64.

4-Nitro-*o*-aminophenol-6-sulphonic Acid

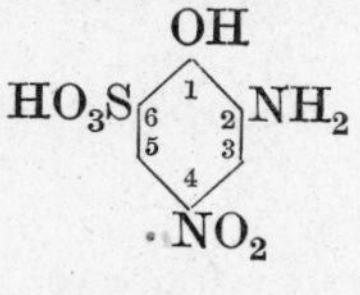

$C_6H_6O_6N_2S$ MW, 234

Prisms + $1H_2O$, needles + $2H_2O$. M.p. 285° decomp.

King, *J. Chem. Soc.*, 1921, **119**, 1415.
Badische, D.R.P., 123,611, (*Chem. Zentr.*, 1901, II, 797).

5-Nitro-*o*-aminophenol-4-sulphonic Acid.

Yellow cryst. Sol. H_2O.

M.L.B., D.R.P., 188,378, (*Chem. Zentr.*, 1907, II, 1467).

6-Nitro-*o*-aminophenol-4-sulphonic Acid.

Prisms. Sol. hot H_2O with reddish-yellow col. Spar. sol. EtOH with yellow col. $FeCl_3 \longrightarrow$ greenish-yellow col.

Na salt: reddish-brown needles. Very sol. H_2O with red col.

K salt: brown needles from H_2O. Sol. hot H_2O with brownish-yellow col.

Badische, D.R.P., 121,427, (*Chem. Zentr.*, 1901, I, 1396).
M.L.B., D.R.P., 148,213, (*Chem. Zentr.*, 1904, I, 414).
Hillyer, U.S.P., 1,504,044, (*Chem. Abstracts*, 1924, **18**, 3194).

6-Nitro-*p*-aminophenol-2-sulphonic Acid

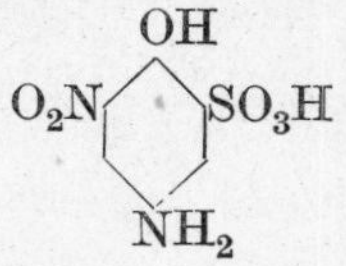

$C_6H_6O_6N_2S$ MW, 234

Reddish-brown needles from H_2O. Does not melt below 290°. Spar. sol. hot H_2O. Insol. EtOH.

Badische, D.R.P., 113,337, (*Chem. Zentr.*, 1900, II, 656).
King, *J. Chem. Soc.*, 1921, **119**, 1415.

2-Nitro-4-aminophenoxyacetic Acid

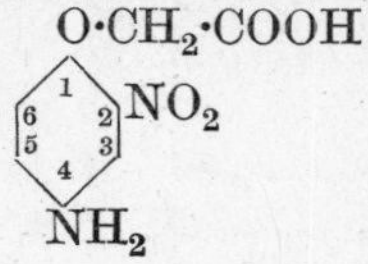

$C_8H_8O_5N_2$ MW, 212

Brownish-yellow prisms from H_2O. M.p. 196°.

N-*Acetyl*: reddish-yellow needles from H_2O. M.p. 205°.

Howard, *Ber.*, 1897, **30**, 2106.
Girard, *Bull. soc. chim.*, 1924, **35**, 772.

3-Nitro-4-aminophenoxyacetic Acid.
Brown needles. M.p. 185°.
N-*Acetyl*: cryst. from H_2O. M.p. 174°.
N-*Benzoyl*: yellow needles from AcOH. M.p. 176–7°. Sol. warm EtOH, AcOH.

See second reference above and also Reverdin, *Ber.*, 1909, **42**, 4113.

3-Nitro-α-aminophenylacetic Acid

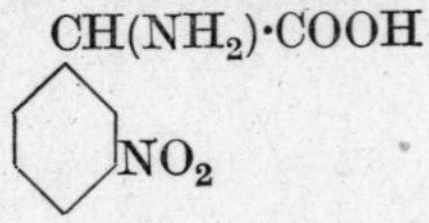

$C_8H_8O_4N_2$ MW, 196

Needles. M.p. 172° decomp. Sol. H_2O. Insol. EtOH. Easily sol. HCl.

Plöchl, Loë, *Ber.*, 1885, **18**, 1179.

2-Nitro-4-aminophenylacetic Acid

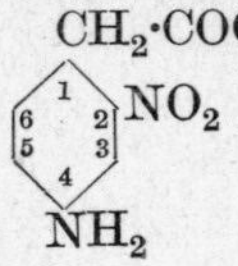

$C_8H_8O_4N_2$ MW, 196

Reddish-brown needles. M.p. 184–6°. Sol. H_2O, EtOH. Mod. sol. Et_2O. Insol. CS_2, C_6H_6. sol. acids, alk.
Me ester: $C_9H_{10}O_4N_2$. MW, 210. M.p. 96°.
Et ester: $C_{10}H_{12}O_4N_2$. MW, 224. Yellow needles. M.p. 100°.

Gabriel, Meyer, *Ber.*, 1881, **14**, 824.

3-Nitro-4-aminophenylacetic Acid.
Orange-yellow plates or needles from H_2O. M.p. 143·5–144·5°. Sol. H_2O, EtOH, Et_2O, AcOH. Mod. sol. $CHCl_3$, C_6H_6. Insol. CS_2.

Gabriel, *Ber.*, 1882, **15**, 836.

3-Nitro-6-amino-α-picoline

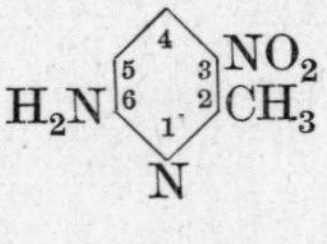

$C_6H_7O_2N_3$ MW, 153

M.p. 188°. Spar. sol. Et_2O, C_6H_6, ligroin. Very spar. sol. H_2O. Dil. acids ⟶ yellow sols. Non-volatile in steam.

Seide, *Chem. Zentr.*, 1923, **3**, 1022.

5-Nitro-6-amino-α-picoline.
M.p. 141°. Spar. sol. H_2O, Et_2O, C_6H_6, ligroin. Insol. EtOH. Dil. acids ⟶ yellow sols. Volatile in steam.

See previous reference.

5-Nitro-2-amino-β-picoline

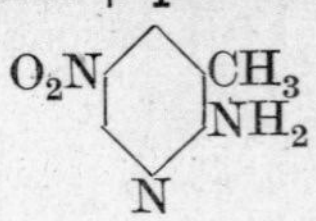

$C_6H_7O_2N_3$ MW, 153

Yellow prisms from EtOH. M.p. 255°. Sol. hot EtOH. Spar. sol. H_2O. Sol. min. acids with yellow col.

Seide, *Ber.*, 1924, **57**, 1805.

3-Nitro-2-amino-γ-picoline

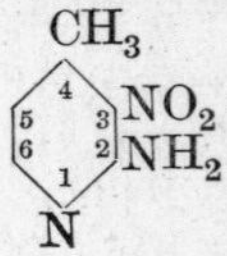

$C_6H_7O_2N_3$ MW, 153

Yellow needles from H_2O. M.p. 136°. Sol. H_2O, EtOH, acids. Volatile in steam.

Seide, *Ber.*, 1924, **57**, 794.

5-Nitro-2-amino-γ-picoline.
Yellow prisms from EtOH. M.p. 220°. Mod. sol. EtOH. Spar. sol. H_2O.

See previous reference.

3-Nitro-2-aminopyridine

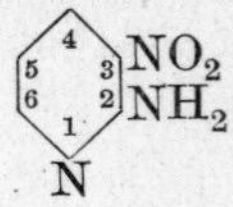

$C_5H_5O_2N_3$ MW, 139

Yellow needles. M.p. 164°.
N-*Me*: $C_6H_7O_2N_3$. MW, 153. Golden-yellow plates. M.p. 63–4°. B.p. 262–262·5°/740 mm. decomp. Sol. H_2O, usual org. solvents.
N-NO_2: 3-nitropyridyl-2-nitramine. $C_5H_4O_4N_4$. MW, 184. Yellow plates from H_2O. M.p. 137°.

Tschitschibabin, Kirssanow, *Ber.*, 1928, **61**, 1228.
Chichibabin, D.R.P., 374,291, (*Chem. Abstracts*, 1924, **18**, 2176). *Note*: this is the alternative spelling of the author's name given in Chem. Abstracts.

5-Nitro-2-aminopyridine.
Yellow leaflets. M.p. 188°.
N-*Me*: cryst. M.p. 181°.
N-NO_2: 5-nitropyridyl-2-nitramine. Cryst. from H_2O. Decomp. on heating. Sol. dil. alkalis. Insol. dil. acids.

See previous references.

3-Nitro-4-aminopyridine.

Yellow needles from H_2O. M.p. 200°. Sol. hot H_2O, EtOH.

B,HCl : prisms. M.p. 258–9°. Easily decomp.

B_2,H_2PtCl_6 : yellow plates. M.p. 256°.

Picrate : needles. M.p. 197–8°.

Koenigs, Mields, Gurlt, *Ber.*, 1924, **57**, 1183.
Koenigs, Freter, *ibid.*, 1190.

***N*-Nitroaminopyridine.**

See Pyridylnitramine.

3-Nitro-4-aminoquinaldine

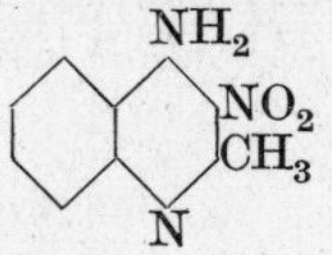

$C_{10}H_9O_2N_3$ MW, 203

Pale yellow needles. M.p. 201°. Sublimes.

Conrad, Limpach, *Ber.*, 1888, **21**, 1982.

5-Nitro-2-aminoquinoline

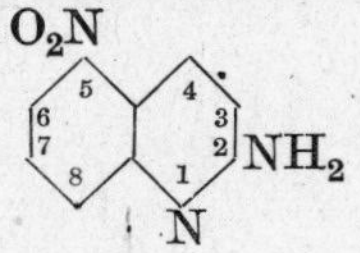

$C_9H_7O_2N_3$ MW, 189

Orange prisms from toluene. M.p. 239°. Sol. EtOH. Mod. sol. C_6H_6. Spar. sol. Et_2O.

Fischer, Guthmann, *J. prakt. Chem.*, 1916, **93**, 378.

6-Nitro-2-aminoquinoline.

Yellow prisms from toluene. M.p. 265°. Sol. EtOH, Et_2O, Py. Mod. sol. C_6H_6.

See previous reference.

8-Nitro-2-aminoquinoline.

Yellow cryst. from toluene. M.p. 159°. Sol. Py. Mod. sol. EtOH, C_6H_6. Spar. sol. Et_2O.

$B,HgCl_2$: yellow cryst. powder. M.p. 216°.

Picrate : orange cryst. M.p. 257°.

N-*Acetyl* : needles from AcOH.Aq. M.p. 211°. Very sol. AcOH. Mod. sol. EtOH, Et_2O, C_6H_6.

N-*Benzoyl* : needles from EtOH.Aq. M.p. 166°. Sol. C_6H_6, AcOH, Py. Mod. sol. Et_2O.

See previous reference.

6-Nitro-4-aminoquinoline.

Yellow needles from EtOH. M.p. 272° decomp. Sol. dil. min. acids. Insol. alkalis. $KMnO_4 \longrightarrow$ 5-nitro-anthranilic acid.

N-*NO_2* : 6-nitro-4-quinolylnitramine. $C_9H_6O_4N_4$. MW, 234. Golden-yellow needles from 50% EtOH. Decomp. at 203°. Sol. alkalis.

Tschitschibabin, Witkovsky, Lapschin, *Ber.*, 1925, **58**, 807.

8-Nitro-5-aminoquinoline.

Needles. M.p. 280°. Sol. warm H_2O, EtOH. Almost insol. Et_2O, C_6H_6, pet. ether.

B,HCl : yellow needles. M.p. about 250° decomp.

Dikshoorn, *Rec. trav. chim.*, 1929, **48**, 237.

5-Nitro-6-aminoquinoline.

Yellow needles from toluene. M.p. 178° (173–4°).

N-p-*Toluenesulphonyl* : yellow cryst. from EtOH. M.p. 168°.

Picrate : m.p. 270°.

Bryd, *Chem. Zentr.*, 1932, I, 3066.
Kaufmann, Zeller, *Ber.*, 1917, **50**, 1629.

8-Nitro-7-aminoquinoline.

Cryst. M.p. 194°.

Fourneau, Tréfouel, Tréfouel, Benoit, *Chem. Abstracts*, 1932, **26**, 1592.

5-Nitro-8-aminoquinoline.

Orange-red plates or needles from C_6H_6. M.p. 197°. Sol. EtOH. Less sol. Et_2O, C_6H_6, $CHCl_3$. Spar. sol. hot H_2O. Insol. pet. ether.

Dikshoorn, *Rec. trav. chim.*, 1929, **48**, 517.
Slater, *J. Chem. Soc.*, 1931, 1940.

6-Nitro-8-aminoquinoline.

Red cryst. from EtOH. M.p. 194°.

B_2,H_2PtCl_6 : red cryst. Decomp. at 180°.

Methiodide : red needles. M.p. 176°. Sol. hot EtOH. Spar. sol. cold H_2O.

N-*Acetyl* : light yellow needles. M.p. 224°. Spar. sol. H_2O, EtOH. Sublimes.

Claus, Hartmann, *J. prakt. Chem.*, 1896, **53**, 207.
Kaufmann, Hüssy, *Ber.*, 1908, **41**, 1740.

***N*-Nitroaminoquinoline.**

See Quinolylnitramine.

4-Nitro-2-aminoresorcinol (3-*Nitro*-2 : 6-*dihydroxyaniline*)

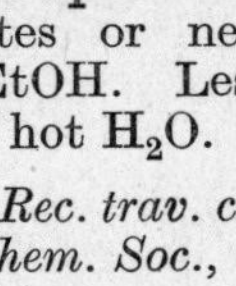

$C_6H_6O_4N_2$ MW, 170

Brown cryst. from EtOH.Aq. M.p. 182°.

Sol. EtOH, Et_2O. Spar. sol. H_2O. Reduces cold $NH_3.AgNO_3$.

Benedikt, v. Hubl, *Monatsh.*, 1881, **2**, 324.
Heller, Lindner, Georgi, *Ber.*, 1923, **56**, 1868.

6-Nitro-4-aminoresorcinol (*5-Nitro-2 : 4-dihydroxyaniline*).

Red cryst. from Et_2O–ligroin. M.p. 160–1° decomp. Very sol. EtOH, Me_2CO, Et_2O. Less sol. C_6H_6, $CHCl_3$, ligroin. Sol. acids, alkalis.

Di-Me ether: $C_8H_{10}O_4N_2$. MW, 198. Red needles from EtOH. M.p. 136–7°. Sol. Me_2CO. Mod. sol. EtOH. N-*Acetyl*: pale yellow needles from EtOH. M.p. 173°. Sol. hot AcOH. Mod. sol. Me_2CO.

N-*Acetyl*: yellow needles from EtOH or AcOH. M.p. 261° decomp. Very sol. Me_2CO. Spar. sol. Et_2O, C_6H_6, $CHCl_3$, ligroin.

Triacetyl deriv.: plates from toluene. M.p. 176° decomp. Sol. EtOH, Me_2CO, $CHCl_3$, AcOH, AcOEt. Spar. sol. C_6H_6, Et_2O. Insol. ligroin.

Vermeulen, *Rec. trav. chim.*, 1919, **38**, 110.
Heller, Sourlis, *Ber.*, 1910, **43**, 2583.

5-Nitro-3-aminosalicylic Acid

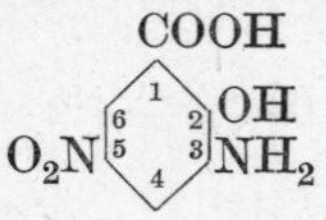

$C_7H_6O_5N_2$ MW, 198

Red needles + H_2O from H_2O. M.p. 234° decomp. Sol. EtOH. Less sol. H_2O. NH_3 ⟶ deep red sol. HCl ⟶ yellow sol.

Hübner, Babcock, Schaumann, *Ber.*, 1879, **12**, 1345.
Meldola, Foster, Brightman, *J. Chem. Soc.*, 1917, **111**, 540.

3-Nitro-5-aminosalicylic Acid.

Plates from H_2O. M.p. 240° decomp. Spar. sol. $CHCl_3$, C_6H_6.

Cassella, D.R.P., 85,989.

4-Nitro-2-aminostilbene

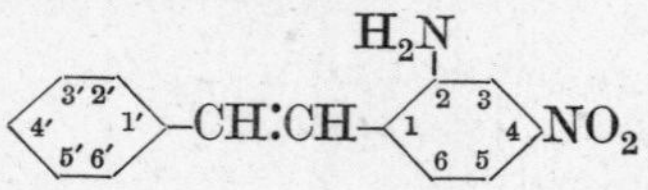

$C_{14}H_{12}O_2N_2$ MW, 240

Red cryst. from EtOH. M.p. 142–3°. Sol. EtOH, C_6H_6.

B,HCl: yellow cryst. from AcOH or HCl. M.p. 218–19°. Decomp. by H_2O.

N-*Acetyl*: light yellow needles from EtOH. M.p. 220°.

Thiele, Escales, *Ber.*, 1901, **34**, 2845.

2'-Nitro-2-aminostilbene.

Amorph. Easily decomp.

Bischoff, *Ber.*, 1888, **21**, 2077.

2-Nitro-4-aminostilbene.

Dark red cryst. from EtOH. M.p. 110–11°.

B,HCl: golden-yellow cryst. M.p. 223°.

N-*Acetyl*: orange plates. M.p. 192–3°.

Thiele, Escales, *Ber.*, 1901, **34**, 2846.

4'-Nitro-4-aminostilbene.

Purplish-red plates from $PhNO_2$. M.p. 229–30°. Sol. hot $PhNO_2$. Spar. sol. EtOH, Et_2O, C_6H_6. Insol. H_2O.

B,HCl: yellow needles.

N-*Di-Me*: $C_{16}H_{16}O_2N_2$. MW, 268. Red plates from C_6H_6. M.p. 250–1°. Sol. EtOH, C_6H_6, AcOH.

Strakosch, *Ber.*, 1873, **6**, 329.

4-Nitro-4'-aminostilbene-2-carboxylic Acid

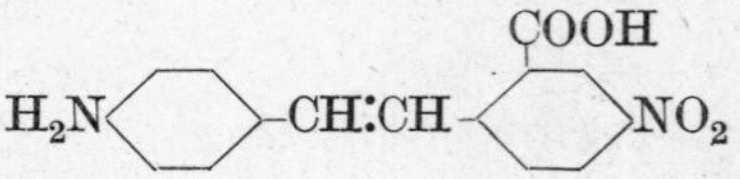

$C_{15}H_{12}O_4N_2$ MW, 284

N-*Di-Me*: $C_{17}H_{16}O_4N_2$. MW, 312. Red cryst. from AcOH. M.p. 206° decomp. Sol. EtOH, AcOH. Spar. sol. C_6H_6, $CHCl_3$. Very spar. sol. Et_2O, ligroin. *Me ester*: $C_{18}H_{18}O_4N_2$. MW, 326. Red cryst. from MeOH. M.p. 158–9°. Sol. EtOH, Et_2O, $CHCl_3$, AcOH. Sol. C_6H_6 with golden-orange fluor. *Et ester*: $C_{19}H_{20}O_4N_2$. MW, 340. Red needles from EtOH. M.p. 139–40°. Sol. C_6H_6 with strong golden-orange fluor.

Pfeiffer, Engelhardt, Alfuss, *Ann.*, 1928, **467**, 176.

2-Nitro-4'-aminostilbene-4-carboxylic Acid

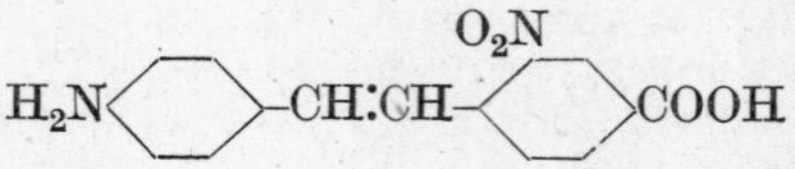

$C_{15}H_{12}O_4N_2$ MW, 284

Brownish-yellow leaflets from AcOH. M.p. 255–63°.

Me ester: $C_{16}H_{14}O_4N_2$. MW, 298. Red needles from EtOH. M.p. 161°.

Et ester: $C_{17}H_{16}O_4N_2$. MW, 312. Red leaflets from EtOH. M.p. 134°.

Nitrile: $C_{15}H_{11}O_2N_3$. MW, 265. Red leaflets from EtOH. M.p. 202°. *Acetyl*: golden-yellow needles + C_2H_5OH from EtOH. M.p. 245°. *Benzoyl*: yellow cryst. from AcOH. M.p. 242°.

N-*Di-Me*: *Me ester*, orange leaflets from MeOH. M.p. 134°. *Et ester*: violet needles or yellow leaflets from EtOH. M.p. 129–30°.

N-*Acetyl*: golden-yellow powder from AcOH. M.p. 275°.

N-*Benzoyl*: orange cryst. from AcOH. M.p. 297°.

Pfeiffer, Kalckbrenner, Behr, *J. prakt. Chem.*, 1925, **109**, 220.

5-Nitro-2-aminoterephthalic Acid

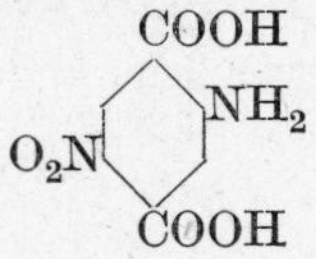

$C_8H_6O_6N_2$ MW, 226

Pale yellow cryst. Decomp. about 260°. Sol. hot H_2O, hot EtOH.

Di-Me ester: $C_{10}H_{10}O_6N_2$. MW, 254. Pale yellow prisms from EtOH. M.p. 187°. Sol. Py. Spar. sol. EtOH, Et_2O, $CHCl_3$, C_6H_6. N-*Acetyl*: pale yellow prisms from EtOH. M.p. 142°. Very sol. $CHCl_3$. Sol. EtOH, Me_2CO, AcOH, C_6H_6, Py. Spar. sol. Et_2O, CS_2, ligroin.

Kauffmann, Weissel, *Ann.*, 1912, **393**, 16.

5-Nitro-*o*-aminothiophenol

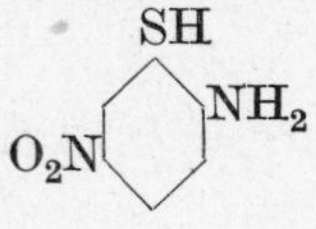

$C_6H_6O_2N_2S$ MW, 170

Orange-yellow plates from EtOH.Aq., pale yellow needles from AcOH. M.p. 84°. Alkalis ⟶ brownish-red sols.

Jacobsen, Kwaysser, *Ann.*, 1893, **277**, 242.

2-Nitro-6-aminothymol

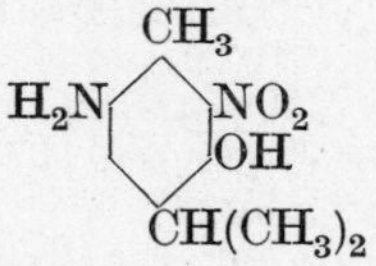

$C_{10}H_{14}O_3N_2$ MW, 210

Reddish-brown needles from EtOH. Very sol. EtOH.

Et ether: $C_{12}H_{18}O_3N_2$. MW, 238. Plates from EtOH. M.p. 111–12°. Sol. EtOH, CS_2. *B,HCl*: needles. Decomp. at 200°. N-*Acetyl*: needles from EtOH.Aq. M.p. 119°. N-*Benzoyl*: needles from EtOH.Aq. M.p. 138°. Spar. sol. Et_2O.

N-*Benzoyl*: yellow needles from ligroin. M.p. 158–60°. Sol. EtOH, C_6H_6, toluene. Spar. sol. ligroin.

O : N-*Diacetyl*: yellow prisms from C_6H_6. M.p. 157–9°.

Soderi, *Gazz. chim. ital.*, 1895, **25**, ii, 404.
Gaebel, *Ber.*, 1902, **35**, 2794.

6-Nitro-4-amino-*m*-toluic Acid

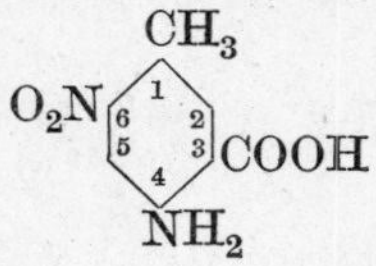

$C_8H_8O_4N_2$ MW, 196

Red cryst. from EtOH or AcOEt. M.p. 239–40° decomp. Sol. H_2O. Spar. sol. C_6H_6. Alk. salts are yellow.

Me ester: $C_9H_{10}O_4N_2$. MW, 210. Red cryst. M.p. 128°. Sol. EtOH.

N-2 : 4-*Dinitrophenyl*: $C_{14}H_{10}O_8N_4$. MW, 362. Yellow needles from AcOH. M.p. 298°. Spar. sol. common org. solvents.

N-*Acetyl*: $C_{10}H_{10}O_5N_2$. MW, 238. Yellow triclinic cryst. M.p. 223–5° decomp. Spar. sol. H_2O, C_6H_6, xylene. Sol. EtOH, AcOH, AcOEt.

Errera, Maltese, *Gazz. chim. ital.*, 1905, **35**, 370, 378.

4-Nitro-6-amino-*m*-toluic Acid.

Yellow needles from H_2O. M.p. about 235°. Sol. EtOH, AcOH. Spar. sol. C_6H_6. Alk. salts are dark yellow. H_2SO_4 at 200° ⟶ 4-nitro-*o*-toluidine.

Me ester: pale yellow needles from EtOH. M.p. 169°.

N-*Acetyl*: pale yellow plates from EtOH. M.p. 254–5° decomp.

See previous reference.

5-Nitro-2-amino-*p*-toluic Acid

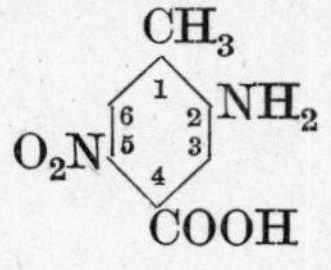

$C_8H_8O_4N_2$ MW, 196

Yellowish-red needles from H_2O. M.p. 220° decomp. Sol. EtOH, Et_2O. Spar. sol. H_2O.

Claus, Beysen, *Ann.*, 1891, **266**, 235.

6-Nitro-2-amino-*p*-toluic Acid.

Lemon-yellow needles from H_2O. M.p. 214°. Sol. EtOH, Et_2O. Sublimes.

Na salt: yellow needles + $\frac{3}{4}H_2O$.

Mg salt : yellow cryst. + $5H_2O$.
Ba salt : golden-yellow plates + $4H_2O$. Spar. sol. H_2O.

See previous reference.

6-Nitro-3-amino-*p*-toluic Acid.
Needles from EtOH. M.p. 235–6°. Spar. sol. H_2O. Heat with HCl in sealed tube to 150° ⟶ 6-nitro-*m*-toluidine.

Fileti, Crosa, *Gazz. chim. ital.*, 1888, **18**, 303.

3-Nitro-4-aminotriphenylmethane

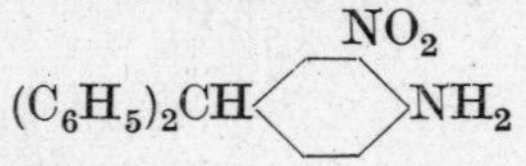

$C_{19}H_{16}O_2N_2$ MW, 304

Golden-yellow cryst. from EtOH.Aq. M.p. 98°. Very sol. most org. solvents.

Thomae, *J. prakt. Chem.*, 1905, **71**, 568.

Nitroaminoveratrol.
See under Nitroaminocatechol.

2-Nitro-*n*-amyl Alcohol (2-*Nitropentanol*-1)

$CH_3{\cdot}CH_2{\cdot}CH_2{\cdot}CH(NO_2){\cdot}CH_2OH$

$C_5H_{11}O_3N$ MW, 133

Liq. B.p. 130–6°/28 mm.

Jones, Kenner, *J. Chem. Soc.*, 1930, 926.

1-Nitro-*sec*.-*n*.-amyl Alcohol (1-*Nitro*-2-*pentanol*)

$CH_3{\cdot}CH_2{\cdot}CH_2{\cdot}CH(OH){\cdot}CH_2{\cdot}NO_2$

$C_5H_{11}O_3N$ MW, 133

B.p. 117°/17 mm., 87–8°/3 mm. D_4^{20} 1·0847. n_D^{20} 1·4421.
Acetyl : b.p. 111–13°/10 mm. D_4^{20} 1·0898. n_D^{20} 1·4339.

See previous reference and also
Schmidt, Rutz, *Ber.*, 1928, **61**, 2145.

***o*-Nitroaniline**

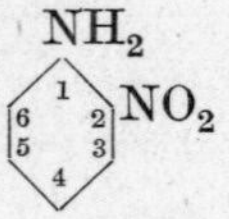

$C_6H_6O_2N_2$ MW, 138

Golden-yellow plates or needles from H_2O. M.p. 71·5°. Very sol. Et_2O. Sol. EtOH, $CHCl_3$. Spar. sol. cold H_2O. $k = 0{\cdot}56 \times 10^{-14}$ at 25°. Electrolytic reduction ⟶ *o*-phenylenediamine.
B,HCl : plates. Decomp. at 155°. Insol. C_6H_6, pet. ether.
B,HI : plates. Decomp. at 141°.
B_2,H_2SO_4 : needles. M.p. 144°.
B,$C_6H_3(NO_2)_3$-1 : 3 : 5 : brownish-yellow needles. M.p. 91°.
Picrate : red cryst. from EtOH. M.p. 73°.
N-*Me* : *see o*-Nitro-*N*-methylaniline.
N-*Di-Me* : *see o*-Nitro-*N*-dimethylaniline.
N-*Di-Et* : *see o*-Nitro-*N*-diethylaniline.
N-*Dipropyl* : *see o*-Nitro-*N*-dipropylaniline.
N-*Phenyl* : *see* 2-Nitrodiphenylamine.
N-*Diphenyl* : *see* 2-Nitrotriphenylamine.
N-*Benzyl* : reddish-yellow prisms from EtOH. M.p. 74–5°.
N-*Dibenzyl* : *see o*-Nitro-*N*-dibenzylaniline.
N-*Formyl*: *o*-nitroformanilide. Yellow needles from EtOH. M.p. 122°. Very sol. AcOH, C_6H_6, Me_2CO, $CHCl_3$. Sol. hot H_2O, EtOH, Et_2O, CS_2.
N-*Acetyl* : *see o*-Nitroacetanilide.
N-*Diacetyl* : cryst. from EtOH. M.p. 94°. Mod. sol. EtOH.
N-*Chloroacetyl* : light yellow needles from EtOH. M.p. 90–3° (88°). Sol. EtOH, C_6H_6, AcOH. Insol. H_2O. Alc. KOH ⟶ red col.
N-*Dichloroacetyl* : light yellow cryst. from EtOH. M.p. 78–80°. Alc. KOH ⟶ orange-red col.
N-*Trichloroacetyl* : yellow needles from EtOH. M.p. 70–2° (65°). Very sol. EtOH. Insol. H_2O.
N-*Propionyl* : yellow cryst. from EtOH. M.p. 63°. Sol. hot H_2O, EtOH, Et_2O, C_6H_6.
N-*Benzoyl* : golden-yellow needles from EtOH. M.p. 98°. Very sol. Et_2O. Sol. EtOH. Spar. sol. H_2O.
N-*Dibenzoyl* : plates from EtOH. M.p. 182°.

Votoček, Burda, *Ber.*, 1915, **48**, 1004.
Sakellarios, Jatrides, *Ber.*, 1925, **58**, 2286.
Ehrenfeld, Puterbaugh, *Organic Syntheses*, Collective Vol. I, 381.

***m*-Nitroaniline.**
Yellow needles from H_2O. M.p. 114°. B.p. above 285°. D_4 1·430. 0·114 parts sol. in 100 parts H_2O at 20°. Sol. MeOH, Et_2O. Mod. sol. C_6H_6. $k = 4{\cdot}0 \times 10^{-12}$ at 25°.
B,HF : cryst. M.p. 207–9°.
B,HCl : cryst. Very sol. H_2O, EtOH.
B,HBr : yellow plates.
Picrate : yellow needles from EtOH. M.p. 143°.
Styphnate : yellowish needles from C_6H_6. M.p. 137°. Sol. EtOH, C_6H_6, AcOEt. Decomp. by $CHCl_3$, CCl_4.
Dioxalate : needles from H_2O. M.p. 119°.
m-*Nitrobenzoic acid add. comp.* : yellow needles from Et_2O. M.p. 88–9°.
2 : 4 : 6-*Trinitrobenzoic acid add. comp.* : yellow needles from hot EtOH. M.p. 139°.

B,$C_6H_3(NO_2)_3$-1 : 3 : 5 : yellow needles. M.p. 98°.

Trichloroacetic acid add. comp. : pale yellow needles. M.p. 147°.

N-*Me* : *see m*-Nitro-*N*-methylaniline.

N-*Di-Me* : *see m*-Nitro-*N*-dimethylaniline.

N-*Et* : *see m*-Nitro-*N*-ethylaniline.

N-*Di-Et* : *see m*-Nitro-*N*-diethylaniline.

N-*Phenyl* : *see* 3-Nitrodiphenylamine.

N-*Benzyl* : yellow leaflets from EtOH.Aq. M.p. 107°.

N-*Dibenzyl* : *see m*-Nitro-*N*-dibenzylaniline.

N-*Diphenyl* : *see* 3-Nitrotriphenylamine.

N-*Formyl* : *m*-nitroformanilide. Cryst. M.p. 134°. Sol. hot H_2O, EtOH, C_6H_6. Spar. sol. Et_2O, ligroin.

N-*Acetyl* : *see m*-Nitroacetanilide.

N-*Diacetyl* : cryst. from Et_2O. M.p. 76–7°. Sol. Et_2O, C_6H_6.

N-*Chloroacetyl* : plates or prisms from EtOH.Aq. M.p. 116° (101–2°).

N-*Benzoyl* : plates from amyl alcohol. M.p. 157°. Sol. Et_2O, $CHCl_3$. Spar. sol. cold EtOH. Insol. H_2O.

N-*Dibenzoyl* : prisms from EtOH. M.p. 150–1°.

Lyford, U.S.P., 1,878,950, (*Chem. Abstracts*, 1933, **27**, 307).
Vorontzov, *Chem. Abstracts*, 1931, **25**, 4861.

p-Nitroaniline.

Pale yellow needles from H_2O. M.p. 148°. D_4 1·424. Sol. 45 parts boiling, 1250 parts H_2O at 18·5°. Sol. MeOH, EtOH, Et_2O. Mod. sol. C_6H_6, toluene. Non-volatile in steam. $k = 1{\cdot}1 \times 10^{-12}$ at 25°.

B,HF : m.p. 173–4°.

B,HCl : leaflets.

Picrate : yellowish-red needles. M.p. 100°.

N-*Me* : *see p*-Nitro-*N*-methylaniline.

N-*Di-Me* : *see p*-Nitro-*N*-dimethylaniline.

N-*Et* : *see p*-Nitro-*N*-ethylaniline.

N-*Di-Et* : *see p*-Nitro-*N*-diethylaniline.

N-*Propyl* : *see p*-Nitro-*N*-propylaniline.

N-*Dipropyl* : *see p*-Nitro-*N*-dipropylaniline.

N-*Phenyl* : *see* 4-Nitrodiphenylamine.

N-*Diphenyl* : *see* 4-Nitrotriphenylamine.

N-*Benzyl* : yellow plates from EtOH.Aq. M.p. 147° (142–3°).

N-*Dibenzyl* : *see p*-Nitro-*N*-dibenzylaniline.

N-*Formyl* : *p*-nitroformanilide. Brownish-yellow cryst. from H_2O. M.p. 194–5°.

N-*Acetyl* : *see p*-Nitroacetanilide.

N-*Chloroacetyl* : leaflets from EtOH. M.p. 85–185·5°.

N-*Dichloroacetyl* : cryst. from toluene. M.p. 128–30°.

N-*Trichloroacetyl* : needles from EtOH. M.p. 146–7°.

N-*Propionyl* : yellowish-brown plates. M.p. 182°.

N-*Benzoyl* : yellowish needles. M.p. 199°. Spar. sol. EtOH. Insol. H_2O, $CHCl_3$. N-*Formyl* : needles from AcOH. M.p. 165°. Sol. EtOH, Me_2CO, C_6H_6, AcOH, AcOEt. Spar. sol. Et_2O. Insol. H_2O.

N-*Dibenzoyl* : prisms from AcOEt. M.p. 203°. Sol. Me_2CO, C_6H_6, AcOH, AcOEt. Insol. H_2O, EtOH, Et_2O.

Votoček, Burda, *Ber.*, 1915, **48**, 1004.
Vasserman, *Chem. Abstracts*, 1931, **25**, 5404.
Merrill, U.S.P., 1,786,766, (*Chem. Abstracts*, 1931, **25**, 716).

***N*-Nitroaniline.**

See Phenylnitramine.

***o*-Nitroaniline-4-sulphonic Acid** (2-*Nitrosulphanilic acid*)

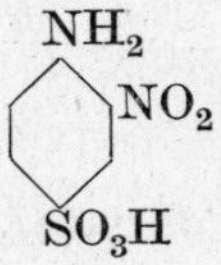

$C_6H_6O_5N_2S$ MW, 218

Yellow needles. Sol. H_2O. Less sol. EtOH.

Chloride : $C_6H_5O_4N_2ClS$. MW, 236·5. Pale yellow plates from Et_2O. M.p. 59–60°.

Amide : $C_6H_7O_4N_3S$. MW, 217. Golden plates or needles from H_2O. M.p. 206–7°.

N-*Phenyl* : *see* 2-Nitrodiphenylamine-4-sulphonic Acid.

Goslich, *Ann.*, 1876, **180**, 103.
Nietzki, Lerch, *Ber.*, 1888, **21**, 3220.
Fischer, *Ber.*, 1891, **24**, 3788.
Bayer, E.P., 235,598, (*Chem. Abstracts*, 1926, **20**, 917).

***m*-Nitroaniline-4-sulphonic Acid** (3-*Nitrosulphanilic acid*)

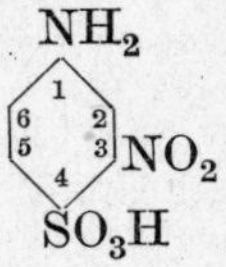

$C_6H_6O_5N_2S$ MW, 218

Needles. Spar. sol. hot H_2O.

Nietzki, Helbach, D.R.P., 86,096 ; *Ber.*, 1896, **29**, 2448.
Hunter, Sprung, *J. Am. Chem. Soc.*, 1931, **53**, 1440.

***m*-Nitroaniline-6-sulphonic Acid** (5-*Nitro-orthanilic acid*).

Yellowish-brown prisms. $k = 8{\cdot}5 \times 10^{-3}$ at 25°.

Bayer, D.R.P., 294,547, (*Chem. Zentr.*, 1916, II, 780).

***p*-Nitroaniline-2-sulphonic Acid** (4-*Nitro-orthanilic acid*)

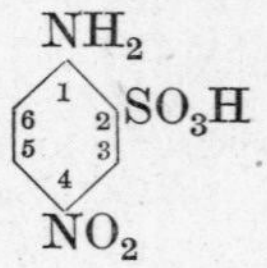

$C_6H_6O_5N_2S$ MW, 218

Yellow cryst.

Amide: $C_6H_7O_4N_3S$. MW, 217. Yellow needles from H_2O. M.p. 207°.

N-*Phenyl*: *see* 4-Nitrodiphenylamine-2-sulphonic Acid.

Fischer, *Ber.*, 1891, **24**, 3789.
Scott, Cohen, *J. Chem. Soc.*, 1922, **121**, 2038.
Bayer, E.P., 235,598, (*Chem. Abstracts*, 1926, **20**, 917).

***p*-Nitroaniline-3-sulphonic Acid** (4-*Nitrometanilic acid*).

Pale yellow needles from H_2O. Sol. H_2O. Spar. sol. EtOH. Insol. Et_2O.

Eger, *Ber.*, 1888, **21**, 2581.
Kalle, D.R.P., 150,982, (*Chem. Zentr.*, 1904, I, 1235).

ω-*p*-Nitroanilinobenzyl Alcohol.

See 4-Nitro-*N*-α-hydroxybenzylaniline.

3-Nitroanisaldehyde (3-*Nitro-4-methoxybenzaldehyde*)

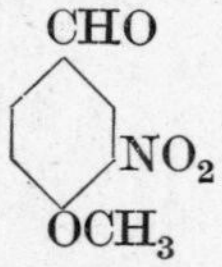

$C_8H_7O_4N$ MW, 181

Needles from $CHCl_3$–ligroin or EtOH–$CHCl_3$. M.p. 86–7°. Sol. usual solvents.

Oxime: *anti*, needles. M.p. 170°. Very sol. Et_2O, Me_2CO. Sol. warm EtOH, C_6H_6. *Syn*: yellowish needles. M.p. 168–70°. Spar. sol. usual solvents.

Phenylhydrazone: yellow plates from EtOH. M.p. 130·5°.

p-*Nitrophenylhydrazone*: red cryst. M.p. 244°.

Einhorn, Grabfield, *Ann.*, 1888, **243**, 370.
Ciusa, *Chem. Zentr.*, 1907, I, 548.

2-Nitroanisic Acid (2-*Nitro-4-methoxybenzoic acid*)

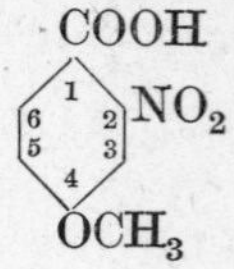

$C_8H_7O_5N$ MW, 197

Needles from H_2O. M.p. 195–6°. Sol. EtOH, Me_2CO. Spar. sol. Et_2O, C_6H_6.

Ullmann, Dootson, *Ber.*, 1918, **51**, 20.
Simonsen, Rau, *J. Chem. Soc.*, 1917, **111**, 236.

3-Nitroanisic Acid (3-*Nitro-4-methoxybenzoic acid*).

Needles from H_2O. M.p. 186–7° (195–6°). Sol. EtOH, Et_2O. Spar. sol. hot H_2O. Distils under 14 mm. press.

Me ester: $C_9H_9O_5N$. MW, 211. Yellow plates. M.p. 109–10°.

Et ester: $C_{10}H_{11}O_5N$. MW, 225. Plates from EtOH. M.p. 97–8° (71–2°).

Propyl ester: $C_{11}H_{13}O_5N$. MW, 239. Cryst. from EtOH. M.p. 63°. B.p. 213–15°/16 mm.

Allyl ester: $C_{11}H_{11}O_5N$. MW, 237. Cryst. M.p. 50°. B.p. 207°/11 mm.

Hexyl ester: $C_{14}H_{19}O_5N$. MW, 281. Yellow oil. B.p. 224–6°/11 mm.

Chloride: $C_8H_6O_4NCl$. MW, 215·5. Cryst. from pet. ether. M.p. 56°.

Nitrile: $C_8H_6O_3N_2$. MW, 178. Needles from EtOH. M.p. 149–50°.

Anilide: needles from EtOH. M.p. 163°.

Ashley, Perkin, Robinson, *J. Chem. Soc.*, 1930, 392.
Sabalitschka, Tiedge, *Arch. Pharm.*, 1934, **272**, 383.

3-Nitro-*o*-anisidine (3-*Nitro-2-aminoanisole*)

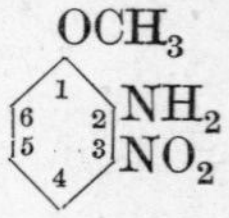

$C_7H_8O_3N_2$ MW, 168

Yellow or bright scarlet needles from EtOH. M.p. 76°.

N-*Me*: $C_8H_{10}O_3N_2$. MW, 182. Dark red needles. M.p. 58°. Sol. EtOH. N-*Acetyl*: prisms from Et_2O. M.p. 105–6°.

N-*Acetyl*: 3-nitro-*o*-acetanisidide. Pale yellow needles from EtOH.Aq. M.p. 158–9°.

Blanksma, *Chem. Zentr.*, 1908, II, 1826.
Ingold, Ingold, *J. Chem. Soc.*, 1926, 1317, 1324.

4-Nitro-*o*-anisidine (*4-Nitro-2-amino-anisole*).

Orange-red needles from EtOH or Et_2O. M.p. 118°. Very sol. Me_2CO. Sol. EtOH, AcOEt, AcOH, boiling C_6H_6. Spar. sol. ligroin.

N-*Me* : orange cryst. from pet. ether. M.p. 87°. N-*Acetyl* : m.p. 126·5–127·5°.

N-*Di-Me* : $C_9H_{12}O_3N_2$. MW, 196. Yellow cryst. from EtOH. M.p. 68–9°.

N-*Acetyl* : 4-nitro-*o*-acetanisidide. Needles from H_2O. M.p. 175–6°.

N-*Benzoyl* : yellow needles from EtOH. M.p. 160–1°. Spar. sol. EtOH, Et_2O.

N-p-*Toluenesulphonyl* : cryst. from AcOH. M.p. 128°.

Fabr. de Thann et Mulhouse, D.R.P., 98,637, (*Chem. Zentr.*, 1898, II, 951).
Vermeulen, *Rec. trav. chim.*, 1906, **25**, 18.
Meldola, Woolcott, Wray, *J. Chem. Soc.*, 1896, **69**, 1330.
Ingold, Ingold, *J. Chem. Soc.*, 1926, 1323.

5-Nitro-*o*-anisidine (*5-Nitro-2-amino-anisole*).

Pale yellow needles. M.p. 139–40°.

N-*Me* : yellow needles from MeOH or pet. ether. M.p. 101–2°. N-*Acetyl* : m.p. 119–120·5°.

N-*Di-Me* : yellow needles. M.p. 99°. Sol. boiling EtOH.

N-*Acetyl* : 5-nitro-*o*-acetanisidide. Pale yellow cryst. from AcOEt. M.p. 153–4°. Sol. boiling C_6H_6. Insol. ligroin.

N-*Benzoyl* : needles from EtOH. M.p. 149–50°.

N-*Benzenesulphonyl* : yellow plates. M.p. 181°.

N-p-*Toluenesulphonyl* : yellow prisms. M.p. 175° (169–70°).

Meldola, Eyre, *Chem. News*, 1901, **83**, 286.
Gribov, Ivanov, Salomatina, *Chem. Abstracts*, 1934, **28**, 1029.
du Pont, U.S.P., 1,963,598, (*Chem. Abstracts*, 1934, **28**, 5084).
See also previous references.

6-Nitro-*o*-anisidine (*6-Nitro-2-amino-anisole*).

Yellow needles from ligroin. M.p. 67°.

N-*Acetyl* : 6-nitro-*o*-acetanisidide. Pale yellow prisms from MeOH or AcOH.Aq. M.p. 103–4°.

Ingold, Ingold, *J. Chem. Soc.*, 1926, 1318.

2-Nitro-*m*-anisidine (*2-Nitro-3-amino-anisole*)

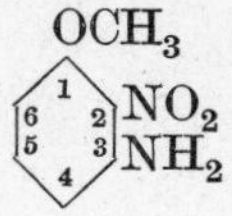

$C_7H_8O_3N_2$ MW, 168

Yellow needles. M.p. 143°.

N-*Acetyl* : 2-nitro-*m*-acetanisidide. Brown cryst. M.p. 265°. Sol. EtOH, C_6H_6. Sublimes.

Reverdin, Widmer, *Ber.*, 1913, **46**, 4073.

4-Nitro-*m*-anisidine (*4-Nitro-3-amino-anisole*).

Brown needles. M.p. 131°. Sublimes.

N-*Acetyl* : 4-nitro-*m*-acetanisidide. Needles from EtOH. M.p. 125°. Sol. EtOH, AcOH. Mod. sol. ligroin.

Meldola, Stephens, *J. Chem. Soc.*, 1906, **89**, 924.
See also previous reference.

5-Nitro-*m*-anisidine (*5-Nitro-3-amino-anisole*).

Orange cryst. M.p. 120°. Sol. hot H_2O. Mod. sol. EtOH, C_6H_6. Insol. ligroin.

N-*Acetyl* : 5-nitro-*m*-acetanisidide. Cryst. M.p. 200°. Sol. EtOH, AcOEt. Less sol. C_6H_6. Insol. H_2O, ligroin.

Vermeulen, *Rec. trav. chim.*, 1906, **25**, 20.
Höchst, D.R.P., 222,062, (*Chem. Zentr.*, 1910, I, 2001).

6-Nitro-*m*-anisidine (*6-Nitro-3-amino-anisole*).

Yellow needles from EtOH. M.p. 169° (161°). Sol. EtOH, Me_2CO, AcOH. Sublimes easily.

N-*Acetyl* : 6-nitro-*m*-acetanisidide. Golden-yellow needles from H_2O. M.p. 165°. Sol. EtOH, AcOH. Spar. sol. H_2O. Insol. ligroin.

Reverdin, Widmer, *Ber.*, 1913, **46**, 4072.
Höchst, D.R.P., 285,638, (*Chem. Zentr.*, 1915, II, 511).

2-Nitro-*p*-anisidine (*2-Nitro-4-amino-anisole*)

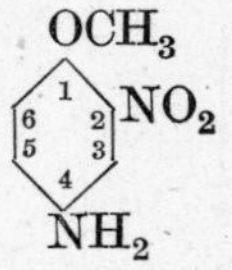

$C_7H_8O_3N_2$ MW, 168

Orange prisms and plates from Et_2O–ligroin. M.p. 57–57·5°. Sol. hot H_2O, Me_2CO, EtOH, Et_2O. Mod. sol. C_6H_6. Spar. sol. toluene. 10% HCl ⟶ pale yellow sol.

B_2,H_2SO_4: yellowish-brown cryst. from H_2O. M.p. 243°. Spar. sol. cold H_2O.

N-*Di-Me*: $C_9H_{12}O_3N_2$. MW, 196. Red cryst. from EtOH. M.p. 46°.

N-*Acetyl*: 2-nitro-*p*-acetanisidide. Yellow needles from H_2O. M.p. 153°. Sol. H_2O. Spar. sol. C_6H_6, ligroin.

N-*Chloroacetyl*: golden-yellow needles from AcOEt. M.p. 149·5–151·5°. Sol. Me_2CO. Spar. sol. $CHCl_3$. Almost insol. H_2O.

Heidelberger, Jacobs, *J. Am. Chem. Soc.*, 1919, **41**, 1455.
Höchst, D.R.P., 101,778, (*Chem. Zentr.*, 1899, I, 1175).
Klemenc, *Ber.*, 1914, **47**, 1411.

3-Nitro-*p*-anisidine (3-*Nitro*-4-*amino-anisole*).

Dark red prisms from H_2O or EtOH. M.p. 129° (123°). Sol. H_2O, EtOH, Et_2O. Spar. sol. C_6H_6. Volatile in steam.

N-*Acetyl*: 3-nitro-*p*-acetanisidide. Yellow needles from EtOH. M.p. 117°. Sol. hot H_2O, EtOH, Et_2O, C_6H_6, AcOH.

N-*Benzoyl*: plates from EtOH. M.p. 140°. Sol. hot EtOH, C_6H_6, AcOH.

N-o-*Nitrobenzoyl*: orange needles. M.p. 172°. Sol. Me_2CO, hot C_6H_6. Spar. sol. EtOH, AcOH. Conc. $H_2SO_4 \longrightarrow$ bluish-green col.

N-m-*Nitrobenzoyl*: orange cryst. M.p. 165–6°. Sol. Me_2CO, EtOH, AcOH.

N-p-*Nitrobenzoyl*: orange needles from AcOH. M.p. 204°. Sol. Me_2CO, hot AcOH. Spar. sol. EtOH.

Reverdin, *Ber.*, 1896, **29**, 2595; 1911, **44**, 2365.
Reverdin, de Luc, *Ber.*, 1912, **45**, 352.

***o*-Nitroanisole**

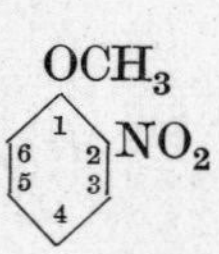

$C_7H_7O_3N$ MW, 153

Cryst. M.p. 10°. B.p. 272°, 150·5–151°/19 mm. Insol. H_2O. D_4^{20} 1·2540. n_D^{20} 1·56204. Volatile in steam.

Ullmann, *Ann.*, 1903, **327**, 114.
Weltz, U.S.P., 1,578,943, (*Chem. Abstracts*, 1926, **20**, 1631).
Clemmensen, U.S.P., 1,875,916, (*Chem. Abstracts*, 1933, **27**, 102).
Aoyama, Morita, *Chem. Abstracts*, 1934, **28**, 141.

***m*-Nitroanisole.**

Needles from EtOH, plates from C_6H_6–ligroin. M.p. 38–9°. B.p. 258°. Insol. H_2O. D^{18} 1·373. Volatile in steam.

Bantlin, *Ber.*, 1878, **11**, 2100.

***p*-Nitroanisole.**

Prisms from EtOH. M.p. 54°. B.p. 259°. D_4^{75} 1·2012. Sol. EtOH, Et_2O. Sol. 13,923 parts H_2O at 15°. Spar. sol. cold pet. ether.

v. Blom, *Helv. Chim. Acta*, 1921, **4**, 1029.
v. Erp, *Ber.*, 1923, **56**, 217.
Rarick, Brewster, Dains, *J. Am. Chem. Soc.*, 1933, **55**, 1289.

***m*-Nitroanisole-6-sulphinic Acid** (4-*Nitro*-2-*methoxybenzenesulphinic acid*)

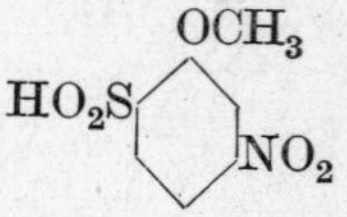

$C_7H_7O_5NS$ MW, 217

Needles from AcOEt. M.p. 127–9°.

Holmes, Ingold, Ingold, *J. Chem. Soc.*, 1926, 1688.

***p*-Nitroanisole-2-sulphinic Acid** (5-*Nitro*-2-*methoxybenzenesulphinic acid*)

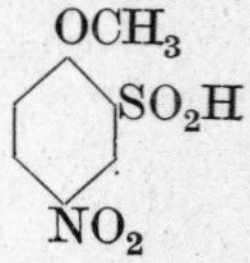

$C_7H_7O_5NS$ MW, 217

Prisms from AcOEt. M.p. 134–6°.

See previous reference.

***o*-Nitroanisole-4-sulphonic Acid** (3-*Nitro*-4-*methoxybenzenesulphonic acid*)

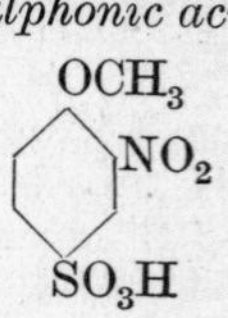

$C_7H_7O_6NS$ MW, 233

Plates from H_2O, prisms from AcOEt–C_6H_6. Very sol. H_2O, AcOEt.

Me ester: $C_8H_9O_6NS$. MW, 247. Prisms from toluene–ligroin. M.p. 83°. Decomp. by H_2O.

Chloride: $C_7H_6O_5NSCl$. MW, 251·5. Needles from C_6H_6–pet. ether. M.p. 66°. Sol. C_6H_6, toluene. Spar. sol. ligroin, pet. ether.

Amide: $C_7H_8O_5N_2S$. MW, 232. Yellowish needles from H_2O. M.p. 146·3°.

Gnehm, Knecht, *J. prakt. Chem.*, 1906, **74**, 92.

9-Nitroanthracene (ms-*Nitroanthracene*)

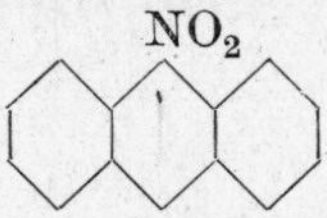

$C_{14}H_9O_2N$ MW, 223

Yellow needles from EtOH, prisms from AcOH or xylene. M.p. 146°. Distils in vacuo above 300°. Very sol. C_6H_6, CS_2. Spar. sol. EtOH, AcOH. Insol. aq. alkalis.

Dimroth, *Ber.*, 1901, **34**, 221; D.R.P., 127,399, (*Chem. Zentr.*, 1902, I, 235).

4-Nitroanthragallol (4-*Nitro*-1 : 2 : 3-*trihydroxyanthraquinone*)

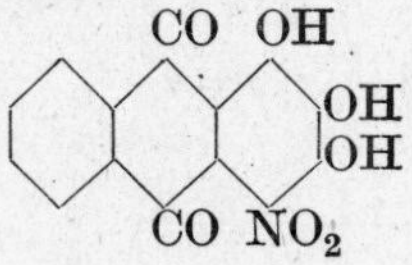

$C_{14}H_7O_7N$ MW, 301

Golden-brown cryst. from hot EtOH–ligroin. M.p. 224° decomp. Sol. EtOH, AcOH. Less sol. Et_2O, C_6H_6, $CHCl_3$. Insol. H_2O, pet. ether.

Triacetyl: yellow needles from Ac_2O–AcOH. M.p. 233°.

Tribenzoyl: cryst. from AcOH. M.p. 209°. Sol. EtOH, C_6H_6, AcOH. Insol. H_2O.

Bamberger, Böck, *Monatsh.*, 1897, **18**, 288; 1901, **22**, 719.

3-Nitroanthranilic Acid (3-*Nitro*-o-*aminobenzoic acid*)

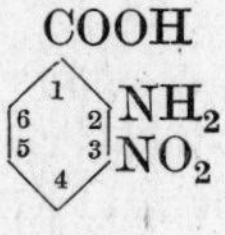

$C_7H_6O_4N_2$ MW, 182

Yellow needles from H_2O. M.p. 208–9°. Very sol. EtOH, Et_2O. Spar. sol. C_6H_6, $CHCl_3$. D^{15} 1·558. Spar. volatile in steam.

Et ester: $C_9H_{10}O_4N_2$. MW, 210. Yellow plates. M.p. 109°. Mod. sol. H_2O, EtOH. Readily volatile in steam. N-*Acetyl*: needles from H_2O. M.p. 102°. Sol. EtOH, Et_2O. Spar. sol. H_2O, $CHCl_3$, pet. ether. Sublimes at 140°. N-*Benzoyl*: cryst. from ligroin. M.p. 85·5°. Sol. EtOH, Et_2O, C_6H_6, $CHCl_3$. Spar. sol. ligroin.

N-*Me*: $C_8H_8O_4N_2$. MW, 196. Reddish-brown needles from EtOH.Aq. M.p. 146°. Sol. EtOH, Et_2O. Spar. sol. H_2O.

N-*Acetyl*: yellow needles from hot H_2O or AcOH. M.p. 180–1°.

Chapman, Stephen, *J. Chem. Soc.*, 1925, **127**, 1795.
Keller, *Arch. Pharm.*, 1908, **246**, 32.
Zacharias, *J. prakt. Chem.*, 1891, **43**, 435.

4-Nitroanthranilic Acid (4-*Nitro*-o-*aminobenzoic acid*).

Orange prisms from EtOH.Aq. M.p. 269°. Sol. xylene. Spar. sol. hot H_2O. Sweet taste.

Me ester: $C_8H_8O_4N_2$. MW, 196. Orange needles. M.p. 157°. Sol. EtOH, ligroin.

Et ester: $C_9H_{10}O_4N_2$. MW, 210. Orange prisms from EtOH. M.p. 100°. Very sol. hot EtOH, Et_2O. N-*Acetyl*: pale yellow plates. M.p. 112°.

N-*Et*: $C_9H_{10}O_4N_2$. MW, 210. Golden-yellow needles or plates. M.p. 223°. *Et ester*: $C_{11}H_{14}O_4N_2$. MW, 238. Pale yellow needles from EtOH or C_6H_6. M.p. 80°.

N-*Phenyl*: *see* 5-Nitrodiphenylamine-2-carboxylic Acid.

N-*Acetyl*: needles from EtOH.Aq. M.p. 217°. Sol. EtOH, Et_2O, $CHCl_3$. Insol. C_6H_6, ligroin.

Amide: pale yellow needles from EtOH. M.p. 218–23°. *Guanidine salt*: cryst. M.p. 247°.

Wheeler, Barnes, *Am. Chem. J.*, 1898, **20**, 221.
Wheeler, Jones, *Am. Chem. J.*, 1910, **44**, 444.
I.G., E.P., 285,877, (*Chem. Abstracts*, 1929, **23**, 156).
See also first reference above.

5-Nitroanthranilic Acid (5-*Nitro*-o-*aminobenzoic acid*).

Yellow needles from EtOH.Aq. M.p. 280° (263°). Sol. hot H_2O, EtOH, Et_2O. Insol. C_6H_6, $CHCl_3$, xylene. Hot conc. KOH ⟶ 5-nitrosalicylic acid.

Me ester: $C_8H_8O_4N_2$. MW, 196. Greenish-yellow needles from EtOH.Aq. M.p. 168°. Sol. usual org. solvents. Spar. sol. H_2O. Spar. volatile in steam. Sublimes.

Et ester: $C_9H_{10}O_4N_2$. MW, 210. Yellow needles from EtOH. M.p. 148°. Sol. EtOH, Et_2O, C_6H_6, Me_2CO, $CHCl_3$, AcOH. Spar. sol. pet. ether. N-*Acetyl*: needles from EtOH. M.p. 153°. Sol. EtOH, Et_2O, C_6H_6, $CHCl_3$, AcOH. Insol. H_2O.

N-*Me*: $C_8H_8O_4N_2$. MW, 196. Pale yellow leaflets from EtOH. M.p. 259° decomp. Sol. EtOH, Et_2O. Insol. H_2O. *Et ester*: $C_{10}H_{12}O_4N_2$. MW, 224. Greenish-yellow needles from

EtOH.Aq. M.p. 103°. Sol. EtOH, Et_2O. Sublimes. *Methylamide*: golden-yellow needles from hot H_2O. M.p. 204°. Sol. EtOH. Spar. sol. hot H_2O, Et_2O. Sublimes in needles. N-*Acetyl*: plates from Et_2O. M.p. 66°. Sol. EtOH. Spar. sol. cold H_2O.

N-*Phenyl*: *see* 4-Nitrodiphenylamine-2-carboxylic Acid.

N-o-*Tolyl*: $C_{14}H_{12}O_4N_2$. MW, 272. Yellow needles from EtOH. M.p. 253–4°.

N-p-*Tolyl*: yellow needles from AcOH. M.p. 262·5°.

Amide: $C_7H_7O_3N_3$. MW, 181. Yellow needles from EtOH–Me_2CO. M.p. 230°. Sol. Me_2CO. Spar. sol. hot H_2O, EtOH.

Methylamide: yellow needles from EtOH.Aq. M.p. 230–1° decomp. Very sol. warm H_2O, EtOH. Spar. sol. $CHCl_3$. Insol. C_6H_6.

Dimethylamide: m.p. 213–14°.

Ethylamide: golden-yellow needles from EtOH. M.p. 156° decomp. Sol. AcOH. Spar. sol. H_2O, $CHCl_3$.

Anilide: $C_{13}H_{11}O_3N_3$. MW, 257. Needles from AcOH. M.p. 203°. Spar. sol. H_2O, EtOH, $CHCl_3$. Insol. Et_2O, C_6H_6.

Methylanilide: m.p. 183–4°.

Ethylanilide: m.p. 144–5°.

Ethyl-o-toluidide: m.p. 147–8°.

N-*Acetyl*: yellow needles from H_2O. M.p. 216–17°.

Hydrazide: yellow needles from H_2O. M.p. 214–18° decomp. Sol. H_2O, EtOH. Insol. Et_2O, $CHCl_3$. Reduces $NH_3.AgNO_3$ and Fehling's.

Thieme, *J. prakt. Chem.*, 1891, **43**, 470.
Grohmann, *Ber.*, 1891, **24**, 3810.
Kratz, *J. prakt. Chem.*, 1896, **53**, 215.
Bayer, D.R.P., 309,951, (*Chem. Zentr.*, 1919, II, 179).
Chapman, Stephen, *J. Chem. Soc.*, 1925, **127**, 1796.

6-Nitroanthranilic Acid (6-*Nitro*-o-*amino-benzoic acid*).

Yellow needles from H_2O. M.p. 184°. Very sol. EtOH, Et_2O, Me_2CO, AcOH. Sol. hot H_2O. Spar. sol. C_6H_6, $CHCl_3$, CS_2. Sweet taste. Dil. $H_2SO_4 \longrightarrow$ *m*-nitroaniline.

Anilide: $C_{13}H_{11}O_3N_3$. MW, 257. Yellow needles from $CHCl_3$. M.p. 137°.

N-*Carbethoxyl*: $C_{10}H_{10}O_6N_2$. MW, 254. Yellowish needles from EtOH.Aq. or H_2O. M.p. 187°.

N-*Acetyl*: cryst. from H_2O. M.p. 212–14°. decomp. Sol. hot EtOH, cold Me_2CO, hot AcOEt. Spar. sol. hot $CHCl_3$, C_6H_6. Insol. Et_2O, pet. ether. *Amide*: cryst. M.p. 218–19°.

N-*Propionyl*: cryst. from AcOEt. M.p. 218°.

Curtius, Semper, *Ber.*, 1913, **46**, 1168.
Bogert, Chambers, *J. Am. Chem. Soc.*, 1905, **27**, 653.
Bogert, Seil, *ibid.*, 1309.

***ms*-Nitroanthranol** (9-*Nitro*-10-*hydroxy-anthracene*)

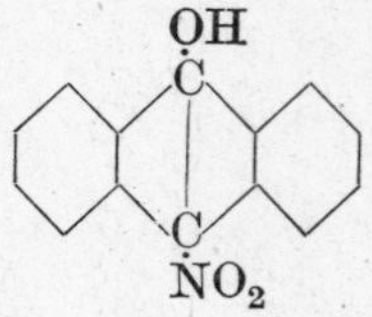

$C_{14}H_9O_3N$ MW, 239

Red needles. Sol. Et_2O, C_6H_6, $CHCl_3$.

Acetyl: yellow plates or needles from $CHCl_3$–pet. ether. M.p. 182°.

Benzoyl: yellow prisms from $CHCl_3$–pet. ether. M.p. 238° decomp. Spar. sol. EtOH.

Meyer, Sander, *Ann.*, 1913, **396**, 150.

1-Nitroanthraquinone

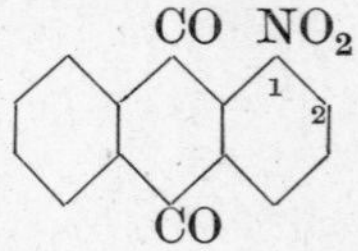

$C_{14}H_7O_4N$ MW, 253

Needles from AcOH. M.p. 230°. B.p. 270°/7 mm. Sol. C_6H_6, $CHCl_3$, AcOH. Spar. sol. EtOH, Et_2O. Insol. H_2O. Sublimes in yellow plates.

Boettger, Petersen, *Ann.*, 1873, **166**, 147.
Lauth, *Bull. soc. chim.*, 1903, **29**, 1133.

2-Nitroanthraquinone.

Yellow needles from EtOH or AcOH. M.p. 184·5–185°. Distils in vacuo. Sol. Me_2CO, $CHCl_3$, hot AcOH, amyl alcohol. Mod. sol. EtOH, Et_2O. Spar. sol. ligroin. Conc. $H_2SO_4 \longrightarrow$ yellow sol. $\longrightarrow$ reddish-yellow on heating.

Scholl, Schneider, Eberle, *Ber.*, 1904, **37**, 4434.
Datta, Varma, *J. Am. Chem. Soc.*, 1919, **41**, 2048.

5-Nitroanthraquinone-1-carboxylic Acid

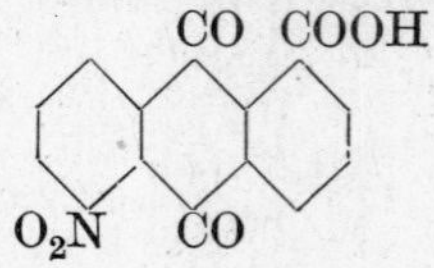

$C_{15}H_7O_6N$ MW, 297

Yellow plates. Decomp. above 330°. Sol. boiling Me_2CO, Py, $PhNO_2$. Spar. sol. boiling

EtOH, AcOH, toluene. Insol. Et_2O, ligroin. Conc. H_2SO_4 ⟶ yellow sol.

Nitrile: $C_{15}H_6O_4N_2$. MW, 278. Yellow plates. M.p. about 390°. Sol. boiling Py, $PhNO_2$. Spar. sol. AcOH, toluene. Insol. EtOH, Et_2O.

Ullmann, v. der Schalk, *Ann.*, 1912, **388**, 208.

1-Nitroanthraquinone-2-carboxylic Acid

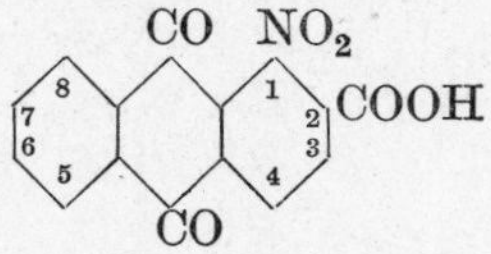

$C_{15}H_7O_6N$ MW, 297

Needles from EtOH or AcOH. M.p. 285–7°. Sol. hot Me_2CO. Insol. Et_2O, ligroin.

Me ester: $C_{16}H_9O_6N$. MW, 311. M.p. 249–51°.

Et ester: $C_{17}H_{11}O_6N$. MW, 325. Pale yellow plates from AcOH. M.p. 233–4°.

Propyl ester: $C_{18}H_{13}O_6N$. MW, 339. M.p. 182–3°.

Isopropyl ester: m.p. 204–6°.

Butyl ester: $C_{19}H_{15}O_6N$. MW, 353. M.p. 174–5°.

sec.-n-*Butyl ester*: m.p. 155–6°.

Isobutyl ester: m.p. 159–60°.

Amyl ester: $C_{20}H_{17}O_6N$. MW, 367. M.p. 166–8°.

Isoamyl ester: m.p. 165–7°.

Hexyl ester: $C_{21}H_{19}O_6N$. MW, 381. M.p. 153–4°.

Cetyl ester: m.p. 105–6°.

Allyl ester: $C_{18}H_{11}O_6N$. MW, 337. M.p. 184–5°.

Benzyl ester: m.p. 211–12°.

Menthyl ester: m.p. 189–90°.

Amide: $C_{15}H_8O_5N_2$. MW, 296. Yellow plates or prisms from AcOH. M.p. 299–301°. Spar. sol. most org. solvents.

Sah, Ma, *J. Chinese Chem. Soc.*, 1933, **1**, 51.
Badische, D.R.P., 256,344, (*Chem. Zentr.*, 1913, I, 759).
Terres, *Ber.*, 1913, **46**, 1639.

5-Nitroanthraquinone-2-carboxylic Acid. Yellow needles from AcOH. Sol. AcOH, chlorobenzene, hot toluene.

Amide: $C_{15}H_8O_5N_2$. MW, 296. Cryst. from AcOH or $PhNO_2$. M.p. 330° decomp.

Eckert, *Monatsh.*, 1914, **35**, 295.

1-Nitroanthraquinone-5-sulphonic Acid

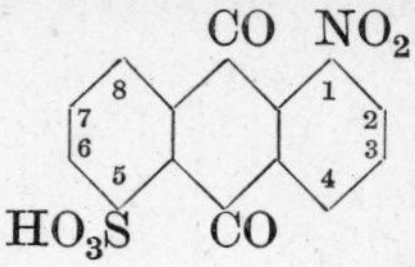

$C_{14}H_7O_7NS$ MW, 333

Cryst. from H_2O.

Chloride: $C_{14}H_6O_6NClS$. MW, 351·5. Yellow needles from $PhNO_2$. M.p. 277°. Sol. hot C_6H_6, toluene. Spar. sol. Me_2CO, AcOH.

Ullmann, Kertész, *Ber.*, 1919, **52**, 552.
Maki, Nagai, *Chem. Abstracts*, 1931, **25**, 948.

1-Nitroanthraquinone-6-sulphonic Acid (5-*Nitroanthraquinone-2-sulphonic acid*).

Yellowish plates from dil. HNO_3. M.p. 255° decomp. Spar. sol. cold H_2O.

Chloride: $C_{14}H_6O_6NClS$. MW, 351·5. Yellowish needles. M.p. 194°. Sol. hot toluene, AcOH. Insol. EtOH, Et_2O.

Claus, *Ber.*, 1882, **15**, 1514.
Höchst, D.R.P., 145,188, (*Chem. Zentr.*, 1903, II, 1038).

1-Nitroanthraquinone-7-sulphonic Acid (8-*Nitroanthraquinone-2-sulphonic acid*).

Cryst. powder. M.p. 250° decomp. Sol. H_2O, EtOH, AcOH. Alkalis ⟶ red col.

See last reference above and also
Claus, *Ber.*, 1882, **15**, 1516.

1-Nitroanthraquinone-8-sulphonic Acid. Cryst. from H_2O.

Chloride: yellow needles. M.p. 245°.

Ullmann, Kertész, *Ber.*, 1919, **52**, 552.
Maki, Nagai, *Chem. Abstracts*, 1931, **25**, 948.

2-Nitroanthraquinone-7-sulphonic Acid (7-*Nitroanthraquinone-2-sulphonic acid*).

Cryst. from H_2O.

Na salt: white needles from H_2O.

Gubelmann, Weiland, Stallmann, *J. Am. Chem. Soc.*, 1931, **53**, 1035.
Newport Chemical Corp., U.S.P., 1,810,010, (*Chem. Abstracts*, 1931, **25**, 4559).

***ms*-Nitroanthrone**

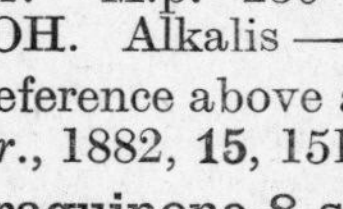

$C_{14}H_9O_3N$ MW, 239

Cryst. from C_6H_6–ligroin. M.p. 140°. Alkalis ⟶ red sols.

Di-Me acetal: needles. M.p. 135° decomp. Very sol. CS_2. Spar. sol. EtOH, C_6H_6, $CHCl_3$.

Meyer, *Organic Syntheses*, Collective Vol. I, 382.

2-Nitroazobenzene

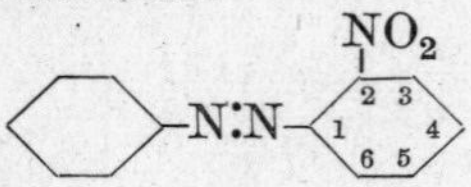

$C_{12}H_9O_2N_3$ MW, 227

Dark orange-red prisms from EtOH. M.p. 70·5–71°. Sol. EtOH, $CHCl_3$, AcOH, C_6H_6, ligroin.

Bamberger, Hübner, *Ber.*, 1903, **36**, 3818.

3-Nitroazobenzene.
Orange needles. M.p. 95·5–96°. Sol. EtOH, AcOH, ligroin.

Bamberger, Hübner, *Ber.*, 1903, **36**, 3811.

4-Nitroazobenzene.
Orange plates or needles from ligroin. M.p. 135°. Sol. EtOH, Me_2CO, $CHCl_3$, AcOH, C_6H_6, ligroin.

See previous reference and also
Angeli, Allesandri, *Atti accad. Lincei*, 1911, **20**, 171.

5-Nitroazobenzene-2-carboxylic Acid (o-*Benzeneazo-*p*-nitrobenzoic acid*)

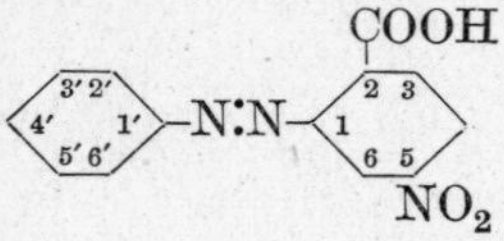

$C_{13}H_9O_4N_3$ MW, 271

Anilide: $C_{19}H_{14}O_3N_4$. MW, 332. Orange-red cryst. from EtOH. M.p. 180·5°.

Sachs, Sichel, *Ber.*, 1903, **36**, 4375.

2-Nitroazobenzene-4-carboxylic Acid (p-*Benzeneazo-*m*-nitrobenzoic acid*).
Red needles from EtOH. M.p. 215°. Sol. EtOH, Et_2O, C_6H_6.

Et ester: $C_{15}H_{13}O_4N_3$. MW, 299. Red needles. M.p. 139°.

Werner, Peters, *Ber.*, 1906, **39**, 191.

3-Nitroazobenzene-4′-sulphonic Acid

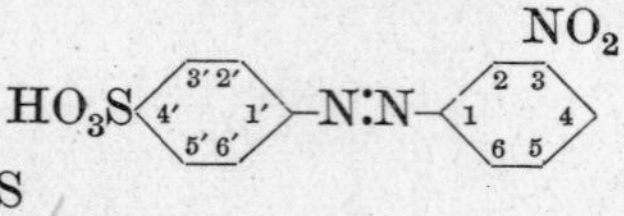

$C_{12}H_9O_5N_3S$ MW, 307

Leaflets. Sol. H_2O. Reduction ⟶ *m*-phenylenediamine + sulphanilic acid.

K salt: orange-red plates. Spar. sol. cold H_2O.

Janovsky, *Monatsh.*, 1882, **3**, 504.

4-Nitroazobenzene-4′-sulphonic Acid.
Orange-yellow needles + $3H_2O$ from H_2O, plates from dil. HNO_3. 3·1 parts sol. 100 parts H_2O at 10°. Zn + HCl ⟶ *p*-phenylenediamine + sulphanilic acid.

K salt: orange-yellow plates. 0·161 parts sol. 100 parts H_2O at 17°, 1·76 parts sol. 100 parts H_2O at 82°.

Janovsky, *Monatsh.*, 1883, **4**, 276.

2-Nitroazoxybenzene

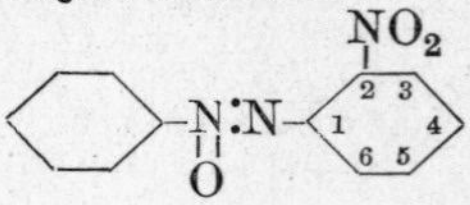

$C_{12}H_9O_3N_3$ MW, 243

Yellow needles or prisms. M.p. 49°. Very sol. Et_2O, C_6H_6. Less sol. EtOH.

Angeli, Alessandri, *Atti. accad. Lincei*, 1911, **20**, 896.
Zinin, *Ann.*, 1860, **114**, 218.

4-Nitroazoxybenzene.
Pale yellow cryst. from EtOH. M.p. 153°.

See previous references.

Nitrobarbituric Acid.
See Dilituric Acid.

Nitrobenzaldazine.
See under Nitrobenzaldehyde.

***o*-Nitrobenzaldehyde**

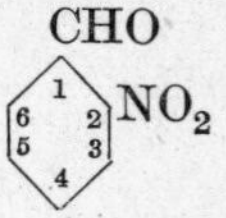

$C_7H_5O_3N$ MW, 151

Bright yellow needles from H_2O. M.p. 43–4°. B.p. 153°/23 mm. Sol. most org. solvents. Spar. sol. H_2O. Volatile in steam. Ox. ⟶ *o*-nitrobenzoic acid. Exposure of C_6H_6 sol. to sunlight ⟶ *o*-nitrosobenzoic acid.

syn-*Oxime*: cryst. from C_6H_6. M.p. 154°. Boiling the C_6H_6 sol. ⟶ *anti*-oxime.

anti-*Oxime*: needles. M.p. 102–3° (96–7°). Sol. EtOH, Et_2O, C_6H_6. Spar. sol. CS_2, pet. ether. Sol. alkalis. Irradiation of C_6H_6 sol. ⟶ *syn*-oxime.

Semicarbazone: yellow needles from H_2O. M.p. 256° (242°) decomp. Spar. sol. H_2O. Insol. most org. solvents.

Hydrazone : *see o*-Nitrobenzylidenehydrazine.
o-*Nitrophenylhydrazone* : orange cryst. from Py. M.p. 223°.
o-*Tolylhydrazone* : scarlet prisms. M.p. 149·5°.
m-*Tolylhydrazone* : red prisms. M.p. 129·5°.
p-*Tolylhydrazone* : red prisms. M.p. 150·5°.
Benzylidenehydrazone : *o* - nitrobenzaldazine. Yellow cryst. M.p. 105°.
Di-Me acetal : $C_9H_{11}O_4N$. MW, 197. B.p. 274–6°, 138–9°/11 mm.
Di-Et acetal : $C_{11}H_{15}O_4N$. MW, 225. B.p. 154–6°/18 mm., 148°/11 mm.
Diacetate : *see o*-Nitrobenzylidene diacetate.
Anil : *see o*-Nitrobenzylideneaniline.
2-*Chloroanil* : m.p. 116·5°.
3-*Chloroanil* : m.p. 77–8°.
4-*Chloroanil* : m.p. 92·5°.
2-*Bromoanil* : m.p. 119°.
3-*Bromoanil* : m.p. 77–8°.
4-*Bromoanil* : m.p. 99°.

Bamberger, Fodor, *Ber.*, 1910, **43**, 3334.
Einhorn, *Ber.*, 1884, **17**, 121.
Ciamician, Silber, *Ber.*, 1901, **34**, 2041; 1903, **36**, 4268.
Fischer, Giebe, *Ber.*, 1897, **30**, 3058.
Curtius, Lublin, *Ber.*, 1900, **33**, 2463.
Brady, Dunn, *J. Chem. Soc.*, 1913, **103**, 1614.
Senier, Clarke, *J. Chem. Soc.*, 1914, **105**, 1920.
Chattaway, Clemo, *J. Chem. Soc.*, 1923, **123**, 3041.

m-Nitrobenzaldehyde.

Needles from H_2O. M.p. 58°. B.p. 164°/23 mm. Sol. most org. solvents. Spar. sol. H_2O. Heat of comb. C_p 800·3 Cal. Volatile in steam. Ox. ⟶ *m*-nitrobenzoic acid.
syn-*Oxime* : plates from Et_2O. Heated above 85° ⟶ *anti*-oxime. *Me ether* : needles from Et_2O. M.p. 72–4°.
anti-*Oxime* : needles from Et_2O. M.p. 121–3°. D^{120} 1·043. Irradiation in C_6H_6 ⟶ *syn*-oxime. *Me ether* : needles. M.p. 63–63·5°.
Semicarbazone : yellow needles from EtOH. M.p. 246°.
Thiosemicarbazone : needles from EtOH. M.p. 163°.
Phenylsemicarbazone : m.p. 195°.
Phenylthiosemicarbazone : needles from EtOH. M.p. 132°.
Hydrazone : *see m*-Nitrobenzylidenehydrazine.
o-*Tolylhydrazone* : reddish-orange prisms. M.p. 170°.
m-*Tolylhydrazone* : yellow prisms. M.p. 127·5°.
p-*Tolylhydrazone* : yellow cryst. M.p. 150·5°.
Benzylidenehydrazone : *m* - nitrobenzaldazine. Yellow plates from $CHCl_3$. M.p. 125°.
p-*Bromophenylhydrazone* : m.p. 151°.
Di-Me acetal : b.p. 162–4°/19 mm. D^{15} 1·209.
Di-Et acetal : b.p. 178°/21 mm. D^{15} 1·131.
Diacetate : *see m*-Nitrobenzylidene diacetate.
Anil : *see m*-Nitrobenzylideneaniline.
4-*Chloroanil* : m.p. 81°. *B,HCl* : m.p. 132°.
4-*Nitroanil* : m.p. 153°.

Ehrlich, *Ber.*, 1882, **15**, 2010.
Freundler, *Compt. rend.*, 1904, **138**, 289.
Goldschmidt, *Ber.*, 1890, **23**, 2170; 1891, **24**, 2809; 1904, **37**, 183.
Brady, Dunn, *J. Chem. Soc.*, 1913, **103**, 1614.
Curtius, Lublin, *Ber.*, 1900, **33**, 2463.
Chattaway, Clemo, *J. Chem. Soc.*, 1923, **123**, 3041.

p-Nitrobenzaldehyde.

Prisms from H_2O. M.p. 106°. Sublimes. Sol. EtOH, AcOH, C_6H_6. Spar. sol. H_2O, Et_2O, pet. ether. Spar. volatile in steam. Mod. stable towards oxidising agents. Used in preparation of triphenylmethane dyes.
syn-*Oxime* : plates from amyl alcohol. M.p. 182–4°. Fusion ⟶ *anti*-oxime. *Me ether* : needles. M.p. 67–8°. Volatile in steam. *Et ether* : m.p. 70–1°.
anti-*Oxime* : needles from H_2O. M.p. 133° (128–9°). Sol. EtOH, Et_2O, AcOH. Spar. sol. H_2O, C_6H_6, pet. ether. Irradiation in C_6H_6 ⟶ *syn*-oxime. *Me ether* : needles from C_6H_6–ligroin. M.p. 105° (101–2°). Volatile in steam. *Et ether* : m.p. 107–8°.
Semicarbazone : needles + $2H_2O$ from H_2O. M.p. anhyd. 211°.
Hydrazone : *see p*-Nitrobenzylidenehydrazine.
Phenylhydrazone : dark red cryst. with metallic lustre from EtOH. M.p. 153–4°.
p-*Nitrophenylhydrazone* : cryst. M.p. 249°.
2 : 4-*Dinitrophenylhydrazone* : orange needles from xylene or quinoline. M.p. 320°.
o-*Tolylhydrazone* : m.p. 162°.
m-*Tolylhydrazone* : crimson needles. M.p. 109°.
p-*Tollyhydrazone* : m.p. 161·5°.
Benzylidenehydrazone : *p*-nitrobenzaldazine. Yellow needles from AcOH. M.p. 300°.
Di-Me acetal : m.p. 23–5°. B.p. 294–6°.
Diacetate : *see p*-Nitrobenzylidene diacetate.
Anil : *see p*-Nitrobenzylideneaniline.
2-*Chloroanil* : m.p. 121°.
3-*Chloroanil* : m.p. 77–8°.

4-*Chloroanil* : m.p. 128°.

Fischer, Grieff, *Ber.*, 1880, **13**, 670; 1881, **14**, 2525.
Law, Perkin, *J. Chem. Soc.*, 1908, **93**, 1635.
Fischer, Giebe, *Ber.*, 1897, **30**, 3057.
Thiele, Winter, *Ann.*, 1900, **311**, 355.
Ciamician, Silber, *Ber.*, 1903, **36**, 4269.
Goldschmidt, Kjellin, *Ber.*, 1891, **24**, 2553.
Brady, Dunn, *J. Chem. Soc.*, 1913, **103**, 1614.
Curtius, Lublin, *Ber.*, 1900, **33**, 2463.
Brady, *J. Chem. Soc.*, 1931, 758.
Chattaway, Clemo, *J. Chem. Soc.*, 1923, **123**, 3041.

ω-Nitrobenzaldoxime.
See Benzonitrolic Acid.

***o*-Nitrobenzamide**

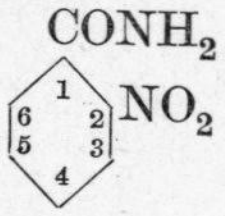

$C_7H_6O_3N_2$ MW, 166

Needles from EtOH.Aq. M.p. 174–6°. B.p. 317°. Sol. EtOH, hot H_2O.

N-*Di-Me* : $C_9H_{10}O_3N_2$. MW, 194. Cryst. from EtOH. M.p. 78°.

Reissert, *Ber.*, 1908, **41**, 3815.
Kalle, D.R.P., 204,477, (*Chem. Zentr.*, 1909, I, 114).
Löb, *Ber.*, 1894, **27**, 3093.

***m*-Nitrobenzamide.**
Needles from H_2O. M.p. 141–3°. B.p. 310–15°.
N-*Me* : $C_8H_8O_3N_2$. MW, 180. M.p. 174°.
N-*Et* : $C_9H_{10}O_3N_2$. MW, 194. M.p. 120°. Sol. hot H_2O.
N-*Acetyl* : m.p. 198°. Sol. hot H_2O, EtOH, Et_2O, C_6H_6, Me_2CO.
N-*Benzoyl* : m.p. 133–4°.

Claus, *J. prakt. Chem.*, 1895, **51**, 401.
Pinner, *Ber.*, 1895, **28**, 483.
Kao, Ma, *J. Chem. Soc.*, 1931, 443.

***p*-Nitrobenzamide.**
Needles from H_2O. M.p. 200° (197–8°).
N-*Me* : cryst. from H_2O. M.p. 218°.
N-*Et* : cryst. from EtOH. M.p. 149°.

Basterfield, Greig, *Chem. Zentr.*, 1933, II, 1022.
Reichenbach, Beilstein, *Ann.*, 1864, **132**, 143.
Blanksma, *Rec. trav. chim.*, 1902, **21**, 417.
See also last reference above.

Nitrobenzanilide.
See under Nitrobenzoic Acid.

3-Nitrobenzanthrone

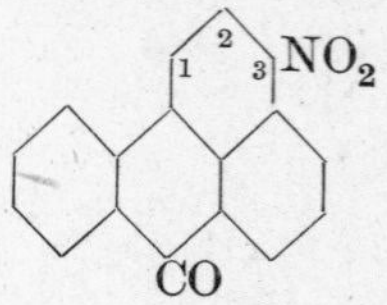

$C_{17}H_9O_3N$ MW, 275

Greenish-yellow needles from AcOH. M.p. 244–5°. Sol. conc. H_2SO_4 ⟶ yellow sol. Red. ⟶ 3-aminobenzanthrone.

Lüttringhaus, Neresheimer, *Ann.*, 1929, **473**, 285.

Nitrobenzene

$C_6H_5{\cdot}NO_2$

$C_6H_5O_2N$ MW, 123

Liq. with characteristic odour. F.p. 5·85°. B.p. 210·85°/760 mm., 184·5°/400 mm., 139·9°/100 mm., 120·2°/50 mm., 108·2°/30 mm., 85·4°/10 mm., 53·1°/1 mm. $D_4^{1\cdot5}$ 1·3440 (solid), D_4^0 1·2229 (liq.), D_4^{10} 1·2125, D_4^{25} 1·1732. n_D^{20} 1·55296. Misc. with most org. solvents. Spar. sol. H_2O. Aq. sol. tastes sweet. Volatile in steam. Vapour is poisonous. Heat of comb. C_v 734·8 Cal. Alkaline or acid reduction ⟶ nitrosobenzene ⟶ β-phenylhydroxylamine ⟶ aniline. Electrolytic reduction in weak acid ⟶ aniline; in strong acid ⟶ *p*-aminophenol.

Nitrobenzeneazonaphthol.
See under Naphthoquinone.

Nitrobenzene-2 : 4-disulphonic Acid

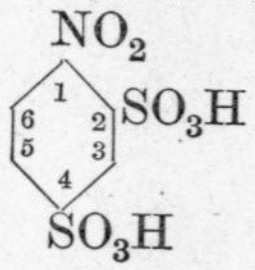

$C_6H_5O_8NS_2$ MW, 283

Hygroscopic needles from H_2O. M.p. 199° decomp.

Heinzelmann, *Ann.*, 1877, **188**, 162.

Nitrobenzene-3 : 5-disulphonic Acid.
Dichloride : $C_6H_3O_6NCl_2S_2$. MW, 320. Cryst. from CCl_4. M.p. 97–8°.
Diamide : $C_6H_7O_6N_3S_2$. MW, 281. Leaflets from H_2O. M.p. 242°.

Heinzelmann, *Ann.*, 1877, **188**, 165.
Bennet, Willis, *J. Chem. Soc.*, 1929, 266.

Nitrobenzene-*o*-sulphinic Acid

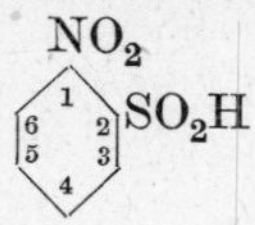

$C_6H_5O_4NS$ MW, 187

Needles. M.p. 134° (124°). Sol. EtOH, AcOH. Spar. sol. H_2O.
Na salt: yellow leaflets. M.p. 123°.
Me ester: $C_7H_7O_4NS$. MW, 201. Plates from MeOH. M.p. 106°.
Et ester: $C_8H_9O_4NS$. MW, 215. Prisms from EtOH. M.p. 58°.

Claasz, *Ann.*, 1911, **380**, 314.
Zincke, Farr, *Ann.*, 1912, **391**, 73.

Nitrobenzene-*m*-sulphinic Acid.
Needles. M.p. 98° (95–6°). Sol. H_2O, EtOH, Et_2O, Me_2CO. Insol. C_6H_6. Phenol + conc. $H_2SO_4 \longrightarrow$ blue col.
Et ester: prisms. M.p. 100°.
Bromide: $C_6H_4O_3NBrS$. MW, 250. M.p. 68°.
Anilide: m.p. 122°.

Limpricht, *Ann.*, 1894, **278**, 242.
Flürscheim, *J. prakt. Chem.*, 1905, **71**, 526.

Nitrobenzene-*p*-sulphinic Acid.
Needles or prisms from H_2O. M.p. 159° (120°). Sol. AcOH, EtOH. Spar. sol. H_2O.
Me ester: m.p. 141°.

Zincke, Lenhardt, *Ann.*, 1913, **400**, 16.
Limpricht, *Ber.*, 1887, **20**, 1240.

Nitrobenzene-*o*-sulphonic Acid

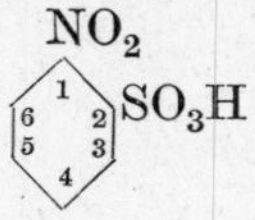

$C_6H_5O_5NS$ MW, 203

Very hygroscopic cryst. M.p. about 70°.
Chloride: $C_6H_4O_4NClS$. MW, 221·5. Cryst. from ligroin. M.p. 68–9°. Sol. Et_2O. Spar. sol. ligroin.
Bromide: $C_6H_4O_4NBrS$. MW, 266. M.p. 63–4°.
Amide: $C_6H_6O_4N_2S$. MW, 202. Needles from 50% EtOH. M.p. 193°.
Me-amide: $C_7H_8O_4N_2S$. MW, 216. M.p. 113°.
Et-amide: $C_8H_{10}O_4N_2S$. MW, 230. M.p. 103°.
Hydrazide: $C_6H_7O_4N_3S$. MW, 217. Prisms. M.p. 101° decomp.
Anilide: $C_{12}H_{10}O_4N_2S$. MW, 278. Cryst. from Me_2CO. M.p. 115°.
N-*Me-anilide*: $C_{13}H_{12}O_4N_2S$. MW, 292. M.p. 73°.
β-*Naphthalide*: $C_{16}H_{12}O_4N_2S$. MW, 328. Needles from EtOH. M.p. 138°.

Obermiller, *J. prakt. Chem.*, 1914, **89**, 70, 82.
Ullmann, Gross, *Ber.*, 1910, **43**, 2703.
Davies, Storrie, Tucker, *J. Chem. Soc.*, 1931, 624.

Nitrobenzene-*m*-sulphonic Acid.
Deliquescent plates. Sol. hot EtOH. $SOCl_2$ at 180–200° $\longrightarrow$ *m*-dichlorobenzene.
p-*Nitrophenyl ester*: m.p. 132–3°.
Chloride: needles from ligroin. M.p. 64° (61°). Sol. hot EtOH. Insol. H_2O.
Bromide: prisms from C_6H_6–ligroin. M.p. 68°.
Amide: needles from 50% EtOH. M.p. 167–8°.
Me amide: yellow prisms from EtOH. M.p. 125°.
Et-amide: plates from EtOH. M.p. 81°.
N-*Dichloroamide*: $C_6H_4O_4N_2Cl_2S$. MW, 271. Yellow plates from $CHCl_3$–pet. ether. M.p. 121°.
Hydrazide: prisms. M.p. 130° decomp.
Anilide: yellow plates from EtOH. M.p. 126°.
Benzylamide: $C_{13}H_{12}O_4N_2S$. MW, 292. Yellow plates from EtOH. M.p. 101°.
o-*Toluidide*: $C_{13}H_{12}O_4N_2S$. MW, 292. Yellow plates from EtOH. M.p. 164°.
p-*Toluidide*: yellow plates from EtOH. M.p. 132°.

Obermiller, *J. prakt. Chem.*, 1914, **89**, 70, 81.

Nitrobenzene-*p*-sulphonic Acid.
Hygroscopic cryst. M.p. 95°.
Et ester: $C_8H_9O_5NS$. MW, 231. Plates. M.p. 91°.
Phenyl ester: $C_{12}H_9O_5NS$. MW, 279. Needles from AcOH. M.p. 114°.
m-*Nitrophenyl ester*: m.p. 133°.
p-*Nitrophenyl ester*: m.p. 156°.
p-*Tolyl ester*: $C_{13}H_{11}O_5NS$. MW, 293. M.p. 106°.
Chloride: needles from ligroin. M.p. 80°.
Amide: prisms from 50% EtOH. M.p. 179–80°.
Me-amide: m.p. 110°.
Et-amide: m.p. 103°.
Hydrazide: yellow prisms. M.p. 150–2° decomp.
Anilide: cryst. from EtOH. M.p. 135–6°.
N-*Me-anilide*: m.p. 117–18°.

p-*Toluidide*: m.p. 179–80°.

Obermiller, *J. prakt. Chem.*, 1914, **89**, 84.
Deményi, *Rec. trav. chim.*, 1929, **48**, 1145.
Bell, *J. Chem. Soc.*, 1928, 2776.

o-Nitrobenzhydrazide (o-*Nitrobenzoylhydrazine*)

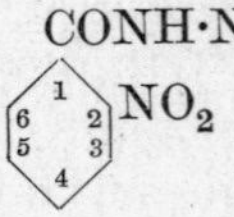

$C_7H_7O_3N_3$ MW, 181

Yellowish-brown cryst. from H_2O. M.p. 123°. Sol. H_2O, EtOH. Insol. Et_2O, $CHCl_3$, C_6H_6.

Curtius, Trachmann, *J. prakt. Chem.*, 1895, **51**, 168.

m-Nitrobenzhydrazide (m-*Nitrobenzoylhydrazine*).

Needles from H_2O. M.p. 152°. Spar. sol. H_2O, EtOH. Insol. Et_2O, C_6H_6, $CHCl_3$.

Meng, Sah, *Science Reports National Tsinghua Univ.*, 1934, **2**, 348.
See also previous reference.

p-Nitrobenzhydrazide (p-*Nitrobenzoylhydrazine*).

Yellowish needles from H_2O. M.p. 210°. Spar. sol. H_2O, EtOH. Insol. Et_2O, C_6H_6, $CHCl_3$.

Curtius, Trachmann, *J. prakt. Chem.*, 1895, **51**, 168.

m-Nitrobenzhydroxamic Acid (N-m-*Nitrobenzoyl-hydroxylamine*)

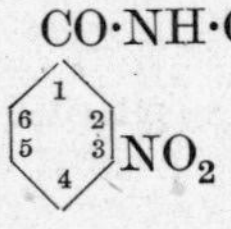

$C_7H_6O_4N_2$ MW, 182

Granules from $CHCl_3$ or C_6H_6. M.p. 153° (151°). Gives red col. with $FeCl_3$.Aq.

O-*Benzoyl*: needles from MeOH. M.p. 153–4°.

O-m-*Nitrobenzoyl*: needles from EtOH. M.p. 153–4°.

Werner, Skiba, *Ber.*, 1899, **32**, 1662.
Meisenheimer, Patzig, *Ber.*, 1906, **39**, 2542.
Angelico, Fanara, *Gazz. chim. ital.*, 1901, **31**, 33.

p-Nitrobenzhydroxamic Acid.

Needles from EtOH or xylene. M.p. 177° decomp. Sol. hot H_2O, NaOH.Aq.

O-*Benzoyl*: plates from AcOH or EtOH. M.p. 185° decomp. (178°).

O-p-*Nitrobenzoyl*: needles from EtOH. M.p. 174° decomp. (173–6°).

Werner, Skiba, *Ber.*, 1899, **32**, 1665.
Holleman, *Rec. trav. chim.*, 1897, **16**, 187.

2-Nitrobenzidine (2-*Nitro*-4 : 4′-*diaminodiphenyl*)

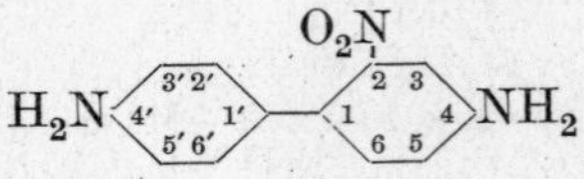

$C_{12}H_{11}O_2N_3$ MW, 229

Red needles from H_2O. M.p. 143° (140–1°). A labile form, m.p. 117°, is also described.

4′-N-*Acetyl*: yellow plates from EtOH or H_2O. M.p. 186–7°.

4 : 4′-N : N-*Diacetyl*: cryst. from AcOH. Does not melt below 310°. Insol. H_2O, EtOH, Et_2O, AcOEt, $CHCl_3$, C_6H_6. Spar. sol. AcOH.

4 : 4′-N : N-*Di*-p-*toluenesulphonyl*: m.p. 164°.

4 : 4′-N : N-*Dibenzylidene*: brownish-yellow cryst. from C_6H_6. M.p. 157°.

4 : 4′-N : N-*Di*-p-*nitrobenzylidene*: yellow cryst. from xylene. M.p. 205–6°.

Cain, May, *J. Chem. Soc.*, 1910, **97**, 725.
Ponte, *Chem. Abstracts*, 1934, **28**, 2345.
Täuber, *Ber.*, 1890, **23**, 796.
Sako, *Bull. Chem. Soc. Japan*, 1934, **9**, 150.

3-Nitrobenzidine.

Red cryst. from EtOH. M.p. 208–10°. Prac. insol. EtOH.

3 : 4′-N : N-*Diacetyl*: yellow needles from dil. AcOH. M.p. 249–50°.

Le Fèvre, Turner, *J. Chem. Soc.*, 1928, 253.

2-Nitrobenzil

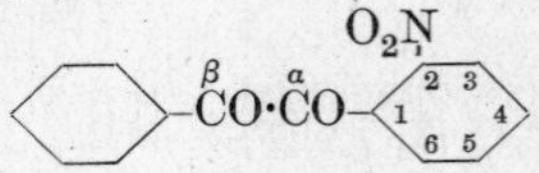

$C_{14}H_9O_4N$ MW, 255

Yellow needles with green reflex from EtOH. M.p. 102° (98°). Sol. Et_2O, C_6H_6. Spar. sol. EtOH, AcOH. $CrO_3 \longrightarrow$ benzoic and o-nitrobenzoic acids.

Monoxime: α-, needles or plates from EtOH. M.p. 185° decomp. β-, m.p. 265° decomp.

Dioxime: yellowish prisms from EtOH. M.p. 244° decomp. Prac. insol. EtOH. Sol. alkalis with red col.

List, *Ber.*, 1893, **26**, 2453.
Chattaway, Coulson, *J. Chem. Soc.*, 1928, 1083.

3-Nitrobenzil.

Cryst. from EtOH or Me_2CO. M.p. 120°. Sol. Me_2CO, $CHCl_3$, C_6H_6, hot AcOH. Mod. sol. EtOH. $CrO_3 \longrightarrow$ benzoic and *m*-nitrobenzoic acids.

See last reference above.

4-Nitrobenzil.

Yellow plates or needles from EtOH. M.p. 142°. Sol. Et_2O, $CHCl_3$. Sn + HCl $\longrightarrow$ 4′-aminodeoxybenzoin. $CrO_3 \longrightarrow$ benzoic and *p*-nitrobenzoic acids.

Dioxime: two forms. (i) M.p. 225° decomp. Prac. insol. EtOH, Et_2O, C_6H_6. EtOH at 170° $\longrightarrow$ (ii). (ii) Needles from C_6H_6–ligroin. M.p. 185°. Sol. EtOH.

Phenylhydrazone: (i) yellow plates. M.p. 200°. (ii) Orange plates. M.p. 162°.

Phenylosazone: orange needles from AcOH. M.p. 216°.

List, *Ber.*, 1893, **26**, 2456.
Hausmann, *Ber.*, 1890, **23**, 532.
Chattaway, Coulson, *J. Chem. Soc.*, 1928, 1083.

6-Nitrobenziminazole

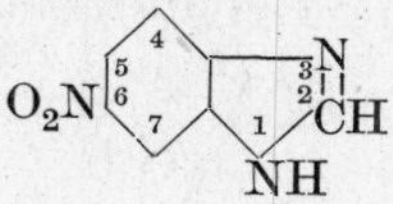

$C_7H_5O_2N_3$ MW, 163

Needles from H_2O. M.p. 203°. Sol. EtOH. Insol. H_2O, Et_2O, C_6H_6, $CHCl_3$. Sol. acids and alkalis.

N-*Me*: $C_8H_7O_2N_3$. MW, 177. *Methiodide*: yellow prisms and needles from H_2O. M.p. 259°.

Bamberger, Berlé, *Ann.*, 1893, **273**, 340.
Fischer, Hess, *Ber.*, 1903, **36**, 3968.

***o*-Nitrobenzoic Acid**

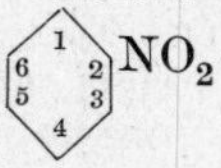

$C_7H_5O_4N$ MW, 167

Needles from H_2O. M.p. 146–8°. D_4^{20} 1·575. Sol. EtOH, Et_2O, $CHCl_3$. Spar. sol. H_2O, C_6H_6, ligroin. Spar. volatile in steam. Does not melt under boiling H_2O. Heat of comb. C_p 730·4 Cal., C_v 731·1 Cal. $k = 6{\cdot}56 \times 10^{-3}$ at 25°, $1{\cdot}6 \times 10^{-3}$ at 100°. NaHg $\longrightarrow$ azobenzene-2 : 2′-dicarboxylic acid. NaOH + Zn dust $\longrightarrow$ hydrazobenzene-2 : 2′-dicarboxylic acid. Zn + HCl $\longrightarrow$ anthranilic acid.

Me ester: $C_8H_7O_4N$. MW, 181. M.p. − 13°. B.p. 275°, 183°/22 mm., 169°/19 mm. D^{20} 1·2855. Sol. MeOH, EtOH, Et_2O, $CHCl_3$, C_6H_6. Insol. ligroin.

Et ester: $C_9H_9O_4N$. MW, 195. M.p. 30°. B.p. 173°/18 mm.

Propyl ester: $C_{10}H_{11}O_4N$. MW, 209. B.p. 173–5°/16 mm.

d-*Amyl ester*: $C_{12}H_{15}O_4N$. MW, 237. B.p. 238°/69 mm. D^{18} 1·135. n_D 1·5132. $[\alpha]_D^{18}$ +1·17°.

l-*Menthyl ester*: $C_{17}H_{23}O_4N$. MW, 305. Prisms from EtOH. M.p. 62–4°. B.p. 185°/2 mm. D_4^{20} 1·1140, D_4^{180} 0·983. $[\alpha]_D^{65}$ −125°.

Anhydride: $C_{14}H_8O_7N_2$. MW, 316. M.p. 135°. Explodes on rapid heating. Sol. EtOH, AcOH. Spar. sol. H_2O, Et_2O.

Chloride: *see* *o*-Nitrobenzoyl chloride.

Amide: *see* *o*-Nitrobenzamide.

Nitrile: *see* *o*-Nitrobenzonitrile.

Anilide: *o*-nitrobenzanilide. $C_{13}H_{10}O_3N_2$. MW, 242. Needles from EtOH. M.p. 155°.

N-*Me-anilide*: $C_{14}H_{12}O_3N_2$. MW, 256. Needles from EtOH. M.p. 94°.

2 : 4-*Dichloroanilide*: $C_{13}H_8O_3N_2Cl_2$. MW, 311. Plates from EtOH. M.p. 153°.

o-*Nitroanilide*: $C_{13}H_9O_5N_3$. MW, 287. Needles from AcOH. M.p. 167–8°.

Hydrazide: *see* *o*-Nitrobenzhydrazide.

Azide: $C_7H_4O_3N_4$. MW, 192. Yellow prisms from Et_2O. M.p. 37·5° (36°).

Beilstein, Kuhlberg, *Ann.*, 1872, **163**, 138.
Reimer, Gatewood, *J. Am. Chem. Soc.*, 1920, **42**, 1475.
Noyes, *Ber.*, 1883, **16**, 53.
Monnet, Reverdin, Noelting, *Ber.*, 1879, **12**, 443.
Curtius, Melsbach, *J. prakt. Chem.*, 1910, **81**, 523.
Adams, Wirth, French, *J. Am. Chem. Soc.*, 1918, **40**, 425.
Pinnow, Müller, *Ber.*, 1895, **28**, 151.

***m*-Nitrobenzoic Acid.**

Prisms. M.p. 140–1°. Known in two labile and one stable modifications. Melts under hot H_2O. D_4^{20} 1·494. Sol. EtOH, Et_2O, $CHCl_3$. Spar. sol. H_2O, pet. ether. Heat of comb. C_p 727 Cal., C_v 727·7 Cal. $k = 3{\cdot}45 \times 10^{-4}$ at 25°. Zn + HCl $\longrightarrow$ *m*-aminobenzoic acid. Zn + NaOH $\longrightarrow$ azoxybenzene-3 : 3′-dicarboxylic acid and azobenzene-3 : 3′-dicarboxylic acid.

Me ester: needles. M.p. 78°. B.p. 279°. Spar. sol. EtOH.

Et ester: m.p. 47° (41°). B.p. 296–8°.

d-*Amyl ester*: b.p. 223–5°/52 mm. D^{19} 1·144. n_D 1·5187. $[\alpha]_D^{75}$ + 5·58°.

l-*Menthyl ester*: b.p. 186°/2 mm. D_4^{20} 1·1173. D_4^{180} 0·9787. $[\alpha]_D^{20}$ − 82·52°.

Anhydride: cryst. from C_6H_6. M.p. 163°. Insol. EtOH, Et_2O.
Chloride: *see m*-Nitrobenzoyl chloride.
Amide: *see m*-Nitrobenzamide.
Nitrile: *see m*-Nitrobenzonitrile.
Anilide: *m*-nitrobenzanilide. Leaflets from EtOH. M.p. 153–4°.
2 : 4-*Dichloroanilide*: plates from AcOH. M.p. 183°.
o-*Nitroanilide*: m.p. 138°.
m-*Nitroanilide*: m.p. 227°.
p-*Nitroanilide*: m.p. 249°.
p-*Toluidide*: needles from EtOH. M.p. 162°.
Hydrazide: *see m*-Nitrobenzhydrazide.
Azide: plates from dil. EtOH. M.p. 68°.

Kamm, Segur, *Organic Syntheses*, Collective Vol. I, 383.
Müller, *Z. physik. Chem.*, 1912, **79**, 172.
Marshall, Acree, *Ber.*, 1910, **43**, 2329.
Adams, Wirth, French, *J. Am. Chem. Soc.*, 1918, **40**, 425.
Beilstein, Kuhlberg, *Ann.*, 1867, **143**, 336.

p-Nitrobenzoic Acid.

Leaflets from H_2O. M.p. 238°. Sublimes. D^{20} 1·61. Sol. EtOH, Et_2O, $CHCl_3$, Me_2CO, boiling H_2O. Spar. sol. CS_2, C_6H_6. Insol. ligroin. Heat of comb. C_p 728·8 Cal., C_v 729·6 Cal. $k = 4{\cdot}0–4{\cdot}3 \times 10^{-4}$ at 25°. $(NH_4)_2S \longrightarrow$ *p*-aminobenzoic acid. NaHg $\longrightarrow$ azoxybenzene-4 : 4′-dicarboxylic acid. Unaffected by Zn+HCl.
Me ester: m.p. 96°.
Et ester: leaflets from EtOH. M.p. 57°.
Propyl ester: leaflets from EtOH. M.p. 35°.
Isopropyl ester: needles from EtOH. M.p. 108–10°.
d-*Amyl ester*: b.p. 250–2°/80 mm. D^{17} 1·14. n_D 1·5203. $[\alpha]_D^{75} + 6{\cdot}29°$.
l-*Menthyl ester*: prisms from EtOH. M.p. 61–3°. D^{65} 1·077. $[\alpha]_D^{20} - 88{\cdot}3°$.
Benzyl ester: $C_{14}H_{11}O_4N$. MW, 257. Yellow plates from EtOH. M.p. 84°.
2-*Naphthyl ester*: $C_{17}H_{12}O_4N$. MW, 294. Needles from MeOH. M.p. 166°.
Anhydride: yellowish leaflets from AcOEt. M.p. 189–90°.
Chloride: *see p*-Nitrobenzoyl chloride.
Amide: *see p*-Nitrobenzamide.
Nitrile: *see p*-Nitrobenzonitrile.
Anilide: *p*-nitrobenzanilide. Leaflets from Et_2O. M.p. 211° (204°).
o-*Nitroanilide*: leaflets from AcOH. M.p. 216°.
m-*Nitroanilide*: plates from EtOH. M.p. 185°.
p-*Nitroanilide*: m.p. 266°.
p-*Toluidide*: needles from EtOH. M.p. 203° (192°).
Hydrazide: *see p*-Nitrobenzhydrazide.
Azide: plates from dil. EtOH. M.p. 69°.

Kamm, Matthews, *Organic Syntheses*, Collective Vol. I, 385.
Robertson, *ibid.*, 389.
Schlosser, Skraup, *Monatsh.*, 1881, **2**, 519.
Beilstein, Kuhlberg, *Ann.*, 1872, **163**, 128.
Meyer, *Monatsh.*, 1901, **22**, 426.

Nitrobenzoic Acid Sulphonic Acid.
See Nitrosulphobenzoic Acid.

4′-Nitrobenzoin

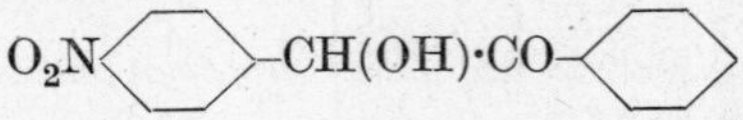

$C_{14}H_{11}O_4N$ MW, 257

Acetyl: leaflets from 90% EtOH. M.p. 125°. Sol. $CHCl_3$, Me_2CO, C_6H_6. Spar. sol. Et_2O, pet. ether.
Benzoyl: cryst. M.p. 137°.

Francis, Keane, *J. Chem. Soc.*, 1911, **99**, 346.

o-Nitrobenzonitrile

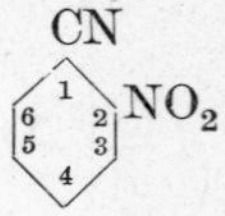

$C_7H_4O_2N_2$ MW, 148

Needles from H_2O or AcOH. M.p. 109–10°. Sol. EtOH, $CHCl_3$, AcOH, CS_2, C_6H_6, hot H_2O. Spar. sol. pet. ether. Zn + HCl $\longrightarrow$ *o*-aminobenzonitrile + *o*-aminobenzamide.

Pinnow, Müller, *Ber.*, 1895, **28**, 151.
Reissert, *Ber.*, 1908, **41**, 3812.
Kalle, D.R.P., 210,563, (*Chem. Zentr.*, 1909, II, 78).

m-Nitrobenzonitrile.

Needles from H_2O. M.p. 117–18°. Sol. Et_2O, AcOH. Mod. sol. EtOH, hot H_2O. Insol. pet. ether. Sublimes. Volatile in steam.

Beilstein, Kuhlberg, *Ann.*, 1868, **146**, 336.
Sandmeyer, *Ber.*, 1885, **18**, 1494.

p-Nitrobenzonitrile.

Leaflets from EtOH. M.p. 149°. Sol. $CHCl_3$, AcOH, hot EtOH. Spar. sol. H_2O, Et_2O. Sublimes. Volatile in steam.

Bogert, Kohnstamm, *J. Am. Chem. Soc.*, 1903, **25**, 479.
Borsche, *Ber.*, 1909, **42**, 3597.
Neber, Hartung, Ruopp, *Ber.*, 1925, **58**, 1239.

2-Nitrobenzophenone

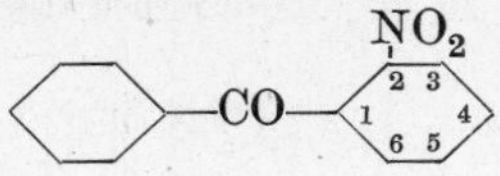

$C_{13}H_9O_3N$ MW, 227

Cryst. from EtOH. M.p. 105°. Mod. sol. EtOH. Sn + HCl ⟶ 2-aminobenzophenone. Sn + AcOH ⟶ phenylanthranil. HNO_3 ⟶ 2 : 2′-, 2 : 3′- and 2 : 4′-dinitrobenzophenone.
Oxime: needles from dil. EtOH.

v. Tatschalow, *J. prakt. Chem.*, 1902, **65**, 308.
Geigy, Koenigs, *Ber.*, 1885, **18**, 2403.
Meyer, *Ber.*, 1893, **26**, 1251.
Boëtius, Römisch, *Ber.*, 1935, **68**, 1927.

3-Nitrobenzophenone.

Needles from EtOH. M.p. 95° (92°). B.p. 234°/18 mm. $SnCl_2$ + HCl ⟶ 3-aminobenzophenone. Zn + NaOH ⟶ 3 : 3′-dibenzoylazoxybenzene. HNO_3 ⟶ 2 : 3′-, 3 : 3′- and 3 : 4′-dinitrobenzophenone.
Phenylhydrazone: yellow needles from EtOH. M.p. 116°.

Becker, *Ber.*, 1882, **15**, 2092.
Geigy, Koenigs, *Ber.*, 1885, **18**, 2401.
Montagne, *Rec. trav. chim.*, 1916, **36**, 260.

4-Nitrobenzophenone.

Plates from EtOH. M.p. 138°. Sol. hot EtOH. Mod. sol. C_6H_6. Spar. sol. CS_2, ligroin. Sn + HCl ⟶ 4-aminobenzophenone. Zn + NaOH ⟶ 4 : 4′-dibenzoylazobenzene and 4 : 4′-dibenzoylazoxybenzene. HNO_3 ⟶ 2 : 4′, 3 : 4′- and 4 : 4′-dinitrobenzophenone.
Monoxime: α-, yellow needles from C_6H_6. M.p. 159°. *Me ether*: yellow leaflets from MeOH. M.p. 93°. N-*Me*: yellow plates from MeOH. M.p. 147°. β-, cryst. from C_6H_6. M.p. 136°. *Me ether*: plates from MeOH. M.p. 96°. N-*Me*: yellow needles from EtOH. M.p. 186°.
Phenylhydrazone: orange-red cryst. from EtOH. M.p. 142°.

Baeyer, Villiger, *Ber.*, 1904, **37**, 605.
Carré, *Ann. chim. phys.*, 1910, **19**, 228.
Schroeter, *Ber.*, 1909, **42**, 3360 (*Footnote*).
Reddelien, *J. prakt. Chem.*, 1915, **91**, 237.
Sutton, Taylor, *J. Chem. Soc.*, 1931, 2192.
Brady, Mehta, *J. Chem. Soc.*, 1924, **125**, 2297.

4-Nitrobenzophenone-2-carboxylic Acid

(5-*Nitro-o-benzoylbenzoic acid*)

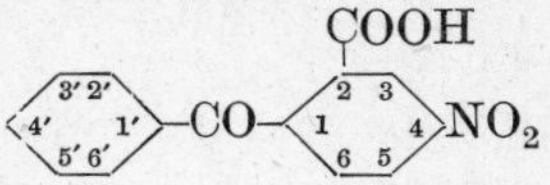

$C_{14}H_9O_5N$ MW, 271

Leaflets + 1MeOH from MeOH. M.p. 212°. Spar. sol. H_2O, MeOH, Et_2O. Conc. H_2SO_4 ⟶ 2-nitroanthraquinone.
Me ester: $C_{15}H_{11}O_5N$. MW, 285. Prisms from MeOH. M.p. 124°.

Rainer, *Monatsh.*, 1908, **29**, 178, 431.

5-Nitrobenzophenone-2-carboxylic Acid

(4-*Nitro-o-benzoylbenzoic acid*).

Pale yellow needles from H_2O or C_6H_6. M.p. 164–5° (161°). Sol. EtOH, Me_2CO, $CHCl_3$, AcOH. Spar. sol. H_2O, C_6H_6. Conc. H_2SO_4 ⟶ 2-nitroanthraquinone.
Me ester: prisms from MeOH–Et_2O. M.p. 104·5°. Sol. MeOH, Et_2O, $CHCl_3$.

See previous reference and also
Kliegl, *Ber.*, 1905, **38**, 295.

3′-Nitrobenzophenone-2-carboxylic Acid

(2-o-*Nitrobenzoylbenzoic acid*).

Pale yellow prisms from MeOH. M.p. 186°. Sol. EtOH, Et_2O, $CHCl_3$. Spar. sol. H_2O.
Me ester: prisms from propyl alcohol. M.p. 108–9° (105°). Sol. EtOH, C_6H_6. Spar. sol. H_2O.
Et ester: $C_{16}H_{13}O_5N$. MW, 299. M.p. 84°.

Lang, *Monatsh.*, 1905, **26**, 972.
Rainer, *Monatsh.*, 1908, **29**, 180.
Hahn, Reid, *J. Am. Chem. Soc.*, 1924, **46**, 1651.

2′-Nitrobenzophenone-4-carboxylic Acid

(4-o-*Nitrobenzoylbenzoic acid*)

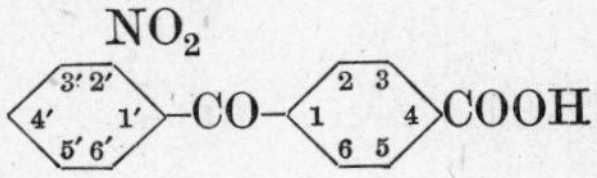

$C_{14}H_9O_5N$ MW, 271

Cryst. from EtOH. M.p. 235–6°. Sol. EtOH, Me_2CO, AcOH. Spar. sol. H_2O, Et_2O, $CHCl_3$, C_6H_6. Insol. ligroin.

Kliegl, *Ber.*, 1908, **41**, 1849.

3′-Nitrobenzophenone-4-carboxylic Acid

(4-m-*Nitrobenzoylbenzoic acid*).

Plates from EtOH. M.p. 242°. Sol. AcOH. Spar. sol. EtOH, Et_2O. Insol. H_2O, $CHCl_3$, C_6H_6.
Chloride: $C_{14}H_8O_4NCl$. MW, 289·5. Cryst.

from C_6H_6. M.p. 94·5°. Sol. AcOH, $CHCl_3$, C_6H_6.

Amide: $C_{14}H_{10}O_4N_2$. MW, 270. Plates from EtOH.Aq. M.p. 204°.

Limpricht, Lenz, *Ann.*, 1895, **286**, 316.

4′-Nitrobenzophenone-4-carboxylic Acid (4-p-*Nitrobenzoylbenzoic acid*).

Needles. M.p. 255°. Sol. EtOH, $CHCl_3$, AcOH. Spar. sol. C_6H_6, ligroin.

Chloride: cryst. from CS_2. M.p. 124°.

Limpricht, Samietz, *Ann.*, 1895, **286**, 330.

o-Nitrobenzoylacetic Acid

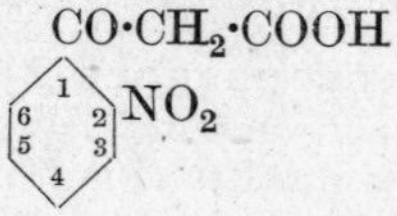

$C_9H_7O_5N$ MW, 209

Needles from H_2O. M.p. 117–20° decomp. Sol. EtOH. Spar. sol. C_6H_6. Insol. pet. ether. Boiling $H_2O \longrightarrow$ *o*-nitroacetophenone. Mild red. $\longrightarrow$ indigo.

Et ester: $C_{11}H_{11}O_5N$. MW, 237. Needles from EtOH. M.p. 35–6°.

Needham, Perkin, *J. Chem. Soc.*, 1904, **85**, 152.
Gabriel, Gerhard, *Ber.*, 1921, **54**, 1069.

m-Nitrobenzoylacetic Acid.

Cryst. from H_2O. M.p. 150° decomp.

Et ester: prisms from EtOH. M.p. 78–9°.

Bülow, Hailer, *Ber.*, 1902, **35**, 933.
Reich, *Chem. Abstracts*, 1918, **12**, 1877.

p-Nitrobenzoylacetic Acid.

Needles from C_6H_6. M.p. 135° decomp. Sol. EtOH, Et_2O, $CHCl_3$, CS_2, pet. ether. Spar. sol. C_6H_6. Alc. $FeCl_3 \longrightarrow$ reddish-brown col. Heated with alkalis or dil. $H_2SO_4 \longrightarrow$ *p*-nitroacetophenone.

Me ester: $C_{10}H_9O_5N$. MW, 223. Prisms. M.p. 106–7°. Sol. $CHCl_3$, C_6H_6, pet. ether. Spar. sol. EtOH. Alc. $FeCl_3 \longrightarrow$ violet-brown col.

Et ester: needles from EtOH. M.p. 74–6°. Sol. EtOH, Et_2O. $FeCl_3 \longrightarrow$ violet-brown col.

Perkin, Bellenot, *J. Chem. Soc.*, 1886, **49**, 443.
Bülow, Hailer, *Ber.*, 1902, **35**, 931.

o-Nitrobenzoylacetone

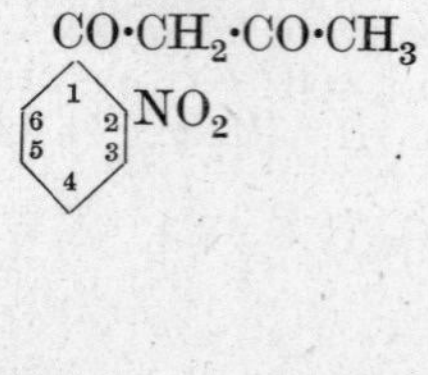

$C_{10}H_9O_4N$ MW, 207

Yellow cryst. from ligroin. M.p. 55°. Sol. EtOH, Et_2O, alkalis. Spar. sol. ligroin. Prac. insol. H_2O.

Gevekoht, *Ann.*, 1883, **221**, 332.

m-Nitrobenzoylacetone.

Needles from EtOH. M.p. 114–15°. $SnCl_2 \longrightarrow$ *m*-aminobenzoylacetone.

Gabriel, Gerhard, *Ber.*, 1921, **54**, 1617.

p-Nitrobenzoylacetone.

Needles. M.p. 102° (softens at 98°). $SnCl_2 \longrightarrow$ *p*-aminobenzoylacetone.

Gabriel, Gerhard, *Ber.*, 1921, **54**, 1618.

Nitrobenzoylbenzoic Acid.

See Nitrobenzophenone-carboxylic Acid.

o-Nitrobenzoyl chloride

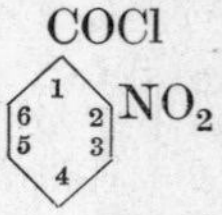

$C_7H_4O_3NCl$ MW, 185·5

M.p. 20°. B.p. 148°/9 mm., 105°/0·5 mm. (97°/1 mm.).

Meyer, *Monatsh.*, 1901, **22**, 426.
Schroeter, Eisleb, *Ann.*, 1909, **367**, 128.

m-Nitrobenzoyl chloride.

Cryst. M.p. 35°. B.p. 275–8°, 183–4°/50–5 mm., 154–5°/18 mm. Very sol. Et_2O.

See first reference above.

p-Nitrobenzoyl chloride.

Yellow needles from ligroin. M.p. 75°. B.p. 202–5°/105 mm., 150–2°/15 mm.

Meyer, *Monatsh.*, 1901, **22**, 426.
Adams, Jenkins, *Organic Syntheses*, Collective Vol. I, 387.

o-Nitrobenzoylformic Acid (o-*Nitrophenylglyoxylic acid*)

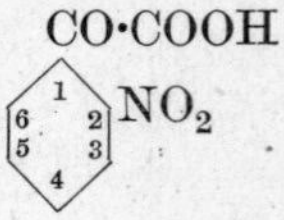

$C_8H_5O_5N$ MW, 195

Prisms + H_2O from H_2O. M.p. 46–7°, anhyd. 123° (156–7° decomp.). Sol. Me_2CO, AcOH. Mod. sol. EtOH. Spar. sol. Et_2O, AcOEt, ligroin, toluene. $FeSO_4$ + NaOH $\longrightarrow$ isatin.

Et ester: $C_{10}H_9O_5N$. MW, 223. Cryst. from C_6H_6–ligroin. M.p. 43–44·5°. Sol. most org. solvents. *Oxime*: needles from boiling H_2O, leaflets from EtOH.Aq. M.p. 163°. Sol. warm EtOH, Et_2O, C_6H_6. Spar. sol. H_2O, CS_2.

Amide: $C_8H_6O_4N_2$. MW, 194. Prisms from H_2O. M.p. 199°. Sol. boiling H_2O. Spar. sol. EtOH, Et_2O.
Nitrile: $C_8H_4O_3N_2$. MW, 176. Prisms from pet. ether. M.p. 54°.
Oxime: brownish-yellow cryst. + H_2O from EtOH.Aq. M.p. 87–8°.

Borsche, *Ber.*, 1909, **42**, 3599.
Claisen, Shadwell, *Ber.*, 1879, **12**, 352.
Claisen, Thompson, *ibid.*, 1945 (*Note*).
Heller, *Ber.*, 1911, **44**, 2419.

***m*-Nitrobenzoylformic Acid** (m-*Nitrophenylglyoxylic acid*).
Prisms from C_6H_6. M.p. 105°.

Baker, *J. Chem. Soc.*, 1931, 2422.

***p*-Nitrobenzoylformic Acid** (p-*Nitrophenylglyoxylic acid*).
Cryst. from C_6H_6. M.p. 150°.

See previous reference.

Nitrobenzoylhydrazine.
See Nitrobenzhydrazide.
Nitrobenzoylpyridine.
See Nitrophenyl pyridyl Ketone.
6-Nitrobenzthiazole (5-*Nitrobenzthiazole*)

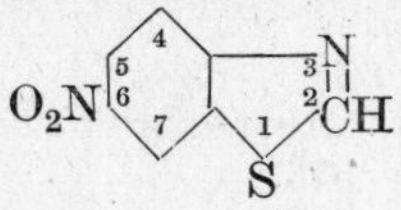

$C_7H_4O_2N_2S$ MW, 180

Yellowish leaflets. M.p. 176–7°.

Jacobson, Kwaysser, *Ann.*, 1893, **277**, 244.

4-Nitro-1 : 2 : 3-benztriazole (7-*Nitro*-1 : 2 : 3-*benztriazole*)

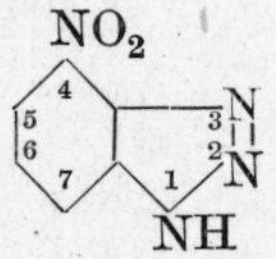

$C_6H_4O_2N_4$ MW, 164

Pale yellow needles from EtOH. M.p. 229°.

Fries, Güterbock, Kühn, *Ann.*, 1934, **511**, 229.
Borsche, Rantscheff, *Ann.*, 1911, **379**, 164.

5-Nitro-1 : 2 : 3-benztriazole (6-*Nitro*-1 : 2 : 3-*benztriazole*).
Long, pale yellow needles. M.p. 211°. Sol. EtOH, Et_2O. Spar. sol. cold H_2O. Sublimes with partial decomp. Reacts acid. Undecomp. by acids or alkalis.

N-*Me*: $C_7H_6O_2N_4$. MW, 178. Cryst. from EtOH. M.p. 163°. Sol. hot C_6H_6, H_2O, EtOH, $CHCl_3$, AcOH. Spar. sol. cold H_2O.

Nietzki, Hagenbach, *Ber.*, 1897, **30**, 544.
Zincke, *Ann.*, 1900, **311**, 290.
Pinnow, Koch, *Ber.*, 1897, **30**, 2852.
Macciotta, *Chem. Abstracts*, 1933, **27**, 4528.

***N*-Nitrobenzylacetamide.**
See under Nitrobenzylamine.
***N*-Nitrobenzylacetanilide.**
See under Nitrobenzylaniline.
***o*-Nitrobenzylacetone** (4-o-*Nitrophenylbutanone*-2)

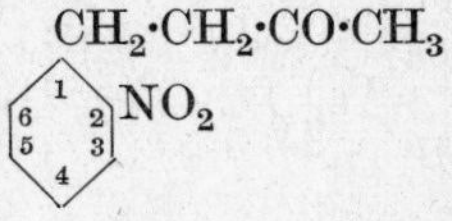

$C_{10}H_{11}O_3N$ MW, 193

Liq. B.p. 183–5°/13 mm. Zn + NH_4OH ⟶ tetrahydroquinaldine.
Oxime: cryst. M.p. 97°. Sol. EtOH, HCl.Aq.
Semicarbazone: powder. M.p. 169–70°. Insol. H_2O, EtOH.

Alber, *J. prakt. Chem.*, 1905, **71**, 45.

***p*-Nitrobenzylacetone** (4-p-*Nitrophenylbutanone*-2).
Needles from EtOH or Et_2O. M.p. 42° (40–1°). B.p. 204°/13 mm. Sol. EtOH, Et_2O.
Oxime: needles or plates from EtOH. M.p. 120°. Sol. hot EtOH.
Semicarbazone: powder. M.p. 198·5°. Sol. acids. Prac. insol. EtOH. Insol. H_2O.
Phenylhydrazone: yellow cryst. M.p. 103°. Decomp. on keeping.

Alber, *J. prakt. Chem.*, 1905, **71**, 44.
Fichter, Wortsmann, *Ber.*, 1904, **37**, 1994.
Mech, *Compt. rend.*, 1906, **143**, 752.

***o*-Nitrobenzyl Alcohol**

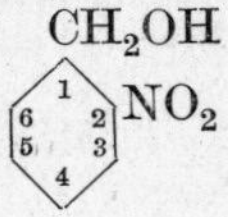

$C_7H_7O_3N$ MW, 153

Needles from H_2O. M.p. 74°. B.p. 270°, 168°/20 mm. Sol. EtOH, Et_2O.
Benzoyl: m.p. 101–2°.

Pierron, *Bull. soc. chim.*, 1901, **25**, 853.
Bamberger, *Ber.*, 1918, **51**, 609.
Schenck, *Ber.*, 1934, **67**, 1571.
Kalle, D.R.P., 104,360, (*Chem. Zentr.*, 1899, II, 950).

m-Nitrobenzyl Alcohol.

Needles from H_2O. M.p. 27°. B.p. 175–80°/3 mm. $D_{15}^{18\cdot5}$ 1·296. Sol. H_2O, EtOH, Et_2O.

Benzoyl : m.p. 71–2°.

Grimaux, *Compt. rend.*, 1867, **65**, 211.
Becker, *Ber.*, 1882, **15**, 2090.
Thorp, Wildman, *J. Am. Chem. Soc.*, 1915, **37**, 373.

p-Nitrobenzyl Alcohol.

Cryst. from H_2O. M.p. 93°. B.p. 185°/12 mm. Sol. H_2O, EtOH.

Formyl : cryst. from EtOH. M.p. 31°.
Acetyl : m.p. 78°.
Propionyl : cryst. from EtOH. M.p. 33°.
Butyryl : cryst. from EtOH. M.p. 35°.
Palmityl : cryst. from EtOH. M.p. 42–42·5°.
Benzoyl : m.p. 94–5°.

Dieffenbach, D.R.P., 214,949, (*Chem. Zentr.*, 1909, II, 1781).
Basler, *Ber.*, 1883, **16**, 2715.
Norris, Watt, Thomas, *J. Am. Chem. Soc.*, 1916, **38**, 1077.
Reid, *J. Am. Chem. Soc.*, 1917, **39**, 306.

o-Nitrobenzylamine

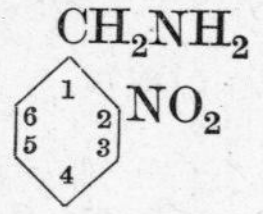

$C_7H_8O_2N_2$ MW, 152

Non-volatile liq. Sol. H_2O. Insol. conc. KOH. Absorbs CO_2 from the air.

N-*Formyl* : *N-o*-nitrobenzylformamide. Cryst. from H_2O. M.p. 88–90°.

N-*Acetyl* : *N-o*-nitrobenzylacetamide. Needles. M.p. 97–9°.

N - *Benzoyl* : *N - o* - nitrobenzylbenzamide. Needles from EtOH. M.p. 110°.

N-o-*Toluyl* : needles from EtOH. M.p. 134–5°.

N-p-*Toluyl* : cryst. from EtOH. M.p. 140–2°.

N-*Benzenesulphonyl*: *N-o*-nitrobenzylbenzenesulphonamide. Yellow cryst. from C_6H_6. M.p. 92°.

N-*Me* : $C_8H_{10}O_2N_2$. MW, 166. Oil. Sol. H_2O. *B,HCl* : plates. M.p. 175–176·5°. N-*Acetyl* : m.p. 57–8°.

N-*Et* : $C_9H_{12}O_2N_2$. MW, 180. Oil. *B,HCl* : cryst. from EtOH. M.p. 184–6°.

N-*Di-Et* : $C_{11}H_{16}O_2N_2$. MW, 208. Yellow liq. B.p. 175–7°/42 mm. Spar. sol. H_2O. *Picrate* : m.p. 117°.

N-*Allyl* : $C_{10}H_{12}O_2N_2$. MW, 192. Oil. Misc. with EtOH. Spar. sol. H_2O. *B,HCl* : needles from EtOH–Et_2O. M.p. 136–7°. *B_2,H_2PtCl_6* : yellow needles from EtOH–Et_2O. M. p. 163°.

N-*Phenyl* : *see* o-Nitrobenzylaniline.

Picrate : yellow needles. M.p. 206–8°.

Wolff, *Ber.*, 1892, **25**, 3031.
Gabriel, Jansen, *Ber.*, 1891, **24**, 3092.
Noelting, Kregczy, *Bull. soc. chim.*, 1916, **19**, 335.
Ing, Manske, *J. Chem. Soc.*, 1926, 2348.

m-Nitrobenzylamine.

N-*Acetyl*: *N-m*-nitrobenzylacetamide. Needles. M.p. 91°.

N-*Benzenesulphonyl* : colourless needles or yellow prisms from C_6H_6. M.p. 123–4°.

N-*Me* : oil. *B,HCl* : needles from H_2O. M.p. 181°.

N-*Di-Et* : yellow liq. B.p. 206–8°/42 mm. Sol. most org. solvents. Spar. sol. H_2O. *Picrate* : m.p. 161°.

N-*Phenyl* : *see m*-Nitrobenzylaniline.

Benzylidene : prisms. M.p. 42°.

m-*Nitrobenzylidene* : leaflets. M.p. 141°.

p-*Nitrobenzylidene* : needles. M.p. 115°.

See last two references above and also Gabriel, Hendess, *Ber.*, 1887, **20**, 2869.

p-Nitrobenzylamine.

Needles. M.p. 40°. Strong base. Absorbs CO_2 from the air.

B,HCl : m.p. 222°.

N-*Acetyl*: *N-p*-nitrobenzylacetamide. Needles from H_2O. M.p. 133°.

N - *Benzoyl* : *N - p* - nitrobenzylbenzamide. Needles from EtOH. M.p. 155–6°.

N-*Benzenesulphonyl*: *N-p*-nitrobenzylbenzenesulphonamide. Orange-yellow leaflets from C_6H_6. M.p. 118°.

N-*Me* : yellow oil. Sol. most org. solvents. *B,HCl* : needles from EtOH. M.p. 226°. *B_2,H_2PtCl_6* : yellowish-red plates from EtOH.Aq. M.p. 220°. *B,$(COOH)_2$* : needles from EtOH.Aq. M.p. 188°.

N-*Di-Me* : $C_9H_{12}O_2N_2$. MW, 180. Yellow oil. Volatile in steam.

N-*Et* : yellow oil. *B,HCl* : cryst. from EtOH.Aq. M.p. 226°. *B,$(COOH)_2$* : plates from EtOH.Aq. M.p. 207°.

N-*Di-Et* : yellow liq. B.p. 219–21°/42 mm. Sol. most org. solvents. Spar. sol. H_2O. *Picrate*: m.p. 131°.

N-*Propyl* : $C_{10}H_{14}O_2N_2$. MW, 194. *B,HCl* : needles from EtOH.Aq. M.p. 225°. *B_2,H_2PtCl_6*: yellow needles from EtOH.Aq. M.p. 177°. *B,$(COOH)_2$* : leaflets from EtOH.Aq. M.p. 228°.

N-*Isoamyl* : $C_{12}H_{18}O_2N_2$. MW, 222. *B,HCl* : prisms from EtOH – Et_2O. M.p. 204°. *B_2,H_2PtCl_6* : orange plates from EtOH.Aq.

I.p. 206°. *Picrate* : m.p. 144°. *B,(COOH)*$_2$: eaflets from EtOH.Aq. M.p. 223°.

N-*Allyl* : yellow oil. *B,HCl* : needles from EtOH–Et$_2$O. M.p. 226°. *B*$_2$*,H*$_2$*PtCl*$_6$: reddish-yellow prisms from EtOH. M.p. 174°. *Picrate* : needles. M.p. 146°. *B,(COOH)*$_2$: leaflets from EtOH.Aq. M.p. 224°.

N-*Phenyl* : *see* *p*-Nitrobenzylaniline.

Benzylidene : prisms. M.p. 71°.

m-*Nitrobenzylidene* : plates. M.p. 115°.

p-*Nitrobenzylidene* : needles. M.p. 150°.

v. Braun, Deutsch, *Ber.*, 1912, **45**, 2197.
Curtius, *J. prakt. Chem.*, 1914, **89**, 526.
Noelting, Kregczy, *Bull. soc. chim.*, 1916, **19**, 335.
Salkowski, *Ber.*, 1889, **22**, 2142.
Paal, Sprenger, *Ber.*, 1897, **30**, 62.
Ing, Manske, *J. Chem. Soc.*, 1926, 2348.

N-4-Nitrobenzyl-*p*-aminophenol

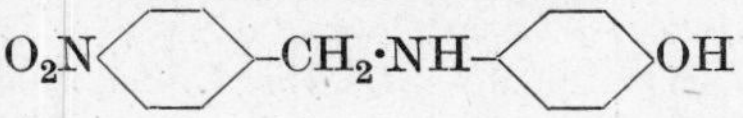

$C_{13}H_{12}O_3N_2$ MW, 244

Reddish-brown cryst. from $CHCl_3$ or C_6H_6, m.p. 114–15°, cryst. + $1H_2O$ from solvents containing H_2O, m.p. 87–8°. Sol. Na_2CO_3.Aq.

B,HCl : m.p. 191°.

O-*Benzoyl* : cryst. from C_6H_6. M.p. 218–20°. *B,HCl* : m.p. 110–12°.

N-*Benzoyl* : yellowish needles. M.p. 208–10°.

Bakunin, Profilo, *Gazz. chim. ital.*, 1907, **37**, ii, 241.

o-Nitrobenzylaniline

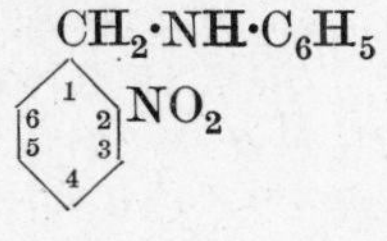

$C_{13}H_{12}O_2N_2$ MW, 228

Needles from EtOH. Two forms : (i) m.p. 47° ; (ii) m.p. 44° (metastable). Zn + HCl ⟶ 2-phenylindazole. Zn + AcOH ⟶ *o*-aminobenzylaniline.

N-*Me* : $C_{14}H_{14}O_2N_2$. MW, 242. Red cryst. from EtOH. M.p. 72°. Spar. sol. ligroin.

N-*Et* : $C_{15}H_{16}O_2N_2$. MW, 256. Brown cryst. from EtOH. M.p. 66°. Sol. $CHCl_3$, C_6H_6. Spar. sol. EtOH, Et_2O. Insol. ligroin. *Hydrochloride* : m.p. about 158°. *Chloroplatinate* : orange ppt. M.p. 116–17° decomp.

N-*Formyl* : *N*-*o*-nitrobenzylformanilide. Yellow needles or plates from CS_2.

N-*Acetyl* : *N*-*o*-nitrobenzylacetanilide. Cryst. M.p. 75°. Spar. sol. ligroin.

N-*Benzoyl* : *N*-*o*-nitrobenzylbenzanilide. Cryst. M.p. 101°. Sol. $CHCl_3$. Spar. sol. EtOH, Et_2O.

N-*Benzenesulphonyl* : needles from EtOH. M.p. 143°. Spar. sol. Et_2O, C_6H_6.

N-*Nitroso* : prisms from Et_2O. M.p. 84° (80·5–81°). Sol. $CHCl_3$, C_6H_6. Spar. sol. ligroin.

Lellman, Stickel, *Ber.*, 1886, **19**, 1605.
Gabriel, *Ber.*, 1887, **20**, 2229.

m-Nitrobenzylaniline.

Orange-red needles from EtOH. M.p. 84°. Sol. EtOH, $CHCl_3$, C_6H_6. Spar. sol. Et_2O.

B,HCl : m.p. 100–20°.

N-*Me* : yellow leaflets from EtOH. M.p. 51–2°. *Picrate* : m.p. 112–13°.

N-*Et* : reddish-brown prisms from EtOH. M.p. 69°. Very sol. $CHCl_3$, C_6H_6. Sol. EtOH, Et_2O. Insol. ligroin. *B,HCl* : prisms from $CHCl_3$. M.p. 186°. *Picrate* : cryst. from $CHCl_3$–ligroin. M.p. 131°.

N-*Acetyl* : *N*-*m*-nitrobenzylacetanilide. Yellow needles from Et_2O. M.p. 48°. Sol. EtOH, Et_2O, $CHCl_3$, C_6H_6. Insol. H_2O.

Purgotti, Monti, *Gazz. chim. ital.*, 1900, **30**, ii, 256.
Reilly, Moore, Drum, *J. Chem. Soc.*, 1928, 563.
Gabriel, Hendess, *Ber.*, 1887, **20**, 2869.

p-Nitrobenzylaniline.

Orange prisms from EtOH.Aq. M.p. 72° (68°). Sol. Et_2O, C_6H_6, hot EtOH. Fe + AcOH ⟶ *p*-aminobenzylaniline.

N-*Et* : yellow cryst. M.p. 67°. Very sol. $CHCl_3$, C_6H_6. Sol. EtOH, Et_2O. Insol. ligroin, pet. ether.

N-*Nitroso* : straw-yellow leaflets or needles. M.p. 75·5–76°. Sol. Me_2CO, $CHCl_3$, C_6H_6, hot EtOH. Spar. sol. ligroin.

Höchst, D.R.P., 97,847, (*Chem. Zentr.*, 1898, II, 696).
Paal, Sprenger, *Ber.*, 1897, **30**, 69.

2-Nitrobenzyl-*o*-anisidine

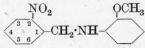

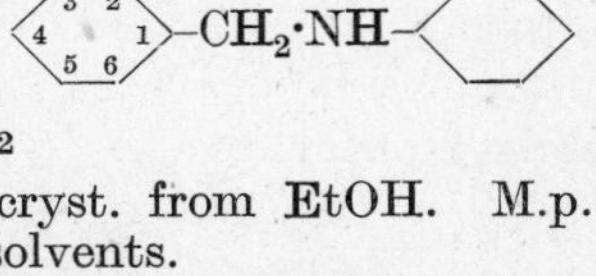

$C_{14}H_{14}O_3N_2$ MW, 258

Orange cryst. from EtOH. M.p. 80°. Sol. most org. solvents.

B,HCl : prisms from EtOH. M.p. 158°.

Paal, Schilling, *J. prakt. Chem.*, 1896, **54**, 277.

4-Nitrobenzyl-*o*-anisidine.

Red cryst. from EtOH. M.p. 95°. Sol. EtOH, Et_2O, AcOH, C_6H_6.

N-*Formyl*: yellowish plates from EtOH. M.p. 102°.

N-*Acetyl*: yellowish plates from EtOH. M.p. 78°.

Paal, Benker, *Ber.*, 1899, **32**, 1253.

2-Nitrobenzyl-*p*-anisidine

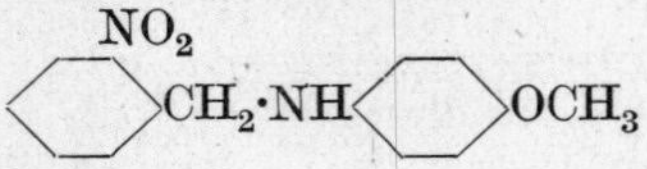

$C_{14}H_{14}O_3N_2$ MW, 258

Red leaflets from EtOH.Aq. M.p. 73°. Sol. most org. solvents. Spar. sol. ligroin.

B,HCl: needles from EtOH–Et_2O. M.p. 185°.

N-*Formyl*: cryst. from EtOH. M.p. 69°.

Paal, Schilling, *J. prakt. Chem.*, 1896, **54**, 283.

***o*-Nitrobenzyl bromide**

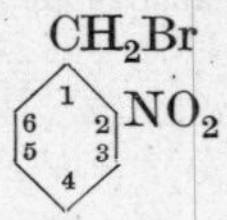

$C_7H_6O_2NBr$ MW, 216

Cryst. from EtOH.Aq. M.p. 46–7°. Sol. EtOH, Et_2O, C_6H_6, ligroin. Darkens on exposure to light.

Norris, Watt, Thomas, *J. Am. Chem. Soc.*, 1916, **38**, 1077.
Opolski, Kowalski, Pilewski, *Ber.*, 1916, **49**, 2282.

***m*-Nitrobenzyl bromide.**

Needles or plates. M.p. 58–9°.

See first reference above and also
Wachendorff, *Ann.*, 1877, **185**, 277.

***p*-Nitrobenzyl bromide.**

Needles from EtOH. M.p. 99–100°. Easily sol. EtOH, Et_2O, AcOH. Spar. sol. cold H_2O.

Brewster, *J. Am. Chem. Soc.*, 1918, **40**, 406.
Lyons, Reid, *J. Am. Chem. Soc.*, 1917, **39**, 1727.
Mourev, Brown, *Bull. soc. chim.*, 1921, **29**, 1006.
See also previous references.

***o*-Nitrobenzyl chloride**

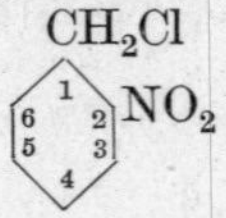

$C_7H_6O_2NCl$ MW, 171·5

Cryst. from ligroin. M.p. 48–9°. Sol. EtOH Et_2O, C_6H_6.

Kumpf, *Ann.*, 1884, **224**, 100.
Noelting, *Ber.*, 1884, **17**, 385.
Holleman, *Rec. trav. chim.*, 1914, **33**, 12.

***m*-Nitrobenzyl chloride.**

Pale yellow needles from ligroin. M.p 45–7° (44·8°). B.p. 173–83°/30–5 mm. Volatil in steam. Sol. EtOH, Et_2O, C_6H_6.

Gabriel, Borgmann, *Ber.*, 1883, **16**, 2064.
Abelli, *Gazz. chim. ital.*, 1883, **13**, 98.
Holleman, *Rec. trav. chim.*, 1914, **33**, 12.
Norris, Taylor, *J. Am. Chem. Soc.*, 1924 **46**, 753.

***p*-Nitrobenzyl chloride.**

Plates or needles from EtOH M.p. 71° Sol. EtOH, Et_2O.

Beilstein, Gietner, *Ann.*, 1886, **139**, 337.
Noelting, *Ber.*, 1884, **17**, 385.
Alway, *J. Am. Chem. Soc.*, 1902, **24**, 1062
Norris, Taylor, *J. Am. Chem. Soc.*, 1924 **46**, 753.

***o*-Nitrobenzyl cyanide** (o-*Nitrophenylacetonitrile*)

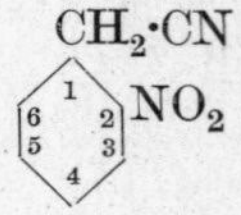

$C_8H_6O_2N_2$ MW, 16

Prisms from AcOH or EtOH, needles fron H_2O. M.p. 84°. B.p. 178°/12 mm. Sol. H_2O Spar. sol. EtOH, Me_2CO, $CHCl_3$, C_6H_6. Alkali ⟶ deep bluish-violet col.

Salkowski, *Ber.*, 1884, **17**, 507.
Bamberger, *Ber.*, 1886, **19**, 2635.
Reissert, *Ber.*, 1908, **41**, 3814.
Pschorr, Hoppe, *Ber.*, 1910, **43**, 2547.

***m*-Nitrobenzyl cyanide** (m-*Nitrophenyl acetonitrile*).

Cryst. from Et_2O–ligroin. M.p. 61–2°. Sol $CHCl_3$. Mod. sol. EtOH, Et_2O, C_6H_6. Spar sol. ligroin.

Haller, *Ann.*, 1908, **358**, 357.
Salkowski, *Ber.*, 1884, **17**, 506.

***p*-Nitrobenzyl cyanide** (p-*Nitrophenylacetonitrile*).

Plates. M.p. 116–17°. Mod. sol. H_2O, EtOH Et_2O, $CHCl_3$, C_6H_6. Sol. alc. KOH with intens carmine col.

Robertson, *Organic Syntheses*, Collectiv Vol. I, 389.
Bucklow, *Ber.*, 1900, **33**, 170.
Gabriel, *Ber.*, 1881, **14**, 2342.

N-Nitrobenzylformanilide.
See under Nitrobenzylaniline.

N-2-Nitrobenzylhydroxylamine

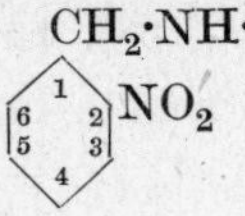

$C_7H_8O_3N_2$ MW, 168

Needles from C_6H_6. M.p. 70°. At 140° becomes dark blue in col.

B,HCl : needles. M.p. 185° decomp.

Kjellin, Kuylenstjerna, *Ber.*, 1897, **30**, 517.

N-3-Nitrobenzylhydroxylamine.
Needles from H_2O. M.p. 79·5–80·5°.
B,HCl : m.p. 145–6°.

Behrend, *Ann.*, 1891, **265**, 245.

N-4-Nitrobenzylhydroxylamine.
Needles from H_2O. M.p. 120–5°. Sol. EtOH. Spar. sol. Et_2O. Insol. ligroin. Reduces Fehling's.

B,HCl : needles. M.p. 180–2° decomp.

Behrend, Leuchs, *Ann.*, 1890, **257**, 243.
Behrend, König, *Ann.*, 1891, **263**, 193.

O-4-Nitrobenzylhydroxylamine

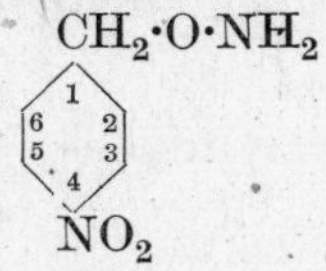

$C_7H_8O_3N_2$ MW, 168

Prisms from C_6H_6–ligroin. M.p. 56°. Does not reduce Fehling's.

B,HCl : leaflets from EtOH. M.p. 217°. Part. hydrolysed by boiling H_2O.

Brady, Klein, *J. Chem. Soc.*, 1927, 881.

o-Nitrobenzylideneacetone (o-*Nitrobenzalacetone, methyl* o-*nitrostyryl ketone*)

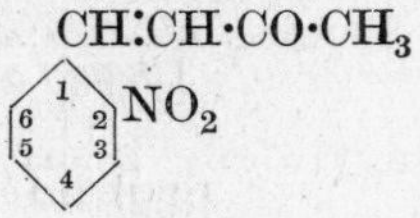

$C_{10}H_9O_3N$ MW, 191

Needles from Et_2O or EtOH.Aq. M.p. 60° (58–9°). Sol. EtOH, Et_2O, $CHCl_3$, C_6H_6. Insol. ligroin. $SnCl_2$ + HCl ⟶ quinaldine. Dil. HOCl ⟶ *o*-nitrocinnamic acid.

Drewsen, *Ber.*, 1883, **16**, 1954.
Fischer, Kuzel, *ibid.*, 36.
M.L.B., D.R.P., 20,255.

m-Nitrobenzylideneacetone (m-*Nitrobenzalacetone, methyl* m-*nitrostyryl ketone*).
Prisms from AcOH. M.p. 94–5°.
Phenylhydrazone : m.p. 155°.

Vorländer, *Ann.*, 1897, **294**, 293.
Ruhemann, *J. Chem. Soc.*, 1903, **83**, 1375.

p-Nitrobenzylideneacetone (p-*Nitrobenzalacetone, methyl* p-*nitrostyryl ketone*).
M.p. 110°. Sol. conc. H_2SO_4 with yellowish-red col.

Phenylhydrazone : red cryst. from EtOH. M.p. 195–6°.
p-*Chlorophenylhydrazone* : m.p. 218–19°.
o-*Tolylhydrazone* : m.p. 180–1.°

M.L.B., D.R.P., 20,255.
Baeyer, Becker, *Ber.*, 1883, **16**, 1969.
Auwers, Voss, *Ber.*, 1909, **42**, 4425.

ω-Nitrobenzylideneacetone (ω-*Nitrobenzalacetone*)

$$C_6H_5{\cdot}CH{:}CH{\cdot}CO{\cdot}CH_2NO_2$$

$C_{10}H_9O_3N$ MW, 191

Yellowish plates from EtOH. M.p. 97–8° after sintering at 83°. Sol. hot alkalis with yellow col.

Harries, *Ann.*, 1901, **319**, 254.

2-Nitrobenzylidene-o-aminophenol

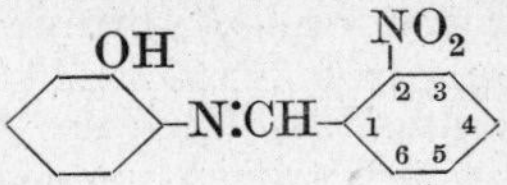

$C_{13}H_{10}O_3N_2$ MW, 242

Yellow needles from C_6H_6. M.p. 107° (104°). Sol. most org. solvents. Slowly darkens on exposure to light.

Me ether : *see* 2-Nitrobenzylidene-*o*-anisidine.

Levi, *Gazz. chim. ital.*, 1929, **59**, 544.
Senier, Clarke, *J. Chem. Soc.*, 1914, **105**, 1920.

3-Nitrobenzylidene-o-aminophenol.
Yellowish needles from EtOH. M.p. 135°. Sol. most org. solvents.

Pope, *J. Chem. Soc.*, 1908, **93**, 535.

4-Nitrobenzylidene-o-aminophenol.
Yellow needles from C_6H_6 or CCl_4. M.p. 158–60° (154°). Sol. EtOH, AcOEt, toluene. Insol. pet. ether, ligroin. Alc. NaOH ⟶ red col.

Me ether : *see* 4-Nitrobenzylidene-*o*-anisidine.

Levi, *Gazz. chim. ital.*, 1929, **59**, 544.
Pope, *J. Chem. Soc.*, 1908, **93**, 536.
Möhlau, Adams, *Chem. Zentr.*, 1907, I, 108.

2-Nitrobenzylidene-*m*-aminophenol

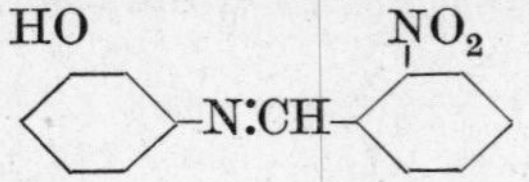

$C_{13}H_{10}O_3N_2$ MW, 242

Yellow prisms. M.p. 106–7°.
Me ether: *see* 2-Nitrobenzylidene-*m*-anisidine.

Senier, Clarke, *J. Chem. Soc.*, 1914, **105**, 1921.

2-Nitrobenzylidene-*p*-aminophenol

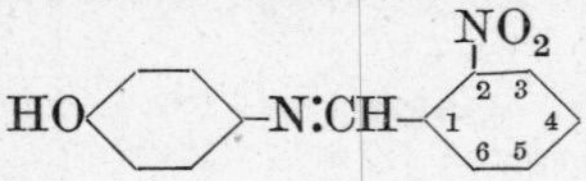

$C_{13}H_{10}O_3N_2$ MW, 242

Yellowish needles from EtOH.Aq. M.p. 163° (159°).
Me ether: *see* 2-Nitrobenzylidene-*p*-anisidine.
B,HCl: m.p. 216°.

Pope, Fleming, *J. Chem. Soc.*, 1908, **93**, 1918.
Senier, Clarke, *J. Chem. Soc.*, 1914, **105**, 1921.

3-Nitrobenzylidene-*p*-aminophenol.
Brown needles from EtOH.Aq. M.p. 154°.

Pope, *J. Chem. Soc.*, 1908, **93**, 534.

4-Nitrobenzylidene-*p*-aminophenol.
Yellow prisms from Et_2O. M.p. 168°. Sol. most org. solvents. Insol. ligroin.
Me ether: *see* 4-Nitrobenzylidene-*p*-anisidine.
Et ether: *see* 4-Nitrobenzylidene-*p*-phenetidine.

Pope, *J. Chem. Soc.*, 1908, **93**, 533.

***o*-Nitrobenzylideneaniline** (o-*Nitrobenzaldehyde anil*)

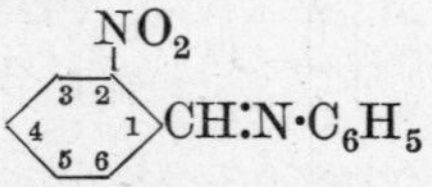

$C_{13}H_{10}O_2N_2$ MW, 226

Yellow leaflets from 80% EtOH. M.p. 69·5°. B.p. 220°/15 mm.

Knoevenagel, *Ber.*, 1898, **31**, 2609 (*Footnote*).

***m*-Nitrobenzylideneaniline** (m-*Nitrobenzaldehyde anil*).
Needles from EtOH. M.p. 66° (61°). Sol. AcOH. $NH_2OH \longrightarrow$ *m*-nitrobenz-*anti*-aldoxime.

Lazorenko, *Jahresber. Fortschr. Chem.*, 1870, 760.
Schwalbe, *Chem. Zentr.*, 1903, I, 231.

***p*-Nitrobenzylideneaniline** (p-*Nitrobenzaldehyde anil*).
Yellowish leaflets from Et_2O. M.p. 93°.

Fischer, *Ber.*, 1881, **14**, 2525.

2-Nitrobenzylidene-*o*-anisidine

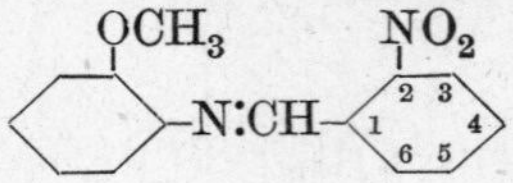

$C_{14}H_{12}O_3N_2$ MW, 256

Yellow cryst. M.p. 64–5°.

Senier, Clarke, *J. Chem. Soc.*, 1914, **105**, 1921.

4-Nitrobenzylidene-*o*-anisidine.
Yellow plates from EtOH.Aq. M.p. 111°.
B,HCl: m.p. 141°.

Pope, Fleming, *J. Chem. Soc.*, 1908, **93**, 1917.

2-Nitrobenzylidene-*m*-anisidine

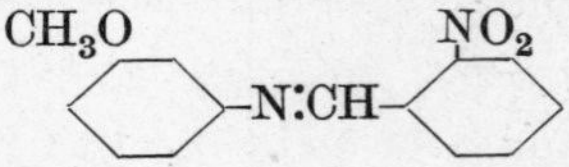

$C_{14}H_{12}O_3N_2$ MW, 256

Yellow cryst. M.p. 74–5°.

Senier, Clarke, *J. Chem. Soc.*, 1914, **105**, 1921.

2-Nitrobenzylidene-*p*-anisidine

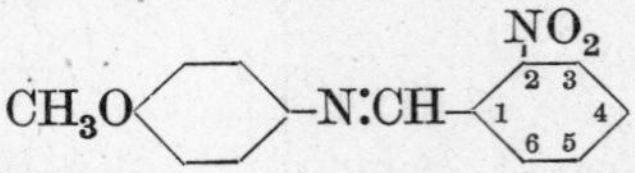

$C_{14}H_{12}O_3N_2$ MW, 256

Yellow cryst. M.p. 80–1°.

See previous reference.

4-Nitrobenzylidene-*p*-anisidine
Yellow leaflets from EtOH. M.p. 139°.
B,HCl: m.p. 200°.

Pope, Fleming, *J. Chem. Soc.*, 1908, **93**, 1917.

***o*-Nitrobenzylidene bromide**

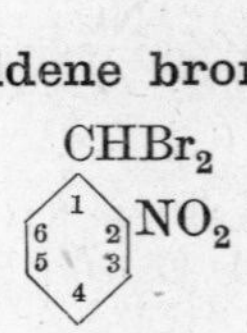

$C_7H_5O_2NBr_2$ MW, 295

Prisms from EtOH. M.p. 46°. Boiling alkalis $\longrightarrow$ *o*-nitrobenzaldehyde.

Reissert, *Ber.*, 1897, **30**, 1043.

m-Nitrobenzylidene bromide.
Needles from EtOH. M.p. 101–2°.

Wachendorff, *Ann.*, 1877, **185**, 278.

***p*-Nitrobenzylidene bromide.**
Needles from EtOH. M.p. 82°. Sol. EtOH, Et_2O. Spar. sol. H_2O. Ox. ⟶ *p*-nitrobenzoic acid. Heat with aniline ⟶ pararosaniline.

Reinhardt, *Ber.*, 1913, **46**, 3598.
See also previous reference.

***o*-Nitrobenzylidene chloride**

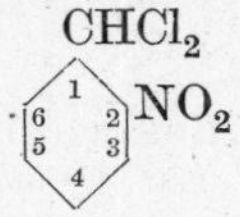

$C_7H_5O_2NCl_2$ MW, 206

Cryst. from EtOH. M.p. 27°. B.p. 143–4°/12 mm. Turns brown when exposed to light. Decomp. on long standing in air. Warm conc. HCl ⟶ *o*-nitrobenzaldehyde.

Kliegl, *Ber.*, 1907, **40**, 4939.
Kliegl, Haas, *Ber.*, 1911, **44**, 1214.

***m*-Nitrobenzylidene chloride.**
Cryst. from EtOH. M.p. 65°. Sol. hot EtOH, Et_2O. Red. ⟶ *m*-toluidine.

Widman, *Ber.*, 1880, **13**, 676.
Kliegl, Haas, *Ber.*, 1909, **42**, 2585.
Holleman, *Rec. trav. chim.*, 1914, **33**, 18.

***p*-Nitrobenzylidene chloride.**
Prisms from EtOH. M.p. 46° (42°). Sol. EtOH, Et_2O.

See last two references above.

***o*-Nitrobenzylidene diacetate**

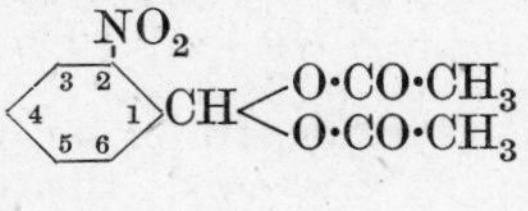

$C_{11}H_{11}O_6N$ MW, 253

Prisms from ligroin. M.p. 90° (87–8°). Sol. most org. solvents.

Thiele, Winter, *Ann.*, 1900, **311**, 356.
Baeyer, D.R.P., 121,788, (*Chem. Zentr.*, 1901, II, 70).
Bakunin, Parlati, *Gazz. chim. ital.*, 1906, **36**, 265.
Bakunin, Fisceman, *Gazz. chim. ital.*, 1916, **46**, 93.

***m*-Nitrobenzylidene diacetate.**
Cryst. from EtOH. M.p. 72°. Sol. most org. solvents.

See last reference above and also
Bakunin, Parlati, *Gazz. chim. ital.*, 1906, **36**, 266.

***p*-Nitrobenzylidene diacetate.**
Prisms from EtOH. M.p. 127° (125°). Sol. most org. solvents.

Thiele, Winter, *Ann.*, 1900, **311**, 355.
Baeyer, D.R.P., 121,788, (*Chem. Zentr.*, 1901, II, 70).
Bakunin, Parlati, *Gazz. chim. ital.*, 1906, **36**, 266.
Kohler, Reimer, *Am. Chem. J.*, 1904, **31**, 169.
Bakunin, Fisceman, *Gazz. chim. ital.*, 1916, **46**, 93.

1 : 2-*p*-Nitrobenzylideneglycerol

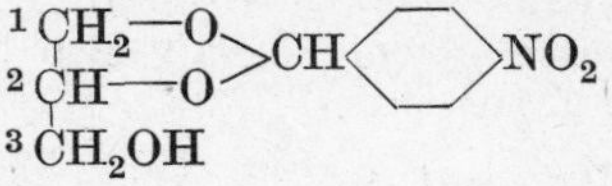

$C_{10}H_{11}O_5N$ MW, 225

Liq. B.p. 177–9°/0·3 mm. HCl (gas) at 100° ⟶ equilibrium mixture with the 1 : 3-isomer in ratio 2 : 1. Sol. EtOH, Et_2O, Me_2CO, C_6H_6. Insol. H_2O, ligroin. Two series of derivatives known which are geometrical isomers.

Me ether: $C_{11}H_{13}O_5N$. MW, 239. α-*Form*: yellow prisms from MeOH. M.p. 47°. Sol. most org. solvents. Insol. H_2O, ligroin. β-*Form*: feathery cryst. M.p. 42°. Somewhat more sol. than α-isomer.

Benzoyl: α-*form*, greenish-yellow cryst. from AcOEt. M.p. 115°. β-*Form*: cryst. from EtOH. M.p. 178°.

p-*Nitrobenzoyl*: α-*form*, straw-yellow needles from toluene. M.p. 117–18°. Sol. EtOH, Et_2O, Me_2CO, $CHCl_3$, C_6H_6. Insol. H_2O. β-*Form*: cryst. from toluene. M.p. 110°.

Hibbert, Sturrock, *J. Am. Chem. Soc.*, 1928, **50**, 3374.
Hibbert, Carter, *ibid.*, 3376.
Hibbert, Platt, Carter, *J. Am. Chem. Soc.*, 1929, **51**, 3641.

1 : 3-*p*-Nitrobenzylideneglycerol.
Cryst. from C_6H_6. M.p. 88°. On standing m.p. rises slowly to 98° although recryst. from C_6H_6 invariably gives the comp. m.p. 88°. HCl (gas) at 100° ⟶ equilibrium mixture with the 1 : 2-isomer in ratio 1 : 2. Forms two series of derivs. which are geometrical isomers.

Me ether: α-*form*, greyish needles from EtOH. M.p. 139°. Sol. EtOH, Et_2O, Me_2CO, C_6H_6, ligroin. Insol. H_2O. β-*Form*: needles from EtOH. M.p. 106°. Slightly more sol. than the α-form.

Benzoyl: α-*form*, plates from AcOEt. M.p. 204° Sol. Et_2O, AcOEt, Me_2CO, C_6H_6, hot ligroin. Insol. H_2O. β-*Form*: m.p. 159°. Rather more sol. than α-form.

p-*Nitrobenzoyl*: α-*form*, spicules from toluene M.p. 208°. β-*Form*: needles from toluene. M.p. 202°.

See previous references.

o-Nitrobenzylidenehydrazine (o-*Nitrobenzaldehyde hydrazone*)

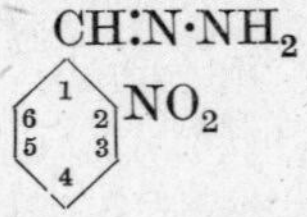

$C_7H_7O_2N_3$ MW, 165

Yellow prisms from EtOH. M.p. 76°. Very sol. most org. solvents.

Curtius, Lublin, *Ber.*, 1900, **33**, 2463.

m-Nitrobenzylidenehydrazine (m-*Nitrobenzaldehyde hydrazone*).

Yellow plates from EtOH. M.p. 107°. Mod. sol. org. solvents.

See previous reference.

p-Nitrobenzylidenehydrazine (p-*Nitrobenzaldehyde hydrazone*).

Orange prisms from EtOH. M.p. 134°.

See previous reference.

o-Nitrobenzylidenemalonic Acid

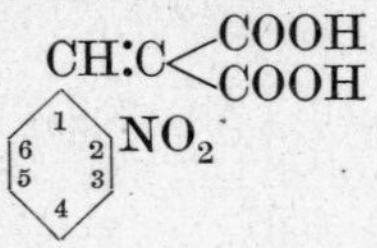

$C_{10}H_7O_6N$ MW, 237

Needles from H_2O. M.p. 162°. Sol. H_2O, Et_2O. Spar. sol. $CHCl_3$. Insol. CS_2, C_6H_6. $FeSO_4$ + NH_4OH ⟶ carbostyril-3-carboxylic acid. Boiling with H_2O ⟶ *o*-nitrobenzaldehyde, CO_2, malonic and *o*-nitrocinnamic acids.

Di-Me ester: $C_{12}H_{11}O_6N$. MW, 265. M.p. 65–6°.

Di-Et ester: $C_{14}H_{15}O_6N$. MW, 293. M.p. 53°.

Mononitrile: *o*-nitro-α-cyanocinnamic acid. $C_{10}H_6O_4N_2$. MW, 218. Yellow cryst. from AcOH. M.p. 226–8° (223°). Sol. EtOH. *Me ester*: $C_{11}H_8O_4N_2$. MW, 232. Needles from EtOH. M.p. 142°. *Et ester*: $C_{12}H_{10}O_4N_2$. MW, 246. Yellow plates from EtOH. M.p. 96°. Sol. EtOH, $CHCl_3$, C_6H_6. Spar. sol. cold EtOH, ligroin. Prac. insol. hot H_2O. *Amide*: $C_{10}H_7O_3N_3$. MW, 217. Needles from dil. EtOH. M.p. 173–4°. Sol. H_2O, EtOH, Me_2CO. Spar. sol. Et_2O.

Di-nitrile: $C_{10}H_5O_2N_3$. MW, 199. Needles from EtOH or AcOH. M.p. 137·5–138°. Sol Me_2CO, $CHCl_3$. Spar. sol. Et_2O, ligroin.

Meyer, *Monatsh.*, 1907, **28**, 53.
Stuart, *J. Chem. Soc.*, 1885, **47**, 155.
Heller, Wunderlich, *Ber.*, 1914, **47**, 1621 2890.
Sudborough, Lloyd, *J. Chem. Soc.*, 1898 **73**, 88.
Issoglio, *Chem. Zentr.*, 1904, I, 878.
Baker, Eccles, *J. Chem. Soc.*, 1927, 2127
Fiquet, *Ann. chim. phys.*, 1893, **29** 491.

m-Nitrobenzylidenemalonic Acid.

Cryst. M.p. 209–10° (205°) decomp. Sol. hot H_2O (part. decomp.). Spar. sol. Et_2O, cold H_2O Boiling with H_2O ⟶ CO_2, *m*-nitrobenzaldehyde, malonic and *m*-nitrocinnamic acids.

Di-Me ester: m.p. 99–100°.

Di-Et ester: plates from EtOH. M.p. 75–6° (73°).

Mononitrile: *m*-nitro-α-cyanocinnamic acid. Needles from EtOH.Aq. or Me_2CO. M.p. 173–5° (172°). *Me ester*: needles. M.p. 135–6°. *Et ester*: (i) colourless form. Prisms from EtOH or needles from EtOH–C_6H_6. M.p. 135° (127–8°). Sol. EtOH, Et_2O, $CHCl_3$, C_6H_6. Spar. sol ligroin. Insol. H_2O. (ii) Yellow form. Yellow cryst. from EtOH or C_6H_6. M.p. 135°.

Kötz, Kempe, *J. prakt. Chem.*, 1907, **75** 507.
Sudborough, Lloyd, *J. Chem. Soc.*, 1898 **73**, 88.
Bertini, *Gazz. chim. ital.*, 1901, **31**, 275.
Baker, Eccles, *J. Chem. Soc.*, 1927, 2127.
Boehm, *Arch. Pharm.*, 1929, **267**, 702.

p-Nitrobenzylidenemalonic Acid.

Cryst. M.p. 227° decomp. Heat ⟶ *p*-nitrocinnamic acid + CO_2. Boiling with H_2O ⟶ *p*-nitrobenzaldehyde, CO_2, malonic and *p*-nitrocinnamic acids.

Di-Me ester: needles from EtOH. M.p. 136–7°.

Di-Et ester: needles from EtOH. M.p. 93°. Sol. hot EtOH, ligroin, C_6H_6. Spar. sol. Et_2O.

Mononitrile: *p*-nitro-α-cyanocinnamic acid. Plates from EtOH. M.p. 208°. *Et ester*: needles. M.p. 169–70°. Sol. EtOH.

Knoevenagel, *Ber.*, 1898, **31**, 2593, 2613.
Stuart, *J. Chem. Soc.*, 1883, **43**, 408; 1885, **47**, 158.
Fiquet, *Ann. chim. phys.*, 1893, **29**, 489.
Boehm, *Arch. Pharm.*, 1929, **267**, 702.
Baker, Eccles, *J. Chem. Soc.*, 1927, 2127.

o-Nitrobenzylidene-1-naphthylamine

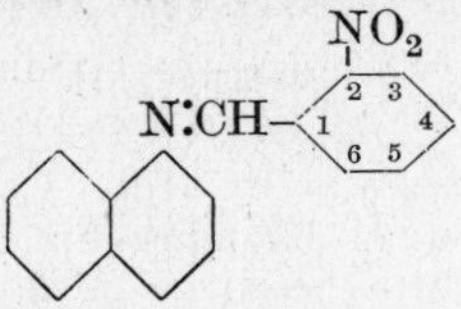

$C_{17}H_{12}O_2N_2$ MW, 276

Yellow solid. M.p. 118–118·5°.

Senier, Clarke, *J. Chem. Soc.*, 1914, **105**, 1923.

m-Nitrobenzylidene-1-naphthylamine.
Yellow plates from ligroin. M.p. 102–3°. Sol. Et_2O, $CHCl_3$. Spar. sol. ligroin.

Zenoni, *Gazz. chim. ital.*, 1893, **23**, ii, 222, 519.

o-Nitrobenzylidene-2-naphthylamine

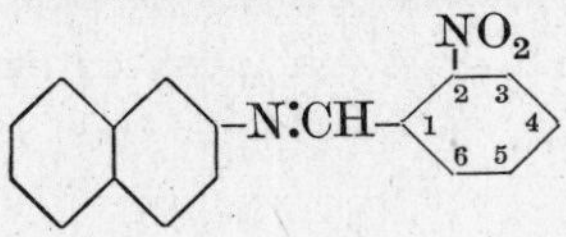

$C_{17}H_{12}O_2N_2$ MW. 276

Yellow cryst. from pet. ether. M.p. 95–6° (91°).

Senier, Clarke, *J. Chem. Soc.*, 1914, **105**, 1924.

m-Nitrobenzylidene-2-naphthylamine.
Yellow plates from EtOH. M.p. 90°. Sol. Et_2O, $CHCl_3$, C_6H_6. Spar. sol. EtOH.

Haase, *Ber.*, 1903, **36**, 593.

p-Nitrobenzylidene-2-naphthylamine.
Yellow needles. M.p. 120–1°. Very sol. Et_2O, Me_2CO. Mod. sol. EtOH, ligroin.

Zenoni, *Gazz. chim. ital.*, 1893, **23**, ii, 223, 519.

4-Nitrobenzylidene-p-phenetidine

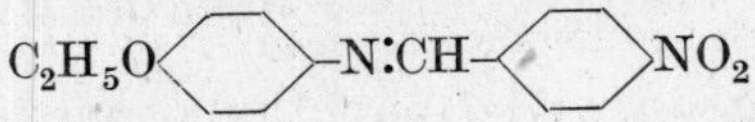

$C_{15}H_{14}O_3N_2$ MW, 270

Yellow, needles from EtOH. M.p. 130·5°. *B,HCl* : m.p. 196°.

Pope, Fleming, *J. Chem. Soc.*, 1908, **93**, 1917.

2-Nitrobenzylidene-o-toluidine

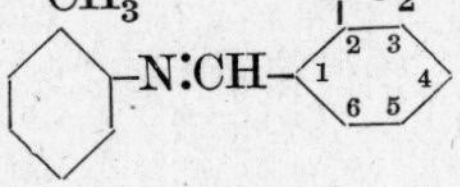

$C_{14}H_{12}O_2N_2$ MW, 240

Yellow cryst. M.p. 81–81·5°.

Senier, Clarke, *J. Chem. Soc.*, 1914, **105**, 1918.

3-Nitrobenzylidene-o-toluidine.
Yellow prisms from EtOH. M.p. 78–9°. Very sol. Et_2O, CS_2, C_6H_6. Sol. EtOH.

Ruhemann, Watson, *J. Chem. Soc.*, 1904, **85**, 1179.

2-Nitrobenzylidene-m-toluidine

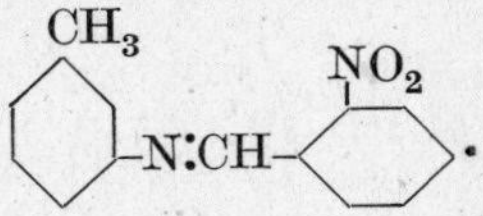

$C_{14}H_{12}O_2N_2$ MW, 240

Yellow solid. M.p. 52–3°.

Senier, Clarke, *J. Chem. Soc.*, 1914, **105**, 1918.

2-Nitrobenzylidene-p-toluidine

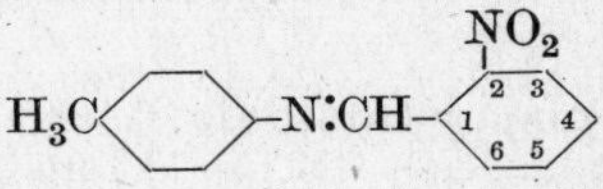

$C_{14}H_{12}O_2N_2$ MW, 240

Yellow solid. M.p. 73–4°.

Senier, Clarke, *J. Chem. Soc.*, 1914, **105**, 1919.

3-Nitrobenzylidene-p-toluidine.
Yellow needles. M.p. 96°. Sol. C_6H_6. Spar. sol. EtOH.

Ullmann, *Ber.*, 1903, **36**, 1024.

4-Nitrobenzylidine-p-toluidine.
Yellow leaflets. M.p. 124·5°. Sol. Et_2O, C_6H_6, hot EtOH.

Ullmann, *Ber.*, 1903, **36**, 1022.

o-Nitrobenzyl iodide

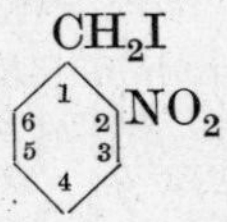

$C_7H_6O_2NI$ MW, 265

Plates. M.p. 75°.

Kumpf, *Ann.*, 1884, **224**, 103.

m-Nitrobenzyl iodide.
Yellow cryst. M.p. 84·5–86°.

Poggi, *Atti accad. Lincei*, 1925, **2**, 423.

p-Nitrobenzyl iodide.

Needles from EtOH. M.p. 127° (124°). Spar. sol. cold EtOH.

Finkelstein, *Ber.*, 1910, **43**, 1531.
Knoll, D.R.P., 230,172, (*Chem. Zentr.*, 1911, I, 359).
Kumpf, *Ann.*, 1884, **224**, 99.

o-Nitrobenzylmalonic Acid

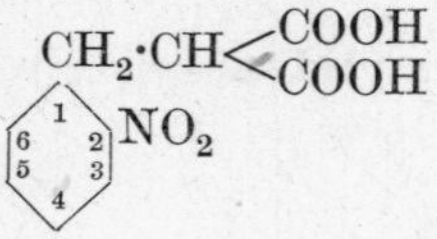

$C_{10}H_9O_6N$ MW, 239

Needles from H_2O. M.p. 164° decomp. Sol. MeOH, EtOH, Et_2O, AcOH, hot H_2O. Insol. $CHCl_3$, C_6H_6, ligroin.

Diamide : $C_{10}H_{11}O_4N_3$. MW, 237. Needles from H_2O. M.p. 234° decomp. Sol. AcOEt, hot EtOH.

Reissert, *Ber.*, 1896, **29**, 634, 644.
Baker, Eccles, *J. Chem. Soc.*, 1927, 2126.

m-Nitrobenzylmalonic Acid.

Cryst. from H_2O. M.p. 171° (164°) decomp.

Diamide : cryst. from H_2O. M.p. 203°.

Amide-nitrile : $C_{10}H_9O_3N_3$. MW, 219. Needles from EtOH. M.p. 147–8°. Sol. H_2O, EtOH, Me_2CO, $CHCl_3$. Spar. sol. Et_2O.

Issoglio, *Chem. Zentr.*, 1904, I, 878.
Gulland, Haworth, Virden, Callow, *J. Chem. Soc.*, 1929, 1666.
Baker, Eccles, *J. Chem. Soc.*, 1927, 2127.

p-Nitrobenzylmalonic Acid.

Yellow powder. Decomp. at 100°.

Di-Me ester : $C_{12}H_{13}O_6N$. MW, 267. Cryst. from MeOH. M.p. 82·5–83·5°.

Di-Et ester : $C_{14}H_{17}O_6N$. MW, 295. Prisms from EtOH.Aq. M.p. 168·5°. Sol. EtOH, Me_2CO. Mod. sol. warm H_2O. Spar. sol. Et_2O.

Monohydrazide : m.p. 137°.

Lellmann, Schleich, *Ber.*, 1887, **20**, 434.
Reissert, *Ber.*, 1896, **29**, 635.
Curtius, *J. prakt. Chem.*, 1930, **125**, 139.
Baker, Eccles, *J. Chem. Soc.*, 1927, 2128.

o-Nitrobenzyl Mercaptan

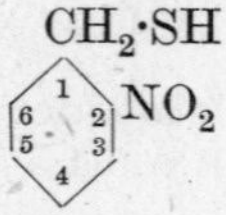

$C_7H_7O_2NS$ MW, 169

Yellow needles from MeOH or AcOEt. M.p 42–4° (47°, 29·5°). B.p. 149°/15 mm.

Gabriel, Stelzner, *Ber.*, 1896, **29**, 161.
Price, Twiss, *J. Chem. Soc.*, 1909, **9** 1727.

m-Nitrobenzyl Mercaptan.

Yellowish-white needles. M.p. 14° (11–12° B.p. 164°/18 mm.

See last reference above and also
Lutter, *Ber.*, 1897, **30**, 1068.

p-Nitrobenzyl Mercaptan.

Yellow needles or plates from EtOH. M.p 58° (55°, 52·5°, 51°). B.p. 164°/15 mm.

Carbamate : m.p. 140–1°.

Price, Twiss, *J. Chem. Soc.*, 1909, **9** 1727.
Poggi, *Atti accad. Lincei*, 1925, **2**, 424.
Horn, *J. Am. Chem. Soc.*, 1921, **43**, 2607

o-Nitrobenzyl-1-naphthylamine

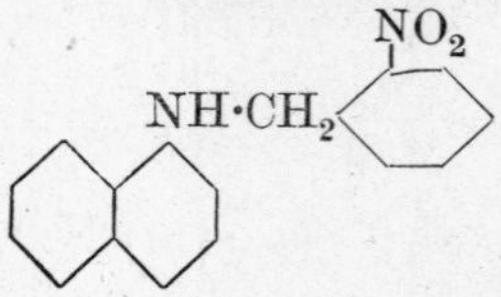

$C_{17}H_{14}O_2N_2$ MW, 27

Yellow needles from EtOH. M.p. 97°. Sol Et_2O, $CHCl_3$, AcOH, C_6H_6. Spar. sol. EtOH ligroin. Insol. H_2O.

N-*Acetyl* : *N-o*-nitrobenzyl-1-acetnaphthalide Leaflets from EtOH. M.p. 130°.

Darier, Mannassewitch, *Bull. soc. chim.* 1902, **27**, 1057.

m-Nitrobenzyl-1-naphthylamine.

Orange-yellow prisms from EtOH. M.p. 94° Spar. sol. EtOH, Et_2O, C_6H_6.

N-*Acetyl* : yellow needles from EtOH. M.p 109–10°.

See previous reference.

p-Nitrobenzyl-1-naphthylamine.

Orange leaflets from EtOH. M.p. 126–7° Sol. Et_2O, C_6H_6. Spar. sol. EtOH, ligroin.

N-*Acetyl* : *N-p*-nitrobenzyl-1-acetnaphthalide Needles from EtOH. M.p. 112–13°.

See previous reference.

o-Nitrobenzyl-2-naphthylamine

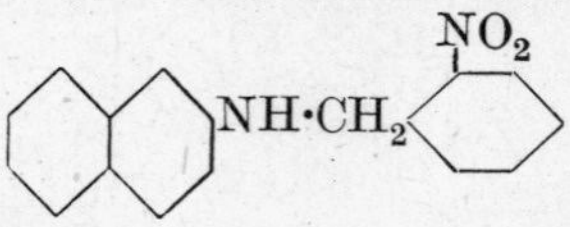

$C_{17}H_{14}O_2N_2$ MW, 278

Red leaflets from EtOH–AcOH. M.p. 162°. Sol. $CHCl_3$, C_6H_6, CS_2. Spar. sol. most org. solvents.

N-*Acetyl* : *N-o*-nitrobenzyl-2-acetnaphthalide. Prisms from EtOH. M.p. 117–18°.

N-*Nitroso* : yellow leaflets from EtOH. M.p. 102°. Sol. $CHCl_3$, C_6H_6. Very spar. sol. ligroin.

Darier, Mannassewitch, *Bull. soc. chim.*, 1902, **27**, 1057.

Busch, Brand, *J. prakt. Chem.*, 1895, **52**, 410.

m-Nitrobenzyl-2-naphthylamine.

Needles from EtOH. M.p. 80°.

Darier, Mannassewitch, *Bull. soc. chim.*, 1902, **27**, 1060.

p-Nitrobenzyl-2-naphthylamine.

Yellow leaflets from EtOH.Aq. M.p. 121·5°. Sol. Et_2O, C_6H_6. Spar. sol. EtOH.

See previous reference.

2-Nitrobenzyl-p-phenetidine

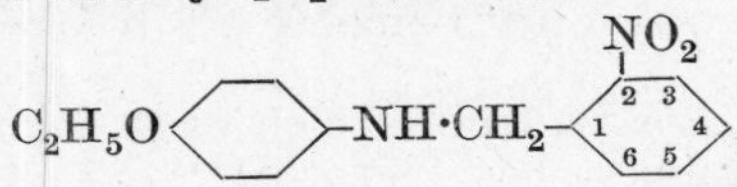

$C_{15}H_{16}O_3N_2$ MW, 272

Red plates from EtOH.Aq. M.p. 52°. Sol. most org. solvents. Spar. sol. ligroin.

B,HCl : needles from EtOH–HCl. M.p. 163°.

N-*Formyl* : plates from C_6H_6. M.p. 96°.

Paal, Küttner, *J. prakt. Chem.*, 1893, **48**, 555.

2-Nitrobenzyl-o-toluidine

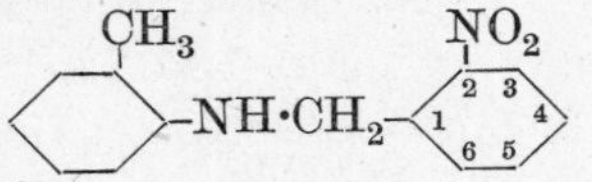

$C_{14}H_{14}O_2N_2$ MW, 242

Cryst. from EtOH. M.p. 96°. D^{15} 1·278. Sol. EtOH, Et_2O, AcOH, C_6H_6.

N-*Formyl* : yellow needles from EtOH.Aq. M.p. 76°.

N-*Nitroso* : needles from EtOH. M.p. 64–5°.

Lellmann, Mayer, *Ber.*, 1892, **25**, 3582.

3-Nitrobenzyl-o-toluidine.

Cryst. from EtOH. M.p. 62°. Sol. $CHCl_3$, CS_2, C_6H_6, hot EtOH. Spar. sol. Et_2O. Insol. H_2O, pet. ether.

Purgotti, Monti, *Gazz. chim. ital.*, 1900, **30**, ii, 258.

4-Nitrobenzyl-o-toluidine.

Red needles. M.p. 93°.

Lellmann, Mayer, *Ber.*, 1892, **25**, 3582.

3-Nitrobenzyl-m-toluidine

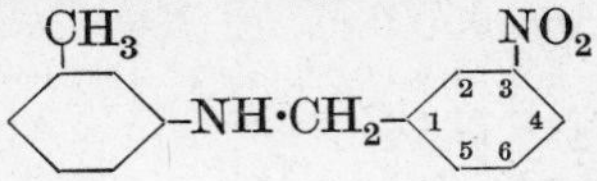

$C_{14}H_{14}O_2N_2$ MW, 242

Cryst. from EtOH. M.p. 67°. Sol. $CHCl_3$, C_6H_6, CS_2, hot EtOH. Spar. sol. Et_2O. Insol. H_2O, pet. ether.

Purgotti, Monti, *Gazz. chim. ital.*, 1900, **30**, ii, 258.

2-Nitrobenzyl-p-toluidine

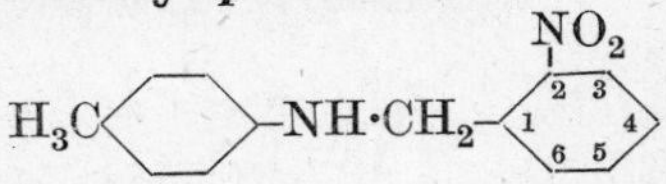

$C_{14}H_{14}O_2N_2$ MW, 242

Yellow cryst. M.p. 72°. Sol. most org. solvents. Spar. sol. ligroin.

N-*Formyl* : needles from EtOH. M.p. 79°.

N-*Acetyl* : *N*-2-nitrobenzylacet-*p*-toluidide. Cryst. from $CHCl_3$–Et_2O. M.p. 65°.

N-*Benzenesulphonyl* : cryst. from EtOH. M.p. 124°.

N-*Nitroso* : yellow needles from EtOH. M.p. 80°.

Lellmann, Stickel, *Ber.*, 1886, **19**, 1609.

Busch, *J. prakt. Chem.*, 1895, **51**, 271.

3-Nitrobenzyl-p-toluidine.

Needles from EtOH. M.p. 86°. Sol. $CHCl_3$, C_6H_6, CS_2, hot EtOH. Spar. sol. pet. ether.

Purgotti, Monti, *Gazz. chim. ital.*, 1900, **30**, ii, 258.

4-Nitrobenzyl-p-toluidine.

Yellow cryst. M.p. 68°.

Lellmann, Mayer, *Ber.*, 1892, **25**, 3582.

o-Nitrobenzylurea

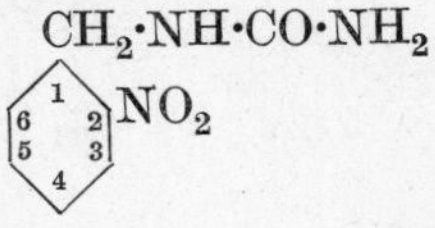

$C_8H_9O_3N_3$ MW, 195

Needles from H_2O. M.p. 150°.

Gabriel, Jansen, *Ber.*, 1891, **24**, 3092.

p-Nitrobenzylurea.

Yellow needles from EtOH. M.p. 196–7°. Sol. EtOH, AcOH. Insol. H_2O, C_6H_6.

Hafner, *Ber.*, 1890, **23**, 339.

Nitrobiuret

$NO_2·NH·CO·NH·CO·NH_2$

$C_2H_4O_4N_4$ MW, 148

Cryst. powder from H_2O. M.p. 165° (223°) decomp. Sol. hot H_2O, EtOH. Spar. sol. cold H_2O. Aq. sol. reacts acid. Boiling $H_2O \longrightarrow$ urea + CO_2 + N_2O. Does not give biuret reaction with $CuSO_4$ + alkali.

Thiele, Uhlfelder, *Ann.*, 1898, **303**, 95.
Davis, Blanchard, *J. Am. Chem. Soc.*, 1929, **51**, 1801.

Nitrobromoform.
See Bromopicrin.

1-Nitrobutane

$CH_3{\cdot}CH_2{\cdot}CH_2{\cdot}CH_2NO_2$

$C_4H_9O_2N$ MW, 103

Colourless liq. B.p. 151–2°. Sol. aq. alkalis.

Züblin, *Ber.*, 1877, **10**, 2083.
Rây, Neogi, *J. Chem. Soc.*, 1906, **89**, 1902.

2-Nitrobutane

$CH_3{\cdot}CH_2{\cdot}CH(NO_2){\cdot}CH_3$

$C_4H_9O_2N$ MW, 103

Liq. B.p. 138–9°/747 mm. D^0 0·9877.

Meyer, Locher, *Ann.*, 1876, **180**, 134.
Bewad, *J. prakt. Chem.*, 1901, **63**, 194.

Nitrobutanol.
See Nitrobutyl Alcohol.

2-Nitro-*n*-butyl Alcohol (*2-Nitrobutanol-1*)

$CH_3{\cdot}CH_2{\cdot}CH(NO_2){\cdot}CH_2OH$

$C_4H_9O_3N$ MW, 119

Liq. B.p. 127–30°/25 mm. $D^{11.5}$ 1·1365. Sol. EtOH, Et_2O, AcOH. Mod. sol. H_2O.

Henry, *Bull. soc. chim.*, 1896, **15**, 1223.
Pauwels, *Chem. Zentr.*, 1898, I, 193.

1-Nitro-*sec.*-*n*-butyl Alcohol (*1-Nitrobutanol-2*)

$CH_3{\cdot}CH_2{\cdot}CH(OH){\cdot}CH_2NO_2$

$C_4H_9O_3N$ MW, 119

Thick liq. B.p. 204°/767 mm., slight decomp., 123–5°/35 mm. D^{18} 1·191, $D^{3.5}$ 1·144. *Acetyl*: b.p. 105–6°/11 mm. D_4^{20} 1·1224. n_D^{20} 1·4285.

Schmidt, Rutz, *Ber.*, 1928, **61**, 2142.
See also first reference above.

3-Nitro-*sec.*-*n*-butyl Alcohol (*3-Nitrobutanol-2*)

$CH_3{\cdot}CH(NO_2){\cdot}CH(OH){\cdot}CH_3$

$C_4H_9O_3N$ MW, 119

B.p. 112–13°/38 mm. $D^{7.8}$ 1·116.

Henry, *Bull. soc. chim.*, 1896, **15**, 1224.

***N*-Nitrobutylamine.**
See Butylnitramine.

***o*-Nitro-*n*-butylbenzene** (*1-o-Nitrophenyl-n-butane*)

$CH_2{\cdot}CH_2{\cdot}CH_2{\cdot}CH_3$

NO_2

$C_{10}H_{13}O_2N$ MW, 179

B.p. 260° part decomp., 131–3°/15 mm. D_4^{20} 1·071. Sn + HCl $\longrightarrow$ *o*-amino-*n*-butylbenzene. Volatile in steam.

Read, Mullin, *J. Am. Chem. Soc.*, 1928, **50**, 1763.
Reilly, Hickinbottom, *J. Chem. Soc.*, 1920, **117**, 116.

***m*-Nitro-*n*-butylbenzene** (*1-m-Nitrophenyl-n-butane*).

B.p. 275°/752 mm. Misc. with $CHCl_3$, $PhNO_2$, Py, pet, ether. Volatile in steam.

Reilly, Hickinbottom, *J. Chem. Soc.*, 1920, **117**, 118.

***p*-Nitro-*n*-butylbenzene** (*1-p-Nitrophenyl-n-butane*)

B.p. 143–5°/15 mm. D_4^{20} 1·065. Sn + HCl $\longrightarrow$ *p*-amino-*n*-butylbenzene.

Read, Mullin, *J. Am. Chem. Soc.*, 1928, **50**, 1763.

α-Nitro-*n*-butylbenzene (*1-Nitro-1-phenyl-n-butane*)

$C_6H_5{\cdot}CH(NO_2){\cdot}CH_2{\cdot}CH_2{\cdot}CH_3$

$C_{10}H_{13}O_2N$ MW, 179

B.p. 250–6°/758 mm. decomp., 151–2°/25 mm. D_0^0 1·0756, D_D^{20} 1·0592. n_D^{20} 1·50746.

Konowalow, *Ber.*, 1895, **28**, 1857.

ω-Nitro-*n*-butylbenzene (*4-Nitro-1-phenyl-n-butane*)

$C_6H_5{\cdot}CH_2{\cdot}CH_2{\cdot}CH_2{\cdot}CH_2NO_2$

$C_{10}H_{13}O_2N$ MW, 179

B.p. 160–5°/15 mm.

v. Braun, Kruber, *Ber.*, 1912, **45**, 397.

***o*-Nitro-*sec.*-*n*-butylbenzene** (*2-o-Nitrophenyl-n-butane*)

$CH(CH_3){\cdot}CH_2{\cdot}CH_3$

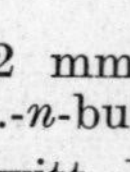

NO_2

$C_{10}H_{13}O_2N$ MW, 179

B.p. 123–6°/12 mm. D_4^{20} 1·065. Sn + HCl $\longrightarrow$ *o*-amino-*sec.*-*n*-butylbenzene.

Read, Hewitt, Pike, *J. Am. Chem. Soc.*, 1932, **54**, 1194.

p-Nitro-sec.-n-butylbenzene (2-p-*Nitrophenyl*-n-*butane*).

B.p. 142–4°/12 mm. 130°/9 mm. D_4^{20} 1·065. Sn + HCl ⟶ *p*-amino-*sec*.-*n*-butylbenzene.

See previous reference and also
Glattfeld, Wertheim, *J. Am. Chem. Soc.*, 1921, **43**, 2684.
Harrison, Kenyon, Shepherd, *J. Chem. Soc.*, 1926, 660.

ω-Nitro-sec.-n-butylbenzene (4-*Nitro*-2-*phenylbutane*)

$$C_6H_5{\cdot}\overset{CH_3}{CH}{\cdot}CH_2{\cdot}CH_2NO_2$$

$C_{10}H_{13}O_2N$ MW, 179

B.p. 138°/12 mm.

v. Braun, Grabowski, Kirschbaum, *Ber.*, 1913, **46**, 1282.

o-Nitro-tert.-butylbenzene

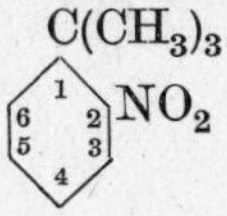

$C_{10}H_{13}O_2N$ MW, 179

Yellow liq. B.p. 250·5°/765 mm., 114·5°/10 mm. D^{15} 1·074. Sol. EtOH, Et_2O, C_6H_6. Volatile in steam. Sn + HCl ⟶ *o*-amino-*tert*.-butylbenzene.

Seńkowski, *Ber.*, 1890, **23**, 2414.
Shoesmith, Mackie, *J. Chem. Soc.*, 1928, 2334.

m-Nitro-tert.-butylbenzene.

Yellowish-red liq. M.p. below 20°. B.p. 250–2°/704 mm.

Gelzer, *Ber.*, 1888, **21**, 2946.
Seńkowski, *Ber.*, 1891, **24**, 2974.
Cf. Shoesmith, Mackie, *J. Chem. Soc.*, 1928, 2334.

p-Nitro-tert.-butylbenzene.

B.p. 265–7°/757 mm. slight decomp., 142–3°/17 mm., 125–30°/10 mm. Sn + HCl ⟶ *p*-amino-*tert*.-butylbenzene. Dil. HNO_3 ⟶ *p*-nitrobenzoic acid.

Malherbe, *Ber.*, 1919, **52**, 319.
Shoesmith, Mackie, *J. Chem. Soc.*, 1928, 2336.

ω-Nitro-tert.-butylbenzene

$$C_6H_5{\cdot}\overset{CH_3}{\underset{CH_3}{C}}{\cdot}CH_2NO_2$$

$C_{10}H_{13}O_2N$ MW, 179

Yellow oil. B.p. 141–3°/15 mm. D_0^0 1·0993, D_0^{20} 1·0840. n_D^{27} 1·52138. Sol. alkalis.

Konowalow, *Jahresber. Fortschr. Chem.*, 1895, 1538.

2-Nitro-4-butylphenol

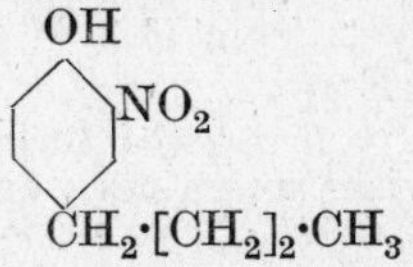

$C_{10}H_{13}O_3N$ MW, 195

B.p. 125°/3·5 mm.

Baranger, *Bull. soc. chim.*, 1931, **49**, 1213.

5-Nitro-3-tert.-butyltoluene

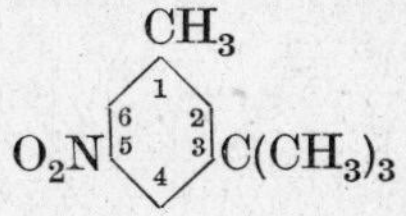

$C_{11}H_{15}O_2N$ MW, 193

M.p. 32°. B.p. 120°/15 mm.

Baur-Thurgau, *Ber.*, 1897, **30**, 303.

6-Nitro-3-tert.-butyltoluene.

Liq. B.p. 160–2° in vacuo. Volatile in steam.

Baur, *Ber.*, 1891, **24**, 2835.

2-Nitro-4-tert.-butyltoluene.

Yellow oil. B.p. 138–9°.

Battegay, Haeffely, *Bull. soc. chim.*, 1924, **35**, 981.

1-Nitrobutyric Acid

$$CH_3{\cdot}CH_2{\cdot}CH(NO_2){\cdot}COOH$$

$C_4H_7O_4N$ MW, 133

Et ester: $C_6H_{11}O_4N$. MW, 161. Yellow oil. B.p. 123°/20 mm. n_D^{18} 1·4535. Spar. sol. H_2O. Easily sol. EtOH, Et_2O, C_6H_6.

Schmidt, Widmann, *Ber.*, 1909, **42**, 1896.

Nitrocaffeic Acid.

See Nitro-3 : 4-dihydroxycinnamic Acid.

3-Nitro-d-camphor (α-*Nitro*-d-*camphor*)

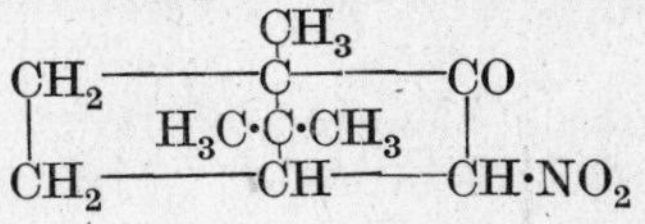

$C_{10}H_{15}O_3N$ MW, 197

Nitro-form.

Prisms from C_6H_6. M.p. 103° (100–1°). Very sol. C_6H_6, $CHCl_3$. Sol. EtOH, Et_2O, ligroin. Spar. sol. pet. ether. Shows mutarotation. $[\alpha]_D^{15}$ − 124° ⟶ − 104° in C_6H_6. $[\alpha]_D^{13}$ − 27° ⟶ − 15° in $CHCl_3$. $[\alpha]_D^{13}$ − 26° ⟶ − 9° in EtOH. $[\alpha]_D^{13}$ − 3° ⟶ + 8° in AcOH.

Aci-form. 3-Isonitro-*d*-camphor.
Not obtained pure in free state.

NH_4 salt: cryst. from EtOH. M.p. 178°. $[\alpha]_{546}$ + 384° in H_2O. Sol. H_2O. Mod. sol. EtOH. Spar. sol. Me_2CO. Insol. $CHCl_3$, C_6H_6, pet. ether.

Na salt: cryst. from EtOH. Very sol. H_2O, EtOH. Insol. Et_2O.

Cu salt: green cryst. from EtOH. Sol. EtOH, Et_2O with brown col. Insol. H_2O.

Anhydride: $C_{20}O_{28}O_5N_2$. MW, 376. Exists in two forms. (i) Cryst. from EtOH. M.p. 193°. $[\alpha]_{546}$ + 242° in C_6H_6. (ii) Greenish-yellow needles from EtOH. M.p. 184°. $[\alpha]_{546}$ − 6° in C_6H_6.

Lowry, Steele, *J. Chem. Soc.*, 1915, **107**, 1040.
Lowry, *J. Chem. Soc.*, 1898, **73**, 995.
Forster, *J. Chem. Soc.*, 1902, **81**, 868.
Cazeneuve, *Bull. soc. chim.*, 1888, **49**, 92.
Lowry, Robertson, *J. Chem. Soc.*, 1904, **85**, 1545.

N-Nitrocarbamic Acid

$NO_2 \cdot NH \cdot COOH$

$CH_2O_4N_2$ MW, 106

K salt: needles. Decomp. by H_2O. Sol. very conc. KOH. Explodes on heating.

Me ester: $C_2H_4O_4N_2$. MW, 120. Plates or prisms. M.p. 88°. Decomp. at 120–30°.

Et ester: *see* Nitrourethane.

Amide: *see* Nitrourea.

Thiele, Dent, *Ann.*, 1898, **302**, 249.

2-Nitrocarbanilide

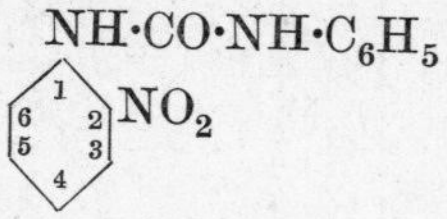

$C_{13}H_{11}O_3N_3$ MW, 257

Yellowish needles from H_2O or EtOH. M.p. 231–3° (170°). Sol. hot EtOH. Insol. Et_2O, pet. ether.

Manuelli, Comanducci, *Gazz. chim. ital.*, 1899, **29**, ii, 141.

3-Nitrocarbanilide.

Pale yellow needles. M.p. 198·5°.

Leuckart, *J. prakt. Chem.*, 1890, **41**, 322.
See also previous reference.

4-Nitrocarbanilide.

Cryst. from EtOH.Aq. M.p. 212° (202°).

See previous references.

1-Nitrocarbazole

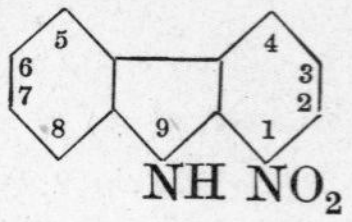

$C_{12}H_8O_2N_2$ MW, 212

Yellow needles from AcOH. M.p. 187°. Mod. sol. CS_2. Spar. sol. pet. ether. Alc. KOH ⟶ bluish-red sol.

Lindemann, *Ber.*, 1924, **57**, 555.
I.G., D.R.P., 511,021, (*Chem. Abstracts*, 1931, **25**, 1262).

3-Nitrocarbazole.

Cryst. M.p. 214° (205°). Spar. sol. C_6H_6, $CHCl_3$, AcOH. Insol. Et_2O, pet. ether.

N-*Acetyl*: needles from C_6H_6. M.p. 237–8°. Sol. $CHCl_3$. Spar. sol. EtOH. Almost insol. pet. ether.

N-*Benzoyl*: yellow plates from AcOH. M.p. 181°. Sol. Et_2O, warm C_6H_6, ligroin.

N-*Nitroso*: pale yellow needles from EtOH. M.p. 166·5° decomp. Sol. hot AcOEt. Mod. sol. $CHCl_3$. Spar. sol. ligroin.

N-*Me*: $C_{13}H_{10}O_2N_2$. MW, 226. Yellow needles from EtOH. M.p. 173° (169–71°).

N-*Et*: $C_{14}H_{12}O_2N_2$. MW, 240. Yellow needles from EtOH. M.p. 126–8°.

Lindemann, *Ber.*, 1924, **57**, 555.
Mazzara, *Ber.*, 1891, **24**, 281.
Mazzara, Leonardi, *Gazz. chim. ital.*, 1892, **22**, ii, 443.
Stevens, Tucker, *J. Chem. Soc.*, 1923, **123**, 2143.

3-Nitrocarbostyril (3-*Nitro-2-hydroxy-quinoline*)

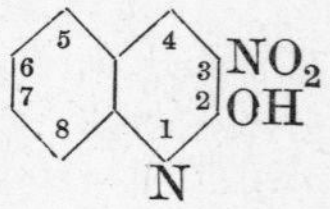

$C_9H_6O_3N_2$ MW, 190

Fine needles from EtOH. Does not melt below 320°. Spar. sol. EtOH, Me_2CO, AcOH.

Friedländer, Lazarus, *Ann.*, 1885, **229**, 243.

4-Nitrocarbostyril (4-*Nitro-2-hydroxy-quinoline*).

Yellow needles from AcOH. M.p. 260°. Insol. EtOH. Sol. dil. alkalis.

See previous reference.

5-Nitrocarbostyril (5-*Nitro-2-hydroxy-quinoline*).

Golden-yellow needles or leaflets from EtOH. M.p. 304°. Very spar. sol. EtOH.

Me ether: $C_{10}H_8O_3N_2$. MW, 204. Yellow needles. M.p. 151°. Sol. EtOH. Insol. H_2O.

N-*Me*: 5-nitro-*N*-methyl-α-quinolone. $C_{10}H_8O_3N_2$. MW, 204. Yellow needles from EtOH or H_2O. M.p. 167°. Sol. Et_2O, C_6H_6. Sublimes.

N-*Et*: 5-nitro-*N*-ethyl-α-quinolone. $C_{11}H_{10}O_3N_2$. MW, 218. Cryst. from MeOH. M.p. 135°. Sol. EtOH, C_6H_6, hot H_2O.

Claus, Setzer, *J. prakt. Chem.*, 1896, **53**, 392.
Fischer, Guthmann, *J. prakt. Chem.*, 1916, **93**, 383.
Decker, Remfry, *Ber.*, 1905, **38**, 2776.

6-Nitrocarbostyril (*6-Nitro-2-hydroxy-quinoline*).

Yellowish needles from H_2O. M.p. 283° (277°).

Me ether: $C_{10}H_8O_3N_2$. MW, 204. Needles from C_6H_6. M.p. 189–90°. Very sol. C_6H_6, $CHCl_3$, toluene. Sol. Et_2O, EtOH, ligroin. Insol. H_2O.

Et ether: $C_{11}H_{10}O_3N_2$. MW, 218. Needles from C_6H_6. M.p. 156–8°.

N-*Me*: 6-nitro-*N*-methyl-α-quinolone. Yellow needles from EtOH. M.p. 226° (222°). Sublimes with slight decomp.

N-*Et*: 6-nitro-*N*-ethyl-α-quinolone. Yellow needles from EtOH. M.p. 183°. Sublimes.

Decker, *J. prakt. Chem.*, 1901, **64**, 89.
Fischer, Guthmann, *J. prakt. Chem.*, 1916, **93**, 378.
Kaufmann, de Petherd, *Ber.*, 1917, **50**, 343.

7-Nitrocarbostyril (*7-Nitro-2-hydroxy-quinoline*).

Pale yellow needles from 1000 parts boiling amyl alcohol. M.p. about 340°. Spar. sol. most org. solvents.

N-*Me*: 7-nitro-*N*-methyl-α-quinolone. Yellow needles from EtOH. M.p. 198–9°. Sol. C_6H_6.

N-*Et*: 7-nitro-*N*-ethyl-α-quinolone. Needles from EtOH. M.p. 168–9°.

Decker, *J. prakt. Chem.*, 1901, **64**, 99.

8-Nitrocarbostyril (*8-Nitro-2-hydroxy-quinoline*).

Yellow prisms from H_2O. M.p. 168° (163°). Spar. sol. cold EtOH.

B,HCl: m.p. 159–60°.

N-*Me*: 8-nitro-*N*-methyl-α-quinolone. Yellow needles from C_6H_6. M.p. 133–4° (128° from EtOH).

N-*Et*: 8-nitro-*N*-ethyl-α-quinolone. Yellow cryst. M.p. 96°. Very sol. C_6H_6.

Decker, Pollitz, *J. prakt. Chem.*, 1901, **64**, 91.
Fischer, Guthmann, *J. prakt. Chem.*, 1916, **93**, 378.
Decker, *Ber.*, 1905, **38**, 1151.

5-Nitrocarvacrol (*5-Nitro-2-hydroxy-*p-*cymene*)

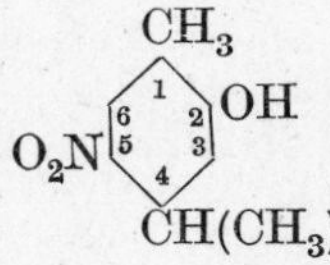

$C_{10}H_{13}O_3N$ MW, 195

Pale yellow prisms from C_6H_6–ligroin. M.p. 87°. Sol. EtOH, Et_2O. Spar. sol. H_2O.

Kehrmann, Schön, *Ann.*, 1900, **310**, 109.

6-Nitrocarvacrol (*6-Nitro-2-hydroxy-*p-*cymene*).

Needles. M.p. 116–17°.

Aschan, *Chem. Zentr.*, 1919, I, 227.

3-Nitrocatechol

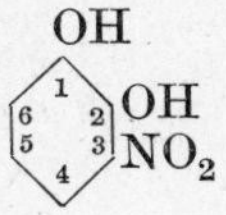

$C_6H_5O_4N$ MW, 155

Yellow needles from pet. ether. M.p. 86·5°. NaOH ⟶ reddish-purple sol.

1-*Me ether*: 3-nitroguaiacol. $C_7H_7O_4N$. MW, 169. Yellow needles. M.p. 62°. Sol. H_2O. Spar. sol pet. ether. Sublimes. 2-*Acetyl*: leaflets from pet. ether. M.p. 40°. Sol. usual org. solvents. 2-*Benzoyl*: plates from EtOH. M.p. 88–9°.

2-*Me ether*: 6-nitroguaiacol. M.p. 102–3°.

Di-Me ether: 3-nitroveratrol. $C_8H_9O_4N$. MW, 183. Needles from EtOH. M.p. 64–5°. Sol. EtOH, Et_2O, C_6H_6. Insol. H_2O, ligroin.

Vermeulen, *Rec. trav. chim.*, 1906, **25**, 23.
Klemenc, *Monatsh.*, 1912, **33**, 704.
Berkenheim, Albitzkaja, *Chem. Zentr.*, 1935, I, 2794.

4-Nitrocatechol.

Yellow needles from H_2O. M.p. 176°. Sol. H_2O, EtOH, Et_2O. Spar. sol. C_6H_6. KOH ⟶ reddish-purple sol.

1-*Me ether*: 4-nitroguaiacol. $C_7H_7O_4N$. MW, 169. Pale yellow needles from H_2O. M.p. 105°. Dil. KOH ⟶ orange sol. 2-*Et ether*: $C_9H_{11}O_4N$. MW, 197. Cryst. from EtOH.

M.p. 100–2° 2-*Acetyl*: needles from hot H_2O. M.p. 101–2°. Sol. boiling EtOH. Insol. cold H_2O.

2-*Me ether*: 5-nitroguaiacol. Yellow needles from H_2O. M.p. 103–4°. Sol. EtOH, Et_2O, boiling H_2O. Dil. KOH ⟶ orange-yellow sol. 1-*Et ether*: M.p. 85–6° 1-*Acetyl*: needles from H_2O. M.p. 108–9°. Sol. H_2O.

Di-Me ether: 4-nitroveratrol. $C_8H_9O_4N$. MW, 183. Yellow needles from EtOH.Aq. M.p. 96°. B.p. about 230°/15–20 mm. Sol. EtOH, Et_2O. Spar. sol. H_2O, ligroin.

1-*Et ether*: $C_8H_9O_4N$. MW, 183. Pale yellow prisms from MeOH.Aq. M.p. 113–14°. *Benzoyl*: needles from MeOH. M.p. 101–2°.

Di-Et ether: $C_{10}H_{13}O_4N$. MW, 211. Pale yellow needles. M.p. 73–5°.

Diacetyl: m.p. 98°.

Dibenzoyl: needles from EtOH. M.p. 156°. Spar. sol. MeOH.

Cardwell, Robinson, *J. Chem. Soc.*, 1915, **107**, 258.
Pollecoff, Robinson, *J. Chem. Soc.*, 1918, **113**, 647.
Riedel, D.R.P., 264,012, (*Chem. Zentr.*, 1913, II, 1181).

2-Nitrochalkone (ω-2-*Nitrobenzylideneacetophenone*)

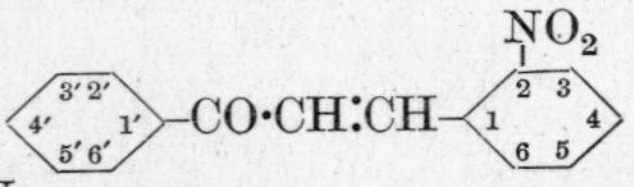

$C_{15}H_{11}O_3N$ MW, 253

Pale brown needles from EtOH. M.p. 125°. Sol. EtOH, Et_2O, AcOH. Sol. conc. H_2SO_4 with greenish-red fluor.

Semicarbazone: golden-yellow leaflets from EtOH. M.p. 177·5°.

Phenylhydrazone: cryst. from EtOH. M.p. 162–4°.

Sorge, *Ber.*, 1902, **35**, 1067.
Tanasescu, Georgescu, *J. prakt. Chem.*, 1934, **139**, 189.

3-Nitrochalkone.

Yellow needles from EtOH or C_6H_6. M.p. 145–6°. Sol. C_6H_6. Mod. sol. EtOH, $CHCl_3$, AcOH. Insol. Et_2O, ligroin.

Phenylhydrazone: yellow cryst. from EtOH. M.p. 101–3°.

Ruhemann, *J. Chem. Soc.*, 1903, **83**, 1377.
See also previous references.

4-Nitrochalkone.

Pale yellow needles from EtOH, plates from C_6H_6. M.p. 164°. Sol. $CHCl_3$. Insol. Et_2O, ligroin.

Semicarbazone: cryst. from EtOH. M.p. 178–9°.

Phenylhydrazone: red needles from EtOH. M.p. 148–50°.

Sorge, *Ber.*, 1902, **35**, 1068.
Tanasescu, Georgescu, *J. prakt. Chem.*, 1934, **139**, 189.

2′-Nitrochalkone.

Needles from EtOH. M.p. 128–9° (124°). Conc. H_2SO_4 ⟶ pale yellow sol.

Hydrazone: m.p. 146–7°.

Engler, Dorant, *Ber.*, 1895, **28**, 2498.

3′-Nitrochalkone.

Cryst. from EtOH. M.p. 131°. Conc. H_2SO_4 ⟶ orange-yellow sol.

Dilthey, Neuhaus, Schommer, *J. prakt. Chem.*, 1929, **123**, 235.

4′-Nitrochalkone.

Yellowish cryst. from EtOH. M.p. 149–50°. Conc. H_2SO_4 ⟶ yellowish-orange sol.

See previous reference.

β-Nitrochalkone (α-*Nitrochalkone*, ω-*nitro*-ω-*benzylideneacetophenone*)

$$C_6H_5{\cdot}CO{\cdot}\overset{NO_2}{\overset{|}{C}}{:}CH{\cdot}C_6H_5$$

$C_{15}H_{11}O_3N$ MW, 253

Yellow cryst. from AcOH, plates from Et_2O or C_6H_6. M.p. 90°. Sol. most org. solvents.

Wieland, *Ann.*, 1903, **328**, 237.

Nitrochloroform.

See Chloropicrin.

4-Nitrochrysazin (4-*Nitro*-1 : 8-*dihydroxyanthraquinone*)

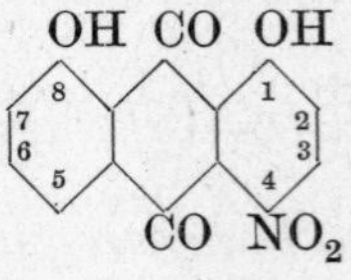

$C_{14}H_7O_6N$ MW, 285

Orange-yellow cryst. from chlorobenzene. M.p. 232–4°. Alkalis give red sols. Conc. H_2SO_4 ⟶ orange-yellow sol.

Di-Me ether: $C_{16}H_{11}O_6N$. MW, 313. Greenish-yellow needles from chlorobenzene. M.p. 232–3°. Spar. sol. org. solvents. Insol. H_2O, alkalis. Conc. H_2SO_4 ⟶ orange-red sol.

M.L.B., D.R.P., 193,104, (*Chem. Zentr.*, 1908, I, 428).

3-Nitrocinchoninic Acid (3-*Nitroquinoline-4-carboxylic acid*)

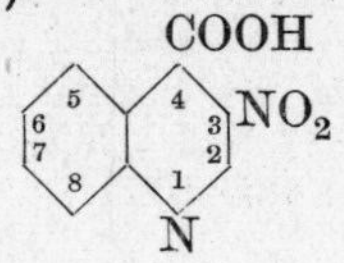

$C_{10}H_6O_4N_2$ MW, 218

Needles from EtOH. M.p. 204°.

Badische, D.R.P., 335,197, (*Chem. Zentr.*, 1921, II, 962).

5-Nitrocinchoninic Acid.

Yellowish cryst. powder. M.p. 275–8° decomp. Sol. hot AcOH, conc. HCl. Spar. sol. other solvents.

Königs, Lossow, *Ber.*, 1899, **32**, 717.

6-Nitrocinchoninic Acid.

Cryst. M.p. above 280° decomp.

Strache, *Monatsh.*, 1889, **10**, 645.

***o*-Nitrocinnamaldehyde**

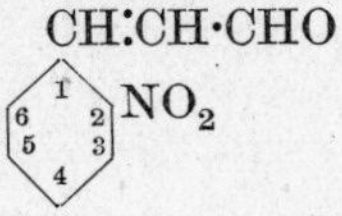

$C_9H_7O_3N$ MW, 177

Needles from Et_2O or EtOH. M.p. 127–127·5°. Sol. hot H_2O, $CHCl_3$. Less sol. EtOH, Et_2O.

anti-*Oxime*: pearly leaflets from EtOH. M.p. 134°. *Acetyl*: m.p. 107°.

syn-*Oxime*: cryst. from Me_2CO.Aq. M.p. 140°. *B,HCl*: m.p. 144°.

Mills, Evans, *J. Chem. Soc.*, 1920, **117**, 1037.

Brady, Grayson, *J. Chem. Soc.*, 1924, **125**, 1421.

***m*-Nitrocinnamaldehyde.**

Needles from H_2O, prisms from EtOH. M.p. 116°. Sol. C_6H_6, AcOH. Spar. sol. H_2O, cold EtOH, Et_2O.

anti-*Oxime*: yellow plates from EtOH. M.p. 157°. *Acetyl*: m.p. 136°.

syn-*Oxime*: yellow cryst. powder from Me_2CO.Aq. M.p. 163°. *B,HCl*: m.p. 175°.

Phenylhydrazone: red plates from EtOH. M.p. 160°.

Kinkelin, *Ber.*, 1885, **18**, 484.

Brady, Grayson, *J. Chem. Soc.*, 1924, **125**, 1420.

***p*-Nitrocinnamaldehyde.**

Needles from H_2O or EtOH. M.p. 141–2°. Sol. usual solvents.

anti-*Oxime*: yellow cryst. from EtOH. M.p. 178–9°. *Acetyl*: yellow cryst. M.p. 158°.

Phenylhydrazone: orange-red cryst. from EtOH. M.p. 180–1°.

Anil: needles from EtOH. M.p. 132–3°.

Einhorn, Gehrenbeck, *Ann.*, 1889, **253**, 348.

Fecht, *Ber.*, 1907, **40**, 3898.

***o*-Nitrocinnamic Acid**

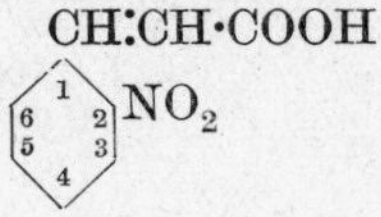

$C_9H_7O_4N$ MW, 193

Cis:

Yellowish cryst. from C_6H_6 or $CHCl_3$. M.p. 146–7° (143°). Sol. EtOH, hot C_6H_6. Spar. sol. $CHCl_3$. Warm conc. $H_2SO_4 \longrightarrow$ dark blue sol. Bromine in sunlight $\longrightarrow$ *trans* form.

Trans:

Needles from EtOH. M.p. 240°. Sol. boiling EtOH. Insol. H_2O. Turns red in sunlight. Ultraviolet absorption in Py.Aq. $\longrightarrow$ 22% *cis* form.

Me ester: $C_{10}H_9O_4N$. MW, 207. Needles from H_2O. M.p. 73°. B.p. 187–9°/15 mm. Very sol. boiling EtOH. Spar. sol. boiling H_2O.

Et ester: $C_{11}H_{11}O_4N$. MW, 221. Yellow cryst. from EtOH. M.p. 44°. Very sol. warm EtOH, Et_2O, C_6H_6, CS_2.

Menthyl ester: cryst. from 95% EtOH. M.p. 49·5°.

Cyclohexyl ester: m.p. 55–6°.

p-*Nitrobenzyl ester*: cryst. from EtOH. M.p. 132°.

Phenacyl ester: m.p. 126°.

Chloride: $C_9H_6O_3NCl$. MW, 211·5. Cryst. M.p. 64·5°. Sol. Et_2O, C_6H_6.

Amide: $C_9H_8O_3N_2$. MW, 192. Needles from H_2O. M.p. 185°. Sol. 100 parts H_2O. Sol. hot EtOH, Me_2CO, AcOH. Spar. sol. Et_2O, C_6H_6, $CHCl_3$, AcOEt. Insol. ligroin.

Chloroamide: $C_9H_7O_3N_2Cl$. MW, 226·5. Needles from AcOH. M.p. 142°. Insol. Et_2O, $CHCl_3$, ligroin.

Nitrile: $C_9H_6O_2N_2$. MW, 174. Needles from H_2O. M.p. 92°. B.p. 194–6°/7–8 mm. Sol. about 460 parts H_2O. Spar. sol. ligroin.

Tanasescu, *Bull. soc. chim.*, 1927, **41**, 1074.

Weerman, *Ann.*, 1913, **401**, 9.

Stoermer, Heymann, *Ber.*, 1912, **45**, 3100.

Pschorr, *Ber.*, 1898, **31**, 1295.

Sudborough, Lloyd, *J. Chem. Soc.*, 1898, **73**, 85.

m-Nitrocinnamic Acid.

Cis :

Needles. M.p. 158°. Bromine in sunlight ⟶ *trans* form.

Trans :

Needles from EtOH. M.p. 200–1°. Sol. 100 parts EtOH. Ultraviolet absorption in $EtOH \cdot NH_3$.Aq. ⟶ 22% *cis* form.

Me ester : $C_{10}H_9O_4N$. MW, 207. Pale yellow prisms from MeOH. M.p. 123–4°. Sol. C_6H_6, $CHCl_3$. Spar. sol. MeOH, EtOH, Et_2O, CS_2.

Et ester : $C_{11}H_{11}O_4N$. MW, 221. Prisms from AcOH. M.p. 78–9°.

Menthyl ester : m.p. 85°.

p-*Nitrobenzyl ester* : cryst. from EtOH. M.p. 173·5–174°.

Phenacyl ester : m.p. 145·5°.

p-*Bromophenacyl ester* : m.p. 178°.

Amide : $C_9H_8O_3N_2$. MW, 192. Leaflets from MeOH. M.p. 195–6°. Sol. EtOH, hot H_2O, AcOH. Insol. Et_2O, C_6H_6, $CHCl_3$, ligroin.

Chloroamide : $C_9H_7O_3N_2Cl$. MW, 226·5. Cryst. from AcOH. M.p. 178° decomp.

Hydrazide : pale yellow cryst. from EtOH. M.p. 139°. *B,HCl* : m.p. 212° decomp. *Benzoyl* : m.p. 185·5°.

Dihydrazide : pale yellow cryst. from EtOH. M.p. 279° decomp. *B,HCl* : m.p. 256° decomp.

Azide : m.p. 117–18°.

Wollring, *Ber.*, 1914, **47**, 112.
Weerman, *Ann.*, 1913, **401**, 15.
Sudborough, Lloyd, *J. Chem. Soc.*, 1898, **73**, 85.
Thayer, *Organic Syntheses*, Collective Vol. I, 390.

p-Nitrocinnamic Acid.

Cis :

Yellow cryst. from toluene or $CHCl_3$. M.p. 143°. Sol. C_6H_6, EtOH. Bromine ⟶ *trans* form.

Trans :

Prisms from EtOH. M.p. 286°. Spar. sol. boiling H_2O, EtOH, Et_2O. Insol. CS_2, pet. ether.

Me ester : $C_{10}H_9O_4N$. MW, 207. Needles from EtOH. M.p. 161°. B.p. 281–6°. Spar. sol. EtOH. Insol. Et_2O.

Et ester : $C_{11}H_{11}O_4N$. MW, 221. Plates from AcOH. M.p. 141–2°. Insol. cold EtOH. Spar. volatile in steam.

Menthyl ester : m.p. 92·5°.

Phenyl ester : $C_{15}H_{11}O_4N$. MW, 269. Needles from EtOH. M.p. 152°.

p-*Nitrobenzyl ester* : cryst. from EtOH. M.p. 186·5°.

Phenacyl ester : m.p. 146·2°.

p-*Bromophenacyl ester* : m.p. 191°.

Chloride : $C_9H_6O_3NCl$. MW, 211·5. Cryst. M.p. 124·5°. B.p. 205–10°.

Amide : $C_9H_8O_3N_2$. MW, 192. Needles from EtOH. M.p. 217°. Spar. sol. EtOH. Insol. H_2O, Et_2O, C_6H_6.

Chloroamide : $C_9H_7O_3N_2Cl$. MW, 226·5. Needles from AcOH. M.p. 169° decomp.

Wollring, *Ber.*, 1914, **47**, 112.
Pfeiffer, Haefelin, *Ber.*, 1922, **55**, 1771.
Weerman, *Ann.*, 1913 **401**, 18.
Beilstein, Kuhlberg, *Ann.*, 1872, **163**, 126.

o-Nitrocinnamylideneacetone

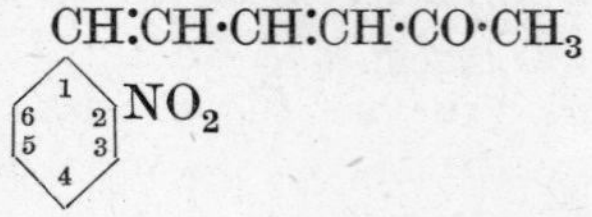

$C_{12}H_{11}O_3N$ MW, 217

Needles. M.p. 73·5°. Sol. usual solvents. Conc. H_2SO_4 ⟶ orange-yellow sol.

Diehl, Einhorn, *Ber.*, 1885, **18**, 2327.

p-Nitrocinnamylideneacetone.

Needles from EtOH. M.p. 132°. Sol. usual solvents.

Einhorn, Gehrenbeck, *Ann.*, 1889, **253**, 353.

3-Nitro-o-coumaraldehyde

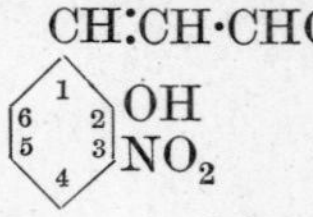

$C_9H_7O_4N$ MW, 193

Golden-yellow needles from AcOH.Aq. M.p. 133°. Sol. hot H_2O. Mod. sol. EtOH, AcOH. Less sol. Et_2O.

Me ether : $C_{10}H_9O_4N$. MW, 207. Yellow prisms from EtOH. M.p. 115°.

v. Miller, Kinkelin, *Ber.*, 1887, **20**, 1933.

5-Nitro-o-coumaraldehyde.

Yellow needles from H_2O. M.p. 200° decomp. Sol. EtOH, AcOH. Spar. sol. H_2O.

See previous reference.

3-Nitro-o-coumaric Acid

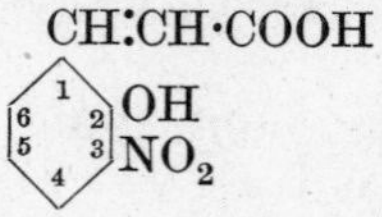

$C_9H_7O_5N$ MW, 209

Cis : 3-Nitrocoumarinic acid.

Yellow prisms from EtOH. M.p. 150° decomp. (rapid heat.). Warm H_2O or EtOH ⟶ 8-nitrocoumarin.

Me ether : $C_{10}H_9O_5N$. MW, 223. Leaflets. M.p. 135–6°. *Me ester* : $C_{11}H_{11}O_5N$. MW, 237. Prisms from EtOH. M.p. 69°.

Trans :

Yellow cryst. from EtOH. M.p. 241–2°. Spar. sol. EtOH.

Me ether : yellow prisms from EtOH. M.p. 193°. *Me ester* : needles from EtOH. M.p. 88–9°.

v. Miller, Kinkelin, *Ber.*, 1889, **22**, 1706.

5-Nitro-*o*-coumaric Acid.

Cis : 5-Nitrocoumarinic acid.

Me ether : $C_{10}H_9O_5N$. MW, 223. Needles from EtOH or AcOH.Aq. M.p. 202–3°. *Me ester* : $C_{11}H_{11}O_5N$. MW, 237. Needles from EtOH. M.p. 124–5°. *Et ester* : $C_{12}H_{13}O_5N$. MW, 251. Needles from EtOH. M.p. 75–7°.

Et ether : $C_{11}H_{11}O_5N$. MW, 237. Needles. M.p. 171–2°. *Me ester* : $C_{12}H_{13}O_5N$. MW, 251. Needles from EtOH. M.p. 111–13°. *Et ester* : $C_{13}H_{15}O_5N$. MW, 265. Needles from EtOH. M.p. 104–5°.

Trans :

Needles. M.p. 247° decomp. Turns yellow in air.

Me ether : needles from H_2O. M.p. 239°. Sol. EtOH, Et_2O. Spar. sol. H_2O. Needles from EtOH. M.p. 163°. *Et ester* : needles from EtOH. M.p. 85°.

Et ether : needles from EtOH.Aq. M.p. 194–5°. *Me ester* : needles from EtOH. M.p. 141–2°.

Me ester : $C_{10}H_9O_5N$. MW, 223. Needles. M.p. 211°.

Acetyl : needles from hot AcOH. M.p. 217°, solidifies and remelts at 259°.

Clayton, *J. Chem. Soc.*, 1910, **97**, 2106.
Dey, Row, *J. Chem. Soc.*, 1924, **125**, 563.

2-Nitro-*m*-coumaric Acid

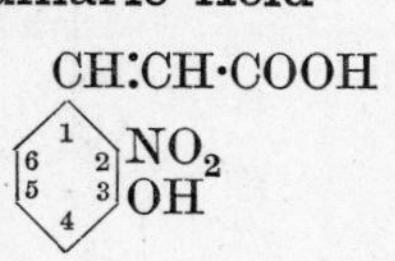

$C_9H_7O_5N$ MW, 209

Needles from H_2O. M.p. 218°. Sol. EtOH, Et_2O, AcOH. Spar. sol. H_2O, C_6H_6. Insol. $CHCl_3$, pet. ether. Sweet taste.

Luff, *Ber.*, 1889, **22**, 292.

4-Nitro-*m*-coumaric Acid.

Golden-yellow needles from EtOH. M.p. 248°. Sol. EtOH, Et_2O. Mod. sol. H_2O.

Me ether : $C_{10}H_9O_5N$. MW, 223. Needles from EtOH. M.p. 218° decomp. *Me ester* : $C_{11}H_{11}O_5N$. MW, 237. Needles from EtOH. M.p. 163° (143°). Sol. EtOH, Et_2O, C_6H_6. Mod. sol. $CHCl_3$.

Ulrich, *Ber.*, 1885, **18**, 2572.
See also previous reference.

5-Nitro-*m*-coumaric Acid.

Cryst. Sol. hot H_2O, EtOH, Et_2O, AcOH. Decomp. on heating.

Luff, *Ber.*, 1889, **22**, 295.

6-Nitro-*m*-coumaric Acid.

Needles from EtOH. M.p. 216°. Very sol. EtOH. Sol. hot H_2O, Et_2O, AcOH.

Me ether : $C_{10}H_9O_5N$. MW, 223. Needles from EtOH. M.p. 224·5–225·5°. Spar. sol. Et_2O, C_6H_6, $CHCl_3$. Insol. ligroin. *Et ester* : $C_{12}H_{13}O_5N$. MW, 251. Needles from EtOH. M.p. 72·5°. Spar. sol. Et_2O, ligroin.

Eichengrün, Einhorn, *Ann.*, 1891, **262**, 171.
See also previous reference.

3-Nitro-*p*-coumaric Acid

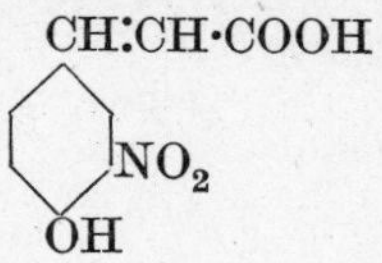

$C_9H_7O_5N$ MW, 209

Yellow needles from EtOH. M.p. 223° (198°) decomp. Insol. cold H_2O.

Me ether : $C_{10}H_9O_5N$. MW, 223. Prisms or plates from EtOH, needles from H_2O. M.p. 247–8°. Spar. sol. hot H_2O, Et_2O, $CHCl_3$. *Me ester* : $C_{11}H_{11}O_5N$. MW, 237. Cryst. from EtOH. M.p. 125°. *Et ester* : $C_{12}H_{13}O_5N$. MW, 251. Prisms from EtOH. M.p. 99–100°.

Me ester : $C_{10}H_9O_5N$. MW, 223. Yellow needles from EtOH. M.p. 142–4°.

Et ester : $C_{11}H_{11}O_5N$. MW, 237. Yellow needles from EtOH. M.p. 110–11°.

Johnson, Kohmann, *J. Am. Chem. Soc.*, 1915, **37**, 165.

6-Nitrocoumarin

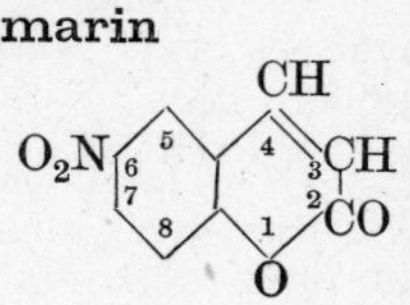

$C_9H_5O_4N$ MW, 191

Needles. M.p. 185°. Mod. sol. boiling H_2O, EtOH, Et_2O.

Oxime: pale yellow needles. M.p. 249–50°.

Phenylhydrazone: red needles from AcOH. M.p. 213°.

Clayton, *J. Chem. Soc.*, 1910, **97**, 2106.
Clayton, Godden, *J. Chem. Soc.*, 1912, **101**, 213.

8-Nitrocoumarin.

Prisms from C_6H_6. M.p. 191°.

See previous references.

Nitrocoumarinic Acid.

See under Nitro-*o*-coumaric Acid.

2-Nitrocoumarone

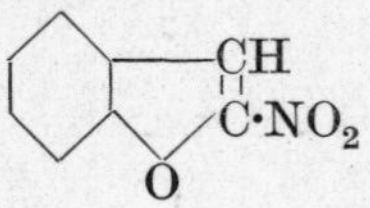

$C_8H_5O_3N$ MW, 163

Needles. M.p. 134°. Sol. Et_2O, C_6H_6, $CHCl_3$. Mod. sol. MeOH, EtOH. Spar. sol. ligroin.

Stoermer, Richter, *Ber.*, 1897, **30**, 2094.
Stoermer, Kahlert, *Ber.*, 1902, **35**, 1641.

6-Nitrocresidine.

See under 6-Nitro-3-amino-*p*-cresol.

3-Nitro-*o*-cresol

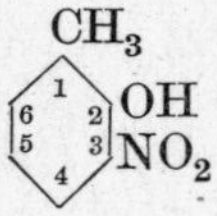

$C_7H_7O_3N$ MW, 153

Prisms from EtOH.Aq. or pet. ether. M.p. 70°. B.p. 102–3°/9 mm. Very sol. EtOH, Et_2O. Insol. H_2O.

Me ether: $C_8H_9O_3N$. MW, 167. Needles from pet. ether. M.p. 30°. B.p. 121–2°/10 mm.

Et ether: $C_9H_{11}O_3N$. MW, 181. Yellow oil. B.p. 249–50°.

Propyl ether: $C_{10}H_{13}O_3N$. MW, 195. Yellow oil. B.p. 210–12°. Sol. EtOH, Et_2O. Insol. H_2O.

Benzoyl: needles from EtOH or pet. ether. M.p. 42°. B.p. 218–20°/9 mm.

p-*Toluenesulphonyl*: cryst. from EtOH. M.p. 66°. B.p. 205–10°/0·5 mm. Sol. Me_2CO, C_6H_6, $CHCl_3$, CCl_4. Spar. sol. EtOH.

Gibson, *J. Chem. Soc.*, 1925, **127**, 44.
Spiegel, Munblit, Kaufmann, *Ber.*, 1906, **39**, 3242.

4-Nitro-*o*-cresol.

Yellow needles from ligroin. M.p. 118°. Sol. EtOH, Et_2O, C_6H_6. Spar. sol. H_2O, CS_2, ligroin.

Me ether: needles from EtOH or C_6H_6–ligroin. M.p. 74°. Spar. sol. EtOH, Et_2O, AcOH. Insol. H_2O.

Et ether: needles from EtOH. M.p. 61°. Sol. EtOH, Et_2O. Insol. H_2O. Volatile in steam.

Acetyl: needles. M.p. 74°. Sol. boiling H_2O, most org. solvents.

p-*Toluenesulphonyl*: prisms from EtOH. M.p. 123–4°. Sol. AcOH. Spar. sol. MeOH, EtOH.

Ullmann, Fitzenkam, *Ber.*, 1905, **38**, 3790.
Spiegel, Munblit, Kaufmann, *Ber.*, 1906, **39**, 3241.

5-Nitro-*o*-cresol.

Needles + H_2O from H_2O or EtOH.Aq., yellow plates from C_6H_6. M.p. 30–40°, anhyd. 96°. B.p. 186–90°/9 mm.

Me ether: needles from EtOH or pet. ether. M.p. 64°. Sol. Me_2CO, C_6H_6, $CHCl_3$, CCl_4.

Et ether: needles from EtOH.Aq. M.p. 71°. Sol. EtOH, Et_2O, C_6H_6, CS_2, hot ligroin.

Benzoyl: m.p. 128°. Mod. sol. Me_2CO, C_6H_6, $CHCl_3$, CCl_4. Spar. sol. EtOH, Et_2O, pet. ether.

p-*Toluenesulphonyl*: cryst. from EtOH. M.p. 107°.

Gibson, *J. Chem. Soc.*, 1925, **127**, 44.

6-Nitro-*o*-cresol.

Yellowish needles from H_2O. M.p. 147°. Sol. EtOH, Et_2O. Spar. sol. cold H_2O. Sweet taste.

Me ether: needles from MeOH.Aq. M.p. 52–3°.

p-*Toluenesulphonyl*: plates from EtOH. M.p. 94°.

Noelting, *Ber.*, 1904, **37**, 1020.
Simonsen, Nayak, *J. Chem. Soc.*, 1915, **107**, 832.

2-Nitro-*m*-cresol

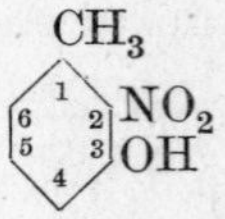

$C_7H_7O_3N$ MW, 153

Yellow needles from pet. ether. M.p. 41°. Sol. usual org. solvents. Odour of iodoform.

Me ether: $C_8H_9O_3N$. MW, 167. Yellow plates from EtOH. M.p. 54°. Volatile in steam.

Acetyl: needles from EtOH. M.p. 59°.

Benzoyl: needles from EtOH. M.p. 79°.

Sol. Me_2CO, C_6H_6, AcOEt, CCl_4. Spar. sol. EtOH, pet. ether.

Barger, Schlittler, *Helv. Chim. Acta*, 1932, **15**, 389.
Gibson, *J. Chem. Soc.*, 1923, **123**, 1269.
Cf. also Corbellini, Ravazzoni, *Atti accad. Lincei*, 1931, **13**, 132.

4-Nitro-*m*-cresol.

Yellow plates from Et_2O or C_6H_6. M.p. 56°. Sol. EtOH, Et_2O, C_6H_6. Spar. sol. H_2O. Volatile in steam.

Me ether: cryst. M.p. 62°.

Et ether: $C_9H_{11}O_3N$. MW, 181. Prisms rom pet. ether. M.p. 55° (50–1°).

Acetyl: plates from EtOH. M.p. 48°.

Benzoyl: prisms. M.p. 77°.

Gibson, *J. Chem. Soc.*, 1923, **123**, 1269.

5-Nitro-*m*-cresol.

Pale yellow cryst. + H_2O from H_2O, cryst. rom C_6H_6. M.p. 60–2°, anhyd. 90–1°. Very ol. EtOH, Et_2O. Less sol. C_6H_6. Non-volatile n steam.

Me ether: cryst. M.p. 70°. *Et ether*: cryst. rom Et_2O. M.p. 53–4°.

Nevile, Winther, *Ber.*, 1882, **15**, 2986.
Blanksma, *Rec. trav. chim.*, 1908, **27**, 25.
Hoshino, Kotake, *Ann.*, 1935, **516**, 76.

6-Nitro-*m*-cresol.

Needles from H_2O. M.p. 129°. Very sol. EtOH, Et_2O, C_6H_6, $CHCl_3$. Spar. sol. H_2O.

Me ether: needles from ligroin. M.p. 55°. Sol. most org. solvents.

Et ether: needles from EtOH. M.p. 45°.

Acetyl: fine needles from EtOH. M.p. 34°.

Benzoyl: needles. M.p. 74°.

Staedel, *Ann.*, 1883, **217**, 51.
Gibson, *J. Chem. Soc.*, 1923, **123**, 1269.
See also last reference above.

2-Nitro-*p*-cresol

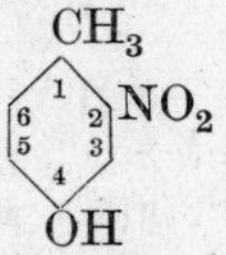

$C_7H_7O_3N$ MW, 153

Yellow prisms from Et_2O. M.p. 79°. Very ol. EtOH, Et_2O. Spar. sol. cold H_2O, C_6H_6, CS_2, groin.

Me ether: $C_8H_9O_3N$. MW, 167. Yellow prisms. M.p. 17°. B.p. 266–7°. Volatile in steam.

Holleman, Hoeflake, *Rec. trav. chim.*, 1916, **36**, 272.
Copisarow, *J. Chem. Soc.*, 1929, 251.

3-Nitro-*p*-cresol.

Yellow needles from EtOH.Aq. M.p. 36·5° (32°). B.p. 125°/22 mm., 114·5°/7·5 mm. Very sol. EtOH, Et_2O, and most other org. solvents. Spar. sol. H_2O.

Me ether: pale yellow cryst. M.p. 8·5°. B.p. 274°, 159°/15 mm. D_4^{25} 1·2025. n_D^{25} 1·5536. Sol. Et_2O. Insol. EtOH.

Et ether: $C_9H_{11}O_3N$. MW, 181. B.p. 275–85° decomp.

Benzoyl: prisms. M.p. 100–1°.

Baranger, *Bull. soc. chim.*, 1931, **49**, 1214.
Derick, Ralph, Flett, U.S.P., 1,394,150, (*Chem. Abstracts*, 1922, **16**, 423).
Brasch, Freyss, *Ber.*, 1891, **24**, 1960.
Neunhöffer, Kölbel, *Ber.*, 1935, **68**, 255.

Nitrocresotic Acid.

See Nitrohydroxytoluic Acid.

3-Nitro-ψ-cumene

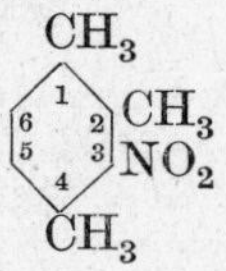

$C_9H_{11}O_2N$ MW, 165

Cryst. M.p. 30°.

Huender, *Rec. trav. chim.*, 1915, **34**, 10.
Mayer, *Ber.*, 1887, **20**, 971.

5-Nitro-ψ-cumene.

Yellowish needles. M.p. 71° (70°). B.p. 265°.

Schultz, *Ber.*, 1909, **42**, 3605.
Huender, *Rec. trav. chim.*, 1915, **34**, 14.

6-Nitro-ψ-cumene.

Prisms from EtOH. M.p. 20°.

Edler, *Ber.*, 1885, **18**, 629.

3-Nitro-ψ-cumidine

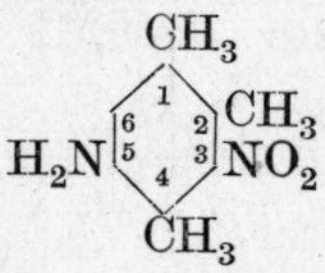

$C_9H_{12}O_2N_2$ MW, 180

Golden-yellow needles. M.p. 138°. Sol. EtOH. Spar. sol. boiling H_2O. Sublimes. Volatile in steam.

Huender, *Rec. trav. chim.*, 1915, **34**, 17.
Blanksma, *Rec. trav. chim.*, 1905, **24**, 48.

6-Nitro-ψ-cumidine.

Light red needles from EtOH.Aq. M.p. 46–7°. Very sol. Et_2O.

Acetyl: needles or prisms from EtOH. M.p. 202–4° (199°). Mod. sol. EtOH, AcOH, $CHCl_3$. Insol. Et_2O.

Propionyl: cryst. from EtOH. M.p. 167°. Sol. Me_2CO, C_6H_6, $CHCl_3$, Py, isoamyl alcohol, CCl_4. Spar. sol. Et_2O, ligroin.

Edler, *Ber.*, 1885, **18**, 629.
Bogert, Bender, *J. Am. Chem. Soc.*, 1914, **36**, 573.

3-Nitrocuminaldehyde

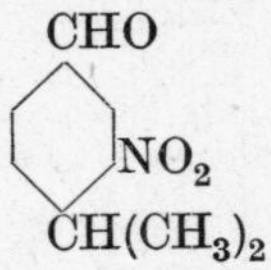

$C_{10}H_{11}O_3N$ MW, 193

Yellow cryst. from EtOH. M.p. 54°.

Oxime: needles from C_6H_6–ligroin. M.p. 74–6°. Sol. EtOH, Et_2O, C_6H_6, $CHCl_3$. Insol. H_2O, ligroin.

Semicarbazone: needles from EtOH. M.p. 222°. Sol. boiling EtOH. Spar. sol. AcOH, $CHCl_3$. Insol. H_2O, Et_2O, ligroin. Turns yellow in air.

Phenylhydrazone: m.p. 123°.

Lippmann, Strecker, *Ber.*, 1879, **12**, 76.
Pizzuti, *Gazz. chim. ital.*, 1910, **40**, ii, 236.

2-Nitrocuminic Acid

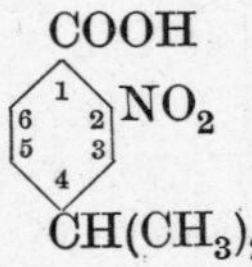

$C_{10}H_{11}O_4N$ MW, 209

Plates from 50% AcOH or ligroin. M.p. 99°. Sol. EtOH, Et_2O, C_6H_6. Spar. sol. ligroin.

Widman, *Ber.*, 1886, **19**, 269.

3-Nitrocuminic Acid.

Prisms from EtOH. M.p. 158–9°. Sol. EtOH, Et_2O. Insol. H_2O. $k = 2{\cdot}15 \times 10^{-4}$ at 25°.

Me ester: $C_{11}H_{13}O_4N$. MW, 223. Cryst. from EtOH. M.p. 64°. Sol. warm EtOH, Et_2O, C_6H_6.

Et ester: $C_{12}H_{15}O_4N$. MW, 237. Liq. B.p. 290° decomp.

Nitrile: $C_{10}H_{10}O_2N_2$. MW, 190. Cryst. from EtOH. M.p. 71°. Very sol. EtOH, Et_2O.

Widman, *Ber.*, 1888, **21**, 2232.
Alexejew, *J. Russ. Phys.-Chem. Soc.*, 1885, **17**, 112.

Nitrocyanoacetic Acid

$NO_2{\cdot}CH(CN){\cdot}COOH$

$C_3H_2O_4N_2$ MW, 130

Me ester: $C_4H_4O_4N_2$. MW, 144. Needles + $1H_2O$. M.p. 76°. Sol. H_2O, MeOH. Spar. sol. Et_2O. *K salt*: leaflets from H_2O. M.p. 264–6° decomp. *Hydrazine salt*: $N_2H_4{\cdot}C_4H_4O_4N_2$. Cryst. from MeOH. M.p. 168°. Very sol. H_2O.

Et ester: $C_5H_6O_4N_2$. MW, 158. Not obtained pure. Prisms from H_2O. Sol. EtOH. Insol. Et_2O, $CHCl_3$, C_6H_6. *K salt*: cryst. M.p. 240°.

Amide: fulminuric acid. $C_3H_3O_3N_3$. MW, 129. Prisms from EtOH. M.p. 145° (136–49° decomp.). Sol. H_2O, EtOH. Spar. sol. Et_2O. Insol. $CHCl_3$, C_6C_6, ligroin. *NH_4 salt*: prisms. Spar. sol. cold H_2O. Insol. EtOH, Et_2O. *K salt*: prisms. Sol. 10 parts cold H_2O. Insol. EtOH, Et_2O.

Hydrazide: colourless needles + $1H_2O$ or yellow anhyd. prisms. M.p. above 285°.

Ulpiani, *Gazz. chim. ital.*, 1912, **42**, i, 225.
Darapsky, Hillers, *J. prakt. Chem.*, 1915, **92**, 324.
Conrad, Schulze, *Ber.*, 1909, **42**, 740.
Nef, *Ann.*, 1894, **280**, 329.

Nitrocyanobenzoic Acid.

See under Nitrophthalic Acid.

Nitro-α-cyanocinnamic Acid.

See under Nitrobenzylidenemalonic Acid.

Nitrocyanophenol.

See under Nitrohydroxybenzoic Acid *and* Nitrosalicylic Acid.

Nitrocyclohexane

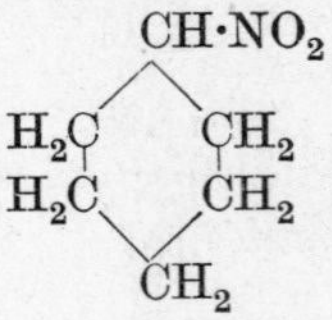

$C_6H_{11}O_2N$ MW, 129

F.p. − 34°. B.p. 205·5–206°, 109°/40 mm. D_0^0 1·0853, D_4^{19} 1·0680. n_D^{19} 1·4612. $SnCl_2$ + HCl ⟶ cyclohexanone oxime. Sn + HCl ⟶ cyclohexanone + aminocyclohexane.

Nametkin, *Ber.*, 1909, **42**, 1372.

Nitrocyclopentane

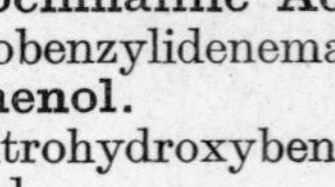

$C_5H_9O_2N$ MW, 115

B.p. 90–1°/40 mm. D_4^{23} 1·0776. n_D^{23} 1·4518. HNO_3 ⟶ glutaric acid.

Nametkin, *Chem. Zentr.*, 1912, I, 1702.

6-Nitro-*m*-cymene

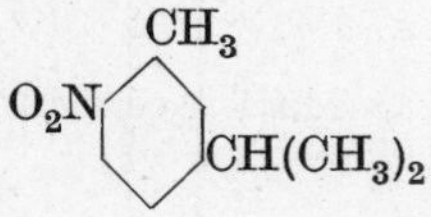

$C_{10}H_{13}O_2N$ MW, 179

Liq. B.p. 230–40°.

Meyer, Bernhauer, *Monatsh.*, 1929, **53** and **54**, 741.

2-Nitro-*p*-cymene

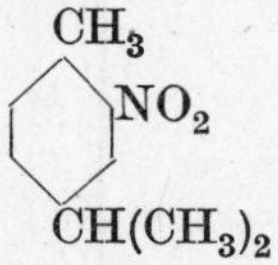

$C_{10}H_{13}O_2N$ MW, 179

Liq. B.p. 130–5°/14 mm., 129–32°/15 mm. D_4^{20} 1·0744. n_D^{20} 1·53093.

Inoue, Horiguchi, *Chem. Abstracts*, 1933, **27**, 3464.
Demonbreun, Kremers, *Chem. Abstracts*, 1923, **17**, 3906.

2-Nitrodeoxybenzoin (ω-o-*Nitrophenylacetophenone, phenyl* o-*nitrobenzyl ketone*)

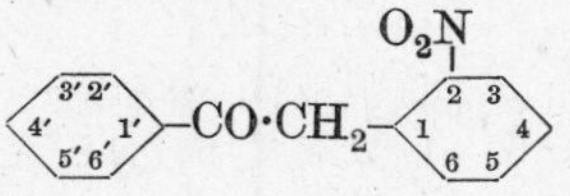

$C_{14}H_{11}O_3N$ MW, 241

Needles from C_6H_6–ligroin. M.p. 73–4°. Sol. EtOH, Et_2O, C_6H_6, AcOH. CrO_3 ⟶ 2-nitrobenzil. Zn dust + NH_3.Aq. ⟶ 2-phenylindole. Alc. KOH ⟶ blue col.

Oxime: needles from EtOH. M.p. 118°. Alkalis ⟶ red sols.

List, *Ber.*, 1893, **26**, 2453.

4-Nitrodeoxybenzoin (ω-p-*Nitrophenylacetophenone, phenyl* p-*nitrobenzyl ketone*).

Prisms from EtOH. M.p. 145° (140–2°). Sol. 597 parts cold, 22·5 parts boiling 95% EtOH. Mod. sol. boiling AcOH. Spar. sol. boiling Et_2O. CrO_3 ⟶ 4-nitrobenzil. Alc. KOH ⟶ violet col.

Oxime: needles from EtOH. M.p. 107° (105°).

See previous reference and also Golubeff, *Ber.*, 1878, **11**, 1939.

α-Nitrodeoxybenzoin (ω-*Nitro*-ω-*phenylacetophenone*)

$$C_6H_5\cdot CO\cdot \overset{NO_2}{CH}\cdot C_6H_5$$

$C_{14}H_{11}O_3N$ MW, 241

Di-Me acetal: needles from MeOH. M.p. 202–3°.

Wieland, Blümich, *Ann.*, 1921, **424**, 106.

Nitrodiaminoanisole.

See under Nitrodiaminophenol.

2-Nitro-1 : 4-diaminoanthraquinone

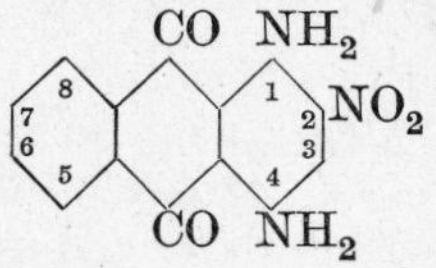

$C_{14}H_9O_4N_3$ MW, 283

Greenish-blue needles. Sol. inert solvents with blue col. Conc. H_2SO_4 ⟶ colourless sol. ⟶ blue on warming with boric acid.

N : N′-*Diacetyl*: yellowish-brown needles from AcOH. M.p. 237° decomp. Conc. H_2SO_4 ⟶ pale yellow sol. ⟶ blue on adding formaldehyde.

N : N′-*Dibenzoyl*: orange needles. Sol. conc. H_2SO_4 with red col.

M.L.B., D.R.P., 254,185, (*Chem. Zentr.*, 1913, I, 197).
Bayer, D.R.P., 267,445, (*Chem. Zentr.*, 1914, I, 88).

5-Nitro-1 : 4-diaminoanthraquinone.

N : N′-*Diacetyl*: red cryst. Py sol. is yellowish-red. Conc. H_2SO_4 ⟶ yellow sol.

Sulphate: dark violet prisms from $PhNO_2$. Sol. Py with violet-blue col.

Bayer, D.R.P., 268,984, (*Chem. Zentr.*, 1914, I, 588).

3′-Nitro-2 : 4-diaminoazobenzene

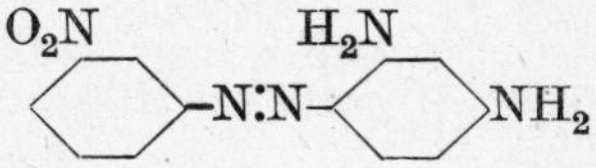

$C_{12}H_{11}O_2N_5$ MW, 257

Yellow cryst. from EtOH.Aq. M.p. 204°.

Tetra-Me: $C_{16}H_{19}O_2N_5$. MW, 313. Free base cannot be cryst. Sol. EtOH, Et_2O, C_6H_6. Insol. H_2O. *B,HCl*: dark violet needles + H_2O from dil. HCl. M.p. anhyd. 198°. Sol. H_2O with yellow col.

Leonhardt, D.R.P., 37,021.
Sachs, Appenzeller, *Ber.*, 1908, **41**, 110.

3-Nitro-2 : 6-diaminobenzaldehyde

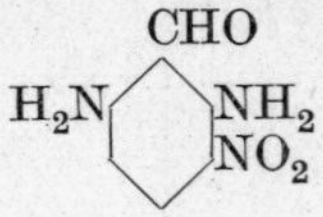

$C_7H_7O_3N_3$ MW, 181

Yellow needles from trichlorobenzene. M.p. 250–1°.

I.G., E.P., 339,699, (*Chem. Zentr.*, 1931, II, 1925); D.R.P., 521,724, (*Chem. Zentr.*, 1931, I, 3722).
Kalischer, Ritter, Honold, U.S.P., 1,876,955, (*Chem. Abstracts*, 1933, **27**, 993).

6-Nitro-4 : 4′-diamino-3 : 3′-dimethyldiphenyl (*6-Nitro-4 : 4′-diamino-3 : 3′-ditolyl*, *6-nitro-3 : 3′-dimethylbenzidine*, *6-nitro-*o*-tolidine*)

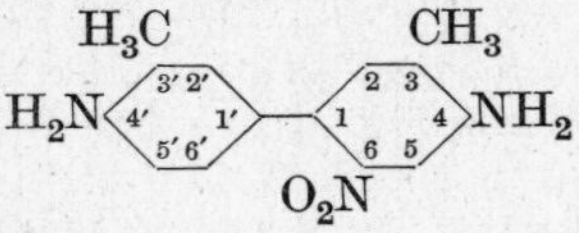

$C_{14}H_{15}O_2N_3$ MW, 257

Red needles from toluene. M.p. 156°. Sol. AcOH. Mod. sol. C_6H_6. Less sol. EtOH. Spar. sol. Et_2O. Insol. ligroin.
4 : 4′-N-*Diacetyl* : yellow needles. M.p. 290°.
4 : 4′-N-*Dibenzylidene* : leaflets. M.p. 147°.

Löwenherz, *Ber.*, 1892, **25**, 1032.

Nitro-4 : 4′-diaminodiphenyl.
See Nitrobenzidine.

4-Nitro-2 : 4′-diaminodiphenylmethane

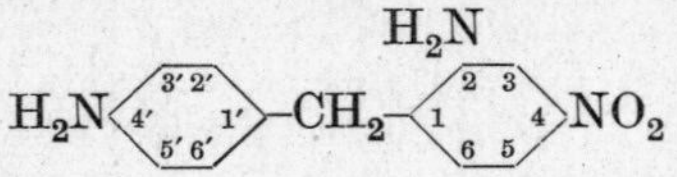

$C_{13}H_{13}O_2N_3$ MW, 243

Orange needles from boiling EtOH. M.p. 157–8°. Sol. about 23 parts boiling EtOH.
B,2HCl : leaflets from H_2O. M.p. 262° decomp.
Diacetyl deriv. : needles from boiling MeOH. M.p. 239–40°. 1·2 parts sol. 100 parts boiling MeOH.
Tetra-acetyl : prisms from boiling EtOH. M.p. 201·5–202·5°. Sol. 100 parts boiling EtOH.

King, *J. Chem. Soc.*, 1920, **117**, 989.

2-Nitro-4 : 4′-diaminodiphenylmethane.
Yellow needles from EtOH. M.p. 100–1°.
4 : 4′-N-*Tetra-Me* : $C_{17}H_{21}O_2N_3$. MW, 299. Deep red needles from EtOH. M.p. 96–96·5° (95°). Sol. warm EtOH, C_6H_6, AcOH. Spar. sol. ligroin.
4 : 4′-N-*Tetra-Et* : $C_{21}H_{29}O_2N_3$. MW, 355 Red prisms. M.p. 79–80°.

Epstein, D.R.P., 139,989, (*Chem. Zentr.* 1908, I, 798).
Bayer, D.R.P., 79,250.
Ullmann, Marié, *Ber.*, 1901, **34**, 4314.

5-Nitro-2 : 3-diaminophenol (*5-Nitro-3 hydroxy-*o*-phenylenediamine*)

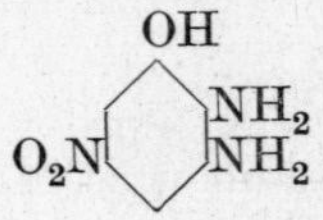

$C_6H_7O_3N_3$ MW, 16

Me ether : 5 - nitro - 2 : 3 - diaminoanisole $C_7H_9O_3N_3$. MW, 183. Dark red needles from H_2O. M.p. 131–2°.

Borsche, *Ber.*, 1917, **50**, 1348.

4-Nitro-2 : 6-diaminophenol (*5-Nitro-2 hydroxy-*m*-phenylenediamine*)

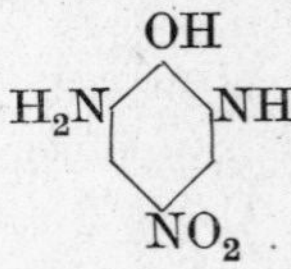

$C_6H_7O_3N_3$ MW, 16

Yellow needles or plates + H_2O. Mod. so EtOH. Spar. sol. H_2O, Et_2O.
N-*Acetyl* : cryst. Sol. AcOH. Mod. so Et_2O. Spar. sol. EtOH.

Griess, *Ann.*, 1870, **154**, 202.
Cassella, D.R.P., 161,341, (*Chem. Zentr* 1905, II, 181).

Nitrodiaminotoluene.
See Nitrotolylenediamine.

2′′-Nitro-4 : 4′-diaminotriphenylmethan

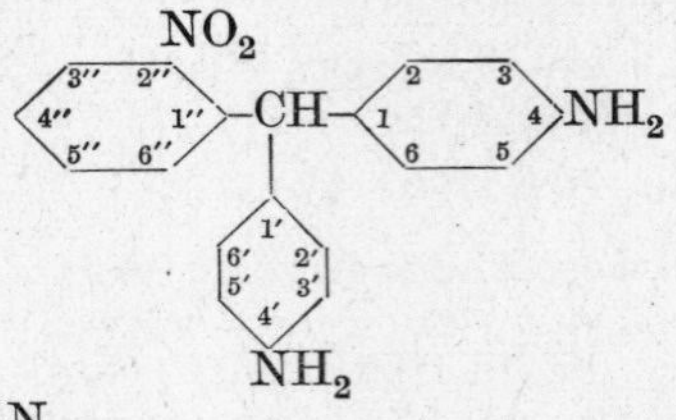

$C_{19}H_{17}O_2N_3$ MW, 31

Yellowish-red cryst. from C_6H_6–ligroin.
4 : 4′-N-*Di-Me* : $C_{21}H_{21}O_2N_3$. MW, 34 Golden-yellow prisms from EtOH–C_6H_6. M.p. 159–60°. Mod. sol. H_2O, ligroin. Spar. so EtOH.
4 : 4′-N-*Di-Et* : $C_{23}H_{25}O_2N_3$. MW, 375. Ye

lowish-red cryst. from C_6H_6–EtOH. M.p. 109–10°.

Fischer, Schmidt, *Ber.*, 1884, **17**, 1889.
Renouf, *Ber.*, 1883, **16**, 1304.

3''-Nitro-4 : 4'-diaminotriphenylmethane.

Yellow cryst. from Et_2O–ligroin. M.p. 136°. Sol. EtOH, Et_2O. Less sol. C_6H_6. Spar. sol. ligroin. Insol. H_2O.

4 : 4'-N-*Di-Me* : yellow prisms from EtOH, golden needles from C_6H_6. M.p. 152°. Sol. C_6H_6. Spar. sol. EtOH, Et_2O, ligroin. *Dimethiodide* : needles from EtOH. M.p. 225° decomp.

4 : 4'-N-*Di-Et* : yellow needles with green fluor. from EtOH. M.p. 95–6°.

Fischer, Ziegler, *Ber.*, 1880, **13**, 671.

4''-Nitro-4 : 4'-diaminotriphenylmethane.

Yellow cryst. from EtOH. Sol. Me_2CO, C_6H_6, $CHCl_3$. Less sol. EtOH, Et_2O. Spar. sol. ligroin. Insol. H_2O.

4 : 4'-N-*Di-Me* : golden-yellow plates from toluene–EtOH. M.p. 176–7°. Spar. sol. EtOH, ligroin. Insol. H_2O. *Dimethiodide* : yellow needles from H_2O. M.p. 220° decomp. Spar. sol. EtOH.

4 : 4'-N-*Di-Et* : reddish-brown plates from EtOH.Aq. M.p. 113°.

Fischer, *Ber.*, 1881, **14**, 2526; 1882, **15**, 677.

6-Nitro-2 : 4-diamino-*m*-xylene (5-*Nitro*-2 : 4-*dimethyl*-m-*phenylenediamine*)

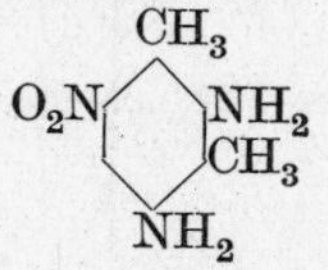

$C_8H_{11}O_2N_3$ MW, 181

Orange-yellow needles from H_2O. M.p. 151–2°. Sol. EtOH. Spar. sol. H_2O.

Noelting, Thesmar, *Ber.*, 1902, **35**, 630.

2-Nitro-4 : 6-diamino-*m*-xylene (5-*Nitro*-4 : 6-*dimethyl*-m-*phenylenediamine*)

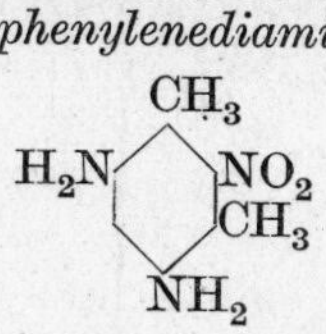

$C_8H_{11}O_2N_3$ MW, 181

Red prisms from EtOH or H_2O. M.p. 212–13°. Sol. EtOH. Mod. sol. boiling H_2O. Sublimes.

N : N'-*Di-Et* : $C_{12}H_{19}O_2N_3$. MW, 237. Yellow cryst. Sol. EtOH, Et_2O.

Fittig, Velguth, *Ann.*, 1868, **148**, 6.
Bussenius, Eisenstuck, *Ann.*, 1860, **113**, 159.

5-Nitro-2 : 3-diamino-*p*-xylene (4-*Nitro*-3 : 6-*dimethyl*-o-*phenylenediamine*)

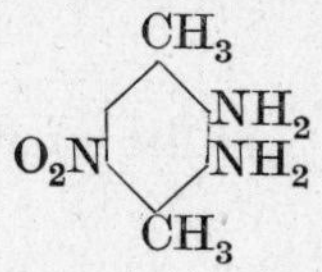

$C_8H_{11}O_2N_3$ MW, 181

Light red needles from C_6H_6 or EtOH.Aq. M.p. 169°. Sol. Et_2O, AcOH. Mod. sol. hot H_2O. Spar. sol. pet. ether.

2-N-*Phenyl* : 4-nitro-6-amino-2 : 5-dimethyldiphenylamine. $C_{14}H_{15}O_2N_3$ MW, 257. Orange-yellow leaflets. M.p. 171°. Sol. EtOH, AcOH. Less sol. C_6H_6. Spar. sol. pet. ether. N'-*Acetyl* : yellow leaflets from C_6H_6–pet. ether. M.p. 203°.

Fries, Noll, *Ann.*, 1912, **389**, 374.
Fries, Arnemann, *Ann.*, 1927, **454**, 160.

2-Nitrodiazoaminobenzene

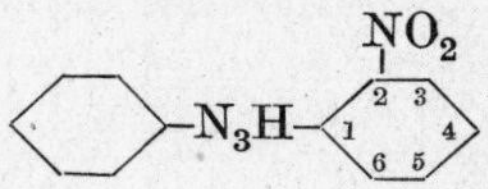

$C_{12}H_{10}O_2N_4$ MW, 242

Orange-yellow needles from EtOH. M.p. 104·5–105°. Sol. $CHCl_3$, Me_2CO, AcOH, C_6H_6.

Bamberger, *Ber.*, 1895, **28**, 237.

3-Nitrodiazoaminobenzene.

Yellow prisms from Et_2O. M.p. 131°.

Goldschmidt, Molinari, *Ber.*, 1888, **21**, 2572.

4-Nitrodiazoaminobenzene.

Yellow needles from C_6H_6. M.p. 148° decomp.

N-*Me*: $C_{13}H_{12}O_2N_4$. MW, 256. Yellow cryst. from ligroin. M.p. 134°. Spar. sol. hot EtOH.

N-*Et* : $C_{14}H_{14}O_2N_4$. MW, 270. Yellow cryst. from ligroin. M.p. 115–16°. Sol. Et_2O, C_6H_6, $CHCl_3$, hot EtOH.

N-*Phenyl* : $C_{18}H_{14}O_2N_4$. MW, 318. Brownish-red. M.p. 63°. Sol. EtOH, Et_2O, C_6H_6. Insol. H_2O.

Nölting, Binder, *Ber.*, 1887, **20**, 3014.
Bamberger, *Ber.*, 1895, **28**, 839.

9-Nitro-1 : 2 : 5 : 6-dibenzanthracene (9-*Nitro*-1 : 2 : 5 : 6-*dinaphthanthracene*)

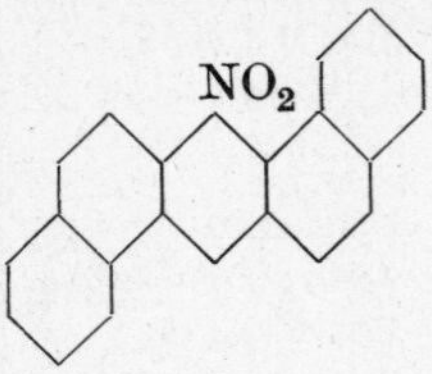

$C_{22}H_{13}O_2N$ MW, 323

Orange-yellow needles from xylene. M.p. 217–18°.

Cook, *J. Chem. Soc.*, 1931, 3276.

2-Nitrodibenzoylmethane

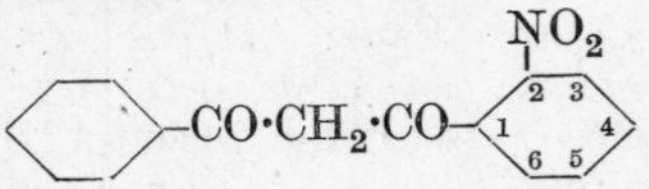

$C_{15}H_{11}O_4N$ MW, 269

Needles from EtOH. M.p. 116°. Alc. $FeCl_3$ ⟶ red col.

Gabriel, Gerhard, *Ber.*, 1921, **54**, 1615.

3-Nitrodibenzoylmethane.

Yellowish cryst. from AcOH. M.p. 135°. Sol. C_6H_6, $CHCl_3$, AcOH. Less sol. MeOH, EtOH. Spar. sol. Et_2O, ligroin. Alc. $FeCl_3$ ⟶ brownish-violet col.

Mono-semicarbazone : cryst. from MeOH.Aq. M.p. 120–5° decomp.

Bodforss, *Ber.*, 1916, **49**, 2804 ; 1918, **51**, 215.

4-Nitrodibenzoylmethane.

Yellow needles from EtOH. M.p. 160°. Sol. C_6H_6. Spar. sol. $CHCl_3$, EtOH. Practically insol. Et_2O. $FeCl_3$ ⟶ red col.

Di-Me acetal : $C_{17}H_{17}O_5N$. MW, 315. Plates from EtOH or pet. ether. M.p. 91°. Mod. sol. usual solvents.

Wieland, *Ber.*, 1904, **37**, 1151.

***o*-Nitro-*N*-dibenzylaniline**

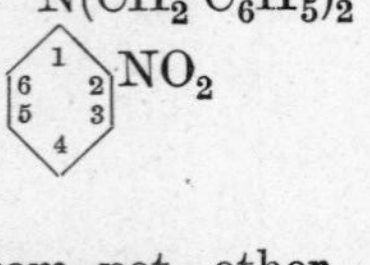

$C_{20}H_{18}O_2N_2$ MW, 318

Yellow plates from pet. ether. M.p. 32–3°. Sol. EtOH, Me_2CO, C_6H_6, AcOH, pet. ether.

Desai, *J. Indian Chem. Soc.*, 1928, **5**, 428.

***m*-Nitro-*N*-dibenzylaniline.**

Golden-yellow needles from EtOH. M.p. 73–4°. Sol. EtOH, Et_2O, Me_2CO, C_6H_6, toluene.

B,HCl : needles from AcOH. M.p. 140–2°.

See previous reference.

***p*-Nitro-*N*-dibenzylaniline.**

Yellow plates from AcOH. M.p. 132–3°. Sol. Me_2CO, C_6H_6. Mod. sol. AcOH. Almost insol. cold EtOH.

See previous reference.

***o*-Nitro-*N*-diethylaniline**

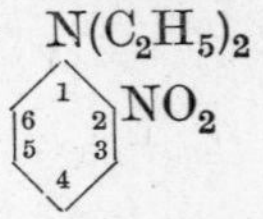

$C_{10}H_{14}O_2N_2$ MW, 194

Orange-yellow oil with pungent odour. Distils in vacuo. Sol. EtOH, Et_2O. Less sol. H_2O.

B,HCl : cryst. from EtOH. Decomp. at 156°.

B,HBr: plates from EtOH. Decomp. at 160°. Hygroscopic.

B,HI : needles from EtOH. M.p. 112°. Hygroscopic.

B,H_2SO_4 : plates from EtOH. M.p. 143°.

Picrate : golden-yellow plates. M.p. 119–20°. Sol. hot EtOH, Et_2O. Spar. sol. H_2O.

Weissenberger, *Monatsh.*, 1912, **33**, 830.

***m*-Nitro-*N*-diethylaniline.**

Dark yellow oil. B.p. 288–90°.

Picrate : cryst. from EtOH. M.p. 138°.

Noelting, Stricker, *Ber.*, 1886, **19**, 550.

***p*-Nitro-*N*-diethylaniline.**

Yellow needles from ligroin, plates from EtOH. M.p. 77–8°. Sol. hot EtOH. Spar. sol. ligroin

Hollemann, de Mooy, *Rec. trav. chim.* 1916, **35**, 32.

Davies, *Bull. soc. chim.*, 1935, 2, 295.

2-Nitrodiethyl Ether.

See under 2-Nitroethyl Alcohol.

4-Nitro-*N*-diethyl-*o*-toluidine

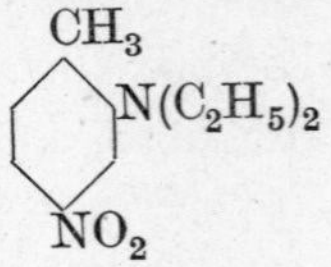

$C_{11}H_{16}O_2N_2$ MW, 20

Yellow oil. B.p. 283° (295–7°/727 mm.). Sol EtOH, Et_2O. Volatile in steam.

Ullmann, Mühlhauser, *Ber.*, 1902, **35** 335.

Möhlau, Klimmer, Kahl, *Chem. Zentr.* 1902, II, 378.

3-Nitro-*N*-diethyl-*p*-toluidine

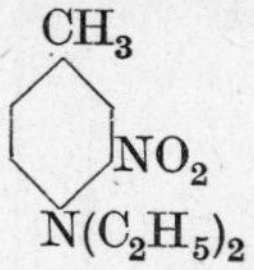

$C_{11}H_{16}O_2N_2$ MW, 208

Yellow oil. B.p. 101–2°/0·7 mm.

Schmidt, Fischer, *Ber.*, 1920, **53**, 1533.

ω-Nitro-3 : 4-dihydroxyacetophenone (4-*Nitroacetylcatechol*)

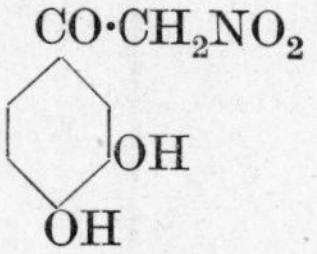

$C_8H_7O_5N$ MW, 197

Yellowish cryst. M.p. 188° decomp. Sol. 10 parts hot H_2O. Sol. EtOH, Me_2CO. Spar. sol. Et_2O, C_6H_6. Dil. NaOH ⟶ intense red sol. $FeCl_3$ ⟶ green col.

Di-Me ether: $C_{10}H_{11}O_5N$. MW, 225. Needles from AcOEt. M.p. 144°. Sol. AcOEt. Spar. sol. EtOH, Et_2O, C_6H_6.

M.L.B., D.R.P., 195,814, (*Chem. Zentr.*, 1908, I, 1225).

Nitrodihydroxyaniline.

See Nitroaminocatechol, Nitroaminoresorcinol *and* Nitroaminohydroquinone.

Nitrodihydroxyanthraquinone.

See Nitroalizarin, Nitrochrysazin, Nitrohystazarin, *and* Nitroquinizarin.

3-Nitro-2 : 4-dihydroxyazobenzene

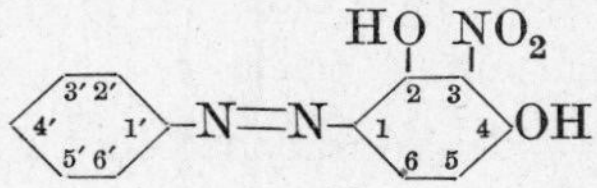

$C_{12}H_9O_4N_3$ MW, 259

Dark red needles from AcOH. M.p. 171°. Sol. alkalis with orange-red col.

Kauffmann, de Pay, *Ber.*, 1906, **39**, 327.

2′-Nitro-2 : 4-dihydroxyazobenzene (o-*Nitrobenzeneazoresorcinol*).

Red needles from EtOH. M.p. 180°. Forms dark red Ba salt.

Elbs *et al.*, *J. prakt. Chem.*, 1924, **108**, 217.

4′-Nitro-2 : 4-dihydroxyazobenzene (p-*Nitrobenzeneazoresorcinol*).

Red cryst. powder from MeOH. M.p. 199–200°. Spar. sol. AcOH, toluene, boiling EtOH.

Forms brownish-red Na salt insol. H_2O. Reagent for magnesium.

Meldola, *J. Chem. Soc.*, 1885, **47**, 660.
Orton, Everatt, *J. Chem. Soc.*, 1908, **93**, 1018.
Fischer, Taurinsch, *Ber.*, 1931, **64**, 236.

4′-Nitro-2 : 5-dihydroxyazobenzene (p-*Nitrobenzeneazohydroquinone*)

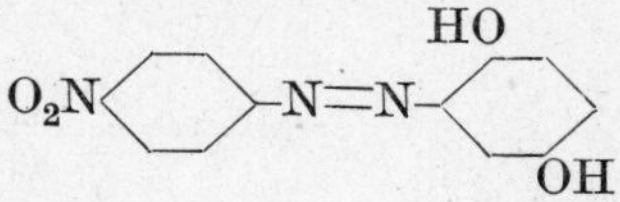

$C_{12}H_9O_4N_3$ MW, 259

Plates from EtOH. Decomp. at 185–90°.

5-*Benzoyl*: brown needles from AcOH.Aq. M.p. 195–7°.

Witt, Johnson, *Ber.*, 1893, **26**, 1910.

2′-Nitro-3 : 4-dihydroxyazobenzene (o-*Nitrobenzeneazocatechol*)

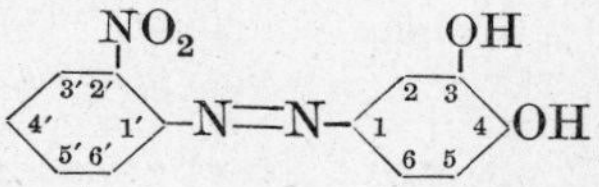

$C_{12}H_9O_4N_3$ MW, 259

3-*Me ether*: $C_{13}H_{11}O_4N_3$. MW, 273. Red cryst. M.p. 144°. Readily sol. org. solvents. Sol. alkalis with wine-red col.

Di-Me ether: o-nitrobenzeneazoveratrol. $C_{14}H_{13}O_4N_3$. MW, 287. Red cryst. M.p. 152°. Sol. most org. solvents.

Colombano, Leonardi, *Gazz. chim. ital.*, 1907, **37**, ii, 467.

3′-Nitro-3 : 4-dihydroxyazobenzene (m-*Nitrobenzeneazocatechol*).

3-*Me ether*: red needles from EtOH.Aq. M.p. 124°. *Acetyl*: cryst. from ligroin. M.p. 95–7°. Sol. EtOH, Et_2O, $CHCl_3$.

See previous reference.

4′-Nitro-3 : 4-dihydroxyazobenzene (p-*Nitrobenzeneazocatechol*).

Red cryst. Sol. in alkalis with blue col., in ammonia and alkali carbonates with violet col., and in conc. H_2SO_4 with red col.

3-*Me ether*: brown cryst. from EtOH.Aq. M.p. 125–35°.

Diacetyl: orange-red needles from MeOH. M.p. 126–7°.

Witt, Mayer, *Ber.*, 1893, **26**, 1074.

5-Nitro-2 : 3-dihydroxybenzaldehyde

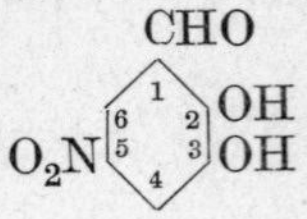

$C_7H_5O_5N$ MW, 183

3-*Me ether*: $C_8H_7O_5N$. MW, 197. Pale yellow needles from EtOH. M.p. 142°.

Di-Me ether: *see* 5-Nitro-2 : 3-dimethoxybenzaldehyde.

3-*Me-2-Et ether*: $C_{10}H_{11}O_5N$. MW, 225. Pale yellow plates. M.p. 137°. p-*Me-anil*: pale yellow needles from EtOH. M.p. 148°.

2-*Me-3-Et ether*: needles from $CHCl_3$. M.p. 118·5°.

3-*Et ether*: $C_9H_9O_5N$. MW, 211. Pale yellow cryst. from EtOH. M.p. 158°.

Di-Et ether: $C_{11}H_{13}O_5N$. MW, 239. Pale yellow needles. M.p. 71°. p-*Me-anil*: needles from EtOH. M.p. 105–6°.

Davies, *J. Chem. Soc.*, 1923, **123**, 1580.
Davies, Rubenstein, *ibid.*, 2844.
Rubenstein, *J. Chem. Soc.*, 1925, 2268.

6-Nitro-2 : 3-dihydroxybenzaldehyde.

3-*Me ether*: 2-*benzenesulphonyl*, yellow needles from EtOH. M.p. 145°. Turns greenish-blue in sunlight.

Di-Me ether: *see* 6-Nitro-2 : 3-dimethoxybenzaldehyde.

3-*Me-2-Et ether*: prisms from EtOH.Aq. M.p. 57°. p-*Nitrophenylhydrazone*: brown needles. M.p. 188–9°. p-*Me-anil*: golden prisms. M.p. 88°.

Di-Et ether: needles from EtOH.Aq. M.p. 75–6°. Turns green in air. p-*Nitrophenylhydrazone*: bright yellow needles. M.p. 268–70°.

See previous references.

Nitro-2 : 4-dihydroxybenzaldehyde.
See Nitroresorcylic Aldehyde.
Nitro-2 : 5-dihydroxybenzaldehyde.
See Nitrogentisic Aldehyde.
Nitro-3 : 4-dihydroxybenzaldehyde.
See Nitroprotocatechuic Aldehyde.
4-Nitro-2 : 3-dihydroxybenzoic Acid

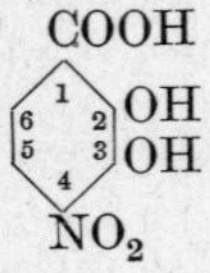

$C_7H_5O_6N$ MW, 199

2-*Me ether*: $C_8H_7O_6N$. MW, 213. Leaflets from H_2O. M.p. 186–7°. Mod. sol. H_2O.

Di-Me ether: *see* 4-Nitro-2 : 3-dimethoxybenzoic acid.

Cain, Simonsen, Smith, *J. Chem. Soc.*, 1914, **105**, 1341.

5-Nitro-2 : 3-dihydroxybenzoic Acid.

3-*Me ether*: needles from H_2O. M.p. 227° decomp. $FeCl_3 \longrightarrow$ reddish-brown col.

Di-Me ether: *see* 5-Nitro-2 : 3-dimethoxybenzoic acid

3-*Et ether*: $C_9H_9O_6N$. MW, 227. Needles from EtOH. M.p. 205°. Spar. sol. H_2O. Alc. $FeCl_3 \longrightarrow$ brownish-violet col. rapidly turning brown.

2-*Me-3-Et ether*: $C_{10}H_{11}O_6N$. MW, 241. Needles from 90% EtOH. M.p. 177°. Spar. sol. cold H_2O. No col. with $FeCl_3$.

3-*Me-2-Et ether*: needles. M.p. 169°. Spar. sol. cold H_2O.

Di-Et ether: $C_{11}H_{13}O_6N$. MW, 255. Needles. M.p. 118°.

Klemenc, *Monatsh.*, 1914, **35**, 98.
Davies, *J. Chem. Soc.*, 1923, **123**, 1588.
Davies, Rubenstein, *J. Chem. Soc.*, 1923, **123**, 2848.

6-Nitro-2 : 3-dihydroxybenzoic Acid.

Di-Me ether: *see* 6-Nitro-2 : 3-dimethoxybenzoic acid.

3-*Me-2-Et ether*: cryst. from hot H_2O. M.p. 119–20°. Mod. sol. hot H_2O.

3-*Me ether*: 2-*benzenesulphonyl*, leaflets from EtOH.Aq. M.p. 218°.

Davies, *J. Chem. Soc.*, 1923, **123**, 1585.
Rubenstein, *J. Chem. Soc.*, 1925, 2269.

Nitro-2 : 4-dihydroxybenzoic Acid.
See Nitro-β-resorcylic Acid.
Nitro-2 : 5-dihydroxybenzoic Acid.
See Nitrogentisic Acid.
Nitro-2 : 6-dihydroxybenzoic Acid.
See Nitro-γ-resorcylic Acid.
Nitro-3 : 4-dihydroxybenzoic Acid.
See Nitroprotocatechuic Acid.
Nitro-3 : 5-dihydroxybenzoic Acid.
See Nitro-α-resorcylic Acid.
3′-Nitro-2 : 4-dihydroxybenzophenone

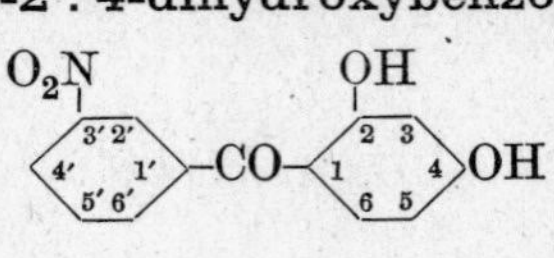

$C_{13}H_9O_5N$ MW, 259

Yellow needles from EtOH.Aq. M.p. 228°.

Di-Me ether: $C_{15}H_{13}O_5N$. MW, 287. Cryst. rom EtOH. M.p. 116–17°.

Yamashita, *Bull. Chem. Soc. Japan*, 1928, **3**, 180.

4′-Nitro-2 : 4-dihydroxybenzophenone.
Pale yellow cryst. from EtOH.Aq. M.p. 03°. Sol. EtOH, AcOH. Less sol. Et_2O, $CHCl_3$, ot H_2O. $FeCl_3$ ⟶ reddish-brown col. KOH ⟶ dark red sol.
Di-Me ether: pale yellow cryst. from pet. ther. M.p. 123–4°.

See previous reference.

4′-Nitro-2 : 5-dihydroxybenzophenone.
Di-Me ether: $C_{15}H_{13}O_5N$. MW, 287. Yellow ryst. from EtOH. M.p. 126°. Sol. C_6H_6, $CHCl_3$. Mod. sol. EtOH, AcOH, AcOEt, CS_2. par. sol. Et_2O, ligroin. Conc. H_2SO_4 ⟶ ntense red col. *Oxime*: exists in two forms. i) Cryst. from EtOH. M.p. 195°. Sol. AcOH. par. sol. EtOH, $CHCl_3$, Et_2O, ligroin. In boiling oluene passes into second form. (ii) Cryst. I.p. 145°. More sol. than first form. *Phenyl-ydrazone*: exists in three forms. M.ps., 165°, 45° and 81°.

Kauffmann, de Pay, *Ber.*, 1912, **45**, 778.

5-Nitro-2 : 3-dihydroxybenzyl Alcohol

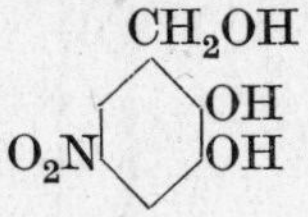

$C_7H_7O_5N$ MW, 185

2 : 3-*Di-Me ether*: $C_9H_{11}O_5N$. MW, 213. Needles from MeOH. M.p. 67°.
3-*Me*-2-*Et ether*: $C_{10}H_{13}O_5N$. MW, 227. Pale yellow prisms from EtOH. M.p. 132°.
Di-Et ether: $C_{11}H_{15}O_5N$. MW, 241. Needles rom EtOH. M.p. 75°.

Rubenstein, *J. Chem. Soc.*, 1926, 649.

3′-Nitro-3 : 4-dihydroxychalkone

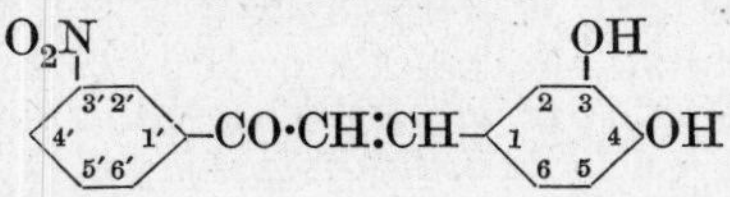

$C_{15}H_{11}O_5N$ MW, 285

Yellow needles from EtOH.Aq. M.p. 217°.
Di-Et ether: $C_{19}H_{19}O_5N$. MW, 341. Yellow needles from EtOH–Et_2O. M.p. 103°.
Diacetyl: needles from EtOH. M.p. 179°. Sol. EtOH, Et_2O, C_6H_6. Spar. sol. H_2O.

Rupe, Wasserzug, *Ber.*, 1901, **34**, 3530.

3-Nitro-4 : 4′-dihydroxychalkone.
Di-Me ether: $C_{17}H_{15}O_5N$. MW, 313. Yellow needles from EtOH. M.p. 160°. Sol. Me_2CO, $CHCl_3$, AcOH. Spar. sol. MeOH, EtOH. Insol. Et_2O, ligroin. *Perchlorate*: m.p. 177–80°.

Pfeiffer, Segall, *Ann.*, 1928, **460**, 130.

2-Nitro-α : 3-dihydroxycinnamic Acid

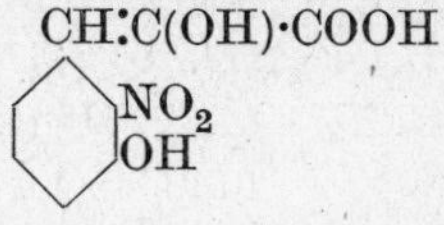

$C_9H_7O_6N$ MW, 225

Di-Me ether: $C_{11}H_{11}O_6N$. MW, 253. Needles from AcOH. M.p. 202° decomp. No col. with $FeCl_3$. Alk. salts yellow.

Blaikie, Perkin, *J. Chem. Soc.*, 1924, **125**, 334.

5-Nitro-2 : 3-dihydroxycinnamic Acid

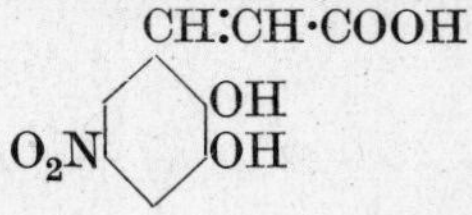

$C_9H_7O_6N$ MW, 225

Di-Me ether: prisms from EtOH. M.p. 231° (229°). Ox. ⟶ 5-nitro-*o*-veratric acid. *Me ester*: $C_{12}H_{13}O_6N$. MW, 267. Needles from EtOH. M.p. 154–5°. *Et ester*: $C_{13}H_{15}O_6N$. MW, 281. Prisms from EtOH. M.p. 116° (111°).
2-*Me*-3-*Et ether*: $C_{12}H_{13}O_6N$. MW, 267. Needles from EtOH. M.p. 200–1°.
Di-Et ether: $C_{13}H_{15}O_6N$. MW, 281. Prisms from EtOH. M.p. 199°.

Rubenstein, *J. Chem. Soc.*, 1926, 651.
Chakravarti, Perkin, *J. Chem. Soc.*, 1929, 194.

6-Nitro-2 : 3-dihydroxycinnamic Acid.
Di-Me ether: needles from EtOH.Aq. M.p. 210–15°. *Et ester*: needles from EtOH.Aq. M.p. 86°.

See first reference above.

2-Nitro-3 : 4-dihydroxycinnamic Acid (2-*Nitrocaffeic acid*)

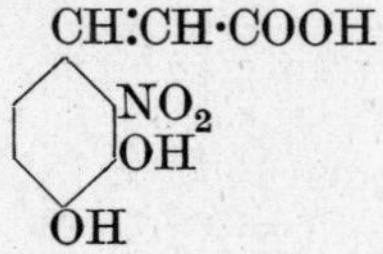

$C_9H_7O_6N$ MW, 225

Trans:
Di-Me ether: needles from EtOH. M.p. 229° after softening at 217°.

Gulland, Virden, *J. Chem. Soc.*, 1928, 932.

5-Nitro-3 : 6-dihydroxy-ψ-cumene (5-*Nitro*-3 : 6-*dihydroxy*-1 : 2 : 4-*trimethylbenzene*)

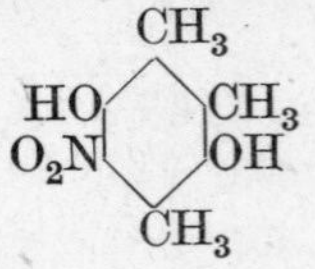

$C_9H_{11}O_4N$ MW, 197

Golden-yellow needles from Et_2O. M.p. 106°. Sol. EtOH, Et_2O, $CHCl_3$, AcOH. Less sol. hot H_2O.

Nef, *Ann.*, 1887, **237**, 18.

4-Nitro-2 : 5-dihydroxydiphenyl

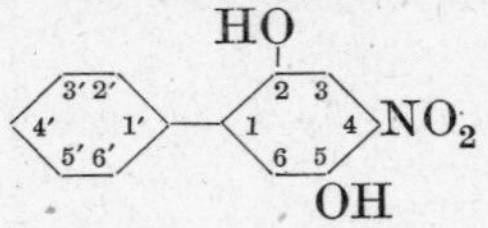

$C_{12}H_9O_4N$ MW, 231

Di-Me ether : $C_{14}H_{13}O_4N$. MW, 259. M.p. 102–3°.

Di-Et ether : $C_{16}H_{17}O_4N$. MW, 287. M.p. 92°.

Dibutyl ether : $C_{20}H_{25}O_4N$. MW, 343. M.p. 41–2°.

Dibenzyl ether : $C_{26}H_{21}O_4N$. MW, 411. M.p. 136–8°.

I.G., F.P., 739,053, (*Chem. Abstracts*, 1933, **27**, 1893); D.R.P., 566,521, (*Chem. Abstracts*, 1933, **27**, 2459).

4-Nitro-2 : 4′-dihydroxydiphenyl.
Yellow cryst. M.p. 187°. Sol. alkalis and alk. carbonates.

Finzi, Mangini, *Gazz. chim. ital.*, 1932, **62**, 673.

5-Nitro-3 : 6-dihydroxy-2-methylbenzoquinone.
See 5-Nitro-3 : 6-dihydroxytoluquinone.

3-Nitro-1 : 2-dihydroxynaphthalene (3-*Nitro*-β-*naphthohydroquinone*)

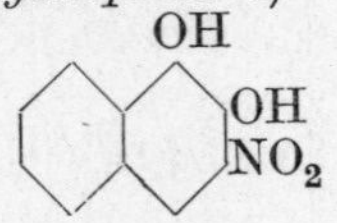

$C_{10}H_7O_4N$ MW, 205

Red plates from EtOH or C_6H_6, needles from H_2O. M.p. 159·5° (152–3°). Sol. EtOH, AcOH. Spar. sol. H_2O. Sublimes in red needles.

Diacetyl : orange leaflets. M.p. 196–7°.

Zincke, Noack, *Ann.*, 1897, **295**, 12.

Nitro-9 : 10-dihydroxyphenanthrene.
See Nitrophenanthrahydroquinone.

2-Nitro-3 : 4-dihydroxyphenylacetic Acid

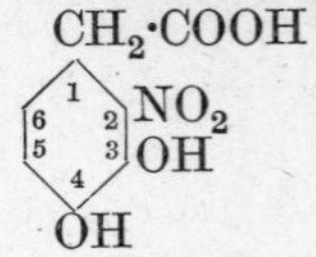

$C_8H_7O_6N$ MW, 213

Orange-yellow needles from xylene. M.p. 171°. Sol. EtOH. Sol. NaOH with orange col. $FeCl_3 \longrightarrow$ intense green col.

3-*Me ether* : *see* 2-Nitrohomovanillic Acid.

3 : 4-*Dibenzyl ether* : $C_{22}H_{19}O_6N$. MW, 393. Needles from EtOH.Aq., m.p. 85°.

3 : 4-*Dicarbethoxyl* : needles from C_6H_6, m.p. 115°; needles from AcOH, m.p. 127°.

Di-Me ether : *see* 2-Nitrohomoveratic Acid.

Gulland, *J. Chem. Soc.*, 1931, 2872.

6-Nitro-3 : 4-dihydroxyphenylacetic Acid.
Yellow needles from toluene. M.p. 212°. Sol. H_2O. NaOH $\longrightarrow$ cherry-red sol. $FeCl_3 \longrightarrow$ dark green col.

Anilide : needles from EtOH. M.p. 201–2°.

3-*Me ether* : *see* 6-Nitrohomovanillic Acid.

Di-Me ether : *see* 6-Nitrohomoveratric Acid.

See previous reference.

6-Nitro-3 : 4-dihydroxyphthalic Acid (6-*Nitronorhemipinic acid*)

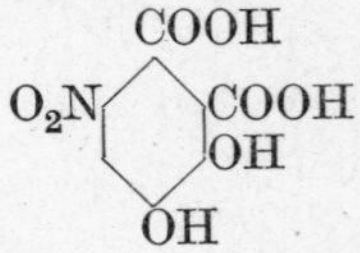

$C_8H_5O_8N$ MW, 243

4-*Me ether* : $C_9H_7O_8N$. MW, 257. Needles from EtOH, leaflets from AcOEt–pet. ether M.p. 220° (205–6° decomp.). Sol. H_2O, EtOH, AcOEt. Spar. sol. C_6H_6. *Di-Me ester* $C_{11}H_{11}O_8N$. MW, 285. Leaflets from C_6H_6 M.p. 145–6°. Sol. hot H_2O. KOH $\longrightarrow$ yellow sol. 2-*Me ester*-1-*anilide* : $C_{17}H_{16}O_7N_2$. MW, 360. Cryst. from C_6H_6. M.p. 170° decomp 1-*Anilide* : $C_{16}H_{14}O_7N_2$. MW, 346. Cryst. powder from $Me_2CO–CCl_4$. M.p. 192°. Mod. sol. Me_2CO. Spar. sol. H_2O, AcOEt. $FeCl_3 \longrightarrow$ ruby-red col. 2-*Anilide* : pale yellow prisms from $Me_2CO–CCl_4$. M.p. 183–4° decomp. Sol EtOH, Me_2CO. Spar. sol. H_2O, Et_2O, C_6H_6, CCl_4. Sol. alkalis and NH_3.Aq. with blood-red col.

Di-Me ether : *see* 6-Nitrohemipinic Acid.

Elbel, *Ber.*, 1886, **19**, 2312.
Wegscheider, Klemenc, *Monatsh.*, 1911 **32**, 386.

6-Nitro-3 : 4-dihydroxy-1-propylbenzene

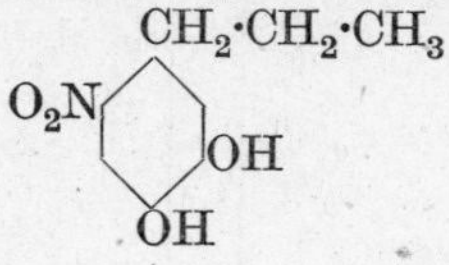

$C_9H_{11}O_4N$ MW, 197

Yellowish-green cryst. M.p. 73°. Very sol. H_2O and most org. solvents.

3-*Me ether*: $C_{10}H_{13}O_4N$. MW, 211. Cryst. + H_2O. M.p. 78°.

4-*Me ether*: cryst. M.p. 52°. 3-*Et ether*: $C_{12}H_{17}O_4N$. MW, 239. Yellow needles. M.p. 60°.

Di-Me ether: $C_{11}H_{15}O_4N$. MW, 225. Yellowish prisms. M.p. 81–2°.

Thoms, Biltz, *Arch. Pharm.*, 1904, **242**, 88.

Nitro-αγ-dihydroxypropylbenzene.
See 1-*o*-Nitrophenyltrimethylene Glycol.

3-Nitro-2 : 6-dihydroxypyridine

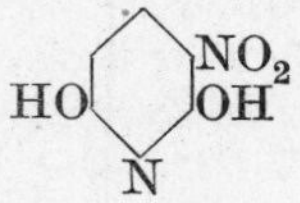

$C_5H_4O_4N_2$ MW, 156

Yellow needles from H_2O. Decomp. at 321°. Sol. alkalis with yellow col.

Gattermann, Skita, *Ber.*, 1916, **49**, 499.

3-Nitro-2 : 4-dihydroxyquinoline

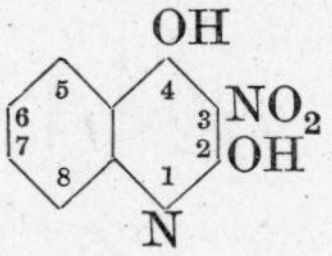

$C_9H_6O_4N_2$ MW, 206

Yellow prisms from AcOH. Decomp. at 225°. Sol. alkalis and NH_3.Aq.

Acetyl: yellow cryst. M.p. 194° decomp.

Gabriel, *Ber.*, 1918, **51**, 1500.
Ashley, Perkin, Robinson, *J. Chem. Soc.*, 1930, 382.

8-Nitro-5 : 6-dihydroxyquinoline.
Di-Me ether: $C_{11}H_{10}O_4N_2$. MW, 234. Cryst. M.p. 126–8°.

I.G., D.R.P., 531,083, (*Chem. Abstracts*, 1931, **25**, 5434).

3-Nitro-2 : 4-dihydroxytoluene (3-*Nitrocresorcinol*)

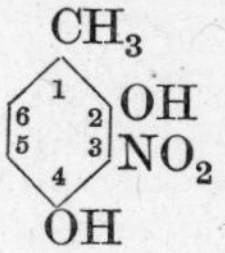

$C_7H_7O_4N$ MW, 169

Red cryst. from EtOH. M.p. 112°. Sol. EtOH, C_6H_6, AcOH, pet. ether. Sol. cold Na_2CO_3.Aq. Volatile in steam.

Henrich, Fleischmann, *Ber.*, 1930, **63**, 1337.

5-Nitro-2 : 4-dihydroxytoluene (5-*Nitrocresorcinol*).

Orange-red needles from C_6H_6 or ligroin. M.p. 125°. Sol. cold Na_2CO_3.Aq. Non-volatile in steam.

See previous reference.

6-Nitro-2 : 5-dihydroxytoluene.
See 6-Nitrotoluhydroquinone.

Nitro-3 : 4-dihydroxytoluene.
See Nitrohomocatechol.

Nitro-3 : 5-dihydroxytoluene.
See Nitro-orcinol.

5-Nitro-3 : 6-dihydroxytoluquinone (5-*Nitro*-3 : 6-*dihydroxy-2-methylbenzoquinone, tolunitranilic acid*)

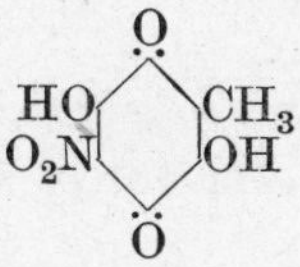

$C_7H_5O_6N$ MW, 199

Yellow needles + H_2O from H_2O. M.p. 180° decomp.

Kehrmann, Brasch, *J. prakt. Chem.*, 1889, **39**, 378.

Nitrodihydroxytrimethylbenzene.
See Nitrodihydroxy-ψ-cumene.

2 - Nitro - 4′ : 4″ - dihydroxytriphenyl - methane

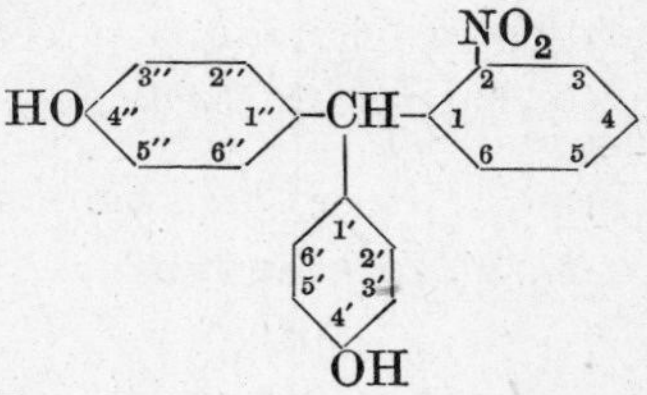

$C_{19}H_{15}O_4N$ MW, 321

Brown amorph. powder. M.p. 92°. Sol. EtOH, Et_2O, AcOH, Me_2CO, AcOEt. Spar.

sol. C_6H_6. Alkalis ⟶ red sols. ⟶ intense green fluor. with EtOH. Conc. H_2SO_4 ⟶ intense red sol.

Di-Me ether : $C_{21}H_{19}O_4N$. MW, 349. Brown amorph. powder.

Diacetyl : yellow amorph. powder.

Dibenzoyl : yellowish powder from 96% EtOH. M.p. 155°. C_6H_6 ⟶ reddish-brown sol. with green fluor.

Tănăsescu, Simonescu, *J. prakt. Chem.*, 1934, **141**, 319.

3 - Nitro - 4′ : 4″ - dihydroxytriphenyl - methane.

Reddish powder. M.p. 90–1°. Sol. EtOH, Me_2CO, AcOEt, AcOH. Less sol. C_6H_6. Alkalis ⟶ yellow sols. ⟶ green fluor. with EtOH.

Di-Me ether : yellow amorph. powder from MeOH. M.p. 70°.

Dibenzoyl : amorph. powder from 96% EtOH. M.p. 89°.

See previous reference.

4 - Nitro - 4′ : 4″ - dihydroxytriphenyl - methane.

Yellowish amorph. powder. M.p. 130°. Sol. EtOH, Me_2CO, Et_2O, AcOH. Less sol. C_6H_6, xylene. Conc. H_2SO_4 ⟶ red sol.

Di-Me ether : reddish amorph. powder. Sol. Et_2O.

Dibenzoyl : powder. Sol. C_6H_6. Less sol. 96% EtOH.

See previous reference.

6-Nitro-1 : 2-diketohydrindene (6-*Nitro-indandione*-1 : 2)

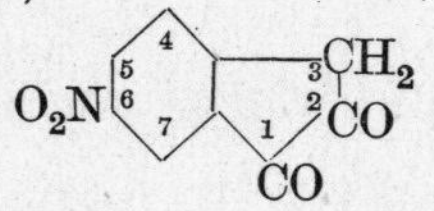

$C_9H_5O_4N$ MW, 191

Pale orange-brown needles. Decomp. about 150°. Sol. alkalis with reddish-brown col.

2-*Oxime* : plates from EtOH, prisms from EtOH. M.p. about 240° decomp. (196°). Mod. sol. AcOH. Spar. sol. EtOH. Alkalis ⟶ deep purple sols. which rapidly turn brown.

Ingold, Piggott, *J. Chem. Soc.*, 1923, **123**, 1488.

v. Braun, Heider, *Ber.*, 1916, **49**, 1279.

5-Nitro-2 : 3-dimethoxybenzaldehyde

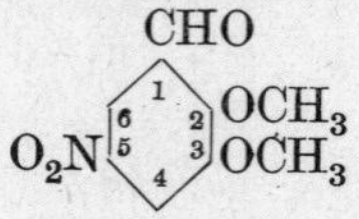

$C_9H_9O_5N$ MW, 211

Needles from MeOH. M.p. 115° (116–17°). Very sol. hot MeOH. Spar. sol. boiling H_2O.

Di-Me acetal : prisms from MeOH. M.p. 89° (96–7°).

Oxime : needles from EtOH. M.p. 155°.

Semicarbazone : needles from EtOH.Aq. M.p. 210°.

Phenylhydrazone : red plates from EtOH. M.p. 179°.

Anil : needles from EtOH. M.p. 122°.

p-*Me-anil* : needles from EtOH. M.p. 143°.

Perkin, Robinson, Stoyle, *J. Chem. Soc.*, 1924, **125**, 2358.

Davies, *J. Chem. Soc.*, 1923, **123**, 1580.

6-Nitro-2 : 3-dimethoxybenzaldehyde.

Needles from C_6H_6–ligroin. M.p. 110°.

Di-Me acetal : cubes from MeOH. M.p. 72°. Turns green in air.

Oxime : needles from EtOH.Aq. M.p. 130°.

Semicarbazone : needles from EtOH.Aq. M.p. 227–8°.

Phenylhydrazone : brownish-orange prisms from EtOH. M.p. 138°.

Anil : needles from EtOH. M.p. 84°.

p-*Me-anil* : plates from EtOH. M.p. 104°.

Perkin, Robinson, Stoyle, *J. Chem. Soc.*, 1924, **125**, 2358.

3-Nitro-2 : 4-dimethoxybenzaldehyde (3-*Nitroresorcylic aldehyde dimethyl ether*)

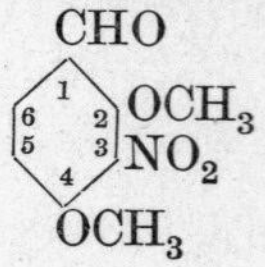

$C_9H_9O_5N$ MW, 211

Cryst. M.p. 104–5°.

Srikantia, Iyengar, Santanam, *J. Chem. Soc.*, 1932, 527.

5-Nitro-2 : 4-dimethoxybenzaldehyde (5-*Nitroresorcylic aldehyde dimethyl ether*).

Needles from MeOH. M.p. 188–9°. Spar. sol. alcohols. No col. with $FeCl_3$.

Oxime : pale yellow. M.p. 184–5°.

Hydrazone : orange plates. M.p. 169–70°.

Rao, Srikantia, Iyengar, *J. Chem. Soc.*, 1925, **127**, 558.

3-Nitro-2 : 5-dimethoxybenzaldehyde (3-*Nitrogentisic aldehyde dimethyl ether*)

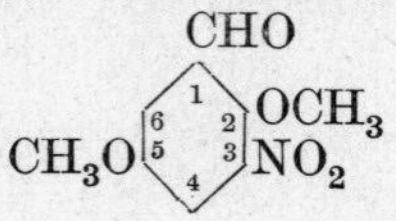

$C_9H_9O_5N$ MW, 211

Pale yellow needles from $CHCl_3$. M.p. 113°.

Rubenstein, *J. Chem. Soc.*, 1925, **127**, 2000.

6-Nitro-2 : 5-dimethoxybenzaldehyde (6-*Nitrogentisic aldehyde dimethyl ether*).
Pale yellow needles from EtOH. M.p. 159°.
p-*Nitrophenylhydrazone* : scarlet prisms. M.p. 245–50° decomp.

See previous reference.

Nitro-3 : 4-dimethoxybenzaldehyde.
See Nitroveratric Aldehyde.

4-Nitro-2 : 3-dimethoxybenzoic Acid

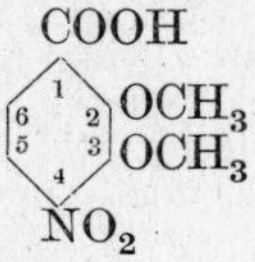

$C_9H_9O_6N$ MW, 227

Two compounds of this structure have been described in the literature.
1. Pale yellow needles from H_2O. M.p. 94–5°.

Majima, Okazaki, *Ber.*, 1916, **49**, 1494.

2. Prisms from AcOEt. M.p. 215–16°. Spar. sol. H_2O.
Et ester : $C_{11}H_{13}O_6N$. MW, 255. Needles from EtOH. M.p. 142–3°.

Cain, Simonsen, Smith, *J. Chem. Soc.*, 1914, **105**, 1339.

5-Nitro-2 : 3-dimethoxybenzoic Acid.
Needles from H_2O. M.p. 176° (174–5°).
Me ester : $C_{10}H_{11}O_6N$. MW, 241. Needles from MeOH.Aq. M.p. 76–7°.
Et ester : needles from EtOH. M.p. 79°.
Nitrile : $C_9H_8O_4N_2$. MW, 208. Brownish needles from MeOH.Aq. M.p. about 127–8°. Sol. most org. solvents.

Gibson, Simonsen, Rau, *J. Chem. Soc.*, 1917, **111**, 77.

6-Nitro-2 : 3-dimethoxybenzoic Acid.
Leaflets or needles from H_2O. M.p. 189–90° (184–5°). Mod. sol. hot C_6H_6. Spar. sol. cold H_2O.
Me ester : needles from MeOH. M.p. 81°.

Perkin, Robinson, *J. Chem. Soc.*, 1914, **105**, 2390.
Cain, Simonsen, *ibid.*, 161.

3-Nitro-2 : 4-dimethoxybenzoic Acid (3-*Nitro-β-resorcylic acid dimethyl ether*)

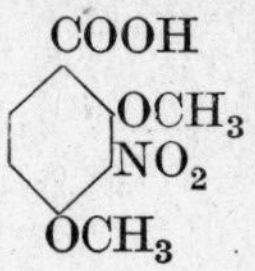

$C_9H_9O_6N$ MW, 227

Needles from H_2O. M.p. 210–12°.
Me ester : $C_{10}H_{11}O_6N$. MW, 241. Prisms from MeOH. M.p. 118–19°.

Dodswell, Kenner, *J. Chem. Soc.*, 1927, 587.

3-Nitro-2 : 5-dimethoxybenzoic Acid (3-*Nitrogentisic acid dimethyl ether*)

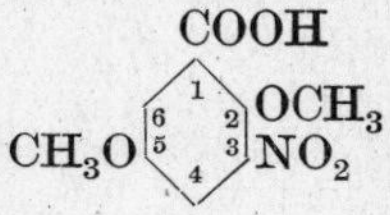

$C_9H_9O_6N$ MW, 227

Yellowish needles from H_2O. M.p. 181–3°. Spar. sol. H_2O. Alkalis ⟶ yellow sols.
Me ester : $C_{10}H_{11}O_6N$. MW, 241. Needles from C_6H_6. M.p. 71–2°.

Klemenc, *Monatsh.*, 1912, **33**, 1253.

6-Nitro-2 : 5-dimethoxybenzoic Acid (6-*Nitrogentisic acid dimethyl ether*).
Me ester : yellow cryst. powder from C_6H_6–pet. ether. M.p. 117–18°.

Klemenc, *Monatsh.*, 1914, **35**, 105.

3-Nitro-2 : 6-dimethoxybenzoic Acid (3-*Nitro-γ-resorcylic acid dimethyl ether*)

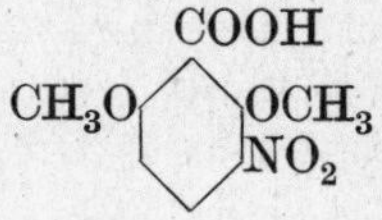

$C_9H_9O_6N$ MW, 227

Nitrile : $C_9H_8O_4N_2$. MW, 208. Yellow needles from EtOH. M.p. 112°.

Blanksma, *Chem. Zentr.*, 1912, II, 339.

Nitro-3 : 4-dimethoxybenzoic Acid.
See Nitroveratric Acid.

2-Nitro-3 : 5-dimethoxybenzoic Acid (2-*Nitro-α-resorcylic acid dimethyl ether*)

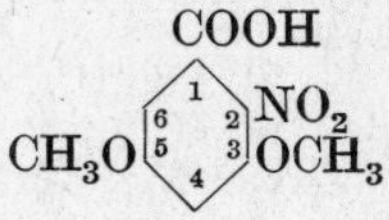

$C_9H_9O_6N$ MW, 227

Cryst. M.p. 232°. Turns yellow in air.

Et ester: $C_{11}H_{13}O_6N$. MW, 255. Needles. M.p. 131°.

Amide: $C_9H_{10}O_5N_2$. MW, 226. Pale yellowish leaflets from EtOH. M.p. 199°.

I.G., D.R.P., 501,609, (*Chem. Zentr.*, 1930, II, 1773).

4-Nitro-3 : 5-dimethoxybenzoic Acid (4-*Nitro-α-resorcylic acid dimethyl ether*).

Yellow needles from H_2O, prisms from EtOH or AcOH. M.p. 225°. Sol. hot EtOH, AcOH. Spar. sol. H_2O. Sublimes in needles with part. decomp.

Et ester: pale yellow needles from EtOH or Et_2O. M.p. 130°.

Einhorn, Pfyl, *Ann.*, 1900, **311**, 62.

Nitro-3 : 4-dimethoxyphenylacetic Acid.
See Nitrohomoveratric Acid.

Nitro-3 : 4-dimethoxytoluene.
See Nitrohomoveratrol.

3-Nitro-2 : 4-dimethylacetophenone

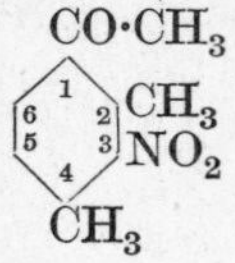

$C_{10}H_{11}O_3N$ MW, 193

Prisms from AcOH. M.p. 72°.

Claus, *J. prakt. Chem.*, 1890, **41**, 499.

5-Nitro-2 : 4-dimethylacetophenone.
Needles from EtOH. M.p. 67°. Very sol. hot EtOH. Sublimes in needles.

See previous reference.

***N*-Nitrodimethylamine.**
See Dimethylnitramine.

3-Nitro-*p*-dimethylaminobenzoic Acid

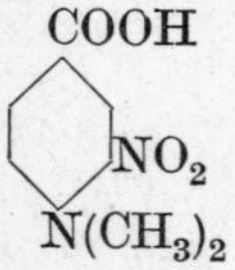

$C_9H_{10}O_4N_2$ MW, 210

Golden-yellow needles from toluene or $CHCl_3$. M.p. 222–3° (213°). Very sol. EtOH. Insol. H_2O.

Me ester: $C_{10}H_{12}O_4N_2$. MW, 224. Yellow leaflets from EtOH.Aq. M.p. 71·5°. Very sol. EtOH, Me_2CO, C_6H_6, $CHCl_3$, AcOH. Mod. sol. ligroin. Spar. sol. H_2O.

Et ester: $C_{11}H_{14}O_4N_2$. MW, 238. Pale yellow leaflets from EtOH. M.p. 80–1°.

Amide: $C_9H_{11}O_3N_3$. MW, 209. Cryst. from H_2O. M.p. 210°. Sol. $CHCl_3$. Mod. sol. EtOH. Insol. Et_2O, ligroin.

Nitrile: $C_9H_9O_2N_3$. MW, 191. Yellow plates. M.p. 114–15°. Mod. sol. EtOH, C_6H_6.

Noelting, Demant, *Ber.*, 1904, **37**, 1030.
Reverdin, Delétra, *Ber.*, 1906, **39**, 972.
Reverdin, *Ber.*, 1907, **40**, 2443.

***o*-Nitro-*N*-dimethylaniline**

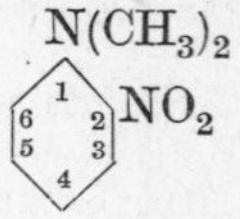

$C_8H_{10}O_2N_2$ MW, 166

Orange-yellow oil. F.p. — 20°. B.p. 151–3°/30–3 mm. n_D 1·61021. Mod. sol. H_2O. Easily volatile in steam.

B,HCl: needles. M.p. 173–4°. Sol. H_2O, hot EtOH, $CHCl_3$.

B,HBr: prisms from EtOH. Decomp. at 172°.

B,HI: cryst. Decomp. at 126°. Unstable.

B,H_2SO_4: plates from EtOH. M.p. 168° (126–7°).

$B,HAuCl_4$: yellowish prisms. Decomp. at 152°. Spar. sol. EtOH.

Picrate: pale yellow prisms from EtOH. M.p. 102–103·5°. Very sol. Me_2CO. Sol. hot EtOH, Et_2O.

$C_8H_{10}O_2N_2,C_6H_3(NO_2)_3$-1 : 3 : 5 : yellowish-red cryst. M.p. 112°.

Friedländer, *Monatsh.*, 1898, **19**, 636.
Weissenberger, *Monatsh.*, 1912, **33**, 826.

***m*-Nitro-*N*-dimethylaniline.**
Red cryst. from Et_2O or EtOH–Et_2O. M.p. 60–1°. B.p. 280–5°. Volatile in steam.

Methiodide: plates from H_2O.

Methonitrate: prisms or plates from H_2O. M.p. 220–40° decomp.

Methopicrate: yellow prisms from EtOH.Aq. M.p. 151–3°.

Picrate: yellow cryst. M.p. 119°.

Ullmann, *Ann.*, 1903, **327**, 112.
Vorländer, Siebert, *Ber.*, 1919, **52**, 294.

***p*-Nitro-*N*-dimethylaniline.**
Yellow needles with blue reflex from EtOH. M.p. 163°. Sol. warm EtOH, AcOH. Insol. H_2O.

B,2HCl: m.p. about 53°.

Tingle, Blanck, *J. Am. Chem. Soc.*, 1908, **30**, 1405.
Davies, *Bull. soc. chim.*, 1935, **2**, 295.

4-Nitro-1 : 3-dimethylanthraquinone

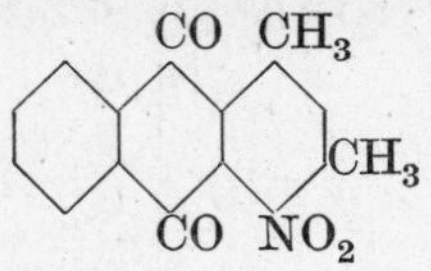

$C_{16}H_{11}O_4N$ MW, 281

Pale yellow needles from AcOH. M.p. 234°. Turns orange-yellow in air.

Scholl, *Ber.*, 1910, **43**, 353.

4′-Nitro-2 : 4-dimethylazobenzene

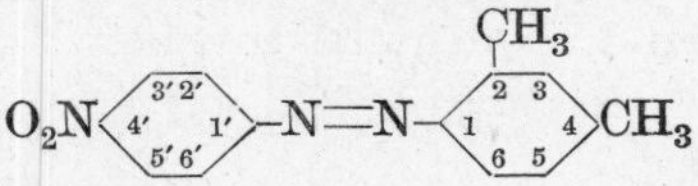

$C_{14}H_{13}O_2N_3$ MW, 255

Orange-red needles from EtOH. M.p. 128·5–29·5°. Sol. hot Me_2CO, C_6H_6, hot ligroin.

Bamberger, *Ber.*, 1907, **40**, 1913, 1923, 1932.

4′-Nitro-3 : 4-dimethylazobenzene. Orange-red needles. M.p. 135·5°.

Bamberger, Blangey, *Ann.*, 1911, **384**, 318.

6-Nitro-2 : 4′-dimethylazobenzene. Red prisms from AcOH. M.p. 65·5–66°. Sol. EtOH, Et_2O, AcOH.

Meisenheimer, Hesse, *Ber.*, 1919, **52**, 1172.

2-Nitro-4 : 4′-dimethylazobenzene. Orange-red cryst. from EtOH. M.p. 80°. Sn + HCl ⟶ *p*-toluidine and 3 : 4-diaminotoluene.

Janovsky, *Monatsh.*, 1889, **10**, 586.

5-Nitro-2 : 4-dimethylbenzaldehyde

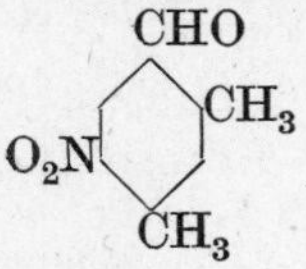

$C_9H_9O_3N$ MW, 179

Yellowish needles from ligroin. M.p. 81°.

Gattermann, *Ann.*, 1906, **347**, 372.

6-Nitro-2 : 5-dimethylbenzaldehyde

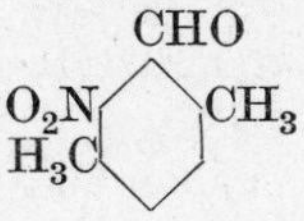

$C_9H_9O_3N$ MW, 179

Yellow needles or leaflets from EtOH. M.p. 120°.

Semicarbazone : needles from EtOH. M.p. 183°.

Azine : yellowish needles from EtOH. M.p. 162°.

Gattermann, *Ann.*, 1912, **393**, 221.

2-Nitro-3 : 5-dimethylbenzaldehyde

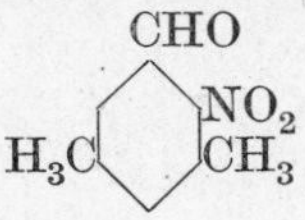

$C_9H_9O_3N$ MW, 179

Needles. M.p. 102–3°. Sol. EtOH, pet. ether.

Bamberger, Weiler, *J. prakt. Chem.*, 1898, **58**, 360.

5-Nitro-1 : 2-dimethylbenziminazole

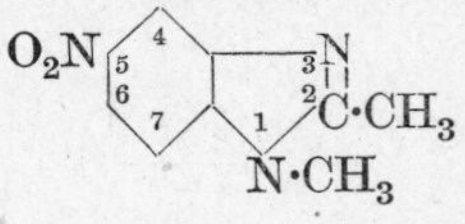

$C_9H_9O_2N_3$ MW, 191

Yellow plates from EtOH or $PhNO_2$. M.p. 226°.

Freis, Modrow, Raeke, Weber, *Ann.*, 1927, **454**, 219.

6-Nitro-1 : 2-dimethylbenziminazole. Cryst. from 90% EtOH. M.p. 242°.

Phillips, *J. Chem. Soc.*, 1931, 1151.

6-Nitro-2 : 5-dimethylbenziminazole. Needles + H_2O from H_2O. M.p. 201–2°. Very sol. EtOH, Et_2O, Me_2CO, C_6H_6. Sol. hot H_2O.

Maron, Salzberg, *Ber.*, 1911, **44**, 2999.
Niementowsky, *Ber.*, 1896, **19**, 724.
Ladenburg, *Ber.*, 1875, **8**, 677.

7-Nitro-2 : 5-dimethylbenziminazole. Needles. M.p. 246°. Sol. EtOH. Spar. sol. Et_2O.

Bankiewicz, *Ber.*, 1888, **21**, 2402.

5-Nitro-2 : 7-dimethylbenziminazole. Cryst. from hot H_2O. M.p. 186°. Sol. EtOH. Spar. sol. cold H_2O. Sol. dil. HCl. Cold dil. NaOH ⟶ yellow sol.

Kym, Ringer, *Ber.*, 1915, **48**, 1675.

6-Nitro-4 : 7-dimethylbenziminazole. Pale yellow needles from 50% EtOH. M.p. 221°. Sol. EtOH, AcOH. Spar. sol. C_6H_6, pet. ether. Sol. bases with yellow col.

Fries, Noll, *Ann.*, 1912, **389**, 375.

3-Nitro-2 : 4-dimethylbenzoic Acid (3-*Nitro*-unsym.-m-*xylylic acid*)

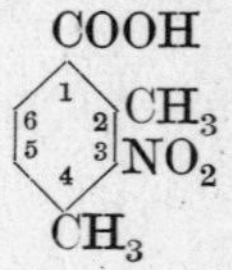

$C_9H_9O_4N$ MW, 195

Yellow prisms from EtOH. M.p. 179° (135°). Sol. EtOH. Spar. sol. hot H_2O, C_6H_6.

Amide: $C_9H_{10}O_3N_2$. MW, 194. Plates from H_2O. M.p. 138°.

Nitrile: $C_9H_8O_2N_2$. MW, 176. M.p. 120–1°.

Wheeler, Hoffman, *Am. Chem. J.*, 1911, **45**, 441.
Borsche, *Ann.*, 1912, **386**, 366.

5-Nitro-2 : 4-dimethylbenzoic Acid.

Needles from H_2O. M.p. 197·5–198·5°. Sol. EtOH, Et_2O, $CHCl_3$, CS_2. Spar. sol. H_2O.

Et ester: $C_{11}H_{13}O_4N$. MW, 223. Needles from EtOH.Aq. M.p. 75–6°.

Amide: m.p. 183°.

Nitrile: $C_9H_8O_2N_2$. MW, 176. Needles from EtOH. M.p. 108–9°.

Fisher, Walling, *J. Am. Chem. Soc.*, 1935, **57**, 1701.
Ahrens, *Ann.*, 1892, **271**, 18.
Borsche, *Ann.*, 1912, **386**, 366.

6-Nitro-2 : 4-dimethylbenzoic Acid.

Yellow needles. M.p. 180°. Sol. EtOH. Spar. sol. H_2O.

Nitrile: yellow needles from H_2O or EtOH. M.p. 126°. Volatile in steam.

Kalle, D.R.P., 239,092, (*Chem. Zentr.*, 1911, II, 1292).

4-Nitro-2 : 5-dimethylbenzoic Acid

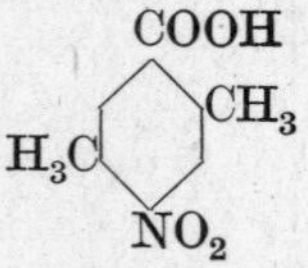

$C_9H_9O_4N$ MW, 195

Cryst. from ligroin. M.p. 165·5–166·5°.

Nitrile: cryst. from EtOH. M.p. 160–1°. Sublimes.

Fisher, Walling, *J. Am. Chem. Soc.*, 1935, **57**, 1702.

2-Nitro-3 : 5-dimethylbenzoic Acid (2-*Nitro*-sym.-m-*xylylic acid, 2-nitromesitylenic acid*)

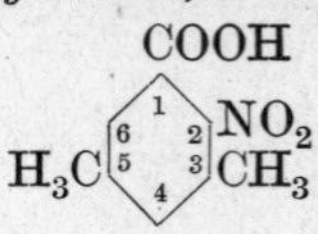

$C_9H_9O_4N$ MW, 195

Needles from hot H_2O. M.p. 210–12°. Sol. hot H_2O. Spar. sol. cold H_2O.

Et ester: $C_{11}H_{13}O_4N$. MW, 223. Plates from EtOH. M.p. 65–6°. Sol. EtOH. Insol. H_2O.

Schmitz, *Ann.*, 1878, **193**, 162, 167.

4-Nitro-3 : 5-dimethylbenzoic Acid (4-*Nitro*-sym.-m-*xylylic acid, 4-nitromesitylenic acid*).

Prisms from H_2O or dil. alc. sol. M.p. 179° (174–6°). Cryst. from conc. alc. sol. M.p. 214–20° (223°): latter on recryst. from H_2O $\longrightarrow$ former (m.p. 179°).

Et ester: prisms from EtOH. M.p. 72°. Sol. EtOH. Insol. H_2O.

Jacobsen, *Ber.*, 1878, **11**, 2054.
Fittig, Brueckner, *Ann.*, 1868, **147**, 48.
Wheeler, Hoffman, *Am. Chem. J.*, 1910, **44**, 119.
Schmitz, *Ann.*, 1878, **193**, 162, 167.

3-Nitro-2 : 4-dimethylbenzophenone

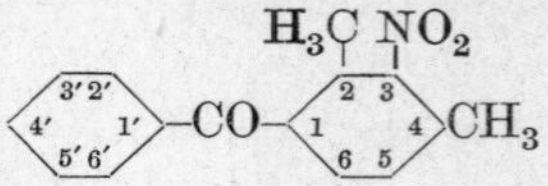

$C_{15}H_{13}O_3N$ MW, 255

Brown prisms from MeOH. M.p. 79·5–80°. Sol. usual org. solvents. Spar. sol. H_2O.

Chardonnens, *Helv. Chim. Acta*, 1929, **12**, 659.

5-Nitro-2 : 4-dimethylbenzophenone.

Yellowish prisms from MeOH. M.p. 62–3°. Sol. usual org. solvents. Spar. sol. H_2O.

See previous reference.

3′-Nitro-2 : 4-dimethylbenzophenone.

Yellowish leaflets from EtOH. M.p. 64°. Sol. hot EtOH, Me_2CO, C_6H_6, AcOH, CS_2.

Oxime: cryst. from ligroin. M.p. 131–49°. Sol. Me_2CO, Et_2O, $CHCl_3$. Less sol. EtOH, C_6H_6, CS_2. Spar. sol. ligroin.

Limpricht, Falkenberg, *Ann.*, 1895, **286**, 333.

3′-Nitro-2 : 5-dimethylbenzophenone.

Needles from EtOH. M.p. 97–8°.

Limpricht, Falkenberg, *Ann.*, 1895, **286**, 341.

3'-Nitro-3 : 4-dimethylbenzophenone.
Yellow plates from EtOH. M.p. 100°. Sol. neutral solvents.

Limpricht, Falkenberg, *Ann.*, 1895, **286**, 339.

Nitrodimethylcarbostyril.
See Nitrohydroxydimethylquinoline.
Nitrodimethyldiphenyl.
See Nitroditolyl.
Nitrodimethyldiphenyl Ether.
See Nitroditolyl Ether.
2-Nitro-4 : 4'-dimethyldiphenylamine

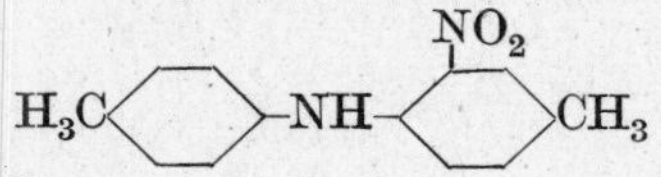

$C_{14}H_{14}O_2N_2$ MW, 242

Red plates from EtOH. M.p. 85°. Sol. most org. solvents.

Lellmann, *Ber.*, 1882, **15**, 831.

3-Nitro-2 : 5-dimethylfuran

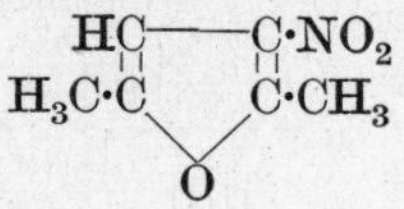

$C_6H_7O_3N$ MW, 141

Liq. B.p. 105–10°/22 mm., 88–92°/9 mm. D^{25} 1·25. n_D^{20} 1·3140.

Gilman, Burtner, *Rec. trav. chim.*, 1932, **51**, 670.

5-Nitro-2 : 4-dimethyl-β-furoic Acid (5-*Nitro*-2 : 4-*dimethylfuran*-3-*carboxylic acid*)

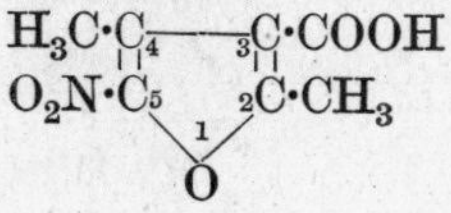

$C_7H_7O_5N$ MW, 185

Cryst. M.p. 182°.

Gilman, Burtner, *Rec. trav. chim.*, 1932, **51**, 667.

4-Nitro-2 : 5-dimethyl-β-furoic Acid (4-*Nitro*-2 : 5-*dimethylfuran*-3-*carboxylic acid*).
Cryst. M.p. 176°.
Et ester: $C_9H_{11}O_5N$. MW, 213. Liq. B.p. 119–20°/20 mm.

See previous reference.

4-Nitro-5 : 6-dimethylindazole

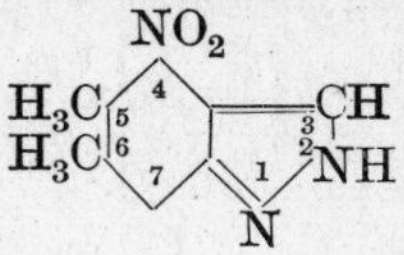

$C_9H_9O_2N_3$ MW, 191

Leaflets from C_6H_6–ligroin. M.p. 204°. Sol. hot C_6H_6. Insol. H_2O, ligroin. Sol. alkalis with dark yellow col.

Noelting, *Ber.*, 1904, **37**, 2596.

7-Nitro-5 : 6-dimethylindazole.
Pale yellow needles from C_6H_6. M.p. 180·5–181·5°. Sol. conc. alkalis with orange col.

See previous reference.

4-(or **6-**)**Nitro-2 : 3-dimethylindole**

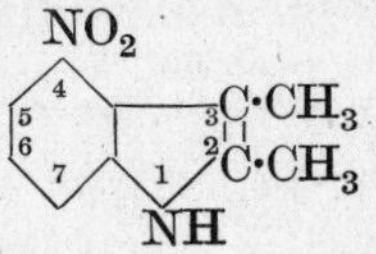

$C_{10}H_{10}O_2N_2$ MW, 190

Orange-red needles from ligroin, m.p. 126°; orange prisms from EtOH, m.p. 142°.
N-*Acetyl*: pale yellow needles from EtOH. M.p. 170°.

Bauer, Strauss, *Ber.*, 1932, **65**, 313.
Plant, Tomlinson, *J. Chem. Soc.*, 1933, 958.

5-Nitro-2 : 3-dimethylindole.
Orange prisms from EtOH, yellow prisms from ligroin. M.p. 188–9° (186°).

See previous references.

7-Nitro-2 : 3-dimethylindole.
Golden-yellow leaflets from ligroin. M.p. 164°.

Bauer, Strauss, *Ber.*, 1932, **65**, 313.

1-Nitro-2 : 6-dimethylnaphthalene

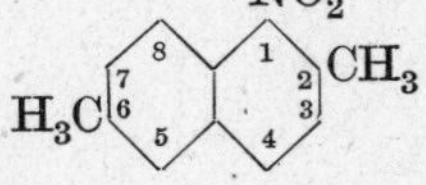

$C_{12}H_{11}O_2N$ MW, 201

Yellow leaflets from AcOH. M.p. 68°.

Mayer, Alken, *Ber.*, 1922, **55**, 2278.

4-Nitro-2 : 6-dimethylnaphthalene.
Yellow needles from MeOH. M.p. 84–5°.

Veselý, Štursa, *Chem. Zentr.*, 1933, I, 3078.

4-(or 6-)Nitro-3 : 3-dimethyloxindole

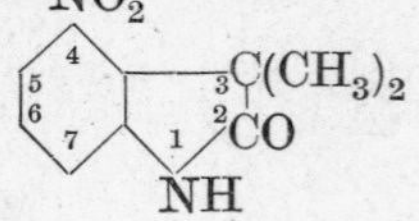

$C_{10}H_{10}O_3N_2$ MW, 206

Cryst. from EtOH. M.p. 167°.

Brunner *et al.*, *Monatsh.*, 1931, **58**, 369.

5-Nitro-3 : 3-dimethyloxindole.

Yellowish-red leaflets from EtOH. M.p. 262°. Sublimes at 190–220°/8 mm. Mod. sol. boiling EtOH.

N-*Me*: $C_{11}H_{12}O_3N_2$. MW, 220. Needles from EtOH. M.p. 203–4° (201–2°).

See previous reference.

7-Nitro-3 : 3-dimethyloxindole.

Yellow needles from EtOH. M.p. 194°. Sublimes at 145–60°/10–13 mm.

See previous reference.

2-Nitro-3 : 5-dimethylphenylacetic Acid

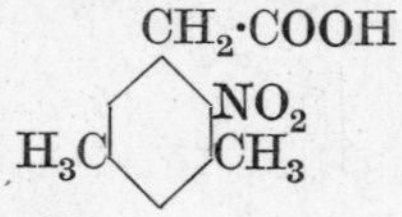

$C_{10}H_{11}O_4N$ MW, 209

Needles from H_2O. M.p. 139°. Sol. EtOH, Et_2O. Mod. sol. hot H_2O.

Wispek, *Ber.*, 1883, **16**, 1579.

Nitrodimethylphenylenediamine.

See Nitrodiaminoxylene.

8-Nitro-2 : 6-dimethylquinoline (8-*Nitro-6-methylquinaldine*)

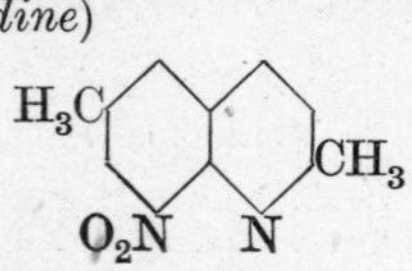

$C_{11}H_{10}O_2N_2$ MW, 202

Orange needles from EtOH. M.p. 114°. Sol. hot EtOH. Insol. H_2O.

B,HCl: grey powder.

Bartow, McCollum, *J. Am. Chem. Soc.*, 1904, **26**, 702.

5-Nitro-6 : 8-dimethylquinoline

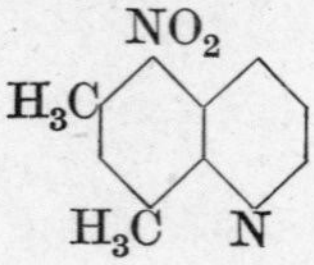

$C_{11}H_{10}O_2N_2$ MW, 202

Yellowish needles from EtOH. M.p. 107–8°. Sol. usual solvents. Insol. cold H_2O. Spar. volatile in steam.

Noelting, Trautmann, *Ber.*, 1890, **23**, 3681.

4-Nitro-*N*-dimethyl-*o*-toluidine

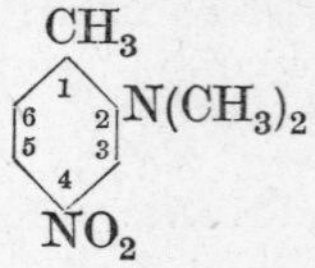

$C_9H_{12}O_2N_2$ MW, 180

Yellowish-red oil. F.p. 15° (14°). B.p. 184°/77 mm., 178°/40 mm., 160°/16 mm. Sol. most org. solvents.

B,HCl: yellow plates. M.p. 197° (192°) decomp.

Methiodide: golden-yellow needles or prisms from H_2O. M.p. 195° (rapid heat.).

Methonitrate: yellowish needles. M.p. 230–5°.

Methochloroaurate: yellow leaflets. M.p. 226° decomp.

Methochloroplatinate: orange prisms. M.p. about 233° decomp.

Methopicrate: yellow needles from H_2O. M.p. about 202°.

Gnehm, Blumer, *Ann.*, 1899, **304**, 107.
Vorländer, Siebert, *Ber.*, 1919, **52**, 300.

5-Nitro-*N*-dimethyl-*o*-toluidine.

Leaflets or plates from EtOH. M.p. 47·5°. Very sol. EtOH, Et_2O. Mod. sol. dil. H_2SO_4.

Bernthsen, *Ber.*, 1892, **25**, 3133.

6-Nitro-*N*-dimethyl-*o*-toluidine.

Golden-yellow cryst. from Et_2O. M.p. 25–25·5°. B.p. 191–2°/100 mm. Sol. EtOH, Et_2O.

v. Tatschalow, *J. prakt. Chem.*, 1902, **65**, 240.

5-Nitro-*N*-dimethyl-*m*-toluidine

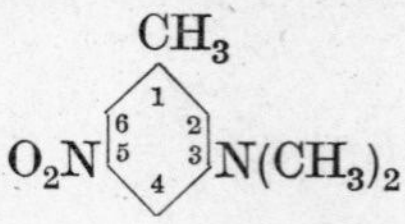

$C_9H_{12}O_2N_2$ MW, 180

Rhombic cryst. from H_2O. M.p. 52°. Spar. sol. H_2O. Volatile in steam.

Haibach, *J. prakt. Chem.*, 1902, **65**, 244.

6-Nitro-*N*-dimethyl-*m*-toluidine.

Yellow needles from EtOH.Aq. M.p. 84°.

Methiodide: yellow needles from H_2O. M.p. 165°.

Methonitrate: prisms from EtOH. M.p. 195° decomp.

Methopicrate: yellow needles or prisms from EtOH. M.p. 205°.

Vorländer, Siebert, *Ber.*, 1919, **52**, 303.

2-Nitro-*N*-dimethyl-*p*-toluidine

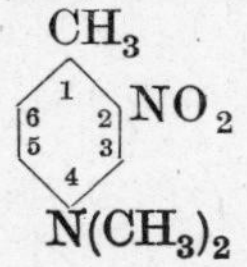

$C_9H_{12}O_2N_2$ MW, 180

Orange-red prisms from EtOH. M.p. 38° (35°). Sol. Et_2O, Me_2CO, C_6H_6. Spar. sol. cold EtOH. Insol. H_2O. Volatile in steam.

Picrate: yellow prisms. M.p. 147°. Spar. sol. H_2O, EtOH.

Methiodide: yellowish prisms. M.p. 195°.

Methobromide: yellow prisms from EtOH. M.p. 192°.

Methonitrate: cryst. from EtOH. M.p. 205–20° decomp.

Methopicrate: yellow needles. M.p. 203°.

Haibach, *J. prakt. Chem.*, 1902, **65**, 248.
Vorländer, Siebert, *Ber.*, 1919, **52**, 307.

3-Nitro-*N*-dimethyl-*p*-toluidine.
Cryst. from MeOH. M.p. 24·5–25°.

Pinnow, *Ber.*, 1895, **28**, 3041.

4-Nitrodiphenic Acid (*4-Nitrodiphenyl-2 : 2′-dicarboxylic acid*)

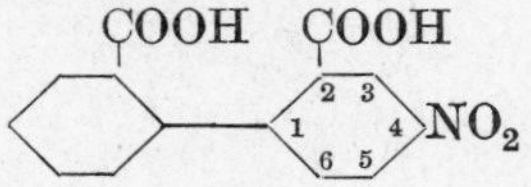

$C_{14}H_9O_6N$ MW, 287

Needles from H_2O. M.p. 217° (214–16°). Sol. EtOH, Et_2O. Mod. sol. hot H_2O, C_6H_6. Spar. sol. cold H_2O. Conc. H_2SO_4 at 155° $\longrightarrow$ 7-nitrofluorenone-4-carboxylic acid.

Dichloride: $C_{14}H_7O_4NCl_2$. MW, 324. Yellow cryst. from C_6H_6–pet. ether. M.p. 90–2°.

Anhydride: $C_{14}H_7O_5N$. MW, 269. Needles from Ac_2O. M.p. 207–207·5° (205–7°).

2-(or 2′)-*Nitrile*: prisms from AcOH. M.p. 194–5°. *Me ester*: needles from AcOH. M.p. 123–4°.

Bell, Robinson, *J. Chem. Soc.*, 1927, 1697, 2238.
Moore, Huntress, *J. Am. Chem. Soc.*, 1927, **49**, 1328.
Strasburger, *Ber.*, 1883, **16**, 2347.
Schmidt, Austin, *Ber.*, 1903, **36**, 3733.
Werner, Piguet, *Ber.*, 1904, **37**, 4313.

5-Nitrodiphenic Acid (*5-Nitrodiphenyl-2 : 2′-dicarboxylic acid*).

Plates from H_2O. M.p. 268°. Sol. MeOH, EtOH, Et_2O. Mod. sol. hot H_2O, C_6H_6. Spar. sol. cold H_2O. H_2SO_4 at 160° $\longrightarrow$ 6(?)-nitrofluorenone-4-carboxylic acid.

Anhydride: cryst. from Ac_2O. M.p. 193–5°.

Schmidt, Austin, *Ber.*, 1903, **36**, **3734**.
Bell, Robinson, *J. Chem. Soc.*, 1927, 2238.

6-Nitrodiphenic Acid (*6-Nitrodiphenyl-2 : 2′-dicarboxylic acid*).

d-.

$[\alpha]_{5461}$ + 65·2° in EtOH. Racemised by boiling Ac_2O. $H_2SO_4 \longrightarrow$ 5-nitrofluorenone-4-carboxylic acid.

l-.

$[\alpha]_{5461}$ − 66·4° in EtOH. Racemised by boiling Ac_2O.

dl-.

Cryst. M.p. 248–50° decomp. Sol. EtOH, Et_2O, Me_2CO, AcOH. Spar. sol. C_6H_6, $CHCl_3$, ligroin. $H_2SO_4 \longrightarrow$ 5-nitrofluorenone-4-carboxylic acid.

Dichloride: yellow powder. M.p. 87°.

Schmidt, Kämpf, *Ber.*, 1903, **36**, **3737**.
Bell, Robinson, *J. Chem. Soc.*, 1927, 1696, 2236.

2-Nitrodiphenyl

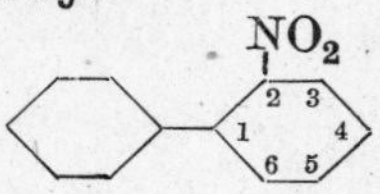

$C_{12}H_9O_2N$ MW, 199

Plates from EtOH. M.p. 37°. B.p. 320°, 200–5°/30 mm., 165–70°/13 mm., 160–6°/4 mm. Sol. EtOH, Et_2O. Insol. H_2O. Sn + HCl $\longrightarrow$ 2-aminodiphenyl. $HNO_3 \longrightarrow$ 2 : 4′- + 2 : 2′-dinitrodiphenyl.

Hübner, *Ann.*, 1881, **209**, 341.
Bell, Kenyon, Robinson, *J. Chem. Soc.*, 1926, 1242.
Jenkins, McCullough, Booth, *Ind. Eng. Chem.*, 1930, **22**, 32.
Morgan, Walls, *J. Soc. Chem. Ind.*, 1930, **49**, 15T.
I.G., F.P., 764,374, (*Chem. Abstracts*, 1934, **28**, 5476).

3-Nitrodiphenyl.

Yellow plates or needles from dil. EtOH. M.p. 62° (58·5°). Sol. EtOH, AcOH, ligroin. Volatile in steam. $CrO_3 \longrightarrow$ *m*-nitrobenzoic acid. Sn + HCl ⟶ 3-aminodiphenyl. HNO_3 ⟶ 3 : 4′- + 3 : 2′-dinitrodiphenyl.

Jacobson, Loeb, *Ber.*, 1903, **36**, 4083.
Fichter, Sulzberger, *Ber.*, 1904, **37**, 882.
Blakey, Scarborough, *J. Chem. Soc.*, 1927, 3003.

4-Nitrodiphenyl.

Yellow needles from EtOH. M.p. 114–114·5°. B.p. 223–4°/30 mm. Sol. Et_2O, $CHCl_3$. Mod. sol. EtOH. CrO_3 ⟶ *p*-nitrobenzoic acid. Sn + HCl ⟶ 4-aminodiphenyl. HNO_3 ⟶ 4 : 4′- + 2 : 4′-dinitrodiphenyl.

Hübner, *Ann.*, 1881, **209**, 340.
Bamberger, *Ber.*, 1895, **28**, 404.
Bell, Kenyon, Robinson, *J. Chem. Soc.*, 1926, 1242.
Jenkins, McCullough, Booth, *Ind. Eng. Chem.*, 1930, **22**, 32.
Morgan, Walls, *J. Soc. Chem. Ind.*, 1930, **49**, 15T.

2-Nitrodiphenylamine

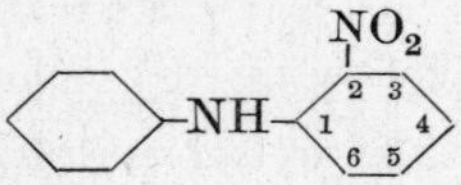

$C_{12}H_{10}O_2N_2$ MW, 214

Orange plates from EtOH.Aq. M.p. 75·5°.

N-*Nitroso*: plates from MeOH. M.p. 99–100°. Hot 3% alc. H_2SO_4 ⟶ 2-nitrodiphenylamine.

Ullmann, Nadai, *Ber.*, 1908, **41**, 1872.
Ullmann, D.R.P., 194,951, (*Chem. Zentr.*, 1908, I, 1115).

3-Nitrodiphenylamine.

Red plates from EtOH.Aq. M.p. 114°. Sol. EtOH, Et_2O, C_6H_6. Spar. sol. ligroin. Conc. H_2SO_4 + HNO_3 ⟶ violet col.

N-*Nitroso*: needles. M.p. 89–90°.

Ullmann, *Ann.*, 1907, **355**, 331.

4-Nitrodiphenylamine.

Yellow needles. M.p. 133°. Sol. EtOH, AcOH. Conc. H_2SO_4 ⟶ violet sol. ⟶ blue on adding HNO_3. 1% NaOH ⟶ intense red sol.

N-*Nitroso*: needles from AcOH. M.p. 133·5° (130°).

Lellmann, *Ber.*, 1882, **15**, 826.
Goldberg, D.R.P., 187,870, (*Chem. Zentr.*, 1907, II, 1465).

4-Nitrodiphenylamine-2-carboxylic Acid

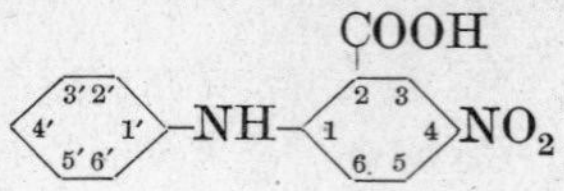

$C_{13}H_{10}O_4N_2$ MW, 258

Yellow needles from EtOH. M.p. 247–8°. Sublimes.

Et ester: $C_{15}H_{14}O_4N_2$. MW, 286. Yellow plates from EtOH. M.p. 121°.

Anilide: $C_{19}H_{15}O_3N_3$. MW, 333. Yellow cryst. from EtOH. M.p. 159°.

Schöpff, *Ber.*, 1890, **23**, 3441.
Grohmann, *Ber.*, 1891, **24**, 3810.

5 - Nitrodiphenylamine - 2 - carboxylic Acid.

Orange-yellow needles from toluene. M.p. 230°. Mod. sol. EtOH, C_6H_6. Spar. sol. ligroin.

Ullmann, Wagner, *Ann.*, 1907, **355**, 363.

2 - Nitrodiphenylamine - 4 - carboxylic Acid.

Red needles from EtOH. M.p. 254°. Sol. EtOH, Me_2CO, $CHCl_3$. Mod. sol. C_6H_6. Insol. ligroin.

Me ester: $C_{14}H_{12}O_4N_2$. MW, 272. Cryst. M.p. 127°.

Et ester: $C_{15}H_{14}O_4N_2$. MW, 286. Cryst. M.p. 123°. Sol. Me_2CO, C_6H_6, $CHCl_3$. Spar. sol. ligroin.

Amide: $C_{13}H_{11}O_3N_3$. MW, 257. Yellow needles from EtOH. M.p. 157°.

Anilide: $C_{19}H_{15}O_3N_3$. MW, 333. Red needles from EtOH. M.p. 215–16°. Sol. EtOH, $CHCl_3$, C_6H_6, Me_2CO, AcOH. Insol. ligroin.

Schöpff, *Ber.*, 1889, **22**, 3282; 1890, **23**, 3443.
Grohmann, *Ber.*, 1890, **23**, 3450.

4-Nitrodiphenylamine-2-sulphonic Acid

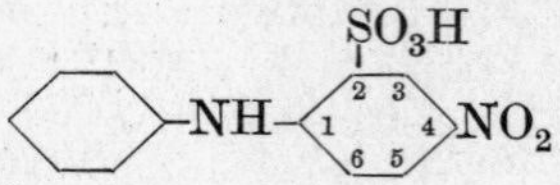

$C_{12}H_{10}O_5N_2S$ MW, 294

Olive-green leaflets from HCl. Very sol. H_2O, EtOH.

Chloride: $C_{12}H_9O_4N_2ClS$. MW, 312·5. Greenish-yellow needles from Et_2O. M.p. 102–4°. Sol. Et_2O, C_6H_6, $CHCl_3$.

Amide: $C_{12}H_{11}O_4N_3S$. MW, 293. Reddish-yellow cryst. from EtOH. M.p. 173°. Insol. H_2O.

Anilide: $C_{18}H_{15}O_4N_3S$. MW, 369. Greenish-ellow needles from EtOH. M.p. 164°.

Fischer, *Ber.*, 1891, **24**, 3798.
Ullmann, Dahmen, *Ber.*, 1908, **41**, 3746.

2-Nitrodiphenylamine-4-sulphonic Acid. Orange cryst. from H_2O. Decomp. at 220°.
Amide: red cryst. from EtOH. M.p. 162°.
Anilide: orange-yellow needles from EtOH. .p. 157°. Sol. EtOH, Me_2CO, AcOH.

Fischer, *Ber.*, 1891, **24**, 3791.

5-Nitrodiphenyl-2-carboxylic Acid

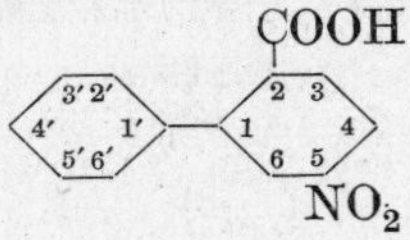

$_{13}H_9O_4N$ MW, 243

Nitrile: m.p. 132–4°.

Jones, Braker, U.S.Ps., 1,922,206, 1,922,207, (*Chem. Abstracts*, 1933, **27**, 5087).

6-Nitrodiphenyl-2-carboxylic Acid. Needles from 50% AcOH. M.p. 187–8°.

Sadler, Powell, *J. Am. Chem. Soc.*, 1934, **56**, 2652.

2′-Nitrodiphenyl-2-carboxylic Acid. Needles from $CHCl_3$. M.p. 168° (165–166·5°).
Brucine salt: nodules from Me_2CO. M.p. 18° decomp. $[\alpha]_D - 20{\cdot}7°$ in $CHCl_3$.
Quinidine salt: needles from EtOH. M.p. 96–8°. $[\alpha]_D + 136°$ in $CHCl_3$.
Strychnine salt: needles from EtOH. M.p. 16°. $[\alpha]_D - 25°$ in $CHCl_3$.

Bell, *J. Chem. Soc.*, 1934, 838.
See also previous reference.

4′-Nitrodiphenyl-2-carboxylic Acid. Needles from EtOH. M.p. 222–5°. Sol. hot EtOH. Prac. insol. H_2O.

Kühling, *Ber.*, 1895, **28**, 525; 1896, **29**, 166.
Grieve, Hey, *J. Chem. Soc.*, 1932, 1891 (*Footnote*).
Schmitz, *Ann.*, 1878, **193**, 123.

6-Nitrodiphenyl-3-carboxylic Acid

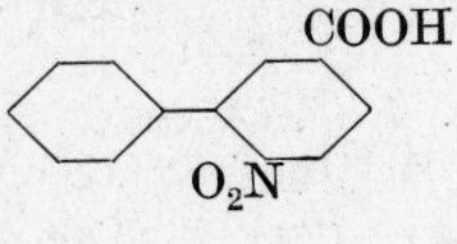

$C_{13}H_9O_4N$ MW, 243

M.p. 227°. Sublimes. (The above structure is the most probable but has not been definitely established.)

Wardner, Lowy, *J. Am. Chem. Soc.*, 1932, **54**, 2513.

2-Nitrodiphenyl-4-carboxylic Acid

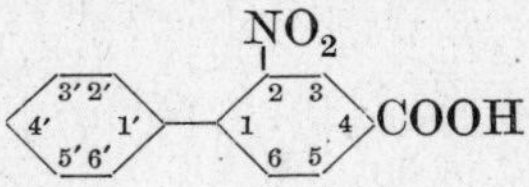

$C_{13}H_9O_4N$ MW, 243

Pale yellow needles from EtOH. M.p. 191°.

Grieve, Hey, *J. Chem. Soc.*, 1932, 1894.

2′-Nitrodiphenyl-4-carboxylic Acid. Needles from EtOH. M.p. 250°.

Grieve, Hey, *J. Chem. Soc.*, 1932, 1892; 1933, 970.

4′-Nitrodiphenyl-4-carboxylic Acid. Needles from EtOH. M.p. 344–6° (340°). Prac. insol. pet. ether, C_6H_6. $HNO_3 \longrightarrow$ 2 : 4′-dinitrodiphenyl-4-carboxylic acid.
Et ester: $C_{15}H_{13}O_4N$. MW, 271. Yellow needles from dil. EtOH. M.p. 112°.
Chloride: $C_{13}H_8O_3NCl$. MW, 261·5. M.p. 194°.

Grieve, Hey, *J. Chem. Soc.*, 1932, 1891; 1933, 971.
I.G., F.P., 735,846, (*Chem. Abstracts*, 1933, **27**, 1001); E.P., 390,556, (*Chem. Abstracts*, 1933, **27**, 4936).

Nitrodiphenyl-2 : 2′-dicarboxylic Acid. *See* Nitrodiphenic Acid.

1-Nitrodiphenylene oxide (1-*Nitrodibenzfuran*)

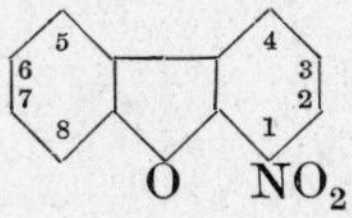

$C_{12}H_7O_3N$ MW, 213

Yellow needles from EtOH. M.p. about 110°. B.p. 190–205°/15 mm.

Borsche, Schacke, *Ber.*, 1923, **56**, 2500.
Ryan, Keane, M'Gahon, *Chem. Abstracts*, 1928, **22**, 70.

2-Nitrodiphenylene oxide (2-*Nitrodibenzfuran*).
Yellowish needles from AcOH. M.p. 181–2°. Spar. sol. hot EtOH.

Borsche, Bothe, *Ber.*, 1908, **41**, 1940.
Cullinane, *J. Chem. Soc.*, 1930, 2267.

3-Nitrodiphenylene oxide (3-*Nitrodibenzfuran*).

Needles from EtOH. M.p. 141°.

Ryan, Keane, M'Gahon, *Chem. Abstracts*, 1928, **22**, 70.

2-Nitrodiphenyl Ether

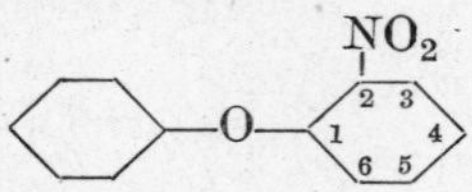

$C_{12}H_9O_3N$ MW, 215

Yellow liq. B.p. 235°/60 mm. part decomp., 195–7°/45 mm., 183–5°/8 mm. Sol. EtOH, Et_2O, $CHCl_3$, AcOH, C_6H_6. Spar. sol. ligroin. Insol. H_2O. D^{15} 1·258, $D^{21 \cdot 5}$ 1·2539. n_D^{20} 1·575. $SnCl_2 \longrightarrow$ 2-aminodiphenyl ether.

Haeussermann, Teichmann, *Ber.*, 1896, **29**, 1447.
Ullmann, *ibid.*, 1880.
Jones, Cook, *J. Am. Chem. Soc.*, 1916, **38**, 1537.
Lock, *Monatsh.*, 1930, **55**, 177.
Brewster, Groening, *Organic Syntheses*, 1934, XIV, 67.

3-Nitrodiphenyl Ether.

Yellow liq. B.p. 337°/758 mm. part decomp., 202–4°/14 mm. D^{15} 1·2451.

Ullmann, Sponagel, *Ber.*, 1905, **38**, 2212; *Ann.*, 1906, **350**, 103.
Lock, *Monatsh.*, 1930, **55**, 179.

4-Nitrodiphenyl Ether.

Plates from MeOH or Et_2O. M.p. 61° (56°). B.p. about 320°, 188–90°/8 mm. Sol. Et_2O, C_6H_6. Mod. sol. EtOH. $SnCl_2 \longrightarrow$ 4-aminodiphenyl ether.

Haeussermann, Teichmann, *Ber.*, 1896, **29**, 1446.
Mailhe, Murat, *Bull. soc. chim.*, 1912, **11**, 446.
Brewster, Groening, *Organic Syntheses*, 1934, XIV, 66.
Rarick, Brewster, Dains, *J. Am. Chem. Soc.*, 1933, **55**, 1289.
Suter, *J. Am. Chem. Soc.*, 1929, **51**, 2583.
Lock, *Monatsh.*, 1930, **55**, 182.
Raiford, Colbert, *J. Am. Chem. Soc.*, 1926, **48**, 2659.

Nitrodiphenyl Ether Carboxylic Acid.
See Nitrophenoxybenzoic Acid.

Nitrodiphenyl Ether Sulphonic Acid.
See under Nitrophenol-sulphonic Acid.

2-Nitrodiphenylmethane

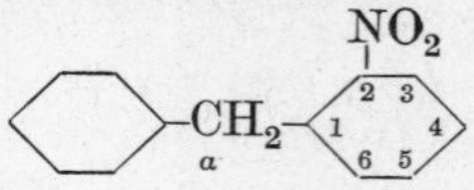

$C_{13}H_{11}O_2N$ MW, 21

Dark yellow liq. B.p. 183–4°/10 mm.

Carré, *Bull. soc. chim.*, 1909, **5**, 119.
Gabriel, Stelzner, *Ber.*, 1896, **29**, 1303.

3-Nitrodiphenylmethane.

Liq. Sol. EtOH, Et_2O, C_6H_6. Cannot b distilled. Non-volatile in steam.

Becker, *Ber.*, 1882, **15**, 2091.

4-Nitrodiphenylmethane.

Cryst. from ligroin. M.p. 31°. B.p. 202°/1 mm. Sol. EtOH, Et_2O, C_6H_6. Spar. sol ligroin. $CrO_3 \longrightarrow$ 4-nitrobenzophenone. Spar volatile in steam.

Baeyer, Villiger, *Ber.*, 1904, **37**, 605.
Basler, *Ber.*, 1883, **16**, 2716.

α-Nitrodiphenylmethane (*Diphenylnitro methane*).

Oil. D_0^0 1·1900, D_0^{20} 1·1727.

Konowalow, *Ber.*, 1896, **29**, 2197.

2-Nitrodiphenyl sulphide

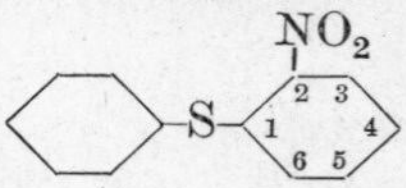

$C_{12}H_9O_2NS$ MW, 231

Yellow needles from ligroin. M.p. 80·2° (77°). Sol. EtOH, Et_2O. Insol. pet. ether Conc. $H_2SO_4 \longrightarrow$ green sol.

Bourgeois, Huber, *Bull. soc. chim.*, 1911, **9**, 947.
Mauthner, *Ber.*, 1906, **39**, 3597.

4-Nitrodiphenyl sulphide.

Pale yellow prisms from ligroin. M.p. 55°. B.p. 288·2°/100 mm., 240°/25 mm.

See first reference above and also
Kehrmann, Bauer, *Ber.*, 1896, **29**, 2364.

5-Nitrodiphenyl sulphide 2-carboxylic Acid (S-*Phenyl*-4-*nitrothiosalicylic acid*)

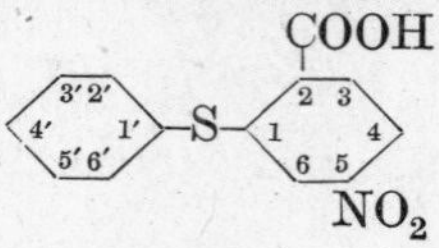

$C_{13}H_9O_4NS$ MW, 275

Yellow cryst. from AcOH. M.p. 210–11°. Sol. EtOH, AcOH. Insol. C_6H_6, ligroin.

Mayer, *Ber.*, 1909, **42**, 3066.

2'-Nitrodiphenyl sulphide 2-carboxylic cid.

Yellow cryst. from AcOH. M.p. 165–6°. par. sol. EtOH, $CHCl_3$. Insol. ligroin. PCl_5 ⟶ 4-nitrothioxanthone.

Me ester: $C_{14}H_{11}O_4NS$. MW, 289. Yellow ryst. from MeOH. M.p. 92°.

Et ester: $C_{15}H_{13}O_4NS$. MW, 303. Yellow ryst. from EtOH. M.p. 75–6°.

Mayer, *Ber.*, 1909, **42**, 3060.

3'-Nitrodiphenyl sulphide 2-carboxylic cid.

Yellow cryst. from AcOH. M.p. 168–9°. ol. hot EtOH, AcOH. Spar. sol. C_6H_6. OCl_2 + $AlCl_3$ ⟶ 1-nitrothioxanthone.

Me ester: yellow cryst. M.p. 112–14°.

Mayer, *Ber.*, 1909, **42**, 3064.

4'-Nitrodiphenyl sulphide 2-carboxylic cid.

Yellow prisms from EtOH. M.p. 229–31°. par. sol. hot EtOH, AcOH. Insol. H_2O, HCl_3, C_6H_6, ligroin. Sol. alkalis ⟶ deep ed sols. PCl_5 ⟶ 2-nitrothioxanthone.

Me ester: yellow cryst. from MeOH. M.p. 31·5°.

Et ester: yellow needles from EtOH. M.p. 27°.

Mayer, *Ber.*, 1909, **42**, 3050.

2-Nitrodiphenyl sulphone

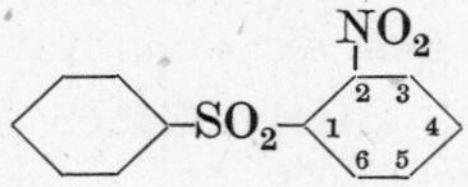

$C_{12}H_9O_4NS$ MW, 263

Cryst. from EtOH. M.p. 147·5°. Sol. warm EtOH, C_6H_6, AcOH. Insol. H_2O.

Ullmann, Pasdermadjian, *Ber.*, 1901, **34**, 1153.
Bourgeois, Huber, *Bull. soc. chim.*, 1911, **9**, 947.

3-Nitrodiphenyl sulphone.

Needles from EtOH. M.p. 80·5–81°.

Olivier, *Rec. trav. chim.*, 1915, **35**, 110.

4-Nitrodiphenyl sulphone.

Needles from EtOH.Aq. M.p. 143°. Sol. EtOH, C_6H_6, AcOH. Insol. Et_2O.

Ullmann, Pasdermadjian, *Ber.*, 1901, **34**, 1154.
Bourgeois, Huber, *Bull. soc. chim.*, 1911, **9**, 947.

5-Nitrodiphenyl sulphone 2-carboxylic Acid (4-*Nitro-2-phenylsulphonebenzoic acid*)

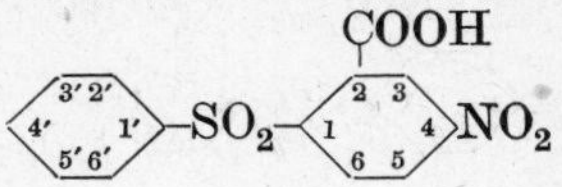

$C_{13}H_9O_6NS$ MW, 307

Needles from H_2O. M.p. 196°. Sol. Me_2CO. Spar. sol. H_2O.

Chloride: $C_{13}H_8O_5NClS$. MW, 325·5. Cryst. from $CHCl_3$. M.p. 109°. Sol. Et_2O, $CHCl_3$, C_6H_6, ligroin.

Amide: $C_{13}H_{10}O_5N_2S$. MW, 306. Prisms from EtOH. M.p. 191–2°. Sol. hot EtOH, Me_2CO. Spar. sol. H_2O, Et_2O, $CHCl_3$.

Norris, *Am. Chem. J.*, 1900, **24**, 483.

2'-Nitrodiphenyl sulphone 2-carboxylic Acid.

Needles. M.p. 197–9°. Sol. EtOH, AcOH. Spar. sol. H_2O.

Me ester: $C_{14}H_{11}O_6NS$. MW, 321. Needles from MeOH. M.p. 127°.

Mayer, *Ber.*, 1909, **42**, 3061.

3'-Nitrodiphenyl sulphone 2-carboxylic Acid.

Cryst. from AcOH. M.p. 190°.

Mayer, *Ber.*, 1909, **42**, 3065.

4'-Nitrodiphenyl sulphone 2-carboxylic Acid.

Yellow cryst. from AcOH. M.p. 196·5°. Sol. EtOH, AcOH. Spar. sol. C_6H_6.

Me ester: yellow needles from MeOH. M.p. 136°.

Et ester: $C_{15}H_{13}O_6NS$. MW, 335. Cryst. from EtOH. M.p. 101°.

Mayer, *Ber.*, 1909, **42**, 3053.

2-Nitrodiphenyl sulphone 4-carboxylic Acid (3-*Nitro-4-phenylsulphonebenzoic acid*).

Yellowish cryst. from EtOH. M.p. 255–60°. Sol. EtOH, AcOH. Insol. C_6H_6.

Ullmann, Pasdermadjian, *Ber.*, 1901, **34**, 1155.

4'-Nitrodiphenyl-4-sulphonic Acid

$C_{12}H_9O_5NS$ MW, 279

Et ester: $C_{14}H_{13}O_5NS$. MW, 307. M.p. 168–9°.

Chloride: $C_{12}H_8O_4NClS$. MW, 297·5. Needles from AcOH. M.p. 178°.

Amide: $C_{12}H_{10}O_4N_2S$. MW, 278. M.p. 228°.

Gabriel, Dambergis, *Ber.*, 1880, **13**, 1408.

2′-Nitrodiphenyl sulphoxide 2-carboxylic Acid

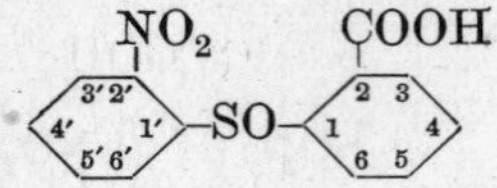

$C_{13}H_9O_5NS$ MW, 291

Pale yellow leaflets from AcOH. M.p. 277°. Sol. $PhNO_2$. Spar. sol. EtOH. Insol. C_6H_6, $CHCl_3$.

Me ester: $C_{14}H_{11}O_5NS$. MW, 305. Yellowish leaflets from MeOH. M.p. 147–8°.

Et ester: $C_{15}H_{13}O_5NS$. MW, 319. Needles from ligroin. M.p. 120°.

Mayer, *Ber.*, 1909, **42**, 3060.

3′-Nitrodiphenyl sulphoxide 2-carboxylic Acid.

Yellow needles from AcOH. M.p. 223°.

Me ester: needles from AcOH. M.p. 137–8°.

See previous reference.

4′-Nitrodiphenyl sulphoxide 2-carboxylic Acid.

Pale yellow leaflets from AcOH or EtOH. M.p. 216–17°. Sol. EtOH. Less sol. AcOH.

Me ester: needles from AcOH–ligroin. M.p. 143·5°.

Et ester: cryst. from ligroin. M.p. 107–107·5°.

See previous reference.

***o*-Nitro-*N*-dipropylaniline**

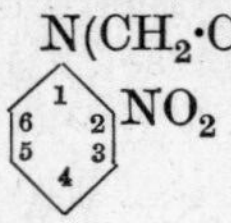

$C_{12}H_{18}O_2N_2$ MW, 222

Orange-yellow oil. Sol. most org. solvents. Spar. sol. H_2O.

B,HBr: plates. Spar. sol. EtOH.

B,HI: needles.

B,HAuCl$_4$: yellow prisms from EtOH.

Picrate: golden plates from EtOH. M.p. 93–4°.

Weissenberger, *Monatsh.*, 1912, **33**, 836.

***p*-Nitro-*N*-dipropylaniline.**

Yellowish-green cryst. M.p. 59°.

Nagornow, *Chem. Zentr.*, 1898, I, 886.

2-Nitro-4 : 4′-ditolyl (2-*Nitro*-4 : 4′-*dimethyldiphenyl*)

$C_{14}H_{13}O_2N$ MW, 227

Yellow plates from MeOH. M.p. 69–70° B.p. 220–5°/29 mm. $HNO_3 \longrightarrow$ 2 : 3′-dinitro 4 : 4′-ditoyl.

Marler, Turner, *J. Chem. Soc.*, 1932, 2393

3-Nitro-4 : 4′-ditolyl (3-*Nitro*-4 : 4′-*dimethyl diphenyl*).

Plates from MeOH. M.p. 80–1°. B.p. 220 30°/20 mm. $HNO_3 \longrightarrow$ 2 : 3′-dinitro-4 : 4′ ditolyl.

See previous reference.

2-Nitro-4 : 4′-ditolylamine (2-*Nitro*-4 : 4′ *dimethyldiphenylamine*)

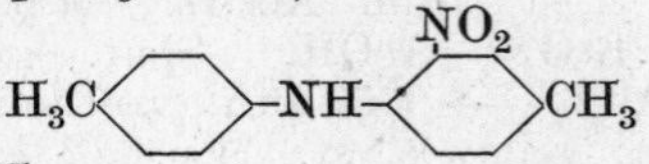

$C_{14}H_{14}O_2N_2$ MW, 24

Red leaflets from EtOH. M.p. 85°. Sol most org. solvents.

N-*Benzoyl*: yellow prisms from EtOH. M.p 167°. Sol. EtOH, AcOH.

Lellmann, *Ber.*, 1882, **15**, 831.

4-Nitro-2 : 2′-ditolyl Ether (4-*Nitro*-2 : 2′ *dimethyldiphenyl ether*)

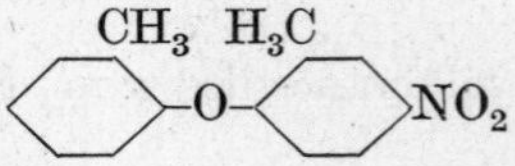

$C_{14}H_{13}O_3N$ MW, 24

Yellow needles from Et_2O. M.p. 125°. B.p about 180°/60 mm.

Mailhe, *Bull. soc. chim.*, 1913, **13**, 170.

4-Nitro-3 : 3′-ditolyl Ether (4-*Nitro*-3 : 3′ *dimethyldiphenyl ether*)

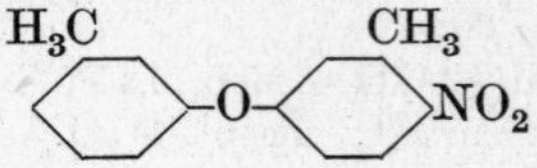

$C_{14}H_{13}O_3N$ MW, 24

M.p. 48°. B.p. 245–350°/50 mm. Sol. Et_2O.

Mailhe, *Bull. soc. chim.*, 1913, **13**, 171.

2-Nitro-4 : 4′-ditolyl Ether (2-*Nitro*-4 : 4′ *dimethyldiphenyl ether*)

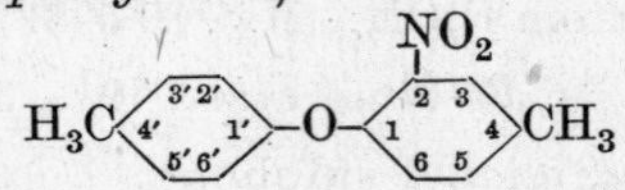

$C_{14}H_{13}O_3N$ MW, 24

Prisms from EtOH. M.p. 50°. B.p. 220°/1 mm. Sol. Et_2O, $CHCl_3$, C_6H_6. Mod. sol. EtOH pet. ether.

Reilly, Drumm, Barrett, *J. Chem. Soc.* 1927, 72.

3-Nitro-4 : 4′-ditolyl Ether (3-*Nitro*-4 : 4′-*dimethyldiphenyl ether*).

B.p. 206°/11 mm. Sol. Et_2O, C_6H_6. Less sol. EtOH. Insol. H_2O.

Reilly, Barrett, *J. Chem. Soc.*, 1927, 1399.

Nitrodulcitol.

See under Dulcitol.

3-Nitrodurene (3-*Nitro*-1 : 2 : 4 : 5-*tetramethylbenzene*)

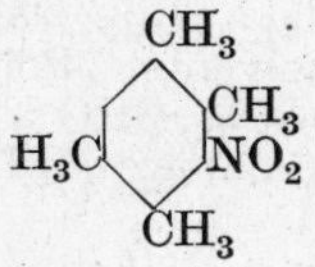

$C_{10}H_{13}O_2N$ MW, 179

Pale yellow prisms from EtOH. M.p. 112–13°.

Smith, Taylor, *J. Am. Chem. Soc.*, 1935, **57**, 2463.

ω-Nitrodurene (1′-*Nitro*-1 : 2 : 4 : 5-*tetramethylbenzene*)

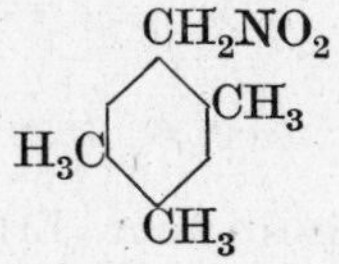

$C_{10}H_{13}O_2N$ MW, 179

Prisms from MeOH, AcOH or pet. ether. M.p. 52·5°. B.p. 143–4°/10 mm. Very sol. EtOH, Et_2O, C_6H_6, $CHCl_3$. Sweet odour. Spar. volatile in steam.

Willstätter, Kubli, *Ber.*, 1909, **42**, 4154.

4-Nitrodurenol (4-*Nitro*-2 : 3 : 5 : 6-*tetramethylphenol*)

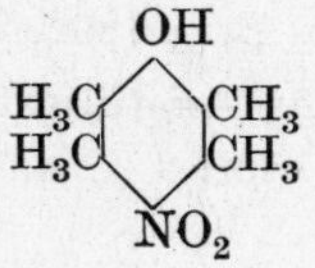

$C_{10}H_{13}O_3N$ MW, 195

Cryst. from EtOH. M.p. 130°. Very sol. EtOH.

Jacobsen, Schnapauff, *Ber.*, 1885, **18**, 2844.

Nitroerythritol.

See under meso-Erythritol.

Nitroethane.

(i) $CH_3{\cdot}CH_2NO_2$ (ii) $CH_3{\cdot}CH{:}NO_2H$

$C_2H_5O_2N$ MW, 75

Probably a mixture of (i) and (ii) (*aci-nitroethane, isonitroethane*). Metallic derivs. of (ii) are known.

B.p. 114–114·8°. D_4^4 1·0685, D_{25}^{25} 1·0461, $D_4^{24\cdot3}$ 1·0472. Non-misc. with H_2O. $n_\gamma^{24\cdot3}$ 1·40102. Heat of comb. C_p (vapour) 322·3 Cal., C_v 322·45 Cal. Sol. alkalis with salt formation. Fe + AcOH ⟶ ethylamine.

Na salt: white powder. Very sol. H_2O. Spar. sol. EtOH.

Neogi, Chowdhuri, *J. Chem. Soc.*, 1916, **109**, 701.
Kraus, D.R.P., 294,755, (*Chem. Zentr.*, 1916, II, 861).
Kissel, *Ber.*, 1882, **15**, 1574.
Götting, *Ann.*, 1888, **243**, 115.
Auger, *Bull. soc. chim.*, 1900, **23**, 333.
Meyer, *Ann.*, 1875, **175**, 88.
Krause, Swiss P., 75,523, (*Chem. Abstracts*, 1918, **12**, 41).

2-Nitroethyl Alcohol (2-*Nitroethanol*, β-*nitroethyl alcohol*, 1-*nitro-2-hydroxyethane*)

$NO_2{\cdot}CH_2{\cdot}CH_2OH$

$C_2H_5O_3N$ MW, 91

Liq. with pungent odour. B.p. 194°/765 mm., 119–20°/35 mm., 102°/10 mm. D^{15} 1·270. Sol. H_2O, EtOH, Et_2O. Aq. sol. ⟶ no col. with $FeCl_3$. Sn + HCl ⟶ 2-aminoethyl alcohol.

Et ether: 2-nitrodiethyl ether. $C_4H_9O_3N$. MW, 119. Liq. with sharp odour and bitter taste. B.p. 178°. D^{16} 1·148.

Wilkendorf, Trénel, *Ber.*, 1923, **56**, 619.
Wieland, Sakellarios, *Ber.*, 1919, **52**, 903; 1920, **53**, 201.
Demuth, Meyer, *Ann.*, 1890, **256**, 29.
Henry, *Rec. trav. chim.*, 1899, **18**, 259.

***N*-Nitroethylamine.**

See Ethylnitramine.

***m*-Nitro-*N*-ethylaniline**

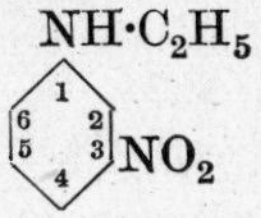

$C_8H_{10}O_2N_2$ MW, 166

Reddish-yellow needles from EtOH or ligroin. M.p. 59–60°. Sol. EtOH, Et_2O, ligroin. Volatile in steam.

N-Acetyl: pale yellow needles. M.p. 88–9°.

Noelting, Stricker, *Ber.*, 1886, **19**, 546.

***p*-Nitro-*N*-ethylaniline.**

Yellow cryst. with bluish-violet lustre from EtOH. M.p. 96°. Sol. warm EtOH, Et_2O, C_6H_6. Spar. sol. CS_2, ligroin.

N-Acetyl: plates. M.p. 118–19°. Sol. EtOH,

C_6H_6. Spar. sol. H_2O, Et_2O. Insol. CS_2, ligroin.

N-*Nitroso*: straw-yellow needles. M.p. 119·5–120°.

N-*Benzyl*: yellow prisms with blue reflex from EtOH. M.p. 63°.

Schweitzer, *Ber.*, 1886, **19**, 149.

β-Nitro-*N*-ethylaniline

$C_6H_5 \cdot NH \cdot CH_2 \cdot CH_2NO_2$

$C_8H_{10}O_2N_2$ MW, 166

Plates. M.p. 37°. Sol. acids and alkalis.

N-*Nitroso*: m.p. about 62°.

Wieland, Sakellarios, *Ber.*, 1919, **52**, 903.

2-Nitroethylbenzene

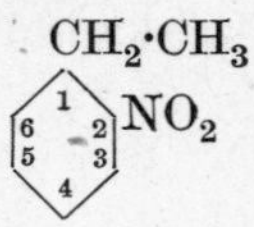

$C_8H_9O_2N$ MW, 151

F.p. − 23°. B.p. 227–8°. $D^{24·5}$ 1·126. n_D^{19} 1·5407.

Schultz, Flachsländer, *J. prakt. Chem.*, 1902, **66**, 160.
Schreiner, *J. prakt. Chem.*, 1910, **81**, 558.
Cline, Reid, *J. Am. Chem. Soc.*, 1927, **49**, 3153.

3-Nitroethylbenzene.
B.p. 242–3°. D^0 1·1345.

Béhal, Choay, *Bull. soc. chim.*, 1894, **11**, 211.

4-Nitroethylbenzene.
F.p. − 32°. B.p. 245–6°. D^{25} 1·124. n_D^{19} 1·5458.

Schultz, Flachsländer, *J. prakt. Chem.*, 1902, **66**, 162.
Schreiner, *J. prakt. Chem.*, 1910, **81**, 558.

4-Nitro-2-ethylbenzoic Acid

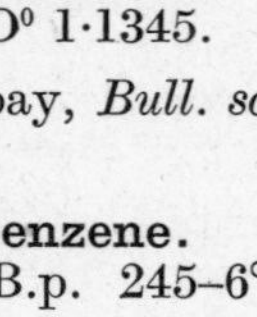

$C_9H_9O_4N$ MW, 195

Cryst M.p. 126°. Sol. EtOH, Et_2O, Me_2CO, AcOH. Insol. pet. ether. HNO_3 at 150° ⟶ 4-nitrophthalic acid.

Giebe, *Ber.*, 1896, **29**, 2536.

5-Nitro-2-ethylbenzoic Acid.
Cryst. M.p. 164°. Sol. EtOH, Et_2O, Me_2CO, AcOH, AcOEt. Insol. pet. ether. HNO_3 at 150° ⟶ 4-nitrophthalic acid.

See previous reference.

Nitroethylene

$CH_2\colon CH \cdot NO_2$

$C_2H_3O_2N$ MW, 73

Pale yellow liq. B.p. 98·5°. $D^{13·8}$ 1·073. Sol. most org. solvents. Polymerises readily. $SnCl_2$ + HCl ⟶ $CH_3 \cdot CHO$ + NH_2OH. Zn + AcOH ⟶ ethylamine. Dil. H_2SO_4 ⟶ 2-nitroethyl alcohol.

Wieland, Sakellarios, *Ber.*, 1919, **52**, 901.

4-Nitro-*N*-ethyl-*o*-toluidine

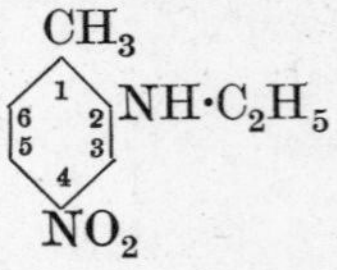

$C_9H_{12}O_2N_2$ MW, 180

Yellowish-red needles from EtOH. M.p. 81–2°.

N-*Acetyl*: plates from EtOH. M.p. 90°. Very sol. EtOH. Spar. sol. pet. ether.

Ullmann, Mühlhauser, *Ber.*, 1902, **35**, 329.
Hantzsch, *Ber.*, 1910, **43**, 1673.
MacCallum, *J. Chem. Soc.*, 1895, **67**, 247.

5-Nitro-*N*-ethyl-*o*-toluidine.
Dark yellow plates from EtOH. M.p. 98°.

N-*Acetyl*: plates or prisms from EtOH.Aq. M.p. 96–7°. Very sol. EtOH.

Bernthsen, *Ber.*, 1892, **25**, 3137.

4-Nitro-*N*-ethyl-*m*-toluidine

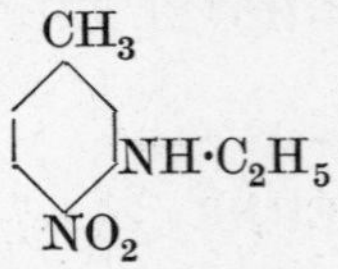

$C_9H_{12}O_2N_2$ MW, 180

Yellowish-red needles from EtOH.Aq. M.p. 60°.

Fischer, Rigaud, *Ber.*, 1902, **35**, 1259.

2-Nitro-*N*-ethyl-*p*-toluidine

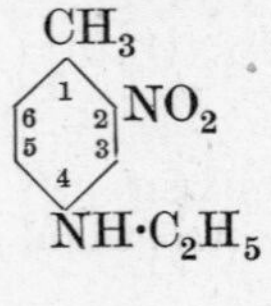

$C_9H_{12}O_2N_2$ MW, 180

Red prisms or yellow needles. M.p. 50° (46–7°). Sol. EtOH, Et_2O.

Noelting, Stricker, *Ber.*, 1886, **19**, 549.
Jaubert, *Bull. soc. chim.*, 1899, **21**, 20.

3-Nitro-*N*-ethyl-*p*-toluidine.
Red cryst. from EtOH. M.p. 58–9°. Sol. Et_2O, C_6H_6, hot EtOH.
N-*Acetyl* : liq. B.p. 245–50°/15 mm.

Gattermann, *Ber.*, 1885, **18**, 1483.
Niementowski, *Ber.*, 1887, **20**, 1884.

6-Nitro-4-ethyl-*o*-toluidine

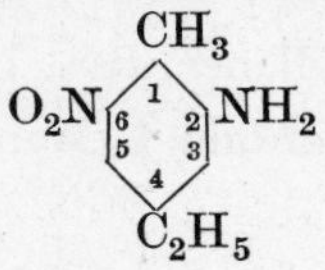

$C_9H_{12}O_2N_2$ MW, 180

Yellow needles from EtOH. M.p. 96°.
N-*Acetyl* : needles from EtOH. M.p. 166°.

Brady, Day, *J. Chem. Soc.*, 1934, 120.

3-Nitro-5-ethyl-*o*-toluidine.
Red prisms from pet. ether. M.p. 64°.
N-*Acetyl* : pale yellow needles from EtOH.Aq. M.p. 142°.

Morgan, Pettet, *J. Chem. Soc.*, 1934, 420.

4-Nitro-5-ethyl-*o*-toluidine.
Golden needles. M.p. 74°.
N-*Acetyl* : m.p. 143°.

See previous reference.

4-Nitro-6-ethyl-*m*-toluidine

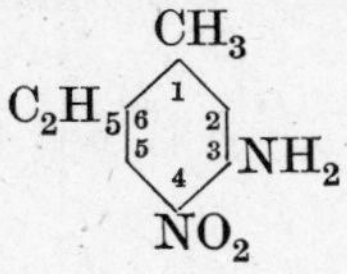

$C_9H_{12}O_2N_2$ MW, 180

Orange prisms from CCl_4. M.p. 90°.
N-*Acetyl* : yellow needles from 95% EtOH. M.p. 103°.

See previous reference.

5-Nitroeugenol (5-*Nitro*-4-*hydroxy*-3-*methoxyallylbenzene*)

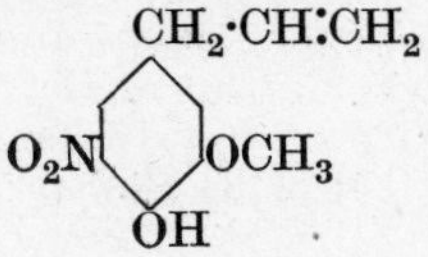

$C_{10}H_{11}O_4N$ MW, 209

Yellow needles from EtOH. M.p. 43–4°. Volatile in steam. Sol. EtOH, Et_2O. Very spar. sol. H_2O.
Acetyl : plates from EtOH. M.p. 61°.

Levin, Lowy, *J. Am. Chem. Soc.*, 1933, **55**, 1996.
Weselsky, Benedikt, *Monatsh.*, 1882, **3**, 388.
Klemenc, *Monatsh.*, 1912, **33**, 379.

3-Nitroflavopurpurin (3-*Nitro*-1 : 2 : 6-*trihydroxyanthraquinone*)

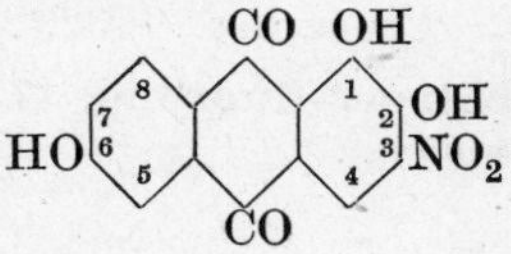

$C_{14}H_7O_7N$ MW, 301

Red cryst.

Bayer, D.R.P., 74,562.

4-Nitroflavopurpurin (4-*Nitro*-1 : 2 : 6-*trihydroxyanthraquinone*).
Reddish-yellow cryst. from AcOH or EtOH. Decomp. above 200°. Mod. sol. EtOH, AcOH. NH_3.Aq. ⟶ reddish-orange sol. NaOH ⟶ deep red sol. Conc. H_2SO_4 ⟶ yellowish-red sol.

Bayer, D.R.P., 74,598.
M.L.B., D.R.P., 70,515.

2-Nitrofluorene

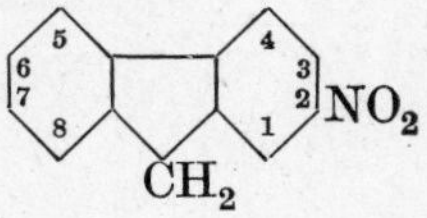

$C_{13}H_9O_2N$ MW, 211

Needles from 50% AcOH. M.p. 156° (154°).

Diels, *Ber.*, 1901, **34**, 1759.
Diels, Schill, Tolson, *Ber.*, 1902, **35**, 3289.
Kuhn, *Organic Syntheses*, 1933, XIII, 74.

3-Nitrofluorene.
Yellow needles from $CHCl_3$–pet. ether. M.p. 105°.

Bardout, *Chem. Zentr.*, 1932, I, 941.

9-Nitrofluorene.
Leaflets from C_6H_6. M.p. 181–2° decomp. Sol. Me_2CO, $CHCl_3$. Mod. sol. EtOH, C_6H_6, AcOH. Insol. H_2O, ligroin. Above m.p. ⟶ fluorenone.

Wislicenus, Waldmüller, *Ber.*, 1908, **41**, 3338.

2-Nitrofluorene-9-carboxylic Acid (2-*Nitrodiphenyleneacetic acid*)

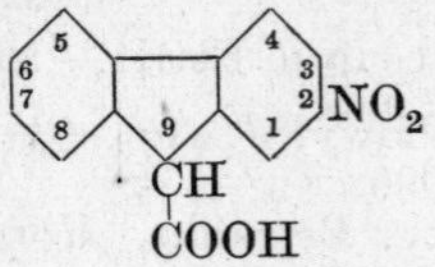

$C_{14}H_9O_4N$ MW, 255

Yellow needles from Me_2CO–$CHCl_3$. M.p. 186–7°. Sol. Me_2CO, EtOH. Spar. sol. C_6H_6, $CHCl_3$. Heat above m.p. ⟶ 2-nitrofluorene.

Rose, *J. Chem. Soc.*, 1932, 2361.

1-(or 3)-Nitro-2-fluorenol (1-(or 3)-*Nitro-2-hydroxyfluorene*)

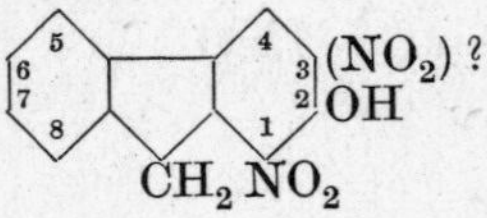

$C_{13}H_9O_3N$ MW, 227

Cryst. from MeOH. M.p. 145·6°.

Ruiz, *Chem. Zentr.*, 1930, II, 1074.

7-Nitro-2-fluorenol (7-*Nitro-2-hydroxyfluorene*).

M.p. 219–20° decomp.

See previous reference.

Nitrofluorenol-carboxylic Acid.

See Nitrohydroxyfluorene-carboxylic Acid.

2-Nitrofluorenone

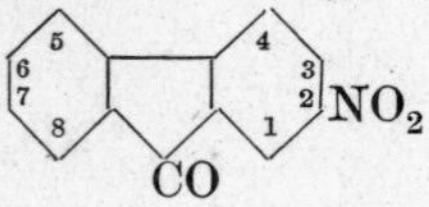

$C_{13}H_7O_3N$ MW, 225

Yellow cryst. M.p. 222–3° (218·5°). Spar. sol. cold EtOH. Sublimes easily. Conc. H_2SO_4 ⟶ reddish-yellow sol.

Oxime: m.p. 258° (rapid heat.). *Acetyl*: pale yellow cryst. from EtOH. M.p. 228°.

Hydrazone: yellow leaflets. M.p. 214°.

Phenylhydrazone: red needles. M.p. 210–14° decomp. (rapid heat.). Sol. Me_2CO, C_6H_6, $CHCl_3$. Spar. sol. EtOH, AcOH.

Azine: brown cryst. powder from xylene. M.p. 305–6°.

Diels, *Ber.*, 1901, **34**, 1764.
Langecker, *J. prakt. Chem.*, 1931, **132**, 145.
Bardout, *Chem. Zentr.*, 1935, II, 1706.

3-Nitrofluorenone.

Yellowish-brown needles from EtOH. M.p. 232°. Spar. sol. EtOH, Et_2O.

Oxime: exists in two forms. (i) Yellowish-brown needles from EtOH. M.p. 240°. (ii) Cryst. M.p. 217° decomp.

Bardout, *Chem. Zentr.*, 1932, I, 941; 1935, II, 1706.

4-Nitrofluorenone.

Cryst. from AcOH. M.p. 173–4°. Sol. usual solvents. Conc. H_2SO_4 ⟶ green sol. ⟶ brown on warming.

Oxime: dark green needles. M.p. 255–6° decomp.

Semicarbazone: brown powder. Does not melt below 350°.

Schmidt, Bauer, *Ber.*, 1905, **38**, 3742.

2-Nitrofluorenone-1-carboxylic Acid

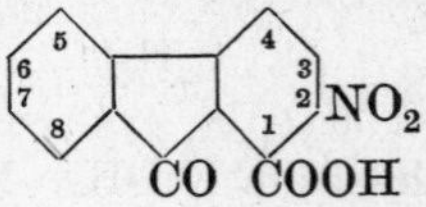

$C_{14}H_7O_5N$ MW, 269

Yellow needles. M.p. 233–5° decomp.

v. Braun, Manz, *Ann.*, 1932, **496**, 195.

6-Nitrofluorenone-4-carboxylic Acid.

Cryst. from AcOH. M.p. 282°.

Bell, Robinson, *J. Chem. Soc.*, 1927, 2238.

7-Nitrofluorenone-4-carboxylic Acid.

Yellow needles from AcOH. M.p. 262–262·5° decomp.

Me ester: $C_{15}H_9O_5N$. MW, 283. Bright yellow needles from C_6H_6. M.p. 199·5–200°.

Chloride: $C_{14}H_6O_4NCl$. MW, 287·5. Yellow needles from C_6H_6. M.p. 203·5–204°.

Amide: $C_{14}H_8O_4N_2$. MW, 268. Yellow needles from AcOH. M.p. 263·5–264°. Sol. hot AcOH. Insol. H_2O, EtOH, $CHCl_3$, Et_2O, chlorobenzene.

Moore, Huntress, *J. Am. Chem. Soc.*, 1927, **59**, 1329.

Nitroform.

See Trinitromethane.

Nitroformaldehyde

$NO_2{\cdot}CHO$

CHO_3N MW, 75

Free compound not known.

Phenylhydrazone: exists in two forms. α-. Orange-red prisms from C_6H_6, $CHCl_3$ or ligroin. M.p. 74·5–75·5°. β-. Golden-yellow needles from EtOH. M.p. 84·5–85·5°. Less sol. than α-form.

Methylphenylhydrazone: yellow plates or

needles. M.p. 91–2°. Sol. EtOH, C_6H_6. Spar. sol. ligroin. Conc. $H_2SO_4 \longrightarrow$ red sol.

1-*Naphthylhydrazone* : dark red needles from EtOH. M.p. 120°.

Bamberger, Schmidt, Levinstein, *Ber.*, 1900, **33**, 2060.
Bamberger, Schmidt, *Ber.*, 1901, **34**, 590.

Nitroformaldoxime.
See Methylnitrolic Acid.

Nitroformanilide.
See under Nitroaniline.

5-Nitro-β-furaldehyde

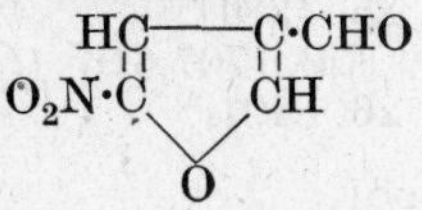

$C_5H_3O_4N$ MW, 141

Cryst. from pet. ether. M.p. 76°.
Diacetate : cryst. from pet. ether. M.p. 87°.
Hydrazone : m.p. 122° decomp.

Gilman, Burtner, *J. Am. Chem. Soc.*, 1933, **55**, 2908.

2-Nitrofuran

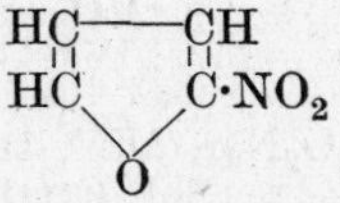

$C_4H_3O_3N$ MW, 113

Yellowish cryst. from pet. ether. M.p. 29°. Sol. H_2O, Et_2O. Alkalis $\longrightarrow$ orange-brown sols.

Rinkes, *Rec. trav. chim.*, 1931, **50**, 590.
Freure, Johnson, *J. Am. Chem. Soc.*, 1931, **53**, 1142.

Nitrofuran-carboxylic Acid.
See Nitrofuroic Acid *and* Nitropyromucic Acid.

5-Nitrofurfural (5-*Nitrofurfuraldehyde*, 5-*nitro-2-furoic aldehyde*)

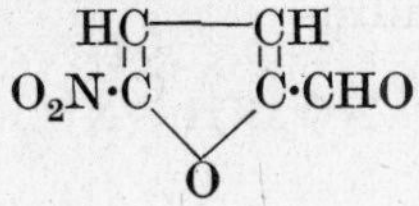

$C_5H_3O_4N$ MW, 141

Cryst. from pet. ether. M.p. 35–6°. B.p. 128–32°/10 mm. Mod. sol. H_2O.
Oxime : exists in two forms. (i) Cryst. M.p. 121°. (ii) Cryst. from EtOH. M.p. 153°.

Gilman, Wright, *J. Am. Chem. Soc.*, 1930, **52**, 2552.

5-Nitro-α-furoic Acid.
See 5-Nitropyromucic Acid.

5-Nitro-β-furoic Acid (5-*Nitrofuran*-3-*carboxylic acid*)

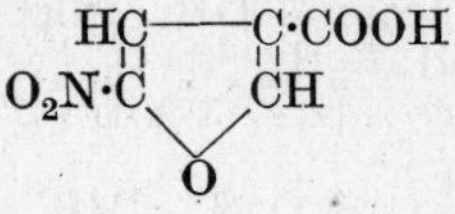

$C_5H_3O_5N$ MW, 157

Cryst. from hot H_2O. M.p. 138°.
Et ester : $C_7H_7O_5N$. MW, 185. Cryst. from EtOH. M.p. 56°.

Gilman, Burtner, *J. Am. Chem. Soc.*, 1933, **55**, 2907.

2-Nitrogallic Acid (2-*Nitro*-3 : 4 : 5-*trihydroxybenzoic acid*)

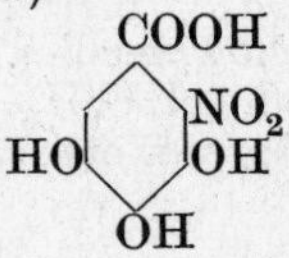

$C_7H_5O_7N$ MW, 215

Tri-Me ether : 2-nitro-3 : 4 : 5-trimethoxybenzoic acid. $C_{10}H_{11}O_7N$. MW, 257. Prisms from EtOH.Aq. M.p. 164°. Sol. EtOH, Et_2O. Spar. sol. hot H_2O, C_6H_6. Turns yellowish-brown in air. *Me ester* : $C_{11}H_{13}O_7N$. MW, 271. Yellowish plates or prisms from ligroin. M.p. 67–8°. Sol. EtOH, Et_2O. Insol. H_2O. *Et ester* : $C_{12}H_{15}O_7N$. MW, 285. Yellowish cryst. from EtOH.Aq. M.p. 68–70°. *Amide* : $C_{10}H_{12}O_6N_2$. MW, 214. Needles from EtOH. M.p. 182–4°.
Tri-Et ether : 2-nitro-3 : 4 : 5-triethoxybenzoic acid. $C_{13}H_{17}O_7N$. MW, 299. Needles from H_2O. M.p. 104°. Sol. EtOH, Et_2O. Spar. sol. H_2O.

Pollak, Feldscharek, *Monatsh.*, 1908, **29**, 146.
Harding, *J. Chem. Soc.*, 1911, **99**, 1592.

3-Nitrogentisic Acid (3-*Nitro*-2 : 5-*dihydroxybenzoic acid*)

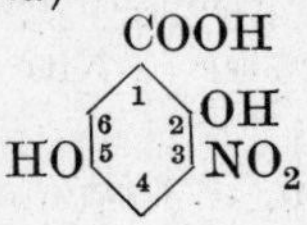

$C_7H_5O_6N$ MW, 199

Yellow cryst. + $2H_2O$ from H_2O. M.p. 230° decomp. Sol. EtOH, boiling H_2O. Spar. sol. most org. solvents. Sol. NH_3.Aq., carbonates, with red col. Caustic alkalis $\longrightarrow$ deep violet sols. $\longrightarrow$ ruby-red on dilution. $FeCl_3 \longrightarrow$ brown col.

5-*Me ether* : $C_8H_7O_6N$. MW, 213. Yellow needles from H_2O. M.p. 181°. Very sol.

MeOH. Mod. sol. boiling H_2O. $FeCl_3 \longrightarrow$ reddish-brown col. *Me ester*: $C_9H_9O_6N$. MW, 227. Yellow cryst. from MeOH. M.p. 138–9°. Spar. sol. cold MeOH, C_6H_6.

Di-Me ether: *see* 3-Nitro-2 : 5-dimethoxybenzoic Acid.

Me ester: $C_8H_7O_6N$. MW, 213. Yellow needles from C_6H_6 or H_2O. M.p. 158°. Spar. sol. cold H_2O, C_6H_6. KOH $\longrightarrow$ violet sol. $\longrightarrow$ orange on dilution. $FeCl_3 \longrightarrow$ green col. rapidly turning reddish-yellow.

Klemenc, *Monatsh.*, 1912, **33**, 1249.
v. Hemmelmayr, *Monatsh.*, 1913, **34**, 819.

4-Nitrogentisic Acid (*4-Nitro-2 : 5-dihydroxybenzoic acid*).

5-*Me ether*: yellow needles from C_6H_6 or H_2O. M.p. 191–2°. Mod. sol. C_6H_6. *Me ester*: yellow leaflets from C_6H_6–pet. ether. M.p. 103°. Sol. C_6H_6.

Klemenc, *Monatsh.*, 1914, **35**, 102.

6-Nitrogentisic Acid (*6-Nitro-2 : 5-dihydroxybenzoic acid*).

5-*Me ether*: yellowish leaflets from boiling H_2O. M.p. 221° decomp. Spar. sol. hot C_6H_6. Sublimes in needles or leaflets at 150°. *Me ester*: cryst. from C_6H_6. M.p. 125–6°.

Di-Me ether: *see* 6-Nitro-2 : 5-dimethoxybenzoic Acid.

See previous reference.

3-Nitrogentisic Aldehyde (*3-Nitro-2 : 5-dihydroxybenzaldehyde*)

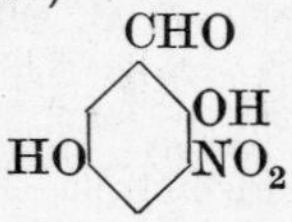

$C_7H_5O_5N$ MW, 183

5-*Me ether*: $C_8H_7O_5N$. MW, 197. Bright yellow needles from AcOH. M.p. 132°. $FeCl_3 \longrightarrow$ red col. p-*Nitrophenylhydrazone*: scarlet prisms. Decomp. at 250°.

Di-Me ether: *see* 3-Nitro-2 : 5-dimethoxybenzaldehyde.

Rubenstein, *J. Chem. Soc.*, 1925, 2000.

Nitroglycerin (*Glycerol trinitrate, nitroglycerol*)

$CH_2{\cdot}O{\cdot}NO_2$
$CH{\cdot}O{\cdot}NO_2$
$CH_2{\cdot}O{\cdot}NO_2$

$C_3H_5O_9N_3$ MW, 227

Exists in two solid forms. (i) *Labile*, cryst. M.p. 2·0°. (ii) *Stable*, cryst. M.p. 13·1°. D_4^4 1·6144, D_4^{15} 1·6009, D_4^{25} 1·5918. Sol. 800 part H_2O, 4 parts EtOH, 18 parts MeOH, 120 part CS_2. Misc. with Et_2O, $CHCl_3$, AcOH, phenol. Spar. sol. ligroin, pet. ether, glycerol. Explodes violently on rapid heating or on detonation. Possesses sweet burning taste. Used as heart stimulant, constituent of many explosives, *e.g.* dynamite, cordite, gelignite.

Hepworth, *J. Chem. Soc.*, 1919, **115**, 843.
Giua, *Chem. Abstracts*, 1930, **24**, 5498.
Evers, D.R.P., 513,396, (*Chem. Abstracts*, 1931, **25**, 1384).
Schmid, F.P., 707,616, (*Chem. Abstracts*, 1932, **26**, 849).

Nitroglycerol.
See Nitroglycerin.

Nitroglycide.
See under Glycide.

4-Nitroglyoxaline (*4-Nitroiminazole*)

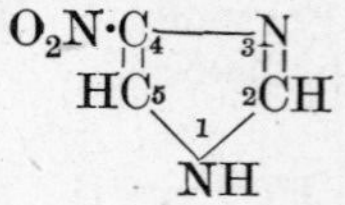

$C_3H_3O_2N_3$ MW, 113

N-*Me*: $C_4H_5O_2N_3$. MW, 127. Needles from H_2O. M.p. 133–4°. Sol. EtOH, Me_2CO, $CHCl_3$. Spar. sol. H_2O, Et_2O.

Hazeldine, Pyman, Winchester, *J. Chem. Soc.*, 1924, **125**, 1431.

5-Nitroglyoxaline (*5-Nitroiminazole*).

N-*Me*: prisms from Et_2O. M.p. 55°. Sol. EtOH, Me_2CO, $CHCl_3$. Mod. sol. H_2O, Et_2O. *Picrate*: yellow needles from H_2O. M.p. 153·5°.

See previous reference.

Nitroguaiacol.
See under Nitrocatechol.

Nitroguanidine

$$NO_2{\cdot}NH{\cdot}\overset{NH}{\overset{\|}{C}}{\cdot}NH_2$$

$CH_4O_2N_4$ MW, 104

Needles or prisms from H_2O. M.p. 232°. decomp. Sol. 11 parts boiling H_2O, 375 parts at 19·3°. Spar. sol. EtOH. Insol. Et_2O. Heat of comb. C_p 210·3 Cal. Decomp. by alkalis.

B,HCl: plates or prisms.

B,HNO₃: plates from hot conc. HNO_3. M.p. 140°.

Davis, *Organic Syntheses*, Collective Vol. I, 392.

4-Nitro-*sym.*-hemimellitenol (2-*Nitro*-3 : 4 : 5-*trimethylphenol*, 4-*nitro*-5-*hydroxy*-1 : 2 : 3-*trimethylbenzene*)

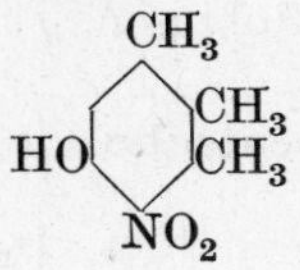

$C_9H_{11}O_3N$ MW, 181

Yellow cryst. M.p. 96–8°.

Auwers *et al.*, *Chem. Abstracts*, 1925, **19**, 2340.

6-Nitrohemipinic Acid (6-*Nitro*-3 : 4-*dimethoxyphthalic acid*)

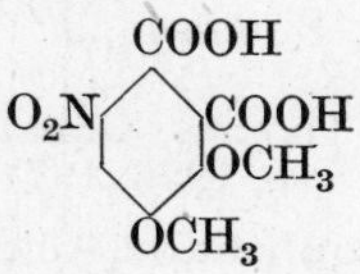

$C_{10}H_9O_8N$ MW, 271

Yellow prisms + H_2O from H_2O. M.p. 166° (155°). $k = 1{\cdot}99 \times 10^{-2}$ at 25°. Above m.p. ⟶ anhydride.

1-*Me ester*: $C_{11}H_{11}O_8N$. MW, 285. Cryst. from C_6H_6 or H_2O. M.p. 146–7°. $k = 1{\cdot}28 \times 10^{-2}$ at 25°. Spar. sol. C_6H_6. *Anilide*: $C_{17}H_{16}O_7N_2$. MW, 360. Cryst. from C_6H_6–pet. ether. M.p. 148–9°. $FeCl_3$ ⟶ red col.

2-*Me ester*: needles from C_6H_6. M.p. 142–4°. $k = 1{\cdot}47 \times 10^{-2}$ at 25°. Spar. sol. C_6H_6. *Anilide*: cryst. from C_6H_6. M.p. 170° decomp.

Di-Me ester: $C_{12}H_{13}O_8N$. MW, 299. Leaflets from EtOH.Aq. M.p. 83–4°.

Anhydride: $C_{10}H_7O_7N$. MW, 253. Prisms or plates from C_6H_6. M.p. 154–5°. Sol. C_6H_6.

Wegscheider, Klemenc, *Monatsh.*, 1910, **31**, 725; 1911, **32**, 386.
Wegscheider, v. Rušnow, *Monatsh.*, 1908, **29**, 546.
Wegscheider, Strauch, *ibid.*, 568.

1-Nitroheptane

$$CH_3{\cdot}[CH_2]_5{\cdot}CH_2NO_2$$

$C_7H_{15}O_2N$ MW, 145

Pale yellow oil. B.p. 193–5°. D^{17} 0·9476. Sol. EtOH, Et_2O. Insol. H_2O. Fe + AcOH ⟶ *n*-heptylamine.

Worstall, *Am. Chem. J.*, 1898, **20**, 210; 1899, **21**, 223.

2-Nitroheptane

$$CH_3{\cdot}[CH_2]_4{\cdot}\underset{}{\overset{NO_2}{CH}}{\cdot}CH_3$$

$C_7H_{15}O_2N$ MW, 145

Liq. B.p. 194–8°. D^0 0·9466. Sol. warm conc. KOH.

Konowalow, *J. Russ. Phys.-Chem. Soc.*, 1893, **25**, 481.

Nitrohexahydrotoluene.
See Nitromethylcyclohexane.

1-Nitrohexane

$$CH_3{\cdot}[CH_2]_4{\cdot}CH_2NO_2$$

$C_6H_{13}O_2N$ MW, 131

Stable liq. B.p. 180–1° (193–4°/765 mm.), 112°/75 mm. D^{20} 0·9488. Sol. EtOH, aq. alkalis. Insol. H_2O. Almost odourless. Sweet taste. Fe + AcOH ⟶ *n*-hexylamine.

Worstall, *Am. Chem. J.*, 1898, **20**, 207; 1899, **21**, 219.
Henry, *Rec. trav. chim.*, 1905, **24**, 358.

2-Nitrohexane

$$CH_3{\cdot}[CH_2]_3{\cdot}\overset{NO_2}{CH}{\cdot}CH_3$$

$C_6H_{13}O_2N$ MW, 131

Liq. B.p. 176° (175–8°). D^0 0·9509, D_0^{20} 0·9357. Sol. boiling conc. KOH. Zn + AcOH in EtOH ⟶ 2-aminohexane + methyl butyl ketone.

Konowalow, *Compt. rend.*, 1892, **114**, 26.
Shoriugin, Lopchiev, *Ber.*, 1934, **67**, 1362.

2-Nitrohippuric Acid (o-*Nitrobenzoylglycine*)

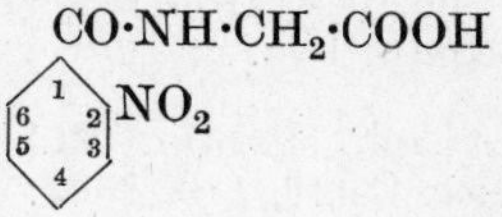

$C_9H_8O_5N_2$ MW, 224

Leaflets from H_2O. M.p. 191° (188°). Sol. EtOH, hot H_2O. Spar. sol. Et_2O.

Et ester: $C_{11}H_{12}O_5N_2$. MW, 252. Needles from EtOH. M.p. 81°.

Knoop, Oesterlin, *Z. physiol. Chem.*, 1927, **170**, 186.

3-Nitrohippuric Acid (m-*Nitrobenzoylglycine*).

Needles from H_2O. M.p. 165–7° (162°). Sol. EtOH, Et_2O, hot H_2O.

Et ester: needles from H_2O. M.p. 75°. Sol. EtOH, C_6H_6. Spar. sol. hot H_2O.

Nitrile: $C_9H_7O_3N_3$. MW, 205. Leaflets from EtOH. M.p. 118°. Sol. EtOH, C_6H_6. Sol. conc. NaOH.

Hydrazide: needles + H_2O from H_2O. M.p. anhyd. 159°.

Conrad, *J. prakt. Chem.*, 1877, **15**, 254.
Klages, Haack, *Ber.*, 1903, **36**, 1647.
Curtius, *J. prakt. Chem.*, 1914, **89**, 485.

4-Nitrohippuric Acid (p-*Nitrobenzoylglycine*).

Orange-red prisms from H_2O. M.p. 129°. Sol. EtOH, Et_2O, hot H_2O.

Et ester: needles from EtOH. M.p. 142° (144°). Sol. Et_2O, ligroin.

Nitrile: needles from EtOH. M.p. 145°. Sol. EtOH, AcOH. Spar. sol. Et_2O, ligroin.

Hydrazide: yellow needles from H_2O. M.p. 203·5°. *Benzylidene*: yellow powder. M.p. 216°.

Azide: yellow powder. M.p. 70–2° decomp. Unstable.

Jaffé, *Ber.*, 1874, **7**, 1673.
Sieber, Smirnow, *Monatsh.*, 1887, **8**, 90.
Klages, Haack, *Ber.*, 1903, **36**, 1648.
Curtius, *J. prakt. Chem.*, 1916, **94**, 129.

o-Nitrohomoanisic Acid (2-*Nitro*-4-*methoxyphenylacetic acid*)

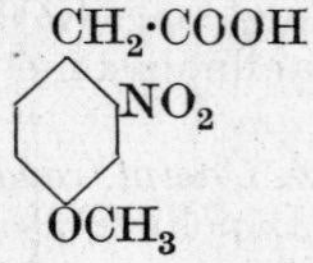

$C_9H_9O_5N$ MW, 211

Yellow needles from 50% AcOH. M.p. 157–8° decomp.

Kermack, Perkin, Robinson, *J. Chem. Soc.*, 1921, **119**, 1631.
Schlittler, *Helv. Chim. Acta*, 1932, **15**, 394.

5-Nitrohomocatechol (5-*Nitro*-3 : 4-*dihydroxytoluene*)

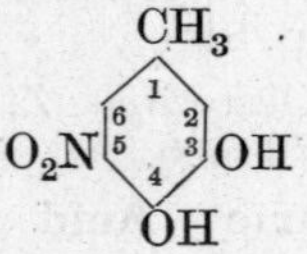

$C_7H_7O_4N$ MW, 169

Golden-yellow plates from H_2O. M.p. 82–3° (79–80°). Sol. hot H_2O, EtOH, Et_2O. Volatile in steam.

4-*Me ether*: $C_8H_9O_4N$. MW, 183. *Acetyl*: yellow prisms from pet. ether. M.p. 60–1°.

Di-Me ether: *see* 5-Nitrohomoveratrol.

3-*Acetyl*: yellow needles from 80% EtOH. M.p. 104–5°.

Cousin, *Ann. chim. phys.*, 1898, **13**, 537.
Gulland, Robinson, *J. Chem. Soc.*, 1926, 1978.

6-Nitrohomocatechol (6-*Nitro*-3 : 4-*dihydroxytoluene*).

Yellow needles from H_2O. M.p. 180–2° decomp. Sol. EtOH, Et_2O. Spar. sol. pet. ether. Insol. H_2O. $FeCl_3 \longrightarrow$ green col.

3-*Me ether*: light yellow prisms from MeOH.Aq. M.p. 138–40°. Sol. most org. solvents. Alkalis $\longrightarrow$ red sols. 4-*Acetyl*: yellowish needles from EtOH. M.p. 138–9°.

Di-Me ether: *see* 6-Nitrohomoveratrol.

Cousin, *Ann. chim. phys.*, 1898, **13**, 537.
Cardwell, Robinson, *J. Chem. Soc.*, 1915, **107**, 258.
Graesser-Thomas, Gulland, Robinson, *J. Chem. Soc.*, 1926, 1974.

4-Nitrohomophthalic Acid

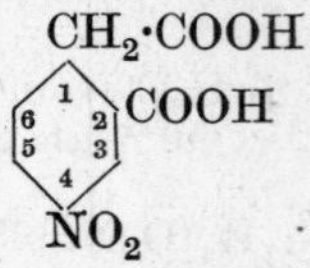

$C_9H_7O_6N$ MW, 225

Needles from H_2O. M.p. 220° decomp. (215°).

Di-Me ester: $C_{11}H_{11}O_6N$. MW, 253. Needles from MeOH. M.p. 99° (93·5°).

Borsche, Dracout, Hanau, *Ber.*, 1934, **67**, 675.
Ingold, Piggott, *J. Chem. Soc.*, 1923, **123**, 1497.

5-Nitrohomophthalic Acid.

Cryst. from H_2O. M.p. 184·5°.

Di-Et ester: $C_{13}H_{15}O_6N$. MW, 281. Cryst. M.p. 57°.

Heusler, Schieffer, *Ber.*, 1899, **32**, 34.

2-Nitrohomoterephthalic Acid

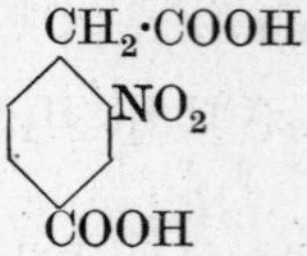

$C_9H_7O_6N$ MW, 225

Leaflets from AcOH. M.p. 222°. Sol. hot H_2O, EtOH. Spar. sol. Et_2O. Insol. C_6H_6, pet. ether. Above m.p. $\longrightarrow$ 2-nitro-*p*-toluic acid. $(NH_4)_2S \longrightarrow$ oxindole-6-carboxylic acid.

Di-Me ester: $C_{11}H_{11}O_6N$. MW, 253. Leaflets from MeOH. M.p. 76·5°.
4-*Nitrile*: $C_9H_6O_4N_2$. MW, 206. *Et ester*: $C_{11}H_{10}O_4N_2$. MW, 234. Yellowish needles from EtOH. M.p. 96°.

Borsche, Stackmann, Makaroff-Semljanski, *Ber.*, 1916, **49**, 2225.
Fileti, Cairola, *J. prakt. Chem.*, 1892, **46**, 563.

2-Nitrohomovanillic Acid (2-*Nitro*-4-*hydroxy*-3-*methoxyphenylacetic acid*)

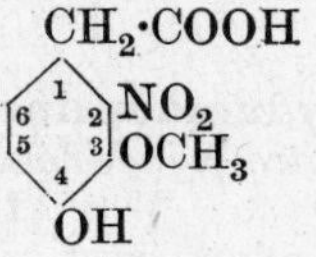

$C_9H_9O_6N$ MW, 227

Orange-yellow needles from H_2O, leaflets from toluene. M.p. 161°. Sol. EtOH. NaOH ⟶ orange sol. $FeCl_3$ ⟶ faint green col.
Benzyl ether: $C_{16}H_{15}O_6N$. MW, 317. Plates from C_6H_6. M.p. 144°. *Benzyl ester*: $C_{23}H_{21}O_6N$. MW, 407. Cryst. from C_6H_6–pet. ether, m.p. 80°; cryst. from EtOH, m.p. 101°.
Me ether: *see* 2-Nitrohomoveratric Acid.
Carbethoxyl: platelets + C_6H_6 from C_6H_6. M.p. 110–18° (solvent free) 132–3°.

Gulland, *J. Chem. Soc.*, 1931, 2872.

5-Nitrohomovanillic Acid (5-*Nitro*-4-*hydroxy*-3-*methoxyphenylacetic acid*).
Yellow needles from H_2O. M.p. 217° decomp. Sol. hot H_2O, hot MeOH. Spar. sol. C_6H_6. Sol. alkalis with blood-red col.
Me ether: *see* 5-Nitrohomoveratric Acid.
Me ester: $C_{10}H_{11}O_6N$. MW, 241. Yellow needles or plates from MeOH. M.p. 101–12°. Very sol. C_6H_6.

Klemenc, *Monatsh.*, 1912, **33**, 382.

6-Nitrohomovanillic Acid (6-*Nitro*-4-*hydroxy*-3-*methoxyphenylacetic acid*).
Long yellow needles from H_2O. M.p. 184°. NaOH ⟶ orange-red sol.
Me ether: *see* 6-Nitrohomoveratric Acid.
Benzyl ether: yellow needles from EtOH. M.p. 222°.

Douglas, Gulland, *J. Chem. Soc.*, 1931, 2898.

2-Nitrohomoveratric Acid (2-*Nitro*-3 : 4-*dimethoxyphenylacetic acid*)

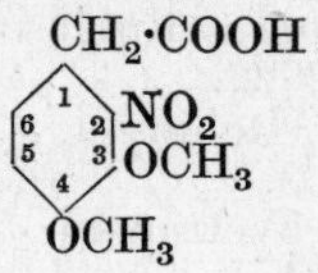

$C_{10}H_{11}O_6N$ MW, 241

Yellow leaflets from H_2O. M.p. 146°. Sol. most org. solvents. Mod. sol. hot H_2O.
Nitrile: $C_{10}H_{10}O_4N_2$. MW, 222. Needles from MeOH. M.p. 68–9°. Sol. hot H_2O.

Kay, Pictet, *J. Chem. Soc.*, 1913, **103**, 955.
Avenarius, Pschorr, *Ber.*, 1929, **62**, 323.
Slotta, Laversen, *J. prakt. Chem.*, 1934, **139**, 226.

5-Nitrohomoveratric Acid (5-*Nitro*-3 : 4-*dimethoxyphenylacetic acid*).
Yellowish needles from H_2O. M.p. 113–14°. Sol. boiling C_6H_6.

Klemenc, *Monatsh.*, 1912, **33**, 385.

6-Nitrohomoveratric Acid (6-*Nitro*-3 : 4-*dimethoxyphenylacetic acid*).
Needles from AcOH.Aq. M.p. 202–4°. Sol. AcOH, AcOEt. Spar. sol. C_6H_6, $CHCl_3$, cold H_2O.
Benzyl ester: needles from EtOH. M.p. 117°.

Oxford, Raper, *J. Chem. Soc.*, 1927, 419.

2-Nitrohomoveratrol (2-*Nitro*-3 : 4-*dimethoxytoluene*)

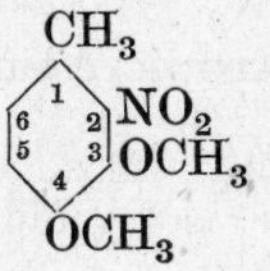

$C_9H_{11}O_4N$ MW, 197

Oil. B.p. 115–17°/1 mm., 108–10°/0·5 mm.

Oberlin, *Arch. Pharm.*, 1925, **263**, 641.
Cf. Gulland, Robinson, *J. Chem. Soc.*, 1926, 1976.

5-Nitrohomoveratrol (5-*Nitro*-3 : 4-*dimethoxytoluene*).
Needles from EtOH. M.p. 59°. Very sol. EtOH, Et_2O. Insol. H_2O. Volatile in steam.

Gulland, Robinson, *J. Chem. Soc.*, 1926, 1977.

6-Nitrohomoveratrol (6-*Nitro*-3 : 4-*dimethoxytoluene*).
Yellow needles from EtOH or ligroin. M.p.

120° (118°). Spar. sol. EtOH, ligroin. Insol. H_2O. Conc. $H_2SO_4 \longrightarrow$ orange-yellow sol.

Heap, Jones, Robinson, *J. Chem. Soc.*, 1927, 2022.
Cardwell, Robinson, *J. Chem. Soc.*, 1915, **107**, 258.
Harding, Weizmann, *J. Chem. Soc.*, 1910, **97**, 1131.

1-Nitrohydantoin

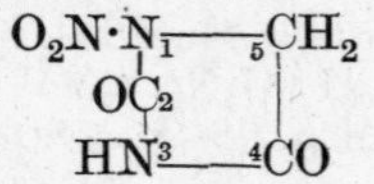

$C_3H_3O_4N_3$ MW, 145

Needles from H_2O. M.p. 170° decomp. Long heating with $H_2O \longrightarrow CO_2 +$ nitroamino-acetamide.

Franchimont, Klobbie, *Rec. trav. chim.*, 1888, **7**, 12.
Franchimont, van Erp, *Rec. trav. chim.*, 1896, **15**, 168.

2-Nitrohydratropic Acid (1-o-*Nitrophenyl-propionic acid*)

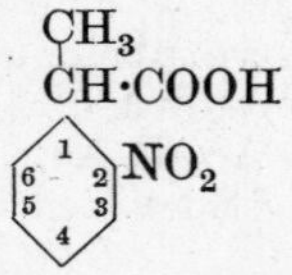

$C_9H_9O_4N$ MW, 195

Cryst. from EtOH.Aq. M.p. 110°. Sol. EtOH, Et_2O. Mod. sol. hot H_2O. Spar. sol. CS_2. $KMnO_4 \longrightarrow$ *o*-nitrobenzoic acid.

Trinius, *Ann.*, 1885, **227**, 262.

4-Nitrohydratropic Acid (1-p-*Nitrophenyl-propionic acid*).

Leaflets from CS_2. M.p. 87–8°. Sol. EtOH, C_6H_6, CS_2. Spar. sol. cold H_2O. $CrO_3 \longrightarrow$ *p*-nitrobenzoic acid.

Nitrile: $C_9H_8O_2N_2$. MW, 176. Cryst. from C_6H_6–ligroin. M.p. 73–5°. Sol. EtOH, Et_2O, C_6H_6.

Opolski, Kowalski, Pilewski, *Ber.*, 1916, **49**, 2282.
See also previous reference.

***m*-Nitrohydrazobenzene**

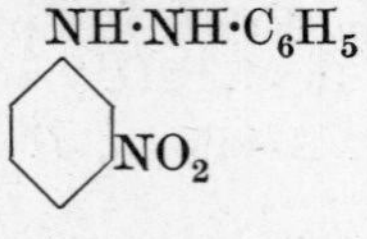

$C_{12}H_{11}O_2N_3$ MW, 229

Yellow cryst. from EtOH. M.p. 85–6°.

Meisenheimer, *Ber.*, 1920, **53**, 358.

6-Nitro-1-hydrindamine (6-*Nitro*-1-*amino-hydrindene*, 6-*nitro*-1-*indanamine*)

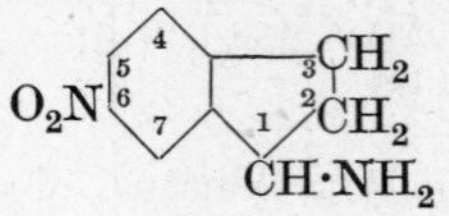

$C_9H_{10}O_2N_2$ MW, 178

Prisms from Et_2O. M.p. 60–1°.

N-*Acetyl*: needles from EtOH or AcOH.Aq. M.p. 180°.

Ingold, Piggott, *J. Chem. Soc.*, 1923, **123**, 1483.

4-Nitro-5-hydrindamine (4-*Nitro*-5-*amino-hydrindene*, 4-*nitro*-5-*indanamine*).

Orange-red cryst. M.p. 128–9°.

N-*Benzoyl*: yellow cryst. M.p. 125–6°.

Borsche, Bodenstein, *Ber.*, 1926, **59**, 1909.

4-Nitrohydrindene (4-*Nitroindane*)

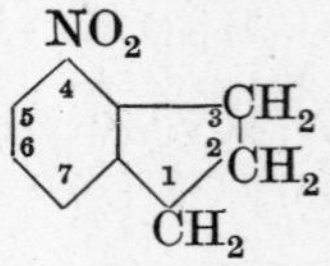

$C_9H_9O_2N$ MW, 163

White solid. M.p. 44–44·5°. B.p. 139°/10 mm.

Lindner, Brukin, *Ber.*, 1927, **60**, 436.

5-Nitrohydrindene (5-*Nitroindane*).

Yellow solid. M.p. 40–40·5°. B.p. 152°/14 mm.

See previous reference.

5-Nitrohydrindene-2 : 2-dicarboxylic Acid

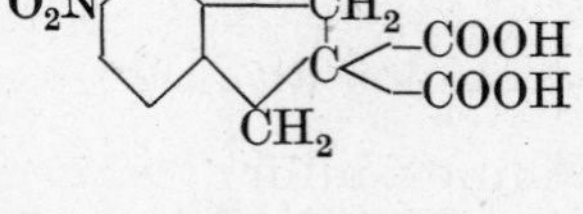

$C_{11}H_9O_6N$ MW, 251

Pale yellow needles from H_2O. M.p. 166–7°. Sol. EtOH, Et_2O, AcOH. Spar. sol. $CHCl_3$. Above m.p. or heated in boiling anisole $\longrightarrow$ 5-nitrohydrindenic acid. $KMnO_4$ in Na_2CO_3.Aq. $\longrightarrow$ 4-nitrophthalic acid.

Mills, Parker, Prowse, *J. Chem. Soc.* 1914, **105**, 1538.

5-Nitro-2-hydrindenic Acid (5-*Nitrohydrindene*-2-*carboxylic acid*, 5-*nitroindane*-2-*carboxylic acid*)

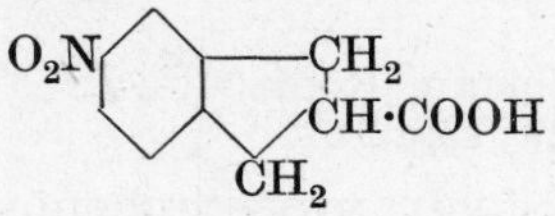

$C_{10}H_9O_4N$ MW, 207

d-.

Cryst. from toluene. M.p. 116°. $[\alpha]_D^{20}$ +29·6°, $[\alpha]_{546}^{20}$ + 36·4° in toluene.

l-.

Cryst. from H_2O. M.p. 116°. $[\alpha]_D^{17}$ − 29·0°, $[\alpha]_{546}^{17}$ − 36·5° in H_2O.

Quinine salt: m.p. 104–7°. $[\alpha]_D^{20}$ − 102·1°, $[\alpha]_{546}^{20}$ − 121·9° in H_2O.

dl-.

Needles from H_2O. M.p. 122·5°. Sol. EtOH, Me_2CO, Et_2O. Mod. sol. C_6H_6, toluene.

Mills, Parker, Prowse, *J. Chem. Soc.*, 1914, **105**, 1540.

2-Nitro-1-hydrindone (2-*Nitroindanone*-1)

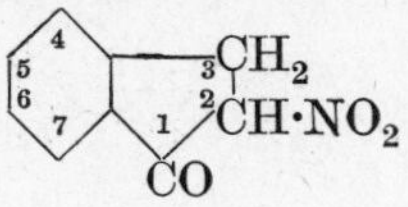

$C_9H_7O_3N$ MW, 177

Yellow needles from C_6H_6–ligroin. M.p. 117° decomp. Sol. usual org. solvents. Mod. sol. H_2O. Spar. sol. ligroin. Reduces $NH_3.AgNO_3$ and Fehling's.

Thiele, Weitz, *Ann.*, 1910, **377**, 15.

4-Nitro-1-hydrindone (4-*Nitroindanone*-1). Prisms from EtOH.Aq. M.p. 104–5°.

Oxime: brown cryst. M.p. 212–13°.

Hoyer, *J. prakt. Chem.*, 1934, **139**, 94.

6-Nitro-1-hydrindone (6-*Nitroindanone*-1). Leaflets from EtOH, AcOEt or pet. ether. M.p. 74°. Very sol. Et_2O, C_6H_6, $CHCl_3$. Sol. MeOH, EtOH, AcOEt. Spar. sol. pet. ether.

Oxime: prisms from AcOEt. M.p. 193–5°.

Semicarbazone: decomp. at 240°.

Ingold, Piggott, *J. Chem. Soc.*, 1923, **123**, 1485.

5-Nitro-2-hydrindone (5-*Nitroindanone*-2)

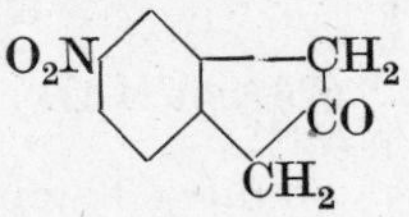

$C_9H_7O_3N$ MW, 177

Brown needles with gold lustre from EtOH. M.p. 141–141·5°. Sol. EtOH, Et_2O, AcOH. Spar. sol. H_2O. Alkalis ⟶ intense reddish-purple sols.

Heusler, Schieffer, *Ber.*, 1899, **32**, 33.

***o*-Nitrohydrocinnamic Acid**

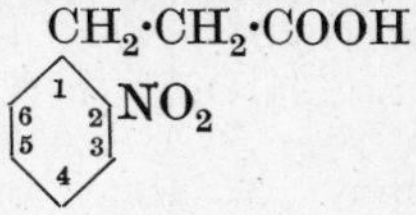

$C_9H_9O_4N$ MW, 195

Yellow cryst. from H_2O. M.p. 115° (113°). Sn + HCl ⟶ hydrocarbostyril.

Me ester: $C_{10}H_{11}O_4N$. MW, 209. B.p. 171–2°/12 mm.

Chloride: $C_9H_8O_3NCl$. MW, 213·5. Needles from pet. ether. M.p. 43°.

Amide: $C_9H_{10}O_3N_2$. MW, 194. Needles from H_2O. M.p. 121–2°.

Bromoamide: yellow needles. M.p. 136–7°.

Jaenisch, *Ber.*, 1923, **56**, 2448.

***m*-Nitrohydrocinnamic Acid.**

Yellow needles from H_2O. M.p. 117–18°. Sol. Et_2O, AcOH. Less sol. EtOH, C_6H_6. Spar. sol. cold H_2O, CS_2.

Gabriel, Steudemann, *Ber.*, 1882, **15**, 846.

***p*-Nitrohydrocinnamic Acid.**

Needles from H_2O. M.p. 163–4°. Sol. hot EtOH. Mod. sol. hot Et_2O. Spar. sol. hot H_2O. CrO_3 ⟶ *p*-nitrobenzoic acid.

Et ester: $C_{11}H_{13}O_4N$. MW, 223. Cryst. from EtOH. M.p. 33–4°.

Amide: $C_9H_{10}O_3N_2$. MW, 194. Needles from boiling H_2O. M.p. 174–5°. Sol. EtOH, Et_2O. Spar. sol. hot C_6H_6, $CHCl_3$.

Methylamide: $C_{10}H_{12}O_3N_2$. MW, 208. Needles from H_2O or $CHCl_3$. M.p. 166–7°. Spar. sol. EtOH, Et_2O.

Dimethylamide: $C_{11}H_{14}O_3N_2$. MW, 222. M.p. 90–1°. Sol. EtOH, Et_2O, $CHCl_3$. Spar. sol. H_2O.

Beilstein, Kuhlberg, *Ann.*, 1872, **163**, 132.
Taverne, *Rec. trav. chim.*, 1897, **16**, 255.

2-Nitrohydroquinone (2-*Nitroquinol*)

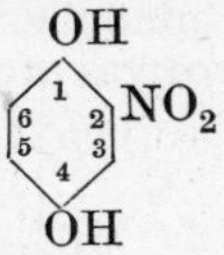

$C_6H_5O_4N$ MW, 155

Yellow cryst. from H_2O. M.p. 133–4°. Very sol. EtOH, Et_2O. Sol. H_2O, C_6H_6. Spar. sol. ligroin. Non-volatile in steam.

1-*Me ether*: $C_7H_7O_4N$. MW, 169. Pale yellow needles from H_2O. M.p. 97–9°. Sol. boiling H_2O, C_6H_6. Acids ⟶ yellow sols. Alkalis ⟶ orange sols. *Acetyl*: needles from MeOH. M.p. 106°. Very sol. boiling MeOH. Volatile in steam.

4-*Me ether*: orange needles from EtOH or ligroin. M.p. 80° (83°). Volatile in steam.

Di-Me ether: $C_8H_9O_4N$. MW, 183. Golden-yellow needles from 50% EtOH. M.p. 72–3°. B.p. 169°/13 mm. Sublimes in needles. Sol. hot 50% EtOH.

Et ether: $C_8H_9O_4N$. MW, 183. Golden needles. M.p. 83°.

Di-Et ether: $C_{10}H_{13}O_4N$. MW, 211. Golden-yellow needles from 60% EtOH. M.p. 49°.

Benzyl ether: $C_{13}H_{11}O_4N$. MW, 245. Yellow needles from H_2O. M.p. 156–8°.

Dibenzyl ether: $C_{20}H_{17}O_4N$. MW, 335. Yellow needles from EtOH. M.p. 83° (78°).

4-*Acetyl*: yellow cryst. from EtOH. M.p. 84°.

Diacetyl: needles or plates from EtOH.Aq. M.p. 86° (80°).

Dipropionyl: pale yellow plates from EtOH.Aq. M.p. 86°. Sol. EtOH, Et_2O, $CHCl_3$. Spar. sol. cold H_2O.

4-*Benzoyl*: golden-yellow needles from EtOH. M.p. 95–6°. Sol. org. solvents. Spar. sol. cold H_2O. *Acetyl*: cryst. from EtOH. M.p. 122°. Sol. hot EtOH, Me_2CO.

Dibenzoyl: needles from EtOH. M.p. 142°. Mod. sol. org. solvents. Insol. H_2O.

Kauffmann, Fritz, *Ber.*, 1910, **43**, 1214.
Richter, *Ber.*, 1916, **49**, 1401.
Kehrmann, Sandoz, Monnier, *Helv. Chim. Acta*, 1921, **4**, 941.
Kehrmann, Klopfenstein, *Helv. Chim. Acta*, 1923, **6**, 954.
Elbs, *J. prakt. Chem.*, 1893, **48**, 179.
Weselsky, Benedikt, *Monatsh.*, 1881, **2**, 369.
Nietzki, *Ann.*, 1882, **215**, 146.
Schiff, Pellizzari, *Ann.*, 1883, **221**, 371.
Klemenc, *Monatsh.*, 1914, **35**, 91.

Nitrohydroxyacetanilide.
See under Nitroaminophenol.

3-Nitro-2-hydroxyacetophenone

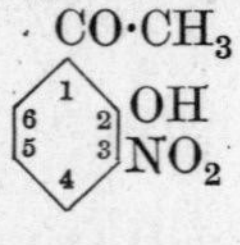

$C_8H_7O_4N$ MW, 181

Needles from AcOH.Aq. M.p. 89–90°. Sol. C_6H_6, AcOH. Mod. sol. boiling H_2O, EtOH.

Oxime: needles from C_6H_6. M.p. 182°. Turns yellow in air.

Acetyloxime: needles from C_6H_6. M.p. 136–7°.

Lindemann, Romanoff, *J. prakt. Chem.*, 1929, **122**, 214.

5-Nitro-2-hydroxyacetophenone.

Needles from AcOH.Aq. M.p. 111–12°. Sol. EtOH, C_6H_6, AcOH. Spar. sol. H_2O.

Oxime: needles from EtOH or C_6H_6. M.p. 231°. Sol. AcOH. Turns yellow in air.

Acetyloxime: cryst. from C_6H_6. M.p. 167°.

See previous reference.

3-Nitro-4-hydroxyacetophenone.

Pale yellow needles from ligroin. M.p. 135° (130°).

Me ether: $C_9H_9O_4N$. MW, 195. Needles from EtOH. M.p. 99·5°.

Stockhausen, Gattermann, *Ber.*, 1892, **25**, 3523.
Pope, *Proc. Chem. Soc.*, 1912, **28**, 332.

5-Nitro-4′-hydroxy-2-aminoazobenzene

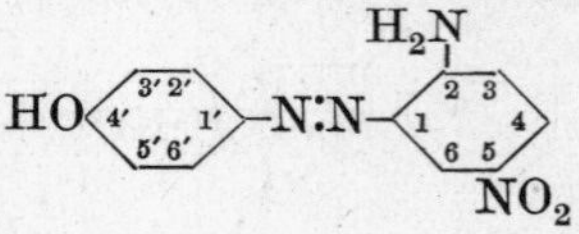

$C_{12}H_{10}O_3N_4$ MW, 258

Me ether: $C_{13}H_{12}O_3N_4$. MW, 272. Brownish-yellow cryst. from AcOH. M.p. 136°.

Borsche, Exss, *Ber.*, 1923, **56**, 2353.

4′-Nitro-6-hydroxy-3-aminoazobenzene.

Golden cryst. from AcOH. M.p. 211°. Conc. alkalis gives indigo-blue col.

N-*Acetyl*: brown needles from AcOH. M.p. 227°. Conc. H_2SO_4 ⟶ yellowish-orange col. Conc. alkali ⟶ blue col.

Grandmougin, Freimann, *J. prakt. Chem.*, 1908, **78**, 395.

Nitrohydroxy-*o*-aminobenzoic Acid.
See Nitrohydroxyanthranilic Acid.

6-Nitro-4-hydroxy-*m*-aminobenzoic Acid

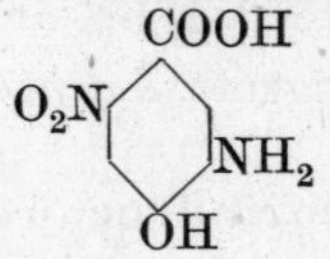

$C_7H_6O_5N_2$ MW, 198

Yellow cryst. Sol. hot H_2O. Sol. alkalis with yellowish-brown col.

Me ether: 6-nitro-3-aminoanisic acid. $C_8H_8O_5N_2$. MW, 212. Pale yellow needles from H_2O. M.p. 187–8°. Very sol. EtOH, AcOEt, Me_2CO. Sol. hot H_2O. N-*Acetyl*: prisms from AcOH, needles from H_2O. M.p. 259–60°.

M.L.B., D.R.P., 184,689, (*Chem. Zentr.*, 1907, II, 764).
Simonsen, Rau, *J. Chem. Soc.*, 1917, **111**, 235.

6-Nitro-3-hydroxy-*p*-aminobenzoic Acid

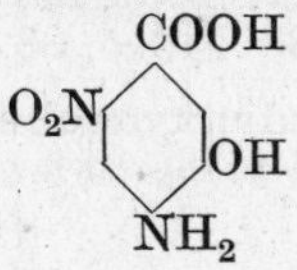

$C_7H_6O_5N_2$ MW, 198

Me ether: $C_8H_8O_5N_2$. MW, 212. Yellow needles from H_2O. Decomp. at 213–14°. Sol. EtOH, Me_2CO, hot H_2O. Mod. sol. AcOEt. Spar. sol. C_6H_6, $CHCl_3$. N-*Acetyl*: leaflets from AcOH. Decomp. at 278–80°.

See second reference above.

4-Nitro-2-hydroxy-4′-aminodiphenyl

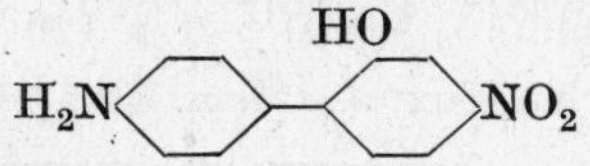

$C_{12}H_{10}O_3N_2$ MW, 230

Orange-red cryst. M.p. 145–6°. Sol. caustic alkalis with intense red col. Sols. in dil. acids are colourless.

Finzi, Mangini, *Gazz. chim. ital.*, 1932, **62**, 664.

4-Nitro-4′-hydroxy-2-aminodiphenylamine

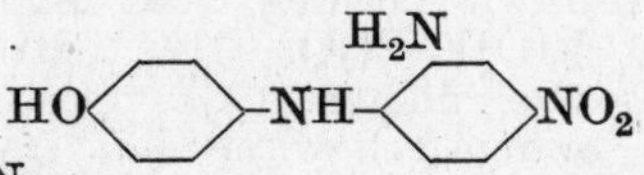

$C_{12}H_{11}O_3N_3$ MW, 245

Brownish-red needles from EtOH.Aq. M.p. 204–5°. Sol. conc. HCl. Mod. sol. H_2O.

Erdmann, *Ann.*, 1908, **362**, 152.

4-Nitro-5-hydroxyanthranilic Acid (4-*Nitro-5-hydroxy-o-aminobenzoic acid*)

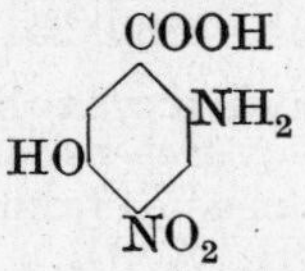

$C_7H_6O_5N_2$ MW, 198

Me ether: $C_8H_8O_5N_2$. MW, 212. Violet-black needles from H_2O. M.p. 217–18°. Sol. H_2O with orange-red col. N-*Benzoyl*: golden-yellow cryst. from AcOH. M.p. 272°. Spar. sol. EtOH, AcOH.

Ruggli, Leonhardt, *Helv. Chim. Acta*, 1924, **7**, 699.

3-Nitro-1-hydroxyanthraquinone

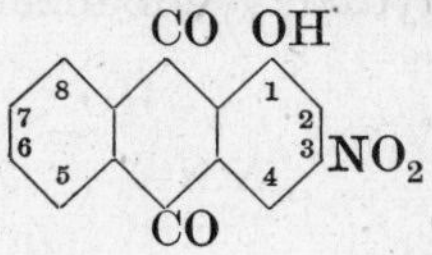

$C_{14}H_7O_5N$ MW, 269

Yellow leaflets from AcOH. M.p. 247–8° (240°). Hot NaOH ⟶ violet sol.

Scholl, Schneider, Eberle, *Ber.*, 1904, **37**, 4435.

4-Nitro-1-hydroxyanthraquinone.

Golden-yellow needles from AcOH. M.p. 268°. Sol. hot AcOH, hot $PhNO_2$. Conc. H_2SO_4 ⟶ yellow sol.

Me ether: $C_{15}H_9O_5N$. MW, 283. Cryst. Sol. EtOH, Py. Conc. H_2SO_4 ⟶ orange-yellow sol.

Bayer, D.R.P., 205,881, (*Chem. Zentr.*, 1909, I, 881); D.R.P., 163,042, (*Chem. Zentr.*, 1905, II, 1062).
Eckert, Steiner, *Monatsh.*, 1914, **35**, 1144.

1-Nitro-2-hydroxyanthraquinone

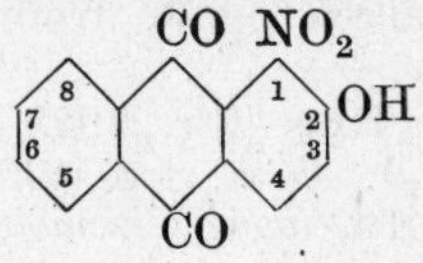

$C_{14}H_7O_5N$ MW, 269

Cryst. M.p. 257°.

Me ether: $C_{15}H_9O_5N$. MW, 283. Yellowish cryst. from $PhNO_2$. M.p. 271°. Spar. sol. AcOH.

Et ether: $C_{16}H_{11}O_5N$. MW, 297. Needles from AcOH. M.p. 243°. Mod. sol. hot AcOH. Spar. sol. EtOH. Insol. H_2O. *Oxime*: yellow needles from AcOH. Spar. sol. AcOH.

Liebermann, Hagen, *Ber.*, 1882, **15**, 1794.
Benesch, *Monatsh.*, 1911, **32**, 449.

5-Nitro-2-hydroxyanthraquinone.

Cryst. from AcOH. Caustic alkalis ⟶ red sols.

Me ether: cryst. powder from MeOH, yellow leaflets from C_6H_6. M.p. 268°.

M.L.B., D.R.P., 167,699, (*Chem. Zentr.*, 1906, I, 1070).

8-Nitro-2-hydroxyanthraquinone.
Pale yellow needles. Conc. $H_2SO_4 \longrightarrow$ yellow sol.
Me ether : needles from C_6H_6. M.p. 238°. Conc. $H_2SO_4 \longrightarrow$ orange sol.

See previous reference.

5-Nitro-2-hydroxyazobenzene (o-*Benzene-azo*-p-*nitrophenol*)

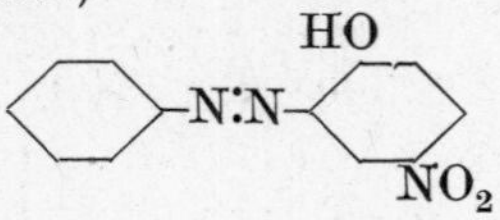

$C_{12}H_9O_3N_3$ MW, 243

Orange-red leaflets from AcOH.Aq. M.p. 150–1°. Sol. usual solvents.

Auwers, Röhrig, *Ber.*, 1897, **30**, 995.

3-Nitro-4-hydroxyazobenzene (p-*Benzene-azo*-o-*nitrophenol*)

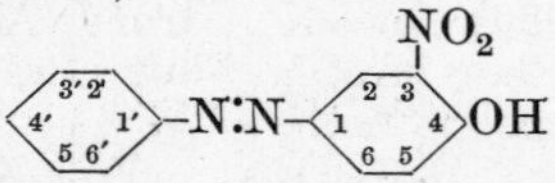

$C_{12}H_9O_3N_3$ MW, 243

Orange-yellow needles from ligroin. M.p. 129°.
Me ether : $C_{13}H_{11}O_3N_3$. MW, 257. Orange-yellow cryst. M.p. 107°.
Acetyl : yellowish-brown prisms from AcOH. M.p. 120·5°. Sol. Me_2CO, Py. Less sol. C_6H_6, $CHCl_3$. Spar. sol. Et_2O. Insol. pet. ether.
Benzoyl : yellow cryst. from C_6H_6. M.p. 132°.

Borsche, Exss, *Ber.*, 1923, **56**, 2356.
Hewitt, *J. Chem. Soc.*, 1900, **77**, 99.
Valori, *Atti accad. Lincei*, 1914, **23**, II, 291.

2′-Nitro-4-hydroxyazobenzene (p-2-*Nitrobenzeneazophenol*).
Dark red needles from MeOH.Aq. M.p. 162–3°. Sol. EtOH, C_6H_6.
Acetyl : yellow cryst. from EtOH. M.p. 109°.

Elbs, Keiper, *J. prakt. Chem.*, 1903, **67**, 581.
Elbs *et al.*, *J. prakt. Chem.*, 1924, **108**, 209.

3′-Nitro-4-hydroxyazobenzene (p-3-*Nitrobenzeneazophenol*).
Dark orange-red or pale yellow cryst. from toluene. M.p. 159° (147°). Sol. EtOH.

Nölting, *Ber.*, 1887, **20**, 2998.

4′-Nitro-4-hydroxyazobenzene (p-4-*Nitrobenzeneazophenol*).
Reddish-brown prisms and golden-yellow leaflets from toluene. M.p. 212–13°. Sol. EtOH. Insol. H_2O.
B,HCl : dark red. M.p. 158–167·5°.
Me ether : $C_{13}H_{11}O_3N_3$. MW, 257. Yellowish-red needles from EtOH. M.p. 157·5–158°. Sol. Et_2O, AcOH.
Acetyl : orange needles. M.p. 147°.
Benzoyl : orange needles. M.p. 195°.

Bamberger, *Ber.*, 1892, **25**, 846.
Nölting, *Ber.*, 1887, **20**, 2997.
Schmidt, *Ber.*, 1905, **38**, 3208.

5-Nitro-4-hydroxyazobenzene-3-carboxylic Acid (5-*Benzeneazo*-3-*nitrosalicylic acid*)

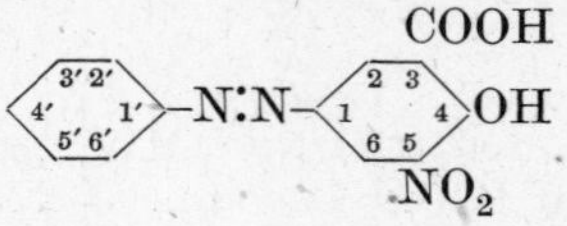

$C_{13}H_9O_5N_3$ MW, 287

Yellowish needles $+ H_2O$ from EtOH.Aq, M.p. 197°. Sol. EtOH, AcOH, boiling H_2O.
Me ester : $C_{14}H_{11}O_5N_3$. MW, 301. Brown needles from EtOH.Aq. M.p. 132–4°.
Et ester : $C_{15}H_{13}O_5N_3$. MW, 315. Yellow needles from 95% EtOH. M.p. 129°.

Hewitt, Fox, *J. Chem. Soc.*, 1901, **79**, 50.

2′-Nitro-4-hydroxyazobenzene-3-carboxylic Acid (5-o-*Nitrobenzeneazosalicylic acid*).
Dark brown cryst. M.p. 215–17°. Sol. hot EtOH, AcOH. Spar. sol. H_2O.

Elbs, Keiper, *J. prakt. Chem.*, 1903, **67**. 583.

3′-Nitro-4-hydroxyazobenzene-3-carboxylic Acid (5-m-*Nitrobenzeneazosalicylic acid*).
Reddish-brown needles from EtOH. M.p. 237°. Sol. EtOH, Et_2O, C_6H_6, $CHCl_3$, AcOH. Insol. H_2O. Sol. alkalis.
Acetyl : orange-yellow needles from EtOH. M.p. 186°. Very sol. EtOH, Et_2O.
Benzoyl : yellow needles from EtOH. M.p. above 240°. Spar. sol. EtOH.
Me ester : $C_{14}H_{11}O_5N_3$. MW, 301. Yellow needles from EtOH. M.p. 167°. Sol. C_6H_6, $CHCl_3$. Spar. sol. EtOH, Et_2O. Conc. H_2SO_4 $\longrightarrow$ blood-red sol.

Gebek, *Ann.*, 1889, **251**, 188.

4′-Nitro-4-hydroxyazobenzene-3-carboxylic Acid (5-p-*Nitrobenzeneazosalicylic acid*).
Orange-brown needles from AcOH.Aq. M.p. 257°. Sol. EtOH, AcOH. Less sol. boiling toluene.
Me ester : orange needles. M.p. 166°. *Acetyl* : orange-yellow needles from EtOH. M.p. 131°.

Et ester : m.p. 220–5°.
Phenyl ester : $C_{19}H_{13}O_5N_3$. MW, 363. Yellow needles from AcOH. M.p. 165°. *Acetyl* : yellow needles from EtOH. M.p. 155°.

Hewitt, Fox, *J. Chem. Soc.*, 1901, **79**, 53.
Grandmougin, Guisan, Freimann, *Ber.*, 1907, **40**, 3453.
Grandmougin, Freimann, *J. prakt. Chem.*, 1908, **78**, 396.

4-Nitro-4′-hydroxyazobenzene-3-carboxylic Acid

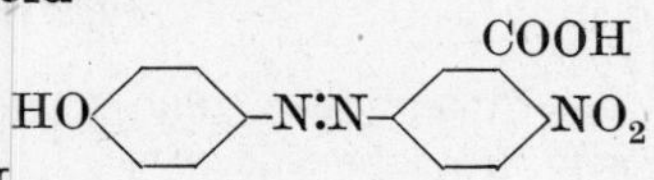

$C_{13}H_9O_5N_3$ MW, 287

Dark red needles from AcOH. M.p. 195°. Sol. most org. solvents. Spar. sol. boiling H_2O. Blood-red sols. in alkalis.

Hewitt, Mitchell, *J. Chem. Soc.*, 1907, **91**, 1261.

Nitro-*o*-hydroxybenzaldehyde.
See Nitrosalicylaldehyde.

2-Nitro-*m*-hydroxybenzaldehyde

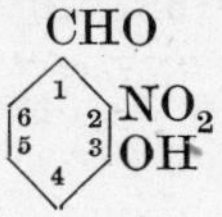

$C_7H_5O_4N$ MW, 167

Needles from ligroin. M.p. 152°.
Me ether : $C_8H_7O_4N$. MW, 181. Plates from hot C_6H_6. M.p. 102°. Sol. EtOH, Et_2O, hot C_6H_6. Spar. sol. H_2O. *Oxime* : cryst. from H_2O. M.p. 170°. Sol. EtOH, Et_2O, C_6H_6, $CHCl_3$. Spar. sol. hot H_2O. p-*Nitrophenylhydrazone* : orange needles. M.p. 222–3°.
Oxime : pale yellow needles. M.p. 172·5°.
Phenylhydrazone : orange-red needles. M.p. 134°.
p-*Nitrophenylhydrazone* : brick-red needles. M.p. 240–50° decomp.

Friedländer, Schenck, *Ber.*, 1914, **47**, 3043.
Rieche, *Ber.*, 1889, **22**, 2350.
Hodgson, Beard, *J. Chem. Soc.*, 1925, 875; 1927, 2375.

4-Nitro-*m*-hydroxybenzaldehyde.
Yellow leaflets. M.p. 128°. Sol. EtOH, Et_2O, C_6H_6, $CHCl_3$. Spar. sol. H_2O, ligroin.
Me ether : cryst. M.p. 104–5°. Sol. EtOH, Et_2O, C_6H_6. Spar. sol. ligroin. Spar. volatile in steam. *Oxime* : m.p. 148°. Sol. EtOH, Et_2O, C_6H_6, $CHCl_3$. Insol. ligroin. p-*Nitrophenylhydrazone* : needles. M.p. 257–8°.

Oxime : dark yellow needles. M.p. 164°.
p-*Nitrophenylhydrazone* : orange-red cryst. M.p. 265–6°.

See previous references.

6-Nitro-*m*-hydroxybenzaldehyde.
Needles. M.p. 167°. Spar. sol. C_6H_6, $CHCl_3$.
Me ether : leaflets from EtOH.Aq. M.p. 83°. Sol. EtOH, Et_2O, C_6H_6. Spar. sol. H_2O, ligroin. Volatile in steam. *Oxime* : m.p. 152°. Sol. EtOH, Et_2O, $CHCl_3$, Me_2CO. Less sol. C_6H_6. p-*Nitrophenylhydrazone* : terracotta needles. M.p. 281–3°.
Et ether : $C_9H_9O_4N$. MW, 195. Cryst. M.p. 62°. *Oxime* : pale yellow cryst. M.p. 125°.
Acetyl deriv. : yellow needles from ligroin. M.p. 74°. Sol. EtOH, Et_2O, C_6H_6, ligroin. Insol. H_2O.
Benzoyl deriv. : m.p. 104–5°.
Oxime : pale yellow needles. M.p. 179–80°.
Semicarbazone : pale yellow cryst. M.p. 245–60° decomp.
Phenylhydrazone : m.p. 185–95° decomp.
o-*Nitrophenylhydrazone* : terracotta needles. M.p. 248–50°.
m-*Nitrophenylhydrazone* : scarlet needles. M.p. 257–8°.
p-*Nitrophenylhydrazone* : deep orange-red needles. Does not melt below 300°.

Friedländer, Schenck, *Ber.*, 1914, **47**, 3043.
Rieche, *Ber.*, 1889, **22**, 2349.
Mason, *J. Chem. Soc.*, 1925, 1195.
Hodgson, Beard, *J. Chem. Soc.*, 1925, 875; 1927, 2375.
Pschorr, Seydel, *Ber.*, 1901, **34**, 4000.

2-Nitro-*p*-hydroxybenzaldehyde

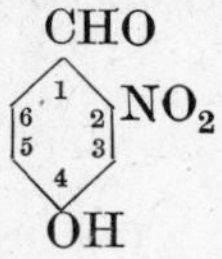

$C_7H_5O_4N$ MW, 167

Yellowish needles from EtOH. M.p. 67°. Sol. Me_2CO, C_6H_6, EtOH, Et_2O. Spar. sol. H_2O. Disagreeable odour.
Phenylhydrazone : red needles from EtOH. M.p. 189–90°.

Sachs, Kantorowicz, *Ber.*, 1906, **39**, 2758.

3-Nitro-*p*-hydroxybenzaldehyde.
Yellowish needles from EtOH. M.p. 144·5° (139–40°). Sol. EtOH, H_2O. Spar. sol. Et_2O, $CHCl_3$. $FeCl_3 \longrightarrow$ red col.

Me ether: *see* 3-Nitroanisaldehyde.

Et ether: $C_9H_9O_4N$. MW, 195. Cryst. from EtOH. M.p. 62°.

Oxime: prisms or needles from EtOH–$CHCl_3$. M.p. 169°. Mod. sol. EtOH, Et_2O, AcOH. Less sol. C_6H_6, $CHCl_3$. Spar. sol. ligroin.

Phenylhydrazone: red needles from EtOH or AcOH. M.p. 175–6°. Sol. EtOH, AcOH, C_6H_6, $CHCl_3$, CS_2. Less sol. Et_2O. O-*Acetyl*: orange-red needles from EtOH. M.p. 134–5°. Sol. Et_2O, C_6H_6, AcOH, $CHCl_3$. Mod. sol. EtOH. N-*Acetyl*: golden-yellow needles from EtOH. M.p. 193–4°. Sol. C_6H_6, $CHCl_3$, AcOH. Mod. sol. EtOH.

p-*Nitrophenylhydrazone*: orange needles from AcOH. M.p. 247–9° decomp.

p-*Bromophenylhydrazone*: red needles from AcOH. M.p. 192–3°.

Paal, *Ber.*, 1895, **28**, 2413.
Auwers, Rohrig, *Ber.*, 1897, **30**, 996.
Fishman, *J. Am. Chem. Soc.*, 1920, **42**, 2299.

Nitro-*o*-hydroxybenzoic Acid.

See Nitrosalicylic Acid.

2-Nitro-*m*-hydroxybenzoic Acid

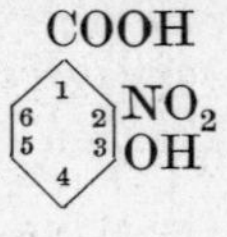

$C_7H_5O_5N$ MW, 183

Plates and prisms + H_2O from H_2O. M.p. 178°. Sol. EtOH, Et_2O. Mod. sol. H_2O. Very sweet.

Me ether: 2-nitro-*m*-methoxybenzoic acid. $C_8H_7O_5N$. MW, 197. Leaflets from H_2O. M.p. 251° decomp. Sol. EtOH, Me_2CO, AcOH. Spar. sol. Et_2O, C_6H_6, $CHCl_3$. NH_3 at 180° $\longrightarrow$ 2-nitro-3-aminobenzoic acid.

Et ester: $C_9H_9O_5N$. MW, 211. Cryst. from EtOH. M.p. 124°. Very sol. EtOH. *Et ether*: $C_{11}H_{13}O_5N$. MW, 239. Plates from EtOH. M.p. 53–4°. NH_3.Aq. at 150° $\longrightarrow$ 2-nitro-3-aminobenzoic acid.

Griess, *Ber.*, 1887, **20**, 407.
Rieche, *Ber.*, 1889, **22**, 2352.
Thieme, *J. prakt. Chem.*, 1891, **43**, 467.

4-Nitro-*m*-hydroxybenzoic Acid.

Yellow leaflets from H_2O. M.p. 230°. Very spar. sol. H_2O.

Me ether: 4-nitro-*m*-methoxybenzoic acid. $C_8H_7O_5N$. MW, 197. Needles. M.p. 233°.

Et ether: $C_9H_9O_5N$. MW, 211. Pale yellow needles from EtOH. M.p. 216·5°. Sol. EtOH, Et_2O. Spar. sol. H_2O. *Et ester*: $C_{11}H_{13}O_5N$. MW, 239. Needles. M.p. 60–1°. Sol. EtOH, Et_2O, $CHCl_3$, AcOH. Insol. H_2O. *Amide*: $C_9H_{10}O_4N_2$. MW, 210. Golden-yellow needles from H_2O. M.p. 202°. Sol. EtOH, AcOH. Spar. sol. Et_2O, C_6H_6.

Me ester: $C_8H_7O_5N$. MW, 197. Needles from EtOH. M.p. 92°.

Et ester: $C_9H_9O_5N$. MW, 211. Yellowish prisms from EtOH. M.p. 84°. Sol. EtOH, Et_2O. Insol. H_2O.

Brenans, Prost, *Compt. rend.*, 1924, **178**, 1285.
Einhorn, Pfyl, *Ann.*, 1900, **311**, 44.
See also previous references.

5-Nitro-*m*-hydroxybenzoic Acid.

Leaflets or plates. M.p. 167°. Sol. EtOH, Et_2O, hot H_2O.

Anilide: needles from AcOH.Aq. M.p. 232°. Sol. AcOH. Mod. sol. EtOH. Insol. H_2O, Et_2O.

Azide: reddish-yellow ppt. Decomp. on heating. Spar. sol. EtOH, Et_2O. Insol. H_2O.

Curtius, Riedel, *J. prakt. Chem.*, 1907, **76**, 260.
Griess, *Ber.*, 1887, **20**, 407.

6-Nitro-*m*-hydroxybenzoic Acid.

Yellow needles or prisms from H_2O. M.p. 171·5–172°. Very sol. H_2O, EtOH, Et_2O.

Me ether: 6-nitro-*m*-methoxybenzoic acid. M.p. 132–3°. Sol. EtOH, Et_2O, $CHCl_3$, C_6H_6, AcOH. Insol. ligroin.

Rieche, *Ber.*, 1889, **22**, 2354.
Beyer, *Rec. trav. chim.*, 1921, **40**, 624.
Brenans, *Compt. rend.*, 1924, **178**, 1285.
See also last reference above.

2-Nitro-*p*-hydroxybenzoic Acid.

Me ether: *see* 2-Nitroanisic Acid.

3-Nitro-*p*-hydroxybenzoic Acid.

Needles or leaflets from H_2O. M.p. 186–7° (182–3°). Sol. EtOH, Et_2O, hot H_2O. No col with $FeCl_3$.

Me ether: *see* 3-Nitroanisic Acid.

Et ether: $C_9H_9O_5N$. MW, 211. Cryst. M.p 200–1°. *Et ester*: $C_{11}H_{13}O_5N$. MW, 239 Cryst. from EtOH. M.p. 64°. *Chloride*: $C_9H_8O_4NCl$. MW, 229·5. M.p. 81–2°. B.p 215–16°/20 mm.

Phenyl ether: *see* 3-Nitro-*p*-phenoxybenzoic Acid.

Me ester: $C_8H_7O_5N$. MW, 197. Yellow needles from EtOH.Aq. M.p. 75–6° (70–1°)

Propyl ether: $C_{11}H_{13}O_5N$. MW, 239. Oil. B.p 144–6°/11 mm. *Benzoyl*: needles from EtOH M.p. 95°. p-*Toluenesulphonyl*: m.p. 86°.

Et ester: $C_9H_9O_5N$. MW, 211. Yellowish

ed prisms from EtOH. M.p. 75–6° (69°). Sol. EtOH, Et_2O, C_6H_6. Insol. H_2O.

Propyl ester: $C_{10}H_{11}O_5N$. MW, 225. Yellow cryst. M.p. 60–1°.

Butyl ester: $C_{11}H_{13}O_5N$. MW, 239. Yellow oil. B.p. 174–6°/8 mm.

Isoamyl ester: $C_{12}H_{15}O_5N$. MW, 253. Yellow needles from EtOH. M.p. 59°. B.p. 117–19°/2 mm.

Benzyl ester: $C_{14}H_{11}O_5N$. MW, 273. Yellowish-brown needles from EtOH. M.p. 82°.

Nitrile: 2-nitro-4-cyanophenol. $C_7H_4O_3N_2$. MW, 164. Yellowish leaflets from very dil. EtOH. M.p. 144–5°. *Acetyl*: m.p. 113–14°.

Carbethoxyl: needles from EtOH.Aq. M.p. 176–7°.

Griess, *Ber.*, 1887, **20**, 408.
Diepolder, *Ber.*, 1896, **29**, 1756.
Thieme, *J. prakt. Chem.*, 1891, **43**, 453.
Einhorn, Pfyl, *Ann.*, 1900, **311**, 67.
Biehringer, Borsum, *Ber.*, 1915, **48**, 1316.
Sabalitschka, Tiedge, *Arch. Pharm.*, 1934, **272**, 383.

5-Nitro-2-hydroxybenzophenone

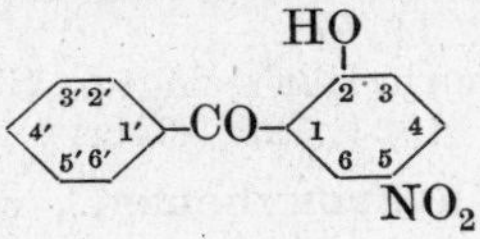

$C_{13}H_9O_4N$ MW, 243

Cryst. from EtOH. M.p. 124–124·5°.

Ullmann, Mallet, *Ber.*, 1898, **31**, 1696.

4′-Nitro-2-hydroxybenzophenone.

Yellow prisms. M.p. 111–13°. Sol. hot EtOH, Et_2O, AcOH. Spar. sol. C_6H_6, ligroin.

Me ether: $C_{14}H_{11}O_4N$. MW, 257. Prisms and leaflets from EtOH or ligroin. M.p. 117–19°. Sol. hot EtOH, AcOH. Spar. sol. Et_2O, hot ligroin.

Auwers, *Ber.*, 1903, **36**, 3896.

3-Nitro-4-hydroxybenzophenone.

Yellowish-brown rhombic cryst. from MeOH. M.p. 120–1°.

Me ether: $C_{14}H_{11}O_4N$. MW, 257. Yellow cryst. from MeOH. M.p. 105°. *Oxime*: yellow. M.p. 179°.

Borsche, *Ber.*, 1917, **50**, 1354.
v. Alphen, *Rec. trav. chim.*, 1930, **49**, 384.

2′-Nitro-4-hydroxybenzophenone.

Et ether: $C_{15}H_{13}O_4N$. MW, 271. Yellow prisms from EtOH. M.p. 115°. Sol. most org. solvents except cold EtOH, ligroin.

Auwers, *Ber.*, 1903, **36**, 3891.

3′-Nitro-4-hydroxybenzophenone.

Yellowish prisms from EtOH.Aq. M.p. 173°. Sol. EtOH, C_6H_6, $CHCl_3$, CS_2. Spar. sol. ligroin.

Me ether: $C_{14}H_{11}O_4N$. MW, 257. Pale yellow cryst. from MeOH. M.p. 95°.

Et ether: $C_{15}H_{13}O_4N$. MW, 271. Prisms from EtOH–ligroin. M.p. 79–81°. Sol. most org. solvents.

Phenyl ether: $C_{19}H_{13}O_4N$. MW, 319. Cryst. M.p. 87–8°. Conc. $H_2SO_4 \longrightarrow$ yellow sol.

v. Alphen, *Rec. trav. chim.*, 1930, **49**, 389.
See also previous reference.

4′-Nitro-4-hydroxybenzophenone.

Yellow needles. M.p. 190–2°. Sol. EtOH, Et_2O, AcOH. Spar. sol. ligroin, pet. ether.

Me ether: needles from EtOH or AcOH. M.p. 121°. Spar. sol. EtOH, Et_2O, AcOH.

Et ether: yellowish needles. M.p. 112°.

Phenyl ether: m.p. 121–2°. Conc. $H_2SO_4 \longrightarrow$ brownish-red sol.

Acetyl: needles from EtOH. M.p. 131°. Spar. sol. EtOH, AcOH. Almost insol. Et_2O, ligroin, pet. ether.

Auwers, *Ber.*, 1903, **36**, 3893.

Nitro-*o*-hydroxybenzyl Alcohol.

See Nitrosaligenin.

4-Nitro-*m*-hydroxybenzyl Alcohol

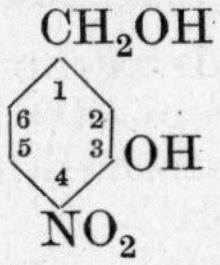

$C_7H_7O_4N$ MW, 169

Needles from C_6H_6. M.p. 97°. Spar. sol. C_6H_6, $CHCl_3$.

Lock, *Ber.*, 1929, **62**, 1185.

6-Nitro-*m*-hydroxybenzyl Alcohol.

Cryst. from H_2O. M.p. 120·5°. Sol. EtOH, Et_2O, Me_2CO. Mod. sol. hot H_2O, C_6H_6, $CHCl_3$, toluene. Alkalis $\longrightarrow$ intense yellow sols. $FeCl_3 \longrightarrow$ reddish-violet col.

Lock, *Ber.*, 1929, **62**, 1184.

3-Nitro-*p*-hydroxybenzyl Alcohol.

Prisms from H_2O. M.p. 97°. Sol. Et_2O, AcOH. Spar. sol. EtOH, C_6H_6.

4-*Me ether*: 3-nitroanisyl alcohol. $C_8H_9O_4N$. MW, 183. Needles from H_2O. M.p. 69°.

4-*Et ether*: $C_9H_{11}O_4N$. MW, 197. Needles from H_2O. M.p. 66°.

Fishman, *J. Am. Chem. Soc.*, 1920, **42**, 2292.
Hart, Hirschfelder, *ibid.*, 2683.

Nitro-*o*-hydroxybenzylamine.
See Nitrosalicylamine.

3-Nitro-*p*-hydroxybenzylamine

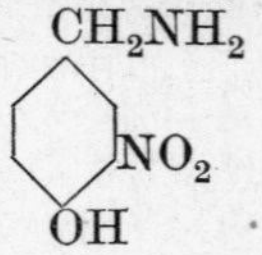

$C_7H_8O_3N_2$ MW, 168

Orange-red needles $+ H_2O$ from H_2O. At 115° loses $H_2O \longrightarrow$ yellow solid, m.p. 225°.

B,HCl : m.p. 242° decomp.

N-*Benzoyl* : yellow needles from EtOH. M.p. 137°.

Einhorn *et al.*, *Ann.*, 1905, **343**, 243.

2-Nitro-*N*-*o*-hydroxybenzylaniline

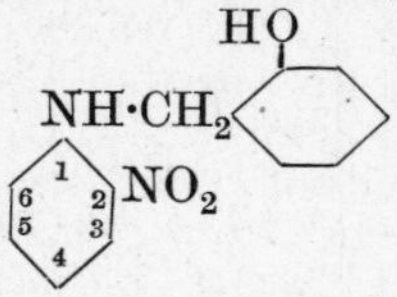

$C_{13}H_{12}O_3N_2$ MW, 244

Dark red plates or needles. M.p. 125°. Very sol. Me_2CO, C_6H_6, $CHCl_3$. Mod. sol. EtOH.

O-*Acetyl* : yellow needles from EtOH.Aq. M.p. 93°. Sol. Et_2O. Insol. ligroin.

Paal, Härtel, *Ber.*, 1899, **32**, 2059.

3-Nitro-*N*-*o*-hydroxybenzylaniline.
Orange needles from EtOH. M.p. 115°.

N-*Acetyl* : prisms from EtOH.Aq. M.p. 126°. Sol. EtOH, C_6H_6, $CHCl_3$.

O : N-*Diacetyl* : needles from EtOH.Aq. M.p. 99°. Sol. C_6H_6, $CHCl_3$, warm EtOH.

See previous reference.

4-Nitro-*N*-*o*-hydroxybenzylaniline.
Golden-yellow plates from EtOH.Aq. M.p. 138°. Sol. org. solvents except ligroin.

O : N-*Diacetyl* : needles from EtOH. M.p. 79°. Sol. C_6H_6, hot $CHCl_3$, AcOH.

See previous reference.

4-Nitro-*N*-α-hydroxybenzylaniline (ω-p-*Nitroanilinobenzyl alcohol*)

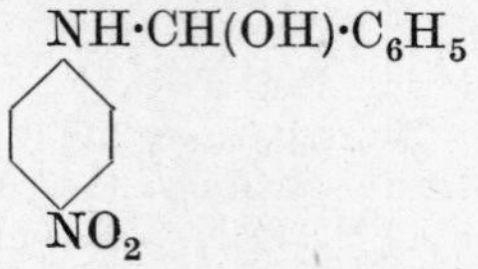

$C_{13}H_{12}O_3N_2$ MW, 244

Yellow prisms. M.p. 85–6°. In vacuo over $H_2SO_4 \longrightarrow$ benzaldehyde-4-nitroanil.

B,HCl : yellow cryst. powder. M.p. about 188°. Sol. EtOH. Insol. Et_2O. Decomp. by cold H_2O.

Dimroth, Zoeppritz, *Ber.*, 1902, **35**, 989.
v. Miller, Plöchl, Rohde, *Ber.*, 1892, **25**, 2054.

5-Nitro-*o*-hydroxybenzyl bromide (α-*Bromo*-5-*nitro*-o-*cresol*)

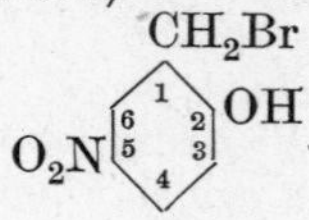

$C_7H_6O_3NBr$ MW, 232

Leaflets from C_6H_6. M.p. 147°. Sol. EtOH. Mod. sol. C_6H_6, AcOH. Spar. sol. ligroin.

Auwers, *Ber.*, 1906, **39**, 3173.

3-Nitro-*p*-hydroxybenzyl bromide (α-*Bromo*-3-*nitro*-p-*cresol*).
Yellow needles from AcOH or pet. ether. M.p. 83–5° (82°). Sol. most solvents. Spar. sol. AcOH, pet. ether, ligroin.

Me ether : $C_8H_8O_3NBr$. MW, 246. Pale yellow needles from pet. ether. M.p. 108°.

Bayer, D.R.P., 132,475, (*Chem. Zentr.*, 1902, II, 81).
Shoesmith, Hetherington, Slater, *J. Chem. Soc.*, 1924, **125**, 1316.

5-Nitro-*o*-hydroxybenzyl chloride (α-*Chloro*-5-*nitro*-o-*cresol*)

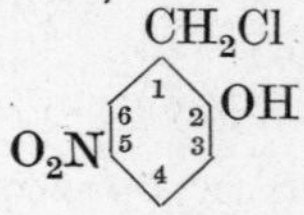

$C_7H_6O_3NCl$ MW, 187·5

Needles or plates from C_6H_6. M.p. 132° (128°). Sol. EtOH, C_6H_6, AcOH, $CHCl_3$. Spar. sol. Et_2O, ligroin. Hot $H_2O \longrightarrow$ 5-nitrosaligenin.

Einhorn, *Ann.*, 1905, **343**, 245.
Bayer, D.R.P., 132,475, (*Chem. Zentr.*, 1902, II, 81).

3-Nitro-*p*-hydroxybenzyl chloride (α-*Chloro*-3-*nitro*-p-*cresol*).
Yellow needles from C_6H_6, ligroin or EtOH, leaflets from pet. ether. M.p. 75° (72°).

See last reference above and also
Stoermer, Behn, *Ber.*, 1901, **34**, 2459.

5-Nitro-*o*-hydroxybenzyl iodide (α-*Iodo*-5-*nitro*-o-*cresol*)

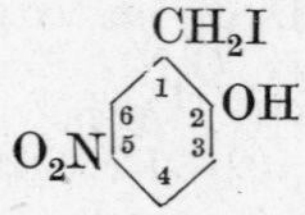

$C_7H_6O_3NI$ MW, 279

Cryst. M.p. 169°.

Bayer, D.R.P., 132,475, (*Chem. Zentr.*, 1902, II, 81).

3-Nitro-*p*-hydroxybenzyl iodide (*α-Iodo*-3-*nitro*-p-*cresol*).
Pale yellow cryst. M.p. 112°.

See previous reference.

2-Nitro-α-hydroxycinnamic Acid (2-*Nitrophenylpyruvic acid, enol form*)

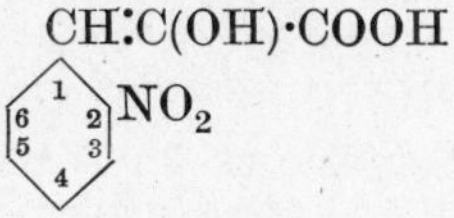

$C_9H_7O_5N$ MW, 209

Me ether: $C_{10}H_9O_5N$. MW, 223. Cryst. from C_6H_6. M.p. 160–1°. Gives no col. with $FeCl_3$. *Me ester*: $C_{11}H_{11}O_5N$. MW, 237. Needles from ligroin. M.p. 67·5–68°. Spar. sol. EtOH. *Et ester*: $C_{12}H_{13}O_5N$. MW, 251. Cryst. from EtOH. M.p. 46–7°. Sol. Et_2O, C_6H_6, $CHCl_3$.
Et ether: $C_{11}H_{11}O_5N$. MW, 237. Needles from C_6H_6. M.p. 146–7°. *Me ester*: $C_{12}H_{13}O_5N$. MW, 251. Brown needles from ligroin. M.p. 49–50°.
Me ester: $C_{10}H_9O_5N$. MW, 223. Yellow cryst. from EtOH. M.p. 92–93·5°.
Et ester: $C_{11}H_{11}O_5N$. MW, 237. Cryst. from ligroin. M.p. 70–1°. $FeCl_3$ ⟶ dark green col. Cu acetate ⟶ green col. *Acetyl*: prisms from C_6H_6. M.p. 95–6°. *Benzoyl*: plates from EtOH or ligroin. M.p. 46–7°. Does not react with $FeCl_3$. Does not decolourise $KMnO_4$ in Me_2CO.

Wislicenus, Thoma, *Ann.*, 1924, **436**, 51.

4-Nitro-α-hydroxycinnamic Acid (4-*Nitrophenylpyruvic acid, enol form*).
Et ester: yellow prisms. M.p. 106°. Mod. sol. usual solvents. Insol. ligroin. Alkalis ⟶ deep red sols. $FeCl_3$ in dil. EtOH ⟶ brownish-green col.

Wislicenus, Schultz, *Ann.*, 1924, **436**, 58.

β-Nitro-α-hydroxydibenzyl.
See β-Nitro-α-hydroxy-*sym.*-diphenylethane.

4′-Nitro-4-hydroxy-2 : 3-dimethylazobenzene

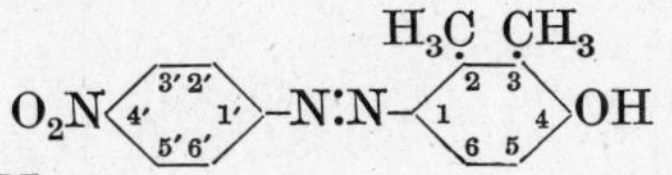

$C_{14}H_{13}O_3N_3$ MW, 271

Me ether: $C_{15}H_{15}O_3N_3$. MW, 285. Dark red needles from EtOH. M.p. 142°. Sol. C_6H_6, AcOH. Spar. sol. EtOH, MeOH. Conc. H_2SO_4 ⟶ bluish-red sol.

Auwers, Michaelis, *Ber.*, 1914, **47**, 1294.

4′-Nitro-4-hydroxy-2 : 5-dimethylazobenzene.
Violet needles from AcOH. M.p. 222–3°. Sol. Et_2O, C_6H_6. Spar. sol. EtOH, AcOH, ligroin.
Me ether: bluish-red needles from AcOH. M.p. 163–4°. Sol. C_6H_6. Mod. sol. EtOH, AcOH. Conc. H_2SO_4 ⟶ red sol.

Auwers, Rietz, *Ann.*, 1907, **356**, 164 (*Note*).

4′-Nitro-4-hydroxy-2 : 6-dimethylazobenzene.
Red needles from AcOH. M.p. 166–7°. Sol. Et_2O, C_6H_6. Mod. sol. AcOH. Spar. sol. EtOH, ligroin.
Me ether: violet needles from AcOH. M.p. 119–20°. Sol. C_6H_6. Mod. sol. AcOH. Spar. sol. EtOH, pet. ether.
Isopropyl ether: $C_{17}H_{19}O_3N_3$. MW, 313. Brownish-violet needles from ligroin. M.p. 92–3°. Sol. usual solvents. Spar. sol. EtOH, pet. ether.
Allyl ether: $C_{17}H_{17}O_3N_3$. MW, 311. Brownish-red needles from pet. ether. M.p. 102–3°.

Auwers, Rietz, *Ann.*, 1907, **356**, 165 (*Note*).
Auwers, Michaelis, *Ber.*, 1914, **47**, 1293.
Ler, *Chem. Abstracts*, 1934, **28**, 4715.

4′-Nitro-2-hydroxy-3 : 5-dimethylazobenzene.
Red needles from AcOH or EtOH. M.p. 194–5° (193°). Sol. Et_2O, C_6H_6. Spar. sol. EtOH, AcOH, ligroin.

See last reference above and also
Auwers, Rietz, *Ann.*, 1907, **356**, 164 (*Note*).

5-Nitro-6-hydroxy-2 : 3-dimethylbenzaldehyde

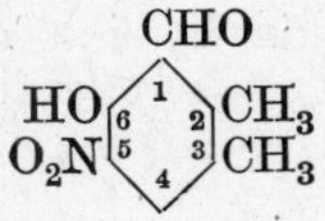

$C_9H_9O_4N$ MW, 195

Dark yellow needles from EtOH. M.p. 86–7°.

Clayton, *J. Chem. Soc.*, 1910, **97**, 1405.

3-Nitro-4-hydroxy-2 : 5-dimethylbenzaldehyde.
Plates from EtOH. M.p. 188°.

Oxime : orange-red needles from H_2O. Decomp. at 160°.

Azine : orange needles from EtOH. Decomp. at 237°.

Gattermann, *Ann.*, 1907, **357**, 325.

5-Nitro-6-hydroxy-3 : 4-dimethylbenzaldehyde.

Needles from EtOH. M.p. 146–7°.

Clayton, *J. Chem. Soc.*, 1910, **97**, 1405.

3-Nitro-6-hydroxy-2 : 4-dimethylpyridine (5-*Nitro*-4 : 6-*dimethyl-α-pyridone*, 3-*nitro*-6-*hydroxy-αγ-lutidine*, 5-*nitro-α-lutidone*)

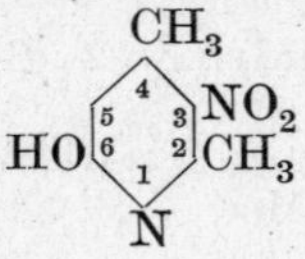

$C_7H_8O_3N_2$ MW, 168

Leaflets. M.p. 260°. Sol. H_2O.

Moir, *J. Chem. Soc.*, 1902, **81**, 116.

5-Nitro-6-hydroxy-2 : 4-dimethylpyridine (3-*Nitro*-4 : 6-*dimethyl-α-pyridone*, 5-*nitro*-6-*hydroxy-αγ-lutidine*, 3-*nitro-α-lutidone*).

Yellow needles from AcOH. M.p. 254°. Sol. alkalis with yellow col. Non-volatile in steam.

Collie, Tickle, *J. Chem. Soc.*, 1898, **73**, 231.
Moir, *J. Chem. Soc.*, 1902, **81**, 104.

3-Nitro-4-hydroxy-2 : 6-dimethylpyridine (3-*Nitro*-2 : 6-*dimethyl-γ-pyridone*, 3-*nitro*-4-*hydroxy-αα′-lutidine*, 3-*nitro-γ-lutidone*).

Yellowish cryst. from AcOH. M.p. about 290–300° decomp. Sol. cold H_2O. Sol. Na_2CO_3.Aq. with yellow col.

Hall, Collie, *J. Chem. Soc.*, 1898, **73**, 238.
Collie, Bishop, *J. Chem. Soc.*, 1925, 962.

3-Nitro-2-hydroxy-4 : 6-dimethylquinoline (3-*Nitro*-4 : 6-*dimethylcarbostyril*)

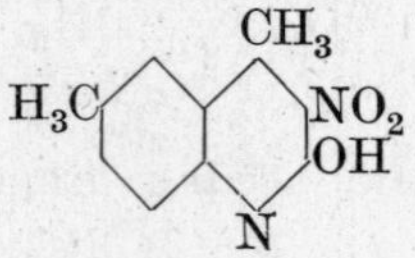

$C_{11}H_{10}O_3N_2$ MW, 218

Prismatic needles from AcOH. M.p. 294°. Spar. sol. EtOH. Insol. H_2O.

Balaban, *J. Chem. Soc.*, 1930, 2346.

6-Nitro-2-hydroxy-4 : 7-dimethylquinoline (6-*Nitro*-4 : 7-*dimethylcarbostyril*)

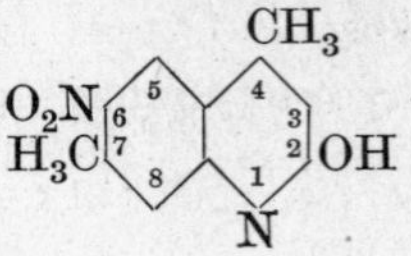

$C_{11}H_{10}O_3N_2$ MW, 21

Leaflets from AcOH. Darkens at 280° wit part. decomp. Spar. sol. AcOH. Insol. EtOH Et_2O.

See previous reference.

8-Nitro-2-hydroxy-4 : 7-dimethylquinoline (8-*Nitro*-4 : 7-*dimethylcarbostyril*).

Yellow plates from AcOH–EtOH. M.p. 226° Sol. hot AcOH. Spar. sol. EtOH.

See previous reference.

6-Nitro-2-hydroxy-4 : 8-dimethylquinoline (6-*Nitro*-4 : 8-*dimethylcarbostyril*)

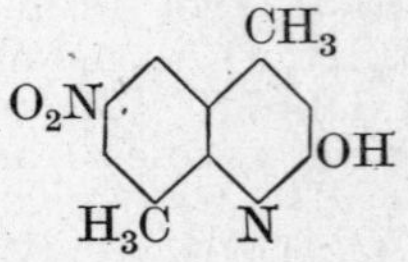

$C_{11}H_{10}O_3N_2$ MW, 21

Needles from AcOH. M.p. 310° decomp Spar. sol. AcOH.

See previous reference.

4-Nitro-2-hydroxydiphenyl

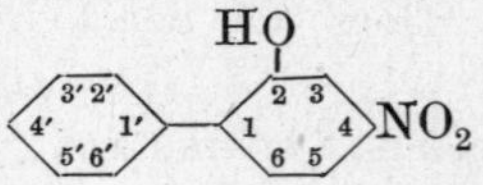

$C_{12}H_9O_3N$ MW, 21

Cryst. from EtOH. M.p. 200–1°.

Finzi, Mangini, *Gazz. chim. ital.*, 1932, 62, 672.

5-Nitro-2-hydroxydiphenyl.

Yellow needles from dil. EtOH or dil. AcOH. M.p. 128° (125–6°). Sol. EtOH, Me_2CO. Moc sol. Et_2O, $CHCl_3$. Insol. ligroin. Sublimes.

Me ether : $C_{13}H_{11}O_3N$. MW, 229. Yellow needles from MeOH. M.p. 95–6°.

Et ether : $C_{14}H_{13}O_3N$. MW, 243. M.p. 110·6°

Borsche, Scholten, *Ber.*, 1917, **50**, 600.
Borsche, *Ann.*, 1900, **312**, 223.
Hill, *Ber.*, 1900, 33, 1241.

2′-Nitro-2-hydroxydiphenyl.

Brown liq.

Me ether : m.p. 80–1°.

Acetyl : cryst. from pet. ether. M.p. 102°.

Mascarelli, Gatti, *Gazz. chim. ital.*, 1931, **61**, 791; *Chem. Abstracts*, 1935, **29**, 4351.

4′-Nitro-2-hydroxydiphenyl.

Needles from dil. EtOH. M.p. 123–4°.

Harris, Christiansen, *Chem. Zentr.*, 1933, II, 3424.

3′-Nitro-3-hydroxydiphenyl.

M.p. 114–16°.

Mascarelli, Gatti, *Gazz. chim. ital.*, 1931, **61**, 325; *Chem. Abstracts*, 1930, **24**, 4777.

3-Nitro-4-hydroxydiphenyl.

M.p. 66°.

Me ether : needles from EtOH. M.p. 91–2°.

Raiford, Colbert, *J. Am. Chem. Soc.*, 1925, **47**, 1454.
Bell, Kenyon, *J. Chem. Soc.*, 1926, 3048.

2′-Nitro-4-hydroxydiphenyl.

Yellow needles. M.p. 138°.

Schultz, Schmidt, Strasser, *Ann.*, 1881, **207**, 351.

4′-Nitro-4-hydroxydiphenyl.

Yellow needles from C_6H_6. M.p. 203° (200–1°).

Me ether : yellow needles from EtOH. M.p. 111°.

p-*Toluenesulphonyl* : cryst. from C_6H_6. M.p. 159° (156–8°).

Bell, Kenyon, *J. Chem. Soc.*, 1926, 3048.
Angeletti, *Chem. Abstracts*, 1927, **21**, 579.

2′-Nitro-2-hydroxydiphenylamine

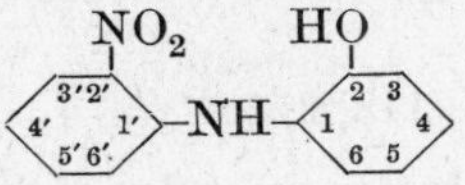

$C_{12}H_{10}O_3N_2$ MW, 230

Me ether : $C_{13}H_{12}O_3N_2$. MW, 244. Red needles. M.p. 83°.

McCombie, Scarborough, Waters, *J. Chem. Soc.*, 1928, 353.

6-Nitro-3-hydroxydiphenylamine.

Leaflets from C_6H_6. M.p. 165°. Sol. EtOH. Spar. sol. C_6H_6.

Et ether : $C_{14}H_{14}O_3N_2$. MW, 258. Orange-yellow needles from EtOH. M.p. 106–106·5°.

Jacobson, Fertsch, Fischer, *Ber.*, 1893, **26**, 684.

2′-Nitro-4-hydroxydiphenylamine.

Me ether : orange-red prisms. M.p. 89°.

McCombie, Scarborough, Waters, *J. Chem. Soc.*, 1928, 353.

4′-Nitro-4-hydroxydiphenylamine.

Yellowish-brown leaflets with steel-blue reflex from H_2O. M.p. 183°. Sol. EtOH, Et_2O, AcOH, AcOEt. Spar. sol. boiling C_6H_6. Insol. CCl_4, ligroin. NaOH ⟶ brown sol. Conc. H_2SO_4 ⟶ pale green sol. ⟶ blue on warming.

Ullmann, D.R.P., 193,448, (*Chem. Zentr.*, 1908, I, 1003).
Ullmann, Jüngel, *Ber.*, 1909, **42**, 1078.

4-Nitro-4′-hydroxydiphenylamine-2-carboxylic Acid

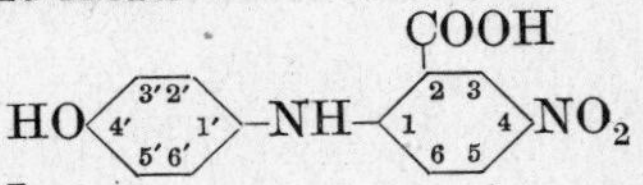

$C_{13}H_{10}O_5N_2$ MW, 274

Orange powder. M.p. 210°. Excess NaOH.Aq. ⟶ intense red col.

Goldstein, Vaymatchar, *Helv. Chim. Acta*, 1928, **11**, 243.

4′-Nitro-4-hydroxydiphenylamine-3-carboxylic Acid.

Brown needles. Sol. hot H_2O with orange-yellow col.

M.L.B., D.R.P., 114,269, (*Chem. Zentr.*, 1900, II, 931).

2-Nitro-2′-hydroxydiphenylamine-4-carboxylic Acid.

Brown needles from EtOH.Aq. M.p. 260–1°. Very sol. Me_2CO. Sol. EtOH. Spar. sol. H_2O, C_6H_6, $CHCl_3$, ligroin.

Schöpff, *Ber.*, 1889, **22**, 3288.

β-Nitro-α-hydroxy-*sym*.-diphenylethane

(β-*Nitro-α-hydroxydibenzyl*)

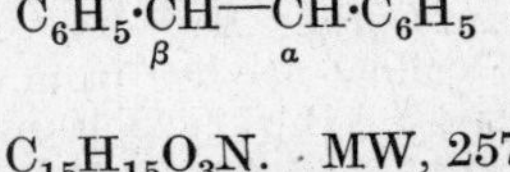

$C_{14}H_{13}O_3N$ MW, 243

Me ether : $C_{15}H_{15}O_3N$. MW, 257. Exists in two forms. (i) Needles from EtOH or pet. ether. M.p. 130–1°. Sol. EtOH, Et_2O, C_6H_6, alkalis. (ii) Prisms from MeOH. M.p. 97–8°. More sol. than (i).

Et ether : $C_{16}H_{17}O_3N$. MW, 271. Needles. M.p. 92°. Mod. sol. usual solvents.

Meisenheimer, Heim, *Ann.*, 1907, **355**, 277.
Heim, *Ber.*, 1911, **44**, 2013.

β-Nitro-α-hydroxy-*unsym.*-diphenylethane

$(C_6H_5)_2C(OH)\cdot CH_2NO_2$

$C_{14}H_{13}O_3N$ MW, 243

Prisms from AcOH. M.p. 107–8°. Sol. Et_2O, hot AcOH. Mod. sol. EtOH, C_6H_6. Spar. sol. pet. ether. Insol. H_2O. CrO_3 in boiling AcOH ⟶ benzophenone.

Et ether: $C_{16}H_{17}O_3N$. MW, 271. Cryst. from Et_2O–pet. ether. M.p. 91–2°. Sol. Et_2O, hot AcOH. Mod. sol. EtOH, C_6H_6. Spar. sol. pet. ether.

Konowalow, Jatzewitsch, *Chem. Zentr.*, 1905, II, 825.

5-Nitro-2-hydroxydiphenyl Ether

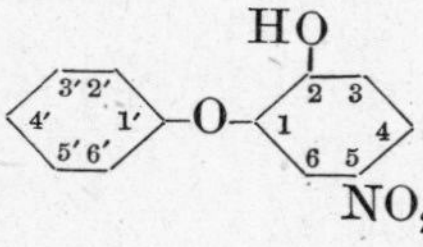

$C_{12}H_9O_4N$ MW, 231

The structure given above has not been definitely established.

Me ether: $C_{13}H_{11}O_4N$. MW, 245. Needles from EtOH. M.p. 70–1°.

Lea, Robinson, *J. Chem. Soc.*, 1926, 412.

2′-Nitro-2-hydroxydiphenyl Ether.

Me ether: yellow needles. M.p. 55°. B.p. 213°/10 mm.

Bouveault, *Bull. soc. chim.*, 1897, **17**, 949.

3′-Nitro-2-hydroxydiphenyl Ether.

Me ether: yellow prisms from MeOH. M.p. 86°.

Buchan, Scarborough, *J. Chem. Soc.*, 1934, 706.

4′-Nitro-2-hydroxydiphenyl Ether.

Needles from C_6H_6. M.p. 109°.

Me ether: yellow needles from EtOH. M.p. 106° (103·5–104°). B.p. 216°/10 mm.

See previous reference and also Bouveault, *Bull. soc. chim.*, 1897, **17**, 949.

3-Nitro-4-hydroxydiphenyl Ether.

Yellow needles from pet. ether. M.p. 51–2°.

Me ether: pale yellow prisms from EtOH. M.p. 73–4°.

Lea, Robinson, *J. Chem. Soc.*, 1926, 412.

2-Nitro-9-hydroxyfluorene-9-carboxylic Acid (2-*Nitro*-9-*fluorenol*-9-*carboxylic acid*)

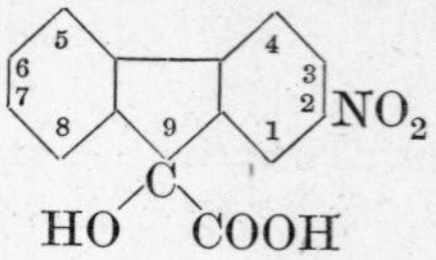

$C_{14}H_9O_5N$ MW, 271

Yellowish-brown prisms. M.p. 160–1° decomp. Sol. EtOH, MeOH, Me_2CO. Mod. sol. Et_2O, C_6H_6, $CHCl_3$. Spar. sol. cold H_2O. Sol. conc. H_2SO_4 with brownish-red col. ⟶ green ⟶ bluish-violet on warming.

Schmidt, Bauer, *Ber.*, 1905, **38**, 3740.

3-Nitro-9-hydroxyfluorene-9-carboxylic Acid (3-*Nitro*-9-*fluorenol*-9-*carboxylic acid*).

Cryst. M.p. 239–40°.

Schmidt, Söll, *Ber.*, 1908, **41**, 3691.

4-Nitro-9-hydroxyfluorene-9-carboxylic Acid (4-*Nitro*-9-*fluorenol*-9-*carboxylic acid*).

Needles from H_2O. M.p. 156–8°. Sol. EtOH, Et_2O, Me_2CO, AcOH. Spar. sol. cold H_2O, C_6H_6, $CHCl_3$. Conc. H_2SO_4 ⟶ brownish-yellow sol. ⟶ green ⟶ blue on warming.

Schmidt, Bauer, *Ber.*, 1905, **38**, 3741.

7-Nitro-2-hydroxyfluorenone

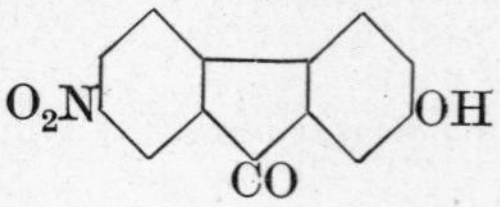

$C_{13}H_7O_4N$ MW, 241

Red cryst. M.p. 298–9°.

Me ether: $C_{14}H_9O_4N$. MW, 255. M.p. 248·5–249·5°.

Eckert, Langecker, *J. prakt. Chem.*, 1928, **118**, 275.

***o*-Nitro-α-hydroxyhydrocinnamic Acid** (β-2-*Nitrophenyl-lactic acid*, o-*nitrobenzylglycollic acid*, α-*hydroxy*-β-2-*nitrophenylpropionic acid*)

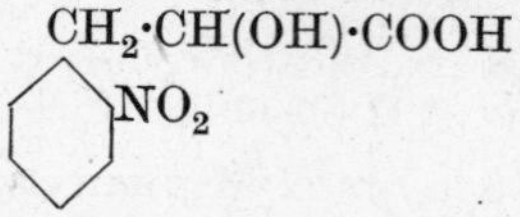

$C_9H_9O_5N$ MW, 211

Needles from H_2O. M.p. 72° (103°). Zn dust + HCl ⟶ 3-hydroxyhydrocarbostyril.

Amide: $C_9H_{10}O_4N_2$. MW, 210. Needles from H_2O. M.p. 195°. Sol. EtOH, Me_2CO, hot H_2O. Spar. sol. Et_2O, $CHCl_3$, C_6H_6.

Nitrile: $C_9H_8O_3N_2$. MW, 192. Plates from $CHCl_3$–pet. ether. M.p. 70–1°.

Heller, *J. prakt. Chem.*, 1923, **106**, 1.
Jaenisch, *Ber.*, 1923, **56**, 2450.

o-Nitro-β-hydroxyhydrocinnamic Acid
(β-2-*Nitrophenylhydracrylic acid*, β-*hydroxy*-β-2-*nitrophenylpropionic acid*)

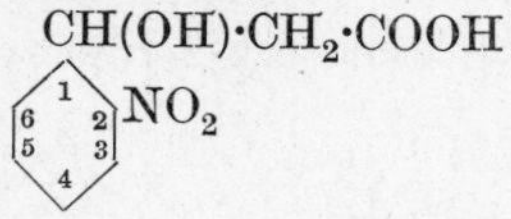

$C_9H_9O_5N$ MW, 211

Plates from H_2O, prisms from Et_2O. M.p. 126°. Sol. H_2O, EtOH, Et_2O. Dil. H_2SO_4 at 190° ⟶ *o*-nitrocinnamic acid.

Me ester: $C_{10}H_{11}O_5N$. MW, 225. Cryst. from very dil. MeOH. M.p. 51°.

Amide: $C_9H_{10}O_4N_2$. MW, 210. Needles from EtOH. M.p. 197°, melting to give a blue col. Sol. H_2O, EtOH, AcOH. Spar. sol. Et_2O, $CHCl_3$, CS_2, ligroin. O-*Acetyl*: prisms from EtOH. M.p. 141–2°.

Baeyer, Drewsen, *Ber.*, 1883, **16**, 2206.
Einhorn, *ibid.*, 2214.
Einhorn, Prausnitz, *Ber.*, 1884, **17**, 1660.

m-Nitro-β-hydroxyhydrocinnamic Acid
(β-3-*Nitrophenylhydracrylic acid*, β-*hydroxy*-β-3-*nitrophenylpropionic acid*).

Leaflets from H_2O. M.p. 105°.

Et ester: $C_{11}H_{13}O_5N$. MW, 239. Cryst. from EtOH.Aq. M.p. 56°.

See last reference above and also
Prausnitz, *Ber.*, 1884, **17**, 596, 598.

p-Nitro-β-hydroxyhydrocinnamic Acid
(β-4-*Nitrophenylhydracrylic acid*, β-*hydroxy*-β-*nitrophenylpropionic acid*).

Cryst. M.p. 130–2°. Sol. EtOH, Et_2O, ligroin, hot H_2O. Spar. sol. C_6H_6, cold H_2O. Sol. undecomp. in cold conc. H_2SO_4. Hot dil. H_2SO_4 ⟶ *p*-nitrocinnamic acid.

Me ester: cryst. from MeOH.Aq. M.p. 73–4°. Sol. EtOH, Et_2O.

Et ester: cryst. from EtOH.Aq. M.p. 45–6°.

Amide: leaflets from H_2O. M.p. 166°. O-*Acetyl*: leaflets. M.p. 146–50°.

Basler, *Ber.*, 1883, **16**, 3003; 1884, **17**, 1494.
Einhorn, Prausnitz, *Ber.*, 1884, **17**, 1661.

5-Nitro-2-hydroxyisophthalic Acid

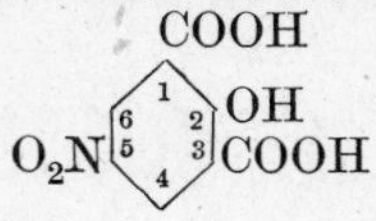

$C_8H_5O_7N$ MW, 227

1-Nitro-4-hydroxy-2-methylanthraquinone

Needles + H_2O. M.p. anhyd. 213–14°. Sol. hot H_2O, EtOH, hot AcOH. Spar. sol. Et_2O. Insol. C_6H_6, $CHCl_3$.

Mononitrile: $C_8H_4O_5N_2$. MW, 208. Yellow cryst. + H_2O from H_2O. M.p. 205°. Sol. H_2O. Very spar. sol. EtOH. Oxidises readily in air. Difficult to hydrolyse.

Hill, *Am. Chem. J.*, 1900, **24**, 13.
Meldola, Foster, Brightman, *J. Chem. Soc.*, 1917, **111**, 545.

5-Nitro-4-hydroxyisophthalic Acid.

Cryst. from EtOH.

Chem. Fab. von Heyden, D.R.P., 555,410, (*Chem. Abstracts*, 1932, **26**, 5105).

Nitrohydroxylepidine.

See Nitrohydroxy-4-methylquinoline.

2-Nitro-4-hydroxy-1-methylanthraquinone

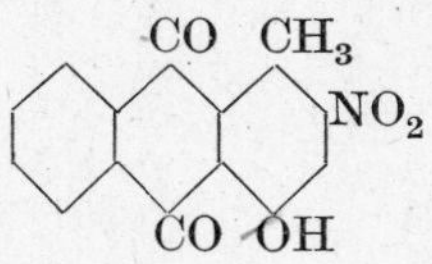

$C_{15}H_9O_5N$ MW, 283

Orange-yellow needles or prisms from EtOH. M.p. 182°. Turns red in air. Alkalis ⟶ reddish-violet sols. Conc. H_2SO_4 ⟶ orange-red sol.

Fischer, Rebsamen, *Ber.*, 1914, **47**, 465.
Fischer, Schweckendick, *ibid.*, 1577.

4-Nitro-3-hydroxy-2-methylanthraquinone

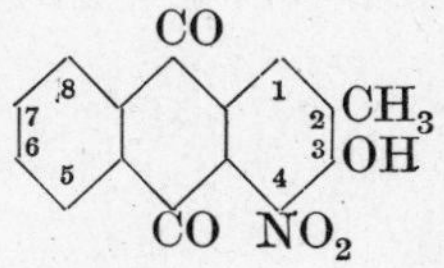

$C_{15}H_9O_5N$ MW, 283

Prisms from AcOH. M.p. 267°.

Me ether: $C_{16}H_{11}O_5N$. MW, 297. Plates from AcOH. M.p. 206°.

Mitter, Pal, *J. Indian Chem. Soc.*, 1930, **7**, 259.

1-Nitro-4-hydroxy-2-methylanthraquinone.

Pale yellow needles from Me_2CO. M.p. 274–5° (241–2°). Sol. EtOH, Me_2CO, toluene. Insol. H_2O.

Eder, Manoukian, *Helv. Chim. Acta*, 1926, **9**, 58.
Keimatsu, Hirano, *Chem. Abstracts*, 1932, 1601.

3-Nitro-4-hydroxy-2-methylanthraquinone.
Pale yellow plates from Me_2CO. M.p. 272–3°.

See first reference above.

5-Nitro-4-hydroxy-2-methylazobenzene

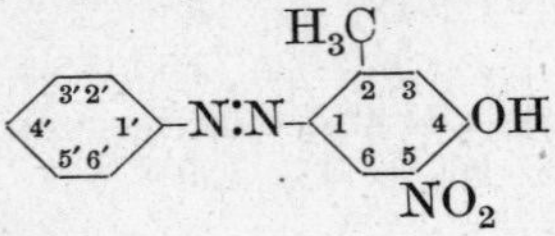

$C_{13}H_{11}O_3N_3$ MW, 257

Yellowish-brown cryst. from pet. ether. M.p. 83–5°. Sol. most org. solvents.

Auwers, Michaelis, *Ber.*, 1914, **47**, 1296.

4′-Nitro-4-hydroxy-2-methylazobenzene.
Violet-brown needles with bronze reflex from toluene, orange-red needles from EtOH.Aq. M.p. 162·5–163·5°. Sol. EtOH, Et_2O, $CHCl_3$. Spar. sol. cold C_6H_6, ligroin.

Me ether: $C_{14}H_{13}O_3N_3$. MW, 271. Orange-red needles and plates from EtOH. M.p. 138°. Sol. C_6H_6. Mod. sol. EtOH, AcOH. Conc. $H_2SO_4 \longrightarrow$ red sol.

Bamberger, *Ber.*, 1895, **28**, 847.
See also previous reference.

3′-Nitro-4′-hydroxy-2-methylazobenzene.
Cryst. from AcOH. M.p. 146°. Very sol. Me_2CO, $CHCl_3$. Sol. AcOH. Spar. sol. EtOH.

Et ether: $C_{15}H_{15}O_3N_3$. MW, 285. Orange needles from AcOH. M.p. 83°. Sol. EtOH.

Acetyl: golden-yellow needles from AcOH. M.p. 108°.

Benzoyl: cryst. from C_6H_6. M.p. 118°.

Hewitt, Lindfield, *J. Chem. Soc.*, 1901, **79**, 156.

2′-Nitro-4-hydroxy-3-methylazobenzene.

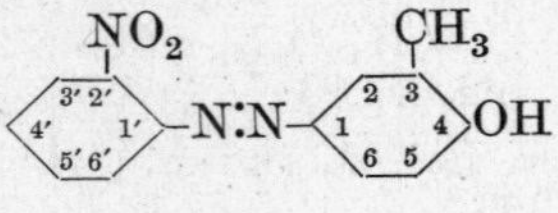

$C_{13}H_{11}O_3N_3$ MW, 257

Orange-red cryst. from C_6H_6 or MeOH.Aq. M.p. 111–12°.

Borsche, *Ann.*, 1907, **357**, 177.

4′-Nitro-4-hydroxy-3-methylazobenzene.
Yellowish-brown cryst. from EtOH. M.p. 202°. Sol. Me_2CO, C_6H_6, $CHCl_3$, ligroin.

Bamberger, *Ber.*, 1895, **28**, 846.

2′-Nitro-6-hydroxy-3-methylazobenzene.
Red needles from EtOH. M.p. 118°.

Acetyl: yellow needles from EtOH. M.p 99–100°.

Goldschmidt, Brubacher, *Ber.*, 1891, 24 2308.

3′-Nitro-6-hydroxy-3-methylazobenzene.
Brown needles from C_6H_6. M.p. 160–1°.

Et ether: $C_{15}H_{15}O_3N_3$. MW, 285. Orang needles from EtOH–C_6H_6. M.p. 121–2°.

Acetyl: orange prisms from C_6H_6. M.p 143–4°.

Meldola, Hanes, *J. Chem. Soc.*, 1894, 65 839.

4′-Nitro-6-hydroxy-3-methylazobenzene.
Brown needles from EtOH, leaflets from AcOH. M.p. 186·5°. Sol. Et_2O, C_6H_6. Spar sol. EtOH, AcOH, ligroin.

Acetyl: red needles from EtOH. M.p. 184° Sol. most org. solvents. Less sol. EtOH, pet ether.

Mehner, *J. prakt. Chem.*, 1902, **65**, 453.
Auwers, *Ann.*, 1909, **365**, 310.

3′-Nitro-4′-hydroxy-3-methylazobenzene.
Yellow needles from pet. ether. M.p. 128·5

Et ether: brown cryst. from EtOH. M.p. 92

Hewitt, Lindfield, *J. Chem. Soc.*, 190 **79**, 157.

2-Nitro-4′-hydroxy-4-methylazobenzene

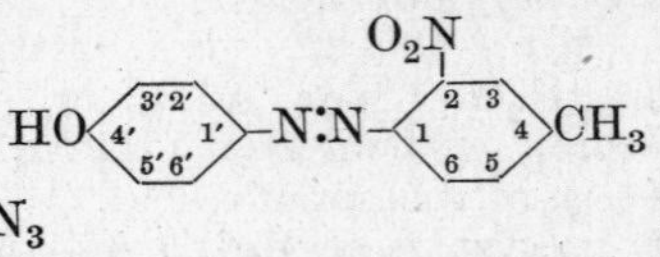

$C_{13}H_{11}O_3N_3$ MW, 2

Brown cryst. from C_6H_6. M.p. 158°.

Hewitt, Mitchell, *J. Chem. Soc.*, 1905, 8 232.

3-Nitro-4′-hydroxy-4-methylazobenzene.
Orange cryst. from AcOH. M.p. 186°. S AcOH. Mod. sol. C_6H_6, Et_2O. Spar. s EtOH.

Acetyl: golden-yellow needles from AcOH.A M.p. 113°. Very sol. EtOH, C_6H_6, AcOH.

Hewitt, Mitchell, *J. Chem. Soc.*, 1905, 8 231.

3'-Nitro-4'-hydroxy-4-methylazobenzene.

Brown plates from AcOH. M.p. 174°. Sol. most ord. solvents. Spar. sol. pet. ether.

Et ether: $C_{15}H_{15}O_3N_3$. MW, 285. Brownish needles from EtOH. M.p. 118°.

Acetyl: brown prisms from EtOH. M.p. 94°.

Benzoyl: yellow cryst. from EtOH. M.p. 129°.

Hewitt, Lindfield, *J. Chem. Soc.*, 1901, **79**, 158.

4'-Nitro-6-hydroxy-3-methylbenzophenone

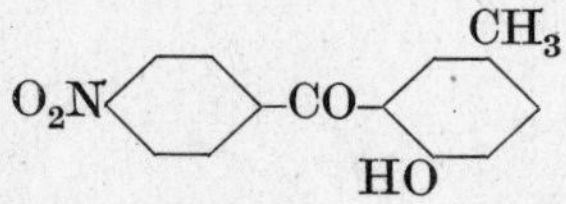

$C_{14}H_{11}O_4N$ MW, 257

Yellow plates from EtOH. M.p. 142–3°. Sol. $CHCl_3$, C_6H_6. Spar. sol. EtOH, ligroin.

Me ether: $C_{15}H_{13}O_4N$. MW, 271. Leaflets from ligroin. M.p. 101–2°.

Auwers, Rietz, *Ber.*, 1907, **40**, 3518.

4-Nitro-4'-hydroxy-2'-methyldeoxybenzoin

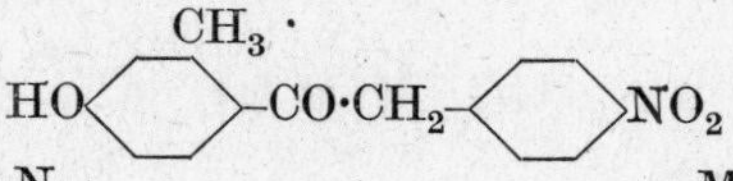

$C_{15}H_{13}O_4N$ MW, 271

Long needles from ligroin. M.p. 128°.

Me ether: $C_{16}H_{15}O_4N$. MW, 285. Plates from ligroin. M.p. 92–3°. *Oxime*: needles. M.p. 164·5–165°.

Hill, Short, *J. Chem. Soc.*, 1935, 1126.

Nitrohydroxy-2-methylquinoline.

See Nitrohydroxyquinaldine.

6-Nitro-2-hydroxy-4-methylquinoline (6-*Nitro-4-methylcarbostyril*, 6-*nitro-2-hydroxylepidine*, 6-*nitro-4-methyl-2-quinolinol*)

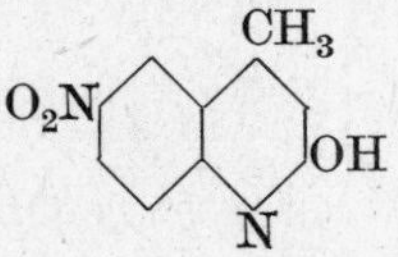

$C_{10}H_8O_3N_2$ MW, 204

Prisms from AcOH. M.p. 340° decomp. Insol. H_2O, EtOH. $KMnO_4 \longrightarrow$ nitrobenzoxazolone.

Balaban, *J. Chem. Soc.*, 1930, 2349.

7-Nitro-8-hydroxy-5-methylquinoline (7-*Nitro-5-methyl-8-quinolinol*)

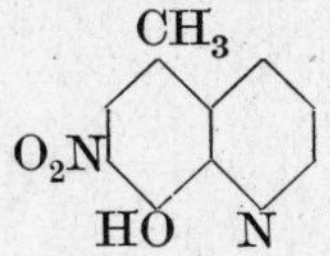

$C_{10}H_8O_3N_2$ MW, 204

Yellow needles from EtOH. M.p. 205–6°. Spar. sol. H_2O.

Noelting, Trautmann, *Ber.*, 1890, **23**, 3667.

5-Nitro-2-hydroxy-6-methylquinoline (5-*Nitro-6-methylcarbostyril*, 5-*nitro-6-methyl-2-quinolinol*)

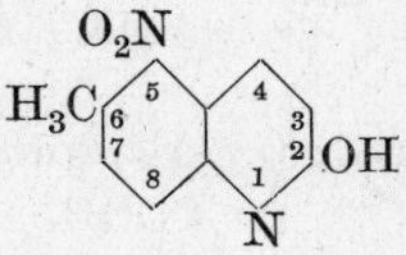

$C_{10}H_8O_3N_2$ MW, 204

N-*Me*: *N*-methyl-α-quinolone. $C_{11}H_{10}O_3N_2$. MW, 218. Cryst. from EtOH. M.p. 192°. Sol. HCl.

Decker, *J. prakt. Chem.*, 1892, **45**, 177.

8-Nitro-2-hydroxy-6-methylquinoline (8-*Nitro-6-methylcarbostyril*, 8-*nitro-6-methyl-2-quinolinol*).

Yellow plates from EtOH. M.p. 200–1°.

N-*Me*: *N*-methyl-α-quinolone. Yellow needles from MeOH. M.p. 165–6°.

Ing, Cahn, *J. Chem. Soc.*, 1931, 2202.

8-Nitro-5-hydroxy-6-methylquinoline (8-*Nitro-6-methyl-5-quinolinol*).

Yellowish-brown leaflets from EtOH or AcOH. Decomp. on heating.

Noelting, Trautmann, *Ber.*, 1890, **23**, 3662.

5-Nitro-8-hydroxy-7-methylquinoline (5-*Nitro-7-methyl-8-quinolinol*)

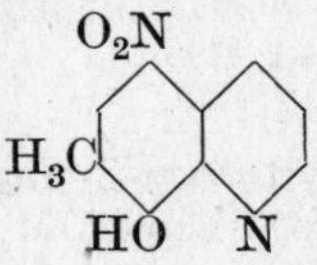

$C_{10}H_8O_3N_2$ MW, 204

Red needles from EtOH, yellow needles from C_6H_6. M.p. 192–3°. Spar. sol. H_2O.

Noelting, Trautmann, *Ber.*, 1890, **23**, 3665.

5-Nitro-2-hydroxy-8-methylquinoline (*5-Nitro-8-methylcarbostyril*, *5-nitro-8-methyl-2-quinolinol*)

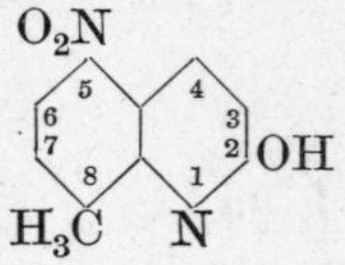

$C_{10}H_8O_3N_2$ MW, 204

N-*Me*: *N*-methyl-α-quinolone. Yellow needles. M.p. 139°.

Decker, *Ber.*, 1905, **38**, 1153.

6-Nitro-5-hydroxy-8-methylquinoline (*6-Nitro-8-methyl-5-quinolinol*).

Orange-red needles from EtOH. M.p. 181–2°.

Noelting, Trautmann, *Ber.*, 1890, **23**, 3677.

3-Nitro-4-hydroxy-1-naphthoic Acid

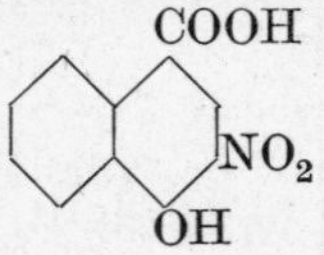

$C_{11}H_7O_5N$ MW, 233

Yellow needles from AcOH. M.p. 258° decomp. Very spar. sol. H_2O with yellow col. Sol. Na_2CO_3.Aq. with red col.

Heller, *Ber.*, 1912, **45**, 676.

4-Nitro-1-hydroxy-2-naphthoic Acid

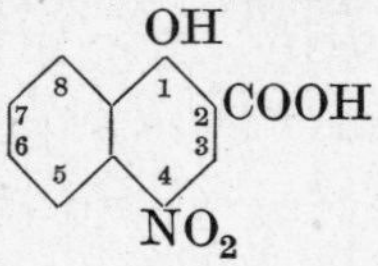

$C_{11}H_7O_5N$ MW, 233

Yellow needles from EtOH.Aq. M.p. 214° decomp. H_2O at 150° ⟶ 4-nitro-1-naphthol.

Me ether: $C_{12}H_9O_5N$. MW, 247. Yellow leaflets from AcOH. M.p. 195–6°.

König, *Ber.*, 1890, **23**, 807.
Borsche, Berkhout, *Ann.*, 1904, **330**, 103.
Dey, *J. Chem. Soc.*, 1915, **107**, 1625.
Froehlicher, Cohen, *J. Chem. Soc.*, 1922, **121**, 1657.

4-Nitro-3-hydroxy-2-naphthoic Acid.

Golden-yellow prisms. M.p. 233–8° decomp. Sol. MeOH, EtOH. Spar. sol. AcOH. Very spar. sol. H_2O.

Me ester: $C_{12}H_9O_5N$. MW, 247. Yellow leaflets from Ac_2O. M.p. 189°. Alk. $KMnO_4$ ⟶ phthalic acid.

Et ester: $C_{13}H_{11}O_5N$. MW, 261. Greenish needles. M.p. 160° (156°). Spar. sol. EtOH, AcOH.

Acetyl: m.p. 235°. *Anilide*: m.p. 236–8°.

Robertson, *J. prakt. Chem.*, 1893, **48**, 534.
Gradenwitz, *Ber.*, 1894, **27**, 2623.
Meisenheimer, Theilacker, Beisswenger, *Ann.*, 1932, **495**, 275.

3-Nitro-2-hydroxy-1:4-naphthoquinone (*3-Nitro-4-hydroxy-1:2-naphthoquinone*)

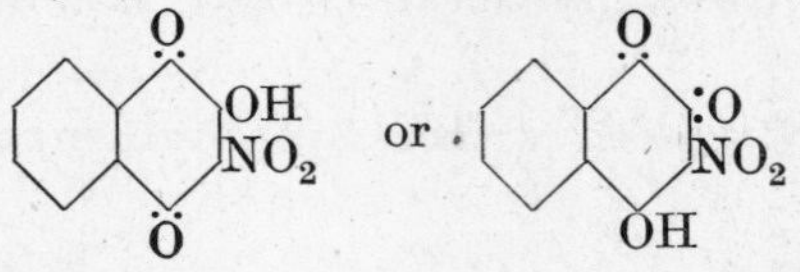

$C_{10}H_5O_5N$ MW, 219

Yellow leaflets from $CHCl_3$. M.p. 157° decomp. Sol. EtOH, Et_2O, hot H_2O. Spar. sol. C_6H_6, $CHCl_3$, ligroin. Dil. HNO_3 ⟶ phthalic acid.

A.G.F.A., D.R.P., 100,611.
Diehl, Merz, *Ber.*, 1878, **11**, 1317.
Kehrmann, *Ber.*, 1888, **21**, 1780.

5-Nitro-2-hydroxyphenanthraquinone

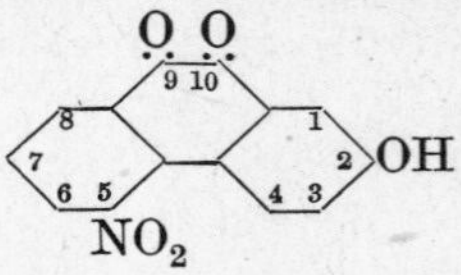

$C_{14}H_7O_5N$ MW, 269

Reddish-brown needles from EtOH.Aq. M.p. about 240° decomp. Sol. EtOH, Et_2O, AcOEt with deep red col. Spar. sol. C_6H_6, AcOH. Sol. conc. H_2SO_4 and alkalis with reddish-brown col.

Acetyl: greenish-yellow needles. M.p. about 220° decomp.

Christie, Holderness, Kenner, *J. Chem. Soc.*, 1926, 671.
Kuhn, Albrecht, *Ann.*, 1927, **455**, 281.

9-Nitro-3-hydroxyphenanthrene (*9-Nitro-3-phenanthranol*)

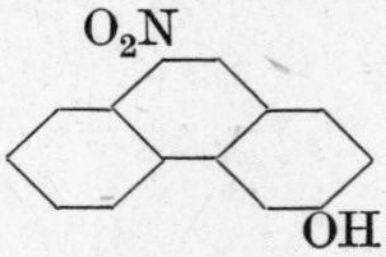

$C_{14}H_9O_3N$ MW, 239

Yellow needles from toluene. M.p. 188–9°.

Acetyl: yellow needles from Me_2CO. M.p. 159°.

Burger, Mosettig, *J. Am. Chem. Soc.*, 1934, **56**, 1745.

Nitrohydroxyphenylcinnamic Acid.
See Nitrohydroxystilbene-carboxylic Acid.

4-Nitro-2-hydroxyphenylurea

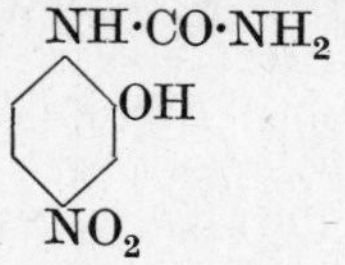

$C_7H_7O_4N_3$ MW, 197

Cryst. from MeOH. M.p. 203° (205°). Sol. EtOH. Insol. cold H_2O, Et_2O, acids. Alkalis ⟶ red sols. Alc. $FeCl_3$ ⟶ olive-green col. Above m.p. ⟶ 6-nitrobenzoxazolone.

Semper, Lichtenstadt, *Ann.*, 1913, **400**, 324.

6-Nitro-3-hydroxyphthalic Acid

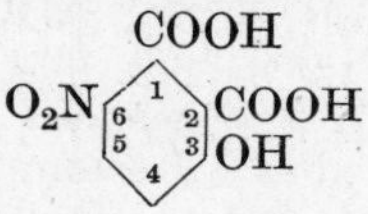

$C_8H_5O_7N$ MW, 227

Dinitrile: $C_8H_3O_3N$. MW, 161. *Me ether*: $C_9H_5O_3N$. MW, 175. M.p. 198°. *Et ether*: $C_{10}H_7O_3N$. MW, 189. M.p. 160°.

Blanksma, *Chem. Zentr.*, 1912, II, 339.

3-Nitro-4-hydroxyphthalic Acid.

Me ether: $C_9H_7O_7N$. MW, 241. Needles from Et_2O.Aq. M.p. 215–17° (212°) decomp. Mod. sol. H_2O, EtOH, AcOEt. Spar. sol. $CHCl_3$, C_6H_6, pet. ether. *Di-Et ester*: $C_{13}H_{15}O_7N$. MW, 297. Needles from EtOH. M.p. 93–4°.

Cain, Simonsen, *J. Chem. Soc.*, 1914, **105**, 162.

Fischer, Kern, *J. prakt. Chem.*, 1916, **94**, 42.

5-Nitro-4-hydroxyphthalic Acid.

Me ether: prisms from H_2O. M.p. 201° decomp. *Di-Me ester*: needles from EtOH. M.p. 115°.

See first reference above.

3-Nitro-2-hydroxypyridine

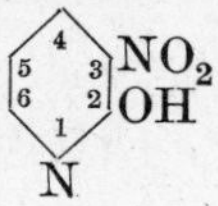

$C_5H_4O_3N_2$ MW, 140

Me ether: $C_6H_6O_3N_2$. MW, 154. M.p. 110°. Sol. EtOH, Et_2O.

Magidson, Menshikov, *Chem. Abstracts*, 1929, **23**, 1640.

5-Nitro-2-hydroxypyridine.

Yellow needles from H_2O. M.p. 184°. Sol. hot H_2O. Spar. sol. Et_2O, C_6H_6, $CHCl_3$, CS_2, ligroin. Sol. alkalis. No col. with $FeCl_3$.

Me ether: $C_6H_6O_3N_2$. MW, 154. Needles from H_2O. M.p. 110°. Easily sol. Et_2O, EtOH.

Et ether: $C_7H_8O_3N_2$. MW, 168. M.p. 95° (72°).

Butyl ether: $C_9H_{12}O_3N_2$. MW, 196. B.p. 148–50°/22 mm.

Benzyl ether: $C_{12}H_{10}O_3N_2$. MW, 230. M.p. 107–8°.

β-*Methoxyethyl ether*: b.p. 160–5°/22 mm. M.p. 65–6°.

N-*Me-pyridone*: $C_6H_6O_3N_2$. MW, 154. Cryst. from EtOH–Et_2O. M.p. 172°.

Tschitschibabin, *J. Russ. Phys.-Chem. Soc.*, 1914, **46**, 1236.

Chemische Fabrik. von Heyden, D.R.P., 568,549, (*Chem. Zentr.*, 1933, I, 3468).

Pieroni, *Atti accad. Lincei*, 1927, **5**, 303.

Räth, E.P., 288,628, (*Chem. Abstracts*, 1929, **23**, 607).

Räth, *Ann.*, 1930, **484**, 52.

6-Nitro-3-hydroxypyridine.

Et ether: pale yellow needles from EtOH. M.p. 31–2°. B.p. 175°/50 mm. Sol. Et_2O. Mod. sol. EtOH. Spar. sol. H_2O.

Koenigs, Gerdes, Sirot, *Ber.*, 1928, **61**, 1022.

3-Nitro-4-hydroxypyridine.

Yellow plates or needles. M.p. 269–70° decomp. Sol. hot H_2O, hot EtOH. Insol. Et_2O, C_6H_6.

Et ether: needles. M.p. 49–50°. Easily sol. EtOH, Et_2O. Spar. sol. H_2O. *B,HCl*: needles. M.p. 160°. *Chloroplatinate*: needles. M.p. 246–8° decomp.

Koenigs, Freter, *Ber.*, 1924, **57**, 1188.

3-Nitro-4-hydroxyquinaldine

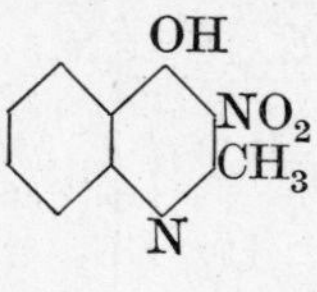

$C_{10}H_8O_3N_2$ MW, 204

Needles from AcOH. Decomp. at 280–5°. Spar. sol. boiling EtOH, C_6H_6. Sol. conc. min. acids.

Me ether: $C_{11}H_{10}O_3N_2$. MW, 218. Pale yellow needles from H_2O or 50% AcOH. M.p. 192°.

N-*Oxide*: decomp. at 227°. Sol. NaOH ⟶ orange-red col.

Conrad, Limpach, *Ber.*, 1887, **20**, 950; 1888, **21**, 1971.
Stark, *Ber.*, 1907, **40**, 3432.
Gabriel, Gerhard, *Ber.*, 1921, **54**, 1076.

Nitro-2-hydroxyquinoline.
See Nitrocarbostyril.

5-Nitro-6-hydroxyquinoline

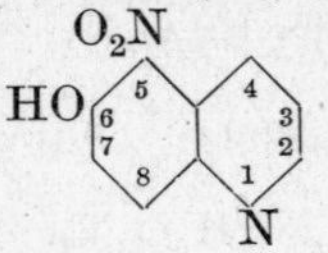

$C_9H_6O_3N_2$ MW, 190

Needles. M.p. 139–40°. Sol. hot EtOH, alkalis, min. acids. $FeCl_3$ ⟶ red col. Sublimes.

Me ether: $C_{10}H_8O_3N_2$. MW, 204. Cryst. from EtOH. M.p. 104–5°. *B,HCl*: cryst. M.p. 219°. *B,HNO₃*: m.p. 195°. Sol. warm EtOH. Insol. H_2O. *B_2,H_2SO_4*: m.p. 205°. *Picrate*: m.p. 211°. Sol. H_2O, EtOH. *Methiodide*: cryst. from H_2O. M.p. 275°. Sol. warm H_2O. Insol. EtOH. *Methiopicrate*: yellow needles from EtOH. M.p. 186°.

Et ether: $C_{11}H_{10}O_3N_2$. MW, 218. Prisms or needles. M.p. 111°. Sol. 20 parts cold EtOH. Sweet taste. *B,HNO_3*: m.p. 193°. Insol. cold H_2O.

Vis, *J. prakt. Chem.*, 1893, **48**, 27.
Decker, Engler, *Ber.*, 1909, **42**, 1740.
Claus, Hofmann, *J. prakt. Chem.*, 1897, **55**, 519.

8-Nitro-6-hydroxyquinoline.
Cryst. M.p. 230° decomp.
Me ether: cryst. M.p. 159–60°.
Et ether: m.p. 158°.
Propyl ether: $C_{12}H_{12}O_3N_2$. MW, 232. Prisms. M.p. 89°.
Butyl ether: $C_{13}H_{14}O_3N_2$. MW, 246. M.p. 92°.
Isoamyl ether: $C_{14}H_{16}O_3N_2$. MW, 260. M.p. 83°.
Octyl ether: $C_{17}H_{22}O_3N_2$. MW, 302. Cryst. M.p. 61°.
Allyl ether: $C_{12}H_{10}O_3N_2$. MW, 230. M.p. 114·5°.
Phenyl ether: $C_{15}H_{10}O_3N_2$. MW, 266. M.p. 142°.

Bayer, E.P., 267,457, (*Chem. Abstracts*, 1928, **22**, 1216).
Magidson, Strukov, *Arch. Pharm.*, 1933, **271**, 359.

8-Nitro-7-hydroxyquinoline.
Yellow plates. M.p. 255° decomp. $FeCl_3$ in EtOH.Aq. ⟶ reddish-yellow col.
Me ether: $C_{10}H_8O_3N_2$. MW, 204. Pale yellow prisms from $CHCl_3$. M.p. 178°. *B,HNO_3*: yellow needles. M.p. 155–6° decomp.

Skraup, *Monatsh.*, 1882, **3**, 534.
Balaban, *J. Chem. Soc.*, 1932, 2626.

5-Nitro-8-hydroxyquinoline.
Yellow needles from EtOH or AcOH. M.p. 178°. Sol. AcOH, hot HCl. Spar. sol. EtOH, Et_2O. Sol. alkalis. Volatile in steam.
B,HCl: yellow needles from EtOH. M.p. 258°.
Me ether: $C_{10}H_8O_3N_2$. MW, 204. Cryst. from EtOH. M.p. 151–5°. Sol. hot EtOH. Insol. H_2O.
Et ether: $C_{11}H_{10}O_3N_2$. MW, 218. Yellow needles. M.p. 128°. Sol. hot EtOH. Insol. H_2O. *B,HNO_3*: needles. M.p. 100°. *B_2,H_2PtCl_6*: needles. Decomp. at 248°. *Methiodide*: red cryst. from EtOH, yellow cryst. + $2H_2O$ from H_2O. M.p. 150°.

Vis, *J. prakt. Chem.*, 1892, **45**, 534.
Freyss, Paira, *Chem. Zentr.*, 1903, I, 35.

5-Nitro-8-hydroxyquinoline-7-carboxylic Acid

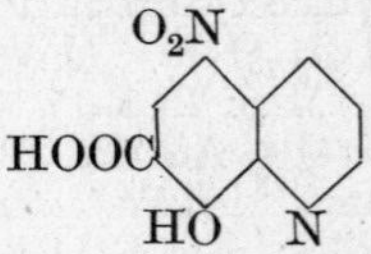

$C_{10}H_6O_5N_2$ MW, 234

Yellow needles from HCl. Decomp. at 200°. Sol. conc. HCl, alkalis, NH_3. Spar. sol. AcOH. Glycerol at 200° ⟶ 5-nitro-8-hydroxyquinoline.
Me ester: $C_{11}H_8O_5N_2$. MW, 248. Needles from EtOH. M.p. 191°. Very sol. C_6H_6, $CHCl_3$, AcOEt.

Einhorn, *Ann.*, 1900, **311**, 65.
Schmitt, Engelmann, *Ber.*, 1887, **20**, 2693.

4′-Nitro-2-hydroxystilbene

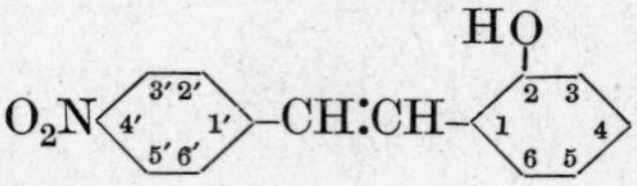

$C_{14}H_{11}O_3N$ MW, 241

Me ether: $C_{15}H_{13}O_3N$. MW, 255. Yellow needles from EtOH. M.p. 122°. Very sol. C_6H_6, $CHCl_3$. Less sol. EtOH, Et_2O, AcOH.

Pfeiffer, *Ber.*, 1915, **48**, 1795.

4'-Nitro-3-hydroxystilbene.
Me ether: yellowish leaflets from EtOH. M.p. 87°. Very sol. C_6H_6, $CHCl_3$. Sol. Et_2O, AcOH. Less sol. EtOH.

See previous reference.

2'-Nitro-4-hydroxystilbene.
Me ether: dark yellow needles from EtOH. M.p. 88–90°. Sol. EtOH, $CHCl_3$.

See previous reference.

4'-Nitro-4-hydroxystilbene.
Yellow needles from EtOH.Aq. M.p. 193°. Alkalis ⟶ deep brown col.
Me ether: orange-yellow leaflets from AcOH; greenish-yellow needles from dil. C_6H_6 sol. M.p. 132–4°. Greenish-yellow form ⟶ orange-yellow at 100°.

Hewitt, Lewcock, *J. Chem. Soc.*, 1931, 444.
See also previous reference.

β-Nitro-4-hydroxystilbene

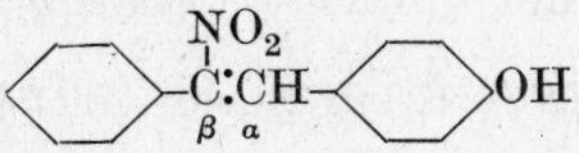

$C_{14}H_{11}O_3N$ MW, 241

Me ether: $C_{15}H_{13}O_3N$. MW, 255. Exists in two forms. (i) Golden-yellow needles from EtOH. M.p. 151°. Insol. Et_2O. (ii) Brownish-orange needles. M.p. 112–13°.

Knoevenagel, Walter, *Ber.*, 1904, **37**, 4509.
Flürscheim, Holmes, *J. Chem. Soc.*, 1932, 1463.

β-Nitro-α-hydroxystilbene.
Me ether: yellow solid. M.p. 87°.

Meisenheimer, Mahler, *Ann.*, 1934, **508**, 190.

4-Nitro-2'-hydroxystilbene-2-carboxylic Acid (5-*Nitro*-2-[o-*hydroxystyryl*]-*benzoic acid*)

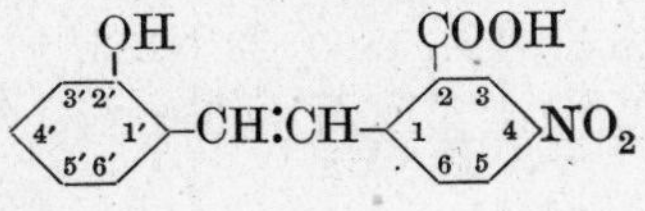

$C_{15}H_{11}O_5N$ MW, 285

Me ether: $C_{16}H_{13}O_5N$. MW, 299. *Nitrile*: $C_{16}H_{12}O_3N_2$. MW, 280. Yellow needles from AcOH. M.p. 146–8°. Sol. AcOH. Spar. sol. boiling EtOH. Very stable to alk. hydrolysis.

Pfeiffer, *Ber.*, 1916, **49**, 2433.

4-Nitro-4'-hydroxystilbene-2-carboxylic Acid (5-*Nitro*-2-[p-*hydroxystyryl*]-*benzoic acid*).
Me ether: yellow needles + H_2O from AcOH. M.p. 215°. Sol. AcOH, hot EtOH. Spar. sol. Et_2O, C_6H_6, $CHCl_3$. Insol. ligroin. *Amide*: $C_{16}H_{14}O_4N_2$. MW, 298. Yellow cryst. powder from xylene. M.p. 255°. *Nitrile*: m.p. 198°. Sol. Me_2CO.
Nitrile: $C_{15}H_{10}O_3N_2$. MW, 266. Orange-yellow needles from AcOH. M.p. 226°. Sol. AcOH, boiling EtOH. KOH ⟶ red sol. *Acetyl*: yellow needles from AcOH. M.p. 176°. *Benzoyl*: yellow needles from AcOH. M.p. 178°.

Pfeiffer, *Ber.*, 1915, **48**, 1796; 1916, **49**, 2437; 1918, **51**, 562.

4-Nitro-4'-hydroxystilbene-3-carboxylic Acid (6-*Nitro*-3-[p-*hydroxystyryl*]-*benzoic acid*)

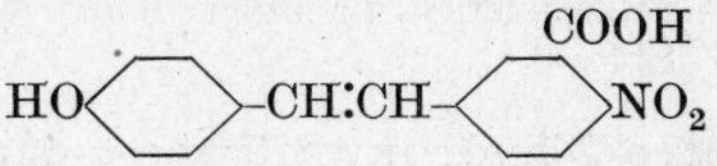

$C_{15}H_{11}O_5N$ MW, 285

Me ether: $C_{16}H_{13}O_5N$. MW, 299. *Nitrile*: $C_{16}H_{12}O_3N_2$. MW, 280. Brownish-orange leaflets from AcOH. M.p. 161°. Sol. EtOH, hot AcOH. Spar. sol. C_6H_6, ligroin.

Pfeiffer, *Ber.*, 1918, **51**, 561.

2-Nitro-2'-hydroxystilbene-4-carboxylic Acid (3-*Nitro*-4-[o-*hydroxystyryl*]-*benzoic acid*)

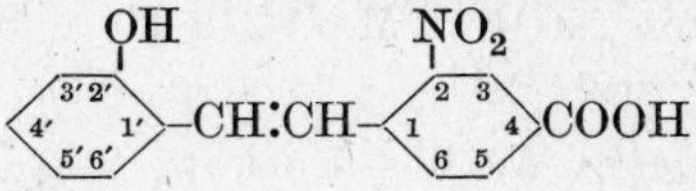

$C_{15}H_{11}O_5N$ MW, 285

Me ether: $C_{16}H_{13}O_5N$. MW, 299. Greenish-yellow cryst. from propionic acid. M.p. 230°. Sol. EtOH, C_6H_6. *Et ester*: $C_{18}H_{17}O_5N$. MW, 327. Yellow needles or leaflets from EtOH. M.p. 101°. Sol. AcOH, C_6H_6. *Nitrile*: $C_{16}H_{12}O_3N_2$. MW, 280. Yellow needles from AcOH. M.p. 183°. Sol. AcOH, C_6H_6.

Pfeiffer, *Ber.*, 1915, **48**, 1803; 1916, **49**, 2431.

2-Nitro-3'-hydroxystilbene-4-carboxylic Acid (3-*Nitro*-4-[m-*hydroxystyryl*]-*benzoic acid*).
Me ether: greenish-yellow needles from AcOH. M.p. 240°. Sol. AcOH, C_6H_6. Very spar. sol. Et_2O. Insol. H_2O, ligroin. *Nitrile*: greenish-yellow needles from AcOH. M.p. 163–4°. Sol. AcOH. Mod. sol. C_6H_6. Spar. sol. EtOH, Et_2O, ligroin.

Pfeiffer, *Ber.*, 1916, **49**, 2434.

2-Nitro-4′-hydroxystilbene-4-carboxylic Acid (3-*Nitro*-4-[p-*hydroxystyryl*]-*benzoic acid*).

Me ether: exists in two forms. (i) Yellow needles or leaflets from AcOH or EtOH. (ii) Orange powder. At 140° (ii) ⟶ (i) and melts at 250°. Sol. hot AcOH. Spar. sol. hot H_2O. *Me ester*: $C_{17}H_{15}O_5N$. MW, 313. Yellow needles from MeOH. M.p. 117–18°. At 100–5° ⟶ orange form. *Et ester*: $C_{18}H_{17}O_5N$. MW, 327. Yellow needles from EtOH. M.p. 103–4°. Sol. Me_2CO, AcOH, Py, CCl_4. *Nitrile*: yellow or orange cryst. from C_6H_6 or AcOH. M.p. 157–8°. At 120–5° yellow ⟶ orange modification.

Nitrile: $C_{15}H_{10}O_3N_2$. MW, 266. M.p. 230–1°. *Acetyl*: yellow leaflets from AcOH. M.p. 225°.

Pfeiffer, *Ber.*, 1915, **48**, 1799; 1916, **49**, 2435; 1918, **51**, 564; *Ann.*, 1916, **411**, 144.

2′-Nitro-2-hydroxystilbene-α-carboxylic Acid (2-*Nitro*-α-[2-*hydroxyphenyl*]-*cinnamic acid*)

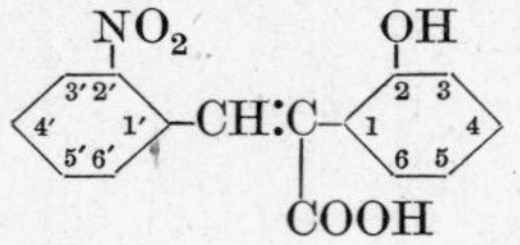

$C_{15}H_{11}O_5N$ MW, 285

Me ether: $C_{16}H_{13}O_5N$. MW, 299. Yellowish plates from EtOH. M.p. 219–20°. Spar. sol. ligroin. Insol. H_2O.

Pschorr, Wolfes, Buckow, *Ber.*, 1900, **33**, 167.

2′-Nitro-4-hydroxystilbene-α-carboxylic Acid (2-*Nitro*-α-[4-*hydroxyphenyl*]-*cinnamic acid*).

Me ether: $C_{16}H_{13}O_5N$. MW, 299. Prisms from toluene, leaflets from EtOH. M.p. 177° decomp. Spar. sol. Et_2O, Me_2CO, C_6H_6, $CHCl_3$. Insol. H_2O, ligroin. *Nitrile*: $C_{16}H_{12}O_3N_2$. MW, 280. Yellow needles from toluene or EtOH. M.p. 162°. Spar. sol. Et_2O, $CHCl_3$. Insol. H_2O, ligroin. Sublimes.

Et ether: $C_{17}H_{15}O_5N$. MW, 313. Yellow prisms from AcOH or toluene. M.p. 158°. Sol. EtOH, Et_2O, C_6H_6, $CHCl_3$. Spar. sol. ligroin. Insol. H_2O.

Pschorr, Wolfes, *Ber.*, 1899, **32**, 3400.
Pschorr, Wolfes, Buckow, *Ber.*, 1900, **33**, 172.
Werner, *Ann.*, 1902, **322**, 152.

4-Nitro-2′-hydroxystilbene-α-carboxylic Acid (2-*Hydroxy*-α-[4-*nitrophenyl*]-*cinnamic acid*).

Me ether: $C_{16}H_{13}O_5N$. MW, 299. *Nitrile*: $C_{16}H_{12}O_3N_2$. MW, 280. Fluor. yellow needles from AcOH. M.p. 190°.

Kauffmann, *Ber.*, 1917, **50**, 1621.

2′-Nitro-3′-hydroxystilbene-α-carboxylic Acid (2-*Nitro*-3-*hydroxy*-α-*phenylcinnamic acid*).

Me ether: leaflets from EtOH.Aq. M.p. 226–7°. Sol. EtOH, $CHCl_3$, AcOH. Spar. sol. Et_2O, toluene. Insol. H_2O, ligroin.

Pschorr, Jaeckel, *Ber.*, 1900, **33**, 1826.

4′-Nitro-3′-hydroxystilbene-α-carboxylic Acid (4-*Nitro*-3-*hydroxy*-α-*phenylcinnamic acid*).

Acetyl: yellowish prisms from EtOH. M.p. 254°.

Pschorr, *Ber.*, 1906, **39**, 3123.

6′-Nitro-3′-hydroxystilbene-α-carboxylic Acid (6-*Nitro*-3-*hydroxy*-α-*phenylcinnamic acid*).

Leaflets from EtOH.Aq. or AcOH.Aq. M.p. 219–20°.

Me ether: $C_{16}H_{13}O_5N$. MW, 299. Leaflets from EtOH. M.p. 165–6°. Spar. sol. C_6H_6, ligroin. Insol. H_2O.

Pschorr, Seydel, *Ber.*, 1901, **34**, 4000.
See also previous reference.

4-Nitro-4′-hydroxystilbene-α-carboxylic Acid (4-*Hydroxy*-α-[4-*nitrophenyl*]-*cinnamic acid*).

Me ether: orange cryst. powder from EtOH. M.p. 231°. Dist. under red. press. ⟶ 4′-nitro-4-methoxystilbene. *Nitrile*: $C_{16}H_{12}O_3N_2$. MW, 280. Yellow needles from EtOH. M.p. 165–6°. Sol. C_6H_6, AcOH.

Acetyl: yellowish cryst. powder from CCl_4–AcOH. M.p. 205°. Heat with EtOH–conc. HCl or piperidine ⟶ 4′-nitro-4-hydroxystilbene.

Remse, *Ber.*, 1890, **23**, 3135.
Hewitt, Lewcock, Pope, *J. Chem. Soc.*, 1912, **101**, 607.

3-Nitro-4-hydroxystyrene

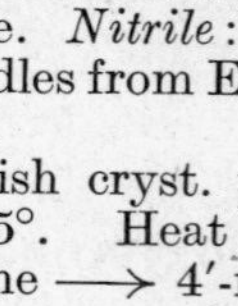

$C_8H_7O_3N$ MW, 165

Me ether: $C_9H_9O_3N$. MW, 179. Cryst. from EtOH. M.p. 89°. Sol. usual org. solvents. Volatile in steam.

Einhorn, Grabfield, *Ann.*, 1888, **243**, 368.

β-Nitro-*o*-hydroxystyrene

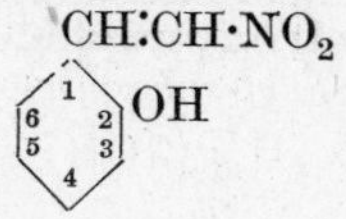

$C_8H_7O_3N$ MW, 165

Yellowish needles. M.p. 133–4°.

Remfry, *J. Chem. Soc.*, 1911, **99**, 286.

β-Nitro-*m*-hydroxystyrene.

Yellowish needles. M.p. 132–3°.

Me ether: $C_9H_9O_3N$. MW, 179. Pale yellow plates or needles from EtOH. M.p. 93–4°. Sol. Me_2CO, $CHCl_3$, C_6H_6. Insol. ligroin.

Benzyl ether: yellow needles from EtOH. M.p. 83°.

Kondo, Ishiwata, *Ber.*, 1931, **64**, 1538.
Gulland, Virden, *J. Chem. Soc.*, 1929, 1795.
Shoesmith, Connor, *J. Chem. Soc.*, 1927, 2232.
See also previous reference.

β-Nitro-*p*-hydroxystyrene.

Yellowish needles or plates from EtOH.Aq. M.p. 165°.

Me ether: anisylidenenitromethane. Yellow needles from EtOH, plates from C_6H_6. M.p. 88°. Sol. hot EtOH. Spar. sol. Et_2O, C_6H_6. Sol. caustic alkalis with yellow col.

Benzyl ether: yellow cryst. from EtOH. M.p. 120°.

Acetyl: yellow needles from EtOH. M.p. 163° (158–9°).

Rosenmund, Pfannkuch, *Ber.*, 1922, **55**, 2365.
Kondo, Shinozaki, *J. Pharm. Soc. Japan*, 1929, **49**, 267.
Knoevenagel, Walter, *Ber.*, 1904, **37**, 4505.
Rosenmund, *Ber.*, 1909, **42**, 4779; 1913, **46**, 1041.
Remfry, *J. Chem. Soc.*, 1911, **99**, 286.
Bouveault, Wahl, *Bull. soc. chim.*, 1903, **29**, 523.
Knoevenagel, D.R.P., 161,171, (*Chem. Zentr.*, 1905, II, 179).

Nitrohydroxystyrylbenzoic Acid.

See Nitrohydroxystilbene-carboxylic Acid.

5-Nitro-2-hydroxy-*m*-toluic Acid (5-*Nitro*-o-*cresotic acid*)

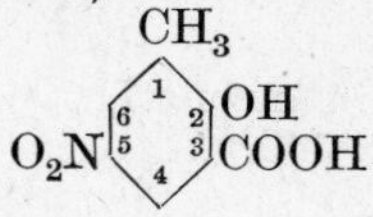

$C_8H_7O_5N$ MW, 197

Needles from EtOH.Aq. M.p. 199°.

Et ester: $C_{10}H_{11}O_5N$. MW, 225. Leaflets from EtOH.Aq. M.p. 63–4°.

Chloride: $C_8H_6O_4NCl$. MW, 215·5. Cryst. from C_6H_6. M.p. 86–8°.

Amide: $C_8H_8O_4N_2$. MW, 196. Yellowish cryst. from EtOH. M.p. 231°. Spar. sol. EtOH, AcOH.

Acetyl: yellowish cryst. from EtOH.Aq. M.p. 142°. Sol. EtOH. Less sol. H_2O, AcOH.

Einhorn, Pfyl, *Ann.*, 1900, **311**, 47.
Fortner, *Monatsh.*, 1901, **22**, 944.

5-Nitro-4-hydroxy-*m*-toluic Acid (5-*Nitro*-p-*cresotic acid*).

Cryst. from AcOH. M.p. 173°.

Et ester: m.p. 104–5°. p-*Toluenesulphonyl*: plates from EtOH. M.p. 110°.

Sane, Chakravarty, Parmanick, *J. Indian Chem. Soc.*, 1932, **9**, 55.

5-Nitro-6-hydroxy-*m*-toluic Acid.

Pale yellow needles from AcOH or C_6H_6. M.p. 240°. Sol. EtOH, Et_2O, AcOH. Mod. sol. hot C_6H_6. Spar. sol. H_2O.

Me ester: $C_9H_9O_5N$. MW, 211. Yellow cryst. M.p. 103°.

Pfister, *J. Am. Chem. Soc.*, 1921, **43**, 375.

2-Nitro-3-hydroxy-*p*-toluic Acid (2-*Nitro*-m-*cresotic acid*)

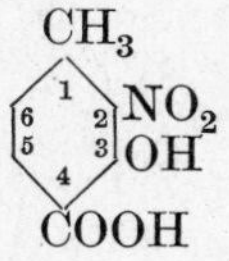

$C_8H_7O_5N$ MW, 97

Et ester: $C_{10}H_{11}O_5N$. MW, 225. Needles from EtOH.Aq. M.p. 73–4°.

Einhorn, Pfyl, *Ann.*, 1900, **311**, 50.

6-Nitro-3-hydroxy-*p*-toluic Acid (6-*Nitro*-m-*cresotic acid*).

Needles from H_2O. M.p. 219° (213°).

Me ether: $C_9H_9O_5N$. MW, 211. Needles from H_2O. M.p. 173–5°. Sol. EtOH, Et_2O, C_6H_6. Spar. sol. H_2O.

Et ether: $C_{10}H_{11}O_5N$. MW, 225. Needles from H_2O. M.p. 161–2°. Very sol. EtOH, Et_2O, C_6H_6. Mod. sol. hot H_2O.

Me ester: $C_9H_9O_5N$. MW, 211. Cryst. from MeOH. M.p. 78°. p-*Toluenesulphonyl*: cryst. M.p. 93°.

Paternò, Canzoneri, *Gazz. chim. ital.*, 1879, **9**, 456.
Clayton, *J. Chem. Soc.*, 1910, **97**, 1402.

5-Nitro-2-hydroxy-*m*-toluic Aldehyde

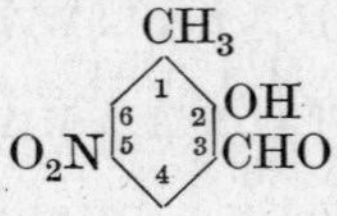

$C_8H_7O_4N$ MW, 181

Yellow cryst. from AcOH, needles from ligroin. M.p. 134°. Sol. Et_2O, C_6H_6, $CHCl_3$. Mod. sol. EtOH, AcOH. Spar. sol. H_2O, ligroin. Sublimes.

Anil: golden-yellow needles from C_6H_6. M.p. 176–7°. Sol. C_6H_6. Mod. sol. EtOH, AcOH. Spar. sol. ligroin.

Phenylhydrazone: yellow needles from EtOH. M.p. 206–7°.

Auwers, Bondy, *Ber.*, 1904, **37**, 3916

5-Nitro-4-hydroxy-*m*-toluic Aldehyde.
Yellow needles. M.p. 141°. Spar. sol. hot H_2O. $FeCl_3 \longrightarrow$ violet col.

Oxime: light yellow leaflets from EtOH. M.p. 214–16°. Spar. sol. boiling EtOH.

Anil: orange-red needles from C_6H_6. M.p. 133·5–134·5°. Sol. C_6H_6. Mod. sol. EtOH, AcOH. Spar. sol. Et_2O, ligroin.

Phenylhydrazone: m.p. 164–6°.

Borsche, *Ber.*, 1917, **50**, 1345.

5-Nitro-6-hydroxy-*m*-toluic Aldehyde.
Yellowish needles from EtOH.Aq. M.p. 152°. Spar. sol. boiling H_2O. Volatile in steam. Forms bisulphite comp.

Phenylhydrazone: m.p. 153–5°.

Schotten, *Ber.*, 1878, **11**, 789.

2-Nitro-3-hydroxy-*p*-toluic Aldehyde

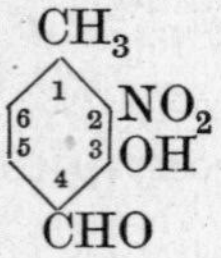

$C_8H_7O_4N$ MW, 181

Yellow needles from EtOH. M.p. 126–7°.

Clayton, *J. Chem. Soc.*, 1910, **97**, 1405.

6-Nitro-3-hydroxy-*p*-toluic Aldehyde.
Yellow needles from EtOH. M.p. 144–5°.

Oxime: yellow needles from EtOH. M.p. 207–8° decomp.

Phenylhydrazone: cryst. M.p. 201–2°.

See previous reference.

Nitrohydroxytrimethylbenzene.
See Nitrohemimellitenol *and* Nitromesitol.

3-Nitro-4-hydroxytriphenylcarbinol (3-*Nitro*-4 : α-*dihydroxytriphenylmethane*)

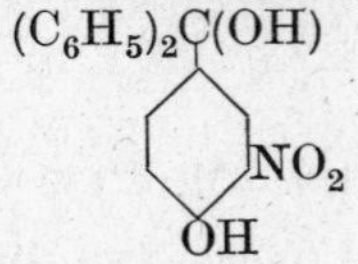

$C_{19}H_{15}O_4N$ MW, 321

Cryst. from 60% AcOH. M.p. 97–8°.

Gomberg, v. Stone, *J. Am. Chem. Soc.*, 1916, **38**, 1604.

1-Nitrohystazarin (1-*Nitro*-2 : 3-*dihydroxy-anthraquinone*)

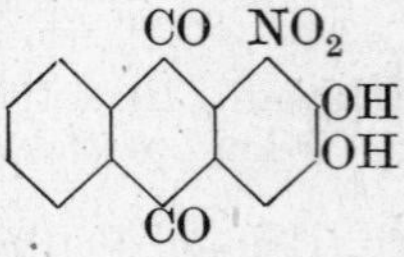

$C_{14}H_7O_6N$ MW, 28

Yellow cryst. from toluene. Sol. EtOH Et_2O, AcOH. Less sol. H_2O, C_6H_6. Dil alkalis $\longrightarrow$ blue sols. Conc. $H_2SO_4 \longrightarrow$ orange-yellow sol. $HNO_3 \longrightarrow$ phthalic acid.

Schrobsdorff, *Ber.*, 1903, **36**, 2939.

4-Nitroindazole

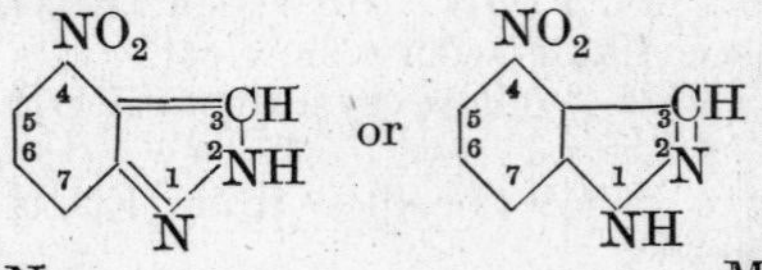

$C_7H_5O_2N_3$ MW, 16

Needles from H_2O. M.p. 203°. Very sol Me_2CO, AcOH. Sol. EtOH, Et_2O, C_6H_6. Insol ligroin. Sol. alkalis with reddish-yellow col Spar. volatile in steam.

N-*Me*: *see* 4-Nitro-methylindazole.

1-o-*Tolyl*: $C_{14}H_{11}O_2N_3$. MW, 253. Needle from EtOH.Aq. M.p. 92–4°. Sol. Et_2O, C_6H_6 AcOH. Mod. sol. EtOH, ligroin.

1-p-*Tolyl*: yellow needles from MeOH. M.p 155–6°.

1-*Benzyl*: $C_{14}H_{11}O_2N_3$. MW, 253. Yellow needles from EtOH. M.p. 97–8°.

2-*Benzyl*: yellow needles from ligroin. M.p 123–4°. Sol. most solvents.

N-*Acetyl*: (i) *Stable form*, needles from

MeOH. M.p. 144·5–145·5°. (ii) *Labile form*: yellow needles from Et_2O. M.p. 119–21°.

N-*Benzoyl*: (i) *Stable form*, needles. M.p. 162–3°. (ii) *Labile form*: yellow needles from Et_2O. M.p. 130–2°.

Noelting, *Ber.*, 1904, **37**, 2562.
Auwers, Schwegler, *Ber.*, 1920, **53**, 1211.
Auwers, Frese, *Ber.*, 1925, **58**, 1372.

5-Nitroindazole.

Leaflets or needles from EtOH. M.p. 208°. Very sol. Me_2CO, AcOH. Sol. EtOH, Et_2O, C_6H_6. Insol. ligroin. Spar. volatile in steam. Conc. alkalis ⟶ red sols. ⟶ yellow on dilution.

N-*Acetyl*: (i) *Stable form*, needles from EtOH. M.p. 158–9°. (ii) *Labile form*: needles from Me_2CO–Et_2O. M.p. 138–9°.

N-*Benzoyl*: (i) *Stable form*, leaflets from C_6H_6. M.p. 193–4°. (ii) *Labile form*: prisms from Me_2CO. M.p. 155°.

N-*Me*: *see* 5-Nitro-methylindazole.

See first two references above.

6-Nitroindazole.

Needles from toluene. M.p. 181°. Sol. EtOH, Et_2O, C_6H_6. Insol. ligroin.

N-*Me*: *see* 6-Nitro-methylindazole.

N-*Et*: $C_9H_9O_2N_3$. MW, 191. Needles from EtOH.Aq. M.p. 91–3°. Sol. EtOH, Et_2O, C_6H_6, conc. HCl.

N-*Benzyl*: $C_{14}H_{11}O_2N_3$. MW, 253. Yellowish needles from MeOH. M.p. 111–12°.

N-*Acetyl*: (i) *Stable form*, needles. M.p. 140–1°. (ii) *Labile form*: leaflets from Et_2O. M.p. 74–5°.

1-*Chloroacetyl*: yellowish needles from C_6H_6. M.p. 149°. Sol. hot C_6H_6. Spar. sol. cold MeOH.

1-*Dichloroacetyl*: cryst. from 3 parts C_6H_6 + 1 part pet. ether. M.p. 137–8°. Sol. Me_2CO, C_6H_6.

1-*Trichloroacetyl*: yellowish cryst. from C_6H_6–pet. ether. M.p. 101–2°.

N-*Benzoyl*: (i) *Stable form*, needles. M.p. 164–5°. (ii) *Labile form*: needles from Et_2O. M.p. 133–4°.

1-o-*Nitrobenzoyl*: yellowish cryst. from toluene. M.p. 206–7°. Spar. sol. most solvents. Stable.

1-m-*Nitrobenzoyl*: cryst. from toluene. M.p. 212–13°. Spar. sol. most solvents. Stable.

1-p-*Nitrobenzoyl*: needles from $PhNO_2$. M.p. 236–7°. Spar. sol. most solvents. Stable.

1-o-*Toluyl*: yellowish needles from Me_2CO. M.p. 188°. Mod. sol. Me_2CO. Stable.

1-m-*Toluyl*: yellowish needles from Me_2CO. M.p. 159–60°.

1-p-*Toluyl*: needles. M.p. 165–6°. Mod. sol. Me_2CO. Spar. sol. MeOH. Stable.

Witt, Noelting, Grandmougin, *Ber.*, 1890, **23**, 3636.
Auwers, Demuth, *Ann.*, 1927, **451**, 298.
See also previous references.

7-Nitroindazole.

Cryst. from EtOH. M.p. 186·5–187·5°.

N-*Me*: *see* 7-Nitro-methylindazole.

1-*Acetyl*: needles from 50% AcOH. M.p. 147°. Sol. Me_2CO, AcOH. Mod. sol. EtOH, Et_2O, C_6H_6. Spar. sol. pet. ether.

2-*Acetyl*: yellow leaflets from Et_2O. M.p. 132·5–134°.

1-*Benzoyl*: needles from MeOH or EtOH. M.p. 132–3°. Sol. Me_2CO. Mod. sol. AcOH, C_6H_6. Spar. sol. EtOH, Et_2O.

2-*Benzoyl*: yellow needles from Me_2CO. M.p. 185°.

1-o-*Nitrobenzoyl*: brownish cryst. from toluene–pet. ether. M.p. 173–5°. Sol. Me_2CO. Stable.

1-p-*Nitrobenzoyl*: yellow needles from toluene. M.p. 155–7°. Sol. Me_2CO.

Noelting, *Ber.*, 1904, **37**, 2575.
Auwers, Schwegler, *Ber.*, 1920, **53**, 1211.
Auwers, Demuth, *Ann.*, 1927, **451**, 302.

6-Nitroindazole-1-carboxylic Acid

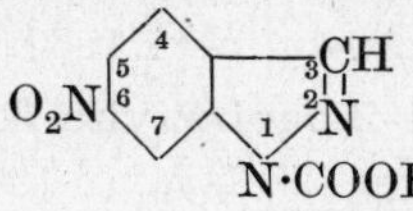

$C_8H_5O_4N_3$ MW, 207

Me ester: $C_9H_7O_4N_3$. MW, 221. Yellow needles from MeOH. M.p. 169°. Sol. AcOH. Spar. sol. EtOH.

Et ester: $C_{10}H_9O_4N_3$. MW, 235. Yellow needles from EtOH. M.p. 147–8°. Sol. EtOH, C_6H_6. Spar. sol. MeOH.

Chloride: $C_8H_4O_3N_3Cl$. MW, 225·5. Needles from Me_2CO. M.p. 140–1°. Sol. Me_2CO. Spar. sol. warm Et_2O, pet. ether.

Amide: $C_8H_6O_3N_4$. MW, 206. Yellow needles from AcOH. M.p. 219–20°. Spar. sol. org. solvents.

Anilide: $C_{14}H_{10}O_3N_4$. MW, 282. M.p. 205–7°.

Auwers, Demuth, *Ann.*, 1927, **457**, 297.

6-Nitroindazole-3-carboxylic Acid.

Yellow plates from AcOH. M.p. 277–82° decomp.

Et ester: needles from EtOH. M.p. 264–6°. Sol. MeOH, EtOH. NaOH ⟶ orange-red sol. N-*Me*: $C_{11}H_{11}O_4N_3$. MW, 249. Cryst. from MeOH. M.p. 178°.

Hahn, Just, *Ber.*, 1932, **65**, 721.

2-Nitroindene

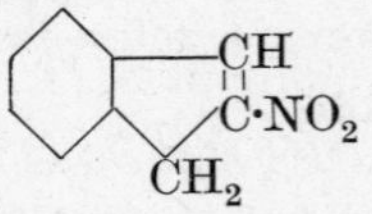

$C_9H_7O_2N$ MW, 161

Cryst. from AcOH. M.p. 141°. Zn dust + AcOH ⟶ 2-hydrindone oxime.

Wallach, Beschke, *Ann.*, 1904, **336**, 2.

3-Nitroindole

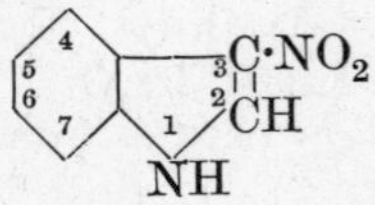

$C_8H_6O_2N_2$ MW, 162

Yellow needles from C_6H_6. M.p. 210°.
N-*Et*: $C_{10}H_{10}O_2N_2$. MW, 190. Needles from, pet. ether. M.p. 102°.

Angelico, Velardi, *Gazz. chim. ital.*, 1904, **34**, ii, 60.

6-Nitroindole.
Yellow prisms from 70% EtOH. M.p. 139–140·5°.

Majima, Kotake, *Ber.*, 1930, **63**, 2241.

1-Nitroindole-2-carboxylic Acid

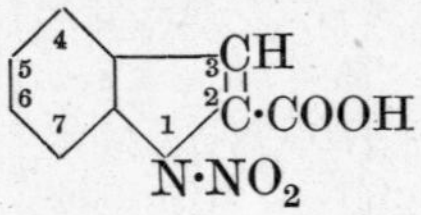

$C_9H_6O_4N_2$ MW, 206

Yellow cryst. from MeOH. M.p. 189° decomp. Spar. sol. usual org. solvents. Sol. alkalis, alk. carbonates, conc. H_2SO_4 with yellowish-red col. Reduces Fehling's on heating.

Reissert, *Ber.*, 1896, **29**, 663.

3-Nitroindole-2-carboxylic Acid.
Yellow leaflets from xylene. M.p. 203° decomp. Above m.p. ⟶ 3-nitroindole.

Angelico, Velardi, *Gazz. chim. ital.*, 1904, **34**, ii, 65.

6-Nitroindole-3-carboxylic Acid.
Yellow needles from EtOH. Decomp. about 275–8°. Alk. salts spar. sol. H_2O with orange-red col.

Et ester: $C_{11}H_{10}O_4N_2$. MW, 234. Yellowish needles from EtOH. M.p. 198–9°.

Majima, Kotake, *Ber.*, 1930, **63**, 2240.

5-Nitroisatin (5-*Nitro-ψ-isatin*)

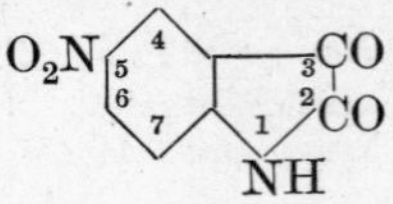

$C_8H_4O_4N_2$ MW, 192

Yellow needles from EtOH. M.p. 245° decomp. Sol. EtOH. Spar. sol. H_2O. Sol. alkalis with red col.
N-*Acetyl*: yellow needles from C_6H_6. M.p. 193–4°. Insol. H_2O.
3-*Oxime*: *benzyl ether*, yellow needles. M.p. 234–5°. Sol. Me_2CO, C_6H_6. Spar. sol. EtOH.
3-*Phenylhydrazone*: yellow cryst. from EtOH. M.p. 284°.
N-*Me*: *see* 5-Nitro-1-methylisatin.

Rupe, Kersten, *Helv. Chim. Acta*, 1926, **9**, 578.
Liebermann, Kraus, *Ber.*, 1907, **40**, 2501.
Korczyński, Marchlewski, *Ber.*, 1902, **35**, 4337.
Schunck, Marchlewski, *Ber.*, 1895, **28**, 546.
Rupe, Stöcklin, *Helv. Chim. Acta*, 1924, **7**, 564.

6-Nitroisatin (6-*Nitro-ψ-isatin*).
Red needles from EtOH. M.p. 244° decomp.
3-*Phenylhydrazone*: brown powder from EtOH. M.p. 286°.

See first reference above.

2-Nitroisoamyl Alcohol (3-*Nitro-2-methylbutanol-4*, *nitroisobutylcarbinol*)

$$(CH_3)_2CH{\cdot}CH(NO_2){\cdot}CH_2OH$$

$C_5H_{11}O_3N$ MW, 133

B.p. 138–9°/38 mm. D^{13} 1·0966. Insol. H_2O.
Nitrate: b.p. 135°/17 mm. Insol. H_2O. Spar. volatile in steam.

Shaw, *Chem. Zentr.*, 1898, I, 439.
Wieland, Rahn, *Ber.*, 1921, **54**, 1775.

α-Nitroisoamylbenzene

$$C_6H_5{\cdot}CH(NO_2){\cdot}CH_2{\cdot}CH(CH_3)_2$$

$C_{11}H_{15}O_2N$ MW, 193

B.p. 159–61°/20 mm. D_0^0 1·08991, D_0^{20} 1·07362. n_D^{20} 1·53140.

Konowalow, Jegorow, *Chem. Zentr.*, 1899, I, 776.

2-Nitroisobutane (tert.-*Nitrobutane*)

$(CH_3)_3C{\cdot}NO_2$

$C_4H_9O_2N$ MW, 103

Cryst. M.p. 24°. B.p. 126–126·5°/748 mm. Misc. with EtOH, Et_2O, C_6H_6. Insol. alkalis. Sn + HCl ⟶ *tert.*-butylamine.

Bewad, *J. prakt. Chem.*, 1893, **48**, 359, 367.
Hass, Hodge, Vanderbilt, U.S.P., 1,976,667, (*Chem. Abstracts*, 1934, **28**, 5830).

3-Nitroisobutane

$(CH_3)_2CH{\cdot}CH_2NO_2$

$C_4H_9O_2N$ MW, 103

B.p. 137–40° (158–9°/755 mm.). $D^{7.5}$ 0·987.

Demole, *Ann.*, 1875, **175**, 142.

2-Nitroisobutyl Alcohol

$(CH_3)_2C(NO_2){\cdot}CH_2OH$

$C_4H_9O_3N$ MW, 119

Needles or plates from MeOH. M.p. 82°. Sol. EtOH, Et_2O. Spar. sol. H_2O.

Henry, *Bull. soc. chim.*, 1895, **13**, 1002.

α-Nitroisobutylbenzene

$C_6H_5{\cdot}CH(NO_2){\cdot}CH(CH_3)_2$

$C_{10}H_{13}O_2N$ MW, 179

Oil. B.p. 244° decomp., 145–6°/25 mm. n_D^{20} 1·50746.

Aci-form: 1-isonitroso-2-methyl-1-phenylpropane. Cryst. M.p. about 54° decomp. Stable only in Et_2O and in the cold. Sol. Na_2CO_3.

Konowalow, *Ber.*, 1895, **28**, 1858; 1896, **29**, 2197.

1-Nitroisobutylene

$(CH_3)_2C{:}CH{\cdot}NO_2$

$C_4H_7O_2N$ MW, 101

Yellow oil with pungent odour. B.p. 154–8° part. decomp., 80°/40 mm., 50°/10 mm. D_0^0 1·052. Insol. H_2O. Sol. alkalis. AlHg in Et_2O or Zn + AcOH in Et_2O ⟶ isobutyraldoxime. H_2O at 100° ⟶ acetone and nitromethane.

Haitinger, *Ann.*, 1878, **193**, 368, 382.

1-Nitroisobutyric Acid

$(CH_3)_2C(NO_2){\cdot}COOH$

$C_4H_7O_4N$ MW, 133

Cryst. M.p. 95°. Very sol. EtOH, Et_2O. Sol. hot $CHCl_3$. Mod. sol. H_2O. Very spar. sol. CS_2. Decomp. readily, *e.g.*, by heating with H_2O, xylene or $PhNO_2$ ⟶ a blue oil.

Me ester: $C_5H_9O_4N$. MW, 147. B.p. 73–4°/12 mm.

Amide: $C_4H_8O_3N_2$. MW, 132. Leaflets from Et_2O. M.p. 117–18°. Sol. H_2O, EtOH. Spar. sol. Et_2O. Hot dil. H_2SO_4 ⟶ CO_2, N_2O and acetone.

Nitrile: $C_4H_6O_2N_2$. MW, 114. Cryst. from ligroin. M.p. 35°. B.p. 97°/45 mm., 73°/12 mm. Sol. EtOH. Spar. sol. H_2O.

Steinkopf, Supan, *Ber.*, 1911, **44**, 2893, 2896.
Piloty, v. Schwerin, *Ber.*, 1901, **34**, 1865.
Pedersen, *J. Phys. Chem.*, 1934, **38**, 559.

5-Nitroisoeugenol

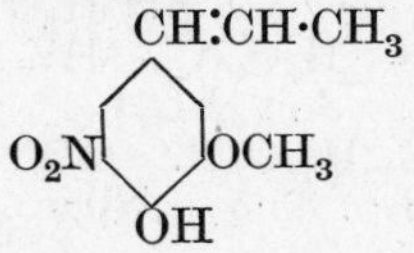

$C_{10}H_{11}O_4N$ MW, 209

Yellowish-red powder. Decomp. about 150°. Sol. EtOH, $CHCl_3$. Insol. H_2O. Very sol. dil. alkalis.

Acetyl: yellowish-brown amorph. powder. Decomp. above 200°. Sol. EtOH, $CHCl_3$, AcOH.

Puxeddu, Cornella, *Gazz. chim. ital.*, 1906, **36**, ii, 451.

Nitro-isonitroso-ethane.
See Ethylnitrolic Acid.

Nitro-isonitroso-methane.
See Methylnitrolic Acid.

2-Nitroisophthalic Acid

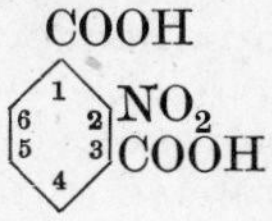

$C_8H_5O_6N$ MW, 211

Prisms from MeOH. M.p. 315° (300°). Sol. to 0·216% in H_2O at 25°. Sol. EtOH, Et_2O.

Mono-Me ester: $C_9H_7O_6N$. MW, 225. Needles from H_2O. M.p. 197°. Very sol. MeOH. *Chloride*: $C_9H_6O_5NCl$. MW, 243·5. Leaflets from C_6H_6. M.p. 121°.

Di-Me ester: $C_{10}H_9O_6N$. MW, 239. Needles from H_2O. M.p. 135°. Insol. pet. ether.

Monoamide: $C_8H_6O_5N_2$. MW, 210. Plates from MeOH. M.p. 252°. *Me ester*: $C_9H_8O_5N_2$. MW, 224. Needles from MeOH. M.p. 190–1°.

Wohl, *Ber.*, 1910, **43**, 3480.
Noelting, Gachot, *Ber.*, 1906, **39**, 73.

4-Nitroisophthalic Acid.

Needles from H_2O. M.p. 258–9° (245°). Very sol. hot H_2O, EtOH, Et_2O. Sol. to 0·967% in H_2O at 25°. k (first) = $1·03 \times 10^{-2}$ at 25°; (second) = $2·63 \times 10^{-4}$ at 25°.

1-*Me ester*: $C_9H_7O_6N$. MW, 225. Needles from C_6H_6. M.p. 153·5–154°. $k = 1·09 \times 10^{-2}$ at 25°.

3-*Me ester*: powder from C_6H_6. M.p. 192–4°. $k = 8·4 \times 10^{-4}$ at 25°.

Di-Me ester: yellowish cryst. from C_6H_6. M.p. 87–88·5°.

Axer, *Monatsh.*, 1920, **41**, 159.
Noyes, *Am. Chem. J.*, 1888, **10**, 485.

5-Nitroisophthalic Acid.

Leaflets + H_2O from H_2O. M.p. anhyd. 249° (255–6°). Very sol. hot H_2O, EtOH, Et_2O.

Di-Me ester: $C_{10}H_9O_6N$. MW, 239. Needles. M.p. 123° (121°). Sol. EtOH.

Di-Et ester: $C_{12}H_{13}O_6N$. MW, 267. Needles from EtOH. M.p. 83·5°. Spar. sol. H_2O, cold EtOH.

Möller, *Ber.*, 1909, **42**, 433 (*Note*).
Huisinga, *Rec. trav. chim.*, 1908, **27**, 265.
Meyer, Wesche, *Ber.*, 1917, **50**, 444.

1-Nitroisopropyl Alcohol

$CH_3·CH(OH)·CH_2NO_2$

$C_3H_7O_3N$ MW, 105

F.p. about −20°. B.p. 112°/13 mm. D^{18} 1·1910. Sol. H_2O, EtOH, Et_2O. $CrO_3 \longrightarrow$ nitroacetone.

Acetyl: b.p. 94–5°/8 mm. D_4^{20} 1·1588. n_D^{20} 1·4242.

Henry, *Chem. Zentr.*, 1898, II, 887.
Schmidt, Rutz, *Ber.*, 1928, **61**, 2145.

Nitro-*p*-isopropylbenzoic Acid.

See Nitrocuminic Acid.

Nitroisopropylcresol.

See Nitrocarvacrol *and* Nitrothymol.

5-Nitroisovanillic Acid (*5-Nitro-3-hydroxy-anisic acid*)

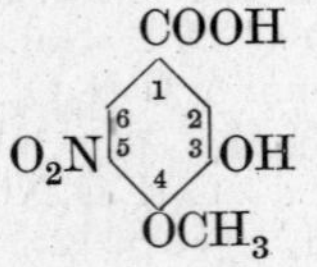

$C_8H_7O_6N$ MW, 213

Needles from H_2O or C_6H_6. M.p. 174°. Sol. hot H_2O, EtOH, Et_2O.

Acetyl: needles. M.p. 168–9°. Sol. EtOH, Et_2O. Spar. sol. cold H_2O.

Matsomoto, *Ber.*, 1878, **11**, 133.
Klemenc, *Monatsh.*, 1914, **35**, 95.

6-Nitroisovanillic Acid (*6-Nitro-3-hydroxy-anisic acid*).

Yellow prisms from boiling H_2O. M.p. 181° decomp. Sol. MeOH, EtOH, Me_2CO, Et_2O. Mod. sol. AcOH, boiling H_2O. Spar. sol. C_6H_6, $CHCl_3$. Alc. $FeCl_3 \longrightarrow$ greenish-brown col. Alk. sols are orange-yellow.

Me ester: $C_9H_9O_6N$. MW, 227. Cryst. from EtOH.Aq. M.p. 143°.

Acetyl: plates from EtOH.Aq. M.p. 214° decomp.

Greenwood, Robinson, *J. Chem. Soc.*, 1932, 1371.

2-Nitroisovanillin

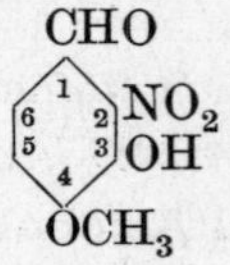

$C_8H_7O_5N$ MW, 197

Leaflets from EtOH. M.p. 148–9°. Turns brown in sunlight.

Me ether: *see* 2-Nitroveratric Aldehyde.

Et ether: $C_{10}H_{11}O_5N$. MW, 225. Cryst. from EtOH. M.p. 76–7°.

Phenylhydrazone: dark violet needles from AcOH. M.p. 157–8°.

Pschorr, Stoehrer, *Ber.*, 1902, **35**, 4396.
Späth, Tharrer, *Ber.*, 1933, **66**, 912.

5-Nitroisovanillin.

Needles from H_2O. M.p. 113°. Sol. most org. solvents. Mod. sol. H_2O.

Acetyl: yellowish needles from H_2O. M.p. 86°. Sol. EtOH, Et_2O, C_6H_6, $CHCl_3$. Spar. sol. H_2O. *Phenylhydrazone*: yellow needles from EtOH. M.p. 165°.

Me ether: *see* 5-Nitroveratric Aldehyde.

Benzoyl: needles from EtOH. M.p. 120–1°. *Phenylhydrazone*: orange cryst. from EtOH. M.p. 205–6°.

Phenylhydrazone: yellowish-red prisms from EtOH. M.p. 170°.

Pschorr, Stoehrer, *Ber.*, 1902, **35**, 4398.
Hinkel, Ayling, Morgan, *J. Chem. Soc.*, 1935, 817.

6-Nitroisovanillin.

Yellow needles from EtOH. M.p. 189°. Sol. AcOH, $CHCl_3$, C_6H_6, hot EtOH. Spar. sol. ligroin, hot H_2O. Darkens rapidly in light.

Phenylhydrazone: red leaflets from EtOH. M.p. 200–1°.

Me ether: *see* 6-Nitroveratric Aldehyde.

Pschorr, Stoehrer, *Ber.*, 1902, **35**, 4394.

4-Nitroisoxazole

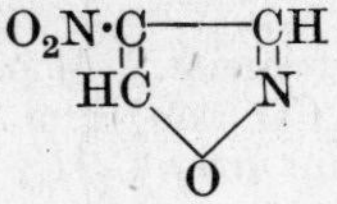

$C_3H_2O_3N_2$ MW, 114

Plates from Et_2O–ligroin. M.p. 46–7°. Sol. EtOH, Et_2O. Spar. sol. CS_2. Very spar. sol. ligroin. Sol. alkalis with deep yellow col.

Hill, Lorrey, *Am. Chem. J.*, 1899, **22**, 106.

7-Nitrokairoline.

See under 7-Nitro-1 : 2 : 3 : 4-tetrahydroquinoline.

Nitrolactic Acid

$O_2N{\cdot}CH_2{\cdot}CH(OH){\cdot}COOH$

$C_3H_5O_5N$ MW, 135

Prisms from Et_2O–$CHCl_3$. M.p. 76–7°. Very sol. H_2O, EtOH, Et_2O. Spar. sol. $CHCl_3$. Zn + HCl ⟶ isoserine.

Hill, Black, *Am. Chem. J.*, 1904, **32**, 231.

3-Nitrolepidine

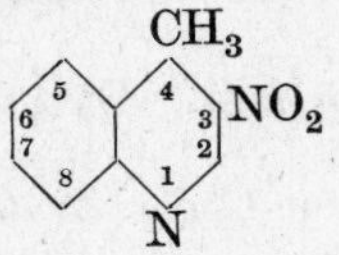

$C_{10}H_8O_2N_2$ MW, 188

Prisms from hot H_2O. M.p. 118°. Volatile in steam.

Badische, D.R.P., 335,197, (*Chem. Abstracts*, 1923, **17**, 1803).

8-Nitrolepidine.

Leaflets from EtOH. M.p. 126–7°. Mod. sol. cold EtOH.

Busch, Koenigs, *Ber.*, 1890, **23**, 2687.

Nitromalic Acid.

See under Malic Acid.

Nitromalondialdehyde

$O_2N{\cdot}CH{<}^{CHO}_{CHO}$ or $O_2N{\cdot}C{\lessdot}^{CHO}_{CH{\cdot}OH}$

$C_3H_3O_4N$ MW, 117

Prisms from Et_2O. M.p. 50–1°. Sol. EtOH, Et_2O, $CHCl_3$, C_6H_6. Mod. sol. ligroin. Decomp. in aq. sol. ⟶ formic acid and trinitrobenzene. Na deriv. with hydrazine sulphate ⟶ a red ppt. which with warm HCl ⟶ 4-nitropyrazole. With acetone in alk. sol. ⟶ *p*-nitrophenol.

Dioxime: known only in form of aq. sol. of Na salt. Slight excess of HCl + aq. sol. of Na salt ⟶ yellow ppt. ⟶ nitroisoxazole.

Monoanil: yellow plates from EtOH. M.p. 143–4°. *Oxime*: yellow cryst. M.p. 162°. *Oxime acetate*: m.p. 115–16°.

Dianil: yellow needles from EtOH.Aq. M.p. 93–4°.

Mono-p-tolylimide: m.p. 176–7°.

Di-p-tolylimide: m.p. 138°.

Monophenylhydrazone: yellow needles. M.p. 101°, re-solidifies on further heating ⟶ 4-nitro-1-phenylpyrazole.

Di-phenylhydrazone: orange-red solid. M.p. 98° decomp. Heat with C_2H_5OH ⟶ 4-nitro-1-phenylpyrazole.

Hill, Torrey, *Am. Chem. J.*, 1899, **22**, 89.
Hill, Sanger, *Ber.*, 1882, **15**, 1908.

Nitromalonic Acid

$O_2N{\cdot}CH{<}^{COOH}_{COOH}$

$C_3H_3O_6N$ MW, 149

Di-Me ester: $C_5H_7O_6N$. MW, 177. Yellowish oil. Readily sol. alkalis. *NH_4 salt*: m.p. about 166° decomp. *K salt*: yellow plates from EtOH. M.p. 206–206·5°. Very sol. H_2O.

Di-Et ester: $C_7H_{11}O_6N$. MW, 205. Colourless oil with fruity odour. B.p. 152–3°/37–38 mm., 134–5°/14 mm., 127°/10 mm. D^0_0 1·220, D^{20}_4 1·1988. Insol. H_2O. NH_3.Aq. at 100° ⟶ nitroacetamide. *NH_4 salt*: leaflets from EtOH. M.p. 152–3° (162°). Very sol. H_2O. Insol. Et_2O. *K salt*: prisms from EtOH. M.p. 154°. Very sol. H_2O, EtOH, hot Me_2CO. Insol. Et_2O, $CHCl_3$, C_6H_6, ligroin.

Diamide: $C_3H_5O_4N_3$. MW, 147. Prisms from H_2O. M.p. 172°. Insol. EtOH.

Mononitrile: *see* Nitrocyanoacetic Acid.

Dianilide: $C_{15}H_{13}O_4N_3$. MW, 299. Pale yellow plates from EtOH. M.p. 141–2°.

Di-N-methylanilide: $C_{17}H_{17}O_4N_3$. MW, 327. Prisms. M.p. 156° decomp.

Ulpiani, *Gazz. chim. ital.*, 1912, **42**, i, 223, 400.
Franchimont, Klobbie, *Rec. trav. chim.*, 1889, **8**, 283.
Ratz, *Monatsh.*, 1904, **25**, 60.

o-Nitromandelic Acid

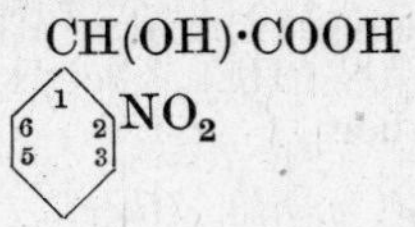

$C_8H_7O_5N$ MW, 197

d-.

Plates from $CHCl_3$. M.p. 100–1°. $[\alpha]^{20}_{5461}$ + 490° in Me_2CO.

Et ester: $C_{10}H_{11}O_5N$. MW, 225. Pale yellow oil. B.p. 165–6°/4 mm. $[\alpha]_D^{20\cdot5}$ + 302° in Me_2CO.

Acetyl: prisms from C_6H_6. M.p. 95–6°. $[\alpha]_D^{20\cdot5}$ + 289° in Me_2CO.

Brucine salt: cryst. + $2H_2O$ from H_2O. M.p. anhyd. 137° decomp. $[\alpha]_{5461}^{20}$ + 291° in Me_2CO.

l-.

Plates from $CHCl_3$. M.p. 100–1°. $[\alpha]_{5461}^{20}$ — 594° in Me_2CO.

r-.

Cryst. from $CHCl_3$ or hot H_2O. M.p. 140°. Sol. H_2O, EtOH, Et_2O. Zn + AcOH or $SnCl_2$ + HCl ⟶ dioxindole. Cold alk. $KMnO_4$ ⟶ *o*-nitrobenzoylformic acid.

Me ester: $C_9H_9O_5N$. MW, 211. M.p. 74·5°. Sol. EtOH, Et_2O. Spar. sol. ligroin.

Et ester: needles from Et_2O–ligroin. M.p. 49–50°. *Benzoyl*: prisms from EtOH–pet. ether. M.p. 76–7° (72°).

Amide: $C_8H_8O_4N_2$. MW, 196. O-*Acetyl*: cryst. from MeOH. M.p. 128°. O-*Benzoyl*: cryst. from EtOH or C_6H_6. M.p. 129°.

Nitrile: *o*-nitrobenzaldehyde cyanhydrin. $C_8H_6O_3N_2$. MW, 178. Needles from C_6H_6. M.p. 95°. Sol. EtOH, Et_2O, Me_2CO. Sol. conc. H_2SO_4 with red col. Hyd. by boiling conc. HCl. *Acetyl*: cryst. from $CHCl_3$–ligroin. M.p. 52°. *Benzoyl*: cryst. from EtOH. M.p. 90–1°. Spar. sol. ligroin.

Me ether: $C_9H_9O_5N$. MW, 211. Plates from H_2O. M.p. 81–2°.

Acetyl: prisms from $CHCl_3$–pet. ether. M.p. 102–3°.

McKenzie, Stewart, *J. Chem. Soc.*, 1935, 106.
Albert, *Ber.*, 1916, **49**, 1385.
Heller, Mayer, *Ber.*, 1906, **39**, 2336.
Engler, Zielke, *Ber.*, 1889, **22**, 208.

m-Nitromandelic Acid.

r-.

Rhombic cryst. from Et_2O–pet. ether. M.p. 119–20°. Sol. H_2O, EtOH, Et_2O. Spar. sol. $CHCl_3$, C_6H_6, ligroin.

Et ester: needles from pet. ether. M.p. 63°. Sol. EtOH, Et_2O, $CHCl_3$, AcOH, C_6H_6. Spar. sol. cold pet. ether.

Beyer, *J. prakt. Chem.*, 1885, **31**, 391, 395.
Evans, Brooks, *J. Am. Chem. Soc.*, 1908, **30**, 408.
Engler, Wöhrle, *Ber.*, 1887, **20**, 2203.

p-Nitromandelic Acid.

dl-.

Cryst. from toluene. M.p. 126–7°. Sol EtOH, Et_2O, Me_2CO, AcOH, hot H_2O.

Me ester: prisms from C_6H_6. M.p. 87°.

Et ester: needles from ligroin. M.p. 75–6°.

Nitrile: *p*-nitrobenzaldehyde cyanhydrin. Yellow needles. M.p. 109–10°. Sol. EtOH, Et_2O, AcOH, AcOEt, Me_2CO, hot C_6H_6. Very spar. sol. ligroin.

Benzoyl: yellowish prisms from toluene. M.p. 185–6° part. decomp.

Heller, Fritsch, *Ber.*, 1913, **46**, 285.
Engler, Zielke, *Ber.*, 1889, **22**, 205, 208.

Nitromannitol.

See under Mannitol.

8-Nitro-p-menthane

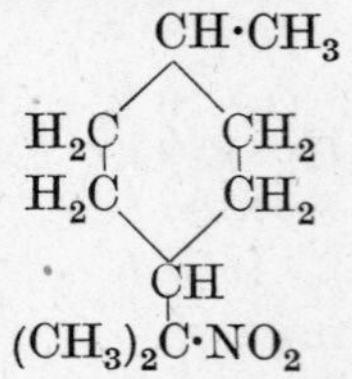

$C_{10}H_{19}O_2N$ MW, 185

B.p. 135–7°/25 mm. D_0^0 1·0005, D_0^{22} 0·9871. n_D^{22} 1·46241.

Konowalow, *Chem. Zentr.*, 1904, I, 1517.

4-Nitromenthone

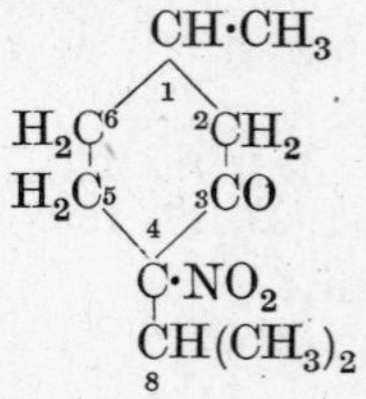

$C_{10}H_{17}O_3N$ MW, 199

Oil. B.p. 135–40°/15 mm. D_0^0 1·0856, D_0^{20} 1·0591.

Konowalow, Ischewsky, *Ber.*, 1898, **31**, 1478.

8-Nitromenthone.

Needles. M.p. 80°. Very sol. MeOH, EtOH, AcOEt, C_6H_6.

Harries, Roeder, *Ber.*, 1898, **31**, 1809; 1899, **32**, 3365.

6-Nitro-2-mercaptobenzthiazole (5-*Nitro*-1-*mercaptobenzthiazole*)

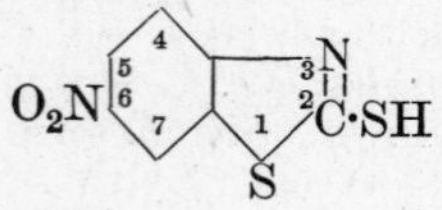

$C_7H_4O_2N_2S_2$ MW, 212

Yellow needles from AcOH. M.p. 255–7°.

Teppema, Sebrell, *J. Am. Chem. Soc.*, 1927, **49**, 1780.
Naugatuck, F.P., 741,910, (*Chem. Abstracts*, 1933, **27**, 3642).
Sebrell, U.S.P., 1,958,770, (*Chem. Abstracts*, 1934, **28**, 4632).

4-Nitromesidine (*4-Nitro-2-aminomesitylene*)

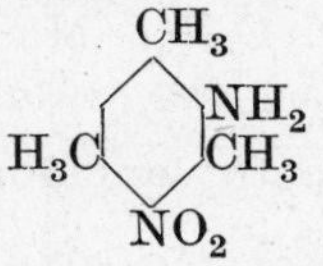

$C_9H_{12}O_2N_2$ MW, 180

Golden-yellow needles from EtOH. M.p. 75°. Very sol. EtOH, Et_2O.

Acetyl: needles from EtOH. M.p. 191°. Mod. sol. boiling EtOH. Sol. conc. HCl.

Benzoyl: cryst. M.p. 168·5°.

m-*Nitrobenzoyl*: m.p. 207–8°.

Benzenesulphonyl: cryst. from C_6H_6. M.p. 162–3°.

Morgan, Micklethwait, *J. Chem. Soc.*, 1906, **89**, 1299.
Hübner, v. Schack, *Ber.*, 1877, **10**, 1711.
Ladenburg, *Ann.*, 1875, **179**, 165.
Kuster, Stallberg, *Ann.*, 1894, **278**, 214.

Nitromesitol (*4-Nitro-2-hydroxymesitylene, 3-nitro-2 : 4 : 6-trimethylphenol*)

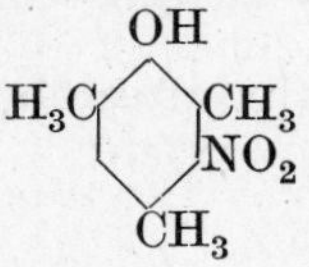

$C_9H_{11}O_3N$ MW, 181

Yellow leaflets from H_2O. M.p. 64°. Sol. EtOH, Et_2O. Spar. sol. cold H_2O. Volatile in steam.

Knecht, *Ann.*, 1882, **215**, 98.

Nitromesitylene

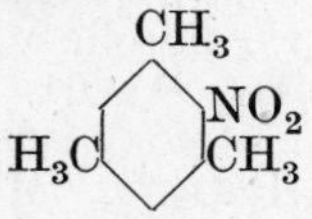

$C_9H_{11}O_2N$ MW, 165

Prisms from EtOH. M.p. 44° (41–2°). B.p. 255°. Very sol. hot EtOH. CrO_3 in AcOH at 60–70° ⟶ 4-nitro-3 : 5-dimethylbenzoic acid.

Bamberger, Rising, *Ber.*, 1900, **33**, 3625.
Ladenburg, *Ann.*, 1875, **179**, 170.
Francis, *Ber.*, 1906, **39**, 3801.
Powell, Johnson, *Organic Syntheses*, 1934, XIV, 68.

ω-Nitromesitylene (*3 : 5-Dimethylphenylnitromethane*)

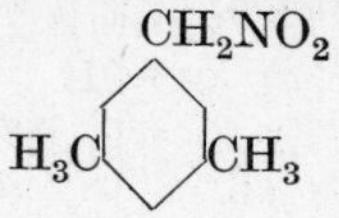

$C_9H_{11}O_2N$ MW, 165

Cryst. from EtOH. M.p. 46·8°. Sol. EtOH, Et_2O, C_6H_6. Spar. sol. pet. ether. Volatile in steam. Heat of comb. C_v 1206·33 Cal. Sol. caustic alkalis and hot Na_2CO_3.Aq. giving Na salt of *aci*-form.

Aci-*Form*: ω-isonitromesitylene; 3 : 5-dimethylphenylisonitromethane

$$(CH_3)_2C_6H_3\cdot CH{:}NO_2H$$

Needles from C_6H_6. M.p. about 63° decomp. Sol. EtOH, Et_2O, Me_2CO, AcOEt, C_6H_6. Spar. sol. pet. ether. Passes into normal nitro form on standing, especially in sunlight.

Konowalow, *Ber.*, 1895, **28**, 1862; 1896, **29**, 2201.

1-Nitromesityl oxide (*5-Nitro-2-methyl-2-pentenone-4*)

$$(CH_3)_2C{:}CH\cdot CO\cdot CH_2NO_2$$

$C_6H_9O_3N$ MW, 143

Yellow pungent liq. B.p. 95–6°/23 mm. $D^{27\cdot3}$ 1·212. Semicarbazide ⟶ nitroacetone semicarbazone.

Anil: yellow leaflets. M.p. 84–5°.

Harries, *Ann.*, 1901, **319**, 248.

Nitromethane

$$CH_3\cdot NO_2$$

CH_3O_2N MW, 61

F.p. — 17° (— 28·5°). B.p. 101–101·5°/764·7 mm. D_4^4 1·1580, D_{15}^{15} 1·1441, D_{20}^{20} 1·1382, D_4^{15} 1·1437, D_4^{25} 1·1297. $n_D^{21\cdot6}$ 1·38133, n_D^{25} 1·37970. Heat of comb. C_p 169·8 Cal. (180·90 Cal.) (vapour), 169·5 Cal. (liq.); C_v 170·25 Cal. (vapour), 169·95 Cal. (liq.). Aq. sol. reacts acid to litmus. $SnCl_2$ ⟶ methylamine and *N*-methylhydroxylamine. Nascent HNO_2 ⟶ methylnitrolic acid. Hot conc. H_2SO_4 ⟶ CO and hydroxylamine.

Steinkopf, Kirchoff, *Ber.*, 1909, **42**, 3439.
Wahl, *Bull. soc. chim.*, 1909, **5**, 180.
Walden, *Ber.*, 1907, **40**, 3216, 4301.
Hirano, *Chem. Abstracts*, 1931, **25**, 69.
Wang, Tseng, *ibid.*, 681.
Pritzl, Adkins, *J. Am. Chem. Soc.*, 1931, **53**, 234.
Krause, Swiss P., 74,333, (*Chem. Abstracts*, 1917, **11**, 2027).
Whitmore, Whitmore, *Organic Syntheses*, Collective Vol. I, 393.

2-Nitro-*p*-methylacetophenone (*Methyl 2-nitro-p-tolyl ketone*)

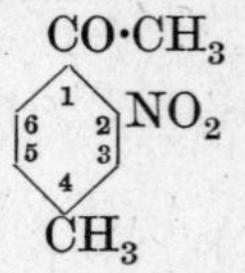

$C_9H_9O_3N$ MW, 179

Yellow oil. Zn dust + NaOH ⟶ 6 : 6′-dimethylindigo.

Duff, *J. Chem. Soc.*, 1914, **105**, 2185.

3-Nitro-*p*-methylacetophenone (*Methyl 3-nitro-p-tolyl ketone*).

Yellow needles from pet. ether. M.p. 61°. Sol. EtOH. Spar. sol. cold pet. ether. Dil. HNO_3 ⟶ 2-nitro-*p*-toluic acid.

Oxime: prisms from EtOH. M.p. 133°.

Semicarbazone: yellow powder from AcOH. M.p. 262° decomp.

2 : 4-*Dinitrophenylhydrazone*: orange-yellow plates from xylene. M.p. 232°.

Errera, *Gazz. chim. ital.*, 1891, **21**, i, 92.
Brady, Day, *J. Chem. Soc.*, 1934, 120.

1-Nitro-3-methylacridine

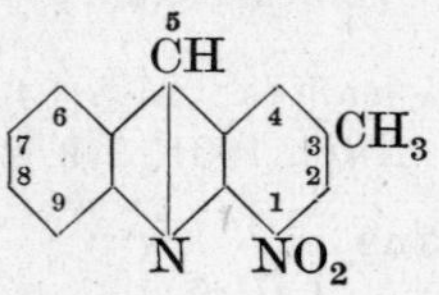

$C_{14}H_{10}O_2N_2$ MW, 238

Brown needles from MeOH. M.p. 201–2°.

Mayer, Stein, *Ber.*, 1917, **50**, 1317.

3-Nitro-5-methylacridine.

Brownish-yellow needles from EtOH. Does not melt below 300°.

Jensen, Rethwisch, *J. Am. Chem. Soc.*, 1928, **50**, 1149.

4-Nitro-1-methylacridone

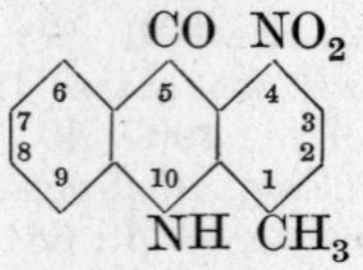

$C_{14}H_{10}O_3N_2$ MW, 254

Yellow prisms from C_6H_6. Does not melt below 300°.

Clemo, Perkin, Robinson, *J. Chem. Soc.*, 1924, **125**, 1774.

8-Nitro-2-methylacridone.

Light brown cryst. from EtOH.Aq. Does not melt below 300°. Mod. sol. C_6H_6. Conc. H_2SO_4 ⟶ greenish-blue col. Hot alkalis ⟶ reddish-violet fluor.

Tanasescu, Macarovici, *Bull. soc. chim.*, 1933, **53**, 372.

1-Nitro-3-methylacridone.

Red cryst. from C_6H_6. M.p. 250°.

Mayer, Stein, *Ber.*, 1917, **50**, 1317.

1-Nitro-10-methylacridone (1-*Nitro*-N-*methylacridone*).

Yellow needles from EtOH. M.p. 168°.

Lehmstedt, Hundertmark, *Ber.*, 1931, **64**, 2391.

3-Nitro-10-methylacridone (3-*Nitro*-N-*methylacridone*).

Yellow needles from AcOH. M.p. 276°. Mod. sol. usual org. solvents.

Lehmstedt, Hundertmark, *Ber.*, 1931, **64**, 2390.

9-Nitro-10-methylacridone (9-*Nitro*-N-*methylacridone*).

Yellow prisms from xylene. M.p. 176–7°.

Burton, Gibson, *J. Chem. Soc.*, 1924, **125**, 2503.

***N*-Nitromethylamine.**

See Methylnitramine.

3-Nitro-*p*-methylaminobenzoic Acid

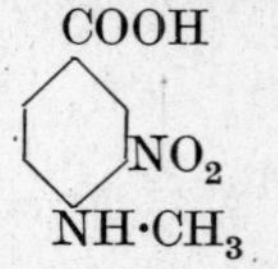

$C_8H_8O_4N_2$ MW, 196

Yellow needles from EtOH. M.p. 303–5° (288°).

Me ester: $C_9H_{10}O_4N_2$. MW, 210. Yellow cryst. from C_6H_6–ligroin. M.p. 145°. Sol. warm EtOH, C_6H_6, AcOH. Very spar. sol. ligroin.

Et ester: $C_{10}H_{12}O_4N_2$. MW, 224. Yellow needles from EtOH. M.p. 101–2°. Sol. EtOH, Et_2O, C_6H_6, $CHCl_3$, AcOH, conc. HCl. Insol. H_2O.

N-*Acetyl*: yellow needles from EtOH. M.p. 190°.

Noelting, Demant, *Ber.*, 1904, **37**, 1029.
Thieme, *J. prakt. Chem.*, 1891, **43**, 458.
Reverdin, de Luc, *Bull. soc. chim.*, 1908, 3, 133.

_o_-Nitro-_N_-methylaniline

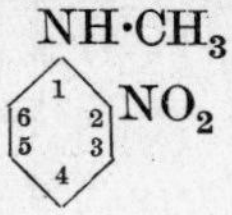

$C_7H_8O_2N_2$ MW, 152

Red needles with blue reflex from pet. ether. M.p. 37°. Sol. usual org. solvents. Spar. sol. cold H_2O, ligroin. Sol. conc. acids.

N-*Acetyl*: m.p. 70°.

N-*Nitroso*: yellowish needles from EtOH. M.p. 36°.

Fischer, Veiel, *Ber.*, 1905, **38**, 321.
Hempel, *J. prakt. Chem.*, 1890, **41**, 168.

_m_-Nitro-_N_-methylaniline.

Reddish-yellow needles or prisms from EtOH. M.p. 68°. Sol. EtOH, Et_2O. Mod. sol. hot H_2O.

N-*Acetyl*: needles from H_2O. M.p. 94–5°.

N-*Benzoyl*: m.p. 104–5°.

N-*Nitroso*: leaflets from EtOH or Me_2CO. M.p. 76° (68–70°). Sol. EtOH. Volatile in steam.

Ullmann, *Ann.*, 1903, **327**, 112.
Meldola, Salmon, *J. Chem. Soc.*, 1888, **53**, 777.
Hodgson, Smith, *J. Chem. Soc.*, 1931, 1509.
Schmidt, Schumacher, *Ber.*, 1921, **54**, 1419.

_p_-Nitro-_N_-methylaniline.

Brownish-yellow prisms with violet reflex from EtOH. M.p. 152°. Sol. EtOH, C_6H_6. Spar. sol. ligroin.

N-*Formyl*: yellow prisms from EtOH. M.p. 118–20°.

N-*Acetyl*: plates from H_2O. M.p. 152–3°.

N-*Benzoyl*: prisms from EtOH.Aq. M.p. 111–12°.

N-β-*Chloroethyl*: greenish-brown cryst. from EtOH. M.p. 90°.

N-*Benzyl*: yellow needles from MeOH. M.p. 68–9°.

N-*Nitroso*: needles from hot EtOH. M.p. 104° (101°). Sol. usual solvents. Spar. sol. H_2O, ligroin.

Meldola, Salmon, *J. Chem. Soc.*, 1888, **53**, 775.
Morgan, Grist, *J. Chem. Soc.*, 1918, **113**, 690.
Hodgson, Smith, *J. Chem. Soc.*, 1931, 1510.
Stoermer, Hoffmann, *Ber.*, 1898, **31**, 2528.

***N*-Nitro-*N*-methylaniline.**

See Methylphenylnitramine.

Nitro-_N_-methylanisidine.

See under Nitroanisidine.

Nitro-_N_-methylanthranilic Acid.

See under Nitroanthranilic Acid.

1-Nitro-2-methylanthraquinone

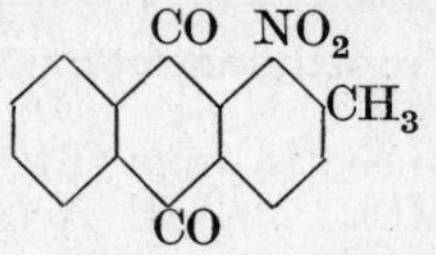

$C_{15}H_9O_4N$ MW, 267

Pale yellow needles from AcOH. M.p. 269–70°. Sol. $PhNO_2$. Spar. sol. C_6H_6, $CHCl_3$, AcOH, AcOEt. Almost insol. EtOH, Et_2O. Na_2S.Aq. ⟶ 1-amino-2-methylanthraquinone. Conc. H_2SO_4 ⟶ yellow sol. ⟶ reddish-brown ⟶ brown on heating. Sol. gives alkali-soluble, purple ppt. on dilution.

Römer, Link, *Ber.*, 1883, **16**, 697.
Fierz, U.S.P., 1,540,467, (*Chem. Abstracts*, 1925, **19**, 2210).
Locker, Fierz, *Helv. Chim. Acta*, 1927, **10**, 642.

4-Nitro-2-methylazobenzene (6-*Benzene-azo*-m-*nitrotoluene*)

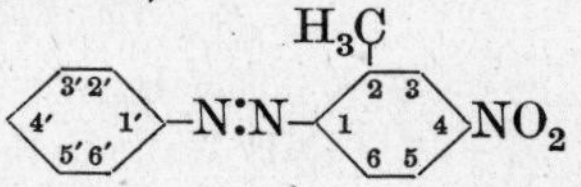

$C_{13}H_{11}O_2N_3$ MW, 241

Red prisms from EtOH, red needles from H_2O. M.p. 98–9°. Sol. usual solvents. Spar. sol. H_2O, pet. ether.

Meisenheimer, Hesse, *Ber.*, 1919, **52**, 1174.

6-Nitro-2-methylazobenzene (2-*Benzene-azo*-m-*nitrotoluene*).

Red oil. B.p. 215°/11 mm.

See previous reference.

2′-Nitro-2-methylazobenzene (2-o-*Nitro-benzeneazotoluene*).

Brownish-red needles from EtOH. M.p. 108–9°. Sol. Et_2O, Me_2CO, $CHCl_3$, C_6H_6, AcOH, hot EtOH, hot ligroin.

Bamberger, Hübner, *Ber.*, 1903, **36**, 3818.

2-Nitro-4-methylazobenzene (4-*Benzene-azo*-m-*nitrotoluene*).

Red leaflets or needles. M.p. 71–71·5°. Sol. Me_2CO, $CHCl_3$, C_6H_6, AcOH, hot EtOH, hot ligroin.

Bamberger, Hübner, *Ber.*, 1903, **36**, 3821.

3-Nitro-4-methylazobenzene (4-*Benzeneazo*-o-*nitrotoluene*).

Orange-red or golden needles from EtOH. M.p. 105°.

Meisenheimer, *Ber.*, 1920, **53**, 367.
Burns, McCombie, Scarborough, *J. Chem. Soc.*, 1928, 2931.

2′-Nitro-4-methylazobenzene (4-o-*Nitrobenzeneazotoluene*).

Orange-red needles from EtOH. M.p. 88°. Sol. Et_2O, $CHCl_3$, Me_2CO, AcOH, C_6H_6, hot EtOH, hot ligroin.

Bamberger, Hübner, *Ber.*, 1903, **36**, 3819.

4′-Nitro-4-methylazobenzene (4-p-*Nitrobenzeneazotoluene*).

Red needles from EtOH. M.p. 183° (180°). Sol. $CHCl_3$, hot ligroin. Spar. sol. EtOH, Et_2O.

Bamberger, *Ber.*, 1902, **35**, 1427.
Burns, McCombie, Scarborough, *J. Chem. Soc.*, 1928, 2931.
Bigiavi, Sabatelli, *Gazz. chim. ital.*, 1927, **57**, 557.

4-Nitro-2-methylbenziminazole

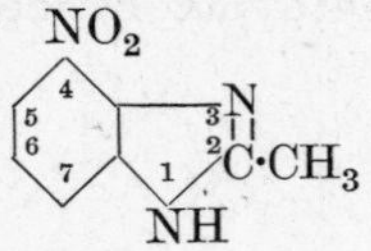

$C_8H_7O_2N_3$ MW, 177.

Yellowish needles from EtOH.Aq. M.p. 217°

Borsche, Rantscheff, *Ann.*, 1911, **379**, 164.

5-Nitro-2-methylbenziminazole.

Yellowish needles or plates from H_2O. M.p. 221°. Sol. hot H_2O, min. acids, caustic alkalis.

Kym, Ratner, *Ber.*, 1912, **45**, 3245.
Kym, Jurkowski, *Ber.*, 1916, **49**, 2689.
Phillips, *J. Chem. Soc.*, 1928, 176.

6-Nitro-2-methylbenziminazole.

Yellowish-brown needles from H_2O. M.p. 219° (216°). Sol. hot H_2O, EtOH, C_6H_6, $CHCl_3$, toluene. Mod. sol. Et_2O. Sol. dil. acids.

Heim, *Ber.*, 1888, **21**, 2307.
Fischer, Hess, *Ber.*, 1903, **36**, 3970.

6-Nitro-3-methylbenziminazole.

Needles from hot H_2O. M.p. 199–200°. Sol. EtOH. Spar. sol. cold H_2O. Very sol. dil. HCl. Sol. dil. NaOH with yellow col.

Kym, Ringer, *Ber.*, 1915, **48**, 1676.

2-Nitro-4-methylbenzophenone (*Pheny 2-nitro*-p-*tolyl ketone*)

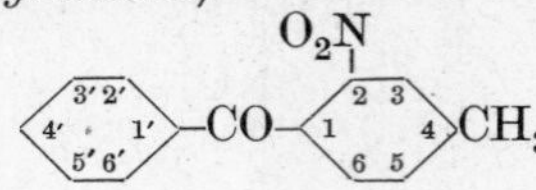

$C_{14}H_{11}O_3N$ MW, 24

Plates or needles from EtOH. M.p. 126–7° Sol. C_6H_6, $CHCl_3$, hot AcOH. Sublimes easily CrO_3 in AcOH ⟶ benzoic acid + *p*-nitro benzoic acid.

Plascuda, Zincke, *Ber.*, 1874, **7**, 983.
See also Limpricht, *Ann.*, 1895, **286**, 324.

3-Nitro-4-methylbenzophenone (*Pheny 3-nitro*-p-*tolyl ketone*).

Cryst. from EtOH or AcOH in pale yellow plates. M.p. 130–2°. Very sol. C_6H_6, Me_2CO $CHCl_3$, AcOH, CS_2. Sol. EtOH, Et_2O, ligroin Spar. sol. H_2O.

Blakey, Scarborough, *J. Chem. Soc.*, 1928 2492.
Weiss, Katz, *Monatsh.*, 1928, **50**, 109.
Chardonnens, *Helv. Chim. Acta*, 1929 **12**, 654.

2′-Nitro-4-methylbenzophenone (2-*Nitrophenyl* p-*tolyl ketone*).

Prisms from EtOH or AcOH. M.p. 155° Sol. warm C_6H_6, $CHCl_3$, AcOH. Spar. sol. hot EtOH, Et_2O, ligroin.

Kliegl, *Ber.*, 1908, **41**, 1845.
Boëtius, Römisch, *Ber.*, 1935, **68**, 1931.

3′-Nitro-4-methylbenzophenone (3-*Nitrophenyl* p-*tolyl ketone*).

Leaflets. M.p. 111°. Sol. Et_2O, $CHCl_3$ C_6H_6. Spar. sol. EtOH. Can be distilled in small quantities.

Limpricht, Lenz, *Ann.*, 1895, **286**, 307.

4′-Nitro-4-methylbenzophenone (4-*Nitrophenyl* p-*tolyl ketone*).

Needles. M.p. 122–4°. Sol. EtOH, Et_2O, C_6H_6, $CHCl_3$, AcOH, CS_2. Sublimes.

Oxime: needles from Et_2O–ligroin. M.p. 145°. Sol. EtOH, Et_2O, C_6H_6. Less sol. ligroin.

Phenylhydrazone: red needles from EtOH. M.p. 154°. Sol. Et_2O, C_6H_6, $CHCl_3$. Spar. sol. ligroin.

Limpricht, Samietz, *Ann.*, 1895, **286**, 321.

Nitromethylbenzophenone-carboxylic Acid.

See Nitrotoluylbenzoic Acid.

5-Nitro-2-methylbenzthiazole (4-*Nitro*-1-*methylbenzthiazole*)

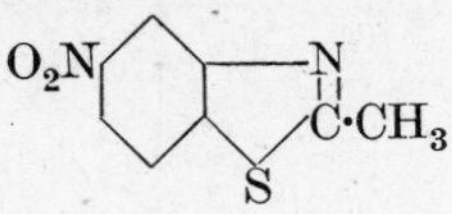

$C_8H_6O_2N_2S$ MW, 194

Long needles from EtOH, C_6H_6, or AcOH. M.p. 139°. Stable to alkalis. Sol. conc. H_2SO_4.

Fries, *Ann.*, 1927, **454**, 177.

4-Nitro-1-methyl-1 : 2 : 3-benztriazole

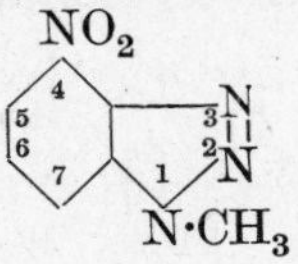

$C_7H_6O_2N_4$ MW, 178

Needles from EtOH. M.p. 173°.

Fries, Güterbock, Kühn, *Ann.*, 1934, **511**, 232.

5-Nitro-1-methyl-1 : 2 : 3-benztriazole.
Cryst. from EtOH. M.p. 163°. Sol. hot C_6H_6, $CHCl_3$.

Pinnow, Koch, *Ber.*, 1897, **30**, 2852.

6-Nitro-1-methyl-1 : 2 : 3-benztriazole.
Pale yellow needles from EtOH. M.p. 187°.

Brady, Reynolds, *J. Chem. Soc.*, 1930, 2672.

7-Nitro-1-methyl-1 : 2 : 3-benztriazole.
Pale yellow needles from EtOH. M.p. 203°.

Fries, Güterbock, Kühn, *Ann.*, 1934, **511**, 232.

7-Nitro-5-methyl-1 : 2 : 3-benztriazole.
Pale yellow needles from EtOH. M.p. 277° decomp.

Lindemann, Krause, *J. prakt. Chem.*, 1927, **115**, 256.

Nitro-*N*-methylbenzylamine.
See under Nitrobenzylamine.

Nitromethylcarbostyril.
See Nitro-2-hydroxymethylquinoline.

2-Nitro-α-methylcinnamic Acid

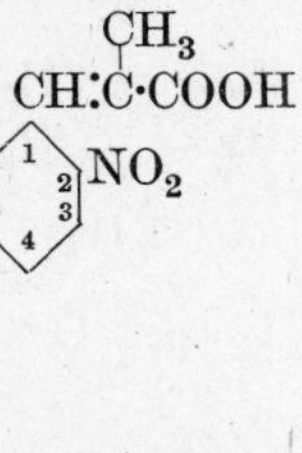

$C_{10}H_9O_4N$ MW, 207

Cryst. from EtOH.Aq. M.p. 164–5°. Sol. EtOH, Et_2O. Spar. sol. C_6H_6, ligroin. $KMnO_4$ ⟶ *o*-nitrobenzoic acid.

Edeleano, *Ber.*, 1887, **20**, 620.

3-Nitro-α-methylcinnamic Acid.
Powder. M.p. 197·5°. Sol. warm EtOH, Et_2O, AcOH, C_6H_6. Spar. sol. ligroin.
Et ester: $C_{12}H_{13}O_4N$. MW, 235. B.p. 197°/11 mm.

v. Miller, Rohde, *Ber.*, 1890, **23**, 1900.
Maxwell, Adams, *J. Am. Chem. Soc.*, 1930, **52**, 2967.

4-Nitro-α-methylcinnamic Acid.
Rhombic cryst. from AcOH. M.p. 208°. Mod. sol. hot EtOH, AcOH. Spar. sol. other solvents. $KMnO_4$ ⟶ *p*-nitrobenzoic acid.
Me ester: $C_{11}H_{11}O_4N$. MW, 221. Leaflets from EtOH. M.p. 115°.

Edeleano, *Ber.*, 1887, **20**, 620.

4-Nitro-β-methylcinnamic Acid

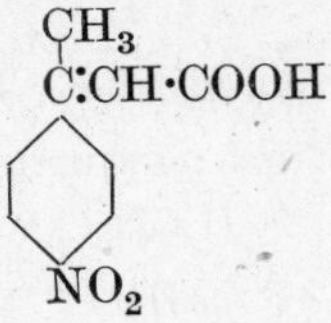

$C_{10}H_9O_4N$ MW, 207

Pale yellowish needles from AcOH. M.p. 168–9°. Dil. HNO_3 at 160° ⟶ *p*-nitrobenzoic acid.
Me ester: $C_{11}H_{11}O_4N$. MW, 221. M.p. 121–2°.
Et ester: $C_{12}H_{13}O_4N$. MW, 235. Cryst. from EtOH. M.p. 74°.

Schroeter, Wulfing, *Ber.*, 1907, **40**, 1594.
Vorländer, *ibid.*, 4535.

2-Nitro-*m*-methylcinnamic Acid

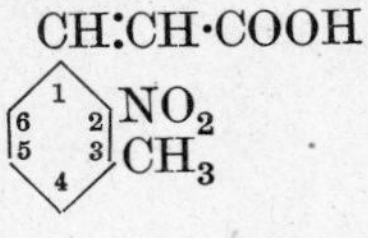

$C_{10}H_9O_4N$ MW, 207

Prisms. M.p. 244°.
Me ester: $C_{11}H_{11}O_4N$. MW, 221. M.p. 83°.

Chakravarti, Venkatasubbam, *Chem. Zentr.*, 1934, I, 1329.

4-Nitro-*m*-methylcinnamic Acid.
Needles from EtOH. M.p. 251°.

Me ester: yellow needles from EtOH. M.p. 124°.

See previous reference.

6-Nitro-*m*-methylcinnamic Acid.
Needles from C_6H_6. M.p. 224°.
Me ester: prisms from MeOH. M.p. 91°.

See previous reference.

3-Nitro-*p*-methylcinnamic Acid

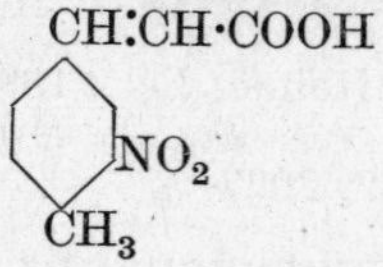

$C_{10}H_9O_4N$ MW, 207

Yellow plates or needles. M.p. 173·5° (170–1°). Sol. EtOH, hot H_2O, Et_2O. Insol. ligroin. *Me ester*: $C_{11}H_{11}O_4N$. MW, 221. Needles from Et_2O–ligroin. M.p. 109°. Sol. EtOH, Et_2O, C_6H_6.
Et ester: $C_{12}H_{13}O_4N$. MW, 235. Yellow plates from EtOH or Et_2O–ligroin. M.p. 97°. Sol. EtOH, Et_2O, C_6H_6.

Gattermann, *Ann.*, 1906, **347**, 360.
Hanztik, Bianchi, *Ber.*, 1899, **32**, 2285.

5-Nitro-4-methyl-*o*-coumaric Acid

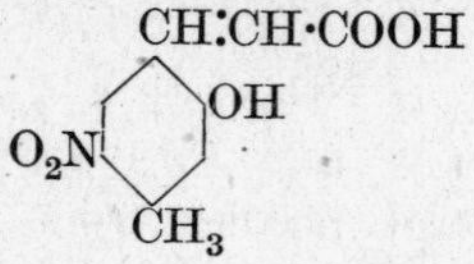

$C_{10}H_9O_5N$ MW, 223

Needles. M.p. 219° decomp.
Me ester: $C_{11}H_{11}O_5N$. MW, 237. Needles from EtOH.Aq. M.p. 187°. *Me ether*: $C_{12}H_{13}O_5N$. MW, 251. Needles. M.p. 136°.

Dey, Row, *J. Chem. Soc.*, 1924, **125**, 563.

6-Nitro-7-methylcoumarin

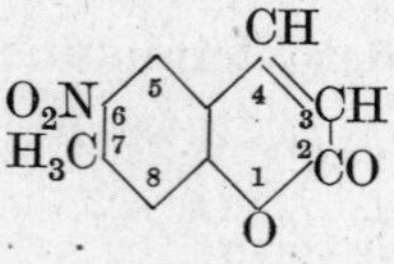

$C_{10}H_7O_4N$ MW, 205

Needles from AcOH. M.p. 223–4°. P_2S_5 in xylene ⟶ 6-nitro-7-methylthiocoumarin. Alk. $KMnO_4$ ⟶ 5-nitro-4-methylsalicylic acid.

Clayton, *J. Chem. Soc.*, 1910, **97**, 1397.

8-Nitro-7-methylcoumarin.
Needles from AcOH. M.p. 165–6°.

See previous reference.

5-Nitro-2-methylcoumarone

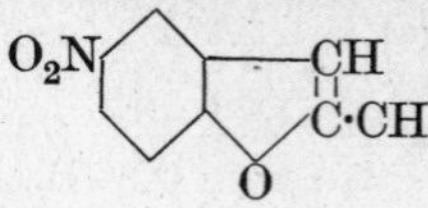

$C_9H_7O_3N$ MW, 177

Needles from EtOH.Aq. M.p. 97°. Sol. Et_2O, C_6H_6, AcOH, AcOEt, ligroin, hot EtOH. Mod. sol. hot H_2O. Volatile in steam. Warm conc. H_2SO_4 ⟶ deep red sol.

Hale, *Ber.*, 1912, **45**, 1601.

1-Nitro-1-methylcyclobutane

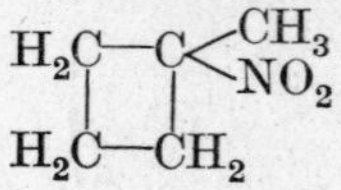

$C_5H_9O_2N$ MW, 115

B.p. 80–2°/30 mm. D_4^{20} 1·0795. n_D^{20} 1·4589.

Rosanow, *Chem. Zentr.*, 1916, I, 925.

1-Nitro-1-methylcyclohexane

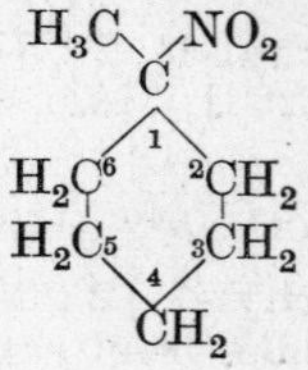

$C_7H_{13}O_2N$ MW, 143

M.p. — 71°. B.p. 118–20°/50 mm., 109–10°/40 mm. D_4^0 1·0547, D_4^{20} 1·0384. n_D^{20} 1·4598. HNO_3 (D 1·2) ⟶ succinic acid and a little oxalic acid.

Nametkin, *Chem. Zentr.*, 1910, II, 1377.
Rosanow, *Chem. Zentr.*, 1924, I, 2426.

3-Nitro-1-methylcyclohexane (3-*Nitrohexahydrotoluene*).
B.p. 119–20°/40 mm. D_4^0 1·0547, D_4^{19} 1·0382. n^{19} 1·4618. Alk. $KMnO_4$ ⟶ 3-methylcyclohexanone and 1- and 2-methyladipic acids.

Nametkin, *Chem. Zentr.*, 1910, II, 1377.

α-Nitromethylcyclohexane (α-*Nitrohexahydrotoluene, cyclohexylnitromethane*)

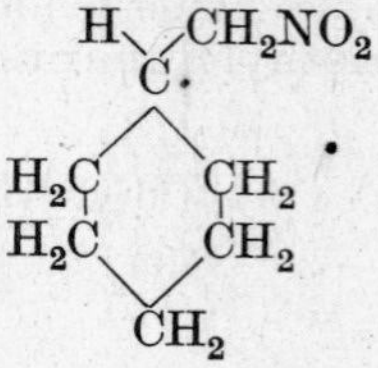

$C_7H_{13}O_2N$ MW, 143

B.p. 123–4°/40 mm., 98°/10 mm. D_4^{20} 1·0482. n_D^{20} 1·4705. HNO_3 (D 1·2) ⟶ adipic acid. Mod. sol. alkalis with yellow col.

Rosanow, *Chem. Zentr.*, 1924, I, 2426.
Zelinsky, *Ber.*, 1908, **41**, 2678.
See also previous reference.

1-Nitro-1-methylcyclopentane

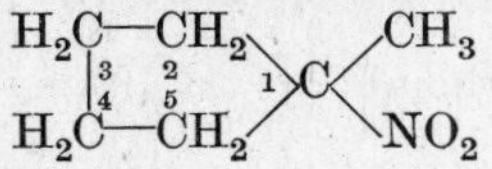

$C_6H_{11}O_2N$ MW, 129

Liq. with terpene-like odour. B.p. 177–84°/750 mm. decomp., 92°/40 mm., 86–8°/30 mm. D_0^0 1·0568, D_4^{20} 1·0395. n_D^{20} 1·4504. Insol. alkalis. HNO_3 ⟶ succinic acid and a little oxalic acid.

See first reference above and also
Nametkin, *Chem. Zentr.*, 1912, I, 1702.

2-Nitro-1-methylcyclopentane.

B.p. 184–5°/758 mm. decomp., 98–9°/40 mm. D_4^{22} 1·0381. n^{22} 1·4488. Sol. alkalis.

See last reference above.

α-Nitromethylcyclopentane (*Cyclopentylnitromethane*)

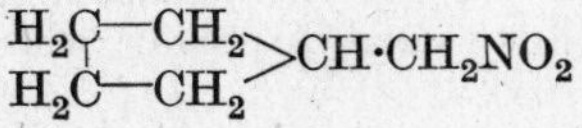

$C_6H_{11}O_2N$ MW, 129

B.p. 110°/35 mm. D_4^{20} 1·0713. n_D^{20} 1·4587. Sol. alkalis with yellow col.

Rosanow, *Chem. Zentr.*, 1916, I, 925.

5-Nitro-2-methyldihydroindole

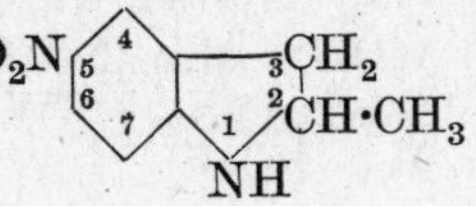

$C_9H_{10}O_2N_2$ MW, 178

Brown needles. M.p. 82°.

N-*Me*: $C_{10}H_{12}O_2N_2$. MW, 192. Dark red needles from EtOH. M.p. 48–9°. Sol. EtOH, Et_2O, $CHCl_3$, C_6H_6. Less sol. ligroin.

N-*Nitroso*: yellow leaflets from EtOH. M.p. 135°. Very sol. $CHCl_3$, C_6H_6. Sol. EtOH, Et_2O. Spar. sol. hot H_2O, ligroin.

Bamberger, Sternitzki, *Ber.*, 1893, **26**, 1296.
Stoermer, Dragendorff, *Ber.*, 1898, **31**, 2540.

6-Nitro-2-methyldihydroindole.

Cryst. M.p. 50°.

B,HCl: m.p. 200° decomp.

N-*Benzoyl*: m.p. 137°. Spar. sol. EtOH.

N-*Nitroso*: m.p. 103–4°. Spar. sol. EtOH.

v. Braun, Grabowski, Rawicz, *Ber.*, 1913, **46**, 3181.

7-Nitro-2-methyldihydroindole.

N-*Nitroso*: dark yellow cryst. M.p. 108°.

Stoermer, Dragendorff, *Ber.*, 1898, **31**, 2540.

6-Nitro-3-methyldihydroindole.

Cryst. M.p. 75°.

B,HCl: m.p. 192°. Mod. sol. EtOH.

N-*Benzoyl*: leaflets. M.p. 148°.

N-*Nitroso*: yellowish. M.p. 100°. Spar. sol. EtOH.

v. Braun, Grabowski, Rawicz, *Ber.*, 1913, **46**, 3180.

4-Nitro-2-methyldiphenyl

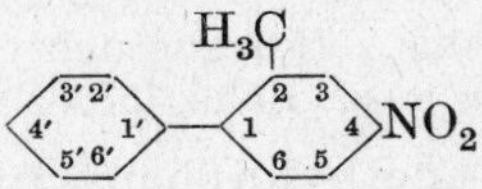

$C_{13}H_{11}O_2N$ MW, 213

Needles from ligroin. M.p. 56–7°. Sol. Et_2O, Me_2CO, $CHCl_3$, C_6H_6. Mod. sol. EtOH.

Bamberger, *Ber.*, 1895, **28**, 405.

6-Nitro-2-methyldiphenyl.

Cryst. from EtOH. M.p. 105–6°. B.p. 155°/3 mm.

Sadler, Powell, *J. Am. Chem. Soc.*, 1934, **56**, 2652.

2′-Nitro-2-methyldiphenyl.

Cryst. from EtOH. M.p. 64–5° (58°). B.p. 150–5°/2 mm.

See previous reference and also
Mascarelli, Gatti, *Atti accad. Lincei*, 1932, **15**, 90.

4′-Nitro-2-methyldiphenyl.

Prisms from EtOH. M.p. 103–4°. Sol. Et_2O, Me_2CO, $CHCl_3$, C_6H_6. Spar. sol. EtOH, ligroin.

Bamberger, *Ber.*, 1895, **28**, 405.
Kühling, *Ber.*, 1895, **28**, 43; 1896, **29**, 166.
Kliegl, Huber, *Ber.*, 1920, **53**, 1647.

4-Nitro-3-methyldiphenyl.

Yellow liq. B.p. 195–200°/18 mm.

Grieve, Hey, *J. Chem. Soc.*, 1932, 2246.

4′-Nitro-4-methyldiphenyl.

Cryst. from EtOH. M.p. 141°. Spar. sol. EtOH. Sol. hot EtOH.

Grieve, Hey, *J. Chem. Soc.*, 1932, 1891.
Gomberg, Pernert, *J. Am. Chem. Soc.*, 1926, **48**, 1379.
Carnelley, *J. Chem. Soc.*, 1876, **29**, 20.

4-Nitro-2-methyldiphenylamine

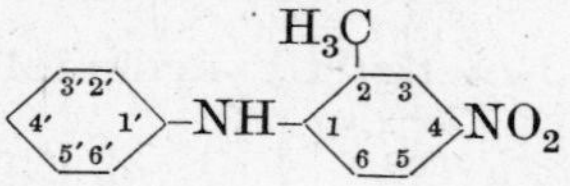

$C_{13}H_{12}O_2N_2$ MW, 228

Golden-yellow plates from C_6H_6. M.p. 140–1°.

Joszt, Lésniański, *Chem. Abstracts*, 1931, **25**, 500.

2′-Nitro-2-methyldiphenylamine.

Orange-yellow needles from EtOH. M.p. 76°.

McCombie, Scarborough, Waters, *J. Chem. Soc.*, 1928, 355.

4′-Nitro-2-methyldiphenylamine.

Yellow leaflets from C_6H_6–ligroin. M.p. 115°. Sol. EtOH, C_6H_6. Spar. sol. Et_2O.

Ullmann, Dahmen, *Ber.*, 1908, **41**, 3749.

6-Nitro-3-methyldiphenylamine.

Yellowish-red plates from EtOH, leaflets from ligroin. M.p. 110°. Sol. hot EtOH. Spar. sol. ligroin.

Schraube, Romig, *Ber.*, 1893, **26**, 581.
Borsche, *Ann.*, 1908, **359**, 76.

2′-Nitro-4-methyldiphenylamine.

Orange-red needles from MeOH.Aq. M.p. 69–70°.

Jacobson, Lischke, *Ann.*, 1898, **303**, 377.
Borsche, Feise, *Ber.*, 1907, **40**, 383.

4′-Nitro-4-methyldiphenylamine.

Yellow needles with blue reflex from EtOH or C_6H_6. M.p. 139°. Sol. boiling EtOH, AcOH. Spar. sol. Et_2O, C_6H_6, ligroin.

Goldberg, D.R.P., 185,663, (*Chem. Zentr.*, 1907, II, 957).
Ullmann, Dahmen, *Ber.*, 1908, **41**, 3751.
Ullmann, D.R.P., 193,448, (*Chem. Zentr.*, 1908, I, 1003).

2-Nitro-*N*-methyldiphenylamine.

Red oil with fishy odour. B.p. 205°/15 mm.

Storrie, Tucker, *J. Chem. Soc.*, 1931, 2261.

6-Nitro-4-methyldiphenylamine-2-carboxylic Acid (*5-Nitro-4-methyl-*N*-phenylanthranilic acid*)

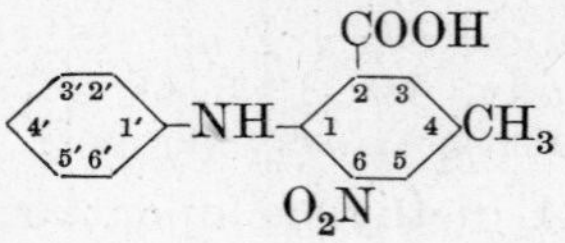

$C_{14}H_{12}O_4N_2$ MW, 272

Brick-red rhombic cryst. from EtOH. M.p. 174°.

Et ester: $C_{16}H_{16}O_4N_2$. MW, 300. Yellowish needles from EtOH. M.p. 136°.

Sane, Chakravarty, Parmanick, *J. Indian Chem. Soc.*, 1932, **9**, 57.

4-Nitro-5-methyldiphenylamine-2-carboxylic Acid (*3-Nitro-5-methyl-*N*-phenylanthranilic acid*).

Me ester: $C_{15}H_{14}O_4N_2$. MW, 286. Yellow cryst. from EtOH. M.p. 84°. Sol. usual org. solvents.

Sane, Joshi, *J. Indian Chem. Soc.*, 1932, **9**, 62.

4-Nitro-2′-methyldiphenylamine-2-carboxylic Acid (*5-Nitro-*N-o-*tolylanthranilic acid*).

Pale yellow needles from EtOH. M.p. 253–4°.

Locher, *Ann.*, 1894, **279**, 275.
Dey, Doraiswami, *J. Indian Chem. Soc.*, 1933, **10**, 318.

5′-Nitro-2′-methyldiphenylamine-2-carboxylic Acid (N-[*5-Nitro-*o-*tolyl*]*-anthranilic acid*).

Cryst. from AcOH. M.p. 220–1°.

Me ester: $C_{15}H_{14}O_4N_2$. MW, 286. Cryst. from MeOH. M.p. 153–5°.

Weiss, Katz, *Monatsh.*, 1928, **50**, 229.

4-Nitro-3′-methyldiphenylamine-2-carboxylic Acid (*5-Nitro-*N-m-*tolylanthranilic acid*).

Bright yellow needles from AcOH. M.p. 256°.

Dey, Doraiswami, *J. Indian Chem. Soc.*, 1933, **10**, 318.

4-Nitro-4′-methyldiphenylamine-2-carboxylic Acid (*5-Nitro-*N-p-*tolylanthranilic acid*).

Yellow needles from AcOH. M.p. 262·5°. Sol. hot EtOH, AcOH. Spar. sol. Et_2O.

See previous reference and also
Kahn, *Ann.*, 1894, **279**, 270.

2′ - Nitro - *N* - methyldiphenylamine - 2 - carboxylic Acid (N-[2-*Nitrophenyl*]-N-*methylanthranilic acid*).

Deep red prisms from EtOH. M.p. 136–7° decomp.

Burton, Gibson, *J. Chem. Soc.*, 1924, **125**, 2502.

2-Nitro-2′-methyldiphenylamine-4-carboxylic Acid

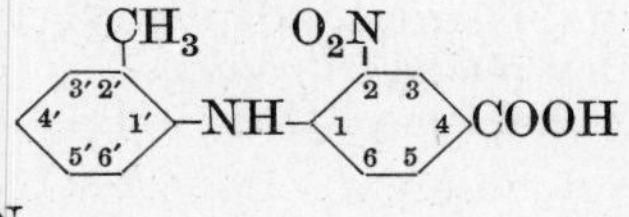

$C_{14}H_{12}O_4N_2$ MW, 272

Light brown needles. M.p. 212°. Sol. EtOH, Et_2O, C_6H_6, $CHCl_3$.

Et ester: $C_{16}H_{16}O_4N_2$. MW, 300. Pale yellow leaflets. M.p. 106°. Sol. EtOH, Et_2O, C_6H_6, $CHCl_3$.

Ullmann, *Ann.*, 1904, **332**, 84.
Heidensleben, *Ber.*, 1890, **23**, 3451.

2-Nitro-4′-methyldiphenylamine-4-carboxylic Acid.

Red needles. M.p. 257°.

Et ester: dark yellow leaflets. M.p. 115°. Sol. EtOH, Et_2O, C_6H_6.

Heidensleben, *Ber.*, 1890, **23**, 3453.
Delétra, Ullmann, *Chem. Zentr.*, 1904, I, 1569.
Schöpff, *Ber.*, 1889, **22**, 3288.

6′-Nitro-2′-methyldiphenyl-2-carboxylic Acid (2-[6-*Nitro*-o-*tolyl*]-*benzoic acid*)

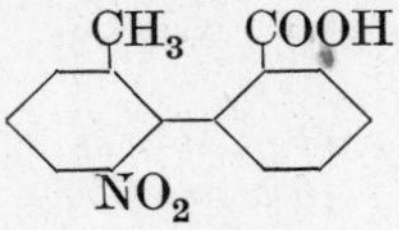

$C_{14}H_{11}O_4N$ MW, 257

d-.

Cryst. from MeOH.Aq. M.p. 173°. $[\alpha]_D^{20}$ + 63·1° in MeOH.

Brucine salt: cryst. + $1\frac{1}{2}H_2O$ from H_2O. M.p. 145–55°, anhyd. 172°. $[\alpha]_D^{20}$ − 57·3° in $CHCl_3$.

l-.

Cryst. from MeOH.Aq. M.p. 174–5°. $[\alpha]_D^{20}$ − 67·7° in MeOH.

Brucine salt: cryst. + H_2O from H_2O. M.p. 169–75°, anhyd. 173–5°. $[\alpha]_D^{20}$ + 30·4° in $CHCl_3$.

dl-.

Pale yellow cryst. from EtOH.Aq. M.p. 171–2°. Sol. most org. solvents. Insol. H_2O.

Stoughton, Adams, *J. Am. Chem. Soc.*, 1930, **52**, 5265.

2′-Nitro-2-methyldiphenyl Ether (o-*Nitrophenyl* o-*tolyl ether*)

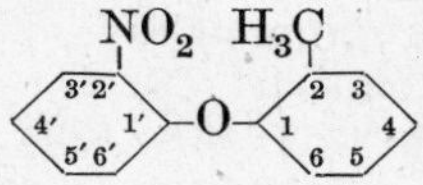

$C_{13}H_{11}O_3N$ MW, 229

Red liq. B.p. 194–6°/14 mm. D^{20} 1·195. Sol. most org. solvents. Insol. H_2O.

Cook, *J. Am. Chem. Soc.*, 1901, **23**, 806.

3′-Nitro-2-methyldiphenyl Ether (m-*Nitrophenyl* o-*tolyl ether*).

Yellow liq. B.p. 235°/14 mm.

Scarborough, Sweeten, *J. Chem. Soc.*, 1934, 53.

4′-Nitro-2-methyldiphenyl Ether (p-*Nitrophenyl* o-*tolyl ether*).

Yellow cryst. from pet. ether. M.p. 35°. B.p. 220–2°/27 mm. Sol. most org. solvents.

See previous reference and also
Cook, Eberly, *J. Am. Chem. Soc.*, 1902, **24**, 1200.

6-Nitro-3-methyldiphenyl Ether (*Phenyl* 6-*nitro*-m-*tolyl ether*).

M.p. 63·5–64·5°.

I.G., D.R.P., 506,339, (*Chem. Abstracts*, 1931, **25**, 302).

2′-Nitro-3-methyldiphenyl Ether (o-*Nitrophenyl* m-*tolyl ether*).

Red liq. B.p. 223°/30 mm. D^{27} 1·208. Sol. most org. solvents. Insol. H_2O.

Cook, *J. Am. Chem. Soc.*, 1901, **23**, 810.

3′-Nitro-3-methyldiphenyl Ether (m-*Nitrophenyl* m-*tolyl ether*).

Yellow prisms from C_6H_6–pet. ether. M.p. 47°.

Scarborough, Sweeten, *J. Chem. Soc.*, 1934, 55.

4′-Nitro-3-methyldiphenyl Ether (p-*Nitrophenyl* m-*tolyl ether*).

Yellow cryst. from EtOH. M.p. 63° (60–1°). B.p. 230–3°/30 mm.

Cook, Frary, *Am. Chem. J.*, 1902, **28**, 486.
Rarick, Brewster, Dains, *J. Am. Chem. Soc.*, 1933, **55**, 1290.

2′-Nitro-4-methyldiphenyl Ether (o-*Nitrophenyl* p-*tolyl ether*).

Yellow cryst. from EtOH. M.p. 49°. B.p. 220°/25 mm., 210°/15 mm.

Cook, Hillyer, *Am. Chem. J.*, 1900, **24**, 526.

Cook, Sherwood, *J. Am. Chem. Soc.*, 1915, **37**, 1836.

Reilly, Drumm, Gray, *Chem. Abstracts*, 1930, **24**, 5290.

Mayer, Krieger, *Ber.*, 1922, **55**, 1661.

3′-Nitro-4-methyldiphenyl Ether (m-*Nitrophenyl* p-*tolyl ether*).

Pale yellow liq. B.p. 220°/23 mm.

Scarborough, Sweeten, *J. Chem. Soc.*, 1934, 56.

4′-Nitro-4-methyldiphenyl Ether (p-*Nitrophenyl* p-*tolyl ether*).

Yellow cryst. from EtOH. M.p. 69° (66°). B.p. 225°/25 mm. Sol. AcOH, C_6H_6.

Fries, Böker, Wallbaum, *Ann.*, 1934, **509**, 83.

Scarborough, Sweeten, *J. Chem. Soc.*, 1934, 55.

Haeussermann, Schmidt, *Ber.*, 1901, **34**, 3770.

Cook, *J. Am. Chem. Soc.*, 1903, **25**, 61.

2′-Nitro-4-methyldiphenylmethane (2-*Nitrophenyl*-p-*tolylmethane*)

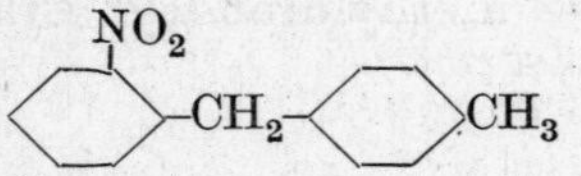

$C_{14}H_{13}O_2N$ MW, 227

Yellow oil. B.p. 195–8°/12 mm. Ox. ⟶ 2′-nitro-4-methylbenzophenone.

Kliegl, *Ber.*, 1908, **41**, 1847.

4-Nitro-2-methyldiphenyl sulphide (*Phenyl* 4-*nitro*-o-*tolyl sulphide*)

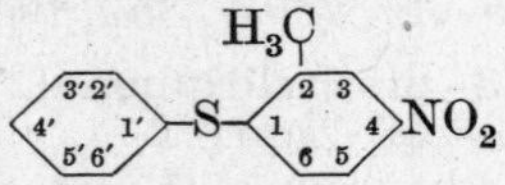

$C_{13}H_{11}O_2NS$ MW, 245

Yellow plates. M.p. 82·8°. B.p. 260°/62 mm. Spar. sol. cold EtOH. Insol. H_2O.

Bourgeois, Henrion, *Bull. soc. chim.*, 1932, **51**, 1421.

2′-Nitro-2-methyldiphenyl sulphide (o-*Nitrophenyl* o-*tolyl sulphide*).

Yellow needles from ligroin. M.p. 86–7°. Sol. EtOH, Et_2O. Insol. pet. ether. Conc. H_2SO_4 ⟶ green sol.

Mauthner, *Ber.*, 1906, **39**, 3598.

4-Nitro-3-methyldiphenyl sulphide (*Phenyl* 4-*nitro*-m-*tolyl sulphide*).

Pale yellow cryst. from EtOH. M.p. 72°.

Bourgeois, Henrion, *Bull. soc. chim.*, 1932, **51**, 1421.

6-Nitro-3-methyldiphenyl sulphide (*Phenyl* 6-*nitro*-m-*tolyl sulphide*).

Cryst. M.p. 59·5°.

See previous reference.

4′-Nitro-4-methyldiphenyl sulphide (p-*Nitrophenyl* p-*tolyl sulphide*).

Yellow needles from EtOH. M.p. 81·5°.

Law, Johnson, *J. Am. Chem. Soc.*, 1930, **52**, 3625.

4-Nitro-2-methyldiphenyl sulphone (*Phenyl* 4-*nitro*-o-*tolyl sulphone*)

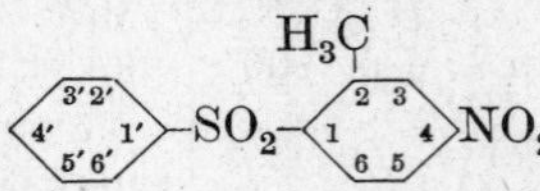

$C_{13}H_{11}O_4NS$ MW, 277

Needles from EtOH. M.p. 104°.

Bourgeois, Henrion, *Bull. soc. chim.*, 1932, **51**, 1421.

5-Nitro-2-methyldiphenyl sulphone (*Phenyl* 5-*nitro*-o-*tolyl sulphone*).

Yellow cryst. from EtOH. M.p. 158°.

Norris, *Am. Chem. J.*, 1900, **24**, 475.

Ullmann, Lehner, *Ber.*, 1905, **38**, 736.

2′-Nitro-4-methyldiphenyl sulphone (o-*Nitrophenyl* p-*tolyl sulphone*).

Cryst. from AcOH. M.p. 156–7°. Easily reduced.

I.G., D.R.P., 562,824, (*Chem. Zentr.*, 1933, I, 309).

General Aniline Works, U.S.P., 1,936,721, (*Chem. Abstracts*, 1934, **28**, 1049).

6-Nitro-3 : 4-methylenedioxyaniline (5-*Nitro*-4-*aminobenzdioxole*)

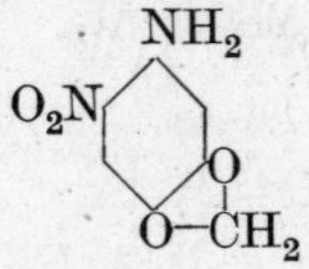

$C_7H_6O_4N_2$ MW, 182

Needles from H_2O or EtOH. M.p. 199°. Sol. warm H_2O. Hot NaOH.Aq. ⟶ blood-red sol.

N-*Me* : $C_8H_8O_4N_2$. MW, 196. M.p. 171°.

N-*Di-Me* : $C_9H_{10}O_4N_2$. MW, 210. M.p. 98°.

N-*Et* : $C_9H_{10}O_4N_2$. MW, 210. M.p. 133°.

N-*Propyl* : $C_{10}H_{12}O_4N_2$. MW, 224. M.p. 15°.

N-*Butyl* : $C_{11}H_{14}O_4N_2$. MW, 238. M.p. 137°.

N-*Amyl* : $C_{12}H_{16}O_4N_2$. MW, 252. M.p. 95°.

N-*Acetyl* : bright yellow needles from AcOEt. I.p. 209°.

Jones, Robinson, *J. Chem. Soc.*, 1917, **111**, 908.
Mameli, *Gazz. chim. ital.*, 1909, **39**, ii, 182.
Parijs, *Rec. trav. chim.*, 1930, **49**, 45.

6-Nitro-3 : 4-methylenedioxycinnamic Acid (6-*Nitropiperonylideneacetic acid*)

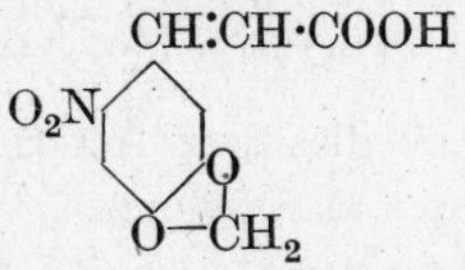

$C_{10}H_7O_6N$ MW, 237

Yellow plates from AcOH. Decomp. at 240°. Spar. sol. EtOH, C_6H_6, $CHCl_3$. Insol. CS_2, igroin. Sol. conc. H_2SO_4 with orange-red col.

Me ester : $C_{11}H_9O_6N$. MW, 251. Pale yellow needles from EtOH. M.p. 152°. Very spar. sol. cold EtOH.

Et ester : $C_{12}H_{11}O_6N$. MW, 265. Yellowish-brown needles from EtOH. M.p. 113–14°.

Feuerstein, Heimann, *J. Chem. Soc.*, 1891, **59**, 156.

3-Nitro-2-methylfuran (3-*Nitrosilvan*)

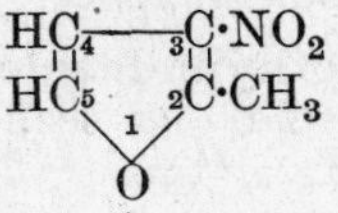

$C_5H_5O_3N$ MW, 127

Oil. M.p. 8°.

Rinkes, *Rec. trav. chim.*, 1931, **50**, 985.

5-Nitro-2-methylfuran (5-*Nitrosilvan*). Leaflets from pet. ether. M.p. 43·5°.

Rinkes, *Rec. trav. chim.*, 1930, **49**, 1120.
Gilman, Wright, *J. Am. Chem. Soc.*, 1932, **54**, 4109.

2-Nitro-3-methylfuran. Yellow needles from pet. ether. M.p. 32·6°.

Rinkes, *Rec. trav. chim.*, 1930, **49**, 1125.

5-Nitro-3-methylfuran. Leaflets from pet. ether. M.p. 29°.

Rinkes, *Rec. trav. chim.*, 1931, **50**, 988.

5-Nitro-2-methyl-β-furoic Acid (5-*Nitro-2-methylfuran-3-carboxylic acid*)

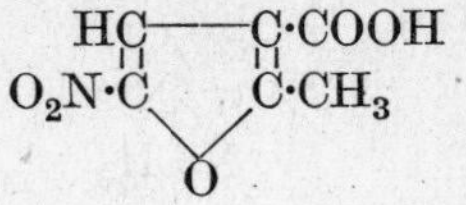

$C_6H_5O_5N$ MW, 171

Pale yellow cryst. M.p. 154–154·5°. Sublimes.

Et ester : $C_8H_9O_5N$. MW, 199. M.p. 52·5°.

Gilman, Burtner, Smith, *Rec. trav. chim.*, 1932, **51**, 407.

Nitromethylglyoxime

$CH_3\cdot C{:}N\cdot OH$
$NO_2\cdot C{:}N\cdot OH$

$C_3H_5O_4N_3$ MW, 147

Prisms or plates from Et_2O. M.p. 97–8° part. decomp. Very sol. H_2O, EtOH, Et_2O. Spar. sol. $CHCl_3$, C_6H_6, pet. ether.

Behrend, Schmitz, *Ann.*, 1893, **277**, 320.
Behrend, Tryller, *Ann.*, 1894, **283**, 210.

6-Nitro-3-methyl-1-hydrindone (6-*Nitro-3-methylindanone*-1)

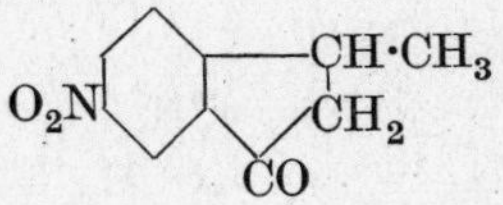

$C_{10}H_9O_3N$ MW, 191

Cryst. from EtOH. M.p. 80°.

Oxime : cryst. from EtOH. M.p. 169°.

Semicarbazone : m.p. 253–4°. Spar. sol. EtOH.

v. Braun, Heider, *Ber.*, 1916, **49**, 1276.

***p*-Nitro-β-methylhydrocinnamic Acid** (2-p-*Nitrophenylbutyric Acid*)

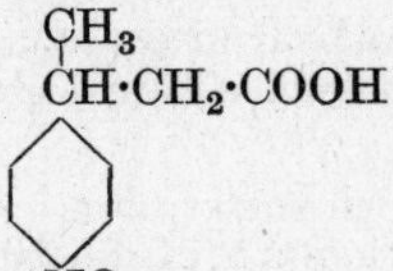

$C_{10}H_{11}O_4N$ MW, 209

Cryst. from EtOH. M.p. 164°.

Me ester : $C_{11}H_{13}O_4N$. MW, 223. M.p. 63–4°.

Chloride : $C_{10}H_{10}O_3NCl$. MW, 227·5. M.p. 58°. B.p. 190–200°/17 mm.

See previous reference and also Schroeter, *Ber.*, 1907, **40**, 1596.

4-Nitro-1-methylindazole

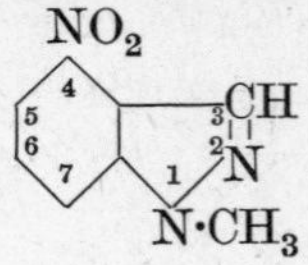

$C_8H_7O_2N_3$ MW, 177

Pale yellow needles from H_2O or pet. ether. M.p. 138–9°. Sol. most solvents.

Auwers, Frese, *Ber.*, 1925, **58**, 1374.

5-Nitro-1-methylindazole.
Pale yellow needles from C_6H_6–pet. ether. M.p. 129°.
Methiodide: golden-yellow leaflets from H_2O. M.p. 203° decomp.

Fries, Tampke, *Ann.*, 1927, **454**, 307.

6-Nitro-1-methylindazole.
Yellow needles from MeOH. M.p. 108–9°. Sol. EtOH, hot MeOH, C_6H_6, AcOH. Mod. sol. hot H_2O. Spar. sol. Et_2O, pet. ether.
Methiodide: reddish needles from EtOH. M.p. 216–17°.

Auwers, Schwegler, *Ber.*, 1920, **53**, 1219.
Auwers, Demuth, *Ann.*, 1927, **451**, 296.

4-Nitro-2-methylindazole

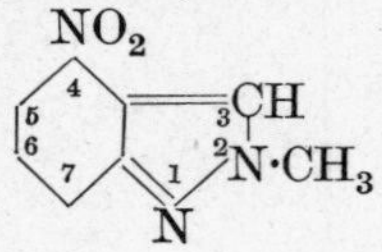

$C_8H_7O_2N_3$ MW, 177

Yellow needles from H_2O. M.p. 101–3°. Very sol. EtOH.

Auwers, Frese, *Ber.*, 1925, **58**, 1374.

5-Nitro-2-methylindazole.
Light red needles from H_2O. M.p. 163°.

Fries, Tempke, *Ann.*, 1927, **454**, 307.

6-Nitro-2-methylindazole.
Light yellow needles from C_6H_6. M.p. 159–60°.

Auwers, Schwegler, *Ber.*, 1920, **53**, 1219.
Auwers, Demuth, *Ann.*, 1927, **451**, 296.

7-Nitro-2-methylindazole.
Yellow needles. M.p. 144–5°.

Noelting, *Ber.*, 1904, **37**, 2576.

5-Nitro-4-methylindazole.
Yellowish needles from AcOH. M.p. 259°. Spar. sol. most solvents.

Noelting, *Ber.*, 1904, **37**, 2586.

6-Nitro-4-methylindazole.
Yellowish needles from EtOH. M.p. 177–8°

See previous reference.

7-Nitro-4-methylindazole.
Golden needles from EtOH. M.p. 180–1°.

See previous reference.

4-Nitro-5-methylindazole.
Pale yellow needles from AcOH.Aq. M.p 198–9°. Yellowish-red sols. in alkalis.

Noelting, *Ber.*, 1904, **37**, 2590.

6-Nitro-5-methylindazole.
Yellow needles from H_2O. M.p. 173–4°. Sol EtOH, C_6H_6. Very sol. Me_2CO, AcOH. Spar sol. ligroin.
N-*Acetyl*: needles from AcOH. M.p. 182–3°

See previous reference.

7-Nitro-5-methylindazole.
Pale yellow needles from EtOH. M.p. 192·5°

Gabriel, Stelzner, *Ber.*, 1896, **29**, 305.
See also previous reference.

4-Nitro-6-methylindazole.
Needles from H_2O. M.p. 206–7°. Sol. usual org. solvents.

Noelting, *Ber.*, 1904, **37**, 2592.

5-Nitro-6-methylindazole.
Needles from AcOH.Aq. M.p. 231–2°.
N-*Acetyl*: needles. M.p. 203–4°. Decomp. easily.

See previous reference.

7-Nitro-6-methylindazole.
Yellowish needles or leaflets from H_2O, EtOH or C_6H_6. M.p. 162°. Sublimes in prisms. Volatile in steam.

See previous reference.

4-Nitro-7-methylindazole.
Cryst. from H_2O. M.p. 222–5°.

Noelting, *Ber.*, 1904, **37**, 2587.

6-Nitro-7-methylindazole.
Cryst. from H_2O. M.p. 175–6°.

See previous reference.

3-Nitro-2-methylindole

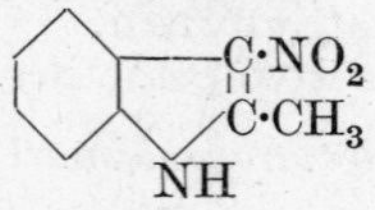

$C_9H_8O_2N_2$ MW, 17[illegible]

Yellow cryst. with violet reflex from boiling EtOH. M.p. about 248° decomp.

N-Et: $C_{11}H_{12}O_2N_2$. MW, 204. Reddish-brown needles from EtOH. M.p. 125°.

Angelico, Velardi, *Gazz. chim. ital.*, 1904, **34**, ii, 61.

5-Nitro-1-methylisatin

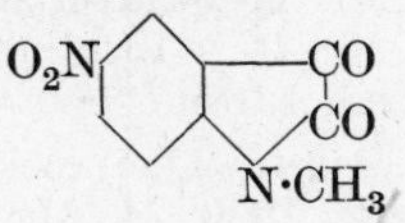

$C_9H_6O_4N_2$ MW, 206

Yellowish-red leaflets from 50% AcOH. M.p. 203°. Mod. sol. EtOH.

Hydrazone: yellow needles from EtOH. M.p. 210° decomp.

Borsche, Hildegard, Weissmann, Fritzsche, *Ber.*, 1924, **57**, 1151.

1-ω-Nitromethylnaphthalene (*α-Naphthylnitromethane*)

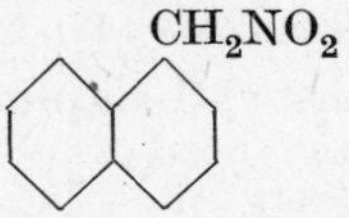

$C_{11}H_9O_2N$ MW, 187

Yellowish needles from pet. ether. M.p. 72–3°.

Wislicenus, Wren, *Ber.*, 1905, **38**, 508.

2-Nitro-1-methylnaphthalene

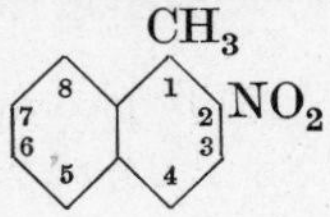

$C_{11}H_9O_2N$ MW, 187

Yellow needles from EtOH. M.p. 58–9°.

Veselý, Štursa, Olejníček, Rein, *Chem. Zentr.*, 1930, I, 2734.

4-Nitro-1-methylnaphthalene.
Pale yellow needles from EtOH. M.p. 71–2°. B.p. 182–3°/18 mm., 176°/12 mm. Sol. usual org. solvents. Conc. $H_2SO_4 \longrightarrow$ red sol. Dil. $HNO_3 \longrightarrow$ 4-nitro-1-naphthoic acid.

Lesser, *Ann.*, 1913, **402**, 11.
See also previous reference.

5-Nitro-1-methylnaphthalene.
Brownish needles from EtOH. M.p. 82–3°.

Veselý, Štursa, Olejníček, Rein, *Chem. Zentr.*, 1930, I, 2734.

6-Nitro-1-methylnaphthalene.
Yellow needles from EtOH. M.p. 76–7°.

See previous reference.

7-Nitro-1-methylnaphthalene.
Yellow needles from EtOH. M.p. 98–9°.

See previous reference.

8-Nitro-1-methylnaphthalene.
Brownish leaflets from EtOH. M.p. 63–4°.

See previous reference.

2-ω-Nitromethylnaphthalene (*β-Naphthylnitromethane*)

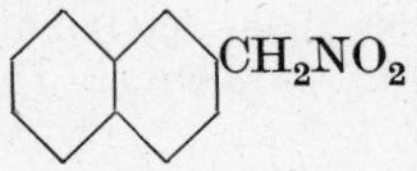

$C_{11}H_9O_2N$ MW, 187

Cryst. M.p. 72° (not sharp). Very sol. org. solvents. Decomp. above m.p.

Wislicenus, Wren, *Ber.*, 1905, **38**, 510.

1-Nitro-2-methylnaphthalene

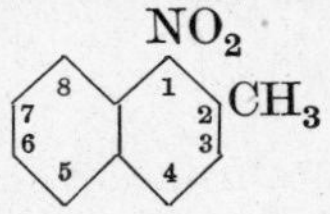

$C_{11}H_9O_2N$ MW, 187

Yellow needles from EtOH. M.p. 81°. B.p. 185–6°/18 mm.

Lesser, *Ann.*, 1913, **402**, 4, 31.
Veselý, Rein, *Chem. Zentr.*, 1929, II, 1669.

3-Nitro-2-methylnaphthalene.
Yellow plates from EtOH. M.p. 117–18°.

Veselý, Štursa, *Chem. Zentr.*, 1934, I, 3589.

5-Nitro-2-methylnaphthalene.
Yellow needles from EtOH. M.p. 61–2°.

Veselý, Páč, *Chem. Zentr.*, 1930, II, 1548.

6-Nitro-2-methylnaphthalene.
Yellow needles from EtOH. M.p. 119°.

See previous reference.

7-Nitro-2-methylnaphthalene.
Yellow cryst. from EtOH. M.p. 102°.

See previous reference.

8-Nitro-2-methylnaphthalene.
Yellow needles from EtOH. M.p. 36–8°.

See previous reference.

1-Nitro-6-methyl-2-naphthoic Acid

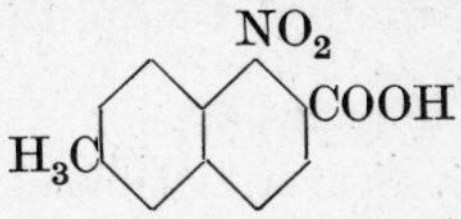

$C_{12}H_9O_4N$ MW, 231

Needles from AcOH. M.p. 238–9°.

Mayer, Alken, *Ber.*, 1932, **55**, 2282.

1-Nitro-6-methyl-2-naphthol

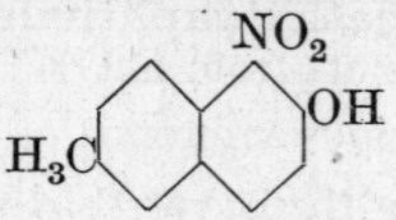

$C_{11}H_9O_3N$ MW, 203

Yellow needles from EtOH.Aq. M.p. 81–2°. Sol. most. org. solvents. Dil. NaOH ⟶ blood-red sol.

Dziewoński, Schoenówna, Waldmann, *Ber.*, 1925, **58**, 1215.

2-Nitro-*N*-methyl-1-naphthylamine

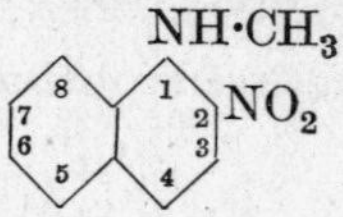

$C_{11}H_{10}O_2N_2$ MW, 202

Dark red needles from pet. ether. M.p. 114°. Sol. EtOH, Et_2O, Me_2CO, AcOH. Insol. H_2O.

Hoogeveen, *Rec. trav. chim.*, 1931, **50**, 37.

4-Nitro-*N*-methyl-1-naphthylamine.
Orange plates. M.p. 184–5°.

Veselý, Vojtěch, *Chem. Zentr.*, 1929, II, 425.

8-Nitro-*N*-methyl-1-naphthylamine.
Cryst. M.p. 81°.
N-*Benzenesulphonyl*: yellow needles from EtOH. M.p. 179°.

See previous reference.

4-Nitro-2-methyl-1-naphthylamine

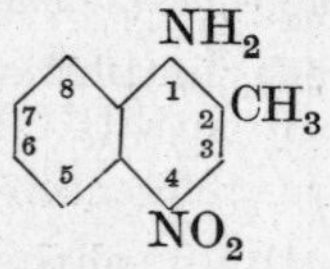

$C_{11}H_{10}O_2N_2$ MW, 202

Orange needles from C_6H_6. M.p. 184–5°. Very sol. EtOH. Spar. sol. C_6H_6.
N-*Acetyl*: pale yellow needles from EtOH. M.p. 240–1°.

Veselý, Kapp, *Chem. Zentr.*, 1924, II, 2751.

2-Nitro-4-methyl-1-naphthylamine.
Cryst. M.p. 179·5°.
N-*Acetyl*: m.p. 224–5°.

Veselý, Štursa, Olejníček, Rein, *Chem. Abstracts*, 1930, **24**, 611.

3-Nitro-4-methyl-1-naphthylamine.
Red plates. M.p. 131–2°.
N-*Acetyl*: yellowish needles. M.p. 230–1°.

Veselý, Štursa, Olejníček, Rein, *Chem. Abstracts*, 1930, **24**, 3008.

2-Nitro-5-methyl-1-naphthylamine.
Cryst. M.p. 178–9°. Insol. 62% H_2SO_4.
N-*Acetyl*: needles from AcOEt. M.p. 245–6°

Veselý, Štursa, Olejníček, Rein, *Chem. Abstracts*, 1930, **24**, 611.

4-Nitro-5-methyl-1-naphthylamine.
Cryst. M.p. 163–4°. Sol. 62% H_2SO_4.
N-*Acetyl*: prisms from AcOEt. M.p. 197–8°

See previous reference.

2-Nitro-6-methyl-1-naphthylamine.
Brownish-red needles from EtOH. M.p. 171°
N-*Acetyl*: yellow needles from EtOH. M.p. 210–11°.

Veselý, Páč, *Chem. Zentr.*, 1930, II, 1548

4-Nitro-6-methyl-1-naphthylamine.
Yellow or orange needles. M.p. 167–9°.
N-*Acetyl*: golden-yellow needles from EtOH M.p. 202°.

See previous reference.

5-Nitro-6-methyl-1-naphthylamine.
Red plates from EtOH or C_6H_6. M.p. 134–6° Sol. EtOH, C_6H_6.
N-*Acetyl*: yellow needles from EtOH. M.p. 192°.
B_2,H_2SO_4: m.p. 270° decomp.

Veselý, Kapp, *Chem. Zentr.*, 1924, II 2751.
Giral, *Chem. Zentr.*, 1934, II, 940.

2-Nitro-7-methyl-1-naphthylamine.
Red needles from EtOH. M.p. 185°.
N-*Acetyl*: yellow needles from AcOEt. M.p 219–20°.

Veselý, Páč, *Chem. Zentr.*, 1930, II, 1548.

4-Nitro-7-methyl-1-naphthylamine.
Orange needles. M.p. 183°.
N-*Acetyl*: yellow needles from AcOH–AcOEt. M.p. 229–30°.

See previous reference.

8-Nitro-7-methyl-1-naphthylamine.
Cryst. from EtOH. M.p. 106–7°.
N-*Acetyl*: m.p. 191–3°.
B_2,H_2SO_4: m.p. 175–80°.

Veselý, Rein, *Chem. Abstracts*, 1928, **22**, 1352.
Giral, *Chem. Zentr.*, 1934, II, 940.

2-Nitro-8-methyl-1-naphthylamine.
Brownish-red needles from EtOH. M.p. 150–2°.
N-*Acetyl* : cryst. from EtOH. M.p. 186–7°.

Veselý, Štursa, Olejníček, Rein, *Chem. Zentr.*, 1930, I, 2735.

4-Nitro-8-methyl-1-naphthylamine.
Orange needles. M.p. 162–3°.
N-*Acetyl* : yellow cryst. from AcOH. M.p. 193–4°.

See previous reference.

1-Nitro-*N*-methyl-2-naphthylamine

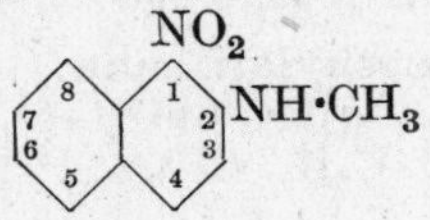

$C_{11}H_{10}O_2N_2$ MW, 202

Red needles from AcOH. M.p. 124–5°.
N-*Acetyl* : greenish-yellow cryst. from EtOH. M.p. 112–13°.
N-*Benzenesulphonyl* : needles from EtOH. M.p. 158–9°.
N-*Nitroso* : needles from EtOH. M.p. 100°.

Meldola, Lane, *J. Chem. Soc.*, 1904, **85**, 1602.

6-Nitro-*N*-methyl-2-naphthylamine.
Golden-yellow plates from EtOH. M.p. 185–6°.
N-*Acetyl* : needles. M.p. 186–7°.
Picrate : m.p. 138–40°.

Veselý, Vojtěch, *Chem. Zentr.*, 1929, II, 425.

4-Nitro-1-methyl-2-naphthylamine

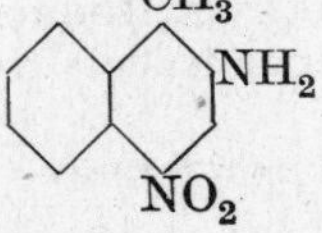

$C_{11}H_{10}O_2N_2$ MW, 202

Orange needles from EtOH. M.p. 126–8°.
N-*Acetyl* : yellow needles from EtOH. M.p. 203–4°.

Veselý, Štursa, Olejníček, Rein, *Chem. Abstracts*, 1930, **24**, 3008.

4-Nitro-3-methyl-1-*p*-nitrophenylpyrazolone-5.
See Picrolonic Acid.

3-Nitro-9-methylphenanthridine

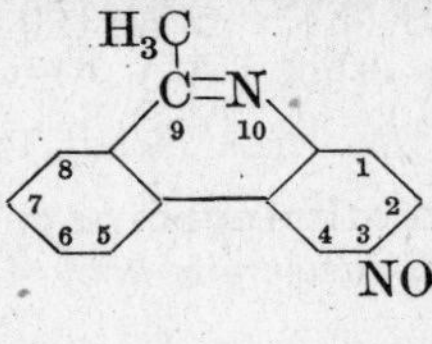

$C_{14}H_{10}O_2N_2$ MW, 238

Brown prisms from C_6H_6. M.p. 201°. Sol. dil. min. acids. Almost insol. dil. AcOH. More sol. in C_6H_6 than in EtOH.

Morgan, Walls, *J. Chem. Soc.*, 1932, 2228.

7-Nitro-9-methylphenanthridine.
Buff needles from C_6H_6. M.p. 243–5°. More sol. in C_6H_6 than in EtOH.

See previous reference.

Nitromethylphenylcinnamic Acid.
See Nitromethylstilbene-α-carboxylic Acid.

4-Nitro-3-methylpyrazole (*4-Nitro-5-methylpyrazole*)

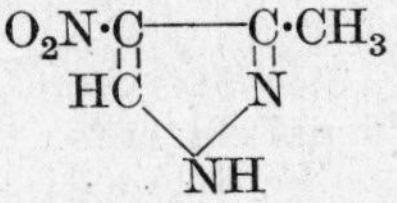

$C_4H_5O_2N_3$ MW, 127

Prisms from H_2O. M.p. 134°. B.p. 325°/748 mm.

Knorr, *Ann.*, 1894, **279**, 228.
Viguier, *Ann. chim. phys.*, 1913, **28**, 469.

4-Nitro-3-methylpyrazolone-5 (*4-Nitro-5-hydroxy-3-methylpyrazole*)

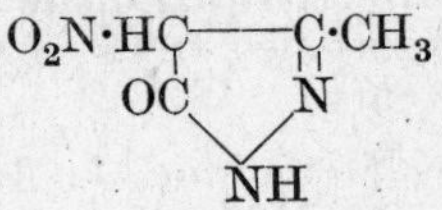

$C_4H_5O_3N_3$ MW, 143

Cryst. from AcOH. M.p. 276°. Spar. sol. EtOH, Me_2CO, amyl alcohol. Insol. pet. ether. Reacts acid.

Betti, Niccoli, *Gazz. chim. ital.*, 1904, **34**, 186.
Bülow, Haas, *Ber.*, 1910, **43**, 2655.

5-Nitro-3-methylpyromucic Acid (*5-Nitro-3-methylfuran-2-carboxylic acid, 5-nitro-3-methyl-α-furoic acid, 5-nitroelsholtzic acid*)

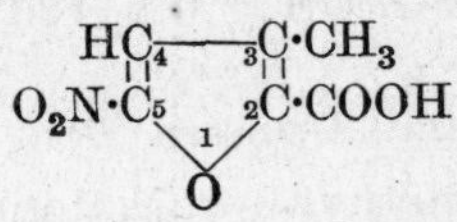

$C_6H_5O_5N$ MW, 171

Cryst. from C_6H_6. M.p. 160°.

Et ester: $C_8H_9O_5N$. MW, 199. Yellow cryst. from C_6H_6–pet. ether. M.p. 61°.

Rinkes, *Rec. trav. chim.*, 1931, **50**, 981.

4-Nitro-5-methylpyromucic Acid (*4-Nitro-5-methylfuran-2-carboxylic acid, 4-nitro-5-methyl-α-furoic acid*).

Needles from Py. M.p. 159–60°.

Me ester: $C_7H_7O_5N$. MW, 185. M.p. 81°.

Rinkes, *Rec. trav. chim.*, 1930, **49**, 1118.

Nitro-2-methylquinoline.

See Nitroquinaldine.

Nitro-4-methylquinoline.

See Nitrolepidine.

5-Nitro-6-methylquinoline

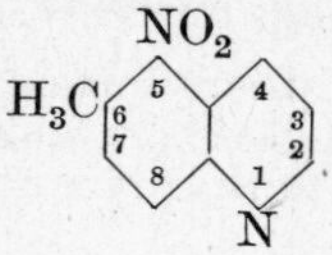

$C_{10}H_8O_2N_2$ MW, 188

Pale yellow needles from EtOH. M.p. 116–17°. Sol. usual solvents. Insol. cold H_2O. Weak base. Fe + AcOH ⟶ 5-amino-6-methylquinoline.

Methiodide: cryst. M.p. 189–90°. Sol. H_2O. Spar. sol. EtOH. Bitter taste.

Noelting, Trautmann, *Ber.*, 1890, **23**, 3655.

Bogert, Fisher, *J. Am. Chem. Soc.*, 1912, **34**, 1570.

8-Nitro-6-methylquinoline.

Pale yellow needles from H_2O. M.p. 122°. Sol. usual solvents.

Bartow, McCollum, *J. Am. Chem. Soc.*, 1904, **26**, 702.

See also previous references.

5-Nitro-8-methylquinoline.

Pale yellow needles from EtOH. M.p. 93°. Sol. usual solvents. Fe + AcOH ⟶ 5-amino-8-methylquinoline. Warm KOH in dil. EtOH ⟶ yellow col. changing through green to red.

Noelting, Trautmann, *Ber.*, 1890, **23**, 3673.

6-Nitro-8-methylquinoline.

Cryst. from EtOH. M.p. 129°. Sol. EtOH. Spar. sol. H_2O.

Lellmann, Ziemssen, *Ber.*, 1891, **24**, 2116.

Nitro-*N*-methyl-α-quinolone.

See under Nitrocarbostyril.

α-Nitro-2-methylstilbene

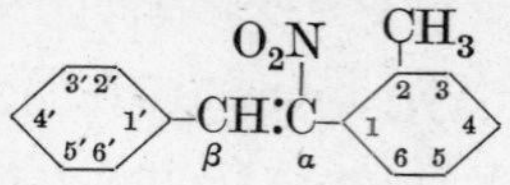

$C_{15}H_{13}O_2N$ MW, 239

Yellow plates from EtOH. M.p. 92°. Sol C_6H_6, $CHCl_3$, CS_2 in cold, MeOH, EtOH, Et_2O AcOH in hot.

Meisenheimer, Beisswenger, Kauffmann Kummer, Link, *Ann.*, 1929, **468**, 202.

β-Nitro-2-methylstilbene.

Needles from EtOH. M.p. 99°.

See previous reference.

α-Nitro-3-methylstilbene.

Yellow plates from MeOH or EtOH. M.p. 82°. Sol. Et_2O, C_6H_6, $CHCl_3$, Py.

See previous reference.

β-Nitro-3-methylstilbene.

Yellow needles from MeOH. M.p. 51°. B.p. 195°/14 mm. Sol. EtOH, Et_2O, C_6H_6. Spar. sol. AcOH.

See previous reference.

2′-Nitro-4-methylstilbene.

Red prisms from EtOH. M.p. 211°.

Pschorr, *Ber.*, 1906, **39**, 3112.

4′-Nitro-4-methylstilbene.

Greenish-yellow leaflets from EtOH. M.p. 150°. Sol. Et_2O, hot EtOH, C_6H_6, $CHCl_3$, AcOH. Less sol. ligroin.

Pfeiffer, *Ber.*, 1915, **48**, 1792.

α-Nitro-4-methylstilbene.

Yellow prisms from EtOH. M.p. 75–6°.

Meisenheimer, Beisswenger, Kauffmann, Kummer, Link, *Ann.*, 1929, **468**, 202.

β-Nitro-4-methylstilbene.

Yellow needles or leaflets from MeOH. M.p. 79°.

See previous reference.

6-Nitro-3-methylstilbene-α-carboxylic Acid (*α-[6-Nitro-3-methylphenyl]-cinnamic acid*)

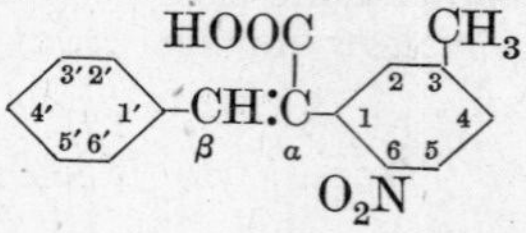

$C_{16}H_{13}O_4N$ MW, 283

Yellowish cryst. from C_6H_6–ligroin. M.p. 202–3°. Spar. sol. C_6H_6, AcOH. Insol. ligroin.

Mayer, Balle, *Ann.*, 1914, **403**, 193.

2′-Nitro-3-methylstilbene-α-carboxylic Acid (2-*Nitro-α-[3-methylphenyl]-cinnamic acid*).

Cryst. from C_6H_6–ligroin. M.p. 141–2°.

Me ester: $C_{17}H_{15}O_4N$. MW, 297. Yellowish needles from ligroin. M.p. 70–1°.

See previous reference.

2-Nitro-3′-methylstilbene-α-carboxylic Acid.

Prisms from AcOH. M.p. 180–1°. Spar. sol. C_6H_6, AcOH.

See previous reference.

2′-Nitro-3′-methylstilbene-α-carboxylic Acid (2-*Nitro-3-methyl-α-phenylcinnamic acid*).

Prisms from C_6H_6–ligroin. M.p. 221°. Spar. sol. MeOH, C_6H_6. Insol. ligroin.

See previous reference.

6′-Nitro-3′-methylstilbene-α-carboxylic Acid (6-*Nitro-3-methyl-α-phenylcinnamic acid*).

Prisms from C_6H_6–ligroin. M.p. 203–4°. Spar. sol. AcOH, C_6H_6. Insol. ligroin.

See previous reference.

2-Nitro-4′-methylstilbene-4-carboxylic Acid

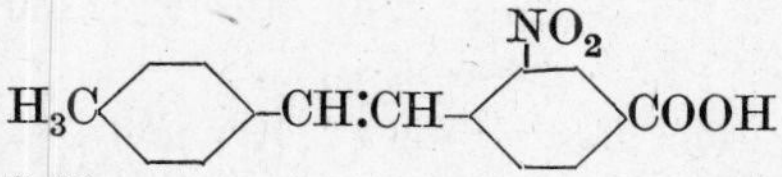

$C_{16}H_{13}O_4N$ MW, 283

Et ester: $C_{18}H_{17}O_4N$. MW, 311. Yellow needles from EtOH. M.p. 99–100°.

Nitrile: $C_{16}H_{12}O_2N_2$. MW, 264. Yellow needles from AcOH. M.p. 170°.

Pfeiffer, *Ann.*, 1916, **411**, 141.

3-Nitro-*N*-methyl-*o*-toluidine

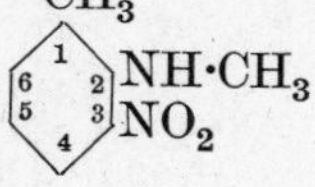

$C_8H_{10}O_2N_2$ MW, 166

Cryst. M.p. 48°.

Gnehm, Blumer, *Ann.*, 1899, **304**, 98.

4-Nitro-*N*-methyl-*o*-toluidine.

Red leaflets from EtOH, yellow needles from ligroin. M.p. 107·5°. Sol. $CHCl_3$, Et_2O. Spar. sol. EtOH, ligroin.

N-*Acetyl*: yellow leaflets from EtOH.Aq. M.p. 119°.

Vorländer, Siebert, *Ber.*, 1919, **52**, 300.
See also previous reference.

5-Nitro-*N*-methyl-*o*-toluidine.

Yellow leaflets from EtOH. M.p. 137°.

N-*Acetyl*: rhombic cryst. from EtOH.Aq. M.p. 97°. Very sol. EtOH.

Bernthsen, *Ber.*, 1892, **25**, 3131.
Kock, *Ann.*, 1888, **243**, 309.

4-Nitro-*N*-methyl-*m*-toluidine

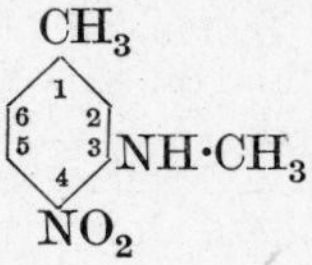

$C_8H_{10}O_2N_2$ MW, 166

Brownish-yellow prisms from MeOH.Aq. M.p. 83°.

Fischer, Rigaud, *Ber.*, 1902, **35**, 1259.

6-Nitro-*N*-methyl-*m*-toluidine.

Yellowish-brown plates with blue reflex. M.p. 92–3°.

Stoermer, Hoffmann, *Ber.*, 1898, **31**, 2535.

2-Nitro-*N*-methyl-*p*-toluidine

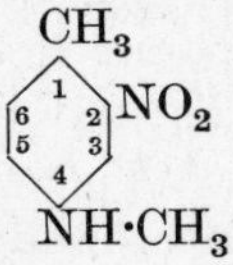

$C_8H_{10}O_2N_2$ MW, 166

Red needles or prisms from EtOH. M.p. 57°.

N-*Acetyl*: light yellow needles from EtOH. M.p. 128–128·5°.

Pinnow, *Ber.*, 1895, **28**, 3040.

3-Nitro-*N*-methyl-*p*-toluidine.

Red needles from EtOH. M.p. 84–5°.

N-*Acetyl*: plates. M.p. 64°. B.p. 250–5°/270 mm. Very sol. usual solvents. *Picrate*: yellow cryst. M.p. 210–12°.

Morgan, Jobling, Barnett, *J. Chem. Soc.*, 1912, **101**, 1212.
Gattermann, *Ber.*, 1885, **18**, 1487.
Niementowski, *Ber.*, 1887, **20**, 1876.

***N*′-Nitro-*N*-methylurea**

$CH_3{\cdot}NH{\cdot}CO{\cdot}NH{\cdot}NO_2$

$C_2H_5O_3N_3$ MW, 119

Needles from C_6H_6. M.p. 159° decomp. Very sol. Me_2CO, AcOEt. Sol. EtOH. Mod. sol. $CHCl_3$, C_6H_6. Spar. sol. H_2O, Et_2O.

Backer, *Rec. trav. chim.*, 1915, **34**, 188.

2-Nitromyristicic Acid

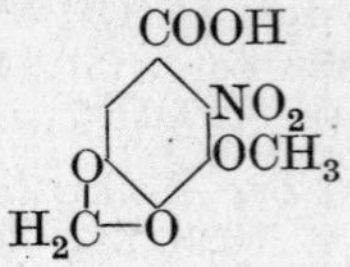

$C_9H_7O_7N$ MW, 241

Needles from H_2O. M.p. 245°. Sol. EtOH, AcOH, AcOEt. Spar. sol. hot H_2O, $CHCl_3$, C_6H_6. Turns yellow on exposure to light.

Et ester: $C_{11}H_{11}O_7N$. MW, 269. Prisms from EtOH. M.p. 82°. Turns yellow on exposure to light.

Salway, *J. Chem. Soc.*, 1909, **95**, 1165; 1911, **99**, 267.

2-Nitromyristicinaldehyde

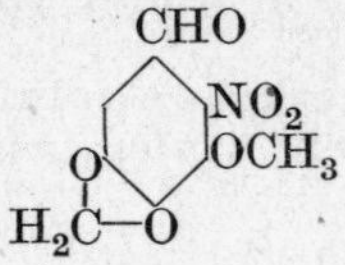

$C_9H_7O_6N$ MW, 225

Needles from EtOH. M.p. 131–2°. Sol. most org. solvents. Spar. sol. pet. ether. Turns deep yellow on exposure to light. $KMnO_4 \longrightarrow$ nitromyristicic acid.

Salway, *J. Chem. Soc.*, 1909, **95**, 1160.

1-Nitro-2-naphthaldehyde

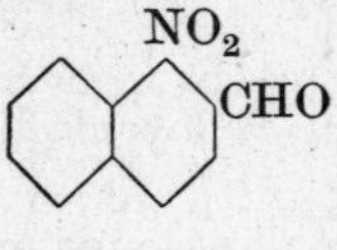

$C_{11}H_7O_3N$ MW, 201

Leaflets from ligroin. M.p. 99°. Volatile in steam. Forms bisulphite comp.

Mayer, Oppenheimer, *Ber.*, 1918, **51**, 1241.

1-Nitronaphthalene

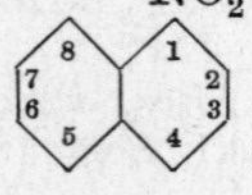

$C_{10}H_7O_2N$ MW, 173

Yellow needles from EtOH. M.p. 61·5° (58·5°). B.p. 304°. D_4 1·331. Very sol. CS_2. Conc. $H_2SO_4 \longrightarrow$ dark red sol.

Picrate: m.p. 71°.

Beilstein, Kuhlberg, *Ann.*, 1873, **169**, 89.
Fichter, Plüss, Swiss P., 150,298, (*Chem. Abstracts*, 1932, **26**, 4830).

2-Nitronaphthalene.

Plates from EtOH.Aq. M.p. 79°. Sol. EtOH, Et_2O, $CHCl_3$, AcOH. Volatile in steam. Zn + AcOH $\longrightarrow$ 2-naphthylamine.

Meisenheimer, Witte, *Ber.*, 1903, **36**, 4157.
du Pont, U.S.P., 1,836,211, (*Chem. Abstracts*, 1932, **26**, 995).

Nitronaphthalene-1:8-dicarboxylic Acid.

See Nitronaphthalic Acid.

1-Nitronaphthalene-3 : 6-disulphonic Acid (4-*Nitronaphthalene*-2 : 7-*disulphonic acid*)

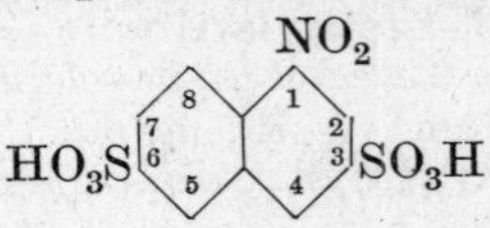

$C_{10}H_7O_8NS_2$ MW, 333

Needles. Very sol. H_2O. Sol. EtOH. Insol. Et_2O.

Dichloride: $C_{10}H_5O_6NCl_2S_2$. MW, 370. Yellow needles from AcOH. M.p. 140–1°. Sol. $CHCl_3$, AcOH, C_6H_6, ligroin. Mod. sol. Et_2O, CS_2. Dist. with $PCl_5 \longrightarrow$ 1 : 3 : 6-trichloronaphthalene.

Diamide: $C_{10}H_9O_6N_3S_2$. MW, 331. Needles M.p. 286–7° decomp. Sol. EtOH. Very spar sol. H_2O. Sol. NH_3.Aq.

Alén, *Ber.*, 1884, **17**, 435 (*Ref.*).
Armstrong, Wynne, *Chem. News*, 1895 **71**, 254.

1-Nitronaphthalene-3 : 7-disulphonic Acid (4-*Nitronaphthalene*-2 : 6-*disulphonic acid*)

Cryst. Very sol. H_2O. Sol. EtOH.

Dichloride: prisms from C_6H_6. M.p. 190–2° Mod. sol. AcOH, C_6H_6. Spar. sol. Et_2O, CS_2 PCl_5 at 200° $\longrightarrow$ 1 : 3 : 7-trichloronaphthalene

Diamide: needles from H_2O. Does not melt below 300°. Spar. sol. H_2O. Very spar. sol EtOH.

Alén, *Ber.*, 1884, **17**, 437 (*Ref.*).
Armstrong, Wynne, *Chem. News*, 1890 **61**, 93.

Nitronaphthalene-disulphonic Acid.

The following Nitronaphthalene disulphonic Acids, for which there is little or no data, have also been prepared:

1-Nitronaphthalene-3 : 8-disulphonic Acid (8-*Nitronaphthalene*-1 : 6-*disulphonic acid*).

Friedländer, *Ber.*, 1895, **28**, 1535.
Armstrong, Wynne, *Chem. News*, 1891 **63**, 124.
Ewer, Pick, D.R.P., 52,724.

1-Nitronaphthalene-4 : 8-disulphonic Acid (4-*Nitronaphthalene*-1 : 5-*disulphonic acid*).

Friedländer, Karamessinis, Schenk, *Ber.*, 1922, **55**, 48.
Cassella, D.R.P., 65,997.

1-Nitronaphthalene-5 : 8-disulphonic Acid (5-*Nitronaphthalene*-1 : 4-*disulphonic acid*).

Gattermann, *Ber.*, 1899, **32**, 1156.
Bayer, D.R.P., 70,857.

2-Nitronaphthalene-4 : 8-disulphonic Acid (3-*Nitronaphthalene*-1 : 5-*disulphonic acid*).

Friedländer, Karamessinis, Schenk, *Ber.*, 1922, **55**, 47.
Tinker, Hansen, U.S.P., 1,836,204, (*Chem. Abstracts*, 1932, **26**, 998).
Cotton, U.S.P., 1,756,537, (*Chem. Abstracts*, 1930, **24**, 3023).
I.G., F.P., 734,616, (*Chem. Abstracts*, 1933, **27**, 1002).

1-Nitronaphthalene-4-sulphinic Acid

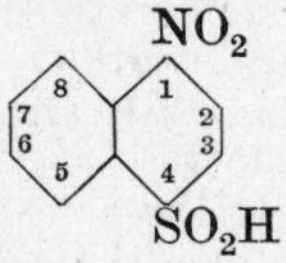

$C_{10}H_7O_4NS$ MW, 237

Yellow needles from H_2O. M.p. 131°. Sol. EtOH, Et_2O, AcOH, AcOEt, Me_2CO. Spar. sol. $CHCl_3$, C_6H_6.

Brunetti, *J. prakt. Chem.*, 1930, **128**, 44.

1-Nitronaphthalene-5-sulphinic Acid.
Cryst. M.p. 140°.
Na salt: yellow leaflets from H_2O.

Reissert, *Ber.*, 1922, **55**, 863.

1-Nitronaphthalene-6-sulphinic Acid.
Prisms with no m.p.

Vorozhtzov, Gribov, *Chem. Abstracts*, 1933, **27**, 2440.

1-Nitronaphthalene-7-sulphinic Acid.
Yellow needles from H_2O. Decomp. at 150–5° without melting.

See previous reference.

1-Nitronaphthalene-8-sulphinic Acid.
Cryst. Deflagrates at 110°. Turns brown in air. Heat with 60% H_2SO_4 in steam $\longrightarrow$ 1-nitronaphthalene.
K salt: golden leaflets + $2H_2O$. Very sol. H_2O.
Ba salt: leaflets + $6H_2O$. Very sol. H_2O.

Erdmann, Süvern, *Ann.*, 1893, **275**, 306.
Reissert, *Ber.*, 1922, **55**, 862.

1-Nitronaphthalene-2-sulphonic Acid

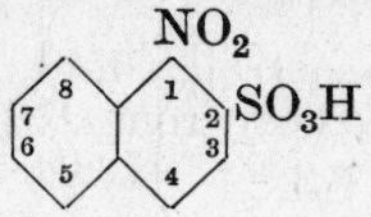

$C_{10}H_7O_5NS$ MW, 253

Green cryst. + H_2O. M.p. 104·7°. Deliquescent.
Na salt: cryst. + $4\frac{1}{2}H_2O$. M.p. 93–4°.
Chloride: $C_{10}H_6O_4NClS$. MW, 271·5. Pink needles from C_6H_6–pet. ether. M.p. 120·5°.
Amide: $C_{10}H_8O_4N_2S$. MW, 252. Needles from 50% EtOH. M.p. 214·3°.

Vorozhtzov, Kozlov, *Chem. Abstracts*, 1933, **27**, 2441.

1-Nitronaphthalene-3-sulphonic Acid.
K salt: needles. Spar. sol. H_2O.
Et ester: $C_{12}H_{11}O_5NS$. MW, 281. Yellow needles from EtOH. M.p. 114·5°. Spar. sol. cold EtOH.
Chloride: yellow needles. M.p. 139·5–140°. Very spar. sol. AcOH. Excess PCl_5 $\longrightarrow$ 1 : 3-dichloronaphthalene.
Amide: needles. M.p. 225°.

Cleve, *Ber.*, 1886, **19**, 2179.
Armstrong, Wynne, *Chem. News*, 1889, **59**, 95.
Erdmann, Süvern, *Ann.*, 1893, **275**, 252.

1-Nitronaphthalene-4-sulphonic Acid.
Cryst. Readily sol. H_2O.
Na salt: needles + H_2O. Very sol. H_2O.
K salt: needles. Spar. sol. cold H_2O.
Ca salt: leaflets + $2H_2O$. Sol. 37 parts H_2O at 17° and 16 parts boiling.
Ba salt: needles + H_2O. Sol. 66 parts cold and 33 parts boiling H_2O.
Me ester: $C_{11}H_9O_5NS$. MW, 267. Needles. M.p. 117°. Spar. sol. EtOH.
Et ester: prisms from EtOH. M.p. 93°.
Chloride: prisms from $CHCl_3$. M.p. 99°.
Amide: cryst. M.p. 188°.

Cleve, *Ber.*, 1890, **23**, 958.
Brunetti, *J. prakt. Chem.*, 1930, **128**, 46.

1-Nitronaphthalene-5-sulphonic Acid.
Prisms + $4H_2O$ from H_2O. Very sol. H_2O. Sol. EtOH. Spar. sol Et_2O, dil. H_2SO_4. Very bitter taste. NaHg $\longrightarrow$ 1-naphthylamine.
NH_4 salt: needles + $1\frac{1}{2}H_2O$. Readily sol. H_2O.
Na salt: plates + $\frac{1}{2}H_2O$. Very sol. H_2O.
K salt: plates + $1H_2O$ from H_2O. Sol. 25 parts H_2O at 17°.
Ca salt: leaflets + $2H_2O$ from H_2O. 100 c.c. H_2O dissolve 0·34 g. at 16° and 7·5 g. at 100°.

Ba salt: needles + $3H_2O$. Spar sol. cold H_2O.

Me ester: prisms from $CHCl_3$. M.p. 117·5°.

Et ester: needles from $CHCl_3$–pet. ether. M.p. 101–2°. Very sol. H_2O. Spar sol. Et_2O, cold EtOH.

Chloride: needles from AcOH or Et_2O. M.p. 113°. Sol. $CHCl_3$,C_6H_6. Spar. sol. Et_2O. Insol. pet. ether.

Amide: yellowish prisms from EtOH. M.p. 236° decomp. (225°). Spar. sol. Et_2O, cold EtOH. Insol. H_2O.

Anilide: cryst. from 90% EtOH. M.p. 123°.

Erdmann, *Ann.*, 1888, **47**, 311.
Cleve, *Ber.*, 1890, **23**, 958.
Erdmann, Süvern, *Ann.*, 1893, **275**, 246.
Steiger, *Helv. Chim. Acta*, 1933, **16**, 798.
Vorozhtzov, Gribov, *Chem. Abstracts*, 1933, **27**, 2440.

1-Nitronaphthalene-6-sulphonic Acid.

Yellow needles + $2H_2O$ from conc. HCl. M.p. 118–19°. Bitter taste. Very sol. H_2O. Sol. EtOH.

NH_4 salt: yellow plates. Sol. 13 parts cold H_2O.

Na salt: yellow cryst. + $3H_2O$. Mod. sol. H_2O.

K salt: plates. Sol. to 3·5% in H_2O at 20°.

Cu salt: $Cu(C_{10}H_6O_5NS)_2,6H_2O$. Green needles. Mod. sol. hot H_2O. Loses $4H_2O$ at 100°.

Ba salt: yellow leaflets + H_2O. Sol. 782 parts H_2O at 22°.

Et ester: yellowish needles from C_6H_6. M.p. 114°.

Chloride: prisms from C_6H_6. M.p. 125·5°. Excess PCl_5 ⟶ 1 : 6-dichloronaphthalene.

Amide: yellow cryst. powder. M.p. 184° (180°). Mod. sol. boiling EtOH. Very spar. sol. boiling H_2O.

Armstrong, Wynne, *Ber.*, 1891, **24**, 654.
Palmaer, *Ber.*, 1888, **21**, 3260.
Cleve, *Ber.*, 1886, **19**, 2179.
Armstrong, *Chem. News*, 1889, **59**, 95.
Erdmann, Süvern, *Ann.*, 1893, **275**, 250.
Cleve, *Bull. soc. chim.*, 1876, **26**, 444.
Vorozhtzov, Gribov, *Chem. Abstracts*, 1933, **27**, 2440.

1-Nitronaphthalene-7-sulphonic Acid.

Yellow needles + $1\frac{1}{2}H_2O$ from HCl.Aq. M.p. 135–6°.

NH_4 salt: yellow plates. Very sol. H_2O.

K salt: yellow needles + $\frac{1}{2}H_2O$. Very sol. H_2O.

Cu salt: $Cu(C_{10}H_6O_5, NS)_2,8H_2O$. Green prisms. Loses $6H_2O$ at 100°.

Ba salt: needles + $3\frac{1}{2}H_2O$. Loses $2\frac{1}{2}H_2O$ at 100° and is anhyd. at 180°. Anhyd. salt is sol. 9·1 parts boiling H_2O and 377 parts H_2O at 17°.

Et ester: yellow needles from EtOH. M.p. 106°.

Chloride: plates from AcOH. M.p. 169° (167°). Spar. sol. AcOH, CS_2. Dist. with PCl_5 ⟶ 1 : 7-dichloronaphthalene.

Amide: yellow prisms from EtOH. M.p. 223°.

Anilide: plates from EtOH. M.p. 172–3°.

Palmaer, *Ber.*, 1888, **21**, 3260.
Erdmann, Süvern, *Ann.*, 1893, **275**, 251.
Cleve, *Bull. soc. chim.*, 1878, **29**, 414.
Vorozhtzov, Gribov, *Chem. Abstracts*, 1933, **27**, 2440.
Fabrowicz, Leśniański, *Chem. Abstracts*, 1932, **26**, 3791.

1-Nitronaphthalene-8-sulphonic Acid.

Needles + $3H_2O$. M.p. 115° decomp. Very sol. H_2O. Sol. EtOH. Spar. sol. Et_2O. Bitter taste.

NH_4 salt: leaflets + $2H_2O$. Easily sol. H_2O.

K salt: needles + H_2O. Very sol. H_2O. Insol. KOH.Aq. PCl_5 ⟶ 1-chloronaphthalene-8-sulphonyl chloride.

Ca salt: leaflets from EtOH.

Me ester: prisms from $CHCl_3$–pet. ether. M.p. 124°. Sol. C_6H_6. Mod. sol. $CHCl_3$. Insol. pet. ether.

Et ester: prisms from $CHCl_3$–pet. ether. M.p. 123·5–124° (118°). Insol. ligroin.

Phenyl ester: $C_{16}H_{11}O_5NS$. MW, 329. M.p. 132·5–133·5°.

Chloride: prisms from $CHCl_3$. Decomp. at 165° (161°). Spar. sol. Et_2O, CS_2, pet. ether.

Amide prisms from EtOH. M.p. 190·5–191·5°.

Me-amide: $C_{11}H_{10}O_4N_2S$. MW, 266. Cryst. from EtOH. M.p. 195·5–196°.

Di-Me-amide: $C_{12}H_{12}O_4N_2S$. MW, 280. Cryst. from EtOH. M.p. 151·5–152·5°.

Et-amide: $C_{12}H_{12}O_4N_2S$. MW, 280. Cryst. from EtOH. M.p. 127·5–128·5°.

Di-Et-amide: $C_{14}H_{16}O_4N_2S$. MW, 308. Cryst. from EtOH. M.p. 115–16°.

Anilide: cryst. from EtOH. M.p. 178–178·5°.

Me-anilide: m.p. 177·5–178°.

Et-anilide: m.p. 170–1°.

Cleve, *Ber.*, 1890, **23**, 950.
Erdmann, *Ann.*, 1888, **247**, 312.
Erdmann, Süvern, *Ann.*, 1893, **275**, 238.
Steiger, *Helv. Chim. Acta*, 1934, **17**, 701.
Vorozhtzov, Gribov, *Chem. Abstracts*, 1933, **27**, 2440.

2-Nitronaphthalene-5-sulphonic Acid

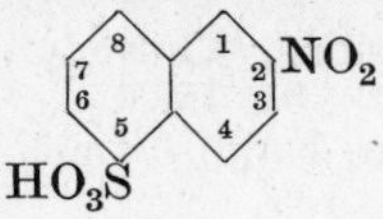

$C_{10}H_7O_5NS$ MW, 253

Chloride: $C_{10}H_6O_4NClS$. MW, 271·5. Yellowish prisms from C_6H_6. M.p. 127°.

Amide: $C_{10}H_8O_4N_2S$. MW, 252. Yellowish plates from EtOH. M.p. 223–4°.

Kappeler, *Ber.*, 1912, **45**, 634.

2-Nitronaphthalene-8-sulphonic Acid.

Chloride: colourless needles from C_6H_6. M.p. 169–70°.

Amide: cryst. from EtOH. M.p. 261–2°.

See previous reference.

1-Nitronaphthalene-3 : 6 : 8-trisulphonic Acid (8-*Nitronaphthalene*-1 : 3 : 6-*trisulphonic acid*)

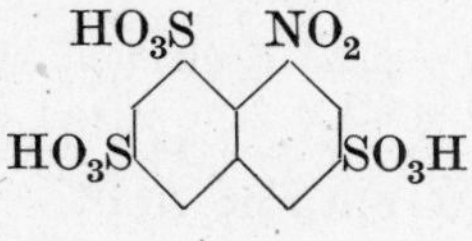

$C_{10}H_7O_{11}NS_3$ MW, 413

Hygroscopic needles.

Na salt: orange-yellow needles or prisms + $6H_2O$.

Ba salt: yellow needles + $8H_2O$. Efflorescent.

Pb salt: orange-yellow needles + $8H_2O$. Mod. sol. H_2O. Efflorescent.

Aniline salt: needles + $2\frac{1}{2}H_2O$. Sol. EtOH, hot H_2O. Spar. sol. Et_2O.

Koch, D.R.P., 56,058.
Kalle, D.R.P., 176,621, (*Chem. Zentr.*, 1906, II, 1746).
Fiery, Schmidt, *Helv. Chim. Acta*, 1921, **4**, 386.

2-Nitronaphthalic Acid (2-*Nitronaphthalene*-1 : 8-*dicarboxylic acid*)

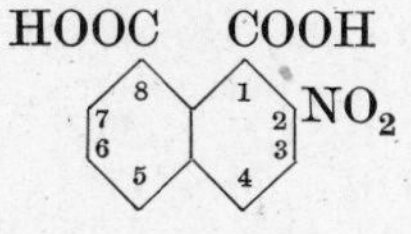

$C_{12}H_7O_6N$ MW, 261

M.p. 173–5°. Heat ⟶ anhydride.

Anhydride: 2-nitronaphthalic anhydride. $C_{12}H_5O_5N$. MW, 243. M.p. 190–200°.

Morgan, Harrison, *J. Soc. Chem. Ind.*, 1930, **49**, 415T.

3-Nitronaphthalic Acid.

Known only as its anhydride.

Anhydride: 3-nitronaphthalic anhydride. Pale brown leaflets from AcOH. M.p. 249° (247°). Insol. H_2O, EtOH, C_6H_6.

Graebe, Briones, *Ann.*, 1903, **327**, 84.
Anselm, Zuckmayer, *Ber.*, 1899, **32**, 3284.

4-Nitronaphthalic Acid.

Yellow needles. Decomp. at 140–50°. On heating readily goes to anhydride. Spar. sol. EtOH, Et_2O, ligroin.

Di-Et ester: $C_{16}H_{15}O_6N$. MW, 317. Yellow solid. M.p. 86°.

Anhydride: 4-nitronaphthalic anhydride. Orange-yellow needles from AcOH. M.p. 220–2°. Sublimes.

Imide: 4-nitronaphthalimide. $C_{12}H_6O_4N_2$. MW, 242. M.p. 284°.

Quincke, *Ber.*, 1888, **21**, 1460.
Dziewoński, *Ber.*, 1903, **36**, 3772.
Graebe, Briones, *Ann.*, 1903, **327**, 82.

1-Nitronaphthanthraquinone (1-*Nitro*-1′ : 2′-*benzanthraquinone*)

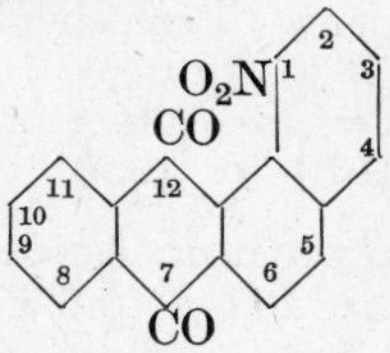

$C_{18}H_9O_4N$ MW, 303

Yellow plates or prisms from C_6H_6. M.p. 277–8°. Sol. $PhNO_2$, boiling AcOH, boiling C_6H_6. Insol. most cold org. solvents. Sol. conc. H_2SO_4 with orange-red col.

Scholl, *Ber.*, 1911, **44**, 2375.

4-Nitronaphthanthraquinone (4-*Nitro*-1′ : 2′-*benzanthraquinone*).

Yellow needles from C_6H_6. M.p. 250–1°. Sol. $CHCl_3$, AcOH, C_6H_6. Insol. EtOH, Et_2O. Sol. conc. H_2SO_4 with orange-red col.

See previous reference.

3-Nitro-1-naphthoic Acid

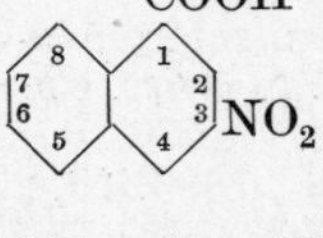

$C_{11}H_7O_4N$ MW, 217

Cryst. from EtOH. M.p. 270·5–271·5°.

Et ester: $C_{13}H_{11}O_4N$. MW, 245. Yellow needles from EtOH or plates from AcOEt. M.p. 87·5–88·5°.

Amide: $C_{11}H_8O_3N_2$. MW, 216. Cryst. from EtOH. M.p. 280–280·8°. Sol. AcOH. Spar. sol. EtOH, xylene. Insol. H_2O.

Leuck, Perkins, Whitmore, *J. Am. Chem. Soc.*, 1929, **51**, 1833.
Dziewoński, Kahl, Dymek, *Chem. Zentr.*, 1935, I, 2169.

4-Nitro-1-naphthoic Acid.

Yellowish needles from EtOH. M.p. 220–1°. Sol. EtOH, $CHCl_3$, AcOH. Spar. sol. C_6H_6, ligroin.

Me ester: $C_{12}H_9O_4N$. MW, 231. M.p. 107·5–108·5°.

Et ester: yellow needles. M.p. 57–8° (54°).

l-*Menthyl ester*: cryst. from EtOH. M.p. 63–63·5°.

Amide: yellow needles from EtOH. M.p. 218°. Spar. sol. hot H_2O.

Nitrile: $C_{11}H_6O_2N_2$. MW, 198. Needles. M.p. 133°. Volatile in superheated steam.

Friedländer, Weisberg, *Ber.*, 1895, **28**, 1841.
Lesser, *Ann.*, 1914, **402**, 16.
Rule, Spence, Bretscher, *J. Chem. Soc.*, 1929, 2520.
Leuck, Perkins, Whitmore, *J. Am. Chem. Soc.*, 1929, **51**, 1835.

5-Nitro-1-naphthoic Acid.

Needles. M.p. 241–2° (239°). Sol. AcOH, warm EtOH. Spar. sol. Et_2O, $CHCl_3$, CS_2, C_6H_6. Prac. insol. pet. ether. Insol. H_2O. Sublimes. Ox. ⟶ 3-nitrophthalic acid. Excess hot HNO_3 (D 1·3) ⟶ 1 : 5-dinitronaphthalene.

Me ester: yellow needles. M.p. 109–10°.

Et ester: needles from EtOH. M.p. 93°.

Isopropyl ester: $C_{14}H_{13}O_4N$. MW, 259. Cryst. from EtOH. M.p. 101·5°.

l-*Menthyl ester*: cryst. from pet. ether. M.p. 102·5°. Triboluminescent.

Amide: cryst. from C_6H_6. M.p. 235–6°.

Nitrile: needles from Et_2O. M.p. 205°. Very sol. $CHCl_3$, C_6H_6. Sol. AcOH, hot EtOH. Spar. sol. Et_2O, CS_2, pet. ether. Fuming HCl at 150–60° ⟶ 5-nitro-1-naphthoic acid.

See last two references above and also
Ekstrand, *J. prakt. Chem.*, 1888, **38**, 156, 241, 276.
Graeff, *Ber.*, 1883, **16**, 2249.

6-Nitro-1-naphthoic Acid.

Cryst. from toluene. M.p. 227–227·5°. Sublimes.

Et ester: cryst. from EtOH. M.p. 111·5–112°.

Amide: needles from EtOH. M.p. 216·5°.

Leuck, Perkins, Whitmore, *J. Am. Chem. Soc.*, 1929, **51**, 1834.
Dziewoński, Kahl, Dymek, *Chem. Zentr.*, 1935, I, 2169.

8-Nitro-1-naphthoic Acid.

Prisms from EtOH. M.p. 215°. Sol. warm AcOH. Spar. sol. Et_2O, C_6H_6. Long heating with HNO_3 (D 1·3) ⟶ 1 : 8-dinitronaphthalene.

Et ester: yellow cryst. from EtOH. M.p. 68–9°. Very sol. EtOH, Et_2O.

l-*Menthyl ester*: yellow pyramids from pet. ether. M.p. 122–3°.

Amide: needles from EtOH. M.p. 280°. Very spar. sol. EtOH.

Rule, Barnett, *J. Chem. Soc.*, 1932, 177.
Ekstrand, *J. prakt. Chem.*, 1888, **38**, 156, 276.
Rule, Spence, Bretscher, *J. Chem. Soc.*, 1929, 2521.

1-Nitro-2-naphthoic Acid

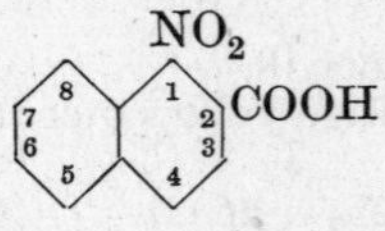

$C_{11}H_7O_4N$ MW, 217

Cryst. from AcOH. M.p. 239°.

Nitrile: $C_{11}H_6O_2N_2$. MW, 198. Brownish cryst. M.p. 138°. Sol. usual org. solvents. Unaffected by prolonged heating with 50% H_2SO_4. Heat with baryta water ⟶ 1-hydroxy-2-naphthoic acid.

Friedländer, Littner, *Ber.*, 1915, **48**, 330.
Mayer, Oppenheimer, *Ber.*, 1918, **51**, 1242.

5-Nitro-2-naphthoic Acid.

Yellowish needles from EtOH. M.p. 295° (286–7°). Sol. Me_2CO. Spar. sol. EtOH, Et_2O, AcOH, $CHCl_3$, C_6H_6, pet. ether. Insol. H_2O.

Me ester: $C_{12}H_9O_4N$. MW, 231. Yellow needles from EtOH. M.p. 112°.

Et ester: $C_{13}H_{11}O_4N$. MW, 245. Yellow plates from EtOH. M.p. 111°.

Isopropyl ester: $C_{14}H_{13}O_4N$. MW, 259. M.p. 75–6°.

Amide: $C_{11}H_8O_3N_2$. MW, 216. Brownish-yellow needles from Me_2CO. M.p. 261–3°.

Nitrile: cryst. from EtOH. M.p. 172–3°

(168°). Sublimes in needles. Very sol. $CHCl_3$. Sol. Et_2O, CS_2, C_6H_6. Mod. sol. EtOH, AcOH. Spar. sol. hot pet. ether. Insol. cold H_2O.

Graeff, *Ber.*, 1883, **16**, 2252.
Friedländer, Heilpern, Spielfogel, *Chem. Zentr.*, 1899, I, 288.
Ekstrand, *J. prakt. Chem.*, 1890, **42**, 275.
Cf. Harrison, Royle, *J. Chem. Soc.*, 1926, 84.

6-Nitro-2-naphthoic Acid.

Pale yellow plates from EtOH. M.p. 310°.

Et ester : brownish-yellow plates from AcOEt, needles from EtOH. M.p. 177°.

Harrison, Royle, *J. Chem. Soc.*, 1926, 89.

7-Nitro-2-naphthoic Acid.

Yellow needles from EtOH. M.p. 262°. Mod. sol. AcOH.

Et ester : needles from EtOH. M.p. 131°.

See previous reference.

8-Nitro-2-naphthoic Acid.

Needles from EtOH. M.p. 295° (288°). Sol. 390 parts cold EtOH. Sublimes. Alk. $KMnO_4$ ⟶ trimellitic acid.

Et ester : plates from C_6H_6 or ligroin. M.p. 121°. Mod. sol. EtOH, ligroin.

Amide : brownish-yellow needles from EtOH or Me_2CO. M.p. 218°.

Nitrile : brown needles from C_6H_6 or EtOH. M.p. 143°.

Friedländer, Heilpern, Spielfogel, *Chem. Zentr.*, 1899, I, 288.
Ekstrand, *J. prakt. Chem.*, 1890, **42**, 292.
Cf. Harrison, Royle, *J. Chem. Soc.*, 1926, 84.

2-Nitro-1-naphthol

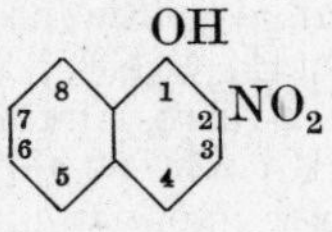

$C_{10}H_7O_3N$ MW, 189

Yellow leaflets from EtOH. M.p. 127–8°. Very spar. sol. H_2O. Volatile in steam.

Me ether : $C_{11}H_9O_3N$. MW, 203. M.p. 80°.

Et ether : $C_{12}H_{11}O_3N$. MW, 217. Yellow needles from ligroin. M.p. 84°. Volatile in steam.

Acetyl : m.p. 118°.

Hodgson, Smith, *J. Chem. Soc.*, 1935, 672.
Veselý, Vojtěch, *Chem. Abstracts*, 1929, **23**, 4466.
Hodgson, Kilner, *J. Chem. Soc.*, 1924, **125**, 807.
Charrier, *Gazz. chim. ital.*, 1915, **45**, i, 524.
Grandmougin, Michel, *Ber.*, 1892, **25**, 973.
Heermann, *J. prakt. Chem.*, 1891, **44**, 240.
Pictet, de Krijanowski, *Chem. Zentr.*, 1903, II, 1109.

3-Nitro-1-naphthol.

Yellow needles. M.p. 167–8°.

Veselý, Dvorák, *Bull. soc. chim.*, 1923, **33**, 329.

4-Nitro-1-naphthol.

Needles from H_2O. M.p. 164°. Very sol. EtOH, AcOH. Non-volatile in steam. Heat with PCl_5 ⟶ 1 : 4-dichloronaphthalene.

Me ether : yellow needles from C_6H_6. M.p. 81° (85–6°).

Et ether : needles from EtOH. M.p. 120° (116–17°).

Carbonate : $(NO_2{\cdot}C_{10}H_6O)_2CO$. Needles from AcOH. M.p. 212°.

m-*Nitrobenzenesulphonyl* : m.p. 135°.

Hodgson, Smith, *J. Chem. Soc.*, 1935, 672.
Bell, *J. Chem. Soc.*, 1933, 287.
Hodgson, Kilner, *J. Chem. Soc.*, 1924, **125**, 807.
Griesheim-Elektron, D.R.P., 117,731, (*Chem. Zentr.*, 1901, I, 548).
Reverdin, Kauffmann, *Ber.*, 1895, **28**, 3050.
Deninger, *J. prakt. Chem.*, 1889, **40**, 301.
Francis, *Ber.*, 1906, **39**, 3802.
Woroshzow, *Chem. Zentr.*, 1911, I, 651; II, 612.

5-Nitro-1-naphthol.

Dark yellow cryst. or red needles from H_2O. M.p. 171° (165°). Sol. AcOH, toluene. Mod. sol. EtOH, Et_2O, hot H_2O. Spar. sol. ligroin. Sol. alkalis with yellowish-brown col.

Me ether : yellow needles from pet. ether. M.p. 96–7°.

Acetyl : needles from EtOH.Aq. M.p. 114°.

Benzoyl : cryst. from MeOH. M.p. 109°.

Kaufler, Bräuer, *Ber.*, 1907, **40**, 327.
Fichter, Kühnel, *Ber.*, 1909, **42**, 4751.
Vorozhtzov, Kulev, *Chem. Abstracts*, 1929, **23**, 3697.

8-Nitro-1-naphthol.
Yellow cryst. from $CHCl_3$. M.p. 130°.
m-*Nitrobenzenesulphonyl* : needles from AcOH. M.p. 166°.

Bell, *J. Chem. Soc.*, 1933, 287.

1-Nitro-2-naphthol

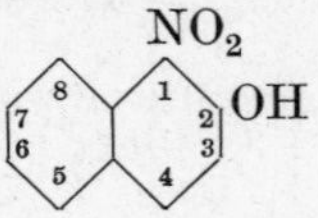

$C_{10}H_7O_3N$ MW, 189

Yellow needles or leaflets from EtOH. M.p. 103°. Readily sol. EtOH.
Me ether : $C_{11}H_9O_3N$. MW, 203. Yellow prisms from AcOH. M.p. 128° (126°). Alc. NH_3 at 160° ⟶ 1-nitro-2-naphthylamine.
Et ether : $C_{12}H_{11}O_3N$. MW, 217. Yellow needles from EtOH or AcOH. M.p. 104–5°. Sol. Et_2O. Spar. sol. AcOH, cold EtOH. Insol. H_2O. Volatile in steam.
Propyl ether : $C_{13}H_{13}O_3N$. MW, 231. Yellow needles from EtOH. M.p. 86°.
Isopropyl ether : yellow leaflets from EtOH. M.p. 63°.
Acetyl : needles from pet. ether. M.p. 61°.
m-*Nitrobenzenesulphonyl* : prisms from AcOH. M.p. 176°.

Hartman, Byers, Dickey, *Organic Syntheses*, 1933, XIII, 78.
Bell, *J. Chem. Soc.*, 1933, 288.
Charrier, *Gazz. chim. ital.*, 1916, **46**, i, 410.
Pictet, de Krijanowski, *Chem. Zentr.*, 1903, II, 1109.
Liebermann, Jacobson, *Ann.*, 1882, **211**, 46.
Francis, *Ber.*, 1906, **39**, 3802.
Davis, *Chem. News*, 1896, **74**, 302.

4-Nitro-2-naphthol.
Yellow needles from pet. ether. M.p. 120°. Sol. alkalis with red col.
Me ether : brown needles from C_6H_6–EtOH. M.p. 100–3°.
m-*Nitrobenzenesulphonyl* : cryst. from AcOH. M.p. 149°.
p-*Toluenesulphonyl* : pale yellow cryst. from EtOH. M.p. 122°.

B.D.C., E.P., 152,437, (*Chem. Abstracts*, 1921, **15**, 761).
Morgan, Evens, *J. Chem. Soc.*, 1919, **115**, 1132.
Bell, *J. Chem. Soc.*, 1933, 288.
Challenor, Ingold, *J. Chem. Soc.*, 1923, **123**, 2080.

5-Nitro-2-naphthol.
Yellow needles from H_2O. M.p. 147°.
Et ether : yellow needles from EtOH. M.p 115°.
m-*Nitrobenzenesulphonyl* : needles from AcOH M.p. 166°.

Friedländer, Szymanski, *Ber.*, 1892, **25** 2079.
Bell, *J. Chem. Soc.*, 1932, 2734.

6-Nitro-2-naphthol.
Yellow needles from H_2O. M.p. 156–8°.
Me ether : m.p. 134°.
Et ether : needles from Et_2O–pet. ether. M.p 114°. Very sol. Me_2CO, $CHCl_3$, C_6H_6. Spar sol. Et_2O, cold EtOH, pet. ether. HNO_3 (D 1·14) at 180–200° ⟶ 4-nitrophthalic acid.

Gaess, *J. prakt. Chem.*, 1892, **45**, 616 1892, **46**, 160.
Davis, *Chem. News*, 1896, **74**, 302.

8-Nitro-2-naphthol.
Yellow needles from H_2O. M.p. 144–5° Sol. EtOH, Et_2O, $CHCl_3$, Me_2CO, C_6H_6.
Me ether : m.p. 69°.
Et ether : yellow needles from pet. ether M.p. 72–3°. Very sol. Et_2O, $CHCl_3$, Me_2CO C_6H_6. Mod. sol. EtOH, pet. ether.
Acetyl : needles from EtOH.Aq. M.p. 101–2°.
m-*Nitrobenzenesulphonyl* : cryst. from AcOH M.p. 144–6°.

Bell, *J. Chem. Soc.*, 1932, 2734.
See also previous references.

2-Nitro-1-naphthol-4-sulphonic Acid

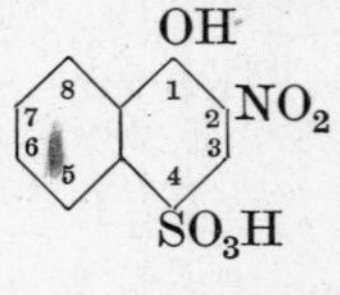

$C_{10}H_7O_6NS$ MW, 269

Heat with HCl under press. at 150–60° ⟶ 2-nitro-1-naphthol.
Mono-K salt : lemon-yellow needles.
Di-K salt : orange-yellow needles.
Et ether : $C_{12}H_{11}O_6NS$. MW, 297. Hot conc. KOH ⟶ 2-nitro-1-naphthol-4-sulphonic acid. Fuming HCl at 150–60° ⟶ 2-nitro-1-naphthol. *K salt* : yellow prisms and plates + $\frac{1}{2}H_2O$ from H_2O.

Witt, Schneider, *Ber.*, 1901, **34**, 3189.

2-Nitro-1-naphthol-7-sulphonic Acid.
Lemon-yellow needles.
Cu salt : cryst. + $5H_2O$ from H_2O.

Finger, *J. prakt. Chem.*, 1909, **79**, 443.

1-Nitro-2-naphthol-6-sulphonic Acid

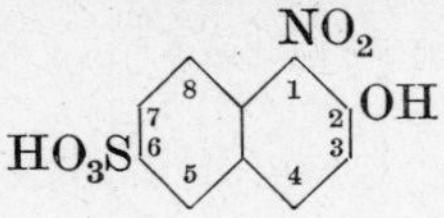

$C_{10}H_7O_6NS$ MW, 269

Et ether: *chloride*, $C_{12}H_{10}O_5NClS$. MW, 315·5. Plates. M.p. 146°. *Amide*: $C_{12}H_{12}O_5N_2S$. MW, 296. Prisms or needles. M.p. 218°.

Heermann, *J. prakt. Chem.*, 1894, **49**, 133.
Lapworth, *Chem. News*, 1895, **71**, 206.

6-Nitro-2-naphthol-4-sulphonic Acid. Brown cryst. + 2–5H_2O which grinds to intense yellow powder.

Ruggli, Knapp, Merz, Zimmermann, *Helv. Chim. Acta*, 1929, **12**, 1042.

6-Nitro-2-naphthol-8-sulphonic Acid. Yellow prisms + 4H_2O from H_2O. At 150° loses 2H_2O. Mod. sol. cold H_2O. Spar. sol. EtOH. Insol. Et_2O.

K salt: orange prisms.
Ba salt: dark yellow prisms + $6\frac{1}{2}H_2O$.

Jacchia, *Ann.*, 1902, **323**, 122.

3-Nitro-1 : 2-naphthoquinone

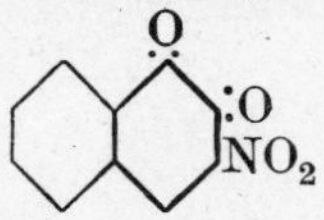

$C_{10}H_5O_4N$ MW, 203

Red cryst. from AcOH. M.p. 158°. Very sol. hot AcOH. Sol. C_6H_6, boiling EtOH. Spar. sol. Et_2O. Insol. CS_2. Hot sulphurous acid ⟶ 3-nitro-1 : 2-dihydroxynaphthalene. Phenylhydrazine ⟶ 3-nitro-1 : 2-dihydroxynaphthalene.

Zincke *et al.*, *Ann.*, 1892, **268**, 273, 297.
Zincke, Noack, *Ann.*, 1897, **295**, 12, (*Footnote*).
Zärtling, *Ber.*, 1890, **23**, 175.

1-Nitro-β-naphthoxyacetic Acid

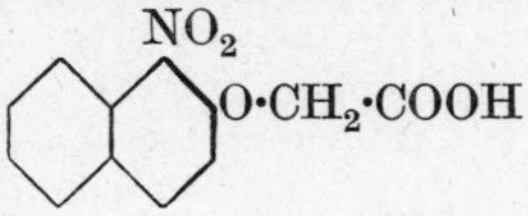

$C_{12}H_9O_5N$ MW, 247

Yellow prisms from AcOH. M.p. 192° (188–9°). Very sol. hot EtOH, hot AcOH. Sol. Et_2O, C_6H_6. Very spar. sol. H_2O.

Et ester: $C_{14}H_{13}O_5N$. MW, 275. Yellowish needles. M.p. 100°.

Chloride: $C_{12}H_8O_4NCl$. MW, 265·5. Yellow leaflets. M.p. 94°. Sol. C_6H_6. Insol. ligroin.

Amide: $C_{12}H_{10}O_4N_2$. MW, 246. Yellow needles from EtOH. M.p. 189°. Sol. Et_2O, hot EtOH. Spar. sol. hot H_2O.

Anilide: yellow needles. M.p. 139°.

Spitzer, *Ber.*, 1901, **34**, 3193.
Lees, Shedden, *J. Chem. Soc.*, 1903, **83**, 758
Badische, D.R.P., 58,614.

1-Nitro-β-naphthoxyacetone

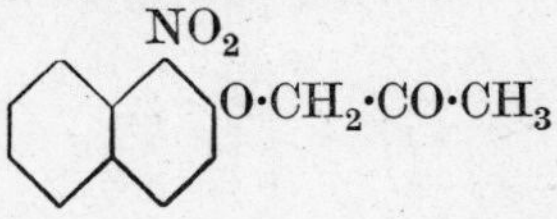

$C_{13}H_{11}O_4N$ MW, 245

Yellowish needles. M.p. 145°. Readily sol. hot EtOH. Mod. sol. Et_2O, AcOH. Insol. H_2O.

Oxime: m.p. 158°.
Semicarbazone: yellowish needles. M.p. 208°.
Phenylhydrazone: yellow plates. M.p. 120°.

Stoermer, Franke, *Ber.*, 1898, **31**, 759.

2-Nitro-1-naphthylamine

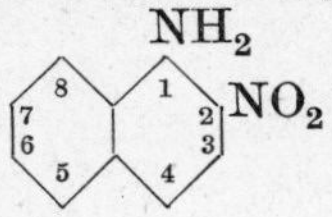

$C_{10}H_8O_2N_2$ MW, 188

Reddish-yellow prisms from EtOH. M.p. 144°. Hot alkali ⟶ 2-nitro-1-naphthol.

N-*Me*: *see* 2-Nitro-*N*-methyl-1-naphthylamine.

N-*Et*: $C_{12}H_{12}O_2N_2$. MW, 216. Red needles. M.p. 77°.

N-*Phenyl*: orange cryst. from EtOH. M.p. 110–11°.

N-*Acetyl*: 2-nitro-1-acetnaphthalide. Yellow needles from EtOH or AcOH. M.p. 199°. Very stable towards HNO_2.

N-*Diacetyl*: yellow prisms from AcOH. M.p. 115°.

N-*Benzoyl*: yellowish prisms from EtOH–AcOH. M.p. 175°. Very sol. EtOH, $CHCl_3$, AcOH, C_6H_6.

Meisenheimer, Patzig, *Ber.*, 1906, **39**, 2541.
Lellmann, *Ber.*, 1887, **20**, 893.
Lellmann, Remy, *Ber.*, 1886, **19**, 797.
Hodgson, Walker, *J. Chem. Soc.*, 1933, 1205.
Hoogeveen, *Rec. trav. chim.*, 1931, **50**, 39.
Bamberger, *Ber.*, 1922, **55**, 3389.

3-Nitro-1-naphthylamine.
M.p. 136–7°.
Acetyl: 3-nitro-1-acetnaphthalide. M.p. 255°.

Veselý, Dvorák, *Bull. soc. chim.*, 1923, **33**, 328.

4-Nitro-1-naphthylamine.
Orange needles from EtOH. M.p. 195° (191°). Mod. sol. EtOH, AcOH. Hot KOH ⟶ NH_3 + 4-nitro-1-naphthol.
N-*Me*: *see* 4-Nitro-*N*-methyl-1-naphthylamine.
N-*Et*: orange cryst. from AcOH. M.p. 179–80° (176–7°). N-*Acetyl*: needles from EtOH. Aq. M.p. 112–13°. N-*Benzoyl*: yellowish prisms from EtOH or C_6H_6. M.p. 121°.
N-*Benzyl*: cryst. from C_6H_6. M.p. 156°.
N-*Acetyl*: 4-nitro-1-acetnaphthalide. Needles. M.p. 190°.
N-*Diacetyl*: yellow needles from EtOH. M.p. 144°.
N-*Benzoyl*: prisms from AcOH. M.p. 224°.
N-*Benzenesulphonyl*: m.p. 173°.
N-p-*Toluenesulphonyl*: yellow needles. M.p. 185°.

Meldola, Streatfield, *J. Chem. Soc.*, 1893, **63**, 1055.
Lellmann, Remy, *Ber.*, 1886, **19**, 797.
Morgan, Couzens, *J. Chem. Soc.*, 1910, **97**, 1693.
Hodgson, Walker, *J. Chem. Soc.*, 1933, 1205.
Chem. Farbr. Griesheim-Elektron, D.R.P., 117,006, (*Chem. Zentr.*, 1901, I, 237).

5-Nitro-1-naphthylamine.
Red needles from H_2O. M.p. 118–19°.
N-*Formyl*: yellow needles. M.p. 199°.
N-*Acetyl*: 5-nitro-1-acetnaphthalide. Brownish prisms from AcOH. M.p. 220°.
N-*Benzenesulphonyl*: needles from EtOH.Aq. M.p. 183°.

Badische, D.R.P., 145,191, (*Chem. Zentr.*, 1903, II, 1097).
Morgan, Jones, *J. Soc. Chem. Ind.*, 1923, **42**, 341T.
Morgan, Micklethwait, *J. Chem. Soc.*, 1906, **89**, 7.
Hodgson, Walker, *J. Chem. Soc.*, 1933, 1346.
Vorozhtzov, Kulev, *Chem. Abstracts*, 1929, **23**, 3697.
Hodgson, E.P., 392,914, (*Chem. Abstracts*, 1933, **27**, 5757).

6-Nitro-1-naphthylamine.
M.p. 143°.
N-*Acetyl*: 6-nitro-1-acetnaphthalide. M.p. 232–3°.

Veselý, Dvorák, *Bull. soc. chim.*, 1923, **33**, 330.

7-Nitro-1-naphthylamine.
Red needles from AcOH. M.p. 133–4° (122–3°).
N-*Acetyl*: 7-nitro-1-acetnaphthalide. M.p. 206–7°.

Schroeter, D.R.P., 563,627, (*Chem. Abstracts*, 1933, **27**, 995).
Schroeter *et al.*, *Ber.*, 1930, **63**, 1317.
Veselý, Dvorák, *Bull. soc. chim.*, 1923, **33**, 330.

8-Nitro-1-naphthylamine.
Red cryst. from pet. ether. M.p. 96–7°.
N-*Me*: *see* 8-Nitro-*N*-methyl-1-naphthylamine.
N-*Acetyl*: 8-nitro-1-acetnaphthalide. Needles from H_2O. M.p. 191°.
N-*Benzenesulphonyl*: needles from EtOH. M.p. 194°.

Morgan, Micklethwait, *J. Chem. Soc.*, 1906, **89**, 7.
Meldola, Streatfield, *J. Chem. Soc.*, 1893, **63**, 1055.
Morgan, Jones, *J. Soc. Chem. Ind.*, 1923, **42**, 341T.

1-Nitro-2-naphthylamine

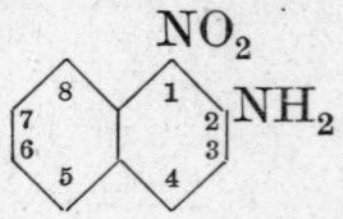

$C_{10}H_8O_2N_2$ MW, 188

Orange-yellow needles from EtOH. M.p. 126–7° (123–4°). Sol. EtOH, Me_2CO, AcOH. Mod. sol. boiling H_2O.
N-*Me*: *see* 1-Nitro-*N*-methyl-2-naphthylamine.
N-*Et*: $C_{12}H_{12}O_2N_2$. MW, 216. Orange-red prisms from EtOH. M.p. 100–1°. N-p-*Toluenesulphonyl*: needles from EtOH. M.p. 152–3°. N-*Nitroso*: cryst. from EtOH. M.p. 90°.
N-*Phenyl*: red prisms from EtOH. M.p. 110–11°.
N-*Acetyl*: 1-nitro-2-acetnaphthalide. Yellow cryst. from EtOH. M.p. 123·5°. Sol. EtOH, AcOH, C_6H_6. Mod. sol. hot H_2O. Spar. sol. Et_2O, ligroin.
N-*Benzoyl*: cryst. + 1 mol. C_6H_6 from C_6H_6. M.p. (benzene-free), 168°.

N-*Benzenesulphonyl*: yellowish prisms. M.p. 156°.

N-p-*Toluenesulphonyl*: orange-yellow prisms from EtOH. M.p. 160–1°.

$B, C_6H_3(NO_2)_3$-1 : 3 : 5 : yellow needles from EtOH. M.p. 115·5–116°.

Hartman, Smith, *Organic Syntheses*, 1933, XIII, 72.
Liebermann, Jacobson, *Ann.*, 1882, **211**, 64.
Meldola, Lane, *J. Chem. Soc.*, 1904, **85**, 1603.
Morgan, Micklethwait, *J. Chem. Soc.*, 1912, **101**, 148.
Veselý, Dvorák, *Bull. soc. chim.*, 1923, **33**, 331.

5-Nitro-2-naphthylamine.

Red needles from EtOH. M.p. 143·5°. Sol. AcOH, C_6H_6, hot EtOH. Insol. ligroin.

N-*Acetyl*: 5-nitro-2-acetnaphthalide. Yellow needles from C_6H_6. M.p. 186°.

N-*Benzoyl*: needles. M.p. 181·5°.

Friedländer, Szymanski, *Ber.*, 1892, **25**, 2077.
Hirsch, D.R.P., 57,491.
Veselý, Dvorák, *Bull. soc. chim.*, 1923, **33**, 327.
Morgan, Chazan, *J. Soc. Chem. Ind.*, 1922, **41**, 1T.

8-Nitro-2-naphthylamine.

Red needles. M.p. 104–5° (103·5°). Sol. EtOH, Et_2O, C_6H_6. Insol. ligroin.

N-*Acetyl*: 8-nitro-2-acetnaphthalide. Yellow needles from EtOH. M.p. 195·5°.

N-*Benzoyl*: greenish-yellow needles from EtOH. M.p. 162°.

See first three references above and also Morgan, Gilmour, *J. Soc. Chem. Ind.*, 1922, **41**, 61T.

4-Nitro-1-naphthylamine-5-sulphonic Acid

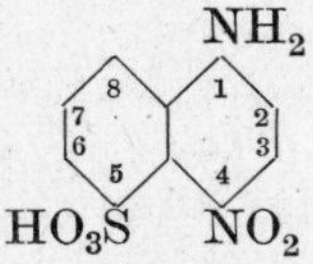

$C_{10}H_8O_5N_2S$ MW, 268

Needles. Spar. sol. H_2O.

Bayer, D.R.P., 133,951, (*Chem. Zentr.*, 1902, II, 867).

4-Nitro-1-naphthylamine-6-sulphonic Acid.

Yellow cryst. from H_2O.

Cassella, D.R.P., 73,502.
Bayer, D.R.P., 228,764, (*Chem. Zentr.*, 1911, I, 105).

4-Nitro-1-naphthylamine-7-sulphonic Acid.

Reddish-brown amorph. powder from H_2O. Mod. sol. hot H_2O.

See first reference above.

5-Nitro-1-naphthylamine-2-sulphonic Acid.

Yellow flakes. Spar. sol. H_2O.

Na salt: yellow leaflets.

Cassella, D.R.P., 70,890.

5-Nitro-1-naphthylamine-4-sulphonic Acid (8-*Nitronaphthionic acid*).

Needles.

N-*Acetyl*: greenish-yellow cryst. Hot dil. $H_2SO_4 \longrightarrow$ 5-nitro-1-naphthylamine. NH_4 *salt*: yellow needles from H_2O.

Nietzki, Zúbelen, *Ber.*, 1889, **22**, 452.
Bucherer, Uhlmann, *J. prakt. Chem.*, 1909, **80**, 221.

6-Nitro-2-naphthylamine-8-sulphonic Acid

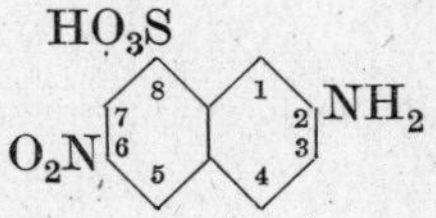

$C_{10}H_8O_5N_2S$ MW, 268

Yellowish amorph. powder.

NH_4 *salt*: dark red prisms.

Ba salt: red cryst. + $4\frac{1}{2}H_2O$

Jacchia, *Ann.*, 1902, **323**, 119
Friedländer, Lucht, *Ber.*, 1893, **26**, 3033.

8-Nitro-2-naphthylamine-6-sulphonic Acid.

Grey powder. Prac. insol. H_2O.

Na salt: orange.

NH_4 *salt*: orange.

Voroshcov, Gribov, *Chem. Abstracts*, 1924, **18**, 1124.

1-Nitro-octane

$CH_3 \cdot [CH_2]_6 \cdot CH_2NO_2$

$C_8H_{17}O_2N$ MW, 159

Yellow liq. B.p. 206–10° part decomp. D^{20} 0·9346.

Worstall, *Am. Chem. J.*, 1898, **20**, 213; 1899, **21**, 228.
Eichler, *Ber.*, 1879, **12**, 1883.

2-Nitro-octane

$CH_3{\cdot}[CH_2]_5{\cdot}CH(NO_2){\cdot}CH_3$

$C_8H_{17}O_2N$ MW, 159

d-.

Pale yellow oil. B.p. 102–5°/23 mm. D^{20}_{20} 0·9224. n^{20}_{D} 1·4324. $[\alpha]^{25}_{D}$ + 15·84° in EtOH.

Na salt: $[\alpha]^{25}_{D}$ + 3·31° in EtOH.

K salt: $[\alpha]^{25}_{D}$ + 3·74 in EtOH.

l-.

B.p. 100–3°/18 mm. D^{20}_{20} 0·9165. n^{20}_{D} 1·4292. $[\alpha]^{25}_{D}$ − 10·8° in EtOH.

dl-.

B.p. 210–12° decomp., 123–4°/40 mm. D^0 0·93645.

Shriver, Young, *J. Am. Chem. Soc.*, 1930, **52**, 3337.
Konowalow, *Chem. Zentr.*, 1899, I, 1063.

3-Nitro-opianic Acid

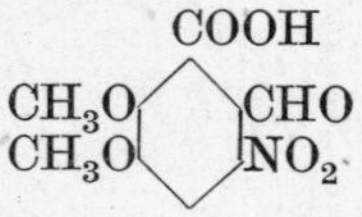

$C_{10}H_9O_7N$ MW, 255

Yellow prisms from H_2O. M.p. 169–70°. Spar. sol. H_2O. $k = 2{\cdot}91 \times 10^{-6}$ at 25°. $KMnO_4$ in hot carbonate sol. ⟶ 6-nitrohemipinic acid.

Me ester: $C_{11}H_{11}O_7N$. MW, 269. Needles from C_6H_6–pet. ether. M.p. 78°. $KMnO_4$ ⟶ 6-nitrohemipinic acid. *Diacetate*: cryst. from C_6H_6. M.p. 159–60°.

ψ-Me ester: 4-nitro-3 : 6 : 7-trimethoxyphthalide. Needles from MeOH. M.p. 181·5–182·5°. Sol. Me_2CO, hot C_6H_6. Stable to $KMnO_4$.

Et ester: $C_{12}H_{13}O_7N$. MW, 283. Yellow needles and plates from C_6H_6. M.p. 80–1°. *Diacetate*: cryst. from C_6H_6–pet. ether. M.p. 100°.

ψ-Et ester: 4-nitro-6 : 7-dimethoxy-3-ethoxyphthalide. Needles from CS_2. M.p. 96°. Very sol. Et_2O. Sol. CS_2, hot C_6H_6. Hyd. by H_2O.

Chloride: $C_{10}H_8O_6NCl$. MW, 273·5. Yellowish leaflets from C_6H_6–ligroin. M.p. 137–8°. Sol. C_6H_6, hot $CHCl_3$. Insol. Et_2O, ligroin.

Amide: $C_{10}H_{10}O_6N_2$. MW, 254. Straw-yellow needles from H_2O. M.p. 203° decomp. Sol. AcOH, hot H_2O. Spar. sol. $CHCl_3$.

Anhydride: $C_{20}H_{16}O_{13}N_2$. MW, 492. Cryst. from AcOEt. M.p. 250°.

Prinz, *J. prakt. Chem.*, 1881, **24**, 357.
Claus, Predari, *J. prakt. Chem.*, 1897, **55**, 173, (*Footnote*).
Wegscheider, Müller, Chiari, *Monatsh.*, 1908, **29**, 742.
Wegscheider, Kuśy, v. Dúbrav, v. Rušnov, *Monatsh.*, 1903, **24**, 801.
Wegscheider, Späth, *Monatsh.*, 1916, **37**, 299.
Wegscheider, Müller, *Ann.*, 1923, **433**, 33.

2-Nitro-orcinol (2-*Nitro*-3 : 5-*dihydroxytoluene*)

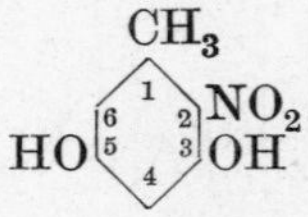

$C_7H_7O_4N$ MW, 169

Yellow needles + H_2O from H_2O. M.p. 122°. Very sol. EtOH, Et_2O. Sol. C_6H_6, $CHCl_3$, ligroin. Non-volatile in steam.

3-*Me ether*: $C_8H_9O_4N$. MW, 183. Brownish-yellow cryst. from C_6H_6–ligroin. M.p. 129–31°. Sol. EtOH, Et_2O, AcOH. Insol. CS_2, ligroin. Non-volatile in steam.

5-*Me ether*: yellow needles from EtOH or ligroin. M.p. 104–6°. Very sol. hot EtOH, C_6H_6, AcOEt. Sol. Et_2O, AcOH. Volatile in steam.

3-*Et ether*: $C_9H_{11}O_4N$. MW, 197. Yellow needles. M.p. 103°. Non-volatile in steam.

5-*Et ether*: yellow needles. M.p. 54°. Volatile in steam.

Henrich, Meyer, *Ber.*, 1903, **36**, 886.
Henrich, Nachtigall, *ibid.*, 893.
Weselsky, Benedikt, *Monatsh.*, 1881, **2**, 370.

4-Nitro-orcinol (4-*Nitro*-3 : 5-*dihydroxytoluene*).

Orange needles from EtOH. M.p. 127°. Sol. EtOH, Et_2O, C_6H_6, $CHCl_3$, AcOH. Mod. sol hot ligroin. Spar. sol. H_2O. Volatile in steam Sublimes.

Henrich, Meyer, *Ber.*, 1903, **36**, 886.
Weselsky, *Ber.*, 1874, **7**, 439.

2-Nitro-oxanilic Acid (*Oxalic acid mono-o-nitroanilide, o-nitrophenyloxamic acid*)

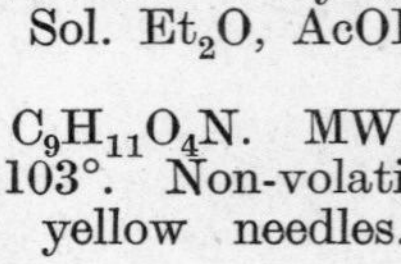

$C_8H_6O_5N_2$ MW, 210

Golden needles from H_2O. M.p. 112°. Sol. hot H_2O, EtOH, AcOH. Spar. sol. Et_2O.

Et ester: $C_{10}H_{10}O_5N_2$. MW, 238. Yellow needles from EtOH or AcOH. M.p. 113° (108°).

o-*Nitroanilide*: *see under* Oxalic Acid.

Aschan, *Ber.*, 1885, **18**, 2937.
Abderhalden, Ehrenwall, Schwab, Zumstein, *Chem. Abstracts*, 1933, **27**, 107.
Kuhlmann, F.P., 649,328, (*Chem. Abstracts*, 1929, **23**, 2988).
Pickard, Allen, Bowdler, Carter, *J. Chem. Soc.*, 1902, **81**, 1568.

3-Nitro-oxanilic Acid (*Oxalic acid mono*-m-*nitroanilide*, m-*nitrophenyloxamic acid*).

M.p. 158°.

Et ester: yellow needles from EtOH. M.p. 150°. Spar. sol. H_2O.

Amide: $C_8H_7O_4N_3$. MW, 209. Needles from AcOH. M.p. 268–9°.

Anilide: yellow needles from $PhNO_2$. M.p. 204°.

m-*Nitroanilide*: *see under* Oxalic Acid.

Anselmino, *Chem. Zentr.*, 1906, I, 753.
Kuhlmann, F.P., 649,328, (*Chem. Abstracts*, 1929, **23**, 2988).
Pickard, Allen, Bowdler, Carter, *J. Chem. Soc.*, 1902, **81**, 1569.
Jacobs, Heidelberger, *J. Am. Chem. Soc.*, 1917, **39**, 1452.

4-Nitro-oxanilic Acid (*Oxalic acid mono*-p-*nitroanilide*, p-*nitrophenyloxamic acid*).

Yellowish needles + $1H_2O$ from H_2O. M.p. 216°. Mod. sol. EtOH. Spar. sol. cold H_2O.

Me ester: $C_9H_8O_5N_2$. MW, 224. Yellow cryst. from MeOH. M.p. 232°.

Et ester: needles from AcOH. M.p. 172° (166°). Very sol. $CHCl_3$, AcOH, AcOEt, Py. Sol. Et_2O, EtOH, Me_2CO, C_6H_6. Very spar. sol. H_2O, pet. ether.

Amide: m.p. 308–10° decomp. Sol. boiling AcOH, AcOEt. Spar. sol. EtOH, Et_2O, $CHCl_3$, C_6H_6.

Anilide: grey needles from AcOEt. M.p. 251–2°.

p-*Nitroanilide*: *see under* Oxalic Acid.

Mumm, Hesse, Volquartz, *Ber.*, 1915, **48**, 391.
Suida, *Monatsh.*, 1910, **31**, 605.
Pickard, Allen, Bowdler, Carter, *J. Chem. Soc.*, 1902, **81**, 1570.
Schultz, Rohde, Herzog, *J. prakt. Chem.*, 1906, **74**, 82.
Aschan, *Ber.*, 1885, **18**, 2936.
Tierie, *Rec. trav. chim.*, 1933, **52**, 420.
Kuhlmann, F.P., 649,328, (*Chem. Abstracts*, 1929, **23**, 2988).

6-Nitro-oxindole

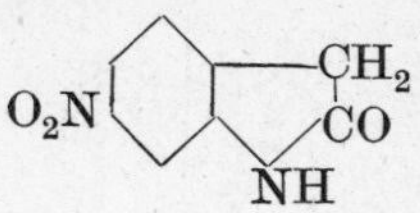

$C_8H_6O_3N_2$ MW, 178

Yellow needles from H_2O or EtOH. Decomp. at 175° ⟶ a colourless sublimate. Sol. alkalis with reddish-yellow col.

Baeyer, *Ber.*, 1879, **12**, 1313.

1-Nitropentane

$CH_3{\cdot}[CH_2]_3{\cdot}CH_2NO_2$

$C_5H_{11}O_2N$ MW, 117

Liq. with rancid odour. B.p. 172–3°/760 mm., 88–90°/64 mm. D^{20} 0·9475. n_D 1·4218. Sweet taste.

Henry, *Rec. trav. chim.*, 1905, **24**, 352.

3-Nitropentane

$CH_3{\cdot}CH_2{\cdot}CH(NO_2){\cdot}CH_2{\cdot}CH_3$

$C_5H_{11}O_2N$ MW, 117

Liq. B.p. 152–5°/746 mm. D^0 0·9575.

Bewad, *J. prakt. Chem.*, 1893, **48**, 380.

***m*-Nitrophenacyl Alcohol** (3-*Nitrobenzoylcarbinol*, 3-*nitro-ω-hydroxyacetophenone*)

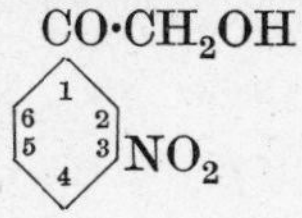

$C_8H_7O_4N$ MW, 181

Pale yellow cryst. M.p. 92·5–93°. Aq. sol. reduces $NH_3.AgNO_3$ and Fehling's. Alk. $Cu(OH)_2$ ⟶ *m*-nitromandelic acid. $KMnO_4$ ⟶ *m*-nitrobenzoic acid.

Acetyl: cryst. from Et_2O–ligroin. M.p. 53°.

Semicarbazone: cryst. from EtOH. M.p. 214°.

Evans, Brooks, *J. Am. Chem. Soc.*, 1908, **30**, 407.
Baker, *J. Chem. Soc.*, 1931, 2422.

***p*-Nitrophenacyl Alcohol** (4-*Nitrobenzoylcarbinol*, 4-*nitro-ω-hydroxyacetophenone*).

M.p. 121°. Sol. hot alkalis.

Acetyl: cryst. from AcOEt–ligroin. M.p. 124°.

Phenylhydrazone: needles from C_6H_6. M.p. 178°.

Baker, *J. Chem. Soc.*, 1931, 2426.
Engler, Zielke, *Ber.*, 1889, **22**, 204.

_o_-Nitrophenacyl bromide (ω-*Bromo*-2-*nitroacetophenone*)

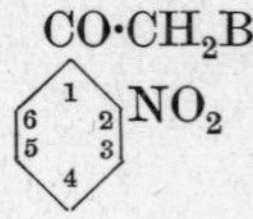

$C_8H_6O_3NBr$ MW, 244

Needles from ligroin. M.p. 55–6°. Sol. EtOH, Et_2O, $CHCl_3$. Spar. sol. ligroin. Alcoholic $(NH_4)_2S$ ⟶ indigo.

Gevekoht, *Ann.*, 1883, **221**, 327.
Arndt, Eistert, Partale, *Ber.*, 1927, **60**, 1369.

_m_-Nitrophenacyl bromide (ω-*Bromo*-3-*nitroacetophenone*).

Needles from EtOH.Aq. M.p. 96°. Sol. EtOH, $CHCl_3$, CS_2. Very spar. sol. Et_2O. $KMnO_4$ ⟶ *m*-nitrobenzoic acid.

Oxime: yellowish needles from C_6H_6–ligroin. M.p. 126·5–127°. *Acetyl*: yellowish needles from C_6H_6–ligroin. M.p. 64–5°.

Korten, Scholl, *Ber.*, 1901, **34**, 1909.
Evans, Brooks, *J. Am. Chem. Soc.*, 1908, **30**, 406.

_p_-Nitrophenacyl bromide (ω-*Bromo*-4-*nitroacetophenone*).

Needles from C_6H_6–pet. ether. M.p. 98°. Sol. Et_2O, Me_2CO, AcOH, C_6H_6, CS_2, hot EtOH.

Baker, *J. Chem. Soc.*, 1931, 2420.

ω-Nitrophenacyl bromide (ω-*Bromo*-ω-*nitroacetophenone*)

$$C_6H_5\cdot CO\cdot CH\Big<^{Br}_{NO_2}$$

$C_8H_6O_3NBr$ MW, 244

Cryst. from Et_2O. M.p. 61·5°. Sol. EtOH and warm aq. Na_2CO_3. Alc. KOH ⟶ intense yellow K salt.

Thiele, Haeckel, *Ann.*, 1902, **325**, 13.

_o_-Nitrophenacyl chloride (ω-*Chloro*-2-*nitroacetophenone*)

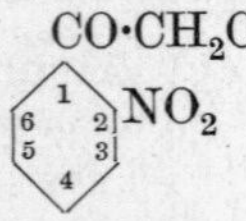

$C_8H_6O_3NCl$ MW, 199·5

Needles from ligroin or MeOH. M.p. 66–7°. Very sol. Et_2O. Sol. EtOH.

Arndt, Eistert, Partale, *Ber.*, 1927, **60**, 1369.

_m_-Nitrophenacyl chloride (ω-*Chloro*-3-*nitroacetophenone*).

Prisms from Et_2O. M.p. 103°.

Baker, *J. Chem. Soc.*, 1931, 2420.
Barkenbus, Clements, *J. Am. Chem. Soc.*, 1934, **56**, 1369.

_p_-Nitrophenacyl chloride (ω-*Chloro*-4-*nitroacetophenone*).

Brown needles from EtOH. M.p. 107°.

Dale, Nierenstein, *Ber.*, 1927, **60**, 1027.

_m_-Nitrophenacyl iodide (ω-*Iodo*-3-*nitioacetophenone*)

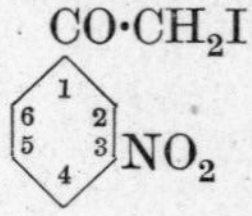

$C_8H_6O_3NI$ MW, 291

Prisms from Et_2O–ligroin. M.p. 96°.

Baker, *J. Chem. Soc.*, 1931, 2420.

_p_-Nitrophenacyl iodide (ω-*Iodo*-4-*nitroacetophenone*).

Needles from AcOEt–ligroin. M.p. 97–8°.

See previous reference.

2-Nitrophenanthrahydroquinone (2-*Nitro*-9 : 10-*dihydroxyphenanthrene*)

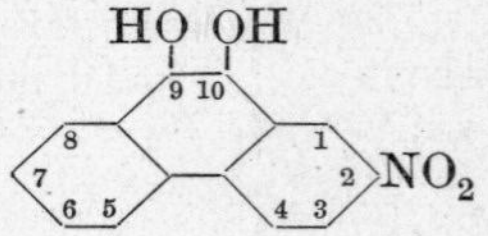

$C_{14}H_9O_4N$ MW, 255

Yellowish-brown cryst. M.p. about 220° decomp. Dil. NaOH ⟶ brownish-violet sol. Conc. H_2SO_4 ⟶ reddish-violet sol.

Di-Me ether: $C_{16}H_{13}O_4N$. MW, 283. Yellow needles from EtOH. M.p. 126–7°. Sol. EtOH, Me_2CO, AcOH.

Diacetyl: pale yellow needles. M.p. 258°.

Schmidt, Austin, *Ber.*, 1903, **36**, 3732.
Jakubowitsch, Worobjowa, *J. prakt. Chem.*, 1935, **143**, 285.

3-Nitrophenanthrahydroquinone (3-*Nitro*-9 : 10-*dihydroxyphenanthrene*).

Red needles with blue reflex from 60% AcOH. M.p. 222–3°. Sol. EtOH, MeOH, Et_2O, AcOH. Spar. sol. C_6H_6. Insol. ligroin. Very dil. NaOH ⟶ blue sol. which absorbs oxygen. Reduces $AgNO_3$ and $FeCl_3$. Conc. H_2SO_4 ⟶ red sol. ⟶ pale yellow on dilution.

Acetyl: yellow needles from Ac_2O. M.p.

234–5° decomp. NaOH ⟶ deep red sol. ⟶ blue on standing.

Schmidt, Kämpf, *Ber.*, 1902, **35**, 3125.
Schmidt, *ibid.*, 3132.

4-Nitrophenanthrahydroquinone (*4-Nitro-9 : 10-dihydroxyphenanthrene*).

Diacetyl : needles from 60% AcOH. M.p. 222–3° decomp.

Schmidt, Kämpf, *Ber.*, 1903, **36**, 3737.

2-Nitrophenanthraquinone

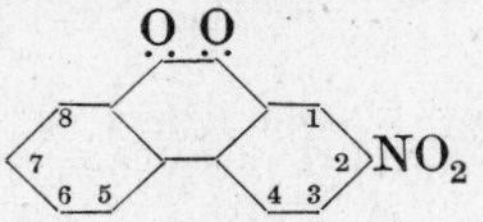

$C_{14}H_7O_4N$ MW, 253

Golden-yellow leaflets from AcOH. M.p. 260° (257°). Spar. sol. AcOH. Insol. EtOH. Sn + HCl ⟶ 2-aminophenanthraquinone.

Oxime : yellowish-green needles. M.p. 213° decomp.

Thiosemicarbazone : red cryst. from Py. M.p. 234–5°.

Schmidt, Heinle, *Ber.*, 1911, **44**, 1497.
Werner, *Ber.*, 1904, **37**, 3086.
Schmidt, Austin, *Ber.*, 1903, **36**, 3731.

3-Nitrophenanthraquinone.

Orange needles from AcOH. M.p. 281–2° (275°). Spar. sol. org. solvents. Conc. H_2SO_4 ⟶ red col. KOH.Aq. ⟶ dark green col.

Imide : green cryst. from C_6H_6. Decomp. at 203°. Sol. C_6H_6. Spar. sol. EtOH, Et_2O, $CHCl_3$.

Oxime : yellow needles from C_6H_6. M.p. 240°. Mod. sol. hot C_6H_6. Spar. sol. other solvents. Alc. $FeCl_3$ ⟶ blood-red col. *Semicarbazone* : greenish-yellow cryst. from EtOH. M.p. 249–50° decomp.

Dioxime : yellowish-red needles from EtOH. M.p. 200° decomp. Sol. CS_2, C_6H_6. Spar. sol. EtOH. *Di-Me* : pale yellow needles from EtOH. M.p. 190–2°. Very sol. $CHCl_3$. Sol. C_6H_6. Spar. sol. EtOH. *Diacetyl* : pale yellow plates from C_6H_6. M.p. 183° decomp. Sol. $CHCl_3$, C_6H_6. Spar. sol. EtOH.

Semicarbazone : m.p. 254° decomp.

Schmidt, Söll, *Ber.*, 1908, **41**, 3683.
Schmidt, Kämpf, *Ber.*, 1902, **35**, 3120.
Schmidt, Schärer, Glatz, *Ber.*, 1911, **44**, 282.

4-Nitrophenanthraquinone.

Pale yellow needles from EtOH. M.p. 179–80°. Very sol. EtOH, Me_2CO, $CHCl_3$, AcOH, AcOEt, C_6H_6. Spar. sol. Et_2O, CS_2. Sol. dil. alkalis. Conc. H_2SO_4 ⟶ dark red sol. ⟶ light brown on dilution.

Oxime : greenish-yellow needles from EtOH. M.p. 169–70°. Mod. sol. EtOH, Me_2CO, AcOEt, C_6H_6. Alc. $FeCl_3$ ⟶ deep brownish-red col.

Thiosemicarbazone : red cryst. from EtOH–Py. M.p. 145°.

Schmidt, Austin, *Ber.*, 1903, **36**, 3731.
Schmidt, Kämpf, *ibid.*, 3736.

2-Nitrophenanthrene

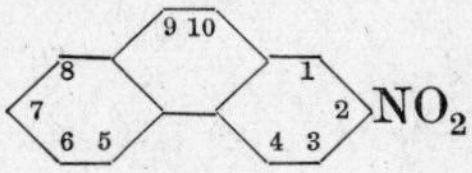

$C_{14}H_9O_2N$ MW, 223

Pale yellow cryst. from EtOH. M.p. 99°. Very sol. EtOH, Et_2O, AcOH, C_6H_6. CrO_3 ⟶ 2-nitrophenanthraquinone.

Schmidt, Heinle, *Ber.*, 1911, **44**, 1494.

3-Nitrophenanthrene.

Dark yellow plates from AcOH. M.p. 170–1°. Mod. sol. Me_2CO, $CHCl_3$, C_6H_6, toluene. Spar. sol. cold EtOH, AcOH. Alc. $(NH_4)_2S$ or $SnCl_2$ in boiling AcOH ⟶ 3-aminophenanthrene.

Schmidt, *Ber.*, 1879, **12**, 1154.
See also Schmidt, *Ber.*, 1901, **34**, 3531.

4-Nitrophenanthrene.

Yellow needles from EtOH. M.p. 80–2°. CrO_3 in AcOH ⟶ 4-nitrophenanthraquinone. $SnCl_2$ in AcOH ⟶ 4-aminophenanthrene.

Schmidt, Heinle, *Ber.*, 1911, **44**, 1494.

9-Nitrophenanthrene.

Pale yellow needles from EtOH. M.p. 116–17°. Sol. $CHCl_3$, C_6H_6. Less sol. EtOH, MeOH, Et_2O. Spar. sol. ligroin. Sol. 49 parts AcOH at 17°. Sol. conc. H_2SO_4 with blood-red col. ⟶ green on warming. Zn dust + alkali ⟶ 9-azophenanthrene. $SnCl_2$ ⟶ 9-aminophenanthrene.

Picrate : pale yellow needles from EtOH. M.p. 78–9°.

Schmidt, Strobel, *Ber.*, 1903, **36**, 2511.
Schmidt, *Ber.*, 1900, **33**, 3257.

2-Nitrophenazine

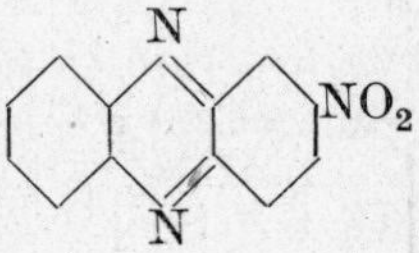

$C_{12}H_7O_2N_3$ MW, 225

Yellow cryst. from EtOH. M.p. 214°. Sol. hot EtOH, hot AcOH. Insol. H_2O. Sublimes. Sol. conc. H_2SO_4 with orange-yellow col.

Kehrmann, Havas, *Ber.*, 1913, **46**, 351.

3-Nitro-*o*-phenetidine (3-*Nitro*-2-*amino-phenetole*)

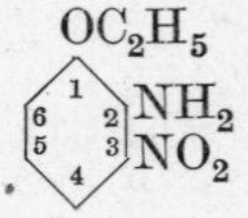

$C_8H_{10}O_3N_2$ MW, 182

Yellow cryst. from H_2O. M.p. 49°.

N-*Me*: $C_9H_{12}O_3N_2$. MW, 196. Dark red cryst. from EtOH. M.p. 59°.

N-*Acetyl*: cryst. from pet. ether. M.p. 64°.

Blanksma, *Chem. Zentr.*, 1908, II, 1826.

4-Nitro-*o*-phenetidine.

Yellow needles from EtOH.Aq. M.p. 99°. Sol. EtOH. Spar. sol. H_2O.

N-*Acetyl*: yellow needles from EtOH. M.p. 199° (196°).

Reverdin, Düring, *Ber.*, 1899, **32**, 164.
See also previous reference.

5-Nitro-*o*-phenetidine.

Yellow needles from EtOH.Aq. M.p. 91°. Sol. EtOH, Et_2O, Me_2CO. Spar. sol. ligroin.

N-*Acetyl*: yellow needles. M.p. 165°.

Reverdin, Düring, *Ber.*, 1899, **32**, 162.
Jacobson, Hönigsberger, *Ber.*, 1903, **36**, 4124.

4-Nitro-*m*-phenetidine (4-*Nitro*-3-*amino-phenetole*)

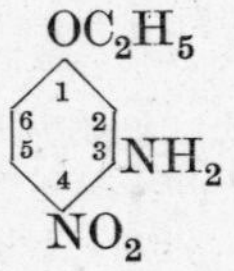

$C_8H_{10}O_3N_2$ MW, 182

Yellow needles from EtOH.Aq. M.p. 105°. Sol. usual org. solvents.

N-*Acetyl*: needles from EtOH. M.p. 95°. Sol. usual org. solvents.

Reverdin, Lokietek, *Bull. soc. chem.*, 1916, **19**, 253.
Hodgson, Clay, *J. Chem. Soc.*, 1930, 963.

5-Nitro-*m*-phenetidine.

Yellow needles from EtOH. M.p. 115°. Sol. hot H_2O, EtOH.

Blanksma, *Rec. trav. chim.*, 1905, **24**, 43.

6-Nitro-*m*-phenetidine.

Needles from EtOH.Aq. M.p. 122–3°. Sol. usual org. solvents. Spar. sol. H_2O. Insol. ligroin.

N-*Acetyl*: golden-yellow needles from H_2O. M.p. 165° (147°). Sol. EtOH, AcOH. Spar. sol. H_2O. Insol. ligroin.

Reverdin, Lokietek, *Bull. soc. chim.*, 1916, **19**, 253.

2-Nitro-*p*-phenetidine (2-*Nitro*-4-*amino-phenetole*)

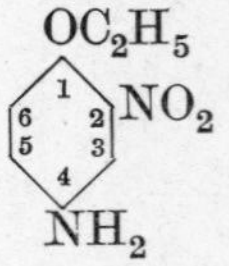

$C_8H_{10}O_3N_2$ MW, 182

Yellow needles from EtOH.Aq. M.p. 40°.

N-*Acetyl*: needles from EtOH. M.p. 123°. Very sol. Me_2CO, $CHCl_3$, AcOH. Sol. C_6H_6. Spar. sol. Et_2O, ligroin.

Reverdin, *Helv. Chim. Acta*, 1927, **10**, 3.

3-Nitro-*p*-phenetidine.

Red prisms from EtOH. M.p. 113° (109°). Sol. Et_2O, $CHCl_3$. Spar. sol. cold EtOH.

N-*Acetyl*: yellow needles from H_2O. M.p. 104°. Sol. EtOH, Et_2O, $CHCl_3$.

N-*Benzenesulphonyl*: yellow needles. M.p. 72°.

N-p-*Toluenesulphonyl*: yellow needles. M.p. 94°.

Kehrmann, Gauhe, *Ber.*, 1898, **31**, 2403.
Reverdin, *Ber.*, 1906, **39**, 3796.

***o*-Nitrophenetole**

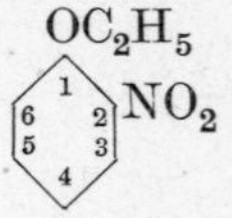

$C_8H_9O_3N$ MW, 167

Yellow oil with green tinge. M.p. 2·1°. B.p. 267°, 149·3°/16 mm., 142·8°/12 mm., 134·2°/8 mm. D^{15} 1·1903. n_D^{20} 1·5425. Sol. EtOH, Et_2O. Insol. H_2O.

Francis, *Ber.*, 1906, **39**, 3803.
Erp, *Ber.*, 1923, **56**, 218.
Richardson, *J. Chem. Soc.*, 1926, 522.

***m*-Nitrophenetole.**

Yellow cryst. M.p. 34°. B.p. 284° (264° slight decomp.), 190°/100 mm., 169°/70 mm. Sn+HCl ⟶ *m*-phenetidine.

Whiston, *J. Soc. Chem. Ind.*, 1924, **43**, 369T.
Reverdin, *Ber.*, 1896, **29**, 2597.

***p*-Nitrophenetole.**

Prisms from Et_2O or EtOH.Aq. M.p. 60° (57–8°). B.p. 283°. D_4^{100} 1·1176, D_4^{125} 1·0937.

Very sol. Et_2O. Sol. hot EtOH, hot pet. ether. Spar. sol. H_2O, cold EtOH, cold pet. ether. Sn+dil. HCl or Fe+HCl ⟶ *p*-phenetidine. Sn+conc. HCl ⟶ 3-chloro-4-aminophenetole.

Gas, Light and Coke Co., E.P., 204,594, (*Chem. Zentr.*, 1925, II, 611).
Richardson, *J. Chem. Soc.*, 1926, 522.
Willgerodt, *Ber.*, 1882, **15**, 1003.
de Bruyn, *Rec. trav. chim.*, 1904, **23**, 36, 43.
Erp, *Ber.*, 1923, **56**, 218.

o-Nitrophenol

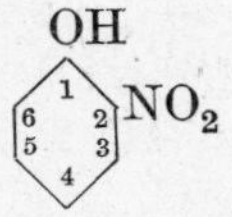

$C_6H_5O_3N$ MW, 139

Sulphur-yellow needles or prisms from EtOH or Et_2O. M.p. 44·9°. B.p. 216°. D_4^{40} 1·2942, D_4^{60} 1·2712, D_4^{80} 1·2482, D_4^{100} 1·2323. Sol. EtOH, Et_2O, CS_2, C_6H_6, hot H_2O. Spar. sol. cold H_2O. Volatile in steam. Heat of comb. C_p 688·2 Cal., C_v 688·6 Cal. $k=6{\cdot}0\times10^{-8}$ at 0°, $7{\cdot}5\times10^{-8}$ ($6{\cdot}8\times10^{-8}$) at 25°, $8{\cdot}3\times10^{-8}$ at 35°. Cold alk. ammonium persulphate ⟶ nitrohydroquinone.

Me ether: *see* o-Nitroanisole.

Et ether: *see* o-Nitrophenetole.

Isobutyl ether: $C_{10}H_{13}O_3N$. MW, 195. Yellow oil. B.p. 275–80°. D^{20} 1·1361.

Allyl ether: $C_9H_9O_3N$. MW, 179. Yellow oil. B.p. 155°/12 mm.

β-*Aminoethyl ether*: β-*o*-nitrophenoxyethylamine. $C_8H_{10}O_3N_2$. MW, 182. Red leaflets from H_2O or plates from Et_2O–C_6H_6. M.p. 72–3°. Very sol. EtOH, Et_2O, boiling C_6H_6. Spar. sol. boiling H_2O.

Phenyl ether: *see* 2-Nitrodiphenyl Ether.

Benzyl ether: $C_{13}H_{11}O_3N$. MW, 229. M.p. 130°.

Acetyl: *o*-nitrophenyl acetate. Needles or prisms from ligroin. M.p. 40–1°. B.p. 253° decomp. Sol. EtOH, Et_2O, C_6H_6. Spar. sol. ligroin.

Chloroacetyl: needles. M.p. 63°.

Bromoacetyl: cryst. from EtOH. M.p. 55·5–56°.

Isobutyryl: *o*-nitrophenyl isobutyrate. Yellow oil. B.p. 163–4°/9 mm.

Lauryl: *o*-nitrophenyl laurate. Cryst. from EtOH. M.p. 35–6°.

Palmityl: *o*-nitrophenyl palmitate. Needles from EtOH. M.p. 51–2°.

Stearyl: *o*-nitrophenyl stearate. Cryst. from EtOH. M.p. 60–1°.

Benzoyl: *o*-nitrophenyl benzoate. Prisms from ligroin. M.p. 59° (55°).

o-*Nitrobenzoyl*: yellowish needles from EtOH. M.p. 125°.

m-*Nitrobenzoyl*: m.p. 129°.

Anisoyl: needles. M.p. 96°.

p-*Bromobenzenesulphonyl*: m.p. 97–8°.

α-*Naphthylurethane*: m.p. 112–13°.

Lukaschewitsch, Stenberg, *Chem. Zentr.*, 1935, II, 212.
Hart, *J. Am. Chem. Soc.*, 1910, **32**, 1105.
Meisenheimer, Hesse, *Ber.*, 1919, **52**, 1166.
Hantzsch, Gorke, *Ber.*, 1906, **39**, 1080.

***m*-Nitrophenol.**

Cryst. from HCl.Aq. M.p. 97° (95·1°). B.p. 194°/70 mm. D_4^{100} 1·2797, D_4^{125} 1·2588, D_4^{150} 1·2359. Heat of comb. C_v 684·8 Cal. $k=1{\cdot}0\times10^{-8}$ at 25°. Very sol. EtOH, Et_2O. Sol. hot H_2O, hot $CHCl_3$. Insol. pet. ether. Sol. dil. acids. Non-volatile in steam. Triboluminescent.

Me ether: *see* m-Nitroanisole.

Et ether: *see* m-Nitrophenetole.

Phenyl ether: *see* 3-Nitrodiphenyl Ether.

Acetyl: *m*-nitrophenyl acetate. Needles from pet. ether. M.p. 55–6°.

Benzoyl: *m*-nitrophenyl benzoate. Cryst. M.p. 95°.

p-*Bromobenzenesulphonyl*: m.p. 108–9°.

p-*Toluenesulphonyl*: prisms from EtOH. M.p. 112–13°.

Phenylurethane: needles from $CHCl_3$. M.p. 129°.

α-*Naphthylurethane*: m.p. 167°.

Bamberger, *Ber.*, 1915, **48**, 1355.
Manske, *Organic Syntheses*, Collective Vol. I, 396.

***p*-Nitrophenol.**

Known in two forms:

(α) Colourless prisms obtained by cryst. from toluene above 63°. Metastable at room temp. Stable to light.

(β) Yellow prisms by cryst. from toluene below 63°. Stable at room temp. Gradually turns red in light.

Ordinary *p*-nitrophenol is a mixture of both forms. M.p. 114°. Heat of comb. C_p 689·1 Cal., C_v 689·5 Cal. $k=6{\cdot}5\times10^{-8}$ at 25°. Very sol. EtOH, Et_2O, hot H_2O. Sol. Na_2CO_3.Aq. Very spar. volatile in steam. Sublimes.

Me ether: *see* p-Nitroanisole.

Et ether: *see* p-Nitrophenetole.

Propyl ether: $C_9H_{11}O_3N$. MW, 181. Oil. B.p. 285–7° part. decomp. Sol. most org. solvents. Insol. H_2O.

Isobutyl ether: $C_{10}H_{13}O_3N$. MW, 195.

Needles from Et_2O. M.p. 39°. B.p. 293–5° decomp.

Isoamyl ether : $C_{11}H_{15}O_3N$. MW, 209. Oil. B.p. 309–10° decomp.

Allyl ether : $C_9H_9O_3N$. MW, 179. Needles. M.p. 36° (18·5°). B.p. 160°/12 mm.

β-*Aminoethyl ether* : β-*p*-nitrophenoxyethylamine. Yellow cryst. from H_2O. M.p. 108–9°. Sol. EtOH, Et_2O, C_6H_6.

Phenyl ether : see 4-Nitrodiphenyl Ether.

Benzyl ether : $C_{13}H_{11}O_3N$. MW, 229. M.p. 187·4°.

Acetyl : *p*-nitrophenyl acetate. Leaflets from EtOH.Aq. M.p. 81–2°. Very sol. C_6H_6. Sol. hot H_2O.

Benzoyl : *p*-nitrophenyl benzoate. Needles. M.p. 142·5°.

o-*Nitrobenzoyl* : needles. M.p. 111°.

p-*Nitrobenzoyl* : cryst. powder. M.p. 159°.

3 : 5-*Dinitrobenzoyl* : cryst.+1AcOH. M.p. 188°.

Anisoyl : needles. M.p. 166°.

p-*Bromobenzenesulphonyl* : m.p. 112°.

α-*Naphthylurethane* : m.p. 150–1°.

Aoyama, Nanai, *Chem. Zentr.*, 1935, II, 2662.
Robertson, *J. Chem. Soc.*, 1902, **81**, 1477.
Pictet, Khotinsky, *Ber.*, 1907, **40**, 1165.

o-Nitrophenol-4 : 6-disulphonic Acid

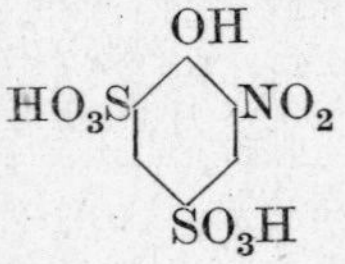

$C_6H_5O_9NS_2$ MW, 299

K salt : orange-yellow prisms + $1\frac{1}{2}H_2O$. $FeCl_3 \longrightarrow$ violet-red col.

Difluoride : $C_6H_3O_7NF_2S_2$. MW, 303. Cryst. M.p. 98·5–99·5°.

Chamot, Pratt, *J. Am. Chem. Soc.*, 1909, **31**, 922; 1910, **32**, 635.
Steinkopf *et al.*, *J. prakt. Chem.*, 1927, **117**, 1.

o-Nitrophenol-4-sulphonic Acid

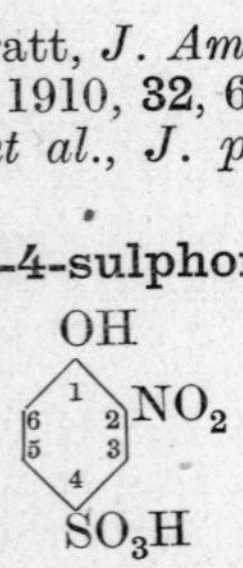

$C_6H_5O_6NS$ MW, 219

Plates from AcOEt–C_6H_6, needles + $3H_2O$ from hot H_2O. M.p. 51·5°, anhyd. 141–2°. Sol. H_2O. Very sol. EtOH, AcOEt, hot $CHCl_3$.

Me ether : see *o*-Nitroanisole-4-sulphonic Aci

Phenyl ether : 2-nitrodiphenyl ether 4-sulphonic acid. Cryst. from C_6H_6. M.p. 89–90°

Fluoride : $C_6H_4O_5NFS$. MW, 221. Cryst. M.p. 66–7°.

Gnehm, Knecht, *J. prakt. Chem.*, 190 **73**, 521.
Kolbe, Gauhe, *Ann.*, 1868, **147**, 71.
Maqueyrol, Loriette, *Bull. soc. chim* 1919, **25**, 371.
Steinkopf *et al.*, *J. prakt. Chem.*, 192 **117**, 1.

m-Nitrophenol-4-sulphonic Acid.

K salt : yellow leaflets from hot H_2O.

Nietzki, Helbach, *Ber.*, 1896, **29**, 2450.

p-Nitrophenol-2-sulphonic Acid.

Prisms or needles or plates + $3H_2O$. Decomp. at 110°. $FeCl_3 \longrightarrow$ deep reddish-brow col. Easily decomp.

K salt : orange-red needles + H_2O. Ver sol. H_2O.

Ca salt : prisms + $3H_2O$.

Ba salt : needles or prisms + H_2O.

Pb salt : needles + $1\frac{1}{2}H_2O$. Insol. H_2O.

Ullmann, Dahmen, *Ber.*, 1908, **41**, 3755
Post, Stuckenberg, *Ann.*, 1880, **205**, 41.

p-Nitrophenol-3-sulphonic Acid.

Cryst. Fe + AcOH $\longrightarrow$ *p*-aminophenol-3-sulphonic acid.

Kalle, D.R.P., 153,123, (*Chem. Zentr* 1904, II, 574).

o-Nitrophenoxyacetic Acid (*Glycollic aci 2-nitrophenyl ether*)

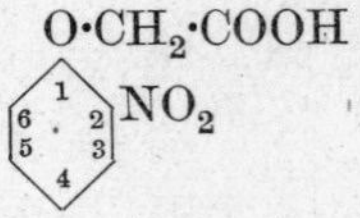

$C_8H_7O_5N$ MW, 19

Prisms from H_2O. M.p. 156·5°. Sol. EtOH $k = 1{\cdot}58 \times 10^{-3}$ at 25°. Non-volatile in steam

Me ester : $C_9H_9O_5N$. MW, 211. Needle M.p. 58°.

Et ester : $C_{10}H_{11}O_5N$. MW, 225. Needles c leaflets from EtOH.Aq. M.p. 46–7°. So EtOH, Et_2O, C_6H_6. Insol. H_2O.

Chloride : $C_8H_6O_4NCl$. MW, 215·5. Yellowish needles from ligroin, prisms from C_6H_6 M.p. 43–44·5°. Sol. most org. solvents.

Amide : $C_8H_8O_4N_2$. MW, 196. Needle from H_2O. M.p. 194·5–199·5° (188°). Spa sol. hot H_2O, EtOH, Me_2CO.

Anilide: $C_{14}H_{12}O_4N_2$. MW, 272. Yellow leaflets. M.p. 118·5°.

Minton, Stephen, *J. Chem. Soc.*, 1922, **121**, 1591.
Jacobs, Heidelberger, *J. Am. Chem. Soc.*, 1917, **39**, 2421.

m-Nitrophenoxyacetic Acid (*Glycollic acid 3-nitrophenyl ether*).

Yellowish needles from H_2O. M.p. 154·5° (151°). Sol. AcOH. Mod. sol. $CHCl_3$, C_6H_6, toluene.

Me ester: needles. M.p. 66·5°.

Et ester: yellow liq. B.p. 208–12°/30 mm., 187°/14 mm.

Chloride: prisms from C_6H_6. M.p. 49–51°.

Amide: yellow prisms. M.p. 178·5°.

Anilide: needles. M.p. 125°.

Minton, Stephen, *J. Chem. Soc.*, 1922, **121**, 1591.
Hewitt, Johnson, Pope, *J. Chem. Soc.*, 1913, **103**, 1631.
Jacobs, Heidelberger, *J. Am. Chem. Soc.*, 1917, **39**, 2191.
Meyer, Duczmal, *Ber.*, 1913, **46**, 3377.

p-Nitrophenoxyacetic Acid (*Glycollic acid 4-nitrophenyl ether*).

Leaflets from MeOH or EtOH. M.p. 184°. Sol. hot EtOH. Spar. sol. H_2O. $k = 1{\cdot}53 \times 10^{-3}$ at 25°.

Me ester: needles. M.p. 100–1° (99°).

Et ester: pale yellow leaflets from EtOH. M.p. 75–6°. B.p. 203–6°/15 mm. Sol. EtOH, Et_2O, C_6H_6.

Propyl ester: m.p. 75–6°.

Amide: prisms or needles. M.p. 156–8° (154–6°). Sol. hot EtOH. Spar. sol. H_2O.

Methylamide: needles from H_2O. M.p. 165·5°. Mod. sol. hot H_2O. Less sol. EtOH, toluene.

Chloride: plates or prisms from C_6H_6. M.p. 86–7°. Sol. Et_2O, C_6H_6.

Anilide: yellow leaflets. M.p. 170°.

p-*Phenetidide*: needles. M.p. 156–7°. Spar. sol. EtOH.

Jacobs, Heidelberger, *J. Am. Chem. Soc.*, 1917, **39**, 2424.
Minton, Stephen, *J. Chem. Soc.*, 1922, **121**, 1591.
Fuchs, D.R.P., 96,492, (*Chem. Zentr.*, 1898, I, 1252).
A.G.F.A., D.R.P., 108,342, (*Chem. Zentr.*, 1900, I, 1177).

o-Nitrophenoxyacetone

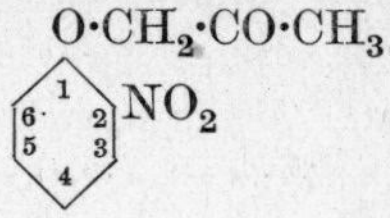

$C_9H_9O_4N$ MW, 195

Needles from H_2O. M.p. 69°. Sol. Et_2O, C_6H_6. Mod. sol. hot H_2O, EtOH. Non-volatile in steam. Gives cryst. bisulphite comp.

Oxime: needles. M.p. 102°. Sol. warm EtOH. Spar. sol. H_2O.

Semicarbazone: cryst. powder. M.p. 178°.

Phenylhydrazone: yellow plates. M.p. 101°.

Stoermer, Brockerhof, *Ber.*, 1897, **30**, 1634.
M.L.B., D.R.P., 97,242, (*Chem. Zentr.*, 1898, II, 525).

p-Nitrophenoxyacetone.

Yellowish leaflets from H_2O or EtOH. M.p. 81°. Sol. Et_2O, $CHCl_3$. Spar. sol. H_2O, EtOH. Gives cryst. bisulphite comp.

Oxime: cryst. M.p. 119°. Mod. sol. hot H_2O, EtOH.

Semicarbazone: cryst. powder from EtOH.Aq. M.p. 216° decomp. Spar. sol. H_2O, EtOH, Et_2O.

Phenylhydrazone: yellow needles from EtOH. M.p. 140°.

See first reference above.

4-Nitro-o-phenoxybenzoic Acid (*5-Nitrodiphenyl ether 2-carboxylic acid*)

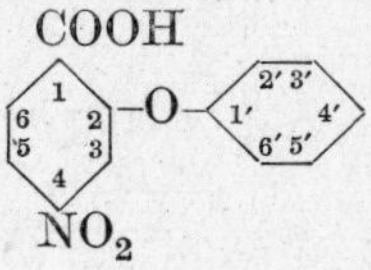

$C_{13}H_9O_5N$ MW, 259

Plates from C_6H_6. M.p. 156°. Sol. EtOH, AcOH, hot C_6H_6. Insol. H_2O, ligroin. Conc. H_2SO_4 at 100° $\longrightarrow$ 2-nitroxanthone.

Ullmann, Wagner, *Ann.*, 1907, **355**, 361.

5-Nitro-o-phenoxybenzoic Acid (*4-Nitrodiphenyl ether 2-carboxylic acid*).

Cryst. from H_2O. M.p. 171–2° (168°). Sol. EtOH, Et_2O, $CHCl_3$. Conc. H_2SO_4 $\longrightarrow$ 3-nitroxanthone.

Haeussermann, Bauer, *Ber.*, 1897, **30**, 740.
Purgotti, *Gazz. chim. ital.*, 1914, **44**, 643.
Brewster, Strain, *J. Am. Chem. Soc.*, 1934, **56**, 118.

2′-Nitro-*o*-phenoxybenzoic Acid (*2′-Nitrodiphenyl ether 2-carboxylic acid*).

Cryst. from C_6H_6. M.p. 153°.

Brewster, Strain, *J. Am. Chem. Soc.*, 1934, **56**, 118.

4′-Nitro-*o*-phenoxybenzoic Acid (*4′-Nitrodiphenyl ether 2-carboxylic acid*).

Cryst. from C_6H_6. M.p. 157°. Conc. H_2SO_4 ⟶ 3-nitroxanthone.

See previous reference.

4′-Nitro-*m*-phenoxybenzoic Acid (*4′-Nitrodiphenyl ether 3-carboxylic acid*)

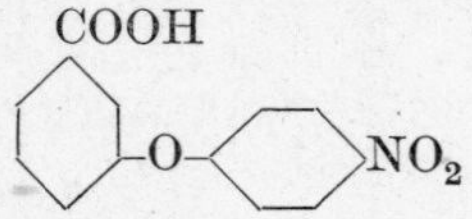

$C_{13}H_9O_5N$ MW, 259

Prisms from dil. AcOH. M.p. 183°.

Scarborough, Sweeten, *J. Chem. Soc.*, 1934, 54.

3-Nitro-*p*-phenoxybenzoic Acid (*2-Nitrodiphenyl ether 4-carboxylic acid*)

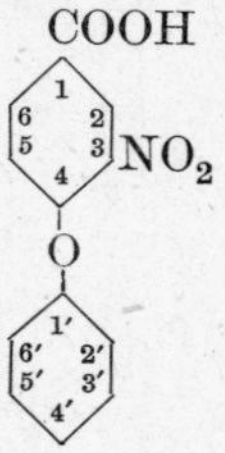

$C_{13}H_9O_5N$ MW, 259

M.p. 174–5°. Sol. EtOH, Et_2O. Mod. sol. C_6H_6. Spar. sol. hot H_2O.

Et ester: $C_{15}H_{13}O_5N$. MW, 287. Yellow cryst. from EtOH. M.p. 93–4°.

Nitrile: $C_{13}H_8O_3N_2$. MW, 240. Yellow prisms from MeOH. M.p. 79°.

Haeussermann, Bauer, *Ber.*, 1897, **30**, 739.
Borsche, *Ber.*, 1923, **56**, 1490.

2′-Nitro-*p*-phenoxybenzoic Acid (*2′-Nitrodiphenyl ether 4-carboxylic acid*).

Needles from H_2O or xylene. M.p. 184° (182–3°). Sol. EtOH, AcOH. Spar. sol. Et_2O. Insol. pet ether.

Me ester: $C_{14}H_{11}O_5N$. MW, 273. Yellow prisms from EtOH. M.p. 88°.

Cook, Hillyer, *Am. Chem. J.*, 1900, **24**, 527.
Mayer, Krieger, *Ber.*, 1922, **55**, 1663, (*Footnote*).

4′-Nitro-*p*-phenoxybenzoic Acid (*4′-Nitrodiphenyl ether 4-carboxylic acid*).

Prisms from boiling EtOH or plates from AcOH.

M.p. 245° (236–7°). Spar. sol. hot EtOH Et_2O, $CHCl_3$. Insol. H_2O.

Me ester: needles from MeOH. M.p. 108–9°

Et ester: needles from MeOH. M.p. 78 (74–5°).

Chloride: $C_{13}H_8O_4NCl$. MW, 277·5. Needle from pet. ether. M.p. 79–80°.

Amide: $C_{13}H_{10}O_4N_2$. MW, 258. M.p 167–8°.

Haeussermann, Bauer, *Ber.*, 1896, **29** 2084.
Suter, Oberg, *J. Am. Chem. Soc.*, 1931 **53**, 1567.
Scarborough, Sweeten, *J. Chem. Soc.* 1934, 55.

Nitrophenoxyethylamine.

See under Nitrophenol.

***o*-Nitrophenoxymalonic Acid**

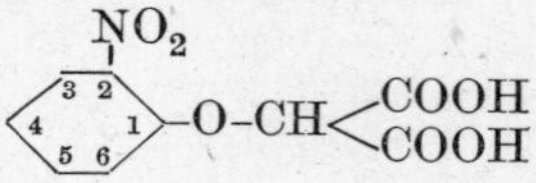

$C_9H_7O_7N$ MW, 241

Di-Me ester: $C_{11}H_{11}O_7N$. MW, 269 Needles from MeOH. M.p. 123°. Sol. most org. solvents. Spar. sol. cold MeOH.

Di-Et ester: $C_{13}H_{15}O_7N$. MW, 297. Needles from C_6H_6. M.p. 116–18°.

Bischoff, *Ber.*, 1907, **40**, 3139.

***m*-Nitrophenoxymalonic Acid.**

Di-Me ester: yellowish leaflets from MeOH M.p. 100°.

Di-Et ester: leaflets. M.p. 78°. Sol. C_6H_6.

See previous reference.

***p*-Nitrophenoxymalonic Acid.**

Needles from Et_2O. Sinters at 160°. Sol Et_2O, Me_2CO, AcOH. Mod. sol. H_2O, EtOH Spar. sol. C_6H_6, ligroin, $CHCl_3$. Decomp. at 168–70° ⟶ *p*-nitrophenoxyacetic acid. Impure acid decomp. slowly on standing.

Di-Me ester: pale yellow prisms or needles M.p. 101°. B.p. 221–2°/15 mm., slight decomp Sol. $CHCl_3$, AcOH, AcOEt. Mod. sol. EtOH C_6H_6. Spar. sol. Et_2O, ligroin.

Di-Et ester: needles from MeOH. M.p. 86° B.p. 241–2°/15 mm., slight decomp. Sol. $CHCl_3$ AcOH. Mod. sol. EtOH, C_6H_6. Spar. sol Et_2O, ligroin.

See previous reference.

1-*o*-Nitrophenoxypropionic Acid (*Lactic acid 2-nitrophenyl ether*)

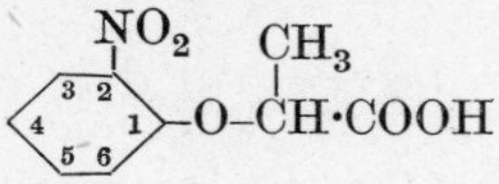

$C_9H_9O_5N$ MW, 211

d-.
Cryst. from EtOH.Aq. M.p. 111–12°. $[\alpha]^{21}_{D}$ + 166·25° in EtOH.

l-.
Cryst. from EtOH.Aq. M.p. 111–12°. $[\alpha]^{21}_{D}$ − 166·00°.

dl-.
Pale yellow needles from EtOH.Aq. M.p. 157–9°. Sol. EtOH, Et_2O, $CHCl_3$. Spar. sol. cold H_2O, C_6H_6, ligroin.
Et ester: $C_{11}H_{13}O_5N$. MW, 225. Needles from EtOH. M.p. 48°. Sol. most org. solvents. Spar. sol. H_2O.
o-*Nitrophenyl ester*: prisms from EtOH. M.p. 137°. Sol. Me_2CO, $CHCl_3$, C_6H_6. Mod. sol. EtOH, ligroin.

Bischoff, *Ber.*, 1900, **33**, 930, 1593; 1906, **39**, 3858.
Fourneau, Sandulesco, *Bull. soc. chim.*, 1922, **31**, 988.

1-*m*-Nitrophenoxypropionic Acid (*Lactic acid 3-nitrophenyl ether*).

d-.
Yellow needles from H_2O. M.p. 101–2°. $[\alpha]^{21}_{D}$ + 51·8°.

l-.
Yellow needles from H_2O. M.p. 101–2°. $[\alpha]^{21}_{D}$ − 51·87°.
Strychnine salt: $[\alpha]^{21}_{D}$ − 25°.

dl-.
Yellow needles. M.p. 109–10°. Sol. H_2O, ligroin. Decomp. slowly in air.
Me ester: b.p. 173–5°/20 mm.
Et ester: oil. B.p. 295–6°/769 mm. slight decomp., 187°/7 mm.
m-*Nitrophenyl ester*: cryst. from MeOH. M.p. 109–10°. Spar. sol. MeOH, EtOH. Insol. H_2O, ligroin.

Bischoff, *Ber.*, 1900, **33**, 1598; 1906, **39**, 3859.
Fourneau, Sandulesco, *Bull. soc. chim.*, 1923, **33**, 459.

1-*p*-Nitrophenoxypropionic Acid (*Lactic acid 4-nitrophenyl ether*).

d-.
Needles from C_6H_6–pet. ether. M.p. 88–90°. $[\alpha]^{21}_{D}$ + 53·7°. Very sol. EtOH, Me_2CO.
Quinidine salt: $[\alpha]^{21}_{D}$ + 172·5°.

l-.
Needles from C_6H_6–pet. ether. M.p. 89–90°. $[\alpha]^{21}_{D}$ − 53·7°.
Yohimbine salt: $[\alpha]^{21}_{D}$ + 20·6°.

dl-.
Needles from EtOH. M.p. 142·5–143°. Sol. EtOH, Et_2O, AcOH. Spar. sol. H_2O, CS_2, $CHCl_3$, ligroin.
Et ester: needles from EtOH. M.p. 59–61·5°. B.p. 195·5°/4 mm.
p-*Nitrophenyl ester*: cryst. from C_6H_6. M.p. 137°. Sol. usual org. solvents.

See second reference above and also Bischoff, *Ber.*, 1900, **33**, 930, 1600; 1906, **39**, 3861.

***o*-Nitrophenylacetaldehyde**

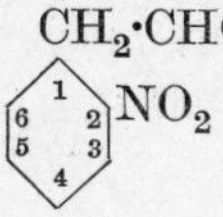

$C_8H_7O_3N$ MW, 165

Yellowish plates. M.p. 22–3°. B.p. 133–5°/5 mm. Sol. EtOH, Et_2O, C_6H_6. Spar. sol. cold H_2O, CCl_4. Insol. ligroin. Fe powder + $NaHSO_3$ ⟶ indole. Alkalis ⟶ red col.
Oxime: needles from H_2O. M.p. 110°. Very sol. EtOH, Et_2O. Sol. C_6H_6.

Weermann, *Ann.*, 1913, **401**, 13.

***m*-Nitrophenylacetaldehyde.**
Needles from H_2O or damp ether. M.p. 78–9°. Sol. EtOH. Mod. sol. Et_2O. Insol. C_6H_6. Alkalis ⟶ yellow col. Volatile in steam.
Oxime: leaflets from C_6H_6. M.p. 105–6°. Sol. Et_2O, C_6H_6. Insol. ligroin.

See previous reference.

***p*-Nitrophenylacetaldehyde.**
Needles. M.p. 85–6°. Very sol. EtOH, Et_2O. Sol. hot H_2O. Alkalis ⟶ deep red col.
Oxime: needles from Et_2O. M.p. 155°. Sol. EtOH, Et_2O. Insol. H_2O, ligroin.

Lipp, *Ber.*, 1886, **19**, 2647.
See also previous reference.

o-Nitrophenylacetic Acid

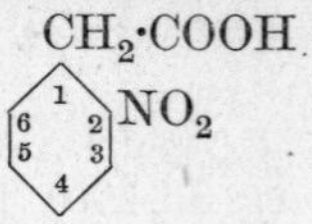

$C_8H_7O_4N$ MW, 181

Needles from EtOH. M.p. 141° (137–8°). $KMnO_4$ ⟶ *o*-nitrobenzoic acid.

Me ester: $C_9H_9O_4N$. MW, 195. Liq. B.p. 264°.

Et ester: $C_{10}H_{11}O_4N$. MW, 209. Cryst. from 95% EtOH. M.p. 69°. Sol. usual org. solvents.

Amide: $C_8H_8O_3N_2$. MW, 180. Plates or needles from EtOH or C_6H_6. M.p. 160–1°.

Nitrile: *see* *o*-Nitrobenzyl cyanide.

Reissert, *Ber.*, 1897, **30**, 1041; 1908, **41** 3814, 3925.
Reissert, Scherk, *Ber.*, 1898, **31**, 395.
Pschorr, Hoppe, *Ber.*, 1910, **43**, 2547.

m-Nitrophenylacetic Acid.

Needles from H_2O. M.p. 120° (117°).

Amide: cryst. from H_2O. M.p. 109–10°. Sol. EtOH, C_6H_6.

Nitrile: *see* *m*-Nitrobenzyl cyanide.

Salkowski, *Ber.*, 1884, **17**, 506.
Heller, *Ann.*, 1908, **358**, 357.
Purgotti, *Gazz. chim. ital.*, 1890, **20**, 596.

p-Nitrophenylacetic Acid.

Yellow needles from H_2O. M.p. 151–2°. Sol. EtOH, Et_2O, C_6H_6. Spar. sol. cold H_2O. $k = 1{\cdot}04 \times 10^{-4}$ at 25°. Sn + HCl ⟶ *p*-aminophenylacetic acid. $K_2Cr_2O_7 + H_2SO_4$ ⟶ *p*-nitrobenzoic acid.

Me ester: needles from ligroin. M.p. 54°. Very sol. EtOH, Et_2O, C_6H_6. Spar. sol. cold H_2O. Alc. KOH ⟶ violet col.

Et ester: leaflets from ligroin. M.p. 69° (65°). B.p. 196–7°/20 mm. Sol. EtOH, Et_2O. Less sol. ligroin.

Benzyl ester: $C_{15}H_{13}O_4N$. MW, 271. Needles from pet. ether. M.p. 92°.

1-*Naphthyl ester*: $C_{18}H_{13}O_4N$. MW, 307. Yellow needles from AcOH, m.p. 152°; yellow plates from EtOH, m.p. 146°.

Chloride: $C_8H_6O_3NCl$. MW, 199·5. Cryst. from CS_2–ligroin, pale yellow plates from pet. ether. M.p. 46–7°. B.p. 135–8°/0·1 mm. Sol. C_6H_6. Spar. sol. ligroin.

Amide: prisms. M.p. 197–8° (191°). Spar. sol. EtOH. Very spar. sol. Et_2O, C_6H_6.

Methylamide: $C_9H_{10}O_3N_2$. MW, 194. Cryst. from Me_2CO or $CHCl_3$. M.p. 159°. Very sol. most org. solvents. Spar. sol. H_2O, pet. ether.

Dimethylamide: $C_{10}H_{12}O_3N_2$. MW, 208 Cryst. from Et_2O. M.p. 90–1°.

Ethylamide: $C_{10}H_{12}O_3N_2$. MW, 208. Cryst M.p. 155°.

Anilide: $C_{14}H_{12}O_3N_2$. MW, 256. Cryst M.p. 198°.

Nitrile: *see* *p*-Nitrobenzyl cyanide.

Hydrazide: yellowish needles from EtOH M.p. 167°. Mod. sol. hot EtOH. Spar. sol hot H_2O, Et_2O. Insol. C_6H_6, $CHCl_3$. *B,HCl* yellowish needles from EtOH. M.p. 251° de comp. Very sol. H_2O.

Azide: cryst. M.p. 45° decomp. Explode on rapid heating.

Taverne, *Rec. trav. chim.*, 1897, **16**, 35 254.
Purgotti, *Gazz. chim. ital.*, 1890, **20**, 595
Borsche, *Ber.*, 1909, **42**, 3596.
Maxwell, *Ber.*, 1879, **12**, 1765.
Pschorr, Wolfes, Buckow, *Ber.*, 1900, **33** 170.
Curtius, *J. prakt. Chem.*, 1914, **89**, 522.
Wedekind, *Ann.*, 1911, **378**, 289.
Robertson, *Organic Syntheses*, Collectiv Vol. I, 389, 398.

o-Nitrophenylacetylene

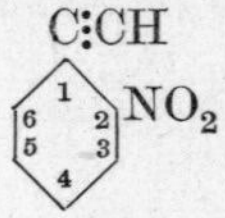

$C_8H_5O_2N$ MW, 147

Needles from EtOH.Aq. M.p. 81–2°. Sol hot H_2O, EtOH. Unpleasant odour. Volatil in steam. $NH_3.AgNO_3$ ⟶ yellowish-whit ppt. $NH_3.CuCl_2$ ⟶ red ppt.

Baeyer, *Ber.*, 1880, **13**, 2259.
Kippenberg, *Ber.*, 1897, **30**, 1130.

m-Nitrophenylacetylene.

Yellow cryst. M.p. 27°. B.p. 120°/11 mm Very sol. EtOH, Et_2O, C_6H_6. Insol. AcOH Volatile in steam. Explodes on dist. under ord press. $NH_3.AgNO_3$ ⟶ greenish-yellow ppt $NH_3.CuCl_2$ ⟶ reddish-brown ppt.

Reich, Koehler, *Ber.*, 1913, **46**, 3737.
Wollring, *Ber.*, 1914, **47**, 111.

p-Nitrophenylacetylene.

Needles from hot H_2O. M.p. 152° (149°) Sol. EtOH, Et_2O, $CHCl_3$, AcOH, CS_2, C_6H_6 Mod. sol. hot H_2O. Spar. sol. ligroin. Turns brown in air. $NH.AgNO_3$ ⟶ yellow ppt $NH_3.CuCl_2$ ⟶ deep red ppt.

Drewsen, *Ann.*, 1882, **212**, 158.
Müller, *ibid.*, 136.
Wieland, *Ann.*, 1903, **328** 233.

ω-o-Nitrophenylbiuret (*Allophanic* o-*nitro-*
ilide)

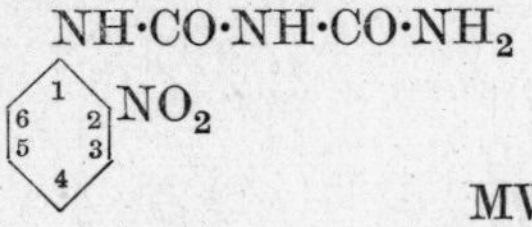

$_8H_8O_4N_4$ MW, 224

Yellow needles from H_2O. M.p. 181°.

Pickard, Allen, Bowdler, Carter, *J. Chem. Soc.*, 1902, **81**, 1568.

ω-m-Nitrophenylbiuret (*Allophanic* m-
itroanilide).

Yellow cryst. from EtOH.Aq. M.p. 178°.
par. sol. NaOH.

See previous reference.

ω-p-Nitrophenylbiuret (*Allophanic* p-*nitro-*
ilide).

Golden-yellow needles from H_2O. M.p. 206°.
l. EtOH.

See previous reference.

Nitrophenylbutane.
See Nitrobutylbenzene.

1-p-Nitrophenylbutyric Acid

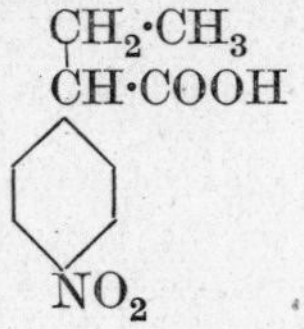

$_{10}H_{11}O_4N$ MW, 209

d-.

Cryst. from H_2O. M.p. 120–2°. $[\alpha]_D^{25} + 17.7°$
AcOEt.

Quinine salt: cryst. from MeOH. M.p.
83–5°. $[\alpha]_D^{25} - 42.2°$ in Py.

l-.

Cryst. from MeOH. M.p. 120–2°. $[\alpha]_D^{25}$
- 17·8° in AcOEt.

Quinine salt: cryst. from MeOH. M.p.
80–2°. $[\alpha]_D^{25} - 53.8°$ in Py.

dl-.

Cryst. from AcOH.Aq. M.p. 118–20°.

Chu, Marvel, *J. Am. Chem. Soc.*, 1933, **55**, 2841.

2-p-Nitrophenylbutyric Acid.
See p-Nitro-β-methylhydrocinnamic Acid.

3-p-Nitrophenylbutyric Acid

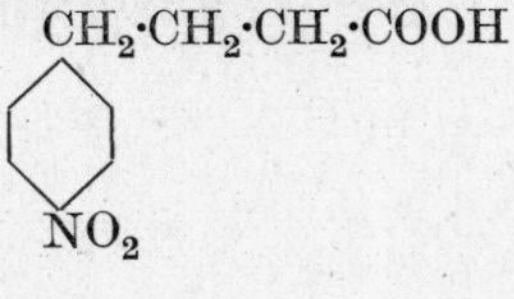

$_{10}H_{11}O_4N$ MW, 209

Prisms from C_6H_6. M.p. 92–3°. Sol. EtOH, Et_2O, Me_2CO, $CHCl_3$, C_6H_6. Insol. H_2O, pet. ether.

Scheer, *J. Am. Chem. Soc.*, 1934, **56**, 744.

o-Nitrophenylcarbamic Acid (o-*Nitrocarbanilic acid*)

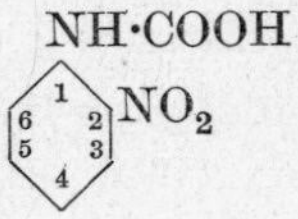

$C_7H_6O_4N_2$ MW, 182

Me ester: $C_8H_8O_4N_2$. MW, 196. Greenish-yellow cryst. from pet. ether. M.p. 53°.
Et ester: *see* o-Nitrophenylurethane.
Isopropyl ester: $C_{10}H_{12}O_4N_2$. MW, 224. Cryst. from pet. ether. M.p. 12°.
Isobutyl ester: $C_{11}H_{14}O_4N_2$. MW, 238. Yellow cryst. M.p. 13°. Sol. EtOH, Et_2O.
Amyl ester: $C_{12}H_{16}O_4N_2$. MW, 252. Cryst. from pet. ether. M.p. — 5°.
Chloride: $C_7H_5O_3N_2Cl$. MW, 200·5. Needles from pet. ether. M.p. 47°. Sol. $CHCl_3$, C_6H_6, pet. ether.
Amide: *see* o-Nitrophenylurea.
Anilide: *see* 2-Nitrocarbanilide.
Nitrile: *see* o-Nitrophenylcyanamide.

Folin, *Am. Chem. J.*, 1897, **19**, 326.
Swartz, *ibid.*, 303.

m-Nitrophenylcarbamic Acid (m-*Nitrocarbanilic acid*).
Me ester: yellow cryst. M.p. 147–9°.
Et ester: *see* m-Nitrophenylurethane.
Chloride: cryst. M.p. 102° decomp.
Amide: *see* m-Nitrophenylurea.
Anilide: *see* 3-Nitrocarbanilide.
Nitrile: *see* o-Nitrophenylcyanamide.

Folin, *Am. Chem. J.*, 1897, **19**, 325.

p-Nitrophenylcarbamic Acid (p-*Nitrocarbanilic acid*).
Me ester: m.p. 179·5°. Spar. sol. Et_2O, C_6H_6. Insol. ligroin. N-*Me*: needles. M.p. 110–11°.
Et ester: *see* p-Nitrophenylurethane.
Propyl ester: m.p. 115°.
Isopropyl ester: m.p. 116° (78°).
Butyl ester: m.p. 95·5°.
Isobutyl ester: m.p. 80° (62°).
Chloride: cryst. Decomp. on heating.
Amide: *see* p-Nitrophenylurea.
Anilide: *see* 4-Nitrocarbanilide.
Nitrile: *see* p-Nitrophenylcyanamide.

Romburgh, *Rec. trav. chim.*, 1929, **48**, 922.
Shriner, Cox, *J. Am. Chem. Soc.*, 1931, **53**, 1604.

α-*o*-Nitrophenylcinnamic Acid (2-*Nitrostilbene-α-carboxylic acid*)

$$C_6H_5 \cdot CH\!:\!C \cdot COOH$$

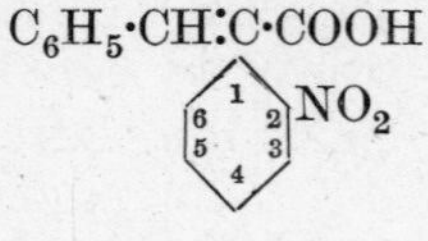

$C_{15}H_{11}O_4N$ MW, 269

Pale yellow needles from EtOH. M.p. 193°.

Borsche, *Ber.*, 1909, **42**, 3601.

α-*p*-Nitrophenylcinnamic Acid (4-*Nitrostilbene-α-carboxylic acid*).

Needles from AcOH. M.p. 224·5°. Sol. Et_2O, hot EtOH, AcOH, C_6H_6.

Me ester : $C_{16}H_{13}O_4N$. MW, 283. Needles from EtOH. M.p. 104°.

Et ester : $C_{17}H_{15}O_4N$. MW, 297. Needles from EtOH. M.p. 86°.

Nitrile : $C_{15}H_{10}O_2N_2$. MW, 250. Yellow needles from EtOH. M.p. 175–6°. Sol. $CHCl_3$, AcOH, C_6H_6. Spar. sol. EtOH, Et_2O. Insol. H_2O.

Borsche, *Ber.*, 1909, **42**, 3597.
v. Walther, Wetzlich, *J. prakt. Chem.*, 1900, **61**, 181.
Remse, *Ber.*, 1890, **23**, 3134.

2-Nitro-α-phenylcinnamic Acid

$$\begin{array}{c} C_6H_5 \\ CH\!:\!C \cdot COOH \end{array}$$

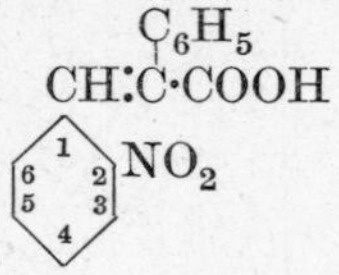

$C_{15}H_{11}O_4N$ MW, 269

Cis :
Short yellow prisms from EtOH or C_6H_6. M.p. 146–7°. Stable to most reagents.

Me ester : $C_{16}H_{13}O_4N$. MW, 283. Yellow needles from EtOH. M.p. 95–6°.

Amide : $C_{15}H_{12}O_3N_2$. MW, 268. Yellow cryst. from $CHCl_3$–pet. ether. M.p. 166–7°.

Anilide : yellow cryst. powder from EtOH. M.p. 148–9°.

p-*Toluidide* : m.p. 181–2°.

Trans :
Yellow cryst. from EtOH. M.p. 195–6°. Mod. sol. Et_2O, C_6H_6, $CHCl_3$. Spar. sol. H_2O, EtOH. Sol. 14 parts hot toluene. $FeSO_4 + NH_3.Aq. \longrightarrow$ 2-amino-α-phenylcinnamic acid.

Me ester : yellow prisms from EtOH. M.p. 75–6°.

Et ester : $C_{17}H_{15}O_4N$. MW, 297. Prisms from pet. ether. M.p. 59°. Mod. sol. cold EtOH.

o-Tolyl ester : $C_{22}H_{17}O_4N$. MW, 359. Yellow prisms from EtOH. M.p. 97–8°. Mod. so EtOH.

Chloride : $C_{15}H_{10}O_3NCl$. MW, 287·5. M. 100°.

Amide : pale yellow needles from toluen M.p. 173–4°.

Nitrile : $C_{15}H_{10}O_2N_2$. MW, 250. Yello needles. M.p. 127–8°.

Anhydride : yellow prisms from EtOH. M. 126°. Spar. sol. hot EtOH.

Anilide : yellow needles from EtOH. M. 136°.

Pschorr, *Ber.*, 1896, **29**, 497.
Bakunin, Parlati, *Gazz. chim. ital.*, 190 **36**, ii, 274.
Bakunin, *Gazz. chim. ital.*, 1895, **25**, 139, 182 ; 1897, **27**, ii, 36, 48.
Stoermer, Prigge, *Ann.*, 1915, **409**, 20.

3-Nitro-α-phenylcinnamic Acid.

Cis :
Needles from EtOH. M.p. 195–6°. Direc sunlight $\longrightarrow$ *trans*-form.

Me ester : leaflets from EtOH. M.p. 115 16°. Sol. hot EtOH.

o-Tolyl ester : needles from EtOH. M. 83–4°.

Anhydride : needles from EtOH. M.p. 129°

Anilide : m.p. 161–2°.

p-*Toluidide* : m.p. 143–4°.

Trans :
Yellow prisms from Et_2O. M.p. 181–2 Sol. boiling EtOH. Mod. sol. Et_2O, CHCl CS_2, C_6H_6, pet. ether. In sunlight partiall converted to *cis*-form.

Me ester : yellowish prisms from EtOH (Et_2O. M.p. 78–9°. Sol. pet. ether.

o-Tolyl ester : cryst. from EtOH. M.p. 118 20°.

Nitrile : yellow cryst. M.p. 133–4°.

Anhydride : yellow needles from Me_2CC M.p. 151°. Mod. sol. Me_2CO, C_6H_6. Spa sol. pet. ether.

Bakunin, *Gazz. chim. ital.*, 1895, **25**, 145, 175 ; 1897, **27**, ii, 36 ; 1902, **3** i, 180.
See also Bakunin, *Gazz. chim. ital.*, 190 **30**, ii, 353 ; 1901, **31**, ii, 83.

4-Nitro-α-phenylcinnamic Acid.

Cis :
Yellowish-green prisms + H_2O from EtOH.Aq yellow leaflets + $\frac{1}{4}C_6H_6$ from C_6H_6. M.p. 144 Very sol. EtOH. Mod. sol. other solvent Sunlight $\longrightarrow$ *trans*-form.

Me ester: needles from EtOH. M.p. 147–148·5°.

o-*Tolyl ester*: needles from EtOH. M.p. 120°.

Anhydride: yellow cryst. from Me_2CO. M.p. 182°.

Anilide: yellow needles. M.p. 167–8°.

p-*Toluidide*: m.p. 181–2°.

Trans:

Yellow prisms or needles from EtOH. M.p. 213–14°. Mod. sol. hot EtOH. Spar. sol. H_2O, Et_2O, $CHCl_3$, C_6H_6. NaHg ⟶ 4-amino-α-phenylhydrocinnamic acid.

Me ester: yellow prisms from EtOH. M.p. 141–2°. Sol. $CHCl_3$, C_6H_6. Less sol. Et_2O. Insol. H_2O, pet. ether.

Phenyl ester: $C_{21}H_{15}O_4N$. MW, 345. Yellow cryst. from EtOH. M.p. 175–6°. Sol. $CHCl_3$, C_6H_6.

o-*Tolyl ester*: yellow needles from EtOH. M.p. 128–9°.

1-*Naphthyl ester*: $C_{25}H_{17}O_4N$. MW, 395. Needles from EtOH. M.p. 126–7°.

Nitrile: orange-red powder. M.p. 117–18°.

Anhydride: yellow cryst. from Me_2CO. M.p. 162°. Mod. sol. C_6H_6. Spar. sol. EtOH, Et_2O.

See previous references.

o-Nitrophenylcyanamide (2-*Nitro*-N-*cyanoaniline*, o-*nitrophenylcarbamic nitrile*)

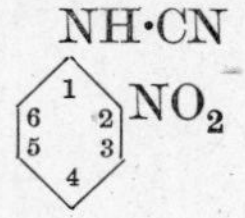

$C_7H_5O_2N_3$ MW, 163

Pale yellow needles. M.p. 152° (146°). Sol. EtOH. Mod. sol. Et_2O, C_6H_6. Spar. sol. H_2O. Sol. alkalis with reddish-brown col.

N-*Benzoyl*: needles from 50% EtOH. M.p. 105°. Sol. EtOH. Spar. sol. Et_2O, C_6H_6. Insol. H_2O.

Pierron, *Bull. soc. chim.*, 1905, **33**, 70.
Arndt, *Ber.*, 1913, **46**, 3528.
Arndt, Rosenau, *Ber.*, 1917, **50**, 1256.

m-Nitrophenylcyanamide (3-*Nitro*-N-*cyanoaniline*, m-*nitrophenylcarbamic nitrile*).

Pale yellow needles. M.p. 133–4° (130°). Sol. EtOH. Less sol. Et_2O, C_6H_6. Sol. alkalis with orange-yellow col.

N-*Benzoyl*: plates. M.p. 109°.

Pierron, *Bull. soc. chim.*, 1905, **33**, 72.
Johnson, Cramer, *J. Am. Chem. Soc.*, 1903, **25**, 491.

p-Nitrophenylcyanamide (4-*Nitro*-N-*cyanoaniline*, p-*nitrophenylcarbamic nitrile*).

Pale yellow needles. M.p. 180°. Sol. EtOH. Less sol. Et_2O. Spar. sol. C_6H_6.

N-*Benzoyl*: plates from EtOH. M.p. 131°.

Pierron, *Bull. soc. chim.*, 1905, **33**, 73.

o-Nitrophenylcyclohexane

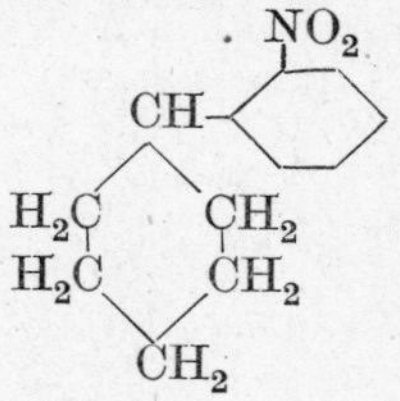

$C_{12}H_{15}O_2N$ MW, 205

M.p. 45°. B.p. 174°/16 mm., 113°/0·5 mm. D_4^{23} 1·111. n_D^{25} 1·5472.

Mayes, Turner, *J. Chem. Soc.*, 1929, 503.
Neunhoeffer, *J. prakt. Chem.*, 1932, **133**, 95.

p-Nitrophenylcyclohexane.

Yellow plates from EtOH. M.p. 58·5°. B.p. 210°/25 mm., 198°/16 mm. Sol. Et_2O, C_6H_6. Spar. sol. EtOH.

See first reference above and also
Kurssanow, *Ann.*, 1901, **318**, 321.

1-Nitro-1-phenylcyclohexane

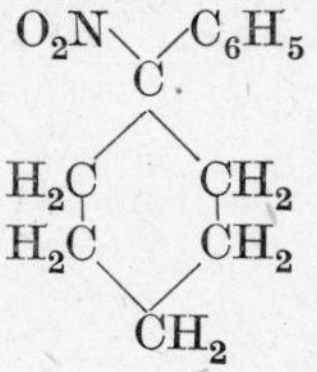

$C_{12}H_{15}O_2N$ MW, 205

Needles. M.p. 54·5–56°. Sol. EtOH, C_6H_6.

Kurssanow, *Chem. Zentr.*, 1907, I, 1744.

3-Nitro-o-phenylenediamine

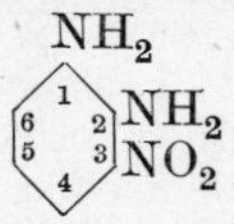

$C_6H_7O_2N_3$ MW, 153

Dark red needles from EtOH.Aq. M.p. 158–9°. Spar. sol. H_2O. HNO_2 ⟶ 4-nitrobenztriazole. Acetic anhydride ⟶ 4-nitro-2-methylbenziminazole.

2-N-*Di-Me*: 6-nitro-2-amino-*N*-dimethylaniline. $C_8H_{11}O_2N_3$. MW, 181. Dark red mass.

1-N-*Benzoyl*: yellow needles from EtOH. M.p. 114°.

2-N-*Phenyl*: *see* 6-Nitro-2-aminodiphenylamine.

Benzoyl: dark yellow needles from EtOH. M.p. 206°.

Borsche, Rantscheff, *Ann.*, 1911, **379**, 163.

4-Nitro-*o*-phenylenediamine.

Dark red needles. M.p. 198° (195°). HNO_2 ⟶ 5-nitrobenztriazole.

1-N-*Me*: 4-nitro-2-amino-*N*-methylaniline. $C_7H_9O_2N_3$. MW, 167. Reddish-brown needles with blue reflex. M.p. 177–8°.

1 : 2-N-*Di-Me*: $C_8H_{11}O_2N_3$. MW, 181. Red prisms. M.p. 172°. Sol. EtOH. Spar. sol. H_2O.

1-N-*Di-Me*: 4-nitro-2-amino-*N*-dimethylaniline. Orange-yellow needles from H_2O. M.p. 63°. Very sol. $CHCl_3$, C_6H_6. Sol. EtOH, Et_2O, CS_2.

1-N-*Phenyl*: *see* 4-Nitro-2-aminodiphenylamine.

1-N-α-*Naphthyl*: $C_{16}H_{13}O_2N_3$. MW, 279. Dark yellow needles from AcOH. Very sol. EtOH, $CHCl_3$, AcOH, Me_2CO. Mod. sol. Et_2O.

1-N-β-*Naphthyl*: brown needles with green reflex from EtOH.Aq., red prisms from EtOH. M.p. 195°. Very sol. Et_2O, $CHCl_3$, Me_2CO, AcOH. Mod. sol. EtOH, C_6H_6. Insol. ligroin. Brown form ⟶ red at 150°. 2-N-*Acetyl*: orange-red needles from boiling EtOH. M.p. 200°. Sol. EtOH, $CHCl_3$, Me_2CO, AcOH. Spar. sol. C_6H_6. Insol. ligroin. 2-N-*Benzoyl*: orange-yellow needles. M.p. 217–18°. Spar. sol. EtOH, $CHCl_3$, C_6H_6, ligroin.

1-N-o-*Tolyl*: $C_{13}H_{13}O_2N_3$. MW, 243. Dark red plates or needles from EtOH.Aq. M.p. 121°. Weak base. 2-N-*Benzoyl*: golden-yellow needles from EtOH. M.p. 164–5°.

1-N-p-*Tolyl*: m.p. 155–6°. 2-N-*Benzoyl*: yellow needles from EtOH. M.p. 210–11°. Sol. warm EtOH. Spar. sol. C_6H_6.

1-N-*Acetyl*: 4-nitro-2-aminoacetanilide. Cryst. from EtOH. M.p. 205°.

2-N-*Acetyl*: 5-nitro-2-aminoacetanilide. Cryst. from EtOH. M.p. 195°.

1 : 2-N-*Diacetyl*: prisms from AcOH.Aq. M.p. 255° (227°). Insol. cold EtOH.

8 : 2-N-*Dibenzoyl*: needles from EtOH. M.p. 235–6°. Sol. EtOH, $CHCl_3$. Spar. sol. Et_2O, ligroin.

Heim, *Ber.*, 1888, **21**, 2305.
Brand, *J. prakt. Chem.*, 1906, **74**, 470.
Kehrmann, Messinger, *J. prakt. Chem.*, 1892, **46**, 573.
Fischer, Hess, *Ber.*, 1903, **36**, 3969.
Muttelet, *Ann. chim. phys.*, 1898, **14**, 401.
Phillips, *J. Chem. Soc.*, 1928, 174.

4-Nitro-*m*-phenylenediamine

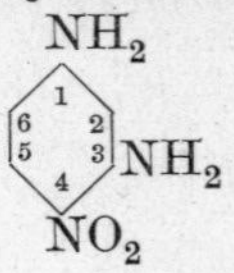

$C_6H_7O_2N_3$ MW, 153

Yellowish-red prisms with blue lustre from H_2O. M.p. 161° (157°). Sol. EtOH, Et_2O. Mod. sol. H_2O. Decomp. by hot KOH.

1-N-*Di-Me*: 4-nitro-3-amino-*N*-dimethylaniline. $C_8H_{11}O_2N_3$. MW, 181. Cryst. M.p. 135°. 3-N-*Et*: $C_{10}H_{15}O_2N_3$. MW, 209. Orange cryst. M.p. 98°. 3-N-*Di-Et*: orange cryst. M.p. 63–4°.

1 : 1 : 3-N-*Tri-Me*: $C_9H_{13}O_2N_3$. MW, 195. Orange needles from MeOH. M.p. 117°.

N-*Tetra-Me*: $C_{10}H_{15}O_2N_3$. MW, 209. Red plates. M.p. 81°.

1-N-*Di-Et*: 4-nitro-3-amino-*N*-diethylaniline. $C_{10}H_{15}O_2N_3$. MW, 209. Yellow cryst. M.p. 139°. 3-N-*Me*: $C_{11}H_{17}O_2N_3$. MW, 223. Yellow cryst. M.p. 96–7°. 3-N-*Et*: $C_{12}H_{19}O_2N_3$. MW, 237. Yellow needles. M.p. 78·5°.

1-N-*Acetyl*: 4-nitro-3-aminoacetanilide. Red prisms from AcOH. M.p. 200°.

1 : 3-N-*Diacetyl*: needles from EtOH or AcOH.Aq. M.p. 246°. Sol. Et_2O, AcOH. Sol. 100 parts EtOH. Insol. H_2O.

1 : 3-N-*Dibenzoyl*: yellow needles from AcOH. M.p. 222°. Spar. sol. EtOH.

1 : 3-N-*Di-p-toluenesulphonyl*: brownish-yellow cryst. M.p. 169°. Sol. alkalis. Spar. sol. H_2O.

Gallinek, *Ber.*, 1897, **30**, 1912.
A.G.F.A., D.R.P., 130,438, (*Chem. Zentr.*, 1902, I, 1083).
Morgan, Wootton, *J. Chem. Soc.*, 1905, **87**, 941.
Romburgh, *Rec. trav. chim.*, 1923, **42**, 804.
Forster, Coulson, *J. Chem. Soc.*, 1922, **121**, 1996.

5-Nitro-*m*-phenylenediamine.

Purplish-red cryst. from H_2O. M.p. 140–1°.

1 : 3-N-*Diacetyl*: yellowish needles. M.p. above 270° decomp. Sol. $PhNO_2$. Insol. other solvents.

Flürscheim, *J. prakt. Chem.*, 1905, **71**, 538.

2-Nitro-*p*-phenylenediamine

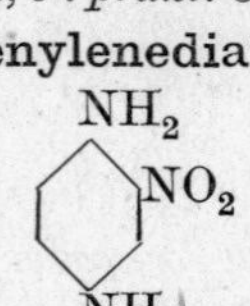

$C_6H_7O_2N_3$ MW, 153

Black needles with strong green reflex from H_2O. M.p. 137° (134–5°).

1-N-*Me* : 2-nitro-4-amino-*N*-methylaniline. $C_7H_9O_2N_3$. MW, 167. Black prisms from H_2O. M.p. 109–10°. Sol. dil. acids with yellowish-red col.

1-N-*Di-Me* : 2-nitro-4-amino-*N*-dimethylaniline. $C_8H_{11}O_2N_3$. MW, 181. 4-N-*Acetyl* : 3-nitro-*p*-dimethylaminoacetanilide. Maroon cryst. M.p. 132°. *Hydrochloride of acetyl* : m.p. 180° decomp. *Picrate of* N-*acetyl* : orange plates. M.p. 172°.

4-N-*Di-Me* : 3-nitro-4-amino-*N*-dimethylaniline. Red needles. M.p. 112°. *Picrate* : greenish-yellow prisms. M.p. 205°. 1-N-*Acetyl* : 2-nitro-*p*-dimethylaminoacetanilide. Red needles. M.p. 116°. *Picrate of* N-*acetyl* : lemon-yellow plates. M.p. 185°.

1-N-*Phenyl* : *see* 2-Nitro-4-aminodiphenylamine.

N-*Tetraphenyl* : $C_{30}H_{23}O_2N_3$. MW, 457. Red needles from AcOH. M.p. 167–8°.

1-N-*Acetyl* : 2-nitro-4-aminoacetanilide. Red needles from H_2O. M.p. 162·5°.

4-N-*Acetyl* : 3-nitro-4-aminoacetanilide. Red needles or leaflets from H_2O. M.p. 189°.

1 : 4-N-*Diacetyl* : yellow needles from H_2O. M.p. 186°.

4-N-*Benzoyl* : yellowish-red needles. M.p. 236°.

1 : 4-N-*Di*-p-*nitrobenzoyl* : yellow leaflets from Py–EtOH. Does not melt below 305°.

Kym, *Ber.*, 1911, **44**, 2923.
Chazel, *Ber.*, 1907, **40**, 3183.
Brand, *J. prakt. Chem.*, 1906, **74**, 470.
Hodgson, Crook, *J. Chem. Soc.*, 1932, 2976.
Phillips, *J. Chem. Soc.*, 1928, 172.
Haeussermann, Bauer, *Ber.*, 1899, **32**, 1913.

o-Nitrophenylethyl Alcohol (o-*Nitro*-β-*hydroxyethylbenzene*)

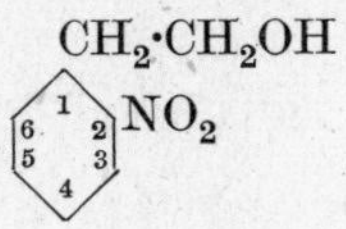

$C_8H_9O_3N$ MW, 167

Colourless oil. B.p. 144–7°/1·3 mm. D^{22} 1·253. n_D^{22} 1·5620. Non-volatile in steam.

Benzoyl : plates from pet. ether. M.p. 55°.

Sabetay, Bléger, Lestrange, *Bull. soc. chim.*, 1931, **49**, 3.

p-Nitrophenylethyl Alcohol (p-*Nitro*-β-*hydroxyethylbenzene*).

Yellowish needles. M.p. 64°. B.p. 177°/16 mm.

Acetyl : b.p. 189°/16 mm.

m-*Nitrobenzoyl* : m.p. 64–5°.

Phenylurethane : m.p. 127–8°.

Pishchimuka, *Chem. Abstracts*, 1917, **11**, 451.
v. Braun, Bartsch, *Ber.*, 1913, **46**, 3053.
Ehrlich, Pistschimuka, *Ber.*, 1912, **45**, 2432.

o-Nitrophenylethylene oxide.

See Nitraldin.

p-Nitrophenylethylene oxide

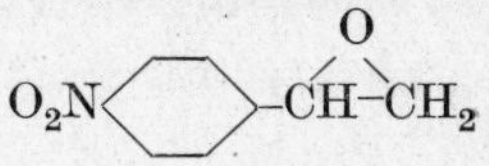

$C_8H_7O_3N$ MW, 165

Prisms from MeOH. M.p. 84–5°.

Arndt, Eistert, Ender, *Ber.*, 1929, **62**, 51.

2-o-Nitrophenylglutaric Acid

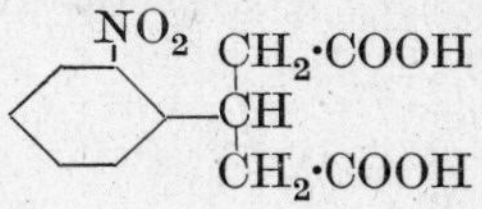

$C_{11}H_{11}O_6N$ MW, 253

Prisms from H_2O. M.p. 205°. Sol. H_2O, EtOH, AcOH, AcOEt. Insol. Et_2O, $CHCl_3$, C_6H_6, pet. ether.

Di-Me ester : $C_{13}H_{15}O_6N$. MW, 281. Prisms from Et_2O. M.p. 65·5°. Very sol. AcOH, AcOEt, C_6H_6.

Anhydride : $C_{22}H_{20}O_{11}N_2$. MW, 488. Needles from C_6H_6. M.p. 130–1°.

Schroeter, Meerwein, *Ber.*, 1903, **36**, 2672; 1907, **40**, 1586.

2-m-Nitrophenylglutaric Acid.

Needles from EtOH.Aq. M.p. 205–6°. Sol. EtOH, Et_2O. Mod. sol. AcOH. Spar. sol. $CHCl_3$, C_6H_6, ligroin, pet. ether.

Anhydride : cryst. M.p. 170·5°. Insol. H_2O, C_6H_6, pet. ether.

Avery, Gere, *Am. Chem. J.*, 1902, **28**, 51.
Knoevenagel, Schürenberg, *Ann.*, 1898, **303**, 235.
See also previous references.

2-p-Nitrophenylglutaric Acid.

Needles from H_2O. M.p. 240° (235°). Sol. EtOH, AcOH. Spar. sol. H_2O. Insol. Et_2O, $CHCl_3$, C_6H_6, ligroin.

Di-Me ester : plates from EtOH. M.p. 65° (62°). Very sol. EtOH. Insol. H_2O.

Anhydride: pale yellow cryst. from AcOEt. M.p. 122·5°. Spar. sol. hot C_6H_6.

Avery, Beans, *Am. Chem. J.*, 1902, **28**, 58.
See also previous references.

2-*p*-Nitrophenylglyceric Acid

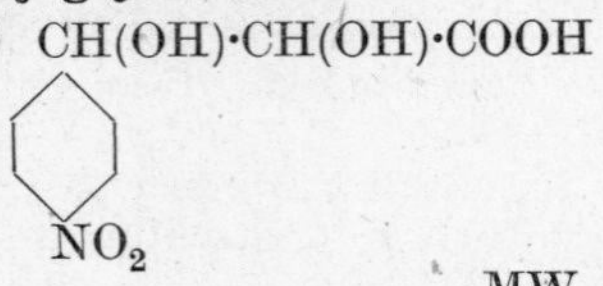

$C_9H_9O_6N$ MW, 227

Yellow leaflets from H_2O. M.p. 167–8°. Sol. EtOH, hot H_2O. Spar. sol. Et_2O.

Lipp, *Ber.*, 1886, **19**, 2645.

2-*o*-Nitrophenylglycidic Acid

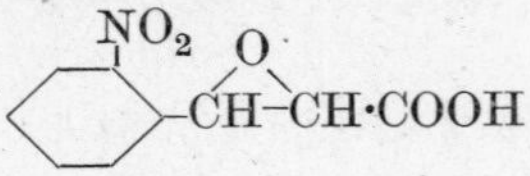

$C_9H_7O_5N$ MW, 209

Plates from C_6H_6, m.p. 124·5–125°: needles $+ 1H_2O$ from H_2O, m.p. 94°. Sol. EtOH, Et_2O, hot H_2O, hot C_6H_6. Insol. ligroin. Heat ⟶ indigo. Conc. H_2SO_4 ⟶ red col.

Me ester: $C_{10}H_9O_5N$. MW, 223. Needles from ligroin. M.p. 65°.

Einhorn, Gernsheim, *Ann.*, 1895, **284**, 135.
Lipp, *Ber.*, 1886, **19**, 2649.

2-*p*-Nitrophenylglycidic Acid.

Cis:
Cryst. from C_6H_6–pet. ether. M.p. 124–5°.

Trans:
Cryst. from EtOH. M.p. 186–8° decomp. Spar. sol. boiling H_2O, cold EtOH.

Kleucker, *Ber.*, 1922, **55**, 1646.
Lipp, *Ber.*, 1886, **19**, 2644.
Erlenmeyer, *Ber.*, 1881, **14**, 1868.

***o*-Nitrophenylglycine**

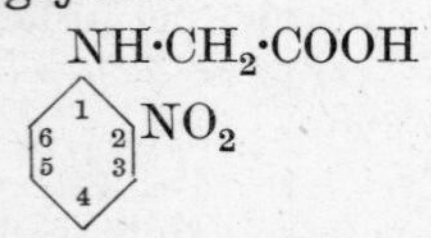

$C_8H_8O_4N_2$ MW, 196

Dark red prisms from EtOH. M.p. 192–3° decomp. Sol. hot EtOH. Spar. sol. H_2O, Et_2O.

Plöchl, *Ber.*, 1886, **19**, 7.
Borsche, Titsingh, *Ber.*, 1907, **40**, 5016.

***m*-Nitrophenylglycine.**

Yellow prisms from H_2O. M.p. 158–9°. Sol. EtOH, pet. ether.

Et ester: $C_{10}H_{12}O_4N_2$. MW, 224. Cryst. from EtOH. M.p. 84°.

m-*Nitroanilide*: cryst. M.p. 201–2°.

Borsche, Titsingh, *Ber.*, 1907, **40**, 5015.
Deutsch, *J. prakt. Chem.*, 1907, **76**, 352.

***p*-Nitrophenylglycine.**

Yellow cryst. from H_2O. M.p. 225° decomp.

N-*Formyl*: brownish-yellow plates from AcOH. M.p. 159–60° decomp. Very sol. hot AcOH. Sol. boiling EtOH. Insol. H_2O, C_6H_6.

N-*Acetyl*: brownish leaflets from AcOH. M.p. 191–2°. Very sol. hot AcOH. Sol. hot EtOH. Insol. cold H_2O.

p-*Nitroanilide*: m.p. 260°.

M.L.B., D.R.P., 88,433.
Badische, D.R.P., 152,012, (*Chem. Zentr.*, 1904, II, 70).
Borsche, Titsingh, *Ber.*, 1907, **40**, 5016.

Nitrophenylhydracrylic Acid.

See Nitro-β-hydroxyhydrocinnamic Acid.

***o*-Nitrophenylhydrazine**

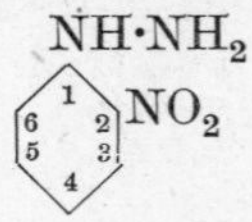

$C_6H_7O_2N_3$ MW, 153

Deep red needles from C_6H_6. M.p. 90°. Sol. hot H_2O. Spar. sol. EtOH, Et_2O, C_6H_6, ligroin.

Formyl deriv.: needles from EtOH. M.p. 177°.

Acetyl deriv.: yellow needles from EtOH. M.p. 140–1°.

Diacetyl deriv.: prisms from EtOH. M.p. 57–8°.

Benzoyl deriv.: yellow needles from EtOH. M.p. 166°.

Bischler, *Ber.*, 1889, **22**, 2801.

***m*-Nitrophenylhydrazine.**

Yellow needles from EtOH. M.p. 93°. Sol. AcOH, $CHCl_3$. Spar. sol. EtOH, C_6H_6, boiling H_2O.

Acetyl deriv.: yellow leaflets from H_2O. M.p. 145°.

Diacetyl deriv.: plates from AcOH. M.p. 150°.

Benzoyl deriv.: prismatic needles from EtOH.Aq. M.p. 151°.

Dibenzoyl deriv.: yellow leaflets from AcOH.Aq. M.p. 153°.

Bischler, Brodsky, *Ber.*, 1889, **22**, 2809.
Hantzsch, Borghaus, *Ber.*, 1897, **30**, 91.

_p_-Nitrophenylhydrazine.

Orange-red leaflets and needles from boiling EtOH. M.p. 157° decomp. Sol. warm EtOH. Mod. sol. Et_2O, $CHCl_3$, hot C_6H_6. Spar. sol. H_2O.

Picrate: red needles from H_2O. M.p. 119–20°. Sol. hot H_2O, EtOH, Me_2CO. Insol. C_6H_6, ligroin.

Bamberger, Kraus, *Ber.*, 1896, **29**, 1834.

_N-m_-Nitrophenylhydroxylamine

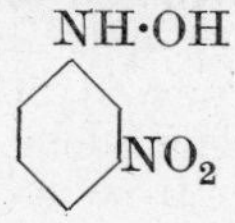

$C_6H_6O_3N_2$ MW, 154

Yellow cryst. from hot C_6H_6. M.p. 118–19°. Sol. EtOH, Et_2O, Me_2CO, hot C_6H_6. Spar. sol. cold H_2O. Reduces $NH_3.AgNO_3$ and Fehling's. Alc.$FeCl_3$ ⟶ 3-nitrosonitrobenzene. Warm 60% H_2SO_4 ⟶ 2-nitro-*p*-aminophenol.

Brand, *J. prakt. Chem.*, 1906, **74**, 464; *Ber.*, 1905, **38**, 4010.

3-Nitro-2-phenylindole

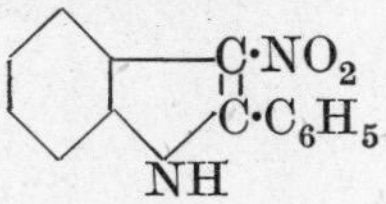

$C_{14}H_{10}O_2N_2$ MW, 238

Yellow cryst. from AcOH or EtOH. M.p. 238–9°. Alk.$KMnO_4$ ⟶ *N*-benzoylanthranilic acid.

Angeli, Angelico, *Gazz. chim. ital.*, 1900, **30**, ii, 275.

3-_o_-Nitrophenylindole

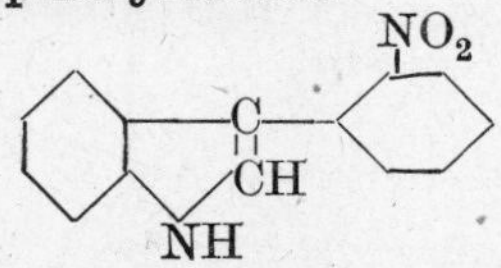

$C_{14}H_{10}O_2N_2$ MW, 238

Orange prismatic needles from C_6H_6–pet. ether. M.p. 119°. Sol. EtOH, C_6H_6. Mod. sol. pet. ether. Ehrlich's reagent ⟶ pink col.

Kermack, Slater, *J. Chem. Soc.*, 1928, 38.

4-Nitro-3-phenylisocarbostyril (*4-Nitro-1-hydroxy-3-phenylisoquinoline*)

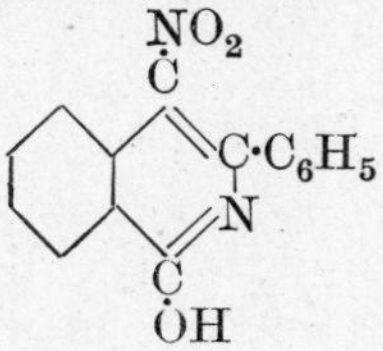

$C_{15}H_{10}O_3N_2$ MW, 266

Yellow cryst. from EtOH. M.p. about 245° decomp. Sol. boiling AcOH. Spar. sol. EtOH, Et_2O, cold C_6H_6. Very spar. sol. CS_2, ligroin.

Me ether: $C_{16}H_{12}O_3N_2$. MW, 280. Yellow cryst. from EtOH. M.p. 167–9°. Sol. Et_2O, $CHCl_3$, C_6H_6, hot AcOH. Mod. sol. hot EtOH. Spar. sol. CS_2, ligroin.

Gabriel, *Ber.*, 1886, **19**, 831.
Wölbling, *Ber.*, 1905, **38**, 3850.

3-_m_-Nitrophenylisocarbostyril (*1-Hydroxy-3-m-nitrophenylisoquinoline*)

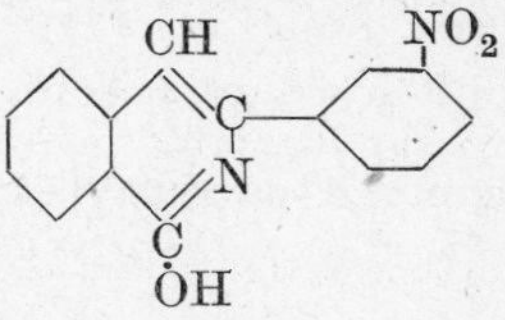

$C_{15}H_{10}O_3N_2$ MW, 266

Cryst. from $PhNO_2$. M.p. 298–300°. Sol. AcOH. Insol. EtOH, Et_2O.

Harper, *Ber.*, 1896, **29**, 2545.

_o_-Nitrophenyl isocyanate (*o-Nitrophenylcarbonimide*)

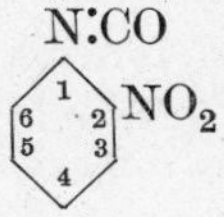

$C_7H_4O_3N_2$ MW, 164

Needles from pet. ether. M.p. 41° (37–8°). Sol. Et_2O, $CHCl_3$, C_6H_6.

Hoeke, *Rec. trav. chim.*, 1935, **54**, 505.

_m_-Nitrophenyl isocyanate (*m-Nitrophenylcarbonimide*).

Leaflets. M.p. 51°. Sol. C_6H_6, Et_2O, $CHCl_3$, toluene, boiling ligroin.

Folin, *Am. Chem. J.*, 1897, **19**, 339.
Hoeke, *Rec. trav. chim.*, 1935, **54**, 505.

_p_-Nitrophenyl isocyanate (*p-Nitrophenylcarbonimide*).

Needles. M.p. 57°. Sol. Et_2O, $CHCl_3$, C_6H_6, toluene, boiling ligroin.

See last reference above.

_o_-Nitrophenyl isothiocyanate (*o-Nitrophenylthiocarbonimide*)

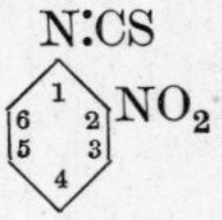

$C_7H_4O_2N_2S$ MW, 180

Yellow plates from Me_2CO.Aq. M.p. 74°.

Dyson, *J. Chem. Soc.*, 1934, 176.

m-Nitrophenyl isothiocyanate (m-*Nitrophenylthiocarbonimide*).

Needles from AcOH. M.p. 60·5°. B.p. 275–80° decomp. Sol. EtOH, Et_2O, $CHCl_3$, AcOH, CS_2, C_6H_6. Spar. sol. H_2O. Combines readily with bases and alcohols.

Steudemann, *Ber.*, 1883, **16**, 549, 2334.

p-Nitrophenyl isothiocyanate (p-*Nitrophenylthiocarbonimide*).

Pale yellow needles from AcOH. M.p. 112–13°. Sol. Et_2O, C_6H_6, warm AcOH.

Jacobson, Klein, *Ber.*, 1893, **26**, 2369.

β-2-Nitrophenyl-lactic Acid.

See *o*-Nitro-α-hydroxyhydrocinnamic Acid.

o-Nitrophenyl 1-naphthyl Ketone

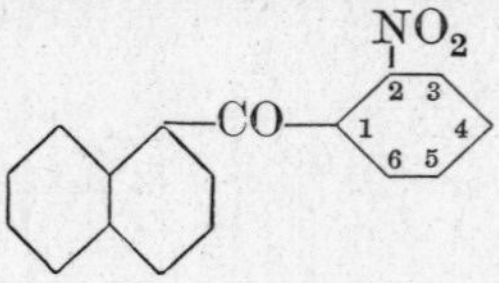

$C_{17}H_{11}O_3N$ MW, 277

Orange-yellow prisms. M.p. 122°.

Berlingozzi, *Chem. Zentr.*, 1934, II, 601.

m-Nitrophenyl 1-naphthyl Ketone.

Reddish-yellow cryst. M.p. 117°.

See previous reference.

p-Nitrophenyl 1-naphthyl Ketone.

Yellow micro-cryst. M.p. 95°.

See previous reference.

o-Nitrophenylpropiolic Acid

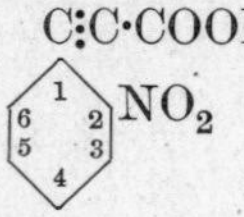

$C_9H_5O_4N$ MW, 191

Needles or leaflets from H_2O. M.p. 157° decomp. Sol. hot H_2O. Spar. sol. $CHCl_3$. Insol. CS_2, ligroin. $k = 1{\cdot}06 \times 10^{-2}$ at 25°. NH_3.Aq. + $FeSO_4$ $\longrightarrow$ *o*-aminophenylpropiolic acid. Hot alkalis $\longrightarrow$ isatin. Heat with $H_2O \longrightarrow$ *o*-nitrophenylacetylene.

Me ester: $C_{10}H_7O_4N$. MW, 205. Yellowish leaflets from CCl_4. M.p. 87–8°. Very sol. MeOH, $CHCl_3$.

Et ester: $C_{11}H_9O_4N$. MW, 219. Pale yellow leaflets from EtOH or Et_2O. M.p. 62°. $(NH_4)_2S \longrightarrow$ indoxylic acid ethyl ester.

Amide: $C_9H_6O_3N_2$. MW, 190. Plates from H_2O. M.p. 159°.

Baeyer, *Ber.*, 1880, **13**, 2258.
Pfeiffer, *Ann.*, 1916, **411**, 148.
Rinkes, *Rec. trav. chim.*, 1929, **48**, 960.

m-Nitrophenylpropiolic Acid.

Needles from C_6H_6–ligroin. M.p. 143°. Sol. EtOH, Et_2O, AcOH, $CHCl_3$, C_6H_6, hot H_2O. Insol. ligroin. Heat with $H_2O \longrightarrow$ *m*-nitrophenylacetylene.

Wollring, *Ber.*, 1914, **47**, 111.
Reich, Koehler, *Ber.*, 1913, **46**, 3735.

p-Nitrophenylpropiolic Acid.

Needles from EtOH or Et_2O. M.p. 181°. Sol. hot EtOH, Et_2O, AcOH. Spar. sol. H_2O, $CHCl_3$, C_6H_6. Very spar. sol. CS_2. Insol. pet. ether. Sol. cold conc. H_2SO_4. Heat with H_2O $\longrightarrow$ *p*-nitrophenylacetylene.

Et ester: needles from Et_2O. M.p. 126°.

Perkin, Bellenot, *J. Chem. Soc.*, 1886, **49**, 441.
Reich, *Compt. rend.*, 1916, **162**, 129.

Nitrophenylpropionic Acid.

See Nitrohydratropic Acid *and* Nitrohydrocinnamic Acid.

2-o-Nitrophenylpyridine

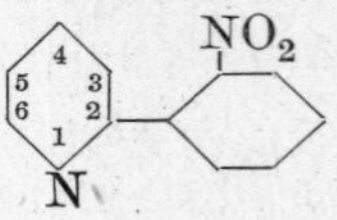

$C_{11}H_8O_2N_2$ MW, 200

Tablets. M.p. 60–1°. Sol. EtOH, Et_2O. Insol. H_2O.

Forsyth, Pyman, *J. Chem. Soc.*, 1926, 2919.

2-m-Nitrophenylpyridine.

Pale yellow needles from EtOH. M.p. 73–4°. Sol. Et_2O. Spar. sol. H_2O, EtOH.

B,HNO₃: needles from $5N/HNO_3$. M.p. 193°.

See previous reference.

2-p-Nitrophenylpyridine.

Needles from EtOH. M.p. 130·5–131·5°. Sol. $CHCl_3$. Spar. sol. EtOH, Et_2O, Me_2CO. Insol. H_2O.

B,HCl: needles from $5N$/HCl. M.p. 185–6°.

Picrate: m.p. 131–131·5°.

Forsyth, Pyman, *J. Chem. Soc.*, 1926, 2916.
Tschitschibabin, Schemjakina, *Chem. Zentr.*, 1923, III, 1024.

3-p-Nitrophenylpyridine.

Buff needles from EtOH. M.p. 148–9°. Sol. $CHCl_3$. Spar. sol. EtOH, Et_2O, Me_2CO. Insol. H_2O.

B,HNO$_3$: needles from *N*/HNO_3. M.p. 198°.

Forsyth, Pyman, *J. Chem. Soc.*, 1926, 2920.

4-*o*-Nitrophenylpyridine.

Plates from Et_2O. M.p. 51–2°.

B,HNO$_3$: prisms from 5*N*/HNO_3. M.p. 178–9°.

Forsyth, Pyman, *J. Chem. Soc.*, 1926, 2924.

4-*m*-Nitrophenylpyridine.

Needles from Me_2CO. M.p. 109–10°. Sol. EtOH, Me_2CO. Spar. sol. Et_2O. Insol. H_2O.

B,HNO$_3$: needles from 5*N*/HNO_3. M.p 222° decomp.

See previous reference.

4-*p*-Nitrophenylpyridine.

Prisms from Me_2CO. M.p. 123–4°. Sol. EtOH, Me_2CO, $CHCl_3$. Spar. sol. Et_2O. Insol. H_2O.

B,HCl : prisms from 5*N*/HCl. M.p. 255°.

Tschitschibabin, Shemyakina, *Chem. Zentr.*, 1923, III, 1024.

o-Nitrophenyl α-pyridyl Ketone (2-o-*Nitrobenzoylpyridine*)

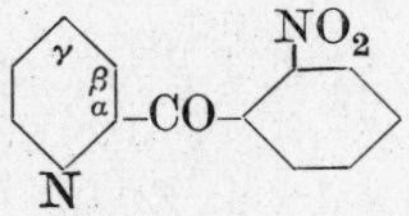

$C_{12}H_8O_3N_2$ MW, 228

Needles from H_2O. M.p. 118°.

Wilson, *J. Chem. Soc.*, 1931, 1937.

***m*-Nitrophenyl α-pyridyl Ketone** (2-m-*Nitrobenzoylpyridine*).

Prisms from EtOH, needles from H_2O. M.p. 122°.

Bryans, Pyman, *J. Chem. Soc.*, 1929, 551.

***p*-Nitrophenyl α-pyridyl Ketone** (2-p-*Nitrobenzoylpyridine*).

Needles from H_2O. M.p. 110° (100°). Sol. EtOH, Et_2O, $CHCl_3$, AcOEt, C_6H_6, ligroin.

B,HCl : needles from EtOH. M.p. 187° (173°).

Phenylhydrazone : yellow cryst. from EtOH. M.p. 171°.

Tschitschibabin, Kuindshi, Benewolenskaja, *Ber.*, 1925, **58**, 1584.
Koenigs, Mensching, Kirsch, *Ber.*, 1926, **59**, 1719.
Bryans, Pyman, *J. Chem. Soc.*, 1929, 551.

***p*-Nitrophenyl β-pyridyl Ketone** (3-p-*Nitrobenzoylpyridine*).

Needles from H_2O. M.p. 106°.

Picrate : plates from H_2O. M.p. 185–7°.

Bryans, Pyman, *J. Chem. Soc.*, 1929, 552.

***m*-Nitrophenyl γ-pyridyl Ketone** (4-m-*Nitrobenzoylpyridine*).

Needles from H_2O. M.p. 129°.

See previous reference.

***p*-Nitrophenyl γ-pyridyl Ketone** (4-p-*Nitrobenzoylpyridine*).

Needles from H_2O. M.p. 123–4°. Sol. EtOH, Et_2O. Mod. sol. H_2O, C_6H_6.

B,HCl : m.p. 202°.

Phenylhydrazone : m.p. 226°.

Tschitschibabin, Kuindshi, Benewolenskaja, *Ber.*, 1925, **58**, 1587.
Koenigs, Mensching, Kirsch, *Ber.*, 1926, **59**, 1722.

***o*-Nitrophenylpyruvic Acid**

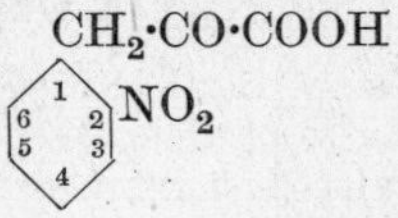

$C_9H_7O_5N$ MW, 209

Enol form : *see* 2-Nitro-α-hydroxycinnamic Acid.

Yellowish needles or leaflets from C_6H_6. M.p. 121°. Very sol. EtOH, Et_2O, AcOH. Mod. sol. hot H_2O. Spar. sol. $CHCl_3$, C_6H_6. Almost insol. ligroin. $FeCl_3$ ⟶ olive-green col.

Me ester : $C_{10}H_9O_5N$. MW, 223. Yellow needles. M.p. 83–7°.

Et ester : $C_{11}H_{11}O_5N$. MW, 237. Needles or prisms from ligroin. M.p. 46–7°. Very sol. Et_2O, Me_2CO, EtOH, $CHCl_3$, C_6H_6, AcOH. Spar. sol. ligroin. $FeCl_3$ gives no immediate col. ⟶ green on standing. Gives no col. with Cu acetate. *Oxime* : needles from EtOH. M.p. 121·2°. *Phenylhydrazone* : yellow needles from EtOH. M.p. 103·5°. $FeCl_3$ in conc. H_2SO_4 ⟶ purplish-red col. *Diphenylhydrazone* : needles. M.p. 107°. *Anil* : red prisms from EtOH. M.p. 92°. Sol. Et_2O, $CHCl_3$. Spar. sol. ligroin. o-*Tolanil* : orange cryst. M.p. 77–8°. m-*Tolanil* : orange cryst. M.p. 138°. p-*Tolanil* : dark red cryst. from EtOH. M.p. 90·5–91·0°. p-*Bromoanil* : dark red prisms. M.p. 136–7°.

Amide : $C_9H_8O_4N_2$. MW, 208. Needles from EtOH. M.p. 165–6°. Sol. AcOH with decomp. Mod. sol. hot H_2O. Spar. sol. Et_2O.

Oxime : needles. M.p. 161° decomp. Sol.

Me_2CO, AcOH. Mod. sol. EtOH, Et_2O. Spar. sol. $CHCl_3$, C_6H_6, pet. ether.

unsym.-*Diphenylhydrazone*: yellow needles from EtOH. M.p. 125°.

unsym.-*Methylphenylhydrazone*: yellow needles from EtOH. M.p. 110°.

Reissert, D.R.P., 92,794; *Ber.*, 1897, **30**, 1036; 1908, **41**, 3813.
Wislicenus, Thoma, *Ann.*, 1924, **436**, 45.

_p_-Nitrophenylpyruvic Acid.

Enol-form: *see* 4-Nitro-α-hydroxycinnamic Acid.

Orange yellow cryst. + AcOH from AcOH. M.p. 194°. Sol. EtOH, Et_2O, Me_2CO. Mod. sol. AcOH. Spar. sol. H_2O, $CHCl_3$, C_6H_6. Insol. ligroin. $FeCl_3$ ⟶ bluish-green col.

Me ester: prisms from MeOH–Me_2CO. M.p. 149°. *Oxime*: pale yellow cryst. from C_6H_6. M.p. 172–3°. Sol. Et_2O, Me_2CO, EtOH. *Phenylhydrazone*: yellowish-green cryst. from MeOH. M.p. 136–45°.

Py salt: yellowish-green needles from Py. M.p. 150°. Sol. Na_2CO_3 with red col.

Reissert, *Ber.*, 1897, **30**, 1047.
Wislicenus, Schultz, *Ann.*, 1924, **436**, 57.
See also first reference above.

2-_o_-Nitrophenylquinoline

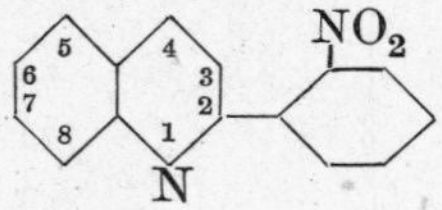

$C_{15}H_{10}O_2N_2$ MW, 250

Needles from MeOH.Aq. M.p. 121–3°.

Le Fèvre, Mathur, *J. Chem. Soc.*, 1930, 2240.

2-_m_-Nitrophenylquinoline.

Pale yellow needles from EtOH. M.p. 123–4°.

Methochloride: needles from EtOH–Et_2O. M.p. 204–5°. Sol. H_2O, MeOH, EtOH. Insol. Et_2O, $CHCl_3$, C_6H_6.

Methopicrate: cryst. from EtOH. M.p. 181–2°.

Le Fèvre, Mathur, *J. Chem. Soc.*, 1930, 2239.

2-_p_-Nitrophenylquinoline.

Pale yellow needles from MeOH.Aq. M.p. 129–31°.

Le Fèvre, Mathur, *J. Chem. Soc.*, 1930, 2240.

1-_o_-Nitrophenylsemicarbazide

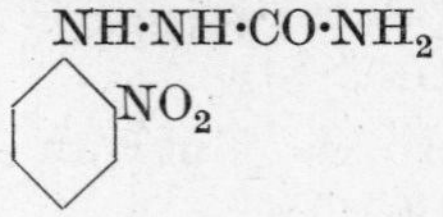

$C_7H_8O_3N_4$ MW, 196

Yellow cryst. from EtOH. M.p. 225° decomp.

Guha, Ghosh, *J. Indian Chem. Soc.*, 1928, **5**, 447.

1-_m_-Nitrophenylsemicarbazide.

Needles from EtOH. M.p. 195° decomp. Sol. hot H_2O, EtOH. Spar. sol. boiling Et_2O, C_6H_6.

Young, Stockwell, *J. Chem. Soc.*, 1898, **73**, 372.

1-_p_-Nitrophenylsemicarbazide.

Yellow needles from H_2O. M.p. 211–12° decomp. Sol. hot H_2O, EtOH, Me_2CO. Spar. sol. C_6H_6. Dil. NaOH ⟶ orange-red sol.

Hyde, *Ber.*, 1899, **32**, 1812.

4-_m_-Nitrophenylsemicarbazide

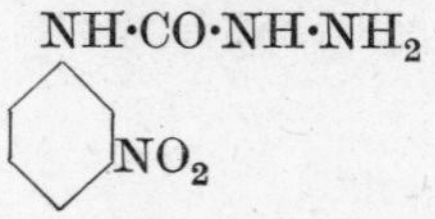

$C_7H_8O_3N_4$ MW, 196

Yellow needles from EtOH. M.p. 138–9°. Sol. 4 parts boiling EtOH. Conc. alkalis ⟶ red col. Reduces Fehling's and $NH_3.AgNO_3$.

Wheeler, Walker, *J. Am. Chem. Soc.*, 1925, **47**, 2794.

_o_-Nitrophenylthiourea

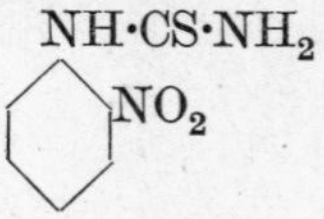

$C_7H_7O_2N_3S$ MW, 197

Yellow cryst. from EtOH. M.p. 140–141·5° (136°). Sol. Et_2O. Sol. alkalis with light red col. Conc. H_2SO_4 ⟶ mauve col.

Arndt, Rosenau, *Ber.*, 1917, **50**, 1255.
Dyson, George, *J. Chem. Soc.*, 1924, **125**, 1707.

_m_-Nitrophenylthiourea.

Yellow cryst. M.p. 120–5° decomp. (157–8°).

See second reference above and also Steudemann, *Ber.*, 1883, **16**, 550.

***p*-Nitrophenylthiourea.**
Yellow cryst. M.p. 189–90°.

Dyson, George, *J. Chem. Soc.*, 1924, **125**, 1707.

Nitrophenyl tolyl Ether.
See Nitromethyldiphenyl Ether.
Nitrophenyl tolyl Ketone.
See Nitromethylbenzophenone.
Nitrophenyltolylmethane.
See Nitromethyldiphenylmethane.
Nitrophenyl tolyl sulphide.
See Nitromethyldiphenyl sulphide.
Nitrophenyl tolyl sulphone.
See Nitromethyldiphenyl sulphone.
1-*o*-Nitrophenyltrimethylene Glycol (2-*Nitro-αγ-dihydroxy*-1-*propylbenzene*)

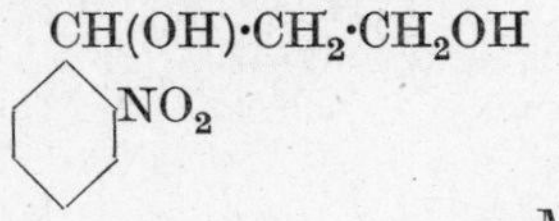

$C_9H_{11}O_4N$ MW, 197

Needles from EtOH. M.p. 108–9°.

Baeyer, Drewsen, *Ber.*, 1882, **15**, 2861.

***o*-Nitrophenylurea**

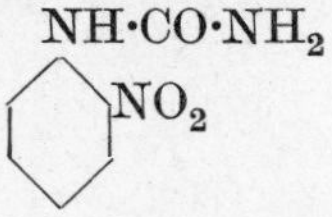

$C_7H_7O_3N_3$ MW, 181

Yellow needles from H_2O. M.p. 183–4° (181°).
N′-*Phenyl*: *see* 2-Nitrocarbanilide.

Arndt, *Ber.*, 1913, **46**, 3529.
Reudler, *Rec. trav. chim.*, 1914, **33**, 46.

***m*-Nitrophenylurea.**
Yellow needles or plates from H_2O. M.p. 196°.
N′-*Phenyl*: *see* 3-Nitrocarbanilide.

Reudler, *Rec. trav. chim.*, 1914, **33**, 46.
Pierron, *Bull. soc. chim.*, 1905, **33**, 72.

***p*-Nitrophenylurea.**
Prisms from EtOH, needles from EtOH.Aq. M.p. 238°. Sol. EtOH, boiling H_2O. Spar. sol. Et_2O, C_6H_6.
N′-*Me*: $C_8H_9O_3N_3$. MW, 195. Yellow needles. M.p. 225–7°. Sol. Me_2CO, hot EtOH, AcOH. Spar. sol. hot H_2O, AcOEt.
N′-*Phenyl*: *see* 4-Nitrocarbanilide.

See previous references and also
Scholl, Nyberg, *Ber.*, 1906, **39**, 2492.

***o*-Nitrophenylurethane** (2-*Nitrocarbanilic acid ethyl ester*)

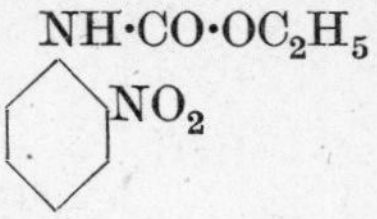

$C_9H_{10}O_4N_2$ MW, 210

Yellow prisms from pet. ether, needles from EtOH. M.p. 58° (56°). Sol. C_6H_6, ligroin. Spar. sol. Et_2O.

Swartz, *Am. Chem. J.*, 1897, **19**, 303.
Vittenet, *Bull. soc. chim.*, 1899, **21**, 588.

***m*-Nitrophenylurethane** (3-*Nitrocarbanilic acid ethyl ester*).
Pale yellow needles. M.p. 56–7° (65°). Sol. EtOH, Et_2O, Me_2CO, $CHCl_3$, C_6H_6. Insol. H_2O.

See previous references and also
Curtius, Struve, Radenhausen, *J. prakt. Chem.*, 1895, **52**, 230.

***p*-Nitrophenylurethane** (4-*Nitrocarbanilic acid ethyl ester*).
Needles from C_6H_6. M.p. 129° (132°). Sol. EtOH, C_6H_6. Insol. boiling ligroin.
N-*Me*: m.p. 45°.

Jacobson, Klein, *Ber.*, 1893, **26**, 2370.
Curtius, Struve, Radenhausen, *J. prakt. Chem.*, 1895, **52**, 233.
Shriner, Cox, *J. Am. Chem. Soc.*, 1931, **53**, 1604.

3-Nitrophloretic Acid (3-*Nitro*-p-*hydrocoumaric acid*, 3-*nitro*-4-*hydroxyhydrocinnamic acid*)

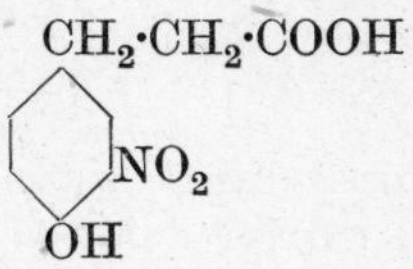

$C_9H_9O_5N$ MW, 211

Orange-yellow needles from H_2O. M.p. 90·5°. Very sol. EtOH. Spar. sol. boiling H_2O.
Me ester: $C_{10}H_{11}O_5N$. MW, 225. Yellow needles from EtOH.Aq. M.p. 64°.
Et ester: $C_{11}H_{13}O_5N$. MW, 239. Yellow needles from EtOH.Aq. M.p. 38°.
Me ether: $C_{10}H_{11}O_5N$. MW, 225. Pale yellow needles from CCl_4. M.p. 128–130·5°.
Amide: $C_{10}H_{12}O_4N_2$. MW, 224. Pale yellow cryst. M.p. 126·5–127°.

Stöhr, *Ann.*, 1884, **225**, 92.
Bougault, *Ann. chim. phys.*, 1902, **25**, 504.
Callow, Gulland, Haworth, *J. Chem. Soc.*, 1929, 1452.

Nitrophloroglucinol (2-*Nitro*-1 : 3 : 5-*tri-hydroxybenzene*)

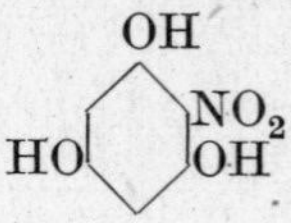

$C_6H_5O_5N$ MW, 171

Red leaflets or prisms + H_2O from H_2O. M.p. 189–91° (186–7°), anhyd. 205°. Sol. AcOH. Mod. sol. EtOH, Et_2O, Me_2CO, AcOEt. Spar. sol. H_2O, $CHCl_3$, C_6H_6. Insol. pet. ether. Sol. Na_2CO_3 with red col.

Leuchs, Geserick, *Ber.*, 1908, **41**, 4182.
Rüdiger, *Arch. Pharm.*, 1914, **252**, 180.

3-Nitrophthalamic Acid (3-*Nitrophthalic acid* 1-*amide*)

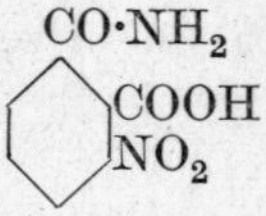

$C_8H_6O_5N_2$ MW, 210

Plates from warm H_2O. M.p. depends on rate of heating. Starts to melt at 150–6°, re-solidifies and then melts at 214–15°. Sol. hot H_2O. Mod. sol. EtOH, Me_2CO, AcOH. Insol. Et_2O, $CHCl_3$, C_6H_6, ligroin. Above 160° ⟶ 3-nitrophthalimide.

NH_4 salt: needles from H_2O. M.p. 172° decomp. Above m.p. ⟶ 3-nitrophthalimide.

Chambers, *J. Am. Chem. Soc.*, 1903, **25**, 608.
Kahn, *Ber.*, 1902, **35**, 3862.
Chapman, Stephen, *J. Chem. Soc.*, 1925, 1795.

3-Nitrophthalanil (3-*Nitrophthalic acid anil*, 3-*nitro*-N-*phenylphthalimide*)

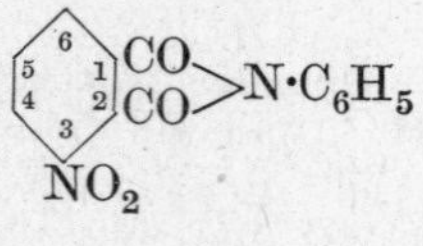

$C_{14}H_8O_4N_2$ MW, 268

Yellowish needles from EtOH–Me_2CO. M.p. 138° (134°). Sol. Me_2CO. Spar. sol. cold EtOH. Insol. H_2O.

Bogert, Boroschek, *J. Am. Chem. Soc.*, 1901, **23**, 748.
Chambers, *J. Am. Chem. Soc.*, 1903, **25**, 611.
Kauffmann, Beisswenger, *Ber.*, 1904, **37**, 2610.

4-Nitrophthalanil (4-*Nitrophthalic acid ani* 4-*nitro*-N-*phenylphthalimide*).

Yellow needles from EtOH–Me_2CO. M.p 194° (192°). Sol. Me_2CO. Spar. sol. EtOH.

Graebe, Buenzod, *Ber.*, 1899, **32**, 1993.
Bogert, Boroschek, *J. Am. Chem. Soc* 1901, **23**, 756.

3-Nitrophthalic Acid

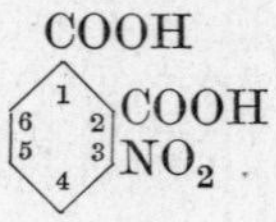

$C_8H_5O_6N$ MW, 21

Pale yellow prisms from H_2O. M.p. 218 Mod. sol. hot H_2O. Sol. hot MeOH, EtOH Spar. sol. Et_2O. Insol. $CHCl_3$, CCl_4, CS_2, C_6H pet. ether. k (first) = $1{\cdot}22 \times 10^{-2}$ at 25° (second) = 4×10^{-5} at 25°. Above 230° ⟶ anhydride.

1-*Me ester*: $C_9H_7O_6N$. MW, 225. Pal yellowish leaflets from hot H_2O. M.p. 164 (157°). $k = 1{\cdot}66 \times 10^{-2}$ at 25°. Conc. NH_3.Aq ⟶ 3-nitro-1-phthalamic acid. l-*Menthy ester*: m.p. 149–50°. $[\alpha]_D^{20}$ − 102° in C_6H *Chloride*: $C_9H_6O_5NCl$. MW, 243·5. Cryst from pet. ether. M.p. 97–9°.

2-*Me ester*: cryst. + H_2O. M.p. anhyd 152–3°. $k = 2{\cdot}1 \times 10^{-3}$ at 25°. l-*Menthy ester*: m.p. 66–7°. $[\alpha]_D^{20}$ − 122·9° in C_6H *Chloride*: cryst. from pet. ether. M.p. 95–7°.

Di-Me ester: $C_{10}H_9O_6N$. MW, 239. Pal yellowish cryst. from MeOH.Aq. M.p. 68–9°.

1-*Et ester*: $C_{10}H_9O_6N$. MW, 239. Needle + $2\frac{1}{2}H_2O$ from H_2O. M.p. 53°, anhyd. 112° l-*Menthyl ester*: m.p. 99°. $[\alpha]_D^{20}$ − 93° in C_6H_6 *Chloride*: $C_{10}H_8O_5NCl$. MW, 257·5. Cryst from pet. ether. M.p. 58–60°.

2-*Et ester*: yellowish needles from EtOH prisms from $CHCl_3$. M.p. 157°. l-*Menthy ester*: m.p. 57–8°. $[\alpha]_D^{20}$ − 125° in C_6H_6 *Chloride*: cryst. from pet. ether. M.p. 74–6°.

Di-Et ester: $C_{12}H_{13}O_6N$. MW, 267. Prism from EtOH, needles from pet. ether. M.p 46°. Sol. EtOH, Et_2O. Insol. H_2O.

1-*Propyl ester*: $C_{11}H_{11}O_6N$. MW, 253 M.p. 122–3°. l-*Menthyl ester*: m.p. 89°. $[\alpha]_D^{20}$ − 83° in C_6H_6. *Chloride*: $C_{11}H_{10}O_5NCl$ MW, 271·5. Cryst. from pet. ether. M.p. 118°

2-*Propyl ester*: m.p. 141–2° (138–9°) l-*Menthyl ester*: m.p. 38–40°. $[\alpha]_D^{20}$ − 116·9° in C_6H_6. *Chloride*: cryst. from pet. ether M.p. 32°.

2-*Isopropyl ester*: cryst. M.p. 152–3°.

2-*Butyl ester*: $C_{12}H_{13}O_6N$. MW, 267. Cryst. M.p. 146–7°.

1-*Isobutyl ester*: m.p. 149°. l-*Menthyl ester*: m.p. 76–7°. $[\alpha]_D^{20}$ − 79° in C_6H_6.

2-*Isobutyl ester*: m.p. 176–7°. l-*Menthyl ester*: liq. $[\alpha]_D^{20}$ − 115·7° in C_6H_6.

1-d-*Amyl ester*: $C_{13}H_{15}O_6N$. MW, 281. Cryst. from C_6H_6. M.p. 116°.

2-d-*Amyl ester*: leaflets from C_6H_6. M.p. 157·5–158·5°. Very sol. Me_2CO. Sol. EtOH, $CHCl_3$. Spar. sol. CS_2, C_6H_6. $[\alpha]_D^{21}$ + 2·2° in Me_2CO, + 2·7° in EtOH.

2-l-*Amyl ester*: $[\alpha]_D^{20}$ − 2·7° in EtOH. *Brucine salt*: cryst. from EtOH.Aq. M.p. 105°.

1-dl-*Amyl ester*: yellowish prisms from C_6H_6. M.p. 117°.

2-dl-*Amyl ester*: cryst. from C_6H_6. M.p. 156–8°.

1-*Isoamyl ester*: exists in two forms. *Stable form*, m.p. 95° (93·5°); *labile form*, m.p. 78°. Very sol. EtOH, Me_2CO. Sol. C_6H_6, hot CCl_4. Spar. sol. CS_2, ligroin.

2-*Isoamyl ester*: cryst. from C_6H_6. M.p. 165–6°. Spar. sol. C_6H_6, CCl_4.

2-l-*Menthyl ester*: $C_{18}H_{23}O_6N$. MW, 349. M.p. 160–2°.

1-*Benzyl ester*: $C_{15}H_{11}O_6N$. MW, 301. M.p. 165°.

2-*Benzyl ester*: m.p. 174°. l-*Menthyl ester*: $[\alpha]_D^{20}$ − 83° in C_6H_6. *Chloride*: $C_{15}H_{10}O_5NCl$. MW, 319·5. Cryst. from pet. ether. M.p. 74–5°.

Dichloride: $C_8H_3O_4NCl_2$. MW, 248. Prisms from Et_2O. M.p. 76–7°. Spar. sol. CCl_4, ligroin. Dry NH_3 ⟶ 3-nitrophthalimide. NH_3.Aq. ⟶ 3-nitrophthalamic acid.

1-*Amide*: *see* 3-Nitrophthalamic Acid.

Diamide: $C_8H_7O_4N_3$. MW, 209. Cryst. powder. M.p. 200–1° decomp. Above m.p. ⟶ 3-nitrophthalimide.

Imide: *see* 3-Nitrophthalimide.

Anil: *see* 3-Nitrophthalanil.

Anilide: $C_{14}H_{10}O_5N_2$. MW, 286. Pale yellow needles from AcOEt. M.p. 181°. Sol. EtOH. Spar. sol. cold H_2O. Reacts acid to litmus. Above m.p. ⟶ 3-nitrophthalanil.

Dianilide: $C_{20}H_{15}O_4N_3$. MW, 361. Needles from EtOH. M.p. 233–4°. Sol. hot EtOH, Et_2O, Me_2CO, $CHCl_3$. Spar. sol. C_6H_6, toluene.

Di-m-nitroanilide: needles from EtOH. M.p. 225–30° decomp.

Di-p-nitroanilide: m.p. 197–200°.

Di-p-toluidide: m.p. 223–4° decomp.

1-*Nitrile*: 6-nitro-2-cyanobenzoic acid. $C_8H_4O_4N_2$. MW, 192. Needles. M.p. 99–100°, resolidifies and then has m.p. 214–15°.

1-*Hydrazide*: needles. Does not melt below 280°. B,N_2H_4: needles from EtOH.Aq. M.p. 157°. N-*Benzylidene*: needles from EtOH. M.p. 177°.

Anhydride: *see* 3-Nitrophthalic Anhydride.

Cohen, Woodroffe, Anderson, *J. Chem. Soc.*, 1916, **109**, 222.
Cohen, Marshall, Woodman, *J. Chem. Soc.*, 1915, **107**, 893.
Wegscheider, Lipschitz, *Monatsh.*, 1900, **21**, 787.
Kahn, *Ber.*, 1902, **35**, 3861.
Miller, *Ann.*, 1881, **208**, 243.
Bogert, Boroschek, *J. Am. Chem. Soc.*, 1901, **23**, 745.
McKenzie, *J. Chem. Soc.*, 1901, **79**, 1136.
Marckwald, *Ber.*, 1902, **35**, 1604.
Marckwald, McKenzie, *Ber.*, 1901, **34**, 486.
Chambers, *J. Am. Chem. Soc.*, 1903, **25**, 607.
Tingle, Bates, *J. Am. Chem. Soc.*, 1910, **32**, 1325.
Culhane, Woodward, *Organic Syntheses*, Collective Vol. I, 399.

4-Nitrophthalic Acid.

Pale yellowish needles from Et_2O. M.p. 165° (160–1°). Sol. H_2O, EtOH, hot AcOEt. Insol. $CHCl_3$, CCl_4, CS_2, C_6H_6, pet. ether. k (first) = $7·6 \times 10^{-3}$ at 25°; (second) = 4×10^{-5} at 25°. Above m.p. ⟶ anhydride.

1-*Me ester*: cryst. + H_2O from H_2O. M.p. anhyd. 131–2°. $k = 4·6 \times 10^{-3}$ at 25°. l-*Menthyl ester*: liq. $[\alpha]_D^{20}$ − 61·6° in C_6H_6.

2-*Me ester*: yellow needles from C_6H_6. M.p. 140–2°.

Di-Me ester: cryst. from EtOH.Aq. M.p. 65–6°.

1-*Et ester*: needles from H_2O. M.p. 127–8°. Sol. H_2O, Et_2O, C_6H_6. $k = 3·05 \times 10^{-3}$ at 25°.

2-*Et ester*: needles from C_6H_6–pet. ether. M.p. 137°. Sol. H_2O. $k = 5·2 \times 10^{-3}$ at 25°.

Di-Et ester: plates from EtOH. M.p. 33–4°. Sol. EtOH, Et_2O. Insol. H_2O.

Diamide: cryst. M.p. 200° decomp. Above m.p. ⟶ 4-nitrophthalimide.

Imide: *see* 4-Nitrophthalimide.

Anil: *see* 4-Nitrophthalanil.

Anilide: pale yellow cryst. from AcOEt. M.p. 192°. Sol. EtOH. Insol. H_2O, Et_2O. Reacts acid to litmus. Above m.p. ⟶ 4-nitrophthalanil.

p-*Toluidide*: needles. M.p. 172°. Insol. cold H_2O, Et_2O.

β-*Naphthylamide*: pale yellow cryst. from

Me_2CO–C_6H_6. M.p. 202–4°. Sol. EtOH, Et_2O. Me_2CO, AcOEt. Spar. sol. $CHCl_3$. Insol. C_6H_6.
Anhydride : *see* 4-Nitrophthalic Anhydride.

Bogert, Boroschck, *J. Am. Chem. Soc.*, 1901, **23**, 752.
Miller, *Ann.*, 1881, **208**, 225.
Seidel, Bittner, *Monatsh.*, 1902, **23**, 418.
Wegscheider, Lipschitz, *Monatsh.*, 1900, **21**, 804.
Wegscheider, Bondi, *Monatsh.*, 1905, **26**, 1048.
Wegscheider, Kuśy, Dúbrav, *Monatsh.*, 1903, **24**, 825.
Tingle, Bates, *J. Am. Chem. Soc.*, 1910, **32**, 1328.

3-Nitrophthalic Anhydride

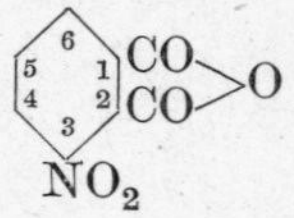

$C_8H_3O_5N$ MW, 193

Needles from AcOH or Me_2CO. M.p. 164°. Sol. hot AcOH. Mod. sol. Me_2CO, hot EtOH. Spar. sol. C_6H_6.

Lawrance, *J. Am. Chem. Soc.*, 1920, **42**, 1871.
Nicolet, Bender, *Organic Syntheses*. Collective Vol. I, 402.

4-Nitrophthalic Anhydride.
Needles from $CHCl_3$–pet. ether. M.p. 119° (114°). Sol. usual org. solvents. Spar. sol. Et_2O. Insol. pet. ether.

See first reference above and also
Crossley, Renouf, *J. Chem. Soc.*, 1909, **95**, 208.

4-Nitrophthalide

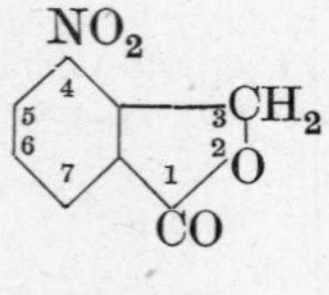

$C_8H_5O_4N$ MW, 179

Leaflets from MeOH. M.p. 136°. Sol. EtOH, $CHCl_3$, AcOH, CS_2, C_6H_6. Spar. sol. H_2O. CrO_3 + AcOH ⟶ 3-nitrophthalic acid.

Beilstein, Kurbatow, *Ann.*, 1880, **202**, 219.
Borsche, Diacont, Hanau, *Ber.*, 1934, **67**, 676.

6-Nitrophthalide.
Yellowish needles from AcOH. M.p. 14 (141°). Very sol. hot $CHCl_3$, AcOH, C_6H Mod. sol. EtOH, Et_2O. Insol. H_2O. D HNO_3 at 140° ⟶ 4-nitrophthalic acid. Sn HCl ⟶ 6-aminophthalide.

See last reference above and also
Hoenig, *Ber.*, 1885, **18**, 3447.
Tasman, *Rec. trav. chim.*, 1927, 4 653.

3-Nitrophthalimide

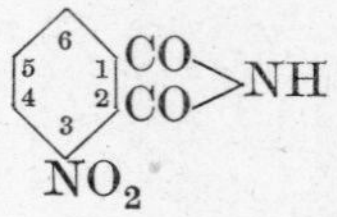

$C_8H_4O_4N_2$ MW, 19

Pale yellow leaflets from EtOH or needl from Me_2CO. M.p. 217–18°. Sol. hot EtO Me_2CO, AcOH. Spar. sol. $CHCl_3$, CS_2, C_6H Insol. H_2O, Et_2O, ligroin. Dil. sols. in EtO and AcOH show blue fluor. Sublimes easily.

N-*Me* : $C_9H_6O_4N_2$. MW, 206. Needles fro CCl_4. M.p. 112–13°.

N-*Et* : $C_{10}H_8O_4N_2$. MW, 220. Yellowis needles from EtOH, plates from CCl_4. M. 105–6°. Sol. hot EtOH. Spar. sol. hot H_2O.

N-β-*Bromoethyl* : plates from CCl_4. M. 115–16°.

N-*Propyl* : $C_{11}H_{10}O_4N_2$. MW, 234. Needle from CCl_4. M.p. 84–5°.

N-*Butyl* : $C_{12}H_{12}O_4N_2$. MW, 248. Prism from CCl_4. M.p. 71–2°.

N-*Amyl* : $C_{13}H_{14}O_4N_2$. MW, 262. Plate from CCl_4. M.p. 93–4°.

N-*Allyl* : $C_{11}H_8O_4N_2$. MW, 232. Plate from CCl_4. M.p. 100–1°.

N-*Phenyl* : *see* 3-Nitrophthalanil.

N-o-*Nitrophenyl* : yellow cryst. from EtOH Me_2CO. M.p. 167°.

N-m-*Nitrophenyl* : light brown cryst. fro EtOH–Me_2CO. M.p. 219°.

N-p-*Nitrophenyl* : yellow cryst. from Me_2CO M.p. 249°. Mod. sol. Me_2CO.

N-o-*Tolyl* : pale yellow needles from EtOH- Me_2CO. M.p. 145°. Sol. Me_2CO. Spar. so EtOH.

N-m-*Tolyl* : yellow needles from EtOH- Me_2CO. M.p. 129°.

N-p-*Tolyl* : pale yellow needles from EtOH- Me_2CO. M.p. 154°.

N-*Benzyl* : $C_{15}H_{10}O_4N_2$. MW. 282. Needle from CCl_4. M.p. 142–3°.

N-p-*Nitrobenzyl*: prisms from AcOH. M.p. 81–2°.

Bogert, Boroschek, *J. Am. Chem. Soc.*, 1901, **23**, 747.
Bogert, Chambers, *J. Am. Chem. Soc.*, 1905, **27**, 652.
Kahn, *Ber.*, 1902, **35**, 3862.
Seidel, Bittner, *Monatsh.*, 1902, **23**, 420.
Chapman, Stephen, *J. Chem. Soc.*, 1925, 1795.
Sah, Ma, *Ber.*, 1932, **65**, 1630.

4-Nitrophthalimide.

Needles from H_2O, yellowish leaflets from EtOH–Me_2CO. M.p. 202° (193–5°). Sol. EtOH, AcOH, Me_2CO. Spar. sol. hot H_2O.

N-*Me*: needles from EtOH. M.p. 179–80°. Sol. Me_2CO, AcOEt, $CHCl_3$, hot EtOH. Mod. sol. C_6H_6, Et_2O, hot H_2O.

N-*Et*: pale yellow leaflets. M.p. 111–12°. Spar. sol. hot H_2O.

N-*Phenyl*: *see* 4-Nitrophthalanil.

N-o-*Nitrophenyl*: pale yellow needles from $PhNO_2$. M.p. 233°. Spar. sol. EtOH, Me_2CO.

N-m-*Nitrophenyl*: yellow needles from $PhNO_2$. M.p. 243°. Spar. sol. EtOH, Me_2CO.

N-p-*Nitrophenyl*: yellow cryst. from $PhNO_2$. M.p. 251–3°. Spar. sol. Me_2CO. Insol. EtOH.

N-o-*Tolyl*: brownish cryst. powder. M.p. 160°. Sol. Me_2CO. Spar. sol. EtOH.

N-m-*Tolyl*: light brownish cryst. from $PhNO_2$. M.p. 197°. Spar. sol. Me_2CO. Insol. EtOH.

N-p-*Tolyl*: yellow cryst. from EtOH–Me_2CO. M.p. 165°. Sol. Me_2CO. Spar. sol. EtOH.

Bogert, Boroschek, *J. Am. Chem. Soc.*, 1901, **23**, 755.
Seidel, Bittner, *Monatsh.*, 1902, **23**, 420.
Chapman, Stephen, *J. Chem. Soc.*, 1925, 1796.
Levy, Stephen, *J. Chem. Soc.*, 1931, 79.

3-Nitro-γ-picoline

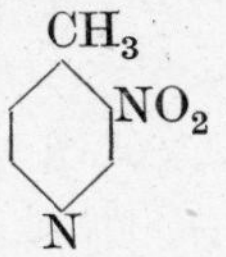

$C_6H_6O_2N_2$ MW, 138

Deliquescent cryst.

B,HCl: prisms from EtOH–pet. ether. M.p. 178°.

B_2,H_2PtCl_6: yellow needles. M.p. 267°.

Picrate: golden-yellow plates. M.p. 118°.

Koenigs, Fulde, *Ber.*, 1927, **60**, 2108.

***N*-Nitropiperidine**

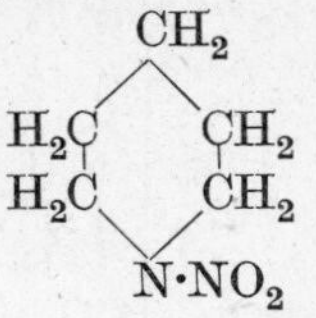

$C_5H_{10}O_2N_2$ MW, 130

M.p. — 5·5°. B.p. 245°/765 mm. slight decomp. $D_4^{26\cdot4}$ 1·1519. $n_D^{26\cdot4}$ 1·4954. Sol. hot H_2O. Volatile in steam.

Bamberger, Kirpal, *Ber.*, 1895, **28**, 536.
Franchimont, van Rijn, Friedmann, *Rec. trav. chim.*, 1907, **26**, 230.

6-Nitropiperonal

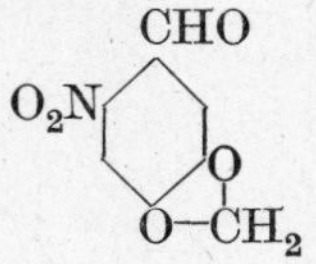

$C_8H_5O_5N$ MW, 195

Needles from H_2O or AcOEt–EtOH. M.p. 98·5° (95·5°). Sol. EtOH, boiling H_2O. Sublimes. Turns yellow in light. 2% $KMnO_4$ ⟶ 6-nitropiperonylic acid.

Oxime: yellow needles from EtOH. M.p. 212° (203°). Sol. Me_2CO, C_6H_6, hot EtOH. Insol. H_2O, pet. ether. *Acetyl*: yellow needles from EtOH. M.p. 142°.

Semicarbazone: decomp. at 272–8°.

Phenylhydrazone: red needles from EtOH. M.p. 218·5° decomp. (212° decomp.).

p-*Nitrophenylhydrazone*: m.p. 248° decomp.

Azine: m.p. 257° decomp.

Semioxamazone: m.p. 325°.

o-*Tolylimide*: yellow needles. M.p. 128°.

p-*Tolylimide*: yellow needles from EtOH. M.p. 121·5°.

Di-Me acetal: needles from MeOH. M.p. 69°. Insol. ligroin.

Parijs, *Rec. trav. chim.*, 1930, **49**, 17.
Bogert, Elder, *J. Am. Chem. Soc.*, 1929, **51**, 534.
Ekeley, Klemme, *J. Am. Chem. Soc.*, 1928, **50**, 2711.

6-Nitropiperonylic Acid

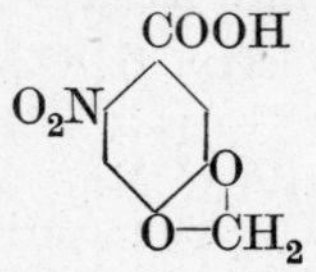

$C_8H_5O_6N$ MW, 211

Yellow needles from H_2O. M.p. 172°. Sol. EtOH, Et_2O.

K salt: yellow needles + $\frac{1}{2}H_2O$. Very sol. H_2O.

Cu salt: green cryst. + $4H_2O$.

Me ester: $C_9H_7O_6N$. MW, 225. Needles from EtOH. M.p. 102°. Sol. warm EtOH. Spar. sol. Et_2O. Insol. H_2O, pet. ether.

Jobst, Hesse, *Ann.*, 1879, **199**, 70.
Oertly, Pictet, *Ber.*, 1910, **43**, 1336.
Mosettig, Czadek, *Monatsh.*, 1931, **57**, 301.

1-Nitropropane

$CH_3{\cdot}CH_2{\cdot}CH_2NO_2$

$C_3H_7O_2N$ MW, 89

Oil. B.p. 130·5–131·5°. D^4 1·0221, $D_4^{24\cdot3}$ 1·0081. $n_D^{24\cdot3}$ 1·40027. Non-miscible with H_2O. Heat of comb. C_v 477·8 Cal.

Neogi, Chowdhuri, *J. Chem. Soc.*, 1916, **109**, 703.
Neogi, *J. Chem. Soc.*, 1914, **105**, 2375.
Meyer, *Ann.*, 1874, **171**, 36.

2-Nitropropane

$CH_3{\cdot}CH(NO_2){\cdot}CH_3$

$C_3H_7O_2N$ MW, 89

Liq. B.p. 115–18° (117–20°). D^0 1·024.

See previous references.

1-Nitropropionic Acid

$CH_3{\cdot}CH(NO_2){\cdot}COOH$

$C_3H_5O_4N$ MW, 119

Needles from CS_2. M.p. 61–61·5° decomp. Sol. H_2O, EtOH, Et_2O, $CHCl_3$, C_6H_6. Spar. sol. CS_2, ligroin.

Et ester: $C_5H_9O_4N$. MW, 147. B.p. 190·5°, 174°/390 mm., 80·5°/10·5 mm. Very sol. EtOH, Et_2O, C_6H_6. Mod. sol. H_2O. *Na salt*: needles from EtOH. M.p. 200°. *NH_4 salt*: cryst. from EtOH. M.p. 119°.

Amide: $C_3H_6O_3N_2$. MW, 118. Needles from $CHCl_3$ or Et_2O. M.p. 68–9°. *NH_4 salt*: m.p. 127–8°.

Steinkopf, Supan, *Ber.*, 1910, **43**, 3246.
Ulpiani, *Atti accad. Lincei*, 1903, **12**, i, 442.
Schmidt, Widman, *Ber.*, 1909, **42**, 1893.

2-Nitropropionic Acid

$O_2N{\cdot}CH_2{\cdot}CH_2{\cdot}COOH$

$C_3H_5O_4N$ MW, 119

Cryst. from $CHCl_3$. M.p. 66–7°. Very sol. H_2O, EtOH, Et_2O. Sol. warm $CHCl_3$. Insol. ligroin. $k = 1{\cdot}62 \times 10^{-4}$ at 25°.

Et ester: $C_5H_9O_4N$. MW, 147. B.p. 161–5°

Chloride: $C_3H_4O_3NCl$. MW, 137·5. B.p 123°/10 mm.

Lewkowitsch, *J. prakt. Chem.*, 1879, **20**, 169.
Barger, Tutin, *Biochem. J.*, 1918, **12**, 405.

***o*-Nitropropiophenone** (*Ethyl 2-nitropheny ketone*)

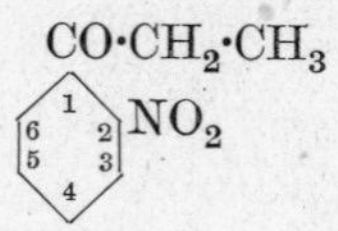

$C_9H_9O_3N$ MW, 17

Cryst. from EtOH. M.p. 85°. B.p. 175°/2 mm., 166–7°/15 mm. Sol. H_2O, EtOH, Et_2O, $CHCl_3$, C_6H_6.

Auwers, Duesberg, *Ber.*, 1920, **53**, 1208.
Comanducci, Pescitelli, *Gazz. chim. ital.*, 1906, **36**, 790.

***m*-Nitropropiophenone** (*Ethyl 3-nitro-phenyl ketone*).

Yellow needles from EtOH. M.p. 100°. Very sol. EtOH, Et_2O, $CHCl_3$, C_6H_6. Sol. boiling H_2O. Spar. sol. petrol. Insol. cold H_2O.

Comanducci, Pescitelli, *Gazz. chim. ital.*, 1906, **36**, 789.

***p*-Nitropropiophenone** (*Ethyl 4-nitrophenyl ketone*).

Yellow cryst. M.p. 114°. Sol. hot H_2O. Very sol. EtOH, Et_2O, $CHCl_3$, C_6H_6.

Comanducci, Pescitelli, *Gazz. chim. ital.*, 1906, **36**, 790.

2-Nitropropyl Alcohol

$CH_3{\cdot}CH(NO_2){\cdot}CH_2OH$

$C_3H_7O_3N$ MW, 105

Thick liq. B.p. 120–2°/32 mm. D^6 1·209. Sol. H_2O, EtOH, Et_2O.

Henry, *Chem. Zentr.*, 1897, I, 741.

3-Nitropropyl Alcohol

$O_2N{\cdot}CH_2{\cdot}CH_2{\cdot}CH_2OH$

$C_3H_7O_3N$ MW, 105

Thick oil. B.p. 138–40°/32 mm. D^{13} 1·173. Sol. H_2O, EtOH, Et_2O.

Henry, *Chem. Zentr.*, 1897, II, 337.

***N*-Nitropropylamine.**
See Propylnitramine.

4-Nitro-*N*-propylaniline

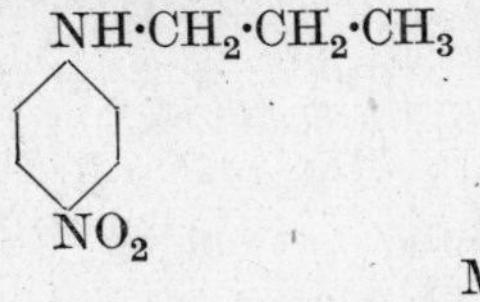

$_9H_{12}O_2N_2$ MW, 180

Yellow cryst. from EtOH. M.p. 64–5°.

Jaeger, v. Kregten, *Chem. Zentr.*, 1912, I, 1302.

***o*-Nitropropylbenzene** (o-*Nitrophenylpropane*)

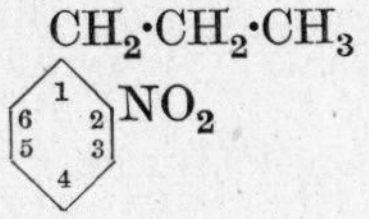

$_9H_{11}O_2N$ MW, 165

Yellow oil. B.p. 133°/26 mm. Odour imilar to nitrobenzene. Volatile in steam.

Brady, Cunningham, *J. Chem. Soc.*, 1934, 122.

***m*-Nitropropylbenzene** (m-*Nitrophenylpropane*).

Yellow oil. B.p. 136°/16 mm. Volatile in team.

See previous reference.

1-Nitropropylene

$CH_3·CH:CH·NO_2$

$C_3H_5O_2N$ MW, 87

Liq. B.p. 37°/10 mm. D_4^{20} 1·0661. n_D^{20} .4527.

Schmidt, Rutz, *Ber.*, 1928, **61**, 2147.

3-Nitropropylene (*Nitroallyl*)

$O_2N·CH_2·CH:CH_2$

$C_3H_5O_2N$ MW, 87

Liq. B.p. 125–30°/760 mm., 87–9°/180 mm. D^{21} 1·051. Sol. EtOH, Et_2O. Insol. H_2O. Volatile in ether vapour. Bitter taste.

Askenasy, Meyer, *Ber.*, 1892, **25**, 1701.

6-Nitroprotocatechuic Acid (6-*Nitro*-3 : 4-*dihydroxybenzoic acid*)

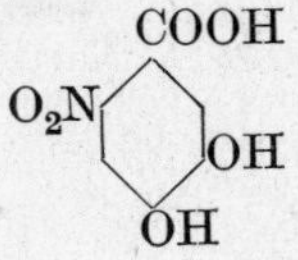

$C_7H_5O_6N$ MW, 199

4-*Me ether* : *see* 6-Nitroisovanillic Acid.
Di-Me ether : *see* 6-Nitroveratric Acid.

Di-Et ether : $C_{11}H_{13}O_6N$. MW, 255. Needles from C_6H_6. M.p. 145·8°.

Perkin, Watson, *J. Chem. Soc.*, 1915, **107**, 206.

2-Nitroprotocatechuic Aldehyde (2-*Nitro*-3 : 4-*dihydroxybenzaldehyde*)

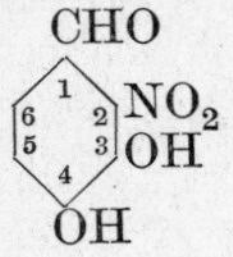

$C_7H_5O_5N$ MW, 183

Yellow needles from Et_2O–ligroin. M.p. 176°.
3-*Me ether* : *see* 2-Nitrovanillin.
4-*Me ether* : *see* 2-Nitroisovanillin.
Di-Me ether : *see* 2-Nitroveratric Aldehyde.

Hayduck, *Ber.*, 1903, **36**, 3528.

5-Nitroprotocatechuic Aldehyde (5-*Nitro*-3 : 4-*dihydroxybenzaldehyde*).

Yellow needles from toluene or H_2O. M.p. 106°. Very sol. H_2O with yellowish-red col.
3-*Me ether* : *see* 5-Nitrovanillin.
4-*Me ether* : *see* 5-Nitroisovanillin.
Di-Me ether : *see* 5-Nitroveratric Aldehyde.

Hayduck, *Ber.*, 1903, **36**, 2933.

6-Nitroprotocatechuic Aldehyde (6-*Nitro*-3 : 4-*dihydroxybenzaldehyde*).

Pale yellow cryst. from 20% EtOH. M.p. 203° decomp. $FeCl_3 \longrightarrow$ dark green col. NaOH $\longrightarrow$ reddish-violet sol.

Azine : orange-yellow amorph. ppt. M.p. about 241°.

Semicarbazone : orange ppt. M.p. 254° decomp.

Phenylhydrazone : reddish-brown ppt. M.p. 203° decomp.

p-*Nitrophenylhydrazone* : red ppt. M.p. 290° decomp.

3-*Me ether* : *see* 6-Nitrovanillin.
4-*Me ether* : *see* 6-Nitroisovanillin.
Di-Me ether : *see* 6-Nitroveratric Aldehyde.

Parijs, *Rec. trav. chim.*, 1930, **49**, 33.

4-Nitropyrazole

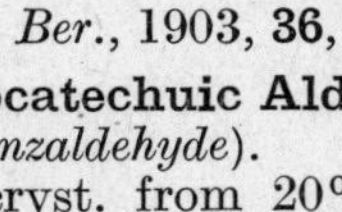

$C_3H_3O_2N_3$ MW, 113

Needles from C_6H_6. M.p. 162°. B.p. 323°.

Buchner, Fritsch, *Ann.*, 1893, **273**, 265.
Knorr, *Ann.*, 1894, **279**, 228.
Hill, Torrey, *Am. Chem. J.*, 1899, **22**, 105.

2-Nitropyridine

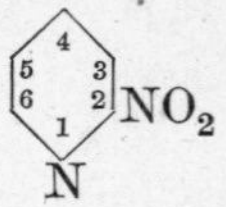

$C_5H_4O_2N_2$ MW, 124

Yellow cryst. M.p. 71°. B.p. 256°. Volatile in steam.

Hertog, Overhoff, *Rec. trav. chim.*, 1930, **49**, 552.
Kirpal, Böhm, *Ber.*, 1931, **64**, 767; 1932, **65**, 680.

3-Nitropyridine.

Needles from C_6H_6–ligroin. M.p. 41°. B.p. 216°. Volatile in steam.

B,HCl: leaflets. M.p. 154°.

B,HNO₃: cryst. from dil. HNO_3. M.p. 150–1°.

B_2,AgNO₃: needles. M.p. 175–6°.

B,HAuCl₄: yellow needles. M.p. 140°.

B_2,H_2PtCl₆: yellow needles. Decomp. at 254°.

Hertog, Overhoff, *Rec. trav. chim.*, 1930, **49**, 552.
Freytag, *J. prakt. Chem.*, 1933, **139**, 44.
Kirpal, Reiter, *Ber.*, 1925, **58**, 699.
Räth, Swiss P., 127,257, (*Chem. Abstracts*, 1929, **23**, 1143).

4-Nitropyridine.

Plates from EtOH.Aq. M.p. 50°.

Kirpal, Böhm, *Ber.*, 1932, **65**, 680.

4-Nitropyrogallol (4-*Nitro*-1 : 2 : 3-*trihydroxybenzene*)

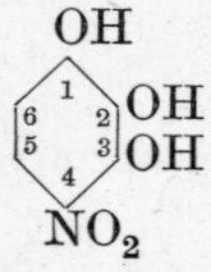

$C_6H_5O_5N$ MW, 171

Yellow needles from H_2O or C_6H_6. M.p. 162°. Sol. EtOH, Et_2O, AcOH, hot H_2O, hot C_6H_6. $FeCl_3$ ⟶ green col.

1 : 3-*Di-Me ether*: $C_8H_9O_5N$. MW, 199. Yellow needles + H_2O from H_2O. M.p. 67–8°. Sol. EtOH, Me_2CO, $CHCl_3$, AcOH. *Acetyl*: yellow cryst. from EtOH. M.p. 92–3°. Sol. Me_2CO, $CHCl_3$. Less sol. AcOH. Insol. H_2O.

Tri-Me ether: $C_9H_{11}O_5N$. MW, 213. Yellow cryst. from EtOH. M.p. 44°. Sol. Et_2O. Mod. sol. EtOH. Insol. H_2O.

Triacetyl: yellow needles from C_6H_6–pet. ether. M.p. 85°. Sol. Et_2O. Spar. sol. EtOH, C_6H_6. Insol. pet. ether.

Benzoyl deriv.: needles from C_6H_6. M.p. 214° decomp. Sol. Et_2O. Spar. sol. H_2O, Et_2O. Alc. $FeCl_3$ ⟶ weak green col.

1-(or 3)-*Carboethoxyl*: yellow leaflets from EtOH.Aq. M.p. 134°. $FeCl_3$ ⟶ green col.

Einhorn, Cobliner, Pfeiffer, *Ber.*, 190-, **37**, 114.
Brand, Collischonn, *J. prakt. Chem.*, 192-, **103**, 329.

5-Nitropyrogallol (5-*Nitro*-1 : 2 : 3-*trihydroxybenzene*).

Brownish-yellow prisms or needles + H_2O from H_2O. M.p. 205° decomp. Spar. sol. cold H_2O. Lime water ⟶ dark red col. $FeCl_3$ ⟶ green col.

1 : 2-(or 1 : 3)-*Di-Me ether*: pale yellow cryst. from EtOH.Aq. M.p. 112–14°. Sol. KOH with orange col.

Tri-Me ether: yellow needles from EtOH, prisms from AcOH. M.p. 100° (99°). Sol. hot EtOH.

Tri-Et ether: $C_{12}H_{17}O_5N$. MW, 255. Needles from EtOH. M.p. 74°.

Harding, *J. Chem. Soc.*, 1914, **105**, 2797.
Schiffer, *Ber.*, 1892, **25**, 722.
Pollak, Goldstein, *Ann.*, 1907, **352**, 168.
Barth, *Monatsh.*, 1880, **1**, 882.
See also Einhorn, Cobliner, Pfeiffer, *Ber.*, 1904, **37**, 104.

5-Nitropyromucic Acid (5-*Nitro-α-furoic acid, 5-nitrofuran-2-carboxylic acid*)

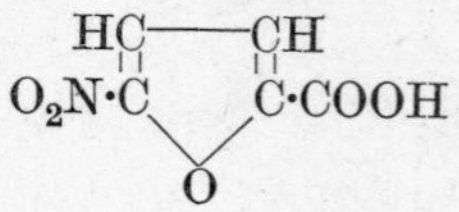

$C_5H_3O_5N$ MW, 157

Pale yellow plates from H_2O. M.p. 184°. Sol. boiling H_2O, EtOH, Et_2O. Spar. sol. C_6H_6. Insol. $CHCl_3$. Sublimes.

Me ester: $C_6H_5O_5N$. MW, 171. Yellowish leaflets. M.p. 78·5°.

Et ester: $C_7H_7O_5N$. MW, 185. Leaflets. M.p. 101°. Sol. boiling EtOH. Spar. sol. Et_2O, C_6H_6.

Chloride: $C_5H_2O_4NCl$. MW, 175·5. Leaflets from $CHCl_3$. M.p. 38°. Sol. $CHCl_3$, Et_2O. Insol. pet. ether.

Amide: $C_5H_4O_4N_2$. MW, 156. Cryst. from EtOH. M.p. 161°. Mod. sol. EtOH. Spar. sol. H_2O, Et_2O.

Anilide: $C_{11}H_8O_4N_2$. MW, 232. Yellow needles from EtOH. M.p. 180°. Spar. sol. EtOH. Insol. H_2O, Et_2O.

p-*Toluidide*: $C_{12}H_{10}O_4N_2$. MW, 246. Yellow prisms. M.p. 162°.

Marquis, *Ann. chim. phys.*, 1905, **4**, 256.
Rinkes, *Rec. trav. chim.*, 1930, **49**, 1169.

3-Nitropyrrole (3-*Isonitrosopyrrolenine*)

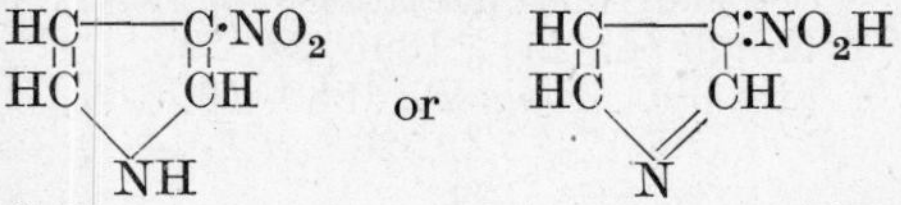

$C_4H_4O_2N_2$ MW, 112

Yellowish prisms or leaflets from ligroin. M.p. 63·5°. At 70° ⟶ a dimer.

Dimer: $C_8H_8O_4N_4$. MW, 224. Yellowish prisms from H_2O. M.p. 101°. Sol. EtOH, Me_2CO, AcOH, AcOEt. Spar. sol. H_2O, $CHCl_3$, C_6H_6. Insol. CCl_4, ligroin.

Hale, Hoyt, *J. Am. Chem. Soc.*, 1915, **37**, 2550.
Angeli, Alessandri, *Atti accad. Lincei*, 1911, **20**, i, 311.

5-Nitroquinaldine (5-*Nitro-2-methylquinoline*)

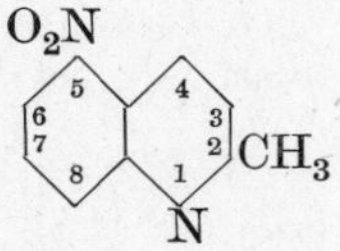

$C_{10}H_8O_2N_2$ MW, 188

Needles from EtOH.Aq. M.p. 82°. Sol. Et_2O. Spar. sol. H_2O. Volatile in steam. $C_6H_5{\cdot}CHO$ at 150° ⟶ 5-nitro-2-styrylquinoline.

Methiodide: orange cryst. from EtOH. M.p. 201°.

Methopicrate: yellow needles. M.p. 151–5°.

Decker, Remfry, *Ber.*, 1905, **38**, 2775.
Doebner, Miller, *Ber.*, 1884, **17**, 1700.

6-Nitroquinaldine.

Yellow needles from H_2O. M.p. 173–4° (164°). Sol. EtOH. Spar. sol. H_2O. Insol. Et_2O. $C_6H_5{\cdot}CHO + ZnCl_2$ ⟶ 6-nitro-2-styrylquinoline.

Methiodide: green cryst. M.p. 214° decomp.

Cohn, Springer, *Monatsh.*, 1903, **24**, 99.
Hamer, *J. Chem. Soc.*, 1921, **119**, 1435.

8-Nitroquinaldine.

Pale yellow needles from EtOH.Aq. M.p. 137°. Sol. EtOH, Et_2O, C_6H_6. Spar. sol. cold H_2O. $C_6H_5{\cdot}CHO + ZnCl_2$ ⟶ 8-nitro-2-styrylquinoline.

Doebner, Miller, *Ber.*, 1884, **17**, 1700.
Claus, Momberger, *J. prakt. Chem.*, 1897, **56**, 378.

5-Nitroquinaldine-3-carboxylic Acid

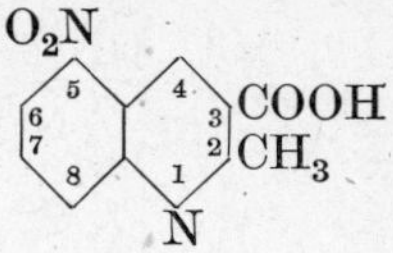

$C_{11}H_8O_4N_2$ MW, 232

Yellow needles from EtOH. M.p. 236°. Insol. H_2O. 10% H_2SO_4 at 150° ⟶ 5-nitroquinaldine.

B,HCl: yellowish-red cryst. M.p. 215° decomp. Sol. H_2O.

Et ester: $C_{13}H_{12}O_4N_2$. MW, 260. Yellowish needles. M.p. 126°. Sol. EtOH, C_6H_6, Et_2O, $CHCl_3$. Spar. sol. H_2O. $B_2H_2PtCl_6$: needles from dil. HCl. Decomp. at 232°.

Claus, Momberger, *J. prakt. Chem.*, 1897, **56**, 375.
Decker, Remfry, *Ber.*, 1905, **38**, 2775.

8-Nitroquinaldine-3-carboxylic Acid.

Yellowish leaflets from EtOH. M.p. 196° decomp. 10% H_2SO_4 at 150° ⟶ 8-nitroquinaldine.

B,HCl: yellow needles. Decomp. at 204°. Spar. sol. H_2O.

Et ester: yellowish cryst. M.p. 137°. Sol. EtOH, Et_2O, C_6H_6, $CHCl_3$. Spar. sol. hot H_2O, pet. ether. Insol. cold H_2O. B_2,H_2PtCl_6: orange-yellow cryst. Decomp. at 175–95°.

See previous references.

5-Nitroquinaldinic Acid (5-*Nitroquinoline-2-carboxylic acid*)

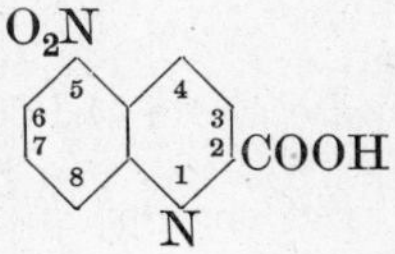

$C_{10}H_6O_4N_2$ MW, 218

Cryst. from H_2O. M.p. 203° decomp. Above m.p. ⟶ 5-nitroquinoline.

Ba salt: needles from H_2O. Spar. sol. H_2O.

Besthorn, Ibele, *Ber.*, 1906, **39**, 2333.

8-Nitroquinaldinic Acid (8-*Nitroquinoline-2-carboxylic acid*).

Cryst. from H_2O. M.p. 177° decomp. Above m.p. ⟶ 8-nitroquinoline.

Ba salt: needles from H_2O. Readily sol. H_2O.

See previous reference.

2-Nitroquinizarin (2-*Nitro*-1 : 4-*dihydroxy-anthraquinone*)

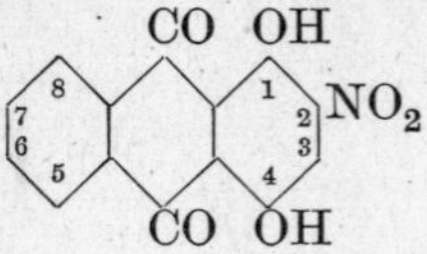

$C_{14}H_7O_6N$ MW, 285

Red needles from $PhNO_2$–AcOH. Dil. NaOH ⟶ bluish-green sol. which decomposes on warming. Conc. H_2SO_4 ⟶ red sol. ⟶ bluish-red with boric acid.

Bayer, D.R.P., 272,299, (*Chem. Zentr.*, 1914, I, 1388).

5-Nitroquinizarin (5-*Nitro*-1 : 4-*dihydroxy-anthraquinone*).

Red cryst. from AcOH. M.p. 244–5°. NaOH ⟶ blue sol. Conc. H_2SO_4 ⟶ rose-pink sol. ⟶ yellowish-red fluor. with boric acid.

Bayer, D.R.P., 90,041.

3-Nitroquinoline

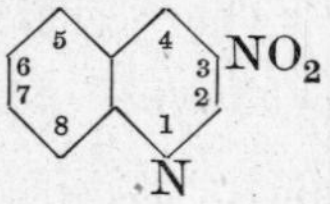

$C_9H_6O_2N_2$ MW, 174

Cryst. M.p. 128°. Volatile in steam.

Badische, D.R.P., 335,197, (*Chem. Zentr.*, 1921, II, 962).

5-Nitroquinoline.

Needles + H_2O from EtOH or Et_2O. M.p. anhyd. 72°. Sol. hot EtOH. Spar. sol. boiling H_2O. Sublimes.

B,HCl : plates. M.p. 214° decomp.

B,HNO_3 : needles from H_2O or EtOH. M.p. 191°.

Methiodide : red prisms from H_2O. M.p. 215° decomp.

Noelting, Trautmann, *Ber.*, 1890, **23**, 3655.
Knueppel, *Ber.*, 1896, **29**, 706.
Decker, *J. prakt. Chem.*, 1901, **63**, 573; *Ber.*, 1905, **38**, 1154.
Le Fèvre, Le Fèvre, *J. Chem. Soc.*, 1935, 1472.

6-Nitroquinoline.

Needles from H_2O or EtOH.Aq. M.p. 153–4° (149–50°). Very sol. C_6H_6. Sol. EtOH, hot H_2O. Spar. sol. Et_2O, ligroin.

B,HBr : cryst. M.p. about 245°. Insol. $CHCl_3$.

Methiodide : orange cryst. M.p. about 245°. Sol. H_2O. Less sol. EtOH.

Tetrachloroiodide : yellow plates from AcOH–HCl. M.p. 131° decomp.

Styphnate : m.p. 189·5–190·5°.

See last reference above and also
Knueppel, *Ber.*, 1896, **29**, 705.
Strache, *Monatsh.*, 1889, **10**, 645.
I.G., F.P., 727,528, (*Chem. Abstracts*, 1932, **26**, 5104).
Hamer, *J. Chem. Soc.*, 1921, **119**, 1432.

7-Nitroquinoline.

Leaflets or needles from EtOH or H_2O. M.p. 132–3°. Sol. Et_2O, $CHCl_3$, hot EtOH. Sublimes.

B,HCl : yellowish needles. M.p. 225° decomp. Hyd. by H_2O.

Methochloride : yellow cryst. M.p. 212–13° decomp.

Methiodide : red plates from H_2O. M.p. 231–2° decomp.

Ethiodide : red needles from EtOH. M.p. 220° decomp.

Knueppel, *Ber.*, 1896, **29**, 706.
Claus, Massau, *J. prakt. Chem.*, 1893, **48**, 170.
Bacharach, Haut, Caroline, *Rec. trav. chim.*, 1933, **52**, 416.

8-Nitroquinoline.

Cryst. from EtOH. M.p. 91–2° (88–9°). Sol. EtOH, Et_2O, C_6H_6. Spar. sol. cold H_2O. $KMnO_4$ ⟶ quinolinic acid.

Knueppel, *Ber.*, 1896, **29**, 705.
Claus, Küttner, *Ber.*, 1886, **19**, 2886.
Besthorn, Ibele, *Ber.*, 1906, **39**, 2333.
Le Fèvre, Le Fèvre, *J. Chem. Soc.*, 1935, 1472.

Nitroquinoline-2-carboxylic Acid.
See Nitroquinaldinic Acid.

Nitroquinoline-4-carboxylic Acid.
See Nitrocinchoninic Acid.

5-Nitroresacetophenone (5-*Nitro*-2 : 4-*dihydroxyacetophenone*)

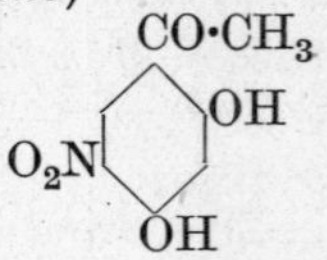

$C_8H_7O_5N$ MW, 197

Yellowish needles from 50% EtOH. M.p. 142°.

4-*Me ether* : nitropeonol. $C_9H_9O_5N$. MW, 211. Needles from EtOH. M.p. 155°.

Oxime : needles from AcOH. M.p. 238°.

'henylhydrazone : orange needles from AcOH. I.p. 215·5–216·5°.

Di-Me ether : $C_{10}H_{11}O_5N$. MW, 225. Ieedles from EtOH. M.p. 131°.

Nencki, Sieber, *J. prakt. Chem.*, 1881, **23**, 150.

Adams, *J. Am. Chem. Soc.*, 1919, **41**, 263.

Lindemann, Könitzer, Romanoff, *Ann.*, 1927, **456**, 307.

2-Nitroresorcinol

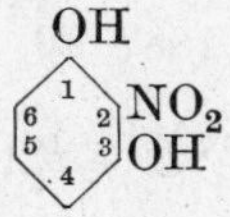

$_6H_5O_4N$ MW, 155

Orange-red prisms from EtOH.Aq. M.p. 5°. Volatile in steam. $k = 0{\cdot}13 \times 10^{-4}$ at 5°. Can be distilled.

Di-Me ether : $C_8H_9O_4N$. MW, 183. Yellow-h needles from EtOH or AcOH. M.p. 131°. ol. $CHCl_3$, C_6H_6, hot EtOH, AcOH. Spar. ol. Et_2O. Prac. insol. ligroin. Turns greenish ı sunlight. Sol. conc. H_2SO_4 with red col.

Di-Et ether : $C_{10}H_{13}O_4N$. MW, 211. M.p. 06–7°.

Kauffmann, de Pay, *Ber.*, 1904, **37**, 726; D.R.P., 145,190, (*Chem. Zentr.*, 1903, II, 973).

Weselsky, Benedikt, *Monatsh.*, 1880, **1**, 887, 894.

4-Nitroresorcinol.

Yellow needles from CCl_4. M.p. 122°. Sol. ItOH, Et_2O, $CHCl_3$, hot C_6H_6. Spar. sol. CCl_4. 'rac. insol. CS_2. $k = 0{\cdot}12 \times 10^{-5}$ at 25°. ublimes. Non-volatile in steam.

1-*Me ether* : $C_7H_7O_4N$. MW, 169. Cryst. I.p. 95°. Volatile in steam.

3-*Me ether* : m.p. 144°.

Di-Me ether : needles from EtOH. M.p. 6–7° (73°). Insol. H_2O, ligroin.

1-*Et ether* : $C_8H_9O_4N$. MW, 183. Yellow eedles. M.p. 79°. Sol. EtOH, Et_2O, AcOH. 'olatile in steam.

3-*Et ether* : needles or plates from EtOH or cOH. M.p. 131°. Non-volatile in steam.

Di-Et ether : m.p. 85°.

Diacetyl : plates from EtOH. M.p. 90–1°.

Dibenzoyl : m.p. 110°.

Weselsky, Benedikt, *Monatsh.*, 1880, **1**, 892.

Blanksma, *Rec. trav. chim.*, 1902, **21**, 322.

Kauffmann, Kugel, *Ber.*, 1911, **44**, 755.

Hollemann, de Mooy, *Rec. trav. chim.*, 1916, **35**, 15.

5-Nitroresorcinol.

Cryst. from H_2O. M.p. 158°.

Me ether : yellow cryst. M.p. 141–2°.

Di-Me ether : yellow needles from AcOEt. M.p. 89°.

Et ether : cryst. from H_2O. M.p. 80°.

Blanksma, *Rec. trav. chim.*, 1908, **27**, 27.

Vermeulen, *Rec. trav. chim.*, 1906, **25**, 26.

4-Nitro-α-resorcylic Acid (4-*Nitro*-3 : 5-*dihydroxybenzoic acid*)

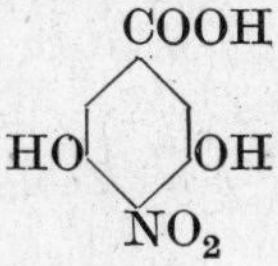

$C_7H_5O_6N$ MW, 199

Dark red needles from H_2O. Decomp. at 212°. Sol. hot H_2O, EtOH, Et_2O. $FeCl_3 \longrightarrow$ reddish-brown col.

Di-Me ether : *see* 4-Nitro-3 : 5-dimethoxybenzoic Acid.

Meyer, *Monatsh.*, 1887, **8**, 430.

5-Nitro-β-resorcylic Acid (5-*Nitro*-2 : 4-*dihydroxybenzoic acid*)

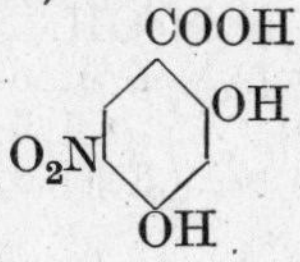

$C_7H_5O_6N$ MW, 199

Yellow leaflets or needles $+ \frac{1}{2}H_2O$ from H_2O. M.p. 215°.

4-*Me ether* : $C_8H_7O_6N$. MW, 213. Needles from H_2O. M.p. about 230° decomp. Spar. sol. H_2O. $FeCl_3 \longrightarrow$ blood-red col.

Me ester : $C_8H_7O_6N$. MW, 213. Leaflets from MeOH. M.p. 167°. Sol. hot EtOH. Spar. sol. H_2O.

Nitrile : $C_7H_4O_4N_2$. MW, 180. Yellow needles from AcOH. M.p. 220°. Sol. EtOH, AcOH. Less sol. C_6H_6. *Diacetyl* : needles from EtOH. M.p. 119°. Sol. AcOH.

Acetyl : cryst. M.p. 150°, solidifies and remelts at 175°. Easily decomp.

Lindemann, Könitzer, Romanoff, *Ann.*, 1927, **456**, 292.

v. Hemmelmayr, *Monatsh.*, 1904, **25**, 25; 1905, **26**, 185.

Gilbody, Perkin, *J. Chem. Soc.*, 1902, **81**, 1056.

3-Nitro-γ-resorcylic Acid (3-*Nitro*-2 : 6-*dihydroxybenzoic acid*)

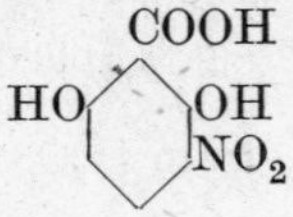

$C_7H_5O_6N$ MW, 199

Nitrile: $C_7H_4O_4N_2$. MW, 180. 6-*Me ether*: $C_8H_6O_4N_2$. MW, 194. M.p. 163°. *Di-Me ether*: *see under* 3-Nitro-2 : 6-dimethoxybenzoic Acid. 6-*Et ether*: $C_9H_8O_4N_2$. MW, 208. M.p. 129°. 6-*Me*-2-*Et ether*: $C_{10}H_{10}O_4N_2$. MW, 222. M.p. 60°. 2-*Me*-6-*Et ether*: m.p. 90°. *Di-Et ether*: $C_{11}H_{12}O_4N_2$. MW, 236. M.p. 66°.

Blanksma, *Chem. Zentr.*, 1912, II, 339.

3-Nitro-β-resorcylic Aldehyde (3-*Nitro*-2 : 4-*dihydroxybenzaldehyde*)

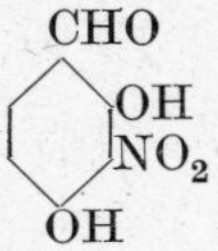

$C_7H_5O_5N$ MW, 183

4-*Me ether*: $C_8H_7O_5N$. MW, 197. Needles from EtOH. M.p. 146–7°. Gives blood-red col. with $FeCl_3$ in MeOH. *Oxime*: needles. M.p. 191–2°. *Phenylhydrazone*: golden-yellow leaflets. M.p. 180°.

Di-Me ether: *see* 3-Nitro-2 : 4-dimethoxybenzaldehyde.

4-*Me*-2-*Et ether*: $C_{10}H_{11}O_5N$. MW, 225. Cryst. M.p. 57–8°.

Srikantia, Iyengar, Santanam, *J. Chem. Soc.*, 1932, 526.

5-Nitro-β-resorcylic Aldehyde (5-*Nitro*-2 : 4-*dihydroxybenzaldehyde*).

Yellowish-brown prisms from C_6H_6. M.p. 148–9°.

4-*Me ether*: needles from EtOH or $CHCl_3$. M.p. 168–9°. Gives red col. with $FeCl_3$. *Oxime*: yellow. M.p. 215–16°. *Phenylhydrazone*: orange. M.p. 197–8°.

Di-Me ether: *see* 5-Nitro-2 : 4-dimethoxybenzaldehyde.

4-*Me*-2-*Et ether*: cryst. M.p. 138–9°. Mod. sol. AcOH, $CHCl_3$. Spar. sol. alcohols. *Oxime*: m.p. 185–6°.

Gattermann, *Ann.*, 1907, **357**, 337.
Rao, Srikantia, Iyengar, *J. Chem. Soc.*, 1925, **127**, 558.

3-Nitrosalicylaldehyde

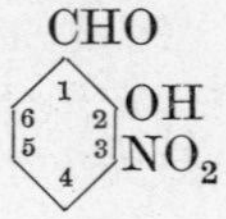

$C_7H_5O_4N$ MW, 1(

Needles from AcOH.Aq. M.p. 109–10°.

Me ether: $C_8H_7O_4N$. MW, 181. Yello prisms from EtOH.Aq. M.p. 102°.

Miller, *Ber.*, 1887, **20**, 1928.

5-Nitrosalicylaldehyde.

Cryst. from AcOH.Aq. M.p. 126°.

Me ether: $C_8H_7O_4N$. MW, 181. Needl from H_2O. M.p. 89–90°. Sol. EtOH, Et_2(*Oxime*: m.p. 183°.

Et ether: $C_9H_9O_4N$. MW, 195. Yellowis needles from EtOH.Aq. M.p. 71–2°. *Sem carbazone*: golden-yellow prisms from EtOI M.p. 234–5° (223°) decomp. *Azine*: leafle from AcOH. M.p. 284–5°. *Phenylhydrazone* red needles from EtOH. M.p. 203–4°.

Oxime: m.p. 225°.

Anil: yellow needles from C_6H_6. M.p. 133 Sol. $CHCl_3$. Mod. sol. C_6H_6, AcOH. Spar. sc MeOH, EtOH, Et_2O, ligroin.

Miller, *Ber.*, 1887, **20**, 1929.
Gattermann, *Ann.*, 1912, **393**, 225.

6-Nitrosalicylaldehyde.

Pale yellow prisms from MeOH or pet. ethe M.p. 54–5°. $FeCl_3 \longrightarrow$ reddish-brown col.

Me ether: cryst. M.p. 111°. Aq.NaOH adde to Me_2CO sol. gives deep blue ppt.

Ashley, Perkin, Robinson, *J. Chem. Soc* 1930, 395.

5-Nitrosalicylamine (5-*Nitro*-o-*hydrox benzylamine*)

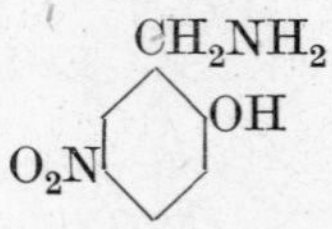

$C_7H_8O_3N_2$ MW, 1(

Yellow leaflets or needles from H_2O. M. 253° decomp. $HNO_2 \longrightarrow$ 5-nitrosaligenin.

B,HCl: yellowish needles. M.p. 250°.

N-*Di-Et*: $C_{11}H_{16}O_3N_2$. MW, 224. Yello needles from EtOH.Aq. M.p. 68–9°. *B,HC* cryst. from EtOH. M.p. 197° decomp.

N-*Chloroacetyl*: yellow needles from Me_2C(M.p. 185–6°.

N-*Benzoyl*: yellowish needles from Me_2CO. [.p. 217–18°.

Einhorn *et al.*, *Ann.*, 1905, **343**, 243; D.R.P., 156,398, (*Chem. Zentr.*, 1905, I, 55).
Tscherniac, D.R.P., 134,979, (*Chem. Zentr.*, 1902, II, 1084).

3-Nitrosalicylic Acid

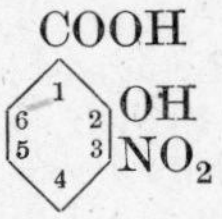

$_7H_5O_5N$ MW, 183

Needles from AcOH. M.p. 148–9° (144°). ol. EtOH, Et_2O, C_6H_6, $CHCl_3$. $k = 1{\cdot}57 \times$ 0^{-2} at 25°.

Me ether: $C_8H_7O_5N$. MW, 197. Needles rom H_2O or EtOH. M.p. 194–5° (191–2°).

Et ether: 3-nitro-2-ethoxybenzoic acid. $_9H_9O_5N$. MW, 211. Needles from H_2O. [.p. 96–7°. *Et ester*: $C_{11}H_{13}O_5N$. MW, 239. ale yellow oil. B.p. 175°/40 mm. Insol. H_2O.

Me ester: $C_8H_7O_5N$. MW, 197. Needles rom MeOH. M.p. 132° (94°).

Et ester: $C_9H_9O_5N$. MW, 211. Plates or eedles from EtOH. M.p. 48·5° (44°). Spar. ol. H_2O, EtOH.

Phenyl ester: *see* β-Nitrosalol.

Chloride: $C_7H_4O_4NCl$. MW, 201·5. Plates rom C_6H_6–pet. ether. M.p. 59–61°.

Amide: $C_7H_6O_4N_2$. MW, 182. Needles rom EtOH, C_6H_6 or H_2O. M.p. 155° (145–6°). eCl_3 ⟶ bluish-red col.

Nitrile: 6-nitro-2-cyanophenol. $C_7H_4O_3N_2$. IW, 164. Golden-yellow prisms from 90% EtOH. M.p. 132–3°. Sol. EtOH, C_6H_6, HCl_3. Spar. sol. Et_2O. Insol. H_2O.

Cousin, Volmar, *Compt. rend.*, 1914, **159**, 330.
Simonsen, Rau, *J. Chem. Soc.*, 1917, **111**, 224.
Zacharias, *J. prakt. Chem.*, 1891, **43**, 435.
Hübner, *Ann.*, 1879, **195**, 34.
Anschütz, Weber, *Ann.*, 1906, **346**, 338.
Meldrum, Hirve, *J. Indian Chem. Soc.*, 1928, **5**, 95.
Fishman, *J. Am. Chem. Soc.*, 1920, **42**, 2296.

4-Nitrosalicylic Acid.

Yellow needles from H_2O or EtOH.Aq. M.p. 235° (226°). Sol. boiling H_2O, EtOH, AcOH. Mod. sol. $CHCl_3$. Spar. sol. C_6H_6. Insol. igroin. Bitter taste. $FeCl_3$ ⟶ red col.

Me ether: $C_8H_7O_5N$. MW, 197. Needles + H_2O from H_2O. M.p. anhyd. 147°. *Me ester*: $C_9H_9O_5N$. MW, 211. Needles from MeOH. M.p. 88–9°.

Phenyl ether: *see* 4-Nitro-*o*-phenoxybenzoic Acid.

Et ester: $C_9H_9O_5N$. MW, 211. Needles from EtOH. M.p. 87°. Sol. Et_2O, C_6H_6. Spar. sol. ligroin. Alc. $FeCl_3$ ⟶ red col. Bitter taste.

Amide: $C_7H_6O_4N_2$. MW, 182. Yellowish needles from EtOH–AcOH. M.p. 192–4°.

Nitrile: 5-nitro-2-cyanophenol. $C_7H_4O_3N_2$. MW, 164. Yellowish needles + H_2O from MeOH.Aq. M.p. anhyd. 160–1°. Very sol. EtOH, Et_2O, AcOH. Spar. sol. hot H_2O, C_6H_6, $CHCl_3$. Hygroscopic. *Acetyl*: yellowish needles from MeOH. M.p. 100°. *Benzoyl*: cryst. from EtOH. M.p. 122°.

Borsche, *Ann.*, 1912, **390**, 10.
Simonsen, Rau, *J. Chem. Soc.*, 1917, **111**, 232.
Ullmann, Wagner, *Ann.*, 1907, **355**, 360.

5-Nitrosalicylic Acid.

Needles from H_2O. M.p. 229–30° (227°). Very sol. EtOH. Sol. hot H_2O. $k = 8{\cdot}9 \times 10^{-3}$ at 25°. $FeCl_3$ ⟶ bluish-red col. Heat with lime ⟶ *p*-nitrophenol. Zn + AcOH ⟶ 5-acetylaminosalicylic acid.

Me ether: $C_8H_7O_5N$. MW, 197. Plates or leaflets from H_2O. M.p. 161°. Sol. EtOH, Me_2CO, hot H_2O, AcOEt. Spar. sol. C_6H_6. Sublimes. *Me ester*: $C_9H_9O_5N$. MW, 211. Needles from EtOH. M.p. 99–100°. *Nitrile*: $C_8H_6O_3N_2$. MW, 178. Cryst. from H_2O. M.p. 126°. Sol. hot EtOH. *Benzoyl*: prisms from EtOH. M.p. 117–18°.

Et ether: 5-nitro-2-ethoxybenzoic acid. $C_9H_9O_5N$. MW, 211. Plates or prisms from H_2O. M.p. 163°. Sol. EtOH, Et_2O. Spar. sol. H_2O. *Et ester*: $C_{11}H_{13}O_5N$. MW, 239. Needles from EtOH. M.p. 98° (68°). *Nitrile*: $C_9H_8O_3N_2$. MW, 192. Cryst. from boiling H_2O. M.p. 101°.

Phenyl ether: *see* 5-Nitro-*o*-phenoxybenzoic Acid.

o-*Tolyl ether*: 4-nitro-2′-methyldiphenyl ether 2-carboxylic acid. Leaflets. M.p. 187–8°. Very sol. EtOH, Et_2O, $CHCl_3$.

m-*Tolyl ether*: 4-nitro-3′-methyldiphenyl ether 2-carboxylic acid. Cryst. M.p. 172°. Very sol. EtOH, Et_2O, $CHCl_3$.

p-*Tolyl ether*: 4-nitro-4′-methyldiphenyl ether 2-carboxylic acid. Cryst. M.p. 165°. Very sol. EtOH, Et_2O, $CHCl_3$.

Me ester: $C_8H_7O_5N$. MW, 197. Cryst. from Et_2O. M.p. 119°.

Et ester: $C_9H_9O_5N$. MW, 211. Needles from EtOH. M.p. 102° (96°). Sol. EtOH, Et_2O. Insol. H_2O.

Phenyl ester: *see* α-Nitrosalol.

2-*Naphthyl ester*: leaflets from EtOH. M.p. 201°.

Amide: $C_7H_6O_4N_2$. MW, 182. Needles from EtOH. M.p. 225°. Sol. hot H_2O, EtOH. $FeCl_3 \longrightarrow$ bluish-red col.

Nitrile: 4-nitro-2-cyanophenol. $C_7H_4O_3N_2$. MW, 164. Yellow needles from H_2O. M.p. 194–6°.

Blanksma, *Chem. Zentr.*, 1908, II, 1827.
Hübner, *Ann.*, 1879, **195**, 15.
Thieme, *J. prakt. Chem.*, 1891, **43**, 469.
Hirsch, *Ber.*, 1900, **33**, 3239.
Simonsen, Rau, *J. Chem. Soc.*, 1917, **111**, 223.
Meldrum, Hirve, *J. Indian Chem. Soc.*, 1928, **5**, 95.
Chattaway, *J. Chem. Soc.*, 1926, 2725.
Kliegl, Hölle, *Ber.*, 1926, **59**, 908.

6-Nitrosalicylic Acid.

Me ether: $C_8H_7O_5N$. MW, 197. Needles from H_2O. M.p. 179–80°. *Amide*: $C_8H_8O_4N_2$. MW, 196. Yellowish needles from EtOH. M.p. 195°. Mod. sol. EtOH, Me_2CO, $CHCl_3$, AcOEt. Spar. sol. Et_2O, C_6H_6, CS_2. *Nitrile*: $C_8H_6O_3N_2$. MW, 178. Needles from $CHCl_3$, Me_2CO or AcOEt. M.p. 171°.

Et ether: *amide*. $C_9H_8O_4N_2$. MW, 210. M.p. 197°. *Nitrile*: $C_9H_8O_3N_2$. MW, 192. Cryst. from EtOH or Me_2CO. M.p. 137°. Spar. sol. H_2O, pet. ether.

Nitrile: 3-nitro-2-cyanophenol. $C_7H_4O_3N_2$. MW, 164. Yellow leaflets from H_2O. M.p. 207–8°. Sol. EtOH, Et_2O. Spar. sol. H_2O. C_6H_6. Insol. ligroin.

Blanksma, *Chem. Zentr.*, 1908, II, 1826.
De Bruyn, *Rec. trav. chim.*, 1883, **2**, 217.

3-Nitrosaligenin (3-*Nitro*-o-*hydroxybenzyl alcohol*)

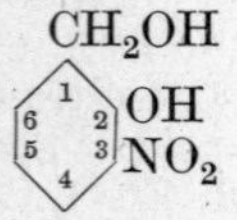

$C_7H_7O_4N$ MW, 169

Yellow needles. M.p. 75°. Sol. EtOH, Et_2O, C_6H_6.

K salt: bright red. Spar. sol. EtOH.

Me ether: $C_8H_9O_4N$. MW, 183. Needles from Et_2O–pet. ether. M.p. 42°. Sol. Et_2O, EtOH, C_6H_6, $CHCl_3$, AcOH. Spar. sol. hot H_2O.

Fishman, *J. Am. Chem. Soc.*, 1920, **42**, 2295.

5-Nitrosaligenin (5-*Nitro*-o-*hydroxybenzyl alcohol*).

Needles. M.p. 128° (126°).

2-*Me ether*: straw coloured needles from EtOH. M.p. 124–5°. Sol. Me_2CO. Mod. sol. hot H_2O, $CHCl_3$. Spar. sol. EtOH. Conc. $H_2SO_4 \longrightarrow$ orange-brown sol.

2-*Acetyl*: pale brown cryst. from C_6H_6. M.p. 106·5–108·5° (106–7°). Sol. EtOH, AcOH. Mod. sol. C_6H_6. Spar. sol. ligroin.

Jacobs, Heidelberger, *J. Biol. Chem.*, 1915, **20**, 675.
Bayer, D.R.P., 136,680, (*Chem. Zentr.*, 1902, II, 1439); D.R.P., 148,977, (*Chem. Zentr.*, 1904, I, 699).

α-Nitrosalol (*Phenyl* 5-*nitrosalicylate*)

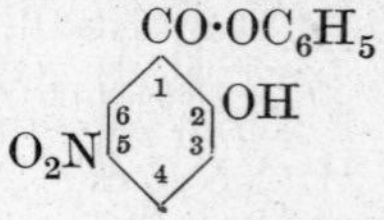

$C_{13}H_9O_5N$ MW, 259

Needles from EtOH or AcOH. M.p. 152°.

Acetyl: needles from EtOH. M.p. 118°.

Knebel, *J. prakt. Chem.*, 1891, **43**, 381.

β-Nitrosalol (*Phenyl* 3-*nitrosalicylate*).

Prisms from EtOH. M.p. 102°.

Acetyl: m.p. 95°.

See previous reference.

***p*-Nitrosoacetanilide.**

See under p-Nitrosoaniline.

***N*-Nitrosoacetanilide**

$$C_6H_5N{<}\begin{matrix}NO\\CO\cdot CH_3\end{matrix}$$

$C_8H_8O_2N_2$ MW, 164

Pale yellow needles from pet. ether. M.p. 50·5–51° decomp. Sol. EtOH, Et_2O, AcOH. Sol. in Et_2O pptes benzene diazonium nitrate. Sol. in ligroin explodes on warming. H_2O_2 in $Et_2O \longrightarrow$ nitrosophenylhydroxylamine. Zn + EtOH (or AcOH) $\longrightarrow$ acetanilide. NaOH $\longrightarrow$ sodium benzene diazoate. $C_6H_6 \longrightarrow$ diphenyl + N + AcOH. Toluene $\longrightarrow$ 2- and 4-methyldiphenyl. $C_6H_5OH \longrightarrow$ 2-hydroxyazobenzene. Dry HCl $\longrightarrow$ acetanilide + NOCl.

Fischer, *Ber.*, 1876, **9**, 463.
v. Pechmann, Frobenius, *Ber.*, 1894, **27**, 651.
Bamberger, *Ber.*, 1894, **27**, 925 (*Footnote*).
Grieve, Hey, *J. Chem. Soc.*, 1934, 1803.

p-Nitrosoaniline (p-*Benzoquinoneimine oxime*)

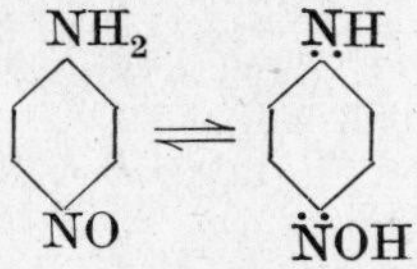

$C_6H_6ON_2$ MW, 122

Steel-blue needles from C_6H_6. M.p. 173–4°. Sol. H_2O with green col. $KMnO_4 \longrightarrow$ *p*-nitroaniline. Sn + HCl $\longrightarrow$ *p*-phenylenediamine. NaOH $\longrightarrow NH_3$ + *p*-nitrosophenol.

N-*Me*: *see* *p*-Nitroso-*N*-methylaniline.

N-*Di-Me*: *see* *p*-Nitroso-*N*-dimethylaniline.

N-*Et*: *see* *p*-Nitroso-*N*-ethylaniline.

N-*Di-Et*: *see* *p*-Nitroso-*N*-diethylaniline.

N-*Propyl*: $C_9H_{12}ON_2$. MW, 164. Steel-blue needles from EtOH.Aq. M.p. 59°. Sol. EtOH, Et_2O, C_6H_6 with green col. Insol. pet. ether.

N-*Dipropyl*: $C_{12}H_{18}ON_2$. MW, 206. Green cryst. from ligroin. M.p. 42°. Sol. EtOH, Et_2O, $CHCl_3$, C_6H_6. *Hydrochloride*: decomp. at 160–5°.

N-*Butyl*: $C_{10}H_{14}ON_2$. MW, 178. Blue needles from EtOH.Aq. M.p. 58–9°. Sol. EtOH, Et_2O, C_6H_6. Spar. sol. H_2O, pet. ether.

N-*Dibutyl*: $C_{14}H_{22}ON_2$. MW, 234. Green oil. *B,HCl*: greenish-yellow cryst. from EtOH–Et_2O. $FeCl_3 \longrightarrow$ red col. *B_2,$CuCl_2$*: green needles from EtOH. M.p. 123–5°. *B,$ZnCl_2$*: m.p. 153° decomp.

N-*Isobutyl*: blue cryst. from EtOH. M.p. 93–4°.

N-*Acetyl*: *p*-nitrosoacetanilide. $C_8H_8O_2N_2$. MW, 164. Green plates or prisms from EtOH. M.p. 174–5° decomp.

Wacher, *Ann.*, 1888, **243**, 291.
Fischer, Schäffer, *Ann.*, 1895, **286**, 151.
Fischer, Hepp, *Ber.*, 1887, **20**, 2475.
Reilly, Hickinbottom, *J. Chem. Soc.*, 1917, **111**, 1030; 1918, **113**, 103.
Jacobs, Heidelberger, *J. Biol. Chem.*, 1915, **21**, 115.

5-Nitroso-o-anisidine (2-*Methoxy*-p-*benzoquinoneimine* 4-*oxime*)

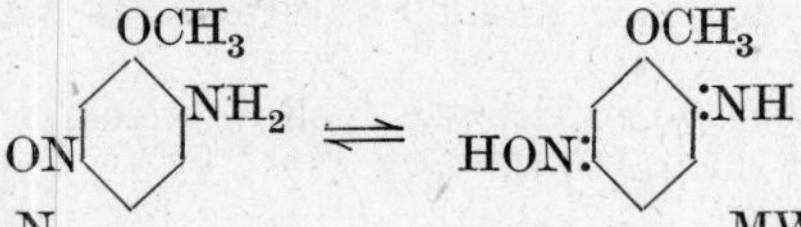

$C_7H_8O_2N_2$ MW, 152

Green cryst. from C_6H_6 or Et_2O. M.p. 107°. Very sol. EtOH, Et_2O, C_6H_6. Spar. sol. H_2O. Sol. acids.

N-*Me*: $C_8H_{10}O_2N_2$. MW, 166. Green plates from Et_2O, blue plates from C_6H_6. M.p. 110°. Sol. MeOH, EtOH, $CHCl_3$, AcOH, C_6H_6. Spar. sol. ligroin.

Best, *Ann.*, 1889, **255**, 178, 186.

6-Nitroso-m-anisidine (3-*Methoxy*-p-*benzoquinoneimine* 4-*oxime*)

$C_7H_8O_2N_2$ MW, 152

Prisms from EtOH. M.p. 209° decomp.

I.G., D.R.P., 561,424, (*Chem. Zentr.*, 1933, II, 444).

Nitrosoanisole.

See under Nitrosophenol.

5-Nitrosoanthranilic Acid (p-*Benzoquinoneimine* 4-*oxime* 2-*carboxylic acid*)

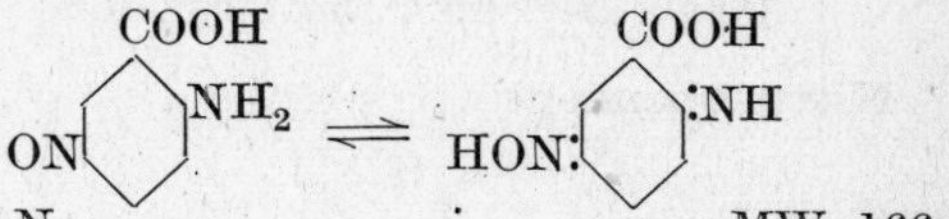

$C_7H_6O_3N_2$ MW, 166

Green cryst. from hot H_2O. Mod. sol. H_2O. Insol. Et_2O.

N-*Me*: *see* 5-Nitroso-*N*-methylanthranilic Acid.

N-*Et*: *see* 5-Nitroso-*N*-ethylanthranilic Acid.

Me ester: $C_8H_8O_3N_2$. MW, 180. Green needles from boiling H_2O. M.p. 167–8°. Dichroic. Sublimes in pale green needles.

Et ester: $C_9H_{10}O_3N_2$. MW, 194. Needles from hot H_2O. M.p. 139°. Spar. sol. EtOH. Dichroic.

Houben, Schreiber, *Ber.*, 1920, **53**, 2358.

1-Nitrosoanthraquinone

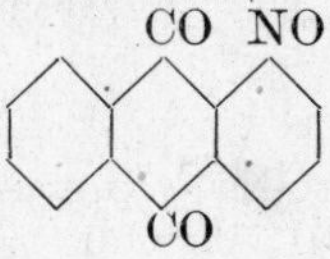

$C_{14}H_7O_3N$ MW, 237

Rose coloured needles from EtOH. M.p. 223–4°.

Beisler, Jones, *J. Am. Chem. Soc.*, 1922, **44**, 2305.

o-Nitrosobenzaldehyde

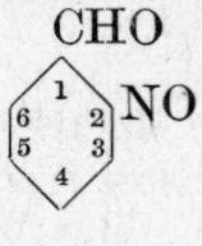

$C_7H_5O_2N$ MW, 135

Needles from CCl_4. M.p. 113–113·5°. Sol. cold Me_2CO, $CHCl_3$, AcOH, warm EtOH, CCl_4, C_6H_6. Spar. sol. Et_2O. Very spar. sol. pet. ether. Dichroic. Volatile in steam with slight decomp.

Bamberger, *Ber.*, 1918, **51**, 624.

_m_-Nitrosobenzaldehyde.

Needles. M.p. 106·5–107°. Gives green sols. in usual solvents. Volatile in steam.

Bamberger, *Ber.*, 1895, **28**, 250.
Alway, *Ber.*, 1903, **36**, 2310.

_p_-Nitrosobenzaldehyde.

Yellow needles from AcOH. M.p. 137–8°. Volatile in steam. Readily polymerised. Conc. $H_2SO_4 \longrightarrow$ deep violet sol.

Kirpal, *Ber.*, 1897, **30**, 1599.
Alway, *Ber.*, 1903, **36**, 2308.

Nitrosobenzene

C_6H_5NO

C_6H_5ON MW, 107

Cryst. from EtOH–Et_2O. M.p. 67·5–68°. B.p. 57–9°/18 mm. Mod. sol. usual solvents. Very volatile. Alk. $H_2O_2 \longrightarrow$ nitrobenzene. Sn + HCl $\longrightarrow$ aniline + chloroaniline. NaOH.Aq. $\longrightarrow$ azoxybenzene.

B_5,CdI_2: cryst. from EtOH. M.p. 114°. Decomp. by H_2O.

Vanino, *Präparative Chemie*, Vol. II, 626.

_o_-Nitrosobenzoic Acid

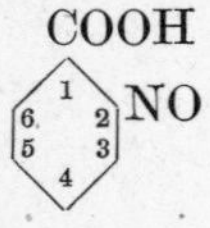

$C_7H_5O_3N$ MW, 151

Cryst. from EtOH or hot AcOH. Darkens at 180°, m.p. 210° decomp. (214°). Sol. hot EtOH, AcOH. Less sol. Et_2O, C_6H_6. Sols. are green.

Me ester: $C_8H_7O_3N$. MW, 165. Needles. M.p. 156·5–157·5° (152–3°). Sol. conc. H_2SO_4 with orange-red col.

Et ester: $C_9H_9O_3N$. MW, 179. Cryst. M.p. 120–1°.

Propyl ester: $C_{10}H_{11}O_3N$. MW, 193. Prisms from C_6H_6 or MeOH. M.p. 95°. Sol. boiling C_6H_6. Mod. sol. hot MeOH.

Isopropyl ester: prisms from C_6H_6–pet. ether. M.p. 117–18°. Sol. boiling MeOH, hot C_6H_6.

Isobutyl ester: $C_{11}H_{13}O_3N$. MW, 207. Needles. M.p. 99–99·5°.

Bamberger, Elger, *Ann.*, 1909, **371**, 339; *Ber.*, 1903, **36**, 3651.
Bamberger, Pyman, *Ber.*, 1909, **42**, 2309, 2326.
Ciamician, Silber, *Ber.*, 1901, **34**, 2044.
Alway, Walker, *Ber.*, 1903, **36**, 2312.

_m_-Nitrosobenzoic Acid.

Cryst. Decomp. at 230°. Gives green sols.

Me ester: cryst. from AcOH. M.p. 93°. Gives bluish-green sols.

Et ester: cryst. from EtOH. M.p. 52–3°. Gives green sols.

Alway, *Ber.*, 1904, **37**, 334.
Alway, Walker, *Ber.*, 1903, **36**, 2313.
Alway, Gortner, *Am. Chem. J.*, 1904, **32**, 401.

_p_-Nitrosobenzoic Acid.

Yellow powder. Decomp. at 250°. Mod. sol. hot EtOH. Spar. sol. AcOH, C_6H_6. Non-volatile in steam.

Me ester: yellow needles from EtOH. M.p. 128·5–129·5°. Sol. hot EtOH, AcOH. Gives green sols.

Et ester: yellow needles from EtOH. M.p. 81°. Sols. are green.

See first two references above and also Alway, Pinckney, *Am. Chem. J.*, 1904, **32**, 399.

5-Nitrosocarvacrol (*Thymoquinone 4-oxime*)

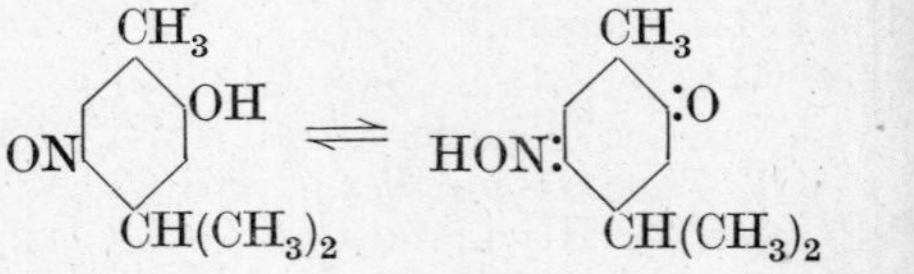

$C_{10}H_{13}O_2N$ MW, 179

Yellowish prisms from C_6H_6, needles from EtOH.Aq. M.p. 153°. Sol. EtOH, Et_2O, $CHCl_3$, C_6H_6. Insol. H_2O. Alk. $K_3Fe(CN)_6 \longrightarrow$ 5-nitrocarvacrol. Sn + HCl $\longrightarrow$ 5-amino-carvacrol.

Phenylsemicarbazone: yellow needles from AcOH. M.p. 204–5°.

Paternò, Canzoneri, *Gazz. chim. ital.*, 1878, **8**, 501.
Mazzara, Plancher, *Gazz. chim. ital.*, 1891, **21**, ii, 155.
Klages, *Ber.*, 1899, **32**, 1518.

4-Nitrosocatechol (*Hydroxy-p-benzoquinone oxime*)

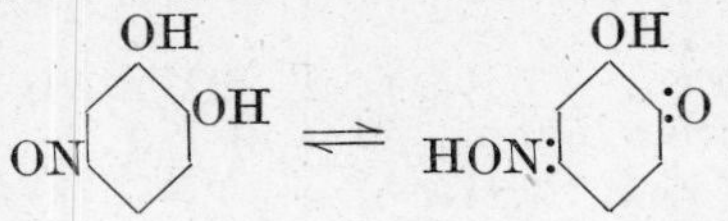

$_6H_5O_3N$ MW, 139

1-*Me ether*: *see* 5-Nitrosoguaiacol.
1-*Et ether*: $C_8H_9O_3N$. MW, 167. Needles. ecomp. on heating. Sol. EtOH, AcOH, C_6H_6. ol. alkalis with red col.

Pfob, *Monatsh.*, 1897, **18**, 479.

m-Nitrosocinnamic Acid

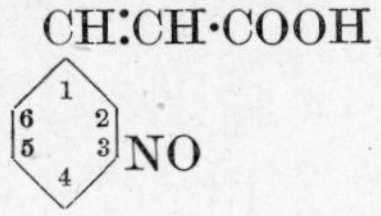

$_9H_7O_3N$ MW, 177

Needles from EtOH. Decomp. at 230°. ols. are green.
Et ester: $C_{11}H_{11}O_3N$. MW, 205. Green lates from EtOH. M.p. 65–6°. Sol. EtOH.

Alway, Bonner, *Am. Chem. J.*, 1904, **32**, 396.

p-Nitrosocinnamic Acid.
Yellow cryst. powder. Decomp. at 220°. ol. EtOH, AcOH.
Me ester: $C_{10}H_9O_3N$. MW, 191. Yellow eedles. M.p. 111–12°.
Et ester: yellow needles from EtOH. M.p. 2–3°. Sol. EtOH, AcOH, C_6H_6 with greenish-ellow col.

See previous reference.

5-Nitroso-o-cresol (*Toluquinone 4-oxime*)

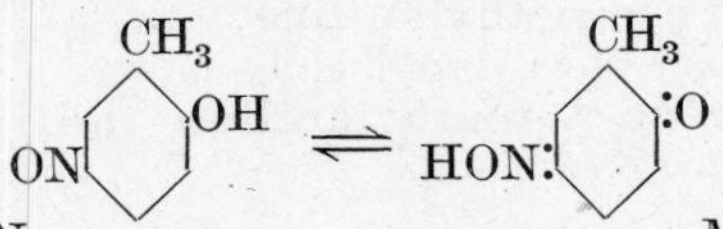

$_7H_7O_2N$ MW, 137

Needles from H_2O. M.p. 134–5° decomp. Sol. EtOH, Et_2O, $CHCl_3$. Less sol. C_6H_6. Spar. sol. H_2O. Alk. $K_3Fe(CN)_6$ ⟶ 5-nitro-*o*-resol.
Me ether: $C_8H_9O_2N$. MW, 151. Pale yellow risms from ligroin. M.p. 73–4°. Sol. most olvents.
2 : 4-*Dinitrophenyl ether*: m.p. 154°.
Acetyl: exists in two stereoisomeric forms. i) Thick prisms. M.p. 112–13°. (ii) Cryst. M.p. 85–7°. Sol. EtOH, Et_2O. Spar. sol. H_2O, ligroin.

Bridge, Morgan, *Am. Chem. J.*, 1898, **20**, 766.
Nölting, Kohn, *Ber.*, 1884, **17**, 370.

6-Nitroso-m-cresol (*Toluquinone 1-oxime*)

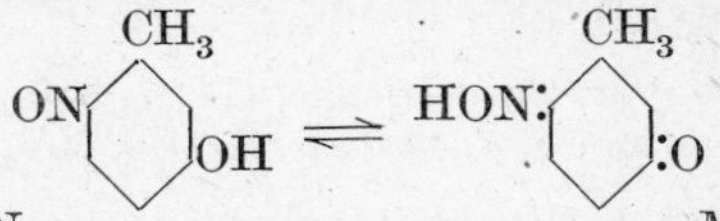

$C_7H_7O_2N$ MW, 137

Needles from H_2O or C_6H_6, prisms from AcOH. M.p. 156° (165°). Sol. EtOH, AcOH, C_6H_6. Less sol. Et_2O. Mod. sol. hot H_2O. Aq. sol. reacts acid. $k = 3{\cdot}5 \times 10^{-7}$ at 25°. Gives Liebermann nitroso reaction.
Me ether: yellow needles from ligroin. M.p. 69°.
Acetyl: prisms from EtOH or ligroin. M.p. 92°.

Bridge, Morgan, *Am. Chem. J.*, 1898, **20**, 774.
Wurster, Riedel, *Ber.*, 1879, **12**, 1799.
v. Erp, *Rec. trav. chim.*, 1911, **30**, 276.

N-Nitrosodiethylamine.
See Diethylnitrosamine.

p-Nitroso-N-diethylaniline

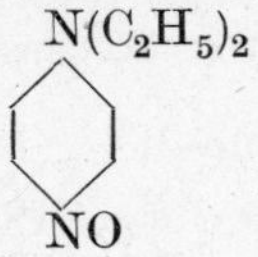

$C_{10}H_{14}ON_2$ MW, 178

Green prisms from Et_2O, green leaflets from Me_2CO. M.p. 87–8° (84°). D^{15} 1·24. Sol. EtOH, Et_2O. Spar. sol. H_2O.

Kopp, *Ber.*, 1875, **8**, 621.

N-Nitrosodimethylamine.
See Dimethylnitrosamine.

p-Nitroso-N-dimethylaniline

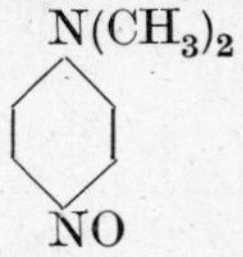

$C_8H_{10}ON_2$ MW, 150

Green plates from Et_2O. M.p. 92·5–93·5° (87·8°). $k = 1{\cdot}95 \times 10^{-10}$ at 25°. Heat of comb. C_p 1123 Cal. Volatile in steam. Readily reduced to *N*-dimethyl-*p*-phenylenediamine. Used as rubber vulcanising accelerator (Accelerene).

B,HCl : yellow needles. M.p. 177° decomp. Heat of comb. C_p 1120·8 Cal.

B,HBr : yellow cryst. Decomp. at 207°.

B,HNO$_3$: m.p. 157–8° decomp.

Trichloroacetate : yellow cryst. M.p. 103°.

Picrate : yellow cryst. Decomp. at 140°. Sol. EtOH. Spar. sol. $CHCl_3$, AcOH, C_6H_6. Insol. Et_2O.

Baeyer, Caro, *Ber.*, 1874, **7**, 810, 963.
Vanino, *Präparative Chemie*, Vol. II, 629.

Nitroso-*N*-dimethyltoluidine.
See under Nitrosotoluidine.

***N*-Nitrosodiphenylamine.**
See under Diphenylamine.

***p*-Nitroso-*N*-dipropylaniline.**
See under *p*-Nitrosoaniline.

***p*-Nitroso-*N*-ethylaniline** (p-*Benzoquinone-ethylimine oxime*)

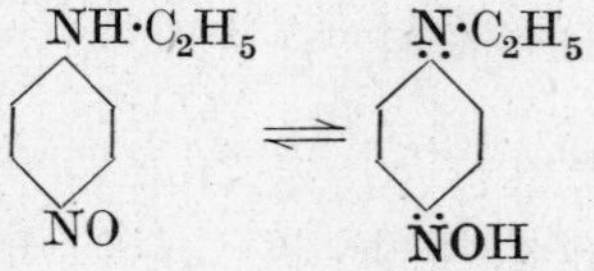

$C_8H_{10}ON_2$ MW, 150

Green plates from C_6H_6. M.p. 78°. Sol. EtOH, Et_2O. Spar. sol. Warm NaOH ⟶ *p*-nitrosophenol + ethylamine.

Oxalate : m.p. 124°.

B$_3$,AgNO$_3$: dark green cryst. from EtOH.Aq. M.p. 121° decomp.

Picrate : yellow needles. M.p. 131°.

Fischer, Hepp, *Ber.*, 1886, **19**, 2993.
Fischer, *Ann.*, 1895, **286**, 156.

***N*-Nitroso-*N*-ethylanthranilic Acid**

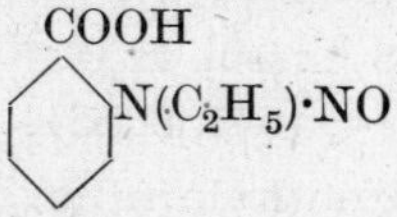

$C_9H_{10}O_3N_2$ MW, 194

Needles. M.p. 90–1°.

Amide : $C_9H_{11}O_2N_3$. MW, 193. Needles from H_2O. M.p. 110°.

Vorländer, v. Schilling, Schrödter, *Ber.*, 1901, **34**, 1645.
Finger, *J. prakt. Chem.*, 1888, **37**, 442.

5-Nitroso-*N*-ethylanthranilic Acid

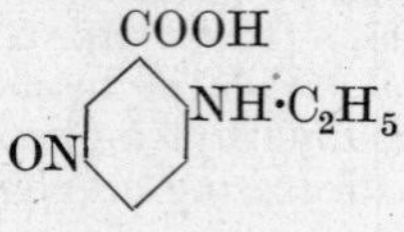

$C_9H_{10}O_3N_2$ MW, 194

Green needles from H_2O, pale green prism[s] from C_6H_6. Decomp. at 142–52°. Sol. EtOH Et_2O.

Me ester : $C_{10}H_{12}O_3N_2$. MW, 208. Gree[n] needles from ligroin. M.p. 91°.

Et ester : $C_{11}H_{14}O_3N_2$. MW, 222. Gree[n] cryst. from ligroin. M.p. 87–8°.

Houben, Brassert, Ettinger, *Ber.*, 1909 **42**, 2752.
Houben, *ibid.*, 3195.

Nitroso-*N*-ethylnaphthylamine.
See under Nitrosonaphthylamine.

Nitroso-*N*-ethyltoluidine.
See under Nitrosotoluidine.

5-Nitrosoguaiacol (2-*Methoxy*-p-*benzoquinone 4-oxime*)

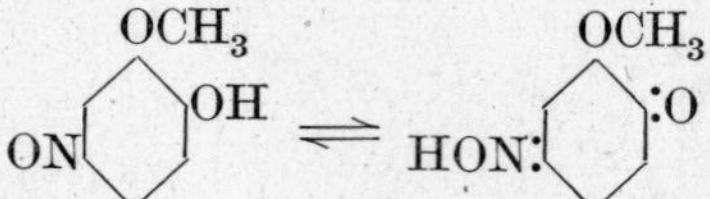

$C_7H_7O_3N$ MW, 15[3]

Yellow leaflets from $CHCl_3$. Decomp. at 165° Sol. EtOH, $CHCl_3$. Less sol. Et_2O, C_6H_6 Spar. sol. H_2O.

Me ether : 4-nitrosoveratrol. $C_8H_9O_3N$ MW, 167. Yellowish-white cryst. M.p. 105–6°. Sol. EtOH, Et_2O, C_6H_6. Spar. sol. H_2O.

Acetyl : cryst. M.p. 156–8° decomp.

Benzoyl : yellow cryst. from EtOH. M.p 188°. Sol. $CHCl_3$, AcOH. Spar. sol. C_6H_6, ligroin. Insol. Et_2O, CS_2.

Pfob, *Monatsh.*, 1897, **18**, 472.
Best, *Ann.*, 1889, **255**, 184.
Bridge, Morgan, *Am. Chem. J.*, 1899, **22**, 486.

Nitrosohydroxyquinoline.
See under Quinolinequinone.

***N*-Nitrosomethylaniline.**
See under Methylaniline.

***p*-Nitroso-*N*-methylaniline** (p-*Benzoquinonemethylimine oxime*)

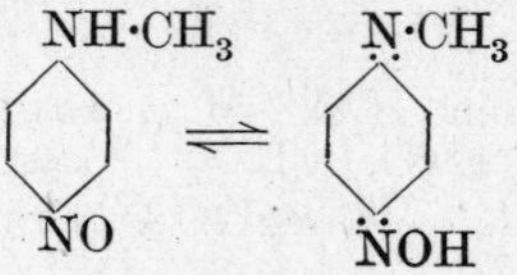

$C_7H_8ON_2$ MW, 136

Bluish plates from C_6H_6. M.p. 118°. Sol. EtOH, Et_2O, $CHCl_3$. Less sol. C_6H_6. Spar. sol. H_2O, ligroin. Possesses acid and basic properties. k (acid) $= 1{\cdot}12 \times 10^{-13}$ at 6°; k (base) $= 1{\cdot}63 \times 10^{-10}$ at 25°.

N-*Et*: $C_9H_{12}ON_2$. MW, 164. Green plates from EtOH.Aq. M.p. 66–7°.
N-β-*Chloroethyl*: $C_9H_{11}ON_2Cl$. MW, 198·5. Green leaflets from EtOH–pet. ether. M.p. 69°.
N-β-*Bromoethyl*: $C_9H_{11}ON_2Br$. MW, 243. Green cryst. from EtOH–pet. ether. M.p. 70°.
N-*Propyl*: $C_{10}H_{14}ON_2$. MW, 178. *B,HCl*: brownish-green leaflets from Et_2O. M.p. 105°. Sol. H_2O, EtOH. Very hygroscopic.

Fischer, Hepp, *Ber.*, 1886, **19**, 2991.
Cain, *Chem. Zentr.*, 1911, I, 1742.
Stoermer, v. Lepel, *Ber.*, 1896, **29**, 2112.

N-Nitroso-N-methylanthranilic Acid

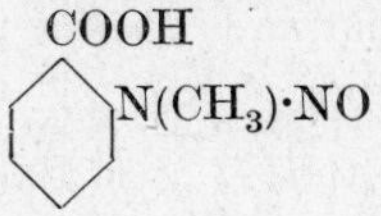

$C_8H_8O_3N_2$ MW, 180

Prisms from C_6H_6. M.p. 128°. Very sol. EtOH, Et_2O. Mod. sol. $CHCl_3$, AcOH. Spar. sol. ligroin.
Me ester: $C_9H_{10}O_3N_2$. MW, 194. Pale yellow oil. B.p. 176–7°/12 mm. $D_4^{18.8}$ 1·2107. $n_D^{18.8}$ 1·55219.
Amide: $C_8H_9O_2N_3$. MW, 179. Needles from EtOH. M.p. 149°.

Fortmann, *J. prakt. Chem.*, 1893, **47**, 400; 1897, **55**, 126.
Zacharias, *J. prakt. Chem.*, 1891, **43**, 449.

5-Nitroso-N-methylanthranilic Acid

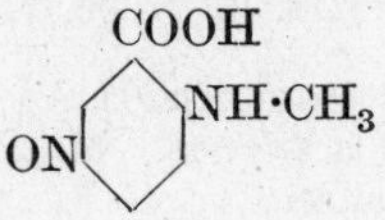

$C_8H_8O_3N_2$ MW, 180

Olive-green cryst. from EtOH or AcOH. Insol. Et_2O, pet. ether. Dil. NaOH on standing ⟶ 5-nitrososalicylic acid.
Me ester: $C_9H_{10}O_3N_2$. MW, 194. Light green needles from pet. ether–ligroin. M.p. 119°. N-*Carbomethoxyl*: green needles from MeOH. M.p. 164–5°. Sol. warm C_6H_6. Insol. pet. ether, ligroin. N-*Carbethoxyl*: green needles from EtOH. M.p. 125° decomp.
Et ester: $C_{10}H_{12}O_3N_2$. MW, 208. Green needles from EtOH. M.p. 89°. Sol. most solvents. Mod. sol. hot H_2O. N-*Carbethoxyl*: needles from EtOH. M.p. 131° decomp.
Phenyl ester: $C_{14}H_{12}O_3N_2$. MW, 256. Green needles from ligroin. M.p. 135–6°.
N-*Carbomethoxyl*: light green. Decomp. at 115–16°.
N-*Carbethoxyl*: green needles. M.p. 115–16° decomp.

Houben, Schreiber, *Ber.*, 1920, **53**, 2351.
Houben, Brassert, *Ber.*, 1907, **40**, 4740.
Houben, Brassert, Ettinger, *Ber.*, 1909, **42**, 2751.
Riedel, D.R.P., 256,461, (*Chem. Zentr.*, 1913, I, 866).

Nitroso-N-methylnaphthylamine.
See under N-Methyl-2-naphthylamine *and* Nitrosonaphthylamine.

Nitrosomethyltoluidine.
See under N-Methyltoluidine *and* Nitrosotoluidine.

Nitrosomethylurea.
See under Methylurea.

1-Nitrosonaphthalene

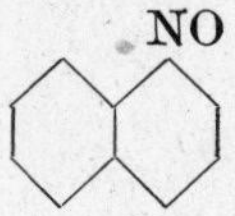

$C_{10}H_7ON$ MW, 157

Pale yellow cryst. from Me_2CO. M.p. 98°. Decomp. about 134°. Sol. AcOEt, $CHCl_3$. Mod. sol. EtOH, Et_2O, C_6H_6. Spar. sol. pet. ether. Decomp. by warm alkalis and acids. Phenol + conc. H_2SO_4 ⟶ blue col.

Willstätter, Kubli, *Ber.*, 1908, **41**, 1938.

2-Nitroso-1-naphthol (1 : 2-*Naphthoquinone 2-oxime*)

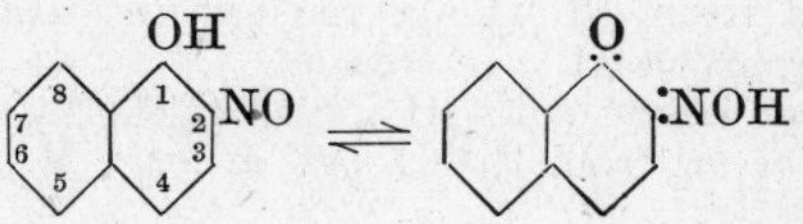

$C_{10}H_7O_2N$ MW, 173

Yellow needles from H_2O or C_6H_6. M.p. 162–4°. Sol. MeOH, EtOH, AcOH, Me_2CO. Less sol. Et_2O, C_6H_6, $CHCl_3$, CS_2, pet. ether. Insol. cold H_2O. Volatile in steam. Conc. H_2SO_4 ⟶ intense red sol.
Me ether: $O{:}C_{10}H_6{:}N{\cdot}OCH_3$. MW, 187. Yellowish-green needles from EtOH.Aq. M.p. 95°. Sol. EtOH. Conc. H_2SO_4 ⟶ intense red sol.
Et ether: $O{:}C_{10}H_6{:}N{\cdot}OC_2H_5$. MW, 201. Greenish-yellow needles. M.p. 101°. Sol. EtOH.
Benzoyl: $O{:}C_{10}H_6{:}N{\cdot}O{\cdot}CO{\cdot}C_6H_5$. Yellow needles from Me_2CO–$CHCl_3$ or AcOEt. M.p. 189–90° (162°). Sol. $CHCl_3$, AcOH, AcOEt.

Less sol. C_6H_6, CS_2. Spar. sol. EtOH, H_2O, Et_2O, ligroin.

Fuchs, *Ber.*, 1875, **8**, 626.
Reverdin, de la Harpe, *Ber.*, 1893, **26**, 1280.
Meisenheimer, Witte, *Ber.*, 1903, **36**, 4169.

4-Nitroso-1-naphthol (1 : 4-*Naphthoquinone-oxime*).

Pale yellow needles from C_6H_6. M.p. 198° (193°). Sol. EtOH, MeOH, Me_2CO, Et_2O. Spar. sol. C_6H_6, $CHCl_3$, CS_2. Sol. alkalis.

Me ether: $O{:}C_{10}H_6{:}N{\cdot}OCH_3$. MW, 187. Pale yellow needles from EtOH, Et_2O or MeOH. M.p. 85° (80–2°). Sol. most solvents. Conc. $H_2SO_4 \longrightarrow$ yellow sol.

Meyer, Lenhardt, *Ann.*, 1913, **398**, 79.
Meisenheimer, *Ann.*, 1907, **355**, 305.

1-Nitroso-2-naphthol (1 : 2-*Naphthoquinone 1-oxime*)

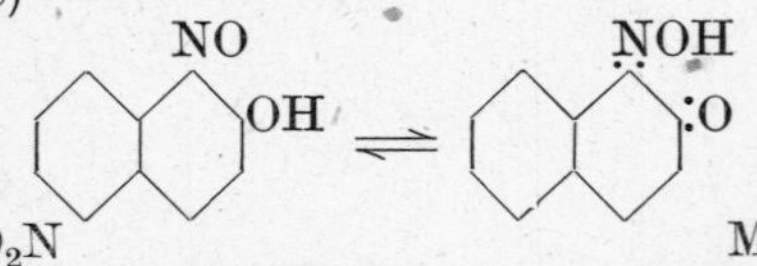

$C_{10}H_7O_2N$ MW, 173

Orange prisms or plates from EtOH or C_6H_6. M.p. 109·5°. Very sol. C_6H_6, CS_2, AcOH. Spar. sol. H_2O, pet. ether. Sol. 42 parts EtOH at 13°. Used as reagent for cobalt.

Me ether: $O{:}C_{10}H_6{:}N{\cdot}OCH_3$. MW, 187. Yellow prisms from ligroin. M.p. 75°. Sol. EtOH, Et_2O, C_6H_6. Mod. sol. hot H_2O. Spar. sol. ligroin. Conc. $H_2SO_4 \longrightarrow$ deep red sol.

Et ether: $O{:}C_{10}H_6{:}N{\cdot}OC_2H_5$. MW, 201. Needles from EtOH.Aq. or ligroin. M.p. 50–60°. Spar. volatile in steam.

Benzyl ether: $O{:}C_{10}H_6{:}N{\cdot}O{\cdot}CH_2{\cdot}C_6H_5$. Pale yellow cryst. from EtOH–pet. ether. M.p. 101° (98°).

Benzoyl: $O{:}C_{10}H_6{:}N{\cdot}O{\cdot}CO{\cdot}C_6H_5$. Yellow cryst. from EtOH. M.p. 114°. Sol. EtOH, AcOH. Spar. sol. H_2O, ligroin.

Benzenesulphonyl: yellow prisms from Me_2CO. M.p. 124–5° decomp. Above m.p. $\longrightarrow$ isomer, m.p. 141°.

Lagodzinski, Hardine, *Ber.*, 1894, **27**, 3076.
Marvel, Porter, *Organic Syntheses*, Collective Vol. I, 403.

2-Nitroso-1-naphthylamine (1 : 2-*Naphthoquinoneimine 2-oxime*)

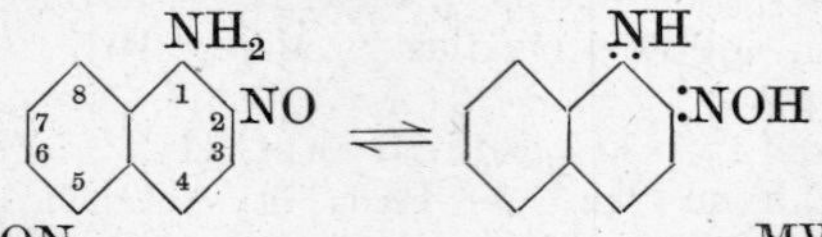

$C_{10}H_8ON_2$ MW, 172

Green prisms from C_6H_6. Sol. EtOH, C_6H_6. Less sol. Et_2O, $CHCl_3$. Spar. sol. hot H_2O, ligroin. Alk. $K_3Fe(CN)_6 \longrightarrow \alpha : \beta$-naphthafurazan.

N-*Et*: $C_{12}H_{12}ON_2$. MW, 200. Green leaflets + H_2O from EtOH.Aq. M.p. 95°.

Harden, *Ann.*, 1889, **255**, 162.

4-Nitroso-1-naphthylamine (1 : 4-*Naphthoquinoneimine 4-oxime*).

N-*Me*: $C_{11}H_{10}ON_2$. MW, 186. Golden cryst. from C_6H_6. M.p. 157° decomp. Mod. sol. EtOH, Et_2O, C_6H_6.

N-*Et*: $C_{12}H_{12}ON_2$. MW, 200. Cryst. from C_6H_6. M.p. 133° decomp. Sol. EtOH, C_6H_6, $CHCl_3$. Insol. ligroin. *Picrate*: green plates. M.p. 174° decomp.

N-*Di-Et*: $C_{14}H_{16}ON_2$. MW, 228. Golden-red cryst. from EtOH. M.p. 165°. Sol. EtOH, Et_2O, C_6H_6. Conc. $H_2SO_4 \longrightarrow$ dark blue sol.

N-*Phenyl*: $C_{16}H_{12}ON_2$. MW, 248. Yellowish-brown leaflets or plates from MeOH.Aq. M.p. 150°.

Fischer, Apitsch, *Ann.*, 1895, **286**, 160.
Kock, *Ann.*, 1888, **243**, 310.
I.G., F.P., 701,915, (*Chem. Abstracts*, 1931, **25**, 4135).

1-Nitroso-2-naphthylamine (1 : 2-*Naphthoquinoneimine 1-oxime*)

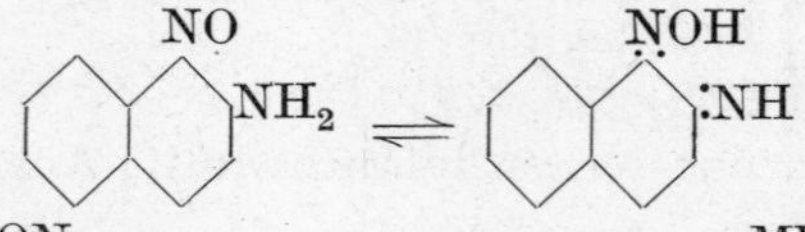

$C_{10}H_8ON_2$ MW, 172

Green needles from EtOH.Aq. M.p. 150–2°. Sol. hot H_2O, org. solvents. Mild ox. agents $\longrightarrow \alpha : \beta$-naphthafurazan.

N-*Me*: $C_{11}H_{10}ON_2$. MW, 186. Dark green prisms or leaflets from MeOH. M.p. 148–9° decomp. *B,HCl*: yellow needles from EtOH–Et_2O. *Picrate*: yellow needles from EtOH.Aq. Mod. sol. EtOH, C_6H_6. Spar. sol. H_2O. *Acetyl*: yellow prisms from C_6H_6. M.p. 140–1° decomp.

N-*Et*: $C_{12}H_{12}ON_2$. MW, 200. Green prisms or plates from MeOH or C_6H_6–ligroin. M.p. 120–1°. N-*Acetyl*: yellow leaflets from EtOH.Aq. Decomp. at 116–18°.

N-*Propyl*: $C_{13}H_{14}ON_2$. MW, 214. Dark green prisms from EtOH. M.p. 115° decomp. Sol. C_6H_6. Mod. sol. EtOH. Spar. sol. H_2O. *B,HCl*: yellow needles from dil. HCl. Decomp. at 280°. *Picrate*: yellow needles from EtOH. Decomp. at 235°. *Acetyl*: yellow leaflets from EtOH.Aq. M.p. 114°.

N-*Butyl*: $C_{14}H_{16}ON_2$. MW, 228. Dark green needles from MeOH, prisms from EtOH. M.p. 98–9°. *Picrate*: yellow needles. Decomp. at 244°. *Acetyl*: leaflets from Et_2O. Turns yellow in air.

N-*Isoamyl*: $C_{15}H_{18}ON_2$. MW, 242. Deep green leaflets or needles from MeOH. M.p. 82°.

N-*Acetyl*: yellow cryst. powder from pet. ether. Decomp. about 136°.

Iljinski, *Ber.*, 1884, **17**, 391.
Fischer, Dietrich, Weiss, *J. prakt. Chem.*, 1920, **100**, 167.

o-Nitrosonitrobenzene

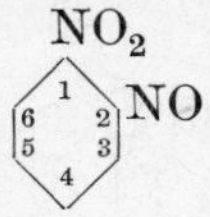

$C_6H_4O_3N_2$ MW, 152

Yellowish cryst. from AcOEt or Me_2CO. M.p. 126–126·5° after turning green at 120°. Sol. hot $CHCl_3$, hot Me_2CO, hot C_6H_6. Mod. sol. hot EtOH, hot ligroin. Spar. sol. Et_2O. Insol. H_2O, pet. ether. Sols. are deep green. Alc. sol. with alkali ⟶ bluish-violet col. Volatile in steam. HNO_3 (D 1·26) ⟶ *o*-dinitrobenzene.

Bamberger, Hübner, *Ber.*, 1903, **36**, 3803.
Meisenheimer, Patzig, *Ber.*, 1906, **39**, 2530.

m-Nitrosonitrobenzene.

Needles. M.p. 90–1° ⟶ a green liq. Sol. $CHCl_3$, Me_2CO, AcOH, C_6H_6, hot EtOH. Spar. sol. Et_2O. Prac. insol. pet. ether. Volatile in steam.

Bamberger, Hübner, *Ber.*, 1903, **36**, 3806.
Alway, Gortner, *Ber.*, 1905, **38**, 1900.
Brand, *ibid.*, 4011.

p-Nitrosonitrobenzene.

Pale yellow needles from EtOH. M.p. 118·5–119° ⟶ a green liq. Sol. with green col. in $CHCl_3$, AcOH, Me_2CO, C_6H_6, hot EtOH. Spar. sol. Et_2O, ligroin. Prac. insol. H_2O. Volatile in steam. HNO_3 (D 1·26) ⟶ *p*-dinitrobenzene. Alc. sol. with alkali ⟶ red col.

Meisenheimer, *Ber.*, 1903, **36**, 4177.
Bamberger, Hübner, *ibid.*, 3809.
Ingold, *J. Chem. Soc.*, 1925, **127**, 517.

4-Nitroso-5-nitro-1-naphthol (5-*Nitro*-1 : 4-*naphthoquinone 4-oxime*)

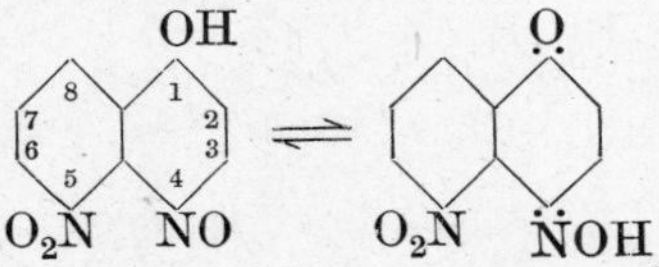

$C_{10}H_6O_4N_2$ MW, 218

Yellow needles from AcOH or EtOH. Decomp. at 250–60°. Sol. EtOH, Et_2O, AcOH, Py. Insol. H_2O. Sol. alkalis with yellow col. Alk. $K_3Fe(CN)_6$ ⟶ 4 : 5-dinitro-1-naphthol. Alk. $KMnO_4$ ⟶ 3-nitrophthalic acid. $SnCl_2$+ HCl in cold ⟶ 4 : 5-diamino-1-naphthol. Sn + HCl in hot ⟶ 5 : 8-dihydroxy-1-naphthylamine.

Acetyl: cryst. from AcOH. M.p. 136°.
Benzoyl: yellow needles. M.p. 210°.

Badische, D.R.P., 90,414.
Friedländer, *Ber.*, 1899, **32**, 3528.
Friedländer, v. Scherzer, *Chem. Zentr.*, 1900, I, 410.
Graebe, Oeser, *Ann.*, 1904, **335**, 145.

4-Nitroso-7-nitro-1-naphthol (7-*Nitro*-1 : 4-*naphthoquinone 4-oxime*).

Yellowish-brown needles from EtOH.Aq. Decomp. above 200°. Sol. conc. H_2SO_4 with yellow col. Sol. alkalis with reddish-brown col. $KMnO_4$ ⟶ 4-nitrophthalic acid.

Graebe, *Ann.*, 1904, **335**, 144.

4-Nitroso-8-nitro-1-naphthol (8-*Nitro*-1 : 4-*naphthoquinone 4-oxime*).

Yellow cryst. from AcOH. Decomp. at 235–40°. Sol. AcOH. Insol. H_2O. Sol. conc. H_2SO_4 and alkalis with yellow col. Alk. $K_3Fe(CN)_6$ ⟶ 4 : 8-dinitro-1-naphthol.

Benzoyl: needles from xylene. M.p. 194°.

Badische, D.R.P., 91,391.
Friedländer, *Ber.*, 1899, **32**, 3528.
Friedländer, v. Scherzer, *Chem. Zentr.*, 1900, I, 411.
Graebe, Oeser, *Ann.*, 1904, **335**, 153.

3-Nitroso-o-nitrotoluene

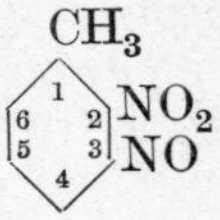

$C_7H_6O_3N_2$ MW, 166

Yellow leaflets from $CHCl_3$. M.p. 92–3° decomp. ⟶ a green col. Spar. sol. usual org. solvents.

Meisenheimer, Hesse, *Ber.*, 1919, **52**, 1173.

4-Nitroso-o-nitrotoluene.

Colourless needles from EtOH.Aq. M.p. 87° ⟶ a green col.

Brand, Zöller, *Ber.*, 1907, **40**, 3333.

5-Nitroso-*o*-nitrotoluene.
Cryst. from EtOH. M.p. 113°. Fuming $HNO_3 \longrightarrow$ 2 : 5-dinitrotoluene.

Kenner, Parkin, *J. Chem. Soc.*, 1920, **117**, 859.

6-Nitroso-*o*-nitrotoluene.
Colourless needles from C_6H_6. M.p. 117° $\longrightarrow$ a green col.

Brand, Zöller, *Ber.*, 1907, **40**, 3331.

2-Nitroso-*m*-nitrotoluene.
Yellow leaflets from EtOH. M.p. 126–7° decomp. $\longrightarrow$ green col. Spar. sol. with green col. in org. solvents. Fuming $HNO_3 \longrightarrow$ 2 : 3-dinitrotoluene.

Meisenheimer, Hesse, *Ber.*, 1919, **52**, 1172.

4-Nitroso-*m*-nitrotoluene.
Pale yellow needles from EtOH. M.p. 145–145·5°. Sol. hot $CHCl_3$, hot Me_2CO, hot C_6H_6. Mod. sol. hot EtOH, hot ligroin. Spar. sol. Et_2O. Sols. are green in col. Fuming $HNO_3 \longrightarrow$ 3 : 4-dinitrotoluene.

Meisenheimer, Hesse, *Ber.*, 1919, **52**, 1167.
Bamberger, Hübner, *Ber.*, 1903, **36**, 3821.

6-Nitroso-*m*-nitrotoluene.
Leaflets from EtOH. M.p. 143–4° decomp. Spar. sol. with green col. in org. solvents. Volatile in steam.

Meisenheimer, Hesse, *Ber.*, 1919, **52**, 1174.

3-Nitroso-*p*-nitrotoluene.
Yellow leaflets from $CHCl_3$. M.p. 141° $\longrightarrow$ a green col. Sol. with green col. in most org. solvents.

Meisenheimer, Hesse, *Ber.*, 1919, **52**, 1169.

***p*-Nitrosophenetole.**
See under p-Nitrosophenol.

***o*-Nitrosophenol** (o-*Benzoquinone monoxime*)

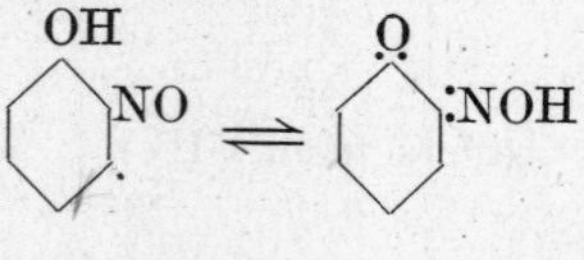

$C_6H_5O_2N$ MW, 123

Pale greenish-yellow needles from pet. ether. Gives deep green sols with org. solvents.
Cu salt: deep red needles from EtOH.
Me ether: *o*-nitrosoanisole. $C_7H_7O_2N$. MW, 137. Leaflets from Me_2CO–pet. ether. M.p. 103° decomp. Sol. EtOH, hot H_2O, AcOH, $CHCl_3$, C_6H_6. Less sol. Et_2O. Spar. sol. pet. ether. $KHSO_4$.Aq. $\longrightarrow$ *o*-nitrophenol. Volatile in steam.

Baudisch, Karzew, *Ber.*, 1912, **45**, 1169.
Baudisch, Rothschild, *Ber.*, 1915, **48**, 1661.
Baudisch, *Ber.*, 1918, **51**, 1058.
Baeyer, Knorr, *Ber.*, 1902, **35**, 3036.

***p*-Nitrosophenol** (p-*Benzoquinone monoxime*)

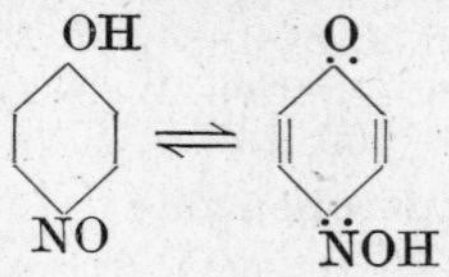

$C_6H_5O_2N$ MW, 123

Pale yellow needles. Turns brown at 124°. Decomp. at 144°. Sol. EtOH, Et_2O, Me_2CO. Mod. sol. H_2O. Sol. alkalis to brown sols turning green on dilution. $k = 3{\cdot}3 \times 10^{-7}$ at 25°. Heat of comb. C_v 715·5 Cal.
Me ether: *p*-nitrosoanisole. $C_7H_7O_2N$. MW, 137. Bluish-green prisms from Et_2O. M.p. 32–4° (23°). Sol. most org. solvents. Spar. sol. ligroin. Insol. H_2O. Easily volatile in steam. Dil. $H_2SO_4 \longrightarrow$ *p*-nitrosophenol.
Et ether: *p*-nitrosophenetole. $C_8H_9O_2N$. MW, 151. Bluish-green prisms from pet. ether. M.p. 33–4°. Sol. EtOH, Et_2O, $CHCl_3$, C_6H_6, pet. ether. Insol. H_2O.

Bridge, *Ann.*, 1893, **277**, 85.
Rising, *Ber.*, 1904, **37**, 44, 46.
Gulinov, *Chem. Zentr.*, 1930, I, 972.
Tseng, Hu, *J. Chinese Chem. Soc.*, 1933, **1**, 183.
See also last reference above.

Nitrosophloroglucinol (2-*Nitroso*-1 : 3 : 5-*trihydroxybenzene*, 3 : 5-*dihydroxy*-o-*benzoquinone 2-oxime*)

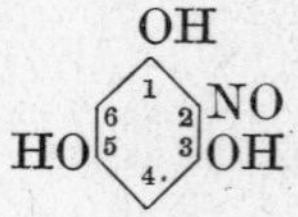

$C_6H_5O_4N$ MW, 155

1-*Me ether*: $C_7H_7O_4N$. MW, 169. Dark red needles from 50% EtOH. Sol. EtOH. Insol. H_2O. Explodes on heating.
1 : 3-*Di-Me ether*: $C_8H_9O_4N$. MW, 183. Yellow needles. M.p. 222°. Sol. boiling H_2O. Mod. sol. EtOH, Et_2O.
1 : 5-*Di-Me ether*: red leaflets. M.p. 175–6°. Sol. EtOH, Et_2O. Spar. sol. boiling H_2O, AcOEt.
1 : 3-*Di-Et ether*: $C_{10}H_{13}O_4N$. MW, 211. Pale yellow needles from EtOH or hot H_2O.

.p. 192–5° decomp. Very sol. EtOH. Insol. t_2O.

1 : 5-*Di-Et ether*: red leaflets from Et_2O. .p. 117°. Sol. EtOH, AcOEt, AcOH. Insol. ›ld H_2O. Sol. dil. alkalis with brownish-ellow col. Sublimes.

Weidel, Pollak, *Monatsh.*, 1897, **18**, 358; 1900, **21**, 29.
Moldauer, *Monatsh.*, 1896, **17**, 464.
Pollak, Gans, *Monatsh.*, 1902, **23**, 949.

2-Nitrosoresorcinol (2-*Nitroso*-1 : 3-*di*-*ydroxybenzene*, 3-*hydroxy*-o-*benzoquinone* 2-*cime*)

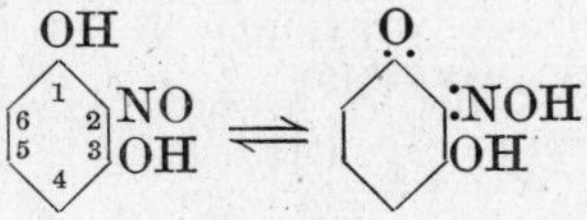

$_6H_5O_3N$ MW, 139

3-*Et ether*: $C_8H_9O_3N$. MW, 167. Yellow eedles. M.p. 102°. Sol. EtOH, Et_2O, C_6H_6.

Kietaibl, *Monatsh.*, 1898, **19**, 544.
Fabre, *Ann. chim.*, 1922, **18**, 49

4-Nitrosoresorcinol (4-*Nitroso*-1 : 3-*dihydr*-*cybenzene*, 4-*hydroxy*-o-*benzoquinone* 1-*oxime*, -*hydroxy*-p-*benzoquinone* 1-*oxime*).

Yellow needles + H_2O from H_2O, brown eedles from $CHCl_3$. Decomp. at 150°. Sol. tOH, Me_2CO, $CHCl_3$. Less sol. H_2O, Et_2O.

1-*Me ether*: $C_7H_7O_3N$. MW, 153. (i) *Stable orm*: yellowish-brown prisms. M.p. 158–9°. ol. EtOH, AcOH, C_6H_6. Spar. sol. H_2O, .cOEt, CS_2. Heat in C_6H_6, CS_2 or toluene ⟶ *bile form*. (ii) *Labile form*: green dichroic lates. At 140° ⟶ *stable form*.

3-*Me ether*: yellow leaflets from AcOH. Decomp. at 160–70°. Sol. EtOH, AcOH. par. sol. AcOEt. Insol. cold Et_2O, CS_2, C_6H_6, groin.

Di-Me ether: $C_8H_9O_3N$. MW, 167. Pale ellow prisms from ligroin. M.p. 115–17°. ol. EtOH, AcOH, C_6H_6. Spar. sol. cold groin.

1-*Et ether*: $C_8H_9O_3N$. MW, 167. (i) *Stable orm*: golden-yellow leaflets. M.p. 146–7°. ol. warm EtOH, Et_2O, C_6H_6. Spar. sol. boiling H_2O. (ii) *Labile form*: green dichroic cryst. t 130–40° ⟶ *stable form*. *Benzoyl*: yellow ryst. from EtOH. M.p. 155°.

3-*Et ether*: yellow leaflets from H_2O, needles rom EtOH. Darkens at 160–70°. Sol. hot I_2O, EtOH. Spar. sol. Et_2O, C_6H_6.

Di-Et ether: $C_{10}H_{13}O_3N$. MW, 195. Pale range cryst. from C_6H_6–ligroin. M.p. 89·5–91·5°. Sol. EtOH, AcOH, Et_2O, C_6H_6. Mod. sol. hot ligroin.

Weselsky, Benedikt, *Monatsh.*, 1880, **1**, 896.
Kietabl, *Monatsh.*, 1898, **19**, 548.
Henrich, *Ber.*, 1902, **35**, 4191; *J. prakt. Chem.*, 1904, **70**, 317.
Henrich, Eisenach, *J. prakt. Chem.*, 1904, **70**, 337.
Henrich, Rhodius, *Ber.*, 1902, **35**, 1478.
Fabre, *Ann. chim.*, 1922, **18**, 49.

5-Nitrososalicylic Acid (p-*Benzoquinone*-*oxime* 2-*carboxylic acid*)

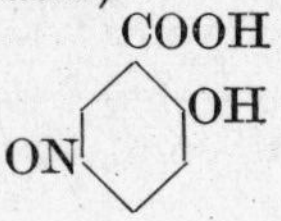

$C_7H_5O_4N$ MW, 167

Green needles from C_6H_6. M.p. 162–3° decomp. (rapid heat.). Explodes at 150° with slow heating. Sol. hot H_2O, Et_2O and most other org. solvents. Gives green sols.

Me ester: $C_8H_7O_4N$. MW, 181. Blue cubes from H_2O or pet. ether. M.p. 89–90°. Sol. EtOH, Et_2O, C_6H_6. Sublimes. Volatile in steam. Alc. $FeCl_3$ ⟶ deep red col.

Et ester: $C_9H_9O_4N$. MW, 195. Blue needles from pet. ether. M.p. 47–8°.

Houben, Brassert, Ettinger, Kellner, *Ber.*, 1909, **42**, 2757.
Houben, Schreider, *Ber.*, 1920, **53**, 2356.

6-Nitrosothymol (*Thymoquinone* 1-*oxime*)

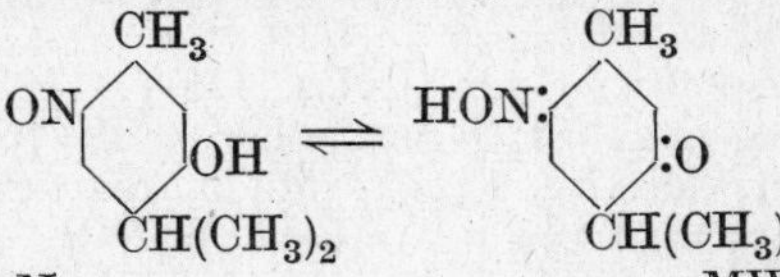

$C_{10}H_{13}O_2N$ MW, 179

Pale yellow needles from $CHCl_3$. M.p. 160–4° (160–2°, rapid heat.). Sol. EtOH, Et_2O, $CHCl_3$. Spar. sol. boiling H_2O. Sol. alkalis with yellowish-red col. Heat of comb. C_p 1334·3 Cal. Alk. $K_3Fe(CN)_6$ ⟶ 4-nitrothymol.

Semicarbazone: m.p. 221–2°.

Schiff, *Ber.*, 1875, **8**, 1500.
Klages, *Ber.*, 1899, **32**, 1518.
Kremers, Wakeman, Hixon, *Organic Syntheses*, Collective Vol. I, 498.

***o*-Nitrosotoluene**

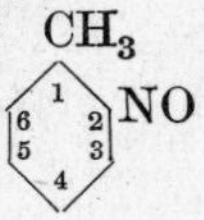

C_7H_7ON MW, 121

Needles or prisms. M.p. 72·5°. Very sol. $CHCl_3$. Sol. EtOH, Et_2O. Volatile in steam.

Bamberger, Rising, *Ann.*, 1901, **316**, 279.
Bamberger, Tschirner, *Ber.*, 1899, **32**, 1677.

***m*-Nitrosotoluene.**
Needles. M.p. 53–53·5°. Volatile in steam.

Bamberger, Rising, *Ann.*, 1901, **316**, 284.
Bamberger, *Ber.*, 1895, **28**, 248.

***p*-Nitrosotoluene.**
Needles from ligroin. M.p. 48·5°. Sol. hot MeOH, C_6H_6. Less sol. hot ligroin. Spar. sol. H_2O. Volatile in steam.

See previous references and also
Wieland, Roseeu, *Ber.*, 1915, **48**, 1119, (*Note* 1).

5-Nitroso-*o*-toluidine (p-*Toluquinoneimine 4-oxime*)

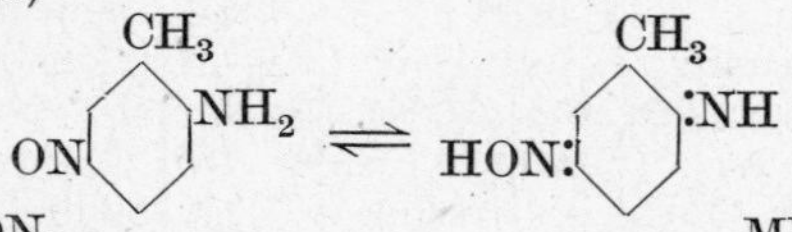

$C_7H_8ON_2$ MW, 136

Green needles from C_6H_6. M.p. 115–16° decomp. Sol. EtOH, Et_2O, hot $CHCl_3$, C_6H_6. Mod. sol. H_2O. Spar. sol. ligroin. Hot NaOH ⟶ 5-nitroso-*o*-cresol.

N-*Me*: $C_8H_{10}ON_2$. MW, 150. Green leaflets from C_6H_6. M.p. 151°. Hot dil. NaOH ⟶ 5-nitroso-*o*-cresol.

N-*Et*: $C_9H_{12}ON_2$. MW, 164. Green leaflets with blue reflex. M.p. 140°.

N-*Butyl*: $C_{11}H_{16}ON_2$. MW, 192. Blue needles from Et_2O–pet. ether. M.p. 50°. Sol. MeOH, Me_2CO, C_6H_6. Mod. sol. CS_2. Spar. sol. Et_2O. Insol. pet. ether. *B,HCl*: greenish-yellow powder. Decomp. at 136°.

N-*Acetyl*: green needles from EtOH. M.p. 135–6°. Spar. sol. Et_2O.

Mehne, *Ber.*, 1888, **21**, 731.
Gnehm, Schröter, *J. prakt. Chem.*, 1906, **73**, 2.
Fischer, Diepolder, *Ann.*, 1895, **286**, 163.
Cain, *J. Chem. Soc.*, 1909, **95**, 715.
Reilly, Hickinbottom, *J. Chem. Soc.*, 1918, **113**, 982.

6-Nitroso-*m*-toluidine (p-*Toluquinoneimine 1-oxime*)

$C_7H_8ON_2$ MW, 136

Steel-blue needles from C_6H_6. M.p. 17 Sol. EtOH, Et_2O. Insol. ligroin.

N-*Di-Me*: $C_9H_{12}ON_2$. MW, 164. Gre leaflets from Et_2O. M.p. 92°. Gives inten green sols.

N-*Acetyl*: green needles from EtOH. M. 128–9°. Sol. AcOH. Spar. sol. Et_2O.

Wurster, Riedel, *Ber.*, 1879, **12**, 1797.
Mehne, *Ber.*, 1888, **21**, 730.
Cain, *J. Chem. Soc.*, 1909, **95**, 715.
I.G., D.R.P., 561,424, (*Chem. Zent* 1933, II, 444).

4-Nitrosoveratrol.
See under 5-Nitrosoguaiacol.

3-Nitroso-*o*-xylene

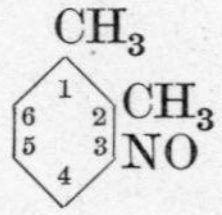

C_8H_9ON MW, 1

Needles. M.p. 91–91·5°. Sol. warm EtO C_6H_6. Mod. sol. Et_2O, $CHCl_3$. Spar. sol. pe ether. Volatile in steam. Reduces alc. Fe ling's on heating.

Bamberger, Rising, *Ann.*, 1901, **316**, 28

4-Nitroso-*o*-xylene.
Pale bluish-green needles from EtOH. M. 44–5°. Very sol. Me_2CO, warm EtOH. Mo sol. pet. ether. Reduces hot Fehling's i presence of EtOH.

See previous reference.

2-Nitroso-*m*-xylene

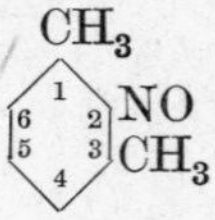

C_8H_9ON MW, 1

Needles. M.p. 144–5° (141·5°). Very s warm EtOH, Me_2CO. Sol. $CHCl_3$, C_6H Spar. sol. Et_2O, ligroin. Does not redu Fehling's.

v. Pechmann, Nold, *Ber.*, 1898, **31**, 560
Bamberger, Rising, *Ann.*, 1901, **316**, 30

4-Nitroso-*m*-xylene.
Prisms from EtOH. M.p. 41·5°. Very so Me_2CO, $CHCl_3$. Sol. pet. ether, ligroin. Vola tile in steam.

See previous references.

2-Nitroso-*p*-xylene

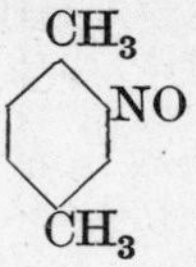

$_8H_9ON$ MW, 135

Needles from EtOH. M.p. 101·5°. Spar. sol. t$_2$O, pet. ether.

Bamberger, Rising, *Ann.*, 1901, **316**, 289.

2′-Nitro-α-stilbazole (2-*o-Nitrostyrylpyr-dine*)

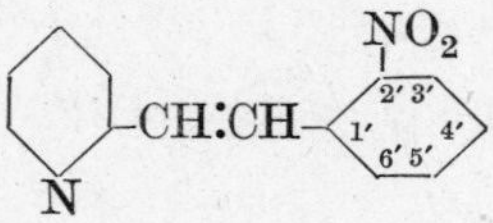

$_{13}H_{10}O_2N_2$ MW, 226

Cis :

Green needles from CS_2. M.p. 95°.

Trans :

Yellow prismatic needles from EtOH. M.p. 01° (95–6°). Sol. $CHCl_3$.

B,HCl : needles from HCl. M.p. 216° (206–2°) decomp.

B,HNO$_3$: needles. M.p. 148°.

B$_2$,H$_2$PtCl$_6$: reddish-yellow cryst. M.p. 20–4° decomp.

Picrate : yellow needles from Me_2CO. M.p. 20°.

Rath, Lehmann, *Ber.*, 1925, **58**, 343.
Shaw, Wagstaff, *J. Chem. Soc.*, 1933, 78.

3′-Nitro-α-stilbazole (3-m-*Nitrostyrylpyr-line*).

Pale yellow needles or leaflets from EtOH. .p. 129° (120°). Sol. EtOH, Et$_2$O, $CHCl_3$, CS_2. par. sol. hot H_2O.

B,HCl : yellow needles from H_2O. M.p. 230°.

B,HAuCl$_4$: pale yellow cryst. powder. .p. 187°.

B,HCl,HgCl$_2$: yellowish needles. M.p. 211° ecomp.

B$_2$,H$_2$PtCl$_6$: yellow needles. M.p. 240° ecomp.

Feist, *Ber.*, 1901, **34**, 465.
Shaw, Wagstaff, *J. Chem. Soc.*, 1933, 78.

4′-Nitro-α-stilbazole (2-p-*Nitrostyrylpyr-line*).

Yellow prisms from pet. ether. M.p. 136° 24°). D_4^{20} 1·319. Darkens in air.

B,HNO$_3$: m.p. 155° decomp.

B$_2$,H$_2$SO$_4$: m.p. 274°.

B,HAuCl$_4$: greyish-yellow powder. M.p.)5° decomp.

B$_2$,H$_2$PtCl$_6$: grey powder. M.p. 206–7° decomp.

Picrate : yellow needles from EtOH. M.p. 272°.

See previous references.

2′-Nitro-γ-stilbazole (4-o-*Nitrostyrylpyr-idine*)

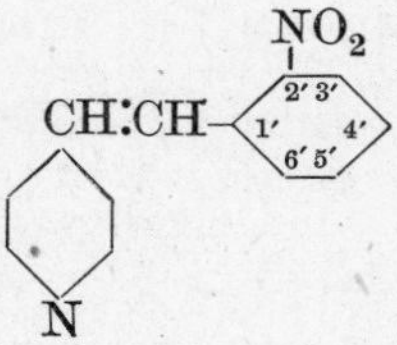

$C_{13}H_{10}O_2N_2$ MW, 226

Cryst. from EtOH. M.p. 98–100°. Sol. EtOH, Et$_2$O, $CHCl_3$, C_6H_6. Insol. H_2O.

B,HCl : m.p. 191–2°.
B,HNO$_3$: m.p. 95°.
B,H$_2$SO$_4$: m.p. 110°.
B,HAuCl$_4$: m.p. 215°.
B$_2$,H$_2$PtCl$_6$: m.p. 206°.
B,HCl,HgCl$_2$: m.p. 175–6°.
Picrate : m.p. 198°.

Löwensohn, *Ber.*, 1907, **40**, 4860.

3′-Nitro-γ-stilbazole (4-m-*Nitrostyrylpyr-idine*).

Brown needles from EtOH. M.p. 138°.

B,HCl : powder from EtOH–Et$_2$O. M.p. 221–2°.

B$_2$,H$_2$PtCl$_6$: yellowish-red leaflets.

Picrate : yellowish-green cryst. Explosive.

Friedländer, *Ber.*, 1905, **38**, 2838.

4′-Nitro-γ-stilbazole (4-p-*Nitrostyrylpyr-idine*).

Yellow needles from EtOH.Aq. M.p. 118–19°. Sol. EtOH, $CHCl_3$, C_6H_6. Mod. sol. Et$_2$O. Insol. H_2O. Sublimes in vacuo.

B,HCl : cryst. from alc. HCl. M.p. 257–8°.

Baumert, *Ber.*, 1906, **39**, 2971.

2-Nitrostilbene

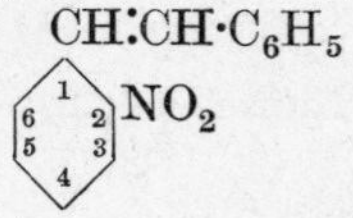

$C_{14}H_{11}O_2N$ MW, 225

Exists in two forms.

(i) Pale yellow needles from EtOH. M.p. 78° (72–3°). Sol. usual solvents. Sol. 100 parts pet. ether at 18°. Irradiation by Hg vapour lamp ⟶ second form.

(ii) Yellow cryst. from pet. ether. M.p. about 42°. Sol. 50 parts pet. ether at 18°.

Stoermer, Prigge, *Ann.*, 1915, **409**, 34.
Pfeiffer, *Ber.*, 1915, **48**, 1052.

4-Nitrostilbene.
Exists in two forms.
(i) Pale yellow needles from EtOH. M.p. 155°. Sol. Et_2O, AcOH, $CHCl_3$, C_6H_6, warm EtOH. Spar. sol. ligroin.
(ii) Brownish-yellow plates from EtOH. M.p. 65°. Sol. EtOH, Et_2O, $CHCl_3$, AcOH, C_6H_6. C_6H_6 + 1 in sunlight ⟶ first form.

Stoermer, Oehlert, *Ber.*, 1922, **55**, 1239.
Pfeiffer, Sergiewskaja, *Ber.*, 1911, **44**, 1109.

Nitrostilbene-α-carboxylic Acid.
See α-Nitrophenylcinnamic Acid.

4-Nitrostilbene-2-carboxylic Acid (5-*Nitro*-o-*styrylbenzoic acid*)

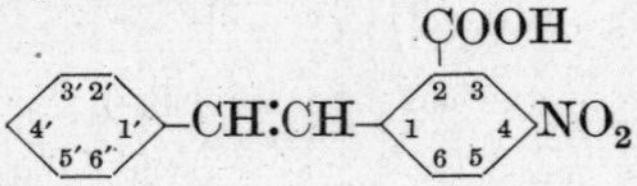

$C_{15}H_{11}O_4N$ MW, 269

Yellow needles from 50% EtOH. M.p. 206°. Sol. Me_2CO. Mod. sol. MeOH, EtOH, Et_2O, AcOH, hot C_6H_6. Insol. ligroin.
Nitrile : 4-nitro-2-cyanostilbene. $C_{15}H_{10}O_2N_2$. MW, 250. Yellow needles from AcOH. M.p. 142°. Sol. boiling AcOH. Mod. sol. C_6H_6. Spar. sol. Et_2O.

Ullmann, Gschwind, *Ber.*, 1908, **41**, 2296.
Pfeiffer, Matton, *Ber.*, 1911, **44**, 1119.

4-Nitrostilbene-3-carboxylic Acid (6-*Nitro*-m-*styrylbenzoic acid*).
Yellow leaflets from AcOH. M.p. 203°. Mod. sol. EtOH, AcOH. Spar. sol. C_6H_6, ligroin.
Nitrile : 4-nitro-3-cyanostilbene. Yellow needles from AcOH. M.p. 187°. Sol. EtOH, Et_2O. Mod. sol. hot AcOH. Spar. sol. C_6H_6, ligroin.

Pfeiffer, *Ber.*, 1918, **51**, 560.

2-Nitrostilbene-4-carboxylic Acid (3-*Nitro*-p-*styrylbenzoic acid*).
Exists in two forms.
(i) *Labile form.*
Pale yellow cryst. from EtOH. M.p. 158°. Sunlight on C_6H_6 sol. + I ⟶ stable form.
Me ester : $C_{16}H_{13}O_4N$. MW, 283. Prisms from EtOH. M.p. 91°. Sunlight ⟶ stable form.
(ii) *Stable form.*
Yellow needles from AcOH. M.p. 236°. Sol. boiling EtOH, AcOH, C_6H_6. Prolonged irradiation ⟶ labile form.
Me ester : needles from MeOH or EtOH. M.p. 122°. Mod. sol. Et_2O, C_6H_6, hot EtOH. Spar. sol. ligroin.
Et ester : $C_{17}H_{15}O_4N$. MW, 297. Pale yellow needles from EtOH. M.p. 124°. Sol. Et_2O, C_6H_6, hot EtOH. Spar. sol. ligroin.
Nitrile : 2-nitro-4-cyanostilbene. Yellow needles or leaflets from AcOH. M.p. 170° Sol. AcOH. Spar. sol. EtOH, Et_2O, C_6H_6.
Quinine salt : pale yellow cryst. from CS_2 M.p. 185°.
Cinchonine salt : yellow prisms from EtOH M.p. 156–7°.
Strychnine salt : yellow cryst. from EtOH M.p. 219°.
Brucine salt : yellow needles from EtOH M.p. 165–8°.

Ullmann, Gschwind, *Ber.*, 1908, **41**, 2295.
Pfeiffer, Matton, *Ber.*, 1911, **44**, 1123.
Stoermer, Oehlert, *Ber.*, 1922, **55**, 1241.
Pfeiffer, du Plessis, Richarz, Stallmann *J. prakt. Chem.*, 1930, **127**, 172.

4-Nitrostilbene-2 : 2′-dicarboxylic Acid

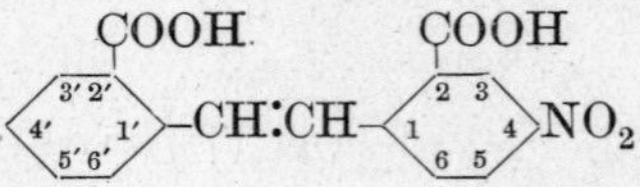

$C_{16}H_{11}O_6N$ MW, 31[illegible]

Yellow needles from *m*-cresol. M.p. about 248°. Very sol. Py. Sol. Me_2CO, warm EtOH AcOH. Spar. sol. hot C_6H_6. Insol. ligroin.
2-*Nitrile* : $C_{16}H_{10}O_4N_2$. MW, 294. Pale yellow needles from AcOH. M.p. 182°. Sol Py. Mod. sol. Me_2CO, hot EtOH. Spar. sol Et_2O, boiling C_6H_6. Insol. pet. ether. *E ester* : $C_{18}H_{14}O_4N_2$. MW, 322. Yellow leaflet or needles from EtOH. M.p. 133°. Sol. AcOH Me_2CO, C_6H_6. Mod. sol. EtOH.

Pfeiffer, Matton, *Ber.*, 1911, **44**, 1118.

2-Nitrostilbene-2′ : 4-dicarboxylic Acid.
Pale yellow needles from *m*-cresol. M.p 257°. Very sol. Py, Me_2CO. Sol. EtOH AcOH. Spar. sol. hot C_6H_6. Insol. ligroin.
Di-Me ester : $C_{18}H_{15}O_6N$. MW, 341. Pale yellow needles from EtOH. M.p. 138°. Sol Et_2O, Me_2CO, AcOH, C_6H_6. Mod. sol. EtOH Insol. ligroin.
4-*Nitrile* : $C_{16}H_{10}O_4N_2$. MW, 294. Yellow needles from *m*-cresol. M.p. 227°. Sol. Py

EtOH, AcOH, Me_2CO. Spar. sol. Et_2O, warm C_6H_6. Insol. ligroin.

See previous reference.

o-Nitrostyrene

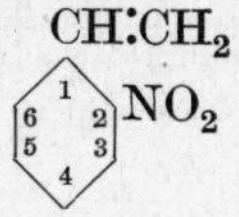

$C_8H_7O_2N$ MW, 149

Oil. F.p. 12–13·5°. Sol. conc. H_2SO_4 with blue col.

Einhorn, *Ber.*, 1883, **16**, 2213.

***m*-Nitrostyrene.**

Yellow oil. F.p. − 5°. Sol. EtOH, Et_2O, $CHCl_3$, AcOH, ligroin.

Prausnitz, *Ber.*, 1884, **17**, 597.

***p*-Nitrostyrene.**

Prisms from ligroin. M.p. 29°. Sol. warm EtOH, Et_2O, C_6H_6, ligroin. Volatile in steam. Decomp. on dist.

Basler, *Ber.*, 1883, **16**, 3003.

ω-Nitrostyrene

$C_6H_5 \cdot CH{:}CH \cdot NO_2$

$C_8H_7O_2N$ MW, 149

Yellowish prisms from EtOH or pet. ether. M.p. 58°. B.p. 250–60° decomp. Very sol. Et_2O, $CHCl_3$, CS_2, C_6H_6. Mod. sol. ligroin. Spar. sol. hot H_2O. Volatile in steam. Heat with $CaCl_2$ ⟶ chloropicrin. In sunlight ⟶ dimeric form, m.p. 180–7° decomp.

Thiele, Haeckel, *Ann.*, 1902, **325**, 7.
Worrall, *Organic Syntheses*, Collective Vol. I, 405.

Nitrostyrylpyridine.

See Nitrostilbazole.

5-Nitro-2-styrylquinoline (5-*Nitrobenzylidenequinaldine*)

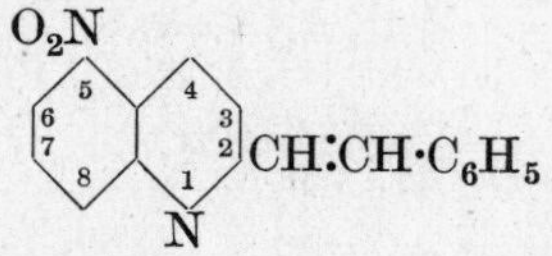

$C_{17}H_{12}O_2N_2$ MW, 276

Pale yellow needles from EtOH.Aq. M.p. 127°. Sol. EtOH, Et_2O, $CHCl_3$, Me_2CO, CS_2, C_6H_6. Insol. H_2O.

B,HCl : golden-yellow needles. M.p. 213°. Sol. EtOH. Insol. H_2O, Et_2O.

B,HAuCl₄ : golden-yellow needles. M.p. 237°. Sol. EtOH. Insol. H_2O, Et_2O.

B₂,H₂PtCl₆ : golden-yellow needles. Decomp. above 199°.

B₂,2HCl,HgCl₂ : yellow needles. M.p. about 249–50°.

Picrate : yellow needles. M.p. 236°. Spar. sol. EtOH. Insol. H_2O, Et_2O.

Schmidt, *Ber.*, 1905, **38**, 3718.

6-Nitro-2-styrylquinoline (6-*Nitrobenzylidenequinaldine*).

Pale yellow needles from EtOH. M.p. 192°. Sol. $CHCl_3$, Me_2CO, CS_2, C_6H_6. Spar. sol. EtOH. Insol. H_2O, Et_2O.

B,HCl : pale yellow needles. M.p. 205°. Sol. EtOH.

B,HAuCl₄ : pale yellow needles. M.p. 218°. Sol. EtOH. Insol. H_2O, Et_2O.

B₂,HCl,HgCl₂ : deep yellow needles. M.p. about 245°. Very spar. sol. EtOH. Insol. H_2O, Et_2O.

See previous reference.

8-Nitro-2-styrylquinoline (8-*Nitrobenzylidenequinaldine*).

Pale yellow needles from EtOH.Aq. M.p. about 142°. Sol. EtOH, C_6H_6, $CHCl_3$, Me_2CO.

B,HCl : reddish-yellow leaflets. Decomp. about 140°. Sol. EtOH.

B,HAuCl₄ : orange needles. M.p. 233°.

B,2HCl,HgCl₂ : orange needles. M.p. 224°.

See previous reference.

2-*o*-Nitrostyrylquinoline (o-*Nitrobenzylidenequinaldine*)

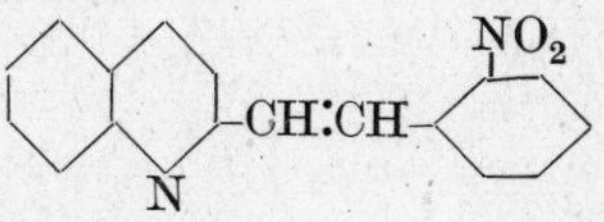

$C_{17}H_{12}O_2N_2$ MW, 276

Yellow cryst. from EtOH. M.p. 103°. Sol. Et_2O, $CHCl_3$, CS_2, C_6H_6. Insol. H_2O.

B,HCl : yellow needles from dil. HCl. M.p. 253°.

B₂,H₂SO₄ : m.p. 238°.

B,HNO₃ : yellow needles from dil. HNO_3. M.p. 178°.

B,HAuCl₄ : yellow needles from EtOH. M.p. 241° decomp.

B₂,H₂PtCl₆ : light brown cryst. M.p. 223°.

Loew, *Ber.*, 1903, **36**, 1666.

2-*m*-Nitrostyrylquinoline (m-*Nitrobenzylidenequinaldine*).

Needles. M.p. 156°.

Picrate: m.p. 261° decomp.

Taylor, Woodhouse, *J. Chem. Soc.*, 1926, 2971.
Wallach, Wüsten, *Ber.*, 1883, **16**, 2009.

2-*p*-Nitrostyrylquinoline (p-*Nitrobenzylidenequinaldine*).

Needles. M.p. 164–5°. Sol. Et_2O, $CHCl_3$, ligroin, hot EtOH.

Bulach, *Ber.*, 1887, **20**, 2047.

4-*o*-Nitrostyrylquinoline (o-*Nitrobenzylidenelepidine*)

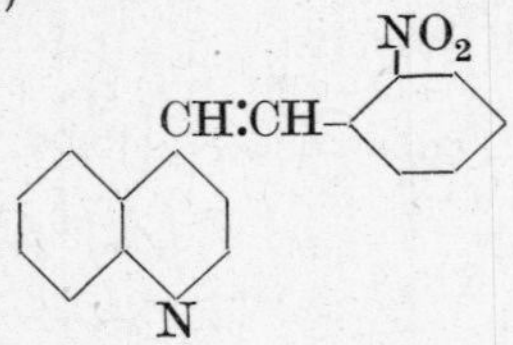

$C_{17}H_{12}O_2N_2$ MW, 276

Yellow leaflets from EtOH. M.p. 162°. Sol. $CHCl_3$, CS_2, C_6H_6. Insol. H_2O.

B,HCl: pale yellow leaflets from dil. HCl. M.p. 257–8°.

B,HNO_3: yellow needles. M.p. 178°.

B,$HAuCl_4$: yellow leaflets from EtOH. M.p. 235°.

B_2,H_2PtCl_6: yellow cryst. Decomp. at 262°.

Methiodide: red cryst. from EtOH. M.p. 237°.

Loew, *Ber.*, 1903, **36**, 1669.

4-*m*-Nitrostyrylquinoline (m-*Nitrobenzylidenelepidine*).

Needles from EtOH. M.p. 131–2°. Spar. sol. cold EtOH.

Heyman, Koenigs, *Ber.*, 1888, **21**, 1429, 2172.

4-*p*-Nitrostyrylquinoline (p-*Nitrobenzylidenelepidine*).

Yellow needles from EtOH. M.p. 221°.

B,HCl: yellow needles from EtOH. M.p. 272°.

B,HBr: yellow needles from EtOH. M.p. 297°.

B,$HAuCl_4$: yellow needles. M.p. 236°.

B_2,H_2PtCl_6: yellowish-brown cryst. Does not melt below 300°.

Picrate: yellow needles from EtOH. M.p. 287°. Sol. MeOH, EtOH, Me_2CO.

Loew, *Ber.*, 1903, **36**, 1670.

Nitrosulphanilic Acid.

See Nitroanilinesulphonic Acid.

4-Nitro-2-sulphobenzoic Acid (4-*Nitrobenzoic acid 2-sulphonic acid*)

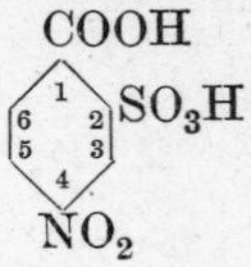

$C_7H_5O_7NS$ MW, 247

Cryst. + H_2O from H_2O. M.p. anhyd. 147°. Very sol. EtOH. PCl_5 at 170° and on pouring into H_2O ⟶ 2-chloro-4-nitrobenzoic acid.

1-*Me ester*: $C_8H_7O_7NS$. MW, 261. Needles from H_2O. M.p. 270° decomp. Very sol. H_2O. Spar. sol. MeOH.

1-*Me-2-Et ester*: $C_{10}H_{11}O_7NS$. MW, 289. Needles. M.p. 68°.

1-*Et-2-Me ester*: prisms from Et_2O. M.p. 80°.

Di-Et ester: $C_{11}H_{13}O_7NS$. MW, 303. Leaflets from EtOH. M.p. 65–6°.

Diphenyl ester: $C_{19}H_{13}O_7NS$. MW, 399. Yellow needles from EtOH. M.p. 119°.

*Di-*o*-nitrophenyl ester*: $C_{19}H_{11}O_{11}N_3S$. MW, 489. Needles from AcOH. M.p. 164°.

*Di-*p*-nitrophenyl ester*: needles. M.p. 152°.

*Di-*p*-tolyl ester*: $C_{21}H_{17}O_7NS$. MW, 427. Needles or plates from C_6H_6. M.p. 117°.

Di-β-naphthyl ester: $C_{27}H_{17}O_7NS$. MW, 499. Needles from AcOH. M.p. 134°.

1-*Me ester 2-chloride*: $C_8H_6O_6NClS$. MW, 279·5. Prisms from MeOH. M.p. 90° (82°).

1-*Et ester 2-chloride*: $C_9H_8O_6NClS$. MW, 293·5. Needles from EtOH. M.p. 68°.

1-*Phenyl ester 2-chloride*: $C_{13}H_8O_6NClS$. MW, 341·5. Needles from AcOH. M.p. 145–7°.

Dichloride: $C_7H_3O_5NCl_2S$. MW, 284. Exists in two forms: (i) cryst. from $CHCl_3$ or Et_2O. M.p. 98° (94°); (ii) needles or plates from pet. ether. M.p. 56–7°. Very sol. $CHCl_3$, Et_2O.

Nitrile: $C_7H_4O_5N_2S$. MW, 228. Prisms + $1H_2O$. M.p. 140–50° (rapid heat.). Very sol. H_2O. 2-*Chloride*: $C_7H_3O_4N_2ClS$. MW, 246·5. Prisms. M.p. 107–8°. Sol. Et_2O, $CHCl_3$, C_6H_6.

Dianilide: $C_{19}H_{15}O_5N_3S$. MW, 397. Needles from EtOH. M.p. 222°.

Kastle, *Am. Chem. J.*, 1889, **11**, 179.
Hausser, *Bull. soc. chim.*, 1891, **6**, 391.
Henderson, *Am. Chem. J.*, 1901, **25**, 1.
Chambers, *Am. Chem. J.*, 1903, **30**, 381.
Holmes, *Am. Chem. J.*, 1901, **25**, 204.

5-Nitro-2-sulphobenzoic Acid (3-*Nitrobenzoic acid 6-sulphonic acid*).

M.p. (+$2H_2O$) 105°, anhyd. 153°. Hydrate sol. H_2O, EtOH. Spar. sol. Et_2O. Insol.

$CHCl_3$, C_6H_6, pet. ether. $PCl_5 \longrightarrow$ 6-chloro-3-nitrobenzoic acid.

Stubbs, *Am. Chem. J.*, 1913, **50**, 195.
Taverne, *Rec. trav. chim.*, 1906, **25**, 64.

5-Nitro-3-sulphobenzoic Acid (3-*Nitrobenzoic acid 5-sulphonic acid*).

Cryst. + $7H_2O$ from H_2O, m.p. 96°; needles + $1H_2O$, m.p. 70°. M.p. anhyd. 159·5° (152°).

3-*Chloride*: $C_7H_4O_6NClS$. MW, 265·5. Needles from C_6H_6. M.p. 170°.

Dichloride: $C_7H_3O_5NCl_2S$. MW, 284. Prisms. M.p. 64°. Sol. C_6H_6, toluene. Mod. sol. CCl_4.

3-*Amide*: $C_7H_6O_6N_2S$. MW, 246. Plates. M.p. 230°.

Diamide: $C_7H_7O_5N_3S$. MW, 245. Needles from H_2O. M.p. 226°.

van Dorssen, *Rec. trav. chim.*, 1910, **29**, 382.
Taverne, *Rec. trav. chim.*, 1906, **25**, 67.
Shah, Bhatt, *J. Chem. Soc.*, 1933, 1373.

2-Nitro-4-sulphobenzoic Acid (2-*Nitrobenzoic acid 4-sulphonic acid*).

Hygroscopic needles + $2\frac{1}{2}H_2O$. M.p. 111°.

1-*Me ester*: cryst. + $2H_2O$. M.p. 95–7°. Hygroscopic. Sol. H_2O, EtOH. Spar. sol. Et_2O. Prac. insol. C_6H_6.

4-*Me ester*: m.p. 140–2°. Insol. cold H_2O.

Di-Me ester: cryst. from C_6H_6. M.p. 86–7°. Sol. Et_2O, hot C_6H_6. Spar. sol. EtOH. Insol. H_2O.

Dichloride: m.p. 160°.

4-*Amide*: m.p. 192°.

Diamide: needles. M.p. 226°.

Wegscheider, Furcht, *Monatsh.*, 1902, **23**, 1139.
Beck, D.R.P., 80,165.
Hart, *Am. Chem. J.*, 1879, **1**, 352.
Hirwe, Jambhekar, *J. Indian Chem. Soc.*, 1933, **10**, 47.

3-Nitro-4-sulphobenzoic Acid (3-*Nitrobenzoic acid 4-sulphonic acid*).

Prisms + $2H_2O$ from H_2O. M.p. 130–1°, anhyd. 159°. Very sol. H_2O. Spar. sol. EtOH. Insol. Et_2O, $CHCl_3$, CS_2.

Hart, *Am. Chem. J.*, 1879, **1**, 343.

6-Nitro-4-sulpho-*m*-toluic Acid (6-*Nitro*-m-*toluic acid 4-sulphonic acid*)

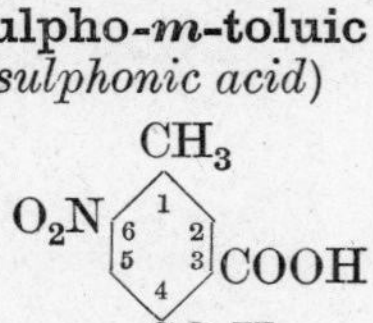

$C_8H_7O_7NS$ MW, 261

Pale yellowish needles + $3H_2O$ from H_2O. M.p. anhyd. 94°. Sol. Me_2CO, AcOH, AcOEt. Insol. Et_2O, CCl_4, ligroin.

Di-Me ester: $C_{10}H_9O_7NS$. MW, 289. Cryst. from MeOH. M.p. 94·5°. Insol. H_2O.

Diphenyl ester: $C_{20}H_{15}O_7NS$. MW, 413. Cryst. from EtOH. M.p. 123°.

4-*Chloride*: $C_8H_6O_6NClS$. MW, 279·5. *Me ester*: $C_9H_8O_6NClS$. MW, 293·5. Plates from ligroin. M.p. 101°. Very sol. EtOH, Et_2O, Me_2CO, $CHCl_3$, C_6H_6. *Et ester*: $C_{10}H_{10}O_6NClS$. MW, 307·5. M.p. 72°.

Dichloride: $C_8H_5O_5NCl_2S$. MW, 298. Exists in two isomeric forms. (i) Rhombohedra or needles from CCl_4. M.p. 134°. (ii) Yellowish needles from CCl_4. M.p. 83°. B.p. 218–20°/21 mm.

Karslake, Bond, *J. Am. Chem. Soc.*, 1909, **31**, 408; 1916, **38**, 1339.

4-Nitro-6-sulpho-*m*-toluic Acid (4-*Nitro*-m-*toluic acid 6-sulphonic acid*).

Needles + H_2O. M.p. 34–7°, anhyd. 150·7°. Very sol. H_2O and most org. solvents.

Di-Me ester: cryst. Decomp. at 302–5°. Very sol. H_2O. Sol. MeOH, EtOH, $CHCl_3$, CCl_4, C_6H_6, ligroin.

Dichloride: prismatic plates from CCl_4 or $CHCl_3$. M.p. 90·2°. Sol. Et_2O, $CHCl_3$. Spar. sol. CCl_4, C_6H_6.

Diamide: $C_8H_9O_5N_3S$. MW, 259. Prismatic plates from 50% EtOH. M.p. 273–4°. Sol. EtOH, Et_2O. Spar. sol. H_2O.

Dianilide: $C_{20}H_{17}O_5N_3S$. MW, 411. Yellow plates from 70% EtOH. M.p. 244·8°. Sol. most org. solvents.

Di-o-toluidide: $C_{22}H_{21}O_5N_3S$. MW, 439. Greenish-yellow prisms from 70% EtOH. M.p. 238·7°. Sol. most org. solvents. Insol. H_2O.

Di-m-toluidide: yellow needles or prisms from EtOH.Aq. M.p. 208·8°.

Di-p-toluidide: needles from EtOH.Aq. M.p. 241·8°.

Karslake, Bond, *J. Am. Chem. Soc.*, 1909, **31**, 406.
Karslake, Huston, *ibid.*, 1058.

2-Nitroterephthalic Acid

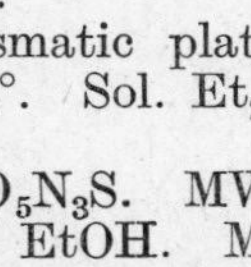

$C_8H_5O_6N$ MW, 211

Needles from hot H_2O. M.p. 268° (262–3°). Sol. hot H_2O, EtOH, Et_2O. k (first) $= 1{\cdot}87 \times 10^{-2}$ at 25°; (second) $= 2{\cdot}0 \times 10^{-4}$ at 25°.

1-*Me ester*: $C_9H_7O_6N$. MW, 225. Cryst. from C_6H_6 or H_2O. M.p. 175–6°. $k = 7{\cdot}7 \times 10^{-4}$ at 25°. l-*Menthyl ester*: cryst. from C_6H_6. M.p. 72–4°. D_4^{20} 1·133. $[\alpha]_D^{20}$ − 68·31°.

4-*Me ester*: needles from C_6H_6. M.p. 133·5–135°. Mod. sol. H_2O. $k = 1{\cdot}9 \times 10^{-2}$ at 25°. l-*Menthyl ester*: needles. M.p. 78–9°. $[\alpha]_D^{18}$ − 141·7° in C_6H_6.

Di-Me ester: $C_{10}H_9O_6N$. MW, 239. Plates from EtOH. M.p. 76°. Sol. C_6H_6. Spar. sol. pet. ether. Volatile in steam.

1-*Et ester*: $C_{10}H_9O_6N$. MW, 239. Cryst. from C_6H_6. M.p. 146–8°. l-*Menthyl ester*: cryst. from C_6H_6. M.p. 48°. D_4^{20} 1·127. $[\alpha]_D^{20}$ − 65·55°.

4-*Et ester*: l-*menthyl ester*, liq. D_4^{20} 1·110. $[\alpha]_D^{20}$ − 91·58°, $[\alpha]_D^{18}$ − 130·5° in C_6H_6.

Di-Et ester: $C_{12}H_{13}O_6N$. MW, 267. Needles from EtOH.Aq. M.p. 57°. Sol. EtOH, Et_2O, Me_2CO, C_6H_6. Mod. sol. H_2O.

1-*Propyl ester*: $C_{11}H_{11}O_6N$. MW, 253. Cryst. from C_6H_6. M.p. 135–7°. l-*Menthyl ester*: b.p. 192°/6 mm. D_4^{20} 1·130. $[\alpha]_D^{20}$ − 62·25°.

4-*Propyl ester*: l-*menthyl ester*, thick liq. D_4^{20} 1·110. $[\alpha]_D^{20}$ − 92·74°, $[\alpha]_D^{18}$ − 129·7° in C_6H_6.

Dipropyl ester: $C_{14}H_{17}O_6N$. MW, 295. Oil. B.p. 228–30°/18 mm.

1-*Butyl ester*: $C_{12}H_{13}O_6N$. MW, 267. Cryst. from C_6H_6. M.p. 132–4°. l-*Menthyl ester*: b.p. 215°/6 mm. D_4^{20} 1·136. $[\alpha]_D^{20}$ − 60·23°.

4-*Butyl ester*: l-*menthyl ester*, thick liq. D_4^{20} 1·099. $[\alpha]_D^{20}$ − 90·51°, $[\alpha]_D^{18}$ − 124·7° in C_6H_6.

1-l-*Menthyl ester*: cryst. from EtOH.Aq. M.p. 75°.

Di-l-*Menthyl ester*: needles from EtOH. M.p. 88°. $[\alpha]_D^{15}$ − 160·5° in C_6H_6.

Dichloride: $C_8H_3O_4NCl_2$. MW, 248. B.p. 174°/8 mm.

Wegscheider, *Monatsh.*, 1900, **21**, 622; 1902, **23**, 407.
Wegscheider, Gehringer, *Monatsh.*, 1908, **29**, 529.
Cohen, de Pennington, *J. Chem. Soc.*, 1918, **113**, 64.
Kauffmann, Weissel, *Ann.*, 1912, **393**, 10.
Soderman, Johnson, *J. Am. Chem. Soc.*, 1925, **47**, 1393.

5-Nitro-1 : 2 : 3 : 4-tetrahydronaphthalene (5-*Nitrotetralin*)

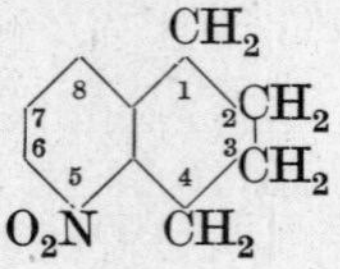

$C_{10}H_{11}O_2N$ MW, 177

4-Nitro-5 : 6 : 7 : 8-tetrahydro-2-naphthol

Cryst. from MeOH. M.p. 34°. B.p. 157°/13 mm. D_{40}^{40} 1·1757.

Schroeter, *Ann.*, 1922, **426**, 39.
Tetralingesellschaft, D.R.P., 299,014, (*Chem. Zentr.*, 1919, IV, 374).

6-Nitro-1 : 2 : 3 : 4-tetrahydronaphthalene (6-*Nitrotetralin*).

Needles from EtOH or MeOH. M.p. 31·4°. B.p. 169°/13 mm. D_{40}^{40} 1·1762.

See previous references.

2-Nitro-5 : 6 : 7 : 8-tetrahydro-1-naphthol (2-*Nitro*-ar-*tetrahydro*-α-*naphthol*)

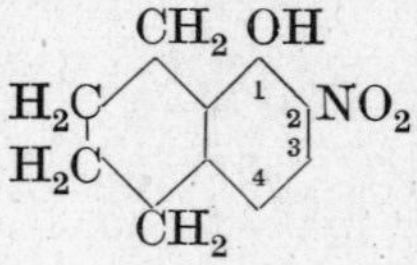

$C_{10}H_{11}O_3N$ MW, 193

Yellow needles from Et_2O. M.p. 56°. Sol. most org. solvents. Spar. sol. H_2O. Volatile in steam. Sweet odour.

Na salt: orange plates or needles from H_2O.

Green, Rowe, *J. Chem. Soc.*, 1918, **113**, 968.

4-Nitro-5 : 6 : 7 : 8-tetrahydro-1-naphthol (4-*Nitro*-ar-*tetrahydro*-α-*naphthol*).

Needles from toluene. M.p. 123°. Non-volatile in steam. Gives yellowish-brown salts.

Rowe, Levin, *J. Chem. Soc.*, 1927, 531.

3-Nitro-5 : 6 : 7 : 8-tetrahydro-2-naphthol (3-*Nitro*-ar-*tetrahydro*-β-*naphthol*)

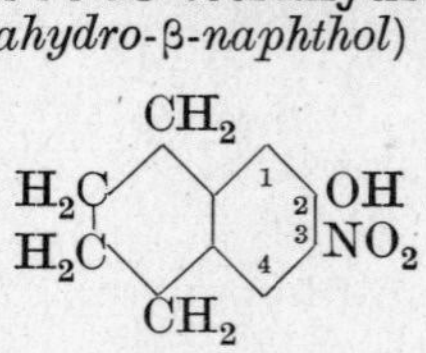

$C_{10}H_{11}O_3N$ MW, 193

Golden-yellow plates from EtOH or CCl_4, needles from AcOH.Aq. M.p. 88–9°. Spar. sol. H_2O.

Acetyl: pale yellow cryst. M.p. 100°.

Thoms, Kross, *Chem. Zentr.*, 1927, I, 3000.

4-Nitro-5 : 6 : 7 : 8-tetrahydro-2-naphthol (4-*Nitro*-ar-*tetrahydro*-β-*naphthol*).

Amorphous.

Schroeter *et al.*, *Ann.*, 1922, **426**, 70.

2-Nitro-5 : 6 : 7 : 8-tetrahydro-1-naphthylamine (2-*Nitro*-ar-*tetrahydro*-α-*naphthylamine*)

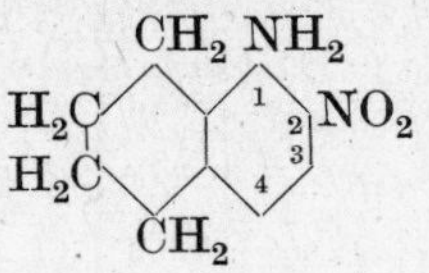

$C_{10}H_{12}O_2N_2$ MW, 192

Orange needles from EtOH. M.p. 87–8°.

N-*Acetyl*: needles from EtOH. M.p. 184–5°. Sol. EtOH, Me_2CO, C_6H_6. Spar. sol. CCl_4.

Schroeter *et al.*, *Ann.*, 1922, **426**, 62.

3-Nitro-5 : 6 : 7 : 8-tetrahydro-1-naphthylamine (3-*Nitro*-ar-*tetrahydro*-α-*naphthylamine*).

Yellow leaflets from EtOH. M.p. 78°.

Acetyl: needles from 60% AcOH. M.p. 194–5°.

See previous reference.

4-Nitro-5 : 6 : 7 : 8-tetrahydro-1-naphthylamine (4-*Nitro*-ar-*tetrahydro*-α-*naphthylamine*).

Pale yellow needles from EtOH.Aq. M.p. 116°. Sol. most org. solvents and dil. acids. Less sol. H_2O.

Acetyl: needles from EtOH.Aq. or H_2O. M.p. 178°. Sol. org. solvents. Mod. sol. H_2O.

Green, Rowe, *J. Chem. Soc.*, 1918, **113**, 959.

1-Nitro-5 : 6 : 7 : 8-tetrahydro-2-naphthylamine (1-*Nitro*-ar-*tetrahydro*-β-*naphthylamine*)

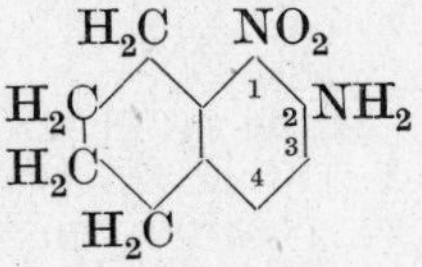

$C_{10}H_{12}O_2N_2$ MW, 192

Red needles from EtOH. M.p. 96°.

Acetyl: needles from Et_2O. M.p. 128–9°.

Schroeter *et al.*, *Ann.*, 1922, **426**, 67.

3-Nitro-5 : 6 : 7 : 8-tetrahydro-2-naphthylamine (3-*Nitro*-ar-*tetrahydro*-β-*naphthylamine*).

Red needles from EtOH. M.p. 125–7°. Sol. Et_2O, C_6H_6, toluene.

N-*Me*: $C_{11}H_{14}O_2N_2$. MW, 206. Fine red needles from EtOH. M.p. 113–15°. Sol. usual org. solvents. *Acetyl*: powder. M.p. 107–108·5°. Sol. most org. solvents.

Acetyl: yellow needles from EtOH. M.p. 135°.

See previous reference.

4-Nitro-5 : 6 : 7 : 8-tetrahydro-2-naphthylamine (4-*Nitro*-ar-*tetrahydro*-β-*naphthylamine*).

Yellow cryst. powder. M.p. 55°. Sol. most org. solvents.

Acetyl: needles from EtOH. M.p. 194°. Spar. sol. Et_2O, C_6H_6.

See previous reference.

6-Nitro-1 : 2 : 3 : 4-tetrahydroquinaldine

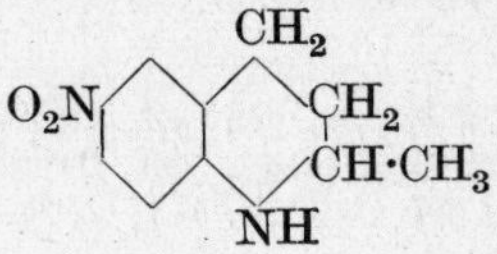

$C_{10}H_{12}O_2N_2$ MW, 192

dl-.

Brownish-red cryst. M.p. 130–2°.

Stoermer, *Ber.*, 1898, **31**, 2540.

6-Nitro-1 : 2 : 3 : 4-tetrahydroquinoline

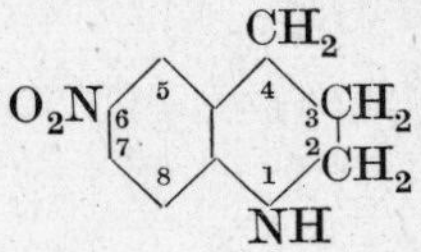

$C_9H_{10}O_2N_2$ MW, 178

Dark yellow needles with bluish reflex. M.p. 163–4°.

N-*Nitroso*: yellow needles. M.p. 154–5°.

Stoermer, *Ber.*, 1898, **31**, 2537.
v. Dorp, *Rec. trav. chim.*, 1904, **23**, 307.

7-Nitro-1 : 2 : 3 : 4-tetrahydroquinoline.

Yellowish-red cryst. from Et_2O–pet. ether. M.p. 90°. Very sol. EtOH, Et_2O.

B,HCl: needles from EtOH. M.p. 203°. Spar. sol. EtOH.

N-*Me*: 7-nitrokairoline. $C_{10}H_{12}O_2N_2$. MW, 192. Red needles from EtOH.Aq. M.p. 93–4°. Sol. usual solvents and conc. acids.

N-*Benzoyl*: m.p. 141°. Spar. sol. EtOH.

N-*Nitroso*: m.p. 118–20°. Spar. sol. EtOH.

v. Braun, Grabowski, Rawicz, *Ber.*, 1913, **46**, 3170, 3173.
Feer, Koenigs, *Ber.*, 1885, **18**, 2390.

8-Nitro-1 : 2 : 3 : 4-tetrahydroquinoline.

Red needles. M.p. 82–3°.

N-*Nitroso*: reddish-brown needles from EtOH. M.p. 99–100°.

Stoermer, *Ber.*, 1898, **31**, 2537.

4-Nitro-2 : 3 : 5 : 6-tetramethylphenol.

See 4-Nitrodurenol.

o-Nitrothioanisole

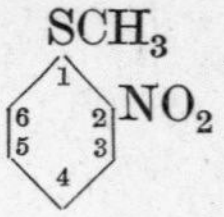

$C_7H_7O_2NS$ MW, 169

Yellow needles from EtOH or H_2O. M.p. 64–5°. Sol. H_2O, EtOH, AcOH, AcOEt, C_6H_6. Less sol. EtOH.Aq. $D_4^{78\cdot2}$ 1·2626. $n_D^{78\cdot2}$ 1·62458.
B,AgNO$_3$: yellow leaflets. M.p. 122°.

Brand, *Ber.*, 1909, **42**, 3988.
Claasz, *Ber.*, 1912, **45**, 1022.
Brand, Kranz, *J. prakt. Chem.*, 1927, **115**, 143.

***p*-Nitrothioanisole.**
Yellow leaflets from ligroin, plates from MeOH. M.p. 72°. $D_4^{80\cdot1}$ 1·2391. $n_D^{80\cdot1}$ 1·64008.

See last reference above and also
Mayer, *Ber.*, 1909, **42**, 3050.
Brand, Wirsing, *Ber.*, 1912, **45**, 1763.

***o*-Nitrothiocarbanilide**

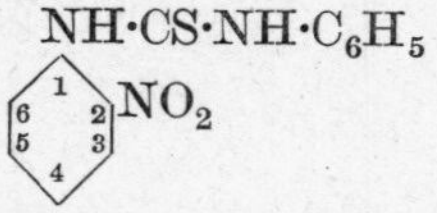

$C_{13}H_{11}O_2N_3S$ MW, 273

Yellow cryst. from AcOH. M.p. 142° (188°). Sol. EtOH. Insol. Et_2O.

Arndt, Rosenau, *Ber.*, 1917, **50**, 1258.
Dyson, *J. Chem. Soc.*, 1934, 176.

***m*-Nitrothiocarbanilide.**
Yellow needles. M.p. 155°. Sol. warm EtOH. Spar. sol. $CHCl_3$, CS_2, C_6H_6.

Bruckner, *Ber.*, 1874, **7**, 1235.
Losanitsch, *Ber.*, 1881, **14**, 2365.

***p*-Nitrothiocarbanilide.**
Pale yellow plates or prisms from EtOH. M.p. 141° (175°).

Hunter, Jones, *J. Chem. Soc.*, 1930, 2206.
Dyson, *J. Chem. Soc.*, 1934, 176.

2-Nitrothiophene

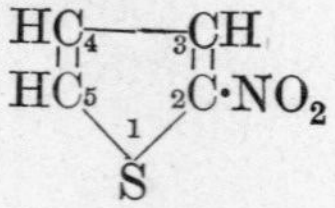

$C_4H_3O_2NS$ MW, 129

Cryst. M.p. 46·5°. B.p. 224–5°. Turns red slowly in air. Sol. hot alkalis with deep reddish-brown col. Volatile in steam. Et_2O sol. causes blisters on skin.

Steinkopf, *Ann.*, 1914, **403**, 18.
Steinkopf, Lützkendorf, D.R.P., 255,394, (*Chem. Zentr.*, 1913, I, 476).
Babasinian, *Organic Syntheses*, 1934, XIV, 76.

3-Nitrothiophene.
Needles from H_2O, leaflets from EtOH. M.p. 77° (75–7°). B.p. 225°, 95°/12 mm.

Steinkopf, Höpner, *Ann.*, 1933, **501**, 183.
Rinkes, *Rec. trav. chim.*, 1933, **52**, 538.

***o*-Nitrothiophenetole**

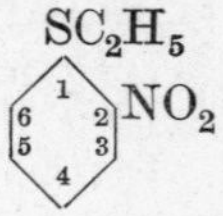

$C_8H_9O_2NS$ MW, 183

Oil. B.p. 149–50°/15 mm.

Foster, Reid, *J. Am. Chem. Soc.*, 1924, **46**, 1939.

***p*-Nitrothiophenetole.**
Yellow needles from 80% AcOH. M.p. 44°.

Brand, Wirsing, *Ber.*, 1913, **46**, 823.
Waldron, Reid, *J. Am. Chem. Soc.*, 1923, **45**, 2402.

***o*-Nitrothiophenol**

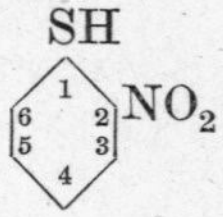

$C_6H_5O_2NS$ MW, 155

Yellow needles from CCl_4. M.p. 57–8°.
S-*Me ether* : *see* *o*-Nitrothioanisole.
S-*Et ether* : *see* *o*-Nitrothiophenetole.
S-*Propyl ether* : $C_9H_{11}O_2NS$. MW, 197. Oil. B.p. 172–4°/7 mm.
S-*Allyl ether* : $C_9H_9O_2NS$. MW, 195. Yellow needles from EtOH. M.p. 54°.
S-*Phenyl ether* : *see* 2-Nitrodiphenyl sulphide.
S-o-*Tolyl ether* : *see* 2′-Nitro-2-methyldiphenyl sulphide.

Brand, *Ber.*, 1909, **42**, 3465.
Claasz, *Ber.*, 1912, **45**, 2427.
Blanksma, *Rec. trav. chim.*, 1901, **20**, 400.
Foster, Reid, *J. Am. Chem. Soc.*, 1924, **46**, 1937.

***p*-Nitrothiophenol.**
Cryst. from Et_2O, $CHCl_3$ or Me_2CO. M.p. 77°. Very sol. Et_2O, $CHCl_3$, Me_2CO. Mod. sol. hot H_2O, EtOH. Spar. sol. AcOH, ligroin.

S-*Me ether*: *see p*-Nitrothioanisole.
S-*Et ether*: *see p*-Nitrothiophenetole.
S-*Propyl ether*: brown oil. D_{25}^{25} 1·1963.
S-*Isopropyl ether*: $C_9H_{11}O_2NS$. MW, 197. Yellow needles from 80% AcOH. M.p. 44·5°.
S-*Allyl ether*: yellow plates from EtOH. M.p. 38–9°.
S-*Butyl ether*: $C_{10}H_{13}O_2NS$. MW, 211. Brown oil. D_{25}^{25} 1·1625.
S-*Isobutyl ether*: brown oil. D_{25}^{25} 1·1573.
S-*Isoamyl ether*: $C_{11}H_{15}O_2NS$. MW, 225. Brown oil. D_{25}^{25} 1·1335.
S-β-*Hydroxyethyl ether*: yellow needles from 80% AcOH. M.p. 59°.
S-β-*Bromoethyl ether*: yellow plates from AcOH. M.p. 58°.
S-*Phenyl ether*: *see* 4-Nitrodiphenyl sulphide.
S-p-*Tolyl ether*: *see* 4′-Nitro-4-methyldiphenyl sulphide.
S-*Benzyl ether*: yellow plates from 80% AcOH. M.p. 123°.
S-*Phenacyl ether*: yellow plates from 80% AcOH. M.p. 118°.
S-*Cyclohexyl ether*: yellow needles from EtOH. M.p. 56–7°.
S-*Benzoyl*: yellow plates from 50% AcOH. M.p. 123–7°.

Foster, Reid, *J. Am. Chem. Soc.*, 1924, **46**, 1939.
Waldron, Reid, *J. Am. Chem. Soc.*, 1923, **45**, 2402.
Fromm, Wittmann, *Ber.*, 1908, **41**, 2267.
Brand, Wirsing, *Ber.*, 1913, **46**, 822.
M.L.B., D.R.P., 228,868, (*Chem. Zentr.*, 1911, I, 50).

1-Nitrothioxanthone

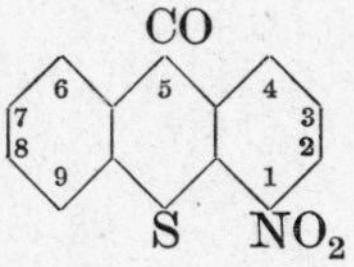

$C_{13}H_7O_3NS$ MW, 257

Yellow needles from C_6H_6, prisms from xylene. M.p. 216–18° (215°). Spar. sol. C_6H_6, AcOH. Very spar. sol. EtOH.

Bayer, D.R.P., 228,756, (*Chem. Zentr.*, 1910, II, 1842).
Mayer, *Ber.*, 1909, **42**, 3062.

2-Nitrothioxanthone.
Leaflets from AcOH. M.p. 247°.

Mayer, *Ber.*, 1909, **42**, 3067.

3-Nitrothioxanthone.
Light brown plates from AcOH. M.p. 219–21°. Spar. sol. AcOH, C_6H_6. Very spar. sol. EtOH.

See previous reference.

4-Nitrothioxanthone.
Plates from AcOH. M.p. 237°. Mod. sol. C_6H_6. Spar. sol. EtOH.

See previous reference.

2-Nitrothymol

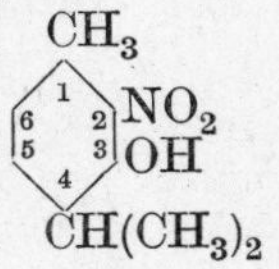

$C_{10}H_{13}O_3N$ MW, 195

Cryst. from EtOH or H_2O. M.p. 119°. Volatile in steam.
Et ether: $C_{12}H_{17}O_3N$. MW, 223. Yellow liq. Volatile in steam.

Robertson, *J. Chem. Soc.*, 1908, **93**, 793 (*Footnote*).
Gaebel, *Ber.*, 1902, **35**, 2797.

6-Nitrothymol.
Needles with bluish fluor. from ligroin–C_6H_6. M.p. 140–2° (137°).
Et ether: yellow plates from EtOH. M.p. 60–1°. Sol. EtOH, Et_2O. Volatile in steam.

Robertson, Briscoe, *J. Chem. Soc.*, 1912, **101**, 1968.
Datta, Varma, *J. Am. Chem. Soc.*, 1919, **41**, 2042.
Kehrmann, Schön, *Ann.*, 1909, **310**, 107.

6-Nitro-*o*-tolidine.
See 6-Nitro-4 : 4′-diamino-3 : 3′-dimethyldiphenyl.

***o*-Nitrotoluene**

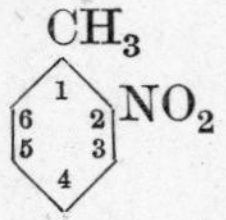

$C_7H_7O_2N$ MW, 137

(α-) Transparent needles. M.p. − 9·55°. (β-) Opaque snow-like cryst. M.p. − 3·85°. β-Form more stable at low temps. and in presence of HNO_3. B.p. 222·3° (219–219·5°/762 mm.). $D_{15}^{19·2}$ 1·1622. $n_D^{20·4}$ 1·54739. $KMnO_4$ ⟶ *o*-nitrobenzoic acid. NaOH ⟶ anthranilic acid. Red. ⟶ *o*-toluidine. NaHg ⟶ *o*-azotoluene and *o*-hydrazotoluene.
$C_7H_7O_2N,AlCl_3$: hygroscopic yellow needles. M.p. 99·5°.
$C_7H_7O_2N,AlBr_3$: yellow needles. M.p. 90°.

$C_7H_7O_2N,SbCl_3$: needles. M.p. 34·5°.
$C_7H_7O_2N,SbBr_3$: needles. M.p. 32° decomp.

Hennaut-Roland, *Bull. soc. chim. Belg.*, 1933, **42**, 80.
Gibson, Duckham, Fairburn, *J. Chem. Soc.*, 1922, **121**, 270.
Clark, Crozier, *Chem. Abstracts*, 1926, **20**, 389.
Hollemann, Vermeulen, *Rec. trav. chim.*, 1914, **33**, 10.
Kohn, *Monatsh.*, 1910, **31**, 745.

m-Nitrotoluene.

M.p. 16°. B.p. 227·2–227·5°/736 mm. D_4^{20} 1·15712. n_D^{21} 1·5470. CrO_3 or $KMnO_4 \longrightarrow$ *m*-nitrobenzoic acid. Red. $\longrightarrow$ *m*-toluidine. NaHg $\longrightarrow$ *m*-azotoluene and *m*-hydrazotoluene.

$C_7H_7O_2N,AlCl_3$: hygroscopic needles. M.p. 99·5°.

$C_7H_7O_2N,AlBr_3$: pale yellow prisms. M.p. 96°.

See first reference above and also
Clarke, Taylor, *Organic Syntheses*, 1923, III, 91.
Gibson, Duckham, Fairburn, *J. Chem. Soc.*, 1922, **121**, 270.

p-Nitrotoluene.

Cryst. from EtOH or Et_2O. M.p. 54·5° (52°). B.p. 237·7°, 104·5°/9 mm., 64–5°/0·052 mm. Spar. sol. H_2O. Mod. sol. MeOH, EtOH. Sol. Et_2O, Me_2CO, AcOEt, CS_2, $CHCl_3$, CCl_4, C_6H_6, toluene, Py. D_4^{75} 1·1038. CrO_3 or $KMnO_4 \longrightarrow$ *p*-nitrobenzoic acid. NaHg in EtOH $\longrightarrow$ *p*-azoxytoluene and *p*-azotoluene. Fe + HCl $\longrightarrow$ *p*-toluidine.

$C_7H_7O_2N,AlCl_3$: hygroscopic plates. M.p. 109°.

$C_7H_7O_2N,AlBr_3$: cryst. M.p. 88°.

$C_7H_7O_2N,SbCl_3$: m.p. 7·5° decomp.

Minnis, U.S.P., 1,920,517, (*Chem. Abstracts*, 1933, **27**, 4819).
Lewin, *J. prakt. Chem.*, 1930, **126**, 219.
Desvergnes, *Chem. Abstracts*, 1925, **19**, 3258.
Gibson, Duckworth, Fairburn, *J. Chem. Soc.*, 1922, **121**, 270.
Hollemann, Vermeulen, *Rec. trav. chim.*, 1914, **33**, 10.

ω-Nitrotoluene.

See Phenylnitromethane.

o-Nitrotoluene-3-sulphonic Acid

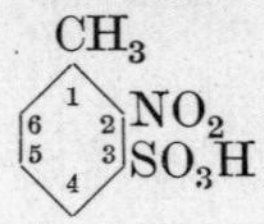

$C_7H_7O_5NS$ MW, 21

Ba salt : leaflets + $2H_2O$. Spar. sol. H_2O.

Chloride : $C_7H_6O_4NClS$. MW, 235·5. M.p 58·5°.

Amide : $C_7H_8O_4N_2S$. MW, 216. M.p. 163·5

Foth, *Ann.*, 1885, **230**, 308.
v. Pechmann, *Ann.*, 1874, **173**, 214.

o-Nitrotoluene-4-sulphonic Acid.

Long pale yellow needles from H_2O. M.p 92°. Very hygroscopic.

Phenyl ester : $C_{13}H_{11}O_5NS$. MW, 29 Needles from EtOH. M.p. 59–60°. So Me_2CO, Et_2O, $CHCl_3$, AcOH, C_6H_6. Mod. so hot EtOH, ligroin.

p-*Nitrophenyl ester* : needles. M.p. 113–14 Sol. $CHCl_3$. Mod. sol. Et_2O. Spar. sol. EtOH ligroin.

o-*Tolyl ester* : needles. M.p. 68–9°.

m-*Tolyl ester* : m.p. 63°.

p-*Tolyl ester* : m.p. 95°.

Fluoride : $C_7H_6O_4NFS$. MW, 219·5. Pa yellow cryst. from CS_2. M.p. 48–9°. So Et_2O, Me_2CO, AcOEt, C_6H_6, pet. ether. Mo sol. EtOH. Spar. sol. cold CS_2. Insol. H_2O Spar. volatile in steam.

Chloride : $C_7H_6O_4NClS$. MW, 235·5. Plate from Et_2O. M.p. 36°.

Amide : $C_7H_8O_4N_2S$. MW, 216. Leaflet from H_2O. M.p. 144·5°. Sol. boiling H_2O, ho EtOH.

Methylamide : $C_8H_{10}O_4N_2S$. MW, 230. Pa yellow prisms from EtOH. M.p. 93°.

Ethylamide : $C_9H_{12}O_4N_2S$. MW, 244. Pa yellow prisms from EtOH. M.p. 87°.

Anilide : $C_{13}H_{12}O_4N_2S$. MW, 292. Crys from EtOH.Aq. M.p. 109°. Sol. EtOH, Et_2O Me_2CO, C_6H_6. Spar. sol. ligroin. Insol. H_2O.

o-*Toluidide* : $C_{14}H_{14}O_4N_2S$. MW, 30 Cryst. from EtOH. M.p. 128°.

p-*Toluidide* : m.p. 130–1°.

p-*Anisidide* : needles from AcOH or EtOH M.p. 81°. Sol. EtOH, Me_2CO, AcOH, Et_2O C_6H_6, hot ligroin. Insol. H_2O.

m-*Phenetidide* : needles from AcOH. M.p 88°. Sol. EtOH, Me_2CO, C_6H_6. Spar. so H_2O, Et_2O, ligroin.

p-*Phenetidide* : cryst. M.p. 128°. *Acetyl* plates. M.p. 172°.

Benzylamide : pale yellow plates from EtOH M.p. 94°.

1-*Naphthylamide*: cryst. from boiling C_6H_6. I.p. 153°. Sol. $CHCl_3$. Mod. sol. EtOH, 't$_2$O, C_6H_6. Insol. boiling H_2O.
2-*Naphthylamide*: cryst. from C_6H_6. M.p. 61°.

Reverdin, Crépieux, *Bull. soc. chim.*, 1901, **25**, 1045; 1902, **27**, 745.
Fichter, Bernouilli, *Ber.*, 1909, **42**, 4309.
Steinkopf *et al.*, *J. prakt. Chem.*, 1927, **117**, 25.
Hirwe, Jambhekar, *J. Indian Chem. Soc.*, 1933, **10**, 48.

o-Nitrotoluene-5-sulphonic Acid.

Chloride: prisms from Et_2O. M.p. 50°. Sol. :t$_2$O, AcOH. Spar. sol. EtOH, ligroin.
Amide: needles. M.p. 133·5°. Sol. EtOH. Spar. sol. cold H_2O.

Foth, *Ann.*, 1885, **230**, 305.

o-Nitrotoluene-6-sulphonic Acid.

Yellow needles + $2H_2O$ from H_2O. M.p. 27°.
Amide: plates from H_2O. M.p. 165°.
Ba salt: red needles from H_2O.

Hirwe, Jambhekar, *J. Indian Chem. Soc.*, 1934, **11**, 242.

m-Nitrotoluene-4-sulphonic Acid

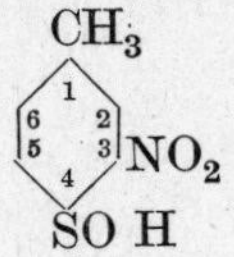

$C_7H_7O_5NS$ MW, 217

Chloride: $C_7H_6O_4NClS$. MW, 235·5. Cryst. rom C_6H_6–pet. ether. M.p. 98–9°. Sol. C_6H_6, $CHCl_3$. Spar. sol. pet. ether.
Amide: $C_7H_8O_4N_2S$. MW, 216. Leaflets rom EtOH.Aq. M.p. 170°.
o-*Anisidide*: yellow needles from AcOH. M.p. 135°.

Zincke, Röse, *Ann.*, 1914, **406**, 134.
Heller, *J. prakt. Chem.*, 1929, **121**, 193.

m-Nitrotoluene-5-sulphonic Acid.

K salt: cryst. from EtOH.
Ba salt: leaflets + $2H_2O$ from H_2O.

v. Dorssen, *Rec. trav. chim.*, 1910, **29**, 379.

m-Nitrotoluene-6-sulphonic Acid.

o-*Toluidide*: cryst. from AcOH. M.p. 177°.
p-*Phenetidide*: m.p. 127°.

Schuloff, Pollak, Reisz, *Ber.*, 1929, **62**, 1849.

p-Nitrotoluene-2-sulphonic Acid

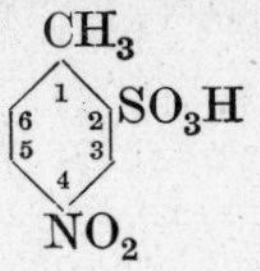

$C_7H_7O_5NS$ MW, 217

Plates + $2H_2O$ from H_2O. M.p. 133·5°. Sol. EtOH, Et_2O, $CHCl_3$.
Phenyl ester: $C_{13}H_{11}O_5NS$. MW, 293. Cryst. from EtOH. M.p. 64°. Alc. alkalis ⟶ orange-yellow sol. ⟶ blue on standing.
p-*Nitrophenyl ester*: m.p. 195°.
Fluoride: $C_7H_6O_4NFS$. MW, 219·5. Prisms from pet. ether. M.p. 57–8°. Sol. Et_2O, Me_2CO, AcOEt, EtOH, C_6H_6.
Chloride: $C_7H_6O_4NClS$. MW, 235·5. Plates or prisms from Et_2O–pet. ether. M.p. 46–7° (43–44·5°). B.p. 183–5°/10 mm.
Amide: $C_7H_8O_4N_2S$. MW, 216. Needles from H_2O. M.p. 186°. Spar. sol. H_2O, EtOH, Et_2O. *Benzoyl*: prisms from EtOH. M.p. 130°. Sol. boiling EtOH. Spar. sol. hot H_2O, Et_2O.
Anilide: $C_{13}H_{12}O_4N_2S$. MW, 292. Rhombic cryst. from Et_2O. M.p. 148°. Sol. AcOH, hot EtOH. Spar. sol. C_6H_6. Very spar. sol. Et_2O.

Steinkopf *et al.*, *J. prakt. Chem.*, 1927, **117**, 36.
Walter, *Chem. Ind.*, 1887, **10**, 309.
Green, Marsden, Scholefield, *J. Chem. Soc.*, 1904, **85**, 1432.
Ullmann, Lehner, *Ber.*, 1905, **38**, 736.
Jenssen, *Ann.*, 1874, **172**, 232.
Osakeyhtio, Norwegian P., 30,325, (*Chem. Abstracts*, 1920, **14**, 2936).
Hintikka, Canadian P., 200,291, (*Chem. Abstracts*, 1920, **14**, 2344).

p-Nitrotoluene-3-sulphonic Acid.

K salt: pale yellow cryst. powder.
Chloride: pale brown oil.

Coffey, *J. Chem. Soc.*, 1926, 3222.

o-Nitrotoluene-α-sulphonic Acid (2-*Nitrobenzylsulphonic acid*)

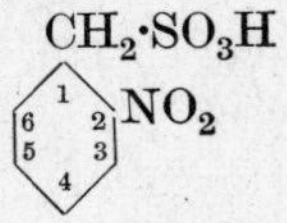

$C_7H_7O_5NS$ MW, 217

Cryst. Very hygroscopic.
Na salt: needles + H_2O from EtOH.

Ba salt: cryst. + $3H_2O$. Spar. sol. H_2O.
Amide: $C_7H_8O_4N_2S$. MW, 216. Cryst. M.p. 137°.

Fischer, D.R.P., 48,722.
Weiss, Reiter, *Ann.*, 1905, **355**, 177.
Marckwald, Frahne, *Ber.*, 1898, **31**, 1855.
Clutterbuck, Cohen, *J. Chem. Soc.*, 1923, **123**, 2512.

m-Nitrotoluene-α-sulphonic Acid (3-*Nitrobenzylsulphonic acid*).

Cryst. + H_2O from H_2O. M.p. 74°. Mod. sol. H_2O, EtOH. Spar. sol. other solvents.
Me ester: $C_8H_9O_5NS$. MW, 231. Cryst. M.p. 99–100° (77°). Sol. EtOH, Et_2O. Insol. H_2O.
Chloride: $C_7H_6O_4NClS$. MW, 235·5. Rhombic cryst. from C_6H_6. M.p. 100°.
Amide: cryst. from H_2O. M.p. 159° decomp. Sol. warm H_2O.
Methylamide: $C_8H_{10}O_4N_2S$. MW, 230. M.p. 106–7°.
Dimethylamide: $C_9H_{12}O_4N_2S$. MW, 244. M.p. 118–19°.
Ethylamide: $C_9H_{12}O_4N_2S$. MW, 244. M.p. 90–1°.

Purgotti, Monti, *Gazz. chim. ital.*, 1900, **30**, ii, 247.
Clutterbuck, Cohen, *J. Chem. Soc.*, 1923, **123**, 2512.
Ingold, Ingold, Shaw, *J. Chem. Soc.*, 1927, 824.

p-Nitrotoluene-α-sulphonic Acid (4-*Nitrobenzylsulphonic acid*).

Needles from C_6H_6. M.p. 71°. Very sol. H_2O, EtOH. Spar. sol. C_6H_6. Insol. Et_2O.
Me ester: m.p. 113°.
Chloride: m.p. 90°.
Amide: prisms from hot H_2O. M.p. 204° (200°).
Methylamide: m.p. 143–5°.
Dimethylamide: m.p. 167°.
Ethylamide: m.p. 110–11°.
Anilide: needles from H_2O. M.p. 220° decomp.
Hydrazide: cryst. from H_2O. M.p. 87° decomp.
Phenylhydrazide: m.p. 156° decomp.

See last two references above and also
Weiss, Reiter, *Ann.*, 1905, **355**, 177.
Mohr, *Ann.*, 1883, **221**, 216.

6-Nitrotoluhydroquinone

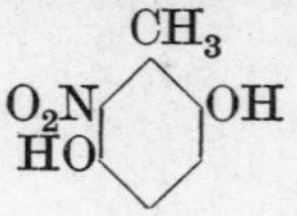

$C_7H_7O_4N$ MW, 1

Red needles from Et_2O–pet. ether. M. 117–18°. Aq. alkalis ⟶ violet sols.

Cohen, Marshall, *J. Chem. Soc.*, 190 **85**, 528.

3-Nitro-o-toluic Acid

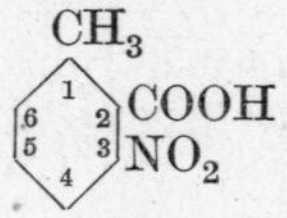

$C_8H_7O_4N$ MW, 18

Pale yellowish needles. M.p. 151–2°.
Me ester: $C_9H_9O_4N$. MW, 195. Needle and leaflets. M.p. 50°.
Chloride: $C_8H_6O_3NCl$. MW, 199·5. Crys from ligroin. M.p. 41°.
Amide: $C_8H_8O_3N_2$. MW, 180. Needle M.p. 158°.
Nitrile: $C_8H_6O_2N_2$. MW, 162. Plates fro C_6H_6. M.p. 109–10°. Sol. usual solvent Sublimes slowly in leaflets.
Anhydride: plates from EtOH. M.p. 174°.

Gabriel, Thieme, *Ber.*, 1919, **52**, 1074 1089.

4-Nitro-o-toluic Acid.

Needles from EtOH.Aq. M.p. 179°. Ver sol. EtOH. Spar. sol. boiling H_2O. Spa volatile in steam.
Me ester: prisms from MeOH. M.p. 69°.
Chloride: needles from $CHCl_3$. M.p. 59–60°
Amide: needles from boiling H_2O. M.p 173–4°. Sol. Me_2CO, hot H_2O, EtOH, AcOH Spar. sol. Et_2O, ligroin.
Methylamide: $C_9H_{10}O_3N_2$. MW, 194 Needles from EtOH.Aq. M.p. 160°. Sol EtOH. Mod. sol. H_2O.
Dimethylamide: $C_{10}H_{12}O_3N_2$. MW, 208 Cryst. from EtOH. M.p. 105–6°. Mod. sol H_2O.
Nitrile: needles from 95% EtOH. M.p 105°. Sol. Me_2CO, $CHCl_3$, C_6H_6, hot EtOH Less sol. hot H_2O, Et_2O, AcOH, CS_2. Spar sol. pet. ether.

Ruggli, Meyer, *Helv. Chim. Acta*, 1922, 5 58.
Jacobsen, Wierss, *Ber.*, 1883, **16**, 1958.
v. Scherpenzeel, *Rec. trav. chim.*, 1901 **20**, 174.
Landsberger, *Ber.*, 1898, **31**, 2880.

5-Nitro-*o*-toluic Acid.

Needles from H_2O. M.p. 152°. Very sol. tOH, hot H_2O.

Nitrile: yellow needles from EtOH. M.p. .3–15°; leaflets by sublimation, m.p. 110°. ol. $CHCl_3$, Me_2CO, C_6H_6. Spar. sol. EtOH, ot H_2O.

Gabriel, Thieme, *Ber.*, 1919, **52**, 1089.
Mayer, *J. prakt. Chem.*, 1915, **92**, 142.

6-Nitro-*o*-toluic Acid.

Cryst. M.p. 184–184·5°.

Me ester: needles from MeOH. M.p. 66°.

Chloride: cryst. from $CHCl_3$. M.p. 68–68·5°.

Amide: needles from H_2O. M.p. 163°.

Methylamide: needles from H_2O. M.p. 31–2°.

Dimethylamide: yellowish cryst. from EtOH. .p. 69·5–70°.

Nitrile: cryst. M.p. 69·5°.

v. Scherpenzeel, *Rec. trav. chim.*, 1901, 20, 172.
Noelting, *Ber.*, 1904, **37**, 1025.

2-Nitro-*m*-toluic Acid

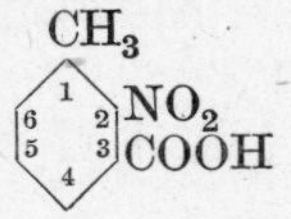

$_8H_7O_4N$ MW, 181

Prisms from EtOH. M.p. 223° (219–20°). ol. hot EtOH. Spar. sol. H_2O.

Me ester: $C_9H_9O_4N$. MW, 195. Cryst. om MeOH. M.p. 74°.

Chloride: $C_8H_6O_3NCl$. MW, 199·5. Cryst. om CS_2. Sol. EtOH, Et_2O.

Amide: $C_8H_8O_3N_2$. MW, 180. Needles om H_2O, prisms from EtOH. M.p. 192°.

Methylamide: $C_9H_{10}O_3N_2$. MW, 194. lates from H_2O. M.p. 135–6°. Spar. sol. t_2O.

Dimethylamide: $C_{10}H_{12}O_3N_2$. MW, 208. ryst. from EtOH. M.p. 88·5°. Sol. H_2O, tOH, Et_2O. Turns red on exposure to light.

Nitrile: $C_8H_6O_2N_2$. MW, 162. Needles om EtOH. M.p. 84°.

Jürgens, *Ber.*, 1907, **40**, 4409.
v. Scherpenzeel, *Rec. trav. chim.*, 1901, 20, 164.
Gabriel, Thieme, *Ber.*, 1919, **52**, 1091.

4-Nitro-*m*-toluic Acid.

Cryst. from hot H_2O. M.p. 134°. Hot lkalis ⟶ red sols.

Me ester: needles from MeOH. M.p. 78–9°.

Amide: needles from EtOH. M.p. 176–7°. Sol. EtOH. Spar. sol. H_2O.

Nitrile: needles from EtOH. M.p. 93–4°. Sol. hot H_2O, EtOH, AcOH. Less sol. C_6H_6.

Findeklee, *Ber.*, 1905, **38**, 3544.
Reissert, Scherk, *Ber.*, 1898, **31**, 390.
Müller, *Ber.*, 1909, **42**, 430.
Pfeiffer, *Ber.*, 1918, **51**, 559.

5-Nitro-*m*-toluic Acid.

Needles from H_2O. M.p. 174°. Very sol. EtOH, Et_2O. Mod. sol. H_2O. Non-volatile in steam.

Me ester: plates from MeOH. M.p. 84–5°.

Chloride: cryst. M.p. about 100°.

Amide: needles from H_2O. M.p. 164–5°. Sol. hot EtOH. Spar. sol. Et_2O.

Nitrile: needles from ligroin. M.p. 104–5°.

Gabriel, Thieme, *Ber.*, 1919, **52**, 1090.
Müller, *Ber.*, 1909, **42**, 433.

6-Nitro-*m*-toluic Acid.

Needles from EtOH. M.p. 219° (212°). Spar. sol. hot H_2O. $k = 3{\cdot}1 \times 10^{-4}$ at 25°. Sublimes.

Me ester: needles from EtOH. M.p. 81–2° (72°). Sol. hot EtOH, Et_2O, C_6H_6. Spar. sol. hot H_2O.

Et ester: $C_{10}H_{11}O_4N$. MW, 209. Prisms from EtOH. M.p. 55°. B.p. 150–6°/9 mm. Very sol. hot EtOH.

Amide: leaflets or prisms from H_2O. M.p. 151°. Mod. sol. hot H_2O.

Nitrile: prisms from EtOH. M.p. 80°. Insol. cold H_2O.

Suida, *Monatsh.*, 1912, **33**, 1282.
Gabriel, Thieme, *Ber.*, 1919, **52**, 1090.
Beilstein, Kreusler, *Ann.*, 1867, **144**, 168.
Müller, *Ber.*, 1909, **42**, 430.

2-Nitro-*p*-toluic Acid

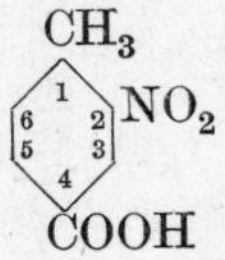

$C_8H_7O_4N$ MW, 181

Prisms from EtOH. M.p. 190°. Sol. EtOH. Spar. sol. cold H_2O.

Me ester: $C_9H_9O_4N$. MW, 195. Yellowish needles from MeOH. M.p. 51°.

Et ester: $C_{10}H_{11}O_4N$. MW, 209. Pale yellow cryst.

Amide: $C_8H_8O_3N_2$. MW, 180. Needles from H_2O. M.p. 166–166·5°. Spar. sol. C_6H_6.

Methylamide: $C_9H_{10}O_3N_2$. MW, 194. M.p. 149°. Sol. EtOH, C_6H_6, hot H_2O.

Dimethylamide: $C_{10}H_{12}O_3N_2$. MW, 208. Cryst. M.p. 49°.

Nitrile: $C_8H_6O_2N_2$. MW, 162. Pale yellow needles from H_2O. M.p. 107°. Sol. Et_2O, Me_2CO, $CHCl_3$, C_6H_6. Less sol. H_2O, EtOH.

Pfeiffer, *Ber.*, 1918, **51**, 563.
Hope, Robinson, *J. Chem. Soc.*, 1911, **99**, 2125.
Pfeiffer, Matton, *Ber.*, 1911, **44**, 1124.
v. Scherpenzeel, *Rec. trav. chim.*, 1901, **20**, 158.

3-Nitro-*p*-toluic Acid.

Needles from H_2O. M.p. 164–5°. Very sol. EtOH. Spar. sol. boiling H_2O, Et_2O, $CHCl_3$, C_6H_6.

Chloride: $C_8H_6O_3NCl$. MW, 199·5. Needles from Et_2O. M.p. 157°.

Amide: needles from C_6H_6 or ligroin. M.p. 153°. Sol. warm H_2O, EtOH, Et_2O, C_6H_6. Insol. ligroin.

Nitrile: needles from H_2O. M.p. 101°. Sol. EtOH, Et_2O, $CHCl_3$, C_6H_6. Insol. ligroin.

Claus, Joachim, *Ann.*, 1891, **266**, 210.
v. Niementowski, Rozański, *Ber.*, 1888, **21**, 1993.
Noyes, *Am. Chem. J.*, 1888, **10**, 474.
Weise, *Ber.*, 1889, **22**, 2429.

Nitrotoluic Acid sulphonic Acid.

See Nitrosulphotoluic Acid.

2-Nitro-*m*-toluic Aldehyde

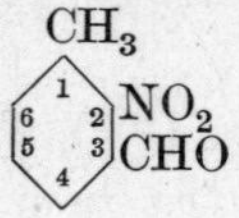

$C_8H_7O_3N$ MW, 165

Needles from H_2O. M.p. 64°. Sol. EtOH, Et_2O, Me_2CO, AcOH, $CHCl_3$, C_6H_6.

Oxime: m.p. 134–5°.

Gilliard, Monnet, Cartier, D.R.P., 113,604, (*Chem. Zentr.*, 1900, II, 751).
Mayer, *Ber.*, 1914, **47**, 406.

4-Nitro-*m*-toluic Aldehyde.

Yellow needles. M.p. 44°.

Oxime: m.p. 104–5°.

Phenylhydrazone: m.p. 141–2°.

See previous references.

6-Nitro-*m*-toluic Aldehyde.

Cryst. from H_2O. M.p. 64°. Very sol. EtOH, Et_2O, Me_2CO, $CHCl_3$, C_6H_6.

Phenylhydrazone: m.p. 108°.

Suida, *Monatsh.*, 1912, **33**, 1281.

2-Nitro-*p*-toluic Aldehyde

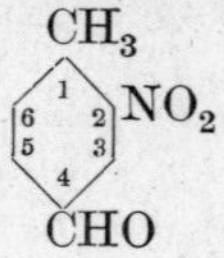

$C_8H_7O_3N$ MW, 16

Pale yellow needles from ligroin. M.p. 48–(42–3°). B.p. 140–5°/15 mm. Mod. sol. EtO Et_2O, C_6H_6.

α-Oxime: pale yellow needles from EtO M.p. 118–20°. *Acetyl*: cryst. from Me_2CO.A M.p. 104°.

β-Oxime: cryst. from Me_2CO.Aq. M.p. 135

B,HCl: m.p. 140° decomp.

Phenylhydrazone: m.p. 105°.

p-*Nitrophenylhydrazone*: m.p. 233°.

Diacetyl: plates from EtOH–ligroin. M. 98–98·5°. Sol. EtOH, Et_2O. Spar. sol. ligroi

Hanzlík, Bianchi, *Ber.*, 1899, **32**, 2286.
Gattermann, *Ann.*, 1906, **347**, 354.
Brady, Cosson, Roper, *J. Chem. Soc* 1925, 2431.
Wahl, *Compt. rend.*, 1934, **198**, 2107.

3-Nitro-*p*-toluic Aldehyde.

Oxime: needles from C_6H_6–ligroin. M. 128°.

M.L.B., D.R.P., 107,095, (*Chem. Zentr.* 1900, I, 886).

3-Nitro-*o*-toluidine

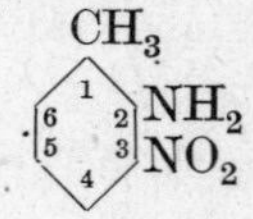

$C_7H_8O_2N_2$ MW, 15

Orange-yellow prisms from EtOH.Aq. M. 97°. Sol. EtOH, Et_2O, $CHCl_3$, C_6H_6. Spa sol. H_2O. D_4^{100} 1·1900.

N-*Acetyl*: 3-nitroacet-*o*-toluidide. M.p. 158

N-*Me*: *see* 3-Nitro-*N*-methyl-*o*-toluidine.

Harrison, *J. Soc. Chem. Ind.*, 1935, **54** 283T.
Meisenheimer, Hesse, *Ber.*, 1919, **52** 1171.

4-Nitro-*o*-toluidine.

Yellow prisms from EtOH. M.p. 107°. So EtOH, Et_2O, Me_2CO. Spar. sol. H_2O.

N-*Formyl*: m.p. 178–9°.

N-*Acetyl*: 4-nitroacet-*o*-toluidide. M.p. 151 Trimorphous.

N-m-*Nitrobenzoyl*: m.p. 193°.

N-p-*Nitrobenzoyl*: m.p. 214°.

N-*Benzenesulphonyl*: m.p. 172°.

N-1-*Naphthalenesulphonyl* : m.p. 244°.
N-2-*Naphthalenesulphonyl* : m.p. 229–30°.
N-*Me* : *see* 4-Nitro-*N*-methyl-*o*-toluidine.
N-*Di-Me* : *see* 4-Nitro-*N*-dimethyl-*o*-toludine.
N-*Et* : *see* 4-Nitro-*N*-ethyl-*o*-toluidine.
N-*Di-Et* : *see* 4-Nitro-*N*-diethyl-*o*-toluidine.
N-*Furfurylidene* : m.p. 153° (75°).
N-*Benzylidene* : m.p. 116°.
N-o-*Nitrobenzylidene* : m.p. 155°.
N-m-*Nitrobenzylidene* : m.p. 185°.
N-p-*Nitrobenzylidene* : m.p. 227°.

Pomeranz, D.R.P. 289,454, (*Chem. Zentr.*, 1916, I, 275).
Ullmann, Grether, *Ber.*, 1902, **35**, 337.
Schiff, Vanni, *Ann.*, 1892, **268**, 322.
Cohen, Dakin, *J. Chem. Soc.*, 1902, **81**, 1333.
McGookin, *J. Chem. Soc.*, 1934, 1743.

5-Nitro-*o*-toluidine.

Yellow needles from H_2O or EtOH. M.p. 129°. Sol. EtOH. Spar. sol. H_2O. D_4^{140} 1·1586.
B,HCl : m.p. 199–200°.
B,HBr : m.p. 240°.
N-*Acetyl* : 5-nitroacet-*o*-toluidide. Needles from H_2O. M.p. 201·6° (198°).
N-*Chloroacetyl* : m.p. 122°.
N-*Benzenesulphonyl* : m.p. 157–9°.
N-p-*Toluenesulphonyl* : m.p. 174°.
N-*Me* : *see* 5-Nitro-*N*-methyl-*o*-toluidine.
N-*Di-Me* : *see* 5-Nitro-*N*-dimethyl-*o*-toluidine.
N-*Et* : *see* 5-Nitro-*N*-ethyl-*o*-toluidine.
N-*Furfurylidene* : m.p. 130°.
N-*Phenyl* : *see* 4-Nitro-2-methyldiphenylamine.

Harrison, *J. Soc. Chem. Ind.*, 1935, **54**, 283T.
Jansen, *Chem. Zentr.*, 1913, II, 761.
Meisenheimer, Hesse, *Ber.*, 1919, **52**, 1171.
Kenner, Parkin, *J. Chem. Soc.*, 1920, **117**, 859.
Bogert, Cook, *J. Am. Chem. Soc.*, 1906, **28**, 1451.

6-Nitro-*o*-toluidine.

Yellow needles from H_2O, yellow leaflets from EtOH. M.p. 92°. B.p. 305° decomp. Sol. EtOH, Et_2O, C_6H_6. Spar. sol. H_2O.
N-*Acetyl* : 6-nitroacet-*o*-toluidide. Prisms from H_2O. M.p. 157·5–158°.
N-*Benzoyl* : m.p. 168°.
N-*Di-Me* : *see* 6-Nitro-*N*-dimethyl-*o*-toluidine.

Wheeler, *Am. Chem. J.*, 1910, **44**, 136.

2-Nitro-*m*-toluidine

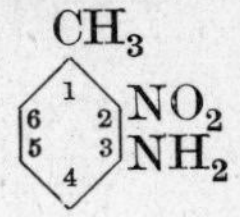

$C_7H_8O_2N_2$ MW, 152

Red prisms. M.p. 108°.
N-*Acetyl* : 2-nitroacet-*m*-toluidide. Prisms from C_6H_6–pet. ether. M.p. 126°.

Morton, McGookin, *J. Chem. Soc.*, 1934, 910.
Burton, Kenner, *J. Chem. Soc.*, 1921, **119**, 1052.

4-Nitro-*m*-toluidine.

Yellow plates from EtOH.Aq. M.p. 110°. Sol. EtOH, Et_2O, $CHCl_3$, C_6H_6.
N-*Acetyl* : 4-nitroacet-*m*-toluidide. Yellow needles from H_2O or pet. ether. M.p. 88–9° (86–7°).
N-*Benzoyl* : m.p. about 83°.
N-*Benzenesulphonyl* : m.p. 137–8°.
N-*Me* : *see* 4-Nitro-*N*-methyl-*m*-toluidine.
N-*Et* : *see* 4-Nitro-*N*-ethyl-*m*-toluidine.
N-*Phenyl* : *see* 6-Nitro-3-methyldiphenylamine.

Elson, Gibson, Johnson, *J. Chem. Soc.*, 1929, 2739.
Harrison, *J. Soc. Chem. Ind.*, 1935, **54**, 283T.
Kenner, Parkin, *J. Chem. Soc.*, 1920, **117**, 858.

5-Nitro-*m*-toluidine.

Brown needles. M.p. 98°. Sol. EtOH, Et_2O, C_6H_6. Spar. sol. H_2O.
N-*Acetyl* : 5-nitroacet-*m*-toluidide. M.p. 187°.
N-*Benzoyl* : m.p. 177°.
N-*Di-Me* : *see* 5-Nitro-*N*-dimethyl-*m*-toluidine.

Morton, McGookin, *J. Chem. Soc.*, 1934, 910.

6-Nitro-*m*-toluidine.

Yellow needles from H_2O. M.p. 135°. Sol. EtOH, Et_2O, hot H_2O. Non-volatile in steam.
N-*Acetyl* : 6-nitroacet-*m*-toluidide. Prisms from EtOH. M.p. 103–4°.
N-*Me* : *see* 6-Nitro-*N*-methyl-*m*-toluidine.
N-*Di-Me* : *see* 6-Nitro-*N*-dimethyl-*m*-toluidine.

Wibaut, *Rec. trav. chim.*, 1913, **32**, 287.
Harrison, *J. Soc. Chem. Ind.*, 1935, **54**, 283T.
Kenner, Parkin, *J. Chem. Soc.*, 1920, **117**, 858.

2-Nitro-*p*-toluidine

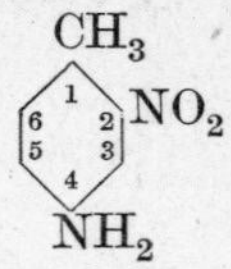

$C_7H_8O_2N_2$ MW, 152

Yellow needles from H_2O. M.p. 78°. Sol. Et_2O, C_6H_6, hot EtOH. Mod. sol. hot H_2O. Spar. sol. CS_2.

B,HCl : m.p. 230–40° (220°).
B,HBr,3H₂O : m.p. 238°.
N-*Formyl* : m.p. 133–4°.
N-*Acetyl* : 2-nitroacet-*p*-toluidide. Yellow needles or leaflets from H_2O. M.p. 144·5°.
N-*Chloroacetyl* : m.p. 129°.
Succinate : $(C_7H_7O_2N_2\cdot OC\cdot CH_2\cdot)$. M.p. 140°.
N-*Benzoyl* : m.p. 168° (172°).
N-*Benzenesulphonyl* : m.p. 160°.
N-p-*Toluenesulphonyl* : m.p. 162–3°.
N-*Me* : *see* 2-Nitro-*N*-methyl-*p*-toluidine.
N-*Di-Me* : *see* 2-Nitro-*N*-dimethyl-*p*-toluidine.
N-*Et* : *see* 2-Nitro-*N*-ethyl-*p*-toluidine.
N-*Butyl* : $C_{11}H_{16}O_2N_2$. MW, 208. M.p. 19°.
N-*Acetyl* : m.p. 48–9°.
N-*Benzylidene* : m.p. 77–8°.

Noelting, Collin, *Ber.*, 1884, **17**, 263.
McGookin, *J. Chem. Soc.*, 1934, 1744.
Morton, McGookin, *ibid.*, 909.

3-Nitro-*p*-toluidine.

Red leaflets from EtOH.Aq. M.p. 117°. Sol. EtOH. Spar. sol. H_2O. Volatile in steam. D_4^{121} 1·164. $k = 5{\cdot}4 \times 10^{-4}$ at 25°.

B,HCl : m.p. 170–1°.
B,HBr : m.p. 229–30°.
N-*Acetyl* : 3-nitroacet-*p*-toluidide. Yellow needles from pet. ether. M.p. 96°.
N-*Diacetyl* : m.p. 78°.
N-*Chloroacetyl* : m.p. 122° (119°).
N-*Trichloroacetyl* : m.p. 54–5°.
N-*Butyryl* : m.p. 62°.
N-*Isovaleryl* : m.p. 88–9°.
Succinate : $(C_7H_7O_2N_2\cdot OC\cdot CH_2\cdot)_2$. M.p. 217°.
N-*Lactyl* : m.p. 86–7°.
N-*Benzoyl* : m.p. 146–8°.
N-o-*Chlorobenzoyl* : m.p. 139°.
N-o-*Nitrobenzoyl* : m.p. 198°.
N-m-*Nitrobenzoyl* : m.p. 188·5°.
N-p-*Nitrobenzoyl* : m.p. 171°.
N-p-*Toluyl* : m.p. 165–6°.
N-*Cinnamoyl* : m.p. 147°.
N-*Benzenesulphonyl* : m.p. 101–2°.
N-p-*Toluenesulphonyl* : m.p. 145–6°.
N-*Di*-p-*toluenesulphonyl* : m.p. 228°.
N-d-*Camphor*-β-*sulphonyl* : m.p. 126–8°.
N-o-*Chlorobenzylidene* : m.p. 149°.
N-p-*Nitrobenzylidene* : m.p. 161·5°.
N-2 : 4-*Dinitrobenzylidene* : m.p. 195°.
N-*Me* : *see* 3-Nitro-*N*-methyl-*p*-toluidine.
N-*Di-Me* : *see* 3-Nitro-*N*-dimethyl-*p*-toluidine.
N-*Et* : *see* 3-Nitro-*N*-ethyl-*p*-toluidine.
N-*Di-Et* : *see* 3-Nitro-*N*-diethyl-*p*-toluidine.

Gattermann, *Ber.*, 1885, **18**, 1483.
A.G.F.A., D.R.P. 164,130, (*Chem. Zentr.*, 1905, II, 1476).
Ullmann, Gross, *Ber.*, 1910, **43**, 2698.
Gindraux, *Helv. Chim. Acta*, 1929, **12**, 933.

3-Nitro-*o*-toluidine-5-sulphonic Acid

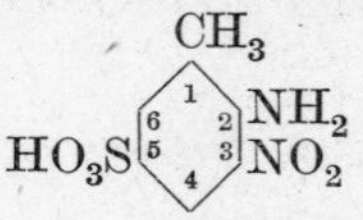

$C_7H_8O_5N_2S$ MW, 232

Yellow needles from H_2O.
K salt : orange-yellow needles. Sol. H_2O.

Gnehm, Blumer, *Ann.*, 1899, **304**, 105.
Nietzki, Pollini, *Ber.*, 1890, **23**, 138.

6-Nitro-*o*-toluidine-4-sulphonic Acid.

Needles. Sol. 102·7 parts H_2O at 19°. Insol. most other solvents.
K salt : leaflets. Spar. sol. cold H_2O.
Ba salt : needles + $2\frac{1}{2}H_2O$. Spar. sol. cold H_2O.

Marckwald, *Ann.*, 1893, **274**, 350.

6-Nitro-*p*-toluidine-3-sulphonic Acid

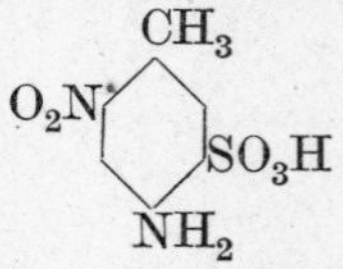

$C_7H_8O_5N_2S$ MW, 232

Pale yellow needles from H_2O. Decomp. on heating. Spar. sol. EtOH.
K salt : orange-red prisms + H_2O. Spar. sol. cold H_2O.
Ba salt : red cryst.

Foth, *Ann.*, 1885, **230**, 300.

3-Nitrotoluquinone

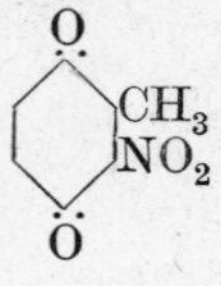

$C_7H_5O_4N$ MW, 167

Ruby red prisms from Et_2O–pet. ether. M.p. 64–5°.

Cohen, Marshall, *J. Chem. Soc.*, 1904, **85**, 527.

3-Nitro-2-*p*-toluylbenzoic Acid (*6-Nitro-4′-methylbenzophenone-2-carboxylic acid*)

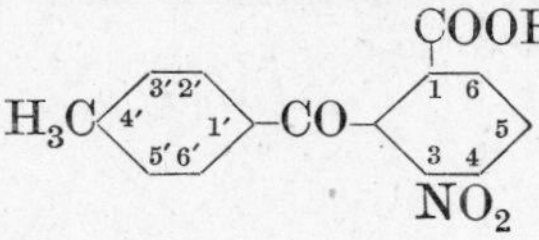

$C_{15}H_{11}O_5N$ MW, 285

Two compounds of this constitution have been described.

(i) Yellow plates from dil. EtOH. M.p. 218–19°.

Mitter, Sarkar, *J. Indian. Chem. Soc.*, 1930, **7**, 625.

(ii) M.p. 123–6° decomp. KOH at 215° ⟶ *p*-toluic and *m*-nitrobenzoic acids.

Lawrance, *J. Am. Chem. Soc.*, 1921, **43**, 2579.

4-Nitro-2-*p*-toluylbenzoic Acid (*5-Nitro-4′-methylbenzophenone-2-carboxylic acid*).

Three compounds of this constitution have been described.

(i) Prisms from AcOH. M.p. 171°.

Mitter, Sarkar, *J. Indian Chem. Soc.*, 1930, **7**, 626.

(ii) M.p. 101–5° decomp. KOH at 215° ⟶ *p*-toluic and *p*-nitrobenzoic acids.

Lawrance, *J. Am. Chem. Soc.*, 1921, **43**, 2579.

(iii) M.p. 216–217·5° (not pure).

Hayashi, Nakayama, *Chem. Abstracts*, 1934, **28**, 5818.

5-Nitro-2-*p*-toluylbenzoic Acid (*4-Nitro-4′-methylbenzophenone-2-carboxylic acid*).

M.p. 187–91° (not pure).

Hayashi, Nakayama, *Chem. Abstracts*, 1934, **28**, 5819.

6-Nitro-2-*p*-toluylbenzoic Acid (*3-Nitro-4′-methylbenzophenone-2-carboxylic acid*).

M.p. 262–5° decomp. KOH at 215° ⟶ *p*-toluic and *o*-nitrobenzoic acids.

Lawrance, *J. Am. Chem. Soc.*, 1921, **43**, 2578.

3′-Nitro-*p*-toluylbenzoic Acid (*3′-Nitro-4′-methylbenzophenone-2-carboxylic acid*).

Cryst. + $1H_2O$. M.p. 205°. Sol. Me_2CO, AcOEt, warm EtOH. Very spar. sol. Et_2O, CS_2, CCl_4. KOH fusion ⟶ benzoic acid.

Et ester: $C_{17}H_{15}O_5N$. MW, 313. Prisms from EtOH. M.p. 122°.

Chloride: $C_{15}H_{10}O_4NCl$. MW, 303·5. Needles from C_6H_6–pet. ether. M.p. 142°. Stable in air.

Amide: $C_{15}H_{12}O_4N_2$. MW, 284. Needles from EtOH or C_6H_6. Decomp. at 200°.

Anhydride: $C_{30}H_{20}O_9N_2$. MW, 552. Needles from EtOH or toluene. M.p. 203°.

Mixed anhydride with acetic acid: $C_{17}H_{13}O_6N$. MW, 327. Cryst. M.p. 145–6°.

Limpricht, *Ann.*, 1898, **299**, 309.

4-Nitro-*m*-tolylacetic Acid (*4-Nitro-3-methylphenylacetic acid*)

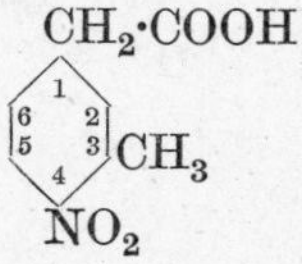

$C_9H_9O_4N$ MW, 195

Nitrile: $C_9H_8O_2N_2$. MW, 176. Cryst. from H_2O or EtOH. M.p. 63° (52°). B.p. 200–5°/22 mm. Sol. boiling EtOH. Mod. sol. boiling H_2O. Alk. $KMnO_4$ ⟶ 4-nitro-*m*-toluic acid.

Barger, Ewins, *J. Chem. Soc.*, 1910, **97**, 2256.

Lifschutz, Jenner, *Ber.*, 1915, **48**, 1740.

6-Nitro-*m*-tolylacetic Acid (*6-Nitro-3-methylphenylacetic acid*).

Cryst. from H_2O. M.p. 149°. Sol. EtOH, Et_2O, Me_2CO, $CHCl_3$.

Reissert, Scherk, *Ber.*, 1898, **31**, 391.

3-Nitro-*p*-tolylacetic Acid (*3-Nitro-4-methylphenylacetic acid*).

Needles from H_2O. M.p. 102°. Sol. EtOH, Et_2O, CS_2. Mod. sol. hot H_2O. Sublimes. $KMnO_4$ ⟶ 3-nitro-*p*-toluic acid.

Claus, Wehr, *J. prakt. Chem.*, 1891, **44**, 90.

5-Nitro-2 : 3-tolylenediamine (*5-Nitro-2 : 3-diaminotoluene*)

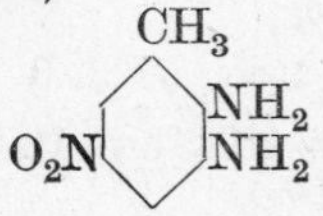

$C_7H_9O_2N_3$ MW, 167

Orange-red needles from EtOH.Aq. M.p. 185°. Very sol. hot EtOH, AcOH. Mod. sol. hot H_2O.

N : N′-*Diacetyl*: yellowish needles from EtOH.Aq. M.p. 234°. Sol. AcOH, hot EtOH. Spar. sol. hot H_2O.

Kym, Ringer, *Ber.*, 1915, **48**, 1674.

5-Nitro-2 : 4-tolylenediamine (5-*Nitro-2 : 4-diaminotoluene*)

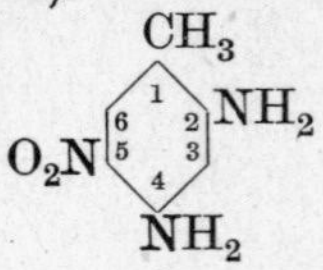

$C_7H_9O_2N_3$ MW, 167

Yellow needles with violet reflex from H_2O. M.p. 154°. Sol. hot EtOH. Mod. sol. hot H_2O. Weak base. Salts decomp. by H_2O.

4-N-*Me*: $C_8H_{11}O_2N_3$. MW, 181. Bronze leaflets from EtOH. M.p. 168°. Sol. $CHCl_3$, AcOH, hot C_6H_6. Spar. sol. ligroin. 2-N-*Acetyl*: yellowish-brown needles from H_2O. M.p. 205·5–207°. Very sol. hot AcOH. Spar. sol. hot H_2O.

4-N-*Di-Me*: $C_9H_{13}O_2N_3$. MW, 195. Yellow needles from EtOH. M.p. 155°.

N : N′-*Diacetyl*: needles from Me_2CO. M.p. 250–1°. Sol. about 300 parts Me_2CO.

N : N′-*Dibenzoyl*: yellow needles from AcOH. M.p. 245°.

N : N′-*Di-benzenesulphonyl*: yellow prisms. M.p. 185°.

N : N′-*Di*-p-*toluenesulphonyl*: yellow cryst. from AcOH. M.p. 210°.

Brady, Day, Reynolds, *J. Chem. Soc.*, 1929, 2265.
Pinnow, *J. prakt. Chem.*, 1900, **62**, 508.
A.G.F.A., D.R.P., 166,600, (*Chem. Zentr.*, 1906, I, 517).
Ruhemann, *Ber.*, 1881, **14**, 2656.
Morgan, Clayton, *J. Chem. Soc.*, 1910, **97**, 2650.
Ladenburg, *Ber.*, 1875, **8**, 1211.
See also Staedel, *Ann.*, 1883, **217**, 155.

6-Nitro-2 : 4-tolylenediamine (6-*Nitro-2 : 4-diaminotoluene*).

Yellowish-orange cryst. from C_6H_6–pet. ether. M.p. 130–1°.

Brady, Day, Reynolds, *J. Chem. Soc.*, 1929, 2266.
Tiemann, *Ber.*, 1870, **3**, 218.

4-Nitro-2 : 5-tolylenediamine (4-*Nitro-2 : 5-diaminotoluene*)

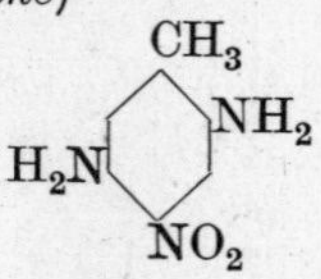

$C_7H_9O_2N_3$ MW, 167

Red needles with bronze reflex from H_2O. M.p. 173°.

N : N′-*Diacetyl*: yellowish prisms from AcOH. M.p. 258° decomp. Very spar. sol. usual solvents.

Morgan, Micklethwait, *J. Chem. Soc.*, 1913, **103**, 1398.

5-Nitro-3 : 4-tolylenediamine (5-*Nitro-3 : 4-diaminotoluene*)

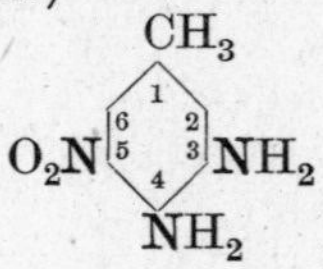

$C_7H_9O_2N_3$ MW, 167

Dark red needles from H_2O. M.p. 158°.

Acetyl: pale yellow needles from MeOH. M.p. 211°.

Lindemann, Krause, *J. prakt. Chem.*, 1927, **115**, 256.
Brady, Day, Reynolds, *J. Chem. Soc.*, 1929, 2265.

6-Nitro-3 : 4-tolylenediamine (6-*Nitro-3 : 4-diaminotoluene*).

4-N-*Me*: $C_8H_{11}O_2N_3$. MW, 181. Dark red needles from hot H_2O or EtOH.Aq. M.p. 180°.

See last reference above.

3-Nitro-*o*-tolylglycine

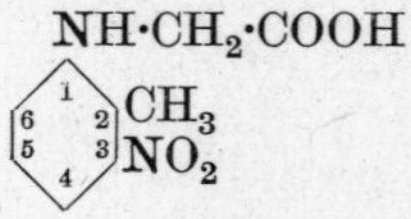

$C_9H_{10}O_4N_2$ MW, 210

Yellowish-brown prisms from EtOH. M.p. 152°. Sol. EtOH, Me_2CO, $PhNO_2$. Spar. sol. hot H_2O, Et_2O, AcOH. Insol. C_6H_6, $CHCl_3$, pet. ether.

Pollak, *J. prakt. Chem.*, 1915, **91**, 297.

4-Nitro-*o*-tolylglycine.

Reddish-brown cryst. from EtOH. M.p. 192°. Very sol. hot H_2O. Sol. EtOH. Spar. sol. Me_2CO, $CHCl_3$. Insol. Et_2O, $PhNO_2$.

Me ester: $C_{10}H_{12}O_4N_2$. MW, 224. Yellow needles from C_6H_6. M.p. 82°. Sol. EtOH, C_6H_6.

Et ester: $C_{11}H_{14}O_4N_2$. MW, 238. Cryst. from C_6H_6. M.p. 87°. Sol. EtOH, Et_2O, C_6H_6. Insol. H_2O, pet. ether.

See previous reference.

5-Nitro-*o*-tolylglycine.

Pale yellow needles from H_2O. M.p. 140°. Very sol. Me_2CO. Sol. EtOH, Et_2O, AcOH. Spar. sol. C_6H_6, cold H_2O.

Me ester: pale yellow needles from C_6H_6. I.p. 108°. Sol. EtOH, AcOH. Spar. sol. :t$_2$O. Insol. H_2O, $CHCl_3$, pet. ether.

Et ester: reddish-brown needles from EtOH. I.p. 42°. Sol. Me_2CO. Mod. sol. EtOH, HCl$_3$, AcOH. Spar. sol. C_6H_6. Insol. H_2O, et. ether.

See previous reference.

4-Nitro-*m*-tolylglycine

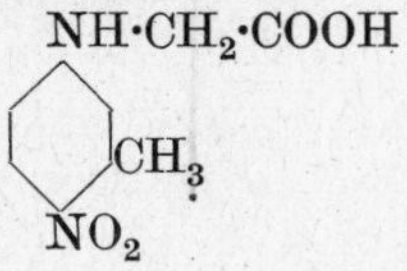

$_9H_{10}O_4N_2$ MW, 210

Yellow cryst. from H_2O. M.p. 145°. Sol. :tOH, Me_2CO, $PhNO_2$. Spar. sol. Et_2O. Inol. cold H_2O, C_6H_6, $CHCl_3$, pet. ether.

Pollak, *J. prakt. Chem.*, 1915, **91**, 304.

2-Nitro-*p*-tolylglycine

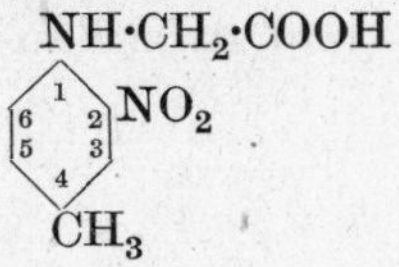

$_9H_{10}O_4N_2$ MW, 210

Reddish-brown prisms from EtOH or AcOH. I.p. 189–90° decomp. Sol. hot EtOH, AcOH. par. sol. cold H_2O, Et_2O.

Et ester: $C_{11}H_{14}O_4N_2$. MW, 238. Bright ellow needles from EtOH. M.p. 65°. Sol. $_6H_6$, ligroin.

Plöchl, *Ber.*, 1886, **19**, 9.
Leuckart, Hermann, *Ber.*, 1887, **20**, 26.

3-Nitro-*p*-tolylglycine.

Yellow prisms from EtOH. M.p. 130°. ery sol. EtOH, AcOH. Spar. sol. Et_2O, hNO$_2$. Insol. cold H_2O, $CHCl_3$, C_6H_6.

NH_4 salt: reddish-brown prisms. M.p. 135°. ol. H_2O, EtOH, Et_2O, AcOH.

Cu salt: green cryst. + H_2O. M.p. 160°. ol. EtOH. Spar. sol. Me_2CO. Insol. cold $_2O$, C_6H_6, Et_2O, $CHCl_3$.

Pollak, *J. prakt. Chem.*, 1915, **91**, 296.

4-Nitro-*o*-tolylurethane

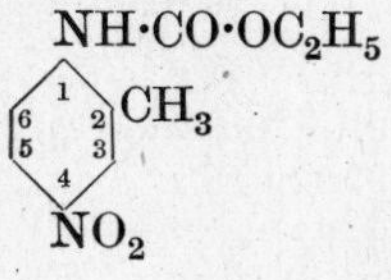

$_{10}H_{12}O_4N_2$ MW, 224

Pale yellow needles from EtOH. M.p. 135°. Sol. boiling H_2O. Mod. sol. C_6H_6, Et_2O. Insol. boiling ligroin.

Vittenet, *Bull. soc. chim.*, 1899, **21**, 591.
Ryan, Cullinane, *Chem. Abstracts*, 1923, **17**, 1792.

5-Nitro-*o*-tolylurethane.

Needles from EtOH. M.p. 137° (129–30°). Sol. EtOH, Et_2O, C_6H_6. Mod. sol. hot H_2O. Spar. sol. boiling ligroin.

See last reference above and also
Schiff, Vanni, *Ann.*, 1892, **268**, 323.

6-Nitro-*o*-tolylurethane.

Prisms. M.p. 131°. Spar. sol. ligroin.

Ryan, Cullinane, *Chem. Abstracts*, 1923, **17**, 1792.

2-Nitro-*p*-tolylurethane

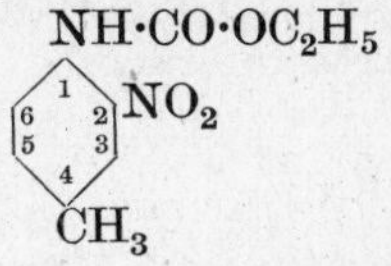

$C_{10}H_{12}O_4N_2$ MW, 224

Yellow needles from EtOH. M.p. 63°. Sol. C_6H_6, Et_2O. Mod. sol. boiling H_2O. Spar. sol. ligroin.

Vittenet, *Bull. soc. chim.*, 1899, **21**, 590.

3-Nitro-*p*-tolylurethane.

Pale yellow needles from EtOH.Aq. M.p. 77–8°. Mod. sol. C_6H_6. Spar. sol. Et_2O. Insol. boiling ligroin.

See previous reference.

5-Nitro-1 : 2 : 3-triaminobenzene

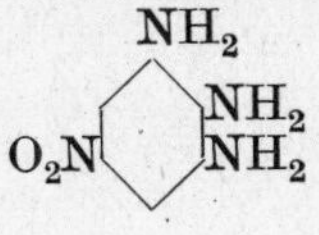

$C_6H_8O_2N_4$ MW, 168

Red cryst. with golden lustre from EtOH. Decomp. at 260°.

Triacetyl deriv.: m.p. 243°.

Nietzki, Hagenbach, *Ber.*, 1897, **30**, 543.

Nitro-1 : 2 : 3-trihydroxybenzene.

See Nitropyrogallol.

3-Nitro-1 : 2 : 4-trihydroxybenzene (3-*Nitrohydroxyhydroquinone*)

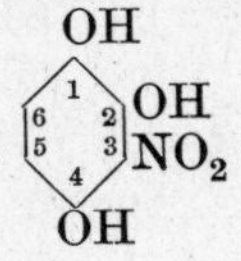

$C_6H_5O_5N$ MW, 171

2-*Me* ether : $C_7H_7O_5N$. MW, 185. Red prisms from C_6H_6. M.p. 86·5–87·5°.

Dakin, *Am. Chem. J.*, 1909, **42**, 493.

5-Nitro-1 : 2 : 4-trihydroxybenzene (5-*Nitrohydroxyhydroquinone*).
Tri-Me ether : $C_9H_{11}O_5N$. MW, 213. Yellow needles from EtOH. M.p. 130°. Sol. boiling EtOH, C_6H_6, AcOH. Spar. sol. hot H_2O, Et_2O. Conc. $H_2SO_4 \longrightarrow$ red sol.
Tri-Et ether : $C_{12}H_{17}O_5N$. MW, 255. Yellow needles from EtOH. M.p. 108–9°. Sol. EtOH, Et_2O, C_6H_6, AcOH.

Brezina, *Monatsh.*, 1901, **22**, 347.
Fabinyi, Széki, *Ber.*, 1906, **39**, 3681.

Nitro-1 : 3 : 5-trihydroxybenzene.
See Nitrophloroglucinol.
Nitro-trimethoxyphthalide.
See under 3-Nitro-opianic Acid.
2-Nitrotriphenylamine

$$\begin{array}{c}C_6H_5\\C_6H_5\end{array}\!\!>\!N-\!\!\left\langle\begin{array}{c}NO_2\\ {}^2\;{}^3\\ {}_1\qquad{}_4\\ {}_6\;{}_5\end{array}\right\rangle$$

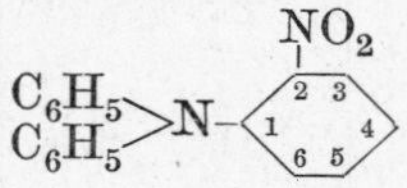

$C_{18}H_{14}O_2N_2$ MW, 290
Yellowish-orange cryst. from EtOH. M.p. 98°.

Piccard, Larsen, *J. Am. Chem. Soc.*, 1917, · **39**, 2009.

3-Nitrotriphenylamine.
Yellow cryst. from MeOH. M.p. 78°. Sol. Et_2O, C_6H_6, AcOEt, $PhNO_2$. Mod. sol. EtOH, AcOH. Insol. H_2O. Conc. $H_2SO_4 \longrightarrow$ colourless sol. turning blue in few seconds.

See previous reference.

4-Nitrotriphenylamine.
Golden-yellow plates from AcOH–AcOEt. M.p. 144° (140°). Very sol. $CHCl_3$. Sol. Me_2CO, C_6H_6, CS_2, AcOEt, hot AcOH. Spar. sol. EtOH, ligroin. Insol. cold AcOH.

Gambarjan, *Ber.*, 1908, **41**, 3510.
Kawai, *J. Chem. Soc. Japan*, 1928, **49**, 235.

3-Nitrotriphenylcarbinol (3-*Nitro-α-hydroxytriphenylmethane*, 3-*nitrotritanol*)

$$\begin{array}{c}C_6H_5\\HO-C\\C_6H_5\end{array}\!\!-\!\!\left\langle\begin{array}{c}NO_2\\ {}^2\;{}^3\\ {}_1\qquad{}_4\\ {}_6\;{}_5\end{array}\right\rangle$$

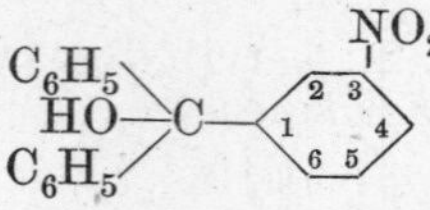

$C_{19}H_{15}O_3N$ MW, 305
Cryst. from ligroin or AcOH.Aq. M.p. 75°.

Tsacher, *Ber.*, 1888, **21**, 190.
Kovachi, *Ann. chim.*, 1918, **10**, 202.

4-Nitrotriphenylcarbinol (4-*Nitro-α-hydroxytriphenylmethane*, 4-*nitrotritanol*).
Prisms from ligroin. M.p. 97–8°.

Baeyer, Villiger, *Ber.*, 1904, **37**, 606.

2-Nitrotriphenylmethane (2-*Nitrotritane*)

$$\begin{array}{c}C_6H_5\\C_6H_5\end{array}\!\!>\!CH-\!\!\left\langle\begin{array}{c}NO_2\\ {}^2\;{}^3\\ {}_1\qquad{}_4\\ {}_6\;{}_5\end{array}\right\rangle$$

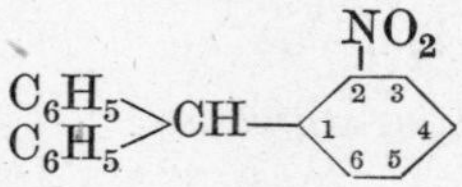

$C_{19}H_{15}O_2N$ MW, 289
Pale yellowish leaflets from EtOH or MeOH. M.p. 93–4°. Sol. hot EtOH, ligroin. Mod. sol. AcOH.

Kliegl, *Ber.*, 1907, **40**, 4941.

3-Nitrotriphenylmethane (3-*Nitrotritane*).
Cryst. from ligroin or Et_2O. M.p. 90°.

Tsacher, *Ber.*, 1888, **21**, 188.
Kovache, *Ann. chim.*, 1918, **10**, 202.

4-Nitrotriphenylmethane (4-*Nitrotritane*).
Leaflets from EtOH. M.p. 93°.

Baeyer, Löhr, *Ber.*, 1890, **23**, 1622.
Stolz, D.R.P., 40,340.

5-Nitrouracil

$$\begin{array}{l}HN^1\!\!-\!\!{}^6CO\\OC^2\quad{}^5C\cdot NO_2\\HN^3\!\!-\!\!{}^4CH\end{array}$$

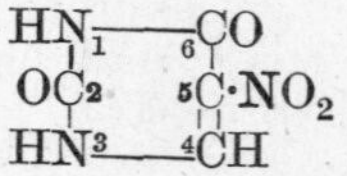

$C_4H_3O_4N_3$ MW, 157
Golden-yellow needles. Decomp. on heating. Spar. sol. H_2O, cold EtOH. Reacts as monobasic acid. $KMnO_4 \longrightarrow CO_2 +$ oxalic acid + urea.
3-N-*Me* : $C_5H_5O_4N_3$. MW, 171. Long needles from EtOH. M.p. 255–6°. Spar. sol. Et_2O, $CHCl_3$, C_6H_6. Reacts acid.
1 : 3-N-*Di-Me* : $C_6H_7O_4N_3$. MW, 185. Long needles from H_2O. M.p. 154·5°.
3-N-*Et* : $C_6H_7O_4N_3$. MW, 185. Long needles from H_2O. M.p. 194·5°.
1-N-*Me*-3-N-*Et* : $C_7H_9O_4N_3$. MW, 199. Pearly cryst. from H_2O. M.p. 73°. Sol. EtOH, Et_2O.
3-N-*Me*-1-N-*Et* : needles from H_2O. M.p. 109°.
Picrate : m.p. 247°.

Johnson, Matsuo, *J. Am. Chem. Soc.*, 1919, **41**, 783.
Biltz, Heyn, *Ann.*, 1917, **413**, 110.
Levene, La Forge, *Ber.*, 1912, **45**, 618.

Nitrourea

$H_2N{\cdot}CO{\cdot}NH{\cdot}NO_2$

$CH_3O_3N_3$ MW, 105

Leaflets or prisms from EtOH. M.p. 159° (150°) decomp. Very sol. Me_2CO, AcOH. Sol. EtOH. Spar. sol. $CHCl_3$, C_6H_6, pet. ether. $k = 7{\cdot}0 \times 10^{-3}$ at 20°. Very stable towards ox. agents. Can be detonated. Not sensitive to percussion or heating.

Backer, *Rec. trav. chim.*, 1912, **31**, 22.
Willstätter, Pfannenstiel, *Ber.*, 1926, **59**, 1870.
Ingersoll, Armendt, *Organic Syntheses*, Collective Vol. I, 408.

Nitrourethane

$O_2N{\cdot}NH{\cdot}CO{\cdot}OC_2H_5$

$C_3H_6O_4N_2$ MW, 134

Plates from Et_2O or ligroin. M.p. 64°. Very sol. EtOH, Et_2O. Sol. H_2O. Spar. sol. ligroin. $k = 4{\cdot}83 \times 10^{-4}$ at 20°. Decomp. at 140° or by heating with H_2O.

Thiele, Lachmann, *Ann.*, 1895, **288**, 287.

2-Nitrovanillic Acid (2-*Nitroprotocatechuic acid* 3-*methyl ether*)

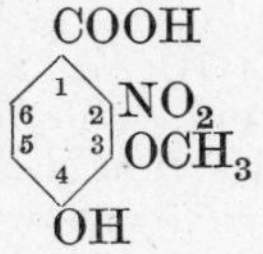

$C_8H_7O_6N$ MW, 213

Needles from EtOH.Aq., cryst. from C_6H_6. Decomp. at 246° (210°). Sol. EtOH, Et_2O. Spar. sol. H_2O. $k = 1{\cdot}2 \times 10^{-4}$ at 25°.

4-*Me ether*: *see* 2-Nitroveratric Acid.

Acetyl: needles from EtOH.Aq. M.p. 181–2°. Sol. EtOH, Et_2O. Spar. sol. hot H_2O.

Tiemann, Matsmoto, *Ber.*, 1876, **9**, 943.
Klemenc, *Monatsh.*, 1914, **35**, 94.

5-Nitrovanillic Acid (5-*Nitroprotocatechuic acid* 3-*methyl ether*).

Pale yellow cryst. from H_2O. M.p. 216°. Sol. EtOH, Et_2O, Me_2CO. Spar. sol. H_2O, $CHCl_3$. NH_3.Aq. ⟶ intense orange-yellow col.

4-*Me ether*: *see* 5-Nitroveratric Acid.

Me ester: $C_9H_9O_6N$. MW, 227. Yellow needles from MeOH or leaflets from Et_2O. M.p. 155° (148–9°). Sol. C_6H_6, EtOH. Less sol. ligroin, Et_2O. Sol. alkalis with red col. *Benzoyl*: yellowish-brown needles from EtOH. M.p. 124–5°. Sol. C_6H_6, warm Et_2O, AcOH, ligroin.

Chloride: $C_8H_6O_5NCl$. MW, 231·5. M.p. 93–4°. Sol. C_6H_6. Spar. sol. Et_2O, ligroin. Insol. pet. ether.

Nitrile: $C_8H_6O_4N_2$. MW, 194. Needles from H_2O. M.p. 140°. *Acetyl*: yellowish needles from EtOH.Aq. M.p. 102°.

Borsche, *Ber.*, 1917, **50**, 1346.
v. Konek, Pacsu, *Ber.*, 1918, **51**, 861.
Klemenc, *Monatsh.*, 1912, **33**, 388; 1914, **35**, 94.

2-Nitrovanillin (2-*Nitroprotocatechuic aldehyde* 3-*methyl ether*)

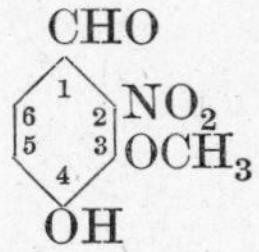

$C_8H_7O_5N$ MW, 197

Needles from EtOH. M.p. 137°. Sol. EtOH, Et_2O, Me_2CO, AcOH. Less sol. hot H_2O, C_6H_6, $CHCl_3$. Spar. sol. ligroin, pet. ether. Turns brown in air.

Me ether: *see* 2-Nitroveratric Aldehyde.

Et ether: $C_{10}H_{11}O_5N$. MW, 225. Cryst. from EtOH. M.p. 106–7°.

Acetyl: needles from EtOH.Aq., prisms from ligroin. M.p. 85–7°. Spar. sol. H_2O, ligroin, pet. ether. Turns yellow in air. *Phenylhydrazone*: reddish-brown plates. M.p. 154°.

Phenylhydrazone: prisms from AcOH. M.p. 161–2°.

Slotta, Lauersen, *J. prakt. Chem.*, 1934, **139**, 224.
Pschorr, Sumuleanu, *Ber.*, 1899, **32**, 3407.
Raiford, Stoesser, *J. Am. Chem. Soc.*, 1928, **50**, 2559.
Späth, Tharrer, *Ber.*, 1933, **66**, 911.

5-Nitrovanillin (5-*Nitroprotocatechuic aldehyde* 3-*methyl ether*).

Pale yellow plates from AcOH. M.p. 178° (172°). Very sol. hot AcOH. Sol. $CHCl_3$, CS_2. Spar. sol. hot EtOH. Insol. Et_2O.

Me ether: *see* 5-Nitroveratric Aldehyde.

Acetyl: yellow cryst. from AcOEt. M.p. 88°. Sol. AcOH, AcOEt.

Oxime: pale orange-yellow needles from EtOH, deep orange-yellow needles from AcOH. M.p. 216° (200–1°). Sol. EtOH, Et_2O. Spar. sol. hot H_2O. *Acetyl*: orange needles + H_2O from EtOH.Aq. M.p. 147°. *Diacetyl*: yellow cryst. from EtOH. M.p. 112°. *B,HCl*: m.p. 204° decomp.

Vogl, *Monatsh.*, 1899, **20**, 384.
Brady, Dunn, *J. Chem. Soc.*, 1915, **107**, 1861.

6-Nitrovanillin (6-*Nitroprotocatechuic aldehyde* 3-*methyl ether*).

Yellow plates from AcOH. M.p. 212° (207°). Sol. hot H_2O, most org . solvens.

Me ether : *see* 6-Nitroveratric Aldehyde.

Et ether : cryst. M.p. 159–60°. Sublimes.

p-*Nitrobenzyl ether* : pale yellow needles from AcOEt. M.p. 212–14°. Sol. Me_2CO, Py, hot C_6H_6, AcOH, AcOEt. Spar. sol. EtOH, Et_2O, $CHCl_3$. *Phenylhydrazone* : brick-red needles from AcOH or EtOH.Aq. M.p. 208°. *Oxime* : pale yellow needles from EtOH. M.p. 158–60°. *Anil* : yellow prisms from EtOH. M.p. 192–3°.

Phenylhydrazone : dark red needles from C_6H_6. M.p. 198°.

Raiford, Stoesser, *J. Am. Chem. Soc.*, 1928, **50**, 2559.
Nair, Robinson, *J. Chem. Soc.*, 1932, 1237.

2-Nitroveratric Acid (2-*Nitroprotocatechuic acid dimethyl ether*, 2-*nitro*-3 : 4-*dimethoxybenzoic acid*)

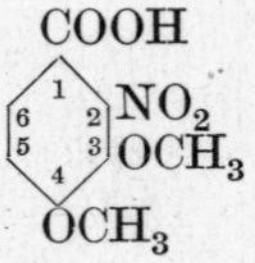

$C_9H_9O_6N$ MW, 227

Needles from H_2O. M.p. 203°. Sol. most ord. solvents. Spar. sol. C_6H_6, pet. ether. Sol. 250 parts boiling, 1000 parts cold H_2O.

Me ester : $C_{10}H_{11}O_6N$. MW, 241. Needles from EtOH.Aq. M.p. 127–8°. Sol. EtOH, Et_2O. Spar. sol. H_2O.

Chloride : $C_9H_8O_5NCl$. MW, 245·5. Needles from toluene. M.p. 78° (73°). Sol. CS_2, toluene, xylene. Spar. sol. C_6H_6, Et_2O. Insol. ligroin. Decomp. by H_2O.

Amide : $C_9H_{10}O_5N_2$. MW, 226. Needles from toluene, plates from H_2O. M.p. 172°. Sol. toluene, xylene. Spar. sol. H_2O, C_6H_6. Insol. Et_2O, $CHCl_3$, AcOEt, CS_2.

Pisovschi, *Ber.*, 1910, **43**, 2140.
Pschorr, Sumuleanu, *Ber.*, 1899, **32**, 3410.

5-Nitroveratric Acid.

Needles from C_6H_6. M.p. 196° (194°). Sol. EtOH, Et_2O. Spar. sol. H_2O, $CHCl_3$, cold C_6H_6. Very spar. sol. pet. ether.

Me ester : needles from MeOH or pet. ether. M.p. 78°. Sol. usual solvents. Mod. sol. MeOH, pet. ether.

Simonsen, Rau, *J. Chem. Soc.*, 1918, **113**, 24.
Klemenc, *Monatsh.*, 1914, **35**, 96.
Zincke, Francke, *Ann.*, 1896, **293**, 192.

6-Nitroveratric Acid.

Yellow needles + $\frac{1}{2}H_2O$. M.p. 185–7° (192-3°). Sol. 25 parts hot H_2O. Sol. EtOH, Et_2O, C_6H_6. Insol. ligroin. $k = 3{\cdot}6 \times 10^{-3}$ at 25°.

Me ester : needles. M.p. 143–4°. Sol. Et_2O, boiling EtOH. Spar. sol. cold H_2O.

Et ester : prisms from EtOH.Aq. M.p. 99-100°. Sol. EtOH, Et_2O. Insol. H_2O.

Nitrile : yellow needles from EtOH. M.p. 165°. Sol. $CHCl_3$. Mod. sol. EtOH, C_6H_6. Conc. $H_2SO_4 \longrightarrow$ green sol. rapidly turning brown.

Keffler, *J. Chem. Soc.*, 1921, **119**, 1479.
Tiemann, Matsmoto, *Ber.*, 1876, **9**, 938.
Simonsen, Rau, *J. Chem. Soc.*, 1918, **113**, 26.
Pschorr, Sumuleanu, *Ber.*, 1899, **32**, 3410.

2-Nitroveratric Aldehyde (2-*Nitroprotocatechuic aldehyde dimethyl ether*, 2-*nitro*-3 : 4-*dimethoxybenzaldehyde*)

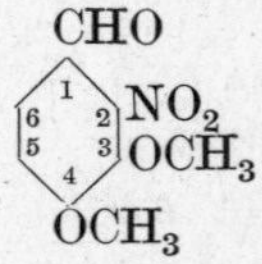

$C_9H_9O_5N$ MW, 21

Prisms from EtOH.Aq. M.p. 64°. Spar. sol. H_2O. Insol. ligroin, pet. ether. Sol. most other solvents. Turns yellow in air.

Phenylhydrazone : yellow plates from AcOH. M.p. 194°.

Pschorr, Stöhrer, *Ber.*, 1902, **35**, 4397.
Pschorr, *Ber.*, 1906, **39**, 3108.
Slotta, Lauersen, *J. prakt. Chem.*, 1934, **139**, 225.

5-Nitroveratric Aldehyde.

Needles from EtOH.Aq. M.p. 90–1°. Sol. EtOH, Et_2O, C_6H_6. Spar. sol. H_2O, pet. ether.

anti-*Oxime* : plates from EtOH. M.p. 151°. *Acetyl* : plates from Me_2CO.Aq. M.p. 115°.

Phenylhydrazone : yellow leaflets. M.p. 108-10°.

Pschorr, Stöhrer, *Ber.*, 1902, **35**, 4399.
Brady, Manjunath, *J. Chem. Soc.*, 1924, **125**, 1067.

6-Nitroveratric Aldehyde.

Yellow needles from EtOH. M.p. 133·5-134·5°. Sol. Et_2O, C_6H_6, AcOH, hot EtOH. Spar. sol. H_2O, ligroin.

Di-Me acetal : prisms from Et_2O–pet. ether. M.p. 54·5–55·5°. Sol. most org. solvents.

anti-*Oxime* : yellow needles from EtOH or C_6H_6. M.p. 178–80°. Sol. hot EtOH. Mod sol. cold EtOH, Et_2O, hot C_6H_6. *Acetyl*: pale yellow leaflets from EtOH. M.p. 152°.

Phenylhydrazone: plates from AcOH. M.p. 216–18°.

See previous references and also
Pschorr, Sumuleanu, *Ber.*, 1899, **32**, 3412.
Marr, Bogert, *J. Am. Chem. Soc.*, 1935, **57**, 1329.

Nitroveratrol.
See under Nitrocatechol.

1-Nitroxanthone

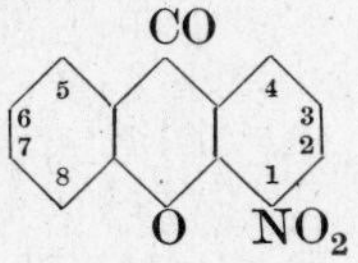

$C_{13}H_7O_4N$ MW, 241

Yellow needles from EtOH. M.p. 127°. $H_2SO_4 \longrightarrow$ green sol.

Dhar, *J. Chem. Soc.*, 1920, **117**, 1063.

2-Nitroxanthone.
Pale yellowish needles from EtOH.Aq. M.p. 176°. Sol. C_6H_6, boiling EtOH. Spar. sol. ligroin. Insol. H_2O. Sol. conc. H_2SO_4 with strong blue fluor.

See previous reference and also
Ullmann, Wagner, *Ann.*, 1907, **355**, 362.

3-Nitroxanthone.
Brown needles from EtOH. M.p. 200°. Insol. usual solvents. Sol. conc. H_2SO_4 with greenish-blue fluor.

Dhar, *J. Chem. Soc.*, 1920, **117**, 1062.
Purgotti, *Gazz. chim. ital.*, 1914, **44**, i, 643.

4-Nitroxanthone.
Brown needles from EtOH. M.p. 210°. Conc. $H_2SO_4 \longrightarrow$ yellow sol.

Dhar, *J. Chem. Soc.*, 1920, **117**, 1061.

3-Nitro-*o*-xylene

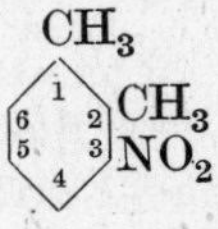

$C_8H_9O_2N$ MW, 151

Needles from EtOH. M.p. 15°. B.p. 240°/760 mm., 136°/29 mm., 131°/20 mm.

Crossley, Wren, *J. Chem. Soc.*, 1911, **99**, 2342.
Crossley, Renouf, *J. Chem. Soc.*, 1909, **95**, 208.

4-Nitro-*o*-xylene.
Yellow prisms from EtOH. M.p. 30°. B.p. 254°/748 mm., 143°/21 mm. Misc. with EtOH above 30°. Sol. most org. solvents.

Diepolder, *Ber.*, 1909, **42**, 2918.
Crossley, Renouf, *J. Chem. Soc.*, 1909, **95**, 207, 215.

2-Nitro-*m*-xylene

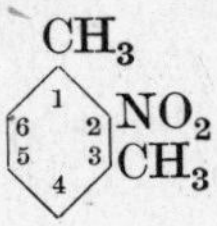

$C_8H_9O_2N$ MW, 151

Liq. B.p. 225°/744 mm. D^{15} 1·112.

Grevingk, *Ber.*, 1884, **17**, 2430.
Miolati, Lotti, *Gazz. chim. ital.*, 1897, **27**, i, 297.

4-Nitro-*m*-xylene.
M.p. 2°. B.p. 237–9° (245·5°/744 mm.). D^1 1·135, $D^{17\cdot5}$ 1·126.

Grevingk, *Ber.*, 1884, **17**, 2429.
Harmsen, *Ber.*, 1880, **13**, 1558.

5-Nitro-*m*-xylene.
Needles from EtOH. M.p. 75°. B.p. 273°/739 mm.

Noyes, *Am. Chem. J.*, 1898, **20**, 800.

2-Nitro-*p*-xylene

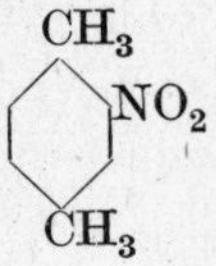

$C_8H_9O_2N$ MW, 151

Pale yellowish liq. B.p. 234–7°. D^{15} 1·132.

Jannasch, *Ann.*, 1875, **176**, 55.

ω-Nitroxylene.
See Tolylnitromethane.

3-Nitro-*o*-xylene-4-sulphonic Acid

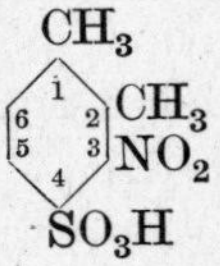

$C_8H_9O_5NS$ MW, 231

Needles + $3H_2O$.

Amide: $C_8H_{10}O_4N_2S$. MW, 230. Prismatic needles from EtOH. M.p. 214°. Spar. sol. EtOH.

Simonsen, *J. Chem. Soc.*, 1913, **103**, 1148.

5-Nitro-*o*-xylene-4-sulphonic Acid.

Needles. Hygroscopic.

Amide : prismatic needles from EtOH. M.p. 157–8°.

See previous reference.

6-Nitro-*o*-xylene-4-sulphonic Acid.

Needles. Easily decomp.

Chloride : $C_8H_8O_4NClS$. MW, 249·5. Plates from C_6H_6–pet. ether. M.p. 69–70°.

Amide : needles from EtOH.Aq. M.p. 180°.

See previous reference.

2-Nitro-*m*-xylene-4-sulphonic Acid

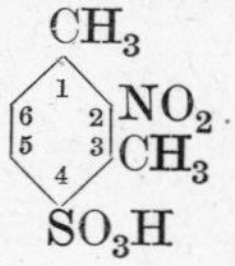

$C_8H_9O_5NS$ MW, 231

Leaflets + H_2O from H_2O. M.p. anhyd. 144°.

Chloride : $C_8H_8O_4NClS$. MW, 249·5. Cryst. M.p. 96°.

Amide : $C_8H_{10}O_4N_2S$. MW, 230. Needles. M.p. 172°. Sol. EtOH, Et_2O.

Claus, Schmidt, *Ber.*, 1886, **19**, 1418.

5-Nitro-*m*-xylene-4-sulphonic Acid.

Leaflets from HNO_3. M.p. 95–100°. Hygroscopic. Sol. H_2O.

Chloride : plates. M.p. 97°. Sol. EtOH, Et_2O, $CHCl_3$, C_6H_6.

Amide : needles from EtOH.Aq. M.p. 108°.

See previous reference.

6-Nitro-*m*-xylene-4-sulphonic Acid.

Needles from dil. HNO_3. M.p. 132° (122°). Sol. dil. HNO_3.

Fluoride : $C_8H_8O_4NFS$. MW, 233. Cryst. from C_6H_6–pet. ether. M.p. 109–10°.

Chloride : cryst. M.p. 98°.

Amide : needles. M.p. 187° (179°).

Limpricht, v. Riesen, *Ber.*, 1885, **18**, 2191.
Steinkopf *et al.*, *J. prakt. Chem.*, 1927, **117**, 41.
See also previous reference.

3-Nitro-*p*-xylene-2-sulphonic Acid

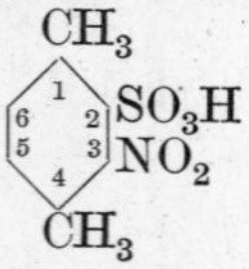

$C_8H_9O_5NS$ MW, 231

Plates + H_2O. M.p. anhyd. 143–5° part. decomp. Mod. sol. EtOH. Insol. Et_2O, $CHCl_3$, C_6H_6, pet. ether.

Phenyl ester : $C_{14}H_{13}O_5NS$. MW, 307. Prism from EtOH. M.p. 83–83·5°.

o-*Tolyl ester* : $C_{15}H_{15}O_5NS$. MW, 321. Prism from EtOH. M.p. 151·5–152°.

m-*Tolyl ester* : plates from EtOH. M.p 107·5–108°.

p-*Tolyl ester* : plates from EtOH. M.p. 76–7°

Chloride : $C_8H_8O_4NClS$. MW, 249·5. Prism from Et_2O–pet. ether. M.p. 109·5–110·5°.

Amide : $C_8H_{10}O_4N_2S$. MW, 230. Needles from 50% EtOH. M.p. 191–2°.

Anilide : $C_{14}H_{14}O_4N_2S$. MW, 306. Bluish needles from EtOH.Aq. M.p. 181·5–182·5° Sol. most org. solvents. Insol. H_2O.

o-*Toluidide* : $C_{15}H_{16}O_4N_2S$. MW, 320. Plates from 50% EtOH. M.p. 143·5–145°.

p-*Toluidide* : needles from EtOH. M.p. 158·5–159°. Sol. EtOH, $CHCl_3$, C_6H_6. Less sol. Et_2O, pet. ether. Insol. H_2O.

Karslake, Huston, *J. Am. Chem. Soc.*, 1914, **36**, 1253.
Huston, *J. Am. Chem. Soc.*, 1915, **37**, 2120.

5-Nitro-*p*-xylene-2-sulphonic Acid.

Plates + H_2O from HCl. M.p. 138–40°. Very hygroscopic. Bitter taste.

Phenyl ester : yellowish plates from EtOH. M.p. 120–120·5°.

o-*Tolyl ester* : needles from EtOH. M.p. 99–100°.

m-*Tolyl ester* : needles from EtOH. M.p. 110–11°.

p-*Tolyl ester* : plates from EtOH. M.p. 117·5–118·5°.

Chloride : plates from Et_2O or Et_2O–pet. ether. M.p. 74·5–75·5°.

Amide : prismatic plates from 50% EtOH. M.p. 197–8°.

Anilide : plates from EtOH. M.p. 130·5–131°.

o-*Toluidide* : yellowish plates from 50% EtOH. M.p. 140·5–141°.

p-*Toluidide* : plates from EtOH. M.p. 143·5–144·5°.

See previous references and also
Choufoer, *Chem. Abstracts*, 1925, **19**, 2195.

6-Nitro-*p*-xylene-2-sulphonic Acid.

Plates + H_2O. Decomp. at 128°. Sol. EtOH. Insol. Et_2O, $CHCl_3$, C_6H_6, CS_2. Very hygroscopic. Bitter taste.

Phenyl ester : plates from EtOH. M.p. 117–18°. Mod. sol. $CHCl_3$, CCl_4, C_6H_6. Insol. H_2O.

o-*Tolyl ester* : cryst. from EtOH. M.p. 66–7°. Mod. sol. EtOH, Et_2O, $CHCl_3$, C_6H_6. Spar. sol. pet. ether. Insol. H_2O.

m-*Tolyl ester*: plates from EtOH. M.p. 71·5–72°. Less sol. than *o*-tolyl ester.
p-*Tolyl ester*: plates from EtOH. M.p. 93·5–94·5°. Less sol. than *m*-tolyl ester.
Fluoride: $C_8H_8O_4NFS$. MW, 233. Cryst. from C_6H_6–pet. ether. M.p. 74–74·5°.
Chloride: prisms from Et_2O–pet. ether. M.p. 31°. Sol. Et_2O, $CHCl_3$, C_6H_6, CS_2. Spar. sol. pet. ether.
Amide: plates from EtOH.Aq. M.p. 172–3°. Sol. EtOH, Et_2O, $CHCl_3$. Insol. H_2O.
Anilide: needles from EtOH.Aq. M.p. 143–4°. Sol. EtOH, Et_2O, $CHCl_3$. Insol. H_2O.
o-*Toluidide*: needles from 50% EtOH. M.p. 126·5–127·5°. Sol. EtOH, $CHCl_3$, CCl_4, C_6H_6. Less sol. Et_2O, pet. ether. Insol. H_2O.
p-*Toluidide*: cryst. from EtOH.Aq. M.p. 135–6°.

Karslake, *J. Am. Chem. Soc.*, 1914, **36**, 1251.
Huston, *J. Am. Chem. Soc.*, 1915, **37**, 2119.
Choufoer, *Chem. Abstracts*, 1925, **19**, 2195.
Steinkopf *et al.*, 1927, **117**, 40.

5-Nitro-*o*-3-xylenol

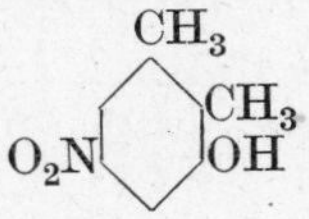

$C_8H_9O_3N$ MW, 167

Orange-yellow needles from C_6H_6 or $CHCl_3$. M.p. 109°.

Crossley, *J. Chem. Soc.*, 1913, **103**, 2180.

5-Nitro-*o*-4-xylenol

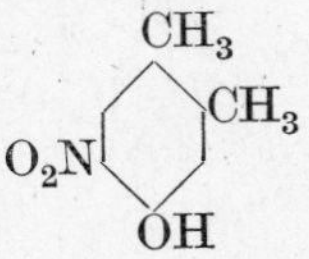

$C_8H_9O_3N$ MW, 167

Yellow rhombic cryst. from EtOH. M.p. 87°. Very sol. $CHCl_3$. Sol. Et_2O, C_6H_6. Spar. sol. pet. ether. Volatile in steam.
Me ether: $C_9H_{11}O_3N$. MW, 181. Pale yellow cryst. from EtOH. M.p. 79°.

Diepolder, *Ber.*, 1909, **42**, 2917.
Cain, Simonsen, *J. Chem. Soc.*, 1914, **105**, 163.

4-Nitro-*m*-2-xylenol

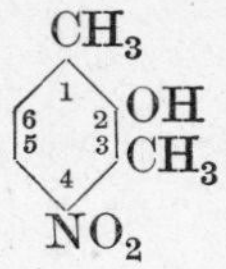

$C_8H_9O_3N$ MW, 167

Leaflets and prisms from C_6H_6, needles from ligroin. M.p. 99–100°.

Auwers, Markovits, *Ber.*, 1908, **41**, 2338.

5-Nitro-*m*-2-xylenol.
Prisms from MeOH. M.p. 169–70°. Very sol. $CHCl_3$. Sol. EtOH. Spar. sol. C_6H_6, ligroin.
Me ether: $C_9H_{11}O_3N$. MW, 181. Pale yellow needles from EtOH. M.p. 92°. Pleasant odour.

Auwers, Markovits, *Ber.*, 1908, **41**, 2335.
Rowe, Bannister, Story, *J. Soc. Chem. Ind.*, 1931, **50**, 79T.

5-Nitro-*m*-4-xylenol

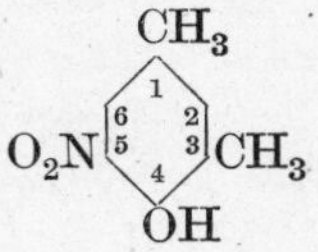

$C_8H_9O_3N$ MW, 167

Yellow needles from EtOH. M.p. 78° (72°). Volatile in steam.
Me ether: $C_9H_{11}O_3N$. MW, 181. Prisms from Et_2O. M.p. 27°. B.p. 269·5°.
p-*Toluenesulphonyl*: plates from EtOH. M.p. 111–12°.

Hodgkinson, Limpach, *J. Chem. Soc.*, 1893, **63**, 105.
Fries, Kann, *Ann.*, 1907, **353**, 354.
Datta, Varma, *J. Am. Chem. Soc.*, 1919, **41**, 2042.
Fox, Turner, *J. Chem. Soc.*, 1930, 1866.

6-Nitro-*m*-4-xylenol.
Yellow needles from HCl. M.p. 95°.
Me ether: needles from EtOH. M.p. 56–7°. Mod. sol. EtOH, Et_2O.

Pfaff, *Ber.*, 1883, **16**, 616.
Bamberger, Reber, *Ber.*, 1907, **40**, 2267.
Maltese, *Gazz. chim. ital.*, 1907, **37**, ii, 284.
Manske, *Organic Syntheses*, Collective Vol. I, 397, *Note* 5.

2-Nitro-*m*-5-xylenol

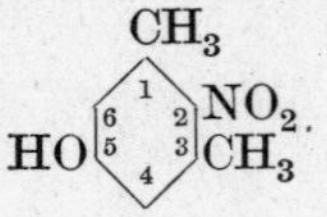

$C_8H_9O_3N$ MW, 167

Yellowish prisms from ligroin. M.p. 107–8°. Non-volatile in steam.

Me ether: $C_9H_{11}O_3N$. MW, 181. Needles from EtOH.Aq. M.p. 53°.

Auwers, Borsche, *Ber.*, 1915, **48**, 1715.
Rowe, Bannister, Seth, Storey, *J. Soc. Chem. Ind.*, 1930, **49**, 469T.

4-Nitro-*m*-5-xylenol.

Yellow needles from ligroin or MeOH.Aq. M.p. 66°. Sol. most org. solvents. Spar. sol. ligroin, pet. ether. Volatile in steam.

Me ether: rhombic plates from MeOH. M.p. 45–6°. Volatile in steam.

See previous references.

3-Nitro-*p*-2-xylenol

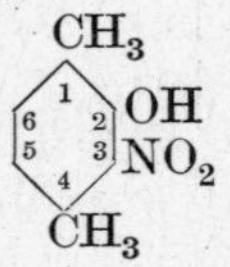

$C_8H_9O_3N$ MW, 167

Golden-yellow needles from pet. ether. M.p. 34–5°. B.p. 236° decomp., 150°/15 mm. Sol. most org. solvents.

Benzoyl: m.p. 79–80°.

Auwers, Michaelis, *Ber.*, 1914, **47**, 1289, *Note* 4.
Oliveri, *Gazz. chim. ital.*, 1882, **12**, 163.

5-Nitro-*p*-2-xylenol.

Pale yellow needles from EtOH.Aq. M.p. 121–3° (115°). Sol. EtOH, Et_2O, hot H_2O.

Et ether: $C_{10}H_{13}O_3N$. MW, 195. M.p. 85°.

Acetyl: yellow prisms from EtOH. M.p. 72–3°. Sol. $CHCl_3$, hot EtOH.

Datta, Varma, *J. Am. Chem. Soc.*, 1919, **41**, 2042.
Noelting, *Ber.*, 1904, **37**, 2593.
See also previous references.

6-Nitro-*p*-2-xylenol.

Yellow leaflets from pet. ether. M.p. 91°. Sol. EtOH, Et_2O. Spar. sol. H_2O. Volatile in steam.

Me ether: $C_9H_{11}O_3N$. MW, 181. Needles from MeOH. M.p. 62–62·5°. Sol. most org solvents.

Sonn, *Ber.*, 1916, **49**, 2589.
Kostanecki, *Ber.*, 1886, **19**, 2321.

4-Nitro-*o*-3-xylidine

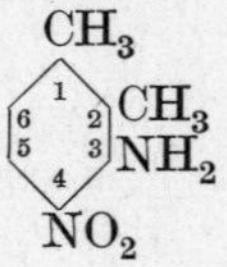

$C_8H_{10}O_2N_2$ MW, 16

Red plates from EtOH. M.p. 118–19°. Sol very conc. HCl.

Acetyl: needles from EtOH. M.p. 160°.

Benzoyl: cryst. M.p. 177–8°. Mod. sol EtOH.

Noelting, Braun, Thesmar, *Ber.*, 1901 **34**, 2246.

5-Nitro-*o*-3-xylidine.

Pale yellow needles from EtOH. M.p 111–12°.

Acetyl: needles from EtOH. M.p. 230–1°.

Benzoyl: m.p. 227–8°. Mod. sol. EtOH.

Crossley, Morrell, *J. Chem. Soc.*, 1911 **99**, 2351.
See also previous reference.

6-Nitro-*o*-3-xylidine.

Brownish-yellow prisms from EtOH. M.p 114°.

Acetyl: yellowish needles from EtOH. M.p 149–50°.

Benzoyl: yellowish cryst. M.p. 208–9°. Mod sol. EtOH.

Noelting, Braun, Thesmar, *Ber.*, 1901 **34**, 2245.

3-Nitro-*o*-4-xylidine

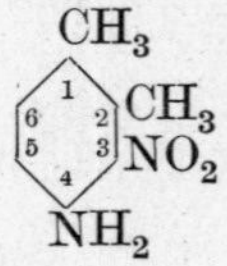

$C_8H_{10}O_2N_2$ MW, 16

Red prisms from EtOH. M.p. 65–6°. Volatil in steam.

Acetyl: needles from EtOH. M.p. 115–16°.

Benzoyl: needles. M.p. 199–200°. Spar. sol EtOH.

Noelting, Braun, Thesmar, *Ber.*, 1901 **34**, 2249.
Crossley, Wren, *J. Chem. Soc.*, 1911, **99** 2342.

5-Nitro-*o*-4-xylidine.

Brownish-red prisms from EtOH. M.p. 139–40°. Mod. sol. org. solvents. Sol. about 40 parts Et_2O.

Acetyl: pale yellow needles from EtOH. M.p. 107°.

Benzoyl: pale yellow needles from EtOH. M.p. 149–50°.

Noelting, Braun, Thesmar, *Ber.*, 1901, **34**, 2248.
Diepolder, *Ber.*, 1909, **42**, 2917.

6-Nitro-*o*-4-xylidine.

Orange leaflets from EtOH. M.p. 74–5°. Volatile in steam.

Acetyl: needles from EtOH. M.p. 209–10°.

Benzoyl: needles from EtOH. M.p. 223–4°.

Noelting, Braun, Thesmar, *Ber.*, 1901, **34**, 2250.
Noelting, Thesmar, *Ber.*, 1902, **35**, 632.

4-Nitro-*m*-2-xylidine

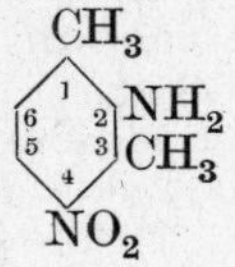

$C_8H_{10}O_2N_2$ MW, 166

Yellow needles from EtOH.Aq. M.p. 81–2°.

Acetyl: pale yellowish needles. M.p. 170°.

Noelting, Stoeklin, *Ber.*, 1891, **24**, 568.
Noelting, Braun, Thesmar, *Ber.*, 1901, **34**, 2259.

5-Nitro-*m*-2-xylidine.

Orange-yellow needles. M.p. 158°.

N-*Acetyl*: m.p. 178°.

Ibbotson, Kenner, *J. Chem. Soc.*, 1923, **123**, 1267.

2-Nitro-*m*-4-xylidine

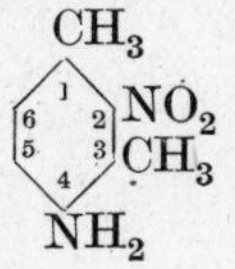

$C_8H_{10}O_2N_2$ MW, 166

Golden-yellow needles. M.p. 81–2° (78°). Sol. EtOH, ligroin, hot H_2O.

Acetyl: needles. M.p. 149°.

Benzoyl: needles from EtOH. M.p. 236°. Spar. sol. EtOH, C_6H_6. Insol. H_2O.

Grevingk, *Ber.*, 1884, **17**, 2425.
Blanksma, *Rec. trav. chim.*, 1909, **28**, 94.
Noelting, Braun, Thesmar, *Ber.*, 1901, **34**, 2260.

5-Nitro-*m*-4-xylidine.

Orange-red needles or plates from ligroin. M.p. 76° (70°).

N-*Me*: $C_9H_{12}O_2N_2$. MW, 180. Red plates with green reflex. M.p. 58°. Very sol. most solvents. Mod. sol. EtOH, ligroin.

Acetyl: yellowish needles from H_2O. M.p. 172–3°.

Benzoyl: needles from EtOH. M.p. 184·5°.

p-*Nitrobenzoyl*: cryst. from AcOH. M.p. 139–40°. Sol. AcOH. Spar. sol. EtOH.

p-*Toluyl*: yellowish needles from EtOH. M.p. 187°. Sol. AcOH. Mod. sol. hot EtOH. Insol. H_2O.

Pinnow, Oesterreich, *Ber.*, 1898, **31**, 2931.
Willgerodt, Schmierer, *Ber.*, 1905, **38**, 1473.
Blanksma, *Rec. trav. chim.*, 1906, **25**, 181.
Hübner, *Ann.*, 1881, **208**, 320.
Ibbotson, Kenner, *J. Chem. Soc.*, 1923, **123**, 1268.

6-Nitro-*m*-4-xylidine.

Orange-red needles. M.p. 123°. Sol. boiling EtOH.

N-*Me*: p-*toluenesulphonyl*, prisms from EtOH. M.p. 135–6°. *Benzenesulphonyl*: prisms from EtOH. M.p. 185–6°.

N-*Di-Me*: $C_{10}H_{14}O_2N_2$. MW, 194. Oil. *Picrate*: cryst. M.p. 170–3° decomp.

Acetyl: needles. M.p. 160°. Sol. EtOH. Mod. sol. C_6H_6. Spar. sol. H_2O.

Diacetyl: plates. M.p. 115°. Very sol. C_6H_6. Spar. sol. EtOH. Insol. H_2O.

Benzoyl: needles from EtOH. M.p. 200°. Mod. sol. EtOH, C_6H_6. Insol. H_2O, pet. ether.

Benzenesulphonyl: prisms from EtOH. M.p. 148·5°.

p-*Toluenesulphonyl*: pale yellow cryst. from EtOH. M.p. 192°.

Noelting, Collin, *Ber.*, 1884, **17**, 265.
Errera, Maltese, *Gazz. chim. ital.*, 1903, **33**, ii, 283.
Fittig, Ahrens, Mattheides, *Ann.*, 1868, **147**, 18.

2-Nitro-*m*-5-xylidine.

Orange prisms from ligroin. M.p. 132°.

Acetyl: prisms from EtOH.Aq. M.p. 163°.

Ibbotson, Kenner, *J. Chem. Soc.*, 1923, **123**, 1267.

4-Nitro-*m*-5-xylidine.

Cryst. from ligroin. M.p. 56°.

Acetyl: m.p. 114°.

Ibbotson, Kenner, *J. Chem. Soc.*, 1923, **123**, 1266.
Noelting, Forel, *Ber.*, 1885, **18**, 2679.

3-Nitro-*p*-2-xylidine

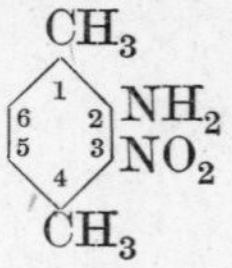

$C_8H_{10}O_2N_2$ MW, 166

Cryst. Volatile in steam.

Benzoyl : needles from EtOH. M.p. 178°.

Hübner, *Ann.*, 1881, **208**, 323.
Noelting, Thesmar, Holzach, *Ber.*, 1902, **35**, 640.

5-Nitro-*p*-2-xylidine.

Plates from EtOH. M.p. 144–5°. Sol. EtOH, Et_2O. Spar. sol. ligroin.

Acetyl : needles from H_2O. M.p. 168–9°.

Benzenesulphonyl : yellow prisms from EtOH.Aq. M.p. 160–3°.

p-*Toluenesulphonyl* : pale yellowish cryst. M.p. 185°.

Noelting, Witt, Forel, *Ber.*, 1885, **18**, 2667.
A.G.F.A., D.R.P., 157,859, (*Chem. Zentr.*, 1905, I, 415).
Fisher, Walling, *J. Am. Chem. Soc.*, 1935, **57**, 1701.

6-Nitro-*p*-2-xylidine.

Golden-yellow needles from EtOH. M.p. 98°. Sol. boiling EtOH. Sublimes with slight decomp.

Acetyl : needles from H_2O. M.p. 180°.

p-*Methylbenzylidene* : pale yellow prisms from EtOH. M.p. 110°.

Fittig, Ahrens, Mattheides, *Ann.*, 1868, **147**, 22.
Blanksma, *Rec. trav. chim.*, 1905, **24**, 49.
v. Kostanecki, *Ber.*, 1886, **19**, 2320.

Nitroxylylic Acid.

See Nitrodimethylbenzoic Acid.

Noctal (*Nostal, isopropyl-β-bromopropenylbarbituric acid*)

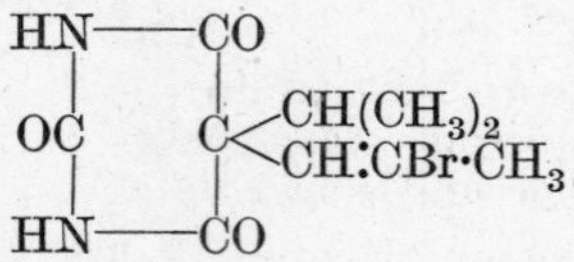

$C_{10}H_{13}O_3N_2Br$ MW, 289

Colourless cryst. M.p. 178°. Sol. EtOH, Me_2CO, AcOH. Mod. sol. Et_2O. Spar. sol. H_2O, $CHCl_3$, C_6H_6. One of most effective narcotics of barbituric series.

Boedecker, Ludwig, *Chem. Abstracts*, 1925, **19**, 1311.

Nonacosane

$CH_3{\cdot}[CH_2]_{27}{\cdot}CH_3$

$C_{29}H_{60}$ MW, 40

Cryst. from pet. ether. M.p. 63·6–64·1 (62·5–63°). B.p. 346–8°/40 mm., 286°/15 mm 179°/0 mm. n_D^{65} 1·4361, n_D^{80} 1·43061.

Krafft, *Ber.*, 1907, **40**, 4783.
Mabery, *Am. Chem. J.*, 1905, **33**, 289.
Gluud, *Ber.*, 1919, **52**, 1040.
Trost, *Chem. Zentr.*, 1936, I, 1241.

Nonadecane

$CH_3{\cdot}[CH_2]_{17}{\cdot}CH_3$

$C_{19}H_{40}$ MW, 26

M.p. 32°. B.p. 330°, 248°/100 mm., 226·5° 50 mm., 212°/30 mm., 193°/15 mm. D^{32} 0·780

Clemmensen, *Ber.*, 1913, **46**, 1841.
Schaal, *Ber.*, 1907, **40**, 4787.
Hildebrandt, Wachter, *J. Am. Chem Soc.*, 1929, **51**, 2487.

Nonadecane-1-carboxylic Acid.

See n-Eicosanic Acid.

Nonadecane-1 : 1-dicarboxylic Acid.

See Octadecylmalonic Acid.

Nonadecane-1 : 19-dicarboxylic Acid.

See Japanic Acid.

Nonadecanoic Acid.

See Nonadecylic Acid.

Nonadecanol-1.

See Nonadecyl Alcohol.

Nonadecanone-2.

See Methyl heptadecyl Ketone.

Nonadecanone-4.

See Propyl pentadecyl Ketone.

Nonadecanone-10.

Caprinone, *q.v.*

Nonadecyl Alcohol (*Nonadecanol*-1)

$CH_3{\cdot}[CH_2]_{17}{\cdot}CH_2OH$

$C_{19}H_{40}O$ MW, 28

Cryst. M.p. 62–3° (61·8–62°). B.p. 166–7° 0·32 mm.

Levene, Taylor, *J. Biol. Chem.*, 1924, 59 905.
Shiina, *Chem. Zentr.*, 1936, I, 755.

Nonadecylic Acid (*Octadecane-1-carboxyli acid, nonadecanoic acid*)

$CH_3{\cdot}[CH_2]_{17}{\cdot}COOH$

$C_{19}H_{38}O_2$ MW, 29

Leaflets from EtOH. M.p. 66·5°. B.p. 297 8°/100 mm.

Schweizer, *Arch. Pharm.*, 1884, **222**, 770
Oskerko, *Chem. Zentr.*, 1914, II, 1264.

Nonadecyl iodide

$CH_3\cdot[CH_2]_{17}\cdot CH_2I$

$C_{19}H_{39}I$ MW, 394

Cryst. M.p. 42·5–43·5°. B.p. 174–174·5°/0·22 mm.

Shiina, *Chem. Zentr.*, 1936, I, 755.
Levene, Taylor, *J. Biol. Chem.*, 1924, **59**, 905.

Nonaldehyde.
See Pelargonic Aldehyde.
Nonamethylene.
See Cyclononane.
Nonanal.
See Pelargonic Aldehyde.
Nonandione-3 : 4.
See Propionylcaproyl.
Nonane (1-*Ethylheptane*)

$CH_3\cdot[CH_2]_7\cdot CH_3$

C_9H_{20} MW, 128

Liq. F.p. — 51°. B.p. 149·5°, 86°/100 mm., 59°/30 mm., 39·5°/11 mm. D_4^{20} 0·7177, D_{15}^{15} 0·7219. n_D^{25} 1·4025, $n_D^{20\cdot5}$ 1·4165.

Krafft, *Ber.*, 1882, **15**, 1692.
Haller, Lassieur, *Compt. rend.*, 1910, **150**, 1017.
Fischer, Klemm, *Chem. Abstracts*, 1930, **24**, 4200.

Nonane-1-carboxylic Acid.
See *n*-Capric Acid.
Nonane-2-carboxylic Acid.
1-Methylpelargonic Acid, *q.v.*
Nonane-1 : 9-dicarboxylic Acid (*Undecanedioic acid*)

$HOOC\cdot[CH_2]_9\cdot COOH$

$C_{11}H_{20}O_4$ MW, 216

Leaflets from H_2O. M.p. 124° (110°). Sol. EtOH, Et_2O. Spar. sol. hot H_2O.
Dichloride: $C_{11}H_{18}O_2Cl_2$. MW, 253. B.p. 191–2°/22 mm.
Diamide: $C_{11}H_{22}O_2N_2$. MW, 214. M.p. 173°.
Dinitrile: $C_{11}H_{18}N_2$. MW, 178. Liq. B.p. 195°/12 mm.
Monoanilide: $C_{17}H_{25}O_3N$. MW, 291. Cryst. from 50% EtOH. M.p. 112·5–113°.
Dianilide: $C_{23}H_{30}O_2N_2$. MW, 366. Cryst. from EtOH. M.p. 160–1° (156°).
Di-p-bromoanilide: m.p. 215°.
Di-o-toluidide: $C_{25}H_{34}O_2N_2$. MW, 394. M.p. 164°.
Di-p-toluidide: m.p. 191°.
α-Anhydride: cryst. from C_6H_6–pet. ether. M.p. 69–70°.
β-Anhydride: wax. M.p. 85–8°.

v. Braun, Danziger, *Ber.*, 1912, **45**, 1975.
Shukow, Schestakow, *J. prakt. Chem.*, 1903, **67**, 416.
Easson, Pyman, *J. Chem. Soc.*, 1931, 3000.
Barnicoat, *J. Chem. Soc.*, 1927, 2928.
Hill, Carothers, *J. Am. Chem. Soc.*, 1933, **55**, 5027.

Nonanol-1.
See Nonyl Alcohol.
Nonanol-2.
See Methylheptylcarbinol.
Nonanol-3.
See Ethyl-*n*-hexylcarbinol.
Nonanol-4.
See Propyl-*n*-amylcarbinol.
Nonanol-5.
See Di-*n*-butylcarbinol.
Nonanol-1-carboxylic Acid.
Hydroxycapric Acid, *q.v.*
Nonanol-2-carboxylic Acid.
See 1-*n*-Heptylhydracrylic Acid.
Nonanone-2.
See Methyl heptyl Ketone.
Nonanone-3.
See Ethyl *n*-hexyl Ketone.
Nonanone-4.
See Propyl *n*-amyl Ketone.
Nonanone-5.
See Di-*n*-butyl Ketone.
1-Nonene (1-*Nonylene*, n-*heptylethylene*)

$CH_3\cdot[CH_2]_6\cdot CH{:}CH_2$

C_9H_{18} MW, 126

B.p. 146°. D^{21} 0·730. n_D^{21} 1·414.

Bourguel, *Bull. soc. chim.*, 1927, **41**, 1475.
Maman, *Chem. Zentr.*, 1936, I, 2332.

2-Nonene (2-*Nonylene*, 1-*methyl-2-hexylethylene*)

$CH_3\cdot[CH_2]_5\cdot CH{:}CH\cdot CH_3$

C_9H_{18} MW, 126

Liq. B.p. 149·4–149·9° (147–8°, 148·5°). D_{15}^{15} 0·7540, D^{21} 0·738. n_D^{21} 1·420. Odour resembles that of petroleum ether.

Clarke, Adams, *J. Am. Chem. Soc.*, 1915, **37**, 2538.
Thoms, Mannich, *Ber.*, 1903, **36**, 2550.
Bourguel, *Bull. soc. chim.*, 1927, **41**, 1475.

4-Nonene (*4-Nonylene, 1-propyl-2-butylethylene*)

$CH_3\cdot[CH_2]_3\cdot CH\colon CH\cdot CH_2\cdot CH_2\cdot CH_3$

C_9H_{18} MW, 126

B.p. 144–6°, 44–6°/12 mm. D^{18} 0·732. n_D^{18} 1·4212.

Kirrmann, *Compt. rend.*, 1926, **182**, 1629.

1-Nonene-1-carboxylic Acid.
See 1-Decylenic Acid.

2-Nonene-9-carboxylic Acid.
See Isodecylenic Acid.

1-Nonenic Acid (*1-Nonylenic acid, 1-octene-1-carboxylic acid, 2-hexylacrylic acid*)

$CH_3\cdot[CH_2]_5\cdot CH\colon CH\cdot COOH$

$C_9H_{16}O_2$ MW, 156

Liq. B.p. 173°/20 mm. Spar. sol. H_2O. Volatile in steam.

Fittig, Schneegans, *Ann.*, 1885, **227**, 80.
Knövenagel, D.R.P., 156,560, (*Chem. Zentr.*, 1905, I, 56).

2-Nonenylethylene.
See Heptoprene.

1-Nonine.
See *n*-Heptylacetylene.

2-Nonine (*Methylhexylacetylene*)

$CH_3\cdot[CH_2]_5\cdot C\vdots C\cdot CH_3$

C_9H_{16} MW, 124

Liq. B.p. 158–9°. D^{18} 0·770. n_D^{18} 1·433.

Truchet, *Ann. chim.*, 1931, **16**, 358.
Bourguel, *Ann. chim.*, 1925, **3**, 395.

3-Nonine (*Ethylamylacetylene*)

$CH_3\cdot[CH_2]_4\cdot C\vdots C\cdot CH_2\cdot CH_3$

C_9H_{16} MW, 124

B.p. 155–7°. D^{20} 0·763. n_D^{20} 1·429.

Truchet, *Compt. rend.*, 1930, **191**, 854.

Nonoic Acid.
See Pelargonic Acid.

Nonylacetylene (*1-Undecine, rutylidene*)

$CH_3\cdot[CH_2]_8\cdot C\vdots CH$

$C_{11}H_{20}$ MW, 152

F.p. — 33°. B.p. 209–10°, 202–4°/745 mm., 110–11°/17 mm., 91°/8 mm. D_4^{25} 0·8666. Sol. most org. solvents. Insol. H_2O.

Thoms, Mannich, *Ber.*, 1903, **36**, 2549.
Bruylants, *Ber.*, 1875, **8**, 413.
Vaughn, *J. Am. Chem. Soc.*, 1933, **55**, 3454.

Nonyl Alcohol (*Nonanol-1*)

$CH_3\cdot[CH_2]_7\cdot CH_2OH$

$C_9H_{20}O$ MW, 144

Found in orange oil. Yellow liq. F.p. — 5°. B.p. 215°, 107·5°/15 mm., 98–101°/12 mm. D_4^0 0·8415, D_4^{20} 0·8279. n_D^{15} 1·43582. Used in rose perfume and cologne waters. Ox. ⟶ pelargonic acid.

3 : 5-*Dinitrobenzoyl* : m.p. 52·2°.
o-*Nitrophenylurethane* : cryst. from pet. ether. M.p. 34°.
m-*Nitrophenylurethane* : cryst. from pet. ether. M.p. 66°.
p-*Nitrophenylurethane* : leaflets from 50% EtOH. M.p. 104°. Sol. EtOH, Me_2CO, $CHCl_3$, C_6H_6. Insol. H_2O, CCl_4, pet. ether.
3 : 5-*Dinitrophenylurethane* : leaflets from pet. ether. M.p. 60°.
1-*Naphthylurethane* : m.p. 65·5°.
4′-*Iodo-4-diphenylurethane* : m.p. 148·4–149·2°.

Krafft, *Ber.*, 1886, **19**, 2221.
Bouveault, Blanc, D.R.P., 164,294, (*Chem. Zentr.*, 1905, II, 1700).
Harding, Weizmann, *J. Chem. Soc.*, 1910, **97**, 304.
Hoppenbrouwers, *Rec. trav. chim.*, 1932, **51**, 951.
Hoeke, *Rec. trav. chim.*, 1935, **54**, 505.

Nonylamine (*1-Aminononane*)

$CH_3\cdot[CH_2]_7\cdot CH_2NH_2$

$C_9H_{21}N$ MW, 143

B.p. 201°.
N-*Acetyl* : leaflets. M.p. 34–5°.
N-*Benzoyl* : m.p. 49°.
Picrate : m.p. 111°.

Thoms, *Chem. Zentr.*, 1901, I, 524.
v. Braun, Sobecki, *Ber.*, 1911, **44**, 1469.
Mailhe, *Bull. soc. chim.*, 1918, **23**, 235.
Jegorow, *J. prakt. Chem.*, 1912, **86**, 529.

Nonylene.
See Nonene.

Nonylenic Acid.
See Nonenic Acid.

Nonylic Acid.
See Pelargonic Acid.

Nonylic Aldehyde.
See Pelargonic Aldehyde.

Nopinane

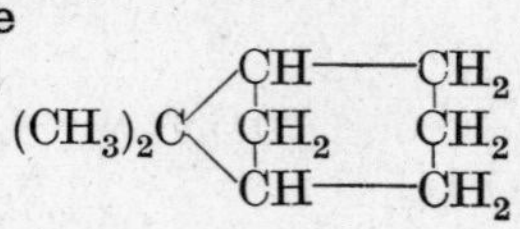

C_9H_{16} MW, 124

B.p. 149°/747 mm. D_{22}^{22} 0·8611. n_D 1·4641.

Semmler, Feldstein, *Ber.*, 1914, **47**, 386.

Nopinene.
See β-Pinene.

Nopinic Acid

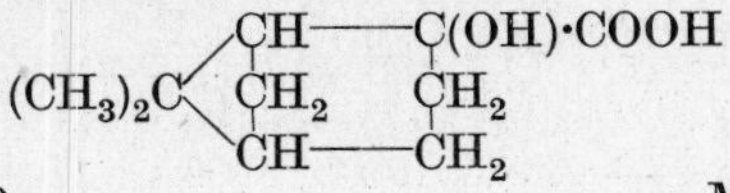

$_{10}H_{16}O_3$ MW, 184

l-.

Needles from H_2O. M.p. 126–8°. Sol. EtOH, t_2O, AcOEt. Spar. sol. H_2O, ligroin. $[\alpha]_D^{18}$ - 16·02° in Et_2O. PbO_2 or $KMnO_4$ in H_2SO_4 → nopinone.

Wallach, Blumann, *Ann.*, 1907, **356**, 228.
Baeyer, Villiger, *Ber.*, 1896, **29**, 1923.
Brus, *Compt. rend.*, 1924, **179**, 501.

Nopinol

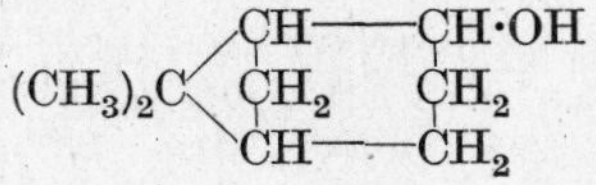

$_9H_{16}O$ MW, 140

Exists in two forms.

α-.

Needles from MeOH. M.p. 101–2°. B.p. 04–5°. $[\alpha]_D^{20}$ − 9·17° in EtOH, $[\alpha]_D^{18}$ − 5·32° ı Et_2O.

Phenylurethane : m.p. 131–2°.

β-.

Viscous liq. $[\alpha]_D^{17}$ − 15·03° in Et_2O.

Phenylurethane : m.p. 95–6°.

Wallach, Blumann, *Ann.*, 1907, **356**, 236.

Nopinone

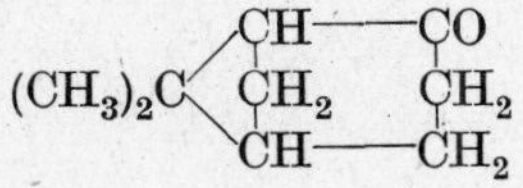

$_9H_{14}O$ MW, 138

d-.

Oil. F.p. about 0°. B.p. 209°, 118·2°/43 ım., 87–8°/14 mm., D_4^0 0·9958, $D_4^{19 \cdot 6}$ 0·9807. $_D^{20}$ 1·4787. $[\alpha]_D^{20}$ + 14·48°, + 38·34° in MeOH, - 33·99° in $CHCl_3$, + 11·51° in Et_2O, + 11·35° ı C_6H_6, + 8·73° in CS_2.

Semicarbazone : needles from MeOH. M.p. 88° (167°).

Hydrazone : cryst. from AcOEt. M.p. 42–3°.

Wallach, Blumann, *Ann.*, 1907, **356**, 231.
Baeyer, Villiger, *Ber.*, 1896, **29**, 1927.
Brus, Peyresblauques, *Compt. rend.*, 1929, **187**, 984.
Schmidt, *Z. angew. Chem.*, 1929, **42**, 126.

Noradrenalin (1-[3 : 4-*Dihydroxyphenyl*]-2-*aminoethanol*, 4-[α-*hydroxy*-β-*aminoethyl*]-*catechol*)

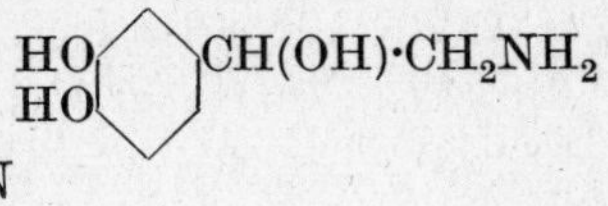

$C_8H_{11}O_3N$ MW, 169

dl-.

Cryst. M.p. 191° decomp. Spar. sol. H_2O, EtOH, Et_2O. Sol. dil. acids and alkalis.

B,HCl : m.p. 141°. Sol. H_2O. Spar. sol. EtOH. Aq. sol. + $FeCl_3$ gives green col.

Oxalate : m.p. 175°. Sol. H_2O.

M.L.B., D.R.P., 157,300, (*Chem. Zentr.*, 1905, I, 315); D.R.P., 193,634, (*Chem. Zentr.*, 1908, I, 430); D.R.P., 195,814, (*Chem. Zentr.*, 1908, I, 1225).

Noragathic Acid

$C_{19}H_{30}O_2$ MW, 290

Prisms from MeOH. M.p. 146–7°. B.p. 195–7°/0·9 mm., 180–3°/0·4 mm. $[\alpha]_D$ + 59·3° in EtOH.

Me ester : $C_{20}H_{32}O_2$. MW, 304. B.p. 151–2°/0·6 mm., 146–8°/0·1 mm. D_4^{23} 1·002. n_D^{23} 1·5087. $[\alpha]_D$ + 57·02° in EtOH.

Ruzicka, Hosking, *Ann.*, 1929, **469**, 188; *Helv. Chim. Acta.*, 1931, **14**, 214.

Norallocholanic Acid

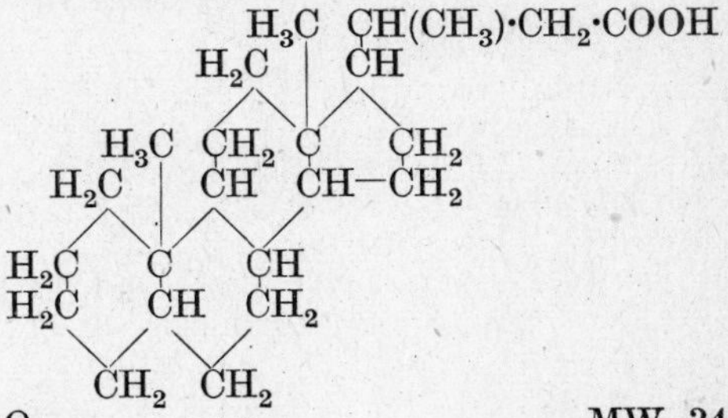

$C_{23}H_{38}O_2$ MW, 346

Plates from Me_2CO. M.p. 170–170·5°.

Me ester : $C_{24}H_{40}O_2$. MW, 360. M.p. 78–9°.

Chuang, *Ann.*, 1933, **500**, 280.
Heilbron, Samant, Simpson, *J. Chem. Soc.*, 1933, 1413.

Noratropine (*Nortropine ester of tropic acid*, dl-*norhyoscyamine*)

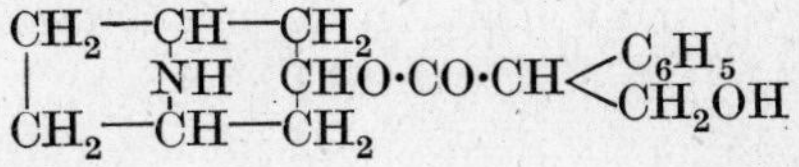

$C_{16}H_{21}O_3N$ MW, 275

Cryst. from Me_2CO. M.p. 113–14°. Sol. EtOH, $CHCl_3$, AcOEt. Mod. sol. Et_2O, Me_2CO, H_2O. Optically inactive. $CH_3I \longrightarrow$ atropine.

B,H₂O : m.p. 73°.

B,HCl : m.p. 193°. Sol. H_2O, EtOH. Prac. insol. Et_2O, Me_2CO.

B_2,H_2SO_4 : needles from H_2O. M.p. 257°. Sol. H_2O, EtOH. Prac. insol. Me_2CO.

$B_2,(COOH)_2$: cryst. from H_2O. M.p. 247–8°.

$B,HAuCl_4$: yellow needles from dil. EtOH. M.p. 157°. Sol. EtOH. Spar. sol. H_2O.

Picrate : needles. M.p. 227°.

Carr, Reynolds, *J. Chem. Soc.*, 1912, **101**, 955.

Norbixin

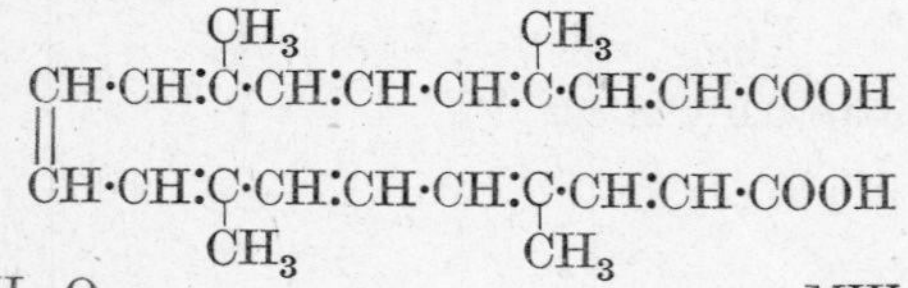

$C_{24}H_{28}O_4$ MW, 380

Cis :

Needles from AcOH. M.p. 254–5°. Sol. MeOH, AcOH, hot EtOH, aq. alkalis. Spar. sol. Et_2O, $CHCl_3$, AcOEt.

Me ester : *see* Bixin.

Di-Me ester : *see under* Bixin.

Trans :

See Isonorbixin.

Kuhn, Grundmann, *Ber.*, 1932, **65**, 1880.
Kuhn, Winterstein, *ibid.*, 646.
Herzig, Faltis, *Ann.*, 1923, **431**, 40.
Vieböck, *Ber.*, 1934, **67**, 377.
Karrer, Helfenstein, Widmer, van Itallie, *Helv. Chim. Acta*, 1929, **12**, 743, 752.

Norborneol

The following compounds have been described under this name :

(a)

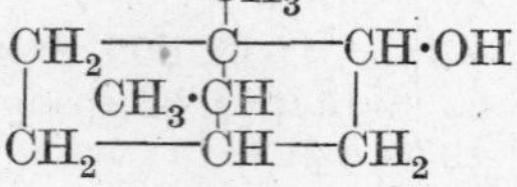

$C_9H_{16}O$ MW, 140

(i) *Santenone alcohol.*

Isolated from East Indian sandalwood oil. M.p. 58–62°. $CrO_3 \longrightarrow$ santenone.

Schimmel, *Bericht vom Oktober*, 1910, 100; *Chem. Zentr.*, 1910, II, 1757.

(ii) *Santenol* (N.B. The nomenclature of the santenols is confused).

M.p. 68–70°. B.p. 195–6°, 87–8°/9 mm. $CrO_3 \longrightarrow$ santenone. $PCl_5 \longrightarrow$ norbornyl chloride. $KMnO_4 \longrightarrow$ santenic acid.

Formate : b.p. 87–94°/9 mm. D^{20} 1·0092. *n* 1·46559.

Acetate : b.p. 89–90·5°/9 mm. D^{20} 0·987. *n* 1·45962.

Semmler, Bartelt, *Ber.*, 1907, **40**, 4467; 1908, **41**, 128, 389.
Aschan, *Ber.*, 1907, **40**, 4923.

(iii) *Norisoborneol, α-santenol* (?).

M.p. 97–8° (91–2°). B.p. 88°/9 mm. $CrO_3 \longrightarrow$ santenone.

Phenylurethane : m.p. 61–2°.

Semmler, Bartelt, *Ber.*, 1907, **40**, 4469.
Aschan, *Ber.*, 1907, **40**, 4923.
Deussen, *J. prakt. Chem.*, 1926, **114**, 114.

(iv) *α-Santenol.*

Needles. M.p. 86°.

Hydrogen diphenate : cryst. from dil. EtOH. M.p. 119–20°.

Komppa, *Ber.*, 1929, **62**, 1751.
Diels, Alder, Petersen, *Ann.*, 1931, **486**, 210.

(b)

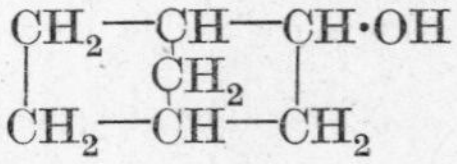

$C_7H_{12}O$ MW, 11

(v) *α-Norborneol, endonorborneol.*

M.p. 149–50°.

Phenylurethane : m.p. 158–9°.

Komppa, Beckmann, *Ann.*, 1934, **512**, 177.

(vi) *β-Norborneol, exonorborneol.*

M.p. 127–8° (123–4°). B.p. 176–7°. $K_2Cr_2O_7 \longrightarrow$ norcamphor.

Phenylurethane : m.p. 147° (144–5°).

Hydrogen phthalate : m.p. 102–3°.

Acetate : b.p. 89–90°/20 mm.

Komppa, Beckmann, *Ann.*, 1934, **512**, 181.
Alder, Stein, Rolland, Schulze, *Ann.*, 1934, **514**, 220, 226.

Norbornylamine

The following compounds have been described under this name :

(a)

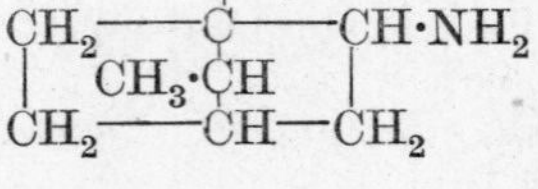

$C_9H_{17}N$ MW, 13

(i) *Santenylamine.*
B.p. 69°/10 mm. D^{20} 0·9163. n_D^{20} 1·47642.
B,HCl : m.p. 272° decomp.
Picrate : m.p. 208°.
Oxalate : decomp. at 280°.

Semmler, Bartelt, *Ber.*, 1908, **41**, 127.

(b)

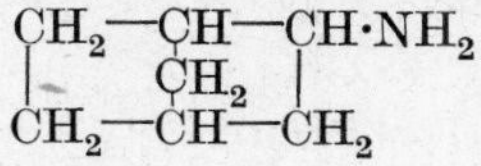
CH2—CH—CH·NH2
CH2
CH2—CH—CH2

$C_7H_{13}N$ MW, 111

(ii) β-*Norbornylamine.*
M.p. 75–80°. B.p. 156–7°.
B,HCl : m.p. about 260° decomp.
Picrate : m.p. 174–5°.
B,HAuCl₄ : m.p. 211–12° decomp.
B₂,H₂PtCl₆ : decomp. above 200°.
Carbamide : m.p. 196–7°.
Phenylthiocarbamide : m.p. 154–5°.

Komppa, Beckmann, *Ann.*, 1934, **512**, 180.

(iii) *Endonorbornylamine.*
B,HCl : m.p. 295°.
Acetyl : m.p. 124°.

Alder, Stein, Rolland, Schulze, *Ann.*, 1934, **514**, 215, 224.

(iv) *Exonorbornylamine.*
B,HCl : does not melt below 345°.
Acetyl : m.p. 139°.

See previous reference.

Norbornylane.
See Norcamphane.

Norbornylene

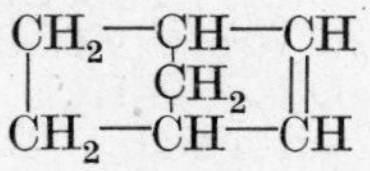
CH2—CH—CH
CH2
CH2—CH—CH

C_7H_{10} MW, 94

M.p. 52–4°. Sublimes.
Dibromide : liq.
Nitrosochloride : needles from $CHCl_3$. M.p. 157–8°.
$C_6H_5N_3$ comp. : m.p. 101–2°.

Komppa, Beckmann, *Ann.*, 1934, **512**, 184.

Norcamphane (*Norbornylane*, 1 : 2 : 2-*bicycloheptane*)

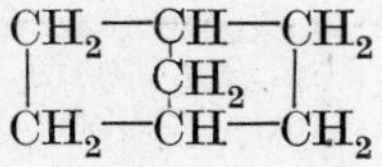
CH2—CH—CH2
CH2
CH2—CH—CH2

C_7H_{12} MW, 96

M.p. 86–7°. Sublimes.

Komppa, Beckmann, *Ann.*, 1934, **512**, 183.

Norcamphene

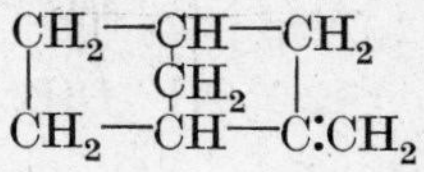
CH2—CH—CH2
CH2
CH2—CH—C:CH2

C_8H_{12} MW, 108

B.p. 123°/755 mm. D_4^{13} 0·8789.
Nitrosochloride : cryst. from AcOEt. M.p. 125°.

Diels, Alder *et al.*, *Ann.*, 1929, **470**, 79.

Norcampholenic Acid

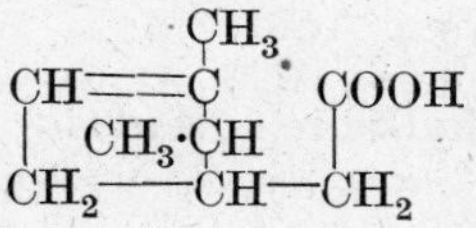
CH3
CH═C COOH
CH3·CH
CH2—CH—CH2

$C_9H_{14}O_2$ MW, 154

B.p. 132–4°/10 mm. D^{20} 1·014. n_D 1·47936.
Nitrile : $C_9H_{13}N$. MW, 135. B.p. 82–3°/9 mm. D^{20} 0·950. n_D 1·4720.

Semmler, Bartelt, *Ber.*, 1908, **41**, 127.

Norcamphor

Two compounds have been described under this name :

(i) *Santenone.*

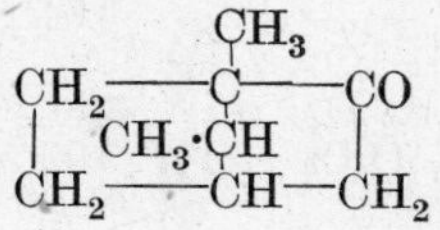
CH3
CH2—C—CO
CH3·CH
CH2—CH—CH2

$C_9H_{14}O$ MW, 138

l-.
Occurs in East Indian sandalwood oil. M.p. 58–61°. B.p. 193–5°. $[\alpha]_D$ − 4·40° in EtOH.
Semicarbazone : m.p. 222–4°.
Oxime : b.p. 110–13°/6 mm.

dl-.
M.p. 55–7° (50–2°, 30°). B.p. 196·5–197°, 75–6°/9 mm. D^{20} 0·966. n_D^{20} 1·4690. $KMnO_4$ ⟶ santenic acid. Na + EtOH ⟶ norisoborneol.
Semicarbazone : m.p. 228–9° (224°).
Oxime : cryst. from pet. ether. M.p. 80–1°. B.p. 116–20°/9 mm.
Oxymethylene deriv. : b.p. 110–13°/9 mm. D^{20} 1·066. n_D 1·50045.
Benzylidene deriv. : b.p. 182–4°/10 mm. D^{20} 1·041. n_D 1·57516.

Semmler, Bartelt, *Ber.*, 1907, **40**, 4467; 1908, **41**, 127.
Schimmel, *Chem. Zentr.*, 1910, II, 1757.
Rimini, *Gazz. chim. ital.*, 1913, **43**, 522.

(ii)

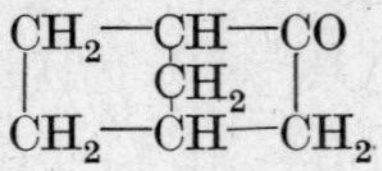

$C_7H_{10}O$ MW, 110

Cryst. M.p. 93–4° (91–2°). Mod. sol. H_2O.

Semicarbazone : m.p. 196·5–197·5°. Sol. EtOH. Spar. sol. C_6H_6.

Hintikka, Komppa, *Chem. Zentr.*, 1918, II, 370.
Komppa, *Ber.*, 1909, **42**, 898 (*Footnote*).
Diels, Alder *et al.*, *Ann.*, 1929, **470**, 76.

Norcamphoric Acid.

See Apocamphoric Acid.

Norcaryophyllenic Acid (3 : 3-*Dimethyl-cyclobutane*-1 : 2-*dicarboxylic acid*)

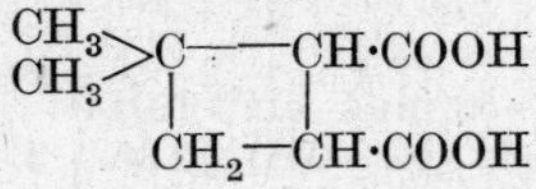

$C_8H_{12}O_4$ MW, 172

Cis form :

d-.

Cryst. from C_6H_6 or dil. HCl. Sinters at 118°. M.p. 125–7° (123·5–124·5°). Sol. H_2O and usual org. solvents. $[\alpha]_{5461}$ + 137° in $CHCl_3$, $[\alpha]_D$ + 118° in $CHCl_3$.

Di-Me ester : $C_{10}H_{16}O_4$. MW, 200. B.p. 107°/12 mm.

Anhydride : $C_{16}H_{22}O_7$. MW, 326. M.p. 38–9°.

Chloride : $C_8H_{11}O_3Cl$. MW, 190·5. B.p. 99–100°/12 mm.

dl-.

Cryst. from H_2O. M.p. 148–9°.

Anhydride : m.p. 40–1°. B.p. 100–2°/1 mm.

Evans, Ramage, Simonsen, *J. Chem. Soc.*, 1934, 1809.
Ramage, Simonsen, *J. Chem. Soc.*, 1935, 532.
Ruzicka, Zimmermann, *Helv. Chim. Acta*, 1935, **18**, 219.
Rydon, *J. Chem. Soc.*, 1936, 593.

Norcephæline (*Noremetine, emetoline*)

$C_{25}H_{32}O_4N_2$ MW, 424

M.p. about 205°. Sol. EtOH, acids and alkalis. Spar. sol. H_2O. Insol. Et_2O.

B,2HCl : amorph. powder. M.p. about 240° decomp. Sol. MeOH. Mod. sol. H_2O. Spar. sol. EtOH. Insol. Me_2CO.

Karrer, *Ber.*, 1916, **49**, 2057.
Carr, Pyman, *J. Chem. Soc.*, 1914, **105**, 1616.
Pyman, *J. Chem. Soc.*, 1917, **111**, 1127.
Hesse, *Ann.*, 1914, **405**, 27.

Norcholanic Acid

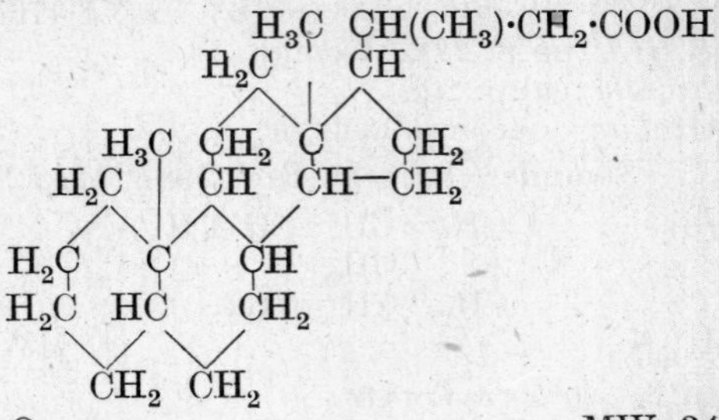

$C_{23}H_{38}O_2$ MW, 346

Needles from AcOH. M.p. 177°.

Me ester : $C_{24}H_{40}O_2$. MW, 360. Needles from MeOH. M.p. 74°.

Et ester : $C_{25}H_{42}O_2$. MW, 374. Prisms from EtOH. M.p. 66–7°.

Wieland, Schlichting, Jacobi, *Z. physiol. Chem.*, 1926, **161**, 94.

Norcitronellol.

See 6-Methyl-2-octenol-8.

Norcodeine (*Normorphine methyl ether*)

$C_{17}H_{19}O_3N$ MW, 285

Needles from AcOEt. M.p. 186°.

B,HCl : cryst. + $3H_2O$. M.p. anhyd. 309°.

B_2,H_2PtCl_6 : yellow leaflets. M.p. 239°.

B,HI : m.p. 257°.

N-β-*Phenylethyl* : $C_{25}H_{27}O_3N$. MW, 389. Cryst. M.p. 114°. Very sol. EtOH. Mod. sol. Et_2O. Spar. sol. pet. ether. *B,HCl* : cryst. M.p. 277°. *B_2,H_2PtCl_6* : m.p. 216–17°.

N-*Cyano* : cryst. from EtOH. M.p. 263°. Sol. EtOH. Mod. sol. $CHCl_3$. Insol. Et_2O. *Acetyl* : cryst. from EtOH. M.p. 184°. Sol. $CHCl_3$. Mod. sol. Et_2O. Sol. 20 parts boiling, 200 parts cold EtOH.

N-*Nitroso* : prisms from EtOH.Aq. M.p. 246°.

N-*Me* : Codeine, *q.v.*

Speyer, Walther, *Ber.*, 1930, **63**, 854.
v. Braun, *Ber.*, 1914, **47**, 2320.

Norconessine

$C_{23}H_{38}N_2$ MW, 342

Occurs in seeds of *Holorrhena antidysenterica*. Dextrorotatory. B.p. 238–40°/0·7 mm.

Di-acid oxalate : m.p. 225–7° decomp. Sol. H_2O, EtOH.

B,2HCl : m.p. 340° decomp. Sol. H_2O, EtOH.

Dimethiodide : m.p. 310–12° decomp.

Haworth, *J. Chem. Soc.*, 1932, 631.

Norcoralydine

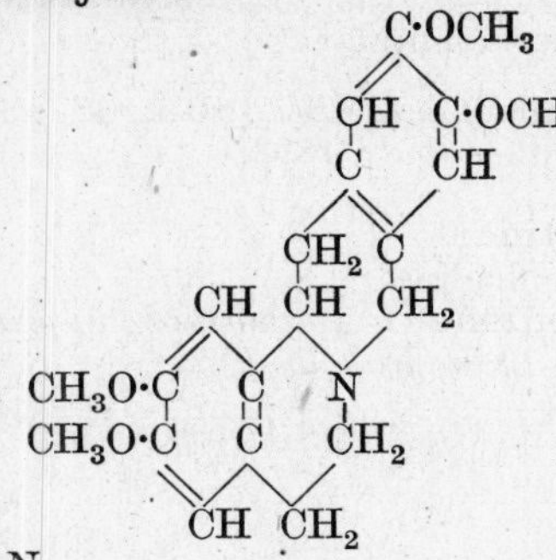

$_{21}H_{25}O_4N$ MW, 355

Plates from dil. EtOH. M.p. 157–8° (151·5–52·5°). Sol. cold dil. H_2SO_4, EtOH, $CHCl_3$. par. sol. C_6H_6. Turns yellow in air. I ⟶ ehydronorcoralydine. $KMnO_4$ ⟶ metahemi-inic acid.

B,HCl : needles from HCl.Aq. M.p. 213°.

B_2,H_2PtCl_6 : orange-red prisms from EtOH. I.p. about 231°.

Picrate : yellow needles from EtOH. M.p. 38°. Spar. sol. H_2O.

Späth, Kruta, *Monatsh.*, 1928, **50**, 341.
Pictet, Chou, *Ber.*, 1916, **49**, 370.

Norcotarnine

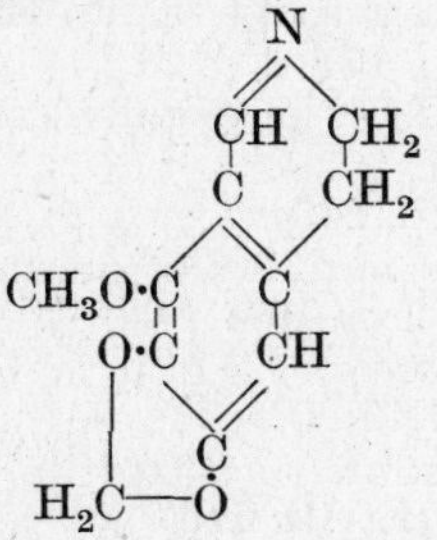

$_{11}H_{11}O_3N$ MW, 205

Yellow flocks from ligroin.

Picrate : yellow needles from EtOH. M.p. 32–4°.

Methiodide : cotarnine hydriodide. M.p. 184–decomp.

Decker, Becker, *Ann.*, 1913, **395**, 330.

Norcotarnone (6-*Hydroxy*-4 : 5-*methylene*-*oxy*-2-*vinylbenzaldehyde*, 2-*hydroxy*-6-*vinyl*-*peronal*)

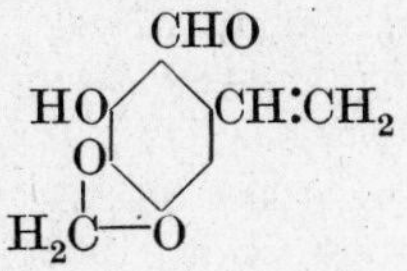

$_{10}H_8O_4$ MW, 192

Yellowish-green cryst. from EtOH. M.p. 89°.

K salt : yellow scales. Spar. sol. cold H_2O.

Me ether : cotarnone. $C_{11}H_{10}O_4$. MW, 206. Plates from EtOH. M.p. 78°. Part. volatile in steam. Insol. cold H_2O. Mod. sol. EtOH, Et_2O, AcOH. $KMnO_4$ ⟶ cotarnic acid. *Oxime*: needles from dil. EtOH. M.p. 130–2°.

Acetyl : needles from EtOH or AcOH. M.p. 84–5°.

Oxime : plates from EtOH. M.p. 202–3°. O-*Acetyl* : m.p. 115–16°. *Diacetyl* : m.p. 100–1°.

Freund, Baker, *Ber.*, 1903, **36**, 1530.
Roser, *Ann.*, 1888, **249**, 163.

Norecgonidine

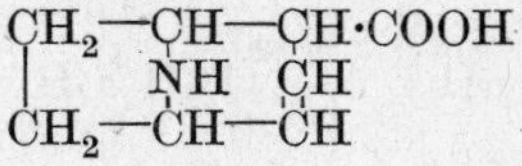

$C_8H_{11}O_2N$ MW, 153

M.p. 254–5°. Sol. H_2O, EtOH. Neutral.

B,HCl : m.p. 257°. Sol. H_2O, EtOH. Insol. Et_2O.

Et ester : $C_{10}H_{15}O_2N$. MW, 181. B.p. 157°/25 mm. *B,HAuCl$_4$* : m.p. 133°.

B_2,H_2PtCl_6 : m.p. 251°.

B,HAuCl$_4$: m.p. 204°.

v. Braun, Müller, *Ber.*, 1918, **51**, 247.

Norecgonine

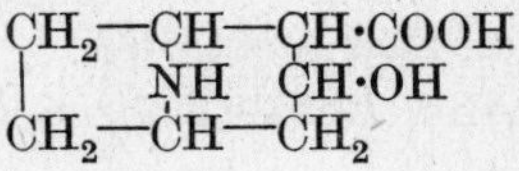

$C_8H_{13}O_3N$ MW, 171

l-.

Needles. M.p. 233°. Sol. H_2O.

B,HAuCl$_4$: yellow needles. M.p. 211°. Spar. sol. H_2O.

O-*Benzoyl* : m.p. 230°. *B,HCl,2H$_2$O* : m.p. 217–18°. *B,HAuCl$_4$* : yellow needles. M.p. 228° decomp. *Me ester* : liq. *B,HAuCl$_4$* : needles from H_2O. M.p. 181–2°. *Et ester* : liq. *B,HAuCl$_4$* : m.p. 160·5°.

N-*Me* : *see l*-Ecgonine.

Einhorn, *Ber.*, 1888, **21**, 3029.
See also Willstätter, Müller, *Ber.*, 1898, **31**, 2655.

Nor-ψ-ecgonine.

d-.

Needles from EtOH–Et_2O. MeI ⟶ *d*-ψ-ecgonine.

Me ester : $C_9H_{15}O_3N$. MW, 185. Cryst. from AcOEt or C_6H_6. M.p. 160°. Sol. MeOH, EtOH. Insol. Et_2O, ligroin.

Et ester : $C_{10}H_{17}O_3N$. MW, 199. Needles

from AcOEt. M.p. 137°. Sol. H_2O, EtOH. Insol. Et_2O.

O-*Benzoyl* : needles from dil. EtOH. *Et ester* : needles from EtOH. M.p. 127°. Sol. $CHCl_3$, AcOEt, C_6H_6. Spar. sol. EtOH. Insol. CS_2, ligroin. B_2,H_2PtCl_6 : m.p. 142°.

N-*Me* : *see* *d*-*ψ*-Ecgonine.

Einhorn, Friedländer, *Ber.*, 1893, **26**, 1482.
See also Willstätter, Müller, *Ber.*, 1898, **31**, 2655.

Norecsantalal (*Nortricycloekasantalal*)

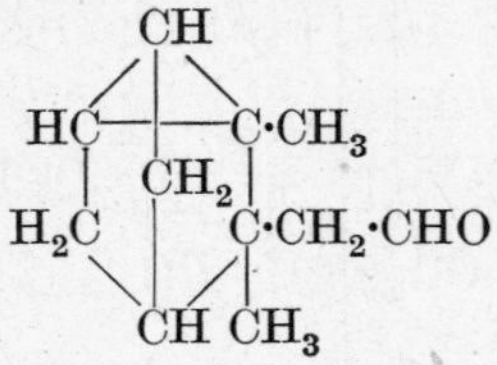

$C_{11}H_{16}O$ MW, 164

Occurs in East Indian sandalwood oil. B.p. 222–4°, 92–4°/11 mm., 86–7°/6 mm. D^{20} 0·9938 (0·9964). n_D^{20} 1·48393. Na + EtOH ⟶ norecsantalol. $NH_3.AgNO_3$ ⟶ norecsantalic acid.

Oxime : b.p. 142–4°/10 mm., 135–7°/7 mm.

Semicarbazone : m.p. 224° (216°). Spar. sol. EtOH.

Semmler, *Ber.*, 1909, **42**, 588; 1910, **43**, 1724, 1893.
Semmler, Zaar, *ibid.*, 1891.

Norecsantalic Acid (*Nortricycloekasantalic acid*)

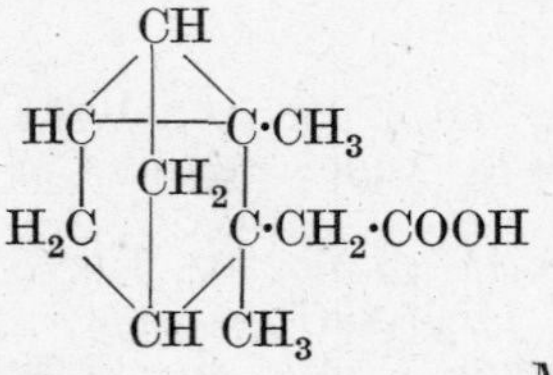

$C_{11}H_{16}O_2$ MW, 180

Cryst. from dil. EtOH. M.p. 93°. B.p. 143–5°/10 mm. $[\alpha]_D$ − 33° 17′ in EtOH.

Me ester : $C_{12}H_{18}O_2$. MW, 194. B.p. 102–4°/10 mm. D^{20} 1·0228. n_D 1·47348.

Semmler, *Ber.*, 1910, **43**, 1724, 1893.

Norecsantalol (*Nortricycloekasantalol*)

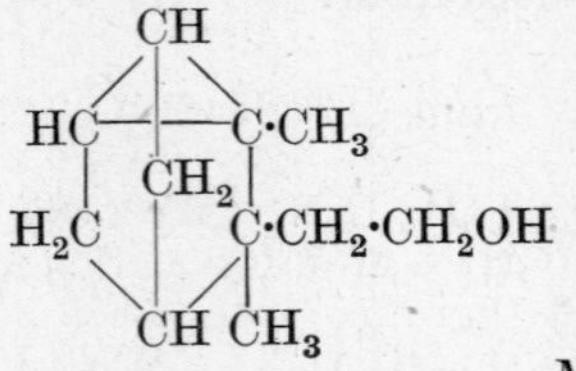

$C_{11}H_{18}O$ MW, 166

B.p. 114–17°/10 mm. D^{20} 0·9958. n_D 1·49049. CrO_3 ⟶ norecsantalal.

Semmler, Zaar, *Ber.*, 1910, **43**, 1890.
Semmler, *ibid.*, 1893.

Noremetine.

See Norcephæline.

Norephedrine (2-*Amino*-1-*phenylpropanol*-1, α-*hydroxy*-β-*aminopropylbenzene*)

$$C_6H_5{\cdot}CH(OH){\cdot}CH(NH_2){\cdot}CH_3$$

$C_9H_{13}ON$ MW, 15[illegible]

l-.

Occurs in Ma Huang and European *Ephedra*. M.p. about 50°. $[\alpha]_D^{20}$ −14·56° in EtOH.

B,HCl : m.p. 171–2°. $[\alpha]_D^{20}$ − 33·27° in H_2O.

$B_2,H_2SO_4,2H_2O$: m.p. anhyd. 285–6° decomp. $[\alpha]_D^{28}$ − 31·99° in H_2O.

Oxalate : m.p. 245° decomp.

B_2,H_2PtCl_6 : m.p. 221° decomp.

$B,HAuCl_4$: m.p. 188°.

N-p-*Nitrobenzoyl* : m.p. 175–6°. $[\alpha]$ − 49·58° in $CHCl_3$.

Hydrogen tartrate + *EtOH* : softens at 130°. M.p. about 160°. $[\alpha]_D^{20}$ − 34·46° (EtOH free).

d-.

M.p. 52°. $[\alpha]_D^{27}$ + 14·76° in EtOH.

B,HCl : m.p. 171–2°. $[\alpha]_D^{27}$ + 33·4° in EtOH.

$B_2,H_2SO_4,2H_2O$: m.p. anhyd. 285–6° decomp. $[\alpha]_D^{27}$ + 31·51°.

Oxalate : m.p. 245°.

B_2,H_2PtCl_6 : m.p. 221·5° decomp.

$B,HAuCl_4$: m.p. 188°.

N-p-*Nitrobenzoyl* : m.p. 175–6°. $[\alpha]$ + 49·95° in $CHCl_3$.

Hydrogen tartrate + *EtOH* : m.p. about 160°. $[\alpha]_D^{27}$ + 34·69° (EtOH free).

dl-.

Plates from Et_2O. M.p. 104–5°.

B,HCl : m.p. 194° (192°).

B_2,H_2SO_4 : m.p. 285–6°.

Hydrogen oxalate : m.p. 245° decomp.

Dioxalate : m.p. 182–3° decomp.

B_2,H_2PtCl_6 : yellow needles from H_2O. M.p. 221·5° decomp.

N-*Acetyl* : m.p. 135°.

N-*Benzoyl* : m.p. 143°.

O : N-*Dibenzoyl* : m.p. 167–8°.

N-p-*Nitrobenzoyl* : cryst. from EtOH. M.p. 189°.

Kanao, *Ber.*, 1930, **63**, 95.
Nagai, Kanao, *Ann.*, 1929, **470**, 157.
Hey, *J. Chem. Soc.*, 1930, 1232.

Nor-ψ-ephedrine (*Norisoephedrine*)

$C_6H_5 \cdot CH(OH) \cdot CH(NH_2) \cdot CH_3$

$C_9H_{13}ON$ MW, 151

l-.

M.p. 77·5–78°. $[\alpha]_D^{20}$ − 32·64° in EtOH.

B,HCl : m.p. 180–1°. $[\alpha]_D^{20}$ − 42·68° in H_2O.

B_2,H_2SO_4 : m.p. 290–1° decomp. $[\alpha]_D^{20}$ − 39·99°.

Oxalate : m.p. 235°.

B_2,H_2PtCl_6 : m.p. 199°.

$B,HAuCl_4$: m.p. 137–8°.

N-p-*Nitrobenzoyl* : m.p. 199°. $[\alpha]_D^{20}$ − 105·13° in $CHCl_3$. *B,HCl* : m.p. 246°. $[\alpha]_D^{22}$ − 54·63° in H_2O.

Hydrogen tartrate : m.p. 202° decomp. $[\alpha]_D^{20}$ − 13·39° in H_2O.

d-.

Occurs in Ma Huang. M.p. 77° (77·5–80°). $[\alpha]_D^{20}$ + 33·14° in EtOH, + 24·7° in H_2O, $[\alpha]_{5461}^{20}$ + 32·2° in MeOH.

B,HCl : m.p. 180–1°. $[\alpha]_D^{20}$ + 42·53° in H_2O.

B_2,H_2SO_4 : m.p. 295° decomp. $[\alpha]_D^{20}$ + 40·12° in H_2O, $[\alpha]_{5461}^{20}$ + 42·9° in H_2O.

Oxalate : m.p. 235° decomp.

B_2,H_2PtCl_6 : m.p. 198°.

$B,HAuCl_4$: m.p. 137–8°.

N-*Benzenesulphonyl* : m.p. 103–4°.

N-*Benzoyl* : m.p. 132°. $[\alpha]_{5461}^{20}$ + 58·3° in MeOH.

O : N-*Dibenzoyl* : m.p. 156–7°. $[\alpha]_{5461}^{20}$ + 28° in MeOH.

N-p-*Nitrobenzoyl* : m.p. 199·5°. $[\alpha]_D^{20}$ + 104·96° in $CHCl_3$.

O-*Benzoyl, HCl* : m.p. 244·5° decomp. $[\alpha]_{5461}^{20}$ − 32·5° in H_2O.

Hydrogen tartrate : m.p. 202°. $[\alpha]_D^{20}$ + 13·36° in H_2O.

dl-.

Plates from pet. ether. M.p. 71°.

B,HCl : m.p. 169°.

B_2,H_2SO_4 : m.p. 290–1° decomp.

Hydrogen oxalate : m.p. 235°.

Dioxalate : m.p. 171° decomp.

B_2,H_2PtCl_6 : m.p. 199·5° decomp.

$B,HAuCl_6$: m.p. 132–3°.

N-*Acetyl* : m.p. 85–6°.

N-p-*Nitrobenzoyl* : m.p. 170°.

O-*Benzoyl* : *B,HCl*, m.p. 220°. *B_2,H_2SO_4* : m.p. 182° decomp. *Picrate* : m.p. 186° decomp.

Smith, *J. Chem. Soc.*, 1928, 51.
Kanao, *Ber.*, 1930, **63**, 98.
Nagai, Kanao, *Ann.*, 1929, **470**, 157.
Hey, *J. Chem. Soc.*, 1930, 1232.
Gibson, Levin, *J. Chem. Soc.*, 1929, 2754.

Noreserethole

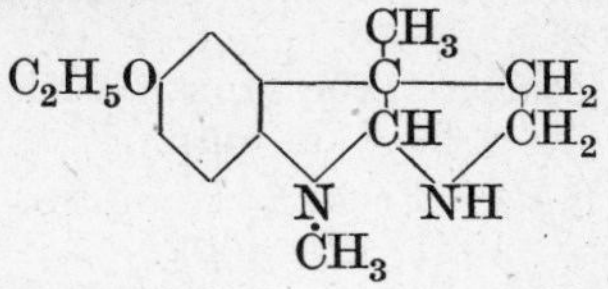

$C_{14}H_{20}ON_2$ MW, 232

d-.

d-*Hydrogen tartrate* : m.p. 188–9°. $[\alpha]_D^{28}$ + 202·1° in H_2O.

l-.

d-*Hydrogen tartrate* : m.p. 190–1°. $[\alpha]_D^{22}$ − 53·3° in H_2O.

dl-.

B.p. 187–92°/12 mm.

B,HCl : m.p. 191–2°.

Benzoyl : m.p. 108°.

$B_2,H_2PtCl_6,\frac{1}{2}H_2O$: m.p. 185° decomp.

Picrate : orange-red prisms from EtOH. M.p. 180–1° (184–5°, 191–2°).

Picrolonate : m.p. 221° (227°).

Robinson, Suginome, *J. Chem. Soc.*, 1932, 314.
Hoshino, Kobayashi, *Ann.*, 1935, **516**, 88.
Julian, Pikl, *J. Am. Chem. Soc.*, 1935, **57**, 563.

Noresermethole

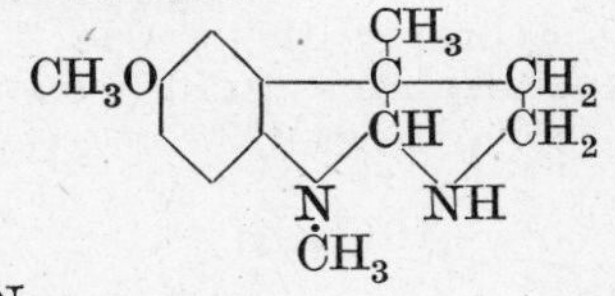

$C_{13}H_{18}ON_2$ MW, 218

dl-.

B.p. 130–2° in high vacuum.

Picrate : orange-red prisms from EtOH. M.p. 162–3°.

Picrolonate,$\frac{1}{2}H_2O$: m.p. 227° decomp.

King, Robinson, *J. Chem. Soc.*, 1932, 1433.
King, Liguori, Robinson, *J. Chem. Soc.*, 1934, 1416.

Norgranatanine.

See Granatanine.

Norgranatoline.

See footnote under Granatoline.

Norharman (β-*Carboline*, 3-*carboline*)

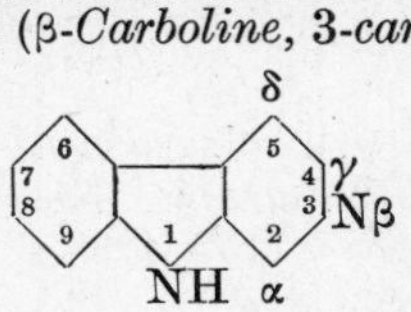

$C_{11}H_8N_2$ MW, 168

Colourless needles. M.p. 198·5°. Sol. EtOH, Et_2O, AcOEt, MeOH, hot H_2O. Spar. sol. C_6H_6, pet. ether. Blue fluor. in dil. acid sol.

Picrate: m.p. 260° decomp.

Kermack, Perkin, Robinson, *J. Chem. Soc.*, 1921, **119**, 1602.

Gulland, Robinson, Scott, Thornley, *J. Chem. Soc.*, 1929, 2926 (*Footnote*).

Norharmine

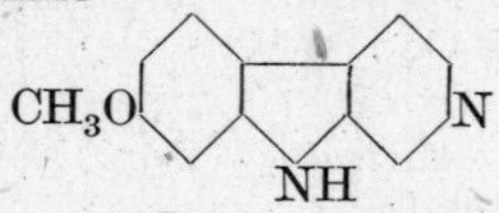

Probable structure

$C_{12}H_{10}ON_2$ MW, 198

Needles from C_6H_6. M.p. 218°. Sol. hot EtOH. Spar. sol. C_6H_6. Sublimes without decomp. Slowly colours pine shaving + HCl.

Hydrochloride: pale yellow prisms from H_2O. Dil. sols. show intense blue fluor.

Aurichloride: pale brown needles from EtOH.

Mercurichloride: pale yellow needles from H_2O.

Perkin, Robinson, *J. Chem. Soc.*, 1912, **101**, 1785.

Kermack, Perkin, Robinson, *J. Chem. Soc.*, 1921, **119**, 1619.

Norhemipinic Acid.

See 3 : 4-Dihydroxyphthalic Acid.

Norhomocamphoric Acid (*Cyclopentane*-1-*carboxylic acid*-3-*acetic acid*, 3-*carboxycyclopentyl-acetic acid*)

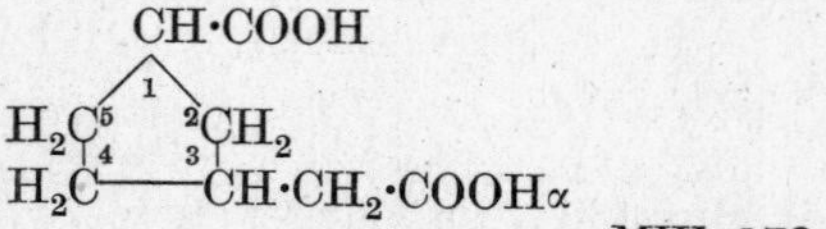

$C_8H_{12}O_4$ MW, 172

Cryst. from Et_2O, H_2O or C_6H_6. M.p. 137–137·5°. Sol. EtOH, Et_2O.

1-*Et ester* α-*Me ester*: $C_{11}H_{18}O_4$. MW, 214. B.p. 135–41°/13 mm. D_4^{17} 1·0683. n_D^{17} 1·4505.

Hintikka, Komppa, *Chem. Zentr.*, 1918, II, 370.

Norhyoscyamine

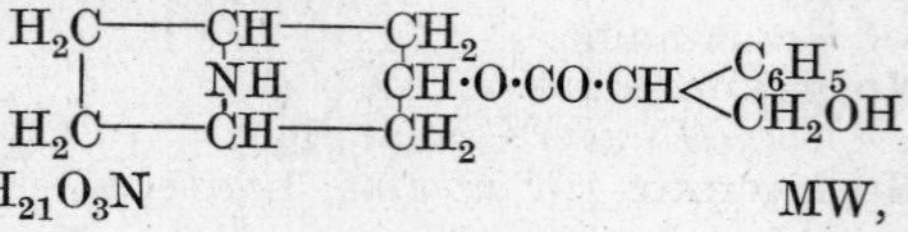

$C_{16}H_{21}O_3N$ MW, 275

l-.

Found in bark of *Scopolia Japonica*, and *Mandragora Officinarum*. Needles from $CHCl_3$–Et_2O. M.p. 140·5° (133–4°). Sol. EtOH, $CHCl_3$. Spar. sol. Et_2O, Me_2CO. Sol. 270 parts H_2O. $[\alpha]_D$ − 21·2° in EtOH.

B,HCl: needles from EtOH–Et_2O. M.p. 207

B_2,H_2SO_4: needles + $3H_2O$ from Me_2CO.A M.p. 249°. Sol. 5 parts H_2O at 15°.

Oxalate: prisms from Me_2CO.Aq. M. 245–6°. Sol. 20 parts H_2O at 15°.

$B,HAuCl_4$: yellow leaflets. M.p. 178–9 (174°). Mod. sol. hot H_2O.

B_2,H_2PtCl_6: needles. M.p. 141°.

Picrate: m.p. 220°.

N-*Me*: *see* Hyoscyamine.

dl-.

See Noratropine.

Carr, Reynolds, *J. Chem. Soc.*, 1912, **101**, 946.

Merck, *Arch. Pharm.*, 1903, **231**, 117.

Hesse, *J. prakt. Chem.*, 1901, **64**, 276.

Norisoborneol.

See under Norborneol.

Norisocampholic Acid (2 : 2 : 3-*Trimethyl cyclopentane*-1-*carboxylic acid*)

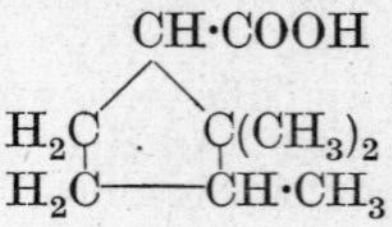

$C_9H_{16}O_2$ MW, 15

Liq. B.p. 130°/12 mm. D_4^{18} 0·9995. n 1·4587.

Chloride: $C_9H_{15}OCl$. MW, 174·5. B.p. 85° 13 mm.

Ethylamide: $C_{11}H_{21}ON$. MW, 183. Cryst from Et_2O. M.p. 68–9°.

v. Braun, Heymons, *Ber.*, 1928, **61**, 2280

Norleucine (1-*Amino*-n-*caproic acid*)

$CH_3{\cdot}CH_2{\cdot}CH_2{\cdot}CH_2{\cdot}CH(NH_2){\cdot}COOH$

$C_6H_{13}O_2N$ MW, 13

d-.

Leaflets from H_2O. M.p. 301°. Sol. t 2% in H_2O at 25°. Very spar. sol. EtOH $[\alpha]_D^{20}$ + 23·14° in HCl, + 6·26° in H_2O. Swee taste. Sublimes partially at 275–80°.

Cu salt: dark blue needles from H_2O Blackens about 255°. Insol. EtOH.

N-*Formyl*: needles from H_2O. M.p. 115–16° $[\alpha]_D^{20}$ − 15·85° in H_2O. Very sol. H_2O, EtOH Et_2O.

N-*Chloroacetyl*: cryst. from AcOEt. M.p 104–6°. $[\alpha]_D^{20}$ + 3·56° in H_2O.

N-*Glycyl*: prisms from EtOH.Aq. M.p 239–40° decomp. $[\alpha]_D^{20}$ − 8·71° in H_2O.

N-*Benzoyl*: m.p. 53°.

l-.

Leaflets from H_2O. M.p. 301°. Sol. 60 part H_2O at 18°. $[\alpha]_D^{20}$ − 26·5° in HCl, − 4·49° in

H_2O. Sublimes partially at 275–80°. Bitter taste.

N-*Formyl* : needles from H_2O. M.p. 115–16°. $[\alpha]_D^{20}$ + 15·53° in H_2O. Very sol. H_2O, EtOH, Et_2O.

N-*Glycyl* : prisms. M.p. 239–40° decomp. $[\alpha]_D^{20}$ + 8·24° in H_2O.

N-β-*Naphthalenesulphonyl* : m.p. 149°. Sol. EtOH, Et_2O. Spar. sol. H_2O. $[\alpha]_D$ — 22·54°.

N-*Benzoyl* : m.p. 53°.

dl-.

Leaflets from H_2O. M.p. 297–300° (275°) (sealed tube). Sol. 83 parts H_2O at 22°.

Et ester : $C_8H_{17}O_2N$. MW, 159. Oil. B.p. 90–1°/11 mm. D^{17} 0·9335. *Picrate* : prisms from H_2O. M.p. 124°.

N-*Me* : $C_7H_{15}O_2N$. MW, 145. Needles from H_2O, leaflets from EtOH. Sublimes at 110°. Sol. 9·8 parts H_2O at 11°, 43·7 parts 94% EtOH at 13°. Insol. Et_2O. Bitter taste. $FeCl_3$ ⟶ intense red col.

N-*Di-Me* : $C_8H_{17}O_2N$. MW, 159. Needles + $2H_2O$ from H_2O, needles from AcOEt. M.p. anhyd. 161–2°. Sol. EtOH, $CHCl_3$. Mod. sol. warm C_6H_6. Spar. sol. AcOEt. Insol. Et_2O, pet. ether. *Methoaurichloride* : yellow leaflets from EtOH. M.p. 142° (137–8°). *Methochloroplatinate* : m.p. 215–16°.

N-*Et* : $C_8H_{17}O_2N$. MW, 159. Leaflets from EtOH. Sublimes without melting. Sol. 9·3 parts H_2O at 15°, 63·5 parts 94% EtOH at 13°. Insol. Et_2O. $FeCl_3$ ⟶ intense red col.

N-*Di-Et* : $C_{10}H_{21}O_2N$. MW, 187. Cryst. from H_2O or EtOH. Very sol. H_2O, EtOH. Insol. Et_2O.

N-*Formyl* : needles from H_2O. M.p. 114·5°. Sol. EtOH, Me_2CO. Spar. sol. Et_2O, AcOEt, C_6H_6, pet. ether.

N-*Chloroacetyl* : prisms from Me_2CO.Aq. M.p. 104–7°. Sol. EtOH, Et_2O, Me_2CO. Insol. H_2O.

N-*Glycyl* : leaflets or prisms from H_2O. M.p. 210–15° decomp. Spar. sol. cold H_2O.

Fischer, Hagenbach, *Ber.*, 1901, **34**, 3764.
Duvillier, *Bull. soc. chim.*, 1895, **13**, 484.
Abderhalden, Weil, *Z. physiol. Chem.*, 1912, **81**, 213.
Abderhalden, Froehlich, Fuchs, *Z. physiol. Chem.*, 1913, **86**, 460.
Yaginuma, Hayakawa, Arai, *Chem. Abstracts*, 1932, **26**, 5073.
Abderhalden, Beckmann, *Z. physiol. Chem.*, 1932, **207**, 93.
Marvel, du Vigneaud, *Organic Syntheses*, Collective Vol. I, 40.

Norlobelanine (*Isolobelanine*, 2 : 6-*diphenacylpiperidine*)

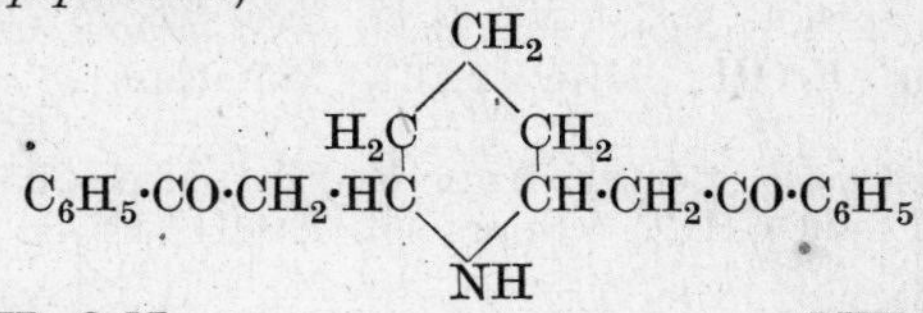

$C_{21}H_{23}O_2N$ MW, 321

One of lobelia alkaloids. Prisms from Et_2O or EtOH.Aq. M.p. 120–1°. Sol. usual solvents. Optically inactive. Red. ⟶ norlobelanidine.

B,HNO₃ : prisms from EtOH.Aq. M.p. 193° decomp.

B,HCl : cryst. from EtOH. M.p. 201–2°.

Methiodide : prisms from C_6H_6. M.p. 183–4°. Turns yellow in air.

Benzoyl : needles from EtOH. M.p. 125–6°.

N-*Me* : Lobelanine, *q.v.*

Wieland, Hermsen, *Ann.*, 1926, **444**, 63.
Wieland, Koschkara, *Ann.*, 1929, **473**, 122.
Wieland, Drishaus, *ibid.*, 117.

Norlobelanidine

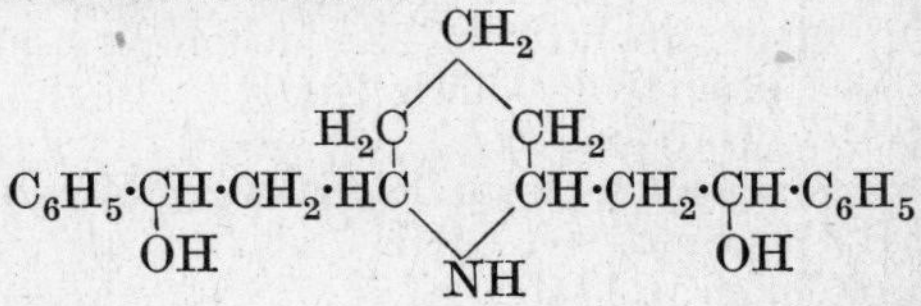

$C_{21}H_{27}O_2N$ MW, 325

One of lobelia alkaloids. Needles from Et_2O. M.p. 120°. Optically inactive.

B,HCl : needles from 80–90% EtOH. M.p. 244° slight decomp.

B,HNO₃ : prisms from H_2O. M.p. 179–80°.

Iodide : needles from Me_2CO.Aq. M.p. 211°.

N-*Me* : Lobelanidine, *q.v.*

Wieland, Koschkara, *Ann.*, 1929, **473**, 123.
Wieland, Drishaus, *ibid.*, 116.

Normenthane.
Isopropylcyclohexane, *q.v.*

Nor-metahemipinic Acid.
See 4 : 5-Dihydroxyphthalic Acid.

Normorphine

$C_{16}H_{17}O_3N$ MW, 271

Cryst. M.p. 263–4°.

B,HCl : cryst. + H_2O from H_2O. M.p. anhyd. 305° decomp.

B₂,H₂PtCl₆ : cryst. + $3H_2O$. M.p. 230–1°.

Me ether : *see* Norcodeine.

O-*Isoamyl* : $C_{21}H_{27}O_3N$. MW, 341. Cryst. M.p. 100°. *B,HCl* : cryst. from EtOH–Et_2O. M.p. 278°. Spar. sol. H_2O. N-*Cyano* : cryst. from EtOH. M.p. 225°. N-*Nitroso* : m.p. 186°.

N-*Cyano* : cryst. from EtOH. M.p. 295–6°. Mod. sol. $CHCl_3$. Spar. sol. EtOH, Et_2O, pet. ether.

N-*Nitroso* : needles from EtOH. M.p. 267° decomp. *Diacetyl* : cryst. from EtOH.Aq. M.p. 202–3°.

Triacetyl : plates from EtOH.Aq. M.p. 164°.

Dibenzoyl : leaflets from EtOH. M.p. 208°. Sol. EtOH.

N-*Me* : Morphine, *q.v.*

Speyer, Walther, *Ber.*, 1930, **63**, 853.
v. Braun, *Ber.*, 1914, **47**, 2320.

Nornarceine

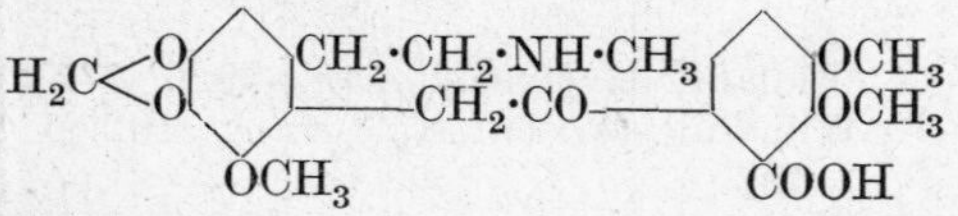

$C_{22}H_{25}O_8N$ MW, 431

Prisms from EtOH, needles + $3H_2O$ from H_2O. M.p. about 205–22° decomp., anhyd. 229° decomp. Sol. boiling EtOH.

N-*Me* : Narceine, *q.v.*

Oxime : leaflets from EtOH.Aq. M.p. 171°. Sol. H_2O. Spar. sol. EtOH.

B,HCl : m.p. 144°.

Rabe, *Ber.*, 1907, **40**, 3283.
Rabe, McMillan, *Ber.*, 1910, **43**, 801.
Polonovski, Polonovski, *Bull. soc. chim.*, 1930, **47**, 365.

Nornicotine (2-[3-*Pyridyl*]-*pyrrolidine*)

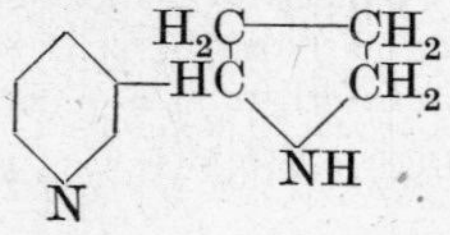

$C_9H_{12}N_2$ MW, 148

d-.

Found in *Duboisia Hopwoodii*. B.p. 117°/3·6 mm. D_4^{10} 1·0757. $n_D^{18\cdot3}$ 1·5490. $[\alpha]_D^{20}$ + 86·3°.

Dipicrate : m.p. 191–2°.

Dipicrolonate : m.p. 252–3°.

l-.

Found in tobacco. B.p. 130·5–131·3°/11 mm., 120°/1 mm., $D^{19\cdot5}$ 1·0737. $n_D^{18\cdot5}$ 1·5378. $[\alpha]_D^{22}$ − 88·8°. Methylation ⟶ *l*-nicotine.

Chloroaurate : m.p. 217°.

Chloroplatinate : decomp. at 295°.

Dipicrate : m.p. 191–2°.

Dipicrolonate : m.p. 250–2°.

N-*Phenylthiourethane* : m.p. 176–7°.

N-*Me* : *see* Nicotine.

N-*Et* : $C_{11}H_{14}N_2$. MW, 176. Oil. B.p. 127–8°/12 mm. *Chloroaurate* : decomp. at 203°. *Picrate* : m.p. 174–6°.

N-*Allyl* : $C_{12}H_{14}N_2$. MW, 188. Liq. B.p. 136–7°/12 mm. *Chloroaurate* : decomp. at 145–8°. *Chloroplatinate* : decomp. at 255°. *Picrate* : cryst. from EtOH. M.p. 180–2°.

N-*Acetyl* : b.p. 212–14°/12 mm. $[\alpha]_D^{20}$ − 3·24° in C_6H_6. *Chloroplatinate* : decomp. at 245°. *Methiodide* : m.p. 201°. *Picrate* : m.p. 151°.

N-*Nitroso* : yellow liq. B.p. 190–2°/0·5 mm. Misc. with H_2O. B_2,H_2PtCl_6 : m.p. 190°. *Methiodide* : m.p. 144°. Hygroscopic.

N-*Urethane* : yellow cryst. from $CHCl_3$–pet. ether. M.p. 164–6°.

v. Braun, Weissbach, *Ber.*, 1930, **63**, 2022.
Späth, Zajic, *Ber.*, 1935, **68**, 1667.
Späth, Hicks, Zajic, *Ber.*, 1935, **68**, 1388; 1936, **69**, 250.
Späth, Marion, Zajic, *Ber.*, 1936, **69**, 251.

Nornicotyrine.

See 2-[3-Pyridyl]-pyrrole.

Nor-opianic Acid (5 : 6-*Dihydroxy*-o-*aldehydobenzoic acid*, 6-*formyl*-o-*pyrocatechuic acid*, 5 : 6-*dihydroxy*-o-*phthalaldehydic acid*)

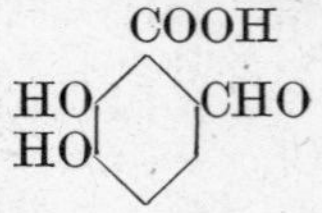

$C_8H_6O_5$ MW, 182

Cryst. + $1\frac{1}{2}H_2O$ from H_2O. M.p. anhyd. 171°. $FeCl_3$ ⟶ deep bluish-green col.

5-*Me ether* : $C_9H_8O_5$. M.W, 196. Cryst. + $2\frac{1}{2}H_2O$. M.p. anhyd. 155–6°. $FeCl_3$ ⟶ dark blue col. *ψ-Me ester*. $C_{10}H_{10}O_5$. MW, 210. M.p. 67–71°. *ψ-Et ester*. $C_{11}H_{12}O_5$. MW, 224. Cryst. from C_6H_6. M.p. 104–6°.

5 : 6-*Di-Me ether* : *see* Opianic Acid.

Wright, *J. Chem. Soc.*, 1877, **32**, 546.
Liebermann, *Ber.*, 1896, **29**, 2033; 1897, **30**, 692.

Norpinic Acid (1 : 1-*Dimethylcyclobutane*-2 : 4-*dicarboxylic acid*)

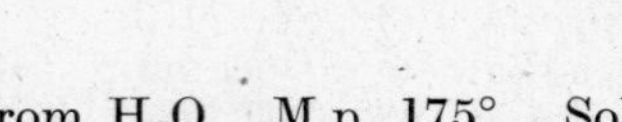

$C_8H_{12}O_4$ MW, 172

Cis :

Prisms from H_2O. M.p. 175°. Sol. AcOEt, hot H_2O. Mod. sol. Et_2O, $CHCl_3$. Sublimes in needles above 100°.

Di-Me ester: $C_{10}H_{16}O_4$. MW, 200. B.p. 28–9°/756 mm., 113–113·8°/11 mm. $D_4^{14·3}$ ·0700. n_D^{17} 1·4459.
Di-Et ester: $C_{12}H_{20}O_4$. MW, 228. B.p. 40°/20 mm.
Anhydride: $C_8H_{10}O_3$. MW, 154. Plates rom Et_2O. M.p. 135°. Warm H_2O ⟶ *cis*-orpinic acid.
Anilide: m.p. 212–13°.

Trans:
Prisms from H_2O. M.p. 146°. Sol. H_2O, EtOH, Et_2O, Me_2CO.

Guha, Gaind, *Chem. Abstracts*, 1934, **28**, 6721.
Kerr, *J. Am. Chem. Soc.*, 1929, **51**, 614.
Östling, *J. Chem. Soc.*, 1912, **101**, 475.
Perkin, Simonsen, *J. Chem. Soc.*, 1909, **95**, 1176.
Kerschbaum, *Ber.*, 1900, **33**, 891.

Nor-ψ-scopine

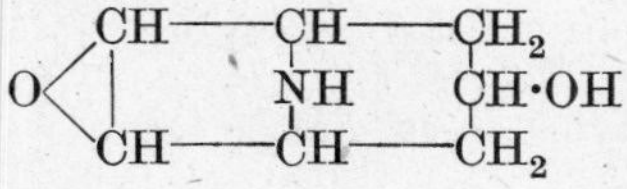

$C_7H_{11}O_2N$ MW, 141

Cryst. M.p. 184°. Excess methyl iodide ⟶ -scopine methiodide.
B,HCl: m.p. 262°.
B,HAuCl₄: m.p. 220°.
Picrate: m.p. 225°.
N-*Me*: *see under* Scopine.

Polonovski, Polonovski, *Compt. rend.*, 1928, **186**, 149.

Norscopoline (*Scopoligenin*)

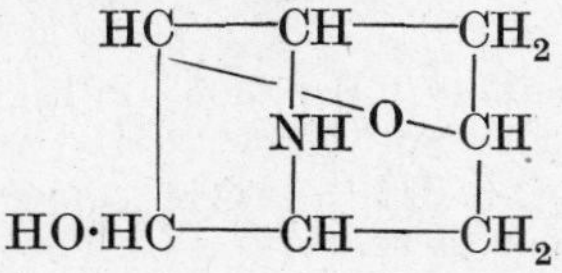

$C_7H_{11}O_2N$ MW, 141

Prisms from EtOH, Et_2O, $CHCl_3$ or pet. ther. M.p. 205–6°. Sol. H_2O, EtOH, $CHCl_3$. par. sol. Et_2O, pet. ether. Sublimes in needles t 120°. Methyl iodide ⟶ scopoline.
B,HCl: m.p. 280°.
B,HAuCl₄: golden-yellow cryst. M.p. 242° 236°).
N-*Me*: *see* Scopoline.

Luboldt, *Arch. Pharm.*, 1898, **236**, 22.
Hess, Merck, Uibrig, *Ber.*, 1915, **48**, 1906.
Polonovski, Polonovski, *Bull. soc. chim.*, 1927, **41**, 1206.

Nortricycloekasantalal.
See Norecsantalal.
Nortricycloekasantalic Acid.
See Norecsantalic Acid.
Nortricycloekasantalol.
See Norecsantalol.
Nortropane (2 : 5-*Trimethylene-pyrrolidine*)

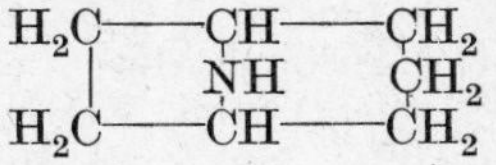

$C_7H_{13}N$ MW, 111

Cryst. M.p. about 60°. B.p. about 161°. Sol. H_2O, EtOH, Et_2O. Absorbs CO_2 from the air.
B,HCl: cryst. M.p. 281° decomp. Very sol. H_2O, EtOH.
B₂,H₂PtCl₆: golden-yellow prisms. Decomp. at 225°.
N-*Phenylguanyl*: needles from EtOH.Aq. M.p. 145°. *B₂,H₂PtCl₆*: decomp. at 208°. Insol. H_2O. *Picrate*: m.p. 157–8°.
N-*Benzoyl*: cryst. M.p. 94–5°. B.p. 204–5°/14 mm.
N-*Hydrocinnamoyl*: thick yellowish oil. B.p. 176–8°/0·4 mm.

Ladenburg, *Ber.*, 1887, **20**, 1649.
v. Braun, *Chem. Zentr.*, 1909, II, 1993; *Ber.*, 1911, **44**, 1259.
Hess, *Ber.*, 1918, **51**, 1014.
v. Braun, Weissbach, *Ber.*, 1930, **63**, 496.

Nortropanol.
See Nortropine.
Nortropanone-3.
See Nortropinone.
Nortropene (*Nortropidine*)

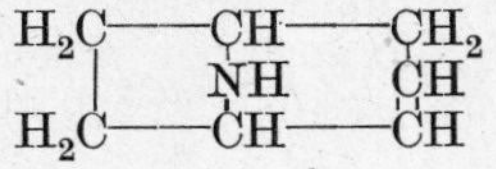

$C_7H_{11}N$ MW, 109

B,HCl: cryst.
B,HAuCl₄: cryst. M.p. 187°.
N-*Acetyl*: liq. Very sol. H_2O. Reacts neutral.

Polonovski, Polonovski, *Bull. soc. chim.*, 1927, **41**, 1202.

Nortropidine.
See Nortropene.
Nortropine (*Nortropanol, tropigenin*)

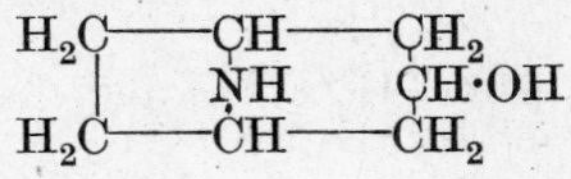

$C_7H_{13}ON$ MW, 127

Needles. M.p. 169° (161°). B.p. 233°. Sol. H_2O, EtOH. Less sol. Et_2O.

B,HCl: m.p. 285°.

B,HNO_2: cryst. from EtOH–Et_2O. M.p. 160°. Sol. H_2O, EtOH. Insol. Et_2O.

$B,HAuCl_4$: golden-yellow leaflets from H_2O. M.p. 215–16° decomp. Sol. EtOH.

B_2,H_2PtCl_6: plates. M.p. 247° decomp. Very sol. H_2O. Insol. EtOH.

N-*Acetyl*: cryst. from EtOH. M.p. 124°. *B,HCl*: m.p. 162°. Spar. sol. Me_2CO.

Polonovski, Polonovski, *Bull. soc. chim.*, 1927, **41**, 1203.
Willstätter, *Ber.*, 1896, **29**, 1579.
Merling, *Ann.*, 1883, **216**, 343.
Chem. Werke Grenzach, D.R.P., 301,870, (*Chem. Zentr.*, 1918, I, 250).

Nortropinone (*Nortropanone*-3, 3-*ketonortropane*)

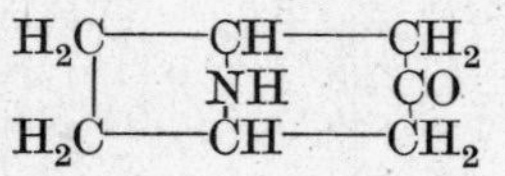

$C_7H_{11}ON$ MW, 125

Needles and leaflets from C_6H_6–ligroin. M.p. 69–70°. Very sol. H_2O, EtOH, C_6H_6. Sol. Et_2O. Spar. sol. ligroin. Hygroscopic. Volatile in steam. Reacts strongly alkaline.

B,HCl: needles from EtOH. M.p. 201° decomp. Very sol. H_2O. Insol. Et_2O. Hygroscopic.

Oxime: leaflets from H_2O. M.p. 181–2°. Very sol. hot H_2O. Sol. EtOH. Spar. sol. Et_2O, Me_2CO, AcOEt, C_6H_6.

$B,HAuCl_4$: golden-yellow prisms from EtOH. M.p. 168° decomp. Very sol. hot EtOH. Decomp. on heating with H_2O.

B_2,H_2PtCl_6: orange-red prisms from H_2O. Decomp. above 200°. Sol. hot H_2O. Insol. EtOH.

Picrate: pale yellow prisms. M.p. 159–60°. Very sol. hot H_2O. Sol. boiling EtOH.

Willstätter, *Ber.*, 1896, **29**, 1581; D.R.P., 89,999, (*Chem. Zentr.*, 1897, I, 352).
Polonovski, Polonovski, *Bull. soc. chim.*, 1927, **41**, 1202.

Norvaline (1-*Amino*-n-*valeric acid*)

$CH_3 \cdot CH_2 \cdot CH_2 \cdot CH(NH_2) \cdot COOH$

$C_5H_{11}O_2N$ MW, 117

d-.

Cryst. from H_2O. Sinters at 305°. $[\alpha]_D^{19}$ $-$ 21·84° in 20% HCl.

Et ester: $C_7H_{15}O_2N$. MW, 145. Liq. B.p. 77·5°/10 mm. N-*Benzoyl*: needles from ligroi M.p. 59°. $[\alpha]_D^{19}$ + 7·98°.

N-*Formyl*: cryst. M.p. 137°. $[\alpha]_D^{18}$ + 2·0 in HCl. Spar. sol. H_2O, EtOH, AcOEt. Ins $CHCl_3$, pet. ether.

N-*Chloroacetyl*: prisms. M.p. 107°. S most ord. solvents. Spar. sol. pet. ether.

N-*Bromoacetyl*: m.p. 95°. $[\alpha]_D^{20}$ $-$ 8·6° EtOH.

N-l-α-*Bromopropionyl*: m.p. 105°. $[\alpha]_D^{20}$ $-$ 1 in H_2O.

N-d-α-*Bromopropionyl*: $[\alpha]_D^{22}$ + 8·5° in EtO Very hygroscopic.

N-*Glycyl*: micro-prisms. Sinters at 22 $[\alpha]_D^{20}$ $-$ 10·17° in H_2O. Sol. H_2O. Spar. s $CHCl_3$. Insol. EtOH, Et_2O, AcOEt, pet. eth

N-*Benzoyl*: cryst. + H_2O from 20% EtO M.p. 64°, anhyd. 97°. $[\alpha]_D^{19}$ $-$ 15·0° in a alkalis.

Brucine salt: needles from EtOH. M.p. 14

l-.

Cryst. from H_2O. Sinters at 307°. [α + 24·2° in 20% HCl.

N-*Formyl*: cryst. M.p. 136°. $[\alpha]_D^{18}$ $-$ 2·1 in EtOH.

N-*Chloroacetyl*: m.p. 108°.

N-*Bromoacetyl*: cryst. from EtOH–pet. eth M.p. 92°. $[\alpha]_D^{20}$ + 9·2° in EtOH.

N-l-α-*Bromopropionyl*: prisms from CHC pet. ether. M.p. 110°. $[\alpha]_D^{20}$ $-$ 9·0° in EtOH

N-d-α-*Bromopropionyl*: $[\alpha]_D^{22}$ + 15° in H_2O.

N-*Glycyl*: micro-prisms. Sinters at 22 $[\alpha]_D^{20}$ + 10·28° in EtOH.

N-*Benzoyl*: needles + H_2O from 20% EtO M.p. 64°, anhyd. 95°. $[\alpha]_D^{20}$ + 14·0° in a alkalis.

dl-.

Silvery leaflets. M.p. 303° (291°) (sealed tub Sol. hot H_2O. Sol. 10 parts H_2O at 18°. Ins EtOH, Et_2O, $CHCl_3$, AcOEt, pet. ether. A sol. has sweet taste.

B,HCl: prisms. M.p. 188° decomp. S H_2O, EtOH. Insol. Et_2O.

B,HNO_3: prisms or plates. Sol. H_2O. Le sol. EtOH. Insol. Et_2O.

Et ester: cryst. M.p. 65°. B.p. 68·5°/8 m D_4^{15} 0·9447. N-*Di-Et*: $C_{11}H_{23}O_2N$. MW, 20 Oil. B.p. 80–5°/10–11 mm. *Picrate*: m. 116°.

N-*Me*: $C_6H_{13}O_2N$. MW, 131. Needl + H_2O from H_2O or EtOH.Aq., cryst. fro MeOH. Sublimes at 252°. Sol. cold H_2 boiling EtOH. Sweet taste.

N-*Di-Me*: $C_7H_{15}O_2N$. MW, 145. Needl from AcOEt. M.p. 182°. Sol. H_2O, EtO

Spar. sol. AcOEt. Insol. Et_2O, pet. ether. *Nitrile*: $C_7H_{14}N_2$. MW, 126. Liq. B.p. 175–6°. *Methiodide*: prisms from H_2O. M.p. 181–2°. *Methochloroaurate*: yellow plates. M.p. 173–4° (160°). *Methochloroplatinate*: orange-yellow prisms. M.p. 219°.

N-*Formyl*: leaflets from EtOH. M.p. 132°. Sol. EtOH. Spar. sol. H_2O, Et_2O, AcOEt. Insol. $CHCl_3$, pet. ether.

Cocker, Lapworth, *J. Chem. Soc.*, 1931, 1399.
Abderhalden, Schweitzer, *Chem. Zentr.*, 1931, I, 798.
Karrer, Schneider, *Helv. Chim. Acta*, 1930, **13**, 1288.
Curtius, Lehmann, *J. prakt. Chem.*, 1930, **125**, 228.
Abderhalden, Kürten, *Chem. Zentr.*, 1921, III, 296.
Menozzi, Belloni, *Gazz. chim. ital.*, 1887, **17**, 116.
Friedmann, *Beiträge zur Chemischen Physiologie und Pathologie*, 1908, **11**, 170.
Schmidt, Dieterle, *Ann.*, 1910, **377**, 48, 51.
Slimmer, *Ber.*, 1902, **35**, 404.

Norwogonin (5 : 7 : 8-*Trihydroxyflavone*)

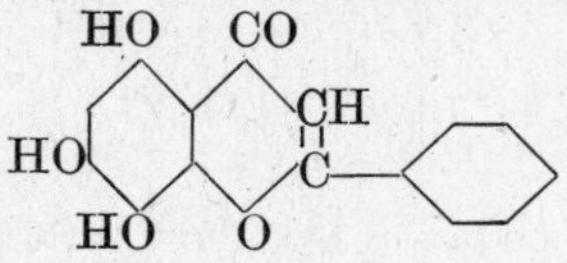

$C_{15}H_{10}O_5$ MW, 270

Yellow needles from AcOH.Aq. M.p. 227–8°.
Triacetyl: needles from EtOH. M.p. 216–17°.
7 : 8-*Di-Me-5-Et ether*: $C_{19}H_{18}O_5$. MW, 326. Needles from EtOH. M.p. 182–3°. Gives no col. with $FeCl_3$.
Tri-Me ether: $C_{18}H_{16}O_5$. MW, 312. Fine needles from H_2O. M.p. 167–8°. Gives no col. with $FeCl_3$. Insol. EtOH.Aq.

Hattori, *J. Chem. Soc. Japan*, 1930, **51**, 472; *Acta Phytochimica*, 1931, **5**, 219; 1932, **6**, 177.
See also Nierenstein, *Acta Phytochimica*, 1932, **6**, 173.

Nostal.
See Noctal.

Novain.
See Carnitine.

Novarsenobenzene.
See Neosalvarsan.

Novatophan.
See under 6-Methyl-2-phenylquinoline-4-carboxylic Acid.

Novocaine (*Ethocaine*, β-*diethylaminoethyl* p-*aminobenzoate*, *Procaine*)

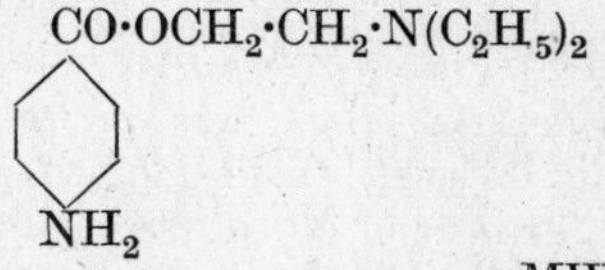

$C_{13}H_{20}O_2N_2$ MW, 236

Needles + $2H_2O$ from EtOH.Aq., plates from Et_2O or ligroin. M.p. 51°, anhyd. 61°. Spar. sol. H_2O. Used extensively as local anæsthetic.
B,HCl: needles. M.p. 153–6°. Very sol. H_2O. Sol. 0·6 parts H_2O, 30 parts EtOH at 25°. Spar. sol. $CHCl_3$. Almost insol. Et_2O. Decolourises acid $KMnO_4$.
B,HI: m.p. 121–2°.
B,HNO_3: cryst. M.p. 100–2°. Sol. H_2O, EtOH.
B,$HClO_3$: m.p. 89°.
Borate: m.p. 168° (159–60°).
Picrate: m.p. 146–7°.
B,p-$NH_2 \cdot C_6H_4 \cdot COOH$: cryst. from EtOH. M.p. 104°.

Einhorn, Uhlfelder, *Ann.*, 1909, **371**, 136.
Dow Chemical Co., U.S.P., 1,501,635, (*Chem. Zentr.*, 1925, I, 901).
Hoffmann–La Roche Co., Swiss P., 118,336, (*Chem. Zentr.*, 1927, II, 977).
Jonesco-Matiu, Iliesco, *Chem. Zentr.*, 1936, I, 3339.

Note.—In view of the confusion existing in the literature regarding Ethocaine, Novocaine and Procaine due to differences between the British, German and American systems, all the data regarding the free base and its salts have been collected under the one name.

Nucitol.
See under Inositol.

Nuclidine.
See Quinuclidine.

NW-Acid.
See 1-Naphthol-4-sulphonic Acid.

O

Obtusatic Acid (*Ramalic acid, protocetraric acid*)

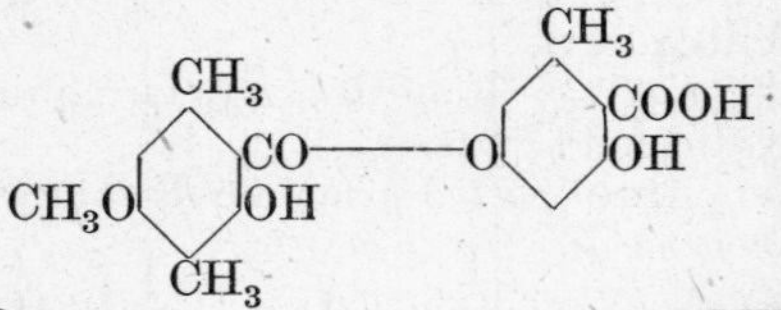

$C_{18}H_{18}O_7$ MW, 346

Occurs in the lichen *Ramalina obtusata*, Arnold. Cryst. from Me_2CO or EtOH. M.p. 203° decomp. Mod. sol. Me_2CO. Spar. sol. Et_2O, $CHCl_3$, C_6H_6. $FeCl_3 \longrightarrow$ red col. with EtOH sol.

Di-Me ether Me ester: $C_{21}H_{24}O_7$. MW, 388. M.p. 126°.

Diacetyl: m.p. 175° decomp. *Me ester*: m.p. 142°.

Asahina, Fuzikawa, *Chem. Abstracts*, 1934, **28**, 2397; *Ber.*, 1932, **65**, 580.
Koller *et al.*, *Monatsh.*, 1932, **61**, 286; 1933, **62**, 241; 1934, **64**, 3.

Ochracin (*Mellein*)

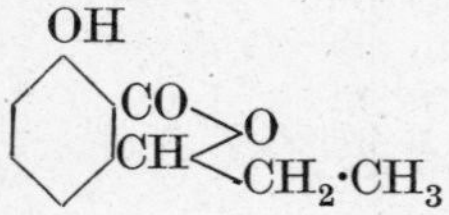

$C_{10}H_{10}O_3$ MW, 178

Fermentation product of the mould *Aspergillus ochraceus*. M.p. 58–58·5°. $FeCl_3 \longrightarrow$ violet col. $[\alpha]_D - 124{\cdot}86°$ ($[\alpha]_D^{12} - 108{\cdot}15°$ in $CHCl_3$).

Acetyl deriv.: m.p. 126–7°.
Benzoyl deriv.: m.p. 101–2°.
Me ether: $C_{11}H_{12}O_3$. MW, 192. M.p. 88–9°.

Yabuta, Sumika, *British Chem. Abstracts*, 1935, **A**, 619.

Ocimene (2 : 6-*Dimethyl*-1 : 5 : 7-*octatriene*)

$CH_2{:}CH{\cdot}C(CH_3){:}CH{\cdot}CH_2{\cdot}CH_2{\cdot}C(CH_3){:}CH_2$

$C_{10}H_{16}$ MW, 136

Occurs in leaves of *Litsea Zeylanica*, C. & T., *Boronia dentigeroides*, Cheel, and *Ocimum basilicum*, L. B.p. 176–8° decomp., 81°/30 mm., 73–4°/21 mm. D_4^{21} 0·799. n_D^{18} 1·4857. Prolonged heating $\longrightarrow$ allo-ocimene (*q.v.*).

Romburg, *Chem. Zentr.*, 1901, I, 1006.
Penfold, *Chem. Abstracts*, 1929, **23**, 3303.
Enklaar, *Rec. trav. chim.*, 1926, **45**, 337.

Octabromoacetylacetone (*Phlorobromin[e], octabromopentandione*-2 : 4)

$CBr_3{\cdot}CO{\cdot}CBr_2{\cdot}CO{\cdot}CBr_3$

$C_5O_2Br_8$ MW, 73[?]

Needles from $CHCl_3$. M.p. 154–5°. Mod. sol Et_2O, $CHCl_3$, C_6H_6, AcOH. Spar. sol. ligroin Insol. H_2O. EtOH $\longrightarrow$ $CBr_3{\cdot}CO{\cdot}CHBr_2$ $NH_3 \longrightarrow CBr_3{\cdot}CO{\cdot}NH_2$.

Benedikt, *Ann.*, 1877, **189**, 165.
Zincke, Kegel, *Ber.*, 1890, **23**, 1717.

Octachloroacetylacetone (*Octachloropentandione*-2 : 4)

$CCl_3{\cdot}CO{\cdot}CCl_2{\cdot}CO{\cdot}CCl_3$

$C_5O_2Cl_8$ MW, 37[?]

Needles or prisms from ligroin. M.p. 42–3° B.p. 165–8°/30–2 mm. Heat with $H_2O \longrightarrow$ $CCl_3{\cdot}COOH + CCl_3{\cdot}CO{\cdot}CHCl_2$.

Zincke, Kegel, *Ber.*, 1890, **23**, 240.

Octachloroanthraquinone

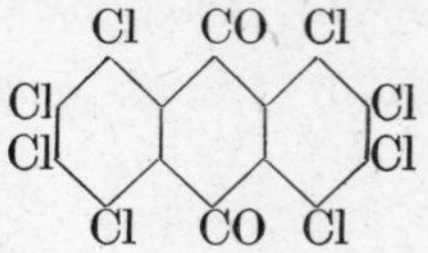

$C_{14}O_2Cl_8$ MW, 48[?]

Yellow needles. Does not melt below 360°.

Eckert, *J. prakt. Chem.*, 1921, **102**, 361.

Octachloronaphthalene

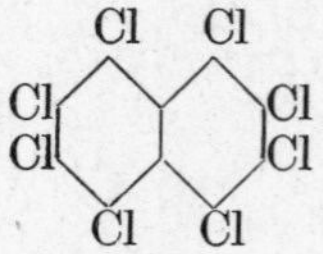

$C_{10}Cl_8$ MW, 40[?]

Cryst. from C_6H_6–CCl_4. M.p. 197·5–198°. B.p. 440–2°/7·4 mm., 258–60°/2·5 mm., 246–50°/0·5 mm.

Schwemberger, Gordon, *Chem. Zentr.*, 1935, II, 514; *Chem. Abstracts*, 1933, **27**, 2439.

Octacosane

$CH_3{\cdot}[CH_2]_{26}{\cdot}CH_3$

$C_{28}H_{58}$ MW, 39[?]

M.p. 64–5° (62°). B.p. 278°/15 mm., 224°/·1 mm. n_D^{65} 1·43539.

Levene, West, Scheer, *J. Biol. Chem.*, 1915, **20**, 521.
Hildebrand, Wachter, *J. Am. Chem. Soc.*, 1929, **51**, 2487.

Octacosane-1 : 28-dicarboxylic Acid

$HOOC·CH_2·[CH_2]_{26}·CH_2·COOH$

$C_{30}H_{58}O_4$ MW, 482

M.p. 108° (123–5°).
Di-Et ester: $C_{34}H_{66}O_4$. MW, 538. M.p. 74°.

Fairweather, *Chem. Abstracts*, 1927, **21**, 3182.
Ruzicka, Brugger, Seidel, Schinz, *Helv. Chim. Acta*, 1928, **11**, 496.

Octacosanic Acid (*Octacosanoic acid, octacosoic acid*)

$CH_3·[CH_2]_{25}·CH_2·COOH$

$C_{28}H_{56}O_2$ MW, 424

M.p. 90·3–90·5° (89°). n_D^{100} 1·4313.
Et ester: $C_{30}H_{60}O_2$. MW, 452. M.p. 64·8–65°.

Bleyberg, Ulrich, *Ber.*, 1931, **64**, 2512.
Holde, Bleyberg, Vohrer, *Chem. Abstracts*, 1931, **25**, 189.

Octacosanol-1.
See Octacosyl Alcohol.

Octacosyl Alcohol (*Octacosanol*)

$CH_3·[CH_2]_{26}·CH_2OH$

$C_{28}H_{58}O$ MW, 426

M.p. 83·2–83·4° (82·9–83·1°).

Bleyberg, Ulrich, *Ber.*, 1931, **64**, 2512.
Pollard, Chibnall, Piper, *Biochem. J.*, 1933, **27**, 1889.

Octacosyl iodide (1-*Iodo*-n-*octacosane*)

$CH_3·[CH_2]_{26}·CH_2I$

$C_{28}H_{57}I$ MW, 520

M.p. 62·8–63·2°.

Bleyberg, Ulrich, *Ber.*, 1931, **64**, 2512.

Octadecane

$CH_3·[CH_2]_{16}·CH_3$

$C_{18}H_{38}$ MW, 254

F.p. 27·5°. (i) Transparent cryst. from Me_2CO. M.p. 27·6°. (ii) Opaque cryst. M.p. 28·02°. B.p. 305–7°, 185–7°/20 mm., 180–3°/15 mm. D_4^{28} 0·7768.

Ueno, *Chem. Abstracts*, 1930, **24**, 4948.
Schrauth, Schenck, Stickdorn, *Ber.*, 1931, **64**, 1317.
Matsui, Arakawa, *Chem. Abstracts*, 1932, **26**, 5264.
Carey, Smith, *J. Chem. Soc.*, 1933, 346.

Octadecane-1 : 18-dicarboxylic Acid

$HOOC·CH_2·[CH_2]_{16}·CH_2·COOH$

$C_{20}H_{38}O_4$ MW, 342

M.p. 124–5° (123°).
Di-Me ester: $C_{22}H_{42}O_4$. MW, 370. M.p. 65·5–66°. B.p. 233–4°/2 mm.
Di-Et ester: $C_{24}H_{46}O_4$. MW, 398. M.p. 54·5–55°. B.p. 230–2°/2 mm.

Chuit, Hausser, *Helv. Chim. Acta*, 1929, **12**, 856.

Octadecanol-1.
See Octadecyl Alcohol.

Octadecanol-3.
See Ethylpentadecylcarbinol.

Octadecanone.
See Ethyl pentadecyl Ketone *and* Methyl hexadecyl Ketone.

Δ⁹-Octadecenyl Alcohol (9-*Octadecenol*-1)

$CH_3·[CH_2]_7·CH{:}CH·[CH_2]_7·CH_2OH$

$C_{18}H_{36}O$ MW, 268

Cis: Oleyl alcohol, oleic alcohol.
Occurs in fish oils. B.p. 205–10°/15 mm. D_4^{20} 0·8489. n_D^{20} 1·4607. Conc. sulphuric acid ⟶ sulphuric esters possessing powerful detergent, wetting, and emulsifying properties.
Acetyl: D_4^{20} 0·8704. n_D^{20} 1·4515.

Reid, Cockerille, Meyer, Cox, Ruhoff, *Organic Syntheses*, 1935, XV, 72.
Noller, Bannerot, *J. Am. Chem. Soc.*, 1934, **56**, 1563.
Hirose, *Chem. Abstracts*, 1930, **24**, 2321.
Toyama, *Chem. Abstracts*, 1924, **18**, 1270.

Trans: elaidyl alcohol, elaidic alcohol.
Constituent of sperm oil. M.p. 36–7° (34°). B.p. 216°/18 mm. D^{40} 0·8388. n_D^{40} 1·4552.
Phenylurethane: m.p. 55°.
β-*Naphthylurethane*: m.p. 71°.

Böeseken, Belinfante, *Rec. trav. chim.*, 1926, **45**, 915.
André, Francois, *Compt. rend.*, 1927, **185**, 279.
Toyama, *Chem. Umschau*, 1924, **31**, 13.

Octadecine-1.
See Hexadecylacetylene.

Octadecyl Alcohol (1-*Hydroxyoctadecane, stearyl alcohol, octadecanol*-1)

$CH_3\cdot[CH_2]_{16}\cdot CH_2OH$

$C_{18}H_{38}O$ MW, 270

Leaflets from EtOH. F.p. 57·95°. M.p. 59·4–59·8°. B.p. 210°/15 mm., 195–205°/0·2 mm. D_4^{59} 0·8124. Conc. $H_2SO_4 \longrightarrow$ sulphuric ester possessing detergent, wetting, and emulsifying properties.

Acetyl: (i) f.p. 30·25. (ii) M.p. 32·85°.
Phenylurethane: needles from EtOH. M.p. 79–80°.
o-*Nitrophenylurethane*: m.p. 70°.
m-*Nitrophenylurethane*: m.p. 77°.
3 : 5-*Dinitrophenylurethane*: m.p. 88°.
Me ether: $C_{19}H_{40}O$. MW, 284. Laminæ from Et_2O–MeOH. M.p. 30–1°.
α-*Glyceryl ether*: *see* Batyl Alcohol.
β-*Glyceryl ether*: $C_{21}H_{44}O_3$. MW, 344. Needles from EtOH. M.p. 62–3°. *Di-phenylurethane*: m.p. 83–4°.

Jantzen, Tiedcke, *J. prakt. Chem.*, 1930, **127**, 277.
Schrauth, Schlenck, Stickdorn, *Ber.*, 1931, **64**, 1318.
Bleyberg, Ulrich, *Ber.*, 1931, **64**, 2510.
Phillips, Mumford, *J. Chem. Soc.*, 1932, 904; 1933, 235.
Tsujimoto, *Chem. Abstracts*, 1921, **15**, 2006.

Octadecylbenzene (1-*Phenyloctadecane*)

$CH_3\cdot[CH_2]_{17}\cdot C_6H_5$

$C_{24}H_{42}$ MW, 330

M.p. 36°. B.p. 249°/15 mm., 147°/0 mm.

Krafft, *Ber.*, 1886, **19**, 2984.

Octadecyl bromide (1-*Bromo-octadecane*)

$CH_3\cdot[CH_2]_{16}\cdot CH_2Br$

$C_{18}H_{37}Br$ MW, 333

Cryst. from EtOH. M.p. 28·5°. Sol. EtOH, AcOEt, pet. ether.

Oskerko, *Chem. Zentr.*, 1914, II, 1264.

Octadecyl chloride (1-*Chloro-octadecane*)

$CH_3\cdot[CH_2]_{16}\cdot CH_2Cl$

$C_{18}H_{37}Cl$ MW, 288·5

B.p. 185–90°/15 mm. D^{20} 0·9041.

Mabery, *Am. Chem. J.*, 1902, **28**, 165.

Δ²-Octadecylenic Acid

$CH_3\cdot[CH_2]_{13}\cdot CH{:}CH\cdot CH_2\cdot COOH$

$C_{18}H_{34}O_2$ MW, 282

Cryst. from AcOH. M.p. 56–7°.
Me ester: $C_{19}H_{36}O_2$. MW, 296. M.p. 36°.

Eckert, Halla, *Monatsh.*, 1913, **34**, 1815.

Δ³-Octadecylenic Acid

$CH_3\cdot[CH_2]_{12}\cdot CH{:}CH\cdot[CH_2]_2\cdot COOH$

$C_{18}H_{34}O_2$ MW, 282

M.p. 52–3°.

See previous reference.

Δ⁵-Octadecylenic Acid.
See Petroselic Acid.

Δ⁹-Octadecylenic Acid.
See Elaidic Acid *and* Oleic Acid.

Δ¹⁰-Octadecylenic Acid

$CH_3\cdot[CH_2]_5\cdot CH{:}CH\cdot[CH_2]_9\cdot COOH$

$C_{18}H_{34}O_2$ MW, 282

F.p. 6–8°.

Fokin, *Chem. Abstracts*, 1912, **6**, 2409.

Δ¹¹-Octadecylenic Acid

$CH_3\cdot[CH_2]_4\cdot CH{:}CH\cdot[CH_2]_{10}\cdot COOH$

$C_{18}H_{34}O_2$ MW, 282

F.p. 36–8°. M.p. 34–6°.

See previous reference.

Octadecylic Acid.
See Stearic Acid.

Octadecyl iodide (1-*Iodo-octadecane*)

$CH_3\cdot[CH_2]_{16}\cdot CH_2I$

$C_{18}H_{37}I$ MW, 380

M.p. 34·5–35° (32·94°). B.p. 160–70°/0·5 mm. Spar. sol. EtOH.

Jantzen, Tiedcke, *J. prakt. Chem.*, 1930, **127**, 277.
Bleyberg, Ulrich, *Ber.*, 1931, **64**, 2510.
Carey, Smith, *J. Chem. Soc.*, 1933, 346.

Octadecylmalonic Acid (*Nonadecane*-1 : 1-*dicarboxylic acid*)

$CH_3\cdot[CH_2]_{17}\cdot CH{<}^{COOH}_{COOH}$

$C_{21}H_{40}O_4$ MW, 356

Cryst. from AcOH. M.p. 109–10°. Sol. Et_2O. Insol. pet. ether.

Amide: $C_{21}H_{41}O_3N$. MW, 355. Cryst. from AcOH. M.p. 126° with loss of CO_2. Insol. Et_2O.
Mononitrile: 1-cyano-*n*-eicosanic acid.

$_1H_{39}O_2N$. MW, 337. Cryst. powder from tOH. M.p. 88°.

Baczewski, *Monatsh.*, 1896, **17**, 544.
Meyer, Brod, Soyka, *Monatsh.*, 1913, **34**, 1132.

Octadeuteronaphthalene

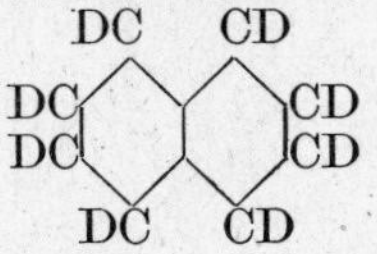

$_{10}D_8$ MW, 136

Cryst. from MeOH.Aq. M.p. 77·5°.

Clemo, McQuillen, *J. Chem. Soc.*, 1935, 1325.

2 : 4-Octadiene (*Propylpropenylethylene, ethylpropylbutadiene*)

$CH_3·CH_2·CH_2·CH:CH·CH:CH·CH_3$

$_8H_{14}$ MW, 110

B.p. 133·5–134°. D_4^{25} 0·7427. n_D^{25} 1·4542.

Mulliken, Wakeman, Gerry, *J. Am. Chem. Soc.*, 1935, **57**, 1607.

2 : 6-Octadiene (*Dicrotyl, propenylethylidene-opane*)

$CH_3·CH:CH·CH_2·CH_2·CH:CH·CH_3$

$_8H_{14}$ MW, 110

B.p. 117–19°.

Charon, *Ann. chim.*, 1899, **17**, 265.

3 : 5-Octadiene (1 : 4-*Diethylbutadiene, propenylethane*)

$CH_3·CH_2·CH:CH·CH:CH·CH_2·CH_3$

$_8H_{14}$ MW, 110

B.p. 138–40°.

Kaufmann, Schweitzer, *Ber.*, 1922, **55**, 262.

***sym.*-Octahydroacridine**

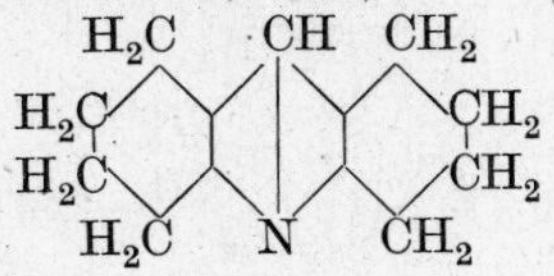

$_{13}H_{17}N$ MW, 187

Cryst. from ligroin. M.p. 69°. B.p. 175°/7 mm.

B_2,H_2PtCl_6 : m.p. 199–200°.
Picrate : m.p. 195°.
Methiodide : m.p. 159°.

Braun, Petzold, Schultheiss, *Ber.*, 1923, **56**, 1349.

***unsym.*-Octahydroacridine**

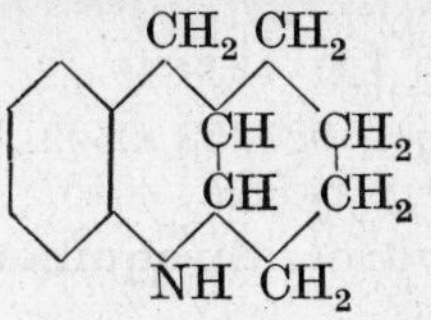

$C_{13}H_{17}N$ MW, 187

d-.

(*a*) M.p. 84·5°. $[\alpha]_D$ + 34°. (*b*) M.p. 72°. $[\alpha]_D$ + 22°.

l-.

(*a*) M.p. 85°. $[\alpha]_D$ — 32°. (*b*) M.p. 72°. $[\alpha]_D$ — 24°.

Camphorsulphonate : (*a*) M.p. 183°. (*b*) M.p. 172°.

dl-.

(*a*) M.p. 84°. B.p. 183°/12 mm. N-*Benzoyl* : m.p. 104°. (*b*) Plates from pet. ether. M.p. 72°. N-*Acetyl* : m.p. 136°. *Picrate* : m.p. 175°. *Methiodide* : m.p. 217°.

Braun, Heymons, Manz, *Ber.*, 1931, **64**, 233.
Perkin, Sedgwick, *J. Chem. Soc.*, 1924, **125**, 2448.

***sym.*-Octahydroanthracene**

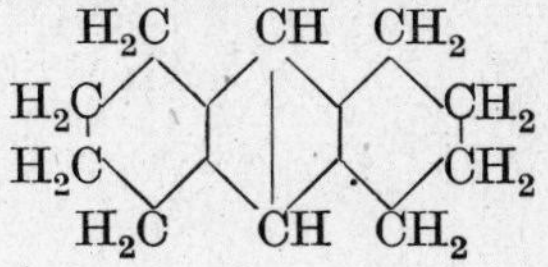

$C_{14}H_{18}$ MW, 186

Leaflets from EtOH. M.p. 39°.

Braun, Bayer, *Ber.*, 1925, **58**, 2679.

***sym.*-Octahydroanthrahydroquinone**

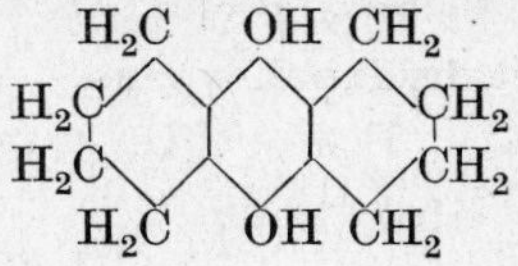

$C_{14}H_{18}O_2$ MW, 218

Cryst. from EtOH. M.p. 242° (234–6°).
Diacetyl : m.p. 224°.

Braun, Bayer, *Ber.*, 1925, **58**, 2680.
Skita, *ibid.*, 2692.

***sym.*-Octahydroanthranol**

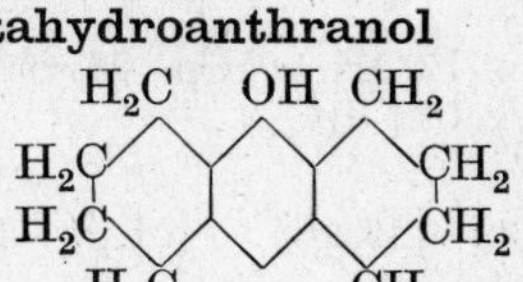

$C_{14}H_{18}O$ MW, 202

Needles from EtOH. M.p. 125°.
Acetyl : m.p. 52°.
Benzoyl : m.p. 129° (128°).

Skita, *Ber.*, 1925, **58**, 2693.
Braun, Bayer, *ibid.*, 2678.

sym.-Octahydroanthraquinone

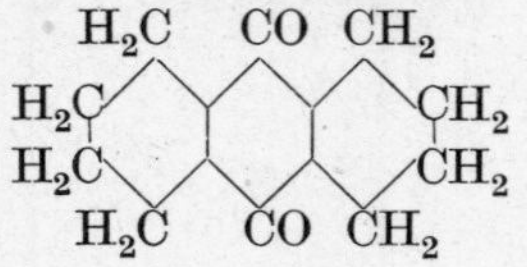

$C_{14}H_{16}O_2$ MW, 216

Cis–cis :
Leaflets from MeOH. M.p. 154–5°.
Cis–trans :
Needles from EtOH. M.p. 186°.
Trans–trans :
Leaflets from AcOEt. M.p. 245°.

Alder, Stein, *Ann.*, 1933, **501**, 283.
Skita, *Ber.*, 1925, **58**, 2692.
Braun, Bayer, *ibid.*, 2678.

sym.-Octahydrochrysene

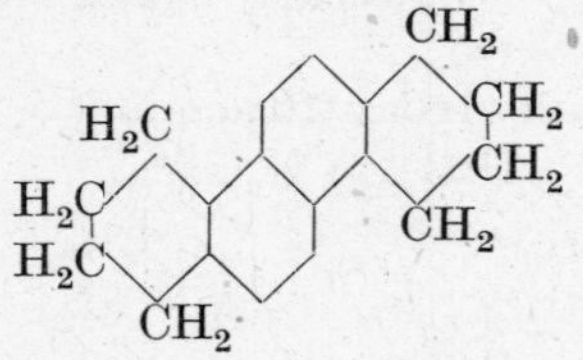

$C_{18}H_{20}$ MW, 236

M.p. 136–8° (138–40°). B.p. 180–1°/0·2 mm.
Picrate : m.p. 139–40°.

Braun, Irmisch, *Ber.*, 1932, **65**, 885.
Cohen, Cook, Hewett, *J. Chem. Soc.*, 1935, 1636.

unsym.-Octahydrochrysene

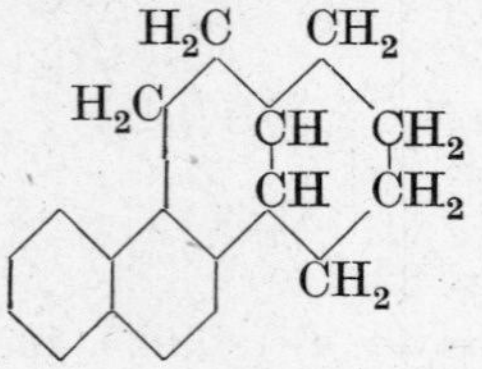

$C_{18}H_{20}$ MW, 236

Cis (?) :
Needles from EtOH. M.p. 78–9°.
Picrate : m.p. 106–106·5°.
Trans (?) :
Needles from MeOH. M.p. 114–114·5°. Forms no picrate.

Cook, Hewett, *J. Chem. Soc.*, 1934, 372.

Octahydro-1 : 2 : 3 : 4-dibenzanthraquinone

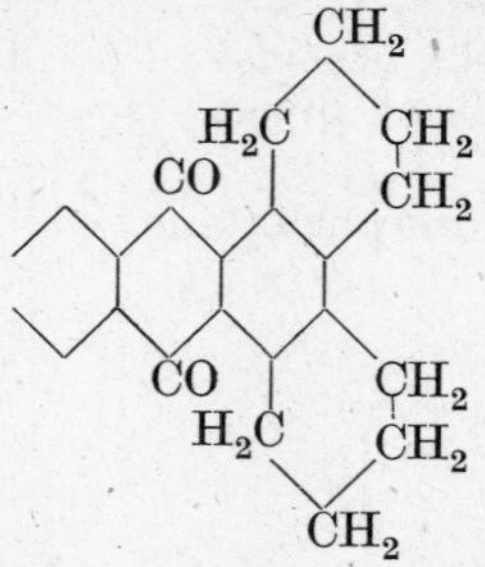

$C_{22}H_{20}O_2$ MW, 31

Yellow cryst. from xylene. M.p. 234°.

See previous reference and also
Barnett, Goodway, Lawrence, *J. Chem. Soc.*, 1935, 1684.

Octahydroindole (*Perhydroindole*)

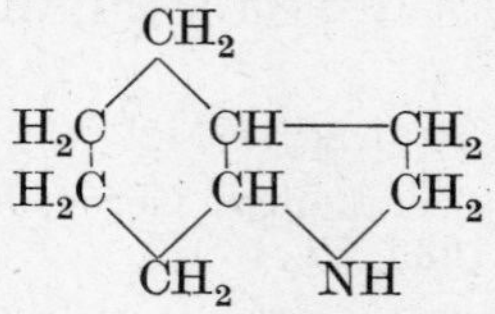

$C_8H_{15}N$ MW, 12

Oil with onion-like odour. B.p. 185·5°/76 mm., 182–3°/720 mm., 64–5°/12 mm. Sol usual org. solvents. Insol. H_2O. React alkaline. D_4^{20} 0·9472. n_D^{20} 1·4892.
B_2,H_2PtCl_6 : reddish-yellow leaflets from EtOH. M.p. about 172–3°. Very sol. warm EtOH. Insol. cold H_2O.
Benzenesulphonyl : cryst. M.p. 70–1°.
Picrate : needles from EtOH. M.p. 137–8° Very sol. hot EtOH, $CHCl_3$. Spar. sol. C_6H_6.

Willstätter, Jaquet, *Ber.*, 1918, **51**, 778.
Willstätter, Seitz, Braun, *Ber.*, 1925, **58**, 385.

1 : 2 : 3 : 4 : 5 : 6 : 7 : 8-Octahydronaphthalene (Δ^9-*Octalin*)

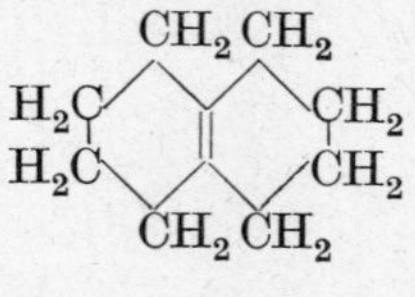

$C_{10}H_{16}$ MW, 136

B.p. 196·5–198·8°/759 mm. D_4^{20} 0·9145. n_D^{20} 1·4978.
Nitrosochloride : m.p. 89–90°.

Hückel, Naab, *Ann.*, 1933, **502**, 144.
Schuikin, *Chem. Zentr.*, 1935, II, 3650.
Cf. Nametkin, Madaeff-Ssitscheff, *Ber.*, 1926, **59**, 373.

1 : 2 : 3 : 4 : 5 : 6 : 7 : 10-Octahydro-naphthalene ($\Delta^{1,9}$-*Octalin*)

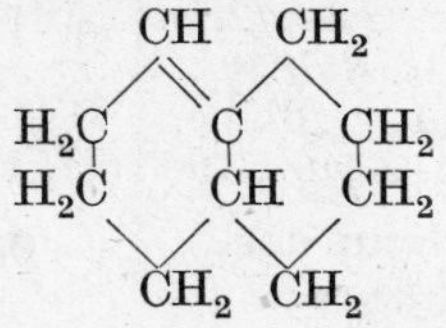

$C_{10}H_{16}$ MW, 136

B.p. 189·5–193·5°/759 mm. $D_4^{20.8}$ 0·9027.
Nitropiperidide : m.p. 179° decomp.
Nitrosochloride : m.p. 127°.

See previous references.

1 : 2 : 3 : 4 : 5 : 6 : 9 : 10-Octahydro-naphthalene (Δ^1-*Octalin*)

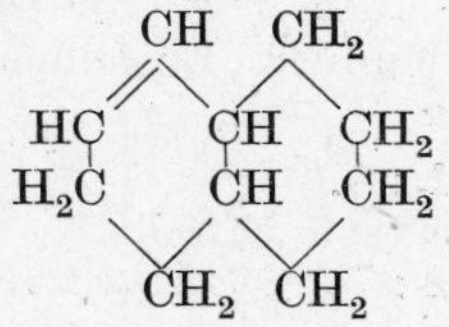

$C_{10}H_{16}$ MW, 136

B.p. 185°. $D_4^{15.6}$ 0·8970.

Hückel, Naub, *Ann.*, 1933, **502**, 150.
Cf. Borsche, Lange, *Ann.*, 1923, **434**, 225.

1 : 2 : 3 : 4 : 5 : 8 : 9 : 10-Octahydro-naphthalene (Δ^2-*Octalin*, β-*naphthanene*)

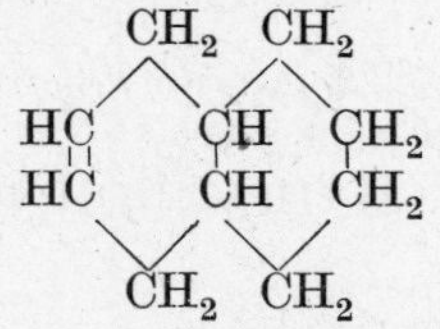

$C_{10}H_{16}$ MW, 136

B.p. 197–9°. D^{20} 0·9103. n_D^{20} 1·4941.
Trans :
M.p. — 24°. D_4^{20} 0·8936. n_D^{20} 1·4841.

Hückel, *Ber.*, 1925, **58**, 1451.
Cf. Borsche, Lange, *Ann.*, 1923, **434**, 225.

***sym*.-Octahydrophenanthraquinone** (*Octanthrone*)

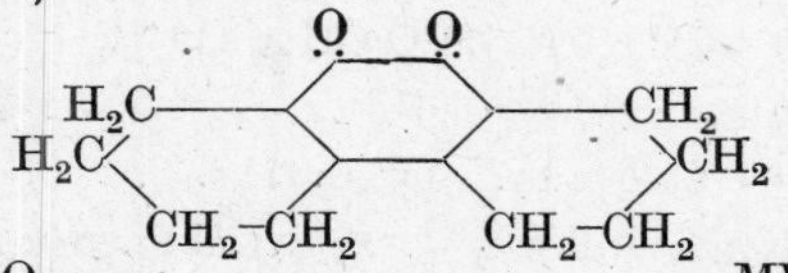

$C_{14}H_{16}O_2$ MW, 216

Red needles from MeOH. M.p. 142°.

Skita, Warnat, *Ber.*, 1925, **58**, 2691.

1 : 2 : 3 : 4 : 5 : 6 : 7 : 8-Octahydrophenanthrene (*Octanthrene*)

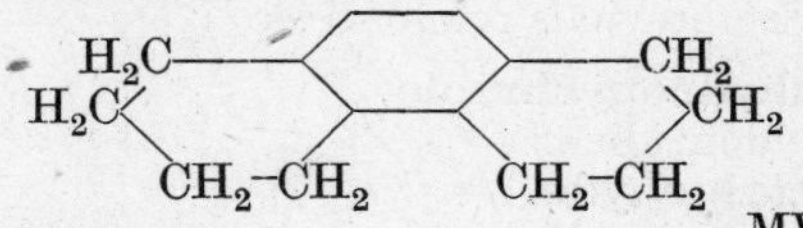

$C_{14}H_{18}$ MW, 186

M.p. 16·7°. B.p. 295°, 167·5°/13 mm. D^{20} 1·026. n_D^{17} 1·5669.

Schroeter, Müller, Huang, *Ber.*, 1929, **62**, 650.
Schroeter, D.R.P., 352,719, (*Chem. Abstracts*, 1923, **17**, 1246).
Kamp, Mosettig, *J. Am. Chem. Soc.*, 1935, **57**, 1107.

1 : 2 : 3 : 4 : 9 : 10 : 11 : 12-Octahydrophenanthrene

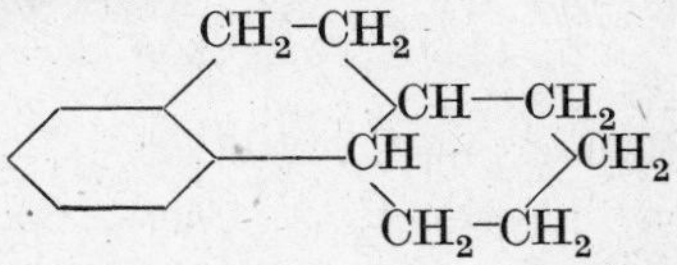

$C_{14}H_{18}$ MW, 186

B.p. 159°/15 mm., 135°/9 mm. (135–7°/6·5 mm.). D_4^{32} 0·997325. $n_D^{19.2}$ 1·5527.

Fulton, Robinson, *J. Chem. Soc.*, 1933, 1465.
Bergs, *Ber.*, 1934, **67**, 243.
Kagehira, *Chem. Abstracts*, 1932, **26**, 443.

1 : 2 : 3 : 4 : 5 : 6 : 7 : 8-Octahydrophenazine

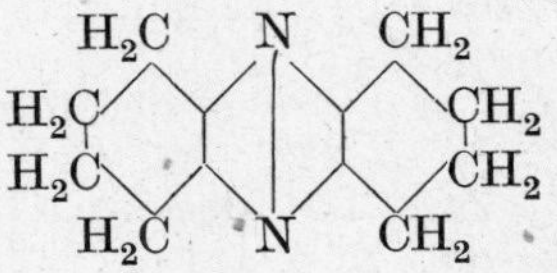

$C_{12}H_{16}N_2$ MW, 188

Cryst. from EtOH.Aq. M.p. 109°.

Clemo, McIlwain, *J. Chem. Soc.*, 1936, 258.

1 : 2 : 3 : 4 : 9 : 10 : 11 : 12-Octahydrophenazine

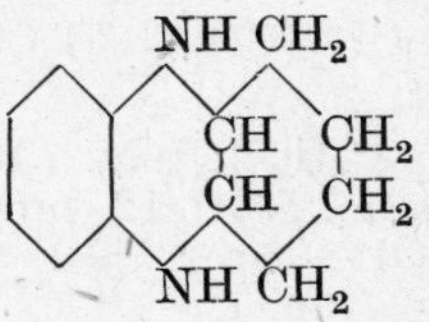

$C_{12}H_{16}N_2$ MW, 188

(i) Needles from EtOH. M.p. 156°.
N : N'*Di-nitroso* : m.p. 126°.

(ii) Plates from EtOH. M.p. 147°.
N : N′-*Dinitroso* : m.p. 109°.

See previous reference.

Octahydropyrindole.
See Indolizidine.

***n*-Octaldehyde.**
See Caprylic Aldehyde.

Octalin.
See Octahydronaphthalene.

$\Delta^{9,10}$-Octalone (1-*Keto-octahydronaphthalene*)

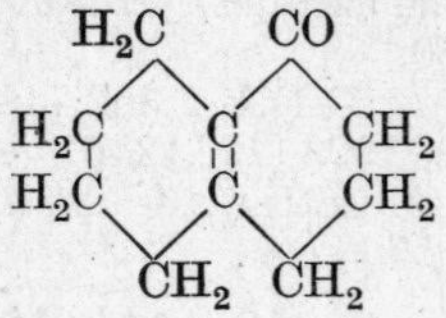

$C_{10}H_{14}O$ MW, 150

B.p. about 140°/9 mm. D_4^{14} 1·000. n_D^{14} 1·4996.
Oxime : m.p. 144–5°. *Benzoyl deriv.* : m.p. 130·5–131·5°.
Semicarbazone : m.p. 242–3°.

Cook, Lawrence, *J. Chem. Soc.*, 1935, 1638.

Octamethylene.
See Cyclo-octane.

Octamethylenediamine (1 : 8-*Diamino*-n-*octane*)

$H_2N{\cdot}CH_2{\cdot}[CH_2]_6{\cdot}CH_2NH_2$

$C_8H_{20}N_2$ MW, 144

Plates. M.p. 52°. B.p. 240–1° (236–40°, 225–6°), 130–40°/20 mm. Sol. H_2O, EtOH, Et_2O. Spar. sol. C_6H_6, ligroin.
B,2HCl : m.p. 274°.
B,2HAuCl₄ : m.p. 188–9° decomp.
B,(COOH)₂ : m.p. 223°.
Di-picrate : m.p. 180° decomp. (182–3°).
N : N′-*Diacetyl* : m.p. 121–2°.

Naegeli, Lendorff, *Helv. Chim. Acta*, 1932, **15**, 53.
Neuberg, Neimann, *Z. physiol. Chem.*, 1905, **45**, 117.

Octamethylene Glycol (1 : 8-*Dihydroxy*-n-*octane, octandiol*-1 : 8)

$HO{\cdot}CH_2{\cdot}[CH_2]_6{\cdot}CH_2OH$

$C_8H_{18}O_2$ MW, 146

Needles from C_6H_6–ligroin. M.p. 63° (60°). B.p. 172°/20 mm., 164°/12 mm., 160–2°/9·5 mm. Sol. EtOH. Spar. sol. H_2O, Et_2O, ligroin.
Diphenylurethane : m.p. 172–172·5°.
Di-Me ether : $C_{10}H_{22}O_2$. MW, 174. B.p. 221°. D^{15} 0·8613. n_D^{15} 1·4257.
Di-n-*amyl ether* : $C_{18}H_{38}O_2$. MW, 286. B.p. 212°/35 mm.

Lespieau, *Compt. rend.*, 1914, **158**, 1188.
Dionneau, *Bull. soc. chim.*, 1910, **7**, 328.
Bouveault, Blanc, D.R.P., 164,294, (*Chem. Zentr.*, 1905, II, 1701).

Octamethylsucrose.
See under Sucrose.

Octanal.
See Caprylic Aldehyde.

Octandiol-1 : 2 (1 : 2-*Dihydroxy*-n-*octane*, n-*hexylethylene glycol*)

$CH_3{\cdot}[CH_2]_5{\cdot}CH(OH){\cdot}CH_2OH$

$C_8H_{18}O_2$ MW, 146

Cryst. from pet. ether. M.p. 35–7°. B.p. 135–6°/20 mm. $[\alpha]_D^{17}$ — 4·7° in EtOH.

Späth, Kuffner, Ensfellner, *Ber.*, 1933, **66**, 598.

Octandiol-1 : 8.
See Octamethylene Glycol.

Octandiol-2 : 7 (2 : 7-*Dihydroxy*-n-*octane*)

$CH_3{\cdot}CH(OH){\cdot}[CH_2]_4{\cdot}CH(OH){\cdot}CH_3$

$C_8H_{18}O_2$ MW, 146

Oil. B.p. 138–9°/15 mm. Sol. ord. org. solvents.
Di-phenylurethane : m.p. 126°.

Blaise, Koehler, *Bull. soc. chim.*, 1910, **7**, 417.

Octandiol-4 : 5 (4 : 5-*Dihydroxy*-n-*octane*, sym.-*dipropylethylene glycol*)

$CH_3{\cdot}[CH_2]_2{\cdot}CH(OH){\cdot}CH(OH){\cdot}[CH_2]_2{\cdot}CH_3$

$C_8H_{18}O_2$ MW, 146

Meso-.
M.p. 123–4°. B.p. 115–18°/10 mm.

Bouveault, Locquin, *Bull. soc. chim.*, 1906, **35**, 644.
Veibel, *Biochem. Z.*, 1931, **239**, 456.

Octandione-2 : 3.
See Acetylcaproyl.

Octandione-2 : 4 (*Acetylvalerylmethane*, 2 : 4-*diketo-octane*)

$CH_3{\cdot}[CH_2]_3{\cdot}CO{\cdot}CH_2{\cdot}CO{\cdot}CH_3$

$C_8H_{14}O_2$ MW, 142

B.p. 64–6°/5 mm. D_{25}^{25} 0·9218.

Kutz, Adkins, *J. Am. Chem. Soc.*, 1930, **52**, 4042.

Octandione-2 : 7.
See 1 : 4-Diacetobutane.

Octandione-3 : 4 (*Propionylvaleryl*, 3 : 4-*di-eto-octane*)

$CH_3{\cdot}[CH_2]_3{\cdot}CO{\cdot}CO{\cdot}CH_2{\cdot}CH_3$

$_8H_{14}O_2$ MW, 142

Dioxime : m.p. about 139–41°.

Fileti, Ponzio, *Gazz. chim. ital.*, 1898, **28**, ii, 264.

Octandione-3 : 5 (*Propionylbutyrylmethane*, : 5-*diketo-octane*)

$CH_3{\cdot}[CH_2]_2{\cdot}CO{\cdot}CH_2{\cdot}CO{\cdot}CH_2{\cdot}CH_3$

$_8H_{14}O_2$ MW, 142

B.p. 189–90°, 75°/20 mm.
Cu deriv. : blue cryst. from EtOH. M.p. 58·5° (157°).

Powell, Seymour, *J. Am. Chem. Soc.*, 1931, **53**, 1050.

Octandione-3 : 6 (sym.-*Dipropionylethane*, : 6-*diketo-octane*)

$CH_3{\cdot}CH_2{\cdot}CO{\cdot}CH_2{\cdot}CH_2{\cdot}CO{\cdot}CH_2{\cdot}CH_3$

$_8H_{14}O_2$ MW, 142

Plates. M.p. 34–5°. B.p. 98°/14 mm.
Dioxime : m.p. 169°.

Blaise, *Compt. rend.*, 1914, **158**, 506.

Octandione-4 : 5.
See Dibutyryl.

***n*-Octane** (1-*Ethylhexane*)

$CH_3{\cdot}[CH_2]_6{\cdot}CH_3$

$_8H_{18}$ MW, 114

F.p. — 56·82°. M.p. — 56·90°. B.p. 25·59°. (125·3–125·6°). D_4^{20} 0·7024 (0·70279). n_D^{20} 1·39750 (1·39760).

Gardiner, Borgstrom, *J. Am. Chem. Soc.*, 1929, **51**, 3375.
Fischer, Klemm, *Z. physik. Chem.*, 1930, **A**, **147**, 275.
Shepard, Henne, Midgley, *J. Am. Chem. Soc.*, 1931, **53**, 1949.
Moldawski, Liwschitz, *Chem. Zentr.*, 1936, I, 758.
Waterman, Kok, *Rec. trav. chim.*, 1934, **53**, 725.
Mair, *Bureau of Standards Journal of Research*, 1932, **9**, 463.
Whitmore, Laughlin, *J. Am. Chem. Soc.*, 1933, **55**, 5056 (*Bibl.*).
Maman, *Chem. Zentr.*, 1936, I, 2332.

Octane-1 : 8-dicarboxylic Acid.
See Sebacic Acid.

Octanol.
See *n*-Octyl Alcohol, *sec.-n*-Octyl Alcohol, Ethyl-*n*-amylcarbinol, *and* Propylbutylcarbinol.

Octanone.
See Ethyl *n*-amyl Ketone, Methyl *n*-hexyl Ketone, *and* Propyl butyl Ketone.

Octanthrene.
See 1 : 2 : 3 : 4 : 5 : 6 : 7 : 8-Octahydrophenanthrene.

Octanthrone.
See Octahydrophenanthraquinone.

Octaverine (1-[3 : 4 : 5-*Triethoxyphenyl*]-6 : 7-*dimethoxyisoquinoline*)

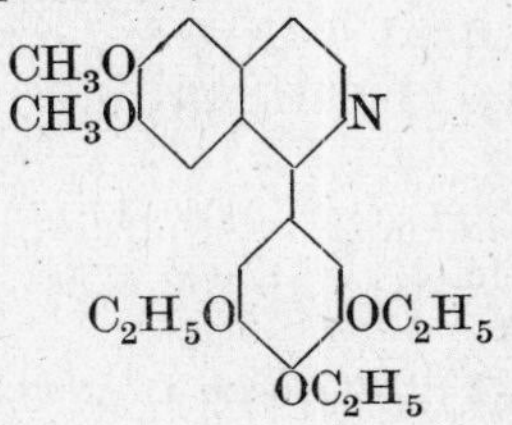

$C_{21}H_{23}O_3N$ MW, 337

B,HCl : m.p. 199–200°.

Ellinger, Koschara, Seegar, *Chem. Abstracts*, 1934, **28**, 4476.
Asta A.G., F.P., 760,825, (*Chem. Abstracts*, 1934, **28**, 4178).

1-Octene (1-*Octylene*)

$CH_3{\cdot}[CH_2]_5{\cdot}CH{:}CH_2$

C_8H_{16} MW, 112

F.p. — 104° C. B.p. 121·85–122·15° (119–119·5°). D_4^{20} 0·7155 (0·715). n_D^{20} 1·40880 (1·4087).

Waterman, Kok, *Rec. trav. chim.*, 1934, **53**, 725 (*Bibl.*).
Whitmore, Herndon, *J. Am. Chem. Soc.*, 1933, **55**, 3429.
Bourguel, *Bull. soc. chim.*, 1927, **41**, 1476.

2-Octene (2-*Octylene*)

$CH_3{\cdot}[CH_2]_4{\cdot}CH{:}CH{\cdot}CH_3$

C_8H_{16} MW, 112

B.p. 124·1–124·7°/745 mm. (123–123·5°). D_4^{20} 0·7248. n_D^{20} 1·4149.

Whitmore, Herndon, *J. Am. Chem. Soc.*, 1933, **55**, 3430.
Klepper, *Chimie et Industrie*, 1929, Special No., 261.
Maman, *Chem. Zentr.*, 1936, I, 2332.
See also last reference above.

1-Octene-1-carboxylic Acid.
See 1-Nonenic Acid.

1-Octenic Acid (2-n-*Amylacrylic acid*, 1-*heptene*-1-*carboxylic acid*)

$CH_3\cdot[CH_2]_4\cdot CH\colon CH\cdot COOH$

$C_8H_{14}O_2$ MW, 142

Nitrile: $C_8H_{13}N$. MW, 123. (*a*) *Cis*: b.p. 74–5°/11 mm. D_4^{20} 0·82854. n_D^{20} 1·44032. (*b*) *Trans*: m.p. 57·6–58°. B.p. 84°/11 mm. D_4^{20} 0·82815. n_D^{20} 1·44344.

Amide: $C_8H_{15}ON$. MW, 141. (*a*) *Cis*: m.p. 66·0–66·4°. (*b*) *Trans*: m.p. 134·7–135·1°.

Bruylants, Fonteyn, *Chem. Abstracts*, 1933, **27**, 5717.

6-Octenic Acid (1-*Heptene*-7-*carboxylic acid*)

$CH_2\colon CH\cdot[CH_2]_4\cdot CH_2\cdot COOH$

$C_8H_{14}O_2$ MW, 142

Et ester: $C_{10}H_{18}O_2$. MW, 170. B.p. 210°.

Carmichael, *J. Chem. Soc.*, 1922, **121**, 2549.

1-Octenol-2 (2-*Hydroxy*-1-*octene*)

$CH_3\cdot[CH_2]_5\cdot C(OH)\colon CH_2$

$C_8H_{16}O$ MW, 128

Me ether: $C_9H_{18}O$. MW, 142. B.p. 166–8°. D_4^{16} 0·8170. n_D^{16} 1·4309.

Moureu, *Compt. rend.*, 1904, **138**, 287.

2-Octenol-4 (4-*Hydroxy*-2-*octene*, *butylpropenylcarbinol*)

$CH_3\cdot[CH_2]_3\cdot CH(OH)\cdot CH\colon CH\cdot CH_3$

$C_8H_{16}O$ MW, 128

B.p. 93·9–95·9°/40 mm.

Mulliken, Wakeman, Gerry, *J. Am. Chem. Soc.*, 1935, **57**, 1606.

2-Octenol-8 (8-*Hydroxy*-2-*octene*)

$HO\cdot CH_2\cdot[CH_2]_4\cdot CH\colon CH\cdot CH_3$

$C_8H_{16}O$ MW, 128

B.p. 187–93°. Sol. EtOH, Et_2O. Spar. sol. H_2O.

Löbl, *Monatsh.*, 1903, **24**, 398.

3-Octenone-5 (*Propylidenemethyl* n-*propyl ketone*, 5-*keto*-3-*octene*)

$CH_3\cdot[CH_2]_2\cdot CO\cdot CH\colon CH\cdot CH_2\cdot CH_3$

$C_8H_{14}O$ MW, 126

B.p. 68–72°/25 mm.

Benary, *Ber.*, 1931, **64**, 2544.

1-Octine (n-*Hexylacetylene*)

$CH_3\cdot[CH_2]_5\cdot C\colon CH$

C_8H_{14} MW, 110

B.p. 127·6–128°.

Mulliken, Wakeman, Gerry, *J. Am. Chem. Soc.*, 1935, **57**, 1607.

2-Octine (*Methyl*-n-*amylacetylene*)

$CH_3\cdot[CH_2]_4\cdot C\colon C\cdot CH_3$

C_8H_{14} MW, 11

B.p. 138–138·4°.

See previous reference.

Octinum (*Octin*, 6-*methylamino*-2-*methyl heptene*-2)

$(CH_3)_2C\colon CH\cdot[CH_2]_2\cdot CH(CH_3)\cdot NH\cdot CH_3$

$C_9H_{19}N$ MW, 14

B.p. 176–8°. Soporific.

Picrate: m.p. 70°.

Knoll, Danish P., 48,717, (*Chem. Zentr.* 1934, II, 1493).

***n*-Octoic Acid.**

See n-Caprylic Acid.

***n*-Octyl Alcohol** (1-*Octanol*, 1-*hydroxy* n-*octane*)

$CH_3\cdot[CH_2]_6\cdot CH_2OH$

$C_8H_{18}O$ MW, 13

M.p. — 16·7°. B.p. 194·45° (195–8°, 195–7°), 98°/19 mm., 90·2°/11·8 mm., 82·8°/7·5 mm. D_4^{20} 0·8270. $n_D^{20\cdot5}$ 1·43035. Heat of comb. C_p 1265·0 Cal., C_v 1262·7 Cal.

3 : 5-*Dinitrobenzoyl*: m.p. 61–2°.

Me ether: *see* Methyl octyl Ether.

Et ether: $C_{10}H_{22}O$. MW, 158. B.p. 189·2° 72–3°/8 mm.

n-*Propyl ether*: $C_{11}H_{24}O$. MW, 172. B.p. 207°.

n-*Butyl ether*: $C_{12}H_{26}O$. MW, 186. B.p. 225–7°.

n-*Heptyl ether*: $C_{15}H_{32}O$. MW, 228. B.p. 278·8°.

Phenylurethane: m.p. 74–74·5° (72°).

o-*Nitrophenylurethane*: m.p. 44°.

m-*Nitrophenylurethane*: m.p. 63°.

3 : 5-*Dinitrophenylurethane*: m.p. 69°.

Blaise, Picard, *Compt. rend.*, 1911, **152**, 269.

Reichstein, Ammann, Trivelli, *Helv. Chim. Acta*, 1932, **15**, 267.

Schrauth, Schenck, Stickdorn, *Ber.*, 1931, **64**, 1318.

Goebel, Marvel, *J. Am. Chem. Soc.*, 1933, **55**, 1696.

Vaughn, Spahr, Nieuwland, *J. Am. Chem. Soc.*, 1933, **55**, 4207.

Deutsche Gold- u. Silber-Scheideanstalt, E.P., 381,185, (*Chem. Abstracts*, 1933, **27**, 3943).

Ruhoff, Reid, *J. Am. Chem. Soc.*, 1933, **55**, 3825.

Deffert, *Bull. soc. chim. Belg.*, 1931, **40**, 385.

sec.-n-Octyl Alcohol (*Methyl*-n-*hexylcarbinol*, *2-hydroxy*-n-*octane*, *octanol-2*, *capryl alcohol*)

$CH_3\cdot[CH_2]_5\cdot CH(OH)\cdot CH_3$

$C_8H_{18}O$ MW, 130

d-.

B.p. 86°/20 mm. $[\alpha]_D^{17} + 9\cdot9°$. D_4^{20} 0·8216.

l-.

B.p. 86°/20 mm. $[\alpha]_D^{17} - 9\cdot9°$.

dl-.

B.p. 179·5°, 110°/120 mm. $D_4^{25\cdot2}$ 0·8188. n_D^{20} 1·42025.

Formyl: $C_9H_{18}O_2$. MW, 158. B.p. 184°/744 mm. D_4^{14} 0·8642.

Acetyl: $C_{10}H_{20}O_2$. MW, 172. B.p. 194·5°/744 mm., 84°/15 mm. D_4^{19} 0·8606. n_D^{20} 1·4141.

Bromoacetyl: $C_{10}H_{19}O_2Br$. MW, 251. B.p. 137°/18 mm.

Propionyl: $C_{11}H_{22}O_2$. MW, 186. B.p. 211°/744 mm., 96°/15 mm. $D_{44}^{20\cdot5}$ 0·8650. n_D^{20} 1·4168.

Butyryl: $C_{12}H_{24}O_2$. MW, 200. B.p. 220°/744 mm., 115°/18 mm. D_4^{17} 0·8587. n_D^{20} 1·4202.

Isobutyryl: b.p. 220°/744 mm. D_4^{14} 0·8554.

Valeryl: $C_{13}H_{26}O_2$. MW, 214. B.p. 127°/17 mm. $D_4^{16\cdot5}$ 0·8560. n_D^{20} 1·4225.

Isovaleryl: b.p. 236·5°/744 mm. D_4^{14} 0·8540.

d-*Caproyl*: $C_{14}H_{28}O_2$. MW, 228. B.p. 141°/17 mm. D_4^{12} 0·8598. n_D^{20} 1·4264.

d-*Heptylyl*: $C_{15}H_{30}O_2$. MW, 242. B.p. 151°/15 mm. D_4^{13} 0·8593. n_D^{20} 1·4290.

d-*Caprylyl*: $C_{16}H_{32}O_2$. MW, 256. B.p. 165°/18 mm. D_4^{12} 0·8557. n_D^{20} 1·4308.

d-*Nonoyl*: $C_{17}H_{34}O_2$. MW, 270. B.p. 174°/17 mm. D_4^{22} 0·8542. n_D^{20} 1·4342.

d-*Undecylyl*: $C_{19}H_{38}O_2$. MW, 298. B.p. 167°/3 mm. D_4^{19} 0·8538. n_D^{20} 1·4373.

d-*Lauryl*: $C_{20}H_{40}O_2$. MW, 312. B.p. 183°/7 mm. $D_4^{16\cdot5}$ 0·8585. n_D^{20} 1·4393.

d-*Myristyl*: $C_{22}H_{44}O_2$. MW, 340. B.p. 197°/4 mm. D_4^{17} 0·8562. n_D^{20} 1·4416.

d-*Palmityl*: $C_{24}H_{48}O_2$. MW, 368. M.p. 32°. B.p. 216°/18 mm. D_4^{45} 0·8372. n_D^{20} 1·4438.

d-*Stearyl*: $C_{26}H_{52}O_2$. MW, 396. M.p. 34°. B.p. 235°/6 mm. D_4^{38} 0·8410.

Phenylacetyl: $C_{16}H_{24}O_2$. MW, 248. B.p. 195°/35 mm., 174°/12 mm. D_4^{20} 0·9578.

Benzoyl: $C_{15}H_{22}O_2$. MW, 234. B.p. 175°/2–5 mm. D_4^{20} 1·0185. n_D^{20} 1·5476.

l-o-*Aminobenzoyl*: $C_{15}H_{23}O_2N$. MW, 249. B.p. 183°/10 mm.

l-m-*Aminobenzoyl*: b.p. 195–9°/18 mm.

l-p-*Aminobenzoyl*: m.p. 69–70°. B.p. 200°/10 mm. *B,HCl*: m.p. 131–3°.

Salicyloyl: $C_{15}H_{22}O_3$. MW, 250. B.p. 170°/10 mm.

Me ether: $C_9H_{20}O$. MW, 144. B.p. 76–7°/44 mm. D_4^{20} 0·8094. n_D^{25} 1·4212.

Et ether: $C_{10}H_{22}O$. MW, 158. B.p. 63–5°/14 mm. D_4^{20} 0·7861. n_D^{25} 1·4136.

n-*Propyl ether*: $C_{11}H_{24}O$. MW, 172. B.p. 76°/18 mm. D_4^{20} 0·7887. n_D^{25} 1·4148.

n-*Butyl ether*: $C_{12}H_{26}O$. MW, 186. B.p. 85–6°/14 mm. D_4^{20} 0·7923. n_D^{25} 1·4168.

n-*Amyl ether*: $C_{13}H_{28}O$. MW, 200. B.p. 99°/15 mm. D_4^{20} 0·7958. n_D^{25} 1·4218.

n-*Hexyl ether*: $C_{14}H_{30}O$. MW, 214. B.p. 115°/15 mm. D_4^{20} 0·7983. n_D^{25} 1·4252.

n-*Heptyl ether*: $C_{15}H_{32}O$. MW, 228. B.p. 129°/18 mm. D_4^{20} 0·8017. n_D^{25} 1·4267.

n-*Octyl ether*: $C_{16}H_{34}O$. MW, 242. B.p. 146°/13 mm. D_4^{20} 0·8038. n_D^{25} 1·4301.

n-*Nonyl ether*: $C_{17}H_{36}O$. MW, 256. B.p. 163°/18 mm. D_4^{20} 0·8042. n_D^{25} 1·4325.

Benzyl ether: $C_{15}H_{24}O$. MW, 220. B.p. 154°/18 mm. D_4^{20} 0·8974.

Diphenylmethyl ether: $C_{21}H_{28}O$. MW, 296. B.p. 202°/10 mm. D_4^{17} 0·9675.

Triphenylmethyl ether: $C_{27}H_{32}O$. MW, 372. B.p. 178°/0·3 mm. D_4^{16} 1·026.

Kenyon, McNicol, *J. Chem. Soc.*, 1923, **123**, 18.
Kenyon, *Organic Syntheses*, 1926, VI, 68.
Waterman, te Nuyl, *Rec. trav. chim.*, 1932, **51**, 533.
Ellis, Reid, *J. Am. Chem. Soc.*, 1932, **54**, 1678.

n-Octylamine (1-*Amino*-n-*octane*)

$CH_3\cdot[CH_2]_6\cdot CH_2NH_2$

$C_8H_{19}N$ MW, 129

B.p. 175–7°/745 mm. (179–80°, 185–7°). $D^{20\cdot8}$ 0·7769.

Picrate: m.p. 111·5–112·5°.

Nyssens, *Chem. Abstracts*, 1931, **25**, 70.
Adamson, Kenner, *J. Chem. Soc.*, 1934, 842.

***sec.*-n-Octylamine** (2-*Amino*-n-*octane*)

$CH_3\cdot[CH_2]_5\cdot CH(NH_2)\cdot CH_3$

$C_8H_{19}N$ MW, 129

B.p. 172–5° (164–5°). D_0^{20} 0·7745. n_D^{25} 1·42319.

Kishner, *Chem. Zentr.*, 1900, I, 653.

n-Octylbenzene (1-*Phenyl*-n-*octane*)

$C_6H_5\cdot[CH_2]_7\cdot CH_3$

$C_{14}H_{22}$ MW, 190

F.p. — 7°. B.p. 264–5°, (262–4°, 261–3°, 257°). D_4^{20} 0·8583. $CrO_3 \longrightarrow$ benzoic acid.

Sabatier, Maihle, *Compt. rend.*, 1914, **158**, 834.
Tilicheev, Kuruindin, *Chem. Abstracts*, 1931, **25**, 3469.
Eisenlohr, Schultz, *Ber.*, 1924, **57**, 1815.

p-Octylbenzoic Acid

COOH

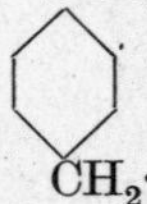

$CH_2·[CH_2]_6·CH_3$

$C_{15}H_{22}O_2$ MW, 234

Leaflets from hot EtOH. M.p. 139°. Spar. sol. H_2O.

Beran, *Ber.*, 1885, **18**, 138.

***n*-Octyl bromide** (1-*Bromo*-n-*octane*)

$CH_3·[CH_2]_6·CH_2Br$

$C_8H_{17}Br$ MW, 193

M.p. — 55·0°. B.p. 201·5°. D_4^{25} 1·10788. n_D^{25} 1·4503.

Kamm, Marvel, *J. Am. Chem. Soc.*, 1920, **42**, 309.
Organic Syntheses, 1921, I, 7; Collective Vol. I, 28.

***sec.-n*-Octyl bromide** (2-*Bromo*-n-*Octane*)

$CH_3·[CH_2]_5·CHBr·CH_3$

$C_8H_{17}Br$ MW, 193

d-.
B.p. 71°/14 mm., 60°/3 mm. D_4^{25} 1·0982. n_D^{25} 1·4475. $[\alpha]_D^{25}$ + 34·2° (+ 29·8°).

l-.
B.p. 83–4°/18 mm. n_D^{20} 1·4500. $[\alpha]_D^{25}$ — 33·1° (— 34·25°).

dl-.
B.p. 72°/14 mm., 61°/3 mm. D_4^{25} 1·0878 (1·09681). n_D^{25} 1·4442 (1·4482).

Ellis, Reid, *J. Am. Chem. Soc.*, 1932, **54**, 1680.
Rule, Smith, Harrower, *J. Chem. Soc.*, 1933, 386.
Shriner, Young, *J. Am. Chem. Soc.*, 1930, **52**, 3332.
Reynolds, Adkins, *J. Am. Chem. Soc.*, 1929, **51**, 279.
Tseng, Hau, Hu, *Chem. Zentr.*, 1936, I, 2917.

***n*-Octyl chloride** (1-*Chloro*-n-*octane*)

$CH_3·[CH_2]_6·CH_2Cl$

$C_8H_{17}Cl$ MW, 148·

B.p. 184°, 78°/15 mm. D_0^4 0·892.

Bouveault, Blanc, *Bull. soc. chim.*, 1904 **31**, 673.
Clark, Streight, *Chem. Abstracts*, 193(**24**, 586.

***sec.-n*-Octyl chloride** (2-*Chloro*-n-*octane*)

$CH_3·[CH_2]_5·CHCl·CH_3$

$C_8H_{17}Cl$ MW, 148·

d-.
B.p. 75°/28 mm., 55–6°/10–11 mm. D 0·8658. n_D^{21} 1·4273. $[\alpha]_D^{17}$ + 20·40° ($[\alpha]_D^{20}$ + 33·70°).

l-.
B.p. 70°/25 mm., 68°/21 mm., 60°/12 mm D_4^{17} 0·8628. n_D^{20} 1·4302. $[\alpha]_D^{17}$ — 20·44°.

dl-.
B.p. 171–3°. D^{15} 0·87075.

Houssa, Phillips, *J. Chem. Soc.*, 1932, 109
Malbot, *Bull. soc. chim.*, 1890, **3**, 69.
Houssa, Kenyon, Phillips, *J. Chem. Soc.* 1929, 1700.
Rule, Smith, Harrower, *J. Chem. Soc.* 1933, 386.
See also last reference above.

Octylene.
See Octene.

Octyl hexadecyl Ketone (*Pentacosanone*-9)

$CH_3·[CH_2]_{15}·CO·[CH_2]_7·CH_3$

$C_{25}H_{50}O$ MW, 36(

Powder from C_6H_6. M.p. 66°. Sol. EtOH. *Semicarbazone*: m.p. 39–41°.

Brigl, *Z. physiol. Chem.*, 1915, **95**, 178.

***n*-Octyl iodide** (1-*Iodo*-n-*octane*)

$CH_3·[CH_2]_6·CH_2I$

$C_8H_{17}I$ MW, 24(

M.p. — 45·7°. B.p. 225–225·5°, 194°/330 mm D_4^{15} 1·33568.

Möslinger, *Ann.*, 1877, **185**, 55.

***sec.-n*-Octyl iodide** (2-*Iodo*-n-*octane*)

$CH_3·[CH_2]_5·CHI·CH_3$

$C_8H_{17}I$ MW, 24(

d-.
B.p. 101°/22 mm. D_4^{17} 1·3314. $[\alpha]_D^{17}$ + 39·83°.

l-.
B.p. 92°/12 mm. D_4^{17} 1·3299. $[\alpha]_D^{17}$ — 40·56°

dl-.
B.p. 190° (210°) part. decomp. $D^{17.5}_{15}$ 1·318.

Pickard, Kenyon, *J. Chem. Soc.*, 1911, **99**, 69.
Cf. Houssa, Kenyon, Phillips, *J. Chem. Soc.*, 1929, 1700.

n-Octylmalonic Acid

$CH_3 \cdot [CH_2]_7 \cdot CH < \begin{matrix} COOH \\ COOH \end{matrix}$

$C_{11}H_{20}O_4$ MW, 216

Prisms from C_6H_6–pet. ether. M.p. 115° (108°).

Di-Et ester: $C_{15}H_{28}O_4$. MW, 272. B.p. 169°/17 mm.

Robinson, *J. Chem. Soc.*, 1924, **125**, 228.
Clutterbuck, Raistrick, Rintoul, *Trans. Roy. Soc.*, 1931, **B, 220**, 301.

4-n-Octylresorcinol (2 : 4-*Dihydroxyoctylbenzene*)

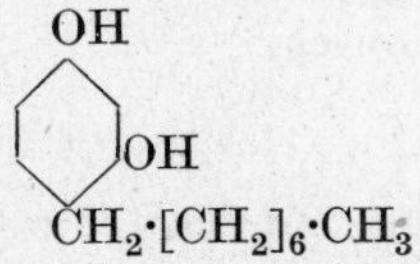

$C_{14}H_{22}O_2$ MW, 222

M.p. 74–5°. B.p. 199–201°/6–7 mm.

Dohme, Cox, Miller, *J. Am. Chem. Soc.*, 1926, **48**, 1692.

n-Octyl thiocyanate

$CH_3 \cdot [CH_2]_6 \cdot CH_2 \cdot CNS$

$C_9H_{17}NS$ MW, 171

B.p. 141–2°/19 mm. D^{25}_4 0·9149. n^{25}_D 1·4642.

Allen, *J. Am. Chem. Soc.*, 1935, **57**, 198.

1-Octyl-2-undecyl-ethylene.
See 9-Heneicosene.
Œnanthaldehyde.
See n-Heptaldehyde.
Œnanthic Acid.
See n-Heptylic Acid.
Œnanthol.
See n-Heptaldehyde.
Œnanthone.
See Di-*n*-hexyl Ketone.
Œnanthylic Acid.
See n-Heptylic Acid.
Œnanthylidene (*Œnanthine*, n-*amylacetylene*, 1-*heptine*)

$CH_3 \cdot [CH_2]_4 \cdot C \vdots CH$

C_7H_{12} MW, 96

F.p. below — 70°. B.p. 99–100° (108–10°), 26°/10 mm. D^{19} 0·750. n^{19}_D 1·418. Red. ⟶ *n*-heptane. $NH_3.AgNO_3$ ⟶ white ppt. $NH_3.Cu_2Cl_2$ ⟶ yellow ppt.

Moureu, André, *Ann. chim.*, 1914, **1**, 116 (*Footnote*).
Bourguel, *Ann. chim.*, 1925, **3**, 191, 325.
Bouis, *Ann. chim.*, 1928, **9**, 461.
Hill, Tyson, *J. Am. Chem. Soc.*, 1928, **50**, 172.
Chem. Fabrik Flörsheim, *Chem. Abstracts*, 1912, **6**, 2072.

Œnidin chloride.
Malvidin chloride, *q.v.*
Œnin chloride (*Primulin chloride, malvidin chloride* 3-β-*glucoside*)

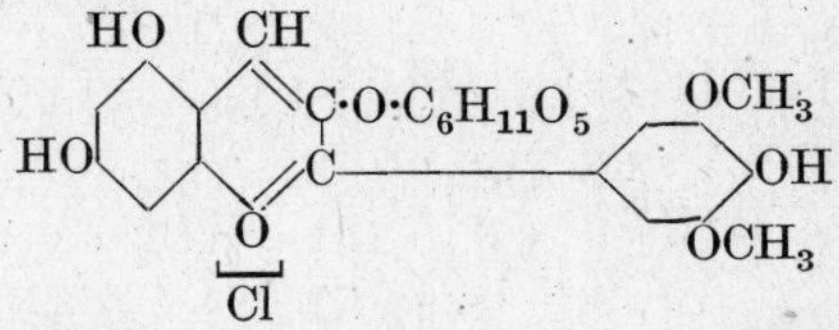

$C_{23}H_{25}O_{12}Cl$ MW, 528·5

Pigment of skins of black grapes. Violet cryst. by transmitted light with yellow metallic cast. Bronze appearance in masses. Gives bluish-violet smear on paper or porcelain.

Picrate: red needles with green reflex. Decomp. at 202°.

Kondo, *Chem. Abstracts*, 1930, **24**, 2748.
Levy, Posternack, Robinson, *J. Chem. Soc.*, 1931, 2701 (*Bibl.*).

Œstriol (*Theelol, follicular hormone hydrate*)

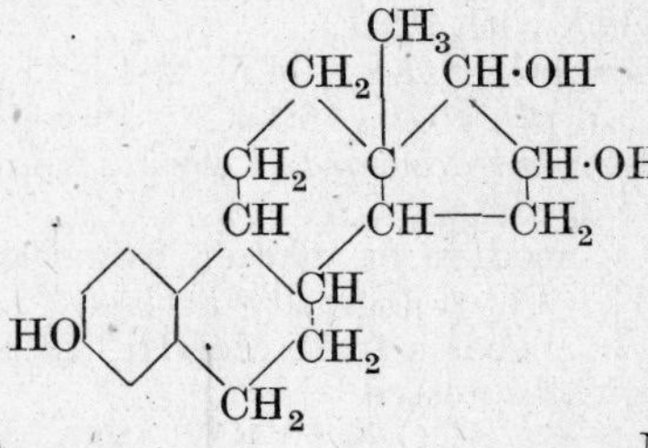

$C_{18}H_{24}O_3$ MW, 288

Isolated from urine of pregnancy. Cryst. from EtOH–AcOEt. M.p. 283° (275°). Sol. 33,000 parts H_2O. Sol. EtOH, Me_2CO, Py. Mod. sol. Et_2O. Spar. sol. pet. ether. Insol. alk. carbonates. Very sol. aq. alkalis. $[\alpha]^{25}_{5461}$ + 71° in EtOH, $[\alpha]_D$ + 34·4° in Py. Heat in vacuo with $KHSO_4$ ⟶ œstrone. Forms Me ether with diazomethane.

Me ether: cryst. from EtOH. M.p. 162·5–164°.

Triacetyl: m.p. 127°. Ten times as physiologically active as œstriol.

Cartland, Meyer, Miller, Rutz, *J. Biol. Chem.*, 1935, **109**, 215.
MacCorquodale, Thayer, Doisy, *J. Biol. Chem.*, 1933, **99**, 329.
Marrian, Haslewood, *Biochem. J.*, 1932, **26**, 25.
Butenandt, Hildebrandt, *Z. physiol. Chem.*, 1931, **199**, 245.
Marrian, *Biochem. J.*, 1930, **24**, 435, 1021.

Œstrone (*Œstrin, theelin, ketohydroxyœstrin, menformon, folliculin, follicular hormone, α-follicular hormone, progynon*)

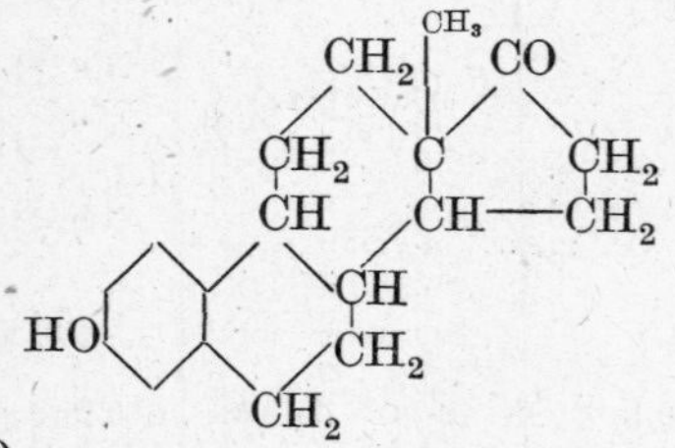

$C_{18}H_{22}O_2$ MW, 270

The œstrus-producing hormone obtained, among other sources, from urine of pregnancy. Colourless cryst. from EtOH. Three polymorphic forms, m.ps. 254°, 256°, 259°. Sol. EtOH, Me_2CO, $CHCl_3$, C_6H_6. Mod. sol. Et_2O, AcOEt. Spar. sol. pet. ether. Insol. H_2O. Sol. alkalis. Insol. alk. carbonates. $[\alpha]_D^{23}$ + 158·5°. Distils undecomp. at 150–200°/0·002 mm. Does not give Liebermann–Burchard reaction. Gives no col. with $FeCl_3$.

Me ether: $C_{19}H_{24}O_2$. MW, 284. Cryst. from EtOH. M.p. 167·5–169·5°. Physiologically inactive. *Semicarbazone*: cryst. from EtOH. M.p. 267° decomp.

Acetyl: needles or plates from EtOH.Aq. M.p. 126°. Physiologically active.

Benzoyl: needles from MeOH. M.p. 217·5°. Physiologically active.

Oxime: $C_{18}H_{23}O_2N$. MW, 285. Needles from EtOH.Aq. Decomp. at 233°. Physiologically active.

Semicarbazone: cryst. from EtOH. M.p. 258–60° decomp. Physiologically inactive.

Marker, Kamm, Oakwood, Laucius, *J. Am. Chem. Soc.*, 1936, **58**, 1503.
Cartland, Meyer, Miller, Rutz, *J. Biol. Chem.*, 1935, **109**, 213.
Curtis, MacCorquodale, Thayer, Doisy, *J. Biol. Chem.*, 1934, **107**, 191.
Kofler, Hauschild, *Z. physiol. Chem.* 1934, **224**, 150.
Butenandt, Störmer, *Z. physiol. Chem.*, 1932, **208**, 129, 149.
Doisy, Veler, Thayer, *J. Biol. Chem.*, 1930, **86**, 499; **87**, 357.
Butenandt, Ziegner, *Z. physiol. Chem.*, 1930, **188**, 1.

Oleandrin

$C_{31}H_{48}O_9$ MW, 564

Glucoside from leaves of *Nerium oleander* (Laurier-rose), Linn. Cryst. from hot MeOH.Aq. M.p. 70–5°. Sol. EtOH, Et_2O. Spar. sol. H_2O. Sublimes.

Windaus, Westphal, *Chem. Abstracts*, 1927, **21**, 299.
Tanret, *Compt. rend.*, 1932, **194**, 914.
Kahlbaum, D.R.P., 577,257, (*Chem. Abstracts*, 1933, **27**, 4032).

Oleanic Acid.

See Oleanolic Acid.

Oleanol

$C_{29}H_{48}O$ MW, 412

Needles from Me_2CO. M.p. 216–20°. $[\alpha]_D^{20}$ + 59° in $CHCl_3$. Gives Liebermann reaction.

Acetyl: needles from EtOH. M.p. 209–10°. $[\alpha]_D^{21}$ + 44·7° in $CHCl_3$.

Winterstein, Stein, *Z. physiol. Chem.*, 1931, **202**, 222.
Kuwada, *Chem. Abstracts*, 1936, **28**, 8237.

Oleanolic Acid (*Panax sapogenin, guagenin, sugar beet sapogenin, "oleanol," caryophyllin, mistletoe sapogenin, oleanic acid*)

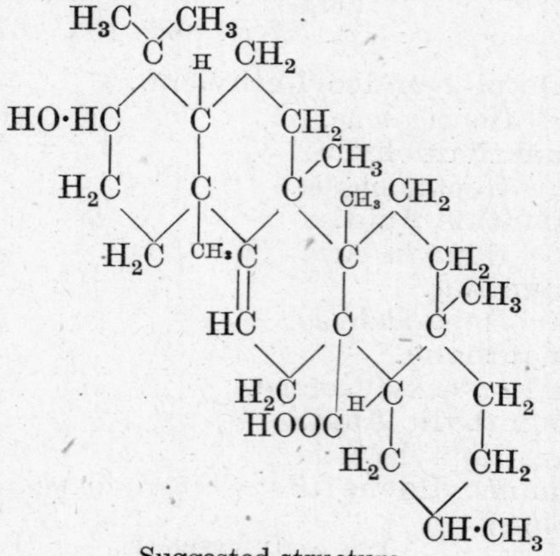

Suggested structure

$C_{30}H_{48}O_3$ MW, 456

Occurs as glucoside in leaves of *Aralia japonica*, (Thunb.), mistletoe, cloves, sugar beet, live leaves, etc. Prisms from EtOH. M.p. 06–8° (305°). Sol. MeOH, EtOH. $[\alpha]_D^{12}$ – 79·5° in $CHCl_3$.

Acetyl: m.p. 268° (258–60°).

Diphenylurethane: m.p. 137–8°.

Me ester: $C_{31}H_{50}O_3$. MW, 470. M.p. 196–° (184°). *Acetyl*: m.p. 223°. *Oxime*: m.p. 46° decomp. (226°).

Kitasato, *Chem. Abstracts*, 1934, **28**, 4051.
Aumüller, Schicke, Wedekind, *Ann.*, 1935, **517**, 211.
Ruzicka, Hofmann, *Helv. Chim. Acta*, 1936, **19**, 114.
Jacobs, Fleck, *J. Biol. Chem.*, 1932, **96**, 341.
Van der Haar, *Rec. trav. chim.*, 1927, **46**, 775, 793.
Ruzicka, Goldberg, Hofmann, *Helv. Chim. Acta*, 1937, **20**, 325.

Note.—The " Oleanol " described by Power, 'utin, *J. Chem. Soc.*, 1908, **93**, 896, appears to e identical with oleanolic acid.

Oleic Acid (*Cis-8-Heptadecylenecarboxylic cid*, *Δ⁹-octadecylenic acid*)

$CH_3\cdot[CH_2]_7\cdot CH{:}CH\cdot[CH_2]_7\cdot COOH$

$C_{18}H_{34}O_2$ MW, 282

F.p. 11·8–12·2° (13·2°). *Labile form*: m.p. 2°. *Stable form*: m.p. 16° (15·4°). B.p. 85·5–286°/100 mm., 203–5°/5 mm., 170–5°/–3 mm. Sol. EtOH, Et_2O. Insol. H_2O. D^{20} ·898. n_D^{20} 1·45823 (1·4610). Heat of comb. C_p 682·0 Cal., C_v 2677·6 Cal.

Me ester: $C_{19}H_{36}O_2$. MW, 296. B.p. 212–3°/15 mm., 160–2°/2–3 mm. D^{18} 0·879.

Et ester: $C_{20}H_{38}O_2$. MW, 310. B.p. 216–7°/151 mm. D^{25} 0·8671.

Propyl ester: $C_{21}H_{40}O_2$. MW, 324. B.p. 66–7°/15 mm.

Isopropyl ester: b.p. 223–4°/15 mm.

Butyl ester: $C_{22}H_{42}O_2$. MW, 338. B.p. 27–8°/15 mm. (235–40°/10–18 mm.).

Isobutyl ester: tebelon. B.p. 226–7°/10 ım., 190°/4 mm. D^{20} 0·86.

tert.-*Butyl ester*: b.p. 223–224·5°/10 mm.

Isoamyl ester: $C_{23}H_{44}O_2$. MW, 352. B.p. 23–4°/10 mm. D^{15} 0·897.

tert.-*Amyl ester*: b.p. 223–225·5°/10 mm.

α-Glyceryl ester: *see* α-Mono-olein.

Vinyl ester: $C_{20}H_{36}O_2$. MW, 308. B.p. 73°/2 mm.

Allyl ester: $C_{21}H_{38}O_2$. MW, 322. B.p. 219–1°/10 mm.

Phenyl ester: $C_{24}H_{38}O_2$. MW, 358. B.p. ıbout 230°/7 mm.

m-*Tolyl ester*: $C_{25}H_{40}O_2$. MW, 372. B.p. about 240°/5 mm.

p-*Chlorophenacyl ester*: $C_{26}H_{40}O_2Cl$. MW, 419·5. M.p. 40°.

p-*Bromophenacyl ester*: $C_{26}H_{40}O_2Br$. MW, 464. M.p. 40°.

p-*Phenylphenacyl ester*: $C_{32}H_{45}O_2$. MW, 461. M.p. 61°.

Menthyl ester: $C_{28}H_{52}O_2$. MW, 420. B.p. about 240°/4 mm.

Stigmasteryl ester: $C_{48}H_{82}O_2$. MW, 690. M.p. 44°.

Chloride: $C_{18}H_{33}OCl$. MW, 300·5. B.p. 213°/13–15 mm., 200°/11 mm., 190°/9 mm.

Amide: $C_{18}H_{35}ON$. MW, 281. M.p. 75–6°.

Anhydride: $C_{36}H_{66}O_3$. MW, 546. M.p. 22–4°. D_4^{15} 0·900. n_D^{20} 1·4630.

Nitrile: $C_{18}H_{33}N$. MW, 263. B.p. 330–5° decomp.

Anilide: m.p. 41°. B.p. 143·5°/10 mm.

Phenylhydrazide: m.p. 72–3°.

Noller, Bannerot, *J. Am. Chem. Soc.*, 1934, **56**, 1563.
Koyama, *Chem. Abstracts*, 1932, **26**, 5067.
Bannister, U.S.P., 1,796,231, (*Chem. Abstracts*, 1931, **25**, 2441).
Skillon, *J. Soc. Chem. Ind.*, 1931, **50**, 131T.
Raymond, *Chimie et Industrie*, Special No., 1929, 523.
Scheffers, *Rec. trav. chim.*, 1927, **46**, 293.
Bertram, *ibid.*, 397.
Holde, Gorgas, *Z. angew. Chem.*, 1926, **39**, 1443.
Robinson, Robinson, *J. Chem. Soc.*, 1925, 175.
Holde, Rietz, *Ber.*, 1924, **57**, 99.
Maihle, *Bull. soc. chim.*, 1920, **27**, 226.
Preiswerk, U.S.P., 1,318,461, (*Chem. Abstracts*, 1920, **14**, 95).
Täufel, Kunkele, *Chem. Zentr.*, 1935, I, 2971.
Brown, Shinowara, *J. Am. Chem. Soc.*, 1937, **59**, 6.

Oleic Alcohol.

See Octadecenyl Alcohol.

Oleodipalmitin

$$C_3H_5\begin{cases} O\cdot CO\cdot[CH_2]_7\cdot CH{:}CH\cdot[CH_2]_7\cdot CH_3 \\ (O\cdot CO\cdot[CH_2]_{14}\cdot CH_3)_2 \end{cases}$$

$C_{53}H_{100}O_6$ MW, 832

Occurs in soya bean oil, butter fat, cocoa fat, etc.

(i) M.p. 27–8°. (ii) Cryst. from $Me{-}C_2O$

$CHCl_3$. M.p. 38° (37°). Remelts at 28°. (iii) M.p. 48°.

Hashi, *Chem. Zentr.*, 1928, I, 1470.
Amberger, *Chem. Abstracts*, 1919, **13**, 3252.

Oleodistearin

$C_3H_5<$ $O{\cdot}CO{\cdot}[CH_2]_7{\cdot}CH{:}CH{\cdot}[CH_2]_7{\cdot}CH_3$ / $(O{\cdot}CO{\cdot}[CH_2]_{16}{\cdot}CH_3)_2$

$C_{57}H_{108}O_6$ MW, 888

Occurs in fat of seeds of *Mangifera indica*, Linn. M.p. 44° (42°, 29–31°).

Amberger, Bromig, *Biochem. Z.*, 1922, **130**, 252.

Oleone (*Dihepadecenyl ketone*)

$CH_3{\cdot}[CH_2]_7{\cdot}CH{:}CH{\cdot}[CH_2]_7$ / $CH_3{\cdot}[CH_2]_7{\cdot}CH{:}CH{\cdot}[CH_2]_7$ $>CO$

$C_{35}H_{66}O$ MW, 502

(i) Pale yellow cryst. from EtOH. M.p. 58·5°. (ii) Pale yellow oil. B.p. 120–75°/20 mm. Red. ⟶ pentatriacontane.
Oxime: m.p. 31°.

Breuer, Weinmann, *Monatsh.*, 1935, **67**, 42.

Oleopalmitostearin

C_3H_5 — $O{\cdot}CO{\cdot}[CH_2]_7{\cdot}CH{:}CH{\cdot}[CH_2]_7{\cdot}CH_3$ / $O{\cdot}CO{\cdot}[CH_2]_{16}{\cdot}CH_3$ / $O{\cdot}CO{\cdot}[CH_2]_{14}{\cdot}CH_3$

$C_{55}H_{104}O_6$ MW, 860

(i) M.p. 31·3°. (ii) M.p. 42°.

Klimont, *Monatsh.*, 1902, **23**, 55.
Hansen, *Chem. Zentr.*, 1902, I, 1116.

Oleyl Alcohol.
See Octadecenyl Alcohol.

Olivetol (5-n-*Amylresorcinol*)

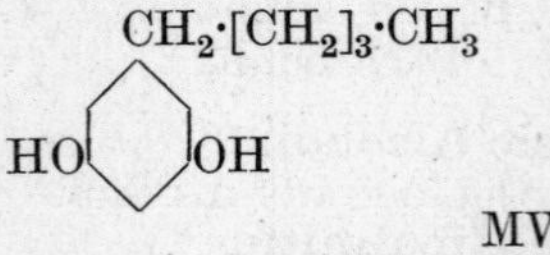

$C_{11}H_{16}O_2$ MW, 180

Prisms + $1H_2O$. M.p. 40–1°. Sol. ord. org. solvents.
Di-Me ether: $C_{13}H_{20}O_2$. MW, 208. B.p. 114°/2 mm.

Asahina, Asano, *Ber.*, 1932, **65**, 478.
Asahina, Nogami, *Ber.*, 1935, **68**, 1501.

Olivetonic Acid

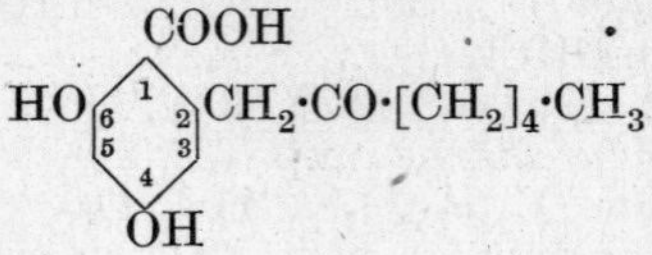

$C_{14}H_{18}O_5$ MW, 26

Needles from hot H_2O. M.p. 159–60°. So EtOH, Et_2O, Me_2CO, hot H_2O. Spar. so C_6H_6, ligroin.
Me ester: $C_{15}H_{20}O_5$. MW, 280. M.p. 85–6
4-*Me ether*: $C_{15}H_{20}O_5$. MW, 280. M.p. 94–5 *Me ester*: $C_{16}H_{22}O_5$. MW, 294. M.p. 80°.
6-*Me ether*: m.p. 119–20°.
Di-Me ether: $C_{16}H_{22}O_5$. MW, 294. Needl from EtOH.Aq. M.p. 93°. *Oxime*: m.p. 120

Asahina, Fuzikawa, *Ber.*, 1935, **68**, 2023

Olivetonide

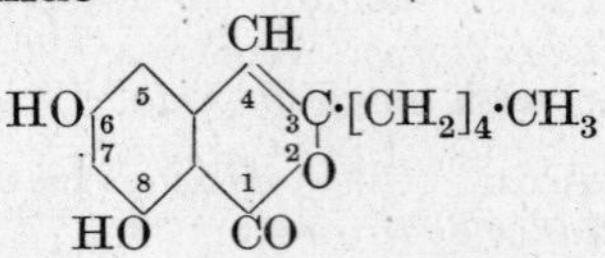

$C_{14}H_{16}O_4$ MW, 24

Needles from ligroin. M.p. 110°.
6-*Me ether*: $C_{15}H_{18}O_4$. MW, 262. Prism from EtOH. M.p. 57°. *Acetyl*: m.p. 60–1
8-*Me ether*: needles from C_6H_6. M.p. 146–7 *Acetyl*: m.p. 84°.
Di-Me ether: $C_{16}H_{20}O_4$. MW, 276. Prism from EtOH. M.p. 94°.
6-*Acetyl*: m.p. 55°.
Diacetyl: m.p. 59°.

Asahina, Fuzikawa, *Ber.*, 1935, **68**, 8: 2023.

Olivetoric Acid

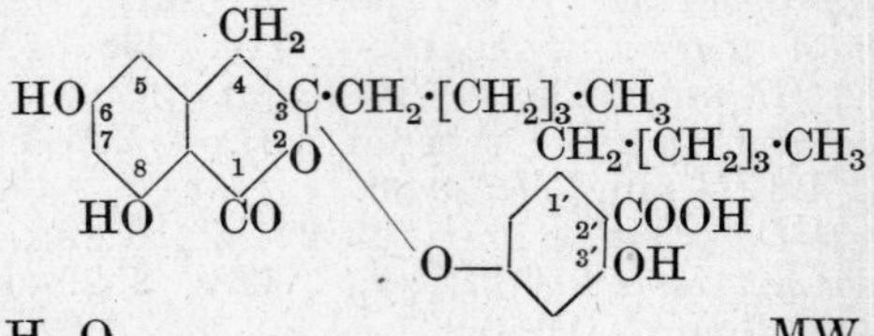

$C_{26}H_{32}O_8$ MW, 47

Occurs in lichens *Alectoria divergens* Ny *Parmelia olivetorum* Nyl, *Evernia olivetorin* Zopf. Cryst. from hot C_6H_6. M.p. 151 Sol. EtOH, Et_2O, Me_2CO, AcOH. Spar. so C_6H_6. Insol. ligroin.
6 : 3′-*Di-Me ether*: *Me ester*, $C_{29}H_{38}O_8$. MW 514. M.p. 123°.

Me ester: $C_{27}H_{34}O_8$. MW, 486. Needles. M.p. 134°.

Asahina, Fuzikawa, *Ber.*, 1935, **68**, 2026.
Asahina, Asano, *Ber.*, 1932, **65**, 584.
See also Hesse, *J. prakt. Chem.*, 1916, **94**, 227.

Olivil

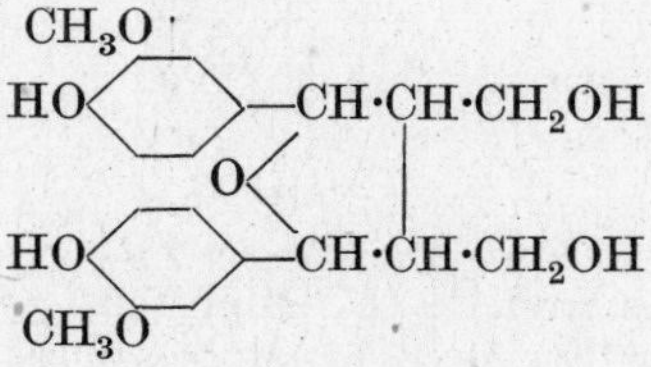

$C_{20}H_{24}O_7$ MW, 376

Occurs in olive-wood resin. Cryst. + $1H_2O$ from H_2O. M.p. 105°, anhyd. 142·5°. $[\alpha]_D^{12}$ − 127°.

Me ether: $C_{21}H_{26}O_7$. MW, 390. M.p. 238°.
Di-Me ether: $C_{22}H_{28}O_7$. MW, 404. M.p. 156°.
Et ether: $C_{22}H_{28}O_7$. MW, 404. M.p. 145°.
Di-Et ether: $C_{24}H_{32}O_7$. MW, 432. M.p. 182°.
Me-Et ether: $C_{23}H_{30}O_7$. MW, 418. M.p. 169°.
Dipropyl ether: $C_{26}H_{36}O_7$. MW, 460. M.p. 135·5°.

Vanzetti, Dreyfuss, *Gazz. chim. ital.*, 1934, **64**, 381.
Dreyfuss, *Gazz. chim. ital.*, 1936, **66**, 96.

Onocerin.
See Onocerol.

Onocerol (*Onocol, onocerin*)

$C_{26}H_{44}O_2$ MW, 288

A phytosterol occurring in *Ononis spinosa*, Linn. Prisms from EtOH. M.p. 232°. Sol. isoamyl alcohol. Spar. sol. Et_2O, $CHCl_3$, AcOEt. Insol. H_2O. Sublimes. $[\alpha]_D^{20}$ + 12·05°.

Diacetyl deriv.: m.p. 224°. $[\alpha]_D^{18}$ + 28·3° in $CHCl_3$.
Di-chloroacetyl deriv.: m.p. 238–44°. $[\alpha]_D^{19}$ + 115° in $CHCl_3$.
Dibenzoyl deriv.: m.p. 237–8°. $[\alpha]_D^{22}$ + 21·3° in $CHCl_3$.
Di-3 : 5-dinitrobenzoyl deriv.: m.p. 290–1°. $[\alpha]_D^{19}$ + 19·3° in $CHCl_3$.
Dianisoyl deriv.: m.p. 232–4°. $[\alpha]_D^{22}$ + 10° in $CHCl_3$.

Schulze, *Z. physiol. Chem.*, 1936, **238**, 35.
Dieterle, Salomon, Gärtner, *Chem. Abstracts*, 1934, **28**, 4065.

Onocol.
See Onocerol.

Opianic Acid (5 : 6-*Dimethoxy*-o-*aldehydobenzoic acid*, 6-*aldehydo*-o-*veratric acid*, 5 : 6-*dimethoxy*-o-*phthalaldehydic acid*)

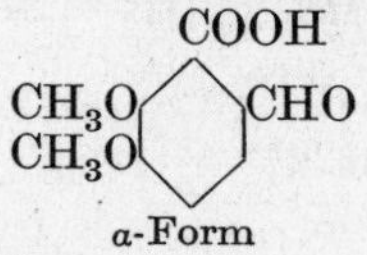

α-Form

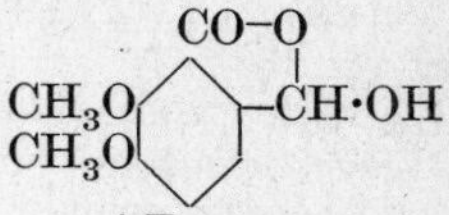

ψ-Form

$C_{10}H_{10}O_5$ MW, 210

Prisms from H_2O. M.p. 150° (146°). Sol. EtOH, Et_2O. $k = 8{\cdot}82 \times 10^{-4}$ at 25°. Ox. ⟶ hemipinic acid. Red. ⟶ meconin.

α-*Me ester*: $C_{11}H_{12}O_5$. MW, 224. Needles from EtOH. M.p. 82–3°. B.p. 232–4°/52 mm.
Diacetyl: m.p. 88–9°. *Semicarbazone*: m.p. 204°.
ψ-*Me ester*: m.p. 105°.
α-*Et ester*: $C_{12}H_{14}O_5$. MW, 238. M.p. 64°.
ψ-*Et ester*: m.p. 92–3°.
ψ-*Propyl ester*: $C_{13}H_{16}O_5$. MW, 252. M.p. 103°.
ψ-tert.-*Amyl ester*: $C_{15}H_{20}O_5$. MW, 280. M.p. 81°.
α-*Benzyl ester*: $C_{17}H_{16}O_5$. MW, 300. M.p. 82–3°.
ψ-*Benzyl ester*: m.p. 94–5°.
ψ-*Chloride*: $C_{10}H_9O_4Cl$. MW, 228·5. Needles from C_6H_6. M.p. 93–4°.
Anhydride: $C_{20}H_{18}O_9$. MW, 402. M.p. 234°.
Oxime: needles. M.p. 82°.
Semicarbazone: m.p. 187°.
Benzoylhydrazone: m.p. 227° decomp.

Kanewskaja *et al.*, *Ber.*, 1936, **69**, 257.
Edwards, Perkin, Stoyle, *J. Chem. Soc.*, 1925, 197.
Kirpal, *Ber.*, 1927, **60**, 382.
Schorigin, Issagulanz, Below, *Ber.*, 1931, **64**, 1931.
Wegscheider, Späth, *Monatsh.*, 1916, **37**, 277.
Rodionow, Fedorova, *Ber.*, 1926, **59**, 2949.

***m*-Opianic Acid** (4 : 5-*Dimethoxy*-o-*aldehydobenzoic acid*, 6-*aldehydoveratric acid*, 4 : 5-*dimethoxy*-o-*phthalaldehydic acid*)

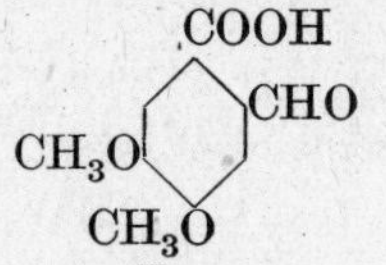

α-Form

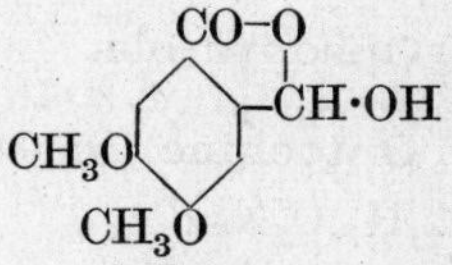

ψ-Form

$C_{10}H_{10}O_5$ MW, 210

Needles from H_2O. M.p. 185°. Sol. AcOH, hot Me_2CO. Spar. sol. H_2O, MeOH.

α-Me ester: $C_{11}H_{12}O_5$. MW, 224. M.p. 93–5°. *Anil*: m.p. about 143°.

ψ-Me ester: m.p. 142–3°.

Anhydride: $C_{20}H_{18}O_9$. MW, 402. M.p. about 230°.

Oxime: m.p. about 140°.

Semicarbazone: m.p. about 227°.

Phenylhydrazone: m.p. 228°.

Vanzetti, Oliverio, Cavinato, *Gazz. chim. ital.*, 1931, **61**, 479.
Perkin, Stoyle, *J. Chem. Soc.*, 1923, **123**, 3171.

ψ-Opianic Acid (3 : 4-*Dimethoxy*-o-*aldehydobenzoic acid*, 2-*aldehydoveratric acid*, 3 : 4-*dimethoxy*-o-*phthalaldehydic acid*)

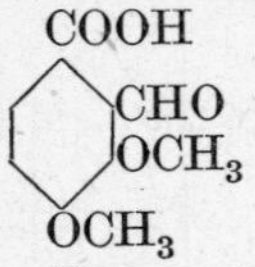

α-Form

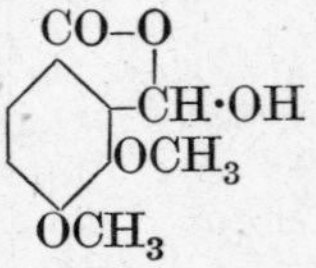

ψ-Form

$C_{10}H_{10}O_5$ MW, 210

Needles from H_2O or C_6H_6. M.p. 121–2°. Sol. hot H_2O, EtOH, $CHCl_3$, C_6H_6. Spar. sol. pet. ether. Hot conc. KOH.Aq. ⟶ veratric acid.

Oxime: needles from H_2O. M.p. 124° decomp.

Perkin, *J. Chem. Soc.*, 1890, **57**, 1064.
Chakravarti, Swaminathan, *Chem. Abstracts*, 1934, **28**, 6720.

Opiazone (6 : 7-*Dimethoxyphthalazone*)

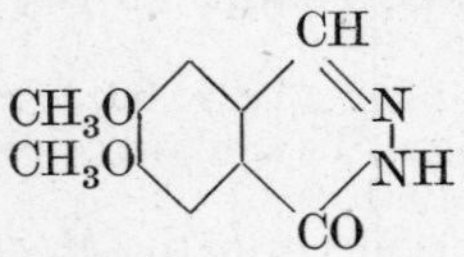

$C_{10}H_{10}O_3N_2$ MW, 206

Needles. M.p. anhyd. 166°. Sol. EtOH, AcOH, hot H_2O.

N-*Acetyl*: m.p. 158–9°.

Liebermann, Bistrzycki, *Ber.*, 1893, **26**, 532.

Opsopyrrole.

See 4-Methyl-3-ethylpyrrole.

Optochine (*Dihydrocupreine ethyl ether*)

$C_{21}H_{28}O_2N_2$ MW, 340

M.p. 80–4° (contains H_2O and toluene). M.p. 123–8° (solvent free). Sol. ord. org. solvents. Mod. sol. C_6H_6, toluene, ligroin. $[\alpha]_D^{26\cdot5}$ — 112·7° in EtOH ($[\alpha]_D^{25}$ — 136·2° in EtOH).

Heidelberger, Jacobs, *J. Am. Chem. Soc.* 1922, **44**, 1097.

Orcacetophenone (4 : 6-*Dihydroxy-2-methylacetophenone*, *methyl* 4 : 6-*dihydroxy*-o-*tolyl ketone*)

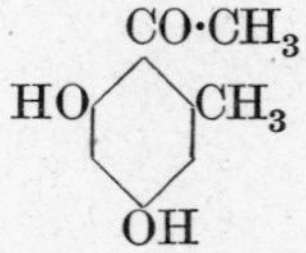

$C_9H_{10}O_3$ MW, 166

Needles from H_2O. M.p. 159°. Sol. EtOH, Et_2O, AcOEt, Me_2CO. Mod. sol. C_6H_6, $CHCl_3$. Spar. sol. H_2O, ligroin.

4-*Me ether*: $C_{10}H_{12}O_3$. MW, 180. M.p. 79°.

6-*Me ether*: m.p. 150°.

Hoesch, *Ber.*, 1915, **48**, 1127.

α-Orcindialdehyde (4 : 6-*Dihydroxy*-2-*methylisophthaldehyde*)

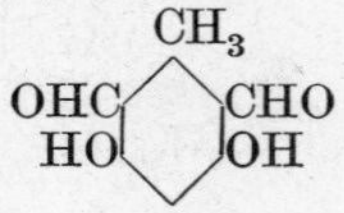

$C_9H_8O_4$ MW, 180

Needles from hot H_2O. M.p. 117–19°. Sol. EtOH, Et_2O, $CHCl_3$. Mod. sol. hot H_2O. Volatile in steam.

Tiemann, Helkenberg, *Ber.*, 1879, **12**, 1003.

β-Orcindialdehyde (2:6-*Dihydroxy*-4-*methylisophthalaldehyde*)

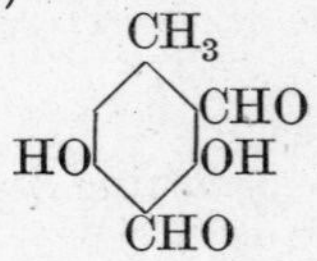

$C_9H_8O_4$ MW, 180

Cryst. from EtOH.Aq. M.p. 168°. Sol. EtOH, Et_2O, $CHCl_3$, hot H_2O.

Tiemann, Helkenberg, *Ber.*, 1879, **12**, 1004.

Orcinol (5-*Methylresorcinol*, 3 : 5-*dihydroxytoluene*)

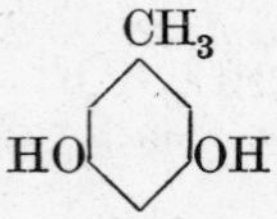

$C_7H_8O_2$ MW, 12

Cryst. + $1H_2O$ from H_2O, leaflets from $CHCl_3$. (i) M.p. 106·5–108°. (ii) M.p. 107·5°. B.p

87–90°. Sol. H_2O, EtOH, Et_2O, C_6H_6. Spar. ol. ligroin, pet. ether. Heat of comb. C_p 24·72 Cal.

Diacetyl : m.p. 25°.

Dibenzoyl : m.p. 88°.

Me ether : $C_8H_{10}O_2$. MW, 138. M.p. 61–2°. .p. 259°/755 mm., 130°/6·5 mm. D^{15} 1·1106. n_D^{20} 1·54734.

Di-Me ether : $C_9H_{12}O_2$. MW, 152. B.p. 44°, 102°/8 mm. D^{15} 1·0478. n_D^{20} 1·52342.

Et ether : $C_9H_{12}O_2$. MW, 152. B.p. 265–70°.

Di-Et ether : $C_{11}H_{16}O_2$. MW, 180. M.p. 6–16·5°. B.p. 251–2°/747·5 mm.

Picrate : m.p. 92°.

Schaum, *Ann.*, 1928, **462**, 207.
Missenden, *Chem. Age*, 1922, **7**, 709 (*Review*).
Walbaum, Rosenthal, *Ber.*, 1924, **57**, 771.
Vogt, Henninger, *Bull. soc. chim.*, 1874, **21**, 273.

β-Orcinol.

See 2 : 6-Dihydroxy-*p*-xylene.

γ-Orcinol.

2 : 4-Dihydroxytoluene, *q.v.*

Orcinol-carboxylic Acid.

See Orsellinic Acid *and* 3 : 5-Dihydroxy-*p*-oluic Acid.

β-Orcylaldehyde (β-*Orcinaldehyde*, 3 : 5-*di-ydroxy*-4-*methyl*-o-*toluic aldehyde*, 4 : 6-*di-ydroxy*-2 : 5-*dimethylbenzaldehyde*)

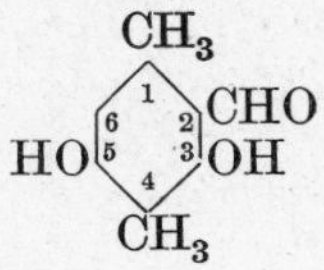

$C_9H_{10}O_3$ MW, 166

Needles from EtOH. M.p. 166°.

5-*Me ether* : *see* Rhizonaldehyde.

Sonn, *Ber.*, 1931, **64**, 185.
Robertson, Stephenson, *J. Chem. Soc.*, 1930, 316.

γ-Orcylaldehyde.

See Atranol, Addendum, Vol. I.

Orcylic Aldehyde.

See 3 : 5-Dihydroxy-*o*-toluic Aldehyde.

Orexine (3-*Phenyl*-3 : 4-*dihydroquinazoline*)

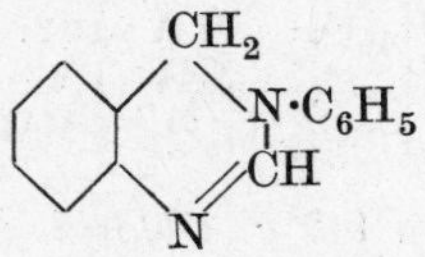

$C_{14}H_{12}N_2$ MW, 208

Plates from Et_2O–ligroin. M.p. 94–6°. Sol. EtOH, Et_2O, $CHCl_3$. Insol. H_2O.

B,HCl,2H₂O : m.p. 80°, anhyd. 221°.

B,HCl,SnCl₂ : m.p. 130–4°.

B₂,H₂PtCl₆ : m.p. 208°.

B₂,H₂SO₄,2H₂O : m.p. 70°, anhyd. 140–3°.

Methiodide : m.p. 170°.

Paal, Busch, *Ber.*, 1889, **22**, 2686.
Kalle, D.R.P., 113,163, (*Chem. Zentr.*, 1900, II, 615).

Oripavine

$C_{18}H_{21}O_3N$ MW, 299

Alkaloid from *Papaver orientalis*. Needles from EtOH. M.p. 200–1°. Sol. $CHCl_3$. Spar. sol. EtOH, Me_2CO. Insol. H_2O.

B,HCl : m.p. 244–5°.

Methiodide : m.p. 207–8°.

Konowalowa, Yunussoff, Orechoff, *Ber.*, 1935, **68**, 2160.

Orixidine

$C_{15}H_{13}O_4N$ MW, 271

Needles from $+ 1\frac{1}{2}H_2O$, EtOH.Aq. M.p. 195°. Cryst. from (+ 1AcOH ?) AcOH. M.p. 142°.

Terasaka, *Chem. Abstracts*, 1932, **26**, 730.

Orixine

$C_{18}H_{23}O_6N(C_{18}H_{21}O_6N)$ MW, 349 (347)

Alkaloid from root of *Orixa japonica*, Thunb. M.p. 152·5°. Sol. EtOH, Et_2O, $CHCl_3$, AcOEt. Insol. pet. ether. $[\alpha]_D^{17}$ + 83·29° in $CHCl_3$.

B,HAuCl₄ : decomp. at 155°.

See previous reference.

Orizabin.

See Jalapin.

Ornithine (1 : 4-*Diamino*-n-*valeric acid*)

$$H_2N{\cdot}CH_2{\cdot}CH_2{\cdot}CH_2{\cdot}CH(NH_2){\cdot}COOH$$

$C_5H_{12}O_2N_2$ MW, 132

d-.

M.p. 140°. Sol. H_2O, EtOH. Spar. sol. Et_2O. $[\alpha]_D^{25}$ + 11·5°.

B,2HCl : $[\alpha]_D$ + 16·8° in H_2O.

B,H₂PtCl₆ : decomp. at 200–10°.

Monosulphate : decomp. at 234°.

Acetate : m.p. 161–2°.

1 : 4-N-*Dibenzoyl* : *see* Ornithuric Acid.

Dipicrate : decomp. at 208°.

dl-.

B,HCl : m.p. 215°.

B,HNO₃ : m.p. 183°.

B,H₂SO₄ : decomp. at 208°.

B_2,H_2SO_4 : m.p. 213°.
Acetate : m.p. 163–4°.
Oxalate : m.p. 218°.
Picrolonate : m.p. 220–1° decomp.
Dipicrolonate : m.p. 235–6°.
4-N-*Benzoyl* : m.p. 285–8°.
Dipicrate : decomp. at 208° (m.p. 195°).

1-N-*Me* : 4-amino-1-methylamino-*n*-valeric acid. $C_6H_{14}O_2N_2$. MW, 146. *$B,HAuCl_4$* : needles. M.p. 130–2°. *Flavianate* : m.p. 222–3°. 4-N-*Benzoyl*-1-N-p-*toluenesulphonyl* : needles from 70% EtOH. M.p. 185°. 1-N-p-*Toluenesulphonyl* : plates from H_2O. M.p. 214–19°. Prac. insol. EtOH, Et_2O, ligroin.

4-N-*Me* : 1-amino-4-methylamino-*n*-valeric acid. *B,HCl* : m.p. about 215–25°. *B,2HCl* : m.p. 157°. Very sol. H_2O. 4-N-*Benzoyl* : m.p. 215°. Sol. H_2O. 1-N-p-*toluenesulphonyl* : decomp. at 245°. 4-N-*Benzoyl*-1-N-p-*toluenesulphonyl* : needles from AcOH. M.p. 188–9°. *Picrate* : decomp. at 205–6°.

Karrer, Escher, Widmer, *Helv. Chim. Acta*, 1926, **9**, 301.
Bergmann, Köster, *Z. physiol. Chem.*, 1926, **159**, 179.
Vickery, Cook, *J. Biol. Chem.*, 1931, **94**, 393.
Lutz, Jirgensons, *Ber.*, 1931, **64**, 1221.
Keimatsu, Sugasawa, *Chem. Abstracts*, 1928, **22**, 1758.
Zimmermann, Canzanelli, *Z. physiol. Chem.*, 1933, **219**, 207.
Thomas, Kapfhammer, Flaschenträger, *Z. physiol. Chem.*, 1922, **124**, 75.
Boon, Robson, *Biochem. J.*, 1935, **29**, 2684.

Ornithuric Acid (1 : 4-N-*Dibenzoylornithine*)

$C_6H_5·CO·NH·[CH_2]_3·CH(NH·CO·C_6H_5)·COOH$

$C_{19}H_{20}O_4N_2$ MW, 340

d-.
Needles or plates from EtOH. M.p. 188–9°. Sol. AcOEt, hot EtOH. Spar. sol. H_2O. Insol. Et_2O. $[\alpha]_D^{20}$ + 8·5° in EtOH.Aq.
Me ester : $C_{20}H_{22}O_4N_2$. MW, 354. M.p. 145–6°.
Et ester : $C_{21}H_{24}O_4N_2$. MW, 368. M.p. 155°.

l-.
M.p. 189°. $[\alpha]_D^{20}$ − 9·22° in NaOH.Aq.

dl-.
Needles from EtOH. M.p. 187–8°.

See first and last references above.

Orotic Acid (*Uracil-4-carboxylic acid*)

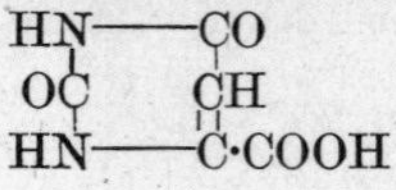

$C_5H_4O_4N_2$ MW, 156

Occurs in milk. Cryst. from H_2O. M.p. 345–6°.
Me ester : $C_6H_6O_4N_2$. MW, 170. M.p. 249°.
Et ester : $C_7H_8O_4N_2$. MW, 184. M.p. 188–9°.

Bachstez, *Ber.*, 1931, **64**, 2683.
Hilbert, *J. Am. Chem. Soc.*, 1932, **54**, 2082.
Johnson, Schroeder, *J. Am. Chem. Soc.*, 1932, **54**, 2942.

Oroxylin-A (5 : 7-*Dihydroxy*-6-*methoxyflavone*)

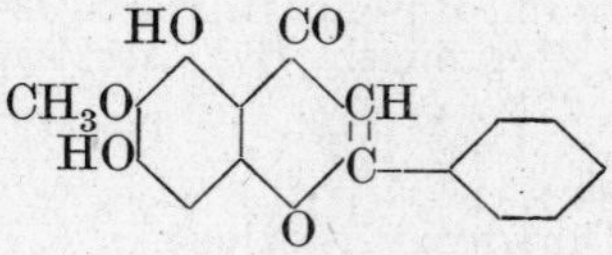

$C_{16}H_{12}O_5$ MW, 284

Colouring matter of root bark of *Oroxylum indicum*, Vent. Yellow needles from EtOH. M.p. 231–2°.
Diacetyl : m.p. 131–2°.
7-*Benzoyl* : m.p. 210°.
7-*Me ether* : $C_{17}H_{14}O_5$. MW, 298. M.p. 155–6°. *Platinichloride* : m.p. 185–7° decomp. 5-*Acetyl* : m.p. 130–1°. 5-*Benzoyl* : m.p. 206–7°.
5 : 7-*Di-Me ether* : $C_{18}H_{16}O_5$. MW, 312. M.p. 165–6°.

Shah, Mehta, Wheeler, *J. Chem. Soc.*, 1936, 591.

Orsellic Acid.
See Orsellinic Acid.

Orsellinic Acid (*Orsellic acid*, 3 : 5-*dihydroxy-o-toluic acid, orcinol-2-carboxylic acid*)

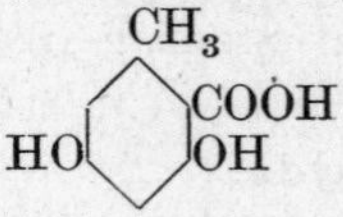

$C_8H_8O_4$ MW, 168

Needles + $1H_2O$ from AcOH.Aq. M.p. 176° decomp. Sol. EtOH, Et_2O. $k = 1·271 \times 10^{-4}$ at 25°.
Me ester : $C_9H_{10}O_4$. MW, 182. M.p. 140°.
Et ester : $C_{10}H_{12}O_4$. MW, 196. M.p. 132°.
Isoamyl ester : $C_{13}H_{18}O_4$. MW, 238. M.p. 76°.
Diacetyl : m.p. 142°. *Chloride* : m.p. 56–8°.
3-*Me ether* : *see* Isoeverninic Acid.

5-*Me ether* : *see* Everninic Acid.
Di-Me ether : *see under* Everninic Acid.
5-*Me*-3-*Et ether* : *see under* Everninic Acid.

Hesse, *Ann.*, 1866, **139**, 35.
Hoesch, *Ber.*, 1913, **46**, 888.
Koller, *Monatsh.*, 1932, **61**, 147.
Sonn, *Ber.*, 1928, **61**, 926.

p-Orsellinic Acid.
See 3 : 5-Dihydroxy-*p*-toluic Acid.
Orthanilic Acid.
See Aniline-*o*-sulphonic Acid.
Orthoacetic Acid (1 : 1 : 1-*Trihydroxyethane*)

$$CH_3 \cdot C \underset{\diagdown OH}{\overset{\diagup OH}{-OH}}$$

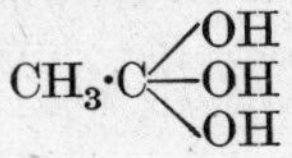

$_2H_6O_3$ MW, 78

Tri-Me ester : $C_5H_{12}O_3$. MW, 120. B.p.
07–9°. D_4^{25} 0·94375. n_D^{25} 1·38585.
Di-Me : *Et ester* : $C_6H_{14}O_3$. MW, 134. B.p.
23–6°. D_4^{25} 0·91915. n_D^{25} 1·38885.
Me-di-Et ester : $C_7H_{16}O_3$. MW, 148. B.p.
35–6°. D_4^{25} 0·90085. n_D^{25} 1·39185.
Me-di-isobutyl ester : $C_7H_{16}O_3$. MW, 148.
3.p. 205–6°.
Me-di-isoamyl ester : $C_9H_{20}O_3$. MW, 176.
3.p. 219–23°.
Tri-Et ester : $C_8H_{18}O_3$. MW, 162. B.p. 144–
°. D_4^{25} 0·8847. n_D^{25} 1·39485.
Et-dipropyl ester : $C_{10}H_{22}O_3$. MW, 190. B.p.
90–4°. D_4^{25} 0·87129. n_D^{25} 1·40635.
Et-di-butyl ester : $C_{12}H_{26}O_3$. MW, 218. B.p.
20–5°. D_4^{25} 0·86461. n_D^{25} 1·41485.
Di-isobutyl ester : $C_{10}H_{22}O_3$. MW, 190. B.p.
07–8°.
Tri-isobutyl ester : $C_{14}H_{30}O_3$. MW, 246.
3.p. 217°.

Sah, *J. Am. Chem. Soc.*, 1928, **50**, 516;
 Chem. Abstracts, 1933, **27**, 5729.
Sigmund, Herschdörfer, *Monatsh.*, 1931,
 58, 284.

Orthobenzoic Acid (ω-*Trihydroxytoluene*)

$$C_6H_5 \cdot C \underset{\diagdown OH}{\overset{\diagup OH}{-OH}}$$

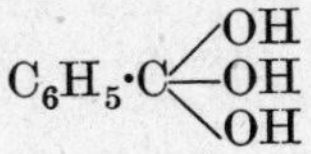

$C_7H_8O_3$ MW, 140

Tri-Et ester : $C_{13}H_{20}O_3$. MW, 224. B.p.
238–40°/747 mm. D_0^{20} 0·9902.
Di-2-naphthyl ester anhydride : needles from
PhNO₂. Does not melt below 350°.

Doebner, *Ann.*, 1890, **257**, 59.
Tschitschibabin, *Ber.*, 1905, **38**, 563.

Orthocarbonic Acid (*Tetrahydroxymethane*)

$$HO \cdot C \underset{\diagdown OH}{\overset{\diagup OH}{-OH}}$$

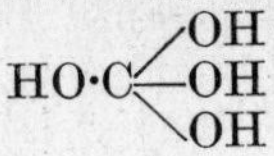

CH_4O_4 MW, 80

Tetra-Me ester : $C_5H_{12}O_4$. MW, 136. M.p.
— 5·5°. B.p. 114°. $D_{18·5}^{18·5}$ 1·0232. n_D^{16} 1·3864.
Tetra-Et ester : $C_9H_{20}O_4$. MW, 192. B.p.
158–9°, 62°/28 mm. $D_4^{18·5}$ 0·9197. $n_D^{18·5}$ 1·39354.
Tetrapropyl ester : $C_{13}H_{28}O_4$. MW, 248. B.p.
224·2°.
Tetra-isobutyl ester : $C_{17}H_{36}O_4$. MW, 304.
B.p. 244·9°.

Hartel, *Ber.*, 1927, **60**, 1841.
Röse, *Ann.*, 1880, **205**, 250.
Wilke, *Z. anorg. allgem. Chem.*, 1921, **119**,
 377.

Orthodene

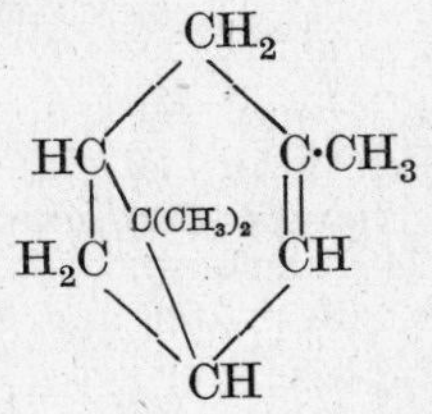

$C_{10}H_{16}$ MW, 136
Occurs in essential oil of *Orthodon lanceolatum*,
Kudo. B.p. 168–70°/757 mm. D_4^{30} 0·8430.
n_D^{30} 1·4670. $[\alpha]_D^{29}$ + 32·6°.

Fujita, *Chem. Abstracts*, 1934, **28**, 1470.

Orthodonene

$C_{15}H_{24}$ MW, 204
Occurs in essential oil of *Orthodon lanceolatum*,
Kudo. B.p. 254°/700 mm. D_4^{30} 0·9017. n_D^{30}
1·4947. $[\alpha]_D^{14}$ — 13·28°.

See previous reference.

Orthoformic Acid (*Trihydroxymethane*)

$$HC \underset{\diagdown OH}{\overset{\diagup OH}{-OH}}$$

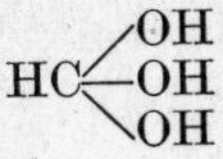

CH_4O_3 MW, 64

Tri-Me ester : $C_4H_{10}O_3$. MW, 106. B.p.
103–5°. D_4^{20} 0·9676. n_D^{20} 1·3793.
Tri-Et ester : $C_7H_{16}O_3$. MW, 148. B.p.
145–7°, 60°/30 mm. D_4^{20} 0·8909. n_D^{20} 1·3922.
Di-Et : *propyl ester* : $C_8H_{18}O_3$. MW, 162.
B.p. 165°/747 mm.; 81°/30 mm. D_4^{20} 0·8813. n_D^{20}
1·3989.
Et-dipropyl ester : $C_9H_{20}O_3$. MW, 176. B.p.
184°/745 mm., 93°/30 mm. D_4^{22} 0·8973. n_D^{20}

Tripropyl ester: $C_{10}H_{22}O_3$. MW, 190. B.p. 196–8°, 190–1°/745 mm., 93°/30 mm. D_4^{20} 0·8805. n_D^{20} 1·4072.

Dipropyl-isoamyl ester: $C_{12}H_{26}O_3$. MW, 218. B.p. 124–30°/24 mm. D_4^{23} 0·8647. n_D^{20} 1·415.

Propyl-di-isoamyl ester: $C_{14}H_{30}O_3$. MW, 246. B.p. 140–7°/30 mm. D_4^{23} 0·8626. n_D^{20} 1·4194.

Tri-isopropyl ester: b.p. 166–8°. D_4^{20} 0·8621. n_D^{20} 1·4000.

Tributyl ester: $C_{13}H_{28}O_3$. MW, 232. B.p. 245–7°. D_4^{20} 0·8693. n_D^{20} 1·4180.

Tri-isobutyl ester: b.p. 224–6°. D_4^{20} 0·8582. n_D^{20} 1·4120.

Tri-isoamyl ester: $C_{16}H_{34}O_3$. MW, 274. B.p. 267–9°, 166°/25 mm. D_4^{20} 0·8628. n_D^{20} 1·4233.

Triphenyl ester: $C_{19}H_{16}O_3$. MW, 292. M.p. 76–7°. B.p. 269–70°/50–5 mm. decomp. Sol. Et_2O, $CHCl_3$, hot EtOH, hot C_6H_6.

Tri-o-tolyl ester: $C_{22}H_{22}O_3$. MW, 334. M.p. 96°.

*Tri-*m*-tolyl ester*: m.p. 50°.

*Tri-*p*-tolyl ester*: m.p. 112°.

Trianilide: trianilinomethane. M.p. 138°. *B,3HCl*: m.p. 240° decomp.

Tri-o-toluidide: m.p. 150–1°. *B,3HCl*: m.p. 212–13°.

*Tri-*m*-toluidide*: m.p. 123°. *B,3HCl*: m.p. 221–2°.

Giacalone, *Gazz. chim. ital.*, 1932, **62**, 577.
Post, Erickson, *J. Am. Chem. Soc.*, 1933, **55**, 3851 (*Bibl.*).
Driver, *J. Am. Chem. Soc.*, 1924, **46**, 2090.
Hunter, *J. Chem. Soc.*, 1924, **125**, 1392.

Orthoform New.
See under 4-Hydroxy-*m*-aminobenzoic Acid.

Orthoform Old.
See under 3-Hydroxy-*p*-aminobenzoic Acid.

Orthopropionic Acid (1 : 1 : 1-*Trihydroxypropane*)

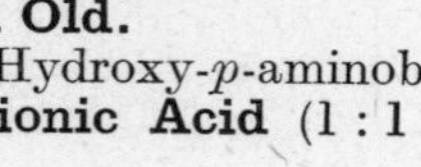

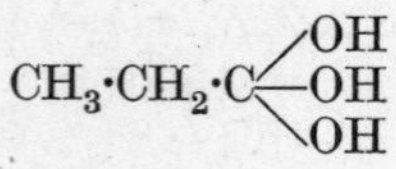

$C_3H_8O_3$ MW, 92

Tri-Et ester: $C_9H_{20}O_3$. MW, 176. B.p. 159–60°.

Kodak-Pathé, F.P., 712,995, (*Chem. Abstracts*, 1932, **26**, 1531).
Sigmund, Herschdörfer, *Monatsh.*, 1931, **58**, 282.

Oryzanin.
See Vitamin B_1.

Oscine.
See Scopoline.

Osotriazole.
See 1 : 2 : 3-Triazole.

Osthol

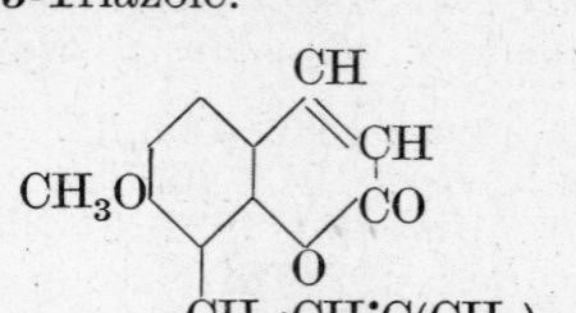

$C_{15}H_{16}O_3$ MW, 244

Occurs in root of *Imperatoria ostruthium*, Linn. Needles from EtOH.Aq. M.p. 83–4° (85°). B.p. 145–50°. Sol. EtOH, MeOH, $CHCl_3$, Me_2CO, AcOEt. Insol. H_2O, pet. ether.

Späth, Holzen, *Ber.*, 1934, **67**, 264.
Yamashita, *Bull. Chem. Soc. Japan*, 1933, **8**, 276.

Ostholic Acid

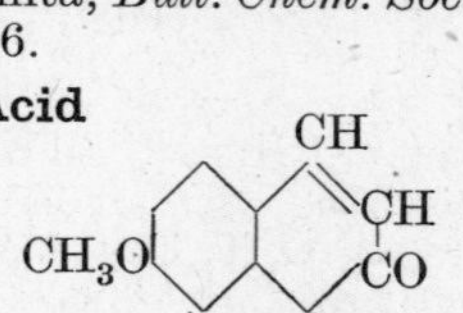

$C_{12}H_{10}O_5$ MW, 234

Needles from AcOEt. M.p. 254–5°.

Me ester: $C_{13}H_{12}O_5$. MW, 248. M.p. 155°.

Späth, Pesta, *Ber.*, 1933, **66**, 759.

Ostreastanol.
See Sitostanol.

Ostreasterol-1

$C_{29}H_{48}O$ MW, 412

Occurs in oysters. M.p. 142–3°. $[\alpha]_D^{20}$ — 43·57° in $CHCl_3$.

Acetyl deriv.: m.p. 134·5°. $[\alpha]_D^{20}$ — 45·95° in $CHCl_3$.

Propionyl deriv.: m.p. 113–14°.

Benzoyl deriv.: m.p. 145–7°.

Bergmann, *J. Biol. Chem.*, 1934, **104**, 317, 553.

Ostreasterol-2

$C_{28}H_{48}O_2$ MW, 416

Plates from EtOH. M.p. 122°.

Acetyl deriv.: prisms. M.p. 104°. $[\alpha_D^{21}]$ — 15·9°.

See previous reference.

Ostruthin

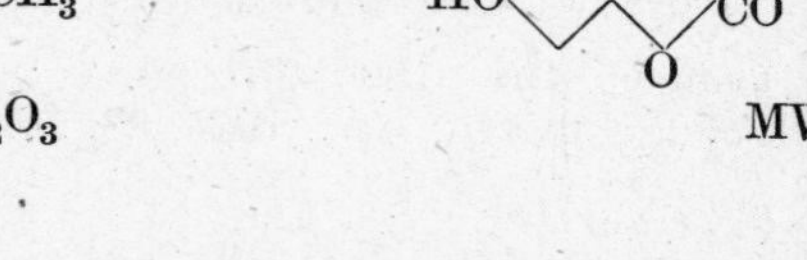

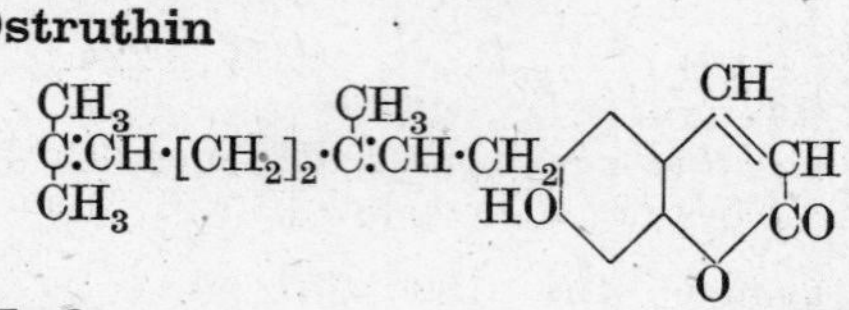

$C_{19}H_{22}O_3$ MW, 298

Occurs in root of *Imperatoria ostruthium*, Linn. ;ryst. from EtOH.Aq. M.p. 119° (117°). Sol. ;HCl$_3$, AcOEt, hot EtOH. Insol. H_2O, pet. ther.

Acetyl deriv. : m.p. 80°.

Me ether : $C_{20}H_{24}O_3$. MW, 312. M.p. 55–5·5°.

Späth, Klager, *Ber.*, 1934, **67**, 859.
Butenandt, Marten, *Ann.*, 1932, **495**, 197.

Ostruthol

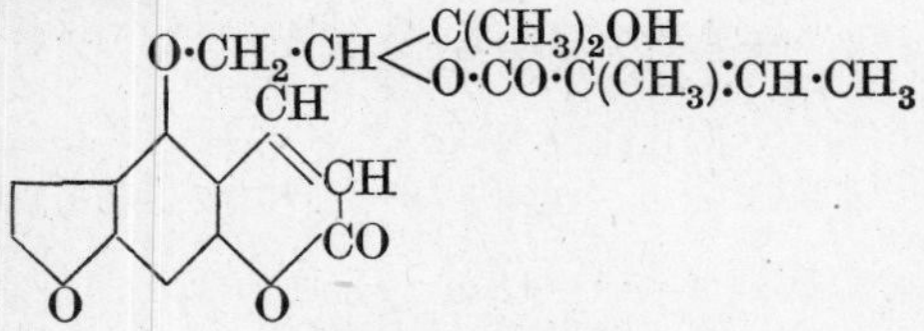

Probable structure

$_{21}H_{22}O_7$ MW, 386

Occurs in *Imperatoria ostruthium*, Linn. ;ryst. from C_6H_6. M.p. 136–7°. B.p. 225°/ ·015 mm. $[\alpha]_D^{15}$ — 18·3° in Py.

Acetyl deriv. : m.p. 125°.

Späth, Christiani, *Ber.*, 1933, **66**, 1150.

Osyritrin.
See Rutin.

Ouabain (*Acocantherin, g-strophanthin*)

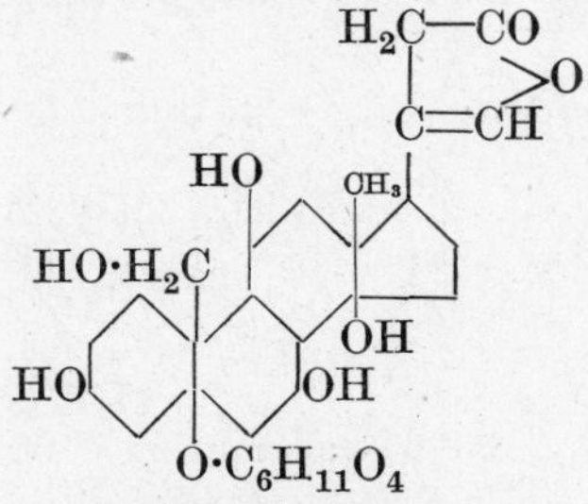

Suggested structure

$_{29}H_{44}O_{12}$ MW, 584

Glucoside occurring in *Acocanthera oabaio.* I.p. 180° (indefinite). Hyd. ⟶ rhamnose + cocanthic acid lactone.

Jacobs, Bigelow, *J. Biol. Chem.*, 1933, **101**, 15.
Sohwurtze, Hann, Keenan, *Chem. Abstracts*, 1930, **24**, 917.
Moir, *Chem. Abstracts*, 1924, **18**, 1825.
Richaud, *Chem. Abstracts*, 1922, **16**, 314.
Catilloni, *Chem. Abstracts*, 1918, **12**, 741.
Klein, *Chem. Abstracts*, 1914, **8**, 988.
Arnaud, *Compt. rend.*, 1888, **107**, 1162.
Fieser, Newman, *J. Biol. Chem.*, 1936, **114**, 705.

Ovoflavine.
See Lactoflavine.

Oxalacetic Acid (*Ketosuccinic acid, hydroxyfumaric acid, hydroxymaleic acid*)

HOOC·CO·CH$_2$·COOH (C-2, C-1)
I

HOOC·C(OH)
HC·COOH
II

HOOC·C(OH)
HOOC·CH
III

$C_4H_4O_5$ MW, 132

II.

Cryst. from Me_2CO–C_6H_6. M.p. 184°. Sol. H_2O, EtOH, Et_2O. Insol. $CHCl_3$, C_6H_6. Heat of comb. C_p 274·10 Cal., C_v 275·78 Cal. $k = 2{\cdot}76 \times 10^{-3}$ at 17°. Py at 50° ⟶ III.

III.

Cryst. from Me_2CO–C_6H_6. M.p. 152°. Sol. EtOH, Me_2CO, AcOEt. Spar. sol. Et_2O. Insol. C_6H_6, $CHCl_3$, ligroin. Heat of comb. C_p 284·9 Cal., C_v 286·58 Cal. $k = 2{\cdot}505 \times 10^{-3}$ at 17°.

I.

A,2NH$_3$: m.p. 75–7° decomp.

A,(CO(NH$_2$)$_2$)$_2$: m.p. 124° decomp.

Di-brucine salt : m.p. 163–6°. Esters and salts are probably of I.

Di-Me ester : $C_6H_8O_5$. MW, 160. M.p. 74° (77°). *Me ether* : $C_7H_{10}O_5$. MW, 174. B.p. 228–30°.

1-*Et ester* : $C_6H_8O_5$. MW, 160. M.p. 102–3°. Sol. H_2O, EtOH, Et_2O. Spar. sol. C_6H_6.

Di-Et ester : $C_8H_{12}O_5$. MW, 188. B.p. 131–2°/24 mm. D_4^{20} 1·130–1·132. $n_D^{16\cdot6}$ 1·45614. *Semicarbazone* : m.p. 162°. p-*Chlorophenylhydrazone* : m.p. 119–20°. p-*Tolylhydrazone* : m.p. 105–6°.

1-*Me* : 2-*Et ester* : $C_7H_{10}O_5$. MW, 174. B.p. 130°/22 mm., 124°/16 mm. *Cu Salt* : green prisms from EtOH. M.p. 134–5°.

2-*Me* : 1-*Et ester* : b.p. 110°/13 mm. *Cu salt* : green needles. M.p. 165–6° (173–4° anhyd.).

2-*Et ester* : 1-*nitrile* : *oxime* : isonitrososuccinic acid Et ester nitrile. M.p. 104°. *Acetyl deriv.* : m.p. 146°.

Di-isoamyl ester : $C_{14}H_{24}O_5$. MW, 272. B.p. 167°/23 mm. *Cu salt* : green needles from EtOH. M.p. 83–5°.

Diamide : $C_4H_6O_3N_2$. MW, 130. M.p. 180° decomp.

Anhydride: *acetyl deriv.*: acetoxymaleic anhydride. M.p. 89–91°.

Oxime: isonitrososuccinic acid. (i) M.p. 126° decomp. (ii) M.p. 88° decomp.

2 : 4-*Dinitrophenylhydrazone*: m.p. 211° decomp.

Diels, Meyer, *Ann.*, 1934, **513**, 139.

U.S. Industrial Alcohol Co., U.S.P., 1,948,201, (*Chem. Abstracts*, 1934, **28**, 2730).

Blanchetière, *Compt. rend.*, 1916, **163**, 206.

Hantzsch, *Ber.*, 1915, **48**, 1407.

Gault, *Compt. rend.*, 1914, **158**, 711.

Fenton, Wilks, *J. Chem. Soc.*, 1912, **101**, 1570.

Meyer, *Ber.*, 1912, **45**, 2860.

Oxalacetoacetic Ethyl Ester

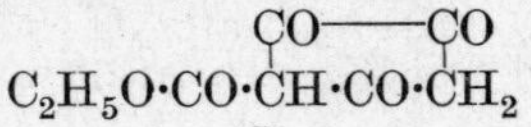

$$CO\text{——}CO$$
$$C_2H_5O\cdot CO\cdot CH\cdot CO\cdot CH_2$$
I

$$CO\text{——}C(OH)$$
$$C_2H_5O\cdot CO\cdot CH\cdot CO\cdot CH$$
II

$$CO\text{——}CH_2$$
$$C_2H_5O\cdot CO\cdot C\text{:}C(OH)\cdot CO$$
III

$C_8H_8O_5$ MW, 184

(a) Yellow needles from Me_2CO. M.p. 145–50° decomp. Sol. H_2O, hot EtOH, hot AcOH. Spar. sol. Et_2O, ligroin.

Phenylhydrazone: m.p. 184–6° decomp.

Di-phenylhydrazone: m.p. 198–202°.

(b) Yellow leaflets from AcOEt. M.p. 105–10°. Sol. H_2O. Mod. sol. ord. org. solvents.

Wislicenus, Schollkopf, *J. prakt. Chem.*, 1917, **95**, 269.

Oxalan (*Oxaluramide*)

$$NH_2\cdot CO\cdot NH\cdot CO\cdot CO\cdot NH_2$$
$C_3H_5O_3N_3$ MW, 131

Cryst. Does not melt below 310°. Insol. H_2O. Sol. H_2SO_4, repptd. by H_2O.

Schenck, *Ber.*, 1905, **38**, 459.

Seemann, *Z. physik. Chem.*, 1905, **44**, 244.

Oxalic Acid

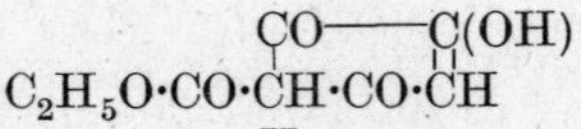

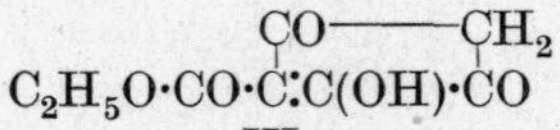

$$COOH$$
$$COOH$$
$C_2H_2O_4$ MW, 90

Occurs in many plants. Cryst. $+ 2H_2O$ from H_2O. M.p. 101·5°, anhyd. 189·5°. Dehydrates on heating and sublimes at 150–60°. Sol. 10·5 parts H_2O at 15°. Mod. sol. EtOH. Spar. sol. Et_2O. $Ca^{\cdot\cdot}$ and $Hg^{\cdot}$ salts very spar. sol. H_2O. k (first) $= 3\cdot4$–$3\cdot6 \times 10^{-2}$ at 25°. $D_4^{18\cdot5}$ 1·653. Heat of comb. C_p 60·2 Cal., C_v 61·1 Cal.

Me ester: $C_3H_4O_4$. MW, 104. B.p. 108–9°.

Di-Me ester: see Dimethyl oxalate.

Me-Et ester: $C_5H_8O_4$. MW, 132. B.p. 173·7°. D_0^0 1·5505.

Et ester: $C_4H_6O_4$. MW, 118. B.p. 117°/15 mm. D_4^{20} 1·2175. *Hydrazide*: m.p. 52–3° decomp.

Di-Et ester: see Diethyl oxalate.

Ethylene ester: $C_4H_4O_4$. MW, 116. M.p. 144°. Readily polymerises.

Propyl ester: $C_5H_8O_4$. MW, 132. B.p. 118–19°/13 mm.

Dipropyl ester: $C_8H_{14}O_4$. MW, 174. M.p. $-46\cdot3°$. B.p. 214–15° (211–12°). D_4^{20} 1·01693. n_D^{20} 1·4168.

Isopropyl ester: $C_5H_8O_4$. MW, 132. B.p. 111°/13 mm. D_4^{20} 1·1657.

Di-isopropyl ester: $C_8H_{14}O_4$. MW, 174. B.p. 189° (193–4°). D_4^{20} 1·00097. n_D^{20} 1·4100.

Dibutyl ester: $C_{10}H_{18}O_4$. MW, 202. F.p. $-29\cdot6°$. B.p. 247–9°. D_4^{20} 0·98732. n_D^{20} 1·4234.

Di-isobutyl ester: b.p. 229–31°. D_4^{20} 0·97373. n_D^{20} 1·4180.

Di-n-amyl ester: $C_{12}H_{22}O_4$. MW, 230. M.p. $-12\cdot8°$. B.p. 154·1°/14·8 mm. D^{20} 0·9722. n_D^{20} 1·4302.

Di-isoamyl ester: b.p. 267–8°.

Di-n-hexyl ester: $C_{14}H_{26}O_4$. MW, 258. M.p. $-9\cdot0°$. B.p. 135–6°/2·5 mm. D^{20} 0·9523. n_D^{20} 1·4331.

Di-n-heptyl ester: $C_{16}H_{30}O_4$. MW, 286. M.p. 12·5°. B.p. 142–4°/2 mm. D^{20} 0·9393. n_D^{20} 1·4372.

Di-n-nonyl ester: $C_{18}H_{34}O_4$. MW, 314. M.p. 11·2°. B.p. 167–9°/3 mm. D^{20} 0·9293. n_D^{20} 1·4404.

Dimyricyl ester: $C_{62}H_{122}O_4$. MW, 930. M.p. 91°.

Diallyl ester: $C_8H_{10}O_4$. MW, 170. B.p. 206–7°/754 mm.

Dicyclohexyl ester: $C_{14}H_{22}O_4$. MW, 254. M.p. 42°.

Diphenyl ester: $C_{14}H_{10}O_4$. MW, 242. M.p. 134°.

Di-o-nitrophenyl ester: $C_{14}H_8O_8N_2$. MW, 332. M.p. 185°.

Di-o-tolyl ester : $C_{16}H_{14}O_4$. MW, 270. M.p. 90–1°.
Di-m-tolyl ester : m.p. 105°.
Di-p-tolyl ester : m.p. 148°.
Di-p-nitrobenzyl ester : $C_{16}H_{12}O_8N_2$. MW, 360. M.p. 204°.
Me ester chloride : $C_3H_3O_3Cl$. MW, 122·5. B.p. 125° (118–20°). D_4^{20} 1·33163.
Et ester chloride : $C_4H_5O_3Cl$. MW, 136·5. B.p. 135°, 30°/10 mm. D_4^{20} 1·2226.
Propyl ester chloride : $C_5H_7O_3Cl$. MW, 150·5. B.p. 156–8°, 50°/12 mm. D_4^{20} 1·16697.
Isobutyl ester chloride : $C_6H_9O_3Cl$. MW, 164·5. B.p. 163–5°, 52°/10 mm. D_4^{20} 1·11532.
Isoamyl ester chloride : $C_7H_{11}O_3Cl$. MW, 178·5. B.p. 183–5°, 68°/10 mm. D_4^{20} 1·09312.
Dichloride : *see* Oxalyl chloride.
Monoamide : *see* Oxamic Acid.
Diamide : *see* Oxamide.
Amide-nitrile : *see under* Cyanoformic Acid.
Mononitrile : *see* Cyanoformic Acid.
sym.-*Dimethylamide* : *see* *sym.*-Dimethyloxamide.
unsym.-*Dimethylamide* : *see* Dimethyloxamic Acid.
Amide-nitrile : *see under* Cyanoformic Acid.
Dinitrile : *see* Cyanogen.
Methylamide : *see* Methyloxamic Acid.
Monoanilide : *see* Oxanilic Acid.
Nitroanilide : *see* Nitro-oxanilic Acid.
Dianilide : *see* Oxanilide.
Di-o-nitroanilide : yellow plates from aniline. M.p. 331° part. decomp.
Di-m-nitroanilide : needles from aniline. M.p. 309–10°.
Di-p-nitroanilide : yellowish needles from aniline. M.p. 358–9° (260°).
Hydrazide : does not melt below 300°.
Dihydrazide : m.p. 241° decomp. N : N′-*Diacetyl* : m.p. 276°. *Hexa-acetyl* : m.p. 156–8°.

Johnson, Partington, *J. Chem. Soc.*, 1930, 1510.
Semenov, Shagalov, Astrakhantzev, *Chem. Abstracts*, 1935, **29**, 6882.
Chrzaszcz, Zakomorry, *Biochem. Z.*, 1935, **279**, 64.
Skinner, *J. Am. Chem. Soc.*, 1933, **55**, 2036.
Rakusin, *Chem.-Ztg.*, 1931, **55**, 128.
Jewel, Butts, *J. Am. Chem. Soc.*, 1931, **53**, 3560.
Sah, Chen, *ibid.*, 3901.
Mugdan, Sint, D.R.P., 606,774, (*Chem. Abstracts*, 1935, **29**, 3691).
du Pont, U.S.P., 1,948,441, (*Chem. Abstracts*, 1934, **28**, 2728).

2-Oxalobutyric Acid

HOOC·CO·CH(CH_3)·CH_2·COOH
I

HOOC·C(OH):C(CH_3)·CH_2·COOH
II

$C_6H_8O_5$ MW, 160

Di-Et ester : $C_{10}H_{16}O_5$. MW, 216. B.p. 163°/5 mm.

Feist, Brewer, *Ann.*, 1922, **428**, 68.

Oxalocrotonic Acid (1-*Hydroxymuconic acid*)

HOOC·CO·CH_2·CH:CH·COOH
I

HOOC·C(OH):CH·CH:CH·COOH
II

$C_6H_6O_5$ MW, 158

Yellow cryst. M.p. about 190° decomp. Sol. EtOH, AcOH, H·COOH. Spar. sol. H_2O. Insol. C_6H_6, $CHCl_3$.

Lapworth, *J. Chem. Soc.*, 1901, **79**, 1279.

Oxalodiacetic Acid.
See Ketipic Acid.

Oxalomalonic Acid

HOOC·CO·CH<(COOH)(COOH)
I

HOOC·C(OH):C<(COOH)(COOH)
II

$C_5H_4O_7$ MW, 176

Tri-Me ester : $C_8H_{10}O_7$. MW, 218. Needles from Et_2O. M.p. 49–50°. Sol. Et_2O, C_6H_6, $CHCl_3$. Spar. sol. EtOH.
Tri-Et ester : $C_{11}H_{16}O_7$. MW, 260. B.p. 220°/10 mm. D_4^{20} 1·153. n_D^{20} 1·4468.

Auwers, Auffenberg, *Ber.*, 1918, **51**, 1103.

Oxalomethylaniline.
See *N*-Methyloxanilic Acid.

1-Oxalopropionic Acid (*Methyloxalacetic acid*)

HOOC·CH(CH_3)·CO·COOH

$C_5H_6O_5$ MW, 146

Di-Et ester : $C_9H_{14}O_5$. MW, 202. Liq. B.p. 137–8°/23 mm., 114–16°/10 mm. Misc. with EtOH, Et_2O. Insol. H_2O. Decomp. on standing. Alc. $FeCl_3$ $\longrightarrow$ intense red col.
Monoamide : $C_5H_7O_4N$. MW, 145. Not isolated. *Phenylhydrazone* : m.p. 99–100°.

Mononitrile : $C_5H_5O_3N$. MW, 127. Yellow cryst. from Et_2O–pet. ether. M.p. 207–8°. Sol. H_2O. Insol. C_6H_6. Reacts acid. Alc. $FeCl_3 \longrightarrow$ red col.

Wislicenus, Arnold, *Ann.*, 1888, **246**, 329.
Wislicenus, Silberstein, *Ber.*, 1910, **43**, 1829.

Oxalosuccinic Acid

HOOC·CO·CH·COOH
        |
       CH_2·COOH
I

HOOC·C(OH):C·COOH
            |
           CH_2·COOH
II

$C_6H_6O_7$ MW, 190

Tri-Et ester : $C_{12}H_{18}O_7$. MW, 274. B.p. 170–5°/12–13 mm. *Phenylhydrazone* : decomp. at 85°.

Wislicenus, Waldmüller, *Ber.*, 1911, **44**, 1564.

Oxaluramide.
See Oxalan.

Oxaluric Acid (*Mono-oxalylurea*)

HOOC·CO·NH·CO·NH_2

$C_3H_4O_4N_2$ MW, 132

Cryst. Decomp. at 208–10°. Sol. H_2O. Spar. sol. ord. org. solvents. Heat of comb. 207·7 Cal. Hot $H_2O \longrightarrow$ oxalic acid + urea.
Me ester : $C_4H_6O_4N_2$. MW, 146. M.p. 192° decomp.
Et ester : $C_5H_8O_4N_2$. MW, 160. M.p. 177–8° decomp.
ω-N-*Formyl* : m.p. 175° decomp.
Amide : *see* Oxalan.
Hydrazide : m.p. 198° decomp.

Fosse, Thomas, Graeve, *Compt. rend.*, 1935, **200**, 1260.
Biltz, Schauder, *J. prakt. Chem.*, 1923, **106**, 147.

Oxalyl bromide

COBr
|
COBr

$C_2O_2Br_2$ MW, 216

Green liq. M.p. — 19·5°. B.p. 102–3°/720 mm., 16–17°/10 mm.

Staudinger, Anthes, *Ber.*, 1913, **46**, 1431.

Oxalylcarbanilide.
See Diphenylparabanic Acid.

Oxalyl chloride

COCl
|
COCl

$C_2O_2Cl_2$ MW, 127

Needles from Et_2O or pet. ether at — 80°. M.p. — 12°. B.p. 63·5–64°/763 mm. $D_4^{13\cdot4}$ 1·4884. $n_D^{12\cdot8}$ 1·434.

Staudinger, *Ber.*, 1908, **41**, 3563; D.R.Ps., 216,918–19, (*Chem. Abstracts*, 1910, **4**, 1087).
Jones, Tasker, *Proc. Chem. Soc.*, 1908, **24**, 271.
Giua, *Chem. Abstracts*, 1925, **19**, 1245.

Oxalyldiacetic Acid.
See Ketipic Acid.
Oxalyl-diacetophenone.
See Diphenacyl Diketone.
Oxalyldimethylurea.
See Dimethylparabanic Acid.
Oxalylguanidine

CO·NH
| >C:NH
CO·NH

$C_3H_3O_2N_3$ MW, 113

Prisms from H_2O. M.p. 266–8° decomp. (sealed tube). Sol. $H_2O \longrightarrow$ oxalic acid + guanidine slowly. Insol. EtOH.

Traube, *Ber.*, 1893, **26**, 2552.

Oxalylmethylurea.
See Methylparabanic Acid.
Oxalylurea.
See Oxaluric Acid *and* Parabanic Acid.
Oxamethane.
See under Oxamic Acid.
Oxamic Acid (*Oxaminic acid, oxalic acid monoamide*)

$CONH_2$
|
COOH

$C_2H_3O_3N$ MW, 89

Cryst. from H_2O. M.p. 210° decomp. Spar. sol. H_2O. Insol. EtOH, Et_2O. Heat of comb. C_p 132·0 Cal., C_v 129·5 Cal.
Me ester : $C_3H_5O_3N$. MW, 103. M.p. 122–3°.
Et ester : oxamethane. $C_4H_7O_3N$. MW, 117. M.p. 114–15°. N-*Acetyl* : m.p. 53·5–54·5°.
Pentachloroethyl ester : $C_4H_2O_3NCl_5$. MW, 289·5. M.p. 134°.
Propyl ester : $C_5H_9O_3N$. MW, 131. M.p. 90–2°.
Isopropyl ester : m.p. 86–7°.
Butyl ester : $C_6H_{11}O_3N$. MW, 145. M.p. 82–4°.
Isobutyl ester : m.p. 89–90°.

Isoamyl ester: $C_7H_{13}O_3N$. MW, 159. M.p. 92–3°.
Amide: *see* Oxamide.
Hydrazide: semioxamazide. M.p. 220–1° decomp. (223–4°).
Diacetyl: $H_2N{\cdot}CO{\cdot}CO{\cdot}NH{\cdot}N(CO{\cdot}CH_3)_2$. M.p. 184–5°.
N-*Me*: *see* Methyloxamic Acid.
N-*Di-Me*: *see* Dimethyloxamic Acid.
Nitroanilide: *see under* Nitro-oxanilic Acid.

Sah, Chen, *J. Am. Chem. Soc.*, 1931, **53**, 3901.
Oelkers, *Ber.*, 1889, **22**, 1569.
Weddige, *J. prakt. Chem.*, 1874, **10**, 196.

Oxamide (*Oxalic acid diamide*)

$$\begin{array}{l} CONH_2 \\ | \\ CONH_2 \end{array}$$

$C_2H_4O_2N_2$ MW, 88

Needles. Spar. sol. EtOH, hot H_2O. Decomp. above 320°. Heat of comb. C_p 203·3 Cal.
N : N′-*Dipropionyl*: m.p. 216° decomp.
N : N′-*Dibutyryl*: m.p. 197°.
N : N′-*Di-isobutyryl*: m.p. 160°.

Kasiwagi, *Bull. Chem. Soc. Japan*, 1926, **1**, 67.
Langebeck, *Ann.*, 1929, **469**, 16.
Bucher, Canadian P., 173,369, (*Chem. Abstracts*, 1918, **12**, 156); U.S.P., 1,194,354, (*Chem. Abstracts*, 1916, **10**, 2500).

Oxanilic Acid (*Oxalic acid monoanilide*)

$$\begin{array}{l} COOH \\ | \\ CO{\cdot}NH{\cdot}C_6H_5 \end{array}$$

$C_8H_7O_3N$. MW, 165

Needles from C_6H_6. M.p. 148–9° (149–50°). Sol. EtOH, Et_2O, $CHCl_3$. Mod. sol. hot H_2O. Spar. sol. C_6H_6, ligroin. $k = 1{\cdot}21 \times 10^{-2}$ at 25°. Heat of comb. C_p 863·1 Cal.
Me ester: $C_9H_9O_3N$. MW, 179. M.p. 114° (111–12°).
Et ester: $C_{10}H_{11}O_3N$. MW, 193. M.p. 66–7°. Heat of comb. C_p 1191·2 Cal. N-*Acetyl*: m.p. 64–5°.
Propyl ester: $C_{11}H_{13}O_3N$. MW, 207. M.p. 92°.
Isopropyl ester: m.p. 52°.
Isobutyl ester: $C_{12}H_{15}O_3N$. MW, 221. M.p. 85°.
Isoamyl ester: $C_{13}H_{17}O_3N$. MW, 235. M.p. 50°.
m-*Tolyl ester*: $C_{15}H_{13}O_3N$. MW, 255. M.p. 94°.
p-*Tolyl ester*: m.p. 132°.
Chloride: $C_8H_6O_2NCl$. MW, 183·5. M.p. 82·5°.
Amide: $C_8H_8O_2N_2$. MW, 164. M.p. 228° (224–5°).
Nitrile: $C_8H_6ON_2$. MW, 146. M.p. 128° decomp.
Anilide: *see* Oxanilide.

Aschan, *Ber.*, 1890, **23**, 1820.
Stobbe, Knebel, *Ber.*, 1921, **54**, 1216.

Oxanilide (sym.-*Diphenyloxamide, oxalic dianilide*)

$$\begin{array}{l} CO{\cdot}NH{\cdot}C_6H_5 \\ | \\ CO{\cdot}NH{\cdot}C_6H_5 \end{array}$$

$C_{14}H_{12}O_2N_2$ MW, 240

Leaflets from C_6H_6 or $PhNO_2$. M.p. 254° (252–3°). B.p. above 360°. Sol. C_6H_6. Spar. sol. hot EtOH. Insol. H_2O, Et_2O. Heat of comb. C_p 1665·4 Cal. Forms a *N*-Na deriv.
N-*Acetyl*: m.p. 197–8°.
N : N′-*Diacetyl*: m.p. 208–9° decomp.
N : N′-*Dibutyryl*: m.p. 156°.
N : N′-*Dibenzoyl*: m.p. 212–13° decomp. (210°).

Bornwater, *Rec. trav. chim.*, 1912, **31**, 108.
Macullum, *J. Soc. Chem. Ind.*, 1923, **42** 468T.

Oxanthranol (10-*Hydroxyanthrone, oxanthrone*)

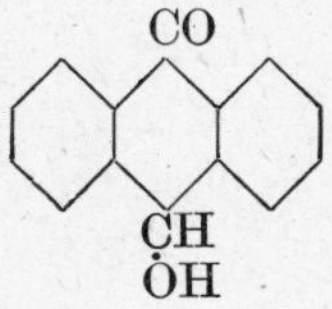

$C_{14}H_{10}O_2$ MW, 210

Keto form of anthrahydroquinone. Colourless cryst. M.p. 167° decomp. Sols. do not fluoresce. Stable in air. Insol. cold alkalis. Sol. hot alc. alkalis, isomerising to anthrahydroquinone. Zn + AcOH ⟶ anthranol.
Acetyl: m.p. 108–9°.
Me ether: 10-methoxyanthrone. $C_{15}H_{12}O_2$. MW, 224. M.p. 102·5° (98°).

Meyer, *Ann.*, 1911, **379**, 60, 77.

Oxanthrone.
See Oxanthranol.
Oxeserolene.
See Hydroxyeserolene.

Oxetone

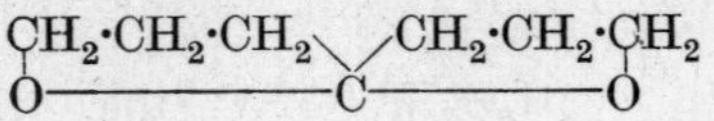

$C_7H_{12}O_2$ MW, 128

F.p. below — 17°. B.p. 159·4°. Mod. sol. cold H_2O. Spar. sol. hot H_2O. Spar. sol. EtOH, Et_2O, $CHCl_3$, C_6H_6. Reduces Tollen's reagent.

Fittig, Ström, *Ann.*, 1892, **267**, 197.
Granichstädten, Werner, *Monatsh.*, 1901, 22, 333.

Oximino-.
See also Isonitroso-.
Oximinoadipic Acid.
See under 1-Ketoadipic Acid.
Oxindole (*2-Hydroxyindole*)

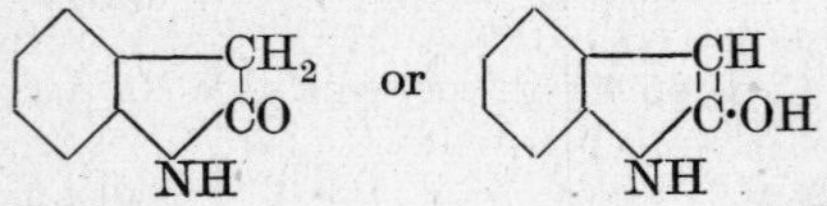

C_8H_7ON MW, 133

Needles from H_2O. M.p. 127°. B.p. 227°/23 mm. Sol. EtOH, Et_2O, hot H_2O. Reduces Tollen's reagent.
N-*Acetyl*: m.p. 126°.

Stollé, *J. prakt. Chem.*, 1930, **128**, 1.
Heller, *Ber.*, 1916, **49**, 2775.
Marschalk, *J. prakt. Chem.*, 1914, **88**, 234.

Oxindole-4-carboxylic Acid

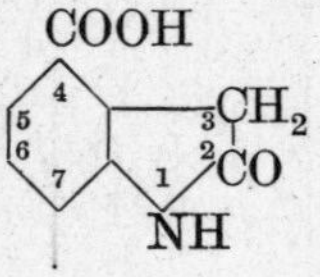

$C_9H_7O_3N$ MW, 177

Yellow cryst. Decomp. above 280°.

Braun, Hahn, *Ber.*, 1923, **56**, 2345.

Oxindole-6-carboxylic Acid.
Brownish-yellow cryst. from EtOH.Aq. M.p. 313°. Spar. sol. ord. org. solvents.

Fileti, Cairola, *Gazz. chim. ital.*, 1892, **22**, ii, 392.

Oxindone.
1 : 2-Diketohydrindene, *q.v.*
Oxine.
See 8-Hydroxyquinoline.
Oxisatin.
Coumarandione, *q.v.*

Oxonic Acid (*Allantoxanic acid*)

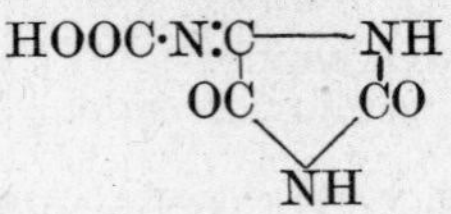

$C_4H_3O_4N_3$ MW, 15

M.p. anhyd. about 261° decomp.

Biltz, Robi, *Ber.*, 1920, **53**, 1967.

Oxonitine

$C_{31}H_{41}O_{12}N$ MW, 61

Needles from AcOH–Me_2CO. M.p. 277° de comp. Spar. sol. ord. org. solvents. [α] — 48·18° in $CHCl_3$.

Majima, Suginome, Shimanuki, *Ber.* 1932, **65**, 595 (*Bibl.*).
Lawson, *J. Chem. Soc.*, 1936, 82.

Oxyacanthine

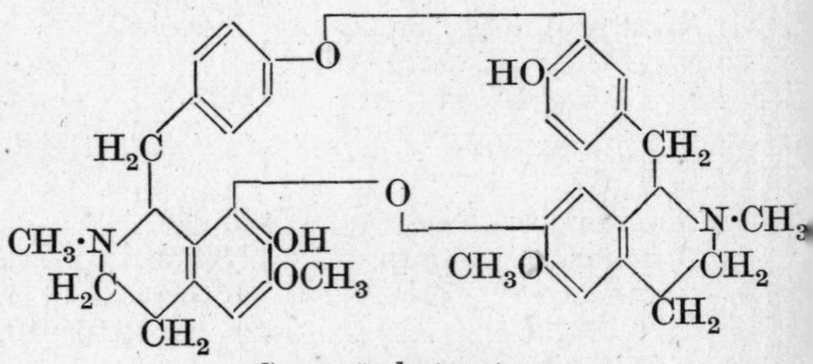

Suggested structure

$C_{38}H_{38}O_6N_2$ MW, 61

Occurs in root of *Berberis vulgaris.* Needles from EtOH. M.p. 217° (208–14°). Sol. $CHCl_3$ C_6H_6. Insol. ligroin. $[\alpha]_D$ + 131·6° in $CHCl_3$.
B,HCl: m.p. 270°.
B,HBr: m.p. 273°.
Me ether: $C_{39}H_{40}O_6N_2$. MW, 632. *B,HCl* m.p. 261°.

Bruchhausen, Gericke, *Chem. Zentr.*, 1931, I, 2761.

Oxyberberine

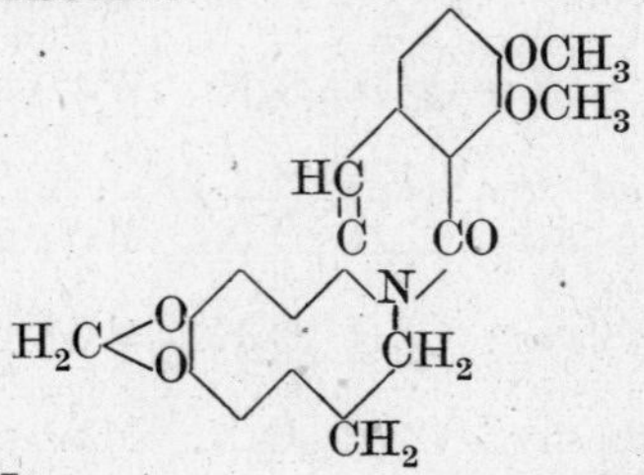

$C_{20}H_{17}O_5N$ MW, 351

Yellow needles from EtOH. M.p. 198–200°. Sol. hot AcOH. Spar. sol. EtOH, C_6H_6. Insol. ligroin.

Perkin, Ray, Robinson, *J. Chem. Soc.*, 1925, 742.
Haworth, Koepfli, Perkin, *J. Chem. Soc.*, 1927, 552.
Späth, Quietensky, *Ber.*, 1925, **58**, 2267.

Oxycyanogen (*Oxycyan*)

$(CNO)_x$

$(CNO)_x$ MW, $(42)_x$

Plates. M.p. — 12·5 to — 11·5°. Decomp. at ord. temp. except in solution. Sol. CS_2, CCl_4. Liberates I from KI.

Hunt, *J. Am. Chem. Soc.*, 1932, **54**, 907.

Oxyhydrastinine

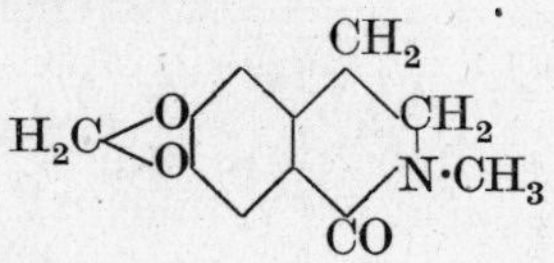

$C_{11}H_{11}O_3N$ MW, 205

Needles from ligroin. M.p. 97–8°. Mod. sol. EtOH, $CHCl_3$, C_6H_6, AcOEt, CS_2. $KMnO_4$ ⟶ hydrastic acid.
B,HBr : m.p. 200°.
B_2,H_2PtCl_6 : m.p. 160°.

Freund, *Ber.*, 1889, **22**, 457.
Perkin, *J. Chem. Soc.*, 1890, **57**, 1034.

Oxy-Koch Acid.
See 1-Naphthol-3 : 6 : 8-trisulphonic Acid.
Oxyneurine.
See Betaine.
Oxypeucedanic Acid

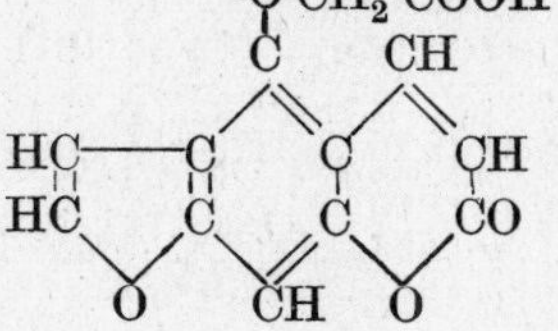

$C_{13}H_8O_6$ MW, 260

Cryst. from AcOH.Aq. M.p. 265°.
Me ester : $C_{14}H_{10}O_6$. MW, 274. Cryst. from MeOH.Aq. M.p. 185°.

Späth, Klager, *Ber.*, 1933, **66, 921.**
Butenandt, Marten, *Ann.*, 1932, **495**, 209.

Oxypeucedanine

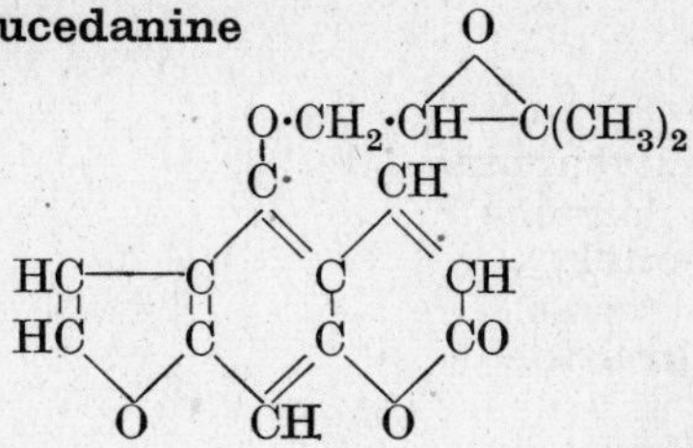

$C_{16}H_{14}O_5$ MW, 286

Occurs in root of *Imperatoria ostruthium*, Linn. Cryst. from Et_2O–$CHCl_3$. M.p. 142–3°. KOH fusion ⟶ phloroglucinol.
Hydrate : cryst. from AcOEt or MeOH.Aq. M.p. 134°. *Monoacetyl* : cryst. from Me_2CO–pet. ether. M.p. 139°. *Diacetyl* : cryst. from $CHCl_3$–pet. ether. M.p. 132–3° (136°). *Monobenzoyl* : cryst. from EtOH.Aq. M.p. 172–172·5°. *Phenylurethane* : cryst. from AcOEt–pet. ether. M.p. 174°.

Späth, Klager, *Ber.*, 1933, **66**, 914.
Butenandt, Marten, *Ann.*, 1932, **495**, 205.

Oxysparteine (*Isolupanine*)

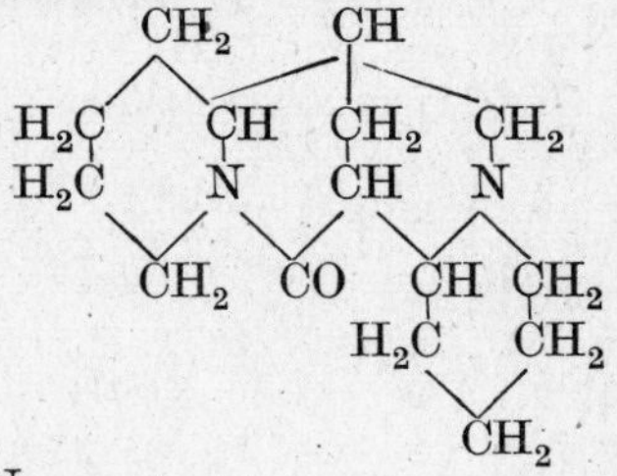

$C_{15}H_{24}ON_2$ MW, 248

Cryst. from pet. ether. M.p. 111°.
B,HI : prisms from EtOH. M.p. 275°.
Methiodide : m.p. 203–4°.

Clemo, Morgan, Raper, *J. Chem. Soc.*, 1936, 1025.

Oxytiglic Acid.
See 1 : 2-Dimethylglycidic Acid.
Ozobenzene (*Benzene triozonide*)

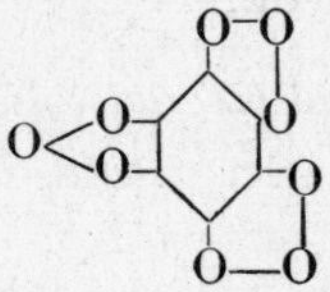

$C_6H_6O_9$ MW, 222

Amorp. Explodes at 50°. Very violent explosive. Insol. EtOH, Et_2O, $CHCl_3$, CS_2, ligroin. H_2O ⟶ CO_2 + H·COOH + CH_3·COOH.

Renard, *Bull. soc. chim.*, 1895, **13**, 940.
Anon., *Chem. Abstracts*, 1920, **14**, 1220.

P

Pachycarpine.
See Sparteine.

Pæonol.
See Peonol.

Palmatine

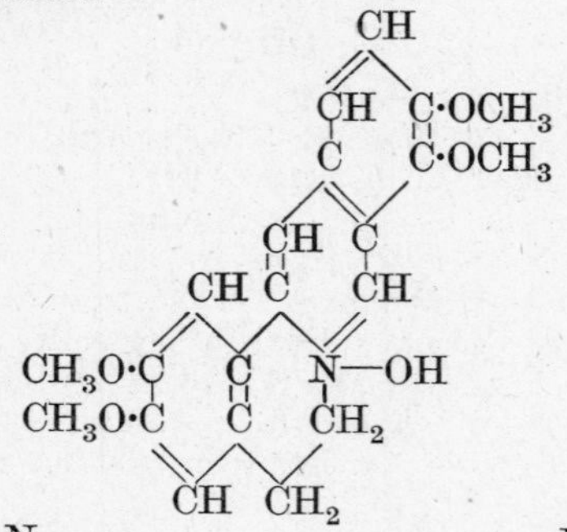

$C_{21}H_{23}O_5N$ MW, 369

Occurs in East African Calumba root.

Iodide: $C_{21}H_{22}O_4NI,2H_2O$. Orange-yellow needles from H_2O. M.p. 241° decomp. (238–40° decomp.). Mod. sol. hot H_2O, EtOH.

B,HNO₃,2H₂O: yellow needles. M.p. 239° decomp.

Chloride: $C_{21}H_{22}O_4NCl,3H_2O$. Greenish-yellow needles from H_2O. M.p. 205° decomp. Sol. H_2O, EtOH.

Sulphate: $(C_{21}H_{22}O_4N)_2SO_4,5H_2O$. Yellow needles. M.p. 250°. Sol. EtOH. Mod. sol. cold H_2O.

$(C_{21}H_{22}O_4NCl)_2,PtCl_4$: yellow cryst. M.p. 236°.

Feist, Sandstede, *Arch. Pharm.*, 1918, **256**, 1.
Feist, Awe, Etzrodt, *Chem. Zentr.*, 1935, I, 2374.
Späth, Quietensky, *Ber.*, 1925, **58**, 2267.
Haworth, Koepfli, Perkin, *J. Chem. Soc.*, 1927, 548.

Palmitaldehyde.
See Palmitic Aldehyde.

Palmitic Acid (*Hexadecylic acid*)

$$CH_3\cdot[CH_2]_{13}\cdot CH_2\cdot COOH$$

$C_{16}H_{32}O_2$ MW, 256

Occurs in form of esters (glycerides) in oils and fats of vegetable and animal origin. Usually obtained from palm-oil, Japan wax or Chinese vegetable tallow. M.p. 63–4° (62·6°). B.p. 390°, 268·5°/100 mm., 219°/20 mm., 215°/15 mm. D_4^{62} 0·8527 (liq.), $D_4^{75\cdot8}$ 0·8465, D_4^{70} 0·8487, D_4^{90} 0·8347. n_D^{60} 1·4339 n_D^{70} 1·4304, $n_D^{74\cdot5}$ 1·4284, n_D^{80} 1·42691. Insol H_2O. Sol. 11 parts EtOH at 20°, 100 part 94–5% EtOH at 0°, 256 parts 75% EtOH at 20°, 2000 parts 50% EtOH at 10°. Sol Et_2O. Spar. sol. pet. ether. Alk. $KMnO$ ⟶ mixture of mono- and di-carboxylic acid of smaller carbon content. Chars with conc H_2SO_4 at 160–80° giving CO and SO_2. P_2O at 200–10° ⟶ palmitone.

$C_{16}H_{31}O_2NH_4 + C_{16}H_{32}O_2$: insol. cold H_2O.

$2(C_{16}H_{31}O_2Na) + C_{16}H_{32}O_2$: m.p. 115–17° Insol. H_2O. Sol. hot EtOH.

$C_{16}H_{31}O_2Na + C_{16}H_{32}O_2$: m.p. 97–8°.

$C_{16}H_{31}O_2Na$: cryst. from EtOH. M.p. about 270°.

$C_{16}H_{31}O_2Na + 2C_{16}H_{32}O_2$: m.p. 81–2°.

$C_{16}H_{31}O_2K + C_{16}H_{32}O_2$: cryst.

$C_{16}H_{31}O_2K$: white tablets. Sol. EtOH.

$(C_{16}H_{31}O_2)_2Ca$: spar. sol. H_2O.

Me ester: $C_{17}H_{34}O_2$. MW, 270. Cryst. from EtOH at −15°. M.p. 30·5° (29·5°). B.p. 415–18°/747 mm., 190·5° (196°)/15 mm., 184°/1[illegible] mm.

Et ester: $C_{18}H_{36}O_2$. MW, 284. Needles M.p. 25° (23·5°). B.p. 184·5–185·5° (191°)/1[illegible] mm. n_D^{50} 1·4278, n_D^{70} 1·4200.

2-*Chloroethyl ester*: $C_{18}H_{35}O_2Cl$. MW, 318·5 Plates from EtOH. M.p. 41·5° (about 44°) B.p. 138° in high vacuum.

2-*Bromoethyl ester*: $C_{18}H_{35}O_2Br$. MW, 363 M.p. 62°. B.p. 144° in high vacuum.

2-*Iodoethyl ester*: $C_{18}H_{35}O_2I$. MW, 410 Plates from EtOH. M.p. 54°.

Propyl ester: $C_{19}H_{38}O_2$. MW, 298. Needles M.p. 20·4° (18·8–19·2°). n_D^{50} 1·4290, n_D^{70} 1·4211.

Butyl ester: $C_{20}H_{40}O_2$. MW, 312. M.p. 16·9°. n_D^{50} 1·4312, n_D^{70} 1·4232.

n-*Amyl ester*: $C_{21}H_{42}O_2$. MW, 326. M.p. 19·4°. n_D^{50} 1·4320, n_D^{70} 1·4241.

Isoamyl ester: m.p. 12·5° (9°). n_D^{50} 1·4315, n_D^{70} 1·4235.

Heptyl ester: $C_{23}H_{46}O_2$. MW, 354. Liq. Solidifies at 8–10°.

Octyl ester: $C_{24}H_{48}O_2$. MW, 368. M.p. 22·5°. n_D^{50} 1·4358, n_D^{70} 1·4277.

Decyl ester: $C_{26}H_{52}O_2$. MW, 396. M.p. 30°.

Dodecyl ester: $C_{28}H_{56}O_2$. MW, 424. Plates from EtOH. M.p. 41°.

Tetradecyl ester: $C_{30}H_{60}O_2$. MW, 452. M.p. 48°.

Pentadecyl ester: $C_{31}H_{62}O_2$. MW, 466. M.p. 57° (55·5°).

Hexadecyl (*cetyl*) *ester*: $C_{32}H_{64}O_2$. MW, 480. Chief constituent of spermaceti. Plates from Et_2O. M.p. 53–4° (51·6°).

Octadecyl ester: $C_{34}H_{68}O_2$. MW, 508. M.p. 59°.

Ceryl ester: $C_{42}H_{84}O_2$. MW, 620. Main constituent of opium wax. M.p. 79°.

Melissyl ester: $C_{46}H_{92}O_2$. MW, 676. A constituent of beeswax. M.p. 72°.

Vinyl ester: $C_{19}H_{34}O_2$. MW, 294. B.p. 165°/2 mm.

Allyl ester: $C_{19}H_{34}O_2$. MW, 294. M.p. 20–5°.

Ethylene glycol mono-ester: $C_{18}H_{36}O_3$. MW, 300. M.p. 51·5°.

Ethylene glycol di-ester: $C_{34}H_{66}O_4$. MW, 538. M.p. 72° (69°). B.p. 226° in high vacuum.

Glycerol mono-ester: *see* Monopalmitin.

Glycerol di-ester: *see* Dipalmitin.

Glycerol tri-ester: *see* Tripalmitin.

Phenyl ester: $C_{22}H_{36}O_2$. MW, 332. M.p. 45°. B.p. 249·5°/15 mm.

o-*Nitrophenyl ester*: $C_{22}H_{35}O_4N$. MW, 377. Needles from EtOH. M.p. 51–2°.

p-*Tolyl ester*: $C_{23}H_{38}O_2$. MW, 346. M.p. 47°. B.p. 258°/15 mm.

Benzyl ester: $C_{23}H_{38}O_2$. MW, 346. M.p. 36°.

p-*Nitrobenzyl ester*: $C_{23}H_{37}O_4N$. MW, 391. M.p. 42–42·5°.

Phenacyl ester: $C_{24}H_{38}O_3$. MW, 374. M.p. 63°.

p-*Chlorophenacyl ester*: $C_{24}H_{37}O_3Cl$. MW, 408·5. M.p. 82°.

p-*Bromophenacyl ester*: $C_{24}H_{37}O_3Br$. MW, 454. M.p. 86° (81·5°).

p-*Iodophenacyl ester*: $C_{24}H_{37}O_3I$. MW, 500. M.p. 90°.

p-*Nitrophenacyl ester*: $C_{24}H_{37}O_5N$. MW, 419. M.p. 42·5°.

Amide: $C_{16}H_{33}ON$. MW, 255. M.p. 106–7°. B.p. 235–6°/12 mm.

Anilide: needles from EtOH. M.p. 90·5° (87·5°). B.p. 282–4°/17 mm., 132·5°/10 mm. Sol. EtOH, Me_2CO, warm AcOH, Et_2O, $CHCl_3$, C_6H_6. Spar. sol. pet. ether. Insol. H_2O.

p-*Bromoanilide*: m.p. 110°.

2 : 4 : 6-*Tribromoanilide*: m.p. 124°.

p-*Toluidide*: cryst. from EtOH. M.p. 96° (93·5°). B.p. 140°/10 mm.

1-*Naphthylamide*: needles. M.p. 112·8° (106°). B.p. 182°/10 mm.

2-*Naphthylamide*: cryst. from EtOH. M.p. 109°. B.p. 198·5°/10 mm.

Phenylhydrazide: m.p. 110·5°.

Diphenylhydrazide: m.p. 124°.

2-*Naphthylhydrazide*: m.p. 135°.

Anhydride: $C_{32}H_{62}O_3$. MW, 494. M.p. 64°. D_4^{70} 0·847, D_4^{83} 0·8383. n_D^{68} 1·4364, n_D^{100} 1·4679.

Chloride: $C_{16}H_{31}OCl$. MW, 274·5. M.p. 12°. B.p 194–5°/17 mm., 198–200°/15 mm.

Nitrile: $C_{16}H_{31}N$. MW, 237. M.p. 31° (29°). B.p. 251°/100 mm., 196°/15 mm. D_4^{31} 0·8224 (liq.), D^{40} 0·8186.

Krafft, *Ber.*, 1888, **21**, 2265.
Chittenden, Smith, *Am. Chem. J.*, 1884, **6**, 218.
Claus, v. Dreden, *J. prakt. Chem.*, 1891, **43**, 149.
Klages, *Ber.*, 1902, **35**, 2260.
Kreis, Hafner, *Ber.*, 1903, **36**, 2769.
Charitschkow, *Chem. Zentr.*, 1905, II, 118.
Bückel, D.R.P., 281,364, (*Chem. Zentr.*, 1915, I, 230).
Holde, Ripper, Zadek, *Ber.*, 1924, **57**, 103.
Whitby, *J. Chem. Soc.*, 1926, 1462.
Wilkie, *J. Soc. Chem. Ind.*, 1927, **46**, 471T.
Hann, Reid, Jamieson, *J. Am. Chem. Soc.*, 1930, **52**, 818.
Dubovitz, *Chem.-Ztg.*, 1930, **54**, 814.
Smith, *J. Chem. Soc.*, 1931, 802.
Deutsche Hydrierwerke, A-G., D.R.P., 572,867, (*Chem. Abstracts*, 1933, **27**, 4433).

Palmitic Aldehyde (*Palmitaldehyde, hexadecylic aldehyde, hexadecanal*)

$CH_3{\cdot}[CH_2]_{13}{\cdot}CH_2{\cdot}CHO$

$C_{16}H_{32}O$ MW, 240

M.p. 34°. B.p. 200–2°/29 mm. Sol. most org. solvents. Insol. H_2O. Polymerises on keeping to trimeride (needles from Et_2O, m.p. 73°).

Oxime: needles from dil. EtOH. M.p. 88°. Sol. Et_2O, $CHCl_3$. Spar. sol. pet. ether, C_6H_6.

Semicarbazone: plates from dil. EtOH. M.p. 109° (107°). Sol. hot $CHCl_3$, C_6H_6.

Thiosemicarbazone: m.p. 109°.

p-*Nitrophenylhydrazone*: yellow cryst. M.p. 96·5°.

Stephen, *J. Chem. Soc.*, 1925, 1876.
Feulgen, Behrens, *Z. physiol. Chem.*, 1928, **177**, 229
Gottfried, Ulzer, *Chem. Abstracts*, 1929, **23**, 1902,
Le Sueur, *J. Chem. Soc.*, 1905, **87**, 1892.
Krafft, *Ber.*, 1880, **13**, 1416.

α-Palmito-α′β-dilaurin

$$\begin{array}{l} CH_2\cdot O\cdot CO\cdot C_{15}H_{31} \\ CH\cdot O\cdot CO\cdot C_{11}H_{23} \\ CH_2\cdot O\cdot CO\cdot C_{11}H_{23} \end{array}$$

$C_{43}H_{82}O_6$ MW, 694

Cryst. from EtOH. M.p. 47–8° (44·8°). n^{70} 1·43965. 100 ccs. EtOH dissolve 0·54 gm. at 23°. Sol. C_6H_6, $CHCl_3$, Et_2O.

Fischer, Bergmann, Bärwind, *Ber.*, 1920, **53**, 1605.
McElroy, King, *J. Am. Chem. Soc.*, 1934, **56**, 1192.

β-Palmito-αα′-dilaurin

$$\begin{array}{l} CH_2\cdot O\cdot CO\cdot C_{11}H_{23} \\ CH\cdot O\cdot CO\cdot C_{15}H_{31} \\ CH_2\cdot O\cdot CO\cdot C_{11}H_{23} \end{array}$$

$C_{43}H_{82}O_6$ MW, 694

M.p. 47·8°. n^{70} 1·43980. 100 ccs. EtOH dissolve 0·38 gm. at 23°.

See second reference above.

α-Palmito-α′β-dimyristin

$$\begin{array}{l} CH_2\cdot O\cdot CO\cdot C_{15}H_{31} \\ CH\cdot O\cdot CO\cdot C_{13}H_{27} \\ CH_2\cdot O\cdot CO\cdot C_{13}H_{27} \end{array}$$

$C_{47}H_{90}O_6$ MW, 750

M.p. 53·0° (47·8°). Sol. Et_2O, $CHCl_3$, hot EtOH. 100 ccs. EtOH dissolve 0·42 gm. at 27·5°. 100 ccs. Me_2CO dissolve 1·82 gm. at 27·5°.

Averill, Roche, King, *J. Am. Chem. Soc.*, 1929, **51**, 870.
Heiduschka, Schuster, *J. prakt. Chem.*, 1928, **120**, 153.

β-Palmito-αα′-dimyristin

$$\begin{array}{l} CH_2\cdot O\cdot CO\cdot C_{13}H_{27} \\ CH\cdot O\cdot CO\cdot C_{15}H_{31} \\ CH_2\cdot O\cdot CO\cdot C_{13}H_{27} \end{array}$$

$C_{47}H_{90}O_6$ MW, 750

M.p. 59·8–60° (49·5°). Sol. Et_2O, $CHCl_3$, hot EtOH. 100 ccs. EtOH dissolve 0·10 gm. at 27·5. 100 ccs. Me_2CO dissolve 0·61 gm. at 27·5°.

Heiduschka, Schuster, *J. prakt. Chem.*, 1928, **120**, 152.
See also first reference above.

α-Palmito-α′β-distearin

$$\begin{array}{l} CH_2\cdot O\cdot CO\cdot C_{15}H_{31} \\ CH\cdot O\cdot CO\cdot C_{17}H_{35} \\ CH_2\cdot O\cdot CO\cdot C_{17}H_{35} \end{array}$$

$C_{55}H_{106}O_6$ MW, 86

Occurs in lard. Plates from C_6H_6–EtOH. M.p. 68·5° (63·2°, 62·6°). n_D^{70} 1·44245.

Amberger, Bromig, *Biochem. Z.*, 192 **130**, 261.
Robinson, Roche, King, *J. Am. Chem Soc.*, 1932, **54**, 708.
Bömer, *Chem. Zentr.*, 1913, I, 1620.

β-Palmito-αα′-distearin

$$\begin{array}{l} CH_2\cdot O\cdot CO\cdot C_{17}H_{35} \\ CH\cdot O\cdot CO\cdot C_{15}H_{31} \\ CH_2\cdot O\cdot CO\cdot C_{17}H_{35} \end{array}$$

$C_{55}H_{106}O_6$ MW, 86

Occurs in lard and in the fat of beef an mutton. Cryst. from Et_2O. M.p. 63·3° (67·9° 64·8°, 68·0°). n_D^{70} 1·4467 (1·44374).

Kreis, Hafner, *Ber.*, 1903, **36**, 1124 2766.
Bömer, Limprich, *Chem. Zentr.*, 1913 I, 1621.
Schuster, *J. pharm. chim.*, 1932, 16 421.
Amberger, Bromig, *Biochem. Z.*, 1922 **130**, 262.
Whitby, *J. Chem. Soc.*, 1926, 1461.
Robinson, Roche, King, *J. Am. Chem Soc.*, 1932, **54**, 708.

Palmitoleic Acid (*Zoomaric acid, 8-hexadecenoic acid, Δ^8-hexadecylenic acid, 8-pentadecylene-1-carboxylic acid*)

$$CH_3\cdot[CH_2]_5\cdot CH{:}CH\cdot[CH_2]_7\cdot COOH$$

$C_{16}H_{30}O_2$ MW, 254

Found as glyceride in oil of whale, cod, walrus, seal, etc. Liq. Dil. alk. $KMnO_4$ in cold ⟶ 8 : 9-dihydroxypalmitic acid.

Me ester: $C_{17}H_{32}O_2$. MW, 268. B.p. 140–1°/5 mm. H ⟶ methyl palmitate. $KMnO_4$ ⟶ heptylic and azelaic acids.

Et ester: $C_{18}H_{34}O_2$. MW, 282. Liq.

Armstrong, Hilditch, *J. Soc. Chem. Ind.*, 1925, **44**, 182T. (See also Hilditch, Vidyarthi, *J. Soc. Chem. Ind.*, 1927, **46**, 172T.)
Schmidt-Nielsen, *Chem. Zentr.*, 1922, I, 1047.
Toyama, *J. Soc. Chem. Ind. Japan*, 1927, **30**, 603.

Palmitone (*Di-pentadecyl ketone, hentriacontanone*-16, 16-*ketohentriacontane*)

$CH_3 \cdot [CH_2]_{13} \cdot CH_2 \cdot CO \cdot CH_2 \cdot [CH_2]_{13} \cdot CH_3$

$C_{31}H_{62}O$ MW, 450

Leaflets from EtOH. M.p. 82·8°. $D_4^{90 \cdot 9}$ 0·7947. Does not form bisulphite comp.

Oxime: needles from EtOH or AcOH. M.p. 59°.

Kipping, *J. Chem. Soc.*, 1890, **57**, 985.

Palmitophenone (*Pentadecyl phenyl ketone, palmitylbenzene*)

$C_6H_5 \cdot CO \cdot [CH_2]_{14} \cdot CH_3$

$C_{22}H_{36}O$ MW, 316

Plates from EtOH. M.p. 59°. B.p. 250·5–251°/15 mm. Mod. sol. Et_2O. Prac. insol. cold EtOH. $D^{75 \cdot 9}$ 0·8692. $n_a^{75 \cdot 9}$ 1·46746. Triboluminescent. $CrO_3 \longrightarrow$ benzoic and pentadecylic acids.

Krafft, *Ber.*, 1886 **19**, 2982.

Palmitylacetic Acid.
See 2-Ketostearic Acid.

***p*-Palmitylanisole.**
See under p-Hydroxypalmitophenone.

Palmitylglycine

$CH_3 \cdot [CH_2]_{14} \cdot CO \cdot NH \cdot CH_2 \cdot COOH$

$C_{18}H_{35}O_3N$ MW, 313

Cryst. from Me_2CO or EtOH. M.p. 125° (121°). Sinters at 119°. Sol. EtOH, Et_2O, Me_2CO, $CHCl_3$, hot C_6H_6. Insol. H_2O, pet. ether.

Et ester: $C_{20}H_{39}O_3N$. MW, 341. Needles from Et_2O. M.p. 80°.

Bondi, Frankl, *Biochem. Z.*, 1909, **17**, 552.
Abderhalden, Funk, *Z. physiol. Chem.*, 1910, **65**, 62.
Karrer, Miyamichi, Storm, Widmer, *Helv. Chim. Acta.*, 1925, **8**, 205.

***p*-Palmitylphenetole.**
See under p-Hydroxypalmitophenone.

***p*-Palmitylphenol.**
See p-Hydroxypalmitophenone.

Panax sapogenin.
See Oleanolic Acid.

Pantocaine (N-*Butylnovocaine*, 2-*dimethylaminoethyl ester of* p-*butylaminobenzoic acid*)

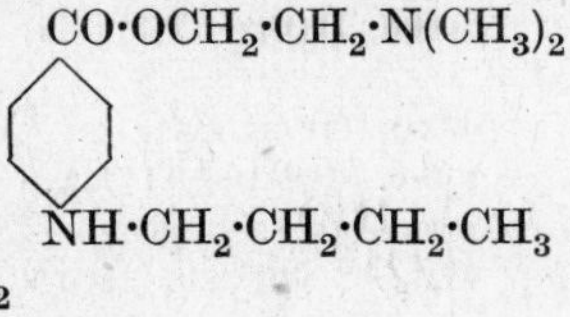

$C_{15}H_{24}O_2N_2$ MW, 264

M.p. 153–4°. Local anæsthetic. Fifteen times as effective as novocaine. Nearly ten times as active as cocaine, but more toxic. Said to cause irritation and turbidity of the cornea.

B,HCl: m.p. 147–8°. Sol. H_2O.

B,HNO$_3$: m.p. 131–2°.

Fussgänger, Schaumann, *Chem. Abstracts*, 1932, **26**, 515.
Eisler, U.S.P., 1,889,645, (*Chem. Abstracts*, 1933, **27**, 1717).
I.G., D.R.P., 582,715, (*Chem. Abstracts*, 1934, **28**, 778).

Papaveraldine (6 : 7-*Dimethoxy*-1-*veratroylisoquinoline, xanthaline*)

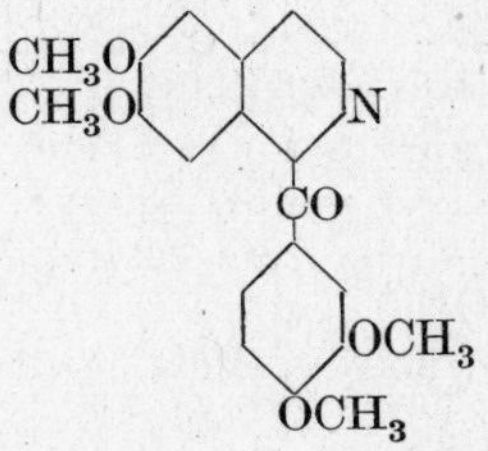

$C_{20}H_{19}O_5N$ MW, 353

Occurs in opium. Cryst. from C_6H_6 or pet. ether. M.p. 210° (208°). Sol. min. acids, hot AcOH. Mod. sol. C_6H_6, $CHCl_3$. Spar. sol. EtOH, Et_2O, pet. ether. Insol. H_2O. Zn + H_2SO_4 or AcOH $\longrightarrow$ papaverinol. Zn + Ac_2O $\longrightarrow$ papaverine. $HNO_3 \longrightarrow$ nitropapaveraldine. KOH fusion $\longrightarrow$ veratric acid + 6 : 7-dimethoxyisoquinoline.

B,HCl,2½(?)H$_2$*O*: yellow cryst. from H_2O.

B,H$_2$*SO*$_4$: yellow needles. Decomp. by H_2O.

B,HNO$_3$*,2H*$_2$*O*: yellow needles. Decomp. by hot H_2O.

B$_2$*,H*$_2$*PtCl*$_6$*,H*$_2$*O*: orange-red prisms from dil. HCl. Decomp. at 210°.

Picrate: yellow needles. M.p. 208–9°.

Methiodide, H$_2$*O*: yellow prisms. M.p. 194°.

Methiodide, 3H$_2$*O*: yellow prisms. M.p. 136° (132°).

Oxime: exists in two forms. (i) Needles or prisms. M.p. 235–6°; (ii) prisms from EtOH. M.p. 245°.

Phenylhydrazone: reddish-yellow aggregates from dil. EtOH. M.p. 80–1°.

Stuchlik, *Monatsh.*, 1900, **21**, 828.
Pschorr, *Ber.*, 1904, **37**, 1936.
Dobson, Perkin, *J. Chem. Soc.*, 1911, **99**, 135.
Buck, Haworth, Perkin, *J. Chem. Soc.*, 1924, **125**, 2184.

Papaveric Acid (2-*Veratroylcinchomeronic acid*)

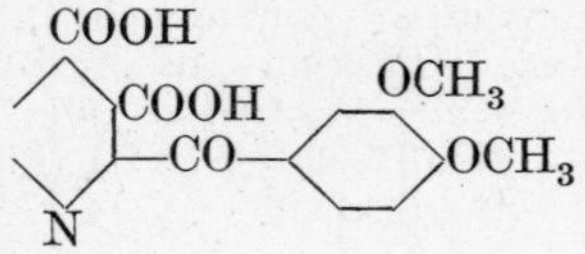

$C_{16}H_{13}O_7N$ MW, 331

Cryst. + H_2O from H_2O. M.p. 233° decomp. Sol. hot dil. EtOH, AcOH, dil. HCl. Spar. sol. cold H_2O, EtOH, Et_2O, Me_2CO, $CHCl_3$, CS_2, C_6H_6, pet. ether. Sol. conc. H_2SO_4 with reddish-yellow col. KOH fusion ⟶ protocatechuic acid. Ac_2O ⟶ papaveric anhydride. HNO_3 ⟶ nitropapaveric acid.

$K_2A,2\frac{1}{2}H_2O$: plates from dil. EtOH. Sol. H_2O. Spar. sol. EtOH.

B,HCl: orange-red cryst. from HCl.Aq.

$B,HCl,2\frac{1}{2}H_2O$: yellow needles.

Oxime: needles from EtOH. M.p. 154–7°. Sol. H_2O, EtOH.

Phenylhydrazone: yellow needles from EtOH. M.p. 190°.

3-*Me ester*: $C_{17}H_{15}O_7N$. MW, 345. Cryst. from MeOH. M.p. 156°. Sol. MeOH. Spar. sol. H_2O.

4-*Me ester*: needles from H_2O or MeOH. M.p. 198° decomp. (196°). Sol. EtOH, Me_2CO, AcOEt. Spar. sol. H_2O, MeOH. Insol. Et_2O.

Di-Me ester: $C_{18}H_{17}O_7N$. MW, 359. Plates from Me_2CO. M.p. 121–2° (122–4°). Sol. Me_2CO, AcOEt.

3-*Et ester*: $C_{18}H_{17}O_7N$. MW, 359. Needles. M.p. 187–8°. Spar. sol. H_2O.

4-*Et ester*: needles from EtOH. M.p. 184°. Spar. sol. H_2O.

Anhydride: $C_{32}H_{24}O_{13}N_2$. MW, 644. Needles from C_6H_6. M.p. 169–70°.

Methochloride, H_2O: yellow plates. M.p. 182–4° decomp.

Goldschmiedt, *Monatsh.*, 1885, **6**, 380; 1888, **9**, 357.
Goldschmiedt, Strache, *Monatsh.*, 1889, **10**, 159, 692.
Goldschmiedt, Kirpal, *Monatsh.*, 1896, **17**, 496.
Kirpal, *Monatsh.*, 1897, **18**, 464.
Schranzhofer, *Monatsh.*, 1893, **14**, 525.
Wegscheider, *Monatsh.*, 1902, **23**, 338, 388.
Goldschmiedt, Honigschmid, *Monatsh.*, 1903, **24**, 681.

Papaverine (6 : 7-*Dimethoxy*-1-*veratryliso quinoline, papaveroline tetramethyl ether*)

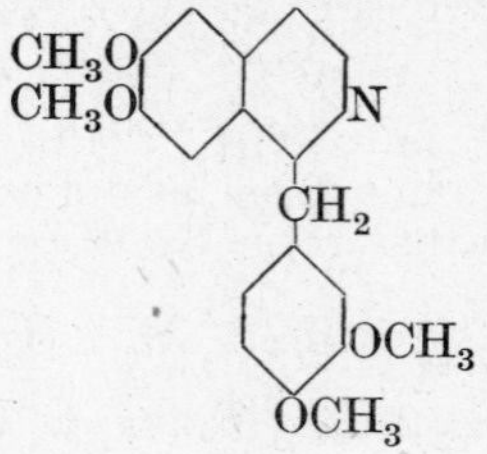

$C_{20}H_{21}O_4N$ MW, 339

Occurs in opium (0·8–1·0%). Prisms from EtOH–Et_2O. Needles from $CHCl_3$–pet. ether. M.p. 147°. Sol. hot EtOH, $CHCl_3$, Me_2CO Mod. sol. hot C_6H_6. Prac. insol. H_2O, pet ether. 1 part dissolves in 86 parts 97% EtOH at 15° and in 258 parts Et_2O at 10°. Sol conc. H_2SO_4 colourless, changing to violet on warming. D_4 1·308–1·337. Optically inactive. Triboluminescent. $Na_2Cr_2O_7$ ⟶ papaveraldine. $KMnO_4$ ⟶ papaveraldine, papaveric acid, 6 : 7-dimethoxyisoquinoline-1-carboxylic acid, pyridine-2 : 3 : 4-tricarboxylic acid, meta-hemipinic acid, veratric acid, oxalic acid, CO_2 and NH_3. Sn + HCl ⟶ tetrahydropapaverine. Br ⟶ bromopapaverine. HNO_3 ⟶ nitropapaverine. Nitrous fumes ⟶ nitrosopapaverine. HNO_2 ⟶ papaveraldoxime, m.p. 235–6°. Boiling conc. HCl ⟶ papaveroline dimethyl ether. HI ⟶ papaveroline. Dist. with KOH ⟶ methylamine, protocatechuic acid, homocatechol dimethyl ether and oxalic acid.

B,HCl: plates from H_2O. M.p. 220–1° decomp. (210–13° decomp.). Sol. 37·3 parts H_2O at 18°.

B,HBr: cryst. from H_2O or dil. EtOH. M.p. 213–14° decomp.

B,HI: m.p. 200° decomp. Sol. hot H_2O, EtOH. Dimorphous.

$B,HFeCl_4,H_2O$: red plates. M.p. 195°.

$B,HFeCl_4,2H_2O$: orange prisms. M.p. 195°.

$B_2,H_2PtCl_6,\frac{1}{2}H_2O$: m.p. 186°.

$B_2,H_2PtCl_6,2H_2O$: orange prisms from conc. HCl. M.p. 198°. Insol. H_2O, EtOH, Et_2O.

Acid oxalate: needles or prisms from H_2O. M.p. 196°. Sol. hot H_2O. Spar. sol. hot EtOH.

Succinate: plates from EtOH. M.p. 171°. Sol. hot H_2O.

Salicylate: plates from EtOH. M.p. 130°.

Benzoate: cryst. from EtOH. M.p. 145°. Sol. EtOH. Insol. H_2O.

Methiodide, $4H_2O$: cryst. from dil. EtOH.

I.p. 60–5° (55–60°), 195° anhyd. Sol. $CHCl_3$. Iod. sol. C_6H_6. Insol. Et_2O.

Ethiodide: yellow cryst. from dil. EtOH. I.p. 216° decomp. Sol. $CHCl_3$. Spar. sol. $_6H_6$. Insol. Et_2O.

Picrate: yellow plates from EtOH. M.p. 83° (179° decomp., 154°).

Picrolonate: needles from EtOH. M.p. 221°.

Pictet, Gams, *Ber.*, 1909, **42**, 2943.
Buck, Haworth, Perkin, *J. Chem. Soc.*, 1924, **125**, 2179.
Rosenmund, Nothnagel, Riesenfeldt, *Ber.*, 1927, **60**, 392.
Späth, Burger, *ibid.*, 704.
Mannich, Walther, *Arch. Pharm.*, 1927, **265**, 1.
Kindler, Peschke, *Arch. Pharm.*, 1934, **272**, 236.

Papaverinol (*Hydroxyxanthaline*)

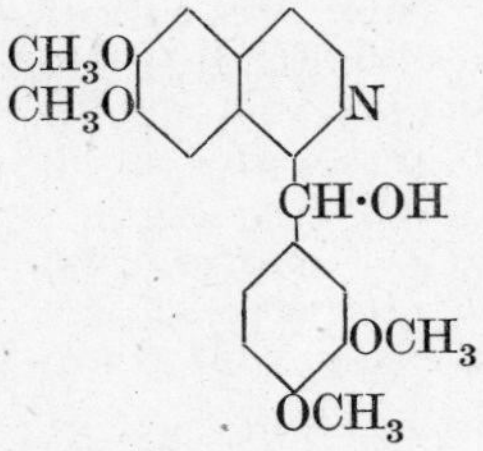

$C_{20}H_{21}O_5N$ MW, 355

Prisms from dil. MeOH. M.p. 137°. Sol. MeOH, EtOH, Me_2CO, $CHCl_3$, C_6H_6. Spar. sol. H_2O, Et_2O. Ox. ⟶ papaveraldine.

B,HCl: yellow needles from EtOH–Et_2O. M.p. 200–2°.

B_2,H_2PtCl_6: orange-yellow needles from dil. HCl. M.p. 168° decomp.

O-*Benzoyl*: amorph. Sol. EtOH, $CHCl_3$, AcOH. *Picrate*: yellow needles from EtOH. M.p. 126° decomp.

O-p-*Bromobenzoyl*: cryst. M.p. 194°.

Methochloride: prisms from EtOH. M.p. 205–6°.

Methiodide: needles from MeOH or EtOH–Et_2O. M.p. 188° (not sharp), 200° decomp. with rapid heating.

Picrate: yellow prisms from EtOH. M.p. 168–71° decomp.

Stuchlik, *Monatsh.*, 1900, **21**, 814.
Gadamer, *Arch. Pharm.*, 1915, **253**, 284.
King, L'Ecuyer, Pyman, *J. Chem. Soc.*, 1936, 732.

Papaveroline (6 : 7-*Dihydroxy*-1-[3 : 4-*dihydroxybenzyl*]-*isoquinoline*)

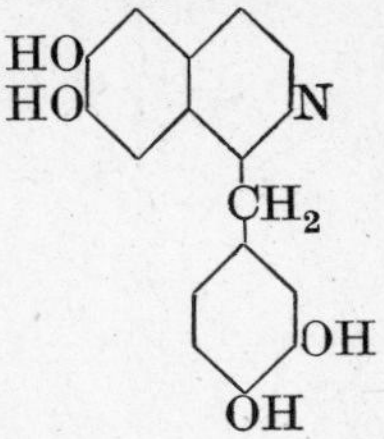

$C_{16}H_{13}O_4N$ MW, 273

Cryst. powder + $2H_2O$. Loses H_2O at 100°. Darkens at 150° and decomp. on further heating without melting. Sol. AcOH, glycerol. Mod. sol. EtOH. Spar. sol. Et_2O, $CHCl_3$. Insol. H_2O, C_6H_6, pet. ether. Sol. dil. min. acids. Dist. with Zn dust ⟶ 1-methylisoquinoline.

B,HCl,H_2O: needles. Sol. hot H_2O.

B,HI,$2H_2O$: needles from H_2O. M.p. anhyd. 230° decomp. Mod. sol. hot H_2O.

B_2,H_2SO_4,$10H_2O$: loses H_2O at 105°.

B_2,$(COOH)_2$,$3H_2O$: needles. Sol. hot H_2O.

Methochloride: m.p. 264° decomp. (235°).

Ethochloride: cryst. M.p. 215°.

Benzylchloride: m.p. 158°.

Methiodide: m.p. 208° decomp. From dil. HCl m.p. 77° (probably hydrated).

Methopicrate: m.p. 210° decomp.

Tetra-Me ether: *see* Papaverine.

O-*Tetrabenzoyl*: m.p. 148°.

Goldschmiedt, *Monatsh.*, 1885, **6**, 967.
Krauss, *Monatsh.*, 1890, **11**, 350.
Claus, Kassner, *J. prakt. Chem.*, 1897, **56**, 344.
Kitasato, Robinson, *J. Chem. Soc.*, 1932, 785.

Para-acetaldehyde.
See Paraldehyde.

Para-anthracene.
See Dianthracene.

Parabanic Acid (*Oxalylurea*)

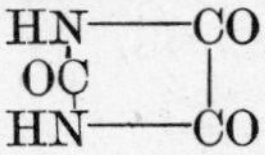

$C_3H_2O_3N_2$ MW, 114

Needles or prisms from boiling H_2O. Part. sublimes at 100°. Decomp. at 243°. Sol. 21 parts H_2O at 8°. Decomp. by boiling aq. alkalis. Salts unstable.

$C_3H_2O_3N_2$,H_2O: cryst. Sol. 7·4 parts H_2O at 8°. Loses H_2O at 150–60°.

Behrend, Asche, *Ann.*, 1918, **416**, 226.
Biltz, Schiemann, *Ber.*, 1926, **59**, 721.

Paraconic Acid (*5-Ketotetrahydrofuran-3-carboxylic acid, butyrolactone-β-carboxylic acid, 5-ketotetrahydro-β-furoic acid*)

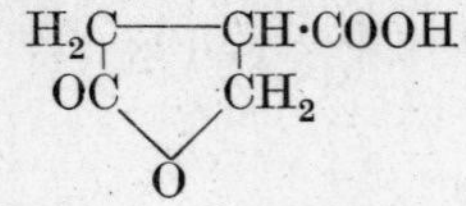

$C_5H_6O_4$ MW, 150

Cryst. M.p. 57–8° (55°). Dist. ⟶ citraconic anhydride.

Fittig, Beer, *Ann.*, 1883, **216**, 84.
Reitter, *Ber.*, 1898, **31**, 2724.

Paracoumarone.
See Coumarone.
Paraformaldehyde.
See under Formaldehyde.
Para-indene.
See Indene.
Paralactic Acid.
See Lactic Acid.
Paraldehyde (*Para-acetaldehyde, 2 : 4 : 6-trimethyl-1 : 3 : 5-trioxan*)

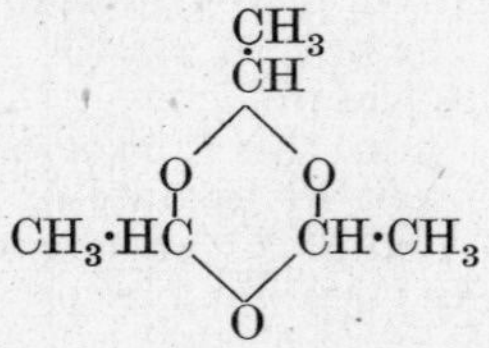

$C_6H_{12}O_3$ MW, 132.

M.p. 12·6° (10°). B.p. 128° (124°). Spar. sol. H_2O. D_4^{10} 1·0037, D_4^{15} 0·9975, D_4^{20} 0·9943, $D_4^{35\cdot5}$ 0·9772, $D_4^{53\cdot7}$ 0·9536, D_4^{75} 0·9264, $D_4^{124\cdot3}$ 0·8738. n_D^{20} 1·4049. Heat of comb. $C_p = 813\cdot2$ Cal. Gives acetaldehyde on warming with a few drops of conc. H_2SO_4, or on boiling with dil. HCl. Ac_2O + conc. H_2SO_4 ⟶ ethylidene diacetate. PCl_5 ⟶ ethylidene chloride. Br water ⟶ acetic acid. Br in $CHCl_3$ ⟶ bromo- and dibromo-acetaldehyde.

Friedel, *Bull. soc. chim.*, 1893, **9**, 385.
Geuther, Cartmell, *Ann.*, 1859, **112**, 16.
Vogt, Nieuwland, *J. Am. Chem. Soc.*, 1921, **43**, 207B.
Morton, Nicolet, U.S.P., 1,300,451, (*Chem. Abstracts*, 1919, **13**, 1861).

Paraldol (*Dimeride of aldol*)

$C_8H_{16}O_4$ MW, 176

Prisms. M.p. 90° (82°, 80–90°). B.p. 90–100° in high vacuo. Sol. H_2O, EtOH. Less sol. Et_2O. Vac. dist. ⟶ aldol. Ox. ⟶ 2-hydroxybutyric acid. Heat in presence of I ⟶ crotonaldehyde. H(+ Ni) ⟶ β butylene glycol.

Nowak, *Monatsh.*, 1901, **22**, 1142.
Wurtz, *Compt. rend.*, 1883, **97**, 1525.

Paranthrene.
See Dianthracene.
Paratophan.
See 6-Methyl-2-phenylquinoline-4-carboxylic Acid.
Paraxanthine (*1 : 7-Dimethylxanthine, 1 : 7 dimethyl-2 : 6-dihydroxy purine*)

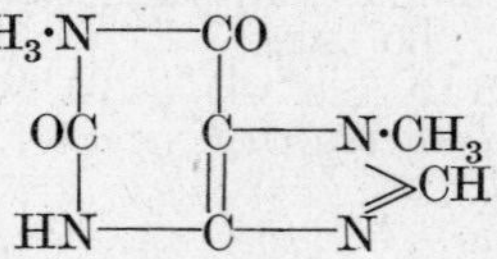

$C_7H_8O_2N_4$ MW, 180

Present in human urine. Plates from H_2O. M.p. 298–9° (289°, 284°). Sol. NH_3.Aq., HCl + HNO_3. Spar. sol. cold H_2O. Mod. sol. hot H_2O. Insol. EtOH, Et_2O, CH_3I ⟶ caffeine.

B,HCl,H₂O : dissociates at 100°. Decomp. in H_2O.
B_2,H_2PtCl_6,H_2O : orange cryst.
$B,HAuCl_4,\frac{1}{2}H_2O$: m.p. 227–8°.
Picrate : yellow ppt. Decomp. in H_2O.

Fischer, *Ber.*, 1897, **30**, 554, 2400.
Fischer, Clemm, *Ber.*, 1898, **31**, 2623.
Fischer, Ach, *Ber.*, 1906, **39**, 423.
Traube, Dudley, *Ber.*, 1913, **46**, 3839.
Boehringer, Sohn, D.R.P., 582,435, (*Chem. Abstracts*, 1933, **27**, 5754); D.R.P., 576,604, (*Chem. Abstracts*, 1933, **27**, 5757).

Parietin.
See Physcione.
Parigenin.
See Sarsasapogenin.
Patchoulene.
See Patschulene.
Patschulene (*Patchoulene*)

$C_{15}H_{24}$ MW, 204

Liq. with cedarwood odour. B.p. 255–6°, 252–3°/743 mm., 112–15°/12–12·5 mm. D_4^{20} 0·9296. n_D^{20} 1·49853. $[\alpha]_D^{20} - 38{\cdot}08°$. Very sol. Et_2O, C_6H_6. Spar. sol. EtOH, AcOH. Insol. HCl, HNO_3, H_2SO_4, but gives red col. with these acids.

Wallach, Tuttle, *Ann.*, 1894, **279**, 394.
Schimmel, *Chem. Zentr.*, 1904, I, 1265.

Pavine (2 : 4-*Dihydropapaverine*)

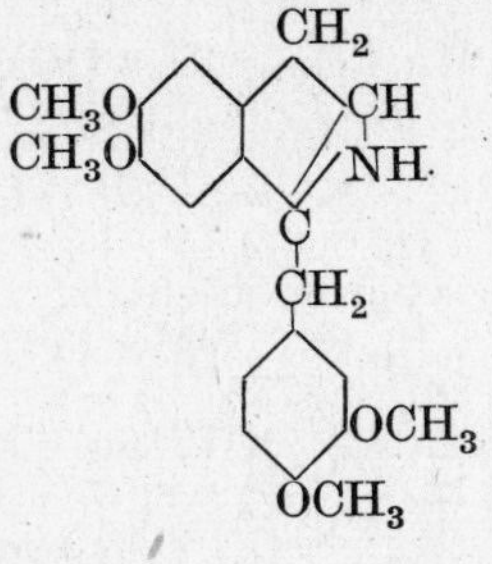

$_{20}H_{23}O_4N$ MW, 341

d-.

Cryst. from C_6H_6. M.p. 224°. $[\alpha]_D^{23} + 150{\cdot}3°$. $CHCl_3$, $+ 198{\cdot}8°$ in AcOH.

d-*Tartrate*: cryst. from Me_2CO–Et_2O. M.p. 56–8° decomp. Very sol. H_2O, org. solvents. $]_D^{22} + 157{\cdot}5°$.

l-.

Cryst. from C_6H_6. M.p. 224°. $[\alpha]_D^{23} - 150{\cdot}8°$. $CHCl_3$.

d-*Tartrate*: cryst. from Me_2CO–Et_2O. M.p. 56–8° decomp. Very sol. H_2O, org. solvents. $]_D^{22} - 150{\cdot}5°$ in H_2O.

dl-.

Prisms from xylene, needles from EtOH. .p. 201–2°. Sol. $CHCl_3$, CS_2, warm Me_2CO, $_6H_6$. Spar. sol. Et_2O, pet. ether.

B,HCl: cryst. $+ 5H_2O$. Decomp. at 325°.

N-*Me*: $C_{21}H_{25}O_4N$. MW, 355. Prisms om Et_2O or C_6H_6. M.p. 140–1°. Sol. most org. lvents. Spar. sol. H_2O, Et_2O, pet. ether. onc. $H_2SO_4 \longrightarrow$ weak yellowish-green col. ,*HCl*: prisms $+ 8H_2O$ from H_2O. M.p. 5–81°. *B,HI*: prisms $+ 6H_2O$ from H_2O. .p. 70–87°. *Picrate*: yellow needles from $_2O$. M.p. 219°. Spar. sol. H_2O, EtOH. *ethiodide*: prisms $+ 2H_2O$ from MeOH. .p. about 280°. Spar. sol. H_2O.

N-*Benzoyl*: prisms from EtOH. M.p. 234–°. Sol. $CHCl_3$. Spar. sol. EtOH, Me_2CO. ery spar. sol. H_2O, Et_2O.

N-*Nitroso*: prisms from EtOH. M.p. 180–2°. ol. warm EtOH. Mod. sol. $CHCl_3$, Me_2CO, $_6H_6$. Spar. sol. Et_2O. Insol. pet. ether.

Picrate: yellow needles. Decomp. at 285°.

Pyman, *J. Chem. Soc.*, 1909, **95**, 1620; 1915, **107**, 177.
Pope, Gibson, *J. Chem. Soc.*, 1910, **97**, 2209.
Pyman, Reynolds, *ibid.*, 1324.

Pectolinarigenin (5 : 7-*Dihydroxy*-6 : 4′-*dimethoxyflavone*)

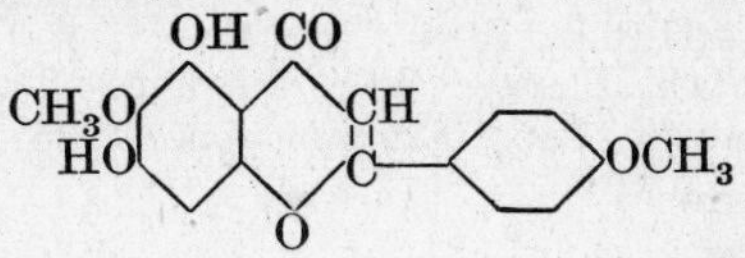

$C_{17}H_{14}O_6$ MW, 314

Yellow needles from EtOH or dil. Me_2CO. M.p. 215–16°.

Diacetyl: needles. M.p. 151°.

7-*Me ether*: $C_{18}H_{16}O_6$. MW, 328. Yellow needles. M.p. 188°. *Acetyl*: m.p. 188°.

Di-Me ether: $C_{19}H_{18}O_6$. MW, 342. M.p. 162°.

Glucoside: *see* Pectolinarin.

Merz, Wu, *Arch. Pharm.*, 1936, **274**, 126.
Robinson, Schwarzenbach, *J. Chem. Soc.*, 1930, 829.

Pectolinarin

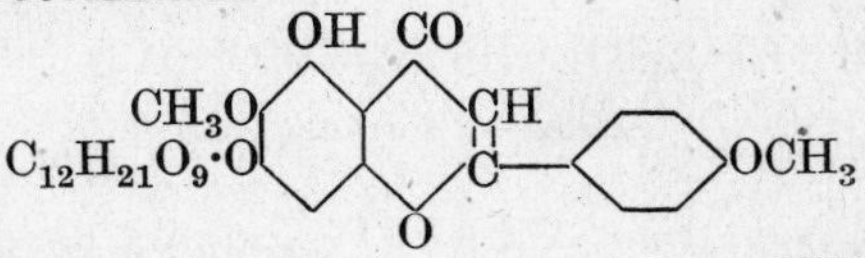

$C_{29}H_{34}O_{15}$ MW, 622

A glucoside from the flowers of *Linaria vulgaris*, Linn. M.p. 240–50° decomp. Hyd. by conc. HCl to glucose, rhamnose and pectolinarigenin.

Hepta-acetyl: cryst. from Et_2O–pet. ether. M.p. 134–8°. $[\alpha]_D^{18} - 68{\cdot}5°$.

See first reference above.

Peganine (*Vasicine*)

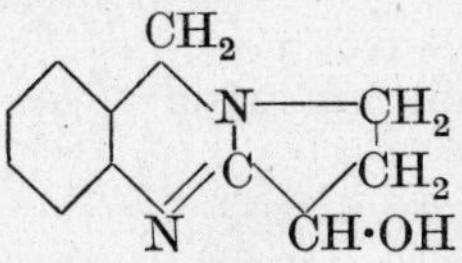

$C_{11}H_{12}ON_2$ MW, 188

l-.

Found in *Adhatoda Vasica*, N. Cryst. from EtOH. M.p. 211–12°. $[\alpha]_D^{14} - 254°$ in $CHCl_3$, $- 61{\cdot}5°$ in EtOH.

dl-.

Needles from EtOH. M.p. 209–10° (196°). Sol. EtOH, $CHCl_3$. Spar. sol. H_2O, Et_2O, C_6H_6.

B,HCl: needles $+ 2H_2O$. M.p. anhyd. 208°.

B,HI: needles $+ 2H_2O$. M.p. anhyd. 195°.

Methiodide: needles from MeOH. M.p. 187°.

Acetyl deriv.: m.p. 122–3°. B.p. 230–40°/0·01 mm.

Picrate: needles. M.p. 199° decomp.

Späth, Kuffner, Platzer, *Ber.*, 1935, **68**, 497, 699, 1384.
Späth, Platzer, *Ber.*, 1936, **69**, 255, 384.
Narang, Ray, *J. Chem. Soc.*, 1936, 686.

Peimine

$C_{26}H_{43}O_3N$ MW, 417

Alkaloid from *Fritillaric Roylei* (Pei-Mu). M.p. 224°.

B,HCl: m.p. 295° decomp.
B,HBr: m.p. 293·5–294°.
B,H_2SO_4: m.p. 278–80°.
B_2,H_2PtCl_6: m.p. 233–5° decomp.
$B,HAuCl_4$: m.p. 164–5°.

Chi, Kao, Chang, *J. Am. Chem. Soc.*, 1936, **58**, 1306.

Pelandjauic Acid (*Pentaspadonic acid*)

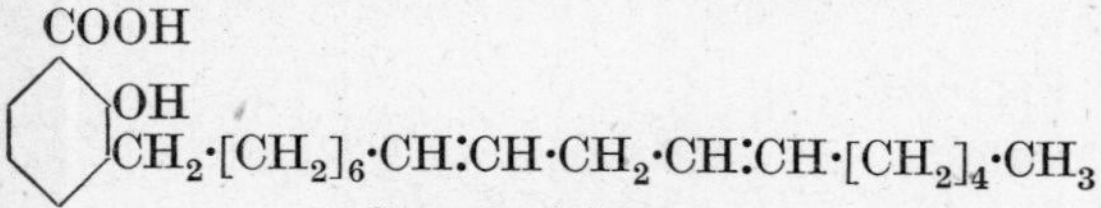

Suggested formula

$C_{24}H_{36}O_3$ MW, 372

Obtained from Minjak Pelandjau, an oily exudation from wood of *Pentaspadon motleyi*, H. Cryst. M.p. 25–6°. $KMnO_4 \longrightarrow$ azelaic and suberic acids.

Me ester: $C_{25}H_{38}O_3$. MW, 386. B.p. 225–35°/0·4 mm. D_4^{12} 0·9170. n_D^{12} 1·51477.

v. Romberg, v. Veen, *Chem. Abstracts*, 1930, **24**, 124.
v. Rombergh, v. Veen, Smit, *Chem. Abstracts*, 1931, **25**, 937.

Pelargone.

See Di-*n*-octyl Ketone.

Pelargonenin chloride (*Pelargonidin 5-β-glucoside*)

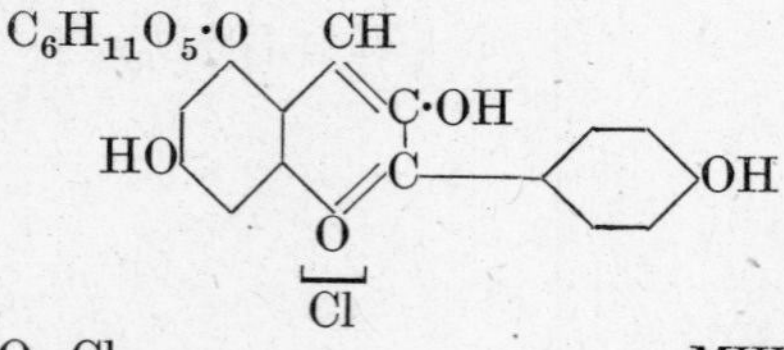

$C_{21}H_{21}O_{10}Cl$ MW, 468·5

Scarlet-red needles. Sol. MeOH. Mod. sol. EtOH. Spar. sol. H_2O, HCl. Acid sols. $\longrightarrow$ red col. with bluish fluor. Na_2CO_3.Aq. $\longrightarrow$ violet-blue col.

Willstätter, Bolton, *Ann.*, 1916, **412**, 136.
Léon, Robertson, Robinson, Seshardi, *J. Chem. Soc.*, 1931, 2673.

Pelargonic Acid (*Nonanoic acid, nonylic acid, nonic acid, octane-1-carboxylic acid*)

$$CH_3{\cdot}[CH_2]_6{\cdot}CH_2{\cdot}COOH$$

$C_9H_{18}O_2$ MW, 158

Oil. F.p. 12·5°. B.p. 253–4°/760 mm., 186°/100 mm. $D_4^{12\cdot5}$ 0·9109, $D_D^{17\cdot5}$ 0·9068. n_D 1·43057. Spar. volatile in steam.

Me ester: $C_{10}H_{20}O_2$. MW, 172. B.p. 213–14°/756 mm. $D^{17\cdot5}$ 0·8765.

Et ester: $C_{11}H_{22}O_2$. MW, 186. F.p. — 36·7°. B.p. 216–19° (227°). D_4^0 0·88156, D_4^{15} 0·86920.

2-*Iodoethyl ester*: b.p. 169°/15 mm.

2-*Diethylaminoethyl ester*: m.p. 131°.

tert.-*Butyl ester*: $C_{13}H_{26}O_2$. MW, 214. Liq. B.p. 242°.

Heptyl ester: $C_{16}H_{32}O_2$. MW, 256. F.p. — 15·54°. B.p. 210°/75 mm., 192·5°/30 mm. D_4^0 0·8745, D_4^{25} 0·8553. n_D^{20} 1·4350.

p-*Chlorophenacyl ester*: m.p. 59°.

p-*Bromophenacyl ester*: m.p. 68·5°.

p-*Iodophenacyl ester*: m.p. 77°.

Chloride: $C_9H_{17}OCl$. MW, 176·5. F.p. — 60·5°. B.p. 215·35°/760 mm., 98°/15 mm. D_4^0 0·95901, D_4^{15} 0·94633.

Nitrile: $C_9H_{17}N$. MW, 139. F.p. — 34·2°. B.p. 224° (214–16°). D_4^0 0·83314, D_4^{15} 0·82207. Sol. EtOH, Et_2O. Insol. H_2O.

Amide: $C_9H_{19}ON$. MW, 157. Cryst. M.p. 98·9° (92–3°). Insol. cold H_2O.

Diethylamide: b.p. 167–9°/16 mm.

Isobutylamide: m.p. 37–8°. B.p. 162°/6 mm.

Anilide: cryst. from EtOH. M.p. 57·5°.

o-*Toluidide*: m.p. 73°.

p-*Toluidide*: cryst. from EtOH. M.p. 84°.

1-*Naphthylamide*: cryst. from EtOH. M.p. 91°.

Anhydride: f.p. 16° (5°). B.p. 207°/15 mm.

Eichler, *Ber.*, 1879, **12**, 1888.
Krafft, *Ber.*, 1882, **15**, 1691.
v. Braun, Sobecki, *Ber.*, 1911, **44**, 1469.
Rochussen, *Chem. Abstracts*, 1930, **24**, 1755.
Deffet, *Chem. Abstracts*, 1932, **26**, 352.
Moses, Reid, *J. Am. Chem. Soc.*, 1932, **54**, 2101.

Pelargonic Aldehyde (*Nonanal, nonanoic aldehyde, nonaldehyde, nonylic aldehyde*)

$$CH_3{\cdot}[CH_2]_6{\cdot}CH_2{\cdot}CHO$$

$C_9H_{18}O$ MW, 142

Found in mandarin and lemon-grass oil. B.p. 190–2°, 80–2°/13 mm. D^{15} 0·8277. n_D^{16} 1·42452. Polymerises readily with H_2SO_4. Oxidises slowly in air.

Di-Me acetal : b.p. 96–8°/15 mm. D_4^{18} 0·8733. $n_D^{18\cdot 5}$ 1·4246.

Di-Et acetal : b.p. 130°/20 mm.

Oxime : leaflets from EtOH.Aq. M.p. 64°. Sol. most org. solvents. Volatile in steam.

Semicarbazone : cryst. from C_6H_6–pet. ether. or MeOH. M.p. 100°.

Thiosemicarbazone : m.p. 77°.

Phenylsemicarbazone : m.p. 131–2°.

o-*Tolylsemicarbazone* : m.p. 120–1°.

p-*Tolylsemicarbazone* : m.p. 155–6°.

m-*Nitrobenzoylhydrazone* : m.p. 87°.

p-*Nitrobenzoylhydrazone* : m.p. 103–4°.

2 : 4-*Dinitrophenylhydrazone* : m.p. 100°.

Strain, *J. Am. Chem. Soc.*, 1935, **57,** 758.

Wagner, *Chem. Abstracts*, 1928, **22**, 3131.

Bagard, *Bull. soc. chim.*, 1907, **1**, 351.

Sabatier, Mailhe, *Compt. rend.*, 1912, **154**, 563; 1906, **158**, 986.

Pelargonidin chloride

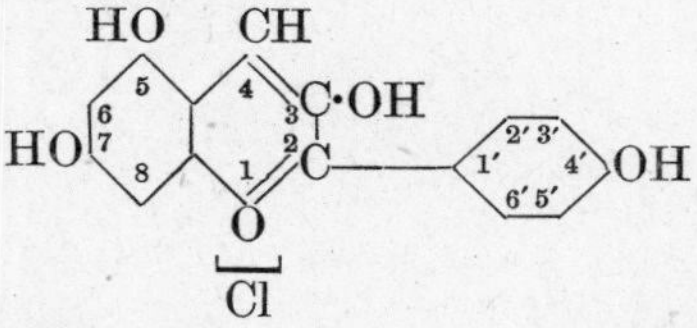

$C_{15}H_{11}O_5Cl$ MW, 306·5

Leaflets from MeOH–Et_2O, needles from MeOH–HCl. Does not melt below 350°. Sol. MeOH, EtOH. Mod. sol. H_2O, $CHCl_3$.

5-*Me ether* : $C_{16}H_{13}O_5Cl$. MW, 320·5. Cryst. Gives orange-red sol. in 0·5% HCl.

7-*Me ether* : $C_{16}H_{13}O_5Cl$. MW, 320·5. Solid. Gives orange-red sol. in 0·5% alc. HCl.

3 : 4′-*Di-Me ether* : $C_{17}H_{15}O_5Cl$. MW, 334·5. Crimson cryst. + H_2O. M.p. 221° decomp.

3-β-*Glucoside* : Callistephin chloride, *q.v.*

4′-β-*Glucoside* : red plates. Decomp. at 184°. Sol. MeOH, EtOH. Spar. sol. cold H_2O, Me_2CO. *Picrate* : red prisms. Decomp. at 146–8°.

5-β-*Glucoside* : *see* Pelargonenin chloride.

7-β-*Glucoside* : scarlet needles. Sol. H_2O, EtOH, 0·5% HCl with deep red col. Na_2CO_3.Aq. ⟶ deep pink col. Alc. NaOH ⟶ violet-red col. *Picrate* : red plates. M.p. 180° decomp.

3 : 5-*Diglucoside* : *see* Pelargonin chloride.

5-*Benzoyl* : indigo plates. Sol. EtOH with violet col. Na_2CO_3.Aq. ⟶ violet col. 4′-*Tetra-acetylglucoside* : reddish-brown needles. Decomp. at 198°. AcOH ⟶ yellowish-red sol. with intense green fluor. Na_2CO_3.Aq. ⟶ bluish-pink sol. ⟶ blue with Me_2CO.

Picrate : reddish plates with golden reflex.

Willstätter, Burdict, *Ann.*, 1916, **412**, 163.

Robertson, Robinson, Sugiura, *J. Chem. Soc.*, 1928, 1533.

Léon, Robertson, Robinson, Seshadri, *J. Chem. Soc.*, 1931, 2673.

Nair, Robinson, *J. Chem. Soc.*, 1934, 1611.

Pelargonin chloride (*Pelargonidin 3 : 5-diglucoside*)

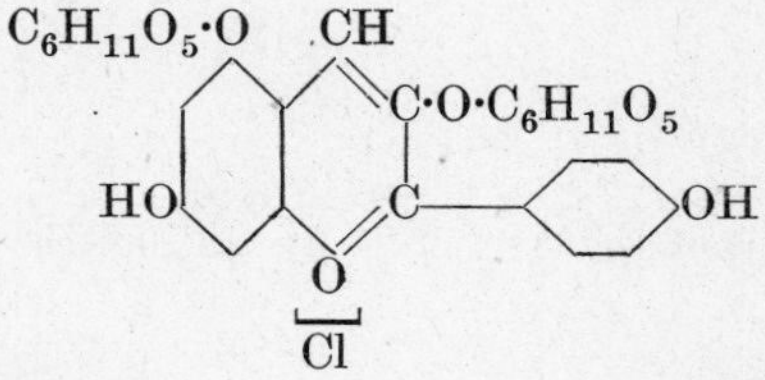

$C_{27}H_{31}O_{15}Cl$ MW, 630·5

Fine red needles + $4H_2O$. M.p. anhyd. 180° decomp. $[\alpha]_D$ − 244°, $[\alpha]_{614}$ − 133° in 0·1% HCl. Sol. H_2O with orange-red sol. turning violet. Spar. sol. MeOH ⟶ red col. with green fluor. 20% HCl ⟶ pelargonidin + glucose.

Karrer, Widmer, *Helv. Chim. Acta*, 1927, **10**, 729.

Robinson, Todd, *J. Chem. Soc.*, 1932, 2488.

Note.—Robinson, Todd, (*loc. cit.*) have shown the identity of pelargonin, monardin (*q.v.*) and salvinin. Karrer and Meuron (*Helv. Chim. Acta*, 1932, **15**, 1214) have confirmed this. It is also possible that punicin may be identical with pelargonin.

Pelletierine

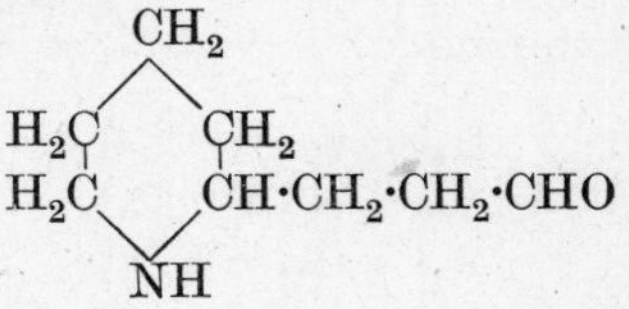

$C_8H_{15}ON$ MW, 141

dl-.

Occurs in root-bark of pomegranate tree (*Runica granatum*). Colourless oil. B.p.

106°/21 mm. Readily absorbs O from air, becoming dark coloured and resinous. Sol. H_2O, Et_2O, $CHCl_3$. Alkaline in reaction.

B,HCl : needles from Me_2CO. M.p. 143–4°.
B,HBr : needles from Me_2CO. M.p. 140°.
Picrate : cryst. from EtOH. M.p. 150–1°.
N-*Acetyl* : b.p. 173–4°/18 mm. *B,HAuCl₄* : m.p. 95–6°.
Oxime : two forms. (i) From pet. ether. M.p. 96–7°; (ii) from Et_2O. M.p. 80°.
Semicarbazone hydrochloride : prisms from 50% AcOH. M.p. 188° decomp.
Hydrazone : b.p. 150°/20 mm.
N-*Carboethoxyl* : yellow oil. B.p. 173–4°/20 mm.
N-*Me* : $C_9H_{17}ON$. MW, 155. B.p. 98–102°/14 mm. Sol. H_2O. *B,HBr* : needles from Me_2CO or C_6H_6. M.p. 152°.

d-.
Sulphate : $[\alpha]_D^{18} + 5.86°$ in H_2O.
d-*Acid tartrate* : $[\alpha]_D^{20} + 21°$ in EtOH.

l-.
Sulphate : $[\alpha]_D^{18} - 5.89°$ in H_2O.
l-*Acid tartrate* : $[\alpha]_D^{20} - 20.94°$ in EtOH.

Hess, Eichel, *Ber.*, 1918, **51**, 743.
Hess, *Ber.*, 1919, **52**, 1005; 1917, **50**, 373.

Note.—Tanret (*Compt. rend.*, 1920, **170**, 1118) maintains that pelletierine occurs naturally in an optically active form, $[\alpha]_D - 31.1°$.

Sulphate : m.p. 133°. $[\alpha]_D - 30.3°$.
B,HCl : m.p. 145°. $[\alpha]_D - 41.2°$.
B,HBr : m.p. 137°. $[\alpha]_D - 32.5°$.
B,HNO₃ : m.p. 82–5°. $[\alpha]_D - 34.8°$.
N-*Acetyl* : b.p. 205–10°/40 mm. $[\alpha]_D + 32.6°$.
Semicarbazone hydrochloride : m.p. 168–70°. $[\alpha]_D - 10.8°$.

This active pelletierine is stated to be sensitive to acids and alkalis, and rapidly racemises.

ψ-Pelletierine (N-*Methylgranatonine*)

$$\begin{array}{ccc}
H_2C\!-\!\!-CH\!\!-\!\!-CH_2 \\
H_2C \quad N\!\cdot\!CH_3 \quad CO \\
H_2C\!-\!\!-CH\!\!-\!\!-CH_2
\end{array}$$

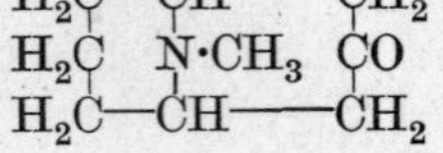

$C_9H_{15}ON$ MW, 153

Found in pomegranates. Prismatic plates from pet. ether. M.p. 48·5°. B.p. 246°/760 mm. Sol. EtOH, Et_2O, $CHCl_3$. Less sol. pet.

ether. Sol. 2·5 parts H_2O. Strong base. $CrO_3 \longrightarrow$ intense green col.

B,HAuCl₄ : pale yellow cryst. from H_2O. M.p. 162° decomp. Sol. boiling H_2O.
Oxime : plates from Et_2O. M.p. 128–9°.
Methiodide : cryst. from EtOH.Aq. Does not melt below 280°.
N-*Oxide* : m.p. 160–2°. *B,HCl* : m.p. 224°.
Picrate : yellow needles from H_2O. M.p. 252–3° decomp.

Ciamician, Silber, *Ber.*, 1892, **25**, 1603; 1893, **26**, 156, 2738.
Piccinini, *Gazz. chim. ital.*, 1899, **29**, i, 408; 1899, **29**, ii, 312.
Hesse, *Ber.*, 1919, **52**, 1011.
Menzies, Robinson, *J. Chem. Soc.*, 1924, **125**, 2163.

Pellotine (N-*Methylanhalonidine*, 8-*hydroxy-6 : 7 - dimethoxy - 1 : 2 - dimethyl - 1 : 2 : 3 : 4 - tetrahydroisoquinoline*)

$$\begin{array}{c}
CH_2 \\
CH_3O\diagup\diagdown CH_2 \\
CH_3O\diagdown\diagup N\!\cdot\!CH_3 \\
HO \quad CH\!\cdot\!CH_3
\end{array}$$

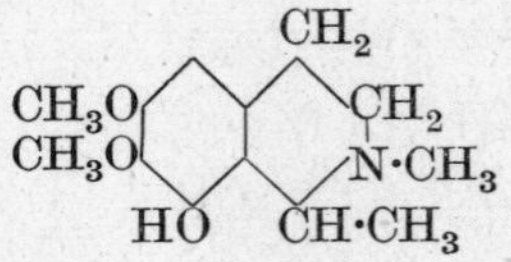

$C_{13}H_{19}O_3N$ MW, 237

Found in *Anhalonium Williamsii*. Plates from EtOH. M.p. 111·5° (110°). Sol. EtOH, Et_2O, Me_2CO, $CHCl_3$. Mod. sol. pet. ether. Spar. sol. H_2O. Aq. sol. reacts strongly alkaline. Conc. $H_2SO_4 \longrightarrow$ yellow col. $\longrightarrow$ reddish-violet with HNO_3. $FeCl_3 \longrightarrow$ blue col. $\longrightarrow$ green on warming. Slightly narcotic. Used as hypnotic.

B,HI : yellowish prisms. M.p. 125–30°. Sol. H_2O, EtOH. Insol. Et_2O.
B₂,H₂PtCl₆ : m.p. 210–12°.
B,HAuCl₄ : orange cryst. M.p. 147–8° decomp.
Methiodide : plates or prisms $+ H_2O$ from MeOH. M.p. 199°. *Me ether* : prisms from H_2O. M.p. 225°. *Et ether* : m.p. 185–6°. *Benzyl ether* : m.p. 193–5°.
Picrate : yellow prisms from H_2O. M.p. 172 3°.

Hefter, *Ber.*, 1894, **27**, 2975; 1901, **34**, 3004.
Späth, *Monatsh.*, 1921, **42**, 97; *Ber.*, 1932, **65**, 1778.
Späth, Boschan, *Monatsh.*, 1933, **63**, 146.
Späth, Becke, *Ber.*, 1934, **67**, 266.
Späth, Kesztler, *Ber.*, 1936, **69**, 755.

Peltogynol

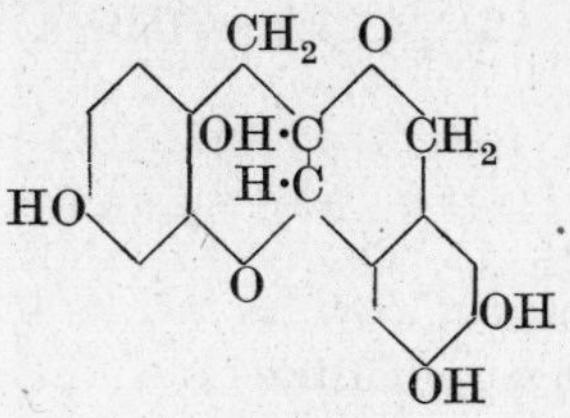

or

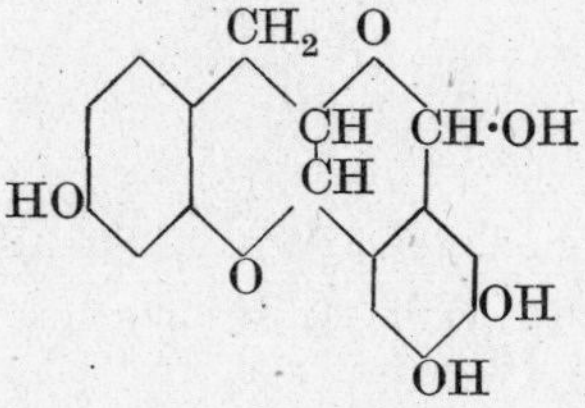

$_{16}H_{14}O_6$ MW, 302

Found in heart-wood of *Peltogyne porphyro-* *ırdia.* Prisms from H_2O. Becomes pink at)0°, dark red at 240° with decomp. and ›ftening. Sol. MeOH, EtOH. Mod. sol. ſe$_2$CO. Spar. sol. cold H_2O, Et_2O, $CHCl_3$, $_6H_6$. Aq.NaOH ⟶ blue sol. ⟶ bright red n standing. Alc. $FeCl_3$ ⟶ blue col. Hot INO$_3$ ⟶ styphnic acid.

Tri-Me ether: $C_{19}H_{20}O_6$. MW, 344. Long eedles or plates from AcOEt. M.p. 198°. ‹]$_D$ + 250° in $CHCl_3$.

Tetra-Me ether: $C_{20}H_{22}O_6$. MW, 358. 'lates. M.p. 175°. $[\alpha]_D^{20}$ + 264° in $CHCl_3$.

Tetra-acetyl: needles from AcOH or C_6H_6–:tOH. M.p. 173°. Sol. AcOEt, $CHCl_3$, C_6H_6. par. sol. H_2O, MeOH, EtOH, Et_2O, pet. :her. $[\alpha]_D^{20}$ + 125° in $CHCl_3$.

Tetrabenzoyl: plates from AcOH. M.p. 244°. 'ery sol. $CHCl_3$. Mod. sol. AcOEt.

Tetra-anisoyl: plates from AcOH. M.p. 18° decomp. Sol. C_6H_6. Mod. sol. Me_2CO. par. sol. MeOH, Et_2O.

Robinson, Robinson, *J. Chem. Soc.*, 1935, 744.

Penta-acetylglucose.
See under Glucose.

Pentabromoacetone

$CBr_3{\cdot}CO{\cdot}CHBr_2$

$_3HOBr_5$ MW, 453

Needles from H_2O or EtOH, prisms from :t$_2$O. M.p. 79–80° (72°). Very sol. org. solvents. Insol. cold H_2O. Sublimes. Volatile in steam.

Jackson, Adams, *J. Am. Chem. Soc.*, 1915, **37**, 2533.

Pentabromoaniline

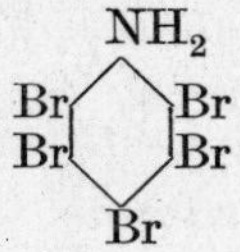

$C_6H_2NBr_5$ MW, 488

Needles from EtOH–toluene(1 : 2). M.p. 261–2°.

Jacobson, Löb, *Ber.*, 1900, **33**, 705.
Hantzsch, Smythe, *ibid.*, 520.

Pentabromoanisole.
See under Pentabromophenol.

Pentabromobenzene

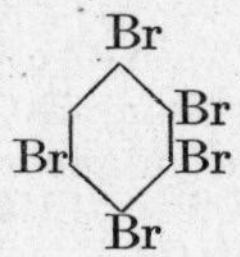

C_6HBr_5 MW, 473

Needles from AcOH or EtOH. M.p. 159–60°. Mod. sol. $CHCl_3$, C_6H_6. Spar. sol. EtOH, Et_2O, AcOH, ligroin. Very spar. volatile in steam.

Jacobson, Löb, *Ber.*, 1900, **33**, 702.
Eckert, Steiner, *Monatsh.*, 1915, **36**, 278.
Eckert, *J. prakt. Chem.*, 1921, **102**, 362.
I.G., D.R.P., 595,461, (*Chem. Zentr.*, 1934, II, 1030).

Pentabromobenzoic Acid (*Perbromobenzoic acid*)

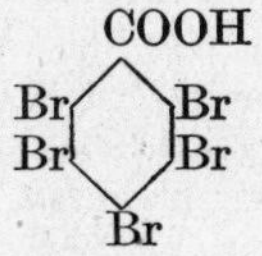

$C_7HO_2Br_5$ MW, 517

Leaflets or needles from EtOH.Aq. M.p. 252° (234–5°). Sol. hot H_2O, EtOH. Spar. sol. pet. ether.

Nitrile: C_7NBr_5. MW, 498. Needles from C_6H_6–EtOH. Does not melt below 300°. Spar. sol. EtOH, Et_2O. Sublimes with slight decomp.

Merz, Weith, *Ber.*, 1883, **16**, 2892.
Blanksma, *Chem. Zentr.*, 1912, II, 1965.

Pentabromoethane

$CBr_3{\cdot}CHBr_2$

C_2HBr_5 MW, 425

Prisms. M.p. 56–7° (54°). B.p. 210°/300 mm. decomp. Very sol. Et_2O. Sol. EtOH.

Bourgoin, *Bull. soc. chim.*, 1875, **23**, 173.
Hunter, Edgar, *J. Am. Chem. Soc.*, 1932, **54**, 2025.

Pentabromophenetole.
See under Pentabromophenol.

Pentabromophenol

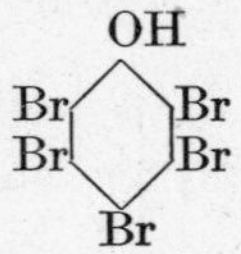

C_6HOBr_5 MW, 489

Needles from EtOH or CS_2. M.p. 229·5° (225°). Sublimes.

Me ether: pentabromoanisole. $C_7H_3OBr_5$. MW, 503. Needles from EtOH. M.p. 173–4°.

Et ether: pentabromophenetole. $C_8H_5OBr_5$. MW, 517. Needles from EtOH. M.p. 136°.

Propyl ether: $C_9H_7OBr_5$. MW, 531. Needles from EtOH. M.p. 98°.

Isopropyl ether: needles from ligroin. M.p. 86°.

n-*Butyl ether*: $C_{10}H_9OBr_5$. MW, 545. M.p. 79–80°.

sec.-n-*Butyl ether*: m.p. 57–8°.

Isobutyl ether: needles from ligroin. M.p. 92–3°.

Isoamyl ether: $C_{11}H_{11}OBr_5$. MW, 559. Needles from ligroin. M.p. 64–5°.

Allyl ether: $C_9H_5OBr_5$. MW, 529. Needles from ligroin. M.p. 167–8°.

Acetyl: prisms from EtOH. M.p. 197° (171°).

Zincke, Birschel, *Ann.*, 1908, **362**, 227.
Bonneaud, *Bull. soc. chim.*, 1910, **7**, 776.
Kohn, Fink, *Monatsh.*, 1923, **44**, 187.
Lucas, Kemp, *J. Am. Chem. Soc.*, 1921, **43**, 1654.
Raiford, Howland, *J. Am. Chem. Soc.*, 1931, **53**, 1054.

1 : 1 : 1 : 2 : 2-Pentabromopropane

$CH_3{\cdot}CBr_2{\cdot}CBr_3$

$C_3H_3Br_5$ MW, 439

Needles from C_6H_6. M.p. 212°.

Loevenich, Loser, Dierichs, *Ber.*, 1927, **60**, 955.

1 : 1 : 2 : 3 : 3-Pentabromopropane

$CHBr_2{\cdot}CHBr{\cdot}CHBr_2$

$C_3H_3Br_5$ MW, 43

Liq. B.p. 165–75°/17 mm. (163–5°/18 mm.)

Prins, D.R.P., 261,689, (*Chem. Abstracts* 1913, II, 394).
Mouneyrat, *Bull. soc. chim.*, 1898, **19**, 809

Pentabromopyridine

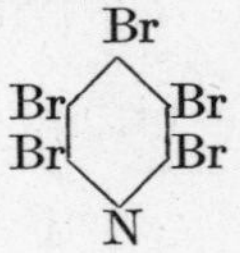

C_5NBr_5 MW, 47

Cryst. from C_6H_6. M.p. 209·5–210°.

Hertog, Wibaut, *Rec. trav. chim.*, 1932 **51**, 940.

Pentabromotoluene

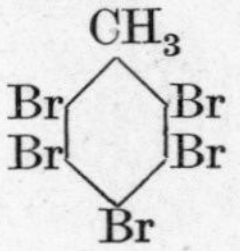

$C_7H_3Br_5$ MW, 48

Needles from C_6H_6. M.p. 282 (280°). D 2·97. Spar. sol. EtOH, AcOH. Sol. abou 102 parts C_6H_6 at 20°.

Bodroux, Taboury, *Bull. soc. chim.* 1912, **11**, 395.
Datta, Chatterjee, *J. Am. Chem. Soc.* 1916, **38**, 2548.
Bodroux, *Ann. chim.*, 1929, **11**, 547.

Pentachloroacetone

$CCl_3{\cdot}CO{\cdot}CHCl_2$

C_3HOCl_5 MW, 230·

Liq. with odour resembling that of chloral B.p. 192°/753 mm. D^{15} 1·69. Sol. 10 part H_2O. Volatile in steam.

B,4H₂O: plates. M.p. 15–17°.

Fritsch, *Ber.*, 1893, **26**, 598; *Ann.*, 1894 **279**, 317.
Staedler, *Ann.*, 1859, **111**, 293.
Buc, U.S.P., 1,391,758, (*Chem. Zentr.* 1922, IV, 940).

Pentachloroaniline

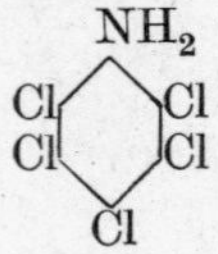

$C_6H_2NCl_5$ MW, 265·

Needles from EtOH. M.p. 232°. Sol. EtOH, Et_2O. Mod. sol. ligroin.

N-*Acetyl*: N-*Me*, m.p. 136–7°. N-*Et*: m.p. 99–100°.

Willegerodt, Wilcke, *Ber.*, 1910, **43**, 2754.
Badische, D.R.P., 176,474, (*Chem. Zentr.*, 1907, I, 142).
Durand, Huguenin, E.P., 217,753, (*Chem. Zentr.*, 1925, I, 301).
Quist, Salo, *Chem. Zentr.*, 1934, II, 594.

Pentachloroanisole.

See under Pentachlorophenol.

Pentachlorobenzene

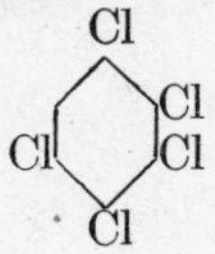

C_6HCl_5. MW, 250·5

Needles from EtOH. M.p. 86° (84°). B.p. 275–7°. D^{10} 1·8422, $D^{16\cdot5}$ 1·8342. Mod. sol. Et_2O, $CHCl_3$, C_6H_6, CS_2, CCl_4. Insol. cold EtOH.

Eckert, Steiner, *Ber.*, 1914, **47**, 2629.
v. der Linden, *Ber.*, 1912, **45**, 413.
Hollemann, *Rec. trav. chim.*, 1920, **39**, 736.

Pentachlorobenzoic Acid (*Perchlorobenzoic acid*)

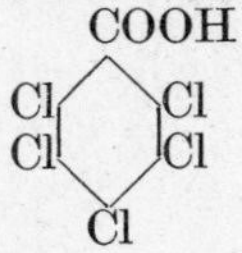

$C_7HO_2Cl_5$ MW, 294·5

Needles. M.p. 201°. Sublimes in vacuo with slight decomp.

Me ester: $C_8H_3O_2Cl_5$. MW, 308·5. Cryst. from MeOH. M.p. 97°.

Chloride: C_7OCl_6. MW, 313. Cryst. from EtOH. M.p. 87°.

Steiner, *Monatsh.*, 1915, **36**, 827.
Merz, Weith, *Ber.*, 1883, **16**, 2885.
Kirpal, Kunze, *Ber.*, 1929, **62**, 2102.

1 : 2 : 2 : 3 : 4-Pentachlorobutane

$CH_2Cl\cdot CHCl\cdot CCl_2\cdot CH_2Cl$

$C_4H_5Cl_5$ MW, 230·5

Liq. B.p. 85°/10 mm. D_4^{20} 1·5543. n_D^{20} 1·5157.

du Pont, U.S.P., 1,964,720, (*Chem. Zentr.*, 1934, II, 3180).
Carothers, Berehet, *J. Am. Chem. Soc.*, 1933, **55**, 1628.

Pentachloroethane (*Pentalin*)

$CHCl_2\cdot CCl_3$

C_2HCl_5 MW, 202·5

Liq. with odour of chloroform. F.p. — 29° (— 22°). B.p. 162·00°, 152·2°/644 mm., 93·6°/103 mm., 69·0°/37 mm. D_4^{15} 1·6846, D_4^{25} 1·6712. n_D^{15} 1·50542. $AlCl_3 \longrightarrow$ tetrachloroethylene.

Mouneyrat, *Bull. soc. chim.*, 1898, **19**, 260.
Salzbergwerk Neustassfurt, D.R.P., 248,982, (*Chem. Zentr.*, 1912, II, 299).
Timmermans, Martin, *J. chim. phys.*, 1926, **23**, 747.
Guyot, *Chimie et Industrie*, 1923, **10**, 13.

Pentachlorophenetole.

See under Pentachlorophenol.

Pentachlorophenol

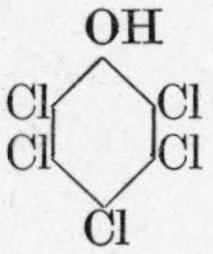

C_6HOCl_5 MW, 266·5

Cryst. + H_2O from EtOH, needles from C_6H_6. M.p. 174°, anhyd. 191°. B.p. 309–10°/754·3 mm. D^{22} 1·978. Very sol. EtOH, Et_2O. Mod. sol. C_6H_6. Spar. sol. cold ligroin. Sublimes in long needles.

Me ether: pentachloroanisole. $C_7H_3OCl_5$. MW, 280·5. Needles from MeOH. M.p. 108°. B.p. 289°/745 mm. decomp. Sol. EtOH. Sublimes readily.

Et ether: pentachlorophenetole. $C_8H_5OCl_5$. MW, 294·5. Prisms from EtOH. M.p. 89–90°. Spar. sol. H_2O.

Propyl ether: $C_9H_7OCl_5$. MW, 308·5. Prisms from EtOH. M.p. 49–50°. Very sol. H_2O.

Butyl ether: $C_{10}H_9OCl_5$. MW, 322·5. Cryst. M.p. 15·5–16·5°. B.p. 343°.

Acetyl: needles from EtOH. M.p. 149·5–150·5° (147–8°). Sol. warm EtOH. Sublimes.

Propionyl: needles from ligroin. M.p. 78·5°. Very sol. Et_2O, C_6H_6.

Butyryl: needles. M.p. 59–62°.

Benzoyl: prisms. M.p. 164–5° (159–60°).

Barral, *Bull. soc. chim.*, 1895, **13**, 342.
Weber, Wolff, *Ber.*, 1885, **18**, 335.
Biltz, Giese, *Ber.*, 1904, **37**, 4019.
Barral, Jambon, *Bull. soc. chim.*, 1900, **23**, 823.
Mathieson, McCombie, *J. Chem. Soc.*, 1931, 1110.
Tiessens, *Rec. trav. chim.*, 1931, **50**, 112.
Tomcsik, *J. pharm. chim.*, 1930, **11**, 101.
I.G., D.R.P., 527,393, (*Chem. Zentr.*, 1931, II, 2785).

1 : 1 : 1 : 2 : 3-Pentachloropropane

$CH_2Cl{\cdot}CHCl{\cdot}CCl_3$

$C_3H_3Cl_5$ MW, 216·5

Needles from hot EtOH. M.p. 179–80°. Sublimes.

Vitoria, *Rec. trav. chim.*, 1905, **24**, 282.
Henry, *ibid.*, 342.

1 : 1 : 2 : 3 : 3-Pentachloropropane

$CHCl_2{\cdot}CHCl{\cdot}CHCl_2$

$C_3H_3Cl_5$ MW, 216·5

Liq. B.p. 198–200°, 126°/90 mm. D_4^{34} 1·6086. $n_D^{16\cdot5}$ 1·5131.

Prins, *J. prakt. Chem.*, 1914, **89**, 421; D.R.P., 261,689, (*Chem. Zentr.*, 1913, II, 394).
Prins, Engelhard, *Rec. trav. chim.*, 1935, **54**, 307.

1 : 1 : 2 : 3 : 3-Pentachloropropylene

$CHCl_2{\cdot}CCl{:}CCl_2$

C_3HCl_5 MW, 214·5

Liq. B.p. 183°, 116°/9 mm. D_4^{34} 1·6317. n_D^{20} 1·5313.

Prins, *J. prakt. Chem.*, 1914, **89**, 419; D.R.P., 261,689, (*Chem. Zentr.*, 1913, II, 394).

Pentachloropyridine

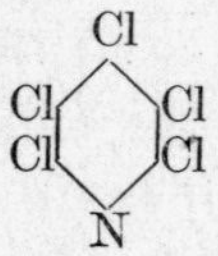

C_5NCl_5 MW, 251·5

Plates or needles from EtOH. M.p. 124°. Mod. sol. hot EtOH. Spar. sol. Et_2O. Insol. H_2O. Volatile in steam. Possesses no basic properties.

Sell, Dootson, *J. Chem. Soc.*, 1897, **71**, 1082; 1898, **73**, 441.
Hertog, Wibaut, Ley, *Rec. trav. chim.*, 1932, **51**, 381.

Pentachlorotoluene

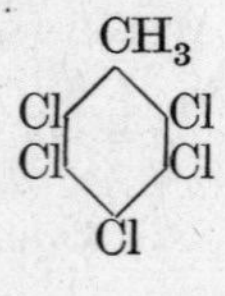

$C_7H_3Cl_5$ MW, 264·5

Needles from C_6H_6. M.p. 218°. B.p. 301° Sol. boiling C_6H_6. Spar. sol. CS_2. Very spar sol. EtOH, Et_2O.

Beilstein, Kuhlberg, *Ann.*, 1869, **150**, 298
Fichter, Glantzstein, *Ber.*, 1916, **49**, 2486

Pentacosane

$CH_3{\cdot}[CH_2]_{23}{\cdot}CH_3$

$C_{25}H_{52}$ MW, 35

Pearly leaflets from EtOH. M.p. 55·5–56°.

Brigl, *Z. physiol. Chem.*, 1915, **95**, 179.

The following pentacosanes have also been described :—

1. From paraffin oil. M.p. 53·8–54°. B.p. 152·5°/0 mm.

Krafft, *Ber.*, 1907, **40**, 4783.

2. From paraffin oil. M.p. 54°. B.p. 282–4°/40 mm. D^{60} 0·7911, D^{90} 0·7854.

Mabery, *Am. Chem. J.*, 1905, **33**, 288.

3. From high-boiling tar. M.p. 53·5–54° B.p. 254°/15 mm. D_D^{65} 1·43202. n_D^{80} 1·42624.

Gluud, *Ber.*, 1919, **52**, 1040, 1049.

Pentacosanic Acid

$CH_3{\cdot}[CH_2]_{22}{\cdot}CH_2{\cdot}COOH$

$C_{25}H_{50}O_2$ MW, 382

Cryst. from Me_2CO. M.p. 84–5°.
Me ester : $C_{26}H_{52}O_2$. MW, 396. Cryst. from Me_2CO. M.p. 61–2°.
Et ester : $C_{27}H_{54}O_2$. MW, 410. Cryst. from Me_2CO. M.p. 58–9°. B.p. 216–17°/0·5 mm.
Nitrile : *n*-tetracosyl cyanide. $C_{25}H_{49}N$. MW, 363. Cryst. from Me_2CO. M.p. 58–9°.

Levene, Taylor, *J. Biol. Chem.*, 1924, **59**, 905.

Pentacosanol-1.
See Pentacosyl Alcohol.
Pentacosanone-9.
See Octyl hexadecyl Ketone.
Pentacosyl Alcohol (*Pentacosanol*-1)

$CH_3{\cdot}[CH_2]_{23}{\cdot}CH_2OH$

$C_{25}H_{52}O$ MW, 368

Cryst. from Me_2CO. M.p. 78·5–79·5°. B.p. 214–16°/0·36 mm.

Levene, Taylor, *J. Biol. Chem.*, 1924, **59**, 916.

Pentadecanal.
See Pentadecylic Aldehyde.

Pentadecane

$CH_3\cdot[CH_2]_{13}\cdot CH_3$

$C_{15}H_{32}$ MW, 212

Cryst. M.p. 10°. B.p. 270·5°/760 mm., 194°/100 mm., 160°/30 mm., 144°/15 mm. D_4^{20} 0·7689.

Krafft, *Ber.*, 1882, **15**, 1700.
Mai, *Ber.*, 1889, **22**, 2134.

Pentadecane-1 : 1-dicarboxylic Acid.
See Tetradecylmalonic Acid.
Pentadecanoic Acid.
See Pentadecylic Acid.
Pentadecanoic Aldehyde.
See Pentadecylic Aldehyde.
Pentadecanol-1.
See Pentadecyl Alcohol.
Pentadecanol-3.
See Ethyldodecylcarbinol.
Pentadecanone-2.
See Methyl tridecyl Ketone.
Pentadecanone-3.
See Ethyl dodecyl Ketone.
Pentadecanone-8.
See Caprylone.

1-Pentadecenol-15 (*Pentadecylenic alcohol*, 14-*pentadecenyl alcohol*, 15-*hydroxy*-1-*pentadecylene*)

$HO\cdot CH_2\cdot[CH_2]_{12}\cdot CH\colon CH_2$

$C_{15}H_{30}O$ MW, 226

Leaflets from pet. ether. M.p. 32–3°. B.p. 170–2°/10 mm.
Phenylurethane : leaflets from EtOH. M.p. 60·5–61°.

Chuit, Boelsing, Hausser, Malet, *Helv. Chim. Acta*, 1927, **10**, 128.

2-Pentadecenol-15 (13-*Pentadecenol*-1, *iso-pentadecylenic alcohol*, 13-*pentadecenyl alcohol*, 15-*hydroxy*-2-*pentadecylene*)

$HO\cdot CH_2\cdot[CH_2]_{11}\cdot CH\colon CH\cdot CH_3$

$C_{15}H_{30}O$ MW, 226

Leaflets from pet. ether. M.p. 40–40·5°. B.p. 170–2°/8 mm.
Phenylurethane : leaflets from EtOH. M.p. 68–68·4°.

Chuit, Boelsing, Hausser, Malet, *Helv. Chim. Acta*, 1927, **10**, 130.

Pentadecenyl Alcohol.
See Pentadecenol.
Pentadecenylsalicylic Acid.
See Ginkgolic Acid.

Pentadecyl Alcohol (*Pentadecanol*-1)

$CH_3\cdot[CH_2]_{13}\cdot CH_2OH$

$C_{15}H_{32}O$ MW, 228

Cryst. M.p. 45–6° (44°).
Formyl : cryst. M.p. 13·69°. B.p. 201·5°/30 mm. D_4^{25} 0·8618. n_D^{20} 1·4399.
Palmityl : cryst. from EtOH. M.p. 55·5°.
Phenylurethane : plates from C_6H_6. M.p. 72°.

Simonini, *Monatsh.*, 1893, **14**, 85.
Gascard, *Ann. chim.*, 1921, **15**, 332.
Ruhoff, Reid, *J. Am. Chem. Soc.*, 1933, **55**, 3825.

Pentadecylamine (1-*Amino*-n-*pentadecane*)

$CH_3\cdot[CH_2]_{13}\cdot CH_2\cdot NH_2$

$C_{15}H_{33}N$ MW, 227

Leaflets or needles. M.p. 36·5° (33°). B.p. 298–301° (301°/720 mm.). Sol. EtOH, Et_2O.
B,HCl : plates from EtOH. M.p. 199°.
Acetyl : needles from pet. ether. M.p. 72°. Sol. EtOH, Et_2O, hot ligroin. Insol. H_2O.

Naegeli, Grüntuch, Lendorff, *Helv. Chim. Acta*, 1929, **12**, 240.

3-Pentadecylcatechol.
See Hydrourushiol.
Pentadecylene-carboxylic Acid.
See Gaidic Acid *and* Palmitoleic Acid.
Pentadecylenic Alcohol.
See Pentadecenol.
Pentadecyl *p*-hydroxyphenyl Ketone.
See *p*-Hydroxypalmitophenone.

Pentadecylic Acid (*Pentadecanoic acid*, *tetradecane*-1-*carboxylic acid*)

$CH_3\cdot[CH_2]_{12}\cdot CH_2\cdot COOH$

$C_{15}H_{30}O_2$ MW, 242

Plates from Me_2CO.Aq. M.p. 53–4° (51°). B.p. 257°/100 mm. Sol. EtOH, Et_2O, $CHCl_3$, C_6H_6, pet. ether.
Me ester : $C_{16}H_{32}O_2$. MW, 256. Needles from EtOH.Aq. M.p. 18·5°.
Et ester : $C_{17}H_{34}O_2$. MW, 270. Needles from EtOH.Aq. M.p. 14°. Sol. most org. solvents.
Chloride : $C_{15}H_{29}OCl$. MW, 260·5. Liq. B.p. 157°/5 mm.
Amide : $C_{15}H_{31}ON$. MW, 241. Needles from EtOH. M.p. 102·5°. Sol. boiling EtOH. Mod. sol. Et_2O. Insol. cold H_2O, pet. ether.

Le Sueur, *J. Chem. Soc.*, 1905, **87**, 1898.
Majima, Nakamura, *Ber.*, 1913, **46**, 4094.
Ford-Moore, Phillips, *Rec. trav. chim.*, 1934, **53**, 857.

Pentadecylic Aldehyde (*Pentadecanal, pentadecanoic aldehyde*)

$CH_3\cdot[CH_2]_{12}\cdot CH_2\cdot CHO$

$C_{15}H_{30}O$ MW, 226

Needles. M.p. 24–5°. B.p. 185°/25 mm., 172–6°/15 mm. Polymerises readily.

Oxime: needles from EtOH.Aq. M.p. 86°. Sol. Et_2O. Spar. sol. EtOH, C_6H_6, pet. ether.

Thiosemicarbazone: cryst. from Et_2O. M.p. 95–96·5°. Spar. sol. EtOH, Me_2CO, AcOEt, C_6H_6. Insol. H_2O, pet. ether.

p-*Bromophenylhydrazone*: cryst. M.p. 40–50°. Unstable.

p-*Nitrophenylhydrazone*: yellow plates from EtOH. M.p. 94–5°. Sol. EtOH, Me_2CO, AcOH, AcOEt, CCl_4, C_6H_6.

2 : 4-*Dinitrophenylhydrazone*: m.p. 107·5°. Sol. AcOEt, $CHCl_3$, C_6H_6, hot Et_2O, Me_2CO, AcOH, CCl_4.

Benzoylhydrazone: plates from EtOH. M.p. 87°.

m-*Nitrobenzoylhydrazone*: plates from EtOH. M.p. 102°. Spar. sol. Et_2O.

Cyanhydrin: *see under* 1-Hydroxypalmitic Acid.

Le Sueur, *J. Chem. Soc.*, 1905, **87**, 1896.
Landa, *Bull soc. chim.*, 1925, **37**, 1235.

3-Pentadecylphenol.
See Hydroginkgol.

Pentadecyl phenyl Ketone.
See Palmitophenone.

5-Pentadecylresorcinol.
See Hydrobilobol.

6-Pentadecylsalicylic Acid.
See Hydroginkgolic Acid.

1 : 2-Pentadiene (*Ethylallene, propylideneethylene*)

$CH_3\cdot CH_2\cdot CH\vdots C\vdots CH_2$

C_5H_8 MW, 68

Mobile liq. B.p. 44–5°. D^{20} 0·6890. n_D^{20} 1·4149.

Bouis, *Bull. soc. chim.*, 1927, **41**, 1160.

1 : 3-Pentadiene (1-*Methylbutadiene*-1 : 3-, 1-*methyldivinyl*, 1-*methylerythrene*, *piperylene*)

$CH_3\cdot CH\vdots CH\cdot CH\vdots CH_2$

C_5H_8 MW, 68

Liq. B.p. 42°. $D_4^{13\cdot6}$ 0·6887, D_4^{20} 0·6830. $n_D^{13\cdot6}$ 1·43443, n_D^{20} 1·4280.

Auwers, Westermann, *Ber.*, 1921, **54**, 2993.
Prévost, *Ann. chim.*, 1928, **10**, 173.
Farmer, Warren, *J. Chem. Soc.*, 1931, 3221.

1 : 4-Pentadiene (*Divinylmethane, allylethylene*)

$CH_2\vdots CH\cdot CH_2\cdot CH\vdots CH_2$

C_5H_8 MW, 68

Liq. B.p. 25·8–26·2°/756 mm. D_4^{20} 0·6594. n_D^{20} 1·3883.

Kogerman, *J. Am. Chem. Soc.*, 1930, **52**, 5060.
Shoemaker, Boord, *J. Am. Chem. Soc.*, 1931, **53**, 1505.

2 : 3-Pentadiene.
See sym.-Dimethylallene.

1 : 3-Pentadiene-1-carboxylic Acid.
See Sorbic Acid.

Pentaerythritol (*Tetrahydroxymethylmethane, tetramethylolmethane, tetrahydroxytetramethylmethane*)

$$\begin{matrix}HO\cdot CH_2\\HO\cdot CH_2\end{matrix}\!>\!C\!<\!\begin{matrix}CH_2OH\\CH_2OH\end{matrix}$$

$C_5H_{12}O_4$ MW, 136

Cryst. from dil. HCl. M.p. 260° (253°). Sol. 18 parts H_2O at 15°. Heat of comb. C_p 661·4 Cal. $HNO_3 \longrightarrow$ oxalic acid. $CrO_3 \longrightarrow$ $H\cdot COOH + CO_2$.

Tetra-Et ether: $C_{13}H_{28}O_4$. MW, 248. Oil. B.p. 220–5°. D_4^0 0·9229, D_4^{16} 0·9082.

Tetra-acetyl: needles from H_2O or C_6H_6. M.p. 82–3°.

Tetranitrate: niperyt, penthrit. Prisms from Me_2CO–EtOH. M.p. 138–40°. Sol. Me_2CO. Spar. sol. EtOH, Et_2O. Reduces Fehling's.

Schwink, *Organic Syntheses*, Collective Vol. I, 417.
Stellbacher, *Chem. Zentr.*, 1919, II, 261.
Deutsche Gold- und Silber-Scheideanstallt v. Roessler, D.R.P., 596,509, (*Chem. Zentr.*, 1933, II, 2190).
Friederich, Brün, *Ber.*, 1930, **63**, 2681.
Bincer, Hess, *Ber.*, 1928, **61**, 539.
Clarke, U.S.P., 1,583,658, (*Chem. Zentr.*, 1926, II, 1191).
Desvergnes, *Chem. Abstracts*, 1933, **27**, 4675.
Dumontel, Giovetti, *Industria chimica*, 1934, **9**, 767 (*Review*).

Pentahomocholine (5-*Dimethylamino*-n-*amyl alcohol*)

$(CH_3)_2N\cdot CH_2\cdot CH_2\cdot CH_2\cdot CH_2\cdot CH_2OH$

$C_7H_{17}ON$ MW, 131

Liq. B.p. 115–16°/25 mm. Misc. with H_2O. Volatile in steam. Weak base.

Methochloride: cryst.

Methiodide: leaflets. M.p. 134°.

Methochloroplatinate: pale yellow needles from EtOH.Aq. M.p. 213°. Very sol. H_2O. Spar. sol. EtOH.

Methochloroaurate: brownish-yellow leaflets from H_2O. M.p. 147°.

v. Braun, *Ber.*, 1916, **49**, 976.

1 : 2 : 3 : 5 : 7-Pentahydroxyanthraquinone (5 : 7-*Dihydroxyanthragallol*)

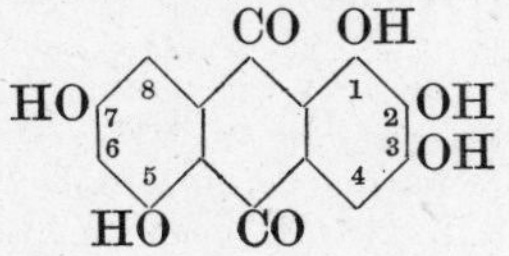

$C_{14}H_8O_7$ MW, 288

Red cryst. from EtOH. Does not melt below 360°. Sol. boiling EtOH, Me_2CO. Spar. sol. Et_2O, AcOH. Insol. H_2O, $CHCl_3$, C_6H_6, ligroin.

Penta-acetyl: pale yellow needles from EtOH. M.p. 229°. Sol. hot EtOH, AcOH.

Noah, *Ber.*, 1886, **19**, 751.
Liebermann, v. Kostanecki, Noah, *Ann.*, 1887, **240**, 273.

1 : 2 : 4 : 5 : 8-Pentahydroxyanthraquinone (*Alizarin Cyanine R*)

Bronze leaflets from $PhNO_2$. Distils undecomp. Conc. $H_2SO_4 \longrightarrow$ blue sol. with red fluor., + boric acid $\longrightarrow$ greenish blue.

Penta-acetyl: leaflets from C_6H_6.

Bayer, D.R.P., 66,153.
Gattermann, *J. prakt. Chem.*, 1891, **43**, 250.

Pentahydroxybenzene

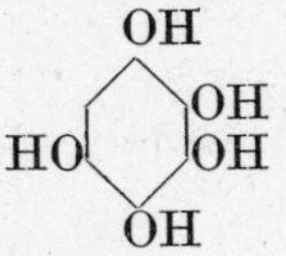

$C_6H_6O_5$ MW, 158

Two compounds of this formula are described in the literature.

1. Cryst. from conc. HI. Very sol. H_2O. Insol. org. solvents.

Wenzel, Weidel, *Chem. Zentr.*, 1903, II, 829.

2. Pale violet needles from AcOEt–C_6H_6. Blackens on heating. Sol. EtOH, Et_2O, AcOEt. Spar. sol. H_2O. Insol. C_6H_6. Alkalis $\longrightarrow$ green sols. $FeCl_3 \longrightarrow$ reddish-brown col.

Penta-acetyl: needles from EtOH–pet. ether.

M.p. 165° decomp. Sol. Et_2O. Spar. sol. H_2O, EtOH, pet. ether.

Einhorn, Cobliner, Pfeiffer, *Ber.*, 1904, **37**, 122.

2 : 3 : 4 : 2′ : 4′-Pentahydroxybenzophenone

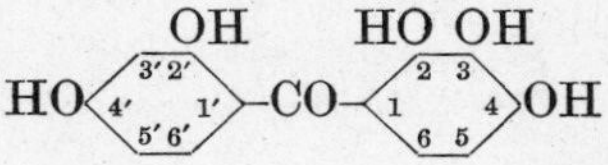

$C_{13}H_{10}O_6$ MW, 262

Yellowish needles + $2H_2O$ from EtOH. M.p. 187° (168–70°). Sol. $H_2O \longrightarrow$ yellow col. $\longrightarrow$ greenish-yellow $\longrightarrow$ olive-green on standing.

Badische, D.R.Ps., 49,149, 50,451.
Atkinson, Heilbron, *J. Chem. Soc.*, 1926, 2690.

2 : 3 : 4 : 3′ : 4′-Pentahydroxybenzophenone.

Yellow needles + $2H_2O$ from boiling H_2O. M.p. anhyd. 192–3°. Sol. hot H_2O, EtOH, Me_2CO, AcOH. Spar. sol. Et_2O. Insol. C_6H_6. Conc. $H_2SO_4 \longrightarrow$ orange sol.

Noelting, Meyer, *Ber.*, 1897, **30**, 2591.

2 : 3 : 4 : 3′ : 5′-Pentahydroxybenzophenone.

3 : 4 : 3′ : 5′-*Tetra-Me ether*: $C_{17}H_{18}O_6$. MW, 318. Pale yellow cryst. from EtOH. M.p. 123–4°. Sol. EtOH, Et_2O, C_6H_6, $CHCl_3$. Spar. sol. AcOH, ligroin. Conc. $H_2SO_4 \longrightarrow$ yellow sol.

Mauthner, *J. prakt. Chem.*, 1913, **87**, 407.

2 : 4 : 6 : 2′ : 4′-Pentahydroxybenzophenone.

Penta-Me ether: $C_{18}H_{20}O_6$. MW, 332. Pale yellow leaflets from EtOH.Aq. M.p. 138°.

Tambor, *Ber.*, 1910, **43**, 1888.

2 : 4 : 6 : 2′ : 6′-Pentahydroxybenzophenone.

2′ : 6′-*Di-Me ether*: $C_{15}H_{14}O_6$. MW, 290. Plates from EtOH.Aq. M.p. 216–18°. Sol. EtOH, $CHCl_3$, C_6H_6. Spar. sol. Et_2O. $FeCl_3 \longrightarrow$ intense blue col.

Korczynski, Nowakowski, *Bull. soc. chim.*, 1928, **43**, 336.

2 : 4 : 6 : 3′ : 4′-Pentahydroxybenzophenone.

See Maclurin.

2 : 4 : 6 : 3′ : 5′-Pentahydroxybenzophenone.

Penta-Me ether: needles. M.p. 132–3°. Sol.

Et_2O, AcOH, $CHCl_3$, C_6H_6, warm EtOH. Spar. sol. ligroin.

Mauthner, *J. prakt. Chem.*, 1913, **87**, 409.

3 : 4 : 5 : 2′ : 4′-Pentahydroxybenzophenone.

Yellow needles from EtOH.Aq. M.p. 242°. Sol. most org. solvents. Spar. sol. H_2O. Alkalis ⟶ intense red col. Alc. $FeCl_3$ ⟶ green col.

3 : 4 : 5-*Tri-Me ether*: $C_{16}H_{16}O_6$. MW, 304. Yellow needles from EtOH.Aq. or H_2O. M.p. 165°. Conc. H_2SO_4 ⟶ intense yellow sol.

Bargellini, Grippa, *Gazz. chim. ital.*, 1927, **57**, 138.
Korczynski, Nowakowski, *Bull. soc. chim.*, 1928, **43**, 335.

3 : 4 : 5 : 3′ : 4′-Pentahydroxybenzophenone.

Yellow needles + $2H_2O$ from H_2O. M.p. anhyd. 266°. Sol. hot H_2O, EtOH, Me_2CO. Mod. sol. hot AcOH. Insol. Et_2O, C_6H_6. Conc. H_2SO_4 ⟶ red col. ⟶ protocatechuic acid on heating.

Penta-Me ether: needles from EtOH. M.p. 119–20°. Conc. H_2SO_4 ⟶ yellow sol. *Oxime*: needles from C_6H_6. M.p. 143°.

Noelting, Meyer, *Ber.*, 1897, **30**, 2591.
v. Kostanecki, Tambor, *Ber.*, 1906, **39**, 4026.
Parkin, Weizmann, *J. Chem. Soc.*, 1906, **89**, 1664.

Pentahydroxycyclohexane.
See Quercitol.

3 : 5 : 6 : 7 : 4′-Pentahydroxyflavone

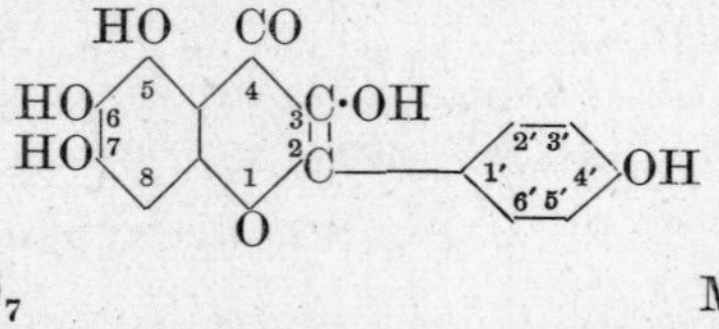

$C_{15}H_{10}O_7$ MW, 302

Yellow micro-needles from AcOH.Aq. Darkens at 270°. Partially melts at 314–20° with decomp. Mg + acid alc. sol. ⟶ pinkish-red col. Alc. $Pb(OAc)_2$ ⟶ orange ppt. changing to greenish-brown. Alc. $FeCl_3$ ⟶ olive-green col.

3 : 6 : 7 : 4′-*Tetra-Me ether*: $C_{19}H_{18}O_7$. MW, 358. Yellow plates from EtOH. M.p. 171°. Alc. $FeCl_3$ ⟶ olive-green col.

Penta-Me ether: *see* Tangeritin.

Goldsworthy, Robinson, *J. Chem. Soc.*, 1937, 48.

3 : 5 : 7 : 2′ : 4′-Pentahydroxyflavone.
See Morin.

3 : 5 : 7 : 3′ : 4′-Pentahydroxyflavone.
See Quercetin.

3 : 7 : 8 : 3′ : 4′-Pentahydroxyflavone

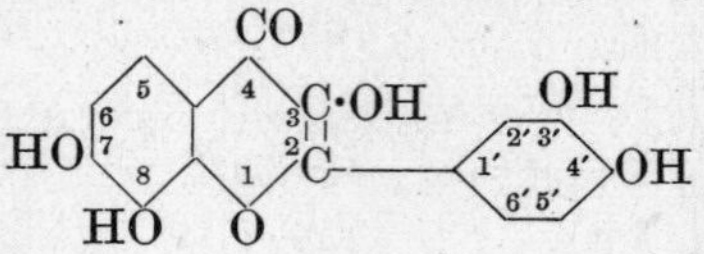

$C_{15}H_{10}O_7$ MW, 30

Pale yellow needles + H_2O from EtOH.Ac M.p. 308° decomp. Conc. H_2SO_4 ⟶ intens yellow col. Dil. NaOH ⟶ reddish-yellow col

7 : 8 : 3′ : 4′-*Tetra-Me ether*: $C_{19}H_{18}O_7$. MW 358. Pale yellow needles from EtOH or AcOH-EtOH. M.p. 217°. Sol. hot AcOH. Spar. sol EtOH. Conc. H_2SO_4 ⟶ intense yellow col *Acetyl*: needles from EtOH.Aq. M.p. 176°.

Penta-acetyl: needles from EtOH. M.p 172–3°.

v. Kostanecki, Rudse, *Ber.*, 1905, **38**, 938

3 : 7 : 3′ : 4′ : 5′-Pentahydroxyflavone.
See Robinetin.

5 : 7 : 3′ : 4′ : 5′-Pentahydroxyflavone.
See Tricetin.

7 : 8 : 3′ : 4′ : 5′-Pentahydroxyflavone.

Yellow needles from EtOH.Aq. Does not melt below 345°.

Penta-acetyl: needles from EtOH. M.p. 263°

Badhwar, Kang, Venkataraman, *J. Chem Soc.*, 1932, 1110.

Pentaketocyclopentane.
See Leuconic Acid.

Pental.
2-Methylbutylene-2, *q.v.*

Pentalin.
See Pentachloroethane.

Pentamethylaniline (*Aminopentamethylbenzene*)

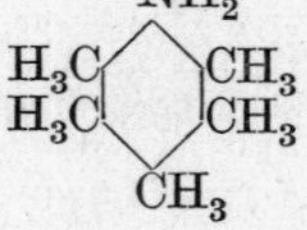

$C_{11}H_{17}N$ MW, 163

Prismatic cryst. from EtOH. M.p. 151–2°. B.p. 277–8°. Sol. EtOH, Et_2O. Insol. H_2O.

N-*Me*: $C_{12}H_{19}N$. MW, 177. Cryst. from EtOH. M.p. 60–1°.

N-*Di-Me*: $C_{13}H_{21}N$. MW, 191. Cryst. M.p. 53–4°.

N-*Formyl*: needles from EtOH.Aq. M.p. 217°.

N-*Acetyl* : needles from EtOH. M.p. 213.

Hoffmann, *Ber.*, 1885, **18**, 1822.
Limpach, *Ber.*, 1888, **21**, 645.
Willstätter, Kubli, *Ber.*, 1909, **42**, 4162.
Dimroth, Leichtlin, Friedemann, *Ber.*, 1917, **50**, 1543.

Pentamethylanisole.
See under Pentamethylphenol.

Pentamethylbenzene

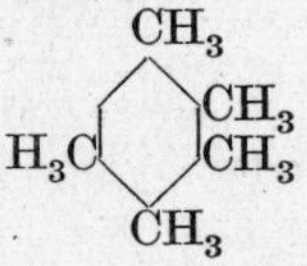

$C_{11}H_{16}$ MW, 148

Prisms from EtOH.Aq. or EtOH–C_6H_6. M.p. 53° (51·5°). B.p. 231°. Very sol. EtOH. Heat of comb. C_v 1551·8 Cal.

Picrate : golden-yellow prisms from EtOH. M.p. 131°.

Jacobsen, *Ber.*, 1887, **20**, 896.
v. Braun, Nelles, *Ber.*, 1934, **67**, 1099.
Smith, *Organic Syntheses*, 1930, X, 34.

Pentamethylbenzoic Acid

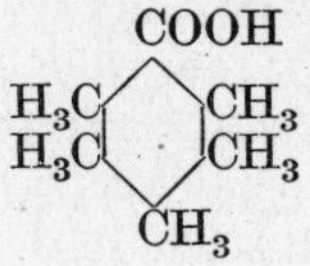

$C_{12}H_{16}O_2$ MW, 192

Needles from boiling H_2O ; leaflets or needles from EtOH.Aq. M.p. 210·5°. Very sol. hot EtOH. Insol. cold H_2O. Volatile in steam. Sublimes. Fuming HNO_3 at 200° ⟶ pentamethylbenzene + CO_2.

Me ester : $C_{13}H_{18}O_2$. MW, 206. Plates from MeOH. M.p. 67·5°. B.p. 299–300°.

Amide : $C_{12}H_{17}ON$. MW, 191. Leaflets from EtOH. M.p. 206°. Insol. H_2O.

Nitrile : $C_{12}H_{15}N$. MW, 173. Needles from EtOH. M.p. 170° (168°). B.p. 294–5° (290–2°). Very sol. hot EtOH. Insol. H_2O.

Jacobsen, *Ber.*, 1889, **22**, 1221.
Hoffmann, *Ber.*, 1885, **18**, 1825.
Clement, *Compt. rend.*, 1934, **198**, 666.

2 : 4 : 5 : 3′ : 4′-Pentamethylbenzophenone

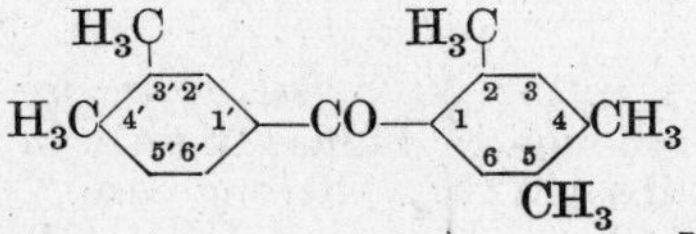

$C_{18}H_{20}O$ MW, 252

Prisms from C_6H_6. M.p. 90°. B.p. 189–90°/3 mm. Very sol. most solvents.

Morgan, Coulson, *J. Chem. Soc.*, 1931, 2327.

2 : 4 : 6 : 3′ : 5′-Pentamethylbenzophenone.

Prisms from pet. ether. M.p. 84–5°. Sol. hot EtOH. Conc. H_2SO_4 ⟶ yellow sol.

Weiler, *Ber.*, 1899, **32**, 1910; 1900, **33**, 344.

Pentamethylene.
See Cyclopentane.

Pentamethylene-aniline.
See N-Phenylpiperidine.

Pentamethylene bromide.
See 1 : 5-Dibromo-*n*-pentane.

Pentamethylene chloride.
See 1 : 5-Dichloro-*n*-pentane.

Pentamethylenediamine.
See Cadaverine.

Pentamethylenedithiocarbamic Acid (*Piperidine* N-*dithiocarboxylic acid*)

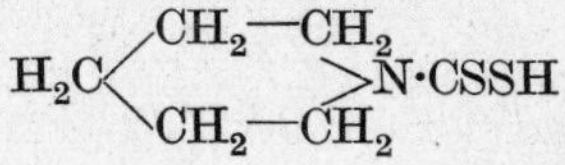

$C_6H_{11}NS_2$ MW, 161

Free acid not known. Salts are powerful vulcanisation accelerators.

Piperidine salt : leaflets from EtOH. M.p. 174°. Well known rapid vulcanisation accelerator.

Phenylhydrazine salt : m.p. 218°.

Me ester : $C_7H_{13}NS_2$. MW, 175. Plates. M.p. 33–4°. B.p. about 260°. Very sol.

Phenyl ester : $C_{12}H_{15}NS_2$. MW, 237. M.p. 116–17.°

p-*Tolyl ester* : $C_{13}H_{17}NS_2$. MW, 251. M.p. 118–19°.

Losanitsch, *Ber.*, 1907, **40**, 2974.
Delépine, *Bull. soc. chim.*, 1902, **27**, 592.
Maas, Wolffenstein, *Ber.*, 1898, **31**, 2689.
Clifford, Lichty, *J. Am. Chem. Soc.*, 1932, **54**, 1166.
I.C.I., E.P., 358,230, (*Brit. Chem. Abstracts*, 1932, 138).

Pentamethyleneglycine.
See Piperidinoacetic Acid.

Pentamethylene Glycol (1 : 5-*Dihydroxypentane*, *pentandiol*-1 : 5)

$$HO{\cdot}CH_2{\cdot}CH_2{\cdot}CH_2{\cdot}CH_2{\cdot}CH_2OH$$

$C_5H_{12}O_2$ MW, 104

Oily liq. with bitter taste. B.p. 238–9° (260°) 155°/31 mm., 134°/12 mm., 119–20°/3 mm. Sol. H_2O, EtOH. Spar. sol. Et_2O. D^0 1·004, D^{11}_{15} 0·999, D^{20}_{20} 0·9939. n^{20}_D 1·4499.

Di-Me ether: $C_7H_{16}O_2$. MW, 132. B.p. 156–7°/760 mm. (159°). D^{15} 0·8616. n^{15}_D 1·4094.

Di-isoamyl ether: $C_{15}H_{32}O_2$. MW, 244. Liq. B.p. 276–7°/759 mm., 159–60°/20 mm. D^{18} 0·844.

Phenyl ether: $C_{11}H_{16}O_2$. MW, 180. B.p. 150–5°/11 mm. *Phenylurethane*: m.p. 93°.

Diacetyl: liq. with fruity odour. F.p. 2°. B.p. 241°/760 mm., 122–3°/3 mm. D^{15} 1·0328, D^{18} 1·021. n^{15}_D 1·4282, n^{19}_D 1·4261.

Succinyl: m.p. 19°. B.p. 88–9°/1 mm. D^{60}_4 1·1373. n^{60}_D 1·4583. *Dimeric form*: m.p. 87°.

Di-p-nitrobenzoyl: cryst. from C_6H_6. M.p. 104·5°.

Carbonate: powder. M.p. 44–6°. Sol. Me_2CO, $CHCl_3$, AcOH, C_6H_6. Insol. EtOH, Et_2O, pet. ether. *Dimeric form*: m.p. 117–18°.

Di-phenylurethane: needles from EtOH or EtOH–$CHCl_3$. M.p. 176°.

Di-1-naphthylurethane: plates. M.p. 147°.

du Pont, U.S.P., 1,995,291, (*Chem. Abstracts*, 1935, **27**, 2975).
Spanagel, Carothers, *J. Am. Chem. Soc.*, 1935, **57**, 931.
Paul, *Bull. soc. chim.*, 1934, **1**, 971.
Wojcik, Adams, *J. Am. Chem. Soc.*, 1933, **55**, 4941.
Bennett, Heathcoat, *J. Chem. Soc.*, 1929, 273.
Müller, Rölz, Gero, *Monatsh.*, 1928, **50**, 107.
v. Braun, Deutsch, Schmatloch, *Ber.*, 1912, **45**, 1250.
Hamonet, *Bull. soc. chim.*, 1905, **33**, 529.
v. Braun, Steindorff, *Ber.*, 1905, **38**, 959.
Lespieau, *Ann. chim. phys.*, 1912, **27**, 175.

Pentamethyleneimine.
See Piperidine.

Pentamethylene iodide.
See 1 : 5-Di-iodo-*n*-pentane.

Pentamethylene oxide.
See Tetrahydropyran.

Pentamethylene sulphide (*Tetrahydrothiopyran*)

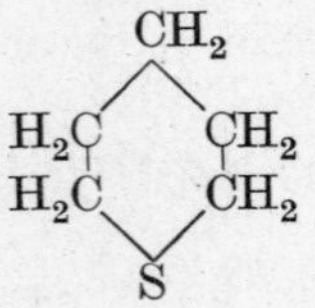

$C_5H_{10}S$ MW, 102

Found in crude Mexican petroleum. Cryst. M.p. 13°. B.p. 141°/755 mm. (141·5–142°/747 mm.). Sol. most org. solvents. Insol. H_2O. D^{15}_4 0·9889, D^{18}_4 0·9943, D^{20}_4 0·9849. n^{18}_D 1·5046. Stable at 200°. Volatile in steam. Tetranitromethane in EtOH ⟶ golden-yellow col. Dil. HNO_3 ⟶ pentamethylene sulphoxide. $KMnO_4$ ⟶ pentamethylene sulphone.

B,HgCl₂: leaflets from EtOH. M.p. 137·5°. Sol. hot EtOH. Insol. H_2O, Et_2O.

Methiodide: needles from EtOH. Sublimes at 192° (162°) without melting. Sol. H_2O. Spar. sol. EtOH. Insol. Et_2O, C_6H_6, ligroin.

Methochloroplatinate: m.p. 225°. Sol. H_2O.

Clarke, *J. Chem. Soc.*, 1912, **101**, 1805.
v. Braun, Trümpler, *Ber.*, 1910, **43**, 548.
Grischkewitsch - Trochimowski, *Chem. Zentr.*, 1923, I, 1503.

Pentamethylene sulphone

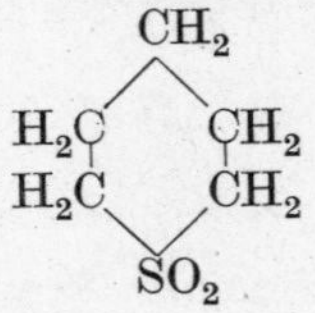

$C_5H_{10}O_2S$ MW, 134

Cryst. from H_2O. M.p. 98·5–99°. Sol. H_2O, EtOH. Less sol. Et_2O. Insol. ligroin.

Grischkewitsch - Trochimowski, *Chem. Zentr.*, 1923, I, 1503.

Pentamethylene sulphoxide

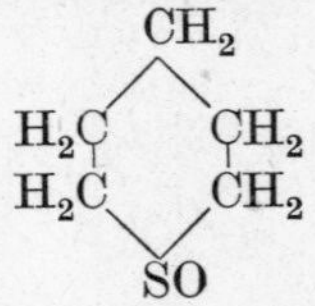

$C_5H_{10}OS$ MW, 118

Yellow liq. which solidifies to glassy mass in exsiccator.

See previous reference.

Pentamethylene-urethane.
See under Piperidine-*N*-carboxylic Acid.

Pentamethylguanidine

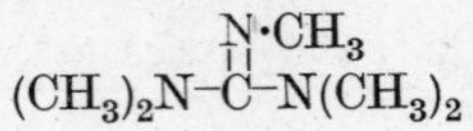

$C_6H_{15}N_3$ MW, 129

Liq. B.p. 155–60°. Sol. H_2O, org. solvents. Very hygroscopic. Fumes slightly in moist air. Readily absorbs CO_2. Strong base.

B,HAuCl₄: needles from H_2O. M.p. 130–2°.

Picrate: yellow needles from H_2O. M.p. 165–6° decomp.

Schenck, *Z. physiol. Chem.*, 1912, **77**, 386.
Lecher, Graf, *Ber.*, 1923, **56**, 1329.

Pentamethylphenol (*Hydroxypentamethylbenzene*)

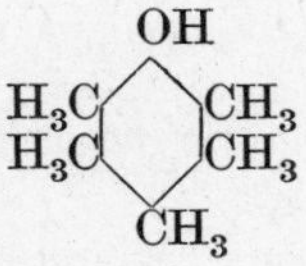

$C_{11}H_{16}O$ MW, 164

Needles from EtOH or pet. ether. M.p. 126°. B.p. 267°. Gives no col. with $FeCl_3$.

Me ether: pentamethylanisole. $C_{12}H_{18}O$. MW, 178. Needles from EtOH. M.p. 63–4°. Sol. EtOH.

Benzoyl: rhombic plates from EtOH. M.p. 127°.

Phenylurethane: needles from EtOH–pet. ether. M.p. 215°.

Hey, *J. Chem. Soc.*, 1931, 1593.
Dimroth, Leichtlin, Friedemann, *Ber.*, 1917, **50**, 1543.
Hofmann, *Ber.*, 1885, **18**, 1826.

2 : 3 : 4 : 5 : 6-Pentamethylpiperazine (2 : 3 : 4 : 5 : 6-*Pentamethylhexahydropyrazine*)

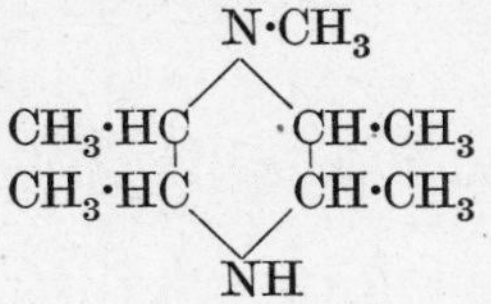

$C_9H_{20}N_2$ MW, 156

γ-Form:

Prisms. M.p. 45°. B.p. 201–2°. Very hygroscopic.

B,H_2O: prisms from Me_2CO. M.p. 73–4°. Sol. EtOH, AcOEt. Spar. sol. C_6H_6, Et_2O.

B,2HCl: needles. M.p. about 300°. Sol. H_2O. Insol. EtOH.

B,HI: prisms from H_2O or EtOH. M.p. 161–2°. Very sol. H_2O, hot EtOH.

B,2HI: prisms from EtOH. M.p. 240° decomp. Sol. H_2O, EtOH, MeOH. Almost insol. Me_2CO, AcOEt.

N-p-*Toluenesulphonyl*: prisms from EtOH, needles from pet. ether. M.p. 124°. *B,HCl*: prisms from EtOH. M.p. 250°. d-*Tartrate*: needles from Me_2CO.Aq. M.p. 174–5°. $[\alpha]_{5461}$ + 9·7° in H_2O. d-*Camphor*-10-*sulphonate*: prisms from H_2O. M.p. 208–11°. $[\alpha]_{5461}$ + 28·4° in $CHCl_3$.

N-*Nitroso*: pale yellow oil. M.p. 24–5°, B.p. 155–7°/15 mm. Very sol. EtOH, Et_2O, CS_2, pet. ether. Less sol. hot than cold H_2O. d-*Camphor*-10-*sulphonate*: cryst. from Me_2CO.Aq. M.p. 213–15° decomp. $[\alpha]_{5461}$ + 15·2° in H_2O.

d-*Tartrate*: cryst. from MeOH. M.p. 164–5°. $[\alpha]_{5461}$ + 20·3° in H_2O.

Di-d-*camphor*-10-*sulphonate*: cryst. from EtOH. M.p. 261°. $[\alpha]_{5461}$ + 20·0° in H_2O.

Phenylthiourea: prisms from pet. ether. M.p. 154°. Sol. EtOH. C_6H_6. Spar. sol. pet. ether.

β-Form:

p-*Toluenesulphonyl*: prisms from EtOH or pet. ether. M.p. 100–1°.

Phenylthiourea: prisms from pet. ether. M.p. 95°.

Kipping, *J. Chem. Soc.*, 1932, 1340; 1933, 143.

Pentanal.
See Valeraldehyde.

1-Pentanalone-2.
See Propylglyoxal.

1-Pentanalone-4.
See Levulinic Aldehyde.

Pentandiol.
See Dihydroxypentane *and* Pentamethylene Glycol.

Pentandione-2 : 3.
See Acetylpropionyl.

Pentandione-2 : 4.
See Acetylacetone.

***n*-Pentane**

$$CH_3{\cdot}CH_2{\cdot}CH_2{\cdot}CH_2{\cdot}CH_3$$

C_5H_{12} MW, 72

Found in American petroleum. F.p. — 129°. B.p. 36·00°. D_4^{20} 0·62632. n_D^{20} 1·35769. Sol. 200 parts H_2O at 16°.

Noller, *Organic Syntheses*, 1931, XI, 84.
Shepard, Henne, Midgley, *J. Am. Chem. Soc.*, 1931, **53**, 1948.

Pentane-1-carboxylic cid.
See n-Caproic Acid.

Pentane-2-carboxylic Acid.
See 1-Methylvaleric Acid.

Pentane-3-carboxylic Acid.
See Diethylacetic Acid.

Pentane-1 : 1-dicarboxylic Acid.
See n-Butylmalonic Acid.

Pentane-1 : 2-dicarboxylic Acid.
See Propylsuccinic Acid.

Pentane-1 : 4-dicarboxylic Acid.
See 1-Methyladipic Acid.

Pentane-1 : 5-dicarboxylic Acid.
See Pimelic Acid.
Pentane-2 : 2-dicarboxylic Acid.
See Methylpropylmalonic Acid.
Pentane-2 : 3-dicarboxylic Acid.
See 1-Methyl-2-ethylsuccinic Acid.
Pentane-2 : 4-dicarboxylic Acid.
See 1 : 3-Dimethylglutaric Acid.
Pentane-3 : 3-dicarboxylic Acid.
See Diethylmalonic Acid.
Pentanol.
See n-Amyl Alcohol, Methyl-n-propylcarbinol, *and* Diethylcarbinol.

1-Pentanolone-2 (*Butyrylcarbinol, 2-keto-n-amyl alcohol*)

$CH_3{\cdot}CH_2{\cdot}CH_2{\cdot}CO{\cdot}CH_2OH$

$C_5H_{10}O_2$ MW, 102

Oil. B.p. 54–6°/11 mm. D_4^{20} 0·9860. n_D^{20} 1·4234.
Me ether : $C_6H_{12}O_2$. MW, 116. B.p. 146–8° (152–3°/745 mm.), 117°/175 mm. D_4^{20} 0·9139. n_D 1·4119. *Semicarbazone* : needles. M.p. 97–8°. Very sol. H_2O, EtOH, Et_2O, AcOEt, C_6H_6. 2 : 4-*Dinitrophenylhydrazone* : m.p. 128·5–129°.
Et ether : $C_7H_{14}O_2$. MW, 130. B.p. 167°, 64–5°/17 mm., 60°/11 mm. D_4^{16} 0·9218. Spar. sol. H_2O. Reduces $NH_3.AgNO_3$. Forms bisulphite comp. *Semicarbazone* : m.p. 86–7°. 2 : 4-*Dinitrophenylhydrazone* : m.p. 163°. *Osazone* : m.p. 110–11°.

Henze, Rigler, *J. Am. Chem. Soc.*, 1934, **56**, 1350.
Maruyama, *Chem. Abstracts*, 1933, **27**, 1863.
Sommelet, *Bull. soc. chim.*, 1911, **9**, 36.
Schmidt, Ascherl, *Ber.*, 1925, **58**, 358.

1-Pentanolone-4.
See 3-Acetopropyl Alcohol.

2-Pentanolone-3 (*Methylpropionylcarbinol, 1-hydroxydiethyl ketone*)

$CH_3{\cdot}CH_2{\cdot}CO{\cdot}CH(OH){\cdot}CH_3$

$C_5H_{10}O_2$ MW, 102

B.p. 152·5°/761 mm., 63°/20 mm., 45–8°/11 mm. D_4^{20} 0·9742. n_D^{20} 1·4218. Vigorously reduces $NH_3.AgNO_3$ and Fehling's.
Me ether : $C_6H_{12}O_2$. MW, 116. B.p. 133°/729 mm.
Et ether : $C_7H_{14}O_2$. MW, 130. B.p. 145°/727 mm.
Butyl ether : $C_9H_{18}O_2$. MW, 158. B.p. 80–2°/35 mm. D_4^{20} 0·8693. n_D^{20} 1·4143.
Semicarbazone : m.p. 208–9°.
Phenylhydrazone : needles from EtOH.Aq. M.p. 107°. Sol. EtOH, Et_2O. Spar. sol. C_6H_6.
Osazone : m.p. 167°.

Vénus-Daniloff, *Bull. soc. chim.*, 1928, **43**, 582.
Henze, Murchison, *J. Am. Chem. Soc.*, 1933, **55**, 4257.
Schmidt, Ascherl, *Ber.*, 1925, **58**, 357.
Gauthier, *Ann. chim. phys.*, 1909, **16**, 324; *Compt. rend.*, 1911, **152**, 1101.

2-Pentanolone-4.
See Acetoisopropyl Alcohol.

3-Pentanolone-2 (*Ethylacetylcarbinol, 1-acetopropyl alcohol, methyl 1-hydroxypropyl ketone*)

$CH_3{\cdot}CH_2{\cdot}CH(OH){\cdot}CO{\cdot}CH_3$

$C_5H_{10}O_2$ MW, 102

B.p. 147–8°/761 mm., 77°/35 mm., 59–59·5°/27 mm. D_4^{20} 0·9500. Misc. with H_2O, EtOH, and most other org. solvents.
Et ether : $C_7H_{14}O_2$. MW, 130. B.p. 76°/67 mm. D^{17} 0·8849. n^{14} 1·4075. *Semicarbazone* : m.p. 93–5°.
Semicarbazone : m.p. 216–17°.
Osazone : m.p. 167°.

Grard, *Ann. chim.*, 1930, **13**, 336.
Vénus-Daniloff, *Bull. soc. chim.*, 1928, **43**, 582.
Bouis, *Bull. soc. chim.*, 1932, **51**, 1177.

Pentanone.
See Diethyl Ketone *and* Methyl propyl Ketone.

Pentantriol-1 : 2 : 3 (*1-Ethyl glycerol, 1 : 2 : 3-trihydroxypentane*)

$CH_3{\cdot}CH_2{\cdot}CH(OH){\cdot}CH(OH){\cdot}CH_2OH$

$C_5H_{12}O_3$ MW, 120

Syrup. B.p. 192°/63·3 mm. D_0^{34} 1·0851. Misc. with H_2O, EtOH. Sol. Et_2O. Sweet taste.
Tribenzoyl : m.p. 99–100°.

Wagner, *Ber.*, 1888, **21**, 3349.
Delaby, *Compt. rend.*, 1923, **176**, 589.

Pentantriol-1 : 2 : 4 (1 : 2 : 4-*Trihydroxypentane*)

$CH_3{\cdot}CH(OH){\cdot}CH_2{\cdot}CH(OH){\cdot}CH_2OH$

$C_5H_{12}O_3$ MW, 120

Liq. B.p. 180°/27 mm. D_0^0 1·135, D_0^{22} 1·120.

Wagner, *Ber.*, 1888, **21**, 3351.

Pentantriol-1 : 2 : 5

$HO{\cdot}CH_2{\cdot}CH_2{\cdot}CH_2{\cdot}CH(OH){\cdot}CH_2OH$

$C_5H_{12}O_3$ MW, 120

Liq. B.p. 190–1°/13 mm. D_{15}^{20} 1·136. n_D^{20} ·42799.

1 : 5-*Di-Me ether*: $C_7H_{16}O_3$. MW, 148. B.p. 4–5°/13 mm. D_{15}^{14} 0·976. n_D^{14} 1·43336. p-*itrobenzoyl*: m.p. 194–5°.

5-*Me* 1-*Et ether*: $C_8H_{18}O_3$. MW, 162. B.p. 9°/13 mm. D_4^{17} 0·955.

Triacetyl: b.p. 173–6°/20 mm., 159°/9 mm. D_{15}^{15} 1·123, D_{15}^{22} 1·112. n_D^{15} 1·4402, n_D^{22} 1·4369.

Triphenylurethane: m.p. 92°.

Paul, *Ann. chim.*, 1932, **18**, 303; *Bull. soc. chim.*, 1933, **53**, 417.

Pentantriol-1 : 3 : 5 (1 : 3 : 5-*Trihydroxy-entane*)

$HO{\cdot}CH_2{\cdot}CH_2{\cdot}CH(OH){\cdot}CH_2{\cdot}CH_2OH$

$_5H_{12}O_3$ MW, 120

Liq. B.p. 188–9°/11 mm.

Blanchard, Paul, *Compt. rend.*, 1935, **200**, 1414.

Pentantriol-2 : 3 : 4 (1 : 3-*Dimethylglycerol*, : 3 : 4-*trihydroxypentane*)

$CH_3{\cdot}CH(OH){\cdot}CH(OH){\cdot}CH(OH){\cdot}CH_3$

$_5H_{12}O_3$ MW, 120

B.p. 244–6°, 152–3°/19 mm. Sol. EtOH, $_2O$. Bitter taste.

Triformyl: m.p. 85°. B.p. 130–4°/15 mm.

Triacetyl: needles from Et_2O. M.p. 121°. .p. 241–3°.

Delaby, Morel, *Bull. soc. chim.*, 1926, **39**, 416.

Reif, *Ber.*, 1908, **41**, 2740.

Pentantrione-2 : 3 : 4 (2 : 3 : 4-*Triketopent-ne*)

$CH_3{\cdot}CO{\cdot}CO{\cdot}CO{\cdot}CH_3$

$_5H_6O_3$ MW, 114

Orange-red oil. B.p. 65–70°/30 mm. Bitter aste. Absorbs H_2O from the air with formation f hydrate, m.p. 52°. Turns brown on standing. Reduces boiling $CuSO_4$.Aq. to Cu.

2-*Oxime*: needles from AcOEt–ligroin. M.p. 5°. Sol. H_2O, EtOH, AcOEt. Insol. ligroin.

2 : 3-*Dioxime*: plates from H_2O. M.p. 128° ecomp. Sol. H_2O, EtOH. Spar. sol. Et_2O, HCl_3. Conc. H_2SO_4 ⟶ green sol.

Semicarbazone: leaflets. M.p. 249°. Sol. AcOH. Spar sol. H_2O, EtOH, pet. ether. lkalis ⟶ yellow sols.

Phenylhydrazone: pale yellow leaflets. M.p. 49°. Sol. AcOH, Me_2CO, C_6H_6. Insol. pet. ther. Conc. H_2SO_4 ⟶ yellow sol.

Di-phenylhydrazone: needles. M.p. 156°.

Wolff, *Ann.*, 1902, **325**, 139.

Sachs, Barschall, *Ber.*, 1901, **34**, 3052.

Pentaphenylethane

$(C_6H_5)_3C{\cdot}CH(C_6H_5)_2$

$C_{32}H_{26}$ MW, 410

Plates from pet. ether. M.p. 166–78° in air, 182–5° in nitrogen. Sol. CS_2, C_6H_6. Spar. sol. Et_2O. Very spar. sol. EtOH, pet. ether. CrO_3 ⟶ triphenylcarbinol + benzophenone.

Gomberg, Cone, *Ber.*, 1906, **39**, 1467.

Bachmann, *J. Am. Chem. Soc.*, 1933, **55**, 2135.

Pentaspadonic Acid.

See Pelandjauic Acid.

Pentatriacontane

$CH_3{\cdot}[CH_2]_{33}{\cdot}CH_3$

$C_{35}H_{72}$ MW, 492

Cryst. from warm EtOH. M.p. 75·0°. B.p. 331°/15 mm. $D_4^{74·7}$ 0·7816. Spar. sol. boiling Et_2O.

Easterfield, Taylor, *J. Chem. Soc.*, 1911, **99**, 2305.

Clemmensen, *Ber.*, 1913, **46**, 1842.

Grün, Ulbrich, Krczil, *Z. angew. Chem.*, 1926, **39**, 421.

1-Pentene (*Propylethylene*, α-*amylene*, 1-*pentylene*)

$CH_3{\cdot}CH_2{\cdot}CH_2{\cdot}CH{:}CH_2$

C_5H_{10} MW, 70

B.p. 39° (29·0–29·8°). D_4^{20} 0·6563. n_D^{20} 1·3711. HI ⟶ 2-iodopentane.

Adams, Kamm, Marvel, *J. Am. Chem. Soc.*, 1918, **40**, 1950.

Leendertse, Tulleners, Waterman, *Rec. trav. chim.*, 1934, **53**, 715.

2-Pentene (sym.-*Methylethylethylene*, β-*amylene*, 2-*pentylene*)

$CH_3{\cdot}CH_2{\cdot}CH{:}CH{\cdot}CH_3$

C_5H_{10} MW, 70

F.p. — 137°, B.p. 36·39°/760 mm. (36°/741 mm.). D_4^{20} 0·651, D_4^{25} 1·6437. n_D^{17} 1·3817, n_D^{20} 1·3308. HI ⟶ 2-iodopentane.

See last reference above and also

Norris, Reuter, *J. Am. Chem. Soc.*, 1927, **49**, 2624.

Norris, *Organic Syntheses*, Collective Vol. I, 421.

Pentene-carboxylic Acid.

See 2-Allylpropionic Acid, 3-Ethylidene-butyric Acid, Hydrosorbic Acid, 1-Methyl-2-

ethylacrylic Acid, 1-Methyl-2-ethylidenepropionic Acid, *and* Propylacrylic Acid.

Pentene-dial.
See Glutacondialdehyde.

1-Pentene-1 : 2-dicarboxylic Acid.
See Propylfumaric Acid *and* Propylmaleic Acid.

1-Pentene-1 : 3-dicarboxylic Acid.
See 1-Ethylglutaconic Acid.

2-Pentene-1 : 2-dicarboxylic Acid.
See Propylidene-succinic Acid.

2-Pentene-2 : 3-dicarboxylic Acid.
See dibasic-Hæmatinic Acid.

2-Pentene-3 : 4-dicarboxylic Acid.
See 1-Methyl-2-ethylidenesuccinic Acid.

2-Pentene-3 : 5-dicarboxylic Acid.
See 1-Ethylideneglutaric Acid.

2-Pentene oxide.
See sym.-Methylethylethylene oxide.

2-Pentene-2 : 3 : 5-tricarboxylic Acid.
See tribasic-Hæmatinic Acid.

Pentenic Acid.
See 2-Ethylidenepropionic Acid, 2-Ethylacrylic Acid, *and* Allylacetic Acid.

Pentenol.
See Allylethyl Alcohol, Ethylvinylcarbinol, Methylallylcarbinol, Methylpropenylcarbinol, *and* 2-Propylidene-ethyl Alcohol.

Pentenone.
See Ethylideneacetone, Ethyl vinyl Ketone, *and* Methyl allyl Ketone.

Penthrit.
See under Pentaerythritol.

1-Pentine (n-*Propylacetylene*)

$$CH_3{\cdot}CH_2{\cdot}CH_2{\cdot}C{\vdots}CH$$

C_5H_8 MW, 68

Liq. F.p. — 95°. B.p. 40° (48–9°). D^{17} 0·694. n_D^{17} 1·388.

Picon, *Compt. rend.*, 1914, **158**, 1346.
Bouis, *Ann. chim.*, 1928, **9**, 402.
Bourguel, *Ann. chim.*, 1925, **3**, 191.
Morehouse, Maass, *Chem. Abstracts*, 1935, **29**, 1059.

2-Pentine (*Methylethylacetylene*)

$$CH_3{\cdot}CH_2{\cdot}C{\vdots}C{\cdot}CH_3$$

C_5H_8 MW, 68

Found in petroleum and fusel oil. F.p. — 101°. B.p. 55·5°/760 mm. $D_4^{17\cdot 2}$ 0·7127. $n_D^{17\cdot 2}$ 1·4045.

Faworsky, *J. prakt. Chem.*, 1888, **37**, 387.
v. Risseghem, *Compt. rend.*, 1914, **158**, 1696.

1-Pentine-1-carboxylic Acid.
See Propylpropiolic Acid.

1-Pentine-4-carboxylic Acid (2-*Acetyleny isobutyric acid*)

$$CH_3{\cdot}\overset{COOH}{CH}{\cdot}CH_2{\cdot}C{\vdots}CH$$

$C_6H_8O_2$ MW, 11

Oil. B.p. 207–8°/768 mm. Spar. sol. H_2O.
Et ester: $C_8H_{12}O_2$. MW, 140. Oil. B.p 165–7°/757 mm. D_4^4 0·95424, D_{20}^{20} 0·93989. n 1·42654.

Perkin, Simonsen, *J. Chem. Soc.*, 1907, **91**, 832.
Gardner, Perkin, *ibid.*, 853.

Pentocystine (4 : 4′-*Diamino*-4 : 4′-*dicarboxy* 1 : 1′-*dibutyl disulphide*)

$$\begin{array}{l} S{\cdot}CH_2{\cdot}CH_2{\cdot}CH_2{\cdot}CH(NH_2){\cdot}COOH \\ S{\cdot}CH_2{\cdot}CH_2{\cdot}CH_2{\cdot}CH(NH_2){\cdot}COOH \end{array}$$

$C_{10}H_{20}O_4N_2S_2$ MW, 29

Needles from H_2O. Decomp. at 269–72°.
Diformyl: cryst. from H_2O. M.p. 120–2°.

du Vigneaud, Dyer, Jones, Patterson, *J. Biol. Chem.*, 1934, **106**, 403.

Pentylene.
See Pentene.

γ-Pentylene Glycol.
See 1 : 4-Dihydroxypentane.

γ-Pentylene oxide.
See 2-Methyltetrahydrofuran.

Peonidin chloride (3 : 5 : 7 : 4′-*Tetrahydroxy* 3′-*methoxyflavylium chloride*)

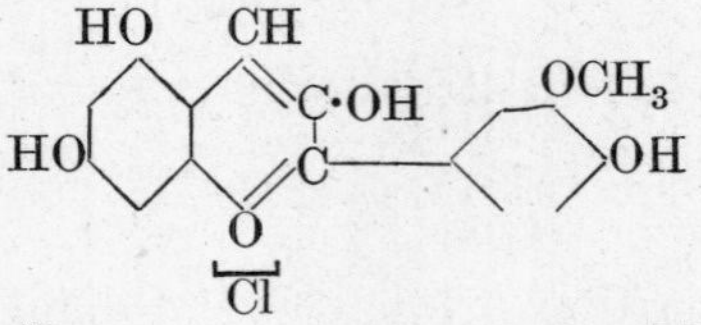

$C_{16}H_{13}O_6Cl$ MW, 336·

Reddish-brown needles + H_2O from 20% HCl. Two modifications of a hydrate containing $1\frac{1}{2}H_2O$ have also been obtained. Sol. EtOH with violet-red col. Mod. sol. cold H_2O with brownish-red col. Spar. sol. dil. HCl.
5-*Benzoyl*: scarlet needles + $\frac{1}{2}H_2O$. Sol MeOH, EtOH.

Nolan, Pratt, Robinson, *J. Chem. Soc.*, 1926, 1968.
Murakami, Robinson, *J. Chem. Soc.* 1928, 1537.
Willstätter, Nolan, *Ann.*, 1915, **408**, 14

Peonin chloride (*7 : 4'-Dihydroxy-3 : 5-di-*
-glucosido-3'-methoxyflavylium chloride)

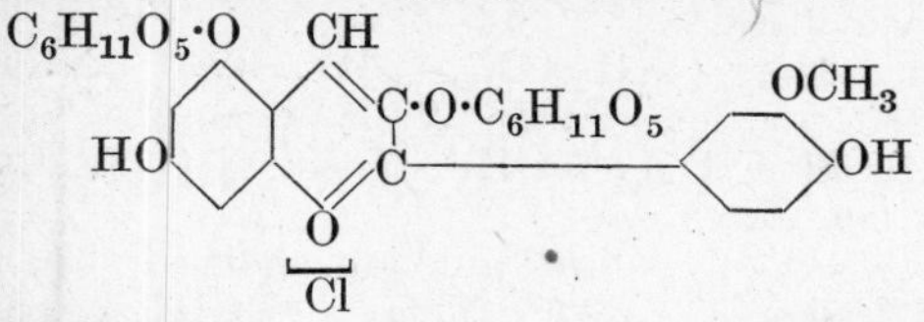

'$_{28}H_{33}O_{16}Cl$ MW, 660·5

Colouring matter of deep violet-red peonies. Reddish-violet needles + H_2O from aq. HCl. Decomp. at 165–7°. Hyd. ⟶ 2 mols. glucose + peonidin chloride.

Robinson, Todd, *J. Chem. Soc.*, 1932, 2493.
Willstätter, Nolan, *Ann.*, 1915, **408**, 136.

Peonol (*2-Hydroxy-4-methoxyacetophenone,* *esacetophenone 4-methyl ether, pœonol*)

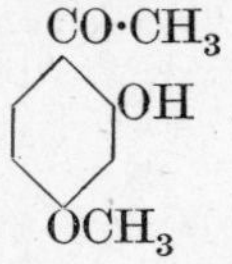

'$_9H_{10}O_3$ MW, 166

Obtained from the root of *Paeonia Moutan* (China, Japan) and a constituent of several ethereal oils *e.g.* from *Paeonia arborea*, Don. Needles from EtOH. M.p. 50°. Sol. EtOH, Et_2O, $CHCl_3$, CS_2, C_6H_6. Volatile in steam. $D^{81\cdot2}$ 1·1310. $n_D^{81\cdot2}$ 1·54322. Gives reddish-violet col. with $FeCl_3$ in aq. or alc. solution. KOH fusion ⟶ resacetophenone, 2 : 4-dihydroxybenzoic acid, and resorcinol. HI ⟶ resacetophenone. Ac_2O ⟶ resacetophenone-4-methyl ether acetate. Br in AcOH ⟶ bromopeonol.

Me ether : 2 : 4-dimethoxyacetophenone. *See under* Resacetophenone.

Et ether : *see under* Resacetophenone.

Acetyl : needles from EtOH. M.p. 46·5°.

Oxime : needles. M.p. 130°. Sol. EtOH, Et_2O, $CHCl_3$, C_6H_6. Spar. sol. H_2O, ligroin.

Hydrazone : plates from dil. EtOH. M.p. 3–5°.

Phenylhydrazone : needles from EtOH. M.p. 08°. Sol. Et_2O, $CHCl_3$, C_6H_6. Spar. sol. EtOH, ligroin. Insol. cold aq. alkalis.

o-*Nitrophenylhydrazone* : deep red prisms from AcOH. M.p. 217°.

m-*Nitrophenylhydrazone* : red plates from AcOH. M.p. 197°.

p-*Nitrophenylhydrazone* : red cryst. from AcOH. M.p. 238–9° (235–6° decomp.).

2 : 4 : 6-*Tribromophenylhydrazone* : needles from EtOH. M.p. 162°. Insol. hot aq. alkalis.

Semicarbazone : needles from EtOH. M.p. 221–2°.

Tahara, *Ber.*, 1891, **24**, 2460.
Brüll, Friedländer, *Ber.*, 1897, **30**, 300.
Nagai, *Ber.*, 1891, **24**, 2847.
Adams, *J. Am. Chem. Soc.*, 1919, **41**, 260.
Lindemann, Könitzer, Romanoff, *Ann.*, 1927, **456**, 304.

Peracetic Acid (*Acetyl hydroperoxide*)

$CH_3\cdot CO\cdot O\cdot OH$

$C_2H_4O_3$ MW, 76

Liq. F.p. + 0·1°. Sol. H_2O, EtOH, Et_2O, H_2SO_4. Explodes violently above 110°. Unpleasant odour. Ketene ⟶ diacetyl peroxide. Strong corrosive action on skin. Used as disinfectant.

Acetyl : *see* Diacetyl peroxide.

Benzoyl : acetyl benzoyl peroxide. Needles from ligroin. M.p. 40–1°. 0·639 parts sol. in 1000 parts H_2O at 25°. Stable when pure. Decomp. when damp or in presence of EtOH, Et_2O or acids. Explodes with hot conc. H_2SO_4. Pure comp. has no oxidising action.

m-*Nitrobenzoyl* : needles from MeOH–ligroin. M.p. 68°. Explodes on heating.

Konsort f. elektrochem. Ind., D.R.P., 269,937, (*Chem. Zentr.*, 1914, I, 716); 272,738, (*Chem. Zentr.*, 1914, I, 1615).
D'Ans, Frey, *Ber.*, 1912, **45**, 1848.
D'Ans, D.R.P., 251,802, (*Chem. Zentr.*, 1912, II, 1413).
Nef, *Ann.*, 1897, **298**, 283.
Freer, Nouy, *Am. Chem. J.*, 1902, **27**, 172.

Perbenzoic Acid (*Benzoyl hydroperoxide*)

$C_6H_5\cdot CO\cdot O\cdot OH$

$C_7H_6O_3$ MW, 138

Plates from pet. ether. M.p. 41–3°. B.p. 97–110°/13–15 mm. Sol. most org. solvents. Spar. sol. H_2O, pet. ether. Very volatile. Sublimes in exsiccator. Volatile in steam. Strong oxidising agent.

Acetyl : *see under* Peracetic Acid.

Benzoyl : *see* Dibenzoyl peroxide.

Braun, *Organic Syntheses*, 1933, XIII, 86.
Tiffeneau, *Organic Syntheses*, Collective Vol. I, 422.
Hibbert, Burt, *J. Am. Chem. Soc.*, 1925, **47**, 2240.
Baeyer, Villiger, *Ber.*, 1900, **33**, 858.
v. Pechmann, Vanino, *Ber.*, 1894, **27**, 1511.
Gambarjan, *Ber.*, 1909, **42**, 4008.
Prileshajew, *Chem. Zentr.*, 1911, I, 1279.

Perbromoacetone.
See Hexabromoacetone.
Perbromobenzoic Acid.
See Pentabromobenzoic Acid.
Perbromoethane.
See Hexabromoethane.
Perbromoethylene.
See Tetrabromoethylene.
Perbromoindone.
See Hexabromoindone-3.
Percaine (*Nupercaine*)

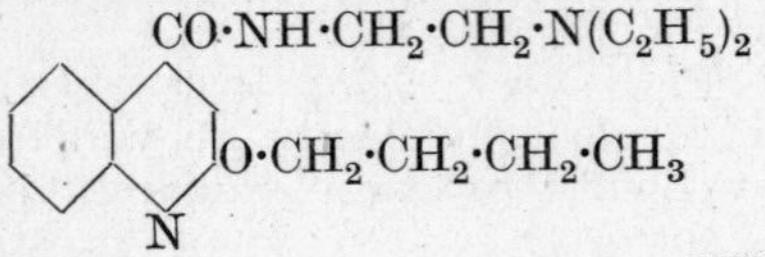

$C_{20}H_{29}O_2N_3$ MW, 343

Plates. M.p. 97–8°. Sol. H_2O, EtOH, C_6H_6. Insol. Et_2O. Aq. sol. shows blue fluor. Local anæsthetic about ten times more powerful than cocaine.

Miescher, *Helv. Chim. Acta,* 1932, **15**, 169.
Uhlmann, *Chem. Zentr.*, 1929, II, 1816.

Perchloroacetone.
See Hexachloroacetone.
Perchlorobenzene.
See Hexachlorobenzene.
Perchlorobenzoic Acid.
See Pentachlorobenzoic Acid.
Perchloroethane.
See Hexachloroethane.
Perchloroethylene.
See Tetrachloroethylene.
Perchloroindone.
See Hexachloroindone-3.
Perchloromethyl Mercaptan (*Thiocarbonyl tetrachloride, trichloromethyl sulphochloride*)

$CCl_3 \cdot SCl$

CCl_4S MW, 186

Pale yellow oil. B.p. 149° (146·5–148°), 73°/50 mm. $D_0^{12·8}$ 1·712, D_4^{11} 1·71785. n_D 1·54835. Decomp. above 200°. $SnCl_2 \longrightarrow CSCl_2 + SnCl_4$. Fe + HCl $\longrightarrow CSCl_2 + CCl_4$. Fe $\longrightarrow CCl_4$.

Helferich, Reid, *J. Am. Chem. Soc.*, 1921, **43**, 591.
Dyson, *Organic Syntheses*, Collective Vol. I, 493.

Pereirine

$C_{20}H_{26}ON_2$ MW, 310

Pale yellow amorph. powder + $\frac{1}{2}H_2O$. M.p. 135° decomp. $[\alpha]_D$ + 137·5° in EtOH. Sol. EtOH, MeOH, Et_2O, $CHCl_3$, AcOEt, C_6H_6, acids. Insol. H_2O. Very bitter taste. Conc. H_2SO_4 $\longrightarrow$ violet-red col.

Me ether: $C_{21}H_{28}ON_2$. MW, 324. Yellow amorph. powder. M.p. 195–7° decomp. Very sol. MeOH, EtOH, AcOEt. Insol. H_2O, Me_2CO, Et_2O, pet. ether.

Methiodide: yellow amorph. powder. M.p. 233–5° decomp. Sol. MeOH, EtOH. Spar. sol. H_2O. Insol. Et_2O, Me_2CO, $CHCl_3$.

Bertho, Moog, *Ann.*, 1934, **509**, 241.

Perezone (*Pipitzahoic acid*)

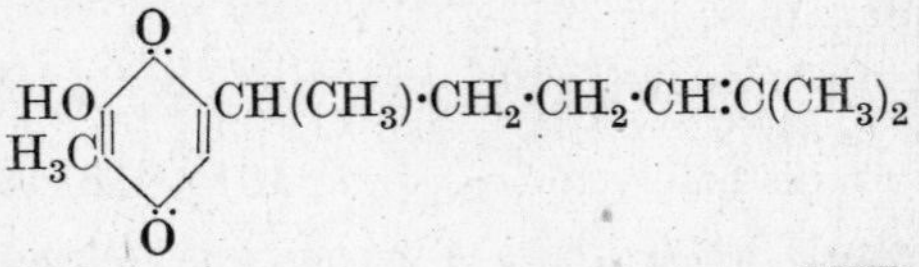

$C_{15}H_{20}O_3$ MW, 248

Found in rind of *Trixis pipitzhuac*. Golden-yellow leaflets from H_2O, plates from Et_2O. M.p. 104–6°. Sol. EtOH, Et_2O, $CHCl_3$, AcOH, C_6H_6. Mod. sol. pet. ether. Insol. H_2O. $[\alpha]_D^{20}$ −17·0° in Et_2O. Volatile in steam. Racemises readily on sublimation. Alkalis $\longrightarrow$ intense purple col.

Me ether: $C_{16}H_{22}O_3$. MW, 262. B.p. 128–33°/0·002 mm.

Fichter, Jetzer, Leepin, *Ann.*, 1913, **395**, 15.
Bayer, D.R.P., 278,090, (*Chem. Zentr.*, 1914, II, 900).
Kögl, Boer, *Rec. trav. chim.*, 1935, **54**, 785.

Performic Acid (*Formyl hydroperoxide*)

$H \cdot CO \cdot O \cdot OH$

CH_2O_3 MW, 62

Only obtained 90% pure. Liq. Misc. with H_2O, EtOH, Et_2O. Mod. sol. $CHCl_3$, C_6H_6. More volatile than formic acid. Strong oxidising agent. Explodes on heating with metals and metallic oxides.

D'Ans, Kneips, *Ber.*, 1915, **48**, 1137.

Perhydroacridine (*Tetradecahydroacridine*)

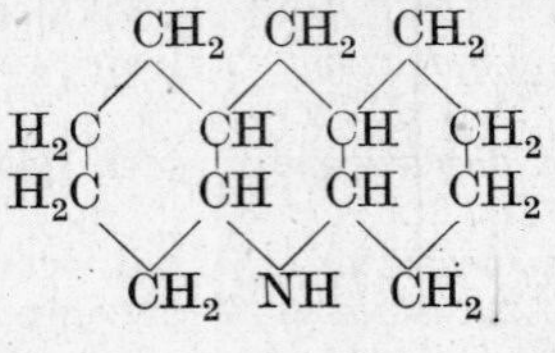

$C_{13}H_{23}N$ MW, 193

Cryst. M.p. 80°. B.p. 140°/14 mm.

B,HCl : does not melt below 300°. Mod. sol. H_2O, EtOH.

N-*Nitroso* : pale yellow. M.p. 217°.
Methiodide : m.p. 266°.
Picrate : cryst. M.p. 167°.

v. Braun, Petzold, Schultheiss, *Ber.*, 1923, **56**, 1349.

Perhydroanthracene (*Tetradecahydro-anthracene*)

$$
\begin{array}{ccc}
& CH_2 \quad CH_2 \quad CH_2 & \\
H_2C \quad CH \quad CH \quad CH_2 \\
H_2C \quad CH \quad CH \quad CH_2 \\
& CH_2 \quad CH_2 \quad CH_2 &
\end{array}
$$

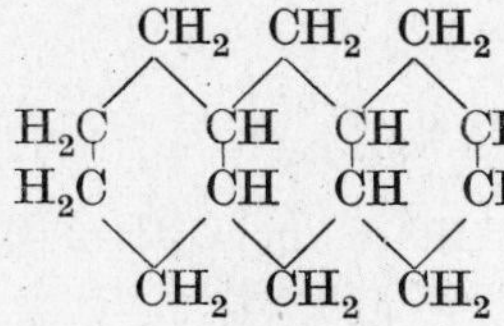

$C_{14}H_{24}$ MW, 192

Two isomeric compounds have been described.
1. Needles from MeOH. M.p. 61·5°.
2. Plates from EtOH. M.p. 93°. B.p. 128°/11 mm.

Fries, Schilling, *Ber.*, 1932, **65**, 1494.
Schroeter, *Ber.*, 1924, **57**, 1998.

Perhydrobenzidine (*Dodecahydrobenzidine*, 4 : 4'-*diaminodicyclohexyl*)

$$
\begin{array}{cc}
CH_2-CH_2 & CH_2-CH_2 \\
H_2N\cdot HC \quad \rangle CH-HC \quad \rangle CH\cdot NH_2 \\
CH_2-CH_2 & CH_2-CH_2
\end{array}
$$

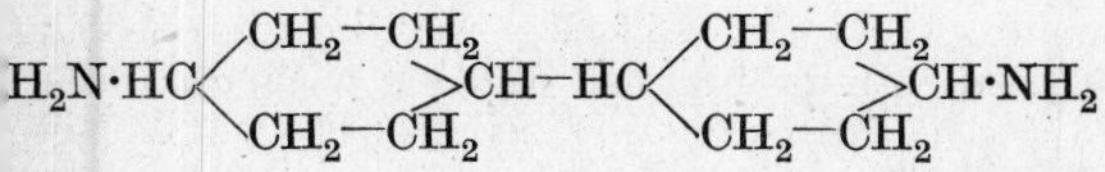

$C_{12}H_{24}N_2$ MW, 196

Cryst. M.p. 59°. B.p. 120°/0·8 mm. Turns yellowish-brown in air. Odour similar to piperidine. Weak base.

B,2HCl : amorph. powder. Decomp. at 290°.
Dipicrate : red needles from EtOH. Decomp. explosively at 247°.

Balaš, Ševčenko, *Chem. Zentr.*, 1931, I, 3112.

Perhydrobixin.
See Bixane.

Perhydrocarotene

$$
\begin{array}{l}
H_2C \quad C(CH_3)_2 \\
H_2C \quad \diamond \quad CH\cdot[CH_2\cdot CH_2\cdot CH(CH_3)\cdot CH_2]_2\cdot CH_2 \\
H_2C \quad CH\cdot CH_3 \\[4pt]
H_2C \quad C(CH_3)_2 \\
H_2C \quad \diamond \quad CH\cdot[CH_2\cdot CH_2\cdot CH(CH_3)\cdot CH_2]_2\cdot CH_2 \\
H_2C \quad CH\cdot CH_3
\end{array}
$$

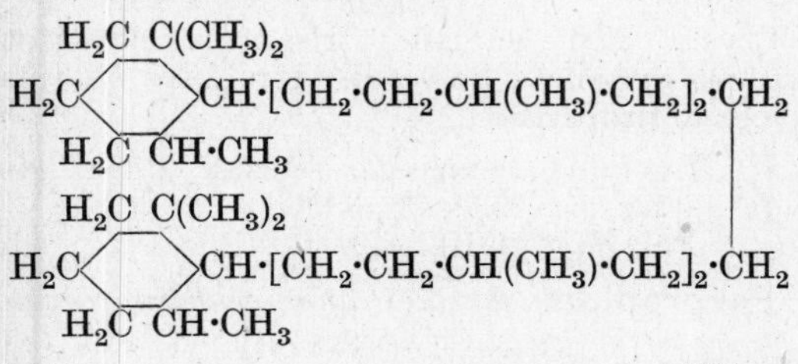

$C_{40}H_{78}$ MW, 558

Needles from Et_2O. M.p. 65°. Sol. Et_2O, C_6H_6. Spar. sol. MeOH, EtOH. Conc. H_2SO_4 $\longrightarrow$ blue sol.

Zechmeister, Cholnoky, Vrabély, *Ber.*, 1928, **61**, 566.

Perhydroindole.
See Octahydroindole.

Peri-Acid.
See 1-Naphthylamine-8-sulphonic Acid.

β-Pericyclocamphane.
See Isobornylene.

Perillic Acid (4-*Isopropenylcyclohexene-1-carboxylic acid*)

$$
\begin{array}{c}
C\cdot COOH \\
H_2C \quad CH \\
H_2C \quad CH_2 \\
CH \\
CH_3\cdot C\!:\!CH_2
\end{array}
$$

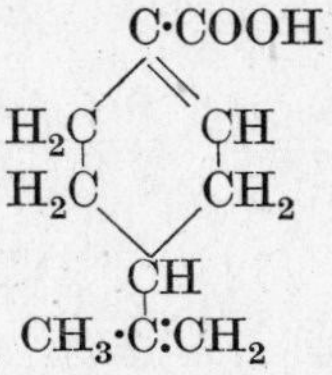

$C_{10}H_{14}O_2$ MW, 166

l-.
Leaflets from EtOH.Aq. M.p. 132–3° (130–1°). B.p. 164–5°/10 mm.
Amide : $C_{10}H_{15}ON$. MW, 165. Cryst. M.p. 164–5°.
Nitrile : $C_{10}H_{13}N$. MW, 147. B.p. 123°/15 mm., 116–18°/11 mm. D^{15} 0·9488, D^{20} 0·9439. n_D^{20} 1·4978.

Schimmel, *Chem. Zentr.*, 1910, II, 1758.
Semmler, Zaar, *Ber.*, 1911, **44**, 55.
Furukawa, Tomizawa, *Chem. Abstracts*, 1920, **14**, 2839.

Perillyl Alcohol ($\Delta^{1,\,8(9)}$-p-*Menthadienol-7*, 1-*hydroxymethyl-4-isopropenylcyclohexene*)

$$
\begin{array}{c}
C\cdot CH_2OH \\
H_2C \quad CH \\
H_2C \quad CH_2 \\
CH \\
CH_3\cdot C\!:\!CH_2
\end{array}
$$

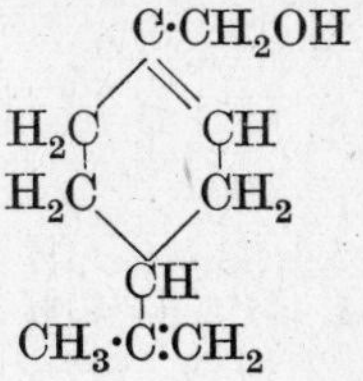

$C_{10}H_{16}O$ MW, 152

Found in ginger-grass oil. B.p. 118–21°/11 mm., 107–10°/12·5 mm. D^{20} 0·9690. n_D 1·4996. $[\alpha]_D$ — 7·0°. CrO_3 $\longrightarrow$ perillyl aldehyde.
Acetyl : b.p. 123–6°/13 mm., 90–1°/4 mm. D^{20} 0·9785. n_D^{20} 1·47615.
Naphthylurethane : m.p. 146–7°.

See last reference above and also
Semmler, Zaar, *Ber.*, 1911, **44**, 54, 460.

Perillyl Aldehyde ($\Delta^{1,8(9)}$-p-*Menthadienal*)

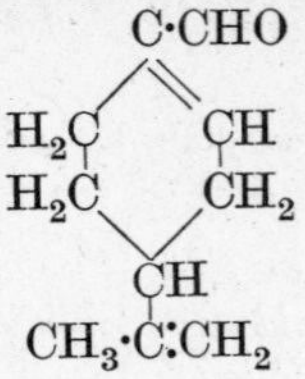

$C_{10}H_{14}O$ MW, 150

l-.

Found in oil of *Perilla nankinensis*, D. B.p. 235–7°/750 mm., 104–5°/10 mm., 91°/4·5 mm. D^{20} 0·9645. n_D^{20} 1·5069. $[\alpha]_D^{20}$ − 145·8°. Reacts with Na_2SO_3 and $NaHSO_3$. $Ag_2O \longrightarrow$ perillic acid.

syn-*Oxime*: prisms. M.p. 129°.

anti-*Oxime*: cryst. M.p. 102°. B.p. 147–8°/12 mm. Very sweet. *B,HCl*: m.p. 114°.

Semicarbazone: m.p. 199–200°.

Semioxamazone: m.p. 228°.

Phenylhydrazone: needles. M.p. 107·5°.

d-.

B.p. 234–6°/743 mm., 99–104°/9 mm. D^{15} 0·9730. n_D^{20} 1·5080. $[\alpha]_D$ + 137°. Reacts with Na_2SO_3 and $NaHSO_3$.

Oxime: m.p. 102°.

Phenylhydrazone: m.p. 107–8°.

Schimmel, *Chem. Zentr.*, 1910, II, 1758.
Semmler, Zaar, *Ber.*, 1911, **44**, 53, 460.
Furukawa, Tomizawa, *Chem. Abstracts*, 1920, **14**, 2839.
Hoshino, *ibid.*, 1410.

Perimidine (1 : 8-*Naphthiminazole*, peri-*naphthiminazole*)

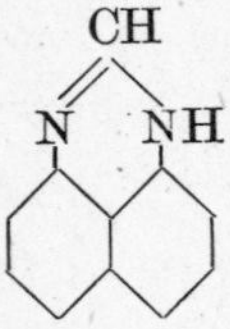

$C_{11}H_8N_2$ MW, 168

Green cryst. from EtOH.Aq. M.p. about 222°. Sol. prac. all org. solvents, acids. Insol. H_2O.

B,HCl: yellowish-green needles from dil. HCl. Decomp. at 300°.

B,HNO_3: long green needles from EtOH or hot H_2O.

Formate: cryst. M.p. 143°, solidifies and then remelts at 220°.

Acetate: cryst. from AcOH.Aq. M.p. 130°, solidifies and then remelts at 221°.

Oxalate: yellow cryst. from hot H_2O or EtOH. Decomp. at 270°.

Pyruvate: m.p. 207°. Very spar. sol. H_2O, EtOH.

Picrate: orange-red cryst. from EtOH. M.p. 232° (226°).

Sachs, *Ann.*, 1909, **365**, 83.

Perimidone

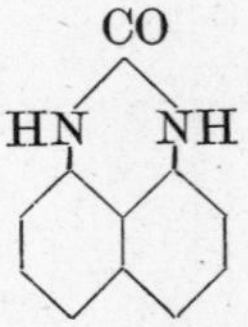

$C_{11}H_8ON_2$ MW, 184

Cryst. from EtOH or C_6H_6. M.p. 304–5°. Spar. sol. most org. solvents.

Sachs, *Ann.*, 1909, **365**, 135.

Periodoacetone.

See Hexaiodoacetone.

Periodoethylene.

See Tetraiodoethylene.

Perlatolic Acid

$C_{25}H_{32}O_7$ MW, 444

Needles from C_6H_6. M.p. 108°. Sol. EtOH, Et_2O, Me_2CO, C_6H_6. Spar. sol. pet. ether, ligroin. Sol. alkalis. Alc. $FeCl_3 \longrightarrow$ violet col. $CHCl_3$ sol. + alkali $\longrightarrow$ red col. on heating showing green fluor. on dilution with H_2O.

Di-Me ether–Me ester: $C_{28}H_{38}O_7$. MW, 486. Needles from MeOH. M.p. 57°.

Asahina, Fuzikawa, *Ber.*, 1935, **68**, 634.

Perparin (6 : 7-*Diethoxy*-1-[3′ : 4′-*diethoxybenzyl*]-*isoquinoline hydrochloride*)

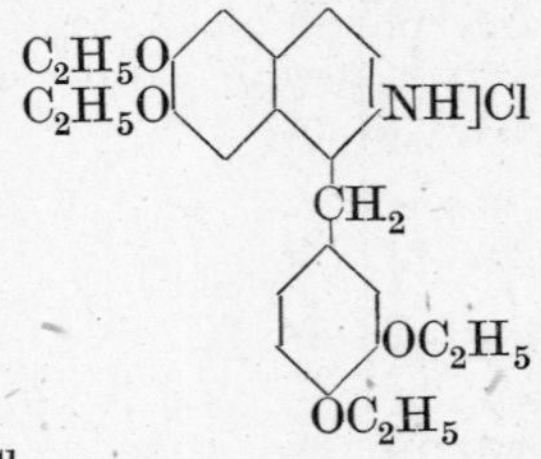

$C_{24}H_{30}O_4NCl$ MW, 431·5

Cryst. M.p. 99–101°. Used as substitute for papaverine. Possesses stronger pharmacological properties.

Issekutz, Leinzinger, Dirner, *Chem. Abstracts*, 1932, **26**, 3836.
Pal, *ibid.*, 2510.

Perpropionic Acid (*Propionyl hydroperoxide*)

$CH_3 \cdot CH_2 \cdot CO \cdot O \cdot OH$

$C_3H_6O_3$ MW, 90

Liq. F.p. — 13·5°. Explodes on heating
$\longrightarrow CO_2 + CH_4 + C_2H_4 + C_2H_6$.
Propionyl : dipropionyl peroxide. Liq. Decomp. above 80°. Misc. with usual solvents.

Clover, Richmond, *Am. Chem. J.*, 1903, **29**, 191.
Konsort f. elektrochem. Ind., D.R.P., 269,937, (*Chem. Zentr.*, 1914, I, 716).
D'Ans, Frey, *Ber.*, 1912, **45**, 1850.
Fichter, Krummenacher, *Helv. Chim. Acta*, 1918, **1**, 146.

Perseitol.
See Persitol.
Perseulose

$$HO\cdot CH_2 - \underset{\underset{H}{|}}{\overset{\overset{OH}{|}}{C}} - \underset{\underset{OH}{|}}{\overset{\overset{H}{|}}{C}} - \underset{\underset{OH}{|}}{\overset{\overset{H}{|}}{C}} - \underset{\underset{H}{|}}{\overset{\overset{OH}{|}}{C}} - CO\cdot CH_2OH$$

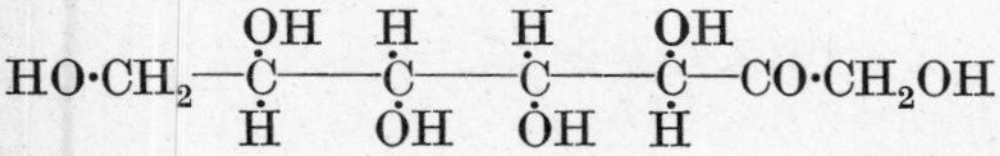

$C_7H_{14}O_7$ MW, 210

Needles from H_2O. M.p. 110–15° decomp. Sol. boiling EtOH. Sweet taste. Aq. sol. shows mutarotation. $[\alpha]_D^{20} - 90\cdot0° \longrightarrow - 81\cdot0°$ in H_2O. Reduces Fehling's.
Phenylosazone : needles from EtOH. M.p. 233°.

Bertrand, *Bull. soc. chim.*, 1909, **5**, 629.
La Forge, *J. Biol. Chem.*, 1916, **28**, 514.

Persitol (*Perseitol*, d-α-mannoheptitol)

$$HO\cdot CH_2 - \underset{\underset{H}{|}}{\overset{\overset{OH}{|}}{C}} - \underset{\underset{OH}{|}}{\overset{\overset{H}{|}}{C}} - \underset{\underset{OH}{|}}{\overset{\overset{H}{|}}{C}} - \underset{\underset{H}{|}}{\overset{\overset{OH}{|}}{C}} - \underset{\underset{H}{|}}{\overset{\overset{OH}{|}}{C}} - CH_2OH$$

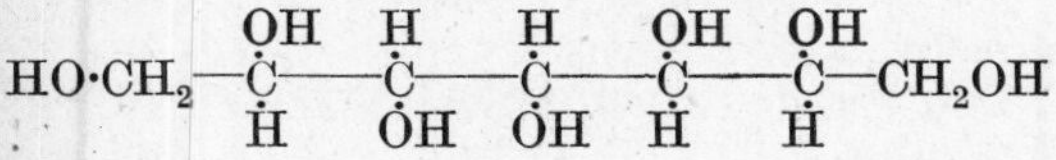

$C_7H_{16}O_7$ MW, 212

Obtained from seeds of *Persea gratissima* or *P. dymifolia*. Needles. M.p. 188°. Sol. H_2O, hot EtOH. Spar. sol. Et_2O. $[\alpha]_D^{20} + 4\cdot53°$. Oxidised by *B. xylinum* to perseulose.
Hepta-acetyl : m.p. 119°. Sol. EtOH. Insol. H_2O.
Heptanitrate : needles from EtOH. M.p. 138°.

Maquenne, *Ann. chim. phys.*, 1890, **19**, 5.
Fischer, *Ber.*, 1890, **23**, 936.
Bertrand, *Compt. rend.*, 1909, **149**, 226.
La Forge, *J. Biol. Chem.*, 1917, **28**, 520.

Peruviol.
See Nerolidol.
Perylene

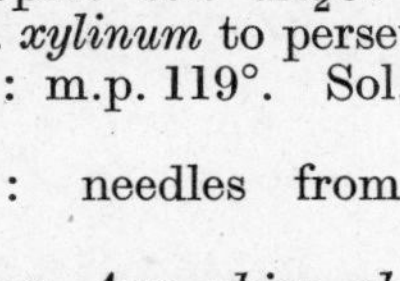

$C_{20}H_{12}$ MW, 252

Bronze plates from toluene or AcOH. M.p. 273–4° (264–5°). Sublimes at 350–400° in bronze leaflets. Sol. $CHCl_3$, CS_2. Less sol. C_6H_6. Mod. sol. AcOH. Spar. sol. EtOH, Et_2O, Me_2CO. Insol. ligroin. Very dil. sols. show blue fluor. Conc. $H_2SO_4 \longrightarrow$ deep green sol. which rapidly changes to bluish-green $\longrightarrow$ blue $\longrightarrow$ reddish-violet. CrO_3 in boiling AcOH $\longrightarrow$ perylenequinone.

Scholl, Seer, Weitzenböck, *Ber.*, 1910, **43**, 2203.
Hansging, Zinke, *Monatsh.*, 1919, **40**, 404.
Marschalk, *Bull. soc. chim.*, 1928, **43**, 1388.
Zinke, Hauswirth, Blank, Grimm, *Monatsh.*, 1932, **61**, 1.
Clar, *Ber.*, 1932, **65**, 846.
Uchida, Takata, *J. Soc. Chem. Ind. Japan*, 1933, **36**, 222.
Morgan, Mitchell, *J. Chem. Soc.*, 1934, 536.

Perylene-3-carboxylic Acid

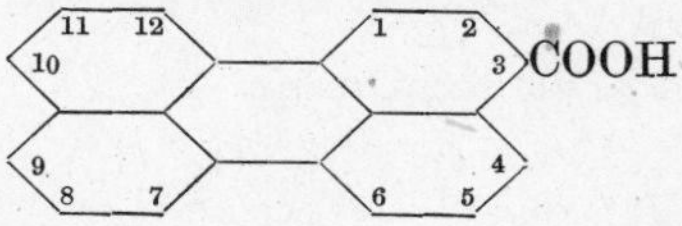

$C_{21}H_{12}O_2$ MW, 296

Yellowish-brown needles from $PhNO_2$. Does not melt below 300°. Sol. H_2SO_4 with violet col. and red fluor. Alkalis $\longrightarrow$ yellow sols. with bluish-green fluor.

I.G., F.P., 635,599, (*Chem. Zentr.*, 1929, I, 2472).

Perylene-3 : 9-dicarboxylic Acid

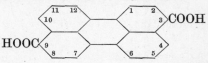

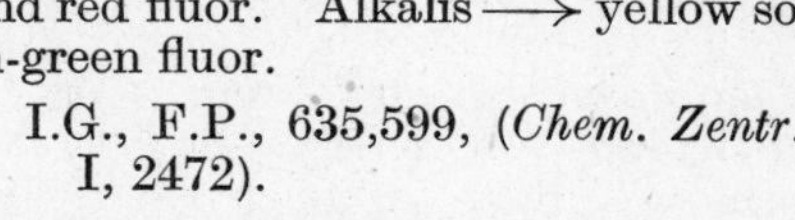

$C_{22}H_{12}O_4$ MW, 340

Orange micro-needles from $PhNO_2$. Sinters about 360°. Conc. $H_2SO_4 \longrightarrow$ red sol. with orange-red fluor. Aq. alkalis $\longrightarrow$ yellow sols. with bluish-green fluor. Spar. sol. org. solvents.
Di-Et ester : $C_{26}H_{28}O_4$. MW, 396. Yellow leaflets from xylene. M.p. 264–5°. Spar. sol. EtOH, toluene, xylene. Sols. are yellow with green fluor.
Dichloride : $C_{22}H_{10}O_2Cl_2$. MW, 377. Red needles from $PhNO_2$. Sol. C_6H_6, toluene, xylene. Sols. are yellow with yellowish-green fluor.

Dinitrile : $C_{22}H_{10}N_2$. MW, 302. Brown cryst. from $PhNO_2$. Does not melt below 360°. Spar. sol. EtOH, AcOH, xylene.

Pongratz, *Monatsh.*, 1927, **48**, 585; 1929, **52**, 9.
Pongratz, Griengl, Cecelsky, *Monatsh.*, 1933, **62**, 71.

Perylene-3 : 10-dicarboxylic Acid.

Reddish-brown needles from $PhNO_2$. Sol. 1000 parts hot $PhNO_2$. Conc. $H_2SO_4 \longrightarrow$ reddish-violet col. slowly changing to brownish-red. Aq. alkalis $\longrightarrow$ yellow sols. with strong green fluor.

Di-Et ester : red leaflets from xylene. M.p. 247–8°.

Dichloride : reddish brown needles from benzoyl chloride.

Dinitrile : brown needles from aniline. M.p. 368–9° (sealed tube). Sol. $PhNO_2$ aniline. Spar. sol. AcOH, xylene with intense green fluor. Conc. $H_2SO_4 \longrightarrow$ reddish-brown col.

Weitzenböck, Seer, *Ber.*, 1913, **46**, 1999.
Funke, *Monatsh.*, 1932, **59**, 193.

1 : 12-Perylenequinone

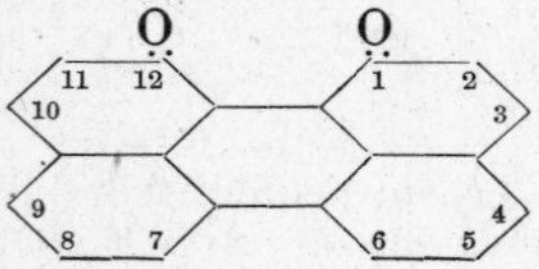

$C_{20}H_{10}O_2$ MW, 282

Reddish-brown needles from C_6H_6. M.p. 287°. Sol. hot AcOH, Py, $PhNO_2$, aniline, chlorobenzene. Spar. sol. hot EtOH, Me_2CO, CCl_4, C_6H_6, toluene. Conc. $H_2SO_4 \longrightarrow$ brown sol. Insol. NaOH.

Zinke, Hanselmayer, *Monatsh.*, 1924, **45**, 232.

3 : 9-Perylenequinone.

Violet needles from $PhNO_2$. Reduced by hydrosulphite to red " vat " with intense green flour.

Zinke, Hirsch, *Monatsh.*, 1929, **52**, 18.

3 : 10-Perylenequinone.

Yellow needles from Py. Decomp. slowly above 350°. Sol. boiling AcOH, Py, $PhNO_2$, aniline, xylene, quinoline. Conc. $H_2SO_4 \longrightarrow$ blood-red sol. with intense fluor.

Zincke, Unterkreuter, *Monatsh.*, 1919, **40**, 407.
Marschalk, *Bull. soc. chim.*, 1927, **41**, 74.

Perylene - 3 : 4 : 9 : 10 - tetracarboxylic Acid

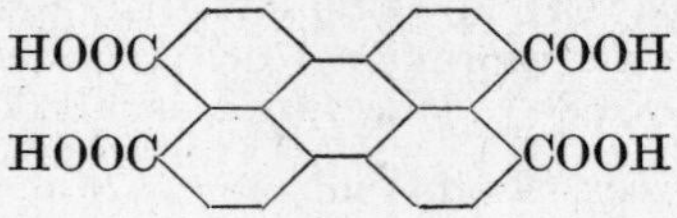

$C_{24}H_{12}O_8$ MW, 428

Brownish-red needles. Hot alkalis $\longrightarrow$ brownish-yellow sols. with deep green fluor. Conc. $H_2SO_4 \longrightarrow$ red sol. with orange-red fluor. Dry dist. of Ca salt $\longrightarrow$ perylene.

Monoimide : brownish-red powder. Very dil alkalis $\longrightarrow$ deep red sols.

Kalle, D.R.P., 394,794, (*Chem. Zentr.* 1924, II, 1276); 408,513, (*Chem. Zentr.* 1925, I, 1811); 412,122, (*Chem. Zentr.* 1925, I, 2666).

Petroselaidic Acid.

See under Petroselic Acid.

Petroselic Acid (*Petroselinic acid, 5-heptadecylene-1-carboxylic acid, Δ^5-octadecylenic acid*)

$CH_3\cdot[CH_2]_{10}\cdot CH{:}CH\cdot[CH_2]_4\cdot COOH$

$C_{18}H_{34}O_2$ MW, 282

Cis :

Found in seeds of *Petroselinum satiuum*. Leaflets. F.p. 27°. M.p. 33–4° (30°). B.p. 237–8°/18 mm. D^{40} 0·8700. n_D^{40} 1·4533. Dil $HNO_3 \longrightarrow$ *trans* acid. Ozone $\longrightarrow$ adipic aldehyde + lauric acid.

Amide : $C_{18}H_{35}ON$. MW, 281. Needles. M.p. 76°.

Triglyceride: tripetroselin. Cryst. F.p. 16·5° M.p. 32° (26·4°). n_D^{40} 1·4619.

Trans : Petroselaidic acid.

Prisms. M.p. 54°.

Palazzo, Tamburello, *Atti accad. Lincei* 1914, **23**, II, 352.
Vongerichten, Köhler, *Ber.*, 1909, **42** 1638.
Steger, Loon, *Rec. trav. chim.*, 1927, **46**, 703.
Hilditch, Jones, *J. Soc. Chem. Ind.*, 1927 **46**, 174T.
Eibner, Widenmeyer, Schild, *Chem. Abstracts*, 1928, **22**, 1487.

Petroselinic Acid.

See Petroselic Acid.

Petunidin (**chloride**)

$C_{16}H_{13}O_7Cl$ MW, 352·5

Forms several hydrates of different cryst forms and solubilities depending on solvent used. Very similar in properties to myrtillidin chloride.

Willstätter, Burdick, *Ann.*, 1916, **412**, 224.
Cf. Bell, Robinson, *J. Chem. Soc.*, 1934 1604.

Petunin (**chloride**)

$C_{28}H_{33}O_{17}Cl$ MW, 676·5

Plates + $2H_2O$. M.p. about 179°. Cryst. are violet by transmitted light, and show copper lustre by reflected light. Sol. MeOH. MeOH+ $FeCl_3$ ⟶ violet col. Na_2CO_3.Aq. ⟶ violet sol. ⟶ blue on standing. 20% HCl ⟶ petunidin chloride + dextrose.

Willstätter, Burdick, *Ann.*, 1916, **412**, 217.

Peucedanine

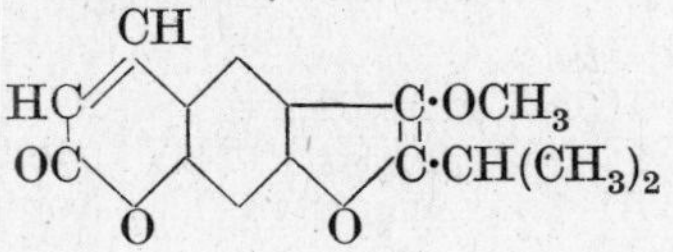

$C_{15}H_{14}O_4$ MW, 258

Found in roots of *Peucedanum officinale*. Prisms or plates. M.p. 109° (76°). Very sol. $CHCl_3$, CS_2. Sol. hot EtOH, Et_2O, AcOH. Spar. sol. C_6H_6, pet. ether. Insol. H_2O. HNO_3 ⟶ styphnic acid. Tasteless. Toxic to fish.

Heut, *Ann.*, 1875, **176**, 71.
Jassoy, Haensel, *Arch. Pharm.*, 1898, **236**, 668.
Späth, Klager, *Ber.*, 1933, **66**, 749.
Späth, Klager, Schlösser, *Ber.*, 1931, **64**, 2203.

Phaeanthine (l-*Tetrandrine*)

Constitution represented by

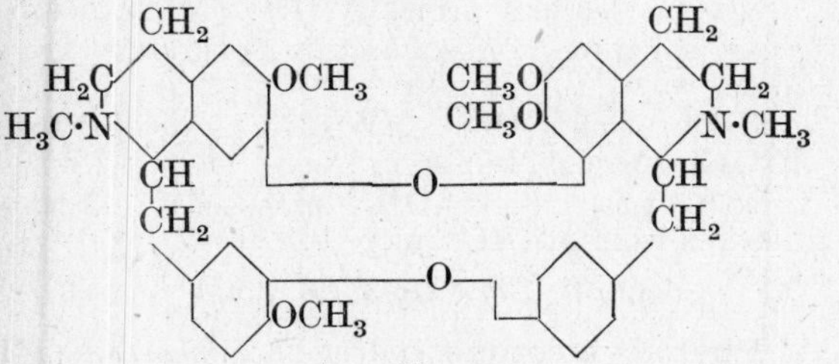

or

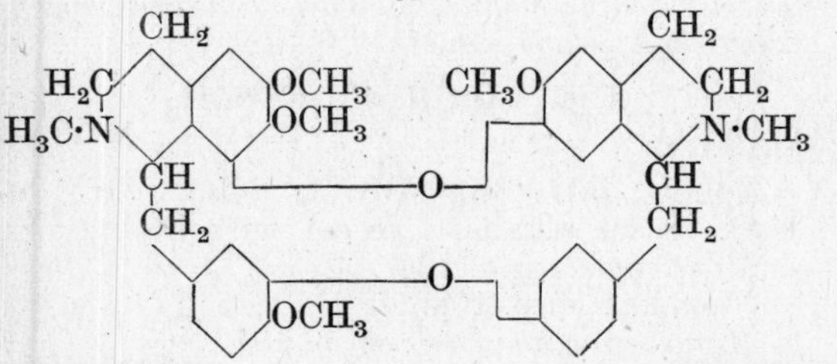

$C_{38}H_{42}O_6N_2$ MW, 622

Alkaloid extracted from *Stephania cepharantha*, *Coceulus lavrifolius*, and *Phaeanthus ebracteolatus*. Hexagonal prisms from Et_2O. M.p. 210°. Sol. Et_2O, $CHCl_3$. Mod. sol. MeOH, Me_2CO. Spar. sol. EtOH. $[\alpha]_D^{30}$ − 278° in $CHCl_3$.

B,2HI : cryst. Decomp. at 268°.
B,2CH₃I : decomp. at 265°.
Picrate : decomp. at 263°.

Kondo, Keimatsu, *Ber.*, 1935, **68**, 1505.

Phaseolunatin.

See Linamarin.

Phellandral (Δ^1-*Tetrahydrocuminaldehyde*)

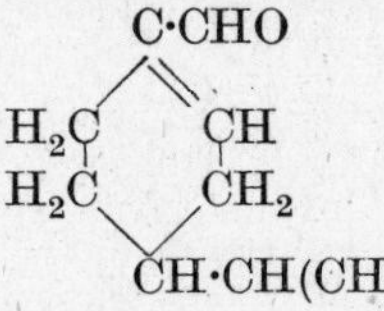

or

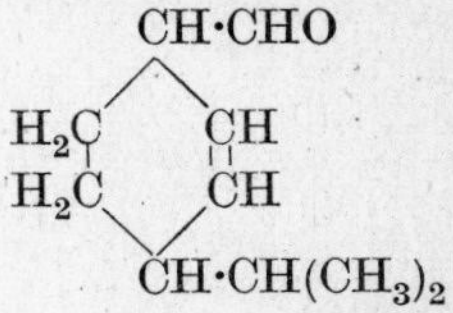

$C_{10}H_{16}O$ MW, 152

Occurs in water-fennel oil. B.p. 220–30°, 89°/5 mm. Mod. sol. H_2O. D^{20} 0·93. n_D^{20} 1·4911 (1·4903). Ox. ⟶ tetrahydrocuminic acid.

Oxime : m.p. 87–8°.
Semicarbazone : m.p. 204–5°.
p-*Nitrophenylhydrazone* : m.p. 169–70°.
2 : 4-*Dinitrophenylhydrazone* : orange-red needles from $CHCl_3$–EtOH. M.p. 202–3°.

Macbeth, Price, *J. Chem. Soc.*, 1935, 152.
Wallach, *Ann.*, 1905, **340**, 13.

α-Phellandrene ($\Delta^{1,5}$-p-*Menthadiene*, 1-*methyl*-4-*isopropylcyclohexadiene*-1 : 5)

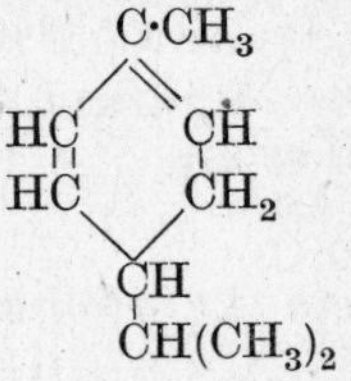

$C_{10}H_{16}$ MW, 136

d-.

Occurs in bitter-fennel, elemi, and ginger-grass oils. B.p. 175–6°, 66–8°/16 mm., 66°/14 mm., 61°/11 mm. D_4^{25} 0·8463. n_D^{20} 1·4777.

α-*Nitrosite* : m.p. 113–14° (rapid heat). $[\alpha]_D^{20}$ − 141° in AcOEt.

β-*Nitrosite* : m.p. 105°. $[\alpha]_D^{19}$ + 45·8° in $CHCl_3$.

l-.

Occurs in oils of pimento, bay, and *Eucalyptus phellandra*, Smith. B.p. 174–7°/759 mm., 171–2°/758·2 mm., 67–8°/22 mm., 58–9°/16 mm.

(60–60·5°/15 mm.). D_4^{20} 0·8425. n_D^{20} 1·4732. $[\alpha]_D^{20}$ — 112·76°.

α-Nitrosite: m.p. 120–1°.

β-Nitrosite: m.p. 105–6°.

dl-.

B.p. 175–6° decomp., 63–5°/15·5 mm. $n_D^{19\cdot5}$ 1·4772.

Read, Storey, *J. Chem. Soc.*, 1930, 2781.
Galloway, Dewar, Read, *J. Chem. Soc.*, 1936, 1597.

β-Phellandrene ($\Delta^{2,1(7)}$-p-*Menthadiene*)

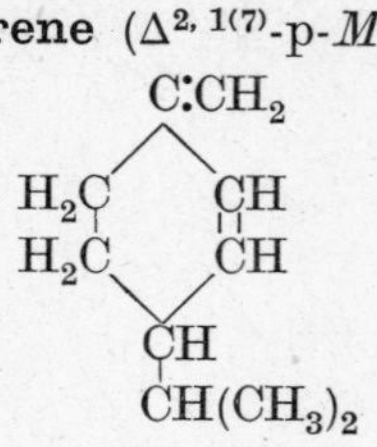

$C_{10}H_{16}$ MW, 136

d-.

Occurs in oil of *Bupleurum fructicosum*, Linn. B.p. 171–2°/766 mm., 57°/11 mm. D^{20} 0·8520. n_D^{20} 1·4788.

α-Nitrosochloride: m.p. 101–2°. $[\alpha]_D$ — 175° in $CHCl_3$.

β-Nitrosochloride: m.p. 100–1°. $[\alpha]_D$ — 285° in $CHCl_3$.

α-Nitrosite: m.p. 102°. $[\alpha]_D^{18\cdot5}$ — 159·3° in $CHCl_3$.

β-Nitrosite: m.p. 97–8°. $[\alpha]_D$ — 159° in $CHCl_3$.

Francesconi, Sernagiotto, *Gazz. chim. ital.*, 1916, **46**, i, 119.
Wallach, *Ann.*, 1905, **340**, 1.

α-Phellandrene Hydrate.
See Δ^2-*p*-Menthenol-1.

Phellogenic Acid.
See Japanic Acid.

Phellonic Acid (1-*Hydroxybehenic acid*)

$CH_3\cdot[CH_2]_{19}\cdot CH(OH)\cdot COOH$

$C_{22}H_{44}O_3$ MW, 356

Cryst. from $CHCl_3$. M.p. 96°.

Et ester: $C_{24}H_{48}O_3$. MW, 384. M.p. 70–1°.

Acetyl: m.p. 79°.

Et ether: $C_{24}H_{48}O_3$. MW, 384. M.p. 60°.

Fileti, *Gazz. chim. ital.*, 1897, **27**, ii, 300.
Zetzsche, Bähler, *Helv. Chim. Acta*, 1931, **14**, 642.

Phenacaine.
See under Holocaine.

Phenacetin.
See under *p*-Phenetidine.

Phenaceturic Acid (*Phenylacetylglycine*)

$C_6H_5\cdot CH_2\cdot CO\cdot NH\cdot CH_2\cdot COOH$

$C_{10}H_{11}O_3N$ MW, 193

Occurs in horse and dog urine. Leaflets from EtOH. M.p. 143° (136°). Sol. EtOH. Spar. sol. H_2O, Et_2O, hot C_6H_6. Hot HCl ⟶ glycine + phenylacetic acid.

Me ester: $C_{11}H_{13}O_3N$. MW, 207. Cryst. from EtOH. M.p. 86·5°. Sol. Et_2O, C_6H_6, $CHCl_3$, hot EtOH.

Et ester: $C_{12}H_{15}O_3N$. MW, 221. Prisms from EtOH. M.p. 82° (79°). Sol. hot EtOH.

Propyl ester: $C_{13}H_{17}O_3N$. MW, 235. Leaflets from H_2O. M.p. 31°.

Amide: $C_{10}H_{12}O_2N_2$. MW, 192. Plates from EtOH.Aq. M.p. 176–7°. Sol. hot H_2O. Insol. EtOH, Et_2O.

Nitrile: $C_{10}H_{10}ON_2$. MW, 174. Needles. M.p. 90·5°. Spar. sol. hot H_2O.

Hotter, *J. prakt. Chem.*, 1888, **38**, 98.

Phenacridol.
See Phenacridone.

Phenacridone (*Phenacridol, benzacridone, benzacridol*)

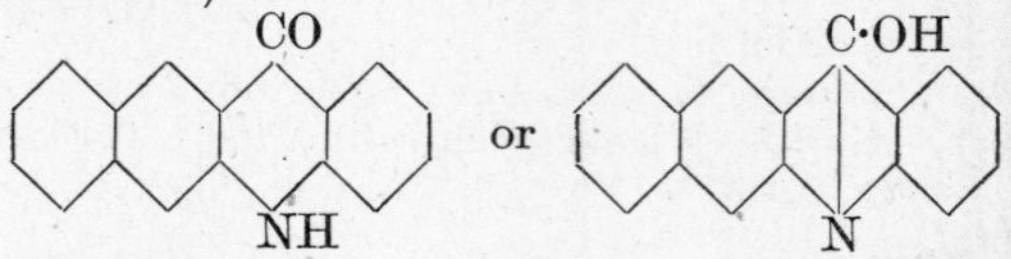

$C_{17}H_{11}ON$ MW, 245

Yellow leaflets from AcOH. M.p. 304–5°. Spar. sol. ord. org. solvents. Sols. show green fluor.

N-*Et*: $C_{19}H_{15}ON$. MW, 273. Needles from EtOH. M.p. 174–5°.

N-*Benzyl*: $C_{24}H_{17}ON$. MW, 335. Yellow needles from EtOH. M.p. 188–9°.

Schöpff, *Ber.*, 1893, **26**, 2590.

Phenacylacetone (*Acetophenoneacetone*, 1-*acetyl-2-benzoylethane*, α : δ-*diketo-*n-*amylbenzene*, ω-*acetonylacetophenone*)

$C_6H_5\cdot CO\cdot CH_2\cdot CH_2\cdot CO\cdot CH_3$

$C_{11}H_{12}O_2$ MW, 176

Yellow oil. B.p. 161°/12 mm. Sol. hot H_2O. Insol. alkalis. No col. with $FeCl_3$.

Monoxime: m.p. 123°.

Dioxime: m.p. 108°.

Mono-semicarbazone: m.p. 191°.

Borsche, Fels, *Ber.*, 1906, **39**, 1926.
See also Finzi, *Gazz. chim. ital.*, 1912, **42**, ii, 356.

Phenacyl Alcohol (*Acetophenone alcohol benzoylcarbinol, ω-hydroxyacetophenone*)

$C_6H_5 \cdot CO \cdot CH_2OH$

$C_8H_8O_2$ MW, 136

Prisms from ligroin, plates from EtOH. M.p. anhyd. 86–7° (73–4° hydrated). B.p. 118–20°/11 mm. Sol. EtOH, Et_2O, $CHCl_3$. Spar. sol. ligroin, hot H_2O. Sublimes at 56°/1 mm.

Me ether: ω-methoxyacetophenone. $C_9H_{10}O_2$. MW, 150. M.p. 7–7·5°. B.p. 228–30°, 118–20°/15 mm. *Semicarbazone*: m.p. 129°. 2 : 4-*Dinitrophenylhydrazone*: m.p. 191–2°.

Et ether: $C_{10}H_{12}O_2$. MW, 164. M.p. 81°. B.p. 134–6°/21 mm. *Oxime*: m.p. 55°.

Phenyl ether: $C_{14}H_{12}O_2$. MW, 212. M.p. 78°. B.p. 255–7°. Volatile in steam. *Oxime*: m.p. 113–14°.

o-*Nitrophenyl ether*: m.p. 118°.
p-*Nitrophenyl ether*: m.p. 144°.
o-*Tolyl ether*: m.p. 84°.
p-*Tolyl ether*: m.p. 68°.
Oxime: m.p. 70°.
Acetyl: m.p. 49° (40°). B.p. 270°.
Benzoyl: m.p. 118·5°. *Oxime*: m.p. 92°.
o-*Nitrobenzoyl*: m.p. 124·5°.
m-*Nitrobenzoyl*: m.p. 104·5°.
p-*Nitrobenzoyl*: m.p. 128·4°.

Rather, Reid, *J. Am. Chem. Soc.*, 1919, **41**, 79.
Wolff, *Ann.*, 1912, **394**, 42.
Dakin, *J. Biol. Chem.*, 1914, **18**, 92.
Allen, Scarrow, *Chem. Zentr.*, 1935, I, 1870.
Hann, Reid, Jamieson, *J. Am. Chem. Soc.*, 1930, **52**, 818.
Kelly, Kleff, *J. Am. Chem. Soc.*, 1932, **54**, 4444.

Phenacyl Aldehyde.
See ω-Formylacetophenone.

Phenacylamine (*Phenomydrol, ω-aminoacetophenone, benzoylmethylamine*)

$C_6H_5 \cdot CO \cdot CH_2NH_2$

C_8H_9ON MW, 135

B,HCl: m.p. 186–7° decomp. (183–4°).
B,HBr: m.p. 217–18° decomp.
Sulphate: m.p. 182°.
N-*Benzoyl*: m.p. 126°.
N-p-*Toluenesulphonyl*: m.p. 79° decomp.
Oxime: m.p. 140°.
Picrate: m.p. 175–6° decomp.

Kindler, D.R.P., 571,795, (*Chem. Abstracts*, 1933, **27**, 4245).
Neber, Huh, *Ann.*, 1935, **515**, 292.
Neber, F.P., 768,604, (*Chem. Abstracts*, 1935, **29**, 475).
Tiffeneau, Orekoff, Roger, *Bull. soc. chim.*, 1931, **49**, 1761.

Phenacyl-*o*-aminobenzoic Acid.
See Phenacylanthranilic Acid.

Phenacyl-*m*-aminobenzoic Acid

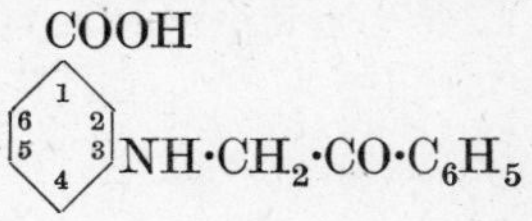

$C_{15}H_{13}O_3N$ MW, 255

Cryst. from EtOH. M.p. 202°. Sol. AcOH, Py.

N-*Acetyl*: m.p. 217°.

Scholtz, *Ber.*, 1918, **51**, 1652.

Phenacyl-*p*-aminobenzoic Acid.
Needles from EtOH. M.p. 211°.

Phenacyl ester: $C_{23}H_{19}O_4N$. MW, 373. M.p. 186°.

N-*Acetyl*: m.p. 176°.

Scholtz, *Ber.*, 1918, **51**, 1653.

Phenacylaniline.
See ω-Anilinoacetophenone.

Phenacylanthranilic Acid (*Phenacyl*-o-*aminobenzoic acid*)

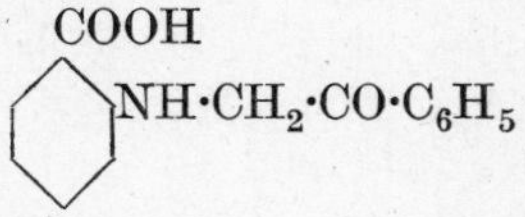

$C_{15}H_{13}O_3N$ MW, 255

Yellow needles from EtOH.Aq. M.p. 190°. Sol. ord. org. solvents.

Phenacyl ester: $C_{23}H_{19}O_4N$. MW, 373. M.p. 180°.

Phenylhydrazone: m.p. 156°.

Scholtz, *Ber.*, 1918, **51**, 1648.

***o*-Phenacylbenzoic Acid** (*Deoxybenzoin*-2-*carboxylic acid, phenyl* o-*carboxybenzyl ketone*)

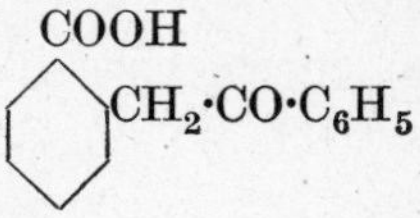

$C_{15}H_{12}O_3$ MW, 240

Needles from EtOH.Aq. M.p. 169–70° (162–3°).

Methylamide : $C_{16}H_{15}O_2N$. MW, 253. M.p. 143–4°.

Auwers, Auffenberg, *Ber.*, 1919, **52**, 109.
Graebe, Trümpy, *Ber.*, 1898, **31**, 377.

Phenacyl bromide (*ω-Bromoacetophenone, bromomethyl phenyl ketone*)

$C_6H_5·CO·CH_2Br$

C_8H_7OBr MW, 199

Prisms from EtOH.Aq. M.p. 51° (50°). B.p. 135°/18 mm. Sol. EtOH, Et_2O, $CHCl_3$, C_6H_6. D^{15} 1·709. $KMnO_4 \longrightarrow$ benzoic acid.
Oxime : (i) m.p. 89·5°. *Acetyl deriv.* : m.p. 145°. (ii) M.p. 96·5–97°.
Semicarbazone : m.p. 146°.

Clibbens, Nierenstein, *J. Chem. Soc.*, 1915, **107**, 1492.
Rather, Reed, *J. Am. Chem. Soc.*, 1919, **41**, 77.

Phenacylcarbinol.
See γ-Hydroxypropiophenone.

Phenacyl chloride (*ω-Chloroacetophenone, chloromethyl phenyl ketone*)

$C_6H_5·CO·CH_2Cl$

C_8H_7OCl MW, 154·5

Leaflets from pet. ether. M.p. 58–9°. B.p. 244–5°, 139–41°/14 mm. Sol. EtOH, Et_2O, C_6H_6. Insol. H_2O. D^{15} 1·324. $CrO_3 \longrightarrow$ benzoic acid.
Oxime : m.p. 88·5–89°. *Acetyl deriv.* : m.p. 67–9°.
Semicarbazone : m.p. 156° (149°, 137°).

Clibbens, Nierenstein, *J. Chem. Soc.*, 1915, **107**, 1492.
Béhal, Detoeuf, *Compt. rend.*, 1911, **153**, 1231.

ω-Phenacylcresol.
See γ-Hydroxyphenylpropiophenone.

Phenacylformaldehyde.
See ω-Formylacetophenone.

Phenacylglycollic Acid (*2-Benzoyl-lactic acid, 1-hydroxy-3-keto-3-phenyl-*n*-butyric acid*)

$C_6H_5·CO·CH_2·CH(OH)·COOH$

$C_{10}H_{10}O_4$ MW, 194

Cryst. M.p. 127° (125–6°). Sol. hot H_2O. Insol. ligroin. Hot alkalis $\longrightarrow$ oxalic acid + acetophenone.

Kozniewski, Marchlewski, *Chem. Zentr.*, 1906, II, 1190.
Koenigs, Wagstaffe, *Ber.*, 1893, **26**, 557.

Phenacylglyoxylic Acid.
See Benzoylpyruvic Acid.

Phenacylhydrazine (*ω-Hydrazinoaceto-phenone*)

$C_6H_5·CO·CH_2·NH·NH_2$

$C_8H_{10}ON_2$ MW, 15

Leaflets from C_6H_6. M.p. 85–6° decomp. Unstable at ord. temps. Sol. hot C_6H_6. Spa sol. EtOH, Et_2O, $CHCl_3$.
B,(COOH)$_2$,H$_2$O : m.p. 149–50° decomp.
N : *N'-Diacetyl* : m.p. 123°.
ω-N-o-*Nitrobenzylidene* : m.p. 156° decomp.
ω-N-m-*Nitrobenzylidene* : m.p. 146–7°.
ω-N-o-*Hydroxybenzylidene* : m.p. 110° de-comp.

Busch, Foerst, *J. prakt. Chem.*, 192 **119**, 287.

Phenacylhydrocinnamic Acid.
See 2-Phenyl-3-benzoylbutyric Acid an 2-Phenyl-2'-benzoylisobutyric Acid.

Phenacylidene bromide (*ω-Dibromoaceto-phenone*)

$C_6H_5·CO·CHBr_2$

$C_8H_6OBr_2$ MW, 27

Plates from $CHCl_3$. M.p. 35–6° (36–7°) B.p. 175–6°/23 mm. $KMnO_4 \longrightarrow$ benzoic acid

Evans, Brooks, *J. Am. Chem. Soc.*, 190 **30**, 406.
Wittorf, *Chem. Zentr.*, 1900, II, 29.

Phenacylidene chloride (*ω-Dichloroaceto-phenone*)

$C_6H_5·CO·CHCl_2$

$C_8H_6OCl_2$ MW, 18

M.p. 20–21·5°. B.p. 249°, 143°/25 mm. 131–2°/11 mm. $KMnO_4 \longrightarrow$ benzoic acid.

Jackson, *J. Am. Chem. Soc.*, 1934, **56** 977.
Gautier, *Ann. chim.*, 1888, **14**, 345, 385.
See also last reference above.

Phenacylidene iodide (*ω-Di-iodoaceto-phenone*)

$C_6H_5·CO·CHI_2$

$C_8H_6OI_2$ MW, 37

Oil. B.p. above 200° decomp. Sol. EtOH Et_2O, C_6H_6, CS_2. Insol. H_2O.

Collet, *Bull. soc. chim.*, 1900, **23**, 830.
Wolff, *Ann.*, 1902, **325**, 143.

2-Phenacylidenemethylfuran.
See Furfurylideneacetophenone.

Phenacyl iodide (ω-*Iodoacetophenone, iodomethyl phenyl ketone*)

$C_6H_5 \cdot CO \cdot CH_2I$

C_8H_7OI MW, 246

M.p. 28–30°. B.p. 158–60°/15 mm.

Truchet, *Ann. chim.*, 1931, **16**, 373.

Phenacyl Mercaptan (ω-*Mercaptoacetophenone*)

$C_6H_5 \cdot CO \cdot CH_2SH$

C_8H_8OS MW, 152

M.p. 23–4°. B.p. 116–22°/4 mm. D_4^{20} 1·1753. Readily decomp. ⟶ H_2S. ZnHg + HCl ⟶ ethylbenzene quantitatively.

Oxime: m.p. 70°.

Phenylhydrazone: m.p. 90–1°.

Groth, *Chem. Abstracts*, 1924, **18**, 1281.

***p*-Phenacylphenol.**

See 4-Hydroxydeoxybenzoin.

Phenalone (peri-*Naphthindenone*, peri-*naphthindone*)

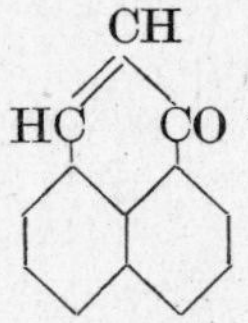

$C_{13}H_8O$ MW, 180

Canary-yellow leaflets from MeOH or cyclohexene. M.p. 153–4°. Basic. Sol. conc. HCl, + H_2O ⟶ red col. Conc. H_2SO_4 ⟶ yellow sol. with intense green fluor.

Badische, D.R.P., 283,066, (*Chem. Zentr.*, 1915, I, 814).

Cook, Hewitt, *J. Chem. Soc.*, 1934, 368, 373.

See also Braun, Manz, Reinsch, *Ann.*, 1929, **468**, 301.

Phenanthrahydroquinone (9 : 10-*Dihydroxyphenanthrene, phenanthraquinol, phenanthrene*-9 : 10-*diol*)

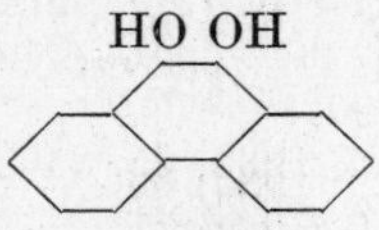

$C_{14}H_{10}O_2$ MW, 210

Needles. M.p. 148°. Sol. EtOH, Et_2O, C_6H_6, hot H_2O. Heat of comb. C_v 1604·3 Cal. Ox. in air ⟶ 9 : 10-phenanthraquinone.

Monoacetyl: m.p. 168–70°.

Diacetyl: m.p. 202°.

Dibenzoyl: m.p. 216–17°.

Mono-o-*xylyl ether*: $C_{22}H_{18}O_2$. MW, 314. Yellow cryst. from ligroin. M.p. 148–9°.

Mono-p-*xylyl ether*: yellow needles from ligroin. M.p. 129–30°.

Braun, Bayer, *Ber.*, 1925, **58**, 2680.

Benrath, Meyer, *J. prakt. Chem.*, 1914, **89**, 258.

Schmidt, Lumpp, *Ber.*, 1910, **43**, 790.

Phenanthrane.

9 : 10-Dihydrophenanthrene, *q.v.*

Phenanthranil (*Phenanthranilic acid lactam*)

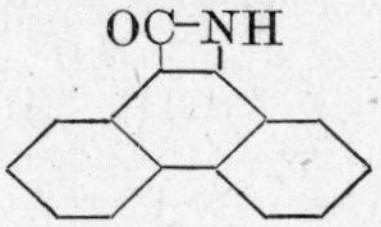

$C_{15}H_9ON$ MW, 219

Needles from C_6H_6. M.p. 241°. Sol. C_6H_6. Sublimes. Na_2CO_3 ⟶ Na salt of acid. Fuming HCl at 170° ⟶ 9-hydroxyphenanthrene.

N-*Acetyl*: m.p. 145°.

Et ether: $C_{17}H_{13}ON$. MW, 247. Needles from pet. ether. M.p. 110°. Sol. EtOH, C_6H_6.

Japp, Knox, *J. Chem. Soc.*, 1905, **87**, 692.

1 : 2-Phenanthraquinone

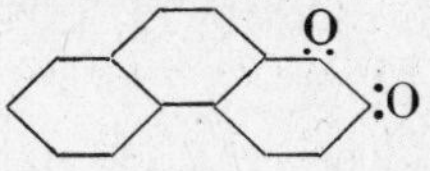

$C_{14}H_8O_2$ MW, 208

Needles from toluene. M.p. 222° decomp. Sol. AcOH. Mod. sol. EtOH, C_6H_6. H_2SO_4 ⟶ blue col. changing rapidly to green.

Fieser, *J. Am. Chem. Soc.*, 1929, **51**, 1896.

1 : 4-Phenanthraquinone

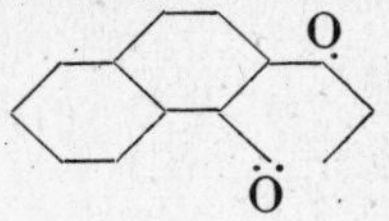

$C_{14}H_8O_2$ MW, 208

Yellow needles from ligroin. M.p. 155°. Sol. EtOH, C_6H_6, AcOH. H_2SO_4 ⟶ violet-red col.

Fieser, *J. Am. Chem. Soc.*, 1929, **51**, 2469.

3 : 4-Phenanthraquinone

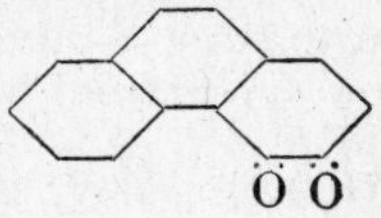

$C_{14}H_8O_2$ MW, 208

Red needles from C_6H_6–ligroin. M.p. 133° decomp. H_2SO_4 ⟶ Prussian-blue col. changing to chrome-green. Red. ⟶ morphol.

Fieser, *J. Am. Chem. Soc.*, 1929, **51**, 946.

9 : 10-Phenanthraquinone

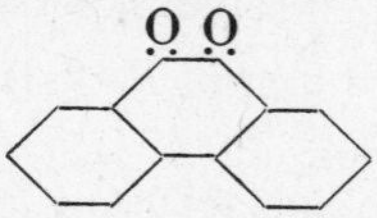

$C_{14}H_8O_2$ MW, 208

Orange-yellow needles. M.p. 206–207·5° (205°, 202°). B.p. above 360°. Sol. Et_2O, hot AcOH. Spar. sol. EtOH, C_6H_6, AcOEt. Insol. H_2O. Sol. conc. H_2SO_4 with dull green col. Sublimes in orange-red plates. $NaHSO_3$ gives unstable bisulphite comp. Ox. ⟶ diphenic acid. Red. ⟶ phenanthrahydroquinone.

Monoxime: m.p. 158°.

Dioxime: m.p. 202° decomp. (rapid heat). *Me ether*: m.p. 222–3°. *Di-Me ether*: m.p. 145–6°. *Diacetyl deriv.*: m.p. 184°.

Monosemicarbazone: m.p. about 220° decomp.

Mono-p-nitrophenylhydrazone: m.p. 245°.

Lewis, Gibbs, U.S.P., 1,288,431, (*Chem. Abstracts*, 1919, **13**, 451).
Tseng, Chu, *Chem. Abstracts*, 1934, **28**, 3730.
Selden, E.P., 170,022, (*Chem. Abstracts*, 1922, **16**, 1137).
Scholl, Schwarzer, *Ber.*, 1922, **55**, 324.
Auwers, *Ann.*, 1911, **378**, 210.
Kenner, Wilson, *J. Chem. Soc.*, 1927, 1111.

Phenanthraquinone-2-carboxylic Acid

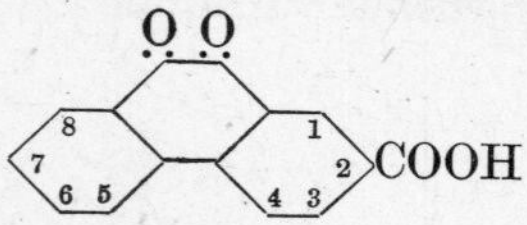

$C_{15}H_8O_4$ MW, 252

Red needles from AcOH. Does not melt below 310°. Spar. sol. hot EtOH, hot Me_2CO. Insol. Et_2O, C_6H_6, CS_2.

Nitrile: $C_{15}H_7O_2N$. MW, 233. Reddish-yellow leaflets from AcOH. M.p. 290°.

Liebermann, Kardos, *Ber.*, 1913, **46**, 201.
Werner, *Ann.*, 1902, **321**, 356.

Phenanthraquinone-3-carboxylic Acid.

Reddish-yellow cryst. from hot AcOH. Does not melt below 315°.

Amide: $C_{15}H_9O_3N$. MW, 251. Orange-red needles. M.p. 290°.

Nitrile: $C_{15}H_7O_2N$. MW, 233. Orang cryst. from AcOH. M.p. 282–3°.

Werner, *Ann.*, 1902, **321**, 355.

Phenanthraquinone-2-sulphonic Acid

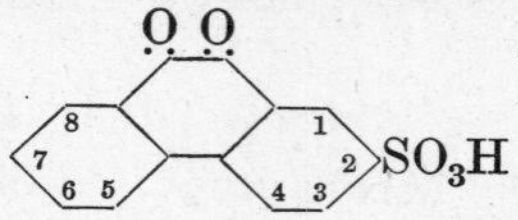

$C_{14}H_8O_5S$ MW, 28

Me ester: $C_{15}H_{10}O_5S$. MW, 302. Yellow leaflets from AcOH. M.p. 196–7° (192–192·5°).

Chloride: $C_{14}H_7O_4ClS$. MW, 306·5. Yellow leaflets or needles from AcOH. M.p. 245–6° decomp.

Sandqvist, *Ann.*, 1911, **379**, 89.

Phenanthraquinone-3-sulphonic Acid.

Me ester: orange-yellow cryst. from AcOH. M.p. 235°.

Chloride: yellowish-red needles. M.p. 257° (228–32° decomp.).

Sandqvist, *Ann.*, 1913, **398**, 136.
Werner, *Ann.*, 1902, **321**, 341.

Phenanthraquinol.

See Phenanthrahydroquinone.

Phenanthrene

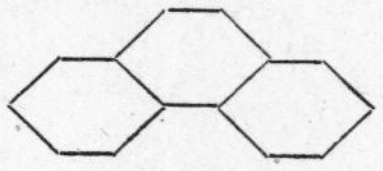

$C_{14}H_{10}$ MW, 178

Constituent of crude anthracene fraction of coal tar. Plates from EtOH. M.p. 101° (98·7–99·5°, 96·5–97·5°). B.p. 340° (332), 210–15°/12 mm. Sol. Et_2O, C_6H_6, $CHCl_3$, Me_2CO, CS_2, CCl_4. Mod. sol. EtOH, MeOH, AcOH, pet. ether. Insol. H_2O. Sols. show blue fluor. D^4 0·9800. n_D 1·59427. Sublimes in leaflets. Ox. ⟶ 9 : 10-phenanthraquinone ⟶ diphenic acid.

Picrate: m.p. 144° (132·8°).

$C_{14}H_{10} + C_6H_2Cl(NO_2)_3$-2 : 1 : 3 : 5 : m.p. 82·4°.

$C_{14}H_{10},C_6H_3(NO_2)_3$-1 : 3 : 5 : m.p. 158°

$C_{14}H_{10},C_6H_2(NO_2)_3NH_2$: m.p. 160–2°.

Zelinsky, Titz, Gaverdovshaia, *Ber.*, 1926, **59**, 2590.
Clar, *Ber.*, 1932, **65**, 846, 1411.
Hönig, *Z. Elektrochem.*, 1929, **35**, 847.
Ruzicka, *Helv. Chim. Acta*, 1934, **17**, 473.
Bachmann, *J. Am. Chem. Soc.*, 1935, **57**, 557.
Nikolaev, *Chem. Abstracts*, 1935, **29**, 7972.
Fieser, Hershberg, *J. Am. Chem. Soc.*, 1935, **57**, 1508.
Iljinski, *Chem. Zentr.*, 1932, I, 1191.

Phenanthrene-acetic Acid.
See Phenanthrylacetic Acid.

Phenanthrene-1-aldehyde

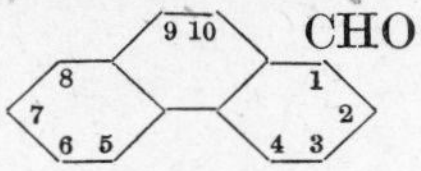

$_{15}H_{10}O$ MW, 206

M.p. 110–11°.

Bachmann, *J. Am. Chem. Soc.*, 1935, **57**, 1382.

Phenanthrene-2-aldehyde.

Needles. M.p. 59–59·5°. Sol. EtOH, MeOH.
Oxime : m.p. 194–5°.
Semicarbazone : m.p. 281–2°.

Mosettig, van de Kamp, *J. Am. Chem. Soc.*, 1933, **55**, 2996.

Phenanthrene-3-aldehyde.

Leaflets from C_6H_6–pet. ether. M.p. 79·5–80°. ;ol. EtOH, MeOH.
Oxime : m.p. 145–145·5°.
Semicarbazone : m.p. 274–5°.

See previous reference.

Phenanthrene-9-aldehyde.

Yellow prisms from EtOH. M.p. 100–1°. 3.p. 231–3°/12 mm. Mod. sol. EtOH.
Oxime : m.p. 157–157·5° (156–7°).
Semicarbazone : m.p. 221–2° (222–222·5°).
p-*Nitrophenylhydrazone* : m.p. 265°.

Hinkel, Ayling, Beynon, *J. Chem. Soc.*, 1936, 344.
Miller, Bachmann, *J. Am. Chem. Soc.*, 1935, **57**, 769.

Phenanthrene-1-carboxylic Acid (1-*Phenanthroic acid*)

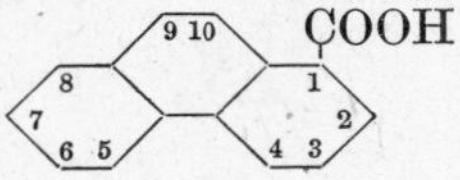

$C_{15}H_{10}O_2$ MW, 222

Needles from EtOH. M.p. 232–3°. Sol. C_6H_6.
Me ester : $C_{16}H_{12}O_2$. MW, 236. M.p. 57°. Sol. ord. org. solvents.
Amide : $C_{15}H_{11}ON$. MW, 221. Plates from AcOH.Aq. M.p. 284°.
Nitrile : $C_{15}H_9N$. MW, 203. Needles from EtOH. M.p. 128°.
Anilide : m.p. 245°.

Bachmann, *J. Am. Chem. Soc.*, 1935, **57**, 1381.
Fieser, *J. Am. Chem. Soc.*, 1932, **54**, 4110.

Phenanthrene-2-carboxylic Acid (2-*Phenanthroic acid*).

Needles from AcOH. M.p. 258·5–260°. Sol. EtOH, AcOH.
Me ester : needles from MeOH. M.p. 96–96·5°.
Et ester : $C_{17}H_{14}O_2$. MW, 250. Needles from pet. ether. M.p. 73–73·5°.
Chloride : $C_{15}H_9OCl$. MW, 240·5. M.p. 101–101·5°.
Amide : needles from C_6H_6. M.p. 242–3°.
Nitrile : cryst. from EtOH. M.p. 108–109·5°.
Anilide : m.p. 217–18°.

Mosettig, van de Kamp, *J. Am. Chem. Soc.*, 1933, **55**, 2996; 1930, **52**, 3708.
Bachmann, *J. Am. Chem. Soc.*, 1935, **57**, 558.

Phenanthrene-3-carboxylic Acid (3-*Phenanthroic acid*, α-*phenanthrene-carboxylic acid*).

Needles from AcOH. M.p. 269° (270°). Sol. EtOH, Et_2O, AcOH. Insol. H_2O. Sublimes.
Me ester : needles from MeOH. M.p. 94·5–95° (97°).
Et ester : needles from pet. ether. M.p. 56–7°.
Chloride : m.p. 116–17°.
Amide : cryst. from EtOH. M.p. 233–4° (227–8°).
Nitrile : needles from EtOH. M.p. 102°.
Anilide : needles from Me_2CO. M.p. 216–17°.

Mosettig, van de Kamp, *J. Am. Chem. Soc.*, 1930, **52**, 3710; 1933, **55**, 2996.
Bachmann, *J. Am. Chem. Soc.*, 1935, **57**, 558.
Kruber, *Ber.*, 1934, **67**, 1005.

Phenanthrene-9-carboxylic Acid (9-*Phenanthroic acid*, β-*phenanthrene-carboxylic acid*).

Cryst. from EtOH. M.p. 252°. Sol. EtOH, Et_2O, AcOH. Insol. H_2O. Sublimes.
Me ester : m.p. 116°.
Et ester : m.p. 61°.
Chloride : m.p. 102°. B.p. 240°/13 mm.
Amide : needles from C_6H_6. M.p. 232–3° (226°).
Nitrile : needles from EtOH. M.p. 103°.
Anilide : m.p. 218°.

Mosettig, van de Kamp, *J. Am. Chem. Soc.*, 1933, **55**, 2996.
Shoppee, *J. Chem. Soc.*, 1933, 39.
Bachmann, *J. Am. Chem. Soc.*, 1934, **56**, 1366.

Phenanthrene-1 : 2-dicarboxylic Acid

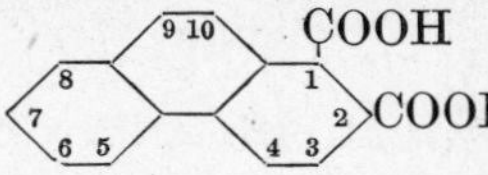

$C_{16}H_{10}O_4$ MW, 266

Anhydride : $C_{16}H_8O_3$. MW, 248. Yellow needles from Ac_2O. M.p. 311–13°.

Fieser, Hershberg, *J. Am. Chem. Soc.*, 1935, **57**, 1508, 1853.

Phenanthrene-1 : 7-dicarboxylic Acid.

Di-Me ester : $C_{18}H_{14}O_4$. MW, 294. Cryst. from MeOH. M.p. 151–2°.

Ruzicka, Graaff, Hosking, *Helv. Chim. Acta*, 1931, **14**, 238.

Phenanthrene-1-sulphonic Acid

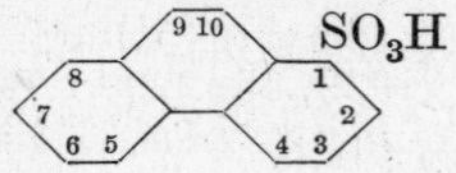

$C_{14}H_{10}O_3S$ MW, 258

p-*Toluidine salt* : needles. M.p. 267°.
Me ester : $C_{15}H_{12}O_3S$. MW, 272. Plates from MeOH. M.p. 102°.

Fieser, *J. Am. Chem. Soc.*, 1929, **51**, 2464.

Phenanthrene-2-sulphonic Acid.

Cryst. + $1H_2O$. M.p. about 150°. Sol. hot toluene, hot $PhNO_2$.
p-*Toluidine salt* : m.p. 291°.
Me ester : (i) m.p. 101·5°. (ii) Leaflets. M.p. 96–8°. Sol. MeOH, EtOH.
Et ester : $C_{16}H_{14}O_3S$. MW, 286. Yellowish-brown leaflets from EtOH. M.p. 88·5°.
Chloride : $C_{14}H_9O_2ClS$. MW, 276·5. Leaflets from AcOH. M.p. 156°.
Amide : $C_{14}H_{11}O_2NS$. MW, 257. Leaflets from EtOH. M.p. 253–4°.
Anilide : m.p. 157–8°.

Sandqvist, *Ann.*, 1911, **379**, 79.
Fieser, *J. Am. Chem. Soc.*, 1929, **51**, 2464.
Ioffe, *Chem. Abstracts*, 1934, **28**, 1694.

Phenanthrene-3-sulphonic Acid (α-*Phenanthrenesulphonic acid*).

Cryst. from $H_2O \longrightarrow$ two hydrates. (i) + $1H_2O$, m.p. 120–1° : (ii) + $2H_2O$, m.p. 88–9°. M.p. anhyd. 175–6°.
p-*Toluidine salt* : m.p. 222°.
Me ester : cryst. from EtOH. M.p. 119–20°.
Et ester : leaflets or needles. M.p. 107–8°. Sol. EtOH, C_6H_6.
Chloride : yellow leaflets from C_6H_6. M.p. 110–11° (108·5°) : solidifies, and remelts at 114°.
Bromide : $C_{14}H_9O_2BrS$. MW, 321. Yellow plates from ligroin. M.p. 140°.
Amide : leaflets from EtOH.Aq. M.p. 189·5–190°.

Sandqvist, *Ann.*, 1909, **369**, 104 ; 1913, **398**, 136.
Fieser, *J. Am. Chem. Soc.*, 1929, **51**, 2464.

Phenanthrene-9-sulphonic Acid (β-*Phenanthrenesulphonic acid*).

Leaflets or needles + $2H_2O$ from H_2O or C_6H_6. M.p. 134°, 174° anhyd.
p-*Toluidine salt* : needles. M.p. 235°.
Me ester : leaflets from MeOH. M.p. 106°.
Et ester : cryst. from EtOH. M.p. 108°.
Chloride : yellow needles from AcOH. M.p. 127° (125·5°).
Amide : needles from EtOH. M.p. 193·5°.

Sandqvist, *Ann.*, 1912, **392**, 76.
Fieser, *J. Am. Chem. Soc.*, 1929, **51**, 2464.
Ioffe, *Chem. Abstracts*, 1934, **28**, 1694.

Phenanthrene - 1 : 8 : 9 : 10 - tetracarboxylic Acid

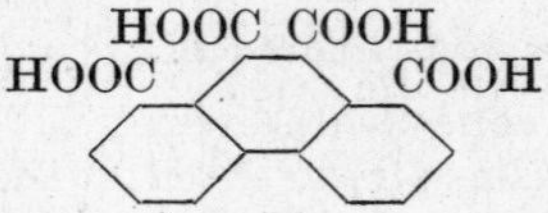

$C_{18}H_{10}O_8$ MW, 354

Tetra-Me ester : $C_{22}H_{18}O_8$. MW, 410. Yellow cryst. M.p. 181–3°.
Di-anhydride : $C_{18}H_6O_6$. MW, 318. Brownish-yellow needles. Does not melt below 400°.

Zinke, Hauswirth, Grimm, *Monatsh.*, 1931, **57**, 405.

Phenanthridine (3 : 4 - *Benzquinoline*, 2 : 3 : 4 : 5-*dibenzpyridine*)

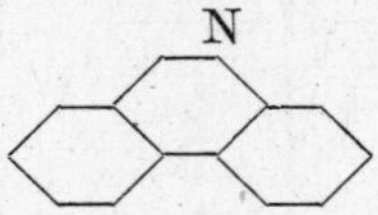

$C_{13}H_9N$ MW, 179

Needles from EtOH.Aq. M.p. 106°. B.p. 349°/769 mm. Sol. EtOH, Et_2O, $CHCl_3$, C_6H_6, CS_2. Spar. sol. H_2O with blue fluor. Spar. volatile in steam.
B,HCl,HgCl₂ : m.p. 197°.
B₂,H₂PtCl₆ : m.p. above 225°.
Methiodide : m.p. 204·5°.
Picrate : m.p. 220°.

Sielisch, Sandke, *Ber.*, 1933, **66**, 433.
Pyl, *Ber.*, 1927, **60**, 287.

Phenanthridine-9-carboxylic Acid

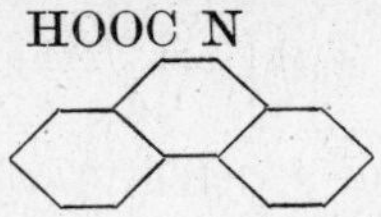

$_{14}H_9O_2N$ MW, 223

Micro-cryst. Sol. EtOH, Me_2CO. Spar. sol. $_6H_6$. Insol. H_2O, pet. ether. Heat ⟶ phen-thridine.

Et ester: $C_{16}H_{13}O_2N$. MW, 251. Needles om pet. ether. M.p. 57–8°.

Walls, *J. Chem. Soc.*, 1934, 108.

Phenanthridone (*Phenanthridol, 10-hydroxy-henanthridine*)

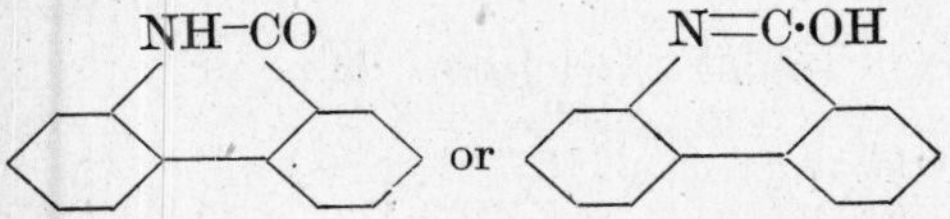

$_{13}H_9ON$ MW, 195

Needles from EtOH. M.p. 293°. Spar. sol. tOH, Et_2O, AcOH. Zn dist. ⟶ phen-nthridine.

Oyster, Adkins, *J. Am. Chem. Soc.*, 1921, **43**, 210.
Meyer, Hofmann, *Monatsh.*, 1916, **37**, 701.
Walls, *J. Chem. Soc.*, 1934, 108; 1935, 1407.
Heidenreich, Tust, U.S.P., 1,880,441, (*Chem. Abstracts*, 1933, **27**, 516).
See also Sielich, Sandke, *Ber.*, 1933, **66**, 434.

Phenanthrindene (*Phenanthrylenemethane*)

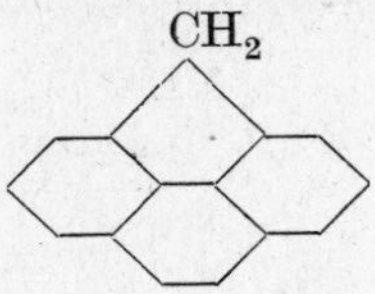

$C_{15}H_{10}$ MW, 190

Needles from EtOH. M.p. 116°. B.p. 353°.
Benzylidene deriv.: m.p. 108°.
Picrate: m.p. 166°.

Kruber, *Ber.*, 1934, **67**, 1004.

Phenanthroic Acid.
See Phenanthrene-carboxylic Acid.

Phenanthrol.
See Hydroxyphenanthrene.

Phenanthrol-carboxylic Acid.
See Hydroxyphenanthrene-carboxylic Acid.

***o*-Phenanthroline** (1 : 10-*Phenanthroline*)

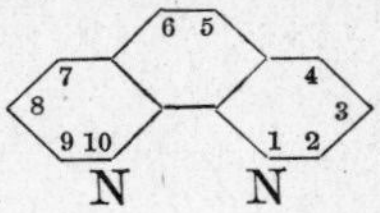

$C_{12}H_8N_2$ MW, 180

Cryst. + $1H_2O$ from H_2O, m.p. 91·5°; cryst. from C_6H_6, m.p. 98–100°. B.p. above 300°. Sol. EtOH, C_6H_6, Me_2CO. Insol. pet. ether. Ferrous salts ⟶ red col. Forms metallic derivs.

Tartarini, Samaja, *Chem. Abstracts*, 1933, **27**, 5741.
Smith, Getz, *Chemical Reviews*, 1935, **16**, 113.
Willink, Wibaut, *Rec. trav. chim.*, 1935, **54**, 282.
Smith, *J. Am. Chem. Soc.*, 1930, **52**, 402.

***m*-Phenanthroline** (1 : 7-*Phenanthroline*)

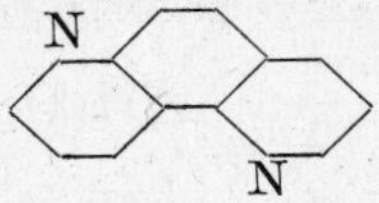

$C_{12}H_8N_2$ MW, 180

Needles. M.p. 65·5°, anhyd. 78–78·5°. B.p. above 360°. Sol. EtOH, hot H_2O. Insol. Et_2O, C_6H_6, ligroin.

Knüppel, *Ber.*, 1896, **29**, 707.
See also Smith, *J. Am. Chem. Soc.*, 1930, **52**, 397.

***p*-Phenanthroline** (*ψ-Phenanthroline*, 4 : 7-*phenanthroline*)

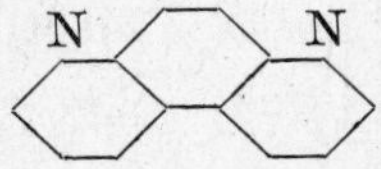

$C_{12}H_8N_2$ MW, 180

Needles from H_2O. M.p. anhyd. 173°. Sol. EtOH, $CHCl_3$. Mod. sol. hot H_2O. Spar. sol. Et_2O, C_6H_6, CS_2.
Hydrochloride: does not melt below 315°.
Sulphate: m.p. 233–4°.
Chromate: decomp. at 225–30°.
Picrate: m.p. 255–6°.
Platinochloride: does not melt below 310°.
Methiodide: m.p. 268–9°.
Di-methiodide: m.p. 271°.

Matsumura, *J. Am. Chem. Soc.*, 1930, **52**, 3196.
Smith, *ibid.*, 402.

Phenanthrone.
Keto form of 9-Hydroxyphenanthrene, *q.v.*

2-Phenanthrylacetic Acid (*Phenanthrene-2-acetic acid*)

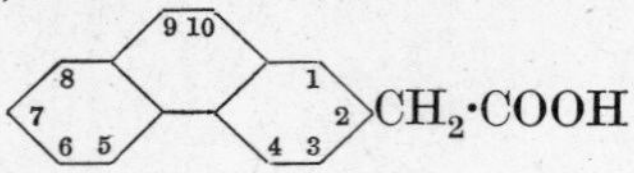

$C_{16}H_{12}O_2$ MW, 236

Needles. M.p. 183·5–184·5°.

Me ester: $C_{17}H_{14}O_2$. MW, 250. Needles. M.p. 78–78·5°.

Nitrile: $C_{16}H_{11}N$. MW, 217. M.p. 106–106·5°.

Mosettig, van de Kamp, *J. Am. Chem. Soc.*, 1933, **55**, 2998.

3-Phenanthrylacetic Acid (*Phenanthrene-3-acetic acid*).

Leaflets. M.p. 177–177·5°.

Me ester: liq. *Picrate*: m.p. 103·5–104°.

Nitrile: m.p. 84·5–85°.

See previous reference.

9-Phenanthrylacetic Acid (*Phenanthrene-9-acetic acid*).

Leaflets. M.p. 220–1° (213–15°).

Me ester: m.p. 75–75·5°.

Amide: $C_{16}H_{13}ON$. MW, 235. Leaflets. M.p. 250–2°.

Nitrile: m.p. 96·5–97°.

See previous reference and also

Willgerodt, Albert, *J. prakt. Chem.*, 1911, **84**, 387.

Phenanthrylamine.

See Aminophenanthrene.

1-Phenanthrylcarbinol (*1-Hydroxymethyl-phenanthrene*)

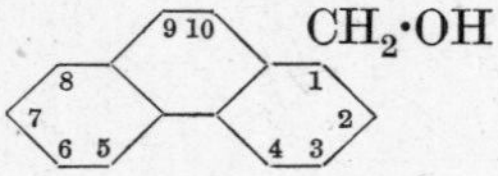

$C_{15}H_{12}O$ MW, 208

M.p. 165°.

Bachmann, *J. Am. Chem. Soc.*, 1935, **57**, 1382.

2-Phenanthrylcarbinol (*2-Hydroxymethyl-phenanthrene*).

Needles from C_6H_6–pet. ether. M.p. 125–125·5°.

Mosettig, van de Kamp, *J. Am. Chem. Soc.*, 1933, **55**, 2998.

3-Phenanthrylcarbinol (*3-Hydroxymethyl-phenanthrene*).

Prisms from C_6H_6–pet. ether. M.p. 103–103·5°.

See previous reference.

9-Phenanthrylcarbinol (*9-Hydroxymethyl-phenanthrene*).

Needles from C_6H_6–pet. ether. M.p. 149–149·5°.

Bachmann, *J. Am. Chem. Soc.*, 1934, **56**, 1366.

Phenanthrylene-methane.

See Phenanthrindene.

9-Phenanthrylmethylamine (*9-Aminomethylphenanthrene*)

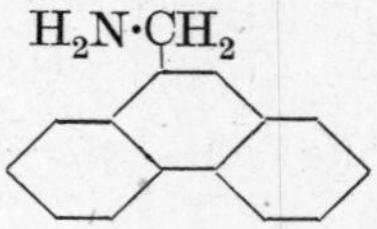

$C_{15}H_{13}N$ MW, 207

Cryst. from Et_2O–ligroin. M.p. 107°.

N-*Acetyl*: m.p. 182–5°.

N-*Benzoyl*: m.p. 167°.

N-*Benzylidene*: m.p. 103·5°.

Picrate: m.p. 241° decomp.

Shoppee, *J. Chem. Soc.*, 1933, 40.

Phenarsazine (*Phenazarsine*)

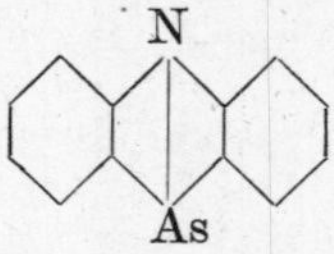

$C_{12}H_8NAs$ MW, 241

M.p. about 310°. Sol. $PhNO_2$. Spar. sol hot xylene.

Wieland, Rheinheimer, *Ann.*, 1921, **423**, 16.

Phenarsazinic Acid (*Phenazarsinic acid*)

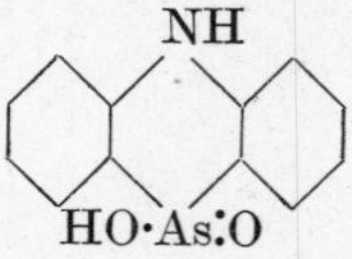

$C_{12}H_{10}O_2NAs$ MW, 275

Cryst. from H_2O. M.p. 365–6° decomp.

B,HCl: m.p. 208°.

Kappelmeier, *Rec. trav. chim.*, 1930, **49**, 83 (*Bibl.*).

Sergeev, Gorkii, *Chem. Abstracts*, 1932, **26**, 2195.

Wieland, Rheinheimer, *Ann.*, 1921, **423**, 22.

See also Razuvaev, Koton, *Chem. Abstracts*, 1933, **27**, 984.

Phenarsine (*Arsanthrene, diarseno*-9 : 10-*anthracene*)

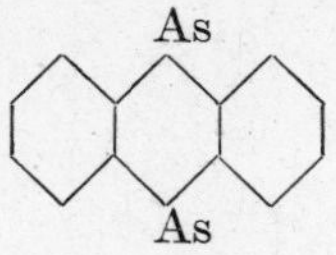

$C_{12}H_8As_2$ MW, 302

Orange-yellow leaflets. M.p. about 340°. Spar. sol. AcOH, Py.

Kalb, *Ann.*, 1921, **423**, 66.

Phenazarsine.
See Phenarsazine.

Phenazarsinic Acid.
See Phenarsazinic Acid.

Phenazine (*Azophenylene*)

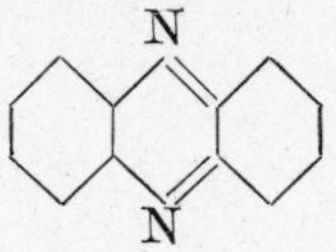

$C_{12}H_8N_2$ MW, 180

Yellowish-red needles, from AcOH. M.p. 171° (170°). B.p. above 360°. Sol. hot EtOH. Mod. sol. Et_2O, C_6H_6. Spar. sol. H_2O. Sublimes. Volatile in steam.

Eckert, Steiner, *Monatsh.*, 1914, **35**, 1153.
Zerewitinoff, Ostromisslensky, *Ber.*, 1911, **44**, 2402.
Kehrmann, Mermod, *Helv. Chim. Acta*, 1927, **10**, 62.
Beschke, *Ann.*, 1913, **398**, 298.
Clemo, McIlwain, *J. Chem. Soc.*, 1934, 1993.

Phenazine-1-carboxylic Acid

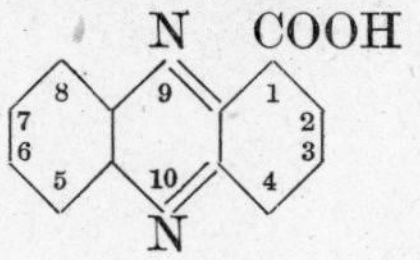

$C_{13}H_8O_2N_2$ MW, 224

Yellow needles from EtOH. M.p. 239°.
Amide : $C_{13}H_9ON_3$. MW, 223. M.p. 234°.

See last reference above and also
Kögl, Tönnis, Groenewegen, *Ann.*, 1932, **497**, 277.

Phenazine-2-carboxylic Acid.
Yellow needles from Me_2CO. M.p. 292–3°.
Amide : $C_{13}H_9ON_3$. MW, 223. M.p. 312°.

Clemo, McIlwain, *J. Chem. Soc.*, 1935, 741.
Kögl, Tönnis, Groenewegen, *Ann.*, 1932, **497**, 288.

Phenazone.
See Antipyrine.

Phenazoxine.
See Phenoxazine.

Pheneserine (*Eseroline phenylurethane*)

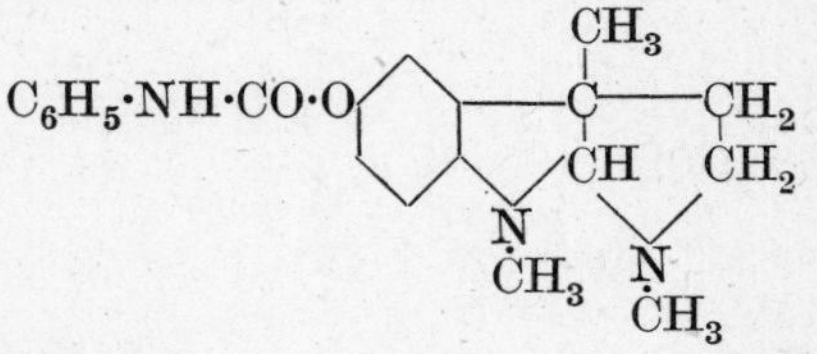

$C_{20}H_{23}O_2N_3$ MW, 337

Prisms. M.p. 150°. NaOH ⟶ eseroline.
Methiodide : m.p. 198°. $[\alpha]_D$ − 92·8° in EtOH.
Picrate : non-cryst. M.p. about 100°.

Polonovski, *Bull. soc. chim.*, 1916, **19**, 46.

Phenetetrol.
See Apionol.

***o*-Phenetidine** (o-*Ethoxyaniline*, o-*aminophenetole*, o-*aminophenol ethyl ether*)

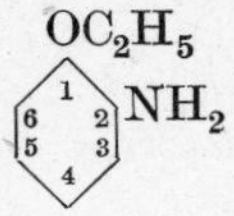

$C_8H_{11}ON$ MW, 137

B.p. 228° (224–9°). $k = 4{\cdot}64 \times 10^{-10}$ at 20°.
$B,C_{10}H_7SO_3H$ (1) : m.p. 185°.
$B,C_{10}H_7SO_3H$ (2) : m.p. 197°.
N-*Formyl* : form-*o*-phenetidide. M.p. 62°. B.p. 292°.
N-*Acetyl* : acet-*o*-phenetidide, *o*-ethoxyacetanilide. $C_{10}H_{13}O_2N$. MW, 179. M.p. 79°.
N-*Lauryl* : m.p. 69·7–70°.
N-*Myristyl* : m.p. 77°.
N-*Palmityl* : m.p. 82–3°.
N-*Stearyl* : m.p. 84·7°.
N-*Benzoyl* : benz-*o*-phenetidide. M.p. 104·2°.
N-1-*Naphthalenesulphonyl* : m.p. 185°.
N-2-*Naphthalenesulphonyl* : m.p. 197°.

Zavelskii, Fomenko, Krolik, *Chem. Abstracts*, 1935, **29**, 467.
Li, Adams, *J. Am. Chem. Soc.*, 1935, **57**, 1568.
Birosel, Huang, *Chem. Abstracts*, 1933, **27**, 5727.

***m*-Phenetidine** (m-*Ethoxyaniline*, m-*aminophenetole*, m-*aminophenol ethyl ether*).
B.p. 248°, 127–8°/11 mm.
N-*Formyl* : form-*m*-phenetidide. Greyish-blue cryst. M.p. 52°.

N-*Acetyl*: acet-*m*-phenetidide. Greyish plates. M.p. 96–7°.

N-*Benzoyl*: see under *m*-Hydroxybenzanilide.

N-*Toluene*-p-*sulphonyl*: m.p. 157°.

Picrate: m.p. 158°.

Reverdin, Lokietek, *Bull. soc. chim.*, 1915, **17**, 407.

p-Phenetidine (p-*Ethoxyaniline*, p-*aminophenetole*, p-*aminophenol ethyl ether*).

M.p. 2·4°. B.p. 254·2–254·7°. $k = 2{\cdot}15 \times 10^{-9}$ at 15°. $D_4^{15{\cdot}9}$ 1·0652. Spar. volatile in steam.

B,HCl: m.p. 234°. Sol. H_2O. Sublimes.

$B,(COOH)_2$: m.p. 201°.

$B_2,(COOH)_2$: m.p. 201°.

Tartrate: vinopyrin. M.p. 192°.

N-*Formyl*: form-*p*-phenetidide. M.p. 68–70°.

N-*Acetyl*: acet-*p*-phenetidide. Phenacetin. $C_{10}H_{13}O_2N$. MW, 179. M.p. 137–8°. Sol. 1400 parts H_2O at 15°, 80 parts at boil. Sol. 6 parts Py at 20°, 67 parts Et_2O at 25°, 20 parts $CHCl_3$ at 25°, 10 parts Me_2CO at 30°, 170 parts C_6H_6 at 30°, 6·5 parts EtOH. Heat of comb. C_p 1303 Cal. NaOBr + NH_3 $\longrightarrow$ brown col. Forms cryst. K deriv. Antipyretic and antineuralgic. B_2,HI: needles. M.p. 147–8°.

N-*Lactyl*: *see under* Lactic acid.

N-*Glycyl*: phenocoll. Needles + $1H_2O$. M.p. 95°, 100·5° anhyd.

N-*Lauryl*: m.p. 109–10°.

N-*Palmityl*: m.p. 117·5°.

N-*Stearyl*: m.p. 112·5°.

Glucoside: m.p. 114°.

N-*Furfurylidene*: m.p. 72–3°.

N-*Benzoyl*: *see under* *p*-Hydroxybenzanilide.

N-*Mandelyl*: *see* Amygdophenine.

N-1-*Naphthalenesulphonyl*: m.p. 201–2°.

N-2-*Naphthalenesulphonyl*: m.p. 207°.

N-*Me*: *see* *N*-Methyl-*p*-phenetidine.

Täufel, Wagner, Dünwald, *Z. Elektrochem.*, 1928, **34**, 115.
Grether, U.S.P., 1,722,417, (*Chem. Abstracts*, 1929, **23**, 4483).
Birosel, Huang, *Chem. Abstracts*, 1933, **27**, 5727.
Ehrhardt, *Ber.*, 1897, **30**, 2015.
Byk, D.R.P., 264,263, (*Chem. Zentr.*, 1913, II, 1179).
Zernik, *Chem. Zentr.*, 1908, I, 1203.
Aoyama, Eguchi, Tashiro, *Chem. Abstracts*, 1935, **29**, 5427.
Zavelskii, Fomenko, Krolik, *ibid.*, 467.
West, *J. Chem. Soc.*, 1925, 494.
Hinsberg, *Ann.*, 1899, **305**, 278.
Tauber, D.R.P., 85,988.

p-Phenetil (*Di*-[4-*ethoxy*]-*benzoyl*, 4 : 4′-*diethoxybenzil*)

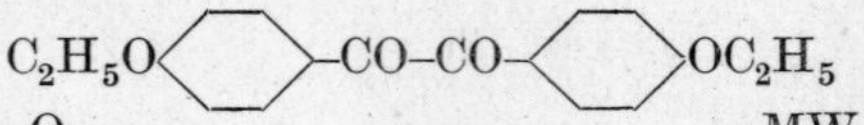

$C_{18}H_{18}O_4$ MW, 298

Prisms from EtOH. M.p. 149°.

Monoxime: m.p. 136°.

Di-phenylhydrazone: m.p. 171°.

Vorländer, *Ber.*, 1911, **44**, 2464.

Phenetole (*Ethyl phenyl ether*, *ethoxybenzene*)

$C_6H_5{\cdot}OC_2H_5$

$C_8H_{10}O$ MW, 122

F.p. − 28·6° (− 30·2°). M.p. − 33°. B.p. 172°, 166°/667·5 mm., 160°/565·5 mm., 92·5°/61·42 mm., 77·5°/31·14 mm., 60°/9·12 mm. Sol. EtOH, Et_2O. Insol. H_2O. Heat of comb. C_p 1057·23 Cal. $D_4^{20{\cdot}2}$ 0·9666. $n_D^{18{\cdot}8}$ 1·5084.

$C_8H_{10}O,SbCl_3$: m.p. 42·2°.

$C_8H_{10}O,SbBr_3$: m.p. 48·8°.

Rodionov, *Bull. soc. chim.*, 1929, **45**, 109.
Zerbe, D.R.P., 563,969, (*Chem. Abstracts*, 1933, **27**, 4812).
Sowa, Hennion, Nieuwland, *J. Am. Chem. Soc.*, 1935, **57**, 710.
Finzi, *Chem. Abstracts*, 1925, **19**, 2648.

Phenetole-2 : 5-disulphonic Acid

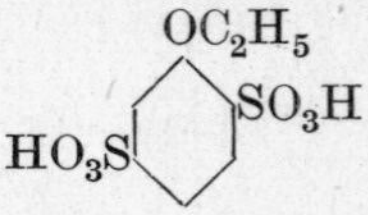

$C_8H_{10}O_7S_2$ MW, 282

Dichloride: $C_8H_8O_5Cl_2S_2$. MW, 319. Plates from Et_2O. M.p. 106–8°.

Diamide: $C_8H_{12}O_5N_2S_2$. MW, 280. Needles from H_2O. M.p. 233°.

Zander, *Ann.*, 1879, **198**, 25.

Phenetole-o-sulphonic Acid

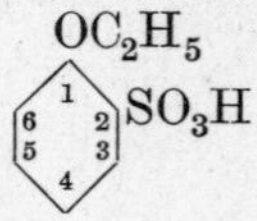

$C_8H_{10}O_4S$ MW, 202

Cryst. mass.

Chloride: $C_8H_9O_3ClS$. MW, 220·5. Plates from pet. ether. M.p. 65–6°.

Amide: $C_8H_{11}O_3NS$. MW, 201. Needles from H_2O. M.p. 163°.

Anilide: m.p. 158°.

Phenylhydrazide: m.p. 132–3°.

Moody, *Chem. News*, 1893, **67**, 35.
Gattermann, *Ber.*, 1899, **32**, 1154.

Phenetole-*m*-sulphonic Acid.
Cryst. Sol. H_2O, EtOH.
Et ester: $C_{10}H_{14}O_4S$. MW, 230. Oil. Decomp. on dist. Volatile in steam.
Chloride: needles from Et_2O. M.p. 38°. Sol. C_6H_6, $CHCl_3$. Spar. sol. EtOH.
Amide: needles from H_2O. M.p. 131° (126°).

Lagai, *Ber.*, 1892, **25**, 1836.

Phenetole-*p*-sulphonic Acid.
Chloride: prisms or leaflets from Et_2O. M.p. 39° (36·5°). Sol. EtOH, Et_2O.
Amide: needles from H_2O, plates from EtOH. M.p. 150° (149°).

Lagai, *Ber.*, 1892, **25**, 1837.
Moody, *Chem. News*, 1892, **65**, 247.
Gattermann, *Ber.*, 1899, **32**, 1155.

***p*-Phenetylurea.**
See Dulcin.

Phenobarbital.
See Luminal.

Phenocoll.
See under p-Phenetidine.

Phenol (*Hydroxybenzene, carbolic acid*)

C_6H_5OH

C_6H_6O MW, 94

Needles. F.p. 41° (40·5°). M.p. 43°. B.p. 182°, 159·7°/400 mm., 90·2°/25 mm. Sol. EtOH, Et_2O. Mod. sol. H_2O. D_4^{25} 1·0710. n_D^{21} 1·5509. $k = 1·3 \times 10^{-10}$ at 25°. $FeCl_3 \longrightarrow$ violet col. Turns pink in air. Corrosive poison. Heat of comb. C_p 732·5 Cal., C_v 734·2 (731–9) Cal. Volatile in steam.
$C_6H_6O,\frac{1}{2}H_2O$: m.p. 16°.
$C_6H_6O,2SbCl_3$: m.p. 37°.
$C_6H_6O,2SbBr_3$: m.p. 66·5°.
$2C_6H_6O,CH_3{\cdot}CO{\cdot}CH_3$: m.p. 15°.
$2C_6H_6O,CH_3{\cdot}CO{\cdot}NH_2$: m.p. 40·8°.
$C_6H_6O,CCl_3{\cdot}COOH$: m.p. 37·6°.
$2C_6H_6O,CO(NH_2)_2$: m.p. 61°.
$C_6H_6O,2CH_3{\cdot}NH_2$: m.p. 8·5–9·5°.
Picrate: m.p. 83·1°.
Phenylurethane: needles from C_6H_6. M.p. 126°. Dist. $\longrightarrow$ phenyl isocyanate. $NH_3 \longrightarrow$ phenylurea.
1-*Naphthylurethane*: m.p. 136–7°.
Sulphite: $C_{12}H_{10}O_3S$. MW, 234. B.p. 185°/15 mm., 143°/0·7 mm.
Hydrogen sulphate: *see* Phenyl hydrogen sulphate.
Hydrogen phosphite: $C_{12}H_{11}O_3P$. MW, 234. B.p. 218–19°/25 mm.
Phosphite: triphenyl phosphite. $C_{18}H_{15}O_3P$. MW, 310. B.p. 360°, 235°/18 mm.
Dihydrogen phosphate: $C_6H_7O_4P$. MW, 174. M.p. 99·5° (97–8°).
Hydrogen phosphate: diphenyl phosphate. $C_{12}H_{11}O_4P$. MW, 250. Needles or leaflets $+ 2H_2O$. M.p. 51°, anhyd. 70°. Sol. EtOH, Et_2O, $CHCl_3$, C_6H_6, hot H_2O.
Phosphate: *see* Triphenyl phosphate.
Orthosilicate: $C_{24}H_{20}O_4Si$. MW, 400. M.p. 47–8°. B.p. 417–20°.
Borate: triphenyl borate. $C_{18}H_{15}O_3B$. MW, 290. Needles from pet. ether. M.p. 50°.
Carbonate: *see* Diphenyl carbonate.
d-α-*Glucoside*: $C_{12}H_{16}O_6$. MW, 256. M.p. 174–5°. $[\alpha]_D^{20}$ − 71° in H_2O.
d-β-*Glucoside*: m.p. 139–41°. $[\alpha]_D^{20}$ − 39·85° in H_2O.

Cappelli, *Gazz. chim. ital.*, 1918, **48**, ii, 107.
Vorozhtzov, Oshuev, *Chem. Abstracts*, 1934, **28**, 1027 (*Review*).
I.G., D.R.P., 613,726, (*Chem. Abstracts*, 1935, **29**, 8298).
du Pont, U.S.P., 2,007,327, *ibid.*, 5864.
Rütgerswerke A.-G., E.P., 427,145, *ibid.*, 6252.
Eikhman, Shemyakin, Vozhdaeva, *ibid.*, 2520.
Tishchenko, Churbakow, *ibid.*, 2520.
Noller, Dutton, *J. Am. Chem. Soc.*, 1933, **55**, 424.
Mizoshita, *Chem. Abstracts*, 1931, **25**, 1812.
Dyson, *Chem. Age*, 1926, **14**, 70 (*Review*).
Battegay, Denivelle, *Compt. rend.*, 1931, **192**, 492.
Bernton, *Ber.*, 1922, **55**, 3361.

Phenoldiazonium chloride.
See Hydroxybenzenediazonium chloride.

Phenol-2 : 4-disulphonic Acid

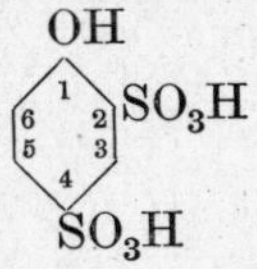

$C_6H_6O_7S_2$ MW, 254

Needles. Decomp. above 100°. Sol. H_2O, EtOH. Insol. Et_2O.
Dichloride: $C_6H_4O_5Cl_2S_2$. MW, 291. Plates from Et_2O. M.p. 89° (86°).
Diamide: $C_6H_8O_5N_2S_2$. MW, 252. Leaflets. M.p. 239°.
Dianilide: m.p. 205°.

Gebauer-Fulnegg, Riesz, Austrian P., 119,960 (*Chem. Abstracts*, 1931, **25**, 1262).

Phenol-2 : 5-disulphonic Acid.

Et ether: phenetole-2 : 5-disulphonic acid. *Dichloride*: $C_8H_8O_5Cl_2S_2$. MW, 319. Plates from Et_2O. M.p. 106–8°. *Diamide*: $C_8H_{12}O_5N_2S_2$. MW, 280. Needles from H_2O. M.p. 233°.

Senhofer, *Sitzb. Akad. Wiss. Wien*, 1878, **78**, ii, 678.

Phenolphthalein (3 : 3-*Di*-[p-*hydroxyphenyl*]-*phthalide*, α-4 : 4′-*trihydroxytriphenylmethane-2-carboxylic acid lactone*)

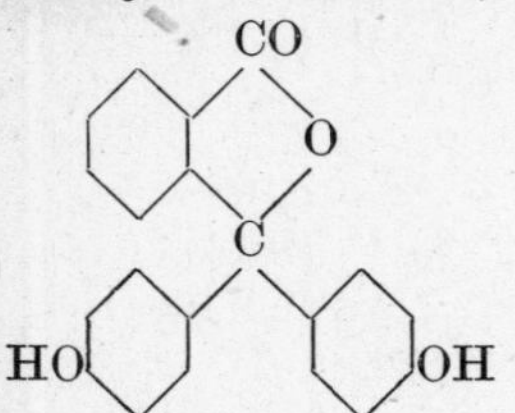

I

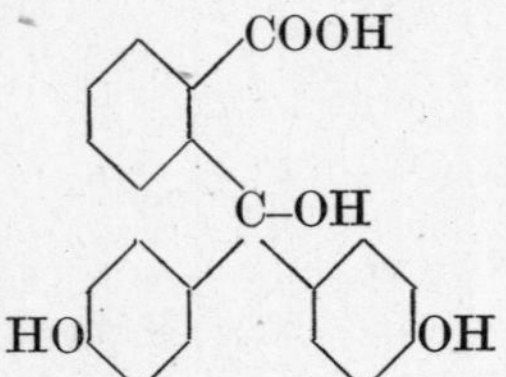

II

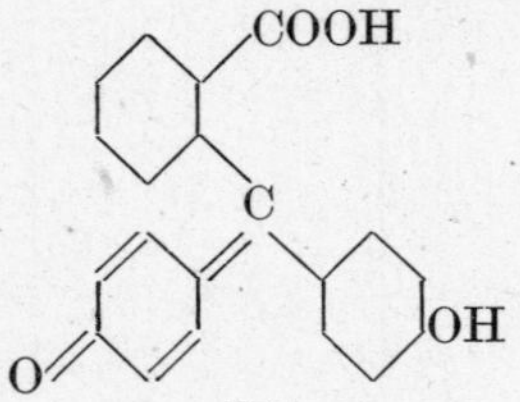

III

I. $C_{20}H_{14}O_4$ MW, 318
II. $C_{20}H_{16}O_5$ MW, 336
III. $C_{20}H_{14}O_4$ MW, 318

I.

Cryst. M.p. 254° (250–3°). Mod. sol. hot H_2O. Sol. hot Et_2O. NaOH ⟶ red col. Used as indicator. Red. ⟶ phenolphthalin.

Me ether: $C_{21}H_{16}O_4$. MW, 332. Needles from C_6H_6. M.p. 198–9° ⟶ glassy mass, m.p. 80°.

Di-Me ether: $C_{22}H_{18}O_4$. MW, 346. Leaflets from EtOH. M.p. 101–2° (97–9°). Sol. hot EtOH.

Di-Et ether: $C_{24}H_{22}O_4$. MW, 374. Leaflets from EtOH. M.p. 122° (118–20°). Sol. C_6H_6.

Diphenyl ether: $C_{32}H_{22}O_4$. MW, 470. Grey cryst. M.p. 105–6°.

Dibenzyl ether: $C_{34}H_{26}O_4$. MW, 498. Leaflets. M.p. 150°. Sol. C_6H_6.

Diacetyl: m.p. 143°.

Di-isovaleryl: m.p. 110°.

Dibenzoyl: m.p. 169°.

Dibenzenesulphonyl: m.p. 112–13°.

III.

Me ester: $C_{21}H_{16}O_4$. MW, 332. Orange-red needles. M.p. 127–30°. Sol. EtOH, $CHCl_3$.

Et ester: *Et ether*, $C_{24}H_{22}O_4$. MW, 374. Yellow cryst. M.p. 98–104°.

Underwood, Barker, *J. Am. Chem. Soc.*, 1930, **52**, 4084.
Molle, *Chem. Abstracts*, 1927, **21**, 2470 (*Bibl.*).
Day, *J. Am. Chem. Soc.*, 1930, **52**, 646.
Lund, *J. Chem. Soc.*, 1930, 1844.
Blicke, Swisher, *J. Am. Chem. Soc.*, 1934, **56**, 902.
Kavalco, U.S.Ps., 1,940,146, 1,940,494, (*Chem. Abstracts*, 1934, **28**, 1366).
Zelinskii, Maksorov, *Ind. Eng. Chem.*, 1931, **24**, 63.

Phenolphthalin (4 : 4′-*Dihydroxytriphenylmethane-2-carboxylic acid*)

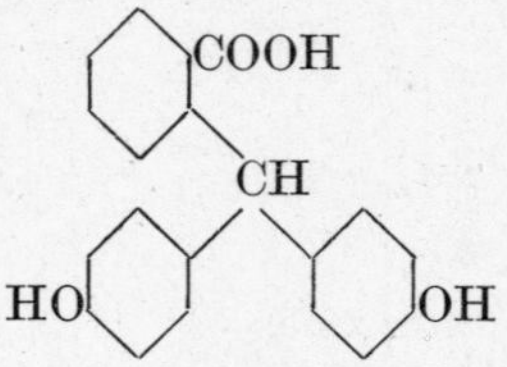

$C_{20}H_{16}O_4$ MW, 320

Needles from H_2O. M.p. 225°. Spar. sol. H_2O. Ox. ⟶ phenolphthalein.

Et ester: $C_{22}H_{20}O_4$. MW, 348. Leaflets or needles from EtOH.Aq. M.p. 150–2° (156–8°).

Di-Me ether: $C_{22}H_{20}O_4$. MW, 348. Needles from EtOH. M.p. 149–50°.

Diacetyl: m.p. 146°.

Baeyer, *Ann.*, 1880, **202**, 80.

Phenol-*o*-sulphonic Acid

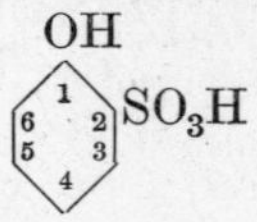

$C_6H_6O_4S$ MW, 174

Cryst. + $\frac{3}{4}H_2O$, partly melts at 50° decomp.: + H_2O, m.p. 145°. Sol. H_2O.

K salt, $2H_2O$: m.p. 235–40°.

Chloride: *acetyl deriv.*, cryst. from ligroin. M.p. 72·2–72·9°. Sol. EtOH, C_6H_6.

Anilide: m.p. 126·5–127·5°. *Acetyl*, m.p. 106–7°.

p-*Toluidide*: m.p. 124–5°. *Acetyl*, m.p. 116–17°.

Hexamethylenetetramine salt: m.p. 140°. B.p. 180°.

Di-hexamethylenetetramine salt: m.p. 160°.

Tomcsik, *Chem. Abstracts*, 1930, **24**, 4517.
Anschütz, *Ann.*, 1918, **415**, 68.

Phenol-*m*-sulphonic Acid.

Needles $+2H_2O$. $FeCl_3 \longrightarrow$ violet col.

K salt, H_2O : m.p. 200–10°.

Chloride : $C_6H_5O_3ClS$. MW, 192·5. Brown oil. Sol. H_2O, EtOH, Et_2O.

Obermiller, *Ann.*, 1911, **381**, 115.
Szathmary, *Ber.*, 1910, **43**, 2485.

Phenol-*p*-sulphonic Acid.

Et ester : *benzoyl deriv.*, m.p. 62°.

Fluoride : $C_6H_5O_3FS$. MW, 176. M.p. 77°.

Chloride : $C_6H_5O_3ClS$. MW, 192·5. *Acetyl*, m.p. 78°. B.p. 148°/12. *Carbethoxyl*, m.p. 75°. *Benzoyl*, m.p. 115–16°.

Amide : $C_6H_7O_3NS$. MW, 173. Cryst. from EtOH. M.p. 176–7°.

Anilide : m.p. 141°. *Acetyl*, m.p. 126–7°.

Aniline salt : m.p. 112–13°.

p-*Toluidide* : m.p. 151–2°. *Acetyl*, m.p. 98–9°.

Piperidide : m.p. 132–3°. *Acetyl*, m.p. 115–16°.

Hexamethylenetetramine salt : m.p. 180–2°.

Di-hexamethylenetetramine salt : m.p. about 190°.

Major, E.P., 328,220, (*Chem. Abstracts*, 1930, **24**, 5509).
Steinkopf, D.R.P., 497,242, (*Chem. Abstracts*, 1930, **24**, 3517).
Fichter, Tamm, *Ber.*, 1910, **43**, 3036.
Anschütz, Molineus, *Ann.*, 1918, **415**, 56.

Phenol-tricarboxylic Acid.

See 5-Hydroxytrimellitic Acid *and* Hydroxytrimesic Acid.

Phenomydrol.

See Phenacylamine.

Phenoprene.

See 2-Phenylbutadiene-1 : 3.

Phenothioxine.

See Phenoxthine.

Phenoxazine (*Phenazoxine*)

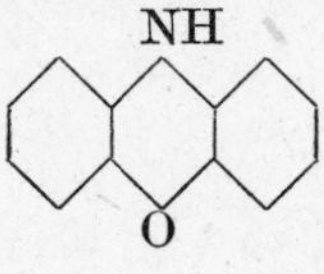

$C_{12}H_9ON$ MW, 183

Leaflets from EtOH. M.p. 156° (153–4°). $FeCl_3 \longrightarrow$ bluish-green col. $H_2SO_4 \longrightarrow$ violet-red col.

Acetyl deriv. : prisms. M.p. 142°.

Cullinane, Davey, Padfield, *J. Chem. Soc.*, 1934, 718.
Kehrmann, Neil, *Ber.*, 1903, **47**, 3107.
Fresenius, *Z. anal. Chem.*, 1934, **96**, 433 (*Review*).

Phenoxthine (*Phenothioxine, dibenzthioxine*)

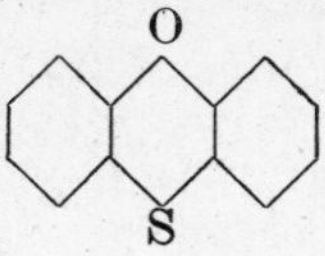

$C_{12}H_8OS$ MW, 200

Cryst. from MeOH. M.p. 59° (57·5–58°). B.p. 185–7°/23 mm. $H_2SO_4 \longrightarrow$ intense violet col.

Suter, McKenzie, Maxwell, *J. Am. Chem. Soc.*, 1936, **58**, 717.
A.G.F.A., D.R.P., 234,743, (*Chem. Abstracts*, 1911, **5**, 2912).
Drew, *J. Chem. Soc.*, 1928, 519.
Ferrario, *Bull. soc. chim.*, 1911, **9**, 536.

Phenoxyacetaldehyde (ω-*Aldehydoanisole, glycollic aldehyde phenyl ether*)

$C_6H_5O{\cdot}CH_2{\cdot}CHO$

$C_8H_8O_2$ MW, 136

Cryst. $+ 1H_2O$. M.p. 38°. B.p. 215° decomp., 118–19°/30 mm., 101–3°/15 mm. Unstable. D_4^{21} 1·1310. n_D^{21} 1·5380.

Oxime : m.p. 95°.

Semicarbazone : m.p. 145°.

Phenylhydrazone : m.p. 86°.

Di-Et acetal : b.p. 257°, 136–8°/16 mm. D_4^{20} 1·0183. n_D^{20} 1·4878.

Rotbart, *Ann. chim.*, 1934, 1, 479.

Phenoxyacetic Acid (*Glycollic acid phenyl ether*)

$C_6H_5O{\cdot}CH_2{\cdot}COOH$

$C_8H_8O_3$ MW, 152

Needles from H_2O. M.p. 98–9°. B.p. 285° decomp. Sol. EtOH, Et_2O, AcOH, C_6H_6, CS_2. $k = 7{\cdot}56 \times 10^{-4}$ at 25°.

o-*Phenylenediamine salt* : m.p. 137°.

m-*Phenylenediamine salt* : m.p. 125–6°.

*Di-*p*-phenylenediamine salt* : m.p. 148–9° decomp.

Me ester : $C_9H_{10}O_3$. MW, 166. B.p. 245°. $D^{17·5}$ 1·150.

Et ester : $C_{10}H_{12}O_3$. MW, 180. B.p. 251°, 145–50°/30 mm. $D^{17·5}$ 1·104.

Phenyl ester : $C_{14}H_{12}O_3$. MW, 228. M.p. 56°. B.p. 320–5°, 236°/73 mm., 185°/30 mm. (196°/13 mm.).

Chloride : $C_8H_7O_2Cl$. MW, 170·5. B.p. 225–6°, 165°/60 mm., 111°/13 mm., 109°/9 mm.

Amide : $C_8H_9O_2N$. MW, 151. Needles from H_2O. M.p. 101·5°.

Anhydride : $C_{16}H_{14}O_5$. MW, 286. Leaflets from Et_2O. M.p. 67–9°.

Nitrile: C_8H_7ON. MW, 133. B.p. 239–40°. $D^{17·5}$ 1·09.

Anilide: m.p. 101·5° (99°).

Monsanto, U.S.P., 1,974,810, (*Chem. Abstracts*, 1934, **28**, 7262).
van Alphen, *Rec. trav. chim.*, 1927, **46**, 144.
Blaise, Picard, *Ann. chim.*, 1912, **26**, 274.

Phenoxyacetone (*Phenyl acetonyl ether, acetol phenyl ether, ω-acetoanisole*)

$C_6H_5O{\cdot}CH_2{\cdot}CO{\cdot}CH_3$

$C_9H_{10}O_2$ MW, 150

Oil. B.p. 229–30°.

Semicarbazone: m.p. 173°.

Guanylhydrazone: m.p. 154.°

St. Wehln, *Ber.*, 1902, **35**, 3553 (*Footnote*).
Stoermer, *Ber.*, 1895, **28**, 1253.

Phenoxyanthraquinone.

See under Hydroxyanthraquinone.

4-Phenoxyazobenzene.

See under 4-Hydroxyazobenzene.

***o*-Phenoxybenzoic Acid** (*Salicylic acid phenyl ether, diphenyl ether 2-carboxylic acid*)

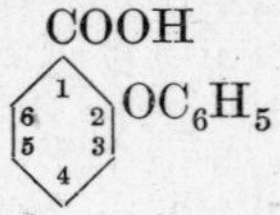

$C_{13}H_{10}O_3$ MW, 214

Leaflets from EtOH.Aq. M.p. 113°. B.p. 355°. Sol. EtOH, Et_2O. Spar. sol. hot H_2O. Dist. ⟶ trace of xanthone.

Me ester: $C_{14}H_{12}O_3$. MW, 228. B.p. 312°.

Et ester: $C_{15}H_{14}O_3$. MW, 242. B.p. above 360°.

Phenyl ester: $C_{19}H_{14}O_3$. MW, 290. Needles from EtOH. M.p. 109°.

Amide: $C_{13}H_{11}O_2N$. MW, 213. Prisms from EtOH. M.p. 131°. Sol. ord. org. solvents.

A.G.F.A., D.R.P., 158,998, (*Chem. Zentr.*, 1905, I, 843).
Ullmann, Zlokasoff, *Ber.*, 1905, **38**, 2117.

***m*-Phenoxybenzoic Acid** (m-*Hydroxybenzoic acid phenyl ether, diphenyl ether 3-carboxylic acid*).

Needles from EtOH.Aq. M.p. 145°. Sol. EtOH, Et_2O. Insol. H_2O.

Griess, *Ber.*, 1888, **21**, 980.

***p*-Phenoxybenzoic Acid** (p-*Hydroxybenzoic acid phenyl ether, diphenyl ether 4-carboxylic acid*).

Prisms from $CHCl_3$. M.p. 159·5°. Sol. EtOH, Et_2O.

Phenyl ester: cryst. from EtOH.Aq. M.p 73–8°. Sol. EtOH, Et_2O, $CHCl_3$, C_6H_6.

Klein, *J. prakt. Chem.*, 1883, **28**, 199.
Griess, *Ber.*, 1888, **21**, 980.
Schönberg, Kraemer, *Ber.*, 1922, **55**, 1190

2-*p*-Phenoxybenzoylbenzoic Acid.

See under 4′-Hydroxybenzophenone-2-carboxylic Acid.

1-Phenoxybutyric Acid

$CH_3{\cdot}CH_2{\cdot}CH(OC_6H_5){\cdot}COOH$

$C_{10}H_{12}O_3$ MW, 18

Needles from H_2O, plates from ligroin M.p. 82–3° (99°). B.p. 258°. Sol. ord. org solvents. $k = 6{\cdot}82 \times 10^{-4}$.

Ag salt: m.p. 202° decomp.

Et ester: $C_{12}H_{16}O_3$. MW, 208. B.p. 250–1° 748 mm., 175–80°/41 mm. Sol. EtOH, Et_2O.

Phenyl ester: $C_{16}H_{16}O_3$. MW, 256. Prism from MeOH. M.p. 48–9°. B.p. 202–3°/25 mm D_{15}^{15} 1·136.

Chloride: $C_{10}H_{11}O_2Cl$. MW, 198·5. B.p 128–31°/38 mm.

Amide: $C_{10}H_{13}O_2N$. MW, 179. M.p. 111 (123°). Sol. Et_2O, Me_2CO, $CHCl_3$, C_6H_6, ho EtOH.

Nitrile: $C_{10}H_{11}ON$. MW, 161. B.p. 228–30°/748 mm. decomp.

Anilide: m.p. 93–4°.

Bischoff, *Ber.*, 1900, **33**, 931; 1901, **34** 1837.

3-Phenoxybutyric Acid

$C_6H_5O{\cdot}CH_2{\cdot}CH_2{\cdot}CH_2{\cdot}COOH$

$C_{10}H_{12}O_3$ MW, 18

Leaflets from ligroin. M.p. 64–5° (60°). Sol EtOH, Et_2O, $CHCl_3$, C_6H_6. Spar. sol. CS_2 ligroin. Insol. H_2O.

Et ester: b.p. 170–3°/25 mm. D_{25}^{33} 1·048. n 1·491.

Amide: leaflets from EtOH.Aq. M.p. 80°.

Nitrile: needles. M.p. 45–6°. B.p. 287–9° 765 mm.

Bentley, Haworth, Perkin, *J. Chem. Soc* 1896, **69**, 168.
Putochin, *Ber.*, 1922, **55**, 2747.
Nair, Peacock, *J. Indian Chem. Soc* 1935, **12**, 318.
Marvel, Tanenbaum, *J. Am. Chem. Soc.* 1922, **44**, 2647.

α-Phenoxydi-1-naphthylmethane.

See under 1 : 1′-Dinaphthylcarbinol.

Phenoxycyclohexane.

See Phenyl cyclohexyl Ether.

Phenoxyethyl Alcohol.
See 2-Hydroxyethyl phenyl Ether.

1-Phenoxyisobutyric Acid

$$\begin{array}{c} CH_3 \\ CH_3 \end{array} > C < \begin{array}{c} OC_6H_5 \\ COOH \end{array}$$

$C_{10}H_{12}O_3$ MW, 180

Needles from H_2O. M.p. 97–8° (98–9°). Sol. EtOH, Et_2O, C_6H_6, $CHCl_3$, AcOH. Mod. sol. hot H_2O. $k = 4.34 \times 10^{-4}$. Volatile in steam.

Et ester : $C_{12}H_{16}O_3$. MW, 208. B.p. 243°, 127°/12 mm.

Phenyl ester : $C_{16}H_{16}O_3$. MW, 256. Needles. M.p. 24–6°. B.p. 194–6°/16 mm.

Chloride : $C_{10}H_{11}O_2Cl$. MW, 198.5. B.p. 112–13°/12.5 mm. (impure).

Amide : $C_{10}H_{13}O_2N$. MW, 179. Needles from EtOH. M.p. 116° (114°).

> Bischoff, *Ber.*, 1900, **33**, 933 ; 1901, **34**, 1837.
> Link, D.R.P., 80,986.
> Gabriel, *Ber.*, 1913, **46**, 1347 (*Footnote*).
> Bargellini, *Gazz. chim. ital.*, 1906, **36**, ii, 334.

1 - Phenoxynaphthalene - 8 - carboxylic Acid.
See under 8-Hydroxy-1-naphthoic Acid.

α-Phenoxyphenylacetic Acid.
See under Mandelic Acid.

1-Phenoxypropionic Acid (*Lactic acid phenyl ether*)

$$CH_3 \cdot CH(OC_6H_5) \cdot COOH$$

$C_9H_{10}O_3$ MW, 166

Needles from H_2O. M.p. 115–16° (112–13°). B.p. 265–6°/758 mm. Sol. EtOH, Et_2O, hot H_2O. $k = 7.75 \times 10^{-4}$. Volatile in steam.

Et ester : $C_{11}H_{14}O_3$. MW, 194. B.p. 243–4°, 160–4°/50 mm., 120–5°/6 mm. $D^{17.5}$ 1.360.

Di-methylaminoethyl ester : $C_{13}H_{19}O_3N$. MW, 237. M.p. 75°. B.p. 116°/0.2 mm. *Picrate* : m.p. 113°. *Picrolonate* : m.p. 148°.

Phenyl ester : $C_{15}H_{14}O_3$. MW, 242. M.p. 52°. B.p. 190°/18 mm. D^{15}_{15} 1.147.

Tropine ester : $C_{17}H_{23}O_3N$. MW, 289. Yellow oil. B.p. 149–50°/0.6 mm. *Picrate* : m.p. 175°. *Picrolonate* : m.p. 200–2°.

Chloride : $C_9H_9O_2Cl$. MW, 184.5. B.p. 146–7°/55 mm., 120°/30 mm., 115°/20 mm., (115–17°/10 mm.).

Amide : $C_9H_{11}O_2N$. MW, 165. Needles from H_2O. M.p. 132–3° (130°). Sol. EtOH, Et_2O, AcOH, CS_2, hot ligroin.

Diphenylamide : m.p. 93°.

Anilide : m.p. 117° (118–19°). B.p. 211–12°/ 14 mm.

Me-anilide : m.p. 57.5°. B.p. 206°/18 mm.

Et-anilide : m.p. 47.5°. B.p. 224–5°/17 mm.

o-*Nitroanilide* : m.p. 88°. B.p. 248°/28 mm.

m-*Nitroanilide* : m.p. 118°.

p-*Nitroanilide* : m.p. 141–2°.

o-*Toluidide* : m.p. 88–90°. B.p. 220–30°/24 mm.

m-*Toluidide* : m.p. 86.5°. B.p. 220°/15 mm.

p-*Toluidide* : m.p. 115°.

Phenylbenzylamide : m.p. 111–12°.

1-*Naphthylamide* : m.p. 131°. B.p. 260°/20 mm.

2-*Naphthylamide* : m.p. 117°.

> Plazek, Rodewald, Krzyzaniak, *Chem. Zentr.*, 1936, I, 1212.
> Fourneau, Sandulesco, *Bull. soc. chim.*, 1922, **31**, 988.

2-Phenoxypropionic Acid (*Hydracrylic acid phenyl ether*)

$$C_6H_5O \cdot CH_2 \cdot CH_2 \cdot COOH$$

$C_9H_{10}O_3$ MW, 166

M.p. 97.5–98°. B.p. 235–45°/771 mm. $k = 5.4 \times 10^{-5}$.

> Powell, *J. Am. Chem. Soc.*, 1923, **45**, 2708.
> Bischoff, *Ber.*, 1900, **33**, 928.

Phenoxypropylene oxide.
See under Glycide.

Phenthiazine.
See Thiodiphenylamine.

Phenuvic Acid (5-*Methyl-2-phenylfuran-3-carboxylic acid*, 5-*methyl-2-phenyl-β-furoic acid*)

$$\begin{array}{c} HC \!\!-\!\!-\!\! C \cdot COOH \\ H_3C \cdot C \qquad C \cdot C_6H_5 \\ O \end{array}$$

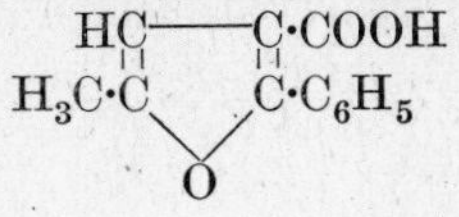

$C_{12}H_{10}O_3$ MW, 202

Needles from EtOH.Aq. M.p. 147–8° (144–5°). Sol. EtOH, C_6H_6, ligroin. Spar. sol. hot H_2O.

Et ester : $C_{14}H_{14}O_3$. MW, 230. Oil. B.p. 193–4°/20 mm.

> Borsche, Fels, *Ber.*, 1906, **39**, 1923, 1927.

Phenylacetaldehyde (α-*Toluic aldehyde*)

$$C_6H_5 \cdot CH_2 \cdot CHO$$

C_8H_8O MW, 120

Cryst. from H_2O. M.p. 33–4°. B.p. 195°, 88°/18 mm., 78°/10 mm. $D^{19.6}_4$ 1.0272. $n^{19.6}_D$ 1.5255. Cold 10% KOH $\longrightarrow$ dimer.

Dimer : amorph. M.p. 50°. Sol. most org. solvents. Depolymerises at 100°.

Cyanhydrin: *see under* α-Hydroxyhydrocinnamic Acid.
Di-Me acetal: oil. B.p. 219–21°/754 mm. D^{18} 1·0042.
Di-Et acetal: b.p. 245–6°.
Oxime: m.p. 98·5°.
Phenylhydrazone: prisms from ligroin. M.p. 62–3°.
Diphenylhydrazone: cryst. from EtOH. M.p. 101–2°.
2 : 4-*Dinitrophenylhydrazone*: golden leaflets from EtOH. M.p. 110°.

Erlenmeyer, Lipp, *Ann.*, 1883, **219**, 182.
Rassow, Burmeister, *J. prakt. Chem.*, 1911, **84**, 487.
Wood, Cowley, *J. Soc. Chem. Ind.*, 1923, **42**, 429T.
Kodama, *Chem. Abstracts*, 1922, **16**, 106.

N-Phenylacetanilide.
See under Diphenylamine.

Phenyl acetate

$CH_3{\cdot}CO{\cdot}OC_6H_5$

$C_8H_8O_2$ MW, 136

B.p. 195·7°. Sol. EtOH, Et_2O, $CHCl_3$. Spar. sol. H_2O. D_4^0 1·0927, D_{15}^{15} 1·0809.

Hoeflake, *Rec. trav. chim.*, 1916, **36**, 30.

N-Phenylacethydrazide.
See Acetylphenylhydrazine.

Phenylacetic Acid (α-*Toluic acid, toluylic acid*)

$C_6H_5{\cdot}CH_2{\cdot}COOH$

$C_8H_8O_2$ MW, 136

Plates from pet. ether. M.p. 76–76·5°. B.p. 265·5°, 144·2–144·8°/12 mm. D_4^{77} 1·091. Sol. EtOH, Et_2O. Spar. sol. cold H_2O. $k = 5{\cdot}56 \times 10^{-5}$ at 25°. Heat of comb. C_v 930·7 Cal.
Me ester: $C_9H_{10}O_2$. MW, 150. B.p. 215°, 131–2°/50 mm. D_0^0 1·0808, D_{16}^{16} 1·0633. n_D^{16} 1·5091.
Et ester: $C_{10}H_{12}O_2$. MW, 164. B.p. 227·1–227·6°, 132–8°/32 mm., 120–5°/17–18 mm. D_4^{20} 1·0333. $n_D^{18·5}$ 1·49921. Used in perfumery.
Propyl ester: $C_{11}H_{14}O_2$. MW, 178. B.p. 238°. D^{18} 1·0142.
Isobutyl ester: $C_{12}H_{16}O_2$. MW, 192. B.p. 247°.
tert.-*Butyl ester*: f.p. − 21°. B.p. 110°/15 mm. D_4^{25} 0·9758. n_D 1·4825.
d-*Amyl ester*: b.p. 265–6°/722·7 mm. D_4^{20} 0·982. n_D^{21} 1·4872. $[\alpha]_D^{22}$ + 4·92°.
l-*Menthyl ester*: liq. B.p. 216°/39 mm., 197°/15 mm., 94–5°/0·25 mm. D_4^{20} 0·9874. $[\alpha]_D^{16·5}$ − 68·15°.
Phenyl ester: $C_{14}H_{12}O_2$. MW, 212. Needles from EtOH.Aq. M.p. 42°. B.p. 158°/7 mm. Sol. EtOH, AcOH, pet. ether. Spar. sol. cold Et_2O. Insol. H_2O.
Benzyl ester: $C_{15}H_{14}O_2$. MW, 226. Oil. B.p. 317–19°, 270°/160 mm., 175–6°/12 mm. D^{17} 1·0938. Sol. EtOH, Et_2O. Spar. sol. cold H_2O.
p-*Nitrobenzyl ester*: m.p. 65°.
p-*Tolyl ester*: m.p. 75–6°.
Fluoride: phenacetyl fluoride. C_8H_7OF. MW, 138. Oil. B.p. 88–9°/17 mm.
Chloride: phenacetyl chloride. C_8H_7OCl. MW, 154·5. Liq. B.p. 170°/250 mm., 104–5°/24 mm., 100°/12 mm. D_4^4 1·1856, D_4^{20} 1·16817.
Bromide: phenacetyl bromide. C_8H_7OBr. MW, 199. B.p. 150–5°/50 mm.
Amide: phenacetamide. C_8H_9ON. MW, 135. Plates or leaflets. M.p. 157°. Sol. EtOH. Spar. sol. H_2O, Et_2O, C_6H_6. N-*Acetyl*: needles from EtOH.Aq. M.p. 129°. N-*Benzoyl*: prisms from C_6H_6, needles from EtOH. M.p. 129–30°.
Methylamide: cryst. from C_6H_6. M.p. 58°. Sol. EtOH, Et_2O, $CHCl_3$. Spar. sol. H_2O, C_6H_6.
Dimethylamide: cryst. M.p. 43·5°. B.p. 155°/10 mm. Sol. H_2O, Et_2O, $CHCl_3$, C_6H_6.
Ethylamide: plates from H_2O. M.p. 73–4°.
Diethylamide: leaflets. M.p. 86°. B.p. 297°.
Dipropylamide: oil. B.p. 183–4°/16 mm.
Nitrile: *see* Benzyl cyanide.
Anhydride: $C_{16}H_{14}O_3$. MW, 254. Needles. M.p. 72°.
Anilide: prisms from EtOH. M.p. 117–18°. Sol. EtOH, Et_2O.
o-*Toluidide*: needles from C_6H_6. M.p. 159°. Sol. EtOH, Me_2CO, $CHCl_3$, C_6H_6. Spar. sol. Et_2O, CS_2, ligroin.
p-*Toluidide*: leaflets from EtOH. M.p. 135–6°. Mod. sol. EtOH, Et_2O.
Hydrazide: needles from H_2O. M.p. 116°. Sol. warm EtOH, H_2O. Mod. sol. hot Et_2O. Reduces warm Fehling's. *B,HCl*: needles. M.p. 215° decomp. Sol. H_2O.

Adams, Thal, *Organic Syntheses*, Collective Vol. I, 265, 427.
Heilbron, Hey, Lythgoe, *J. Chem. Soc.*, 1936, 297.
Sobin, Bachmann, *J. Am. Chem. Soc.*, 1935, **57**, 2458.
Yabroff, Porter, *J. Am. Chem. Soc.*, 1932, **54**, 2453.
Kindler, Giese, Hesse, *Arch. Pharm.*, 1927, **265**, 389.
Wieland, Fischer, *Ann.*, 1925, **446**, 65.
Autenrieth, Thomae, *Ber.*, 1924, **57**, 431.
Adams, Ulich, *J. Am. Chem. Soc.*, 1920, **42**, 599.
Traube, Krahmer, *Ber.*, 1919, **52**, 1296.
Taverne, *Rec. trav. chim.*, 1897, **16**, 34.

1-Phenylacetoacetic Acid

$CH_3·CO·CH(C_6H_5)·COOH$

$C_{10}H_{10}O_3$ MW, 178

Et ester: $C_{12}H_{14}O_3$. MW, 206. Oil. B.p. 145–7°/11 mm. Mod. sol. alkalis. Alc. $FeCl_3$ ⟶ intense violet col.

l-*Menthyl ester*: needles from MeOH. M.p. 69°. B.p. 204–10°/10 mm., 131–3°/0·1 mm. Shows mutarotation.

Nitrile: $C_{10}H_9ON$. MW, 159. Cryst. from EtOH.Aq. or AcOEt–pet. ether. M.p. 90–1°. Very sol. EtOH, Et_2O, $CHCl_3$, C_6H_6. Spar. sol. hot H_2O, pet. ether. Volatile in steam. Alc. $FeCl_3$ ⟶ green col. *Phenylhydrazone*: needles from MeOH. M.p. 114°. *Anil*: leaflets from C_6H_6. M.p. 102–3°.

Anilide: needles from EtOH.Aq. M.p. 97°. Sol. EtOH. Spar. sol. H_2O, Et_2O.

Rupe, *Ann.*, 1913, **398**, 372.
Bodroux, *Bull. soc. chim.*, 1910, **7**, 851.
Beckh, *Ber.*, 1898, **31**, 3161.
Heller, Herrmann, Spielmeyer, *J. prakt. Chem.*, 1928, **120**, 196.

3-Phenylacetoacetic Acid

$C_6H_5·CH_2·CO·CH_2·COOH$

$C_{10}H_{10}O_3$ MW, 178

Et ester: $C_{12}H_{14}O_3$. MW, 206. B.p. 153–5°/9 mm. MeOH + $FeCl_3$ ⟶ deep red col. Tetranitromethane in MeOH ⟶ faint yellowish-green col., without solvent ⟶ reddish-orange col. Does not reduce Fehling's. $NaNO_2$ ⟶ deep blue col.

Cu salt: cryst. from C_6H_6. M.p. 176–8°. Sol. $CHCl_3$. Spar. sol. Et_2O.

Semicarbazone: needles from MeOH.Aq. M.p. 113–16°. Sol. EtOH. Insol. H_2O, Et_2O.

Anil: needles from 75% MeOH. M.p. 96–98·5°. Sol. Et_2O, AcOEt. Spar. sol. cold MeOH, pet. ether, ligroin. Insol. H_2O.

Sonn, Litten, *Ber.*, 1933, **66**, 1512.

Phenylacetol.
See 3-Phenylhydroxyacetone.

Phenylacetone.
See Methyl benzyl Ketone.

Phenylacetonylbenzoylcarbinol (*Acetonebenzil*)

$$\begin{matrix}C_6H_5\\CH_3·CO·CH_2\end{matrix}\!\!>\!C\!<\!\begin{matrix}OH\\CO·C_6H_5\end{matrix}$$

$C_{17}H_{16}O_3$ MW, 268

Prisms from Et_2O. M.p. 78°. Sol. Et_2O, hot EtOH. At 200° ⟶ benzil + acetone. Ox. ⟶ acetic + benzoic acids.

Monoxime: cryst. from EtOH. M.p. 146°. Sol. hot C_6H_6. Mod. sol. Et_2O.

Japp, Miller, *J. Chem. Soc.*, 1885, **47**, 24.

Phenyl acetonyl Ether.
See Phenoxyacetone.

4-Phenyl-1-acetopyrazole (*Acetylphenylpyrazole*)

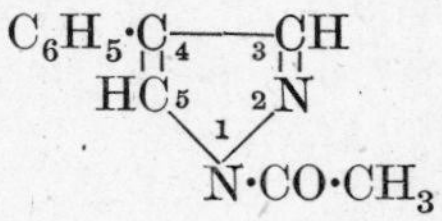

$C_{11}H_{10}ON_2$ MW, 186

Pale yellow needles from MeOH or Et_2O. M.p. 81·5–82·5°. B.p. 159–61°/12 mm. $D_4^{99·9}$ 1·0945. n_D 1·5589.

Auwers, Cauer, *J. prakt. Chem.*, 1930, **126**, 177.

1-Phenyl-3-acetopyrazole (3-*Acetyl*-1-*phenylpyrazole*).

Phenylhydrazone: yellow plates. M.p. 182°.

Diels, Petersen, *Ber.*, 1922, **55**, 3454.

1-Phenyl-4-acetopyrazole (4-*Acetyl*-1-*phenylpyrazole*).

Needles from EtOH.Aq. M.p. 121·5–122·5°. Sol. H_2O.

Oxime: needles from 50% EtOH. M.p. 129–31°. Spar. sol. H_2O.

Phenylhydrazone: needles from EtOH. M.p. 142–4° decomp.

Balbiano, *Gazz. chim. ital.*, 1889, **19**, 197.

***N*-Phenylaceturic Acid.**
See under Phenylglycine.

Phenylacetylacetone (3-*Phenylpentandione*-2 : 4)

$$\begin{matrix}C_6H_5\\CH_3·CO\end{matrix}\!\!>\!CH·CO·CH_3$$

$C_{11}H_{12}O_2$ MW, 176

Oil with odour of pine shavings. M.p. 58–60°. B.p. 127–8°/15 mm. $FeCl_3$ ⟶ purple col.

Cu salt: dark green cryst. Decomp. at 222–4°. Sol. usual org. solvents.

Morgan, Drew, Porter, *Ber.*, 1925, **58**, 333.

Phenylacetylcarbinol (*Methyl α-hydroxybenzyl ketone*, 1-*hydroxy*-1-*phenylacetone*)

$CH_3·CO·CH(OH)·C_6H_5$

$C_9H_{10}O_2$ MW, 150

Yellowish oil. B.p. 205–7°, 135–7°/24 mm., 140–5°/11 mm. Misc. with most org. solvents. Reduces $NH_3.AgNO_3$ and Fehling's.

Acetyl: pale yellow oil. B.p. 165–70°/40 mm.
Oxime: needles from H_2O. M.p. 112–15°.

Semicarbazone: powder from toluene. M.p. 194°. Sol. boiling AcOH. Spar. sol. other solvents.

2 : 4-*Dinitrophenylhydrazone*: orange needles from EtOH. M.p. 170°.

Note: phenylacetylcarbinol is tautomeric (keto-carbinol tautomerism) with methylbenzoylcarbinol (β-hydroxypropiophenone).

Hey, *J. Chem. Soc.*, 1930, 1232.
Meerwein, Hinz, *Ann.*, 1930, **484**, 1.
Favorskiĭ, Tennikova, *Compt. rend.*, 1934, **198**, 1998.
Freudenberg, *Biochem. Z.*, 1932, **245**, 238.
Roger, *Biochem. Z.*, 1931, **230**, 320.
Kotchergine, *Bull. soc. chim.*, 1928, **43**, 573.

Phenylacetyl-carbinol.
See 3-Phenylhydroxyacetone.

Phenylacetylene (*Acetylenylbenzene, ethinylbenzene*)

$C_6H_5{\cdot}C{\vdots}CH$

C_8H_6 MW, 102

Oil. F.p. − 45°. B.p. 142–4°, 49–50°/14 mm. $D_4^{12\cdot5}$ 0·9371. $n_D^{17\cdot4}$ 1·5501. Heat of comb. C_v 1024·5 Cal.

Vaughn, *J. Am. Chem. Soc.*, 1934, **56**, 2064.
Hessler, *Organic Syntheses*, Collective Vol. I, 428.

Phenylacetylene dichloride.
See αβ-Dichlorostyrene.

Phenylacetylglycine.
See Phenaceturic Acid.

2-Phenylacetyl-propionic Acid.
See 4-Phenyl-levulinic Acid.

5-Phenylacridine (ms-*Phenylacridine*)

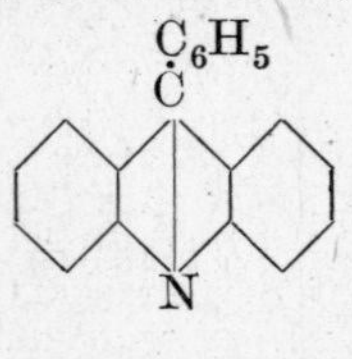

$C_{19}H_{13}N$ MW, 255

Pale yellow leaflets from EtOH. M.p. 184° (181°). B.p. 403–4°. Sol. C_6H_6. Mod. sol. Et_2O. Spar. sol. EtOH. Insol. H_2O. Sol. conc. H_2SO_4. Sols. in acids show green fluor. Sublimes in leaflets. Triboluminescent.

Picrate: cryst. from EtOH. M.p. 227·7°.

Dipicrate: cryst. from EtOH. M.p. 185–6°.

Methohydroxide: plates from C_6H_6. M.p. 140°. Sol. Et_2O, $CHCl_3$, C_6H_6, pet. ether. Insol. H_2O. Sol. acids.

Methochloride: cryst. + $2H_2O$. Decomp. a 225–6°. Very sol. H_2O, EtOH, $CHCl_3$, Py $PhNO_2$. Insol. Et_2O, CCl_4.

Methobromide: greenish-yellow cryst. + H_2O Decomp. at 230°. Sol. H_2O. Mod. sol. EtOH $CHCl_3$, Py, $PhNO_2$, aniline.

Methiodide: black prisms from EtOH. So EtOH, $CHCl_3$, Py, $PhNO_2$. Less sol. H_2O Me_2CO, C_6H_6. Insol. Et_2O, CCl_4.

Methonitrate: yellow needles. Decomp. a 288°. Sol. EtOH, $CHCl_3$.

Ethohydroxide: cryst. from toluene. M.p 136–7°. Sol. Et_2O, Me_2CO, $CHCl_3$.

Ethiodide: dark red needles from H_2O. M.p 223° decomp.

Ethopicrate: yellow needles from EtOH M.p. 181°.

Phenohydroxide: prisms from ligroin. M.p 178°. Sol. Et_2O, EtOH, C_6H_6, hot ligroin Conc. H_2SO_4 ⟶ yellow sol. with intense gree fluor.

Ullmann, Maag, *Ber.*, 1907, **40**, 2520.
Schmid, Decker, *Ber.*, 1906, **39**, 937.
Kaufmann, Albertini, *Ber.*, 1909, **4** 2008.
Bernthsen, *Ann.*, 1884, **224**, 13.
Ullmann, *Ann.*, 1907, **355**, 319.

4-Phenylacridinic Acid.
See 4-Phenylquinoline-2 : 3-dicarboxylic Aci

***N*-Phenylacridone**

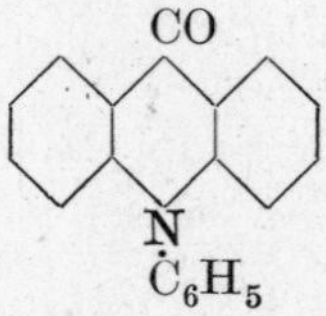

$C_{19}H_{13}ON$ MW, 27

Yellow cryst. from toluene. M.p. 276°. So boiling C_6H_6, amyl alcohol, toluene with yello col. Mod. sol. AcOH with intense blue fluor Spar. sol. MeOH, EtOH. Insol. Et_2O, ligroin Conc. H_2SO_4 ⟶ yellow sol. with intense gree fluor.

Goldberg, Nimcrovsky, *Ber.*, 1907, **4** 2450.

2-Phenylacrolein.
See Cinnamaldehyde.

1-Phenylacrylic Acid.
See Atropic Acid.

2-Phenylacrylic Acid.
See Cinnamic Acid.

1-Phenyladipic Acid (1-*Phenylbutane*-1 : 4-*dicarboxylic acid*)

$$C_6H_5\cdot CH\cdot COOH$$
$$[CH_2]_2$$
$$CH_2\cdot COOH$$

$C_{12}H_{14}O_4$ MW, 222

Cryst. from C_6H_6–Et_2O. M.p. 132–3°.

Case, *J. Am. Chem. Soc.*, 1933, **55**, 2927.

2-Phenyladipic Acid (2-*Phenylbutane*-1 : 4-*dicarboxylic acid*)

$$CH_2\cdot COOH$$
$$C_6H_5\cdot CH$$
$$CH_2$$
$$CH_2\cdot COOH$$

$C_{12}H_{14}O_4$ MW, 222

Plates from C_6H_6–Et_2O. M.p. 148°. Sol. EtOH, Me_2CO, Et_2O. Insol. H_2O.

Di-Et ester: $C_{16}H_{21}O_4$. MW, 277. B.p. 197–200°/10 mm.

v. Braun, Weissbach, *Ber.*, 1931, **64**, 1785.
Planske, *J. Am. Chem. Soc.*, 1931, **53** 1104.

Phenylalanine.
See Aminohydrocinnamic Acid *and* Anilinopropionic Acid.

Phenylaldehydoacetic Acid.
See Phenylformylacetic Acid.

1-Phenylallyl Alcohol (*Vinylphenylcarbinol*, *α-hydroxyallylbenzene*)

$$C_6H_5\cdot CH(OH)\cdot CH{:}CH_2$$

$C_9H_{10}O$ MW, 134

Mobile oil. B.p. 214°/760 mm., 114°/25 mm., 106°/18 mm., 90–2°/11 mm. Decolourises $KMnO_4$. $O_3 \longrightarrow$ mandelic acid + formic acid. Sweet taste. Odourless.

Et ether: $C_{11}H_{14}O$. MW, 162. Oil. B.p. 203–5°/755 mm. Fruity odour.

Benzoyl: mobile oil. B.p. 182°/12 mm.

p-*Nitrobenzoyl*: leaflets from EtOH. M.p. 48°.

Klages, Klenk, *Ber.*, 1906, **39**, 2553.
Rupe, Müller, *Helv. Chim. Acta*, 1921, **4**, 846.
Moureu, Gallagher, *Bull. soc. chim.*, 1921, **29**, 1009.
Meisenheimer, Schmidt, *Ann.*, 1929, **475**, 178.

3-Phenylallyl Alcohol.
See Cinnamyl Alcohol.

Phenylallylamine.
See Allylaniline.

2-Phenylallylcarbinol (2-*Phenyl*-1-*butenol*-4)

$$CH_2{:}C(C_6H_5)\cdot CH_2\cdot CH_2OH$$

$C_{10}H_{12}O$ MW, 148

B.p. 123°/10 mm. D^{20} 1·0272. n_D^{20} 1·5577.

St. Pfau, Plattner, *Helv. Chim. Acta*, 1932, **15**, 1266.

Phenylallylene.
See Methylphenylacetylene.

Phenyl *o*-aminobenzyl Ether.
See under o-Aminobenzyl Alcohol.

***N*-Phenyl-1-amino-8-naphthol-4-sulphonic Acid** (*Phenyl-S acid*, 8-*anilino*-1-*naphthol-5-sulphonic acid*)

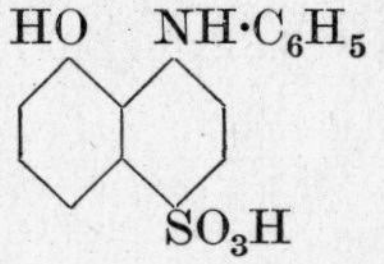

$C_{16}H_{13}O_4NS$ MW, 315

Cryst. Intermediate for azo dyes.

Acid Na salt: needles. Mod. sol. H_2O.

Neutral Na salt: cryst. Mod. sol. cold H_2O.

Bayer, D.R.P., 181,929, (*Chem. Zentr.*, 1907, I, 1653).

***N*-Phenyl-2-amino-5-naphthol-7-sulphonic Acid** (*Phenyl-J acid*, 2-*anilino*-5-*naphthol*-7-*sulphonic acid*, 6-*anilino*-1-*naphthol*-3-*sulphonic acid*)

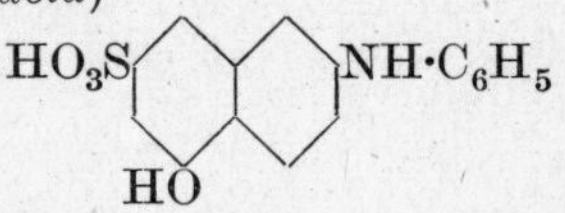

$C_{16}H_{13}O_4NS$ MW, 315

Cryst. Spar. sol. H_2O, EtOH, cold dil. acids. Conc. $H_2SO_4 \longrightarrow$ green sol. Dil. $Na_2CO_3 \longrightarrow$ sol. with violet fluor. Important intermediate for azo dyes.

Leonhardt, D.R.P., 114,248, (*Chem. Zentr.*, 1900, II, 997).
Badische, D.R.P., 122,570, (*Chem. Zentr.*, 1901, II, 670).
Bucherer, Stohmann, *J. prakt. Chem.*, 1905, **71**, 451.

***N*-Phenyl-2-amino-8-naphthol-6-sulphonic Acid** (*Phenyl-gamma acid*, 2-*anilino*-8-*naphthol*-6-*sulphonic acid*, 7-*anilino*-1-*naphthol*-3-*sulphonic acid*)

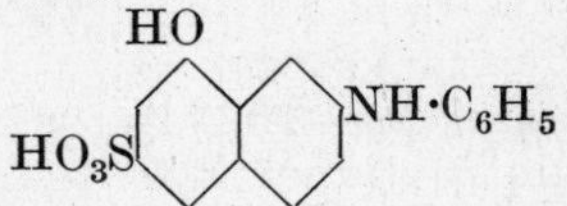

$C_{16}H_{13}O_4NS$ MW, 315

Needles or leaflets. Sol. 35 parts hot, 300 parts cold H_2O. Intermediate for azo dyes.

Ba salt : leaflets. Mod. sol. H_2O.

See last two references above and also Cassella, D.R.P., 79,014.

Levinstein, D.R.P., 99,339, (*Chem. Zentr.*, 1899, I, 160).

Phenyl-aminonaphthyl-methane.

See 4-Benzyl-1-naphthylamine.

1-Phenyl-*n*-amyl Alcohol (*1-Phenyl-pentanol-1*, *butylphenylcarbinol*, *α-hydroxy-*n*-amylbenzene*)

$CH_3{\cdot}CH_2{\cdot}CH_2{\cdot}CH_2{\cdot}CH(C_6H_5)OH$

$C_{11}H_{16}O$ MW, 164

B.p. 137°/21 mm., 132°/14 mm., 121–2°/15 mm.

Urethane : m.p. 75°.

Levene, Mikeska, *J. Biol. Chem.*, 1926, **70**, 355.

Fourneau, Montaigne, Puyal, *Chem. Abstracts*, 1922, **16**, 240.

Roblin, Davidson, Bogert, *J. Am. Chem. Soc.*, 1935, **57**, 155.

3-Phenyl-*n*-amyl Alcohol (*3-Phenyl-pentanol-1*)

$CH_3{\cdot}CH_2{\cdot}CH(C_6H_5){\cdot}CH_2{\cdot}CH_2OH$

$C_{11}H_{16}O$ MW, 164

l-.

B.p. 135–8°/20 mm., 118°/1 mm. $[\alpha]_D^{25}$ − 2·69°.

Levene, Marker, *J. Biol. Chem.*, 1935, **110**, 333.

Lévy, *Compt. rend.*, 1933, **197**, 773.

4-Phenyl-*n*-amyl Alcohol (*4-Phenyl-pentanol-1*)

$CH_3{\cdot}CH(C_6H_5){\cdot}CH_2{\cdot}CH_2{\cdot}CH_2OH$

$C_{11}H_{16}O$ MW, 164

l-.

B.p. 109°/1 mm. $[\alpha]_D^{25}$ — 0·90°.

Levene, Marker, *J. Biol. Chem.*, 1935, **110**, 339.

5-Phenyl-*n*-amyl Alcohol (*5-Phenyl-pentanol-1*, *ω-hydroxy-*n*-amylbenzene*)

$C_6H_5{\cdot}CH_2{\cdot}CH_2{\cdot}CH_2{\cdot}CH_2{\cdot}CH_2OH$

$C_{11}H_{16}O$ MW, 164

B.p. 155°/20 mm., 151°/13 mm.

Phenyl ether : $C_{17}H_{20}O$. MW, 240. Viscous liq. B.p. 198°/14 mm.

Acetyl : b.p. 155°/12 mm.

v. Braun, *Ber.*, 1911, **44**, 2872.

Roblin, Davidson, Bogert, *J. Am. Chem. Soc.*, 1935, **57**, 155.

1-Phenyl-*sec.*-*n*-amyl Alcohol.

See Propylbenzylcarbinol.

2-Phenyl-*sec.*-*n*-amyl Alcohol.

See Methylpropylphenylcarbinol.

5-Phenyl-*sec.*-*n*-amyl Alcohol (*5-Phenyl-pentanol-2*, *δ-hydroxy-*n*-amylbenzene*, *1-phenyl-pentanol-4*)

$C_6H_5{\cdot}CH_2{\cdot}CH_2{\cdot}CH_2{\cdot}CH(OH){\cdot}CH_3$

$C_{11}H_{16}O$ MW, 164

B.p. 134–5°/16 mm. D_4^{25} 0·9643. n_{5875}^{25} 1·51110

Phenylurethane : needles from pet. ether M.p. 57°.

Roblin, Davidson, Bogert, *J. Am. Chem. Soc.*, 1935, **57**, 151.

2-Phenyl-*active*-amyl Alcohol (*2-Methyl-2-phenylbutanol-1*)

$$CH_3{\cdot}CH_2{\cdot}\overset{\displaystyle CH_3}{\underset{\displaystyle C_6H_5}{C}}{\cdot}CH_2OH$$

$C_{11}H_{16}O$ MW, 164

Oil. B.p. 246°, 138°/23 mm.

Benzoyl : cryst. M.p. 46°. B.p. 202–4°/12 mm.

Blondeau, *Compt. rend.*, 1922, **174**, 1424.

3-Phenyl-*active*-amyl Alcohol (*2-Methyl-3-phenylbutanol-1*)

$$CH_3{\cdot}\overset{\displaystyle C_6H_5}{CH}{\cdot}\underset{\displaystyle CH_3}{CH}{\cdot}CH_2OH$$

$C_{11}H_{16}O$ MW, 164

Oil with odour of roses. B.p. 132–3°/13 mm.

Braun *et al.*, *Ann.*, 1927, **451**, 48.

2-Phenylamylamine

$CH_3{\cdot}CH_2{\cdot}CH_2{\cdot}CH(C_6H_5){\cdot}CH_2NH_2$

$C_{11}H_{17}N$ MW, 163

l-.

Liq. B.p. 90°/3 mm.

Levene, Marker, *J. Biol. Chem.*, 1931, **93**, 773.

5-Phenyl-*n*-amylamine (*ω-Amino-*n*-amylbenzene*)

$C_6H_5{\cdot}CH_2{\cdot}CH_2{\cdot}CH_2{\cdot}CH_2{\cdot}CH_2NH_2$

$C_{11}H_{17}N$ MW, 163

Liq. B.p. 131°/15 mm.

N-*Di-Me* : $C_{13}H_{21}N$. MW, 191. B.p. 134–5°/18 mm.

N-*Et* : $C_{13}H_{21}N$. MW, 191. B.p. 295°.

B,HCl : m.p. 144°.

N-*Amyl*: $C_{16}H_{27}N$. MW, 233. B.p. 310°. *B,HCl*: cryst. from H_2O or EtOH. M.p. 184–6°.

N-*Cyclohexyl*: $C_{17}H_{28}N$. MW, 246. B.p. 315°. *B,HCl*: m.p. 246°.

Benzoyl: needles from Et_2O–ligroin. M.p. 60°. B.p. 273–5°/15 mm.

B_2,H_2PtCl_6: leaflets from H_2O. M.p. 220°.

Picrate: cryst. from Et_2O. M.p. 152–3°. Sol. EtOH.

Methiodide: leaflets from H_2O. M.p. 181°. Very sol. $CHCl_3$. Spar. sol. H_2O, EtOH.

Methochloroplatinate: light red cryst. from H_2O. M.p. 219°.

Skita, Wulff, *Ann.*, 1927, **455**, 40.
v. Braun, *Ber.*, 1910, **43**, 2849.
Merck, D.R.P., 238,959, (*Chem. Zentr.*, 1911, II, 1284).

Phenylamylene.
See Phenylpentene.

***N*-Phenylanisidine.**
See under 2- and 4-Hydroxydiphenylamines.

1-Phenylanthracene

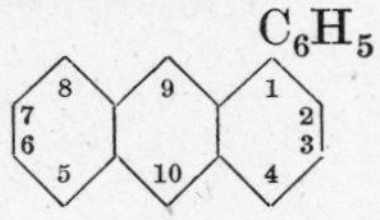

$C_{20}H_{14}$ MW, 254

Yellow prisms from EtOH. M.p. 110–12°. Sol. usual solvents.

Cook, *J. Chem. Soc.*, 1930, 1091.

2-Phenylanthracene.
Pale yellow leaflets from AcOEt. M.p. 207–207·5°. Spar. sol. most solvents.

See previous reference.

9-Phenylanthracene (ms-*Phenylanthracene*).
Leaflets from EtOH. M.p. 152–3°. B.p. 417°. Sol. warm EtOH, Et_2O, $CHCl_3$, CS_2, $CHCl_3$. Sols. show blue fluor.

Baeyer, *Ann.*, 1880, **202**, 61.
Linebarger, *Am. Chem. J.*, 1891, **13**, 554.
Guyot, Catel, *Compt. rend.*, 1905, **140**, 1462.

***N*-Phenylanthranil**

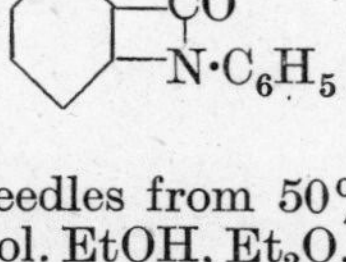

$C_{13}H_9ON$ MW, 195

Pale yellow needles from 50% EtOH. M.p. 169° decomp. Sol. EtOH, Et_2O, Me_2CO, AcOEt, C_6H_6. Spar. sol. H_2O. Sols. show greenish-blue fluor.

B,HCl: pale yellow needles. M.p. 169° decomp.

B,$HgCl_2$: golden-yellow leaflets. M.p. 225–32° decomp.

Drechsler, *Monatsh.*, 1914, **35**, 533.

Phenylanthranilic Acid.
See Diphenylamine-2-carboxylic Acid.

1-Phenylanthraquinone

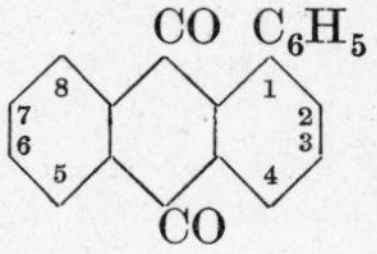

$C_{20}H_{12}O_2$ MW, 284

Yellow needles from AcOH. M.p. 176–8°.

Allen, Overbaugh, *J. Am. Chem. Soc.*, 1935, **57**, 740.

2-Phenylanthraquinone.
Pale yellow needles from MeOH. M.p. 162–5° (160–1°). Sol. AcOH, CCl_4. Mod. sol. EtOH, Et_2O, $CHCl_3$, Me_2CO, CS_2, C_6H_6. Alc. KOH ⟶ red col. Conc. H_2SO_4 ⟶ red col.

Scholl, Neovius, *Ber.*, 1911, **44**, 1079.
Groggins, *Ind. Eng. Chem.*, 1930, **22**, 620.

Phenyl 1-anthraquinonyl Ketone (1-*Benzoylanthraquinone*)

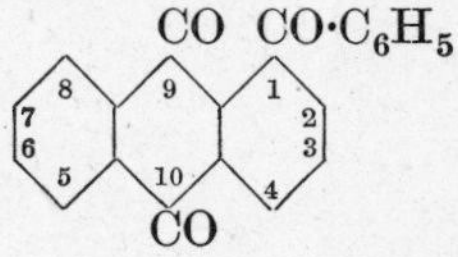

$C_{21}H_{12}O_3$ MW, 312

Yellowish cryst. powder from AcOH. M.p. 229° (225–7°). Sol. conc. H_2SO_4 with pale yellow col.

1-*Oxime*: yellow rhombic leaflets. Decomp. about 218°.

9-*Oxime*: *syn.*, yellow rhombic cryst. Decomp. about 210°. *Anti.*: yellow needles or leaflets. M.p. 230°.

Scholl, Müller, Stix, *Ber.*, 1935, **68**, 801.
Scholl *et al.*, *Ann.*, 1934, **512**, 1.
I.G., D.R.P., 487,254, (*Chem. Abstracts*, 1930, **24**, 2147).
Schaarschmidt, *Ber.*, 1915, **48**, 837.

Phenylarsen-dibromide.
See Phenyldibromoarsine.

Phenylarsen-dichloride.
See Phenyldichloroarsine.

Phenylarsine (*Arsinobenzene*)

$C_6H_5{\cdot}AsH_2$

C_6H_7As MW, 154

Oil. B.p. 148°, 93°/70 mm., 77°/33 mm., 55°/14 mm., 36°/2 mm. Sol. EtOH, Et_2O. In air ⟶ phenylarsinic acid.

As-*Di-Me*: $C_8H_{11}As$. MW, 182. Liq. B.p. 200°. Sol. EtOH, C_6H_6. Insol. H_2O. *Methiodide*: prisms from EtOH. M.p. 248·5° (244°). *Methochloroplatinate*: red plates from hot H_2O. M.p. 219° decomp.

As-*Di-Et*: $C_{10}H_{15}As$. MW, 210. B.p. 240°. *Methiodide*: prisms from EtOH–Et_2O. M.p. 122° (77°). *Ethiodide*: prisms from H_2O. M.p. 112–13°. Sol. EtOH. Insol. Et_2O.

As-*Et*·*Propyl*: $C_{11}H_{17}As$. MW, 224. B.p. 245°.

As-*Phenyl*: *see* Diphenylarsine.

As-*Diphenyl*: *see* Triphenylarsine.

Palmer, Dehn, *Ber.*, 1901, **34**, 3598.
Fichter, Elkind, *Ber.*, 1916, **49**, 245.
Winmill, *J. Chem. Soc.*, 1912, **101**, 719.
Michaelis, Link, *Ann.*, 1881, **201**, 205.
La Coste, Michaelis, *Ann.*, 1880, **201**, 212.

Phenylarsinic Acid (*Phenylarsonic acid*)

$$C_6H_5\cdot \underset{\ddot{O}}{As}(OH)_2$$

$C_6H_7O_3As$ MW, 202

Cryst. from H_2O. M.p. 158–62° decomp. Above m.p. ⟶ anhydride. 3·25 parts sol. 100 parts H_2O at 28°, 24 parts at 84°. Very stable to ox. agents.

Anhydride: amorph. Decomp. on heating.

Di-Me ester: $C_8H_{11}O_3As$. MW, 230. B.p. 188°/95 mm. D^{23} 1·3946. Decomp. by H_2O.

Di-Et ester: $C_{10}H_{15}O_3As$. MW, 258. B.p. 168–70°/15 mm. D^{15} 1·318.

Dichloride: $C_6H_5OCl_2As$. MW, 239. Cryst. M.p. about 100°. Sol. H_2O with decomp.

La Coste, Michaelis, *Ann.*, 1880, **201**, 203.
Michaelis, Loesner, *Ber.*, 1884, **27**, 265.
Michaelis, *Ann.*, 1902, **320**, 293.
Bullard, Dickey, *Organic Syntheses*, 1935, XV, 59.

Phenylarsonic Acid.
See Phenylarsinic Acid.

***N*-Phenylaspartic anil.**
See Anilinosuccinanil.

Phenylaticonic Acid (*Iso-γ-phenylitaconic acid*)

$$\begin{array}{c} C_6H_5\cdot CH \\ \| \\ HOOC\cdot C\cdot CH_2\cdot COOH \end{array}$$

$C_{11}H_{10}O_4$ MW, 206

Prisms from Et_2O. M.p. 149–51° (not sharp). Sol. 15 parts Et_2O, 90 parts H_2O at ord. temps. Spar. sol. $CHCl_3$. Insol. CS_2, ligroin. Sunlight ⟶ phenylitaconic acid. Heat in vacuo at 160–75° ⟶ anhydride. $KMnO_4$ ⟶ benzaldehyde + malonic acid + oxalic acid.

Anhydride: needles from Et_2O–$CHCl_3$. M.p. 138–40°. Sol. $CHCl_3$, C_6H_6. Spar. sol. Et_2O.

Stobbe, Horn, *Ber.*, 1908, **41**, 3983.
Stobbe, *Ber.*, 1908, **41**, 4353.
Fittig, Brooke, *Ann.*, 1899, **305**, 33.

Phenyl azide (*Azidobenzene, diazobenzolimide, phenylazoimide, triazobenzene*)

$$C_6H_5\cdot N\!<\!\begin{array}{c}N\\ \|\\ N\end{array} \quad \text{or} \quad C_6H_5\cdot N{:}N{:}N$$

$C_6H_5N_3$ MW, 119

Pale yellow oil. B.p. 73·5°/22–4 mm., 59°/14 mm. Mod. sol. EtOH, Et_2O. Insol. H_2O. D_0^4 1·12399, D^{10} 1·0980, D^{25} 1·0853. n_D^{11} 1·56104. Possesses aromatic ammoniacal odour. Explodes on dist. at ord. press., or by treatment with conc. H_2SO_4. Volatile in steam. Strongly antipyretic. $N_2H_4\cdot H_2O$ ⟶ C_6H_6 + NH_3 + N. NaHg + EtOH ⟶ hydrazobenzene. Zn + H_2SO_4 ⟶ C_6H_6 + NH_3 + N. Dil. H_2SO_4 ⟶ *p*-aminophenol. Na + EtOH ⟶ aniline + N. Long heating with conc. HCl ⟶ *o*- and *p*-chloroanilines.

Dimroth, *Ber.*, 1902, **35**, 1032 (*Note*).

1-Phenylbarbituric Acid

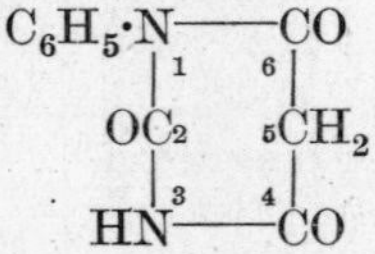

$C_{10}H_8O_3N_2$ MW, 204

Cryst. from EtOH. M.p. 262°.

Macbeth, Nunan, Traill, *J. Chem. Soc.*, 1926, 1252.

5-Phenylbarbituric Acid.
M.p. 258° (250°, 206°).

Lund, *Chem. Zentr.*, 1936, I, 2096.
Bayer, D.R.P., 249,722, (*Chem. Zentr.*, 1912, II, 652).

***p*-Phenylbenzaldehyde.**
See 4-Aldehydodiphenyl.

1-Phenylbenzanthrone

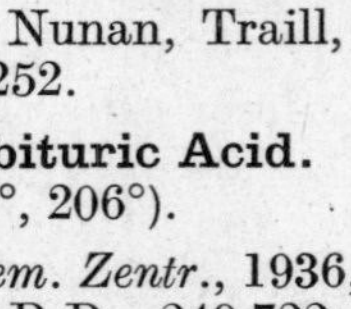

$C_{23}H_{14}O$ MW, 306

M.p. 186°. Sol. conc. H_2SO_4 with orange-red l. showing strong fluor. $Na_2Cr_2O_7 \longrightarrow$ anthra-inone-1-carboxylic acid.

Clar, *Ber.*, 1932, **65**, 858.
I.G., E.P., 286,685, (*Chem. Abstracts*, 1929, **23**, 1139).
Nakanishi, *Chem. Abstracts*, 1934, **28**, 763.

2-Phenylbenzanthrone.

Yellow needles from AcOH. M.p. 199–200°. l. H_2SO_4 to red sol. changing to orange-red.

I.G., E.P., 297,129, (*Chem. Abstracts*, 1929, **23**, 2580).

3-Phenylbenzanthrone.

Yellow needles from AcOH. M.p. 182–3° 81°). Ox. $\longrightarrow$ phenyl 1-anthraquinonyl tone.

Allen, Overbaugh, *J. Am. Chem. Soc.*, 1935, **57**, 1323.
Nakanishi, *Chem. Abstracts*, 1934, **28**, 763.
I.G., D.R.P., 488,607, (*Chem. Abstracts*, 1930, **24**, 2148); E.P., 297,129, (*Chem. Abstracts*, 1929, **23**, 2580).

6-Phenylbenzanthrone.

M.p. 186°. Alk. $KMnO_4 \longrightarrow$ 4-phenylanthra-inone-1-carboxylic acid.

Allen, Overbaugh, *J. Am. Chem. Soc.*, 1935, **57**, 743.

10-Phenylbenzanthrone.

Golden-yellow or yellowish-brown leaflets from H_6 or Py.Aq. M.p. 178–9° (170–1°). Very l. C_6H_6, CS_2, Py. Mod. sol. AcOH. Spar. l. EtOH. Very spar. sol. pet. ether. Sol. nc. H_2SO_4 with red col. showing golden-yellow ıor.

Scholl, Seer, *Ann.*, 1912, **394**, 150.
Schmidlin, Garcia-Banùs, *Ber.*, 1912, **45**, 3184.

Phenylbenzene.

See Diphenyl.

Phenylbenzhydrylcarbinol.

See 2-Hydroxy-1 : 1 : 2-triphenylethane.

Phenyl benzhydryl Ketone.

See Diphenylbenzoylmethane.

2-Phenylbenzil

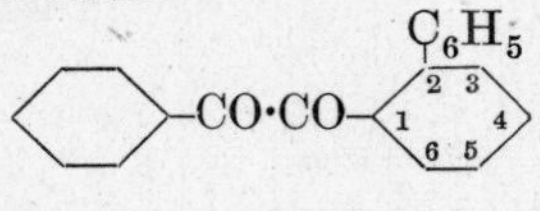

$_{20}H_{14}O_2$ MW, 286

Yellow plates from EtOH. M.p. 80°. Ox. $\rightarrow$ diphenyl-2-carboxylic acid.

Quinoxaline deriv.: m.p. 163°.

Kohler, Nygaard, *J. Am. Chem. Soc.*, 1930, **52**, 4137.

4-Phenylbenzil.

Yellow plates from EtOH. M.p. 105°.

Hatt, Pilgrim, Hurran, *J. Chem. Soc.*, 1936, 94.
Gomberg, Natta, *J. Am. Chem. Soc.*, 1929, **51**, 2244.

1-Phenylbenziminazole

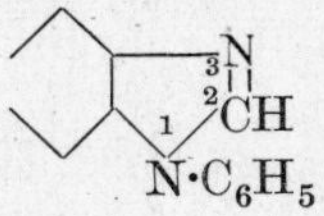

$C_{13}H_{10}N_2$ MW, 194

Needles from ligroin. M.p. 98°. Sol. MeOH, EtOH. Spar. sol. H_2O.

B,HCl,HgCl₂: cryst. from EtOH.Aq. M.p. 145–146·5°.

Fischer, Rigaud, *Ber.*, 1901, **34**, 4204.
Phillips, *J. Chem. Soc.*, 1929, 2823.

2-Phenylbenziminazole.

Plates from AcOH, needles from H_2O. M.p. 291° (280°, 285°). Sol. AcOH. Mod. sol. EtOH. Spar. sol. H_2O, $CHCl_3$, C_6H_6. Forms metallic derivs. with silver and mercury.

B,HCl: needles from EtOH. M.p. 303° (above 306°).

Feigl, Gleich, *Monatsh.*, 1928, **49**, 394.
Fischer, Mann-Tiechler, *J. prakt. Chem.*, 1924, **107**, 45.
Guha, Ray, *J. Indian Chem. Soc.*, 1925, **2**, 93.
Hinsberg, Koller, *J. prakt. Chem.*, 1896, **29**, 1498.

Phenyl benzoate

$C_6H_5{\cdot}CO{\cdot}OC_6H_5$

$C_{13}H_{10}O_2$ MW, 198

Prisms. M.p. 71°. B.p. 314° (299°). Sol. hot EtOH, hot Et_2O. Insol. H_2O. Heat of comb. C_p 1511·3 Cal.

Rasinski, *J. prakt. Chem.*, 1882, **26**, 62.
Reychler, *Chem. Zentr.*, 1908, I, 1042.
Czapek, *Monatsh.*, 1914, **35**, 637.

Phenylbenzoic Acid.

See Diphenyl-carboxylic Acid.

α-Phenylbenzoin.

See Diphenylbenzoylcarbinol.

2-Phenylbenzophenone (*2-Benzoyldiphenyl, phenyl o-xenyl ketone*)

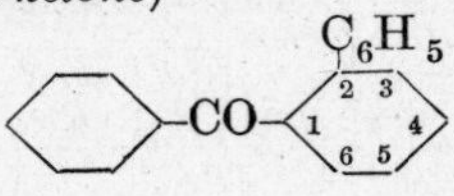

$C_{19}H_{14}O$ MW, 258

Cryst. from ligroin. M.p. 90°.

Schlenk, Bergmann *et al.*, *Ann.*, 1928, **464**, 34.

4-Phenylbenzophenone (4-*Benzoyldiphenyl, phenyl* p-*xenyl ketone*).

Cryst. from EtOH. M.p. 102° (106°). B.p. 419–20°/744 mm. Sol. Et_2O, $CHCl_3$, C_6H_6, hot EtOH. $CrO_3 \longrightarrow$ *p*-benzoylbenzoic acid.

Oxime: needles from EtOH. M.p. 193–4°. Sol. EtOH, Et_2O.

Nenitzescu, Isacescu, Ionescu, *Ann.*, 1931, **491**, 217.
Hey, Jackson, *J. Chem. Soc.*, 1936, 805.
Staudinger, Kon, *Ann.*, 1911, **384**, 97.
Wolf, *Ber.*, 1881, **14**, 2032.

Phenylbenzoylacetic Acid (2-*Keto*-1 : 2-*diphenylpropionic acid*)

$$\begin{array}{c} C_6H_5 \\ | \\ C_6H_5\cdot CO\cdot CH\cdot COOH \end{array}$$

$C_{15}H_{12}O_3$ MW, 240

Free acid unknown.

Me ester: $C_{16}H_{14}O_3$. MW, 254. Liq. Decomp. on dist. $\longrightarrow$ stilbene.

Et ester: $C_{17}H_{16}O_3$. MW, 268. Prisms. M.p. 90°. Very sol. EtOH, Et_2O, C_6H_6.

l-*Menthyl ester*: (i) *keto form*, needles from MeOH. M.p. 116°. Sol. Et_2O, C_6H_6. Spar. sol. cold EtOH. $[\alpha]_D^{20}$ + 21·10° in C_6H_6, − 12·1° in EtOH. Et_2O sol. + $FeCl_3 \longrightarrow$ deep red col. (ii) *Enol form*: $[\alpha]_D^{20}$ − 62·83° in C_6H_6, − 62·6° in EtOH.

Amide: $C_{15}H_{13}O_2N$. MW, 239. Needles from EtOH. M.p. 178°. Sol. EtOH. Spar. sol. Et_2O, hot H_2O.

Nitrile: $C_{15}H_{11}ON$. MW, 221. Plates from AcOH. M.p. 93–4°. Very sol. EtOH, Et_2O, C_6H_6, hot pet. ether. Alk. hyd. $\longrightarrow$ benzoic acid + benzyl cyanide. Conc. H_2SO_4 at 120° $\longrightarrow$ amide. Conc. HCl at 150° $\longrightarrow$ deoxybenzoin. Boiling dil. acids $\longrightarrow$ benzoic + phenylacetic acids.

Anilide: needles from EtOH. M.p. 168–9°.

Oxime: cryst. M.p. 138–9°.

Rupe, Gisiger, *Helv. Chim. Acta*, 1925, **8**, 349.
Ghosh, *J. Chem. Soc.*, 1916, **109**, 117.
Walther, Schickler, *J. prakt. Chem.*, 1897, **55**, 314.

3-Phenyl-1-benzoylbutyric Acid

$$\begin{array}{r} CO\cdot C_6H_5 \\ | \quad\quad \\ C_6H_5\cdot CH_2\cdot CH_2\cdot CH\cdot COOH \end{array}$$

$C_{17}H_{16}O_3$ MW, 268

Free acid not isolated.

Et ester: $C_{19}H_{20}O_3$. MW, 296. B.p. 225–30°/11 mm.

Auwers, Möller, *J. prakt. Chem.*, 192[illegible], **109**, 150.

1-Phenyl-2-benzoylbutyric Acid

$$\begin{array}{c} C_6H_5\cdot CO\ \ C_6H_5 \\ | \quad\quad | \\ CH_3\cdot CH\cdot CH\cdot COOH \end{array}$$

$C_{17}H_{16}O_3$ MW, 26[illegible]

Exists in two forms. (i) Needles from $CHCl_3$–ligroin. M.p. 145°. Sol. EtOH, Et_2O, $CHCl_3$, C_6H_6. Insol. ligroin. (ii) Needles from $CHCl_3$–ligroin. M.p. 131°. Sol. EtOH, Et_2O, $CHCl_3$. Spar. sol. ligroin, cold H_2O.

Me ester: $C_{18}H_{18}O_3$. MW, 282. Exists i[n] two forms. (i) Plates from MeOH. M.p. 105°. (ii) M.p. 87°.

Reimer, Reynolds, *Am. Chem. J.*, 191[illegible], **48**, 216, 218.

3-Phenyl-2-benzoylbutyric Acid

$$\begin{array}{c} CO\cdot C_6H_5 \\ | \quad\quad \\ C_6H_5\cdot CH_2\cdot CH\cdot CH_2\cdot COOH \end{array}$$

$C_{17}H_{16}O_3$ MW, 26[illegible]

Needles from C_6H_6–ligroin. M.p. 100–1°.

Borsche, *Ber.*, 1914, **47**, 1114.

2-Phenyl-3-benzoylbutyric Acid (β-*Phen*[illegible]*acylhydrocinnamic acid*)

$$\begin{array}{c} C_6H_5 \\ | \\ C_6H_5\cdot CO\cdot CH_2\cdot CH\cdot CH_2\cdot COOH \end{array}$$

$C_{17}H_{16}O_3$ MW, 26[illegible]

Needles or plates from H_2O, prisms fro[m] AcOH. M.p. 160° (152–153·5°). Sol. EtOH, AcOH. Spar. sol. Et_2O. Hot $Ac_2O \longrightarrow$ lacton[e].

Me ester: $C_{18}H_{18}O_3$. MW, 282. Needle[s]. M.p. 94°.

Et ester: $C_{19}H_{20}O_3$. MW, 296. M.p. 59–61°.

Lactone: $C_{17}H_{14}O_2$. MW, 250. Needles. So[l.] Et_2O. Hot alc. NaOH regenerates the acid.

Oxime: m.p. 144–145·5°.

Semicarbazone: cryst. from 90% EtOH. M.p. 220° (212·5–213°).

Stobbe, *Ber.*, 1901, **34**, 655.
Vorländer, Knötzsch, *Ann.*, 1897, **29**[illegible], 332.
Kohler, Steele, *J. Am. Chem. Soc.*, 191[illegible], **41**, 1103.
Qudrat-i-Khuda, *J. Indian Chem. Soc*[.], 1931, **8**, 220.

3-Phenyl-3-benzoylbutyric Acid (*2-Desylpropionic acid*)

$$C_6H_5{\cdot}CO{\cdot}\overset{C_6H_5}{CH}{\cdot}CH_2{\cdot}CH_2{\cdot}COOH$$

$C_{17}H_{16}O_3$ MW, 268

Needles from EtOH. M.p. 136° (133–4°). Sol. EtOH, AcOH. Insol. H_2O.

Me ester: needles. M.p. 63–4°.

Et ester: needles. M.p. 33–4°.

Knoevenagel, *Ber.*, 1888, **21**, 1351.
Meerwein, *J. prakt. Chem.*, 1918, **97**, 261.

Phenylbenzoyldiazomethane.
See Azibenzil.

2-Phenyl-1-benzoylisobutyric Acid (*Methylbenzylbenzoylacetic acid, 1-benzyl-1-benzoylpropionic acid*)

$$\begin{matrix}CH_3\\C_6H_5{\cdot}CH_2\end{matrix}\!>C<\!\begin{matrix}CO{\cdot}C_6H_5\\COOH\end{matrix}$$

$C_{17}H_{16}O_3$ MW, 268

Free acid not isolated.

Et ester: $C_{19}H_{20}O_3$. MW, 296. Oil. B.p. 223–8°/19 mm.

Hope, Perkin, *J. Chem. Soc.*, 1909, **95**, 2046.

2-Phenyl-2-benzoylisobutyric Acid (*1-Desylpropionic acid*)

$$\begin{matrix}C_6H_5\\C_6H_5{\cdot}CO\end{matrix}\!>CH{\cdot}CH<\!\begin{matrix}CH_3\\COOH\end{matrix}$$

$C_{17}H_{16}O_3$ MW, 268

Needles from EtOH. M.p. 220° (213·5°). Insol. H_2O.

Knoevenagel, *Ber.*, 1888, **21**, 1353.
Japp, Michie, *J. Chem. Soc.*, 1903, **83**, 299.

2-Phenyl-2′-benzoylisobutyric Acid (*α-Phenacylhydrocinnamic acid, 1-benzyl-2-benzoylpropionic acid*)

$$\begin{matrix}C_6H_5{\cdot}CO{\cdot}CH_2\\C_6H_5{\cdot}CH_2\end{matrix}\!>CH{\cdot}COOH$$

$C_{17}H_{16}O_3$ MW, 268

Needles from MeOH. M.p. 176° (169·5°). Sol. EtOH, $CHCl_3$, AcOH. Mod. sol. MeOH. Spar. sol. Et_2O. Insol. H_2O, pet. ether. Sublimes.

Me ester: $C_{18}H_{18}O_3$. MW, 282. Prisms from MeOH. M.p. 68·5°.

Thiele, Mayr, *Ann.*, 1899, **306**, 186.
Klobb, *Bull. soc. chim.*, 1897, **17**, 411.
Kohler, *Ber.*, 1905, **38**, 1206.

2-Phenyl-1-benzoylpropionic Acid (*Benzylbenzoylacetic acid, α-benzoylhydrocinnamic acid*)

$$\begin{matrix}C_6H_5{\cdot}CO\\C_6H_5{\cdot}CH_2\end{matrix}\!>CH{\cdot}COOH$$

$C_{16}H_{14}O_3$ MW, 254

Me ester: $C_{17}H_{16}O_3$. MW, 268. B.p. 250–55°/50 mm.

Et ester: $C_{18}H_{18}O_3$. MW, 282. B.p. 265–70°/80 mm., 218–20°/12 mm.

l-*Menthyl ester*: needles. M.p. 117°. $[\alpha]_D^{20}$ − 60·83° in C_6H_6.

Perkin, Calman, *J. Chem. Soc.*, 1886, **49**, 155.
Perkin, Stenhouse, *J. Chem. Soc.*, 1891, **59**, 1006.
Jacobson, Ghosh, *J. Chem. Soc.*, 1915, **107**, 961.

1-Phenyl-2-benzoylpropionic Acid (*Phenylphenacylacetic acid*)

$$C_6H_5{\cdot}CO{\cdot}CH_2{\cdot}\overset{C_6H_5}{CH}{\cdot}COOH$$

$C_{16}H_{14}O_3$ MW, 254

d-.

Plates from Et_2O. M.p. 176–8°. $[\alpha]_D$ + 157·3° in AcOEt.

Semicarbazone: needles from MeOH. M.p. 107–10°, resolidifying on further heating, melting again above 160°.

l-.

Plates from Et_2O. M.p. 176–8°. $[\alpha]_D^{16}$ − 157·6° in AcOEt.

dl-.

Prisms from EtOH. M.p. 153° (160°). Sol. EtOH, Et_2O, $CHCl_3$, C_6H_6. Spar. sol. hot H_2O.

Me ester: cryst. from MeOH. M.p. 104°.

Et ester: needles. M.p. 37–8°.

Amide: $C_{16}H_{15}O_2N$. MW, 253. Needles from EtOH. M.p. 149°.

Nitrile: $C_{16}H_{13}ON$. MW, 235. Plates from EtOH. M.p. 127·5°. Sol. EtOH, Et_2O, $CHCl_3$.

Oxime: plates + 1 mol. C_6H_6 from C_6H_6. M.p. 83–7°.

Semicarbazone: cryst. powder from EtOH. M.p. 189–91°.

Lapworth, Wechsler, *J. Chem. Soc.*, 1910, **97**, 41.
Allen, Kimball, *Organic Syntheses*, 1930, X, 80.
Hann, Lapworth, *J. Chem. Soc.*, 1904, **85**, 1368.
Rupe, Schneider, *Ber.*, 1895, **28**, 962.

2-Phenyl-2-benzoylpropionic Acid (β-*Benzoylhydrocinnamic acid, desylacetic acid*)

$$\begin{matrix} C_6H_5 \\ C_6H_5{\cdot}CO{\cdot}CH{\cdot}CH_2{\cdot}COOH \end{matrix}$$

$C_{16}H_{14}O_3$ MW, 254

Cryst. from EtOH. M.p. 162°. Fuming HI ⟶ 2 : 3-diphenylbutyric acid. NaHg ⟶ 2 : 3-diphenyl-3-butyrolactone.

Me ester : $C_{17}H_{16}O_3$. MW, 268. Cryst. from MeOH. M.p. 49°.

Thiele, Straus, *Ann.*, 1901, **319**, 164.
Anschütz, Walter, *Ann.*, 1907, **354**, 147.

2-Phenyl-γ-benzpyrone.
See Flavone.

2-Phenylbenzthiazole

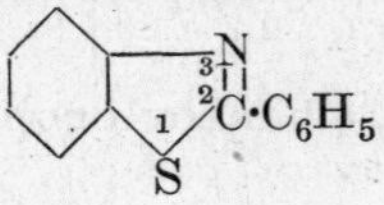

$C_{13}H_9NS$ MW, 211

Needles from EtOH.Aq. M.p. 114°.
Methiodide : m.p. 218°.
Methopicrate : orange-yellow plates. M.p. 125–6°.
Methoperchlorate : needles. M.p. 220°.
Methochloroplatinate : m.p. 243° decomp.
Dibromide : m.p. 119°.
Tetrabromide : m.p. 134–6°.
Hexabromide : m.p. 156° decomp.
$C_{13}H_9NS,C_6H_3(NO_2)_3$-1 : 3 : 5 : yellow needles. M.p. 106°.

Chandri, Desai, Hunter, *J. Indian Chem. Soc.*, 1934, **11**, 252.
Hunter, *J. Chem. Soc.*, 1930, 138.
Clark, *J. Chem. Soc.*, 1928, 2316.
Chapman, *ibid.*, 1894.
Bogert, Abrahamson, *J. Am. Chem. Soc.*, 1922, **44**, 831.

Phenylbenzylacetic Acid.
See 1 : 2-Diphenylpropionic Acid.

Phenylbenzyl Alcohol.
See Hydroxymethyl-diphenyl.

Phenylbenzylamine.
See Benzylaniline.

Phenylbenzylcarbinol (α-*Hydroxydibenzyl, 1-hydroxy-1 : 2-diphenylethane*)

$$C_6H_5{\cdot}CH_2{\cdot}CH(OH){\cdot}C_6H_5$$

$C_{14}H_{14}O$ MW, 198

Needles from EtOH.Aq. or AcOH. M.p. 67–8° (62°). B.p. 167–70°/10 mm. Dist. at ord. press. ⟶ stilbene. HNO_3 (D 1·3) ⟶ deoxybenzoin. H (+ Ni) at 360° ⟶ dibenzyl.

Et ether : α-ethoxydibenzyl. $C_{16}H_{18}O$. MW, 226. B.p. 149–51°/10 mm. Hot dil. H_2SO_4 ⟶ stilbene.

Schmidlin, Garcia-Banùs, *Ber.*, 1912, **45**, 3199.
Marshall, *J. Chem. Soc.*, 1915, **107**, 520.
Limpricht, Schwanert, *Ann.*, 1870, **155**, 62.

Phenyl benzyl Diketone (*Benzoylphenacetyl, phenylbenzylglyoxal,* 1 : 3-*diphenylpropandione*-1 : 2, 1 : 2-*diketo*-1 : 3-*diphenylpropane*)

$$C_6H_5{\cdot}\underset{\beta}{C}O{\cdot}\underset{\alpha}{C}O{\cdot}CH_2{\cdot}C_6H_5$$

or

$$C_6H_5{\cdot}CO{\cdot}C(OH){:}CH{\cdot}C_6H_5$$

$C_{15}H_{12}O_2$ MW, 224

Three modifications have been described :
(i) Yellow needles. M.p. 67°.
(ii) Yellowish-white cryst. M.p. 90°.
(iii) Lemon-yellow needles. M.p. 35–6°. B.p. 191–2°/15 mm.

(i) and (ii) are probably stereoisomers of the enolic form. (iii) is the ketonic form.

Readily oxidised in air.

α-Oxime : ω-isonitroso-ω-benzylacetophenone. Plates from C_6H_6. M.p. 126°. Sol. alkalis with yellow col.

Dioxime : phenylbenzylglyoxime. Plates from AcOH. M.p. 207°.

Di-phenylhydrazone : m.p. 131°.

Wieland, *Ber.*, 1903, **36**, 3018.
Widman, *Ber.*, 1916, **49**, 484.
Jorländer, *Ber.*, 1917, **50**, 416.
Moureu, *Ann. chim.*, 1930, **14**, 301.
Kohler, Barnes, *J. Am. Chem. Soc.*, 1934, **56**, 211.

Phenyl benzyl Ether

$$C_6H_5{\cdot}CH_2{\cdot}O{\cdot}C_6H_5$$

$C_{13}H_{12}O$ MW, 184

Leaflets from EtOH. M.p. 40°. B.p. 286–7°, 178–9°/35 mm., 124–5°/4 mm. Conc. HCl at 100° ⟶ phenol + benzyl chloride.

van Duzee, Adkins, *J. Am. Chem. Soc.*, 1935, **57**, 148.
Baw, *J. Indian Chem. Soc.*, 1926, **3**, 103
Powell, Adams, *J. Am. Chem. Soc.*, 1920, **42**, 656.

***sym*.-Phenylbenzylethylene.**
See 1 : 3-Diphenylpropylene.

Phenylbenzylglycollic Acid.
See 1 : 2-Diphenyl-lactic Acid.

Phenylbenzylglyoxal.
See Phenyl benzyl Diketone.
Phenylbenzylglyoxime.
See under Phenyl benzyl Diketone.
***sym*.-Phenylbenzylhydrazine** (β-*Benzylphenylhydrazine*)

$$C_6H_5{\cdot}CH_2{\cdot}NH{\cdot}NH{\cdot}C_6H_5$$

$C_{13}H_{14}N_2$ MW, 198

Colourless cryst. M.p. 35°. B.p. about 290° decomp. Very sol. prac. all org. solvents. Oxidises in air to benzaldehyde phenylhydrazone.

B,HCl: leaflets from H_2O. M.p. 205° (193–5°). Spar. sol. EtOH, cold H_2O. Insol. Et_2O.

B,(COOH)$_2$: m.p. 190°.

Ponzio, Valente, *Gazz. chim. ital.*, 1908, 38, i, 525.
Schlenk, *J. prakt. Chem.*, 1908, **78,** 51.

***unsym*.-Phenylbenzylhydrazine** (α-*Benzylphenylhydrazine*)

$$\begin{matrix} C_6H_5 \\ C_6H_5{\cdot}CH_2 \end{matrix}\!\!>N{\cdot}NH_2$$

$C_{13}H_{14}N_2$ MW, 198

Colourless oil. B.p. 216–18°/38 mm., 207–8°/10 mm. Part. decomp. on standing.

B,HCl: needles from H_2O. M.p. 170° (166–7°).

d-*Camphor*-β-*sulphonic acid salt*: prisms from AcOEt–Et_2O. M.p. 156–7°.

Methochloride: prisms. M.p. 158–9° decomp. Very sol. H_2O, EtOH. Insol. Et_2O, C_6H_6. *B,AuCl$_3$*: yellow prisms from dil. HCl. M.p. 134° decomp. *B$_2$,PtCl$_4$*: orange needles from dil. HCl. M.p. 162° decomp.

Methiodide: cryst. from EtOH. M.p. 122° decomp. *B$_2$,HgI$_2$*: prisms from MeOH. M.p. 135–6° decomp. *B,HgI$_2$*: yellow prisms from EtOH. M.p. 128–9° decomp.

Ofner, *Monatsh.*, 1904, **25**, 599.
Milrath, *Monatsh.*, 1908, **29**, 910 (*Footnote* 2).
Ruff, Ollendorff, *Ber.*, 1899, **32**, 3235 (*Footnote* 2).
Ponzio, Valente, *Gazz. chim. ital.*, 1908, **38**, i, 520.
Michaelis, Philips, *Ann.*, 1889, **252**, 286.
Singh, *J. Chem. Soc.*, 1914, **105**, 1976.

Phenylbenzylideneacetone.
See Acetostilbene *and* Benzyl styryl Ketone.
Phenylbenzylidenelactic Acid.
See 1-Hydroxy-2 : 3-diphenylvinylacetic Acid.
Phenyl benzyl Ketone.
See Deoxybenzoin.

Phenylbenzylnitrosamine.
See under Benzylaniline.
Phenyl benzyl sulphide.
See under Benzyl Mercaptan.
***sym*.-Phenylbenzylurea**

$$C_6H_5{\cdot}\underset{4}{CH_2}{\cdot}\underset{3}{NH}{\cdot}\underset{2}{CO}{\cdot}\underset{1}{NH}{\cdot}C_6H_5$$

$C_{14}H_{14}ON_2$ MW, 226

Needles from EtOH. M.p. 170° (168°). Sol. EtOH. Insol. H_2O.

1-N-*Me*: $C_{15}H_{16}ON_2$. MW, 240. M.p. 84°. Sol. EtOH, AcOH, C_6H_6.

Ley, Krafft, *Ber.*, 1907, **40**, 703.
Thiele, Pickard, *Ann.*, 1899, **309**, 203.
Kühn, Riesenfeld, *Ber.*, 1891, **24**, 3817.

ω-Phenylbiuret (*Allophanic acid anilide, 1-phenylbiuret, allophanylaniline*)

$$C_6H_5{\cdot}NH{\cdot}CO{\cdot}NH{\cdot}CO{\cdot}NH_2$$

$C_8H_9O_2N_3$ MW, 179

Cryst. from EtOH.Aq. M.p. 167° (various m.p.'s between 156–65° are recorded, due to decomp. on melting). Sol. EtOH. Insol. Et_2O. Does not give biuret reaction. Heat ⟶ NH_3 + cyanuric acid + carbanilide. Heat with aniline ⟶ carbanilide.

Davis, Blanchard, *J. Am. Chem. Soc.*, 1929, **51**, 1809.
Dains, Wertheim, *J. Am. Chem. Soc.*, 1920, **42**, 2307.
Gatewood, *J. Am. Chem. Soc.*, 1925, **47**, 410.
Blair, *J. Am. Chem. Soc.*, 1934, **56**, 904.

***ms*.-Phenylbiuret** (3-*Phenylbiuret, dicarbamylaniline*)

$$C_6H_5{\cdot}N\!\!<\!\begin{matrix} CONH_2 \\ CONH_2 \end{matrix}$$

$C_8H_9O_2N_3$ MW, 179

Needles or prisms from hot H_2O. M.p. 192°. Very sol. EtOH, boiling H_2O. Heat with aniline ⟶ carbanilide. KOH + a little $CuSO_4$ ⟶ reddish-violet col.

See last reference above and also
Schiff, *Ann.*, 1907, **352**, 78.
Weith, *Ber.*, 1877, **10**, 1744.

Phenylboric Acid

$$C_6H_5B(OH)_2$$

$C_6H_7O_2B$ MW, 122

Needles from H_2O. M.p. 221° (216°). Sol. EtOH, Et_2O, hot H_2O. Volatile in steam.

Chlorine water ⟶ chlorobenzene. H_2O_2 ⟶ phenol. Boiling conc. HCl ⟶ benzene.

Ainley, Challenger, *J. Chem. Soc.*, 1930, 2171.
Seaman, Johnson, *J. Am. Chem. Soc.*, 1931, **53**, 713.
Bean, Johnson, *J. Am. Chem. Soc.*, 1932, **54**, 4417.
Krause, Nitsche, *Ber.*, 1922, **55**, 1264.
Krause, D.R.P., 371,467, (*Chem. Abstracts*, 1924, **18**, 992).

Phenylbromoacetic Acid.
See α-Bromophenylacetic Acid.

Phenyl ω-bromobenzyl Ketone.
See Desyl bromide.

4-Phenyl-1 : 2-butadiene (1-*Benzylallene*)

$C_6H_5{\cdot}CH_2{\cdot}CH{:}C{:}CH_2$

$C_{10}H_{10}$ MW, 130

B.p. 72–3°/17 mm. D_4^{20} 0·9220. n_D^{20} 1·5460.

Carothers, Berchet, *J. Am. Chem. Soc.*, 1933, **55**, 2816.

1-Phenyl-1 : 3-butadiene (1-*Phenylerythrene*)

$CH_2{:}CH{\cdot}CH{:}CH{\cdot}C_6H_5$

$C_{10}H_{10}$ MW, 130

Cis :
B.p. 86°/11 mm. n^{28} 1·5950.
Trans :
B.p. 76°/11 mm. n^{28} 1·5920.

Muskat, Herrmann, *J. Am. Chem. Soc.*, 1931, **53**, 266.
Bergmann, Bondi, *Ber.*, 1931, **64**, 1479.

2-Phenyl-1 : 3-butadiene (2-*Phenylerythrene, phenoprene*)

$CH_2{:}CH{\cdot}C(C_6H_5){:}CH_2$

$C_{10}H_{10}$ MW, 130

B.p. 60–1°/17 mm. D_4^{20} 0·9226. n_D^{20} 1·5489.
Dimer : needles from MeOH. M.p. 62°. B.p. 220–5°/10 mm.

Carothers, Berchet, *J. Am. Chem. Soc.*, 1933, **55**, 2816.

4-Phenyl-1 : 3-butadiene-1-carboxylic Acid.
See 2-Styrylacrylic Acid.

4-Phenyl-1 : 3-butadiene-1 : 1-dicarboxylic Acid.
See Cinnamylidenemalonic Acid.

Phenylbutandiol.
See Phenylbutylene Glycol *and* Phenyltetramethylene Glycol.

Phenylbutane.
See Butylbenzene.

Phenylbutenol.
See Methylstyrylcarbinol, 2-Phenylallylcarbinol, Propenylphenylcarbinol, *and* Allylphenylcarbinol.

1-Phenylbutine-1 (1-*Ethyl-2-phenylacetylene*)

$CH_3{\cdot}CH_2{\cdot}C{\vdots}C{\cdot}C_6H_5$

$C_{10}H_{10}$ MW, 13

B.p. 201–3°, 87–90°/18 mm. D^{18} 0·915. n 1·537.

Truchet, *Ann. chim.*, 1931, **16**, 397.
Morgan, *J. Chem. Soc.*, 1876, **29**, 162.
Bergmann, Bondi, *Ber.*, 1933, **66**, 286.

4-Phenylbutine-1 (β-*Phenethylacetylene*)

$C_6H_5{\cdot}CH_2{\cdot}CH_2{\cdot}C{\vdots}CH$

$C_{10}H_{10}$ MW, 13

B.p. 189–91°/758 mm., 83°/15 mm. D_4^0 0·928 D_4^{14} 0·918. n_D^{20} 1·5212. Heat of comb. C_v 1340· Cal.

André, *Bull. soc. chim.*, 1911, **9**, 193.
Moureu, André, *Ann. chim.*, 1914, **1**, 116
Bert, Dorier, Lamy, *Compt. rend.*, 1925 **181**, 555.

1-Phenyl-*n*-butyl Alcohol.
See Propylphenylcarbinol.

2-Phenyl-*n*-butyl Alcohol (α-*Hydroxymethylpropylbenzene*)

$CH_3{\cdot}CH_2{\cdot}CH(C_6H_5){\cdot}CH_2OH$

$C_{10}H_{14}O$ MW, 15

dl-.
B.p. 124–7°/25 mm., 120–1°/15 mm. D 0·989. n_D^{16} 1·43.
Benzoyl : m.p. 115–16°. B.p. 202–3°/18 mm
Phenylurethane : m.p. 58–9°.

d-.
$[\alpha]_D^{25}$ + 1·8°, $[\alpha]_D^{30}$ + 2·54° (+ 1·11°).

Lagerev, *Chem. Zentr.*, 1935, II, 2809.
Levene, Marker, *J. Biol. Chem.*, 1935 **108**, 415.
Rampart, Amagat, *Ann. chim.*, 1927, 8 284.

3-Phenyl-*n*-butyl Alcohol

$CH_3{\cdot}CH(C_6H_5){\cdot}CH_2{\cdot}CH_2OH$

$C_{10}H_{14}O$ MW, 15

l-.
B.p. 117°/8 mm. D_4^{25} 0·986. n_D^{25} 1·5201 $[\alpha]_D^{25}$ − 9·15° ($[\alpha]_D^{30}$ − 2·89°).

dl-.

B.p. 138–40°/33 mm., 125·5–128°/13 mm., 110–11°/6 mm. D_D^{20} 0·9834.

Levene, Marker, *J. Biol. Chem.*, 1931, **93**, 762; 1935, **108**, 413.
Wojcik, Adkins, *J. Am. Chem. Soc.*, 1933, **55**, 4943.
Rupe, van Walraven, *Helv. Chim. Acta*, 1930, **13**, 369.

4-Phenyl-*n*-butyl Alcohol (δ-*Hydroxybutylbenzene*)

$C_6H_5 \cdot CH_2 \cdot CH_2 \cdot CH_2 \cdot CH_2OH$

$C_{10}H_{14}O$ MW, 150

Oil. B.p. 140°/14 mm. Insol. H_2O. D_4^{20} 1·001.
Me ether: $C_{11}H_{16}O$. MW, 164. B.p. 108°/11 mm.
Nitrite: $C_6H_5 \cdot [CH_2]_4 \cdot O \cdot NO$. B.p. 125–30°/15 mm.
p-*Nitrobenzoyl*: m.p. 18–20°.
Phenylurethane: m.p. 51–2°.

Kirner, *J. Am. Chem. Soc.*, 1926, **48**, 1112.
v. Braun, *Ber.*, 1911, **44**, 2871.
v. Braun, Deutsch, *Ber.*, 1912, **45**, 2176.

2-Phenyl-*sec*.-*n*-butyl Alcohol.
See Methylethylphenylcarbinol.

4-Phenyl-*sec*.-*n*-butyl Alcohol (γ-*Hydroxybutylbenzene, methyl-β-phenylethylcarbinol*)

$C_6H_5 \cdot CH_2 \cdot CH_2 \cdot CH(OH) \cdot CH_3$

$C_{10}H_{14}O$ MW, 150

d-.

B.p. 132°/14 mm. D_4^{20} 0·9788. n_D^{20} 1·5168. Volatile in steam.
Formyl: b.p. 120°/15 mm. D_4^{20} 1·0083.
Acetyl: b.p. 130°/15 mm. D_4^{20} 0·9854.
Propionyl: b.p. 141°/16 mm. D_4^{20} 0·9790.

l-.

B.p. 132°/14 mm. n_D^{20} 1·5168. $[\alpha]_D^{20}$ − 19·45° in EtOH. Volatile in steam.

dl-.

Oil with aromatic odour. B.p. 238°/750 mm., 123–4°/15 mm. $D_4^{16\cdot5}$ 0·9899. $n_D^{16\cdot5}$ 1·517.
Acetyl: b.p. 123–4°/15 mm. D_4^{16} 0·991. n_D^{16} 1·4895.
Phenylurethane: m.p. 116–17° (113°).

Hewitt, Kenyon, *J. Chem. Soc.*, 1925, **127**, 1094.
Zechmeister, Rom, *Ann.*, 1929, **468**, 126.
Schlenk, Bergmann, *Ann.*, 1930, **479**, 73.
Packendorff, *Ber.*, 1934, **67**, 906.
Pickard, Kenyon, *J. Chem. Soc.*, 1914, **105**, 1125.

Phenyl-*tert*.-butyl Alcohol.
See Dimethylbenzylcarbinol.

1- *and* 4-Phenylbutylamines.
See Aminobutylbenzene.

2-Phenyl-*n*-butylamine

$$CH_3 \cdot CH_2 \cdot \underset{}{\overset{C_6H_5}{\overset{|}{C}}}H \cdot CH_2NH_2$$

$C_{10}H_{15}N$ MW, 149

B.p. 110°/13 mm.
B,HCl: cryst. from Et_2O. M.p. 156°.

Rampart, Amagat, *Ann. chim.*, 1927, **8**, 285.

1-Phenyl-1-butylene (α-*Butenylbenzene*)

$CH_3 \cdot CH_2 \cdot CH\vdots CH \cdot C_6H_5$

$C_{10}H_{12}$ MW, 132

B.p. 190–3° (186–7°), 89–90°/15 mm., 78°/12 mm., 70–1°/8 mm. D_4^{20} 0·9106. n_D^{16} 1·5381. Na + EtOH ⟶ butylbenzene.
Nitrosite: m.p. 124°.
Dibromide: m.p. 70°.

Auwers, Roth, Eisenlohr, *Ann.*, 1910, **373**, 282.
Klages, *Ber.*, 1904, **37**, 2312.
Lévy, Dvoleitzka-Gombinska, *Bull. soc. chim.*, 1931, **49**, 1769.
For *cis-* and *trans-* forms see
Muskat, Knapp, *Ber.*, 1931, **64**, 785.

4-Phenyl-1-butylene (γ-*Butenylbenzene*)

$C_6H_5 \cdot CH_2 \cdot CH_2 \cdot CH\vdots CH_2$

$C_{10}H_{12}$ MW, 132

B.p. 177–8°/754 mm., 64°/10 mm. D_4^{20} 0·8831. n_D^{20} 1·5059. Heat of comb. C_v 1356·8 Cal. $KMnO_4$ in Me_2CO ⟶ hydrocinnamic acid.

André, *Bull. soc. chim.*, 1911, **9**, 193.
Riiber, *Ber.*, 1911, **44**, 2392.
Gilman, McGlumphy, *Bull. soc. chim.*, 1928, **43**, 1326.

1-Phenyl-2-butylene (β-*Butenylbenzene, crotonylbenzene*)

$CH_3 \cdot CH\vdots CH \cdot CH_2 \cdot C_6H_5$

$C_{10}H_{12}$ MW, 132

Oily liq. B.p. 176°, 81–2°/21 mm., 70°/12 mm. D_4^{20} 0·8831. n_D^{20} 1·5101. Alc. KOH ⟶ 1-phenyl-1-butylene. Ozone in presence of H_2O ⟶ phenylacetaldehyde.

Auwers, Roth, Eisenlohr, *Ann.*, 1911, **385**, 108.
Klages, *Ber.*, 1904, **37**, 2310.
Straus, *Ann.*, 1905, **342**, 257.

2-Phenyl-2-butylene (*α-Methylpropenylbenzene*)

$$CH_3\cdot CH:C(C_6H_5)\cdot CH_3$$

$C_{10}H_{12}$ MW, 132

B.p. 188–9°, 80–1°/20 mm. $D_4^{19\cdot 7}$ 0·9088. $n_D^{19\cdot 7}$ 1·5339. Heat of comb. C_v 1352·8 Cal. $KMnO_4$ in H_2SO_4 ⟶ acetophenone.

Klages, *Ber.*, 1902, **35**, 2641, 3508.
Haller, Bauer, *Ann. chim.*, 1918, **9**, 12.
Thorpe, Wood, *J. Chem. Soc.*, 1913, **103**, 1578.

1-Phenyl-α-butylene Glycol (1-*Phenyl*-1 : 2-*butandiol, αβ-dihydroxybutylbenzene*)

$$CH_3\cdot CH_2\cdot CH(OH)\cdot CH(OH)\cdot C_6H_5$$

$C_{10}H_{14}O_2$ MW, 166

Two forms. (i) M.p. 40–1°. (ii) B.p. 205–8°/72 mm.

Lévy, Dvoleitzka-Gombinska, *Bull. soc. chim.*, 1931, **49**, 1774.

2-Phenyl-α-butylene Glycol (2-*Phenyl*-1 : 2-*butandiol*)

$$CH_3\cdot CH_2\cdot C(C_6H_5)(OH)\cdot CH_2OH$$

$C_{10}H_{14}O_2$ MW, 166

Cryst. from ligroin. M.p. 56°. B.p. 165°/23 mm. Sol. H_2O, EtOH, Et_2O. At 250–300° ⟶ diphenylacetaldehyde. At 400–50° ⟶ deoxybenzoin.

Ramart-Lucas, Salmon-Legagneur, *Bull. soc. chim.*, 1932, **51**, 1078.
Stoermer *et al.*, *Ber.*, 1906, **38**, 2300.

4-Phenyl-α-butylene Glycol (4-*Phenyl*-1 : 2-*butandiol, γδ-dihydroxybutylbenzene*)

$$C_6H_5\cdot CH_2\cdot CH_2\cdot CH(OH)\cdot CH_2OH$$

$C_{10}H_{14}O_2$ MW, 166

Viscous oil. B.p. 180°/13 mm.

v. Braun, *Ber.*, 1923, **56**, 2182.

1-Phenyl-β-butylene Glycol (1-*Phenyl*-1 : 3-*butandiol, αγ-dihydroxybutylbenzene*)

$$CH_3\cdot CH(OH)\cdot CH_2\cdot CH(OH)\cdot C_6H_5$$

$C_{10}H_{14}O_2$ MW, 166

Powder. Sinters at 60°. M.p. about 73·5°. B.p. 175–8°/21 mm., 168–9°/13 mm., 129–31°/2 mm. Sol. EtOH, C_6H_6, ligroin, hot Et_2O. Spar. sol. H_2O.

Diacetyl: b.p. 157°/10 mm., 140°/2 mm. Decomp. on dist. at ord. press.

Michael, Ross, *J. Am. Chem. Soc.*, 1931, **53**, 2412.
Sprague, Adkins, *J. Am. Chem. Soc.*, 1934, **56**, 2670.
Bauer, *Compt. rend.*, 1912, **154**, 1093.

3-Phenyl-β-butylene Glycol (3-*Phenyl*-1 : 3-*butandiol*)

$$CH_3\cdot C(C_6H_5)(OH)\cdot CH_2\cdot CH_2OH$$

$C_{10}H_{14}O_2$ MW, 166

B.p. 130°/1 mm. D^{20} 1·0865. n_D^{20} 1·5341.

St. Pfau, Plattner, *Helv. Chim. Acta*, 1932, **15**, 1266.

1-Phenylbutyraldehyde (*Ethylphenylacetaldehyde*)

$$CH_3\cdot CH_2\cdot CH(C_6H_5)\cdot CHO$$

$C_{10}H_{12}O$ MW, 148

Oil. B.p. 211°, 104–6°/15 mm.
Semicarbazone: m.p. 155°.

Stoermer, *Ber.*, 1906, **39**, 2300.

2-Phenylbutyraldehyde.
See β-Methylhydrocinnamaldehyde.

3-Phenylbutyraldehyde

$$C_6H_5\cdot CH_2\cdot CH_2\cdot CH_2\cdot CHO$$

$C_{10}H_{12}O$ MW, 148

B.p. 129–31°/17 mm. (120–2°/16 mm.).
Semicarbazone: leaflets from MeOH. M.p 104–5°.
Di-Me acetal: b.p. 121–4°/9 mm.

v. Braun, Anton, Fischer, Keller, Manz *Ber.*, 1934, **67**, 225.
v. Braun, Kruber, *Ber.*, 1912, **45**, 394.

1-Phenylbutyric Acid (*Ethylphenylacetic acid*)

$$CH_3\cdot CH_2\cdot CH(C_6H_5)\cdot COOH$$

$C_{10}H_{12}O_2$ MW, 164

Plates from Et_2O. M.p. 42°. B.p. 270°.
Me ester: $C_{11}H_{14}O_2$. MW, 178. B.p. 228°.
Amide: $C_{10}H_{13}ON$. MW, 163. M.p. 86°.
Nitrile: $C_{10}H_{11}N$. MW, 145. B.p. 238–40° 114–15°/15 mm. D^{14} 0·977. Sol. EtOH, C_6H_6 Insol. H_2O. Volatile in steam.

Riiber, *Ber.*, 1903, **36**, 1406.
Rupe, *Ann.*, 1909, **369**, 334.
Neure, *Ann.*, 1889, **250**, 154.
Bodroux, Taboury, *Bull. soc. chim.*, 1910 **7**, 667.

2-Phenylbutyric Acid.
See β-Methylhydrocinnamic Acid.

3-Phenylbutyric Acid (*2-Benzylpropionic acid*)

$C_6H_5{\cdot}CH_2{\cdot}CH_2{\cdot}CH_2{\cdot}COOH$

$C_{10}H_{12}O_2$ MW, 164

Leaflets from H_2O. M.p. 52°. B.p. 290°, 171°/15 mm. Sol. EtOH, Et_2O. Mod. sol. warm H_2O.

Et ester: $C_{12}H_{16}O_2$. MW, 192. B.p. 130–1°/10 mm. D_4^{20} 1·001.

l-*Menthyl ester*: b.p. 205°/10 mm. $[\alpha]_D^{20}$ — 57·0° in C_6H_6.

Chloride: $C_{10}H_{11}OCl$. MW, 182·5. B.p. 140–2°/12 mm., 119°/9 mm.

Amide: $C_{10}H_{13}ON$. MW, 163. Plates from H_2O. M.p. 84·5°. Sol. EtOH, Et_2O.

Nitrile: $C_{10}H_{11}N$. MW, 145. B.p. 142–5°/16 mm., 129–31°/10 mm.

Overbaugh, Allen, Martin, Fieser, *Organic Syntheses*, 1935, XV, 64.
Richard, *Compt. rend.*, 1935, **200**, 1945.
Amagat, *Bull. soc. chim.*, 1927, **41**, 942.
Auwers, Möller, *J. prakt. Chem.*, 1925, **109**, 138.
v. Braun, *Ber.*, 1910, **43**, 2844; 1911, **44**, 2871.
Rupe, *Ann.*, 1913, **395**, 118.

Phenylbutyrolactam.
See Phenylpyrrolidone.

3-Phenylbutyrolactone.
See under 3-Hydroxy-3-phenylbutyric Acid.

3-Phenyl-γ-butyrolactone-2-carboxylic Acid.
See γ-Phenylparaconic Acid.

Phenylcacodyl (*Tetraphenyldiarsine*)

$(C_6H_5)_2As{\cdot}As(C_6H_5)_2$

$C_{24}H_{20}As_2$ MW, 458

Cryst. M.p. 135°. B.p. 200°/1 mm. Sol. EtOH. Less sol. Et_2O. Sol. 100 parts C_6H_6 at 20°.

Michaelis, *Ann.*, 1902, **321**, 148.
Michaelis, Schulte, *Ber.*, 1882, **15**, 1954.
Porter, Borgstrom, *J. Am. Chem. Soc.*, 1919, **41**, 2049.

5-Phenylcapric Acid

$CH_3{\cdot}[CH_2]_3{\cdot}CH(C_6H_5){\cdot}[CH_2]_4{\cdot}COOH$

$C_{16}H_{24}O_2$ MW, 248

B.p. 176–80°/3 mm. D_{25}^{25} 0·9817. n_D^{20} 1·5000.

p-*Bromophenacyl ester*: m.p. 55·5–56°.

Harmon, Marvel, *J. Am. Chem. Soc.*, 1932, **54**, 2523.

9-Phenylcapric Acid

$C_6H_5{\cdot}CH_2{\cdot}[CH_2]_7{\cdot}CH_2{\cdot}COOH$

$C_{16}H_{24}O_2$ MW, 248

Waxy solid. M.p. 41°. B.p. 228–30°/18 mm. Very sol. usual org. solvents.

Et ester: $C_{18}H_{28}O_2$. MW, 276. B.p. 220–4°/20 mm.

Borsche, *Ber.*, 1919, **52**, 2085.

1-Phenylcaproic Acid

$CH_3{\cdot}[CH_2]_3{\cdot}CH(C_6H_5){\cdot}COOH$

$C_{12}H_{16}O_2$ MW, 192

B.p. 182–3°/20 mm. D_4^{19} 1·0225. n_D^{19} 1·5071.

Amide: $C_{12}H_{17}ON$. MW, 191. M.p. 96°.

Nitrile: $C_{12}H_{15}N$. MW, 173. B.p. 151·1–152·5°/20 mm.

Lévy, Jullien, *Bull. soc. chim.*, 1929, **45**, 941.
Dolique, *Ann. chim.*, 1931, **15**, 468.

2-Phenylcaproic Acid

$CH_3{\cdot}[CH_2]_2{\cdot}CH(C_6H_5){\cdot}CH_2{\cdot}COOH$

$C_{12}H_{16}O_2$ MW, 192

d-.

B.p. 152°/4 mm. D_4^{25} 1·025. n_D 1·5078. $[\alpha]_D^{25}$ + 5·93°.

Et ester: $C_{14}H_{20}O_2$. MW, 220. B.p. 123°/2 mm. D_4^{25} 0·969. n_D^{25} 1·4870. $[\alpha]_D^{25}$ + 3·45°.

Levene, Marker, *J. Biol. Chem.*, 1931, **93**, 765.

3-Phenylcaproic Acid

$CH_3{\cdot}CH_2{\cdot}CH(C_6H_5){\cdot}CH_2{\cdot}CH_2{\cdot}COOH$

$C_{12}H_{16}O_2$ MW, 192

dl-.

Cryst. M.p. 104·5–105·5°. B.p. 185°/22 mm.

Chloride: $C_{12}H_{15}OCl$. MW, 210·5. B.p. 138°/18 mm.

Nitrile: $C_{12}H_{15}N$. MW, 173. B.p. 148–50°/19 mm.

l-.

B.p. 156°/4 mm. $[\alpha]_D^{25}$ — 0·61°.

Lévy, *Compt. rend.*, 1933, **197**, 772.
Levene, Marker, *J. Biol. Chem.*, 1935, **110**, 329.

4-Phenylcaproic Acid

$$\begin{array}{c} C_6H_5 \\ CH_3\cdot CH\cdot[CH_2]_2\cdot CH_2\cdot COOH \end{array}$$

$C_{12}H_{16}O_2$ MW, 192

d-.

B.p. 156°/1 mm. D_4^{25} 1·022. $[\alpha]_D^{25}$ + 2·01°.

Et ester: $C_{14}H_{20}O_2$. MW, 220. B.p. 145°/1 mm. D_4^{25} 0·974. $[\alpha]_D^{25}$ + 1·40°.

dl-.

B.p. 173–5°/11 mm.

Chloride: $C_{12}H_{15}OCl$. MW, 210·5. B.p. 134–6°/13 mm.

Levene, Marker, *J. Biol. Chem.*, 1931, **93**, 771.
Nenitzescu, Gavăt, *Ann.*, 1935, **519**, 271.

5-Phenylcaproic Acid

$$C_6H_5\cdot CH_2\cdot[CH_2]_3\cdot CH_2\cdot COOH$$

$C_{12}H_{16}O_2$ MW, 192

Cryst. M.p. 22–4° (11°). B.p. 206–8°/30 mm., 180–90°/17 mm. (186–8°/11 mm.).

Et ester: $C_{14}H_{20}O_2$. MW, 220. B.p. 162–4°/12 mm.

Chloride: $C_{12}H_{15}OCl$. MW, 210·5. B.p. 151–2°/11 mm.

Nitrile: $C_{12}H_{15}N$. MW, 173. B.p. 161–3°/13 mm.

Anilide: m.p. 80°.

p-*Toluidide*: m.p. 78°.

Piperidide: b.p. 177°/0·03 mm.

v. Braun, *Ber.*, 1911, **44**, 2873.
Borsche, *Ber.*, 1919, **52**, 2084.
Staudinger, Müller, *Ber.*, 1923, **56**, 714.
Grateau, *Compt. rend.*, 1930, **191**, 947.

4-Phenylcaprylic Acid

$$\begin{array}{c} C_6H_5 \\ CH_3\cdot CH_2\cdot CH_2\cdot CH\cdot[CH_2]_3\cdot COOH \end{array}$$

$C_{14}H_{20}O_2$ MW, 220

l-.

B.p. 170°/1 mm. D_4^{25} 0·999. $[\alpha]_D^{25}$ − 0·82°.

Et ester: $C_{16}H_{24}O_2$. MW, 248. B.p. 152°/1 mm. D_4^{25} 0·958. $[\alpha]_D^{25}$ − 0·49°.

Levene, Marker, *J. Biol. Chem.*, 1931, **93**, 770.

7-Phenylcaprylic Acid

$$C_6H_5\cdot CH_2\cdot[CH_2]_5\cdot CH_2\cdot COOH$$

$C_{14}H_{20}O_2$ MW, 220

Leaflets. M.p. about 30°. B.p. 209–10°/14 mm.

Borsche, *Ber.*, 1919, **52**, 2084.

Phenylcarbamic Acid (*Carbanilic acid*)

$$C_6H_5\cdot NH\cdot COOH$$

$C_7H_7O_2N$ MW, 137

Not known in free state.

Me ester: phenylurethylan. $C_8H_9O_2N$. MW, 151. Leaflets from EtOH. M.p. 47°.

Et ester: *see* Phenylurethane.

Propyl ester: $C_{10}H_{13}O_2N$. MW, 179. Needles. M.p. 57–9°.

Isopropyl ester: needles from EtOH. M.p. 75–6° (90°).

Butyl ester: $C_{11}H_{15}O_2N$. MW, 193. Leaflets or prisms from pet. ether. M.p. 65·5° (57°).

Isobutyl ester: needles. M.p. 86°.

tert.-*Butyl ester*: needles from pet. ether. M.p. 136°.

dl-*Amyl ester*: $C_{12}H_{17}O_2N$. MW, 207. M.p. 31°.

d-*Amyl ester*: cryst. from ligroin. M.p. 30°.

Isoamyl ester: cryst. from pet. ether. M.p. 55°.

tert.-*Amyl ester*: m.p. 42°.

Allyl ester: cryst. M.p. 70°.

l-*Menthyl ester*: needles from EtOH. M.p. 111–12°. $[\alpha]_D^{20}$ − 77·21° in $CHCl_3$.

dl-*Menthyl ester*: needles from MeOH.Aq. M.p. 104°.

Tropine ester: *see* Uretropine.

Amide: *see* Phenylurea.

Anilide: *see* Carbanilide.

Nitrile: *see* Phenylcyanamide.

Jeffreys, *Am. Chem. J.*, 1901, **22**, 18.
Roemer, *Ber.*, 1873, **6**, 1103.
Lambling, *Bull. soc. chim.*, 1898, **19**, 777.
Piccard, Littlebury, *J. Chem. Soc.*, 1912, **101**, 116.
Weizmann, Garrard, *J. Chem. Soc.*, 1920, **117**, 328.

Phenylcarbazinic Acid.

See Phenylhydrazine-β-carboxylic Acid.

***N*-Phenylcarbazole**

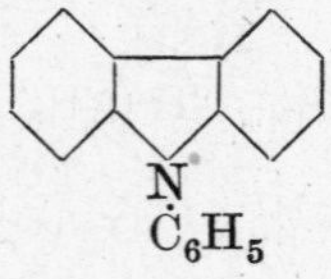

$C_{18}H_{13}N$ MW, 243

Needles or plates from EtOH. M.p. 94–5° (82–4°).

Picrate: red needles from ligroin. M.p. 26–9°.

Cassella, D.R.P., 224,951, (*Chem. Zentr.*, 1910, II, 699).
Eckert, Seidel, Endler, *J. prakt. Chem.*, 1922, **104**, 88.
Montmollin, Montmollin, *Helv. Chim. Acta*, 1923, **6**, 98.
Hager, *Organic Syntheses*, Collective Vol. I, 532 (*Note* 13).

3-Phenylcarbostyril (2-*Hydroxy*-3-*phenyl-uinoline*)

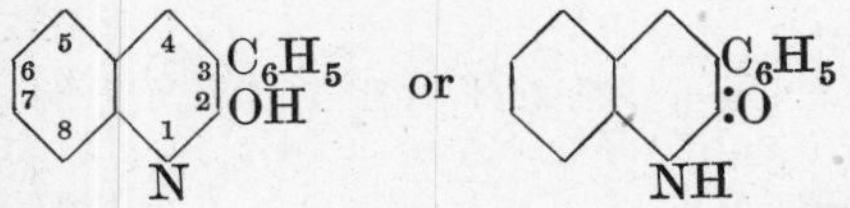

$_{15}H_{11}ON$ MW, 221

Needles from EtOH. M.p. 234–5°. Sol. hot tOH, C_6H_6. Insol. Et_2O.

Bischler, Lang, *Ber.*, 1895, **28**, 292.
Stoermer, Prigge, *Ann.*, 1915, **409**, 27.
Wislicenus, Erbe, *Ann.*, 1920, **421**, 146.

4-Phenylcarbostyril (2-*Hydroxy*-4-*phenyl-uinoline*).

Needles. M.p. 259°. Sol. AcOH, hot C_6H_6. par. sol. hot H_2O, EtOH, $CHCl_3$, CS_2, ligroin. n + H ⟶ 4-phenylquinoline.

Camps, *Arch. Pharm.*, 1899, **237**, 683.

Phenyl *o*-carboxybenzyl Ketone.
See *o*-Phenacylbenzoic Acid.

Phenyl-carboxymethyl-glycine.
See 1-Phenyliminodiacetic Acid.

Phenyl-ω-carboxysarcosine.
See 1-Phenyliminodiacetic Acid.

Phenylcarbylamine.
See Phenyl isocyanide.

Phenylcarbylamine chloride.
See Phenyliminophosgene.

Phenylchloroacetic Acid (1-*Chloro*-1-*phenyl-cetic acid*)

$C_6H_5 \cdot CHCl \cdot COOH$

$C_8H_7O_2Cl$ MW, 170·5

d-.

Cryst. from pet. ether. M.p. 60–1°. $[\alpha]_D^{20}$ + 191·9° in C_6H_6.

Me ester: $C_9H_9O_2Cl$. MW, 184·5. B.p. 78°/40 mm., 124°/8 mm. D_4^{20} 1·1882. $[\alpha]_D^{18}$ + 25·67°.

Et ester: $C_{10}H_{11}O_2Cl$. MW, 198·5. B.p. 62°/45 mm., 138°/19 mm., 133°/12 mm. D_4^{20} ·1594. n_D^{20} 1·5152. $[\alpha]_D^{20}$ + 121·0° in EtOH.

Propyl ester: $C_{11}H_{13}O_2Cl$. MW, 212·5. B.p. 180°/60 mm., 140°/19 mm. D_4^{20} 1·1278. n_D^{20} 1·5095. $[\alpha]_D^{18}$ + 23·94°.

Butyl ester: $C_{12}H_{15}O_2Cl$. MW, 226·5. B.p. 163–4°/20 mm. D^{20} 1·1040.

l-*Menthyl ester*: needles from EtOH.Aq. M.p. 56–7°. $[\alpha]_D^{15\cdot5}$ + 5·7° in EtOH.

Chloride: $C_8H_6OCl_2$. MW, 189. B.p. 120°/23 mm. $[\alpha]_D^{18}$ + 158·33° in CS_2.

l-.

Needles from pet. ether. M.p. 61°. Sol. EtOH, Et_2O, $CHCl_3$, C_6H_6. Spar. sol. cold H_2O. $[\alpha]_D^{18}$ − 163° in EtOH, − 191·3° in C_6H_6.

Me ester: b.p. 123–6°/11 mm. D_4^{18} 1·213. $[\alpha]_D^{15}$ − 86·7°.

Et ester: b.p. 132–3°/15 mm. $D_4^{16\cdot4}$ 1·162. $[\alpha]_D^{20}$ − 108° in EtOH.

l-*Menthyl ester*: needles from EtOH.Aq. M.p. 44·5–45·5°. $[\alpha]_D^{15}$ − 150·1°.

Chloride: b.p. 103°/11 mm. $[\alpha]_{578}^{20}$ − 250°.

Dimethylamide: m.p. 47°. $[\alpha]_{578}$ − 110° in EtOH.

dl-.

Leaflets. M.p. 78°. Very sol. EtOH, Et_2O. Mod. sol. hot ligroin. Spar. sol. H_2O.

Me ester: b.p. 248° decomp.

Et ester: b.p. 142°/19 mm.

l-*Menthyl ester*: cryst. from Et_2O. M.p. 28–9°. B.p. 200–1°/12 mm. D_4^{20} 1·064. $[\alpha]_D^{20}$ − 67·2°.

Chloride: b.p. 120°/15 mm., 110°/4 mm.

Amide: C_8H_8ONCl. MW, 169·5. Needles from C_6H_6. M.p. 116°. Sol. EtOH, Et_2O.

Nitrile: C_8H_6NCl. MW, 151·5. B.p. 131·5°/13 mm., 108–10°/5 mm.

McKenzie, Clough, *J. Chem. Soc.*, 1909, **95**, 784.
Walden, *Ber.*, 1895, **28**, 1295.
Bischoff, Walden, *Ann.*, 1894, **279**, 122.
Meyer, Boner, *Ann.*, 1883, **220**, 44.
Michaël, Jeanprêtre, *Ber.*, 1892, **25**, 1680.
Darapsky, *J. prakt. Chem.*, 1919, **99**, 188.
McKenzie, Barrow, *J. Chem. Soc.*, 1911, **99**, 1916.
McKenzie, Smith, *J. Chem. Soc.*, 1923, **123**, 1962.
Freudenberg, Todd, Seidler, *Ann.*, 1933, **501**, 217.
Barrow, Thorneycroft, *J. Chem. Soc.*, 1934, 724.
Hignett, Kay, *J. Soc. Chem. Ind.*, 1935, **54**, 98T.

Phenyl ω-chlorobenzyl Ketone.
See Desyl chloride.

Phenylchloroform.
See Benzotrichloride.

Phenyl-2-chlorolactic Acid (*2-Chloro-1-hydroxy-2-phenylpropionic acid, cinnamic acid chlorohydrin*)

$C_6H_5 \cdot CHCl \cdot CH(OH) \cdot COOH$

$C_9H_9O_3Cl$ MW, 200·5

l-.

Cryst. M.p. 144°. $[\alpha]_D - 71{\cdot}7°$.

dl-.

Needles from $CHCl_3$. M.p. 141–2°. Sol. EtOH, Et_2O. Spar. sol. $CHCl_3$, C_6H_6, ligroin. Hot $H_2O \longrightarrow CO_2 + HCl +$ phenylacetaldehyde. NaOH ⟶ phenylglycidic acid.

Erlenmeyer, *Ann.*, 1892, **271**, 150; *Ber.*, 1906, **39**, 789.

2-Phenylchroman.
See Flavan.

4-Phenylchroman

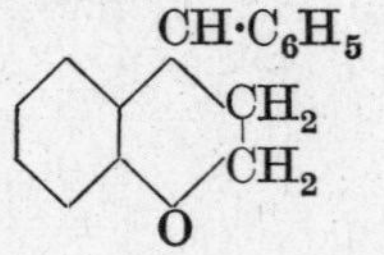

$C_{15}H_{14}O$ MW, 210

Needles from pet. ether. M.p. 38·5°. Addn. of $FeCl_3$ to suspension in $H_2SO_4 \longrightarrow$ reddish-violet col.

Greenwood, Nierenstein, *J. Chem. Soc.*, 1920, **117**, 1597.

2-Phenylchromanone.
See Flavanone.

2-Phenylchromone.
See Flavone.

3-Phenylchromone.
See Isoflavone.

8-Phenylchromone

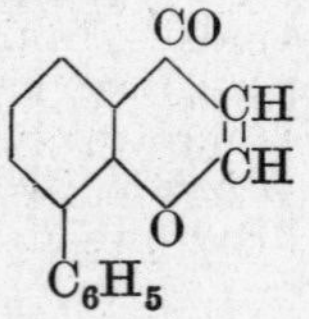

$C_{15}H_{10}O_2$ MW, 222

Needles from EtOH.Aq. M.p. 112°.

Watson, *J. Chem. Soc.*, 1916, **109**, 305.

6-Phenylcinchomeronic Acid (*6-Phenylpyridine-3 : 4-dicarboxylic acid*)

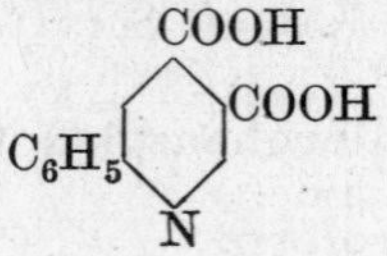

$C_{13}H_9O_4N$ MW, 243

Yellow needles and prisms from H_2O. M 248–50°. Spar. sol. H_2O, Et_2O. Mod. s EtOH.

Di-Me ester: $C_{15}H_{13}O_4N$. MW, 271. Plat from $CHCl_3$. M.p. 74°.

Boehm, Bournot, *Ber.*, 1915, **48**, 1573.

Phenylcinchoninic Acid.
See Phenylquinoline-4-carboxylic Acid.

α-Phenylcinnamaldehyde (*1 : 2-Dipheny acrolein, α-formylstilbene*)

$C_6H_5 \cdot CH{:}C(C_6H_5) \cdot CHO$

$C_{15}H_{12}O$ MW, 2

Cryst. from EtOH. M.p. 94°. B.p. 19 200°/17 mm. Ag_2O in $C_6H_6 \longrightarrow$ 1-pheny cinnamic acid.

Oxime: leaflets from EtOH. M.p. 165–6°.

Semicarbazone: cryst. from EtOH. M. 188·5–189·5°.

Phenylhydrazone: yellow needles from AcOI M.p. 125–6°.

Meerwein, *J. prakt. Chem.*, 1918, **97**, 28
Shoruigan, Isagulyantz, Machinskay *Ber.*, 1933, **66**, 389.

β-Phenylcinnamaldehyde (*2 : 2-Dipheny acrolein*)

$(C_6H_5)_2C{:}CH \cdot CHO$

$C_{15}H_{12}O$ MW, 2

Pale yellow prisms from ligroin. M.p. 44°.

Semicarbazone: m.p. 214–15°.

Phenylhydrazone: yellow needles. M.p. 17

Ziegler, Tiemann, *Ber.*, 1922, **55**, 3413.
Kohler, Larsen, *J. Am. Chem. Soc.*, 193 **57**, 1452.

α-Phenylcinnamic Acid (*Stilbene-α-car oxylic acid, 1 : 2-diphenylacrylic acid*)

$C_6H_5 \cdot CH{:}C(C_6H_5) \cdot COOH$

$C_{15}H_{12}O_2$ MW, 2

Trans:

Needles from ligroin or EtOH.Aq. M. 172°. Sol. EtOH, Et_2O. Mod. sol. hot H_2 Irradiation ⟶ *cis*-form.

Me ester: $C_{16}H_{14}O_2$. MW, 238. Needl from EtOH.Aq. M.p. 77–8°.

Et ester: $C_{17}H_{16}O_2$. MW, 252. Crys M.p. 33–4° (28°). B.p. 214–15°/28 mm., 192 13 mm. $D_4^{18\cdot2}$ 1·0971. $n_D^{18\cdot6}$ 1·5972.

l-*Menthyl ester*: needles or leaflets fro EtOH.Aq. $[\alpha]_D^{20} - 53{\cdot}44°$ in C_6H_6.

Phenyl ester: $C_{21}H_{16}O_2$. MW, 300. Needl

from EtOH–$CHCl_3$. M.p. 142°. Sol. $CHCl_3$. Mod. sol. Me_2CO, C_6H_6. Spar. sol. EtOH, Et_2O.

o-*Tolyl ester*: $C_{22}H_{18}O_2$. MW, 314. Needles from EtOH. M.p. 130°.

Amide: $C_{15}H_{13}ON$. MW, 223. Needles from Me_2CO.Aq. M.p. 127°.

Nitrile: $C_{15}H_{11}N$. MW, 205. Cryst. from EtOH. M.p. 49–51°. B.p. 213–14°/23 mm.

Anilide: cryst. from EtOH. M.p. 141°.

Cis:

Leaflets from EtOH. M.p. 137–8°. More sol. than *trans*- form.

Amide: cryst. from $CHCl_3$–ligroin. M.p. 167–8°.

Nitrile: cryst. from EtOH. M.p. 86°. B.p. 228–30°/23 mm.

Anilide: cryst. from $CHCl_3$–pet. ether. M.p. 179°.

Stoermer, Voht, *Ann.*, 1915, **409**, 39.
Cabella, *Gazz. chim. ital.*, 1884, **14**, 114.
Rupe, *Ann.*, 1909, **369**, 315.
Walther, *J. prakt. Chem.*, 1896, **53**, 454.
v. Braun, Manz, *Ann.*, 1929, **468**, 258.
Pfeiffer, Engelhardt, Alfuss, *Ann.*, 1928, **467**, 158.
Müller, Gawlich, Krentzmann, *Ann.*, 1935, **515**, 111.

β-Phenylcinnamic Acid (2 : 2-*Diphenylacrylic acid*)

$(C_6H_5)_2C{:}CH{\cdot}COOH$

$C_{15}H_{12}O_2$ MW, 224

Leaflets from EtOH. M.p. 162°. Sol. EtOH, Et_2O, AcOH. Spar. sol. H_2O, ligroin.

Me ester: oil. B.p. 194·6–194·8°/13 mm.

Et ester: b.p. 207°/17 mm.

l-*Menthyl ester*: needles from EtOH. M.p. 66–7°. $[\alpha]_D^{20}$ − 37·92° in C_6H_6.

Nitrile: pale yellow needles from MeOH. M.p. 49°.

Anilide: m.p. 130–1°.

Anhydride: $C_{30}H_{22}O_3$. MW, 430. Needles from EtOH. M.p. 118–20°. Cold conc. H_2SO_4 ⟶ green col. ⟶ red on heating.

de Fazi, *Gazz. chim. ital.*, 1915, **45**, ii, 5.
Rupe, *Ann.*, 1909, **369**, 315; 1913, **395**, 142.
Kohler, Reimer, *Am. Chem. J.*, 1905, **33**, 343.
Rupe, Busolt, *Ber.*, 1907, **40**, 4539.
Posner, *J. prakt. Chem.*, 1910, **82**, 439.
Schlenk, Bergmann, *Ann.*, 1928, **463**, 237

***p*-Phenylcinnamic Acid**

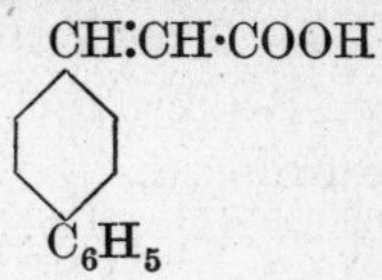

$C_{15}H_{12}O_2$ MW, 224

Needles from 60% AcOH. M.p. 225°.

Et ester: $C_{17}H_{16}O_2$. MW, 252. M.p. 87°.

v. Braun, Nelles, *Ber.*, 1933, **66**, 1465.
Vorländer, *Ber.*, 1935, **68**, 453.
Hey, *J. Chem. Soc.*, 1931, 2478.

Phenylcitraconic Acid (*Benzylmaleic acid*)

$C_6H_5{\cdot}CH_2{\cdot}C{\cdot}COOH$
$\quad\quad\quad\quad HC{\cdot}COOH$

$C_{11}H_{10}O_4$ MW, 206

Cryst. from Et_2O–ligroin. M.p. 105–8°. Very sol. H_2O, Et_2O. Mod. sol. $CHCl_3$. Insol. CS_2, ligroin. Hot H_2O ⟶ phenylitaconic acid. 10% NaOH ⟶ phenylitaconic + phenylaticonic acids. Br in sunlight ⟶ phenylmesaconic acid.

Anhydride: $C_{11}H_8O_3$. MW, 188. Prisms from Et_2O. M.p. 60–1°. Sol. C_6H_6, warm Et_2O, boiling CS_2. Spar. sol. boiling ligroin. H_2O ⟶ phenylcitraconic acid.

Fittig, Brooke, *Ann.*, 1899, **305**, 21.

6-Phenylcoumalin (6-*Phenyl-α-pyrone*)

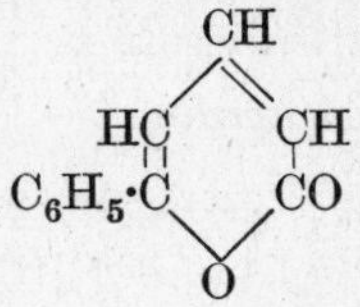

$C_{11}H_8O_2$ MW, 172

Present in Coto bark. Needles from pet. ether or MeOH.Aq. M.p. 68°. Sol. EtOH, Et_2O, $CHCl_3$, AcOH. Mod. sol. warm pet. ether.

Picrate: yellow plates from Et_2O. M.p. 81–2°.

Dimer: cryst. powder. M.p. 219° decomp. Spar. sol. boiling EtOH, Me_2CO. Insol. Et_2O, AcOH, C_6H_6.

Severni, *Gazz. chim. ital.*, 1896, **26**, ii, 338.
Ciamician, Silber, *Ber.*, 1894, **27**, 841.
Kalf, *Rec. trav. chim.*, 1927, **46**, 594.

2-Phenylcoumaran

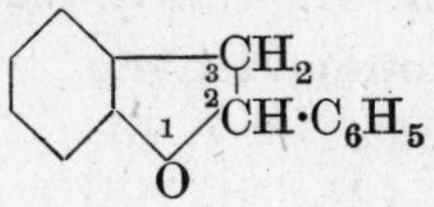

$C_{14}H_{12}O$ MW, 196

Cryst. M.p. 32–3°. Volatile in steam. Conc. H_2SO_4 ⟶ pale yellow col.

Stoermer, Reuter, *Ber.*, 1903, **36**, 3983.

3-Phenylcoumaran.
Needles from EtOH. M.p. 38·5°. B.p. 167°/14 mm. Sol. in conc. H_2SO_4 turns yellow on standing. Conc. H_2SO_4 + $FeCl_3$ ⟶ brownish-green col.

Stoermer, Reuter, *Ber.*, 1903, **36**, 3984.
Stoermer, Kippe, *Ber.*, 1903, **36**, 4006, 4008.

3-Phenylcoumarin

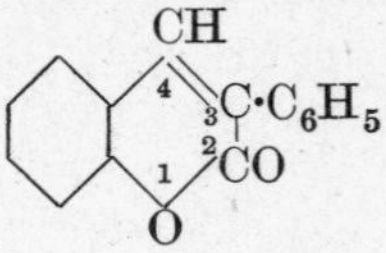

$C_{15}H_{10}O_2$ MW, 222

Needles from AcOH. M.p. 140–1°.
Semicarbazone: pale yellow cryst. Decomp. at 210–13°.

Lovett, Roberts, *J. Chem. Soc.*, 1928, 1977.
Stoermer, Prigge, *Ann.*, 1915, **409**, 27.

4-Phenylcoumarin.
Needles from EtOH or H_2O. M.p. 105°. Sol. most org. solvents. Spar. sol. boiling H_2O. Sol. conc. H_2SO_4.

Stoermer, Friderici, *Ber.*, 1908, **41**, 340.

2-Phenylcoumarone

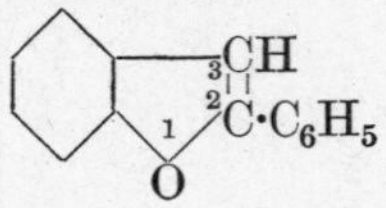

$C_{14}H_{10}O$ MW, 194

Leaflets from EtOH.Aq. M.p. 120–1°. Volatile in steam. Sol. conc. H_2SO_4 with yellow col. showing blue fluor. on heating.

Stoermer, Reuter, *Ber.*, 1903, **36**, 3981.
v. Kostanecki, Tambor, *Ber.*, 1909, **42**, 826.

3-Phenylcoumarone.
Cryst. M.p. 42°. B.p. 316–17°, 177–8°/15 mm. D^{19} 1·1449. Sol. conc. H_2SO_4 with orange-yellow col. showing blue fluor. on heating.

Stoermer, Kippe, *Ber.*, 1903, **36**, 4004.

1-Phenylcrotonaldehyde

$$CH_3{\cdot}CH{:}\underset{}{\overset{C_6H_5}{\overset{|}{C}}}{\cdot}CHO$$

$C_{10}H_{10}O$ MW, 146

B.p. 117°/15 mm. D_0^{18} 1·045. n_D^{18} 1·5605.
Oxime: m.p. 116°.
Semicarbazone: m.p. 201°.

Tiffeneau, Weill, *Compt. rend.*, 1935, **200**, 1217.

2-Phenylcrotonaldehyde.
β-Methylcinnamaldehyde, *q.v.*

1-Phenylcrotonic Acid (*α-Ethylidenephenylacetic acid, β-methylatropic acid*)

$$CH_3{\cdot}CH{:}\overset{C_6H_5}{\overset{|}{C}}{\cdot}COOH$$

$C_{10}H_{10}O_2$ MW, 162

Prisms from EtOH, needles or plates from H_2O. M.p. 136°. Spar. sol. cold H_2O. $KMnO_4$ ⟶ benzoylformic acid + acetaldehyde.
Et ester: $C_{12}H_{14}O_2$. MW, 190. B.p. 128–31°/15 mm. Volatile in steam.
1-*Menthyl ester*: yellow oil. Decomp. on dist. $[\alpha]_D^{20}$ − 46·13° in C_6H_6.
Amide: $C_{10}H_{11}ON$. MW, 161. Plates from C_6H_6. M.p. 98–9°.
Nitrile: $C_{10}H_9N$. MW, 143. B.p. 224–6°/751 mm., 125°/13–14 mm. D_4^{20} 1·013. n_D^{20} 1·5555.

Rupe, Busolt, *Ann.*, 1909, **369**, 332.
Dimroth, Feuchter, *Ber.*, 1903, **36**, 2253.
Knowles, Cloke, *J. Am. Chem. Soc.*, 1932, **54**, 2028.
Pfeiffer, Engelhardt, Alfuss, *Ann.*, 1928, **467**, 158.
Ray, *Chem. Abstracts*, 1928, **22**, 3647.

2-Phenylcrotonic Acid.
See β-Methylcinnamic Acid.

3-Phenylcrotonic Acid (*2-Benzylacrylic acid*)

$$C_6H_5{\cdot}CH_2{\cdot}CH{:}CH{\cdot}COOH$$

$C_{10}H_{10}O_2$ MW, 162

Two forms. (i) Plates from C_6H_6, pearly leaflets from H_2O. M.p. 65°. Sol. EtOH, Et_2O, C_6H_6, CS_2. (ii) Liq. Passes into (i) on heating with dil. HCl.

Bougault, *Compt. rend.*, 1917, **164**, 635.
Fittig, Luib, *Ann.*, 1894, **283**, 55, 302.
Vorländer, Strunck, *Ann.*, 1906, **345**, 244.

1-Phenylcrotonyl Alcohol.
See Propenylphenylcarbinol.

Phenylcyanamide (*Cyananilide, phenylcarbamic nitrile, N-cyanoaniline*)

$$C_6H_5{\cdot}NH{\cdot}CN$$

$C_7H_6N_2$ MW, 118

Cryst. from H_2O or Et_2O. M.p. 47°. Sol. EtOH, Et_2O. Spar. sol. H_2O. Sol. KOH.Aq.

Berger, *Monatsh.*, 1884, **5**, 219.

Phenyl cyanide.
See Benzonitrile.

Phenylcyanoacetic Acid (*α-Cyanophenylacetic acid, phenylmalonic mononitrile*)

$C_6H_5{\cdot}CH(CN){\cdot}COOH$

$C_9H_7O_2N$ MW, 161

Cryst. from Et_2O–ligroin. M.p. 92°. Sol. H_2O, EtOH, Et_2O, hot C_6H_6. Insol. ligroin. At 150–60° ⟶ benzyl cyanide.

Et ester: $C_{11}H_{11}O_2N$. MW, 189. Oil. B.p. 275° slight decomp., 165·5°/20 mm. Misc. with org. solvents. Insol. H_2O.

Amide: $C_9H_8ON_2$. MW, 160. Cryst. from EtOH. M.p. 147°. Sol. hot EtOH. Insol. H_2O.

Methylamide: $C_{10}H_{10}ON_2$. MW, 174. M.p. 102°.

Anilide: needles from EtOH. M.p. 136°. Spar. sol. Et_2O. Insol. H_2O.

o-*Toluidide*: m.p. 139°.

m-*Toluidide*: m.p. 131°.

p-*Toluidide*: needles from EtOH. M.p. 139°.

Merck, D.R.P., 606,349, (*Chem. Zentr.*, 1935, I, 2048).
Heseler, *Am. Chem. J.*, 1904, **32**, 122.

2-Phenyl-3-cyanocinchoninic Acid.
See under 2-Phenylquinoline-3 : 4-dicarboxylic Acid.

Phenylcyclobutane (*Cyclobutylbenzene*)

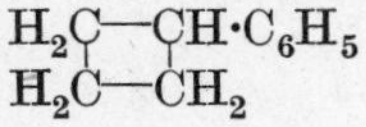

$C_{10}H_{12}$ MW, 132

B.p. 190–1°/755 mm., 101–2°/41 mm. D_4^{20} 0·9378. n_D^{20} 1·5277.

Case, *J. Am. Chem. Soc.*, 1934, **56**, 716.

Phenylcyclohexane (*Cyclohexylbenzene, hexahydrodiphenyl*)

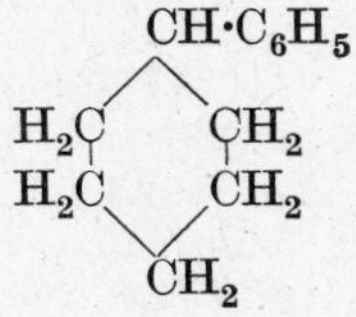

$C_{12}H_{16}$ MW, 160

Plates. M.p. 7–8°. B.p. 235–6°, 156°/80 mm., 127–8°/30 mm., 106°/12 mm. D_4^{20} 0·9502. n_D^{20} 1·5329. Stable to cold $KMnO_4$.

Meerwein, *Ann.*, 1919, **419**, 171.
Bedos, *Compt. rend.*, 1923, **177**, 111.
Case, *J. Am. Chem. Soc.*, 1934, **56**, 716.
Neunhoffer, *J. prakt. Chem.*, 1932, **133**, 95.
Truffault, *Bull. soc. chim.*, 1934, **1**, 391.

Phenylcyclohexane-carboxylic Acid.
See Phenylhexahydrobenzoic Acid.

1-Phenylcyclohexanol (1-*Hydroxyhexahydrodiphenyl*, 1-*phenylhexahydrophenol*)

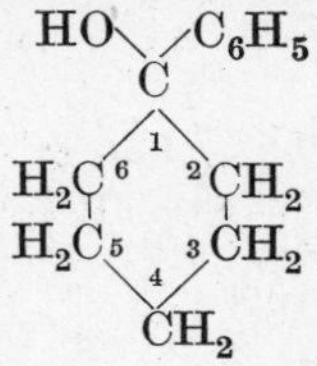

$C_{12}H_{16}O$ MW, 176

Prisms from ligroin. M.p. 63–63·5°. B.p. 156·5–158·5°/28 mm., 141–4°/14 mm. Sol. EtOH, Et_2O, $CHCl_3$, C_6H_6, ligroin. Insol. H_2O.

Auwers, Treppmann, *Ber.*, 1915, **48**, 1216.
Sabatier, Mailhe, *Compt. rend.*, 1904, **138**, 1322.
Kurssanow, *Chem. Zentr.*, 1907, I, 1744.

2-Phenylcyclohexanol (2-*Hydroxyhexahydrodiphenyl*, 2-*phenylhexahydrophenol*).

Cryst. from pet. ether. M.p. 56–7°. B.p. 153–4°/16 mm.

3 : 5-*Dinitrobenzoyl*: cryst. from EtOH. M.p. 121–121·5°.

Phenylurethane: m.p. 137–138·5°.

Phthalate: m.p. 185–6°.

Bedos, *Bull. soc. chim.*, 1926, **39**, 292.
Cook, Hewett, Lawrence, *J. Chem. Soc.*, 1936, 75.

3-Phenylcyclohexanol (3-*Hydroxyhexahydrodiphenyl*, 3-*phenylhexahydrophenol*).

Needles from pet. ether. M.p. 81° (79·5–80·5°). Sol. most org. solvents. Volatile in steam. Odour resembles geranium.

Acetyl: plates from EtOH. M.p. 43–4°. B.p. 300°.

Benzoyl: prisms from EtOH. M.p. 68°.

o-*Nitrobenzoyl*: needles from EtOH. M.p. 70°.

Boyd, Clifford, Probert, *J. Chem. Soc.*, 1920, **117**, 1383.
Crossley, Renouf, *J. Chem. Soc.*, 1915, **107**, 608.

4-Phenylcyclohexanol (*4-Hydroxyhexahydrodiphenyl, 4-phenylhexahydrophenol*).

Needles from C_6H_6. M.p. 132–3°. B.p. 155–8°/13 mm. Very sol. Et_2O. Mod. sol. ligroin. Spar. sol. H_2O.

Kurssanow, *Ann.*, 1901, **318**, 325; *Chem. Zentr.*, 1923, III, 1075.
Wuyts, *Chem. Zentr.*, 1912, II, 1006.

2-Phenylcyclohexanone

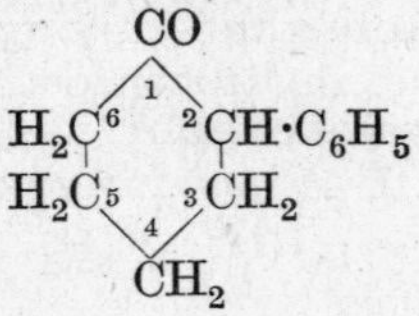

$C_{12}H_{14}O$ MW, 174

Cryst. from pet. ether or EtOH. M.p. 63° (50–3°). B.p. 180°/16 mm. Spar. sol. H_2O. Does not form bisulphite comp.

Oxime: m.p. 169°.

Semicarbazone: m.p. 190°.

Le Brazidec, *Compt. rend.*, 1914, **159**, 775.
v. Braun, Gruber, Kirschbaum, *Ber.*, 1922, **55**, 3670.
Levy, Stiras, *Bull. soc. chim.*, 1931, **49**, 1830.
Cook, Hewett, Lawrence, *J. Chem. Soc.*, 1936, 76.
Sherwood, Short, Woodcock, *ibid.*, 323.

3-Phenylcyclohexanone.

Oil. B.p. 287–8°/736 mm., 169–169·5°/18 mm. Alc. $H_2SO_4 \longrightarrow$ reddish-yellow sol. with green fluor.

Oxime: plates from EtOH. M.p. 128–9°. Sol. most org. solvents. Mod. sol. Et_2O. Insol. pet. ether.

Semicarbazone: prisms from EtOH. M.p. 167°. Sol. MeOH, EtOH, Me_2CO, $CHCl_3$. Mod. sol. Et_2O.

Boyd, Clifford, Probert, *J. Chem. Soc.*, 1920, **117**, 1383.

4-Phenylcyclohexanone.

Cryst. from pet. ether. M.p. 78°.

Semicarbazone: cryst. from EtOH. M.p. 229° decomp.

v. Braun, Weissbach, *Ber.*, 1931, **64**, 1788.

***N*-Phenylcyclohexylamine** (*Hexahydrodiphenylamine, N-cyclohexylaniline*)

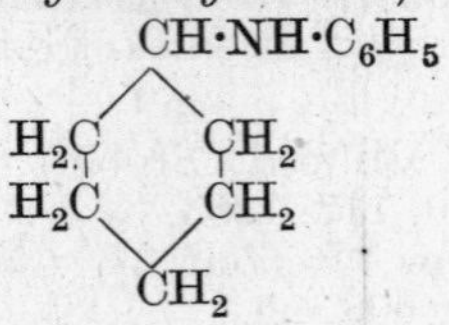

$C_{12}H_{17}N$ MW, 175

M.p. 14°. B.p. 191–2°/73 mm., 180·5–182·5°/66 mm., 134–5°/6 mm. Sol. EtOH, Et_2O, C_6H_6. Insol. H_2O.

B,HCl: needles. M.p. 230·5° (204–5°). Sol. EtOH. Spar. sol. Et_2O.

B_2,H_2SO_4: needles. M.p. 226–227·5°.

B,HBr: needles. M.p. 184°.

B,HI: needles. M.p. 176°.

B,HNO_3: m.p. 173°.

Acetate: needles. M.p. 154–155·5°.

N-*Acetyl*: m.p. 69–70°. Sol. EtOH. Insol. H_2O.

N-p-*Toluenesulphonyl*: m.p. 141–2°.

B_2,H_2PtCl_6: m.p. 177°.

Picrate: yellow prisms. M.p. 164–5°.

Kurssanow, *Chem. Zentr.*, 1907, I, 1744.
Guyot, Fournier, *Bull. soc. chim.*, 1930, **47**, 203.
Skita, Keil, *Ber.*, 1928, **61**, 1682.
Bucherer, Fischbeck, *J. prakt. Chem.*, 1934, **140**, 69.
Hickinbottom, *J. Chem. Soc.*, 1932, 2646.
Hiers, Adams, *J. Am. Chem. Soc.*, 1927, **49**, 1102.
I.G., D.R.P., 483,205, (*Chem. Zentr.*, 1929, II, 2938).
Forge, *Ann. chim.*, 1921, **15**, 291.

Phenyl cyclohexyl Ether (*Hexahydrodiphenyl ether, phenoxycyclohexane*)

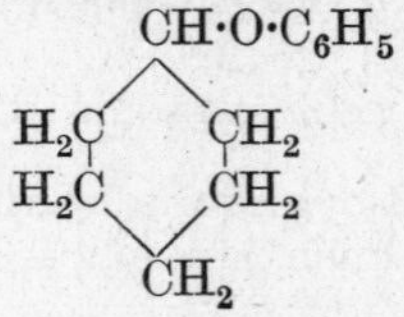

$C_{12}H_{16}O$ MW, 176

B.p. 260–2°, 140°/21·5 mm. D_4^0 1·0241, D_4^{20} 1·0077.

Kurssanow, *J. Russ. Phy.-Chem. Soc.*, 1916, **48**, 1172.
Scranth, Quasebath, *Ber.*, 1924, **57**, 854.
v. Duzee, Adkins, *J. Am. Chem. Soc.*, 1935, **57**, 147.

Phenylcyclopentane (*Cyclopentylbenzene*)

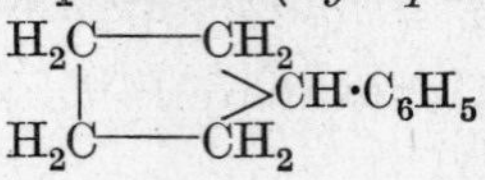

$C_{11}H_{14}$ MW, 146

B.p. 213–15°, 116–17°/37 mm. D_4^{20} 0·9502, D_4[illegible] 0·9432. n_D^{20} 1·5309.

Zelinski, *Ber.*, 1925, **58**, 2755.
v. Braun, Kühn, *Ber.*, 1927, **60**, 2561.
Case, *J. Am. Chem. Soc.*, 1934, **56**, 716.
Dupont, *Chem. Zentr.*, 1936, II, 613.

1-Phenylcyclopentane-1-carboxylic Acid

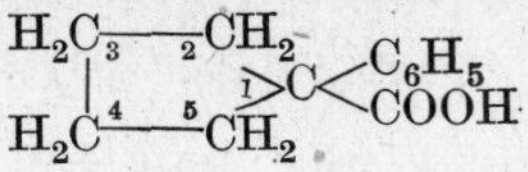

$_{12}H_{14}O_2$ MW, 190

M.p. 158–9°.

Amide: $C_{12}H_{15}ON$. MW, 189. Cryst. from $_6H_6$. M.p. 157–8°.

See third reference above.

2-Phenylcyclopentane-1-carboxylic Acid.

Thick oil. B.p. 190–2°/13 mm.

Chloride: $C_{12}H_{13}OCl$. MW, 208·5. B.p. 50–3°/12 mm.

Anilide: cryst. from Et_2O. M.p. 93–5°.

v. Braun, Kühn, *Ber.*, 1927, **60**, 2560.

3-Phenylcyclopentane-1-carboxylic Acid.

B.p. 196–8°/5 mm.

Chloride: b.p. 159–62°/15 mm.

Amide: $C_{12}H_{15}ON$. MW, 189. M.p. 149°.

Anilide: m.p. 107°.

Nenitzescu, Gavăt, *Ann.*, 1935, **519**, 268.

1-Phenylcyclopentanol

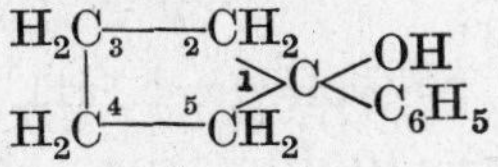

$_{11}H_{14}O$ MW, 162

B.p. 132–3°/18 mm., 121·0–121·1°/6 mm. $_4^{20}$ 1·0530. n_D^{20} 1·5479.

Zelinski, *Ber.*, 1925, **58**, 2755.
Dupont, Chavanne, *Bull. soc. chim. Belg.*, 1933, **42**, 537.

3-Phenylcyclopentanol.

B.p. 155–6°/10 mm.

Acetyl: thick oil. B.p. 154°/12 mm.

Borsche, Menz, *Ber.*, 1908, **41**, 203.

2-Phenylcyclopentanone

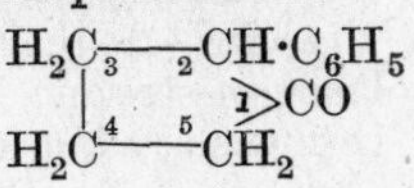

$_{11}H_{12}O$ MW, 160

M.p. 126–7°.

Oxime: m.p. 146° decomp.

Semicarbazone: m.p. 228° decomp.

Mitchovitch, *Compt. rend.*, 1935, **200**, 1601.

3-Phenylcyclopentanone.

B.p. 154–5°/10 mm.

Semicarbazone: leaflets from EtOH. M.p. 181° decomp.

Borsche, Menz, *Ber.*, 1908, **41**, 204.

Phenylcyclopropane (*Cyclopropylbenzene*)

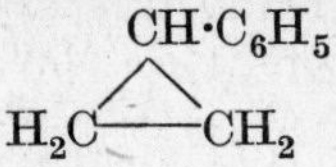

C_9H_{10} MW, 118

B.p. 173·6°/758 mm., 79–80°/37 mm. D_4^{20} 0·9317. n_D^{20} 1·5285. 60% $H_2SO_4 \longrightarrow$ dimer.

Dimer: thick oil. B.p. 330–2°/750 mm. D_0^{17} 1·002. n_D^{17} 1·5710.

Kishner, *Chem. Zentr.*, 1913, II, 2129.
Lespieau, *Compt. rend.*, 1930, **190**, 1129.
Case, *J. Am. Chem. Soc.*, 1934, **56**, 716.

1-Phenylcyclopropane-1-carboxylic Acid

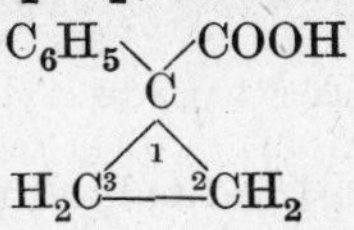

$C_{10}H_{10}O_2$ MW, 162

M.p. 86–7°.

Amide: $C_{10}H_{11}ON$. MW, 161. M.p. 100–1°.

Nitrile: $C_{10}H_9N$. MW, 143. B.p. 250–3°/751 mm., 98–100°/1 mm. D_4^{20} 1·0156. n_D^{20} 1·3676.

Knowles, Cloke, *J. Am. Chem. Soc.*, 1932, **54**, 2028; *Chem. Abstracts*, 1935, **29**, 2156.
See also last reference above.

2 - Phenylcyclopropane - 1 - carboxylic Acid.

Needles from H_2O. M.p. 105°.

Et ester: $C_{12}H_{14}O_2$. MW, 190. Needles from ligroin. M.p. 39°. B.p. 144–8°/15 mm.

Amide: leaflets from hot H_2O. M.p. 187–8°.

Buchner, Geronimus, *Ber.*, 1903, **36**, 3783.

1-Phenylcyclopropane-1 : 2-dicarboxylic Acid

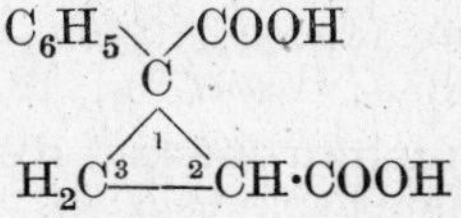

$C_{11}H_{10}O_4$ MW, 206

Free acid unstable.

Anhydride: $C_{22}H_{18}O_7$. MW, 394. Needles from EtOH.Aq. M.p. 99°. Sol. EtOH, Et_2O, C_6H_6. Sol. hot H_2O with acid reaction.

Ruhemann, *J. Chem. Soc.*, 1902, **81**, 1215.

3-Phenylcyclopropane-1 : 2-dicarboxylic Acid.

Cis:

Prisms from EtOH. M.p. 175°. Sol. EtOH,

Et_2O. Less sol. H_2O. Heat in vacuo ⟶ anhydride.

Di-Me ester: $C_{13}H_{14}O_4$. MW, 234. Needles from ligroin. M.p. 63°. B.p. 200–14°/20 mm.

Di-Et ester: $C_{15}H_{18}O_4$. MW, 262. Viscous oil. B.p. 256–7°/120 mm.

Anhydride: cryst. from boiling Et_2O. M.p. 134°. B.p. 282°/190 mm.

Trans:

Needles from H_2O. M.p. 121°.

Buchner, Dessauer, *Ber.*, 1892, **25**, 1147.
Buchner, Perkel, *Ber.*, 1903, **36**, 3777.
Buchner, *Ber.*, 1888, **21**, 2645.
Haerdi, Thorpe, *J. Chem. Soc.*, 1925, 1243.

N-Phenyldiacetamide.
See Diacetanilide.

Phenyl-diaminoditolyl-methane.
See Diaminodimethyltriphenylmethane.

N-Phenyldibenzamide.
See Dibenzanilide.

2-Phenyl-1 : 3-dibenzoylpropane.
See Benzylidene-diacetophenone.

Phenyldibenzylamine.
See Dibenzylaniline.

Phenyldibromoarsine (*Dibromo-phenyl-arsine, phenylarsen-dibromide*)

$C_6H_5AsBr_2$

$C_6H_5Br_2As$ MW, 312

B.p. 285° decomp. D^{15} 2·0983.

La Coste, Michaelis, *Ann.*, 1880, **201**, 203.
Winmill, *J. Chem. Soc.*, 1912, **101**, 723.
Roeder, Blasi, *Ber.*, 1914, **47**, 2752.

Phenyldichloroarsine (*Dichloro-phenyl-arsine, phenylarsen-dichloride*)

$C_6H_5AsCl_2$

$C_6H_5Cl_2As$ MW, 223

B.p. 252–5°.

La Coste, Michaelis, *Ann.*, 1880, **201**, 193.
Winmill, *J. Chem. Soc.*, 1912, **101**, 720.

Phenyl ω-dichlorobenzyl Ketone.
See αα-Dichlorodeoxybenzoin.

5-Phenyl-5 : 10-dihydroacridine

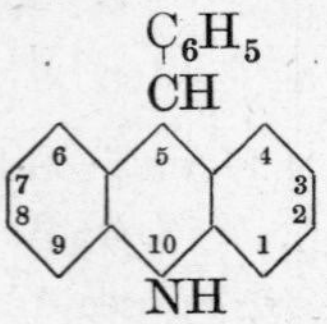

$C_{19}H_{15}N$ MW, 257

Needles from propyl alcohol or C_6H_6. M.p. 170° (163°). Mod. sol. Et_2O, hot EtOH.

N-Me: $C_{20}H_{17}N$. MW, 271. Needles. M.p. 104°.

N-Acetyl: cryst. from C_6H_6–ligroin. M.p. 128°.

Bernthsen, *Ann.*, 1884, **224**, 25.
Bergmann, Blum-Bergmann, v. Christiani, *Ann.*, 1930, **483**, 85.

10-Phenyl-5 : 10-dihydroacridine (*N-Phenyldihydroacridine*).

Needles or prisms from AcOH. M.p. 119°. Very sol. Et_2O, C_6H_6. Sol. EtOH. Insol. H_2O. Alc. sol. shows blue fluor.

Ullmann, Maag, *Ber.*, 1907, **40**, 2518.

2-Phenyl-9 : 10-dihydroanthracene

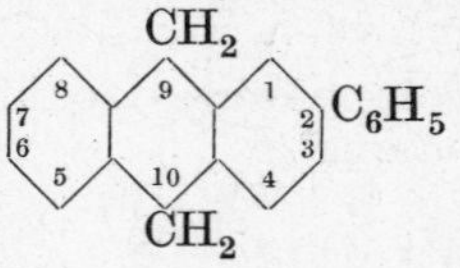

$C_{20}H_{16}$ MW, 25

Yellowish cryst. from AcOH. M.p. 93–6°. Sol. $CHCl_3$, Me_2CO, CCl_4, CS_2. Mod. sol. Et_2O, AcOH. CrO_3 in boiling AcOH ⟶ 2-phenyl-anthraquinone.

Scholl, Neovius, *Ber.*, 1911, **44**, 1081.

9-Phenyl-9 : 10-dihydroanthracene.

Needles from MeOH. M.p. 91–91·5°.

Haack, *Ber.*, 1929, **62**, 1783.

2-Phenyl-2 : 3-dihydrobenz-γ-pyrone.
See Flavanone.

2-Phenyl-2 : 3-dihydroindole (*2-Phenyl-indoline*)

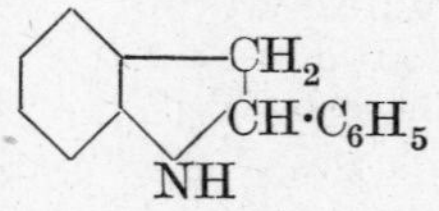

$C_{14}H_{13}N$ MW, 19

Cryst. from ligroin. M.p. 46°. Sol. dil. min. acids. Volatile in steam.

B_2,H_2PtCl_6: yellowish-red needles. M.p. 191° decomp. Insol. EtOH.

Pictet, *Ber.*, 1886, **19**, 1065.
Stoermer, *Ber.*, 1898, **31**, 2540.

1-Phenyl-3 : 4-dihydroisoquinoline

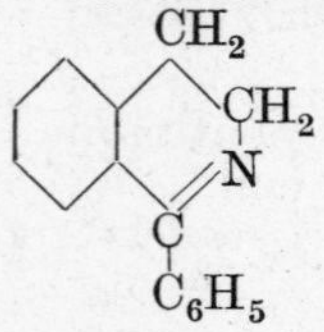

$C_{15}H_{13}N$ MW, 20

Prisms from pet. ether. M.p. 73–4°. B.p. 320°/718 mm., 194–6°/23 mm. Spar. sol. usual org. solvents. Insol. H_2O.

B,HCl : needles. M.p. 225°. Sol. H_2O, EtOH, $CHCl_3$. Insol. Et_2O, pet. ether.

B_2,H_2PtCl_6 : orange prisms from H_2O. M.p. 230–3°.

Picrate : yellow leaflets from $CHCl_3$–Et_2O. M.p. 173–5° (163°). Mod. sol. hot H_2O.

Pictet, Kay, *Ber.*, 1909, **42**, 1975.
Späth, Berger, Kuntara, *Ber.*, 1930, **63**, 139.

3-Phenyl-3 : 4-dihydroquinazoline.
See Orexine.

Phenyl 2 : 4-dihydroxyphenacyl Ether.
See under Fisetol.

3-Phenyl-1 : 2-diketohydrindene (3-*Phenylindandione*-1 : 2)

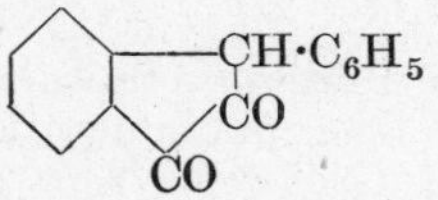

$C_{15}H_{10}O_2$ MW, 222

Needles from ligroin. M.p. 137–8°.

Disemicarbazone : yellow needles from EtOH M.p. 252° decomp.

Pfeiffer, Waal, *Ann.*, 1935, **520**, 192.

2-Phenyl-1 : 3-diketohydrindene (2-*Phenylindandione*-1 : 3)

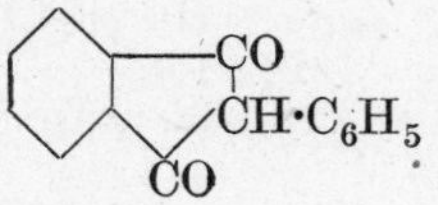

$C_{15}H_{10}O_2$ MW, 222

Leaflets from EtOH. M.p. 147–8° (145°). Sol. usual org. solvents. Insol. H_2O. Sol. conc. H_2SO_4 with blue col. Sol. alkalis with deep red col.

Dioxime : needles from EtOH. M.p. 193–6°.

Nathanson, *Ber.*, 1893, **26**, 2576.
Hantzsch, Gajewski, *Ann.*, 1912, **392**, 303.

4-Phenyldinicotinic Acid (4-*Phenylpyridine*-3 : 5-*dicarboxylic acid*)

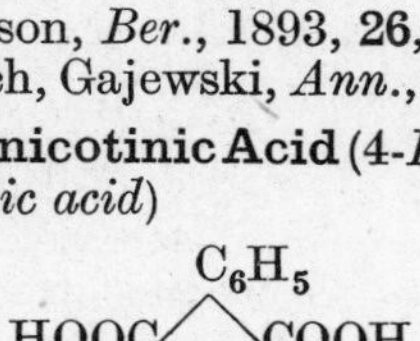

$C_{13}H_9O_4N$ MW, 243

Greenish-yellow plates + $\frac{1}{2}H_2O$. M.p. 229–30°, anhyd. 245–6° decomp.

Weber, *Ann.*, 1887, **241**, 13.

Phenyldiphenacylmethane.
See Benzylidene-diacetophenone.

Phenyl-diphenyl.
See Diphenylbenzene.

Phenyldiphenylenemethane.
See 9-Phenylfluorene.

Phenyldiphenylylmethane.
See *p*-Benzyldiphenyl.

Phenyldithiocarbamic Acid (*Dithiocarbanilic acid*)

$C_6H_5{\cdot}NH{\cdot}CSSH$

$C_7H_7NS_2$ MW, 169

NH_4 salt : yellow prisms. M.p. 108° decomp. Sol. 4 parts H_2O at 35°. Spar. sol. EtOH.

Me ester : phenyldithiourethylan. $C_8H_9NS_2$. MW, 183. Leaflets from EtOH.Aq. M.p. 95–6° (87–8°).

Et ester : *see* Phenyldithiourethane.

Propyl ester : $C_{10}H_{13}NS_2$. MW, 211. Cryst. from pet. ether. M.p. 66–7°.

Allyl ester : $C_{10}H_{11}NS_2$. MW, 209. M.p. 42°.

Isoamyl ester : $C_{12}H_{17}NS_2$. MW, 239. Plates. M.p. 71°.

Phenyl ester : $C_{13}H_{11}NS_2$. MW, 245. Cryst. from EtOH. M.p. 104–6° decomp.

Benzyl ester : $C_{14}H_{13}NS_2$. MW, 259. Cryst. from EtOH. M.p. 84–5°.

Freund, Bachrach, *Ann.*, 1895, **285**, 199.
v. Braun, *Ber.*, 1902, **35**, 3384.
Roshdestwenski, *Chem. Zentr.*, 1910, I, 910.

Phenyldithiourethane (*Dithiocarbanilic acid ethyl ester*)

$C_6H_5{\cdot}NH{\cdot}CS{\cdot}SC_2H_5$

$C_9H_{11}NS_2$ MW, 197

Plates from EtOH. M.p. 60–1°. Very sol. EtOH, Et_2O, C_6H_6. Insol. H_2O.

Will, *Ber.*, 1882, **15**, 1305.
Losanitsch, *Ber.*, 1891, **24**, 3025.

Phenyldi-*o*-tolylmethane (2 : 2′-*Dimethyltriphenylmethane*)

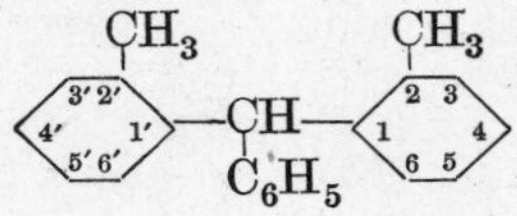

$C_{21}H_{20}$ MW, 272

Cryst. from AcOH. M.p. 104°. B.p. 180–5°/12 mm.

Weiss, Reichel, *Monatsh.*, 1929, **53**, 197.

Phenyldi-*p*-tolylmethane (4 : 4′-*Dimethyltriphenylmethane*).

Needles from MeOH. M.p. 55–6° (52°). Very

sol. Et_2O, $CHCl_3$, CS_2, C_6H_6. Less sol. EtOH, AcOH, ligroin.

Kliegl, *Ber.*, 1905, **38**, 85.
Guyot, Kovache, *Compt. rend.*, 1912, **154**, 122.
Vorländer, *Ber.*, 1911, **44**, 2470.

***o*-Phenylenediacetic Acid** (o-*Xylene-ω : ω′-dicarboxylic acid*)

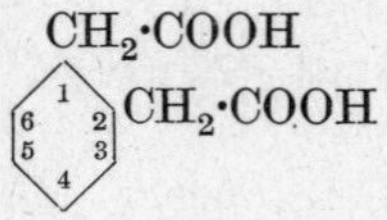

$C_{10}H_{10}O_4$ MW, 194

Needles from H_2O or Et_2O. M.p. 150° (148·5–149°). Sol. EtOH, Et_2O, hot H_2O. $k = 1{\cdot}111 \times 10^{-4}$ at 25°.

Di-Et ester: $C_{14}H_{18}O_4$. MW, 250. Oil. B.p. 185°/15 mm.

Diamide: $C_{10}H_{12}O_2N_2$. MW, 192. Needles from H_2O. M.p. 198°. Spar. sol. EtOH.

Dinitrile: *o*-xylylene dicyanide, ω : ω′-dicyano-*o*-xylene. $C_{10}H_8N_2$. MW, 156. Exists in two forms. (i) Labile. Prisms or needles from MeOH. M.p. 18°. (ii) Stable. Prisms from EtOH. M.p. 60°. Sol. EtOH, Et_2O.

Moore, Thorpe, *J. Chem. Soc.*, 1908, **93**, 175.
Baeyer, Pape, *Ber.*, 1884, **17**, 447.
v. Braun, Kruber, Danziger, *Ber.*, 1916, **49**, 2648.

***m*-Phenylenediacetic Acid** (m-*Xylene-ω : ω′-dicarboxylic acid*).

Needles from H_2O. M.p. 170°.

Di-Me ester: $C_{12}H_{14}O_4$. MW, 222. B.p. 298–300°, 185–7°/15 mm. Sol. EtOH, Et_2O, $CHCl_3$, C_6H_6, CS_2.

Di-Et ester: b.p. 188–9°/12 mm.

Dinitrile: *m*-xylylene dicyanide, ω : ω′-dicyano-*m*-xylene. Cryst. M.p. 28–9°. B.p. 305–10°/300 mm. part. decomp., 170°/20–30 mm. Sol. EtOH, Et_2O, C_6H_6. Insol. H_2O, ligroin.

Kipping, Oddo, *J. Chem. Soc.*, 1888, **53**, 41.
Oddo, *Gazz. chim. ital.*, 1893, **23**, ii, 337.
Titley, *J. Chem. Soc.*, 1928, 2579.

***p*-Phenylenediacetic Acid** (p-*Xylene-ω : ω′-dicarboxylic acid*).

Needles from H_2O. M.p. 244° (236°). Sol. H_2O, EtOH, Et_2O. Spar. sol. $CHCl_3$, CS_2, pet. ether.

Di-Me ester: leaflets. M.p. 56·5–57°. B.p. 189–90°/15 mm.

Di-Et ester: m.p. 59°.

Diamide: leaflets or needles from H_2O. Does not melt below 290°. Spar. sol. usual solvents.

Dinitrile: *p*-xylylene dicyanide, ω : ω′-dicyano-*p*-xylene. Needles from H_2O, prisms from Et_2O. M.p. 98°. Sol. EtOH, Et_2O, $CHCl_3$. Mod. sol. hot H_2O.

See last reference above and also
Zincke, Klippert, *Ber.*, 1876, **9**, 1767.
Kipping, *J. Chem. Soc.*, 1888, **53**, 44.

***o*-Phenylenediamine** (1 : 2-*Diaminobenzene*)

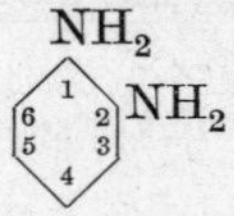

$C_6H_8N_2$ MW, 108

Leaflets from H_2O, plates from $CHCl_3$. M.p. 102–3°. B.p. 256–8°/760 mm. Very sol. EtOH, Et_2O, $CHCl_3$. Sol. hot H_2O. $k = 3{\cdot}3 \times 10^{-10}$ at 25°.

N-*Me*: *see* *N*-Methyl-*o*-phenylenediamine.

N-*Di-Me*: *see* *o*-Aminodimethylaniline.

N : N′-*Di-Me*: *see* *sym.*-Dimethyl-*o*-phenylenediamine.

N-*Et*: *see* *N*-Ethyl-*o*-phenylenediamine.

N-*Di-Et*: *see* *o*-Aminodiethylaniline.

N-*Phenyl*: *see* *o*-Aminodiphenylamine.

N-*Diphenyl*: *see* *o*-Aminotriphenylamine.

N : N′-*Diphenyl*: *see* *sym.*-Diphenyl-*o*-phenylenediamine.

N : N′-*Tetra-Me*: $C_{10}H_{16}N_2$. MW, 164. Oil. B.p. 215–18°/735 mm. Hot $FeCl_3 \longrightarrow$ red col. *B,2HCl*: prisms. M.p. 180°.

N-p-*Tolyl*: *see* 2′-Amino-4-methyldiphenylamine.

N-*Dibenzyl*: $C_{20}H_{20}N_2$. MW, 288. Oil. N′-*Acetyl*: needles from EtOH. M.p. 121–2°. N′-*Benzoyl*: needles from AcOH. M.p. 156°.

N : N′-*Dibenzyl*: cryst. from C_6H_6–pet. ether. M.p. 21°. *B,HCl*: needles from EtOH.Aq. + HCl. M.p. 149°.

N-*Benzylidene*: yellow cryst. from pet. ether. M.p. 60–1°. Sol. EtOH, Et_2O, ligroin. N′-*Acetyl*: golden-yellow leaflets. M.p. 125°.

N : N′-*Dibenzylidene*: prisms from ligroin. M.p. 106°.

N-*Acetyl*: *see* *o*-Aminoacetanilide.

N : N′-*Diacetyl*: needles from H_2O. M.p. 185–6°. Sol. boiling H_2O, EtOH, $CHCl_2$, Me_2CO, AcOH. Spar. sol. Et_2O, C_6H_6, ligroin.

N-*Benzoyl*: cryst. from H_2O. M.p. 140°. Sol. EtOH.

N : N′-*Dibenzoyl*: prisms from AcOH. M.p. 301°. Spar. sol. most org. solvents. N-*Formyl*: needles from $CHCl_3$-ligroin. M.p. 157°. Sol. Me_2CO, AcOEt, hot C_6H_6. Spar. sol. Et_2O.

N-*Propionyl* : cryst. from $CHCl_3$–ligroin. M.p. 124°.

N : N′-*Di*-o-*nitrobenzoyl* : pale yellow needles from AcOH. M.p. 265°. Sol. hot EtOH.

N : N′-*Di*-m-*nitrobenzoyl* : needles from AcOH. M.p. 240°. Mod. sol. hot EtOH, AcOH. Spar. sol. C_6H_6.

N-p-*Nitrobenzoyl* : yellow needles from H_2O. M.p. 200°. Sol. EtOH, AcOH. Spar. sol. H_2O. Insol. C_6H_6.

N : N′-*Di*-p-*nitrobenzoyl* : prisms from AcOH. M.p. 267°. Sol. hot EtOH. Insol. Et_2O, C_6H_6.

N-*Picryl* : red cryst. from xylene. M.p. 177–8° decomp. Sol. Me_2CO, xylene, $PhNO_2$. Spar. sol. EtOH, Et_2O.

N-p-*Toluenesulphonyl* : m.p. 259–260·5°.

Chapman, Perrott, *J. Chem. Soc.*, 1932, 1777.
Hinsberg, König, *Ber.*, 1895, **28**, 2947.
Jacobson, Lischke, *Ann.*, 1898, **303**, 378.
Fischer, Veiel, *Ber.*, 1905, **38**, 323.
Rupe, Porai-Koschitz, *Chem. Zentr.*, 1904, I, 102.
Walther, v. Pulawski, *J. prakt. Chem.*, 1899, **59**, 250.
Mixter, *Am. Chem. J.*, 1884, **6**, 27.
Wolff, *Ann.*, 1913, **399**, 302.
Pinnow, *Ber.*, 1899, **32**, 1402.

***m*-Phenylenediamine** (1 : 3-*Diaminobenzene*).

Rhombic cryst. from EtOH. M.p. 63–4°. B.p. 282–4°/760 mm. D_{10}^{10} 1·1421, $D_4^{57·7}$ 1·10696. $n_D^{57·7}$ 1·63390. Very sol. H_2O, EtOH. Less sol. Et_2O.

N-*Me* : *see* *N*-Methyl-*m*-phenylenediamine.

N-*Di-Me* : *see* *m*-Aminodimethylaniline.

N : N′-*Di-Me* : *see* *sym*.-Dimethyl-*m*-phenylenediamine.

N-*Et* : *see* *N*-Ethyl-*m*-phenylenediamine.

N-*Di-Et* : *see* *m*-Aminodiethylaniline.

N-*Phenyl* : *see* *m*-Aminodiphenylamine.

N-*Diphenyl* : *see* *m*-Aminotriphenylamine.

N : N′-*Diphenyl* : *see* *sym*.-Diphenyl-*m*-phenylenediamine.

N : N′-*Tri-Me* : $C_9H_{14}N_2$. MW, 150. B.p. 270° (280°). Sol. EtOH, C_6H_6. *Methiodide* : cryst. + H_2O. M.p. 192°. Sol. H_2O, EtOH. Insol. Et_2O. *Acetyl* : cryst. from EtOH. M.p. 88°. B.p. 280°.

N : N′-*Tetra-Me* : $C_{10}H_{16}N_2$. MW, 164. Oil. F.p. — 2°. B.p. 266–7°/748 mm. $D^{15·8}$ 0·9849. *Methiodide* : cryst. + $1H_2O$ from H_2O. M.p. 192°.

N : N′-*Tetraphenyl* : $C_{30}H_{24}N_2$. MW, 412. Needles from Me_2CO. M.p. 137·5–138°. Sol. Me_2CO, C_6H_6. Less sol. AcOH. Sol. 800 parts MeOH at 15°.

N : N′-*Di*-p-*tolyl* : *see* Di-*p*-tolyl-*m*-phenylene diamine.

N-1-*Naphthyl* : *m*-aminophenyl-1-naphthylamine. $C_{16}H_{14}N_2$. MW, 234. Prisms. M.p. 94–5°. B.p. 275–80°/12 mm. Very sol. EtOH, C_6H_6. Sol. hot Et_2O. Mod. sol. hot H_2O.

N-2-*Naphthyl* : *m*-aminophenyl-2-naphthylamine. $C_{16}H_{14}N_2$. MW, 234. Needles from EtOH. M.p. 128°. B.p. 320°/40 mm. Very sol. Et_2O, $CHCl_3$. *B,2HCl* : m.p. 210°. *Picrate* : leaflets. M.p. 180° decomp. N′-*Acetyl* : needles from EtOH. M.p. 135°. N : N′-*Diacetyl* : m.p. 147–8°. N′-*Benzoyl* : m.p. 173°. N : N′-*Dibenzoyl* : m.p. 213°.

Dinaphthyl : *see* Dinaphthyl-*m*-phenylenediamine.

N-*Dibenzyl* : $C_{20}H_{20}N_2$. MW, 288. Oil. N′-*Acetyl* : needles from EtOH. M.p. 143–4°. N′-*Benzoyl* : needles from AcOH. M.p. 171–2°.

N : N′-*Tetrabenzyl* : amorph. M.p. 80–1°.

Dibenzylidene : yellowish needles from Et_2O. M.p. 104–5°.

N : N′-*Diformyl* : cryst. from EtOH. M.p. 155°. Sol. hot H_2O, EtOH.

N-*Acetyl* : *see* *m*-Aminoacetanilide.

N : N′-*Diacetyl* : prisms from EtOH.Aq. M.p. 191°.

N-*Benzoyl* : cryst. M.p. 125°.

N : N′-*Dibenzoyl* : needles from AcOH. M.p. 240°. Mod. sol. AcOH. Spar. sol. EtOH.

N-m-*Nitrobenzoyl* : m.p. 142°.

N-p-*Nitrobenzoyl* : light brown needles. M.p. 212°.

N-*Picryl* : orange-red cryst. from Me_2CO. M.p. 206–7°. Sol. Me_2CO. Spar. sol. EtOH, AcOH.

Zincke, Sintenis, *Ber.*, 1872, **5**, 792.
Jaubert, *Bull. soc. chim.*, 1899, **21**, 20.
Pinnow, Wegner, *Ber.*, 1897, **30**, 3110.
Gaess, Elsaesser, *Ber.*, 1893, **26**, 976.
Piccard, Brewster, *J. Am. Chem. Soc.*, 1921, **43**, 2630.
Desai, *J. Indian Chem. Soc.*, 1925, **5**, 425.
B.D.C., E.P., 168,689, (*Chem. Zentr.*, 1922, IV, 376; *Chem. Abstracts*, 1922, **16**, 720).

***p*-Phenylenediamine** (1 : 4-*Diaminobenzene*).

Plates from Et_2O. M.p. 147° (140°). B.p. 267°. Sol. EtOH, Et_2O. Sol. 100 parts cold H_2O. Heat of comb. C_v 843·3 Cal.

N-*Me* : *see* *N*-Methyl-*p*-phenylenediamine.

N-*Di-Me* : *see* *p*-Aminodimethylaniline.

N : N′-*Di-Me* : *see* *sym*.-Dimethyl-*p*-phenylenediamine.

N-*Et* : *see N*-Ethyl-*p*-phenylenediamine.
N-*Di-Et* : *see p*-Aminodiethylaniline.
N-*Phenyl* : *see p*-Aminodiphenylamine.
N-*Diphenyl* : *see p*-Aminotriphenylamine.
N : N'-*Diphenyl* : *see sym.*-Diphenyl-*p*-phenylenediamine.
N : N'-*Tri-Me* : $C_9H_{14}N_2$. MW, 150. Oil. B.p. 265°. Spar. sol. H_2O. *Acetyl* : m.p. 95°.
N : N'-*Tetra-Me* : $C_{10}H_{16}N_2$. MW, 164. Leaflets from EtOH.Aq. or ligroin. M.p. 51°. B.p. 260°. Very sol. EtOH, Et_2O, $CHCl_3$. Sol. ligroin. Spar. sol. cold H_2O. *Methiodide* : leaflets. M.p. 265°.
N : N'-*Tetra-Et* : $C_{14}H_{24}N_2$. MW, 220. Plates from EtOH.Aq. M.p. 52°. B.p. 280°. Very sol. EtOH, Et_2O, $CHCl_3$, C_6H_6, ligroin.
N-*Propyl* : $C_9H_{14}N_2$. MW, 150. Leaflets. B.p. 281°. Sol. EtOH, Et_2O, C_6H_6.
N : N'-*Dipropyl* : $C_{12}H_{20}N_2$. MW, 192. Pale yellow oil. B.p. 155·5–156·5°/6 mm. Sol. EtOH. Spar. sol. hot H_2O. N-*Chloroacetyl* : prisms from EtOH. M.p. 121–121·5°.
N-*Butyl* : plates from pet. ether. M.p. 31·5°. B.p. 302·5–303·5°/760 mm. Sol. most org. solvents. Spar. sol. pet. ether. Insol. H_2O. Turns red in air. *B,2HCl* : plates from EtOH. Does not melt below 200°.
N-*Isobutyl* : leaflets from C_6H_6–ligroin. M.p. 39°.
N-*Isoamyl* : cryst. M.p. 31–2°.
N : N'-*Triphenyl* : cryst. from MeOH. M.p. 77–81°. B.p. 205–15°/0·01 mm. Very sol. Me_2CO, AcOEt, CS_2, C_6H_6. N-*Acetyl* : leaflets from EtOH. M.p. 184°.
N : N'-*Tetraphenyl* : leaflets from Me_2CO. M.p. 199–200°. Very sol. C_6H_6. Spar. sol. Et_2O, EtOH, pet. ether. Sol. 90 parts boiling Me_2CO.
N-o-*Tolyl* : *see* 4'-Amino-2-methyldiphenylamine.
N-p-*Tolyl* : *see* 4'-Amino-4-methyldiphenylamine.
N : N'-*Ditolyl* : *see* Ditolyl-*p*-phenylenediamine.
N-*Benzyl* : plates from Et_2O. M.p. 37°. N'-*Acetyl* : needles from EtOH. M.p. 141–2°. N : N'-*Diacetyl* : prisms from EtOH.Aq. M.p. 116–17°. N'-*Benzoyl* : plates from EtOH. M.p. 182–3°. N : N'-*Dibenzoyl* : needles. M.p. 124°.
N : N'-*Dibenzyl* : needles from EtOH. M.p. 89–90°. Sol. Et_2O. Spar. sol. EtOH–$FeCl_3$ ⟶ intense red col.
N : N'-*Tetrabenzyl* : needles from AcOH. M.p. 152° (149°). Sol. C_6H_6, $CHCl_3$, CS_2. Spar. sol. EtOH.
N-1-*Naphthyl* : plates. M.p. 80·5–81°. B.p. 275–80°/12 mm. Sol. hot EtOH, C_6H_6. Spar. sol. H_2O. N'-*Acetyl* : needles from EtOH. M.p. 162·5°.
N-2-*Naphthyl* : needles from ligroin. M.p. 94°. Very sol. C_6H_6, EtOH, Et_2O, Me_2CO with blue fluor. *B,2HCl* : m.p. 240°. decomp. N'-*Acetyl* : needles from C_6H_6. M.p. 160°.
Dinaphthyl : *see* Dinaphthyl-*p*-phenylenediamine.
N-*Picryl* : black prisms from AcOEt. M.p. 186–7°. Sol. AcOH, amyl alcohol.
Dibenzylidene : plates from EtOH. M.p. 140°.
N-*Formyl* : brownish needles from H_2O. M.p. 125–7°.
N : N'-*Diformyl* : m.p. 205–7°.
N-*Acetyl* : *see p*-Aminoacetanilide.
N : N'-*Diacetyl* : leaflets from hot AcOH. M.p. 303°.
N-*Benzoyl* : leaflets. M.p. 128°. Sol. EtOH, $CHCl_3$. Spar. sol. H_2O.
N : N'-*Dibenzoyl* : leaflets. Does not melt below 300°. Spar. sol. EtOH, Et_2O, AcOH.
N-m-*Nitrobenzoyl* : golden cryst. from EtOH. M.p. 217–18°.
N-p-*Nitrobenzoyl* : cryst. M.p. 228°.

Paul, *Z. angew. Chem.*, 1897, **10**, 149.
Pomeranz, D.R.P., 269,542, (*Chem. Zentr.* 1914, I, 591).
Wurster, *Ber.*, 1879, **12**, 523.
Reilly, Hickinbottom, *J. Chem. Soc.* 1917, **111**, 1032.
Ullmann, Dahmen, *Ber.*, 1908, **41**, 3750.
Philip, *J. prakt. Chem.*, 1886, **34**, 65.
Jacobs, Heidelberger, *J. Biol. Chem.* 1915, **21**, 115.
Quick, *J. Am. Chem. Soc.*, 1920, **42**, 1033.
Norris, Cummings, *J. Ind. Eng. Chem.* 1925, **17**, 305.
Major, *J. Am. Chem. Soc.*, 1931, **53**, 4375.
Andrews, Lowy, *J. Am. Chem. Soc.*, 1934, **56**, 1411.
Hofmann, *Compt. rend.*, 1863, **56**, 994.

o-Phenylenediamine-4-sulphonic Acid
(3 : 4-*Diaminobenzenesulphonic acid*)

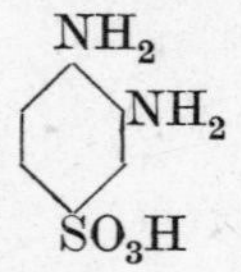

$C_6H_8O_3N_2S$ MW, 188

Needles. Decomp. on melting. Mod. sol. hot H_2O. Turns blue or green in air. $FeCl_3$ ⟶ reddish-brown col.

Nietzki, Lerch, *Ber.*, 1888, **21**, 3221.
Post, Hartung, *Ann.*, 1880, **205**, 100.

_m_-Phenylenediamine-4-sulphonic Acid (2 : 4-*Diaminobenzenesulphonic acid*)

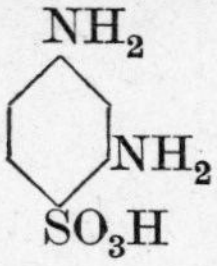

$C_6H_8O_3N_2S$ **MW, 188**

Plates and prisms from H_2O. Spar. sol. cold H_2O. Slowly turns brown in air.

Post, Hartung, *Ann.*, 1880, **205**, 107.
Hunter, Sprung, *J. Am. Chem. Soc.*, 1931, 53, 1440.

_p_-Phenylenediamine-2-sulphonic Acid (2 : 5-*Diaminobenzenesulphonic acid*)

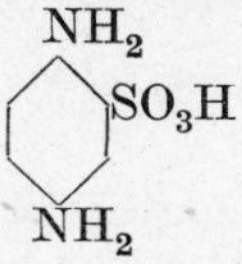

$C_6H_8O_3N_2S$ MW, 188

Plates + $2H_2O$ from H_2O, needles from H_2O with trace H_2SO_4. Mod. sol. H_2O. Insol. EtOH, Et_2O, C_6H_6.

N-*Di-Me* : sol. H_2O. $FeCl_3 \longrightarrow$ red col.

Anilide : leaflets from H_2O. M.p. 171°.

B,HCl : needles. M.p. 215° decomp.

A.G.F.A., D.R.P., 204,972, (*Chem. Zentr.*, 1909, I, 475).
Kalle, D.R.P., 124,907, (*Chem. Zentr.*, 1901, II, 1103).
Fischer, *Ber.*, 1891, **24**, 3789.
Eger, *Ber.*, 1889, **22**, 848.

Phenylene Dimercaptan.
See Dithiocatechol, Dithiohydroquinone, *and* Dithioresorcinol.

Phenylenedimethyldiamine.
See sym.-Dimethylphenylenediamine.

Phenylenedinaphthyldiamine.
See Dinaphthylphenylenediamine.

Phenylenediphenyldiamine.
See sym.-Diphenylphenylenediamine.

_o_-Phenylenedipropionic Acid (o-*Xylylenediacetic acid, benzene*-o-*dipropionic acid*, o-*diethylbenzene*-ω : ω'-*dicarboxylic acid*)

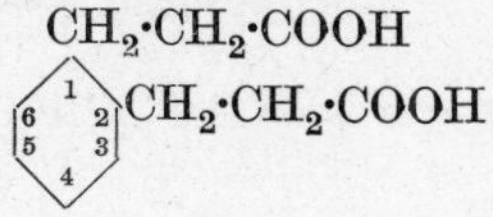

$C_{12}H_{14}O_4$ MW, 222

Needles from H_2O, prisms from EtOH.Aq. M.p. 171° (168°, 162°).

Di-Et ester : $C_{16}H_{22}O_4$. MW, 278. B.p. 200–2°/12 mm.

Diamide : $C_{12}H_{16}O_2N_2$. MW, 220. Needles from EtOH. M.p. 195°.

Titley, *J. Chem. Soc.* 1928, 2578.
Fries, Bestian, *Ber.*, 1936, **69**, 720.

_m_-Phenylenedipropionic Acid (m-*Xylylenediacetic acid, benzene*-m-*dipropionic acid*, m-*diethylbenzene*-ω : ω'-*dicarboxylic acid*).

Plates from H_2O. M.p. 146–7°. Mod. sol. EtOH, Et_2O.

Di-Me ester : $C_{14}H_{18}O_4$. MW, 250. Leaflets from MeOH.Aq. M.p. 51°. Very sol. EtOH, Et_2O, C_6H_6.

Di-Et ester : liq. B.p. 247–50°/60 mm.

Kipping, *J. Chem. Soc.*, 1888, **53**, 33.

_p_-Phenylenedipropionic Acid (p-*Xylylenediacetic acid, benzene*-p-*dipropionic acid*, p-*diethylbenzene*-ω : ω'-*dicarboxylic acid*).

Cryst. from MeOH. M.p. 223–4°. Spar. sol. EtOH. Insol. H_2O.

Di-Me ester : plates from MeOH. M.p. 115°. Spar. sol. cold MeOH.

See previous reference.

Phenyleneditolyldiamine.
See Ditolylphenylenediamine.

Phenylerythrene.
See Phenyl-1 : 3-butadiene.

Phenylethane.
See Ethylbenzene.

Phenyl _p_-ethoxyphenacyl Ether.
See under p-Hydroxyphenacyl Alcohol.

Phenyl ethoxystyryl Ketone.
See under Hydroxychalkone.

β-Phenylethylacetylene.
See 4-Phenylbutine-1.

1-Phenylethyl Alcohol.
See Methylphenylcarbinol.

2-Phenylethyl Alcohol (*Benzylcarbinol*, β-*hydroxyethylbenzene*)

$$C_6H_5{\cdot}CH_2{\cdot}CH_2OH$$

$C_8H_{10}O$ MW, 122

Found in fresh rose petals and neroli oil. B.p. 219–21°/750 mm., 104°/14 mm., 98–100°/12 mm. D_4^{25} 1·0235. $n_D^{16\cdot8}$ 1·5337. Mod. sol. H_2O, EtOH.Aq. Used in perfumery, as also are its esters.

Me ether : *see* Methyl phenylethyl Ether.

Phenyl ether : phenyl phenylethyl ether. $C_{14}H_{14}O$. MW, 198. B.p. 166°/14 mm.

Formyl : b.p. 94°/9 mm. D^{15} 1·054.

Acetyl : b.p. 224°, 118–20°/13 mm. D^{15} 1·038. n_D 1·5108.

Methoxyacetyl : b.p. 149°/18 mm. D_4^{17} 1·0806. n_D^{17} 1·5000.

Oxalate : cryst. from 80% EtOH. M.p. 51·5°.
p-*Nitrobenzoyl* : m.p. 62–3°.
Allophanate : m.p. 186°.
Phenylurethane : m.p. 79–80°.

Skita, Ritter, *Ber.*, 1911, **43**, 3398.
Bouveault, Blanc, *Bull. soc. chim.*, 1904, **31**, 674.
Skita, *Ber.*, 1915, **48**, 1694.
Skita, Mayer, *Ber.*, 1912, **45**, 3584.
Leonard, *J. Am. Chem. Soc.*, 1925, **47**, 1774.

Phenylethylamine.
See Aminoethylbenzene.
β-Phenylethylbenzylamine.
See Benzyl-phenylethylamine.
Phenylethyl bromide.
See Bromoethylbenzene.
Phenylethyl chloride.
See Chloroethylbenzene.
Phenylethylene.
See Styrene.
Phenylethylene bromohydrin.
See Styrene bromohydrin.
Phenylethylene chlorohydrin.
See Styrene chlorohydrin.
Phenylethylenediamine (αβ-*Diaminoethylbenzene*)

$C_6H_5·CH(NH_2)·CH_2NH_2$

$C_8H_{12}N_2$ MW, 136

l-.
M.p. 4–5°. B.p. 104°/1–2 mm. D^{18} 1·034. $[\alpha]_D$ − 35·2°.
N : N′-*Diacetyl*: cryst. from AcOEt. M.p. 174°.
N : N′-*Dibenzoyl* : cryst. from EtOH. M.p. 227°.
d-*Tartrate* : m.p. 220° decomp. $[\alpha]_D$ + 40·8° in H_2O.

dl-.
B.p. 243–6°, 156–7°/42 mm. Very sol. H_2O. Sol. most org. solvents.
Diacetyl : cryst. from AcOEt. M.p. 159° (152°).
Triacetyl : plates from H_2O. M.p. 166°.
Dibenzoyl : leaflets from EtOH. M.p. 217°.
Picrate : yellow cryst. M.p. 160°. Insol. C_6H_6, ligroin.
B,2HCl : needles. Does not melt below 260°.

Reihlen, Hessling, Hühn, Weinbrenner, *Ann.*, 1932, **493**, 25.
Kanewskaja, *J. prakt. Chem.*, 1932, **132**, 340.
Reihlen, Weinbrenner, Hessling, *Ann.*, 1932, **494**, 157.
Feist, Arnstein, *Ber.*, 1893, **28**, 425, 3172.

Phenylethylene dibromide.
See Styrene dibromide.
Phenylethylene dichloride.
See Styrene dichloride.
Phenylethylene Glycol.
See Styrene Glycol.
Phenylethylene oxide.
See Styrene oxide.
Phenylethylhydrazine (*Phenethylhydrazine*, ω-*hydrazinoethylbenzene*)

$C_6H_5·CH_2·CH_2·NH·NH_2$

$C_8H_{12}N_2$ MW, 136

B.p. 137–9°/12–13 mm.
B,HCl : plates from EtOH. M.p. 171°.
Dibenzoyl : needles from 50% EtOH. M.p. 144–5°.

Votoček, Lemings, *Chem. Zentr.*, 1932, II, 1613.

Phenylethyl 1-naphthyl Ketone (ω-*Benzyl*-α-*acetonaphthone*)

$CO·CH_2·CH_2·C_6H_5$

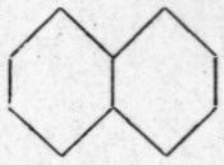

$C_{19}H_{16}O$ MW, 260

Leaflets from 70% EtOH. M.p. 93° (53–4°). B.p. 240–60°/25 mm. Sol. conc. H_2SO_4 with yellow col. turning brownish-red on warming.
Oxime : cryst. from EtOH. M.p. 120°.

Albrecht, *Monatsh.*, 1914, **35**, 1498.
Bergmann, Weiss, *Ber.*, 1931, **64**, 1492.

Phenylethylpiperidine.
See Stilbazoline.
2-Phenylethylpyridine (*Dihydro*-α-*stilbazole*, *phenyl*-2-*pyridylethane*)

$CH_2·CH_2·C_6H_5$

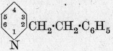

$C_{13}H_{13}N$ MW, 183

Liq. with sweet odour. F.p. − 3°. B.p. 289·5°/766 mm. D^0_4 1·0465. Very sol. EtOH, Et_2O, C_6H_6. Spar. sol. H_2O. Volatile in steam.
B,HAuCl₄ : yellow needles from dil. HCl. M.p. 149–50°.
B,HCl,HgCl₂ : cryst. M.p. 149°.
B₂,H₂PtCl₆ : reddish-yellow needles. M.p. 185–6°.

Baurath, *Ber.*, 1888, **21**, 821.

4-Phenylethylpyridine (γ-*Dihydrostilbazole*, *phenyl*-4-*pyridylethane*).
Needles from EtOH. M.p. 69–71° (65°).

B,HCl : cryst. from EtOH–Et_2O. M.p. 180°.
B,HI : brownish-red leaflets from H_2O. Decomp. about 150°.
$B,HAuCl_4$: yellow leaflets. M.p. 183–5° (166°).
B_2,H_2PtCl_6 : brown leaflets. M.p. 214°.
Picrate : yellow needles. M.p. 162–3°.

Friedländer, *Ber.*, 1905, **38**, 2837.
Fels, *Ber.*, 1904, **37**, 2147.

2-Phenylethylquinoline (*Phenyl*-2-*quinolylethane*)

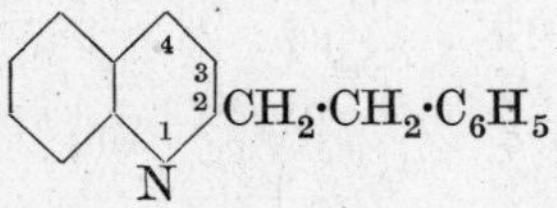

$C_{17}H_{15}N$ MW, 233

Cryst. from C_6H_6 or ligroin. M.p. 28°. B.p. 214–19°/14 mm. Spar. volatile in steam.
Picrate : pale yellow prisms. M.p. about 130°.

Heymann, Koenigs, *Ber.*, 1888, **21**, 1426.
Ziegler, Zeiser, *Ann.*, 1931, **485**, 190.

4-Phenylethylquinoline (*Phenyl*-4-*quinolylethane*).
Cryst. from EtOH.Aq. or ligroin. M.p. 100–1°.

See first reference above.

α-Phenylethyl-succinic Acid (3-*Phenylbutane*-1 : 2-*dicarboxylic acid*)

$$C_6H_5\cdot\underset{|}{\overset{CH_3}{CH}}\cdot CH(CH_2\cdot COOH)\cdot COOH$$

$C_{12}H_{14}O_4$ MW, 222

Needles from C_6H_6 or hot H_2O. M.p. 144–146·5°. Sol. EtOH, Et_2O. Spar. sol. cold C_6H_6.

Stobbe, *Ann.*, 1899, **308**, 127.

β-Phenylethyl-succinic Acid (4-*Phenylbutane*-1 : 2-*dicarboxylic acid*)

$$C_6H_5\cdot CH_2\cdot CH_2\cdot CH(COOH)\cdot CH_2\cdot COOH$$

$C_{12}H_{14}O_4$ MW, 222

Cryst. from H_2O or C_6H_6. M.p. 136°. Sol. EtOH, Et_2O. Spar. sol. C_6H_6. Insol. CS_2, low-boiling pet. ether.
Mono-NH_4 salt : leaflets from H_2O. M.p. 185° decomp.
Anhydride : $C_{12}H_{12}O_3$. MW, 204. Cryst. from pet. ether. M.p. 56°. Sol. $CHCl_3$, C_6H_6. Spar. sol. CS_2, pet. ether.

Thiele, Meisenheimer, *Ann.*, 1899, **306**, 257, 261.

9-Phenylfluorene (*Phenyldiphenylenemethane*)

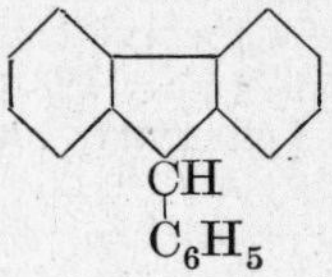

$C_{19}H_{14}$ MW, 242

Needles or leaflets from EtOH or C_6H_6. M.p. 148° (145°). Sol. AcOH, $CHCl_3$, C_6H_6, pet. ether, hot EtOH. Spar. sol. Et_2O. Alc. and benzene solutions show blue fluor. $CrO_3 \longrightarrow$ *o*-benzoylbenzoic acid.

Vorländer, Pritzsche, *Ber.*, 1913, **46**, 1796.
Kliegl, *Ber.*, 1905, **38**, 287.
Koelsch, *J. Am. Chem. Soc.*, 1934, **56**, 482.

Phenyl formate

$$H\cdot CO\cdot OC_6H_5$$

$C_7H_6O_2$ MW, 122

B.p. 173° slight decomp., 107°/25 mm. D^0 1·0879.

Seifert, *J. prakt. Chem.*, 1885, **31**, 467.
Auger, *Compt. rend.*, 1904, **139**, 799.
Adickes, Brunnert, Lücker, *J. prakt. Chem.*, 1931, **130**, 174.

Phenylformylacetanilide.
See under Phenylformylacetic Acid.

Phenylformylacetic Acid (*Phenylaldehydoacetic acid*, β-*hydroxyatropic acid*, α-*hydroxymethylenephenylacetic acid*, 2-*hydroxy*-1-*phenylacrylic acid*, *phenylmalonaldehydic acid*)

$$\underset{\text{aldo-form.}}{C_6H_5\cdot\overset{CHO}{\overset{|}{CH}}\cdot COOH} \rightleftharpoons \underset{\text{enol-form.}}{C_6H_5\cdot\overset{CH\cdot OH}{\overset{||}{C}}\cdot COOH}$$

$C_9H_8O_3$ MW, 164

The acid is unknown in the free state.
Me ester : $C_{10}H_{10}O_3$. MW, 178. α(*enol*)-form : leaflets. M.p. 40–1°. β(probably *aldo*)-form : leaflets from C_6H_6. M.p. 91–3° (87°). *Semicarbazone* : m.p. 159–60°. *Aldo-enol* mixture : b.p. 153–5°/18 mm. n^{20} 1·52425.
Et ester : $C_{11}H_{12}O_3$. MW, 192. α(mainly *enol*)-form : b.p. 135°/15 mm. Alc. sol. $\longrightarrow$ bluish-violet col. with $FeCl_3$. *Formyl* : m.p. 87°. *Acetyl* : b.p. 184°/18 mm. β(probably *aldo*)-form : m.p. 50° (70°). *Semicarbazone* : m.p. 162–5° (130–1°). *Aldo-enol* mixture : b.p. 150–1°/18 mm. n^{20} 1·532. *γ-form* : plates. M.p. 108–10°.
Nitrile : α-formylbenzyl cyanide, α-cyanophenylacetaldehyde. C_9H_7ON. MW, 145. Leaf-

lets from EtOH. M.p. 165–6° (157–8°). Sol. EtOH, C_6H_6, hot H_2O.

Anilide : phenylformylacetanilide. Exists in two modifications. (α-) Plates from pet. ether. M.p. 68°. (β-) Triangular plates from Et_2O or AcOH. M.p. 98°.

Piperidide : exists in two modifications. (α-) M.p. 104–6°. (β-) M.p. 122°.

Décombe, *Ann. chim.*, 1932, **18**, 90, 113.
Wislicenus, Erbe, *Ann.*, 1920, **421**, 119.
Tiffeneau, Levy, *Chem. Abstracts*, 1930, **24**, 2450.
Ghosh, *J. Chem. Soc.*, 1916, **109**, 113.
Wislicenus, *Ann.*, 1917, **413**, 206.

Phenylfumaric Acid

$$C_6H_5 \cdot C \cdot COOH$$
$$HOOC \cdot CH$$

$C_{10}H_8O_4$ MW, 192

Needles from C_6H_6. M.p. 128–9°. Very sol. H_2O. Spar. sol. C_6H_6. Above m.p. ⟶ phenyl-maleic anhydride. Reduces $KMnO_4$.Aq. slowly.

Almström, *Ber.*, 1915, **48**, 2009; *Ann.*, 1916, **411**, 375.

Phenyl furyl Diketone.
See Benzfuril.

Phenyl α-furyl Ketone (2-*Benzoylfuran*, α-*benzofuran*)

$$HC \!\!-\!\! CH$$
$$HC \quad C \cdot CO \cdot C_6H_5$$
$$O$$

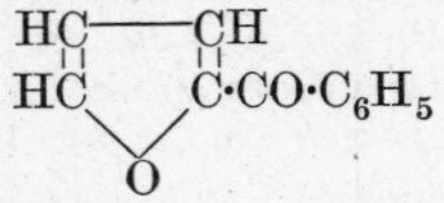

$C_{11}H_8O_2$ MW, 172

B.p. 285°, 186°/46 mm., 164°/19 mm. D^{20} 1·1732. n_D^{20} 1·6055 (1·5798).

Oxime : yellow needles from C_6H_6–pet. ether. M.p. 138° (132°). Very sol. org. solvents.

Semicarbazone : m.p. 182°.

Asahina, Murayama, *Arch. Pharm.*, 1914, **252**, 448.
Marquis, *Bull. soc. chim.*, 1900, **23**, 33.
Gilman, Hewlett, *Chem. Abstracts*, 1930, **24**, 1640.

Phenyl furylvinyl Ketone.
See Furfurylideneacetophenone.

Phenyl-gamma Acid.
See *N*-Phenyl-2-amino-8-naphthol-6-sulphonic Acid.

2-Phenylglutaconic Acid (2-*Phenylpropyl-ene*-1 : 3-*dicarboxylic acid*)

$$C_6H_5$$
$$HOOC \cdot CH_2 \cdot C : CH \cdot COOH$$

$C_{11}H_{10}O_4$ MW, 206

Prismatic plates from AcOEt. M.p. 154–5° Above m.p. ⟶ anhydride. P + HI at 150 ⟶ 2-phenylglutaric acid.

Mono-Et ester : $C_{13}H_{14}O_4$. MW, 234. Needle from C_6H_6–pet. ether. M.p. 78°. Dist. ⟶ anhydride.

Di-Et ester : $C_{15}H_{18}O_4$. MW, 262. B.p. 186 7°/11 mm., 167–8°/5 mm. D_4^{20} 1·1014. $n_?^2$ 1·5240.

Monoamide : $C_{11}H_{11}O_3N$. MW, 205. Needle from AcOEt. M.p. 138°.

Mononitrile : $C_{11}H_9O_2N$. MW, 187. Leaflet from EtOH or AcOH. M.p. 256–7°. Spar. sol H_2O, EtOH.

Anhydride : $C_{11}H_8O_3$. MW, 188. Leaflet from AcOEt. M.p. 206°.

Imide : $C_{11}H_9O_2N$. MW, 187. Prisms from AcOH, leaflets from EtOH. M.p. 256–7°. Spar sol. boiling EtOH. Very spar. sol. H_2O, Et_2O Alc. $FeCl_3$ ⟶ red col.

Monoanilide : cryst. from AcOEt. M.p. 174°

Mono-p-toluidide : cryst. from AcOEt. M.p 184°.

Michael, *J. prakt. Chem.*, 1894, **49**, 22.
Ruhemann, *J. Chem. Soc.*, 1899, **75**, 252
Feist, Pomme, *Ann.*, 1909, **370**, 74.
Guareschi, *Chem. Zentr.*, 1907, I, 459 1901, I, 821.
Bland, Thorpe, *J. Chem. Soc.*, 1912, **101** 868.
Gidvani, Kon, *J. Chem. Soc.*, 1932, 2448

3-Phenylglutaconic Acid (3-*Phenylpropyl-ene*-1 : 3-*dicarboxylic acid*)

$$C_6H_5$$
$$HOOC \cdot CH \cdot CH : CH \cdot COOH$$

$C_{11}H_{10}O_4$ MW, 206

Cryst. from EtOH. M.p. 164°.

Di-Et ester : b.p. 220°/80 mm. D^{30} 1·0712 n_D^{30} 1·50923.

Phalnikar, Nargund, *Chem. Zentr.*, 1936 I, 4556.

2-Phenylglutamic Acid

$$C_6H_5$$
$$HOOC \cdot CH_2 \cdot CH \cdot CH(NH_2) \cdot COOH$$

$C_{11}H_{13}O_4N$ MW, 223

Plates from H_2O. M.p. 179°. Insol. EtOH. *N-Benzoyl* : needles from H_2O. M.p. 171–2°

Harington, *J. Biol. Chem.*, 1925, **64**, 29.

3-Phenylglutamic Acid

$$C_6H_5$$
$$HOOC \cdot CH \cdot CH_2 \cdot CH(NH_2) \cdot COOH$$

$C_{11}H_{13}O_4N$ MW, 223

Rhombic cryst. M.p. 185° decomp. Spar. sol. H_2O.

v. Beznák, *Biochem. Z.*, 1929, **205**, 414.

1-Phenylglutaric Acid (1-*Phenylpropane*-1 : 3-*dicarboxylic acid*)

$$HOOC{\cdot}CH_2{\cdot}CH_2{\cdot}\overset{C_6H_5}{\overset{|}{C}}H{\cdot}COOH$$

$C_{11}H_{12}O_4$ MW, 208

Cryst. from C_6H_6 or Et_2O–pet. ether. M.p. 82–3°. Dist. in vacuo ⟶ anhydride.

Anhydride: $C_{11}H_{10}O_3$. MW, 190. Needles from Et_2O. M.p. 95°. B.p. 218–30°/13 mm.

Fichter, Merckens, *Ber.*, 1901, **34**, 4175.

2-Phenylglutaric Acid (*Benzylidenediacetic acid*, 2-*phenylpropane*-1 : 3-*dicarboxylic acid*)

$$HOOC{\cdot}CH_2{\cdot}\overset{C_6H_5}{\overset{|}{C}}H{\cdot}CH_2{\cdot}COOH$$

$C_{11}H_{12}O_4$ MW, 208

Plates from H_2O, prisms from C_6H_6. M.p. 140°. Sol. EtOH, Et_2O, AcOEt, $CHCl_3$. Spar. sol. C_6H_6. Insol. pet. ether. $k = 7{\cdot}7 \times 10^{-5}$ at 25°. Above m.p. ⟶ anhydride.

Di-Me ester: $C_{13}H_{16}O_4$. MW, 236. Prisms or needles from MeOH. M.p. 86–7°.

Di-Et ester: $C_{15}H_{20}O_4$. MW, 264. B.p. 188–9°/13 mm.

Dichloride: $C_{11}H_{10}O_2Cl_2$. MW, 245. M.p. 46°. B.p. 178–80°/18 mm.

Anhydride: $C_{11}H_{10}O_3$. MW, 190. Cryst. from C_6H_6. M.p. 105°. B.p. 217–19°/15 mm. Sol. Et_2O, $CHCl_3$, C_6H_6. Insol. pet. ether.

Imide: $C_{11}H_{11}O_2N$. MW, 189. Leaflets from H_2O, EtOH or C_6H_6. M.p. 173–4°.

Monoanilide: needles from EtOH.Aq. M.p. 171° (168°).

Mono-p-*toluidide*: needles. M.p. 154–5°.

Anil: needles from EtOH. M.p. 223°.

Michael, *J. prakt. Chem.*, 1887, **35**, 352.
Herrmann, Vorländer, *Chem. Zentr.*, 1899, I, 730.
Avery, Bouton, *Am. Chem. J.*, 1898, **20**, 513.
v. Braun, Weissbach, *Ber.*, 1931, **64**, 1787.

1-Phenylglyceric Acid (1 : 2-*Dihydroxy*-1-*phenylpropionic acid, atroglyceric acid*)

$$HO{\cdot}CH_2{\cdot}\overset{C_6H_5}{\overset{|}{C}}(OH){\cdot}COOH$$

$C_9H_{10}O_4$ MW, 182

Cryst. from H_2O. M.p. 146°. Mod. sol. hot H_2O. Heat ⟶ phenylacetaldehyde.

Nitrile: $C_9H_9O_2N$. MW, 163. Needles from Et_2O. M.p. 55–7° decomp.

Plöchl, Blümlein, *Ber.*, 1883, **16**, 1292.
Fittig, Kast, *Ann.*, 1881, **206**, 30.
McKenzie, Wood, *J. Chem. Soc.*, 1919, **115**, 838.

2-Phenylglyceric Acid (αβ-*Dihydroxyhydrocinnamic acid*)

$$C_6H_5{\cdot}CH(OH){\cdot}CH(OH){\cdot}COOH$$

$C_9H_{10}O_4$ MW, 182

Exists in two stereoisomeric forms.

(i) *d*-.

Needles or plates from C_6H_6. M.p. 95°. Sol. 10 parts Et_2O at 20°. $[\alpha]_D^{20} + 26{\cdot}1°$ in H_2O, $+ 21{\cdot}15°$ in EtOH, $+ 27{\cdot}5°$ in Me_2CO.

l-.

Cryst. M.p. 97–8°. $[\alpha]_D - 25{\cdot}6°$.

dl-.

Needles from Et_2O. M.p. 122°. Sol. 15 parts Et_2O. $k = 2{\cdot}35 \times 10^{-4}$.

Me ester: $C_{10}H_{12}O_4$. MW, 196. Cryst. M.p. 87°. B.p. 110°/0·1 mm. *Dibenzoyl*: cryst. from EtOH. M.p. 113·5°.

Monoacetyl: cryst. from H_2O. M.p. 158°.

Dibenzoyl: needles from C_6H_6. M.p. 187° decomp. Sol. EtOH. Spar. sol. C_6H_6, hot H_2O.

Et ester: prisms from toluene. M.p. 109°.

Phenylhydrazide: m.p. 177°.

(ii) *d*-.

Plates from H_2O. M.p. 166–7° (164°). Sol. 200 parts Et_2O, 25 parts H_2O at 20°. $[\alpha]_D^{20} + 39{\cdot}6°$ in H_2O.

l-.

Plates from H_2O. M.p. 166–7° (164°). Sublimes in high vacuum. $[\alpha]_D^{20} - 39{\cdot}6°$ in H_2O, $- 30{\cdot}5°$ in EtOH, $- 36{\cdot}4°$ in Me_2CO.

dl-.

Plates from H_2O, leaflets from Et_2O or C_6H_6. M.p. 141–2°. Very sol. H_2O, EtOH. Mod. sol. Me_2CO. Spar. sol. $CHCl_3$, CS_2. Insol. C_6H_6, ligroin. Sol. 75 parts Et_2O at 20°. $k = 2{\cdot}54 \times 10^{-4}$. At 160° ⟶ phenylacetaldehyde.

Me ester: cryst. M.p. 67°. B.p. 114°/0·1 mm.

Et ester: *dibenzoyl*, needles from EtOH. M.p. 85°.

Monoacetyl: cryst. from H_2O. M.p. 93·5°.

Diacetyl: leaflets $+ \frac{1}{2}H_2O$ from H_2O. M.p. 88–9°.

Amide: $C_9H_{11}O_3N$. MW, 181. Leaflets from EtOH. M.p. 161–2°. Sol. EtOH, Me_2CO, hot H_2O.

Phenylhydrazide : m.p. 215°.

> Anschütz, Kinnicutt, *Ber.*, 1879, **12**, 539.
> Plöchl, Mayer, *Ber.*, 1897, **30**, 1601.
> Lipp, *Ber.*, 1883, **16**, 1289.
> Riiber, *Ber.*, 1908, **41**, 2413.
> Riiber, Berner, *Ber.*, 1917, **50**, 894.
> Berner, *Chem. Zentr.*, 1919, III, 777.

1-Phenylglycerol (*Stycerine*, 1 : 2 : 3-*tri-hydroxy-1-phenylpropane*)

$$HO \cdot CH_2 \cdot CH(OH) \cdot CH(OH) \cdot C_6H_5$$

$C_9H_{12}O_3$ MW, 168

Cryst. from EtOH. M.p. 100·5° (98–9°). B.p. 184–6°. $D_4^{13·5}$ 1·2213. n_D^{15} 1·5600.
1-*Me ether* : $C_{10}H_{14}O_3$. MW, 182. M.p. 68°.
2-*Me ether* : m.p. 44°. B.p. 153–6°/5–6 mm.
3-*Me ether* : needles. M.p. 54°. B.p. 159°/8 mm. Sol. H_2O, EtOH, Et_2O, C_6H_6. Insol. pet. ether.

> Platt, Hibbert, *Chem. Zentr.*, 1933, I, 3923.
> Tiffeneau, Neuberg-Rabinovitch, Cahmann, *Bull. soc. chim.*, 1935, **2**, 1869.
> See also Prévost, Losson, *Compt. rend.*, 1934, **198**, 659.

Phenylglycide (*Phenylglycidol*)

$$C_6H_5 \cdot CH\!-\!\!-\!\!CH \cdot CH_2OH$$
$$\diagdown \!\! O \!\! \diagup$$

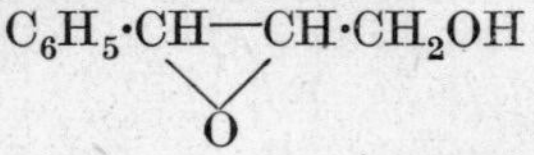

$C_9H_{10}O_2$ MW, 150

Waxy cryst. M.p. 26·5°. B.p. 134–5°/4–5 mm. n_D^{27} 1·5427.
Me ether : $C_{10}H_{12}O_2$. MW, 164. B.p. 130–7°/21–3 mm. n_D^{20} 1·5170.
Acetyl : b.p. 129–32°/3 mm. n_D^{22} 1·5208.
Phenylurethane : cryst. from C_6H_6–pet. ether. M.p. 87°.

> Jahn, Hibbert, *Chem. Zentr.*, 1933, II, 1018.

Phenylglycidic Acid

$$C_6H_5 \cdot CH\!-\!\!-\!\!CH \cdot COOH$$
$$\diagdown \!\! O \!\! \diagup$$

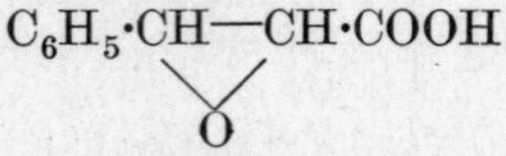

$C_9H_8O_3$ MW, 164

l-.
Na salt : $[\alpha]_D$ — 157·9° in H_2O.
dl-.
Prisms. M.p. 83–4°. B.p. 128–30°/4–5 mm. Spar. sol. H_2O. Stable at ord. temps. Above

m.p. $\longrightarrow$ phenylacetaldehyde. Dil. H_2SO
$\longrightarrow$ phenylacetaldehyde + 2-phenylglyceric aci (both forms).
Et ester : $C_{11}H_{12}O_3$. MW, 192. B.p. 279· slight decomp.
Anilide : needles from EtOH. M.p. 142°.

> Erlenmeyer, *Ber.*, 1906, **39**, 789.
> Dieckmann, *Ber.*, 1910, **43**, 1035.
> Erdmann, D.R.P., 107,228.
> I.G., F.P., 715,657, (*Chem. Zentr.*, 193 II, 2747).
> Kaufmann, D.R.P., 515,034, (*Chem Zentr.*, 1931, I, 1829).

C-Phenylglycine.
α-Aminophenylacetic Acid, *q.v.*
Phenylglycine (*Anilinoacetic acid*)

$$C_6H_5 \cdot NH \cdot CH_2 \cdot COOH$$

$C_8H_9O_2N$ MW, 15

Cryst. M.p. 127–8°. Mod. sol. H_2O. Les sol. Et_2O. $k = 3·8 \times 10^{-6}$ at 25°. Na and salts sol. H_2O, Ca salt spar. sol. H_2O, Fe an Cu salts insol. H_2O. Intermediate in manu facture of indigo.
Me ester : $C_9H_{11}O_2N$. MW, 165. Needles M.p. 48°. Sol. EtOH, Et_2O. Insol. H_2O Volatile in steam.
Et ester : $C_{10}H_{13}O_2N$. MW, 179. Leaflets M.p. 58°. B.p. 273–4°, 163°/18 mm., 140°/8 mm Sol. EtOH, Et_2O. Spar. sol. hot H_2O. Volatil in steam. N-*Carboethoxyl* : thick liq. B.p 177–8°/14 mm.
Isoamyl ester : $C_{13}H_{19}O_2N$. MW, 221. Leaf lets from C_6H_6. M.p. 37–9°. Sol. Et_2O, C_6H_6 amyl alcohol. Insol. H_2O. N-*Isoamyl* $C_{18}H_{29}O_2N$. MW, 291. B.p. 215–16°/20 mm.
Phenyl ester : $C_{14}H_{13}O_2N$. MW, 227. Leaf lets from cold EtOH.Aq. M.p. 82–3°. Sol. cold EtOH, Et_2O, $CHCl_3$, C_6H_6. Hot EtOH $\longrightarrow$ phenylglycine ethyl ester.
p-*Tolyl ester* : $C_{15}H_{15}O_2N$. MW, 241. Pal yellow needles from pet. ether. M.p. 109°.
Amide : $C_8H_{10}ON_2$. MW, 150. Needles from H_2O, leaflets from EtOH. M.p. 136°. Sol EtOH, Me_2CO, hot H_2O. Spar. sol. Et_2O.
Methylamide : m.p. 118°.
Ethylamide : m.p. 53–4°.
Anilide : needles from EtOH. M.p. 113° Sol. EtOH, Et_2O, hot H_2O.
p-*Toluidide* : needles. M.p. 171–2° (165°) Sol. EtOH, Et_2O.
Nitrile : $C_8H_8N_2$. MW, 132. Plates from ligroin–Et_2O. M.p. 48°. Sol. EtOH, Et_2O C_6H_6. Spar. sol. H_2O, ligroin.

Hydrazide: leaflets from EtOH. M.p. 126·5°. Sol. warm H_2O, EtOH. Spar. sol. Et_2O.

Piperidide: m.p. 102–3°.

N-*Me*: *see* N-Phenylsarcosine.

N-*Et*: $C_{10}H_{13}O_2N$. MW, 179. Oil. *Et ester*: $C_{12}H_{15}O_2N$. MW, 207. B.p. 280°/759 mm., 178°/42 mm. Turns brown in air. *Isoamyl ester*: $C_{15}H_{23}O_2N$. MW, 249. B.p. 187°/18 mm. *Amide*: $C_{10}H_{14}ON_2$. MW, 178. M.p. 114–15°. *Nitrile*: $C_{10}H_{12}N_2$. MW, 160. Cryst. M.p. about 24°. B.p. 183°/20 mm., 150–1°/13 mm.

N-*Phenyl*: *see* N-Diphenylglycine.

N-*Formyl*: *see* Formylphenylglycine.

N-*Acetyl*: N-phenylaceturic acid. $C_{10}H_{11}O_3N$. MW, 193. Leaflets from H_2O. M.p. 194°. Sol. EtOH, AcOH, AcOEt. Spar. sol. H_2O, Et_2O, $CHCl_3$, C_6H_6, ligroin. $k = 2{\cdot}6 \times 10^{-4}$ at 25°. *Et ester*: m.p. 194–5°.

N-*Chloroacetyl*: plates or prisms from C_6H_6. M.p. 132–3°. Sol. EtOH, C_6H_6. $k = 3{\cdot}4 \times 10^{-4}$ at 25°. *Me ester*: prisms from ligroin. M.p. 59–60°.

N-*Bromoacetyl*: leaflets from H_2O. M.p. 153° decomp. $k = 3{\cdot}4 \times 10^{-4}$ at 25°. *Me ester*: leaflets from ligroin. M.p. 71°.

N-*Benzoyl*: N-phenylhippuric acid. Amorph. M.p. 63°. Very sol. EtOH, Et_2O, $CHCl_3$, C_6H_6.

Wohl, Blank, D.R.P., 167,698, (*Chem. Zentr.*, 1906, I, 1069).
Mai, *Ber.*, 1902, **35**, 580.
Curtius, *J. prakt. Chem.*, 1888, **38**, 436.
Lippmann, D.R.P., 163,515, (*Chem. Zentr.*, 1905, II, 1475).
Bischoff, *Ber.*, 1889, **22**, 1809.
Badische, D.R.P., 142,559, (*Chem. Zentr.*, 1903, II, 81).
Paal, Otten, *Ber.*, 1890, **23**, 2592.
Fischer, Gluud, *Ann.*, 1909, **369**, 266.
Thorpe, Wood, *J. Chem. Soc.*, 1913, **103**, 1606.
Stollé, *J. prakt. Chem.*, 1914, **90**, 274.
Wessely, *Z. physiol. Chem.*, 1925, **146**, 72.
B.D.C., E.P., 188,933, (*Chem. Abstracts*, 1923, **17**, 1646).
Rebuffat, *Gazz. chim. ital.*, 1887, **17**, 232.

Phenylglycine-o-carboxylic Acid (*Anthranilinoacetic acid*)

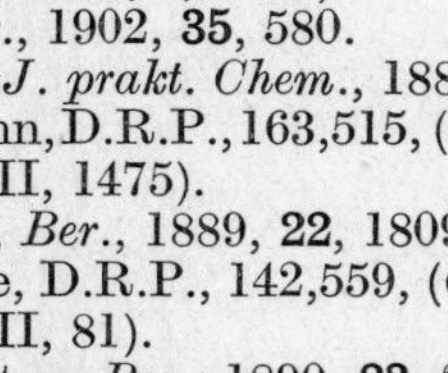

$C_9H_9O_4N$ MW, 195

Needles from MeOH. M.p. 218–20°. Sol. EtOH, Et_2O, AcOH. Mod. sol. hot H_2O. Insol. $CHCl_3$, C_6H_6. Alc. sol. shows blue fluor. Intermediate in manufacture of indigo.

α-*Me ester*: $C_{10}H_{11}O_4N$. MW, 209. M.p. 160°.

β-*Me ester*: m.p. 182°. α-*Amide*: $C_{10}H_{12}O_3N_2$. MW, 208. M.p. 195°. α-*Anilide*: m.p. 140–2°.

Di-Me ester: $C_{11}H_{13}O_4N$. MW, 223. Leaflets. M.p. 97°. Volatile in steam. C_6H_6 and Et_2O sols. show blue fluor. N-*Acetyl*: m.p. 83°. B.p. 205–12°/30 mm.

α-*Et ester*: $C_{11}H_{13}O_4N$. MW, 223. Needles from EtOH. M.p. 152°. Sol. $CHCl_3$. β-*Me ester*: $C_{12}H_{15}O_4N$. MW, 237. M.p. 48°. N-*Acetyl*: m.p. 86–7°. $k = 3{\cdot}8 \times 10^{-4}$ at 25°. N-*Carboethoxyl*: m.p. 114–16°.

β-*Et ester*: m.p. 182°. α-*Amide*: $C_{11}H_{14}O_3N$. MW, 222. Needles from EtOH. M.p. 180–2°. α-*Nitrile*: $C_{11}H_{12}O_2N_2$. MW, 204. Cryst. from EtOH. M.p. 89°. Sol. C_6H_6. Insol. H_2O. α-*Anilide*: m.p. 164–6°. N-*Acetyl*: m.p. 130–2°. N-*Benzoyl*: m.p. 141–3°. N-*Carboethoxyl*: m.p. 106–8°. α-*Hydrazide*: needles from EtOH. M.p. 166°.

Di-Et ester: $C_{13}H_{17}O_4N$. MW, 251. M.p. 75°. N-*Acetyl*: plates or prisms. M.p. 63–4°. B.p. 214–18°/15 mm. decomp. N-*Benzoyl*: m.p. 53–4°. N-*Carboethoxyl*: m.p. 50°.

α-*Amide*: $C_9H_{10}O_3N_2$. MW, 194. M.p. 195°.

Diamide: $C_9H_{11}O_2N_3$. MW, 193. Leaflets from H_2O. M.p. 198–200°.

α-*Nitrile*: $C_9H_8O_2N_2$. MW, 176. Leaflets from EtOH, needles from $CHCl_3$ or C_6H_6. M.p. 184°. Sol. Me_2CO, Et_2O. Mod. sol. boiling EtOH. Insol. C_6H_6. Sols. show violet fluor. β-*Me ester*: $C_{10}H_{10}O_2N_2$. MW, 190. Needles from EtOH. M.p. 106·5°.

β-*Nitrile*: cryst. M.p. 197° decomp.

α-*Anilide*: needles from EtOH. M.p. about 235° decomp. β-*Amide*: m.p. 185°.

N-*Me*: $C_{10}H_{11}O_4N$. MW, 209. Cryst. M.p. 189° decomp.

N-*Et*: $C_{11}H_{13}O_4N$. MW, 223. M.p. 184–6°.

N-*Phenyl*: $C_{15}H_{13}O_4N$. MW, 271. Prisms from MeOH.Aq. M.p. 165–7°.

N-*Benzyl*: $C_{16}H_{15}O_4N$. MW, 285. M.p. 190° decomp. *Di-Me ester*: $C_{18}H_{19}O_4N$. MW, 313. M.p. 82–3°.

N-*Acetyl*: cryst. from MeOH or H_2O. M.p. 214°. $k = 1{\cdot}05 \times 10^{-3}$ at 25°.

N-*Benzoyl*: cryst. from EtOH. M.p. 197°.

α-*Hydrazide*: needles from EtOH. M.p. 200·5°.

Dihydrazide: prisms from EtOH. M.p. 161°. Sol. EtOH. Spar. sol. H_2O. Insol. Et_2O, C_6H_6, pet. ether. *B,2HCl* : m.p. 201°. *Dipicrate* : orange-red plates from H_2O. M.p. 185°.

v. Heyden, D.R.P., 138,207, (*Chem. Zentr.*, 1903, I, 304).
Leonhardt, D.R.P., 126,962, (*Chem. Zentr.*, 1902, I, 82).
Vorländer, *Ber.*, 1902, **35**, 1685.
Vorländer, Mumme, *Ber.*, 1902, **35**, 1699.
Kalle, D.R.P., 206,903, (*Chem. Zentr.*, 1909, I, 807).
Badische, D.R.P., 136,779, (*Chem. Zentr.*, 1902, II, 1351).
Vorländer, v. Schilling, *Ber.*, 1900, **33**, 554.
Houben, *Ber.*, 1913, **46**, 3998.

Phenylglycine-*m*-carboxylic Acid.

Diamide : m.p. 201–2°. Sol. hot H_2O.

α-Nitrile : leaflets from 30% EtOH. M.p. 193°. Sol. hot H_2O, EtOH, Me_2CO, C_6H_6.

Houben, Arnold, *Ber.*, 1908, **41**, 1573.
Lumière, Perrin, *Bull. soc. chim.*, 1903, **29**, 966.

Phenylglycine-*p*-carboxylic Acid.

Cryst. from H_2O. M.p. 219–21° decomp. Spar. sol. H_2O.

α-Amide : prisms from EtOH. M.p. 251°. Spar. sol. H_2O. Insol. Et_2O, C_6H_6. *β-Et ester* : needles from EtOH. M.p. 142°.

α-Nitrile : cryst. powder from Me_2CO. M.p. 177° decomp.

Einhorn, Seuffert, *Ber.*, 1910, **43**, 3001.
Mauthner, Suida, *Monatsh.*, 1890, **11**, 380.
Houben, Arnold, *Ber.*, 1908, **41**, 1572.

Phenylglycollic Acid.

See Mandelic Acid.

Phenylglycollyltropine.

See Homatropine.

Phenylglyoxal (*Benzoylformaldehyde*)

$$\underset{\beta}{C_6H_5\cdot CO}\cdot\underset{\alpha}{CHO}$$

$C_8H_6O_2$ MW, 134

Needles + H_2O from H_2O. M.p. 91°. Sol. usual solvents. Sol. about 35 parts H_2O at 20°. Volatile in steam. Alkalis ⟶ mandelic acid. $KMnO_4$ ⟶ benzoic acid. Above m.p. ⟶ anhydrous compound, a deep yellow oil, b.p. 142°/125 mm., 120°/50 mm.

α-Oxime : *see* Isonitrosoacetophenone.

Dioxime : *see* Phenylglyoxime.

α-Di-Me acetal : b.p. 247–8°, 133–4°/16 mm.

α-Di-Et acetal : b.p. 110°/15 mm.

α-Hydrazone : needles from C_6H_6. M.p. 120–1°. Mod. sol. EtOH, hot C_6H_6. Spar. sol. H_2O, Et_2O.

α-Semicarbazone : pale yellowish leaflets from EtOH. M.p. 217° decomp.

α-Thiosemicarbazone : yellowish prisms from EtOH. M.p. 170°. Spar. sol. H_2O, EtOH Et_2O, $CHCl_3$.

Diphenylhydrazone: *phenylosazone*, yellow leaflets or needles from EtOH. M.p. 152°. Sol EtOH, Et_2O, C_6H_6. Insol. H_2O.

Di-p-nitrophenylhydrazone : m.p. 310–11° decomp.

Wieland, Semper, *Ann.*, 1908, **358**, 57.
Russanow, *Ber.*, 1891, **24**, 3501.
Wolff, Lindenhayn, *Ber.*, 1903, **36**, 4127.
Wolff, *Ann.*, 1912, **394**, 34.
Henze, *Z. physiol. Chem.*, 1931, **198**, 84.
Madelung, Oberwegner, *Ber.*, 1932, **65**, 935.
Riley, Gray, *Organic Syntheses*, 1935, XV, 67.

1-Phenylglyoxaline (1-*Phenyliminazole*)

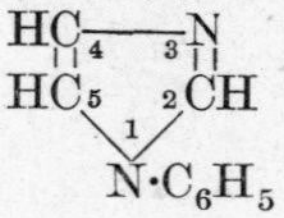

$C_9H_8N_2$ MW, 144

Cryst. M.p. 13°. B.p. 276°. Misc. with most ord. solvents. Insol. H_2O.

$B,2HNO_3$: prisms. M.p. 82–6°.

B_2,H_2PtCl_6 : reddish-yellow leaflets. M.p. 203° decomp. Mod. sol. hot H_2O.

Picrate : yellow needles from EtOH. M.p. 152°. Spar. sol. H_2O, cold EtOH.

Wohl, Marckwald, *Ber.*, 1889, **22**, 576, 1354.
Fischer, Hunsalz, *Ber.*, 1894, **27**, 2206.

2-Phenylglyoxaline (2-*Phenyliminazole*).

Leaflets from C_6H_6, needles from H_2O. M.p. 148–9°. B.p. 340°. Sol. EtOH. Spar. sol. H_2O, C_6H_6.

B,HNO_3 : leaflets from EtOH. M.p. 135°.

Acid oxalate : needles from H_2O. M.p. 219°.

Picrate : needles from H_2O. M.p. 238°.

N-*Me* : *see* 1-Methyl-2-phenylglyoxaline.

Fargher, Pyman, *J. Chem. Soc.*, 1919, **115**, 232.
Maquenne, *Ann. chim. phys.*, 1891, 24, 543.

4-Phenylglyoxaline (4-*Phenyliminazole*).

Leaflets from H_2O. M.p. 128–9°. Very sol. EtOH, Et_2O. Mod. sol. hot H_2O, C_6H_6.

B_2,H_2PtCl_6 : orange-red prisms + $3H_2O$. M.p. 215° decomp.

Pinner, *Ber.*, 1902, **35**, 4135.

Phenylglyoxime (*Phenylglyoxal dioxime*)

$C_6H_5 \cdot C{:}NH{:}O$
$CH{:}N \cdot OH$
α-form

$C_8H_8O_2N_2$ MW, 164

Needles from $CHCl_3$ or EtOH.Aq. M.p. 168°. Sol. EtOH, Et_2O, acids. Spar. sol. C_6H_6. Insol. ligroin.

N-*Me* : $C_9H_{10}O_2N_2$. MW, 178. M.p. 209–10°. Sol. AcOH, dil. HCl. Insol. Na_2CO_3. Gives greenish-yellow sol. in amyl alcohol or NaOH.

O : N-*Di-Me* : $C_{10}H_{12}O_2N_2$. MW, 192. M.p. 135°. Sol. 20% HCl.

Dipropionyl : m.p. 75°.

Diphenylurethane : m.p. 136° decomp.

$C_6H_5 \cdot C{:}N \cdot OH$ b
$CH{:}N \cdot OH$ a
β-form

Needles from EtOH. M.p. 180°. HCl in Et_2O or AcOH ⟶ α-form.

a-*Me ether* : $C_9H_{10}O_2N_2$. MW, 178. Prisms from ligroin. M.p. 113°. b-*Acetyl* : prisms from pet. ether. M.p. 75°.

Di-Me ether : $C_{10}H_{12}O_2N_2$. MW, 192. Plates from EtOH. M.p. 72°. B.p. 240°/740 mm., 137–8°/40 mm.

Diacetyl : m.p. 71–2°.

Dipropionyl : m.p. 89–90°.

Dibenzoyl : m.p. 150°.

Diphenylurethane : m.p. 146–7° decomp.

Longo, *Gazz. chim. ital.*, 1932, **62**, 139.
Ponzio, *Gazz. chim. ital.*, 1930, **60**, 825.
Avogadro, *Gazz. chim. ital.*, 1926, **56**, 713.
Ponzio, Avogadro, *Gazz. chim. ital.*, 1923, **53**, 25, 311.

Phenylglyoxylic Acid.
See Benzoylformic Acid.

Phenylguanazole

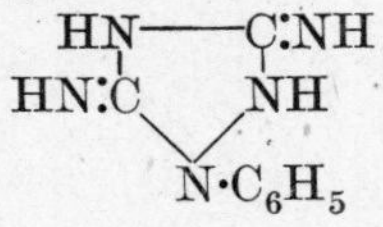

$C_8H_9N_5$ MW, 175

Cryst. M.p. 175°. Sol. EtOH. Mod. sol. $CHCl_3$. Spar. sol. Et_2O, C_6H_6.

B,HCl : needles. M.p. 240°. Sol. H_2O, EtOH.

N-*Nitroso deriv.* : yellow powder. M.p. 245°. Spar. sol. EtOH.

N-*Acetyl deriv.* : prisms from H_2O. M.p. 244°. Sol. warm H_2O, EtOH. Insol. Et_2O.

Diacetyl deriv. : prisms from H_2O. M.p. 212°.

Tetra-acetyl : needles. M.p. 157°.

Pellizzari, Roncagliolo, *Gazz. chim. ital.*, 1901, **31**, i, 477.
Pellizzari, *Gazz. chim. ital.*, 1891, **21**, ii, 146.

Phenylguanidine

$C_6H_5 \cdot NH \cdot C({:}NH) \cdot NH_2$

$C_7H_9N_3$ MW, 135

Cryst. from C_6H_6. M.p. 66–7°. Sol. EtOH, C_6H_6. Spar. sol. H_2O, Et_2O, CCl_4.

B,HNO_3 : needles or prisms. M.p. 128° (118°).

B,HBr : m.p. 71°.

B_2,H_2PtCl_6 : m.p. 197–8°.

B_2,H_2SO_4 : m.p. 205°. Sol. H_2O. Spar. sol. EtOH.

B_2,H_2CO_3 : prisms from H_2O. M.p. 138–40°. Spar. sol. cold H_2O.

Benzoyl deriv. : pale yellow prisms from C_6H_6–pet. ether. M.p. 91–2°. Sol. EtOH, C_6H_6. *Picrate* : yellow prisms from EtOH. M.p. 186°.

Dibenzoyl deriv. : needles from EtOH. M.p. 187°.

Picrate : needles. M.p. 223° (218–20°).

Kampf, *Ber.*, 1904, **37**, 1683.
Wheeler, Johnson, *Am. Chem. J.*, 1901, **26**, 417.
Smith, *J. Am. Chem. Soc.*, 1929, **51**, 477.
Schering-Kahlbaum A.-G., D.R.P., 565,881, (*Chem. Zentr.*, 1933, I, 1685).

***N*-Phenylheptadecylamine.**
See Heptadecylaniline.

1-Phenylheptane.
See *n*-Heptylbenzene.

3-Phenylheptane

$CH_3 \cdot [CH_2]_3 \cdot CH(C_6H_5) \cdot CH_2 \cdot CH_3$

$C_{13}H_{20}$ MW, 176

d-.

B.p. 112°/15 mm. D_4^{25} 0·856. $[\alpha]_D^{25}$ + 0·97°.

dl-.

Obtained by cracking gasoline. B.p. 68–71°/3 mm. n_D^{20} 1·4871.

Levene, Marker, *J. Biol. Chem.*, 1932, **97**, 563.
Tilicheev, Kuruindin, *Chem. Abstracts*, 1931, **25**, 3469.

Phenylheptanol-1.
See Phenylheptyl Alcohol.

1-Phenylheptanol-6 (7-*Phenylheptanol*-2)

$CH_3 \cdot CH(OH) \cdot [CH_2]_5 \cdot C_6H_5$

$C_{13}H_{20}O$ MW, 192

B.p. 169°/50 mm. (164°/23 mm.). D_4^{25} 0·9482 (0·9389). n_D^{25} 1·50575 (1·5028).

Roblin, Davidson, Bogert, *J. Am. Chem. Soc.*, 1935, **57**, 155.
Davies, Dixon, Jones, *J. Chem. Soc.*, 1930, 471.

2-Phenylheptanol-3

C_6H_5
$CH_3\cdot[CH_2]_3\cdot CH(OH)\cdot CH\cdot CH_3$

$C_{13}H_{20}O$ MW, 192

B.p. 156–60°/30 mm.

Lévy, Jullien, *Bull. soc. chim.*, 1929, **45** 941.

3-Phenylheptanol-4

C_6H_5
$CH_3\cdot[CH_2]_2\cdot CH(OH)\cdot CH\cdot CH_2\cdot CH_3$

$C_{13}H_{20}O$ MW, 192

B.p. 145–7°/20 mm.

See previous reference.

4-Phenylheptanol-4 (*Diethylphenylcarbinol, ω-diethylbenzyl alcohol*)

C_6H_5
$CH_3\cdot CH_2\cdot CH_2\cdot C(OH)\cdot CH_2\cdot CH_2\cdot CH_3$

$C_{13}H_{20}O$ MW, 192

B.p. 134°/26 mm. D^0 0·9589, D^{15} 0·9470. n_D 1·516.
Acetyl : b.p. 160°/19 mm. D^{15} 0·8973.

Amouroux, Murat, *Compt. rend.*, 1912, **154**, 993.
Gilman, Fothergill, Parker, *Rec. trav. chim.*, 1929, **48**, 748.

2-Phenylheptanone-3

C_6H_5
$CH_3\cdot[CH_2]_3\cdot CO\cdot CH\cdot CH_3$

$C_{13}H_{18}O$ MW, 190

B.p. 256–7°.
Semicarbazone : m.p. 129°.

Lévy, Jullien, *Bull. soc. chim.*, 1929, **45**, 941.

2-Phenylheptanone-6

C_6H_5
$CH_3\cdot CO\cdot CH_2\cdot CH_2\cdot CH_2\cdot CH\cdot CH_3$

$H_{18}O$ MW, 190

B.p. 136–40°/13 mm. D_4^{20} 0·9629.
p-*Nitrophenylhydrazone* : m.p. 117°.

Nenitzescu, Gavát, *Ann.*, 1935, **519**, 270.

3-Phenylheptanone-2

C_6H_5
$CH_3\cdot[CH_2]_3\cdot CH\cdot CO\cdot CH_3$

$C_{13}H_{18}O$ MW, 190

B.p. 250–1°. D_4^0 0·960.
Oxime : m.p. 63–6°.
Semicarbazone : m.p. 156–8°.

Tiffeneau, Lévy, Jullien, *Bull. soc. chim.*, 1931, **49**, 1788.

3-Phenylheptanone-4

C_6H_5
$CH_3\cdot CH_2\cdot CH_2\cdot CO\cdot CH\cdot CH_2\cdot CH_3$

$C_{13}H_{18}O$ MW, 190

B.p. 242–5°.
Semicarbazone : m.p. 106–7°.

See previous reference.

4-Phenylheptanone-3

C_6H_5
$CH_3\cdot CH_2\cdot CH_2\cdot CH\cdot CO\cdot CH_2\cdot CH_3$

$C_{13}H_{18}O$ MW, 190

B.p. 240–5°.
Semicarbazone : m.p. 108–9°.

Lévy, Jullien, *Bull. soc. chim.*, 1929, **45**, 941.

4-Phenyl-3-heptene (*1-Propyl-1-phenylbutylene*-1, *4-phenyl-3-heptylene*)

C_6H_5
$CH_3\cdot CH_2\cdot CH_2\cdot C\colon CH\cdot CH_2\cdot CH_3$

$C_{13}H_{18}$ MW, 174

B.p. 228°/760 mm. D^{25} 0·8855. n_D^{15} 1·522.

Amouroux, Murat, *Compt. rend.*, 1912, **154**, 993.

1-Phenylheptyl Alcohol (n-*Hexylphenylcarbinol*, 1-*phenylheptanol*-1)

$CH_3\cdot[CH_2]_5\cdot CH(OH)\cdot C_6H_5$

$C_{13}H_{20}O$ MW, 192

B.p. 275°, 176°/40 mm., 156°/25 mm.
Phenylurethane : m.p. 77°.

Colacicchi, *Atti accad. Lincei*, 1910, **19**, ii, 601.

3-Phenylheptyl Alcohol (3-*Phenylheptanol*-1)

C_6H_5
$CH_3\cdot[CH_2]_3\cdot CH\cdot CH_2\cdot CH_2OH$

$C_{13}H_{20}O$ MW, 192

l-.
B.p. 150°/10 mm. D_4^{27} 0·947. $[\alpha]_D^{27}$ − 1·45°.

dl-.
B.p. 116–20°/3 mm. D_{25}^{25} 0·9466. n_D^{20} 1·5070.

Harmon, Marvel, *J. Am. Chem. Soc.*, 1932, **54**, 2525.
Levene, Marker, *J. Biol. Chem.*, 1932, **97**, 563.

5-Phenylheptyl Alcohol (5-*Phenylheptanol*-1)

$$CH_3\cdot CH_2\cdot CH(C_6H_5)\cdot CH_2\cdot CH_2\cdot CH_2\cdot CH_2OH$$

$C_{13}H_{20}O$ MW, 192

d-.
B.p. 145°/1 mm. D_4^{25} 0·952. $[\alpha]_D^{25}$ + 1·47°.
l-.
B.p. 123°/1 mm.

Levene, Marker, *J. Biol. Chem.*, 1931, **93**, 749; 1935, **110**, 329.

7-Phenylheptyl Alcohol (7-*Phenylheptanol*-1)

$$C_6H_5\cdot[CH_2]_6\cdot CH_2OH$$

$C_{13}H_{20}O$ MW, 192

Liq. with faint odour of roses. B.p. 170–2°/15 mm.
Acetyl: b.p. 188–90°/24 mm.

v. Braun, *Ber.*, 1911, **44**, 2878.

Phenylheptylene.
See Phenylheptene.

1-Phenyl-1 : 3-hexadiene (1-*Styryl*-1-*butylene*)

$$CH_3\cdot CH_2\cdot CH{:}CH\cdot CH{:}CH\cdot C_6H_5$$

$C_{12}H_{14}$ MW, 158

Oil B.p. 128°/16 mm. D_4^{12} 0·9253. n_D^{12} 1·60252. Na + EtOH ⟶ 1-phenyl-2-hexene.

Klages, *Ber.*, 1907, **40**, 1770.

6-Phenyl-1 : 3-hexadiene

$$C_6H_5\cdot CH_2\cdot CH_2\cdot CH{:}CH\cdot CH{:}CH_2$$

$C_{12}H_{14}$ MW, 158.

B.p. 99·5–100·5°/11 mm. D_4^{13} 0·9304. n_D^{13} 1·5446.

Cohen, *J. Chem. Soc.*, 1935, 433.

1-Phenylhexahydrobenzoic Acid (1-*Phenylcyclohexane*-1-*carboxylic acid*)

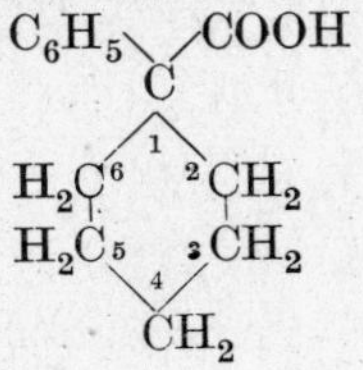

$C_{13}H_{16}O_2$ MW, 204

Cryst. M.p. 121°.
Amide: $C_{13}H_{17}ON$. MW, 203. Cryst. from C_6H_6–pet. ether. M.p. 95–6°.

Case, *J. Am. Chem. Soc.*, 1934, **56**, 716.

2-Phenylhexahydrobenzoic Acid (2-*Phenylcyclohexane*-1-*carboxylic acid*).

Prisms from pet. ether. M.p. 105–7° (104–5°). Sol. MeOH, Et_2O, Me_2CO, $CHCl_3$, warm pet. ether. Spar. sol. H_2O.

Kipping, Perkin, *J. Chem. Soc.*, 1890, **57**, 316.
Ranedo, Léon, *Chem. Abstracts*, 1927, **21**, 1108.
Cook, Hewett, Lawrence, *J. Chem. Soc.*, 1936, 70.

4-Phenylhexahydrobenzoic Acid (4-*Phenylcyclohexane*-1-*carboxylic acid*).

Exists in two forms.
(i) Leaflets from 50% AcOH. M.p. 204° (202°). Fuming HCl at 170° ⟶ (ii).
Me ester: $C_{14}H_{18}O_2$. MW, 218. M.p. 28°. B.p. 172–3°/15 mm.
(ii) Needles from 40% EtOH. M.p. 113°. Sol. EtOH, $CHCl_3$, AcOH. Less sol. Et_2O, pet. ether. Sol. 1000 parts boiling H_2O. Conc. HCl at 180° ⟶ (i).

Rassow, *Ann.*, 1894, **282**, 147.
Nenitzescu, Gavăt, *Ann.*, 1935, **519**, 266.

N-Phenylhexahydroisonicotinic Acid (N-*Phenylpiperidine*-4-*carboxylic acid*, N-*phenylisonipecotic acid*)

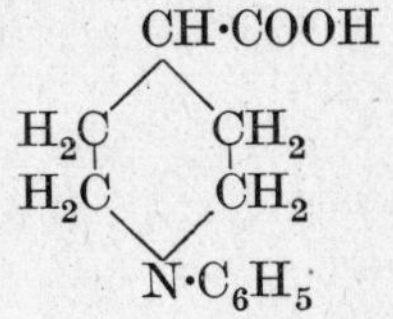

$C_{12}H_{15}O_2N$ MW, 205

Cryst. from EtOH. M.p. 131°.
B,HBr: cryst. from H_2O. M.p. 218–19°.
Me ester: $C_{13}H_{17}O_2N$. MW, 219. Cryst. from ligroin. M.p. 46°.
Anilide: m.p. 210°.
Methiodide: decomp. 180°.
Picrate: cryst. from MeOH. M.p. 207° decomp.

Prelog, Hanousek, *Chem. Abstracts*, 1934, **28**, 5825.

Phenylhexahydrophenol.
See Phenylcyclohexanol.

Phenyl hexahydrostyryl Ketone.
See Hexahydrobenzylideneacetophenone.

1-Phenylhexane (n-*Hexylbenzene*)

$CH_3 \cdot [CH_2]_4 \cdot CH_2 \cdot C_6H_5$

$C_{12}H_{18}$ MW, 162

B.p. 219–20° (215°). D_4^{20} 0·8613. n_D^{20} 1·490.

v. Braun, Deutsch, *Ber.*, 1912, **45**, 2180.
Sabatier, Mailhe, *Compt. rend.*, 1914, **158**, 834.

2-Phenylhexane (ω-*Methylbutyltoluene*)

$CH_3 \cdot [CH_2]_3 \cdot CH(C_6H_5) \cdot CH_3$

$C_{12}H_{18}$ MW, 162

d-.
B.p. 100°/22 mm. D_4^{25} 0·855. $[\alpha]_D^{25}$ + 1·96°.

dl-.
B.p. 208°/760 mm. D_4^{15} 0·869. n^{15} 1·492.

Brochet, *Bull. soc. chim.*, 1893, **9**, 687.
Levene, Marker, *J. Biol. Chem.*, 1931, **93**, 749.

3-Phenylhexane (ω-*Ethylpropyltoluene*)

$CH_3 \cdot CH_2 \cdot CH_2 \cdot CH(C_6H_5) \cdot CH_2 \cdot CH_3$

$C_{12}H_{18}$ MW, 162

d-.
B.p. 103°/25 mm. D_4^{24} 0·863. $[\alpha]_D^{24}$ + 0·57°.

See last reference above.

Phenylhexanol-1.
See Phenylhexyl Alcohol.

1-Phenylhexanol-3 (*Propyl-β-phenylethylcarbinol*)

$CH_3 \cdot CH_2 \cdot CH_2 \cdot CH(OH) \cdot CH_2 \cdot CH_2 \cdot C_6H_5$

$C_{12}H_{18}O$ MW, 178

d-.
Needles. M.p. 34°. B.p. 146°/16 mm. Volatile in steam.
Acid phthalate: m.p. 75°. $[\alpha]_{5893}$ + 25·5°. *Brucine salt*: cryst. from Me_2CO. M.p. 75°. $[\alpha]_{5893}$ − 12·5°.

l-.
Needles. M.p. 34°. B.p. 146°/16 mm. Volatile in steam.
Acid phthalate: m.p. 75°. $[\alpha]_{5893}$ − 25·5°. *Brucine salt*: cryst. from Me_2CO. M.p. 95°. $[\alpha]_{5893}$ − 2·1° in EtOH.
Formyl: b.p. 147°/18 mm. D_4^{20} 0·9872.
Acetyl: b.p. 154°/20 mm. D_4^{20} 0·9725.

dl.-
Acid phthalate: prisms from EtOH. M.p. 108°.

Hewitt, Kenyon, *J. Chem. Soc.*, 1925, 1094.

1-Phenylhexanol-5 (6-*Phenylhexanol*-2)

$CH_3 \cdot CH(OH) \cdot [CH_2]_4 \cdot C_6H_5$

$C_{12}H_{18}O$ MW, 178

B.p. 148°/18 mm. D_4^{20} 0·9567. n_D^{20} 1·50787.
Phenylurethane: needles from pet. ether. M.p. 65°.

Roblin, Davidson, Bogert, *J. Am. Chem. Soc.*, 1935, **57**, 151.

2-Phenylhexanol-3 (*Propyl-α-phenylethylcarbinol*)

$CH_3 \cdot CH_2 \cdot CH_2 \cdot CH(OH) \cdot CH(C_6H_5) \cdot CH_3$

$C_{12}H_{18}O$ MW, 178

B.p. 150–5°/30 mm.

Lévy, Jullien, *Bull. soc. chim.*, 1929, **45**, 941.

1-Phenylhexanone-3 (*Propyl β-phenylethyl ketone*)

$CH_3 \cdot CH_2 \cdot CH_2 \cdot CO \cdot CH_2 \cdot CH_2 \cdot C_6H_5$

$C_{12}H_{16}O$ MW, 176

B.p. 133–5°/8 mm.
Oxime: m.p. 43°.
Semicarbazone: cryst. from C_6H_6. M.p. 79°.

Rupe, Hirschmann, *Helv. Chim. Acta*, 1931, **14**, 698.

1-Phenylhexanone-4 (6-*Phenylhexanone*-3)

$CH_3 \cdot CH_2 \cdot CO \cdot CH_2 \cdot CH_2 \cdot CH_2 \cdot C_6H_5$

$C_{12}H_{16}O$ MW, 176

Colourless oil. B.p. 137–40°/10 mm.
Semicarbazone: cryst. from EtOH. M.p. 149°.

Rupe, Hirschmann, *Helv. Chim. Acta*, 1931, **14**, 700.

1-Phenylhexanone-5 (6-*Phenylhexanone*-2)

$CH_3 \cdot CO \cdot [CH_2]_4 \cdot C_6H_5$

$C_{12}H_{16}O$ MW, 176

B.p. 137°/8 mm.
Semicarbazone: m.p. 143°.

Ramart-Lucas, Labaune, *Ann. chim.*, 1931, **16**, 276.

2-Phenylhexanone-3 (*Propyl α-phenylethyl ketone*)

$CH_3 \cdot [CH_2]_2 \cdot CO \cdot CH(C_6H_5) \cdot CH_3$

$C_{12}H_{16}O$ MW, 176

B.p. 240–2°.
Semicarbazone: m.p. 148–9°.

Lévy, Jullien, *Bull. soc. chim.*, 1929, **45**, 941.

2-Phenylhexanone-5 (5-*Phenylhexanone*-2)

$$CH_3{\cdot}CO{\cdot}CH_2{\cdot}CH_2{\cdot}\underset{}{\overset{C_6H_5}{CH}}{\cdot}CH_3$$

$C_{12}H_{16}O$ MW, 176

B.p. 122–5°/9 mm.
Semicarbazone : m.p. 147°.

Nenitzescu, Gavăt, *Ann.*, 1935, **519**, 270.

3-Phenylhexanone-2

$$CH_3{\cdot}CH_2{\cdot}CH_2{\cdot}\overset{C_6H_5}{CH}{\cdot}CO{\cdot}CH_3$$

$C_{12}H_{16}O$ MW, 176

B.p. 235–6°. D_4^0 0·970.
Oxime : m.p. 42–3°.
Semicarbazone : m.p. 130–1°.

Lévy, Jullien, *Bull. soc. chim.*, 1929, **45**, 941.

3-Phenylhexanone-4 (4-*Phenylhexanone*-3)

$$CH_3{\cdot}CH_2{\cdot}CO{\cdot}\overset{C_6H_5}{CH}{\cdot}CH_2{\cdot}CH_3$$

$C_{12}H_{16}O$ MW, 176

Yellow oil. B.p. 114–16°/13 mm. D^{20} 0·965, D^0 0·978.
Oxime : m.p. 57–8°.
Semicarbazone : m.p. 139–40°. Mod. sol. EtOH, C_6H_6.

Tiffeneau, Lévy, *Bull. soc. chim.*, 1923, **33**, 735.

6-Phenylhexene-1

$$C_6H_5{\cdot}[CH_2]_3{\cdot}CH_2{\cdot}CH{:}CH_2$$

$C_{12}H_{16}$ MW, 160

B.p. 94–5°/10 mm. D_4^{20} 0·8839. n_D^{20} 1·5033.

v. Braun, Deutsch, Schmatlock, *Ber.*, 1912, **45**, 1257.

1-Phenylhexene-2 (sym.-*Propylbenzylethylene*, 1-*propyl*-3-*phenylpropylene*)

$$CH_3{\cdot}CH_2{\cdot}CH_2{\cdot}CH{:}CH{\cdot}CH_2{\cdot}C_6H_5$$

$C_{12}H_{16}$ MW, 160

B.p. 108°/16 mm. D_4^{16} 0·8898. n_D^{16} 1·5058.

Klages, *Ber.*, 1907, **40**, 1771.

2-Phenylhexene-3

$$CH_3{\cdot}CH_2{\cdot}CH{:}CH{\cdot}\overset{C_6H_5}{CH}{\cdot}CH_3$$

$C_{12}H_{16}$ MW, 160

B.p. 84°/10 mm.

Riiber, *Ber.*, 1903, **36**, 1405.

1-Phenyl-1-hexenone-5

$$CH_3{\cdot}CO{\cdot}CH_2{\cdot}CH_2{\cdot}CH{:}CH{\cdot}C_6H_5$$

$C_{12}H_{14}O$ MW, 174

B.p. 153–5°/10 mm.
Semicarbazone : cryst. from AcOEt. M.p. 132.°

Fischer, Wiedemann, *Ann.*, 1935, **520**, 69.

3-Phenyl-2-hexenone-5

$$CH_3{\cdot}CO{\cdot}CH_2{\cdot}\overset{C_6H_5}{C}{:}CH{\cdot}CH_3$$

$C_{12}H_{14}O$ MW, 174

B.p. 138°/14 mm.
Semicarbazone : plates from EtOH. M.p. 185°.

Johnson, Kon, *J. Chem. Soc.*, 1926, 2758.

3-Phenyl-3-hexenone-5

$$CH_3{\cdot}CO{\cdot}CH{:}\overset{C_6H_5}{C}{\cdot}CH_2{\cdot}CH_3$$

$C_{12}H_{14}O$ MW, 174

B.p. 138°/14 mm.
Semicarbazone : plates. M.p. 158°.

See previous reference.

1-Phenylhexyl Alcohol (1-*Phenylhexanol*-1, n-*amylphenylcarbinol*)

$$CH_3{\cdot}[CH_2]_4{\cdot}CH(OH){\cdot}C_6H_5$$

$C_{12}H_{18}O$ MW, 178

Viscous liq. B.p. 170°/50 mm. D_4^{25} 0·9477. n_D^{25} 1·5042.

Davies, Dixon, Jones, *J. Chem. Soc.*, 1930, 470.

2-Phenylhexyl Alcohol (2-*Phenylhexanol*-1)

$$CH_3{\cdot}[CH_2]_3{\cdot}\overset{C_6H_5}{CH}{\cdot}CH_2OH$$

$C_{12}H_{18}O$ MW, 178

d-.
B.p. 127°/1 mm. D_4^{25} 0·967. $[\alpha]_D^{25}$ + 1·96°.

Levene, Marker, *J. Biol. Chem.*, 1931, **93**, 772.

3-Phenylhexyl Alcohol (3-*Phenylhexanol*-1)

$$CH_3{\cdot}[CH_2]_2{\cdot}\overset{C_6H_5}{CH}{\cdot}CH_2{\cdot}CH_2OH$$

$C_{12}H_{18}O$ MW, 178

d-.
B.p. 127°/5 mm. D_4^{25} 0·955. n_D^{25} 1·5101. $[\alpha]_D^{25}$ + 2·51°.

Levene, Marker, *J. Biol. Chem.*, 1931, **93**, 765.

4-Phenylhexyl Alcohol (4-*Phenylhexanol*-1)

$$C_6H_5$$
$$CH_3 \cdot CH_2 \cdot CH \cdot [CH_2]_2 \cdot CH_2OH$$

$C_{12}H_{18}O$ MW, 178

d-.

B.p. 125°/5 mm. $[\alpha]_D^{25} + 0.21°$.

> Levene, Marker, *J. Biol. Chem.*, 1935, **110**, 335.

6-Phenylhexyl Alcohol (6-*Phenylhexanol*-1)

$$C_6H_5 \cdot [CH_2]_5 \cdot CH_2OH$$

$C_{12}H_{18}O$ MW, 178

B.p. 160–1°/13 mm.
Me ether : $C_{13}H_{20}O$. MW, 192. B.p. 140°/13 mm.
Acetyl : b.p. 166–8°/13 mm.

> v. Braun, *Ber.*, 1911, **44**, 2876.
> v. Braun, Deutsch, *Ber.*, 1912, **45**, 2177.

1-Phenylhippuric Acid (1-*Benzoylamino-phenylacetic acid*)

$$C_6H_5$$
$$C_6H_5 \cdot CO \cdot NH \cdot CH \cdot COOH$$

$C_{15}H_{13}O_3N$ MW, 255

Needles from EtOH. M.p. 175·5°. Sol. EtOH, Et$_2$O, hot H$_2$O.
Et ester : $C_{17}H_{17}O_3N$. MW, 283. Cryst. M.p. 84°.
Phenyl ester : $C_{21}H_{17}O_3N$. MW, 331. Needles from EtOH. M.p. 131°.

> Bayer, D.R.P., 55,026.
> Kossel, *Ber.*, 1891, **24**, 4151.

N-Phenylhippuric Acid.

See under Phenylglycine.

1-Phenylhydantoic Acid (α-*Ureido-phenyl-acetic acid*)

$$C_6H_5$$
$$H_2N \cdot CO \cdot NH \cdot CH \cdot COOH$$

$C_9H_{10}O_3N_2$ MW, 194

Prisms from H$_2$O. M.p. 196–196·5° decomp. (178°). Spar. sol. cold H$_2$O.
Et ester : $C_{11}H_{14}O_3N_2$. MW, 222. Cryst. M.p. 139–40°. Sol. EtOH, Et$_2$O, hot H$_2$O.
Amide : $C_9H_{11}O_2N_3$. MW, 193. Prisms from EtOH.Aq. M.p. 223° decomp. Sol. EtOH, hot H$_2$O. Less sol. Et$_2$O, C$_6$H$_6$.

> Pinner, *Ber.*, 1888, **21**, 2326.
> Dakin, Dudley, *J. Biol. Chem.*, 1914, **18**, 49.
> Pinner, Spilker, *Ber.*, 1889, **22**, 697.
> Kossel, *Ber.*, 1891, **24**, 4150.

4-Phenylhydantoic Acid

$$C_6H_5 \cdot NH \cdot CO \cdot NH \cdot CH_2 \cdot COOH$$

$C_9H_{10}O_3N_2$ MW, 194

Needles. M.p. 197° decomp.
Et ester : needles. M.p. 108–9°.

> Bailey, *Am. Chem. J.*, 1902, **28**, 386.

1-Phenylhydantoin

$$C_6H_5 \cdot \underset{1}{N} \text{---} \underset{5}{CH_2}$$
$$O \underset{2}{C} \quad | $$
$$HN \underset{3}{\text{-----}} \underset{4}{CO}$$

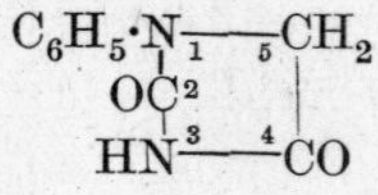

$C_9H_8O_2N_2$ MW, 176

Fine needles. M.p. 193–4°. Mod. sol. EtOH. Spar. sol. H$_2$O.

> Schwebel, *Ber.*, 1877, **10**, 2049.
> Friedrich, Beckurts, *Arch. Pharm.*, 1899, **237**, 337.

3-Phenylhydantoin.

Needles from H$_2$O. M.p. 159–60°. Sol. EtOH, Me$_2$CO, hot C$_6$H$_6$, conc. min. acids. Spar. sol. Et$_2$O.

> Mouneyrat, *Ber.*, 1900, **33**, 2394.

5-Phenylhydantoin.

Needles. M.p. 178°. Sol. EtOH, alkalis. Spar. sol. H$_2$O.
N-*Me* : $C_{10}H_{10}O_2N_2$. MW, 190. Needles from H$_2$O. M.p. 161°. Spar. sol. cold EtOH.
N-*Et* : prisms from H$_2$O. M.p. 94°. Very sol. EtOH, Et$_2$O, C$_6$H$_6$. Spar. sol. H$_2$O.
N-*Acetyl* : needles from C$_6$H$_6$. M.p. 145°.

> Pinner, Lifschütz, *Ber.*, 1887, **20**, 2355.
> Pinner, *Ber.*, 1888, **21**, 2325.
> Lehmann, *Ber.*, 1901, **34**, 372.
> Bergs, D.R.P., 566,094, (*Chem. Abstracts*, 1933, **27**, 1001).

1-Phenylhydracrylic Acid.

See Tropic Acid.

2-Phenylhydracrylic Acid.

See β-Hydroxyhydrocinnamic Acid.

α-Phenylhydratropic Acid.

See 1 : 1-Diphenylpropionic Acid.

Phenylhydrazidine (*Acetylamidrazone*)

$$CH_3 \cdot CO \cdot \underset{\gamma}{C}(NH_2) \underset{\beta}{:} \underset{}{N} \cdot \underset{\alpha}{NH} \cdot C_6H_5$$

$C_9H_{11}ON_3$ MW, 177

Yellow needles. M.p. 183°. Spar. sol. C$_6$H$_6$, ligroin, boiling H$_2$O.

γ-N-*Acetyl*: needles. M.p. 143°. Very sol. $CHCl_3$. Mod. sol. Et_2O. Insol. ligroin.

Phenylhydrazone: cryst. powder or needles. M.p. 224°. Sol. Et_2O, $CHCl_3$, Me_2CO. *B,HNO₂*: needles. M.p. 135°.

Bamberger, Lorenzen, *Ber.*, 1892, **25**, 3541.
Bamberger, Gruyter, *Ber.*, 1893, **26**, 2785; *J. prakt. Chem.*, 1901, **64**, 234.

Phenylhydrazine (*Hydrazinobenzene*)

$C_6H_5{\cdot}NH{\cdot}NH_2$

$C_6H_8N_2$ MW, 108

Plates or prisms. M.p. 23°. B.p. 241–2°, 137–8°/18 mm. $D_4^{20\cdot3}$ 1·0978. $n_D^{20\cdot3}$ 1·60813. Sol. EtOH, Et_2O, $CHCl_3$, C_6H_6. Spar. sol. H_2O, ligroin. Heat of comb. C_v 879·2 Cal. $k = 1{\cdot}62 \times 10^{-9}$ at 15°. Weak base.

B,HF: leaflets. M.p. 166–7° decomp.

B,HCl: leaflets from EtOH. M.p. 240°.

B,HNO₃: leaflets. M.p. 145°.

N′-*Phenyl*: *see* Hydrazobenzene.

N′-*Formyl*: leaflets from EtOH. M.p. 145°. Sol. hot H_2O, EtOH. Spar. sol. cold H_2O, $CHCl_3$, C_6H_6.

N-*Acetyl*: leaflets from C_6H_6–ligroin. M.p. 125–6°. Sol. EtOH, $CHCl_3$, C_6H_6. Spar. sol. Et_2O, ligroin. N′-*Formyl*: cryst. M.p. 77–8°.

N′-*Acetyl*: prisms. M.p. 129°. Sol. hot H_2O, EtOH. Spar. sol. cold H_2O, Et_2O. Reduces Fehling's. N-*Formyl*: cryst. M.p. 86°.

N : N′-*Diacetyl*: plates or needles from EtOH–C_6H_6. M.p. 107–8°. Very sol. boiling H_2O, EtOH, $CHCl_3$. Spar. sol. Et_2O. Reduces cold Fehling's.

N′-*Propionyl*: plates from $CHCl_3$. M.p. 157–8°.

N′-*Butyryl*: plates from H_2O. M.p. 103–4°.

N-*Isobutyryl*: plates or needles from pet. ether. M.p. 46–8°.

N′-*Isobutyryl*: leaflets from H_2O. M.p. 142–3°.

N′-*Isovaleryl*: leaflets from 30% EtOH. M.p. 112–112·5°.

N-*Benzoyl*: needles from H_2O or EtOH.Aq. M.p. 70°. Sol. EtOH, Et_2O, $CHCl_3$. Spar. sol. H_2O. Reduces warm Fehling's.

N′-*Benzoyl*: prisms from EtOH. M.p. 168°. Mod. sol. hot EtOH, C_6H_6. Spar. sol. H_2O, Et_2O.

N : N′-*Dibenzoyl*: prisms from EtOH. M.p. 177–8°. Mod. sol. hot EtOH. Spar. sol. H_2O. Reduces $NH_3.AgNO_3$.

N-*Nitroso*: $C_6H_5N(NO){\cdot}NH_2$. $C_6H_7ON_3$. MW, 137. Yellow cryst. M.p. 51°. Dil. HCl ⟶ phenyl azide. Poisonous. Forms red Cu salt.

Michaelis, Schmidt, *Ann.*, 1889, **252**, 302.
Leighton, *Am. Chem. J.*, 1898, **20**, 677.
Widman, *Ber.*, 1894, **27**, 2964.
Thompson, *J. Soc. Dyers Colourists*, 1921, **37**, 7.
Coleman, *Organic Syntheses*, Collective Vol. I, 432.
Wurster, *Ber.*, 1887, **20**, 2633.
Bamberger, Hauser, *Ann.*, 1910, **375**, 317.

Phenylhydrazine-α-carboxylic Acid (*α-Phenylhydrazinoformic acid*)

$C_6H_5{\cdot}N(NH_2){\cdot}COOH$

$C_7H_8O_2N_2$ MW, 152

Me ester: $C_8H_{10}O_2N_2$. MW, 166. Rhombic prisms from pet. ether. M.p. 69–70°.

Et ester: $C_9H_{12}O_2N_2$. MW, 180. Plates. M.p. 24–5°. B.p. 157°/15 mm. Spar. sol. usual solvents. Alc. $FeCl_3$ ⟶ red col. *B,HCl*: needles. M.p. 157–8°.

Amide: *see* 2-Phenylsemicarbazide.

Rupe, Gebhardt, *Ber.*, 1899, **32**, 11.
Busch, Limpach, *Ber.*, 1911, **44**, 1583.
Willstätter, Ulbrich, Pogány, Maimeri, *Ann.*, 1929, **477**, 168.

Phenylhydrazine-β-carboxylic Acid (*ω-Phenylcarbazinic acid, β-phenylhydrazinoformic acid*)

$C_6H_5{\cdot}NH{\cdot}NH{\cdot}COOH$

$C_7H_8O_2N_2$ MW, 152

Free acid not isolated.

K salt: needles from EtOH. M.p. 243° decomp. Sol. H_2O, EtOH.

Me ester: $C_8H_{10}O_2N_2$. MW, 166. Prisms from H_2O. M.p. 115–17°.

Et ester: $C_9H_{12}O_2N_2$. MW, 180. Cryst. from EtOH.Aq. M.p. 82–3°. Sol. EtOH, Et_2O, Me_2CO, $CHCl_3$, C_6H_6, hot H_2O. Conc. H_2SO_4 sol. with $FeCl_3$ ⟶ intense red col.

Phenyl ester: $C_{13}H_{12}O_2N_2$. MW, 228. Needles. M.p. 122–3°.

Amide: *see* 1-Phenylsemicarbazide.

B,C₆H₅·NH·NH₂: cryst. powder. M.p. 80° decomp.

Busch, Limpach, *Ber.*, 1911, **44**, 1582.
Freundler, *Bull. soc. chim.*, 1901, **25**, 859.
Busch, Stern, *J. prakt. Chem.*, 1899, **60**, 236.
Heller, *Ann.*, 1891, **263**, 281.

Phenylhydrazine-*o*-carboxylic Acid
(o-*Hydrazinobenzoic acid*)

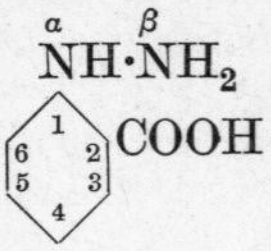

$C_7H_8O_2N_2$ MW, 152

Needles from H_2O. M.p. 249°. Mod. sol. hot H_2O. Spar. sol. EtOH, Et_2O. Reduces Fehling's and $NH_3.AgNO_3$ in the cold.

B,HBr: needles. M.p. 207–10°.

Nitrile: *o*-cyanophenylhydrazine. $C_7H_7N_3$. MW, 133. Leaflets from H_2O. M.p. 152–3°. Sol. EtOH, Et_2O. Insol. ligroin. *B,HCl*: needles. M.p. 160–1°. B_2,H_2SO_4: m.p. 215–16°. *Picrate*: needles. M.p. 238°.

α-N-*Me*: $C_8H_{10}O_2N_2$. MW, 166. Cryst. from ligroin. M.p. 120°. Very sol. EtOH.

Fischer, *Ber.*, 1880, **13**, 680.
Acree, *Am. Chem. J.*, 1907, **37**, 365.
Gabriel, *Ber.*, 1903, **36**, 805.

Phenylhydrazine-*m*-carboxylic Acid
(m-*Hydrazinobenzoic acid*).

Pale yellow leaflets. M.p. 186° decomp. Spar. sol. EtOH, hot H_2O. Insol. Et_2O. Reacts strongly acid. Reduces Fehling's.

Roder, *Ann.*, 1886, **236**, 164.

Phenylhydrazine-*p*-carboxylic Acid
(p-*Hydrazinobenzoic acid*).

Needles or plates from H_2O. M.p. 220–5° decomp. Mod. sol. hot H_2O.

Fischer, *Ann.*, 1882, **212**, 337.
Anchel, Schoenheimer, *J. Biol. Chem.*, 1936, **114**, 543.

Phenylhydrazine-β-sulphonic Acid

$C_6H_5{\cdot}NH{\cdot}NH{\cdot}SO_3H$

$C_6H_8O_3N_2S$ MW, 188

Not known in free state.

NH_4 salt: needles from EtOH. M.p. 208° decomp. Sol. H_2O. Mod. sol. EtOH. Insol. Et_2O, C_6H_6.

Na salt: leaflets from H_2O.

Paal, Kretschmer, *Ber.*, 1894, **27**, 1245.
Bucherer, Schmidt, *J. prakt. Chem.*, 1909, **79**, 402.

Phenylhydrazine-*m*-sulphonic Acid
(*Hydrazinobenzene*-m-*sulphonic acid*)

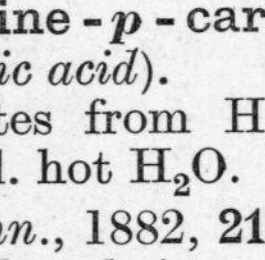

$C_6H_8O_3N_2S$ MW, 188

Plates or needles + $2H_2O$ from H_2O. Sol. 40 parts H_2O at 22°. Sol. hot H_2O. Spar. sol. EtOH, Et_2O.

Limpricht, *Ber.*, 1888, **21**, 3409.

Phenylhydrazine-*p*-sulphonic Acid
(*Hydrazinobenzene*-p-*sulphonic acid*).

Needles or leaflets from H_2O. Sol. 200 parts H_2O at 11°, 30 parts H_2O at 100°. Spar. sol. EtOH.

Thompson, *J. Soc. Dyers Colourists*, 1921, **37**, 7.

α-Phenylhydrazinoacetic Acid

$C_6H_5{\cdot}N(NH_2){\cdot}CH_2{\cdot}COOH$

$C_8H_{10}O_2N_2$ MW, 166

Leaflets from EtOH. M.p. 168° decomp. Spar. sol. EtOH. Insol. Et_2O, $CHCl_3$, C_6H_6. Sol. dil. HNO_3 with red col. Reduces warm Fehling's.

B,HCl: needles. M.p. 170° decomp.

Et ester: $C_{10}H_{14}O_2N_2$. MW, 194. Oil. B.p. 157–61°/7 mm. Sol. EtOH, Et_2O, C_6H_6, ligroin. Insol. H_2O. Reduces hot Fehling's.

Amide: $C_8H_{11}ON_3$. MW, 165. Needles. M.p. 150°. Sol. C_6H_6.

Anilide: needles from EtOH. M.p. 149°. Reduces Fehling's and $NH_3.AgNO_3$ in the cold.

Rupe, Heberlein, *Ann.*, 1898, **301**, 58.
Busch, *Ber.*, 1903, **36**, 3880.
Harries, *Ber.*, 1895, **28**, 1225.

β-Phenylhydrazinoacetic Acid

$C_6H_5{\cdot}NH{\cdot}NH{\cdot}CH_2{\cdot}COOH$

$C_8H_{10}O_2N_2$ MW, 166

Yellow leaflets or needles from EtOH. M.p. 153° (173° decomp.). Mod. sol. EtOH. Spar. sol. Me_2CO, AcOEt, C_6H_6.

B,HCl: leaflets. M.p. 165° decomp.

Et ester: oil. *Oxalate*: leaflets. M.p. 156°.

Phenyl ester: $C_{14}H_{14}O_2N_2$. MW, 242. Leaflets. M.p. 93–4°.

Anilide: m.p. 135°.

See first two references above and also
Busch, Meussdörfer, *J. prakt. Chem.*, 1907, **75**, 124.
Ghosh, Guha, *Chem. Zentr.*, 1934, I, 3050.

1-β-Phenylhydrazinobutyric Acid

$$\begin{matrix} C_6H_5{\cdot}NH{\cdot}NH \\ CH_3{\cdot}CH_2 \end{matrix}\!\!>CH{\cdot}COOH$$

$C_{10}H_{14}O_2N_2$ MW, 194

Needles from MeOH. Sublimes.

Amide: $C_{10}H_{15}ON_3$. MW, 193. Needles

from Et_2O–pet. ether. M.p. 79°. Sol. EtOH, Et_2O. Less sol. C_6H_6.

Nitrile: $C_{10}H_{13}N_3$. MW, 175. Cryst. from Et_2O–pet. ether. M.p. 37°. Sol. EtOH, Et_2O, $CHCl_3$, C_6H_6. Insol. H_2O.

v. Miller, Plöchl, Sender, *Ber.*, 1892, **25**, 2037.

2-α-Phenylhydrazinobutyric Acid

$$\overset{CH_3}{|}$$
$$C_6H_5·N(NH_2)·CH·CH_2·COOH$$

$C_{10}H_{14}O_2N_2$ MW, 194

Plates from EtOH. M.p. 111°. Sol. EtOH, $CHCl_3$. Spar. sol. H_2O, Et_2O.

Lederer, *J. prakt. Chem.*, 1891, **45**, 87.

2-β-Phenylhydrazinobutyric Acid

$$\overset{CH_3}{|}$$
$$C_6H_5·NH·NH·CH·CH_2·COOH$$

$C_{10}H_{14}O_2N_2$ MW, 194

Needles from C_6H_6. M.p. 96–7°. Sol. EtOH, Et_2O. Insol. ligroin.

Prentice, *J. Chem. Soc.*, 1904, **85**, 1671.

Phenylhydrazinoformic Acid.
See Phenylhydrazine-carboxylic Acid.

1-α-Phenylhydrazinoisobutyric Acid

$$C_6H_5·N(NH_2)·C(CH_3)_2·COOH$$

$C_{10}H_{14}O_2N_2$ MW, 194

Amide: $C_{10}H_{15}ON_3$. MW, 193. Needles from C_6H_6. M.p. 118°. Sol. EtOH, C_6H_6, hot H_2O. Spar. sol. ligroin. *B,HCl*: needles from EtOH. M.p. 206°.

v. Walther, Hübner, *J. prakt. Chem.*, 1916, **93**, 132.

1-β-Phenylhydrazinoisobutyric Acid

$$C_6H_5·NH·NH·C(CH_3)_2·COOH$$

$C_{10}H_{14}O_2N_2$ MW, 194

Leaflets from EtOH. M.p. 165–6°.

Amide: leaflets from EtOH. M.p. 117°. Sol. EtOH, Et_2O, $CHCl_3$, C_6H_6. Spar. sol. H_2O, ligroin. Reduces Fehling's on heating.

Nitrile: $C_{10}H_{13}N_3$. MW, 175. Needles from ligroin. M.p. 70°. Sol. EtOH, Et_2O, $CHCl_3$, C_6H_6. Spar. sol. ligroin. Insol. H_2O. Reduces hot Fehling's.

Reissert, *Ber.*, 1884, **17**, 1461.
Eckstein, *Ber.*, 1892, **25**, 3323.

1-β-Phenylhydrazinopropionic Acid

$$\overset{CH_3}{|}$$
$$C_6H_5·NH·NH·CH·COOH$$

$C_9H_{12}O_2N_2$ MW, 180

Needles from MeOH. M.p. 174°.

Et ester: $C_{11}H_{16}O_2N_2$. MW, 208. Liq. Very sol. dil. HCl. Reduces Fehling's in the cold.

Amide: $C_9H_{13}ON_3$. MW, 179. Cryst. from H_2O. M.p. 124°. Sol. EtOH, hot H_2O. Spar. sol. $CHCl_3$, C_6H_6, ligroin.

Nitrile: $C_9H_{11}N_3$. MW, 161. Cryst. from ligroin. M.p. 58°. Very sol. EtOH, Et_2O. Less sol. C_6H_6. Spar. sol. ligroin. Insol. H_2O. Reduces hot Fehling's. Fuming HCl ⟶ amide.

Reissert, *Ber.*, 1884, **17**, 1453; 1892, **25**, 2701.
v. Miller, Plöchl, Rohde, *Ber.*, 1892, **25**, 2060.

1-Phenylhydrindene

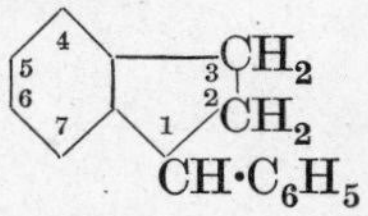

$C_{15}H_{14}$ MW, 194

B.p. 148–50°/13 mm.

Mayer, Stieglitz, *Ber.*, 1921, **54**, 1399.

2-Phenylhydrindene.

Yellow oil. B.p. 162–3°/10 mm. D_4^{16} 1·0821. n_D^{15} 1·5955.

v. Braun, Manz, *Ber.*, 1929, **62**, 1062.

3-Phenyl-1-hydrindenic Acid (*3-Phenylhydrindene-1-carboxylic acid*)

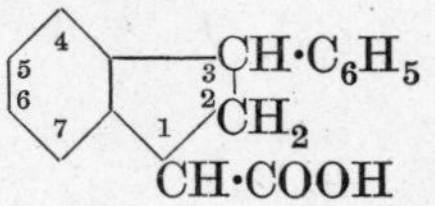

$C_{16}H_{14}O_2$ MW, 238

Needles from AcOH. M.p. 143–144·5°. B.p. 227–9°/14 mm.

Me ester: $C_{17}H_{16}O_2$. MW, 252. Needles from EtOH–pet. ether. M.p. 77–8°. B.p. 204·5–205°/13 mm.

Et ester: $C_{18}H_{18}O_2$. MW, 266. Prisms from EtOH. M.p. 69–70°.

Blum-Bergmann, *Ann.*, 1930, **484**, 38; 1932, **492**, 277.

2-Phenyl-2-hydrindenic Acid (*2-Phenylhydrindene-2-carboxylic acid*).

Cryst. M.p. 194–5°.

Case, *J. Am. Chem. Soc.*, 1934, **56**, 715.

2-Phenyl-1-hydrindone (2-*Phenylindanone*)

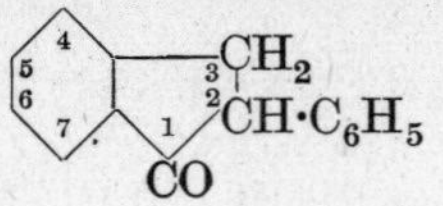

$C_{15}H_{12}O$ MW, 208

Prisms from EtOH. M.p. 77–8°. B.p. 344° decomp. Very sol. $CHCl_3$, Me_2CO, C_6H_6. Sol. EtOH, Et_2O. Spar. sol. ligroin. Reduces warm $NH_3.AgNO_3$.

Semicarbazone: cryst. from MeOH. M.p. 211–12°.

Phenylhydrazone: cryst. from C_6H_6. M.p. 137–8°.

p-*Nitrophenylhydrazone*: yellow leaflets from Me_2CO, red cryst. powder from AcOH. M.p. 174°.

v. Miller, Rohde, *Ber.*, 1892, **25**, 2096.
Auwers, Auffenberg, *Ber.*, 1919, **52**, 107.

3-Phenyl-1-hydrindone (3-*Phenylindanone*).

Prisms from MeOH. M.p. 78°. Very sol. EtOH, Et_2O, AcOH, C_6H_6.

Oxime: needles from EtOH.Aq. M.p. 141°.

Semicarbazone: m.p. 223–5°. Spar. sol. most solvents.

Phenylhydrazone: yellowish cryst. from EtOH. M.p. 130°.

p-*Nitrophenylhydrazone*: red cryst. from AcOH. M.p. 220–1°.

Auwers, Auffenberg, *Ber.*, 1919, **52**, 110.
Liebermann, Hartmann, *Ber.*, 1892, **25**, 2124.
Pfeiffer, de Waal, *Ann.*, 1935, **520**, 189.

4-Phenyl-1-hydrindone (4-*Phenylindanone*).

Thick yellow oil. B.p. 200–5°/11 mm.

Semicarbazone: cryst. M.p. 192°. Very sol. EtOH.

v. Braun, Manz, *Ann.*, 1929, **468**, 276.

Phenylhydrocinnamic Acid.

See 1 : 2-, and 2 : 2-Diphenylpropionic Acids.

Phenyl hydrogen sulphate

$C_6H_5{\cdot}O{\cdot}SO_3H$

$C_6H_6O_4S$ MW, 174

Very unstable.

Na salt: needles. Very hygroscopic. Decomp. easily.

K salt: leaflets from EtOH. Sol. 7 parts H_2O at 15°.

NH_4 salt: cryst. from dil. NH_3.Aq. $FeCl_3$ ⟶ reddish-violet col.

Baumann, *Ber.*, 1878, **11**, 1907.
Czapek, *Monatsh.*, 1914, **35**, 639.
Hofmann, Biesalski, *Ber.*, 1912, **45**, 1396.

3-Phenylhydroxyacetone (*Phenylacetylcarbinol, phenacetylcarbinol, hydroxymethyl benzyl ketone, phenylacetol,* 1-*hydroxy*-3-*phenylacetone, phenylpropanolone*)

$C_6H_5{\cdot}CH_2{\cdot}CO{\cdot}CH_2OH$

$C_9H_{10}O_2$ MW, 150

M.p. 48°. B.p. 144–5°/12–13 mm. Ag_2O ⟶ phenylacetic acid.

Me ether: $C_{10}H_{12}O_2$. MW, 164. B.p. 139–40°/27 mm. *Semicarbazone*: m.p. 127–8°.

Et ether: $C_{11}H_{14}O_2$. MW, 178. B.p. 116–17°/1 mm. *Semicarbazone*: m.p. 100°.

Phenyl ether: $C_{15}H_{14}O_2$. MW, 226. Needles from ligroin. M.p. 43–4°. *Semicarbazone*: needles from MeOH. M.p. 151–2°. *Phenylhydrazone*: yellow cryst. from MeOH. Sinters at 65°, m.p. 94–6°.

Benzyl ether: $C_{16}H_{16}O_2$. MW, 240. B.p. 235°/40 mm. *Semicarbazone*: m.p. about 105°.

Oxime: m.p. 118°.

Semicarbazone: m.p. 134°.

Acetyl: needles from EtOH. M.p. 131°.

p-*Nitrobenzoyl*: plates from EtOH.Aq. M.p. 120°.

Darmon, *Compt. rend.*, 1933, **197**, 1328, 1649.

β-Phenylhydroxylamine (N-*Phenylhydroxylamine*)

$C_6H_5{\cdot}NH{\cdot}OH$

C_6H_7ON MW, 109

Needles from H_2O, C_6H_6 or pet. ether. M.p. 81–2°. Sol. 50 parts cold, 10 parts hot H_2O. Very sol. EtOH, Et_2O, $CHCl_3$, CS_2, hot C_6H_6. Spar. sol. ligroin. Conc. H_2SO_4 ⟶ deep blue sol.

N-*Formyl*: plates or needles. M.p. 70–1°. Sol. EtOH, Et_2O, $CHCl_3$, hot H_2O. Spar. sol. pet. ether.

N-*Acetyl*: needles from ligroin. M.p. 67–67·5°. Sol. EtOH, Et_2O, C_6H_6, hot H_2O. Spar. sol. pet. ether.

O : N-*Diacetyl*: prisms from C_6H_6–pet. ether. M.p. 43°. Sol. EtOH, Et_2O, Me_2CO, C_6H_6, boiling ligroin. Spar. sol. H_2O.

N-*Benzoyl*: needles from pet. ether. M.p. 123–4°. Spar. sol. Et_2O.

O : N-*Dibenzoyl*: cryst. from EtOH. M.p. 121°. Sol. hot EtOH, Et_2O, C_6H_6. Spar. sol. pet. ether.

N-*Carbethoxyl*: prisms from ligroin. M.p. 47·5°. B.p. 160–3°/12 mm. Sol. EtOH, Et_2O, Me_2CO, C_6H_6. Spar. sol. ligroin.

N-*Nitroso*: phenylisonitramine, phenylnitrosohydroxylamine. Needles from ligroin. M.p. 58–9°. Sol. usual solvents. Spar. sol. H_2O.

$k = 5{\cdot}7 \times 10^{-6}$ at 0°. *NH_4 salt*: cupferron. Glistening white plates. Reagent for separation of Fe, Cu, titanium, vanadium, zirconium, uranium.

Wohl, *Ber.*, 1894, **27**, 1435.
Bamberger, Destraz, *Ber.*, 1902, **35**, 1884.
Ciamician, Silber, *Ber.*, 1905, **38**, 1183.
Kamm, *Organic Syntheses*, Collective Vol. I, 435.
Marvel, *ibid.*, 171.

Phenyl-hydroxynaphthylmethane.
See Benzylnaphthol.
Phenyl-hydroxyphenyl-acrylic Acid.
See Hydroxystilbene-α-carboxylic Acid.
Phenyl hydroxyphenyl Diketone.
See Hydroxybenzil.
Phenyl hydroxystyryl Ketone.
See 2-, 3-, and 4-Hydroxychalkones.
Phenyl ω-hydroxy-*p*-tolyl Ketone.
See 4-Hydroxymethyl-benzophenone.
Phenyliminazole.
See Phenylglyoxaline.
Phenyliminodeoxybenzoin.
See Benzil-anil.

1-Phenyliminodiacetic Acid (*Phenyl-ω-carboxysarcosine, phenyl-*N*-carboxymethyl-glycine*)

$$HOOC{\cdot}CH_2{\cdot}NH{\cdot}\underset{}{CH}(C_6H_5){\cdot}COOH$$

$C_{10}H_{11}O_4N$ MW, 209

Needles from H_2O. M.p. 220° decomp. Spar. sol. H_2O. Insol. EtOH, Et_2O.
B,HCl: leaflets. Decomp. at 220–2°.
Di-Me ester: $C_{12}H_{15}O_4N$. MW, 237. Thick oil. B.p. 220–1°/17 mm. D_4^{16} 1·1705, D_4^{25} 1·1622. n^{18} 1·5111.
Di-Et ester: $C_{14}H_{19}O_4N$. MW, 265. B.p. 195–6°/17 mm. Sol. EtOH, Et_2O. Insol. H_2O. D_4^{20} 1·1059. n^{20} 1·4976.
Diamide: $C_{10}H_{13}O_2N_3$. MW, 207. Cryst. M.p. 152–3°.

Stadnikow, *Ber.*, 1908, **41**, 4364; *Chem. Zentr.*, 1909, II, 1989.

***N*-Phenyliminodiacetic Acid** (*Anil-diacetic acid, anilinodiacetic acid*)

$$C_6H_5{\cdot}N(CH_2{\cdot}COOH)_2$$

$C_{10}H_{11}O_4N$ MW, 209

Needles. M.p. 152–5° decomp. Sol. EtOH, hot H_2O. Rather spar. sol. Et_2O. $k = 2{\cdot}73 \times 10^{-4}$ at 25°. Alc. $FeCl_3$ ⟶ reddish-brown col. ⟶ brown ppt. on standing.
Di-Me ester: $C_{12}H_{15}O_4N$. MW, 237. B.p. 216–18°/25 mm., 210–11°/18 mm.
Mono-Et ester: $C_{12}H_{15}O_4N$. MW, 237. Cryst. from H_2O. M.p. 121–2°. B.p. about 230–40°/17 mm. *Anilide*: needles from Et_2O. M.p. 121–2°.
Di-Et ester: $C_{14}H_{19}O_4N$. MW, 265. Oil. B.p. 197–8°/17 mm. (200–6°/6 mm.).
Diamide: $C_{10}H_{13}O_2N_3$. MW, 207. Cryst. from H_2O. M.p. 238° (225°). Spar. sol. EtOH, Et_2O, $CHCl_3$.
Monoanilide: needles from EtOH.Aq. M.p. 215°.
Dianilide: needles from EtOH. M.p. 218°.

Vorländer, Mumme, *Ber.*, 1901, **34**, 1647.
de Mouilpied, *J. Chem. Soc.*, 1905, **87**, 439.
Johnson, Bengis, *J. Am. Chem. Soc.*, 1911, **33**, 749.

Phenyliminophosgene (*Phenylcarbylamine chloride*)

$$C_6H_5{\cdot}N{:}CCl_2$$

$C_7H_5NCl_2$ MW, 174

B.p. 104–6°/30 mm. Vapour is toxic and lachrymatory.

Bly, Perkins, Lewis, *J. Am. Chem. Soc.*, 1922, **44**, 2896.

Phenyliminopropionic Acid.
See under Pyruvic Acid.

2-Phenylindazole

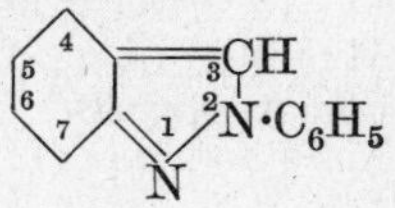

$C_{13}H_{10}N_2$ MW, 194

Needles from EtOH. M.p. 83–4°. B.p. 344–5°. Sol. EtOH, Et_2O, AcOH, C_6H_6. Spar. sol. ligroin. Insol. H_2O. Sol. conc. min. acids. CrO_3 in AcOH, or $KMnO_4$ ⟶ azobenzene-2-carboxylic acid.
B_2,H_2PtCl_6: m.p. 187–8° decomp.
Picrate: yellow needles. M.p. 93–4°.

Reissert, Lemmer, *Ber.*, 1926, **59**, 356.
Paal, *Ber.*, 1891, **24**, 961.
Busch, *Ber.*, 1894, **27**, 2899.
Freundler, *Bull soc. chim.*, 1903, **29**, 745; 1904, **31**, 868.

3-Phenylindazole.
Exists in two forms.
(i) Needles from ligroin. M.p. 107–8°. Heated above m.p. ⟶ (ii).
(ii) Prisms from ligroin. M.p. 115–16°. Heated to higher temps. again ⟶ (i).
1(?)N-*Acetyl*: needles from ligroin. M.p. 69–79°.

Auwers, Schaum, *Ber.*, 1929, **62**, 1672.

3-Phenylindazole-2-carboxylic Acid

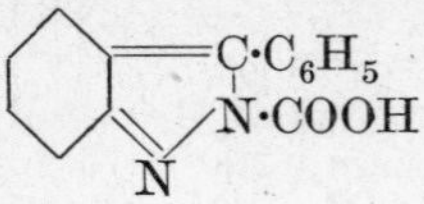

$C_{14}H_{10}O_2N_2$ MW, 238

Me ester: $C_{15}H_{12}O_2N_2$. MW, 252. Needles from MeOH. M.p. 112–13°. Sol. EtOH, AcOH. Prac. insol. C_6H_6, pet. ether.

Et ester: $C_{16}H_{14}O_2N_2$. MW, 266. Needles. M.p. 83–4°.

Auwers, Hüttenes, *Ber.*, 1922, **55**, 1133.

2-Phenylindazole-3-carboxylic Acid

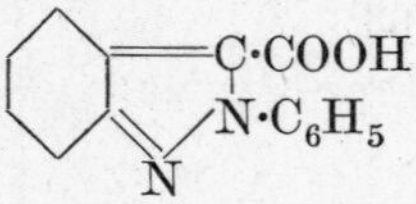

$C_{14}H_{10}O_2N_2$ MW, 238

M.p. 200° decomp. Heat ⟶ 2-phenylindazole.

Me ester: needles from EtOH. M.p. 169–70°.

Amide: $C_{14}H_{11}ON_3$. MW, 237. M.p. 247–8° (243–4°).

Nitrile: $C_{14}H_9N_3$. MW, 219. M.p. 105° (106–7°).

Reissert, Lemmer, *Ber.*, 1926, **59**, 355.
Heller, Spielmeyer, *Ber.*, 1925, **58**, 836.

1-Phenylindole (N-*Phenylindole*)

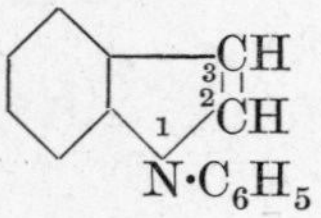

$C_{14}H_{11}N$ MW, 193

Yellowish oil. B.p. 326–7°/757 mm. Sol. EtOH, Et_2O, C_6H_6. Insol. H_2O. Volatile in steam. With pine-splinter + HCl ⟶ bluish-violet col.

Fischer, Hess, *Ber.*, 1884, **17**, 568.
Pfülf, *Ann.*, 1887, **239**, 221.

2-Phenylindole (α-*Phenylindole*)

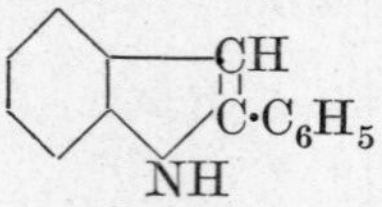

$C_{14}H_{11}N$ MW, 193

Leaflets from EtOH or ligroin. M.p. 189° (187°). B.p. above 360°, about 250°/10 mm. Odour resembles indole. Gradually turns green in air. Sublimes. Spar. volatile in steam. Sol. Et_2O, $CHCl_3$, AcOH, C_6H_6, hot CS_2. Spar. sol. hot H_2O. Insol. dil. min. acids. CrO_3 in boiling AcOH ⟶ benzoic acid.

N-*Me*: $C_{15}H_{13}N$. MW, 207. Cryst. from EtOH, C_6H_6, or ligroin. M.p. 101°. Spar. volatile in steam. Mod. sol. cold conc. HCl, re-pptd. unchanged on dilution.

N-*Et*: $C_{16}H_{15}N$. MW, 221. Needles from EtOH. M.p. 86°.

Picrate: red prisms from EtOH. M.p. 127°.

I.C.I., E.P., 330,332, (*Chem. Abstracts*, 1930, **24**, 5770).
I.G., D.R.P., 574,840, (*Chem. Abstracts*, 1933, **27**, 4541).
Campbell, *J. Chem. Soc.*, 1935, 1210.
Wolff, *Ann.*, 1912, **394**, 107.
Madelung, *Ber.*, 1912, **45**, 1131.
Fischer, Hütz, *Ber.*, 1895, **28**, 587.

3-Phenylindole (β-*Phenylindole*).

Leaflets from ligroin. M.p. 88–9°. Sol. EtOH, Et_2O, C_6H_6. Mod. sol. hot ligroin. Insol. H_2O. $ZnCl_2$ at 170° ⟶ 2-phenylindole.

N-*Me*: cryst. from pet. ether. M.p. 64–5°. Sol. EtOH, Et_2O, C_6H_6. $ZnCl_2$ at 210° ⟶ *N*-methyl-2-phenylindole. *Picrate*: brown needles from C_6H_6–ligroin. M.p. 90°.

N-*Nitroso*: yellow needles from ligroin. M.p. 60–1°. Sol. Et_2O, $CHCl_3$, Me_2CO, C_6H_6.

Picrate: red needles from C_6H_6–ligroin. M.p. 107°.

Fischer, Schmidt, *Ber.*, 1888, **21**, 1073, 1811.
Henle, *Ber.*, 1905, **38**, 1365.
Ince, *Ann.*, 1889, **253**, 38.

1-Phenylindole-2-carboxylic Acid

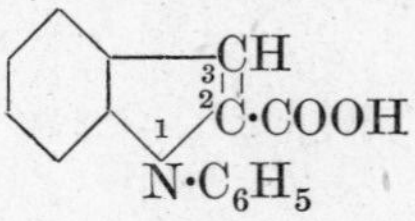

$C_{15}H_{11}O_2N$ MW, 237

Needles from EtOH.Aq. M.p. 176°. Sol. EtOH, Et_2O. Very spar. sol. boiling H_2O. At 200–10° ⟶ 1-phenylindole.

Fischer, Hess, *Ber.*, 1884, **17**, 567.
Pfülf, *Ann.*, 1887, **239**, 221.

3-Phenylindole-2-carboxylic Acid.

Needles from C_6H_6. M.p. 186°.

Et ester: $C_{17}H_{15}O_2N$. MW, 265. Cryst. from EtOH. M.p. 137–8°.

Manske, Perkin, Robinson, *J. Chem. Soc.*, 1927, 6.

N-Phenylisatin

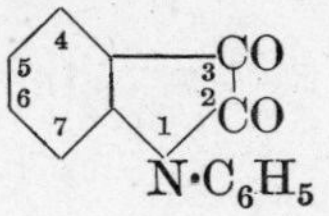

$C_{14}H_9O_2N$ MW, 223

Yellowish-red leaflets from EtOH. M.p. 138°. Mod. sol. EtOH, Et_2O, C_6H_6.

3-Hydrazone: yellow needles from EtOH. M.p. 192°.

Stollé, *Ber.*, 1913, **46**, 3915; D.R.P., 281,046, (*Chem. Zentr.*, 1915, I, 71).
Pfülf, *Ann.*, 1887, **239**, 222.

1-Phenylisoamyl Alcohol.
Isobutylphenylcarbinol, *q.v.*

2-Phenylisoamyl Alcohol (*2-Methyl-3-phenylbutanol-4, 3-methyl-2-phenyl-n-butyl alcohol*)

$$(CH_3)_2CH\cdot CH(C_6H_5)\cdot CH_2OH$$

$C_{11}H_{16}O$ MW, 164

Thick oil. B.p. 130°/15 mm.

Acetyl: liq. B.p. 134°/15 mm.

Ramart-Lucas, Amagat, *Compt. rend.*, 1927, **184**, 30.
Blaise, Courtot, *Bull. soc. chim.*, 1906, **35**, 595.

N-Phenylisoamylamine.
See Isoamylaniline.

1-Phenylisobutane.
See Isobutylbenzene.

2-Phenylisobutane.
tert.-Butylbenzene, *q.v.*

2-Phenylisobutyl Alcohol

$$(CH_3)_2C(C_6H_5)\cdot CH_2OH$$

$C_{10}H_{14}O$ MW, 150

B.p. 122–3°/20 mm.

Phenylurethane: m.p. 59–60°.

Haller, Bauer, *Ann. chim.*, 1918, **9**, 10.

Phenylisobutylamine.
See Aminoisobutylbenzene *and* *N*-Isobutylaniline.

1-Phenylisobutyraldehyde (*Dimethylphenylacetaldehyde*)

$$C_6H_5\cdot C(CH_3)_2\cdot CHO$$

$C_{10}H_{12}O$ MW, 148

B.p. 215–18°, 105–10°/14 mm. D^0 0·9912. Does not form bisulphite comp.

Semicarbazone: m.p. 172°.

Tiffeneau, Dorlencourt, *Ann. chim. phys.*, 1907, **10**, 366; 1909, **16**, 248.

2-Phenylisobutyraldehyde.
See α-Methylhydrocinnamaldehyde.

1-Phenylisobutyric Acid (*1-Methylhydratropic acid, dimethylphenylacetic acid*)

$$C_6H_5\cdot C(CH_3)_2\cdot COOH$$

$C_{10}H_{12}O_2$ MW, 164

Prisms from EtOH. M.p. 80–1°. B.p. 150–5°/10 mm. Conc. H_2SO_4 ⟶ yellow sol. with green fluor.

Me ester: $C_{11}H_{14}O_2$. MW, 178. B.p. 225°.

Et ester: $C_{12}H_{16}O_2$. MW, 192. B.p. 235–6°.

Propyl ester: $C_{13}H_{18}O_2$. MW, 206. B.p. 250°.

Isobutyl ester: $C_{14}H_{20}O_2$. MW, 220. B.p. 260–1°.

Chloride: $C_{10}H_{11}OCl$. MW, 182·5. B.p. 109°/13 mm.

Amide: $C_{10}H_{13}ON$. MW, 163. Cryst. M.p. 160–1°. B.p. 200–5°/60 mm. Spar. sol. Et_2O. Insol. H_2O.

Nitrile: $C_{10}H_{11}N$. MW, 145. B.p. 232°, 114–16°/20 mm. D^{21} 0·966. n_D 1·50665.

Wallach, *Chem. Zentr.*, 1899, II, 1047.
Haller, Bauer, *Compt. rend.*, 1912, **155**, 1582.

2-Phenylisobutyric Acid.
See α-Methylhydrocinnamic Acid.

1-Phenylisocaproic Acid (*3-Methyl-1-phenylvaleric acid, isobutylphenylacetic acid*)

$$(CH_3)_2CH\cdot CH_2\cdot CH(C_6H_5)\cdot COOH$$

$C_{12}H_{16}O_2$ MW, 192

Prisms from pet. ether. M.p. 78–9°.

Nitrile: $C_{12}H_{15}N$. MW, 173. B.p. 263–6°, 136–8°/15 mm. D^{16} 0·942. Sol. EtOH, Et_2O, C_6H_6, AcOH. Insol. H_2O. Volatile in steam.

Bodroux, Taboury, *Bull. soc. chim.*, 1910, **7**, 668.

N-Phenylisocarbostyril (*2-Phenylisoquinolone*)

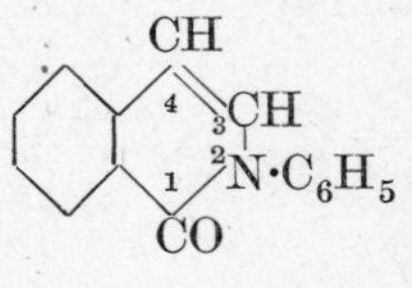

$C_{15}H_{11}ON$ MW, 221

Needles from EtOH.Aq. M.p. 117·5°. Very sol. EtOH. Spar. sol. Et_2O, C_6H_6. Sublimes.

Bamberger, Frew, *Ber.*, 1894, **27**, 203.
Dieckmann, Meiser, *Ber.*, 1908, **41**, 3268.

3-Phenylisocarbostyril (*1-Hydroxy-3-phenylisoquinoline, 3-phenylisoquinolone*)

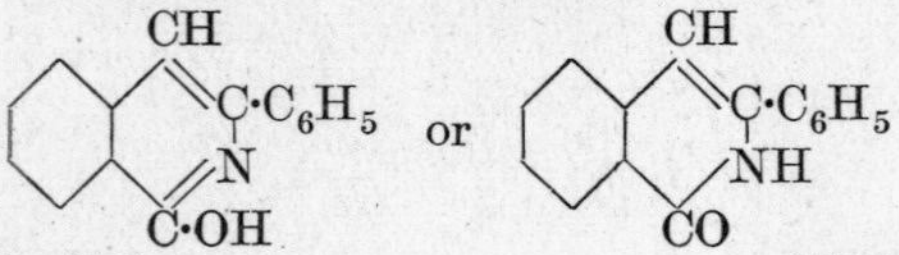

$C_{15}H_{11}ON$ MW, 221

Needles or prisms. M.p. 197°. Sol. hot EtOH, conc. HCl. Dist. with Zn dust in H ⟶ 3-phenylisoquinoline.

Et ether: $C_{17}H_{15}ON$. MW, 249. Needles from EtOH. M.p. 45–6°.

Gabriel, *Ber.*, 1886, **19**, 835.
Wölbling, *Ber.*, 1905, **38**, 3848.

2-Phenylisocrotonic Acid.

Cis form of β-Methylcinnamic Acid. *See* β-Methylcinnamic Acid.

Phenyl isocyanate (*Phenylcarbimide, carbanil*)

$C_6H_5{\cdot}N{:}CO$

C_7H_5ON MW, 119

Pungent lachrymatory liq. B.p. 162–3°/751 mm., 55°/13 mm. $D_4^{19\cdot6}$ 1·0956, $D_4^{25\cdot9}$ 1·08870. $n_D^{19\cdot6}$ 1·53684. Used for characterisation of alcohols and as a dehydrating agent.

Hardy, *J. Chem. Soc.*, 1934, 2011.
Zimmer, D.R.P., 133,760, (*Chem. Zentr.*, 1902, II, 553).

Phenyl isocyanide (*Phenylcarbylamine, benzoisonitrile*)

$C_6H_5{\cdot}NC$

C_7H_5N MW, 103

Liq. with penetrating odour. B.p. 165–6° part. polymerisation, 78°/40 mm. D^{15} 0·977. Very unstable Rapidly turns green and then blue ⟶ slowly to a brown resin. Na + amyl alcohol ⟶ methylaniline. Heated with EtONa in sealed tube ⟶ N : N′-diphenylformamidine.

Biddle, Goldberg, *Ann.*, 1900, **310**, 7.

1-Phenylisohexyl Alcohol (*2-Methyl-4-phenylpentanol-5*)

$(CH_3)_2CH{\cdot}CH_2{\cdot}\overset{C_6H_5}{CH}{\cdot}CH_2OH$

$C_{12}H_{18}O$ MW, 178

B.p. 138–9°/14 mm.

Phenylurethane: cryst. from Et_2O–ligroin M.p. 78°.

Ramart, Amagat, *Ann. chim.*, 1927, **8** 288.

Phenylisonitramine.

See under Phenylhydroxylamine.

Phenylisonitromethane.

See under Phenylnitromethane.

2-Phenylisopentane.

tert.-Amylbenzene, *q.v.*

3-Phenylisopentane (*2-Methyl-3-phenylbutane*)

$CH_3{\cdot}\overset{C_6H_5}{CH}{\cdot}CH(CH_3)_2$

$C_{11}H_{16}$ MW, 148

B.p. 188–9°/753 mm. D_4^{16} 0·8672. n_D^{16} 1·4972

Konowalow, Jegorow, *Chem. Zentr.*, 1899 I, 776.
Klages, *Ber.*, 1903, **36**, 3691.

4-Phenylisopentane.

See Isoamylbenzene.

5-Phenylisophthalic Acid.

See Diphenyl-3 : 5-dicarboxylic Acid.

Phenylisopropyl Alcohol.

See Dimethylphenylcarbinol *and* Methylbenzylcarbinol.

***N*-Phenylisopropylamine.**

N-Isopropylaniline, *q.v.*

1-Phenylisopropylamine (*α-Aminocumene, 2-amino-2-phenylpropane, α-aminoisopropylbenzene*)

$(CH_3)_2C(NH_2){\cdot}C_6H_5$

$C_9H_{13}N$ MW, 135

B.p. 196–7°/762 mm. D_0^{20} 0·9424. n_D^{25} 1·5181

B,HCl: m.p. 235·5°. Sol. EtOH. Very spar sol. Et_2O, C_6H_6. Insol. pet. ether.

B,HNO₂: m.p. 98–9° decomp.

N-*Benzoyl*: needles from EtOH. M.p. 159° Very spar. sol. Et_2O.

Oxalate: needles from EtOH. M.p. 131°.

Konowalow, *Chem. Zentr.*, 1894, II, 33.
Brander, *Rec. trav. chim.*, 1918, **37**, 68.

2-Phenylisopropylamine (*2-Amino-1-phenylpropane, 1-benzylethylamine, β-aminopropylbenzene*)

$C_6H_5{\cdot}CH_2{\cdot}CH(NH_2){\cdot}CH_3$

$C_9H_{13}N$ MW, 135

d-.

B.p. 102°/16 mm. D_4^{15} 0·949. n_D^{20} 1·4704 $[\alpha]_D^{15}$ + 35·6°.

B,HCl: m.p. 156°. $[\alpha]_D^{15}$ + 24·8° in H_2O.

N-*Benzoyl*: cryst. from EtOH. M.p. 159–60°. $[\alpha]_D^{15}$ —14·8° in C_6H_6.

dl-.
B.p. 205° (203°).
B,HCl : m.p. 145–7°. Hygroscopic.
N-*Acetyl* : needles from EtOH.Aq. M.p. 64° initially, 93° on standing.
Picrate : m.p. 143°.

Hey, *J. Chem. Soc.*, 1930, 18.
Jones, Wallis, *J. Am. Chem. Soc.*, 1926, **48**, 180.
Leithe, *Ber.*, 1932, **65**, 664.

1-Phenylisoquinoline

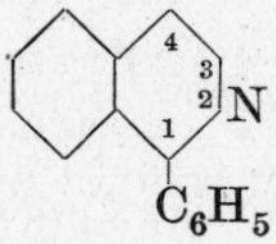

$C_{15}H_{11}N$ MW, 205

Needles from EtOH.Aq. M.p. 95–6°. B.p. 298°/729 mm., 120–40°/1 mm. Spar. volatile in steam.
B,HCl : needles from EtOH–Et_2O. M.p. 235–6°.
B_2,H_2PtCl_6 : yellowish-red prisms from EtOH. M.p. 242–3° decomp.
Picrate : yellow needles from EtOH. M.p. 165°.

Pictet, Gams, *Ber.*, 1910, **43**, 2388.
Späth, Berger, Kuntara, *Ber.*, 1930, **63**, 139.
Rosenmund, Nothnagel, Riesenfeldt, *Ber.*, 1927, **60**, 395.

3-Phenylisoquinoline.
Leaflets from EtOH. M.p. 103–5°. Spar. volatile in steam.
$B,HAuCl_4,H_2O$: m.p. 179–80°.

Gabriel, Neumann, *Ber.*, 1892, **25**, 3573.

Phenylisoquinolone.
See Phenylisocarbostyril.
2-Phenylisoserine.
See 1-Hydroxy-2-amino-2-phenylpropionic Acid.
1-Phenylisosuccinic Acid.
See Methylphenylmalonic Acid.
2-Phenylisosuccinic Acid.
See Benzylmalonic Acid.
Phenyl isothiocyanate

$C_6H_5{\cdot}N{:}CS$

C_7H_5NS MW, 135

Colourless liq. F.P. — 21°. B.p. 221°, 131·8°/63 mm., 120–1°/35 mm., 95°/12 mm. D_4^4 1·1477, D_4^{25} 1·1288, D_4^{35} 1·1202, D_4^{50} 1·1061. $n_D^{23\cdot4}$ 1·64918. Heat of comb. C_v 1019·0 Cal., C_p 1020·3 Cal.

Dains, Brewster, Olander, *Organic Syntheses*, Collective Vol. I, 437.

1-Phenylisovaleric Acid (*Isopropylphenylacetic acid*)

$(CH_3)_2CH{\cdot}CH(C_6H_5){\cdot}COOH$

$C_{11}H_{14}O_2$ MW, 178

Prisms from ligroin. M.p. 61–2°. B.p. 159–60°/14 mm.
Amide : $C_{11}H_{15}ON$. MW, 177. Needles from EtOH.Aq. M.p. 111–12° (68°).
Nitrile : $C_{11}H_{13}N$. MW, 159. B.p. 245–9°/765 mm. $D^{15\cdot5}$ 0·967. Sol. EtOH, C_6H_6. Insol. H_2O. Volatile in steam.
Anilide : m.p. 132–3°.

Bodroux, Taboury, *Bull. soc. chim.*, 1910, **7**, 669.
Haller, Bauer, *Compt. rend.*, 1909, **149**, 9.
Hoffmann, *J. Am. Chem. Soc.*, 1929, **51**, 2546.

2-Phenylisovaleric Acid (β : β-*Dimethylhydrocinnamic acid*)

$(CH_3)_2C(C_6H_5){\cdot}CH_2{\cdot}COOH$

$C_{11}H_{14}O_2$ MW, 178

Cryst. from pet. ether. M.p. 58–58·5°.
Me ester : $C_{12}H_{16}O_2$. MW, 192. B.p. 120°/11 mm.
Anilide : cryst. from 60% MeOH. M.p. 122–3°.

Hoffmann, *J. Am. Chem. Soc.*, 1929, **51**, 2545–6.

3-Phenylisovaleric Acid (2-*Benzylbutyric acid*)

$C_6H_5{\cdot}CH_2{\cdot}CH(CH_3){\cdot}CH_2{\cdot}COOH$

$C_{11}H_{14}O_2$ MW, 178

Oil. B.p. 172°/13 mm. (161°/13 mm.). Sol. EtOH, Et_2O. Insol. H_2O.
Et ester : $C_{13}H_{18}O_2$. MW, 206. B.p. 144–6°/15 mm.
Chloride : $C_{11}H_{13}OCl$. MW, 196·5. B.p. 133–5°/14 mm., 123°/12 mm.
Nitrile : $C_{11}H_{13}N$. MW, 159. B.p. 121°/13 mm.
Anilide : needles from EtOH. M.p. 101°.

Anschütz, Motschmann, *Ann.*, 1915, **407**, 88.
v. Braun, Stuckenschmidt, *Ber.*, 1923, **56**, 1728.

Phenylitaconic Acid (*Benzylidenesuccinic acid, γ-phenylitaconic acid*)

$$C_6H_5{\cdot}CH$$
$$\alpha\ HOOC{\cdot}CH_2{\cdot}C{\cdot}COOH\ \beta$$

$C_{11}H_{10}O_4$ MW, 206

Plates from Et_2O. M.p. 192° (rapid heat.) with loss of H_2O. Sol. 24 parts boiling H_2O. Spar. sol. Et_2O, C_6H_6, cold H_2O. Very spar. sol. $CHCl_3$, CS_2. $k = 1{\cdot}37 \times 10^{-4}$ at 25°. Heat at 180–5° in vacuo ⟶ phenylitaconic anhydride + a little phenylcitraconic anhydride. $KMnO_4$ ⟶ benzaldehyde, malonic and oxalic acids.

Di-Me ester: $C_{13}H_{14}O_4$. MW, 234. Thick oil. B.p. 186°/19 mm. Misc. in all proportions with EtOH, Et_2O, Me_2CO, C_6H_6. Spar. sol. ligroin. Insol. H_2O. Volatile in steam.

α-Et ester: $C_{13}H_{14}O_4$. MW, 234. Needles from H_2O or pet. ether. M.p. 76–9°.

β-Et ester: needles or plates from CS_2. M.p. 72°. Sol. EtOH, Et_2O. Spar. sol. pet. ether, CS_2.

Di-Et ester: $C_{15}H_{18}O_4$. MW, 262. Oil. B.p. 315°, 195°/20 mm. Polymerises slowly in the dark, more rapidly in light. n_α^{20} 1·5243.

Anhydride: $C_{11}H_8O_3$. MW, 188. Leaflets from $CHCl_3$. M.p. 164–6° ⟶ phenylcitraconic anhydride with slight decomp. Sol. 9 parts boiling C_6H_6, 200 parts boiling Et_2O. Very spar. sol. pet. ether, CS_2.

Fittig, Brooke, *Ann.*, 1899, **305**, 21.
Stobbe, *Ber.*, 1908, **41**, 4353.
Hecht, *Monatsh.*, 1903, **24**, 367.

Phenyl-J Acid.
See N-Phenyl-2-amino-5-naphthol-7-sulphonic Acid.

1-Phenyl-lactic Acid.
See Atrolactinic Acid.

2-Phenyl-lactic Acid.
See α-Hydroxyhydrocinnamic Acid.

2-Phenyl-lepidine.
See Flavoline.

1-Phenyl-levulinic Acid (1-*Phenyl*-2-*acetylpropionic acid*)

$$C_6H_5$$
$$CH_3{\cdot}CO{\cdot}CH_2{\cdot}CH{\cdot}COOH$$

$C_{11}H_{12}O_3$ MW, 192

Leaflets from H_2O. M.p. 126°. Sol. EtOH, Et_2O.

Me ester: $C_{12}H_{14}O_3$. MW, 206. M.p. 71°.

Amide: $C_{11}H_{13}O_2N$. MW, 191. Yellow prisms from AcOH.Aq. M.p. 236° decomp.

Phenylhydrazone: needles from EtOH. M.p 140°.

Weltner, *Ber.*, 1885, **18**, 790.
Ruhemann, *J. Chem. Soc.*, 1904, **85**, 1455

4-Phenyl-levulinic Acid (2-*Phenylacetyl-propionic acid*)

$$C_6H_5{\cdot}CH_2{\cdot}CO{\cdot}CH_2{\cdot}CH_2{\cdot}COOH$$

$C_{11}H_{12}O_3$ MW, 19

Needles from $CHCl_3$–ligroin. M.p. 55–6° Sol. Et_2O, CS_2, C_6H_6. Mod. sol. H_2O. Spar sol. ligroin.

Semicarbazone: needles from 50% EtOH M.p. 182–3° decomp.

Stobbe, Russwurm, Schulz, *Ann.*, 1899 **308**, 179.

Phenylmaleic Acid (1-*Phenylethylene*-1 : 2-*dicarboxylic acid*)

$$C_6H_5{\cdot}C{\cdot}COOH$$
$$HC{\cdot}COOH$$

$C_{10}H_8O_4$ MW, 192

Prisms from Et_2O. Mod. sol. H_2O. Very unstable.

Anhydride: needles from CS_2. M.p. 119–119·5°. Sol. Et_2O, $CHCl_3$. Spar. sol. CS_2, ligroin. Cold H_2O ⟶ acid.

Alexander, *Ann.*, 1890, **258**, 77.

1-Phenylmalic Acid

$$C_6H_5{\cdot}C(OH){\cdot}COOH$$
$$CH_2{\cdot}COOH$$

$C_{10}H_{10}O_5$ MW, 21

Prisms from $CHCl_3$. M.p. 187–8°. Sol. 75 parts H_2O at 15°. Sol. Et_2O.

Alexander, *Ann.*, 1890, **258**, 76.

2-Phenylmalic Acid

$$HO{\cdot}CH{\cdot}COOH\ \alpha$$
$$C_6H_5{\cdot}CH{\cdot}COOH\ \beta$$

$C_{10}H_{10}O_5$ MW, 21

Cryst. from Et_2O. M.p. 160°. Sol. 3 parts H_2O at 15°. Insol. $CHCl_3$, C_6H_6, ligroin.

β-Et ester: $C_{12}H_{14}O_5$. MW, 238. Oil. α *Nitrile*: $C_{12}H_{13}O_3N$. MW, 219. Prisms from hot EtOH. M.p. 127–8°. Sol. $CHCl_3$. Spar sol. Et_2O, ligroin.

Alexander, *Ann.*, 1890, **258**, 80.
Börner, *Chem. Zentr.*, 1900, I, 123.

Phenylmalonaldehydic Acid.
See Phenylformylacetic Acid.

Phenylmalonic Acid

$$C_6H_5\cdot CH<\begin{matrix}COOH\\COOH\end{matrix}$$

$C_9H_8O_4$ MW, 180

Prisms from H_2O. M.p. 152–3° decomp. Sol. H_2O, EtOH, Et_2O, Less sol. $CHCl_3$, CS_2, C_6H_6, ligroin. Above m.p. ⟶ phenylacetic acid.

Me ester: $C_{10}H_{10}O_4$. MW, 194. Cryst. from MeOH. M.p. 95°. *Anilide*: m.p. 109°.

Di-Me ester: $C_{11}H_{12}O_4$. MW, 208. Cryst. from ligroin. M.p. 51°. B.p. 147–9°/10 mm.

Et ester: $C_{11}H_{12}O_4$. MW, 208. *Amide*: $C_{11}H_{13}O_3N$. MW, 207. Needles from C_6H_6. M.p. 152°. Sol. EtOH. Insol. H_2O.

Di-Et ester: $C_{13}H_{16}O_4$. MW, 236. B.p. 171°/21 mm., 158–9°/10 mm.

Dichloride: $C_9H_6O_2Cl_2$. MW, 217. B.p. 122°/15 mm.

Diamide: $C_9H_{10}O_2N_2$. MW, 178. Cryst. from EtOH. M.p. 233°. Sol. EtOH. Insol. H_2O.

Nitrile: *see* Phenylcyanoacetic Acid.

Dinitrile: $C_9H_6N_2$. MW, 142. Cryst. from EtOH.Aq. M.p. 68–9°. B.p. 152–3°/21 mm. Sol. EtOH, Et_2O. Spar. sol. H_2O, ligroin.

Nelson, Cretcher, *J. Am. Chem. Soc.*, 1928, **50**, 2758.
Hessler, *Am. Chem. J.*, 1905, **32**, 123.
Wislicenus, *Ber.*, 1894, **27**, 1093.
Staudinger, Hirzel, *Ber.*, 1917, **50**, 1030.
Rising, Stieglitz, *J. Am. Chem. Soc.*, 1918, **40**, 728.
Dox, Yoder, *J. Am. Chem. Soc.*, 1922, **44**, 1564.
Ivanoff, Spassoff, *Bull. soc. chim.*, 1931, **49**, 19.
Blum-Bergmann, *Ber.*, 1932, **65**, 115.

Phenyl Mercaptan.
See Thiophenol.

Phenylmercaptobenzoic Acid.
See Diphenyl sulphide carboxylic Acid.

Phenylmesaconic Acid (*Benzylfumaric acid*)

$$\begin{matrix}C_6H_5\cdot CH_2\cdot C\cdot COOH\\ \quad\quad HOOC\cdot CH\end{matrix}$$

$C_{11}H_{10}O_4$ MW, 206

Needles from H_2O. M.p. 212°. Sol. Et_2O, boiling C_6H_6. Sol. 35 parts boiling H_2O. Spar. sol. cold H_2O. Insol. $CHCl_3$, CS_2, ligroin. Heat with 10% NaOH ⟶ phenylitaconic acid + phenylaticonic acid.

Fittig, Brooke, *Ann.*, 1899, **305**, 31.

Phenylmesitylmethane (*Benzylmesitylene, 1 : 3 : 5-trimethyldiphenylmethane*)

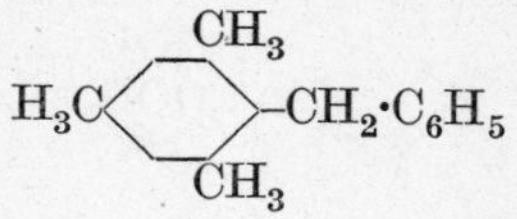

$C_{16}H_{18}$ MW, 210

Needles. M.p. 37°. B.p. 301–3°, 183°/11 mm. CrO_3 ⟶ benzoylmesitylene. HI + P ⟶ toluene + mesitylene.

Louise, *Ann. chim. phys.*, 1885, **6**, 177.
Klages, Allendorff, *Ber.*, 1898, **31**, 1001.

Phenyl *p*-methoxyphenacyl Ether.
See under p-Hydroxyphenacyl Alcohol.

Phenyl methoxystyryl Ketone.
See Anisylideneacetophenone *and under* 2-, and 3-Hydroxychalkones.

Phenyl methylstyryl Ketone.
See Dypnone *and* 2′-, 3′-, and 4′-Methyl chalkones.

1-Phenylnaphthalene

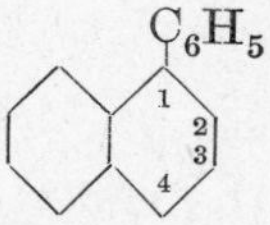

$C_{16}H_{12}$ MW, 204

Cryst. M.p. about 45°. B.p. 334°/760 mm., 186–8°/10 mm. Sol. EtOH, Et_2O, AcOH, C_6H_6. Shows faint blue fluor.

Chattaway, *J. Chem. Soc.*, 1893, **63**, 1185.
Möhlau, Berger, *Ber.*, 1893, **26**, 1198.
Veselý, Štursa, *Chem. Zentr.*, 1936, I, 1221.

2-Phenylnaphthalene.

Leaflets from EtOH. M.p. 101–2°. B.p. 345–6°. Sol. AcOH, C_6H_6. Less sol. EtOH, Et_2O, $CHCl_3$. Volatile in steam. Shows weak blue fluor.

Smith, Takamatsu, *J. Chem. Soc.*, 1881, **39**, 547.
Späth, *Monatsh.*, 1912, **33**, 1046.

Phenylnaphthalene-carboxylic Acid.
See β-Chrysenic Acid *and* Phenylnaphthoic Acid.

2-Phenylnaphthalene-1 : 2′-dicarboxylic Acid.
See Chrysodiphenic Acid.

1-Phenylnaphthalene-2 : 3-dicarboxylic Acid

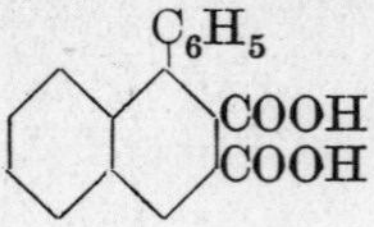

$C_{18}H_{12}O_4$ MW, 292

Leaflets from H_2O. At 255° ⟶ anhydride.

2-*Me ester*: $C_{19}H_{14}O_4$. MW, 306. Needles from EtOH or C_6H_6–ligroin. M.p. 207° decomp.

Di-Me ester: $C_{20}H_{16}O_4$. MW, 320. Leaflets from MeOH.Aq. M.p. 118–20° (121°). Sol. hot EtOH. Spar. sol. Et_2O.

2-*Et ester*: $C_{20}H_{16}O_4$. MW, 320. Needles from C_6H_6–ligroin. M.p. 207° decomp. Sol. most org. solvents. Insol. H_2O.

Di-Et ester: $C_{22}H_{20}O_4$. MW, 348. Plates from ligroin. M.p. 129–30°.

Anhydride: needles from C_6H_6–ligroin. M.p. 255° (257–9°). Sol. $CHCl_3$, AcOH, C_6H_6. Spar. sol. EtOH. Insol. ligroin.

Imide: needles from EtOH. M.p. 246°. Sol. EtOH, AcOH, C_6H_6.

Lanser, Halvorsen, *Ber.*, 1902, **35**, 1407.
Stobbe, *Ber.*, 1907, **40**, 3373.
Michael, Bucher, *Am. Chem. J.*, 1898, **20**, 95.
Pfeiffer, Moller, *Ber.*, 1907, **40**, 3841.

1-Phenylnaphthalene-4-sulphonic Acid

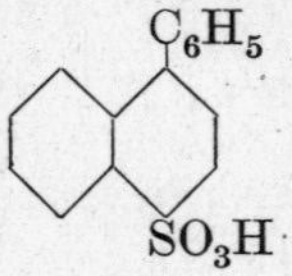

$C_{16}H_{12}O_3S$ MW, 284

Needles from C_6H_6. M.p. 165–7°.

Anilide: cryst. from C_6H_6–pet. ether. M.p. 167°. Very sol. C_6H_6.

v. Braun, Anton, *Ber.*, 1934, **67**, 1053.

***N*-Phenylnaphthastyril**

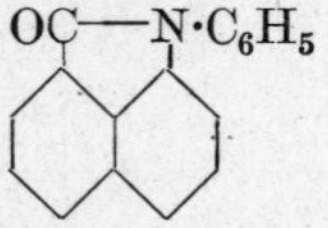

$C_{17}H_{11}ON$ MW, 245

Yellow needles from ligroin. M.p. 104–5°. Mod. sol. usual org. solvents, hot conc. HCl. Sol. hot, insol. cold NaOH.Aq.

I.G., F.P., 778,254, (*Chem. Abstracts*, 1935, **29**, 4600).
Rule, Turner, *J. Chem. Soc.*, 1935, 318.

2-Phenyl-1-naphthoic Acid.

See β-Chrysenic Acid.

4-Phenyl-1-naphthoic Acid (4-*Phenylnaphthalene*-1-*carboxylic acid*)

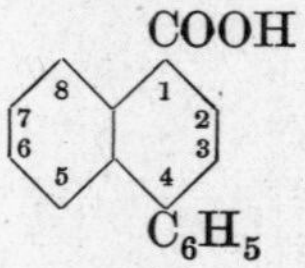

$C_{17}H_{12}O_2$ MW, 248

Cryst. from AcOH.Aq. M.p. 172–3°.

Nitrile: $C_{17}H_{11}N$. MW, 229. Cryst. from C_6H_6. M.p. 114–15°.

v. Braun, Anton, *Ber.*, 1934, **67**, 1054.

5-Phenyl-1-naphthoic Acid (5-*Phenylnaphthalene*-1-*carboxylic acid*).

Cryst. from AcOH. M.p. 229°.

Nitrile: cryst. from C_6H_6. M.p. 73–7°.

See previous reference.

3-Phenyl-1-naphthol (4-*Hydroxy*-2-*phenylnaphthalene*)

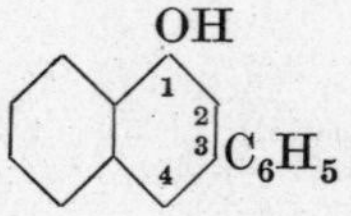

$C_{16}H_{12}O$ MW, 220

Brownish needles from EtOH.Aq. M.p. 100–1°. Sol. EtOH, Et_2O, $CHCl_3$. Spar. sol. boiling H_2O.

Ruhemann, *J. Chem. Soc.*, 1910, **97**, 461.

4-Phenyl-1-naphthol (4-*Hydroxy*-1-*phenylnaphthalene*).

Needles from C_6H_6–pet. ether. M.p. 140°.

v. Braun, Anton, *Ber.*, 1934, **67**, 1053.

***N*-Phenyl-1-naphthylamine**

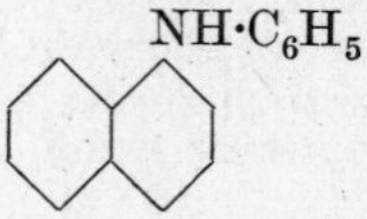

$C_{16}H_{13}N$ MW, 219

Prisms or needles from EtOH, leaflets from ligroin. M.p. 62°. B.p. 335°/528 mm., 226°/8 mm. (200°/10 mm.). Sol. EtOH, Et_2O, $CHCl_3$, AcOH, C_6H_6. Sols. show blue fluor. Heat of comb. C_v 2017 Cal. Conc. H_2SO_4 + HNO_3 ⟶ blue col. ⟶ green ⟶ brown on heating. Rubber vulcanisation acceleration.

N-Acetyl: cryst. from EtOH. M.p. 115°. Sol. EtOH, $CHCl_3$, C_6H_6. Spar. sol. Et_2O.

N-*Benzoyl* : cryst. from EtOH. M.p. 152°. ol. EtOH, Et_2O, C_6H_6.

Knoevenagel, *J. prakt. Chem.*, 1914, **89**, 17.
Knoll, D.R.P., 241,853, (*Chem. Zentr.*, 1912, I, 178).
Streiff, *Ann.*, 1881, **209**, 154.

N-Phenyl-2-naphthylamine

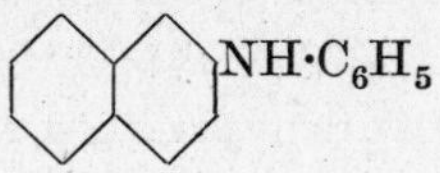

$_{16}H_{13}N$ MW, 219

Needles from MeOH. M.p. 108° (102–4°). .p. 395–399·5°, 237°/13 mm. Mod. sol. EtOH, t_2O, AcOH, C_6H_6. Sols. show blue fluor. eat of comb. C_v 2007 Cal. Rubber vulcanis- ion accelerator.

N-*Acetyl* : cryst. from Et_2O. M.p. 93°. Sol. tOH, Et_2O, AcOH, C_6H_6.

N-*Benzoyl* : needles from EtOH. M.p. 136° 47–8°). Sol. C_6H_6. Spar. sol. EtOH.

N-*Me* : $C_{17}H_{15}N$. MW, 233. M.p. 52–3°.

N-*Et* : $C_{18}H_{17}N$. MW, 247. Leaflets. M.p. 3°.

Streiff, *Ann.*, 1881, **209**, 157.
Cherntzov, Drozdov, *Chem. Abstracts*, 1935, **29**, 2529.
See also first two references above.

4-Phenyl-1-naphthylamine

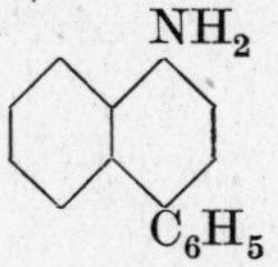

$_{16}H_{13}N$ MW, 219

Cryst. M.p. 73–4°.

N-*Acetyl* : m.p. 167–8°.

Veselý, Štursa, *Chem. Zentr.*, 1933, II, 3850.

Phenylnaphthylamine-carboxylic Acid.

See Naphthylanthranilic Acid.

N-Phenyl-1-naphthylamine-8-sulphonic cid (*Phenyl-peri acid*, 1-*anilinonaphthalene*-8- *ılphonic acid*)

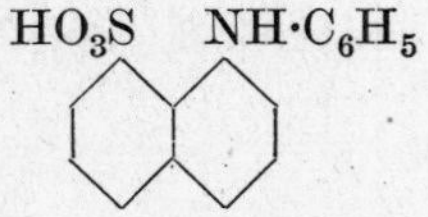

$_{16}H_{13}O_3NS$ MW, 299

Leaflets. Spar. sol. H_2O. Intermediate for zo dyes.

Na salt : needles + H_2O. Very sol. H_2O.

Bayer, D.R.P., 70,349.
Kalle, D.R.P., 170,630, (*Chem. Zentr.*, 1906, II, 473).
A.G.F.A., D.R.P., 158,923, (*Chem. Zentr.*, 1905, I, 909).

4-Phenyl-1 : 2-naphthylenediamine

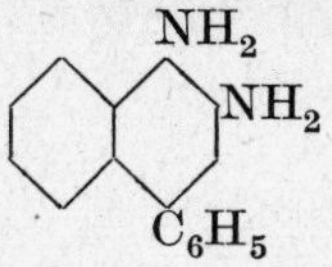

$C_{16}H_{14}N_2$ MW, 234

Cryst. M.p. 100–1°.

Veselý, Štursa, *Chem. Zentr.*, 1933, II, 3850.

2-Phenyl-1 : 3-naphthylenediamine

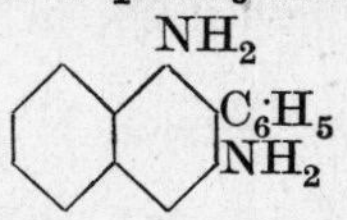

$C_{16}H_{14}N_2$ MW, 234

Plates from MeOH. M.p. 116°. Sol. EtOH, C_6H_6. Spar. sol. cold Et_2O. Insol. pet. ether. Turns red in air.

1 : 3-N-*Di-Me* : $C_{18}H_{18}N_2$. MW, 262. *Cis* : Dimorphous. Needles or prisms from EtOH. M.p. 170°. Needles are stable between 20° and 80°. Prisms formed below 17° and above 80°. *Trans* : cryst. from EtOH. M.p. 159–60°. *Acetyl* : prisms from EtOH. M.p. 203°. *Di-acetyl* : prisms from MeOH.Aq. M.p. 207–8°. p-*Toluenesulphonyl* : needles from EtOH. M.p. 219–20°. *Di*-p-*toluenesulphonyl* : plates from Py. M.p. 305°.

N : N-*Tri-Me* : $C_{19}H_{20}N_2$. MW, 276. Needles from EtOH. M.p. 104–5°. *Acetyl* : needles from EtOH. M.p. 178°.

N : N-*Tetra-Me*: $C_{20}H_{22}N_2$. MW, 290. Prisms from EtOH. M.p. 122°.

3-N-*Acetyl* : plates from EtOH or C_6H_6. M.p. 220°.

1 : 3-N-*Diacetyl* : needles. M.p. 267°.

1 : 3-N-*Di*-p-*toluenesulphonyl* : *cis*, dimorphous prisms from MeOH. M.ps. 203–5° and 188–9°. *Trans* : needles from MeOH. M.p. 173–5°.

N : N-*Tri*-p-*toluenesulphonyl* : needles from MeOH. M.p. 153–4°.

Atkinson, Thorpe, *J. Chem. Soc.*, 1906, **89**, 1934.
Atkinson, Ingham, Thorpe, *J. Chem. Soc.*, 1907, **91**, 589.
Lees, Thorpe, *ibid.*, 1296.
Gibson, Kentish, Simonsen, *J. Chem. Soc.*, 1928, 2131.
Lesslie, Turner, *J. Chem. Soc.*, 1929, 1512.

Phenyl 1-naphthyl Ether (1-*Phenoxy-naphthalene*)

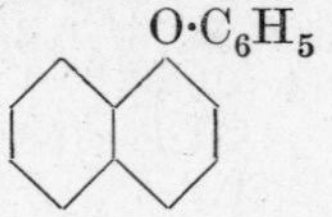

$C_{16}H_{12}O$ MW, 220

Prisms from Et_2O–EtOH. M.p. 55–6°. B.p. 349·5°. Sol. Et_2O, $CHCl_3$, C_6H_6. Mod. sol. EtOH, ligroin.

Ullmann, Sponagel, *Ann.*, 1906, **350**, 90.
Fritzsche, D.R.P., 269,543, (*Chem. Zentr.*, 1914, I, 591).

Phenyl 2-naphthyl Ether (2-*Phenoxy-naphthalene*).

Needles from Et_2O–EtOH. M.p. 46°. B.p. 335·5°/753 mm. Sol. Et_2O, $CHCl_3$, AcOH. Insol. H_2O.

See previous references.

***sym*.-Phenyl-1-naphthylhydrazine** (*Benzenehydrazo-α-naphthalene*)

$C_6H_5{\cdot}NH{\cdot}NH{\cdot}C_{10}H_7$

$C_{16}H_{14}N_2$ MW, 234

Leaflets. M.p. 125°.
Diacetyl: m.p. 264°.

Nietzki, Zehntner, *Ber.*, 1883, **26**, 144.

Phenyl 1-naphthyl Ketone (1-*Benzoyl-naphthalene*)

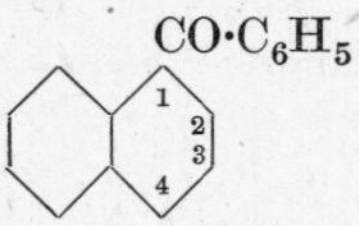

$C_{17}H_{12}O$ MW, 232

Prisms from EtOH. M.p. 75·5–76°. B.p. 385°, 225°/12 mm., 222°/8 mm. Sol. 41 parts EtOH at 12°. Diamagnetic.

Oxime: exists in two forms. (i) Cryst. from EtOH. M.p. 161°. (ii) Cryst. from EtOH. M.p. 127°.

Imide: m.p. 68–9°. B.p. 181·5°/4·5 mm.

Moureu, Mignonac, *Compt. rend.*, 1913, **156**, 1806.
Betti, Poccianti, *Gazz. chim. ital.*, 1915, **45**, i, 374.
Caille, *Compt. rend.*, 1911, **153**, 393.
Szperl, *Chem. Zentr.*, 1930, I, 3436.

Phenyl 2-naphthyl Ketone (2-*Benzoyl-naphthalene*).

Needles from EtOH. M.p. 82°. B.p. 398°/754 mm., 225°/8 mm. Sol. 49 parts EtOH at 12°. Paramagnetic.

Oxime: exists in two forms. (i) Needles fro[m] EtOH. M.p. 174°. (ii) Cryst. from EtO[H]. M.p. 157°.

Semicarbazone: cryst. from EtOH. M.[p.] 175°. Sol. EtOH, Et_2O, $CHCl_3$, CS_2, $C_6H_{[6]}$. Insol. H_2O.

Lecher, *Ber.*, 1913, **46**, 2667; D.R.P. 281,802, (*Chem. Zentr.*, 1915, I, 281).
Poccianti, *Gazz. chim. ital.*, 1915, **45**, i[i], 114.
Barbot, *Bull. soc. chim.*, 1930, **47**, 1314.

Phenyl-1-naphthylmethane (1-*Benzyl-naphthalene*)

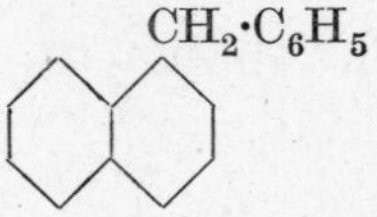

$C_{17}H_{14}$ MW, 21[8]

M.p. 58·5°. B.p. 350°, 217–20°/20 mm. So[l.] EtOH, Et_2O, $CHCl_3$, CS_2, C_6H_6. D^{17} 1·16[6]. Dil. HNO_3 ⟶ phenyl 1-naphthyl ketone.

Picrate: yellow needles. M.p. 100–1°.

Nenitzescu, Isăcescu, Ionescu, *Ann.*, 193[1], **491**, 217.
Miquel, *Bull. soc. chim.*, 1876, **26**, 2.
Roux, *Ann. chim. phys.*, 1887, **12**, 326.
Lecher, D.R.P., 281,802, (*Chem. Zentr.*, 1915, I, 281).
Dziewoński, Dziecielewski, *Chem. Zentr.*, 1928, I, 57.
Gasopoulos, *Chem. Zentr.*, 1933, II, 43.

Phenyl-2-naphthylmethane (2-*Benzyl-naphthalene*)

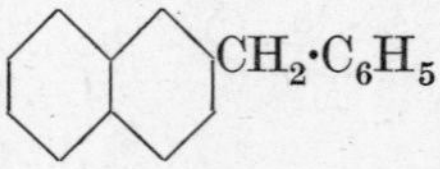

$C_{17}H_{14}$ MW, 21[8]

Prisms. M.p. 55·5°. B.p. 350°. Sol. EtOH, C_6H_6. D^0 1·176. Dil. HNO_3 ⟶ phenyl 2-naphthyl ketone.

Picrate: golden-yellow needles from EtOH. M.p. 93°.

Roux, *Ann. chim. phys.*, 1887, **12**, 326.
Vincent, Roux, *Bull. soc. chim.*, 1883, **40**, 165.
Dziewoński, Wodelski, *Chem. Zentr.*, 1933, I, 774.

Phenyl 1-naphthyl sulphide (1-*Thio-naphthol phenyl ether*)

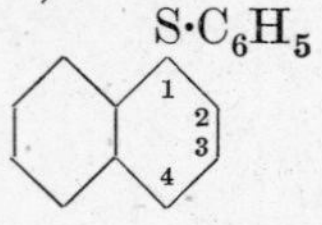

$C_{16}H_{12}S$ MW, 23[6]

Prisms from EtOH.Aq. M.p. 41·8°. B.p. 255–6°/43 mm., 220–5°/11 mm. D_4^{15} 1·167. Mod. sol. EtOH, Et_2O.

Wuyts, *Bull. soc. chim.*, 1906, **35**, 167.
Bourgeois, *Ber.*, 1895, **28**, 2327.

Phenyl 2-naphthyl sulphide (2-*Thionaphthol phenyl ether*).

Needles or leaflets from EtOH. M.p. 51·8°. B.p. 226°/11 mm.

See last reference above.

Phenyl 1-naphthyl sulphone

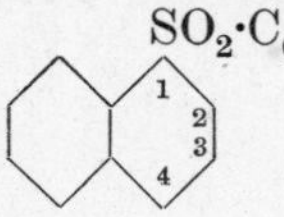

$C_{16}H_{12}O_2S$ MW, 268

Cryst. from EtOH. M.p. 99·5–100·5°. Very sol. hot EtOH, Et_2O, AcOH, C_6H_6.

Michael, Adair, *Ber.*, 1877, **10**, 585.

Phenyl 2-naphthyl sulphone.

Needles from EtOH or Et_2O. M.p. 115–16°.

See previous reference.

6-Phenylnicotinic Acid (6-*Phenylpyridine-3-carboxylic acid*)

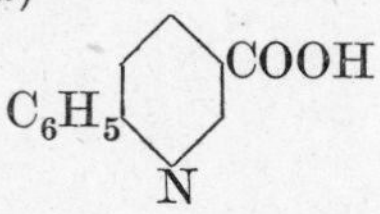

$C_{12}H_9O_2N$ MW, 199

Needles from H_2O. M.p. 232–3° (sinters at 220°). Sol. EtOH, Et_2O. Spar. sol. H_2O, AcOH.

Anilide: leaflets from EtOH. M.p. 199°.

Bemary, Paille, *Ber.*, 1924, **57**, 832.

Phenylnitramine (N-*Nitroaniline, nitraminobenzene*)

$C_6H_5{\cdot}NH{\cdot}NO_2 \rightleftharpoons C_6H_5{\cdot}N{:}N(O){\cdot}OH$

aci-form

$C_6H_6O_2N_2$ MW, 138

Pearly leaflets from pet. ether. M.p. 46–46·5°. Very sol. most org. solvents. Mod. sol. H_2O. Spar. sol. pet. ether. $k = 1{\cdot}7 \times 10^{-5}$ at 18°, $2{\cdot}3 \times 10^{-5}$ at 25°. Explodes on strong heating. Warm dil. min. acids $\longrightarrow$ *o*- and *p*-nitroaniline. Mod. volatile in steam.

N-*Me*: *see* Methylphenylnitramine.

aci-*Me ether*: $C_7H_8O_2N_2$. MW, 152. Yellow oil with odour of heliotrope. Decomp. with explosion on warming.

Bamberger, *Ber.*, 1893, **26**, 485; 1894, **27**, 362, 915.
Degner, v. Pechmann, *Ber.*, 1897, **30**, 647.

Phenyl nitrobenzyl Ketone.
See Nitrodeoxybenzoin.

Phenylnitromethane (ω-*Nitrotoluene*)

$C_6H_5{\cdot}CH_2{\cdot}NO_2 \rightleftharpoons C_6H_5{\cdot}CH{-}N{\cdot}OH$ (with O bridging CH and N)

or

$C_6H_5{\cdot}CH{:}N(O){\cdot}OH$

aci-form

$C_7H_7O_2N$ MW, 137

Yellow liq. B.p. 225–7°, 141–2°/35 mm., 118–19°/16 mm. D_0^0 1·1756, D_0^{20} 1·1598. n_D^{20} 1·53230. Gives no col. with $FeCl_3$. Alkalis $\longrightarrow$ *aci*-form. Electrolytic reduction $\longrightarrow$ benzylamine.

aci-*Form*: phenylisonitromethane. Cryst. from Et_2O–pet. ether. M.p. 84°. Sol. EtOH, Et_2O. Mod. sol. C_6H_6. Insol. pet. ether. Sol. Na_2CO_3.Aq. $FeCl_3 \longrightarrow$ intense reddish-brown col. *NH_4 salt*: powder. M.p. 89–90°.

Hantzsch, Schultze, *Ber.*, 1896, **29**, 700.
Konowalow, *Ber.*, 1895, **28**, 1861.
Hollemann, *Rec. trav. chim.*, 1894, **13**, 405.
Wislicenus, Grützner, *Ber.*, 1909, **42**, 1932.
Schorygin, Ssokolowa, *Chem. Zentr.*, 1930, II, 2637.

***S*-Phenyl-4-nitrothiosalicylic Acid.**
See 5-Nitrodiphenylsulphide-2-carboxylic Acid.

Phenyl 6-nitro-*m*-tolyl Ether.
See 6-Nitro-3-methyldiphenyl Ether.

Phenyl nitrotolyl Ketone.
See Nitromethylbenzophenone.

Phenyl nitrotolyl sulphide.
See Nitromethyldiphenyl sulphide.

Phenyl nitrotolyl sulphone.
See Nitromethyldiphenyl sulphone.

Phenyloctane.
See Octylbenzene.

4-Phenyloxazole

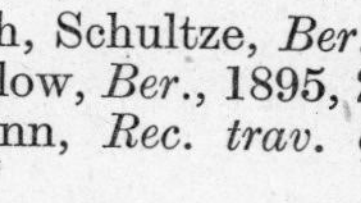

C_9H_7ON MW, 145

Thick liq. M.p. 6°. B.p. 220–2°.

B,HCl: plates. M.p. 80°.

Lewy, *Ber.*, 1887, **20**, 2578.
Blümlein, *Ber.*, 1884, **17**, 2580.

5-Phenyloxazole.

Cryst. M.p. 41–2°.

B_2,AuCl$_3$: orange needles from H_2O. M.p. 149–50°.

Chloroplatinate : long yellow needles. Does not decompose below 275°. Spar. sol. H_2O.

Bachstez, *Ber.*, 1914, **47**, 3165.

2-Phenyl-2-oxazoline (*2-Phenyl-4 : 5-dihydro-oxazole*)

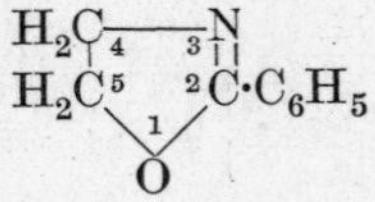

C_9H_9ON MW, 147

B.p. 246–8° (242–3°). Misc. with EtOH, Et_2O. Spar. sol. H_2O.

Picrate : yellow needles. M.p. 177°. Spar. sol. most solvents.

Gabriel, Neumann, *Ber.*, 1892, **25**, 2385.
Gabriel, Stelzner, *Ber.*, 1895, **28**, 2933.
Wenker, *J. Am. Chem. Soc.*, 1935, **57**, 1080.

1-Phenyloxindole

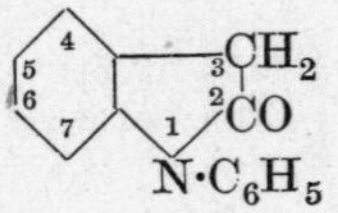

$C_{14}H_{11}ON$ MW, 209

Leaflets from H_2O or ligroin. M.p. 121°. Sol. EtOH, Et_2O. Spar. sol. H_2O.

Stollé, *Ber.*, 1914, **47**, 2120; D.R.P., 335,673, (*Chem. Abstracts*, 1923, **17**, 1802).

3-Phenyloxindole.

Reddish leaflets from EtOH. M.p. 183° (185–7°). Sol. EtOH, C_6H_6. Insol. acids. Sol. KOH.Aq.

N-*Acetyl* : cryst. from EtOH.Aq. M.p. 103°.

Brunner, *Monatsh.*, 1897, **18**, 547.
Meisenheimer, Camparter, *Ber.*, 1924, **57**, 297.

7-Phenylpalmitic Acid

$$CH_3\cdot[CH_2]_7\cdot \underset{}{\overset{C_6H_5}{\overset{|}{C}H}}\cdot[CH_2]_6\cdot COOH$$

$C_{22}H_{36}O_2$ MW, 332

B.p. 190–5°/0·12 mm. D_{25}^{25} 0·9417. n_D^{20} 1·4912.

Et ester : $C_{24}H_{40}O_2$. MW, 360. B.p. 174–80°/0·13 mm. D_{25}^{25} 0·9194. n_D^{20} 1·4808.

p-*Bromophenacyl ester* : m.p. 77–8°.

Harmon, Marvel, *J. Am. Chem. Soc.*, 1932, **54**, 2515.

γ-Phenylparaconic Acid (*3-Phenyl-γ-butyrolactone-2-carboxylic acid*)

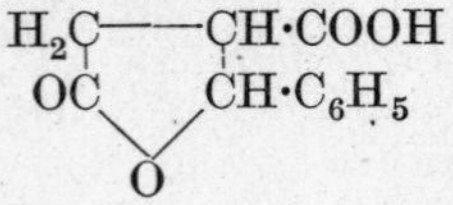

$C_{11}H_{10}O_4$ MW, 206

d-.

Needles $+ \frac{1}{4}H_2O$ from H_2O. M.p. anhyd. 134°. Sol. EtOH, Et_2O, $CHCl_3$, hot H_2O, hot C_6H_6. Insol. CS_2, pet. ether. $[\alpha]_D^{20}$ + 64·3° in EtOH.

l-.

Needles $+ \frac{1}{4}H_2O$ from H_2O. M.p. anhyd. 134°. Sol. EtOH, Et_2O, $CHCl_3$, hot H_2O, hot C_6H_6. Insol. CS_2, pet. ether. $[\alpha]_D^{20}$ − 65·3° in EtOH.

dl-.

Needles $+ \frac{1}{4}H_2O$ from H_2O. M.p. 99°, anhyd. 121°. $k = 4{\cdot}80 \times 10^{-4}$ at 20°. Heat of comb. of hydrate, C_v 1195·9 Cal.

Me ester : $C_{12}H_{12}O_4$. MW, 220. Cryst. from Et_2O. M.p. 69–70°. B.p. 211°/14 mm.

Et ester : $C_{13}H_{14}O_4$. MW, 234. Oil with aromatic odour. B.p. 241–2°/52 mm., 224°/25 mm.

Barbier, Locquin, *Bull. soc. chim.*, 1912, **13**, 233.
Fittig, Jehl, *Ann.*, 1904, **330**, 345.

5-Phenyl-1 : 2-pentadiene (*γδ-Pentadienylbenzene*)

$$C_6H_5\cdot CH_2\cdot CH_2\cdot CH\dot{:}C\dot{:}CH_2$$

$C_{11}H_{12}$ MW, 144

B.p. 76–7°/7 mm. D_4^{20} 0·9169. n_D^{20} 1·5400.

Carothers, Berchet, *J. Am. Chem. Soc.*, 1933, **55**, 2816.

1-Phenyl-1 : 3-pentadiene (*αγ-Pentadienylbenzene*)

$$CH_3\cdot CH\dot{:}CH\cdot CH\dot{:}CH\cdot C_6H_5$$

$C_{11}H_{12}$ MW, 144

Viscous oil. B.p. 240–60°, 116°/16 mm. $D_4^{15\cdot2}$ 0·9325. $n_D^{15\cdot2}$ 1·6000.

Auwers, Eisenlohr, *J. prakt. Chem.*, 1911, **84**, 43.
Pestemer, Wiligot, *Monatsh.*, 1935, **66**, 123.

2-Phenyl-1 : 3-pentadiene

$$\begin{array}{c} \quad\quad\quad\quad\quad C_6H_5 \\ CH_3{\cdot}CH{:}CH{\cdot}C{:}CH_2 \end{array}$$

$_{11}H_{12}$ MW, 144

B.p. 85–6°/15 mm. Readily polymerises.

Kuhn, Hoffer, *Ber.*, 1933, **66**, 1269.

3-Phenylpentandione-2 : 4.
See Phenylacetylacetone.

1-Phenylpentane.
See *n*-Amylbenzene.

2-Phenylpentane (ω-*Methylethyltoluene*)

$$\begin{array}{c} \quad\quad\quad\quad\quad C_6H_5 \\ CH_3{\cdot}CH_2{\cdot}CH_2{\cdot}CH{\cdot}CH_3 \end{array}$$

$_{11}H_{16}$ MW, 148

B.p. 191–3°. D_4^{21} 0·8594. n_D^{21} 1·4875.

Klages, *Ber.*, 1902, **35**, 3509.

3-Phenylpentane (*Diethylphenylmethane*, ec.-n-*amylbenzene*, ω-*diethyltoluene*)

$$\begin{array}{c} \quad\quad C_6H_5 \\ CH_3{\cdot}CH_2{\cdot}CH{\cdot}CH_2{\cdot}CH_3 \end{array}$$

$_{11}H_{16}$ MW, 148

B.p. 180° (187°), 83–5°/22 mm., 38–41°/0·7 m. D_4^{15} 0·8755. n_D^{25} 1·4868.

Levene, Marker, *J. Biol. Chem.*, 1935, **108**, 417.

Phenylpentanol-1.
See Phenyl-*n*-amyl Alcohol.

1-Phenylpentanol-2.
See Propylbenzylcarbinol.

1-Phenylpentanol-4.
See 5-Phenyl-*sec.-n*-amyl alcohol.

2-Phenylpentanol-2.
See Methylpropylphenylcarbinol.

5-Phenylpentanol-2.
See 5-Phenyl-*sec.-n*-amyl Alcohol.

1-Phenylpentanol-3 (*Ethyl-β-phenylethylcarbinol, γ-hydroxy-*n-*amylbenzene*)

$$CH_3{\cdot}CH_2{\cdot}CH(OH){\cdot}CH_2{\cdot}CH_2{\cdot}C_6H_5$$

$_{11}H_{16}O$ MW, 164

d-.

M.p. 38°. B.p. 143°/19 mm. D_4^{20} 0·9687, D_4^{140} 0·8773. $[\alpha]_{5461}$ + 31·8° in EtOH.

Acid phthalate: viscous gum. $[\alpha]_{5461}$ + 42·9° n EtOH. *Strychnine salt*: m.p. 158°. $[\alpha]_{5461}$ – 38·7° in $CHCl_3$.

Formyl: b.p. 135°/15 mm. D_4^{20} 0·9980. n_{5461}^{20} 1·5003. $[\alpha]_{5461}^{20}$ – 13·93°.

Acetyl: b.p. 147°/19 mm. D_4^{20} 0·9829. n_{5461}^{20} ·4920. $[\alpha]_{5461}^{18·5}$ – 11·20°.

l-.

M.p. 38°. B.p. 143°/19 mm.

Acid phthalate: $[\alpha]_{5461}$ – 42·9° in EtOH. *Cinchonidine salt*: m.p. 154°. $[\alpha]_{5461}$ – 54·2° in EtOH.

Propionyl: b.p. 150°/14 mm. D_4^{20} 0·9731. n_{5461}^{20} 1·4878. $[\alpha]_{5461}^{20}$ + 22·47°.

dl.-

Liq. B.p. 143°/19 mm., 130°/15 mm.

Acid phthalate: prisms from AcOH. M.p. 74°.

Phenylurethane: m.p. 74°.

Hewitt, Kenyon, *J. Chem. Soc.*, 1925, 1094.
Roblin, Davidson, Bogert, *J. Am. Chem. Soc.*, 1935, **57**, 151.

2-Phenylpentanol-3 (*Ethyl-α-phenylethylcarbinol*)

$$\begin{array}{c} \quad\quad\quad\quad\quad\quad\quad\quad C_6H_5 \\ CH_3{\cdot}CH_2{\cdot}CH(OH){\cdot}CH{\cdot}CH_3 \end{array}$$

$C_{11}H_{16}O$ MW, 164

B.p. 134–7°/32 mm.

Tiffeneau, Lévy, *Bull. soc. chim.*, 1923, **33**, 759.

3-Phenylpentanol-3 (*Diethylphenylcarbinol*)

$$\begin{array}{c} \quad C_6H_5 \\ CH_3{\cdot}CH_2{\cdot}C(OH){\cdot}CH_2{\cdot}CH_3 \end{array}$$

$C_{11}H_{16}O$ MW, 164

B.p. 223–4°/762 mm., 159–61°/150 mm., 109°/15 mm. D_4^{19} 0·9836. n_D^{20} 1·51655.

Klages, *Ber.*, 1903, **36**, 3692.
Gilman, Fothergill, Parker, *Rec. trav. chim.*, 1929, **48**, 748.

1-Phenylpentanone-2.
See Propyl benzyl Ketone.

1-Phenylpentanone-3 (γ-*Keto*-n-*amylbenzene*)

$$CH_3{\cdot}CH_2{\cdot}CO{\cdot}CH_2{\cdot}CH_2{\cdot}C_6H_5$$

$C_{11}H_{14}O$ MW, 162

B.p. 244°/750 mm., 140°/14 mm. (128°/17 mm.). D_4^0 0·9793. n_D^{20} 1·50882.

Semicarbazone: m.p. 131–2° (82°).

Hewitt, Kenyon, *J. Chem. Soc.*, 1925, 1096.
Maxim, *Ann. chim.*, 1928, **9**, 55.

1-Phenylpentanone-4 (5-*Phenylpentanone*-2, γ-*acetopropylbenzene*, δ-*keto*-n-*amylbenzene*)

$$CH_3{\cdot}CO{\cdot}CH_2{\cdot}CH_2{\cdot}CH_2{\cdot}C_6H_5$$

$C_{11}H_{14}O$ MW, 162

Mobile liq. B.p. 128–30°/15 mm.

Semicarbazone: leaflets from MeOH. M.p. 125°.

Diels, Poetsch, *Ber.*, 1921, **54**, 1585.
Heilbron, Heslop, Irving, Wilson, *J. Chem. Soc.*, 1931, 1340.

2-Phenylpentanone-3 (*ω-Methylbutyryltoluene*)

$$CH_3\cdot CH_2\cdot CO\cdot \underset{}{\overset{C_6H_5}{CH}}\cdot CH_3$$

$C_{11}H_{14}O$ MW, 162

B.p. 225–8° (222–5°). D^0 0·982.
Semicarbazone: m.p. 136°.

Lévy, Jullien, *Bull. soc. chim.*, 1929, **45**, 941.
Lévy, Tabart, *Bull. soc. chim.*, 1931, **49**, 1776.

2-Phenylpentanone-4 (*4-Phenylpentanone-2, β-acetoisopropylbenzene*)

$$CH_3\cdot CO\cdot CH_2\cdot \overset{C_6H_5}{CH}\cdot CH_3$$

$C_{11}H_{14}O$ MW, 162

B.p. 109–10°/11 mm. D_4^{20} 0·9708. n_D^{20} 1·51237.
Oxime: viscous liq. B.p. 160°/20 mm.
Semicarbazone: m.p. 145° (137°).

Rupe, Wild, *Ann.*, 1917, **414**, 124.
Nenitzescu, Gavăt, *Ann.*, 1935, **519**, 260.

3-Phenylpentanone-2 (*ω-Ethylacetyltoluene*)

$$CH_3\cdot CH_2\cdot \overset{C_6H_5}{CH}\cdot CO\cdot CH_3$$

$C_{11}H_{14}O$ MW, 162

B.p. 220–5° (215–20°). D^0 0·979. Does not form bisulphite comp.
Semicarbazone: m.p. 189–90°.

Lévy, Jullien, *Bull. soc. chim.*, 1929, **45**, 941.
Tiffeneau, Lévy, Jullien, *Bull. soc. chim.*, 1931, **49**, 1788.

1-Phenyl-1-pentene (*α-Phenyl-α-amylene, α-pentenylbenzene*)

$$CH_3\cdot CH_2\cdot CH_2\cdot CH{:}CH\cdot C_6H_5$$

$C_{11}H_{14}$ MW, 146

B.p. 217° (202–5°), 94°/14 mm., 87·5°/9 mm. D_4^{22} 0·8782. n_D^{20} 1·5158.
Nitrosite: m.p. 121°.
Dibromide: m.p. 61°.

v. Braun, Köhler, *Ber.*, 1918, **51**, 79.
Prévost, Daujat, *Bull. soc. chim.*, 1930, **47**, 588.
Lévy, Dvoleitzka-Gombinska, *Bull. soc. chim.*, 1931, **49**, 1765.

2-Phenyl-1-pentene (*β-Phenyl-α-amylene*)

$$CH_3\cdot CH_2\cdot CH_2\cdot \overset{C_6H_5}{C}{:}CH_2$$

$C_{11}H_{14}$ MW, 146

B.p. 198–202°. D^0 0·9138.

Tiffeneau, *Ann. chim. phys.*, 1907, **10**, 357.

3-Phenyl-1-pentene (*γ-Phenyl-α-amylene, amenylbenzene*)

$$CH_3\cdot CH_2\cdot \overset{C_6H_5}{CH}\cdot CH{:}CH_2$$

$C_{11}H_{14}$ MW, 146

B.p. 191·5° (173°), 71°/12 mm. D^{23} 0·8458. n^{21} 1·5030.

Dafert, *Monatsh.*, 1883, **4**, 621.
Prévost, Daujat, *Bull. soc. chim.*, 1930, **47**, 588.

5-Phenyl-1-pentene (*ε-Phenyl-α-amylene, δ-pentenylbenzene*)

$$C_6H_5\cdot CH_2\cdot CH_2\cdot CH_2\cdot CH{:}CH_2$$

$C_{11}H_{14}$ MW, 146

B.p. 203–4°, 77–8°/10 mm. D_4^{20} 0·8889. n_D^{20} 1·5065.

v. Braun, Deutsch, Schmatloch, *Ber.*, 1912, **45**, 1255.

1-Phenyl-2-pentene (*α-Phenyl-β-amylene, β-pentenylbenzene*)

$$CH_3\cdot CH_2\cdot CH{:}CH\cdot CH_2\cdot C_6H_5$$

$C_{11}H_{14}$ MW, 146

B.p. 201°, 111°/30 mm., 97–8°/19 mm. $D_4^{16\cdot 2}$ 0·8884. $n_D^{16\cdot 2}$ 1·5089. Alc. KOH at 150° ⟶ 1-phenyl-1-pentene.

Auwers, Roth, Eisenlohr, *Ann.*, 1910, **373**, 284.
Prévost, Daujat, *Bull. soc. chim.*, 1930, **47**, 588.

2-Phenyl-2-pentene (*β-Phenyl-β-amylene*)

$$CH_3\cdot CH_2\cdot CH{:}\overset{C_6H_5}{C}\cdot CH_3$$

$C_{11}H_{14}$ MW, 146

Oil. B.p. 203–5°, 90°/16 mm. $D_4^{26\cdot 5}$ 0·8950. $n_D^{26\cdot 5}$ 1·5196. Acid $KMnO_4$ ⟶ acetophenone. Na + EtOH ⟶ 2-phenylpentane.

Klages, *Ber.*, 1902, **35**, 3509.
Tiffeneau, *Ann. chim. phys.*, 1907, **10**, 363.

3-Phenyl-2-pentene (*γ-Phenyl-β-amylene*)

$$CH_3\cdot CH_2\cdot \overset{C_6H_5}{C}{:}CH\cdot CH_3$$

$C_{11}H_{14}$ MW, 146

B.p. 197–8°/753 mm., 92°/18 mm. D_4^{14} 0·9173. n_D^{15} 1·5266.

Nitrosochloride: needles. M.p. 117°.

Klages, *Ber.*, 1903, **36**, 3692.

5-Phenyl-2-pentene (*ε-Phenyl-β-amylene, γ-pentenylbenzene*)

$C_6H_5·CH_2·CH_2·CH{:}CH·CH_3$

$C_{11}H_{14}$ MW, 146

B.p. 203–4°.

I.G., E.P., 315,312, (*Chem. Zentr.*, 1930, I, 2161).

Phenyl-peri Acid.

See N-Phenyl-1-naphthylamine-8-sulphonic Acid.

Phenylphenacyl acetic Acid.

See 1-Phenyl-2-benzoylpropionic Acid.

Phenyl phenacyl Ketone.

See Dibenzoylmethane.

9-Phenylphenanthridine

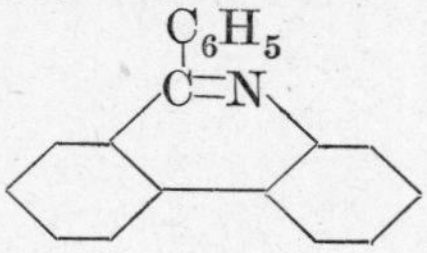

$C_{19}H_{13}N$ MW, 255

Plates from EtOH. M.p. 109°. B.p. above 400°. Sol. EtOH, Et_2O, $CHCl_3$, C_6H_6. Mod. sol. hot H_2O. Spar. sol. ligroin. Volatile in steam. Salts easily hyd. by H_2O.

B,HCl: needles. M.p. 220°.

B,HCl,H₂O: cryst. from dil. HCl. M.p. 95–6°.

Nitrate: needles. M.p. 205°.

$B_2,H_2PtCl_6,2H_2O$: yellow needles. Decomp. about 300° without melting.

Picrate: yellow needles from EtOH. M.p. 242° decomp.

Pictet, Hubert, *Ber.*, 1896, **29**, 1183, 1187.

***N*-Phenyl-*p*-phenetidine.**

See under 4-Hydroxydiphenylamine.

Phenylphenol.

See Hydroxydiphenyl.

Phenylphenylenediamine.

See Aminodiphenylamine.

Phenyl phenylethyl Ether.

See under 2-Phenylethyl Alcohol.

Phenyl phenylethyl Ketone.

See ω-Benzylacetophenone.

α-Phenyl-phenylglycine.

See α-Anilinophenylacetic Acid.

Phenylphosphine (*Phosphaniline*)

$C_6H_5PH_2$

C_6H_7P MW, 110

B.p. 160–1°. D^{15} 1·001. Oxidises very rapidly in air.

B,HI: needles. M.p. 138°. Decomp. by H_2O into its components.

Köhler, Michaelis, *Ber.*, 1877, **10**, 808.

Phenylphosphorous Acid

$C_6H_5·PO(OH)_2$

$C_6H_7O_3P$ MW, 158

Leaflets from H_2O. M.p. 158°. Sol. EtOH, Et_2O. Insol. C_6H_6. Stable in air.

Di-Me ester: $C_8H_{11}O_3P$. MW, 186. B.p. 247°, 101–2°/15 mm. D_0^{20} 1·0849. n_D^{20} 1·5280.

Et ester: $C_8H_{11}O_3P$. MW, 186. Syrup. Decomp. on dist. *Anilide*: m.p. about 105°. Hygroscopic.

Di-Et ester: $C_{10}H_{15}O_3P$. MW, 214. Viscous liq. B.p. 267°.

Phenyl ester: $C_{12}H_{11}O_3P$. MW, 234. Needles from EtOH.Aq. M.p. 57°. *Anilide*: yellow cryst. M.p. 83°. B.p. 235°/25 mm.

Diphenyl ester: $C_{18}H_{15}O_3P$. MW, 310. Needles from EtOH.Aq. M.p. 63·5°.

Dichloride: $C_6H_5OCl_2P$. MW, 195. Viscous liq. B.p. 258°. D^{20} 1·375.

Diamide: $C_6H_9ON_2P$. MW, 156. Leaflets from EtOH. M.p. 189°.

Anhydride: phosphinobenzene. $C_6H_5O_2P$. MW, 140. Cryst. powder from C_6H_6. M.p. 100°.

Anilide: m.p. 125°.

Dianilide: needles from EtOH. M.p. 211°.

Di-p-toluidide: needles from EtOH. M.p. 223°.

Di-phenylhydrazide: needles from EtOH. M.p. 175°.

Aniline salt: needles. M.p. 212°.

Arbusow, *Chem. Zentr.*, 1936, I, 543.
Michaelis, *Ann.*, 1876, **181**, 305,335; 1896, **293**, 217.
Michaelis, Köhler, *Ber.*, 1876, **9**, 521.

4-Phenylphthalic Acid.

See Diphenyl-3 : 4-dicarboxylic Acid.

***N*-Phenylphthalimide.**

See Phthalanil.

***N*-Phenylphthalimidine** (*Phthalidanil*)

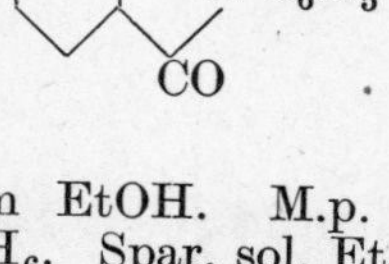

$C_{14}H_{11}ON$ MW, 209

Leaflets from EtOH. M.p. 162–3° (160°). Sol. $CHCl_3$, C_6H_6. Spar. sol. Et_2O. Very spar. sol. boiling H_2O. Insol. dil. acids and alkalis.

CrO_3 in AcOH ⟶ phthalanil. Alk. $KMnO_4$ ⟶ phthalanilic acid.

Anil : needles from Et_2O. M.p. 142–3°. *Hydrochloride* : m.p. 237–8°. B_2,H_2PtCl_6 : red-dish-yellow cryst. from H_2O. M.p. 212-13° decomp.

Rowe, Levin, Burns, Davies, Tepper, *J. Chem. Soc.*, 1926, 704.
Fischer, Wolter, *J. prakt. Chem.*, 1910, **80**, 110.
Thiele, Schneider, *Ann.*, 1909, **369**, 297.
Graebe, Pictet, *Ann.*, 1888, **247**, 306.

3-Phenylphthalimidine

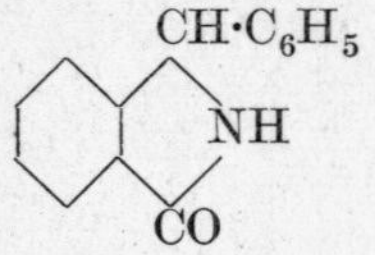

$C_{14}H_{11}ON$ MW, 209

Cryst. from 75% AcOH. M.p. 218–20°. Sol. MeOH, EtOH. Spar. sol. Et_2O. Insol. pet. ether.

N-*Acetyl* : cryst. from AcOH. M.p. 153–5°.

Rose, *J. Am. Chem. Soc.*, 1911, **33**, 390.

4-Phenyl-α-picoline (2-*Methyl*-4-*phenyl-pyridine*)

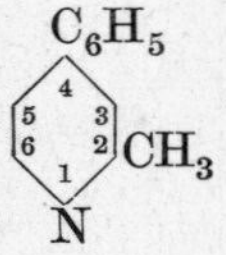

$C_{12}H_{11}N$ MW, 169

Liq. resembling diphenylamine in odour. B.p. 280–90°. Volatile in steam. Turns brown in air.

$B,HClO_4$: m.p. 142–3°.

B_2,H_2PtCl_6 : orange-yellow needles. M.p. 211–13°.

$B,HAuCl_4$: m.p. 161–3°.

Picrate : yellow needles. M.p. 210–13° (203°).

Gohdes, *J. prakt. Chem.*, 1929, **123**, 184.

6-Phenyl-α-picoline (2-*Methyl*-6-*phenyl-pyridine*).

Liq. B.p. 280–1°. Volatile in steam.

$B,HAuCl_4$: yellow needles. M.p. 150–1°. Spar. sol. cold H_2O.

B_2,H_2PtCl_6,H_2O : reddish needles from H_2O. M.p. 200° decomp.

Picrate : yellow needles. M.p. 135°.

Scholtz, *Ber.*, 1895, **28**, 1726.

6-Phenyl-α-picoline-3-carboxylic Acid (2-*Methyl*-6-*phenylnicotinic acid*)

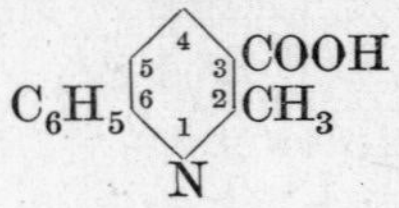

$C_{13}H_{11}O_2N$ MW, 213

Cryst. from EtOH. M.p. 196°. Sol. Me_2CO, AcOEt. Spar. sol. H_2O, Et_2O, C_6H_6, ligroin. Readily sol. dil. acids.

B,HCl : m.p. 288°.

Et ester : $C_{15}H_{15}O_2N$. MW, 241. M.p. 46–46·5°. B.p. 185°/13 mm., 160–1°/2 mm. *Chloroplatinate* : m.p. 196°.

Methylbetaine : m.p. 240° decomp. B_2,H_2SO_4 prisms from EtOH. M.p. 223–4°. $B,HAuCl_4$ yellow needles. M.p. 160–1°.

Mumm, Neumann, *Ber.*, 1926, **59**, 1620.
Späth, Burger, *Monatsh.*, 1928, **49**, 265.
Nienburg, *Ber.*, 1935, **68**, 1475.

6-Phenyl-α-picoline-4-carboxylic Acid (2-*Methyl*-6-*phenylisonicotinic acid*).

Cryst. from EtOH. M.p. 272°. Sol. EtOH, Me_2CO, AcOEt. Spar. sol. H_2O, Et_2O, C_6H_6, ligroin. Sol. dil. HCl.

Et ester : b.p. 194°/16 mm. Solidifies to a mass of needles.

Mumm, Neumann, *Ber.*, 1926, **59**, 1621.

6-Phenyl-α-picoline-3 : 4-dicarboxylic Acid (2-*Methyl*-6-*phenylcinchomeronic acid*)

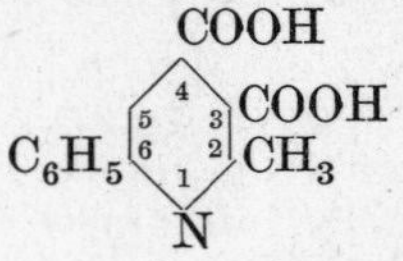

$C_{14}H_{11}O_4N$ MW, 25

Cryst. from EtOH. M.p. 217°. Sol. H_2O, EtOH, AcOH, HCl. Insol. Et_2O, AcOEt, Me_2CO, $CHCl_3$, C_6H_6.

3-*Et ester* : $C_{16}H_{15}O_4N$. MW, 285. Needles from ligroin. M.p. 145°. Sol. Me_2CO, AcOEt. Spar. sol. EtOH, Et_2O, C_6H_6, ligroin. Prac insol. H_2O.

4-*Et ester* : needles from AcOEt. M.p. 185°. Mod. sol. Et_2O, AcOEt, C_6H_6, ligroin. Spar. so H_2O.

Di-Et ester : $C_{18}H_{19}O_4N$. MW, 313. Needles from AcOEt. M.p. 73°. Sol. EtOH, Et_2O, Me_2CO, $CHCl_3$, C_6H_6. Mod. sol. ligroin. *Picrate* m.p. 83°.

4-*Amide* : $C_{14}H_{12}O_3N_2$. MW, 256. Cryst from EtOH. M.p. 199°. Spar. sol. org. solvents

Anhydride : $C_{14}H_9O_3N$. MW, 239. Needles from C_6H_6. M.p. 196°. Sol. Et_2O, AcOEt, C_6H_6, ligroin.

Imide : $C_{14}H_{10}O_2N_2$. MW, 238. Needles from Me_2CO. M.p. 249°.

Mumm, Böhme, *Ber.*, 1921, **54**, 731.
Mumm, Neumann, *Ber.*, 1926, **59**, 1616.

6-Phenylpicolinic Acid (6-*Phenylpyridine-2-carboxylic acid*)

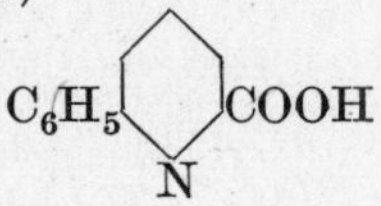

$C_{12}H_9O_2N$ MW, 199

Needles from H_2O. M.p. 109°. Very sol. EtOH. Heat at 190–200° ⟶ 2-phenylpyridine. $FeSO_4$ in H_2O ⟶ red col.

Scholtz, *Ber.*, 1895, **28**, 1728.

***N*-Phenyl-α-pipecoline** (2-*Methyl*-N-*phenylpiperidine*)

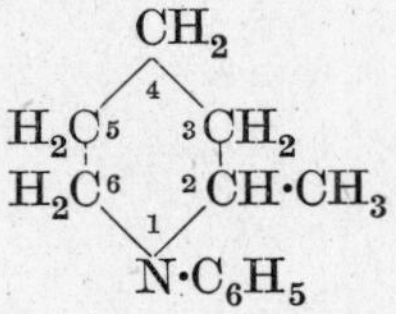

$C_{12}H_{17}N$ MW, 175

B.p. 256·5–257°/710 mm., 143°/20 mm. Sol. EtOH, Et_2O. Very spar. sol. H_2O.

B_2,H_2PtCl_6 : orange-yellow needles. Decomp. at 212°.

Picrate : yellow prisms from EtOH. M.p. 167–8° (162°).

Methiodide : cryst. powder from EtOH–Et_2O. M.p. 145°.

v. Braun, Sobecki, *Ber.*, 1911, **44**, 1045.
Lipp, *Ann.*, 1896, **289**, 245.

6-Phenyl-α-pipecoline (2-*Methyl*-6-*phenyl piperidine*).

B.p. 112–14°/12 mm. D_4^{25} 0·9096. n_D^{25} 1·4882.

Two inactive stereoisomeric forms are known :

α-.

B,HCl : m.p. 191–2°. Sol. Me_2CO.

B_2,H_2PtCl_6 : m.p. 236°.

β-.

B.p. 117·5–118°/11 mm.

B,HCl : cryst. from Me_2CO. M.p. 225°.

B_2,H_2PtCl_6 : m.p. 257°.

Adkins, Kuick, Farlow, Wojcik, *J. Am. Chem. Soc.*, 1934, **56**, 2425.
Singer, McElvain, *J. Am. Chem. Soc.*, 1935, **57**, 1137.
Meisenheimer, Stratman, Theilacker, *Ber.*, 1932, **65**, 423.

***N*-Phenylpiperazine**

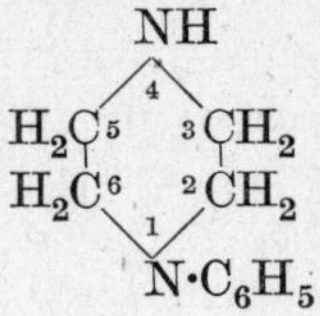

$C_{10}H_{14}N_2$ MW, 162

Oil. B.p. 156–7°/10 mm. D_4^{14} 1·0725. n_D 1·59053.

B,HCl : m.p. 247° decomp.

B,HBr : m.p. 250–2°.

4-*Acetyl* : m.p. 96°. *B,HCl* : m.p. 213–14°.

4-*Benzoyl* : m.p. 96–7°. *B,HCl* : m.p. 244°.

4-p-*Tolylsulphonyl* : m.p. 199–200°.

4-*Benzyl* : m.p. 59°. *B,HCl* : m.p. 228°.

Prelog, Blažek, *Chem. Abstracts*, 1935, **29**, 2959.
Prelog, Driza, *Chem. Abstracts*, 1934, **28**, 1347.
Pollard, MacDowell, *J. Am. Chem. Soc.*, 1934, **56**, 2199.

***N*-Phenylpiperidine** (1-*Phenylpiperidine*, *pentamethylene-aniline*)

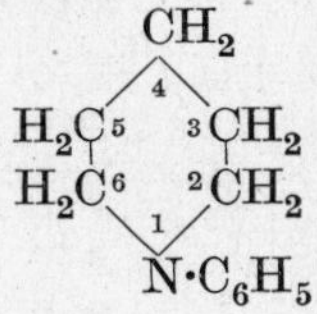

$C_{11}H_{15}N$ MW, 161

B.p. 245–50° (257–8°/752 mm.). Sol. EtOH, Et_2O, $CHCl_3$, C_6H_6.

B,HBr : leaflets from EtOH–Et_2O. M.p. 235°.

B_2,H_2PtCl_6,$2H_2O$: leaflets or needles. Decomp. at 190°.

Picrate : yellow cryst. from EtOH. M.p. 148°.

Methobromide : cryst. from EtOH–Et_2O. M.p. 170° ⟶ *N*-phenylpiperidine + methyl bromide. Somewhat hygroscopic.

Methiodide : cryst. from EtOH–Et_2O. M.p. 146°. Sol. H_2O, EtOH. Gradually turns yellow in air.

Le Fèvre, *J. Chem. Soc.*, 1932, 1378.
Paul, *Bull. soc. chim.*, 1933, **53**, 1489.
v. Braun, *Ber.*, 1907, **40**, 3920.

2-Phenylpiperidine.

Cryst. + $1H_2O$. M.p. 60–1°. The anhyd. base is an oil, b.p. 255–255·5°/767 mm., 110–12°/9 mm. Volatile in steam.

B,HCl : needles from EtOH–Et_2O. M.p. 196–7°.

B,HAuCl_4 : yellow cryst. M.p. 159–60°.

B_2,H_2PtCl_6 : yellow plates. Decomp. about 197°.
Picrate : cryst. from H_2O. M.p. 115–17°.
N-*Benzoyl* : *B,HCl*, m.p. 186–7°.

Adkins, Kuick, Farlow, Wojcik, *J. Am. Chem. Soc.*, 1934, **56**, 2427.
Gabriel, *Ber.*, 1908, **41**, 2013.

3-Phenylpiperidine.
B.p. 255–6°/740 mm. D_{25}^{25} 1·0040. n_D^{25} 1·5473.
B,HCl : m.p. 146–7°.
N-*Benzoyl* : *B,HCl*, m.p. 180–1°.

Walters, McElvain, *J. Am. Chem. Soc.*, 1933, **55**, 4625.

4-Phenylpiperidine.
M.p. 57·5–58° (50°). B.p. 255–7°/727 mm. Insol. H_2O. Absorbs CO_2 from the air.
B,HNO_3 : plates from H_2O. M.p. 139°.
Chloroplatinate : orange leaflets. M.p. 204–7°.
N-*Benzoyl* : *hydrochloride*, m.p. 174–5°.

Forsyth, Pyman, *J. Chem. Soc.*, 1930, 401.
Adkins, Kuick, Farlow, Wojcik, *J. Am. Chem. Soc.*, 1934, **56**, 2427.
Bally, *Ber.*, 1887, **20**, 2590.

***N*-Phenylpiperidine-4-carboxylic Acid.**
See N-Phenylhexahydroisonicotinic Acid.
Phenylpiperidylmethane.
See Benzylpiperidine.
Phenylpropandiol.
See Phenylpropylene Glycol *and* Phenyltrimethylene Glycol.
Phenylpropane.
See Cumene *and* Propylbenzene.
Phenylpropanolone.
See 3-Phenylhydroxyacetone.
Phenylpropargyl Alcohol (*Phenylacetylenylcarbinol, phenylpropiolic alcohol, hydroxymethylphenylacetylene*)

$C_6H_5{\cdot}C{:}C{\cdot}CH_2OH$

C_9H_8O MW, 132

B.p. 137–8°/15 mm. (140°/12 mm.). D_{18}^{18} 1·07. n_D^{18} 1·5873. Heat of comb. C_v 1138·1 Cal. Reduces $NH_3.AgNO_3$.
Me ether : $C_{10}H_{10}O$. MW, 146. B.p. 226°, 115°/16 mm. D_4^{20} 1·0016. n_D^{20} 1·5502.
Propyl ether : $C_{12}H_{14}O$. MW, 174. B.p. 137°/17 mm. D_4^{20} 0·9668. n_D^{20} 1·5326.
Acetyl : b.p. 145–7°/16 mm.

Guest, *J. Am. Chem. Soc.*, 1925, **47**, 862.
Bert, *Compt. rend.*, 1930, **191**, 493.
Lai, *Bull. soc. chim.*, 1933, **53**, 682.
Moureu, André, *Ann. chim.*, 1914, **1**, 119.

Phenylpropargyl Aldehyde.
See Phenylpropiolic Aldehyde.
Phenylpropiolic Acid

$C_6H_5{\cdot}C{:}C{\cdot}COOH$

$C_9H_6O_2$ MW, 146

Needles from H_2O or CS_2. M.p. 137°. Melts under H_2O at approx. 80°. Very sol. EtOH, Et_2O. $k = 5{\cdot}9 \times 10^{-3}$ at 25°. Heat of comb. C_v 1022·0 Cal. Zn + AcOH ⟶ cinnamic acid. NaHg ⟶ hydrocinnamic acid. Dissolving in conc. H_2SO_4 ⟶ benzoylacetic acid. Hot baryta ⟶ phenylacetylene.
Me ester : $C_{10}H_8O_2$. MW, 160. Cryst. M.p. 26°. B.p. 158–9°/48 mm., 132–3°/16 mm. D_4^{25} 1·0830. n_D^{25} 1·5618. Heat of comb. C_v 7478 cal./gm.
Et ester : $C_{11}H_{10}O_2$. MW, 174. Oil. B.p. 260–70° (rapid dist.), 152–3°/21 mm., 144°/13 mm. D_4^{25} 1·0550. n_D^{25} 1·5502. Heat of comb. C_v 7693 cal./gm.
d-*Amyl ester* : $C_{14}H_{16}O_2$. MW, 216. B.p. 210°/55 mm. D_4^{20} 1·0035. $[\alpha]_D$ + 5·58°.
l-*Menthyl ester* : needles. M.p. 63–4°. B.p. 235–8°/30 mm. D_4^{33} 1·0595. n_D^{17} 1·5239. $[\alpha]_D^{21}$ − 58·65° in $CHCl_3$, $[\alpha]_D^{20}$ − 72·6° in C_6H_6.
d-*Bornyl ester* : yellowish cryst. M.p. 45°. B.p. 228–30°/21 mm. D_4^{15} 1·0884. n_D^{17} 1·55. $[\alpha]_D^{21}$ + 31·05° in $CHCl_3$.
p-*Nitrobenzyl ester* : m.p. 83°.
Chloride : C_9H_5OCl. MW, 164·5. B.p. 115–16°/17 mm. (119°/12 mm.).
Amide : C_9H_7ON. MW, 145. Needles from H_2O. M.p. 108–9° (99–100°). Sol. MeOH, EtOH, $CHCl_3$. Spar. sol. Et_2O, cold. H_2O. Conc. H_2SO_4 ⟶ benzoylacetamide. Hydrazine hydrate in EtOH ⟶ 3-phenylpyrazolone-5.
Nitrile : C_9H_5N. MW, 127. M.p. 41°. B.p. 228–9°, 105–6°/13 mm. $D_4^{41\cdot5}$ 1·0046. $n_D^{41\cdot5}$ 1·58535.
Hydrazide : cryst. from EtOH. M.p. 114° ⟶ 3-phenylpyrazolone-5. *B,HCl* : hygroscopic cryst. M.p. 138–9°. Sol. EtOH, Et_2O. *Picrate* : yellow plates + $1H_2O$. M.p. 105–10°.
Azide : needles from Et_2O. M.p. 55°. Insol. H_2O.
Anilide : needles from EtOH. M.p. 126°.
p-*Toluidide* : plates from EtOH. M.p. 142°.

Abbott, *Organic Syntheses*, 1932, XII, 60.
Curtius, Kenngott, *J. prakt. Chem.*, 1926, **112**, 314.
Bogert, Marcus, *J. Am. Chem. Soc.*, 1919, **41**, 88 (*Note* 1).
Michael, *Ber.*, 1901, **34**, 3648.
Moureu *et al.*, *Ann. chim.*, 1914, **2**, 276.

Phenylpropiolic Alcohol.
See Phenylpropargyl Alcohol.

Phenylpropiolic Aldehyde (*Phenylpropargyl aldehyde*)

$C_6H_5{\cdot}C{\vdots}C{\cdot}CHO$

C_9H_6O MW, 130

Oil with odour resembling cinnamaldehyde. B.p. 127–8°/28 mm., 118°/17 mm., 112–13°/15 mm., 104–5°/11 mm. $D_4^{12\cdot6}$ 1·0680. $n_D^{12\cdot6}$ 1·60785. Decomp. on dist. at atmospheric press. Heat of comb. C_v 1081·7 Cal. Aq. alkalis ⟶ phenylacetylene + H·COOH.

Oxime: needles from ligroin. M.p. 108°. Acetic anhydride ⟶ phenylpropiolic nitrile.

Di-Et acetal: b.p. 144–5°/14 mm. D^{13} 0·9940. n_D^{13} 1·52216.

Kalff, *Rec. trav. chim.*, 1927, **46**, 594.
Auwers, Seyfried, *Ann.*, 1930, **484**, 224.
Moureu, Delange, *Bull. soc. chim.*, 1904, **31**, 1329.

2-Phenylpropionaldehyde.
See Hydrocinnamaldehyde.

1-Phenylpropionic Acid.
See Hydratropic Acid.

2-Phenylpropionic Acid.
See Hydrocinnamic Acid.

β-Phenylpropiophenone.
See α-Methyldeoxybenzoin.

1-Phenylpropyl Alcohol.
Ethylphenylcarbinol, *q.v.*

2-Phenylpropyl Alcohol (*β-Hydroxyisopropylbenzene, β-hydroxycumene, hydratropic alcohol*)

$CH_3{\cdot}CH(C_6H_5){\cdot}CH_2OH$

$C_9H_{12}O$ MW, 136

dl-.
B.p. 114°/14 mm. D^0 1·017.
Acid phthalate: prisms from CS_2. M.p. 79°.
Acetyl: b.p. 125°/14 mm., 103–5°/10 mm.
Benzoyl: b.p. 198–200°/20 mm.
p-*Nitrobenzoyl*: plates. M.p. 65°.
Phenylurethane: needles. M.p. 156°.

Ramart, Amagat, *Ann. chim.*, 1927, **8**, 263.
Cohen, Marshall, Woodman, *J. Chem. Soc.*, 1915, **107**, 897.

3-Phenylpropyl Alcohol.
See Hydrocinnamyl Alcohol.

1-Phenylpropylamine (*α-Aminopropylbenzene*)

$CH_3{\cdot}CH_2{\cdot}CH(NH_2){\cdot}C_6H_5$

$C_9H_{13}N$ MW, 135

Oil. B.p. 204–6°/748 mm., 100–5°/35 mm., 99–100°/16 mm. D_0^0 0·9560, D_0^{25} 0·9347. n^{25} 1·51726. Spar. sol. H_2O. Absorbs CO_2.

B,HCl: needles from EtOH. M.p. 189·5° (194°).

N-*Benzoyl*: needles from EtOH. M.p. 115–16°.

N-*Benzenesulphonyl*: needles from EtOH. M.p. 81°.

N-*Me*: α-methylaminopropylbenzene. $C_{10}H_{15}N$. MW, 149. B.p. 96°/20 mm. *B,HCl*: needles or prisms. M.p. 153°.

N-*Et*: α-ethylaminopropylbenzene. $C_{11}H_{17}N$. MW, 163. B.p. 207–8°/729 mm., 99°/20 mm. *B,HCl*: needles or prisms. M.p. 180°.

N-*Phenyl*: α-phenylpropylaniline, α-anilinopropylbenzene. $C_{15}H_{17}N$. MW, 211. Viscous oil. B.p. 192°/20 mm. *B,HCl*: needles from EtOH–Et_2O. M.p. 187°. *B,HNO₃*: needles or prisms. M.p. 174°. Part. hyd. by H_2O.

Hartung, Munch, *J. Am. Chem. Soc.*, 1931, **53**, 1878.
Konowalow, *Chem. Zentr.*, 1894, I, 465.
Busch, Leefhelm, *J. prakt. Chem.*, 1908, **77**, 8.

2-Phenylpropylamine (*β-Aminoisopropylbenzene, β-aminocumene*)

$CH_3{\cdot}CH(C_6H_5){\cdot}CH_2NH_2$

$C_9H_{13}N$ MW, 135

Oil with fishy odour. B.p. 210°, 104°/21 mm. Misc. with EtOH, Et_2O, C_6H_6. Very spar. sol. H_2O. Absorbs H_2O and CO_2 from the air.
B,HCl: m.p. 123–4°.
B_2,H_2PtCl_6: m.p. 229° decomp.
$B,HAuCl_4$: m.p. 124°.
N-*Benzoyl*: cryst. from EtOH. M.p. 85°.
Picrate: m.p. 182°.

See first reference above and also
v. Braun, Grabowski, Kirschbaum, *Ber.*, 1913, **46**, 1281.
Freund, König, *Ber.*, 1893, **26**, 2875.

3-Phenylpropylamine (*γ-Aminopropylbenzene*)

$C_6H_5{\cdot}CH_2{\cdot}CH_2{\cdot}CH_2NH_2$

$C_9H_{13}N$ MW, 135

B.p. 221·5°/755 mm., 75–80°/1 mm. D_4^{25} 0·9760. Misc. with EtOH, Et_2O. Mod. sol. H_2O with strongly alk. reaction. Absorbs CO_2.

B,HCl: leaflets from EtOH–Et_2O. M.p. 218°.

B_2,H_2PtCl_6: yellow leaflets from H_2O. Decomp. at 233°.

Neutral oxalate: needles from H_2O. M.p. 190° decomp.

Acid oxalate: prisms from EtOH. M.p. 156°. Very sol. hot H_2O.

Picrate: lemon-yellow needles from H_2O. M.p. 152–3°.

N-*Me*: γ-methylaminopropylbenzene. $C_{10}H_{15}N$. MW, 149. Odourless oil. B.p. 116°/20 mm. (133–5°/18 mm.). B_2,H_2PtCl_6: red leaflets from H_2O. M.p. 188°. *Picrate*: needles from EtOH. M.p. 93–4°.

N-*Di-Me*: γ-dimethylaminopropylbenzene. $C_{11}H_{17}N$. MW, 163. B.p. 222–4°, 117–18°/26 mm., 99°/14 mm. *B,HCl*: m.p. 146°. B_2,H_2PtCl_6: orange cryst. M.p. 152°. *Methobromide*: cryst. from EtOH–Et_2O. M.p. 143°. *Methiodide*: needles from EtOH. M.p. 179°.

N-*Et*: γ-ethylaminopropylbenzene. $C_{11}H_{17}N$. MW, 163. B.p. 124–6°/25 mm., 118°/16 mm. B_2,H_2PtCl_6: needles. M.p. 134–5°.

N-*Di-Et*: γ-diethylaminopropylbenzene. $C_{13}H_{21}N$. MW, 191. B.p. 137–9°/22 mm.

N-*Propyl*: γ-propylaminopropylbenzene. $C_{12}H_{19}N$. MW, 177. B.p. 134°/17 mm. *Picrate*: orange cryst. from EtOH–Et_2O. M.p. 97°.

N-*Dipropyl*: γ-dipropylaminopropylbenzene. $C_{15}H_{25}N$. MW, 219. B.p. 158–60°/17 mm. B_2,H_2PtCl_6: red cryst. M.p. 91–3°.

N-*Benzoyl*: cryst. from H_2O. M.p. 57–8°.

Hartung, Munch, *J. Am. Chem. Soc.*, 1931, **53**, 1878.
Goodyear, F.P., 751,712, (*Chem. Zentr.*, 1934, I, 126).
v. Braun, Aust, *Ber.*, 1916, **49**, 504.
Emde, *Ann.*, 1912, **391**, 93.
v. Braun, *Ber.*, 1910, **43**, 3218.
Gabriel, Eschenbach, *Ber.*, 1897, **30**, 1128.
Michaelis, Jacobi, *Ber.*, 1893, **26**, 2160.

α-Phenylpropylaniline.

See under 1-Phenylpropylamine.

Phenylpropylene.

See Allylbenzene *and* α-, and β-Methylstyrenes.

1-Phenylpropylene Glycol (*αβ-Dihydroxypropylbenzene, α-methyl-α′-phenylethylene glycol, 1-phenylpropandiol-1 : 2*)

$$CH_3\cdot CH(OH)\cdot CH(OH)\cdot C_6H_5$$

$C_9H_{12}O_2$ MW, 152

Exists in two forms:

(i) Plates from Et_2O–pet. ether. M.p. 56–7° (52–3°). Very sol. H_2O, EtOH, Et_2O, Me_2CO, $CHCl_3$, C_6H_6. Spar. sol. ligroin. Ox. ⟶ benzaldehyde and acetaldehyde.

Dibenzoyl: needles. M.p. 101°.

(ii) Plates from Et_2O. M.p. 92–3°. 20% H_2SO_4 ⟶ phenylacetone. Ox. ⟶ benzaldehyde and acetaldehyde.

Dibenzoyl: m.p. 76–7°.

Lévy, Dvoleitzka-Gombinska, *Bull. soc chim.*, 1931, **49**, 1765.
Zincke, Zahn, *Ber.*, 1910, **43**, 851.
Tiffeneau, *Compt. rend.*, 1906, **142**, 1538.

2-Phenylpropylene Glycol (*αβ-Dihydroxyisopropylbenzene, α-methyl-α-phenylethylene glycol 2-phenylpropandiol-1 : 2*)

$$CH_3\cdot \overset{C_6H_5}{\overset{|}{C}}(OH)\cdot CH_2OH$$

$C_9H_{12}O_2$ MW, 152

Needles from pet. ether. or ligroin–Et_2O. M.p. 44·5° (40–1°). B.p. 158–60°/25 mm., 153°/16 mm. Sol. H_2O, EtOH, Et_2O. Spar. sol. ligroin.

Danilow, Venus-Danilowa, *Ber.*, 1927, **60**, 1063.
Stoermer, *Ber.*, 1906, **39**, 2297.

3-Phenylpropylene Glycol (*βγ-Dihydroxypropylbenzene, 3-phenylpropandiol-1 : 2, benzylethylene glycol*)

$$C_6H_5\cdot CH_2\cdot CH(OH)\cdot CH_2OH$$

$C_9H_{12}O_2$ MW, 152

B.p. 163–5°/15 mm.

Diacetyl: b.p. 282–6°, 163–6°/13 mm. D° 1·128.

Dibenzoyl: m.p. 74–5°.

1-*Phenyl ether*: $C_{15}H_{16}O_2$. MW, 228. Plates from C_6H_6. M.p. 91–2°. Insol. H_2O.

Hershberg, *Helv. Chim. Acta*, 1934, **17**, 351
Fourneau, *Chem. Zentr.*, 1910, I, 1134.

α-Phenylpropyl-malonic Acid (*2-Phenylbutane-1 : 1-dicarboxylic acid, ethylphenylisosuccinic acid*)

$$CH_3\cdot CH_2\cdot \overset{C_6H_5}{\overset{|}{C}H}\cdot CH{<}^{COOH}_{COOH}$$

$C_{12}H_{14}O_4$ MW, 222

Plates + $1H_2O$ from H_2O. M.p. 74°. Sol. EtOH, Et_2O, Me_2CO. At 150° ⟶ 2-phenylvaleric acid.

Di-Et ester: $C_{16}H_{22}O_4$. MW, 278. B.p. 187–8°/22 mm.

Reynolds, *Am. Chem. J.*, 1910, **44**, 315.

γ-Phenylpropyl-malonic Acid (*4-Phenylbutane-1 : 1-dicarboxylic acid*)

$$C_6H_5\cdot CH_2\cdot CH_2\cdot CH_2\cdot CH{<}^{COOH}_{COOH}$$

$C_{12}H_{14}O_4$ MW, 222

Cryst. from C_6H_6–ligroin. M.p. 98° (94°). Sol. most org. solvents except ligroin. Heated above m.p. or better at 200° under reduced press. ⟶ 4-phenylvaleric acid.

Di-Me ester: $C_{14}H_{18}O_4$. MW, 250. B.p. 183–4°/10 mm.

Di-Et ester: b.p. 189–94°/13 mm.

Et ester-nitrile: $C_{14}H_{17}O_2N$. MW, 231. Oil. B.p. 192–3°/11 mm.

v. Braun, Kruber, *Ber.*, 1912, **45**, 386.
Przewalski, *Chem. Zentr.*, 1923, III, 665.
Borsche, *Ber.*, 1912, **45**, 622.

1-Phenylpyrazole

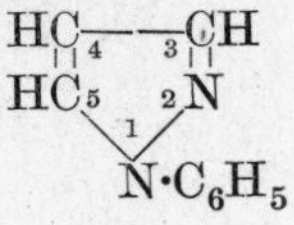

$C_9H_8N_2$ MW, 144

Needles. M.p. 11–11·5°. B.p. 246–7°. Sol. EtOH, Et_2O. Spar. sol. warm H_2O.

Chloroaurate: yellow needles from EtOH–HCl. M.p. 181°.

Alvisi, *Gazz. chim. ital.*, 1892, **22**, i, 161.

3(5)-Phenylpyrazole

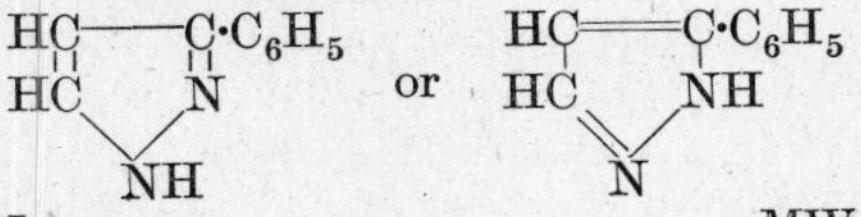

$C_9H_8N_2$ MW, 144

Needles from H_2O. M.p. 79°. B.p. 313–14°, 177–8°/11 mm. Sol. EtOH, Et_2O. $D_4^{99·8}$ 1·0818. $n_{He}^{100·8}$ 1·58890.

B,HCl: cryst. powder. M.p. 144–5°.

B,HNO₃: needles from Et_2O. M.p. 126° decomp. Sol. H_2O, EtOH. Spar. sol. Et_2O, Me_2CO, C_6H_6.

N-*Acetyl*: needles from ligroin. M.p. 64–5°. B.p. 157–8°/10 mm. Sol. Me_2CO, C_6H_6. Spar. sol. EtOH, ligroin. $D_4^{100·3}$ 1·0778. $n_{He}^{100·3}$ 1·56064.

N-o-*Nitrobenzoyl of 3-phenylpyrazole*: cryst. from MeOH. M.p. 107·5–108·5°. Sol. Me_2CO, C_6H_6. Spar. sol. MeOH.

N-o-*Nitrobenzoyl of 5-phenyl pyrazole*: needles from MeOH. M.p. 151–2°. Sol. Me_2CO. Spar. sol. MeOH, C_6H_6.

Auwers, Dietrich, *J. prakt. Chem.*, 1934, **139**, 89.
Auwers, Cauer, *J. prakt. Chem.*, 1930, **126**, 194.
Auwers, Schmidt, *Ber.*, 1925, **58**, 538.
Buchner, Hachumian, *Ber.*, 1902, **35**, 38.
For non-equivalence of positions 3 and 5 see Auwers, *Ann.*, 1933, **508**, 57.

4-Phenylpyrazole.

Plates from EtOH. M.p. 230°. Sol. EtOH, C_6H_6. Spar. sol. Et_2O.

B,HCl: needles. M.p. 215–18°.

N-*Acetyl*: yellow needles from EtOH. M.p. 81·5–82·5°. B.p. 159–61°. Sol. Me_2CO, C_6H_6. Spar. sol. ligroin.

Picrate: yellow cryst. from EtOH. M.p. 155°.

Auwers, Cauer, *J. prakt. Chem.*, 1930, **126**, 194.
Rupe, Huber, *Helv. Chim. Acta*, 1927, **10**, 848.
Buchner, Perkel, *Ber.*, 1903, **36**, 3777.

3-Phenylpyrazole-1-carboxylic Acid

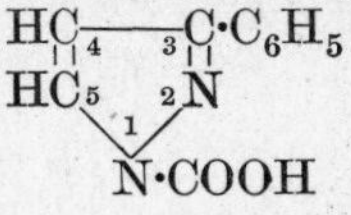

$C_{10}H_8O_2N_2$ MW, 188

Et ester: $C_{12}H_{12}O_2N_2$. MW, 216. B.p. 193°/13 mm. D_4^{19} 1·1694. n_{He}^{19} 1·57904.

Amide: $C_{10}H_9ON_3$. MW, 187. Needles from Me_2CO. M.p. 142–3°. Sol. ord. org. solvents.

Picrate: yellow needles from Et_2O. M.p. 165–6°.

Auwers, Dietrich, *J. prakt. Chem.*, 1934, **139**, 89.
Auwers, Cauer, *J. prakt. Chem.*, 1930, **126**, 197.
Auwers, Ottens, *Ber.*, 1925, **58**, 2076.

4-Phenylpyrazole-1-carboxylic Acid.

Et ester: plates from ligroin. M.p. 78–78·5°. B.p. 192°/9 mm. Very sol. ord. org. solvents. $D_4^{99·9}$ 1·1055. $n_{He}^{99·5}$ 1·54637.

Auwers, Cauer, *J. prakt. Chem.*, 1930, **126**, 193.

5-Phenylpyrazole-1-carboxylic Acid.

Me ester: $C_{11}H_{10}O_2N_2$. MW, 202. Needles from EtOH. M.p. 152°. Sol. ord. org. solvents.

Et ester: cryst. from C_6H_6. M.p. 58–9°. Very sol. MeOH, EtOH. Spar. sol. C_6H_6. $D_4^{78·4}$ 1·1165. $n_{He}^{78·4}$ 1·53860.

Amide: plates from C_6H_6. M.p. 133–4°. Very sol. AcOH. Mod. sol. EtOH, Me_2CO, C_6H_6. Spar. sol. Et_2O.

Auwers, Breyhan, *J. prakt. Chem.*, 1935, **143**, 267.
Auwers, Dietrich, *J. prakt. Chem.*, 1934, **139**, 89.
Auwers, Ottens, *Ber.*, 1925, **58**, 2077.

1-Phenylpyrazole-3-carboxylic Acid

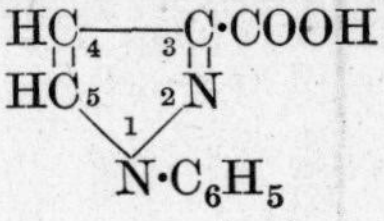

$C_{10}H_8O_2N_2$ MW, 188

Needles from H_2O. M.p. 146°. Sol. EtOH, Et_2O. Spar. sol. cold H_2O.

Me ester : $C_{11}H_{10}O_2N_2$. MW, 202. Needles. M.p. 77°.

Claisen, Roosen, *Ann.*, 1894, **278**, 294.

4-Phenylpyrazole-3-carboxylic Acid.

Plates. M.p. 252–3° with decomp. to 4-phenylpyrazole. Spar. sol. hot H_2O, EtOH, Me_2CO. Insol. $CHCl_3$.

Me ester : prisms from MeOH. M.p. 188–90°. N-*Acetyl* : needles from EtOH. M.p. 129·5–130·5°. Sol. Et_2O. Mod. sol. EtOH. Spar. sol. ligroin.

Et ester : $C_{12}H_{12}O_2N_2$. MW, 216. Plates from EtOH. M.p. 164–5°. Sol. MeOH. Spar. sol. Et_2O.

Nitrile : needles from C_6H_6. M.p. 149·5–150°. Very sol. EtOH, Et_2O. Mod. sol. C_6H_6. Spar. sol. H_2O, ligroin.

Auwers, Ungemach, *Ber.*, 1933, **66**, 1204, 1207.
Auwers, Cauer, *Ann.*, 1929, **470**, 302.
Kohler, Steele, *J. Am. Chem. Soc.*, 1919, **41**, 1104.

5(3) - Phenylpyrazole - 3(5) - carboxylic Acid.

Needles from H_2O or EtOH. M.p. 234° decomp. Sol. MeOH, EtOH. Insol. C_6H_6.

Me ester : $C_{11}H_{10}O_2N_2$. MW, 202. Prisms from MeOH or Et_2O. M.p. 182°.

Et ester : $C_{12}H_{12}O_2N_2$. MW, 216. Needles from MeOH or Et_2O. M.p. 140°. Sol. hot H_2O, EtOH, Et_2O. Very sol. $CHCl_3$. N-*Acetyl* : needles from C_6H_6. M.p. 109–10°.

Hydrazide : m.p. 205°.

Auwers, Dietrich, *J. prakt. Chem.*, 1934, **139**, 93.
Auwers, Mausolf, *Ber.*, 1927, **60**, 1732.
Bülow, *Ber.*, 1904, **37**, 2201.

1-Phenylpyrazole-4-carboxylic Acid

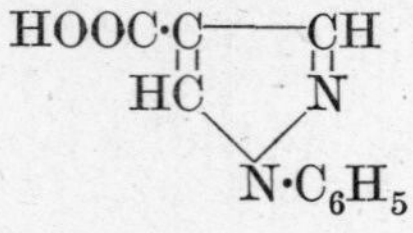

$C_{10}H_8O_2N_2$ MW, 188

Needles from H_2O. M.p. 219–20°. Sol. EtOH. Spar. sol. H_2O, Et_2O. Sublimes in needles.

Me ester : needles from MeOH. M.p. 128–9°.

Et ester : prisms from EtOH. M.p. 96–7°.

Wislicenus, Bindemann, *Ann.*, 1901, **316**, 36.

5-Phenylpyrazole-4-carboxylic Acid.

Needles from H_2O. M.p. 260°. Sol. EtOH. Spar. sol. H_2O. Insol. Et_2O.

Me ester : needles from ligroin. M.p. 111·5–112·5°.

Et ester : needles from EtOH.Aq. M.p. 85–6°.

Anilide : cryst. + 1EtOH from EtOH. M.p. 182°.

o-*Anisidide* : needles from EtOH.Aq. M.p. 127°. Sol. most org. solvents.

p-*Anisidide* : needles from EtOH.Aq. M.p. 161°.

Auwers, Ungemach, *Ber.*, 1933, **66**, 1207.
Dains, Long, *J. Am. Chem. Soc.*, 1921, **43**, 1201.

1-Phenylpyrazole-5-carboxylic Acid

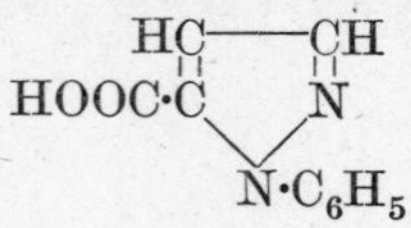

$C_{11}H_8O_4N_2$ MW, 232

Needles from H_2O. M.p. 183°. Sol. EtOH, Et_2O. Spar. sol. cold H_2O.

Me ester : $C_{11}H_{10}O_2N_2$. MW, 202. Needles. M.p. 67°.

Chloride : needles from ligroin. M.p. 53°. B.p. 152°/15 mm.

Rojahn, Seitz, *Ann.*, 1924, **437**, 303.
Claisen, Roosen, *Ann.*, 1894, **278**, 292.

4 - Phenylpyrazole - 1 : 3(5) - dicarboxylic Acid

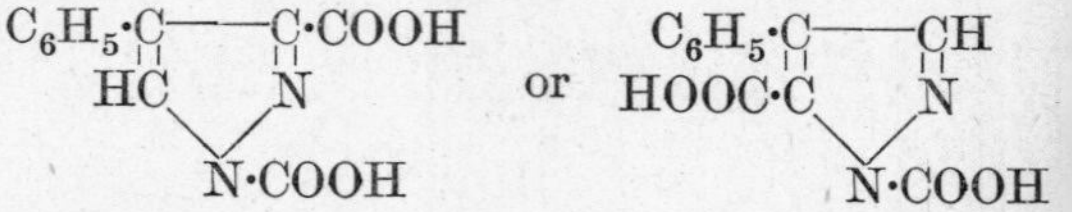

$C_{11}H_8O_4N_2$ MW, 232

3(5)-*Et ester* : $C_{13}H_{12}O_4N_2$. MW, 260. *Anilide* : needles from ligroin. M.p. 105–6°. Sol. ord. org. solvents.

1-*Me*-3(5)-*Et ester* : $C_{14}H_{14}O_4N_2$. MW, 274. Needles from EtOH. M.p. 75–6°. Sol. ord. org. solvents.

Auwers, Ungemach, *Ber.*, 1933, **66**, 1203.

3 - Phenylpyrazole - 1 : 4 - dicarboxylic Acid

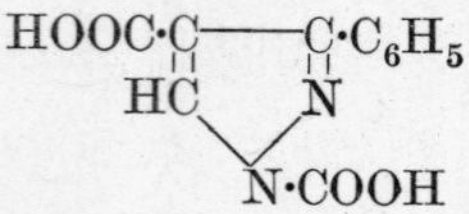

$C_{11}H_8O_4N_2$ MW, 232

4-*Et ester* : $C_{13}H_{12}O_4N_2$. MW, 260. Cryst. from EtOH. M.p. 85–6°. *Anilide* : cryst. from ligroin. M.p. 136–7°. Sol. ord. org. solvents.

Di-Et ester: $C_{15}H_{16}O_4N_2$. MW, 288. Needles from ligroin. M.p. 57·5–58·5°. Sol. ord. org. solvents. Spar. sol. ligroin.

Auwers, Ungemach, *Ber.*, 1933, **66**, 1207.

3(5)-Phenylpyrazole-1 : 5(3)-dicarboxylic Acid.

1-*Me*-5(3)-*Et ester*: $C_{14}H_{14}O_4N_2$. MW, 274. Needles from ligroin. M.p. 80–1°. Sol. ord. org. solvents.

Auwers, Dietrich, *J. prakt. Chem.*, 1934, **139**, 93.

1 - Phenylpyrazole - 3 : 4 - dicarboxylic Acid

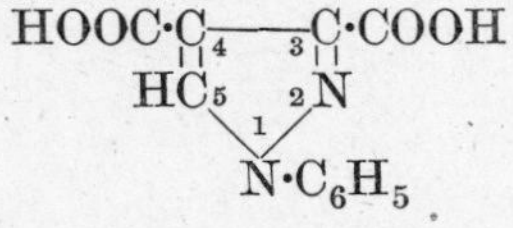

$C_{11}H_8O_4N_2$ MW, 232

Plates from H_2O. M.p. 234° decomp. Spar. sol. cold H_2O, Et_2O.

Di-Me ester: $C_{13}H_{12}O_4N_2$. MW, 260. Tablets. M.p. 97–8°.

Balbiano, *Gazz. chim. ital.*, 1898, **28**, i, 385.

5 - Phenylpyrazole - 3 : 4 - dicarboxylic Acid.

Cryst. M.p. 235° decomp. Very sol. hot H_2O, EtOH. Mod. sol. Et_2O. Resorcinol ⟶ fluorescein reaction.

Buchner, *Ber.*, 1894, **27**, 3247.
Sjollema, *Ann.*, 1894, **279**, 252.

1 - Phenylpyrazole - 3 : 5 - dicarboxylic Acid

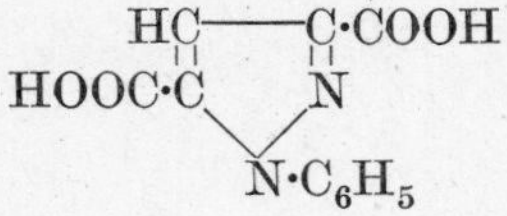

$C_{11}H_8O_4N_2$ MW, 232

Plates from EtOH. M.p. 266° decomp. to 1-phenylpyrazole-3-carboxylic acid. Sol. Et_2O. Spar. sol. cold H_2O, $CHCl_3$, ligroin, C_6H_6.

Di-NH_4 salt: plates. M.p. 210–15° decomp. Very sol. H_2O.

Di-Me ester: $C_{13}H_{12}O_4N_2$. MW, 260. M.p. 127–8°.

Diamide: $C_{11}H_{10}O_2N_4$. MW, 230. Plates from EtOH. M.p. 190°. Very sol. EtOH.

Claisen, Roosen, *Ann.*, 1894, **278**, 286.

4 - Phenylpyrazole - 3 : 5 - dicarboxylic Acid.

Needles + $2H_2O$ from H_2O. Loses H_2O at 130°. M.p. 243–6°. Dist. ⟶ 4-phenylpyrazole.

Me-Et ester: $C_{14}H_{14}O_4N_2$. MW, 274. Rhombohedra or needles from Et_2O. M.p. 104–5°.

Di-Et ester: $C_{15}H_{16}O_4N_2$. MW, 288. Needles from EtOH.Aq. M.p. 96°.

Behaghel, Buchner, *Ber.*, 1902, **35**, 34.

1 - Phenylpyrazole - 4 : 5 - dicarboxylic Acid

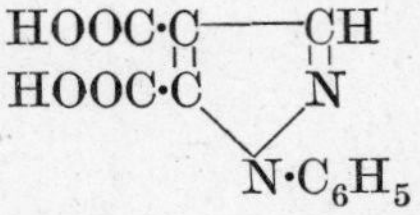

$C_{11}H_8O_4N_2$ MW, 232

Prisms and plates from H_2O. M.p. 216°. Sol. EtOH. Very sol. hot H_2O. Spar. sol. cold H_2O, Et_2O, $CHCl_3$. Dist. ⟶ 1-phenylpyrazole-4-carboxylic acid. Resorcinol ⟶ greenish-red fluorescence.

Ba salt: needles from H_2O. Spar. sol. cold H_2O.

Di-Me ester: $C_{13}H_{12}O_4N_2$. MW, 260. Needles from MeOH. M.p. 75–6°.

Diamide: $C_{11}H_{10}O_2N_4$. MW, 230. Needles from H_2O. M.p. 253–5°.

Dianilide: plates. M.p. 205–6°. Sol. EtOH, AcOEt. Spar. sol. Et_2O, ligroin.

Claisen, *Ann.*, 1897, **295**, 315.

1-Phenylpyrazoline

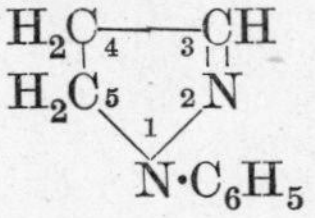

$C_9H_{10}N_2$ MW, 146

Plates from ligroin. M.p. 51–2°. B.p. 273–4°/754 mm. Sol. hot H_2O, EtOH, Et_2O, C_6H_6. Slightly basic. Volatile in steam from slightly acid sol.

Michaelis, Lampe, *Ann.*, 1893, **274**, 319.

3-Phenylpyrazoline.

M.p. 44–5°. B.p. 164°/17 mm. Spar. sol. pet. ether.

Picrate: cryst. from MeOH. M.p. 142–3°.

Nitroso deriv.: m.p. 152·5–153·5°.

Auwers, Heimke, *Ann.*, 1927, **458**, 207.

4-Phenylpyrazoline.

Oil. Oxidises in air to 4-phenylpyrazole.

B,HCl: cryst. from EtOH. M.p. 162°. Sol. H_2O, EtOH. Insol. Et_2O.

$B_2,(COOH)_2$: cryst. from EtOH. M.p. 120°.

B_2,H_2PtCl_6: m.p. 116–17°.

Oliveri, Mandala, *Gazz. chim. ital.*, 1910, **40**, i, 117.
Buchner, Dessauer, *Ber.*, 1903, **36**, 3777.

5-Phenylpyrazoline.
Colourless oil. B.p. 153°/15 mm. $D_4^{15\cdot8}$ 1·1068.
Picrate : m.p. 117–18°.

Auwers, Heimke, *Ann.*, 1927, **458**, 208.

1-Phenylpyrazolone-3

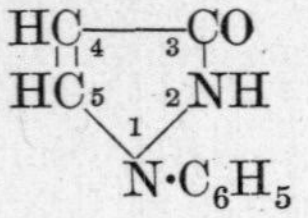

$C_9H_8ON_2$ MW, 160

Needles from H_2O. M.p. 154°. Sol. hot EtOH, $CHCl_3$, C_6H_6, conc. HCl, alkalis. Spar. sol. hot H_2O.
B,HCl : needles. M.p. 111°.
N-*Acetyl* : needles from ligroin. M.p. 62–3°.

Harries, Loth, *Ber.*, 1896, **29**, 519.

1-Phenylpyrazolone-5

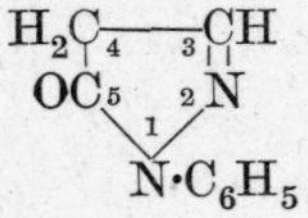

$C_9H_8ON_2$ MW, 160

Prisms and plates from AcOEt. M.p. 118–19°. Sol. acids, alkalis.
B,HCl : needles. M.p. 165°.
Isonitroso deriv. : orange-yellow needles from AcOH.Aq. M.p. 160° decomp.

Claisen, Haase, *Ber.*, 1895, **28**, 38.

3-Phenylpyrazolone-5.
Plates from EtOH. M.p. 236° decomp. Insol. cold EtOH, Et_2O, C_6H_6.
B,HCl : needles. M.p. 196°.
N-*Acetyl* : plates from EtOH. M.p. 122°. Spar. sol. cold EtOH, Et_2O, C_6H_6.
Isonitroso deriv. : yellow needles from H_2O. M.p. 188°. Sol. EtOH, Et_2O, alkalis.

Rothenburg, *J. prakt. Chem.*, 1895, **52**, 23.

1 - Phenyl - 4 - pyrazolone - 3 - carboxylic Acid (1-*Phenyl-isopyrazolone*-3-*carboxylic acid*)

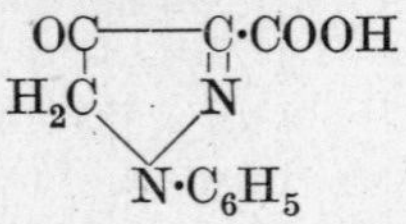

$C_{10}H_8O_3N_2$ MW, 204

Me ester : $C_{11}H_{10}O_3N_2$. MW, 218. Needles from MeOH. M.p. 85–7°. $FeCl_3 \longrightarrow$ blue col.
Et ester : $C_{12}H_{12}O_3N_2$. MW, 232. Pale yellow needles from EtOH. M.p. 258–60°. $FeCl_3 \longrightarrow$ blue col.

Favrel, *Compt. rend.*, 1913, **156**, 1912.

1 - Phenyl - 5 - pyrazolone - 3 - carboxylic Acid

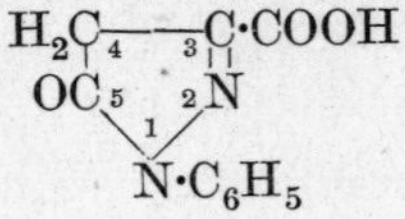

$C_{10}H_8O_3N_2$ MW, 204

Small needles from EtOH or hot H_2O. Loses CO_2 at 230°, m.p. 261°. Sol. EtOH. Insol. H_2O, Et_2O. $FeCl_3 \longrightarrow$ blue col.
Me ester : $C_{11}H_{10}O_3N_2$. MW, 218. Cryst. from MeOH. M.p. 197°.
Et ester : $C_{12}H_{12}O_3N_2$. MW, 232. Prisms from EtOH. M.p. 180–2°. $FeCl_3 \longrightarrow$ blue col.
Et ether : plates from H_2O. M.p. 152–3°. Sol. EtOH, Et_2O, $CHCl_3$. Spar. sol. cold H_2O.
Et ester : needles from EtOH.Aq. M.p. 83–4°.

Leighton, *J. Am. Chem. Soc.*, 1898, **20**, 679.

1 - Phenyl - 5 - pyrazolone - 4 - carboxylic Acid.
M.p. 91–2° decomp. Sol. EtOH, Me_2CO.
Et ester : needles from EtOH.Aq. M.p. 117–18°. Sol. EtOH, Et_2O, Me_2CO, C_6H_6, alkalis. $FeCl_3 \longrightarrow$ dark red col.

Ruhemann, *J. Chem. Soc.*, 1893, **63**, 878.

2 - Phenyl - 5 - pyrazolone - 4 - carboxylic Acid.
Cryst. from EtOH. M.p. 216° decomp. Dist. $\longrightarrow$ 2-phenylpyrazolone-5.

Michaelis, Remy, *Ber.*, 1907, **40**, 1020.

3-Phenylpyridazine (3-*Phenyl*-1 : 2-*diazine*)

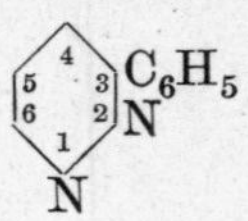

$C_{10}H_8N_2$ MW, 156

Needles from H_2O or ligroin. M.p. 102–3°. B.p. 330–2°. Sol. EtOH, Et_2O. Sublimes.
B,MeI : yellow needles from MeOH–Et_2O. M.p. 179°. Sol. MeOH.
B,HAuCl$_4$: yellow needles. M.p. 159°.
Picrate : cryst. from EtOH. M.p. 127°.

Gabriel, Colman, *Ber.*, 1899, **32**, 401.

4-Phenylpyridazine (4-*Phenyl*-1 : 2-*diazine*).
Cryst. from ligroin. M.p. 86–86·5°. Sol. EtOH, Et_2O, C_6H_6, acids. Spar. sol. ligroin.
B_2,H_2PtCl_6,H_2O : cryst. M.p. 295–300° decomp. Spar. sol. H_2O, EtOH.

Stoermer, Fincke, *Ber.*, 1909, **42**, 3130.

4-Phenylpyridazine-5-carboxylic Acid

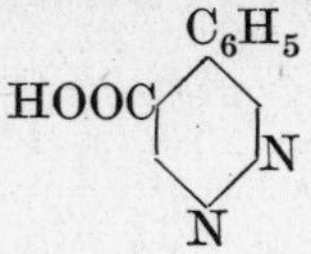

$C_{11}H_8O_2N_2$ MW, 200

Slightly brownish crystals. M.p. 220–1° decomp. Mod. sol. hot EtOH. Spar. sol. hot H_2O. Insol. Et_2O, C_6H_6. Heat with $BaCO_3$ in vacuo ⟶ 4-phenylpyridazine.

See previous reference.

3-Phenylpyridazine-6-carboxylic Acid

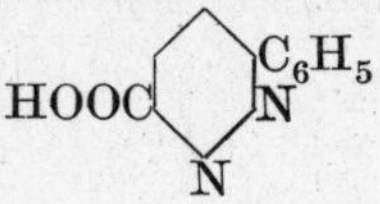

$C_{11}H_8O_2N_2$ MW, 200

Needles from H_2O. M.p. 130–1°.

Paal, Dencks, *Ber.*, 1903, **36**, 494.

2-Phenylpyridine (α-*Pyridylbenzene*)

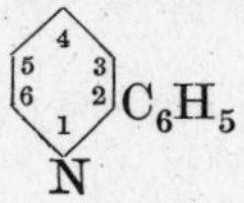

$C_{11}H_9N$ MW, 155

Oil. B.p. 268–9°. Misc. with EtOH, Et_2O, but not H_2O. Difficultly volatile in steam. Neutral $KMnO_4$ ⟶ benzoic acid. Acid $KMnO_4$ ⟶ picolinic acid.

$B_2,H_2PtCl_6,2H_2O$: orange-yellow needles. M.p. 204°. Insol. H_2O, EtOH, Et_2O.

Picrate : yellow needles. M.p. 175°. Very sol. hot EtOH.

Ziegler, Zeiser, *Ber.*, 1930, **63**, 1851.
Bergstrom, McAllister, *J. Am. Chem. Soc.*, 1930, **52**, 2847.

3-Phenylpyridine (β-*Pyridylbenzene*).

Pale yellow oil. B.p. 269–70°/749 mm. Immiscible with H_2O. Sol. EtOH, Et_2O, dil. acids. Difficultly volatile in steam. $KMnO_4$ ⟶ nicotinic acid.

Picrate : pale yellow needles from EtOH. M.p. 162–3°.

Skraup, Cobenzl, *Monatsh.*, 1883, **4**, 456.

4-Phenylpyridine (γ-*Pyridylbenzene*).

Plates from H_2O. M.p. 77–8°. B.p. 274–5°. Mod. sol. hot H_2O. $KMnO_4$ ⟶ isonicotinic acid. Na + EtOH ⟶ 4-phenylpiperidine.

B,MeI : nearly colourless cryst.

$B_2,H_2Cr_2O_7$: orange needles from H_2O. M.p. 155° decomp.

Picrate : yellow needles. M.p. 197·5°.

Overhoff, Tilman, *Rec. trav. chim.*, 1929, **48**, 993.

6-Phenylpyridine-2-carboxylic Acid.

See 6-Phenylpicolinic Acid.

6-Phenylpyridine-3-carboxylic Acid.

See 6-Phenylnicotinic Acid.

Phenylpyridine-dicarboxylic Acid.

See Phenylcinchomeronic Acid, Phenyldinicotinic Acid, *and* Phenylquinolinic Acid.

1-Phenyl-α-pyridone

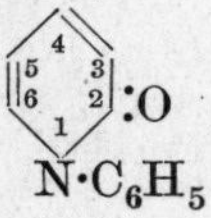

$C_{11}H_9ON$ MW, 171

Cryst. from EtOH or C_6H_6. M.p. 128°. B.p. above 300°.

Tschitschibabin, Geletzki, *Ber.*, 1924, **57**, 1159.

6-Phenyl-α-pyridone.

Yellow scales from C_6H_6. M.p. 197°. Sol. EtOH. Spar. sol. C_6H_6. Insol. H_2O, Et_2O. Zn dust dist. ⟶ 2-phenylpyridine. PCl_3 ⟶ 6-chloro-2-phenylpyridine.

B,HCl : pale yellow needles. M.p. 104°.

Leben, *Ber.*, 1896, **29**, 1678.

1-Phenyl-γ-pyridone

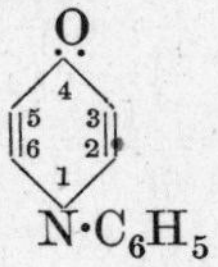

$C_{11}H_9ON$ MW, 171

Needles + $2H_2O$ from H_2O, m.p. anhyd. 104–5° : cryst. from C_6H_6, m.p. 116°. Very sol. warm H_2O, EtOH. Spar. sol. Et_2O.

B,MeI : rhomboids. M.p. 146°.

Picrate : yellow leaflets from EtOH. M.p. 190°.

Borsche, Bonacker, *Ber.*, 1921, **54**, 2682.

6-Phenyl-γ-pyridone.

Cryst. + $\frac{1}{2}H_2O$ from H_2O. M.p. 155°.

Borsch, Peter, *Ann.*, 1927, **453**, 158.

Phenyl-2-pyridylamine.

See 2-Anilinopyridine.

Phenyl-2-pyridylcarbinol (α-[α-*Pyridyl*]-*benzyl alcohol*, 2-α-*hydroxybenzylpyridine*)

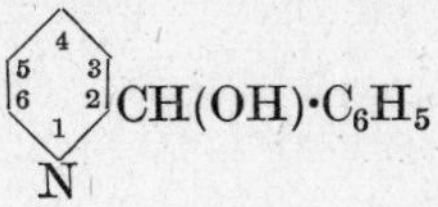

$C_{12}H_{11}ON$ MW, 185

Cryst. from C_6H_6–pet. ether. M.p. 82°. Very sol. EtOH, Et_2O, C_6H_6, dil. min. acids. Insol. H_2O, pet. ether. $KMnO_4 \longrightarrow$ phenyl 2-pyridyl ketone.

B_2,H_2PtCl_6: orange-red plates from H_2O. M.p. 197° decomp. Spar. sol. cold H_2O.

Tschitschibabin, *Ber.*, 1904, **37**, 1371.

Phenyl-4-pyridylcarbinol (*α-[γ-Pyridyl]-benzyl alcohol, 4-α-hydroxybenzylpyridine*).

Cryst. from C_6H_6 or AcOEt. M.p. 126°. Very sol. EtOH, min. acids. Spar. sol. Et_2O, C_6H_6. Insol. H_2O, pet. ether. $KMnO_4 \longrightarrow$ phenyl 4-pyridyl ketone.

B_2,H_2PtCl_6: orange-red scales from H_2O. M.p. 205°. Spar. sol. cold H_2O.

See previous reference.

Phenylpyridylethane.

See Phenylethylpyridine.

Phenyl 2-pyridyl Ketone (*2-Benzoylpyridine*)

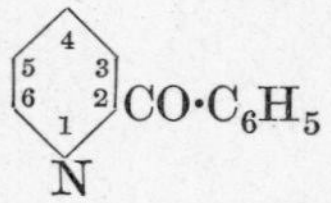

$C_{12}H_9ON$ MW, 183

Oil. B.p. 317°, 170–2°/10 mm. D_0^{20} 1·1558. Red. $\longrightarrow$ phenyl-2-pyridylcarbinol.

B,HCl: cryst. from Me_2CO. M.p. 126–8°.

B_2,H_2PtCl_6: cryst. from dil. HCl. M.p. 193° decomp.

Oxime: two forms. (i) Pale yellow prisms. M.p. 150–2°. (ii) Cryst. M.p. 165–7°.

Phenylhydrazone: yellow cryst. from EtOH. M.p. 136–7°. Spar. sol. cold EtOH.

Picrate: cryst. from EtOH or Me_2CO. M.p. 130°. Sol. MeOH, AcOEt. Spar. sol. C_6H_6.

Crook, McElvain, *J. Am. Chem. Soc.*, 1930, **52**, 4006.
Tschugajew, *Ber.*, 1906, **39**, 3387.
Tschitschibabin, *Chem. Zentr.*, 1902, I, 206.

Phenyl 3-pyridyl Ketone (*3-Benzoylpyridine*).

Cryst. M.p. 42°. B.p. 318–19°. Ox. $\longrightarrow$ nicotinic acid. Red. $\longrightarrow$ 3-benzylpyridine.

B,HCl: needles. M.p. 160–2°.

B_2,H_2PtCl_6: cryst. from dil. HCl. M.p. 245° decomp.

Oxime: two forms. (i) M.p. 141–3°. Sol. hot EtOH. Spar. sol. H_2O. (ii) Prisms from C_6H_6. M.p. 162–3°. Sol. EtOH. Spar. sol. Et_2O. Insol. H_2O. Sol. in dil. HCl, pptd. with $Na_2CO_3 \longrightarrow$ (i).

Phenylhydrazone: m.p. 143·5°.

Picrate: clusters of needles from EtOH. M.p. 161°.

La Forge, *J. Am. Chem. Soc.*, 1928, **50**, 2486.
Tschitschibabin, *Ber.*, 1903, **36**, 2711.

Phenyl 4-pyridyl Ketone (*4-Benzoylpyridine*).

Plates from H_2O, needles from pet. ether. M.p. 71·5–72·5°. B.p. 313·5–314°/742 mm. Very sol. EtOH, Et_2O. Spar. sol. hot H_2O. Red. $\longrightarrow$ phenyl-4-pyridylcarbinol.

B,HCl: cryst. from EtOH–Et_2O. M.p. 195–7°.

Oxime: two forms. (i) Monoclinic prisms from EtOH. M.p. 176–7° decomp. (ii) Cryst. from EtOH. M.p. 152–5°.

Phenylhydrazone: yellow cryst. from EtOH. M.p. 181–2°.

Picrate: monoclinic cryst. from EtOH. M.p. 159–60°.

Crook, McElvain, *J. Am. Chem. Soc.*, 1930, **52**, 4006.
Tschitschibabin, *Chem. Zentr.*, 1902, I, 206.

Phenylpyridylmethane.

See Benzylpyridine.

6-Phenyl-α-pyrone.

See 6-Phenylcoumalin.

2-Phenyl-γ-pyrone

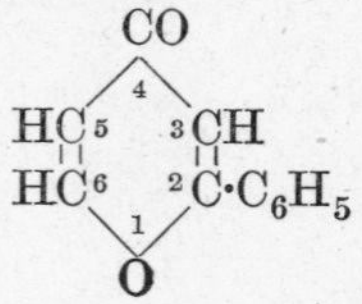

$C_{11}H_8O_2$ MW, 172

Needles from H_2O. M.p. 104°.

Borsche, Peter, *Ann.*, 1927, **453**, 158.

1-Phenylpyrrole

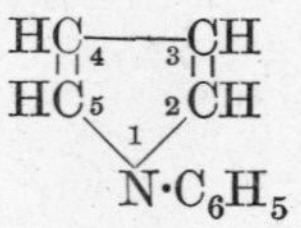

$C_{10}H_9N$ MW, 143

Scales with camphor-like odour. M.p. 62°. B.p. 234°, 140°/38 mm. Very sol. pet. ether. Mod. sol. EtOH, Et_2O, C_6H_6, $CHCl_3$. Insol. H_2O. Readily volatile in steam. Sublimes. Heat of comb. C_v 1283·1 Cal. Turns red in air. Unaffected by acids and alkalis. EtOH–HCl $\longrightarrow$ "pine-chip" violet. Dist. through glowing tube $\longrightarrow$ 2-phenylpyrrole.

Köttnitz, *J. prakt. Chem.*, 1872, **6**, 148.

2-Phenylpyrrole.

Plates from EtOH. M.p. 129°. B.p. 271–2°/726 mm. Very sol. EtOH, Et_2O, $CHCl_3$, C_6H_6. Spar. sol. ligroin. Sublimes. Readily volatile in steam.

Pictet, Crépieux, *Ber.*, 1895, **28**, 1905.

5-Phenylpyrrole-2-aldehyde

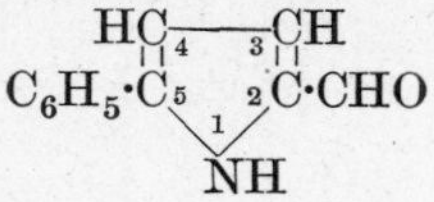

$C_{11}H_9ON$ MW, 171

Needles from C_6H_6–pet. ether. M.p. 138°.

Semicarbazone: greenish plates from EtOH.Aq. M.p. 190°.

p-*Nitrophenylhydrazone*: dark red needles from EtOH. M.p. 222°.

Azine: yellow cryst. from C_6H_6. M.p. 240°.

Plancher, Rossi, Ghigi, *Gazz. chim. ital.*, 1929, **59**, 347.

1-Phenylpyrrole-2-carboxylic Acid

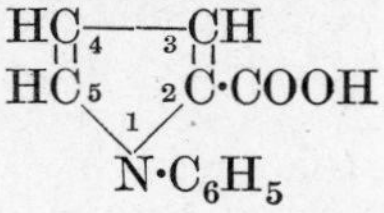

$C_{11}H_9O_2N$ MW, 187

Plates or needles from EtOH or C_6H_6. M.p. 166° decomp. to 1-phenylpyrrole. Very sol. EtOH, $CHCl_3$, AcOH, C_6H_6. Sol. Et_2O. Insol. cold H_2O, pet. ether. Loses CO_2 in boiling water.

Me ester: $C_{12}H_{11}O_2N$. MW, 201. Plates from EtOH.Aq. M.p. 88°. B.p. 282°. Insol. H_2O.

Et ester: $C_{13}H_{13}O_2N$. MW, 215. B.p. 289°.

Anilide: needles from EtOH.Aq. M.p. 136°.

Pictet, Steinmann, *Ber.*, 1902, **35**, 2530.

2-Phenylpyrrole-3-carboxylic Acid.

Cubes. M.p. 192–3° decomp.

Et ester: prisms. M.p. 19°. B.p. 194–5°/6 mm.

Kondo, Suzuki, *Chem. Zentr.*, 1927, II, 1029.

1-Phenylpyrrolidine

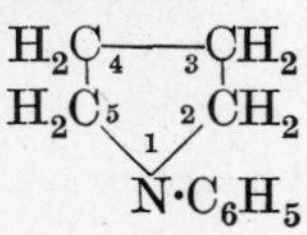

$C_{10}H_{13}N$ MW, 147

Oil. B.p. 110–16°/9 mm. D^{25} 1·0260. n_D^{25} 1·5803.

B_2,H_2PtCl_6: yellow needles from EtOH–HCl. M.p. 174–5° decomp.

$B,2(COOH)_2,\frac{1}{2}H_2O$: cryst. from Me_2CO–pet. ether. M.p. 156°.

Picrate: m.p. 115–16°.

Signaigo, Adkins, *J. Am. Chem. Soc.*, 1936, **58**, 715.

Craig, Hixon, *J. Am. Chem. Soc.*, 1930, **52**, 807.

2-Phenylpyrrolidine.

Oil. B.p. 236–8°. Spar. sol. H_2O giving alk. sol. Absorbs CO_2 from the air.

$B,HAuCl_4$: yellow prisms. M.p. 110°.

B_2,H_2PtCl_6: prisms. M.p. 187–8°.

Picrate: plates. M.p. 148–9°.

La Forge, *J. Am. Chem. Soc.*, 1928, **50**, 2477.

Gabriel, Colman, *Ber.*, 1908, **41**, 520.

3-Phenylpyrrolidine.

Oil. B.p. 120–2°/12 mm. Spar. sol. H_2O. Slowly absorbs CO_2 from the air.

Picrate: cryst. from EtOH. M.p. 166°.

Späth, Breusch, *Monatsh.*, 1928, **50**, 352.

1-Phenylpyrrolidine-2 : 5-dicarboxylic Acid

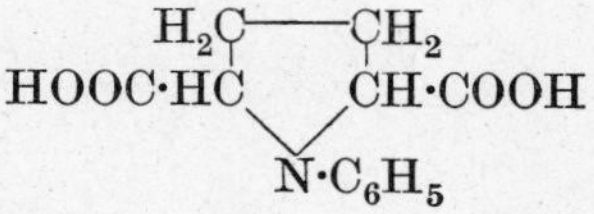

$C_{12}H_{13}O_4N$ MW, 235

Needles from Me_2CO–pet. ether. Decomp. at 252°. Very sol. cold EtOH, hot Me_2CO. Spar. sol. cold Et_2O, H_2O. Insol. $CHCl_3$, pet. ether, C_6H_6. Decolourises acid or alk. $KMnO_4$.

Ba salt, $8H_2O$: needles from EtOH.Aq. Very sol. H_2O. Insol. abs. EtOH.

Di-Me ester: $C_{14}H_{17}O_4N$. MW, 263. Needles from pet. ether. M.p. 88°. B.p. 225–30°/32 mm. Very sol. hot EtOH, Et_2O, Me_2CO, $CHCl_3$, C_6H_6. Insol. cold H_2O, cold EtOH, pet. ether.

Di-Et ester: $C_{16}H_{21}O_4N$. MW, 291. Yellow oil. B.p. 227–8°/30 mm. Immiscible with H_2O.

Monoanilide: needles from $CHCl_3$–C_6H_6. Decomp. at 184°. Very sol. EtOH, Me_2CO. Spar. sol. cold H_2O, pet. ether, C_6H_6.

Le Sueur, Haas, *J. Chem. Soc.*, 1910, **97**, 177.

Le Sueur, *J. Chem. Soc.*, 1909, **95**, 276.

1-Phenylpyrrolidone-2 (N-*Phenyl-γ-butyrolactam*)

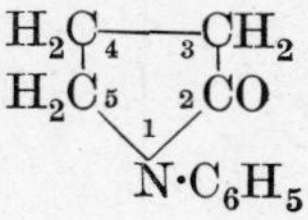

$C_{10}H_{11}ON$ MW, 161

Needles from EtOH.Aq. or C_6H_6–pet. ether, plates from H_2O. M.p. 68–9°. B.p. 180–2°/11 mm.

Lipp, Caspers, *Ber.*, 1925, **58**, 1013.

4-Phenylpyrrolidone-2 (*2-Phenyl-γ-butyrolactam*).

Hexagonal prisms from C_6H_6–pet. ether. M.p. 60°.

N-*Acetyl*: hexagonal plates from EtOH. M.p. 63°.

N-*Benzoyl*: prisms from C_6H_6–pet. ether. M.p. 145°.

Jackson, Kenner, *J. Chem. Soc.*, 1928, 1659.

5-Phenylpyrrolidone-2 (*3-Phenyl-γ-butyrolactam*).

Needles. M.p. 91°.

Köhl, *Ber.*, 1903, **36**, 174.

1-Phenyl-2-pyrrolidone-3-carboxylic Acid

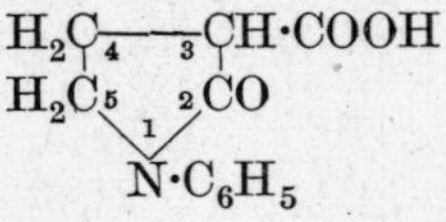

$C_{11}H_{11}O_3N$ MW, 205

M.p. 64–5°.

Küster, Grassner, *Z. physiol. Chem.*, 1925, **145**, 45.

1-Phenyl-3-pyrrolidone-2-carboxylic Acid (*1-Phenyl-3-pyrrolidone-4-carboxylic acid*)

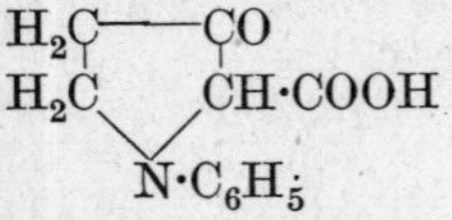

or

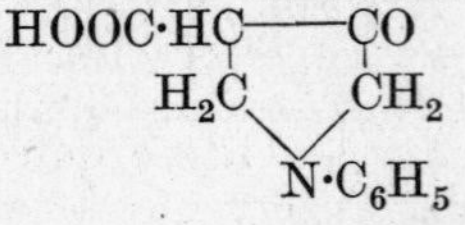

$C_{11}H_{11}O_3N$ MW, 205

Cryst. from H_2O. M.p. 143–4°. Losses CO_2 at 170–80°. $FeCl_3 \longrightarrow$ no col.

Et ester: $C_{13}H_{15}O_3N$. MW, 233. Needles from EtOH, plates from EtOH.Aq. M.p. 69–70°. $FeCl_3 \longrightarrow$ dark violet col.

Phenylhydrazone: m.p. 160–1°.

de Mouilpied, *J. Chem. Soc.*, 1905, **87**, 442.

3-Phenyl-5-pyrrolidone-2-carboxylic Acid

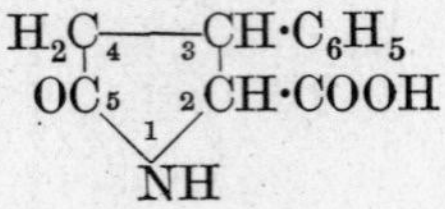

$C_{11}H_{11}O_3N$ MW, 205

Needles and prisms from EtOH. M.p. 196·5–197·5°.

Harington, *J. Biol. Chem.*, 1925, **64**, 29.

1-Phenyl-5-pyrrolidone-3-carboxylic Acid.

Needles from H_2O, plates from EtOH.Aq. M.p. 190° slight decomp. Insol. dil. HCl.

Ag salt: needles from H_2O.

Ba salt: very sol. H_2O.

Chloride: $C_{11}H_{10}O_2NCl$. MW, 223·5. Cryst. Easily decomp. by H_2O.

Anilide: plates from EtOH.Aq. M.p. 185°. Very sol. Et_2O. Spar. sol. H_2O. Sublimes.

Anschütz, Reuter, *Ann.*, 1889, **254**, 141.

2-Phenyl-2-pyrroline

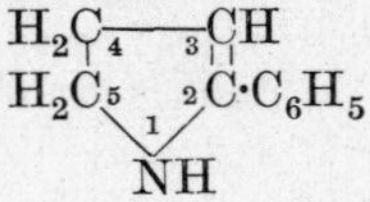

$C_{10}H_{11}N$ MW, 145

Cryst. with strong ammoniacal odour and bitter taste. M.p. 44–5°. B.p. 249°/752 mm. Spar. sol. hot H_2O. Aq. sol. reacts alkaline. Red. $\longrightarrow$ 2-phenylpyrrolidine.

B,HCl: plates from Me_2CO or EtOH–Et_2O. M.p. 210° (206–7°).

B_2,H_2PtCl_6: orange plates or needles from dil. HCl. M.p. 220° decomp. (darkens at 200°).

Picrate: cryst. from MeOH. M.p. 198°.

Gabriel, Colman, *Ber.*, 1908, **41**, 517.
Sonn, Podschus, Schützler, Stephani, *Ber.*, 1935, **68**, 150.
Craig, Bulbrook, Hixon, *J. Am. Chem. Soc.*, 1931, **53**, 1833.

2-Phenyl-3-pyrroline

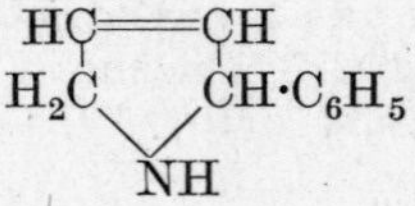

$C_{10}H_{11}N$ MW, 145

M.p. 45°. B.p. 118°/11 mm.

B,HCl: cryst. from EtOH.Aq. M.p. 240°.

Lipp, Seeles, *Ber.*, 1929, **62**, 2458.
Wohl, *Ber.*, 1901, **34**, 1922.

Phenyl 2-pyrryl Ketone (*2-Benzoylpyrrole*)

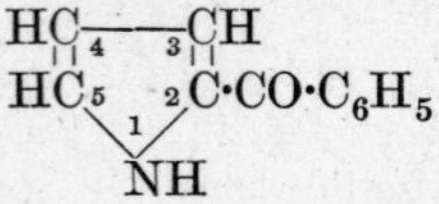

$C_{11}H_9ON$ MW, 117

Needles, plates or prisms from hot H_2O, EtOH.Aq., or pet. ether. M.p. 79°. B.p. 305°. Very sol. EtOH, AcOH, C_6H_6. Sol. pet. ether. Insol. cold H_2O. Stable to boiling KOH.

Oxime: needles from EtOH.Aq. M.p. 147°.

Oddo, Dainotti, *Gazz. chim. ital.*, 1912, **42**, i, 730.
Pictet, *Ber.*, 1904, **37**, 2797.

Phenylpyruvic Acid (*α-Ketohydrocinnamic acid*)

$C_6H_5 \cdot CH_2 \cdot CO \cdot COOH$

$C_9H_8O_3$ MW, 164

Plates from $CHCl_3$. M.p. 157° (153–4°) decomp. Very sol. EtOH, Et_2O. Sol. hot $CHCl_3$, C_6H_6. Spar. sol. boiling H_2O. Insol. cold ligroin. Oxidises in air. Freshly prepared sol. in K_2CO_3 decolourises $KMnO_4$. Reduces boiling Fehling's and Nessler's. Salts react with semicarbazide but free acid does not. Et_2O sol. ⟶ green ring with $FeCl_3$ sol. Ac_2O ⟶ 1-acetoxycinnamic acid. Red. ⟶ benzylglycollic acid.

Na salt, H_2O: insol. EtOH. Stable in air. H_2O of cryst. remains at 100°.

Me ester: $C_{10}H_{10}O_3$. MW, 178. Needles. M.p. 75°. Sol. EtOH, Et_2O, C_6H_6. Insol. H_2O. Oxidises in air ⟶ $C_6H_5 \cdot CHO$. *Semicarbazone*: m.p. 196°.

Et ester: $C_{11}H_{12}O_3$. MW, 192. Needles. M.p. 45°. B.p. 154·5°/15 mm., 117–21°/2·8 mm. Sol. EtOH, Et_2O, C_6H_6. Insol. H_2O. Oxidises in air ⟶ $C_6H_5 \cdot CHO$. $FeCl_3$ ⟶ violet col. Ac_2O ⟶ ethyl 1-acetoxycinnamic ester. Can be separated into 3 forms, 2 enolic *cis–trans* isomerides and one ketonic:—

α. Needles from ligroin. M.p. 52°. β. B.p. 152°/15 mm. γ. M.p. 79°. α and β with $FeCl_3$ ⟶ green col. γ Gives no col. α and β give same phenylurethane of ethyl 1-hydroxycinnamic ester. All give same acetate and benzoate of 1-OH-cinnamic ester, and same ketonic derivatives. *Oxime*: $C_{11}H_{13}O_3N$. MW, 207. Prisms or needles from ligroin. M.p. 57–8°. Sol. EtOH, Et_2O, C_6H_6. Mod. sol. ligroin. Spar. sol. H_2O. *Semicarbazone*: plates from EtOH.Aq. M.p. 159–60° (167°). *Phenylhydrazone*: m.p. 89°. p-*Tolylhydrazone*: orange prisms. M.p. 72°. Sol. EtOH, Me_2CO, C_6H_6. p-*Nitrophenylhydrazone*: yellow cryst. from AcOH. M.p. 181°.

Amide: $C_9H_9O_2N$. MW, 163. M.p. 190°. Sol. hot EtOH. Insol. H_2O, Et_2O, C_6H_6. *Oxime*: needles from H_2O. M.p. 147°.

Anilide: m.p. 126°.

Oxime: $C_9H_9O_3N$. MW, 179. Needles from EtOH.Aq., or H_2O. M.p. 159° (153–67°) decomp. Sol. EtOH, Et_2O, C_6H_6.

Semicarbazone: m.p. 180° decomp.

p-*Nitrophenylhydrazone*: cryst. from EtOH.Aq. M.p. 187–8° decomp.

p-*Tolylhydrazone*: yellow felted needles from EtOH, prisms from Me_2CO. M.p. 158° decomp.

Erlenmeyer, Arbenz, *Ann.*, 1904, **333**, 228.
Bougault, *Compt. rend.*, 1916, **162**, 761.
Gault, Weick, *Bull. soc. chim.*, 1922, **31**, 867.
Feist, Rauterberg, *Ber.*, 1922, **55**, 3702.
Walker, *J. Chem. Soc.*, 1925, 1862.
Kon, Watson, *J. Chem. Soc.*, 1932, 7.

4-Phenylquinaldine (2-*Methyl*-4-*phenylquinoline*)

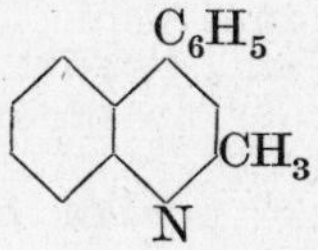

$C_{16}H_{13}N$ MW, 219

Plates from EtOH. M.p. 98–9°. Sol. EtOH, Et_2O, $CHCl_3$, C_6H_6. Spar. sol. ligroin, pet. ether. Sol. dil. acids with blue fluor.

Hydrochloride: needles from EtOH. M.p. 219°.

Sulphate: yellow needles from H_2O. M.p. 235°.

$ZnCl_2$ double salt: needles. M.p. 197°.

$CdCl_2$ double salt: needles. M.p. 208–10°.

$HgCl_2$ double salt: needles from dil. HCl. M.p. 202°.

Chloroplatinate: m.p. 235°.

Picrate: yellow needles from EtOH. M.p. 205–6°. Insol. Et_2O.

Methiodide: m.p. 205°.

Spallino, Salimei, *Gazz. chim. ital.*, 1912, **42**, i, 608.
Fischer, *J. prakt. Chem.*, 1918, **98**, 226.
Beyer, *J. prakt. Chem.*, 1886, **33**, 421.

4-Phenylquinaldinic Acid.

See 4-Phenylquinoline-2-carboxylic Acid.

2-Phenylquinazoline

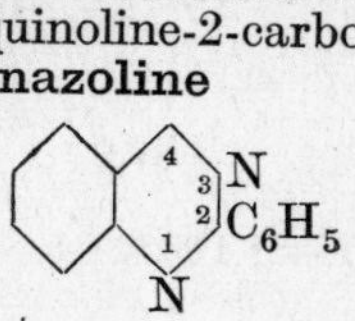

$C_{14}H_{10}N_2$ MW, 206

Needles from EtOH. M.p. 101°. Does not boil below 300°. Sol. EtOH, Et_2O, C_6H_6. Insol. H_2O.

Bischler, Lang, *Ber.*, 1895, **28**, 288.

4-Phenylquinazoline.
Picrate: yellow leaflets from EtOH. M.p. 178°.

Bischler, Barad, *Ber.*, 1892, **25**, 3093.

2-Phenylquinoline

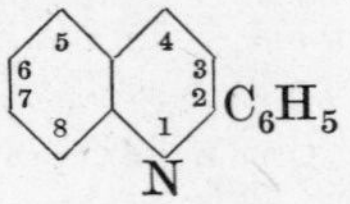

$C_{15}H_{11}N$ MW, 205

Needles from EtOH.Aq. M.p. 86° (80–1°). B.p. 363°, 310°/187 mm. Sol. Et_2O, Me_2CO, AcOEt, C_6H_6, CS_2, hot EtOH. Spar. sol. H_2O. Very spar. sol. pet. ether. Triboluminescent. $KMnO_4$ in dil. H_2SO_4 ⟶ *N*-benzoylanthranilic acid.

Dichromate: m.p. 145–8°.
Ferrichloride: m.p. 169–70°.
Hydrochloride: yellow needles from alc. HCl. M.p. 163–5°.
$B_2,2HCl,AuCl_3$: needles from HCl. M.p. about 204°.
$B,HAuCl_4$: m.p. about 160°.
$B_2,H_2PtCl_6,2H_2O$: yellow needles. Decomp. about 210°.
Picrate: yellow leaflets from EtOH. M.p. 191–2°.
Methiodide: orange-red cryst. from EtOH–Et_2O. M.p. 200°.
Ethiodide: yellow prisms. M.p. 195°.

Doebner, v. Miller, *Ber.*, 1883, **16**, 1665.
Goldschmidt, *Ber.*, 1895, **28**, 986.
Doebner, Gieseke, *Ann.*, 1887, **242**, 294.
Le Fèvre, Pearson, *J. Chem. Soc.*, 1932, 2807.

3-Phenylquinoline.
Plates from Et_2O. M.p. 52°. B.p. 205–7°. Sol. EtOH, Et_2O, $CHCl_3$, C_6H_6. Spar. volatile in steam.

B,HCl: needles from dil. HCl. M.p. 109°.
Picrate: yellow cryst. from EtOH. M.p. 205°.
Methiodide: yellow needles from MeOH. M.p. 224°.
Ethiodide: m.p. 228°.

Friedländer, Göhring, *Ber.*, 1883, **16**, 1836.
Hübner, *Ber.*, 1908, **41**, 482.
Warren, *J. Chem. Soc.*, 1936, 1367.

4-Phenylquinoline.
Needles from Et_2O or ligroin. M.p. 61–2°. Sol. EtOH, Et_2O and most indifferent solvents. Insol. H_2O. Sol. dil. HCl and dil. H_2SO_4 with blue fluor.

Hydrochloride: needles from EtOH–Et_2O. M.p. 96–7°.
Sulphate: plates from H_2O. M.p. 195–6°.
$ZnCl_2$ *double salt*: needles from dil. HCl. M.p. 115–20°.
$CdCl_2$ *double salt*: needles. M.p. 120–2°.
$HgCl_2$ *double salt*: needles. M.p. 197–9°.
B_2,H_2PtCl_6: yellow plates. M.p. 244°.
Picrate: yellow needles from EtOH. M.p. 225°.
Methiodide: yellow needles from EtOH or H_2O. M.p. 222° decomp.

Kenner, Statham, *J. Chem. Soc.*, 1935, 301.
Koenigs, Nef, *Ber.*, 1886, **19**, 2430; 1887, **20**, 622.
Koenigs, Meimberg, *Ber.*, 1895, **28**, 1038.

6-Phenylquinoline.
Plates from EtOH, C_6H_6 or aniline. M.p. 110–11°. B.p. 260°/77 mm. Sol. EtOH, $CHCl_3$, CS_2, C_6H_6. Spar. sol. Et_2O, pet. ether. Very spar. sol. H_2O. Spar. volatile in steam.

Methiodide: yellow prisms from H_2O. M.p. 194° to a red liq.

La Coste, Sorger, *Ann.*, 1885, **230**, 8.

8-Phenylquinoline.
Viscous oil with yellowish-green fluor. B.p. 283°/187 mm., 270–6°/80 mm. Sol. EtOH, Et_2O, $CHCl_3$, CS_2, C_6H_6. Very spar. sol. H_2O.

$B_2,H_2Cr_2O_7$: reddish-yellow leaflets from H_2O. M.p. 125–6°.
Picrate: yellow needles. M.p. about 210°.
Methiodide: yellow cryst. M.p. 163°. Insol. Et_2O.

La Coste, Sorger, *Ann.*, 1885, **230**, 39.
Möhlau, Berger, *Ber.*, 1893, **26**, 2004.

4-Phenylquinoline-2-carboxylic Acid
(*4-Phenylquinaldinic acid*)

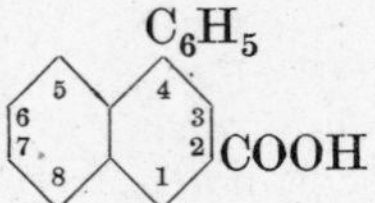

$C_{16}H_{11}O_2N$ MW, 249

Yellow needles from EtOH.Aq. M.p. 171°. At 180–90° ⟶ 4-phenylquinoline.

Chloroplatinate: yellow needles. M.p. 233–4° decomp.
Chloride: $C_{16}H_{10}ONCl$. MW, 267·5. Cryst. from ligroin. M.p. 116° ⟶ red col.

Koenigs, Jaeglé, *Ber.*, 1895, **28**, 1049.
Besthorn, *Ber.*, 1913, **46**, 2766.

2-Phenylquinoline-3-carboxylic Acid.

Needles. M.p. 226° (230° decomp.). Sol. MeOH, AcOH, $PhNO_2$. Spar. sol. C_6H_6.

Me ester : $C_{17}H_{13}O_2N$. MW, 263. M.p. 84°. B.p. 195°/13 mm.

Nitrile : needles from EtOH. M.p. 193–4°.

John, *J. prakt. Chem.*, 1931, **131**, 271.
v. Meyer, *J. prakt. Chem.*, 1914, **90**, 28.

2-Phenylquinoline-4-carboxylic Acid (2-*Phenylcinchoninic acid, cinchophene, atophan, quinophan*).

Needles from MeOH. M.p. 212–13°. Sol. Et_2O, hot EtOH, alkalis, warm min. acids. Insol. H_2O. The acid and several of its derivs. have wide therapeutic use as uric acid eliminants. Oxidised in human organism to 8-hydroxy-2-phenylquinoline-4-carboxylic acid. Dist. with lime ⟶ 2-phenylquinoline.

B,HCl : lemon-yellow cryst. M.p. 223°.

B,HBr : brownish-yellow cryst. M.p. 255°.

B,HI : orange cryst. M.p. 243°.

Me ester : $C_{17}H_{13}O_2N$. MW, 263. Leaflets. M.p. 61°. Bitter taste.

Et ester : $C_{18}H_{15}O_2N$. MW, 277. Cryst. from EtOH. M.p. 51°. Sol. EtOH, Et_2O. *B,HCl* : m.p. 210–11° decomp. *Picrate* : m.p. 144–5°.

Propyl ester : $C_{19}H_{17}O_2N$. MW, 291. M.p. 63–4°.

Butyl ester : $C_{20}H_{19}O_2N$. MW, 305. M.p. 56–7°.

Isobutyl ester : m.p. 39–40°.

Isoamyl ester : $C_{21}H_{21}O_2N$. MW, 319. Yellow oil. B.p. 235–40°/2 mm.

Allyl ester : atoquinol. Needles from EtOH. M.p. 30°. B.p. 265°/15 mm., 215°/0·8 mm. Sol. EtOH, Et_2O, Me_2CO. Insol. H_2O. *B,HCl* : yellow needles from EtOH. M.p. 145–7°. Insol. Et_2O.

Phenyl ester : cryst. from EtOH. M.p. 132°.

p-*Chlorophenyl ester* : m.p. 117–18°.

2-*Naphthyl ester* : yellow cryst. M.p. 130°.

Benzyl ester : yellow cryst. from EtOH. M.p. 77–8°. Sol. C_6H_6. Mod. sol. EtOH, Et_2O. Insol. H_2O.

Phenylethyl ester : m.p. 72°.

Cinnamyl ester : cryst. from Et_2O. M.p. 83°.

Salicyl ester : m.p. 188°.

Chloride : $C_{16}H_{10}ONCl$. MW, 267·5. Yellow cryst. from C_6H_6–ligroin. M.p. 81–2°. *B,HCl* : m.p. about 153° decomp.

Amide : $C_{16}H_{12}ON_2$. MW, 248. M.p. 196°.

Nitrile : $C_{16}H_{10}N_2$. MW, 230. Needles from EtOH. M.p. 140°. B.p. about 365°.

Anhydride : $C_{32}H_{20}O_3N_2$. MW, 480. Needles from C_6H_6. M.p. 185°. *Dimethiodide* : m.p. 132°.

Anilide : cryst. from EtOH. M.p. 198°.

Hydrazide : needles from EtOH. M.p. 222°. Spar. sol. Et_2O, C_6H_6.

Phenylhydrazide : cryst. from AcOH. M.p. 215°.

Azide : needles from pet. ether. M.p. 87°.

Methochloride : prisms + $2H_2O$ from H_2O. M.p. 209–10° decomp., after turning green at about 140°.

Methiodide : red cryst. from EtOH or H_2O. M.p. 160–5° decomp.

Du Puis, Lindwall, *J. Am. Chem. Soc.*, 1935, **56**, 471.
John, *Ber.*, 1926, **59**, 1447.
Rojahn, Schulten, *Arch. Pharm.*, 1926, **264**, 348.
Rosenmund, *Ber.*, 1921, **54**, 2893.
Wülfing, E.P., 325,985, (*Chem. Zentr.*, 1930, II, 93).
Boeringer Sohn, D.R.P., 485,426, (*Chem. Zentr.*, 1931, I, 853); D.R.P., 520,922, (*Chem. Zentr.*, 1931, I, 3173).
Gesellschaft für Chemische Industrie in Basel, U.S.P., 1,378,343, (*Chem. Zentr.*, 1921, IV, 514).
Bayer, D.R.P., 290,703, (*Chem. Zentr.*, 1916, I, 645).
Kalle, D.R.P., 287,304, (*Chem. Zentr.*, 1915, II, 933).

3-Phenylquinoline-4-carboxylic Acid (3-*Phenylcinchoninic acid*).

Prisms from AcOH. M.p. 273°. Somewhat difficultly sol. AcOH, Me_2CO. At 290° ⟶ 3-phenylquinoline.

Me ester : needles from MeOH.Aq. M.p. 73°.

Amide : microcryst. powder from AcOH.Aq. M.p. 274°.

Anilide : needles from EtOH.Aq. M.p. 222°.

Hydrazide : platelets + $1H_2O$ from EtOH.Aq. M.p. 154°.

Hübner, *Ber.*, 1906, **39**, 983.

2-Phenylquinoline-6-carboxylic Acid.

Cryst. from EtOH.Aq. M.p. 277°.

v. Braun, Brauns, *Ber.*, 1927, **60**, 1255.

4-Phenylquinoline-2 : 3-dicarboxylic Acid (4-*Phenylacridinic acid*)

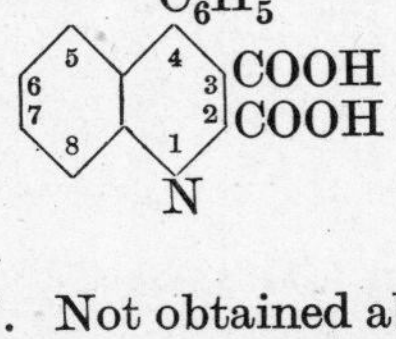

$C_{17}H_{11}O_4N$ MW, 293

M.p. 200–15°. Not obtained absolutely pure.

Claus, Nicolayson, *Ber.*, 1885, **18**, 2706.

2 - Phenylquinoline - 3 : 4 - dicarboxylic Acid.

Needles + $2H_2O$ from H_2O. M.p. 193–4°. Mod. sol. EtOH. Spar. sol. H_2O.

3-*Nitrile*: 2-phenyl-3-cyanocinchoninic acid. $C_{17}H_{10}O_2N_2$. MW, 274. Needles from C_6H_6. M.p. 267–8°.

Engelhard, *J. prakt. Chem.*, 1898, **57**, 471.
v. Meyer, *J. prakt. Chem.*, 1914, **90**, 23.

2 - Phenylquinoline - 4 : 7 - dicarboxylic Acid.

Yellow cryst. powder. M.p. 200°. Sol. AcOEt. Spar. sol. EtOH, Et_2O, $CHCl_3$.

Neumann, D.R.P., 373,285, (*Chem. Zentr.*, 1923, IV, 665).

2 - Phenylquinoline - 4 : 8 - dicarboxylic Acid.

Needles from EtOH or AcOH. Does not melt below 300°. Insol. H_2O, Et_2O, $CHCl_3$, C_6H_6, pet. ether. Heated with soda-lime ⟶ 2-phenylquinoline.

Doebner, Fettback, *Ann.*, 1894, **281**, 2.

6-Phenylquinolinic Acid (6-*Phenylpyridine*-2 : 3-*dicarboxylic acid*)

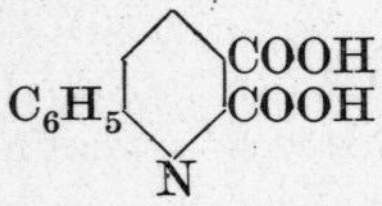

$C_{13}H_9O_4N$ MW, 243

M.p. 148–50° with decomp. to 6-phenylnicotinic acid.

Späth, Burger, *Monatsh.*, 1928, **49**, 270.

Phenyl-2-quinolylamine.
See 2-Anilinoquinoline.

Phenylquinolylethane.
See Phenylethylquinoline.

Phenylquinolylethylene
See Styrylquinoline.

***sym*.-Phenylquinolylhydrazine.**
See under 2-Quinolylhydrazine.

Phenyl 2-quinolyl Ketone (2-*Benzoylquinoline*)

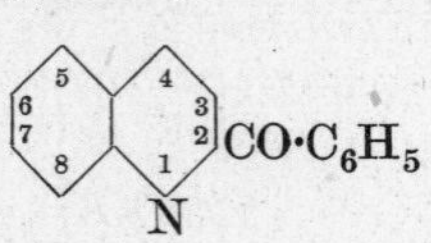

$C_{16}H_{11}ON$ MW, 233

Leaflets from C_6H_6–ligroin. M.p. 111°.

Kaufmann, Dändikler, Burkhardt, *Ber.*, 1913, **46**, 2932.
Besthorn, *Ber.*, 1908, **41**, 2002.

Phenyl 4-quinolyl Ketone (4-*Benzoylquinoline*).

Needles from H_2O. M.p. 60°. B.p. 220–4°/15 mm., 155°/0·5 mm. Sol. usual org. solvents except ligroin. Spar. sol. hot H_2O.

B,HCl: plates from EtOH. Decomp. about 204°.

Oxime: amorphous. *B,HCl*: needles from MeOH. M.p. 256° decomp.

Phenylhydrazone: yellow cryst. from C_6H_6. M.p. 239–40°.

Picrate: yellow cryst. from EtOH. M.p. 214°.

Picrolonate: yellow cryst. from EtOH. Decomp. at 174°.

Methiodide: orange leaflets. M.p. 218° (not sharp).

Kaufmann, Peyer, *Ber.*, 1913, **46**, 60.
Rabe, Pasternack, *ibid.*, 1029.

Note.—Remfrey, Decker, *Ber.*, 1908, **41**, 1008, give m.p. of phenyl 4-quinolyl ketone as 294°.

Phenyl 8-quinolyl Ketone (8-*Benzoylquinoline*).

Plates from MeOH. M.p. 94°. Very sol. EtOH, Et_2O, C_6H_6. Spar. sol. ligroin.

B_2,H_2PtCl_6: yellowish cryst. M.p. 213° decomp.

Oxime: two forms. (i) Cryst. + $1H_2O$ from EtOH. M.p. 121°. (ii) cryst. + $1H_2O$ from EtOH. M.p. 165°.

Phenylhydrazone: yellowish needles from EtOH. M.p. 190°.

Semicarbazone: cryst. from EtOH.Aq. M.p. 188°.

Azine: yellowish needles from C_6H_6. M.p. 287°.

Howitz, Köpke, *Ann.*, 1913, **396**, 42.

Phenylquinolylmethane.
See Benzylquinoline.

2-Phenylquinoxaline

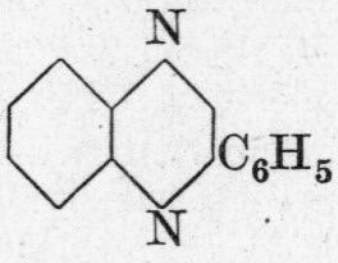

$C_{14}H_{10}N_2$ MW, 206

Needles from EtOH. M.p. 78°. Very sol. EtOH, Et_2O, $CHCl_3$, C_6H_6. Spar. sol. H_2O, pet. ether. Sol. conc. H_2SO_4 and conc. HCl with yellow col.

Hinsberg, *Ann.*, 1896, **292**, 246.
Fischer, Römer, *Ber.*, 1908, **41**, 2350.

Phenyl-S Acid.
See N-Phenyl-1-amino-8-naphthol-4-sulphonic Acid.

Phenyl salicylate.
See Salol.

Phenylsalicylic Acid.
See 3-Hydroxydiphenyl-2-carboxylic Acid *and* 2-Hydroxydiphenyl-3-carboxylic Acid.

1-Phenylsarcosine.
See α-Methylaminophenylacetic Acid.

***N*-Phenylsarcosine** (N-*Methylphenylglycine*, N-*methylanilinoacetic acid*)

$$C_6H_5\cdot\overset{CH_3}{\overset{|}{N}}\cdot CH_2\cdot COOH$$

$C_9H_{11}O_2N$ MW, 165

Cryst. from Et_2O. M.p. 95–100°. Sol. EtOH. Mod. sol. H_2O.

B,HCl: prisms from conc. HCl. M.p. 210° (204°).

Me ester: $C_{10}H_{13}O_2N$. MW, 179. B.p. 140–1°/10 mm. *Methiodide*: yellowish cryst. from H_2O. M.p. 98–9°.

Et ester: $C_{11}H_{15}O_2N$. MW, 193. B.p. 156–7°/17 mm., 148°/12 mm. *Methiodide*: cryst. from H_2O. Decomp. at 129°.

Propyl ester: $C_{12}H_{17}O_2N$. MW, 207. B.p. 175°/24 mm.

Isoamyl ester: $C_{13}H_{19}O_2N$. MW, 221. B.p. 300–2°, 179–81°/17 mm.

l-*Menthyl ester*: plates from EtOH. M.p. 83·5–84·5°. $[\alpha]_D^{20}$ — 51·4° in MeOH.

Amide: $C_9H_{12}ON_2$. MW, 164. Prisms from hot H_2O. M.p. 163°. Mod. sol. EtOH.

Nitrile: $C_9H_{10}N_2$. MW, 146. M.p. 13°. B.p. 266°, 161–3°/21 mm., 148–9°/13 mm. *Methiodide*: cryst. powder from EtOH–Et_2O. M.p. 100° decomp.

Methochloride: prisms from H_2O. M.p. 194–6° decomp.

Methopicrate: needles from EtOH. M.p. 195°.

Methochloroplatinate: prisms from EtOH. M.p. 164° decomp.

Willstätter, Kahn, *Ber.*, 1904, **37**, 416.
Gault, *Bull. soc. chim.*, 1908, **3**, 373.
Knoevenagel, *Ber.*, 1904, **37**, 4083.
Öchslin, *Ann. chim.*, 1914, **1**, 243.
Warunis, Sachs, *Ber.*, 1904, **37**, 2637.

1-Phenylsemicarbazide

$$\underset{4}{H_2N}\cdot\underset{3}{CO}\cdot\underset{2}{NH}\cdot\underset{1}{NH}\cdot C_6H_5$$

$C_7H_9ON_3$ MW, 151

Leaflets from H_2O or EtOH.Aq. M.p. 172°. Sol. MeOH, EtOH, Me_2CO, hot H_2O. Spar. sol. Et_2O, C_6H_6, ligroin, cold H_2O. Fuming HCl ⟶ CO_2, NH_3 and phenylhydrazine.

1-*Nitroso*: yellow needles from H_2O. M.p. 126–7° decomp.

4-*Me*: m.p. 154–5°.

4-*Et*: plates from EtOH.Aq. M.p. 151°. 1-*Nitroso*: yellow needles from Me_2CO. M.p. 86·5° decomp.

1-*Acetyl*: *see unsym.*-Acetylphenylsemicarbazide.

Widman, *Ber.*, 1893, **26**, 2613 (*Footnote*).
Fischer, *Ann.*, 1877, **190**, 113.
Willstätter, Stoll, *Ber.*, 1909, **42**, 4876.

2-Phenylsemicarbazide

$$H_2N\cdot CO\cdot\overset{C_6H_5}{\overset{|}{N}}\cdot NH_2$$

$C_7H_9ON_3$ MW, 151

Needles from EtOH. M.p. 120°. Sol. EtOH, warm H_2O. Very spar. sol. Et_2O, C_6H_6. Reduces warm Fehling's.

B_2,$Cu(NO_3)_2$: blue cryst. from H_2O. M.p. 155°.

Hydrochloride: m.p. 185–6°.

4-*Et*: $C_9H_{13}ON_3$. MW, 179. Plates from EtOH.Aq. M.p. 88°.

Picrate: yellow needles from EtOH. M.p. 163°.

Busch, Walter, *Ber.*, 1903, **36**, 1359.
Pellizzari, *Gazz. chim. ital.*, 1907, **37**, i, 621.

4-Phenylsemicarbazide

$$C_6H_5\cdot NH\cdot CO\cdot NH\cdot NH_2$$

$C_7H_9ON_3$ MW, 151

Plates from H_2O, needles from C_6H_6. M.p. 128°. Sol. EtOH, $CHCl_3$, dil. acids and alkalis. Spar. sol. hot H_2O. Insol. Et_2O.

B,HCl: prisms. M.p. 215°. Sol. H_2O, EtOH.

2-*Me*: $C_8H_{11}ON_3$. MW, 165. M.p. 93–4°.

1 : 1-*Di-Me*: $C_9H_{13}ON_3$. MW, 179. M.p. 108°.

Wheeler, *Organic Syntheses*, Collective Vol. I, 439.
Sah, Ma, *J. Chinese Chem. Soc.*, 1934, **2**, 32.

2-Phenylserine.
See 2-Hydroxy-1-amino-2-phenylpropionic Acid.

8-Phenylstearic Acid

$$CH_3\cdot[CH_2]_8\cdot\overset{C_6H_5}{\overset{|}{CH}}\cdot[CH_2]_7\cdot COOH$$

$C_{24}H_{40}O_2$ MW, 360

M.p. 36·5–38°. B.p. 200–4°/0·09 mm. D_{25}^{25} 0·9340. n_D^{20} 1·4891.

p-*Bromophenacyl ester*: cryst. from EtOH. M.p. 83·5–84·5°.

Harmon, Marvel, *J. Am. Chem. Soc.*, 1932, **54**, 2515.

9-Phenylstearic Acid

$$CH_3\cdot[CH_2]_7\cdot\overset{C_6H_5}{\overset{|}{C}}H\cdot[CH_2]_8\cdot COOH$$

$C_{24}H_{40}O_2$ MW, 360

M.p. 40–41·5°. B.p. 199–205°/0·09 mm. D_{25}^{25} 0·9338. n_D^{20} 1·4894.

p-*Bromophenacyl ester*: cryst. from EtOH. M.p. 71–2°.

See previous reference.

α-Phenylstilbene.

See 1 : 1 : 2-Triphenylethylene.

Phenyl styryl Ketone.

See Chalkone.

Phenylstyrylmethane.

See 1 : 3-Diphenylpropylene.

Phenylsuccinic Acid

$$\begin{array}{l} C_6H_5\cdot CH\cdot COOH\ \alpha \\ \qquad\quad | \\ \qquad\ CH_2\cdot COOH\ \beta \end{array}$$

$C_{10}H_{10}O_4$ MW, 194

d-.

Prisms from H_2O. M.p. 173–4°. Sol. MeOH, EtOH, Me_2CO. $[\alpha]_D^{16\cdot5}$ + 148·3° in EtOH, $[\alpha]_D^{15\cdot4}$ + 173·4° in Me_2CO.

Di-Me ester: $C_{12}H_{14}O_4$. MW, 222. B.p. 161–2°/16 mm. $[\alpha]_D^{15}$ + 169·8° in CCl_4, $[\alpha]_D^{12}$ + 140·9° in EtOH. Racemised by CH_3ONa in MeOH.

Di-Et ester: $C_{14}H_{18}O_4$. MW, 250. B.p. 166°/13 mm. $[\alpha]_D^{13}$ +103·4° in Me_2CO, $[\alpha]_D^{16}$ + 130·6° in CCl_4, $[\alpha]_D^{15\cdot5}$ + 100·8° in EtOH. Very rapidly racemised by CH_3ONa.

Anhydride: $C_{10}H_8O_3$. MW, 176. Needles from C_6H_6–pet. ether. M.p. 83·5–84·5°. Sol. $CHCl_3$, C_6H_6. Spar. sol. CCl_4, pet. ether. $[\alpha]_D^{15}$ + 100·9° in C_6H_6.

l-.

M.p. 173–4°. $[\alpha]_D^{14\cdot5}$ − 173·3° in Me_2CO, $[\alpha]_D^{12\cdot5}$ − 147·1° in MeOH. Not racemised by CH_3ONa.

Anhydride: m.p. 83·5–84·5°. $[\alpha]_D^{14}$ −100·9° in C_6H_6.

dl-.

Leaflets from H_2O. M.p. 168°. Very sol. EtOH, Et_2O, AcOH, Me_2CO. Sol. hot H_2O. Very spar. sol. $CHCl_3$, CS_2. Insol. C_6H_6, ligroin, pet. ether. $k = 1·64 \times 10^{-4}$ at 25°.

α-*Me ester*: $C_{11}H_{12}O_4$. MW, 208. Cryst. from H_2O. M.p. 92°. Sol. MeOH, Me_2CO, $CHCl_3$, C_6H_6. $k = 1·1 \times 10^{-4}$ at 25°. β-*Amide*: $C_{11}H_{13}O_3N$. MW, 207. Cryst. from MeOH.Aq. M.p. 119°. β-*Anilide*: needles from EtOH. M.p. 149°. β-p-*Toluidide*: m.p. 118°.

β-*Me ester*: prisms from H_2O. M.p. 102–3°. Sol. MeOH, Me_2CO, $CHCl_3$, C_6H_6. Insol. ligroin, pet. ether. $k = 0·49 \times 10^{-4}$ at 25°. α-*Amide*: cryst. from H_2O. M.p. 145°. α-*Nitrile*: $C_{11}H_{11}O_2N$. MW, 189. Prisms from C_6H_6–pet. ether. M.p. 55°. B.p. 155–9°/10 mm. α-*Anilide*: cryst. from MeOH.Aq. M.p. 96°. α-p-*Toluidide*: m.p. 118°.

Di-Me ester: prisms from pet. ether. M.p. 57·5–58·5°. B.p. 160–2°/12 mm. Sol. MeOH, Me_2CO, $CHCl_3$, C_6H_6. Insol. H_2O.

α-*Et ester*: $C_{12}H_{14}O_4$. MW, 222. Cryst. from MeOH. M.p. 88–9°. β-*Amide*: $C_{12}H_{15}O_3N$. MW, 221. Cryst. from EtOH.Aq. M.p. 148–50°.

β-*Et ester*: cryst. from MeOH. M.p. 95–6°. α-*Amide*: cryst. from EtOH. M.p. 173°. α-*Nitrile*: $C_{12}H_{13}O_2N$. MW, 203. Oil. B.p. 176°/16 mm.

Di-Et ester: liq. B.p. 160°/10 mm.

Dichloride: $C_{10}H_8O_2Cl_2$. MW, 231. Liq. B.p. 150–1°/12 mm.

α-*Amide*: $C_{10}H_{11}O_3N$. MW, 193. Plates from H_2O. M.p. 158–9°. Sol. EtOH, Me_2CO. Spar. sol. $CHCl_3$, C_6H_6.

β-*Amide*: cryst. from H_2O. M.p. 144–5°. Very spar. sol. C_6H_6.

Diamide: $C_{10}H_{12}O_2N_2$. MW, 192. M.p. 209–10°.

α-*Nitrile*: $C_{10}H_9O_2N$. MW, 175. Needles from EtOH.Aq. M.p. 150°. B.p. 215–18°/10 mm. Sol. EtOH, Et_2O. Spar. sol. H_2O.

Dinitrile: $C_{10}H_8N_2$. MW, 156. Cryst. from H_2O. M.p. 68–9°. Sol. EtOH, Me_2CO, $CHCl_3$.

Anhydride: needles from Et_2O. M.p. 54°. B.p. 204–6°/22 mm., 191–2°/12 mm.

Imide: $C_{10}H_9O_2N$. MW, 175. Prisms from AcOH.Aq. M.p. 90°. B.p. 205–10°/10 mm. Sol. EtOH, Me_2CO, $CHCl_3$, AcOH. Spar. sol. H_2O. N-*Phenyl*: needles from AcOEt. M.p. 138°. N-p-*Tolyl*: needles from C_6H_6. M.p. 139°.

α-*Anilide*: m.p. 175°.

β-*Anilide*: cryst. from MeOH. M.p. 170–1°.

Dianilide: m.p. 222°.

α-p-*Toluidide*: m.p. 175°.

β-p-*Toluidide*: m.p. 168–9°.

Dihydrazide : prisms from H_2O. M.p. 174·5°.
Dihydrochloride : m.p. 150°.

Wren, Williams, *J. Chem. Soc.*, 1916, **109**, 574.
Lapworth, Baker, *Organic Syntheses*, Collective Vol. I, 440.
Curtius *et al.*, *J. prakt. Chem.*, 1930, **125**, 68.
Ramart-Lucas, Papadakis, *Ann. chim.*, 1932, **18**, 32.

Phenylsulphamic Acid (*Aniline-ω-sulphonic acid*)

$C_6H_5{\cdot}NH{\cdot}SO_3H$

$C_6H_7O_3NS$ MW, 173

Plates from EtOH–Et_2O. Does not melt below 280°. Sol. H_2O. Decomp. by steam.
NH_4 salt : plates from EtOH.Aq. M.p. 152°. Sol. H_2O, MeOH. Spar. sol. EtOH. Insol. Et_2O, AcOEt, C_6H_6, ligroin.
Amide : $C_6H_8O_2N_2S$. MW, 172. M.p. 108·5–109°.
Dimethylamide : needles. M.p. 84–5°.
Anilide : m.p. 114°.

Traube, *Ber.*, 1890, **23**, 1654.
Paal, Kretzschmer, *Ber.*, 1894, **27**, 1244.
Bühner, *Ann.*, 1904, **333**, 288.
Battegay, Meybeck, *Compt. rend.*, 1932, **194**, 186.

Phenylsulphoneacetic Acid (*Methyl phenyl sulphone ω-carboxylic acid*)

$C_6H_5{\cdot}SO_2{\cdot}CH_2{\cdot}COOH$

$C_8H_8O_4S$ MW, 200

Needles from Et_2O. M.p. 111·5–112·5°. Sol. H_2O, EtOH, Et_2O. Mod. sol. C_6H_6. Decomp. at 160° $\longrightarrow$ CO_2 + methyl phenyl sulphone.
Et ester : $C_{10}H_{12}O_4S$. MW, 228. Prisms from EtOH. M.p. 45°. Sol. EtOH, Et_2O, C_6H_6. Insol. H_2O.
Chloride : $C_8H_7O_3ClS$. MW, 218·5. Cryst. from Et_2O. M.p. 58°.
Amide : $C_8H_9O_3NS$. MW, 199. Needles from H_2O. M.p. 156°. Sol. H_2O, EtOH. Spar. sol. Et_2O.
Nitrile : $C_8H_7O_2NS$. MW, 181. Needles. M.p. 114°. Sol. EtOH.

Troeger, Hille, *J. prakt. Chem.*, 1905, **71**, 225.
Otto, *J. prakt. Chem.*, 1884, **30**, 339.
Troeger, Vasterling, *J. prakt. Chem.*, 1905, **72**, 338.

1-Phenyltetrahydroindazole

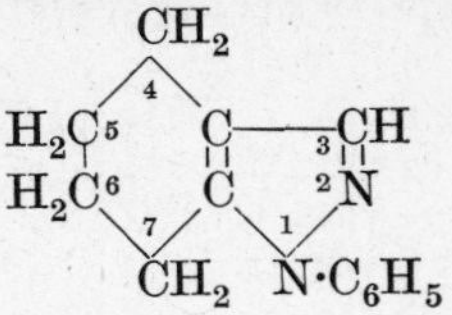

$C_{13}H_{14}N_2$ MW, 198

Plates from ligroin. M.p. 58–9°. B.p. 178°/10 mm. Sol. ord. org. solvents.
Picrate : yellow cryst. from C_6H_6. M.p. 125–6°.

Auwers, Buschmann, Heidenreich, *Ann.*, 1924, **435**, 315.

2-Phenyltetrahydroindazole

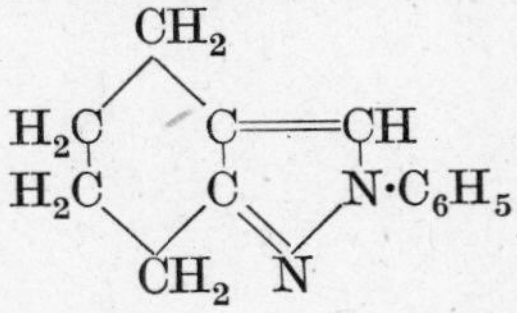

$C_{13}H_{14}N_2$ MW, 198

Prisms. M.p. 48·5–49·5°. B.p. 177°/10 mm. Sol. ord. org. solvents.
Picrate : plates from EtOH. M.p. 126·5–127·5°.

See previous reference.

***N*-Phenyl-1 : 2 : 3 : 4-tetrahydroisoquinoline**

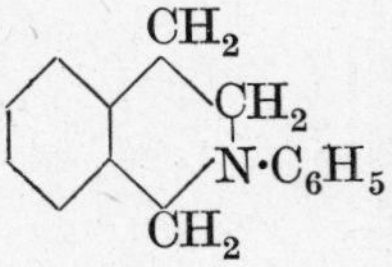

$C_{15}H_{15}N$ MW, 209

B.p. 198°/16 mm. Turns brown rapidly in air.
Picrate : yellow plates from EtOH. M.p. 120°.

v. Braun, Zobel, *Ber.*, 1923, **56**, 2152.

1-Phenyl-1 : 2 : 3 : 4-tetrahydroisoquinoline

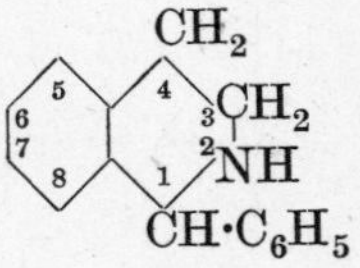

$C_{15}H_{15}N$ MW, 209

l-.
Cryst. from pet. ether. M.p. 84°. $[\alpha]_D^{20}$ — 12·4° in $CHCl_3$.
B,HCl : cryst. from EtOH–Et_2O. M.p. 204°.

dl-.

Prisms from Et_2O. M.p. 97°. Sol. $CHCl_3$, C_6H_6. Spar. sol. EtOH, Et_2O.

N-*Me* : $C_{10}H_{13}N$. MW, 147. Needles + $1H_2O$ from EtOH.Aq. M.p. 120–30°. *Methiodide* : prisms from EtOH.Aq. M.p. 240–3°.

Bitartrate : cryst. from H_2O. M.p. 187°.

Leithe, *Monatsh.*, 1929, **53** and **54**, 961.
Freund, Bode, *Ber.*, 1909, **42**, 1761.

3 - Phenyl - 1 : 2 : 3 : 4 - tetrahydroisoquinoline.

Cryst. M.p. 45–8°. Readily sol. ord. org. solvents.

Gabriel, *Ber.*, 1885, **18**, 3479.

2-Phenyl-1 : 2 : 3 : 4-tetrahydronaphthalene

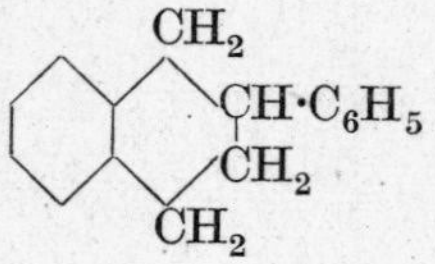

$C_{16}H_{16}$ MW, 208

B.p. 180–1°/13 mm. D_4^{18} 1·0579. n_D^{18} 1·5980.

v. Braun, Manz, *Ann.*, 1929, **468**, 267.
Späth, *Monatsh.*, 1912, **33**, 1046.

1-Phenyl-1 : 2 : 3 : 4-tetrahydronaphthalene-1 : 4-dicarboxylic Acid.

See Isatropic Acid.

2-Phenyl-1 : 4 : 5 : 6-tetrahydropyridine

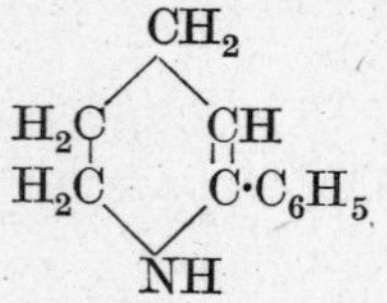

$C_{11}H_{13}N$ MW, 159

F.p. about 18°. B.p. 275–7°/751 mm.

B,HCl : cryst. from HCl. M.p. 86–7°.

B,HAuCl$_4$: cryst. M.p. 118°.

B_2,H_2PtCl_6 : orange-red plates. M.p. 210–11° decomp.

Picrate : yellow needles. M.p. 181°.

Gabriel, *Ber.*, 1908, **41**, 2012.
Cloke, Ayers, *J. Am. Chem. Soc.*, 1934, **56**, 2145.

2-Phenyl-1 : 2 : 3 : 4-tetrahydroquinoline

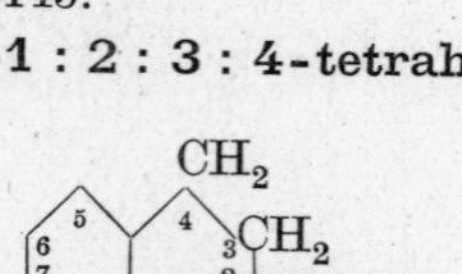

$C_{15}H_{15}N$ MW, 209

Viscous oil. B.p. 341–4°, 196–7°/12 mm. Sol. Et_2O, hot EtOH. Insol. H_2O.

N-*Me* : $C_{16}H_{17}N$. MW, 223. Needles from ligroin. M.p. 106–7°.

Doebner, Miller, *Ber.*, 1886, **19**, 1198.
Freund, *Ber.*, 1904, **37**, 4669.
v. Braun, Petzold, Seemann, *Ber.*, 1922, **55**, 3785.

3-Phenyl-1 : 2 : 3 : 4-tetrahydroquinoline.

Cryst. from EtOH. M.p. 83°.

B,HCl : needles from EtOH.Aq. M.p. 229°.

N-*Acetyl* : prisms from EtOH.Aq. M.p. 78°.

N-*Nitroso* : m.p. 147°.

Picrate : cryst. from EtOH. M.p. 181°.

Picrolonate : yellow powder from EtOH. M.p. 205°.

v. Braun, Petzold, Seemann, *Ber.*, 1922, **55**, 3790.

4-Phenyl-1 : 2 : 3 : 4-tetrahydroquinoline.

Plates from EtOH.Aq. M.p. 74°.

B,HCl,1H$_2$O : needles. M.p. 193–4°. Sublimes at 140°.

Sulphate : needles. M.p. 158°. Spar. sol. H_2O.

B_2,H_2PtCl_6 : m.p. 215° decomp.

N-*Me* : oil. *Picrate* : yellow needles from EtOH. M.p. 222–4°.

N-*Acetyl* : plates from EtOH. M.p. 120°.

N-*Benzoyl* : needles from Et_2O. M.p. 147°.

N-*Nitroso* : yellow needles from EtOH. M.p. 72°.

Picrate : yellow needles from EtOH. M.p. 183°.

Koenigs, Meimberg, *Ber.*, 1895, **28**, 1042.
Höchst, D.R.P., 79,385.

6-Phenyl-1 : 2 : 3 : 4-tetrahydroquinoline.

Amorphous solid. Sol. EtOH, Et_2O, hot H_2O. Insol. $CHCl_3$, C_6H_6.

B,HCl,1½H$_2$O : needles. M.p. 204°. Spar. sol. H_2O.

N-*Me* : amorphous powder from Et_2O. Sol. hot H_2O. Spar. sol. $CHCl_3$. Insol. CS_2, C_6H_6. *Methiodide* : prisms from EtOH. M.p. 194–5°. Insol. Et_2O. *Picrate* : yellow needles from EtOH. M.p. 147°.

N-*Acetyl* : needles from EtOH. M.p. 99–100°.

N-*Benzoyl* : needles from EtOH.Aq. M.p. 137°.

N-*Nitroso* : yellow cryst. from pet. ether. M.p. 111–12°.

Picrate: yellow needles from H_2O. M.p. 165°.

La Coste, *Ann.*, 1885, **230**, 20.

3-Phenyl-5 : 6 : 7 : 8-tetrahydroquinoline

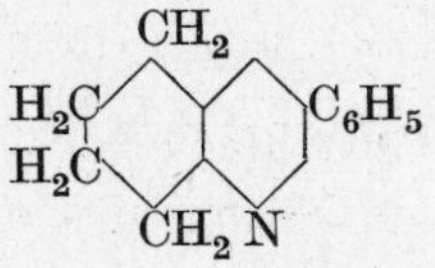

$C_{15}H_{15}N$ MW, 209

Colourless oil. B.p. 211–12°. Misc. with EtOH in all proportions.

B,HCl: m.p. 235°.

Picrolonate: yellow powder from EtOH. M.p. 201°.

Methiodide: m.p. 240–3°.

v. Braun, Petzold, Seemann, *Ber.*, 1922, **55**, 3791.

1-Phenyltetramethylene Glycol (1-*Phenyl*-1 : 4-*butandiol*, αδ-*dihydroxybutylbenzene*)

$HO{\cdot}CH_2{\cdot}CH_2{\cdot}CH_2{\cdot}CH(OH){\cdot}C_6H_5$

$C_{10}H_{14}O_2$ MW, 166

Cryst. from Et_2O. M.p. 75°. Readily sol. org. solvents.

Marshall, Perkin, *J. Chem. Soc.*, 1891, **59**, 890.

1-Phenyl-1 : 2 : 3 : 4-tetrazole

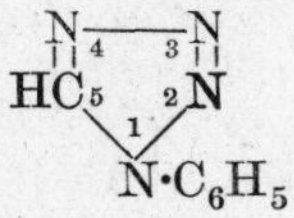

$C_7H_6N_4$ MW, 146

Cryst. from EtOH.Aq. M.p. 65–6°. Sol. EtOH, $CHCl_3$, C_6H_6. Insol. H_2O.

$AgNO_3$ add. comp.: needles. Decomp. at 126°.

$HgCl_2$ add. comp.: needles. M.p. 147°.

Stollé, Henke-Stark, *J. prakt. Chem.*, 1930, **124**, 281.
Freund, Paradies, *Ber.*, 1901, **34**, 3120.
Dimroth, de Montmollin, *Ber.*, 1910, **43**, 2907.

5-Phenyl-1 : 2 : 3 : 4-tetrazole.

Needles from EtOH. M.p. 215° decomp.

Mercuriacetate: needles from EtOH. M.p. 140° decomp.

Knoll, D.R.P., 521,870, (*Chem. Abstracts*, 1931, **25**, 3364).
Stollé, Henke-Stark, *J. prakt. Chem.*, 1930, **124**, 287.

2-Phenylthiazole

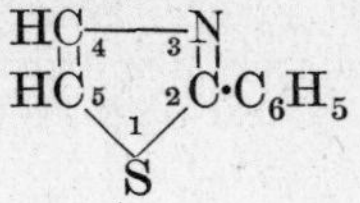

C_9H_7NS MW, 161

B.p. 267–9°/732 mm. (263–4°/772 mm.).

B,HCl: needles + $2H_2O$. M.p. 61–2°.

B_2,H_2PtCl_6: yellow micro-cryst. + $2H_2O$. M.p. 198–9° (173–5°) decomp.

Picrate: m.p. 124–5°.

Hubacher, *Ann.*, 1890, **259**, 234.
Bachstez, *Ber.*, 1914, **47**, 3164.

4-Phenylthiazole.

M.p. 52°. B.p. 273°. Sol. EtOH.

$B,HAuCl_4$: m.p. 174–5° decomp.

B_2,H_2PtCl_6: brownish-yellow needles + $2H_2O$. M.p. 196°.

Picrate: m.p. 164–5°.

Popp, *Ann.*, 1889, **250**, 279.

5-Phenylthiazole.

M.p. 45–6°.

$B,HAuCl_4$: m.p. 185°.

B_2,H_2PtCl_6: yellow micro-cryst. Decomp. at 281–2°.

$B_2,H_2Cr_2O_7$: needles from HCl. M.p. 108–9° decomp.

Picrate: yellow needles from EtOH. M.p. 138–9° decomp.

Bachstez, *Ber.*, 1914, **47**, 3164.

4-Phenylthiazolone

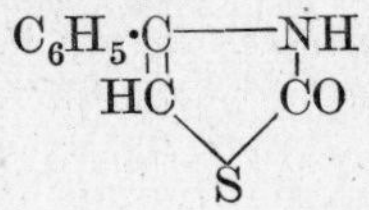

C_9H_7ONS MW, 177

M.p. 204°. Spar. sol. org. solvents. Sol. alkalis.

Hydrazone: needles from EtOH. M.p. 167–8°. N-*Acetyl*: needles from EtOH. M.p. 196–7°.

Dyckerhoff, *Ber.*, 1877, **10**, 120.
Arapides, *Ann.*, 1888, **249**, 15.
Bose, *Quart. J. Indian Chem. Soc.*, 1924, I, 60.

Phenyl 2-thienyl Ketone (2-*Benzoylthiophene*)

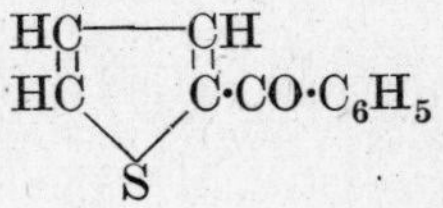

$C_{11}H_8OS$ MW, 188

Needles from pet. ether. M.p. 55–6°. B.p. 300°. Sol. EtOH, Et_2O. Insol. H_2O.

Oxime: *α-form*, needles from EtOH. M.p. 93°. *Acetyl*: m.p. 80°. *β-Form*: m.p. 113–14°. *Acetyl*: m.p. 88–9°.

Minnis, *Organic Syntheses*, 1932, XII, 62.
Steinkopf, D.R.P., 297,203, (*Chem. Zentr.*, 1917, I, 834).
Hantzsch, *Ber.*, 1891, **24**, 60.

Phenylthioacetic Acid (*Thio-α-toluic acid*)

$C_6H_5{\cdot}CH_2{\cdot}CO{\cdot}SH$ or $C_6H_5{\cdot}CH_2{\cdot}CSOH$

C_8H_8OS MW, 152

Oil. Standing in air slowly ⟶ di-phenylacetyl disulphide, m.p. 62°.

Et ester: $C_{10}H_{12}OS$. MW, 180. B.p. 170°/99 mm. D_4^{12} 1·0142.

Amide: phenylthioacetamide. C_8H_9NS. MW, 151. Cryst. from EtOH. M.p. 97·5–98°. Sol. EtOH, Et_2O. Spar. sol. hot H_2O. Dist. ⟶ benzyl cyanide.

Johnson, *J. Am. Chem. Soc.*, 1906, **28**, 1457.
Bernthsen, *Ann.*, 1877, **184**, 293.

Phenylthiocarbamic Acid (*Thiocarbanilic acid*)

$C_6H_5{\cdot}NH{\cdot}CSOH$ or $C_6H_5{\cdot}NH{\cdot}COSH$

C_7H_7ONS MW, 153

O-*Me ester*: C_8H_9ONS. MW, 167. Cryst. from EtOH. M.p. 97° (93–4°). Sol. EtOH, Et_2O, Me_2CO, $CHCl_3$, AcOH, C_6H_6. Insol. H_2O.

S-*Me ester*: leaflets from EtOH.Aq. M.p. 83–4°. Sol. EtOH, Et_2O, C_6H_6. Insol. H_2O. Sol. conc. H_2SO_4, reppd. by H_2O.

Et ester: *see* Phenylthiourethane.

O-*Propyl ester*: $C_{10}H_{13}ONS$. MW, 195. Needles from EtOH. M.p. 48°. Sol. EtOH, Et_2O, $CHCl_3$, C_6H_6.

O-*Isopropyl ester*: cryst. from EtOH. M.p. 85·5°.

O-*Butyl ester*: $C_{11}H_{15}ONS$. MW, 209. Needles from Et_2O–pet. ether. M.p. 53°.

O-*Isobutyl ester*: prisms. M.p. 80·5°.

O-*Isoamyl ester*: $C_{12}H_{17}ONS$. MW, 233. Cryst. M.p. about 21°.

S-*Isoamyl ester*: needles from Et_2O. M.p. 67°.

O-*Allyl ester*: needles from ligroin. M.p. 64·5–65·5°.

O-l-*Menthyl ester*: cryst. from EtOH.Aq. M.p. 74–5°. $[\alpha]_D^{20}$ − 63·07° in EtOH.

O-*Phenyl ester*: $C_{13}H_{11}ONS$. MW, 239. Needles from $CHCl_3$. M.p. 142°. *Ag salt*: bronze-yellow cryst. from $CHCl_3$–EtOH. M.p. 186°.

S-*Phenyl ester*: needles from EtOH. M.p. 122–122·5°.

O-*Benzyl ester*: cryst. from EtOH. M.p. 82–82·5°.

S-*Benzyl ester*: prisms from C_6H_6. M.p. 96–7°.

Amide: *see* Phenylthiourea.

Bettschart, Bistrzycki, *Helv. Chim. Acta*, 1919, **2**, 131.
Schneider, Wrede, *Ber.*, 1914, **47**, 2040.
Wheeler, Barnes, *Am. Chem. J.*, 1900, **24**, 71.
Orndorff, Richmond, *Am. Chem. J.*, 1899, **22**, 456.

Phenylthioglycollic Acid (*Phenylmercaptoacetic acid, thioanisole-ω-carboxylic acid, carboxymethyl phenyl sulphide*)

$C_6H_5{\cdot}S{\cdot}CH_2{\cdot}COOH$

$C_8H_8O_2S$ MW, 168

Needles. M.p. 61–2°. Spar. sol. cold H_2O.

Me ester: $C_9H_{10}O_2S$. MW, 182. B.p. 262–3°. D_{25}^{25} 1·1728. n_D^{25} 1·5569.

Et ester: $C_{10}H_{12}O_2S$. MW, 196. B.p. 265°, 144·5°/14 mm. D_{25}^{25} 1·1322. n_D^{25} 1·5429.

Propyl ester: $C_{11}H_{14}O_2S$. MW, 210. B.p. 270° decomp. D_{25}^{25} 1·1021. n_D^{25} 1·5348.

Butyl ester: $C_{12}H_{16}O_2S$. MW, 224. B.p. 280° decomp. D_{25}^{25} 1·0816. n_D^{25} 1·5308.

Chloride: C_8H_7OClS. MW, 186·5. B.p. 115–16°/3 mm. D_{25}^{25} 1·2581.

Amide: C_8H_9ONS. MW, 167. Needles from EtOH. M.p. 104°. Sol. EtOH. Spar. sol. H_2O, Et_2O.

Uyeda, *J. Chem. Soc. Japan*, 1931, 410.
Pummerer, *Ber.*, 1910, **43**, 1407.

Phenylthioglycollic Acid o-carboxylic Acid (S-*Carboxymethylthiosalicylic acid*, o-*carboxyphenylthioglycollic acid*)

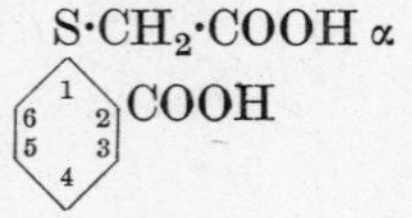

$C_9H_8O_4S$ MW, 212

Needles from AcOEt. M.p. 213°. Sol. EtOH, Me_2CO, AcOH, AcOEt. Mod. sol. hot H_2O. Spar. sol. Et_2O. Insol. C_6H_6, ligroin.

2-*Me-ester*: $C_{10}H_{10}O_4S$. MW, 226. Cryst. from hot H_2O. M.p. 151°.

α-*Me ester*: cryst. M.p. 126–127·5°.

Di-Me ester: $C_{11}H_{12}O_4S$. MW, 240. Needles from MeOH. M.p. 52°. Insol. H_2O.

2-*Et ester*: $C_{11}H_{12}O_4S$. MW, 240. M.p. 137°.

2-*Nitrile*: *o*-cyanophenylthioglycollic acid. $C_9H_7O_2NS$. MW, 193. Yellow needles from H_2O. M.p. 140°. Sol. EtOH, Et_2O. Spar. sol. cold H_2O, C_6H_6, ligroin. *Me ester*: $C_{10}H_9O_2NS$. MW, 207. Needles from MeOH. M.p. 87–8°.

Friedländer, *Ann.*, 1907, **351**, 402.
Höchst, D.R.P., 216,725, (*Chem. Zentr.*, 1910, I, 130).
Lesser, D.R.P., 229,067, (*Chem. Zentr.*, 1911, I, 104).
Wegscheider, Joachimowitz, *Monatsh.*, 1914, **35**, 1049.

Phenylthioglycollic Acid *p*-carboxylic Acid (p-*Carboxyphenylthioglycollic acid*).

Yellow cryst. M.p. 267–9° decomp. Sol. EtOH, Me_2CO, AcOH. Spar. sol. H_2O, Et_2O, $CHCl_3$, C_6H_6, ligroin.

Di-Me ester: needles from ligroin. M.p. 63–4°.

Di-Et ester: $C_{13}H_{16}O_4S$. MW, 268. Needles from ligroin. M.p. 98°.

Friedländer, Chwala, *Monatsh.*, 1907, **28**, 279.

2-Phenylthiophene

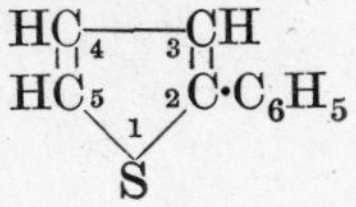

$C_{10}H_8S$ MW, 160

Needles from EtOH. M.p. 40–1°. Sol. EtOH, AcOEt. Mod. sol. Et_2O, C_6H_6, CS_2, ligroin. Volatile in steam.

Kues, Paal, *Ber.*, 1886, **19**, 3142.

3-Phenylthiophene.

Cryst. from EtOH. M.p. 91·4–92°. B.p. 254–60°/725 mm. Sol. ord. org. solvents. Volatile in steam.

Bamberger, *Ber.*, 1897, **30**, 367.
Chrzaszczewska, *Chem. Zentr.*, 1926, II, 2905.

Phenylthiosalicylic Acid.

See Diphenyl sulphide 2-carboxylic Acid.

1-Phenylthiosemicarbazide

$$\underset{4}{H_2N}\cdot\underset{3}{CS}\cdot\underset{2}{NH}\cdot\underset{1}{NH}\cdot C_6H_5$$

$C_7H_9N_3S$ MW, 167

Prisms from EtOH. M.p. 200–1° decomp. Mod. sol. hot EtOH. Spar. sol. H_2O, Et_2O, $CHCl_3$, C_6H_6.

4-N-*Me*: needles. M.p. 170° (163–4°).

4-N-*Acetyl*: prisms from EtOH. M.p. 178–9°.

4-N-*Propionyl*: prisms from EtOH. M.p. 155–6° decomp.

1-N-*Benzoyl*: cryst. from EtOH. M.p. 223°

4-N-*Benzoyl*: prisms from EtOH. Mp. 136–7°.

1 : 4-N-*Dibenzoyl*: needles. M.p. 188°.

Fromm, Trnka, *Ann.*, 1925, **442**, 154.
Fischer, Besthorn, *Ann.*, 1882, **212**, 324.
Busch, Opfermann, Walther, *Ber.*, 1904, **37**, 2332.
Dixon, *J. Chem. Soc.*, 1889, **55**, 303; 1896, **69**, 860.

2-Phenylthiosemicarbazide

$$H_2N\cdot CS\cdot \overset{C_6H_5}{N}\cdot NH_2$$

$C_7H_9N_3S$ MW, 167

Cryst. from hot H_2O. M.p. 153°. Sol. EtOH, hot H_2O. Spar. sol. C_6H_6.

4-N-*Me*: needles from EtOH.Aq. M.p. 91°. Sol. EtOH, Me_2CO, AcOH. Mod. sol. Et_2O, $CHCl_3$.

4-N-*Et*: prisms from EtOH. M.p. 121–2°.

Picrate: yellow cryst. from EtOH. M.p. 145°.

Pellizzari, *Gazz. chim. ital.*, 1907, **37**, 622.
Rolla, *Gazz. chim. ital.*, 1908, **38**, 345.
Dixon, *J. Chem. Soc.*, 1889, **55**, 302.

4-Phenylthiosemicarbazide

$$C_6H_5\cdot NH\cdot CS\cdot NH\cdot NH_2$$

$C_7H_9N_3S$ MW, 167

Plates from EtOH. M.p. 140° decomp. Spar. sol. C_6H_6. Insol. ligroin.

2-N-*Me*: plates from EtOH. M.p. 143°.

1 : 2-N-*Di-Me*: prisms from EtOH. M.p. 115°.

2-N-*Et*: needles. M.p. 109–10°.

1 : 2-N-*Dibenzoyl*: yellow cryst. from EtOH. M.p. 195°.

1 : 1 : 2 : 4-N-*Tetrabenzoyl*: yellowish-green cryst. from EtOH. M.p. 148°.

Fromm, Trnka, *Ann.*, 1925, **442**, 154.
Busch, *Ber.*, 1909, **42**, 4600.
Freund, Hempel, *Ber.*, 1895, **28**, 77.
Knorr, Köhler, *Ber.*, 1906, **39**, 3264.

Phenylthiourea

$$\underset{3}{H_2N}\cdot\underset{2}{CS}\cdot\underset{1}{NH}\cdot C_6H_5$$

$C_7H_8N_2S$ MW, 152

Needles from hot H_2O. M.p. 154°. Sol. EtOH.

3-N-*Me*: $C_8H_{10}N_2S$. MW, 166. Needles. M.p. 113°. Sol. EtOH.

3-N-*Di-Me*: $C_9H_{12}N_2S$. MW, 180. Prisms from EtOH. M.p. 134–5°.

3-N-*Et*: $C_9H_{12}N_2S$. MW, 180. Cryst. from EtOH or C_6H_6. M.p. 99–99·5°.

3-N-*Di-Et*: $C_{11}H_{16}N_2S$. MW, 208. Yellow oil. B.p. 182°/15 mm.

1-N-*Acetyl*: prisms from EtOH.Aq. M.p. 139° decomp.

3-N-*Acetyl*: m.p. 173° (171°). Cryst. from dil. EtOH. Mod. sol. EtOH, Et_2O. Prac. insol. H_2O. Sol. dil. alkalis.

3-N-*Propionyl*: prisms from EtOH. M.p. 129–30°.

1-N-*Benzoyl*: cryst. from EtOH. M.p. about 140°.

3-N-*Benzoyl*: needles. M.p. 148–9°.

1-N-*Phenylacetyl*: prisms from EtOH. M.p. 113–14°.

Salkowski, *Ber.*, 1891, **24**, 2728.
Gebhardt, *Ber.*, 1884, **17**, 3038.
Streiger, *Monatsh.*, 1916, **37**, 649.
Schiff, *Ann.*, 1868, **148**, 338.
Hugershoff, *Ber.*, 1899, **32**, 3659.

Phenylthiourethane

$C_6H_5·NH·CS·OC_2H_5$ (i)
$C_6H_5·NH·CO·SC_2H_5$ (ii)

$C_9H_{11}ONS$ MW, 181

(i) "Xanthogenanilide." Cryst. from EtOH. M.p. 71–2°. Insol. H_2O, EtOH, Et_2O. Sol. alkalis. Heat with EtI ⟶ S-ether.

(ii) Needles from EtOH. M.p. 73°. Sol. EtOH. Insol. H_2O.

Will, *Ber.*, 1882, **15**, 341.
Hofmann, *Ber.*, 1870, **3**, 774.
Jacobson, Klein, *Ber.*, 1893, **26**, 2364.
Biilmann, *Ann.*, 1906, **348**, 141.

Phenyltoluene.
See Methyldiphenyl.

6-Phenyl-*m*-toluic Acid.
See 2-Methyldiphenyl-4-carboxylic Acid.

***N*-Phenyltoluidine.**
See Methyldiphenylamine.

Phenyl-tolyl.
See Methyldiphenyl.

Phenyltolylamine.
See Methyldiphenylamine.

Phenyltolylcarbinol.
See Methylbenzhydrol.

Phenyl *p*-tolyl Diketone.
See 4-Methylbenzil.

4-*N*-Phenyl-1 : 3 : 4-tolylenediamine.
See 2-Amino-4-methyldiphenylamine.

1-Phenyl-1-*p*-tolylethane (α-*Methylphenyl*-p-*tolylmethane*)

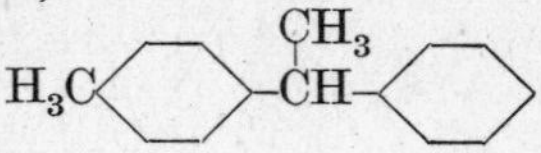

$C_{15}H_{16}$ MW, 196

Oil. B.p. 280–2°, 154–155·8°/14 mm. $D_4^{17·2}$ 0·9847. $n_D^{17·2}$ 1·56590.

Auwers, *Ber.*, 1916, **49**, 2401.
Kraemer, Spilker, *Ber.*, 1891, **24**, 2788.

1-Phenyl-2-*p*-tolylethane.
See 4-Methyldibenzyl.

Phenyl tolyl Ether.
See under Cresol.

1-Phenyl-2-tolylethylene.
See Methylstilbene.

Phenyl-*o*-tolylguanidine

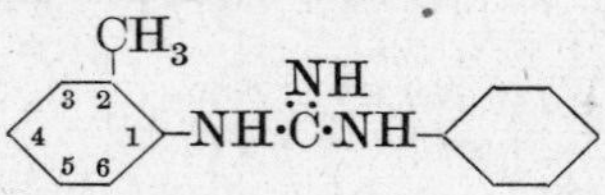

$C_{14}H_{15}N_3$ MW, 225

Needles from AcOH. M.p. 123–5°. Sol. EtOH, $CHCl_3$, C_6H_6. Mod. sol. H_2O.

Heller, Bauer, *J. prakt. Chem.*, 1902, **65**, 384.
Heuser, U.S.P., 1,669,242, (*Chem. Abstracts*, 1928, **22**, 2172).

Phenyl-*p*-tolylguanidine.

Needles from ligroin. M.p. 120–2°. Sol. EtOH, C_6H_6. Mod. sol. H_2O.

Heller, Bauer, *J. prakt. Chem.*, 1902, **65**, 385.

***sym.*-Phenyltolylhydrazine.**
See Methylhydrazobenzene.

Phenyl *o*-tolyl Ketone (2-*Methylbenzophenone*)

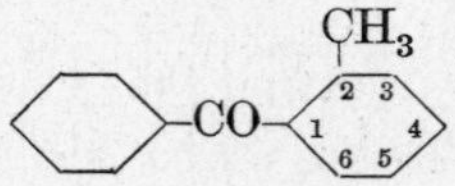

$C_{14}H_{12}O$ MW, 196

B.p. 309·5°/762 mm., 168°/12 mm.

Oxime: phenyl-*syn*-form. M.p. 105°. Phenyl-*anti*-form: m.p. 69°.

Ketimide: oil. B.p. 136–7°/4 mm. $D_4^{18·5}$ 1·0614. $n_D^{18·5}$ 1·6065.

Smith, *Ber.*, 1891, **24**, 4047.
Goldschmidt, Stöcker, *Ber.*, 1891, **24**, 2805.

Phenyl *m*-tolyl Ketone (3-*Methylbenzophenone*).

Oil. B.p. 311–13°/723 mm. $D^{17·5}$ 1·088. Misc. with EtOH, Et_2O, $CHCl_3$, AcOH, C_6H_6.

Oxime: cryst. from EtOH. M.p. 100–1°.

Ador, Rilliet, *Ber.*, 1879, **12**, 2300.
Goldschmidt, Stöcker, *Ber.*, 1891, **24**, 2807.

Phenyl p-tolyl Ketone (4-*Methylbenzophenone*).

Dimorphous. Stable form, m.p. 59–60°. Metastable form, m.p. 55°. B.p. 311–12°/720 mm. Sol. Et_2O, C_6H_6. Mod. sol. EtOH.

Oxime: two forms. (i) Needles from EtOH.Aq. M.p. 153–4°. O-*Me ether*: needles from EtOH.Aq. M.p. 70·5–72°. N-*Me*: plates from ligroin. M.p. 91–2°. N-*Acetyl*: prisms. M.p. 124–5°. (ii) Needles from EtOH. M.p. 136–137·5°. O-*Me ether*: oil. B.p. 184–5°/16 mm. N-*Me*: prisms from ligroin. M.p. 113–14°.

Semicarbazone: cryst. from EtOH. M.p. 121–2°.

Hydrazone: cryst. from EtOH. M.p. 80–1°.

2 : 4-*Dinitrophenylhydrazone*: m.p. 199–200°.

Ketimide: m.p. 37°. B.p. 147°/5 mm. D_4^{20} 1·0617. n_D^{20} 1·6097.

Staudinger, Goldstein, *Ber.*, 1916, **49**, 1926.
Marshall, *J. Chem. Soc.*, 1915, **107**, 516.
Meyer, *Monatsh.*, 1907, **28**, 1223.
Semper, Lichtenstadt, *Ber.*, 1918, **51**, 936.
Bruzau, *Ann. chim.*, 1934, **1**, 352.

Phenyl-m-tolylmethane (m-*Benzyltoluene*, 3-*methyldiphenylmethane*)

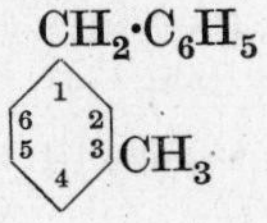

$C_{14}H_{14}$ MW, 182

B.p. 275°/747 mm., 268–269·5°/725 mm. $D^{17·5}$ 0·997.

Ador, Rilliet, *Ber.*, 1879, **12**, 2300.

Phenyl-p-tolylmethane (p-*Benzyltoluene*, 4-*methyldiphenylmethane*).

B.p. 279–80°, 145·5–155·7°/13·5 mm. D^{18} 0·994. $n_a^{14·7}$ 1·56922. Sol. EtOH, Et_2O, $CHCl_3$, AcOH.

Weiler, *Ber.*, 1900, **33**, 464.
Hirst, Cohen, *J. Chem. Soc.*, 1895, **67**, 828.
v. Meyer, *J. prakt. Chem.*, 1910, **82**, 539.

Phenyl o-tolyl sulphide (2-*Methyldiphenyl sulphide*)

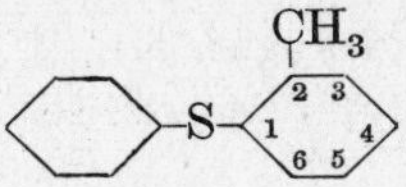

$C_{13}H_{12}S$ MW, 200

Oil. B.p. 304·5°/724 mm., 222·5°/100 mm. D_4^0 1·1131, D_4^{30} 1·0893.

Bourgeois, *Ber.*, 1895, **28**, 2322.
Ziegler, *Ber.*, 1890, **23**, 2471.

Phenyl m-tolyl sulphide (3-*Methyldiphenyl sulphide*).

Oil. F.p. − 6·5°. B.p. 309·5°, 164·5°/11 mm. D_4^0 1·1058, D_4^{15} 1·0937.

Bourgeois, *Ber.*, 1895, **28**, 2323.

Phenyl p-tolyl sulphide (4-*Methyldiphenyl sulphide*).

Oil. F.p. 15·7°. B.p. 311·5°, 167·5°/11 mm. $D^{15·7}$ 1·0900.

See previous reference and also
Ziegler, *Ber.*, 1890, **23**, 2471.

Phenyl o-tolyl sulphone (2-*Methyldiphenyl sulphone*)

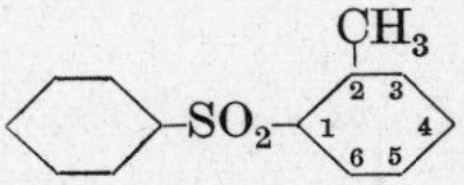

$C_{13}H_{12}O_2S$ MW, 232

Plates from EtOH. M.p. 80–1°. Sol. EtOH, Et_2O, C_6H_6. Spar. sol. ligroin. Insol. H_2O.

Ullmann, Lehner, *Ber.*, 1905, **38**, 734.

Phenyl m-tolyl sulphone (3-*Methyldiphenyl sulphone*).

Needles. M.p. 109°.

Courtot, Frenkiel, *Compt. rend.*, 1934, **199**, 558.

Phenyl p-tolyl sulphone (4-*Methyldiphenyl sulphone*).

Plates from EtOH. M.p. 124·5°. Spar. sol. C_6H_6, AcOH.

Michael, Adair, *Ber.*, 1878, **11**, 116.
Olivier, *Rec. trav. chim.*, 1914, **33**, 249.

Phenyl o-tolyl sulphoxide

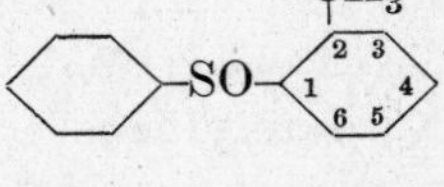

$C_{13}H_{12}OS$ MW, 216

Prisms. M.p. 42°. B.p. 220°/11 mm.

Courtot, Frenkiel, *Compt. rend.*, 1934, **199**, 558.

Phenyl *m*-tolyl sulphoxide.
B.p. 215°/12 mm.

See previous reference.

Phenyl *p*-tolyl sulphoxide.
M.p. 73°.

See previous reference.

***N*-Phenyl-*N'*-*o*-tolylthiourea** (o-*Methylthiocarbanilide*)

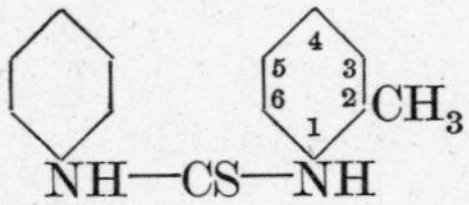

$C_{14}H_{14}N_2S$ MW, 242

Needles. M.p. 141–2°. Sol. EtOH, Et_2O. Spar. sol. H_2O. Phenylhydrazine ⟶ 1-phenyl-4-*o*-tolylthiosemicarbazide.

Walther, Stenz, *J. prakt. Chem.*, 1906, **74**, [2], 226.
Naunton, *J. Soc. Chem. Ind.*, 1926, **45**, 377T.

***N*-Phenyl-*N'*-*m*-tolylthiourea** (m-*Methylthiocarbanilide*).

Prisms from EtOH. M.p. 91–2°. Very sol. Et_2O, $CHCl_3$, C_6H_6, CS_2. $AgNO_3$ in EtOH ⟶ phenyl-*m*-tolylurea.

Dixon, *J. Chem. Soc.*, 1895, **67**, 557.

***N*-Phenyl-*N'*-*p*-tolylthiourea** (p-*Methylthiocarbanilide*).

M.p. 142°. Very sol. EtOH. Sol. Et_2O. Spar. sol. H_2O. Hydrazine ⟶ 4-*p*-tolylthiosemicarbazide. Phenylhydrazine ⟶ 1-phenyl-4-*p*-tolylthiosemicarbazide.

Gebhardt, *Ber.*, 1884, **17**, 3035.

***N*-Phenyl-*N'*-*o*-tolylurea** (o-*Methylcarbanilide*)

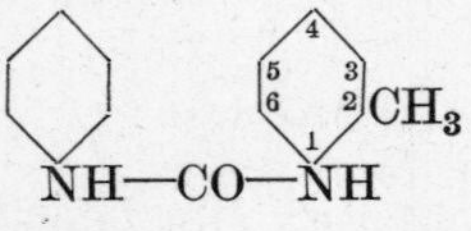

$C_{14}H_{14}ON_2$ MW, 226

Needles from EtOH. M.p. 212° (196°).

Sonn, *Ber.*, 1914, **47**, 2442.

***N*-Phenyl-*N'*-*m*-tolylurea** (m-*Methylcarbanilide*).

Needles from EtOH. M.p. 173–4°.

Buchka, Schachtebeck, *Ber.*, 1889, **22**, 840.

***N*-Phenyl-*N'*-*p*-tolylurea** (p-*Methylcarbanilide*).

Needles from EtOH. M.p. 226°. Spar. sol. cold EtOH.

Mayer, *Bull. soc. chim.*, 1916, **19**, 430.

1-Phenyl-1 : 2 : 3-triazole

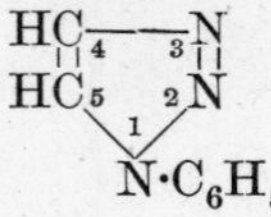

$C_8H_7N_3$ MW, 145

Plates from warm H_2O. M.p. 56°. B.p. 172–4°/18·5 mm.

Bertho, *Ber.*, 1925, **58**, 862.
Dimroth, Fester, *Ber.*, 1910, **43**, 2222.

1-Phenyl-1 : 2 : 4-triazole

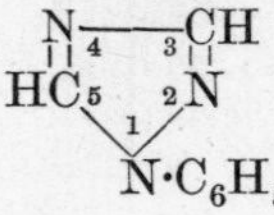

$C_8H_7N_3$ MW, 145

Needles. M.p. 47°. B.p. 266°. Sol. EtOH.

B,HNO₃ : needles. M.p. 141°. Spar. sol. cold H_2O.

B_2,H_2PtCl_6 : yellow needles + $3H_2O$ from HCl. Also orange-red prisms + $2H_2O$. Boiling H_2O ⟶ $B_2,PtCl_4$, yellow powder. Insol. H_2O, HCl.

Picrate : cryst. from H_2O. M.p. 159°.

Pellizzari, *Gazz. chim. ital.*, 1911, **41**, ii, 20.
Widman, *Ber.*, 1893, **26**, 2615.

3-Phenyl-1 : 2 : 4-triazole.

Needles. M.p. 119·5–120°.

B,HCl : needles. M.p. 195°.

Acetyl : m.p. 90°.

B_2,H_2PtCl_6 : yellow plates + $2H_2O$ from dil. HCl. Decomp. at 255°.

See first reference above and also
Young, Oates, *J. Chem. Soc.*, 1901, **79**, 665.

1-Phenyl-1 : 2 : 5-triazole

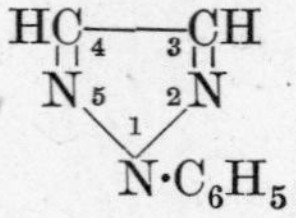

$C_8H_7N_3$ MW, 145

B.p. 223–4°/716 mm. Spar. sol. H_2O. Misc. with EtOH.

Jonas, Pechmann, *Ann.*, 1891, **262**, 290.

3-Phenyl-1 : 2 : 5-triazole.

Scales from EtOH.Aq. or C_6H_6. M.p. 143–5°. Exhibits acidic and basic properties.

B,HCl : cryst. powder. M.p. 140°. Insol. cold H_2O.

Oliveri-Mandalà, Coppola, *Chem. Zentr.*, 1910, II, 225.

1-Phenyl-1 : 3 : 4-triazole

$$\underset{N\cdot C_6H_5}{\underset{|}{HC_5 \quad \underset{2}{}CH}}\quad \overset{N\overset{4}{=\!=\!=}\overset{3}{=\!=\!=}N}{}$$

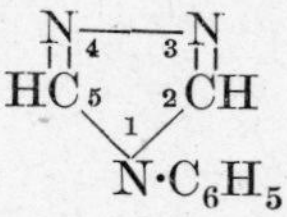

$C_8H_7N_3$ MW, 145

Prisms from H_2O, needles from C_6H_6. M.p. 122°. Sol. H_2O, EtOH. Spar. sol. Et_2O. Decomp. on dist. $KMnO_4 \longrightarrow 1 : 3 : 4$-triazole. $CuSO_4 \longrightarrow$ light blue ppt. $AgNO_3$ and $HgCl_2$ $\longrightarrow$ white ppts.
B_2, H_2PtCl_6 : needles from HCl.
Picrate : needles from EtOH. M.p. 172°.

Heller, Köhler, Gottfried, Arnold, Herrmann, *J. prakt. Chem.*, 1928, **120**, 62.
Pellizzari, Massa, *Atti accad. Lincei*, 1901, **10**, I, 366.

5-Phenyl-1 : 3 : 4-triazole.
Pale yellow plates from EtOH.Aq. M.p. 177°.

De, Roy-Choudhury, *J. Indian Chem. Soc.*, 1928, **5**, 275.

1-Phenyltricarballylic Acid

$$\begin{array}{l} C_6H_5\cdot CH\cdot COOH \\ CH\cdot COOH \\ CH_2\cdot COOH \end{array}$$

$C_{12}H_{12}O_6$ MW, 252

Two forms.
(i) Needles from Me_2CO or C_6H_6, scales from H_2O. M.p. 199° decomp. Very sol. hot H_2O, Me_2CO. Spar. sol. $CHCl_3$, boiling C_6H_6, CS_2.
(ii) Prisms $+ 1H_2O$ from warm H_2O. M.p. 110° (in closed capillary, m.p. 110–15°, then solidifies and remelts at 196–201°).

Wegscheider, *Ber.*, 1911, **44**, 908.
Stobbe, Fischer, *Ann.*, 1901, **315**, 231.
Hecht, *Monatsh.*, 1903, **24**, 370.

1-Phenyltrimethylene Glycol (1-*Phenylpropandiol*-1 : 3, *αγ-dihydroxypropylbenzene*)

$HO\cdot CH_2\cdot CH_2\cdot CH(OH)\cdot C_6H_5$

$C_9H_{12}O_2$ MW, 152

Colourless odourless oil. B.p. 175°/11 mm. 165°/10 mm.).
Dibenzoyl : needles from ligroin. M.p. 51°.
Di-p-nitrobenzoyl : m.p. 110–110·5°.

Di-Me ether : $C_{11}H_{16}O_2$. MW, 180. B.p. 215–17° part. decomp., 94–5°/15 mm., 89–91°/12 mm. D_4^{19} 0·983.

Rupe, Müller, *Helv. Chim. Acta*, 1921, **4**, 844.
St. Pfau, Plattner, *Helv. Chim Acta*, 1932, **15**, 1265.
Straus, Berkow, *Ann.*, 1913, **401**, 155.

2-Phenyltrimethylene Glycol (2-*Phenylpropandiol*-1 : 3, *ββ'-dihydroxyisopropylbenzene*)

$\underset{HO\cdot CH_2\cdot CH\cdot CH_2OH}{\overset{C_6H_5}{}}$

$C_9H_{12}O_2$ MW, 152

Viscous oil. B.p. 176°/13 mm. D_4^{19} 1·1161. n_D^{19} 1·54267.
Diacetyl : b.p. 162–4°/13 mm.
Methylene ether : b.p. 128–30°/13 mm. D_4^{18} 1·1111. n_D^{18} 1·53063.

Prins, *Chem. Abstracts*, 1920, **14**, 1119, 1662.

1-Phenyluracil

$$\begin{array}{l} C_6H_5\cdot N\overset{1}{\rule{1.2em}{0.4pt}}\overset{6}{\rule{1.2em}{0.4pt}}CO \\ OC_2 \qquad {}_5CH \\ HN\underset{3}{\rule{1.2em}{0.4pt}}\underset{4}{\rule{1.2em}{0.4pt}}CH \end{array}$$

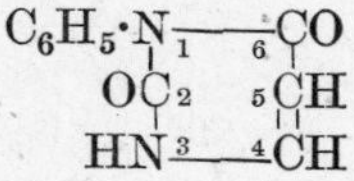

$C_{10}H_8O_2N_2$ MW, 188

Cryst. from H_2O. M.p. 247°. Spar. sol. H_2O, MeOH, EtOH, Py. Insol. Et_2O, AcOEt, Me_2CO, $CHCl_3$, ligroin, C_6H_6.

Buerger, Johnson, *J. Am. Chem. Soc.*, 1934, **56**, 2755.

4-Phenyluracil.
Microscopic needles and prisms from EtOH or AcOH.Aq. M.p. 269–70° decomp. Sol. 100 parts H_2O at 100°, 35 parts EtOH at 78°. Sol. AcOH, KOH. Spar. sol. Et_2O. Stable to HCl, $NH_2\cdot NH_2$, CH_3I.
K salt : cryst. from H_2O. Decomp. above 300°.
1-*Me* : plates from EtOH. M.p. 228–30°. Sol. boiling EtOH, boiling $CHCl_3$.
1 : 3-*Di-Me* : plates from EtOH. M.p. 122–122·5°. Sol. boiling EtOH, $CHCl_3$.

Evans, Johnson, *J. Am. Chem. Soc.*, 1930, **52**, 4999.
Johnson, Hemingway, *J. Am. Chem. Soc.*, 1915, **37**, 379.
Warmington, *J. prakt. Chem.*, 1893, **47**, 203.

5-Phenyluracil.

Microscopic plates from H_2O or EtOH. Does not melt below 350°. Sol. alkalis. Spar. sol. hot H_2O, hot EtOH.

Wheeler, Bristol, *Am. Chem. J.*, 1904, **33**, 448.

1-Phenylurazole

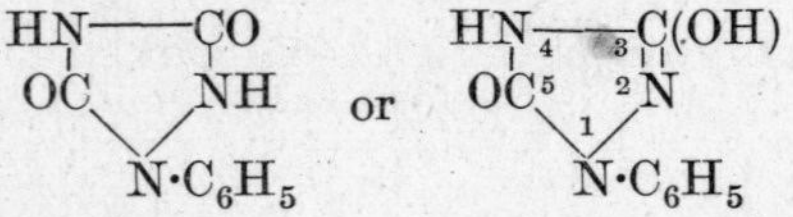

$C_8H_7O_2N_3$ MW, 177

Plates from H_2O. M.p. 263–4°. Sol. hot H_2O, alkalis. Spar. sol. H_2O, EtOH, Et_2O, $CHCl_3$. Behaves as monobasic acid. Reddens litmus. CO_2 liberated from carbonates. Stable to boiling alk. sols. $FeCl_3 \longrightarrow$ violet col. *O*-acyl and *O*-alkyl comps. with HCl $\longrightarrow$ *N*-comps. $PCl_5 \longrightarrow$ 1-phenyl-3 : 5-dichlorotriazole.

Ag salt: m.p. 252° decomp. Very sol. NH_4OH. Insol. dil. HNO_3.

Ba salt: plates + $2H_2O$. Decomp. at 280–300°.

2-*Me*: $C_9H_9O_2N_3$. MW, 191. Needles. M.p. 183°. Very sol. EtOH, Et_2O, alkalis. Spar. sol. H_2O. Stable to H_2SO_4 at 100°. *Ag salt*: m.p. 250° decomp. Insol. dil. HNO_3. Very sol. NH_4OH.

4-*Me*: m.p. 225°. Sol. $CHCl_3$. 2-*Acetyl*: needles from EtOH. M.p. 94–5°. 2-*Benzoyl*: cryst. M.p. 185° Very sol. EtOH, Et_2O. Insol. H_2O. 3-*Me ether*: needles from alk. EtOH.Aq. M.p. 95°. 3-*Et ether*: cryst. from alk. EtOH.Aq. M.p. 95°.

2 : 4-*Di-Me*: $C_{10}H_{11}O_2N_3$. MW, 205. Prisms or plates from EtOH.Aq., or ligroin. M.p. 95°. Very sol. hot H_2O, EtOH, C_6H_6. Mod. sol. Et_2O. NaOH $\longrightarrow$ 1-phenyl-2 : 4-dimethylsemicarbazide and 1-phenyl-2-methylurazole.

2-*Et*: $C_{10}H_{11}O_2N_3$. MW, 205. M.p. 119°. Very sol. hot H_2O, hot EtOH, Et_2O, $CHCl_3$. Spar. sol. cold H_2O, cold EtOH. *Ag salt*: m.p. 239° decomp.

2-*Me*-4-*Et*: $C_{11}H_{13}O_2N_3$. MW, 219. Cryst. from alk. EtOH.Aq. M.p. 113°.

3-*Me ether*: $C_9H_9O_2N_3$. MW, 191. Plates. M.p. 197°. Gives mono K salt. HCl $\longrightarrow$ phenylurazole.

3(5)-*Et ether*: $C_{10}H_{11}O_2N_3$. MW, 205. Two forms. May be 3- and 5-Et ethers. (i) M.p. 141°. Very sol. EtOH, Et_2O, C_6H_6. Insol. H_2O, alkalis. Spar. sol. ligroin. EtOH–HCl $\longrightarrow$ phenylurazole. (ii) Needles from EtOH. M.p. 152°. Sol. hot H_2O, alkalis. Behaves a monobasic acid.

3 : 5-*Di-Et ether*: $C_{12}H_{15}O_2N_3$. MW, 233 Needles from EtOH.Aq. M.p. 53°. Sol. EtOH Et_2O, C_6H_6. Spar. sol. H_2O. HCl $\longrightarrow$ phenyl urazole.

2-*Acetyl*: needles from H_2O, plates from C_6H_6 M.p. 175°.

2 : 4-*Diacetyl*: needles from C_6H_6. M.p. 169° Insol. H_2O. EtOH $\longrightarrow$ 2-acetyl.

2 : 4-*Dibenzoyl*: m.p. 178–80°.

Murray, Dains, *J. Am. Chem. Soc.*, 1934 **56**, 144.

Dains, Wertheim, *J. Am. Chem. Soc.* 1920, **42**, 2308.

Brunel, Acree, *Am. Chem. J.*, 1912, **43** 505.

Acree, *Am. Chem. J.*, 1907, **38**, 1; *Ber.* 1903, **36**, 3139; *Ber.*, 1902, **35**, 557.

4-Phenylurazole.

Prisms from H_2O. M.p. 203°. Sol. EtOH Spar. sol. Et_2O. Oxidising agents $\longrightarrow$ deep re col.

N-*Me*: cryst. M.p. 188°. Very sol. hot H_2O EtOH. Strongly acidic.

Thiele, Stange, *Ann.*, 1894, **283**, 45.

Phenylurea

$$C_6H_5\cdot \underset{1}{NH}\cdot \underset{2}{CO}\cdot \underset{3}{NH_2}$$

$C_7H_8ON_2$ MW, 13

Needles or plates from H_2O, tablets fron EtOH. M.p. 147°. Sol. hot H_2O, EtOH. Spar sol. cold H_2O, Et_2O. Heat of comb. C_p 88 Cal. Heat $\longrightarrow$ *N* : *N'*-diphenylurea. H_2SO $\longrightarrow$ sulphanilic and sulphocarbanilic acids $NaNO_2 \longrightarrow$ *N*-nitroso-*N*-phenylurea. Hydr azine $\longrightarrow$ 4-phenylsemicarbazide. NaOEt $\longrightarrow$ mono-Na deriv.

B,HCl: plates. M.p. 114–16° decomp. De comp. by H_2O.

B,HNO$_3$: plates. M.p. 134–5° decomp Decomp. by H_2O.

B$_2$,*HAuCl*$_4$: red needles. M.p. 147°. De comp. by H_2O.

B$_3$,*H*$_2$*PtCl*$_6$: orange cryst. M.p. 173–5 decomp.

1-N-*Acetyl*: needles from hot H_2O. M.p. 167°

2-N-*Acetyl*: *see sym.*-Acetylphenylurea.

2-N-*Benzoyl*: needles from EtOH. M.p. 210° (202°). Spar. sol. cold EtOH, Et_2O Insol. H_2O.

1-N-*Nitroso*: $C_6H_5N(NO)\cdot CO\cdot NH_2$. $C_7H_7O_2N_3$ MW, 165. Yellow needles from Et_2O–pet ether. M.p. 95° decomp. Sol. EtOH. Spar. sol. Et_2O, C_6H_6.

Palit, *J. Indian Chem. Soc.*, 1934, **11**, 479.
Mauguin, *Ann. chim. phys.*, 1911, **22**, 346.
Pickard, Kenyon, *J. Chem. Soc.*, 1907, **91**, 902.
Schiff, *Ann.*, 1907, **352**, 83.
Stieglitz, Earle, *Am. Chem. J.*, 1903, **30**, 418.
Hoffmann, *Ann.*, 1849, **70**, 130.
Doht, Haager, *Monatsh.*, 1903, **24**, 853.

Phenylurethane (*Phenylcarbamic ethyl ester, carbanilic acid ethyl ester*)

$C_6H_5{\cdot}NH{\cdot}CO{\cdot}OC_2H_5$

$C_9H_{11}O_2N$ MW, 165

Needles from H_2O, plates from EtOH.Aq. M.p. 53°. B.p. 237° (slight decomp.), 152°/14 mm. Very sol. EtOH, Et_2O. Insol. cold H_2O. Heat of comb. C_p 1128·3 Cal. EtOH sol. with $AgNO_3$ + drop of NaOH ⟶ deep red to black col. NH_3 ⟶ aniline + urea. P_2O_5 ⟶ phenyl isocyanate. $R{\cdot}NH_2$ ⟶ $C_6H_5{\cdot}NH{\cdot}CO{\cdot}NH{\cdot}R$.

K deriv.: needles. Decomp. by H_2O.

N-*Acetyl*: cryst. from ligroin. M.p. 59°. B.p. 142°/10 mm.

N-*Benzoyl*: m.p. 160–1°.

N-*Nitroso*: $C_9H_{10}O_3N_2$. MW, 194. Pale yellow needles from pet. ether. M.p. 61–2°. Sol. EtOH, Et_2O, AcOH.

Binaghi, *Gazz. chim. ital.*, 1932, **62**, 469.
Nekrassow, Melnikow, *J. prakt. Chem.*, 1930, **126**, 92.
Weizmann, Garrard, *J. Chem. Soc.*, 1920, **117**, 328.
Nijk, *Rec. trav. chim.*, 1920, **39**, 700.

3-Phenyluric Acid

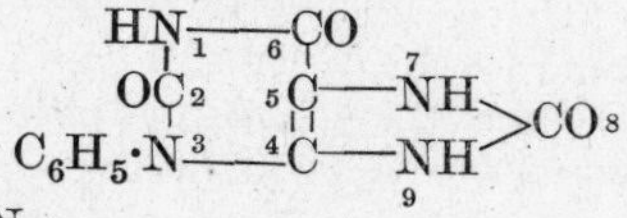

$C_{11}H_8O_3N_4$ MW, 244

Cryst. + $1H_2O$ from EtOH.Aq. or AcOH.Aq. Decomp. at 270–300°. Sol. hot EtOH, AcOH. Spar. sol. cold H_2O.

1-*Me*: $C_{12}H_{10}O_3N_4$. MW, 258. Yellowish needles from AcOH. Does not melt below 340°.

1 : 7 : 9-*Tri-Me*: $C_{14}H_{14}O_3N_4$. MW, 286. Cryst. from H_2O. M.p. 229°.

Hepner, Frenkenberg, *Helv. Chim. Acta*, 1932, **15**, 536.

9-Phenyluric Acid.

Plates + $2H_2O$ from H_2O. Sol. 120 parts H_2O at 100°. Anhyd. at 130°. Decomp. at 320°. Spar. sol. EtOH. Sol. warm H_2SO_4. Reduces $NH_3.AgNO_3$. Gives murexide reaction.

Fischer, *Ber.*, 1900, **33**, 1704.

Phenyl-ψ-uric Acid

$C_{11}H_{10}O_4N_4$ MW, 262

Aggregates of microscopic needles from H_2O. Contains H_2O of cryst. Contains $\frac{1}{2}H_2O$ at 120°, chars above this temp. Sol. 350 parts H_2O. Reduces $NH_3.AgNO_3$. Gives murexide reaction. HCl ⟶ 9-phenylurea. Na, K and NH_4 salts spar. sol. cold H_2O.

Fischer, *Ber.*, 1900, **33**, 1703.

1-Phenylvaleraldehyde (*α-Phenyl*-n-*valeraldehyde*)

$CH_3{\cdot}CH_2{\cdot}CH_2{\cdot}CH(C_6H_5){\cdot}CHO$

$C_{11}H_{14}O$ MW, 162

Oil. B.p. 122–3°/28 mm.

Semicarbazone: m.p. 115–16°.

Darzens, *Compt. rend.*, 1904, **139**, 1216.

4-Phenylvaleraldehyde

$C_6H_5{\cdot}CH_2{\cdot}CH_2{\cdot}CH_2{\cdot}CH_2{\cdot}CHO$

$C_{11}H_{14}O$ MW, 162

Oil with lemon odour. B.p. 129–31°/10 mm.

p-*Nitrophenylhydrazone*: pale yellow cryst. powder from EtOH.Aq. M.p. 82–4°.

Di-Me acetal: $C_{13}H_{20}O_2$. MW, 208. B.p. 136–9°/11 mm.

v. Braun, Kruber, *Ber.*, 1912, **45**, 399.

1-Phenylvaleric Acid (*α-Phenyl*-n-*valeric acid, 1-phenylbutane-1-carboxylic acid, propylphenylacetic acid*)

$CH_3{\cdot}CH_2{\cdot}CH_2{\cdot}CH(C_6H_5){\cdot}COOH$

$C_{11}H_{14}O_2$ MW, 178

d-.

Viscous oil. B.p. 165°/14 mm. D_4^{20} 1·047. $[\alpha]_D$ + 72·10°, $[\alpha]_D$ + 58·81° in $CHCl_3$, $[\alpha]_D$ + 33·1° in Et_2O.

l-.

$[\alpha]_D$ − 14·1° in Et_2O.

dl-.

Needles from ligroin. M.p. 52°. B.p. 280°. Resolved into active components with *l*-menthylamine.

Amide: $C_{11}H_{15}ON$. MW, 177. Cryst. from EtOH.Aq. M.p. 83–5°. Sol. org. solvents. Spar. sol. H_2O.

Nitrile: $C_{11}H_{13}N$. MW, 159. B.p. 254–5°/750 mm., 125–8°/13 mm. D^{15} 0·960. Immiscible with H_2O. Misc. with EtOH, C_6H_6. Volatile in steam.

Levene, Marker, *J. Biol. Chem.*, 1930, **88**, 53.
Bayer, D.R.P., 249,241, (*Chem. Zentr.*, 1912, II, 396).
Pickard, Yates, *J. Chem. Soc.*, 1909, **95**, 1017.

2-Phenylvaleric Acid (β-*Phenyl*-n-*valeric acid*, β-*ethylhydrocinnamic acid*, 2-*phenylbutane*-1-*carboxylic acid*)

$$CH_3{\cdot}CH_2{\cdot}\overset{C_6H_5}{\overset{|}{C}}H{\cdot}CH_2{\cdot}COOH$$

$C_{11}H_{14}O_2$ MW, 178

d-.

B.p. 142°/5 mm. $[\alpha]_D^{25}$ + 2·86° in C_6H_6.

l-.

B.p. 140°/4 mm. $[\alpha]_D^{25}$ — 16·5° in C_6H_6.

Et ester: $C_{13}H_{18}O_2$. MW, 206. B.p. 110°/2 mm. $[\alpha]_D^{25}$ — 7·41°.

dl-.

Cryst. from Et_2O. M.p. 66°. Very sol. EtOH, Et_2O.

Me-anilide: b.p. 206°/12 mm.

Et-anilide: b.p. 214°/15 mm.

Maxim, Ioanid, *Chem. Zentr.*, 1928, II, 755.
Levene, Marker, *J. Biol. Chem.*, 1935, **110**, 333; 1932, **97**, 388; 1931, **93**, 763.

3-Phenylvaleric Acid (γ-*Phenyl*-n-*valeric acid*, 3-*phenylbutane*-1-*carboxylic acid*)

$$CH_3{\cdot}\overset{C_6H_5}{\overset{|}{C}}H{\cdot}CH_2{\cdot}CH_2{\cdot}COOH$$

$C_{11}H_{14}O_2$ MW, 178

l-.

B.p. 137°/1 mm. $[\alpha]_D^{20}$ — 1·06°.

Et ester: $C_{13}H_{18}O_2$. MW, 206. B.p. 112°/1 mm. $[\alpha]_D^{25}$ — 1·23°.

dl-.

Cryst. M.p. 13°. B.p. 210°/85 mm., 170°/10 mm., 147°/1 mm. D_1^{15} 1·0554.

Chloride: $C_{11}H_{13}OCl$. MW, 196·5. B.p. 118–19°/13 mm.

Nitrile: $C_{11}H_{13}N$. MW, 159. B.p. 125–6°/13 mm.

Levene, Marker, *J. Biol. Chem.*, 1935, **110**, 338.
Braun, Stuckenschmidt, *Ber.*, 1923, **56**, 1727.
Mayer, Stamm, *ibid.*, 1431.
Eijkmann, *Chem. Zentr.*, 1904, I, 1416.

4-Phenylvaleric Acid (δ-*Phenyl*-n-*valeric acid*, 4-*phenylbutane*-1-*carboxylic acid*)

$$C_6H_5{\cdot}CH_2{\cdot}CH_2{\cdot}CH_2{\cdot}CH_2{\cdot}COOH$$

$C_{11}H_{14}O_2$ MW, 178

Plates from hot H_2O, prisms from pet. ether. M.p. 57° (61°). Sol. ord. org. solvents. Spar. sol. hot H_2O.

Me ester: $C_{12}H_{16}O_2$. MW, 192. B.p. 173°/35 mm.

Et ester: $C_{13}H_{18}O_2$. MW, 206. B.p. 150°/11 mm.

Amide: $C_{11}H_{15}ON$. MW, 177. M.p. 109°.

Nitrile: $C_{11}H_{13}N$. MW, 159. B.p. 157–61°/17 mm.

Anilide: plates from MeOH. M.p. 89–90°.

Staudinger, Müller, *Ber.*, 1923, **56**, 713.
Rupe, *Ann.*, 1909, **369**, 343.
v. Braun, Deutsch, *Ber.*, 1912, **45**, 2178.

4-Phenyl-γ-valerolactone.

See under 3-Hydroxy-4-phenyl-*n*-valeric Acid.

N-Phenylvaline.

See 1-Anilinoisovaleric Acid.

3-Phenylvinylacetic Acid.

See Styrylacetic Acid.

Phenylvinylacrylic Acid.

See Styrylacrylic Acid.

1-Phenylvinyl Alcohol (α-*Hydroxystyrene*)

$$CH_2{:}C(OH){\cdot}C_6H_5$$

C_8H_8O MW, 120

Me ether: $C_9H_{10}O$. MW, 134. Oil with aromatic odour. B.p. 197°. D_0^{21} 1·003. n_D^{25} 1·5400. Dil. H_2SO_4 ⟶ acetophenone. Semicarbazide acetate ⟶ semicarbazone of acetophenone.

Et ether: $C_{10}H_{12}O$. MW, 148. Oil. B.p. 209–10°, 88–9°/11 mm. D_4^{20} 0·9709. $n_D^{17\cdot5}$ 1·5304. Alc. HCl ⟶ acetophenone.

Isoamyl ether: $C_{13}H_{18}O$. MW, 190. B.p. 255–9°. D^0 0·943.

Phenyl ether: $C_{14}H_{12}O$. MW, 196. B.p. 151°/14 mm. D_{17}^{17} 1·10729.

Auwers, *Ber.*, 1911, **44**, 3520.
Moureu, *Compt. rend.*, 1903, **137**, 261.
Tiffeneau, *Compt. rend.*, 1907, **145**, 813.

2-Phenylvinyl Alcohol (β-*Hydroxystyrene*)

$C_6H_5 \cdot CH{:}CH \cdot OH$

C_8H_8O MW, 120

Me ether: oil. B.p. 210–13°, 99°/13 mm. $D_4^{23\cdot3}$ 0·9894. $n_D^{24\cdot3}$ 1·5620. Dil. H_2SO_4 ⟶ phenylacetaldehyde.

Et ether: oil with aromatic odour. B.p. 223–6°, 105°/14 mm. $D_4^{21\cdot4}$ 0·9714. $n_D^{21\cdot2}$ 1·5502. Forms unstable add. comp. with Br. Boiling H_2O ⟶ phenylacetaldehyde.

Propyl ether: $C_{11}H_{14}O$. MW, 162. B.p. 238–41°. $D_0^{15\cdot5}$ 0·966. $n_D^{15\cdot5}$ 1·542.

Isobutyl ether: $C_{12}H_{16}O$. MW, 176. B.p. 248–51°. D_0^{16} 0·946. n_D^{16} 1·5342.

Phenyl ether: b.p. 180°/16 mm., 157–8°/7 mm. Na + EtOH ⟶ ethylbenzene. HI ⟶ 2-phenylnaphthalene. Forms unstable bromine add. comp. Acid hyd. ⟶ phenylacetaldehyde.

Acetyl: two stereoisomeric forms. *Cis*: b.p. 68°/0 mm. D^{20} 1·073. n_D^{20} 1·5553. *Trans*: b.p. 68°/0 mm. D^{20} 1·065. n_D^{20} 1·5518. Red. ⟶ 2-phenylethyl alcohol. Catalytic red. ⟶ 2-phenylethyl acetate. Hyd. ⟶ phenylacetaldehyde.

Böeseken, Kremer, *Rec. trav. chim.*, 1931, **50**, 830.
Späth, *Monatsh.*, 1915, **36**, 6.
Auwers, Eisenlohr, *J. prakt. Chem.*, 1910, **82**, 100.
Stoermer, Biesenbach, *Ber.*, 1905, **38**, 1961.
Moureu, *Compt. rend.*, 1903, **137**, 288.

5-Phenylxanthene

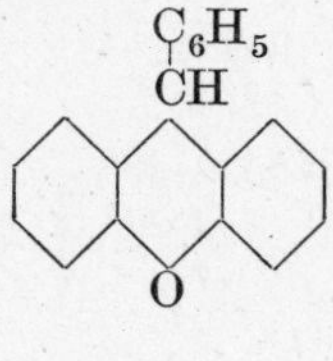

$C_{19}H_{14}O$ MW, 258

Cryst. from boiling EtOH. M.p. 145°. Sol. C_6H_6. Spar. sol. EtOH, AcOH, ligroin. Insol. cold H_2SO_4.

Ruszig, *Z. angew. Chem.*, 1919, **32**, 39.
Baeyer, *Ann.*, 1907, **354**, 170.

Phenyl xenyl Ketone.
See Phenylbenzophenone.

Phenyl-xylene.
See Dimethyldiphenyl.

Phenyl *p*-xylyl Ketone.
See 4-Methyldeoxybenzoin.

Phloracetophenone (2 : 4 : 6-*Trihydroxyacetophenone, acetophloroglucinol*)

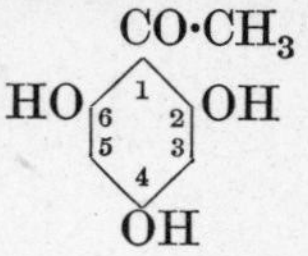

$C_8H_8O_4$ MW, 168

Needles from H_2O. M.p. anhyd. 219°. Sol. EtOH, Et_2O, Me_2CO, AcOH. Spar. sol. $CHCl_3$, hot C_6H_6.

2-*Me ether*: $C_9H_{10}O_4$. MW, 182. M.p. 205–7°.

4-*Me ether*: m.p. 136–7° (139–40°).

2 : 4-*Di-Me ether*: $C_{10}H_{12}O_4$. MW, 196. Constituent of fruit of *Xanthoxylum alatum*, Roxb., and volatile oil of *X. aubertia*, DC. Cryst. from EtOH. M.p. 85–8°. Sol. EtOH, Et_2O, alkalis. Insol. H_2O. *Oxime*: m.p. 108–10°. *Acetyl*: prisms from EtOH. M.p. 107°.

2 : 6-*Di-Me ether*: $C_{10}H_{12}O_4$. MW, 196. Prisms from AcOEt. M.p. 185·5°. 4-*Benzoyl*: m.p. 119°.

Tri-Me ether: $C_{11}H_{14}O_4$. MW, 210. Prisms. M.p. 103° (100°).

2-*Me*-4-*Et ether*: $C_{11}H_{14}O_4$. MW, 210. M.p. 56–7°.

4-*Me*-2-*Et ether*: m.p. 133–4°.

2 : 4-*Di-Me*-6-*Et ether*: $C_{12}H_{16}O_4$. MW, 224. M.p. 69–70°.

2 : 6-*Di-Me*-4-*Et ether*: m.p. 81–2°.

2 : 4-*Di-Et ether*: $C_{12}H_{16}O_4$. MW, 224. Needles from EtOH.Aq. M.p. 85°.

Tri-Et ether: $C_{14}H_{20}O_4$. MW, 252. Plates from EtOH.Aq. M.p. 75°.

Triacetyl: m.p. 103°.

2-*Benzoyl*: m.p. 168°.

4-*Benzoyl*: m.p. 210–11°.

Tribenzoyl: m.p. 117–18°.

Gulati, Seth, Venkataraman, *J. Chem. Soc.*, 1934, 1765; *Organic Syntheses*, 1935, XV, 70.
Tseng, *Chem. Zentr.*, 1935, II, 2826.
Sonn, *Ber.*, 1928, **61**, 2300.
Shinoda, Sato, *Chem. Abstracts*, 1928, **22**, 2947.
Howells, Little, *J. Am. Chem. Soc.*, 1932, **54**, 2452.
Kostanecki, Tambor, *Ber.*, 1899, **32**, 2262.

Phloramine.
See 5-Aminoresorcinol.

Phloraspin

$C_{23}H_{28}O_8$ MW, 432

Constituent of *Filix mas* extract. Needles from Me_2CO.Aq. M.p. 211°. Mod. sol. $CHCl_3$,

Me_2CO, AcOEt, AcOH, hot EtOH, hot xylene. Spar. sol. Et_2O, C_6H_6, pet. ether, ligroin. $FeCl_3 \longrightarrow$ reddish-brown col. in EtOH. Sol. alkalis or conc. $H_2SO_4 \longrightarrow$ butyric acid. Possibly identical with flavaspidin, *q.v.*

Boehm, *Ann.*, 1903, **329**, 338.

Phlorbenzophenone (2 : 4 : 6-*Trihydroxybenzophenone*)

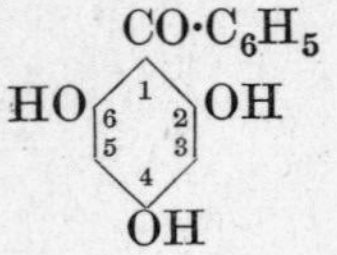

$C_{13}H_{10}O_4$ MW, 230

Yellow needles + $1H_2O$ from H_2O. M.p. 165°. NaOH $\longrightarrow$ red col. $FeCl_3 \longrightarrow$ brownish-red col. Reduces $NH_3.AgNO_3$ and Fehling's. Sol. EtOH, Et_2O, AcOEt. Spar. sol. $CHCl_3$, C_6H_6, ligroin.

2-*Me ether*: *see* Isocotoin.

4-*Me ether*: *see* Cotoin.

2 : 4-*Di-Me ether*: $C_{15}H_{14}O_4$. MW, 258. 6-*Acetyl*: prisms from EtOH. M.p. 83°.

2 : 6-*Di-Me ether*: plates from EtOH.Aq. M.p. 178–9°. 4-*Benzoyl*: prisms from EtOH. M.p. 172°.

4-*Me*-2 : 6-*Di-Et ether*: $C_{18}H_{20}O_4$. MW, 300. M.p. 82–3°.

2 : 4-*Di-Me*-6-*Et ether*: $C_{17}H_{18}O_4$. MW, 286. M.p. 103–4°.

4-*Benzoyl*: needles from C_6H_6. M.p. 186°.

2 : 4 : 6-*Tribenzoyl*: prisms from MeOH. M.p. 125–6° (172°).

Canter, Curd, Robertson, *J. Chem. Soc.*, 1931, 1254.
Hoesch, *Ber.*, 1915, **48**, 1131.
Klarmann, Figdor, *J. Am. Chem. Soc.*, 1926, **48**, 804.

Phlorbutyrophenone (2 : 4 : 6-*Trihydroxybutyrophenone*)

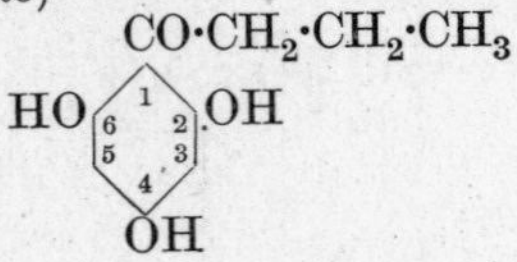

$C_{10}H_{12}O_4$ MW, 196

Cryst. + $1H_2O$. M.p. 183° anhyd. (181°).

(?) 2-*Me ether*: $C_{11}H_{14}O_4$. MW, 210. Needles. M.p. 130°.

(?) 4-*Me ether*: leaflets. M.p. 113°.

2 : 4-*Di-Me ether*: $C_{12}H_{16}O_4$. MW, 224. Prisms from EtOH.Aq. M.p. 70°.

2 : 6-*Di-Me ether*: prisms from AcOEt. M.p. 107°. 4-*Benzoyl*: m.p. 86°.

4-*Benzoyl*: m.p. 164°.

Canter, Curd, Robertson, *J. Chem. Soc.*, 1931, 1252.

Phloretic Acid (*Phloretinic acid*, p-*hydrocoumaric acid, 4-hydroxyhydrocinnamic acid*)

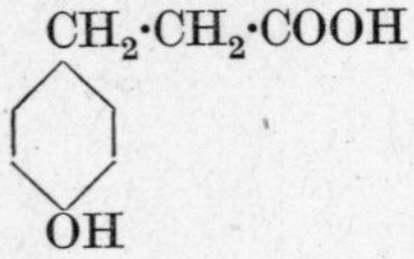

$C_9H_{10}O_3$ MW, 166

Occurs in human urine. Prisms from Et_2O. M.p. 129–30°. Sol. EtOH, Et_2O, hot H_2O. Insol. CS_2. $k = 1{\cdot}73 \times 10^{-5}$ at 25° ($2{\cdot}03 \times 10^{-5}$). No col. with $FeCl_3$.

Me ester: $C_{10}H_{12}O_3$. MW, 180. Cryst. from Et_2O–pet. ether. M.p. 40–1°. B.p. 186–7°/17 mm.

Et ester: $C_{11}H_{14}O_3$. MW, 194. M.p. 45°. B.p. 193°/18 mm.

Amide: $C_9H_{11}O_2N$. MW, 165. Prisms. M.p. 127–8° (125°). *Acetyl deriv.*: m.p.133–4°.

Nitrile: C_9H_9ON. MW, 147. Prisms. M.p. 58–9°.

Me ether: *see* p-Methoxyhydrocinnamic Acid.

Et ether: p-ethoxyhydrocinnamic acid. $C_{11}H_{14}O_3$. MW, 194. Cryst. from H_2O. M.p. 106·5° (104°).

Carbomethoxyl: m.p. 86–7° (83–4°).

Stöhr, *Ann.*, 1884, **225**, 59.
Bayer, D.R.P., 233,551, (*Chem. Zentr.*, 1911, I, 1334).
Fischer, Nouri, *Chem. Abstracts*, 1917, II, 1649.
Zemplén, Csūrōs, Gerecs, Aczél, *Ber.*, 1928, **61**, 2492.

Phloretin (*Dihydronarigenin, asebogenol*, ω-p-*hydroxyphenylpropiophenone*)

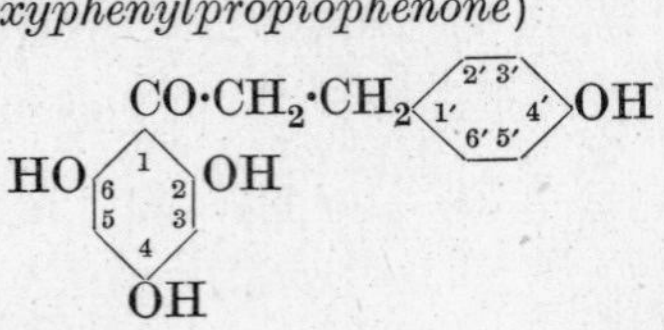

$C_{15}H_{14}O_5$ MW, 274

Needles from EtOH.Aq. M.p. 262–4° (274°) decomp. (varies with rate of heating). Sol. hot Me_2CO. Spar. sol. $CHCl_3$. Insol. Et_2O.

Triacetyl deriv.: m.p. 188–9°.

Tetra-acetyl: m.p. 165° (96°).

2 : 4 : 4′-*Tri-Me ether*: $C_{18}H_{20}O_5$. MW, 316. M.p. 109–10°. *Acetyl deriv.*: m.p. 62–3°.

2 : 6 : 4′-*Tri-Me ether*: m.p. 142°.

β-*Glucoside*: *see* Phloridzin.

Bridel, Kramer, *Compt. rend.*, 1931, **193**, 748.
Müller, Robertson, *J. Chem. Soc.*, 1933, 1171.
Rosenmund, Rosenmund, *Ber.*, 1928, **61**, 2612.
Shinoda, Sato, Kawagoe, *Chem. Abstracts*, 1930, **24**, 604.
See also last two references above.

Phlorhizin.
See Phloridzin.

Phlorhizoside.
See Phloridzin.

Phloridzin (*Phlorrhizin, phlorizin, phlorhizin, 2-phloretin-*β*-glucoside, phlorhizoside, asebotoside, asebotin.* See formula under Phloretin above)

$C_{21}H_{24}O_{10}$ MW, 436

Occurs in *Micromelum teprocarpum*, Turcz. Needles. M.p. 108°. Solidifies at 138° and remelts at 170° (about 150°).

Tri-Me ether: $C_{24}H_{30}O_{10}$. MW, 478. M.p. 75–6°. *Tetra-acetyl deriv.*: m.p. 94–5°.

Bridel, Kramer, *Compt. rend.*, 1931, **193**, 748.
Zemplén, Csūrōs, Gerecs, Aczél, *Ber.*, 1928, **61**, 2486.
Müller, Robertson, *J. Chem. Soc.*, 1933, 1170.

Phlorin (*Phloroglucinol-*β*-glucoside*)

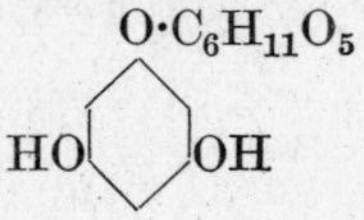

$C_{12}H_{16}O_8$ MW, 288

Cryst. M.p. 231–3°. Sol. H_2O, EtOH, MeOH. Spar. sol. Me_2CO. Insol. Et_2O, AcOEt, amyl alcohol. $[\alpha]_D^{22}$ — 74·58°.

Cremer, Seuffert, *Ber.*, 1912, **45**, 2565.

Phlorisobutyrophenone (2 : 4 : 6-*Trihydroxyisobutyrophenone*)

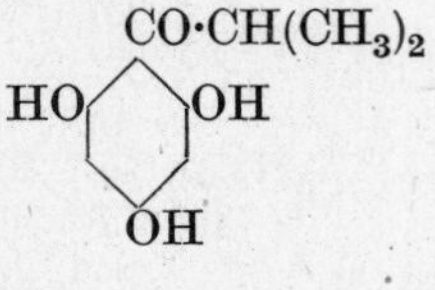

$C_{10}H_{12}O_4$ MW, 196

Needles + $1H_2O$ from hot H_2O. M.p. 68°, anhyd. 138–40°.

Karrer, Rosenfeld, *Helv. Chim. Acta*, 1921, **4**, 711.

Phlorizin.
See Phloridzin.

Phlorobromin.
See Octabromoacetylacetone.

Phloroglucide (*Phloroglucidol*)

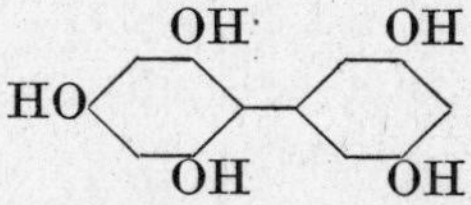

Probable structure

$C_{12}H_{10}O_5$ MW, 234

Leaflets + $2H_2O$ from H_2O. Does not melt. Spar. sol. EtOH, hot H_2O. Insol. Et_2O.

Penta-acetyl: m.p. 105–7°.
Mono-Me ether: $C_{13}H_{12}O_5$. MW, 248. Cryst. from H_2O. M.p. 222–5°. *Tetra-acetyl deriv.*: m.p. 102–5°.
Penta-Me ether: $C_{17}H_{20}O_5$. MW, 304. Cryst. from EtOH. M.p. 117–20°.
Mono-Et ether: $C_{14}H_{16}O_5$. MW, 262. Cryst. from H_2O. M.p. 165–8°.

Herzig, Kohn, *Monatsh.*, 1908, **29**, 677.
Wichelhaus, *Ber.*, 1919, **52**, 2054.
Cross, Bevan, *J. Chem. Soc.*, 1911, **99**, 1456.

Phloroglucidol.
See Phloroglucide.

Phloroglucinaldehyde.
See 2 : 4 : 6-Trihydroxybenzaldehyde.

Phloroglucinol (1 : 3 : 5-*Trihydroxybenzene*)

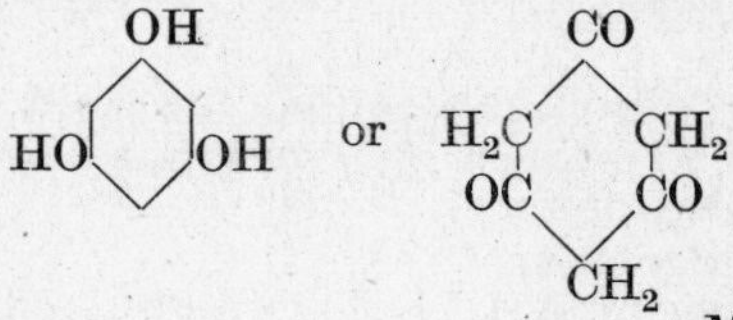

$C_6H_6O_3$ MW, 126

Leaflets or plates + $2H_2O$ from H_2O. M.p. 117°, 217–19° anhyd., rapid heat.; 200–9° slow heat. Sol. EtOH, Et_2O, Py. Mod. sol. H_2O. Heat of comb. C_v 617·65 Cal. $k = 4{\cdot}5 \times 10^{-10}$ at 25°. $FeCl_3$ in EtOH ⟶ bluish-violet col. Sol. in H_2O + drop NH_3.Aq. ⟶ violet-red col.

$C_6H_6O_3,1NH_3$: m.p. 88–91°.
$2C_6H_6O_3,(C_2H_5)_3N$: m.p. 103–4°.
Triacetyl: m.p. 104°.
Tribenzoyl: m.p. 185°.
Mono-p-hydroxybenzoyl deriv.: m.p. 218°.
Trioxime: blackens at 140°. Explodes at 155°.
Picrate: m.p. 101–3°.

Mono-Me ether: $C_7H_8O_3$. MW, 140. M.p. 78° (78–81°, 77–80°). B.p. 213°/16 mm., 188–9°/12 mm.
Di-Me ether: $C_8H_{10}O_3$. MW, 154. Cryst. from C_6H_6–ligroin. M.p. 36–8°. B.p. 172–5°/17 mm.
Tri-Me ether: $C_9H_{12}O_3$. MW, 168. Prisms from EtOH. M.p. 52·5° (54–5°). B.p. 255·5°. Sol. EtOH, Et_2O, C_6H_6.
Mono-Et ether: $C_8H_{10}O_3$. MW, 154. Leaflets + $2H_2O$ from H_2O. M.p. 84–6°. B.p. 220°/15 mm. (220–1°/30 mm.).
Di-Et ether: $C_{10}H_{14}O_3$. MW, 182. Needles from H_2O. M.p. 88–9°. B.p. 188–9°/20 mm. Volatile in steam. *Me ether*: $C_{11}H_{16}O_3$. MW, 196. B.p. 147–8°/13 mm.
Tri-Et ether: $C_{12}H_{18}O_3$. MW, 210. Cryst. M.p. 43°. B.p. 175°/24 mm. Sol. EtOH, Et_2O. Volatile in steam.
Triphenyl ether: $C_{24}H_{18}O_3$. MW, 354. Prisms from Et_2O. M.p. 112°. B.p. 290–3°/20 mm. Sol. Et_2O, C_6H_6, $CHCl_3$. Spar. sol. EtOH, AcOH, ligroin.
Dibenzyl ether: $C_{20}H_{18}O_3$. MW, 306. M.p. 62–4°. Sol. ord. org. solvents.
Tribenzyl ether: $C_{27}H_{24}O_3$. MW, 396. M.p. 39–41°. Sol. ord. org. solvents.
Glucoside: *see* Phlorin.

Herzig, Aigner, *Monatsh.*, 1900, **21**, 444.
Clarke, Hartman, *Organic Syntheses*, 1929, IX, 74.
Goris, Canal, *Compt. rend.*, 1935, **201**, 1435.

Phloroglucinol-dicarboxylic Acid.
See 2 : 4 : 6-Trihydroxyisophthalic Acid.
Phloroglucite.
See Phloroglucitol.
Phloroglucitol (*Phloroglucite, hexahydrophloroglucinol,* 1 : 3 : 5-*trihydroxycyclohexane, cyclohexantriol*-1 : 3 : 5)

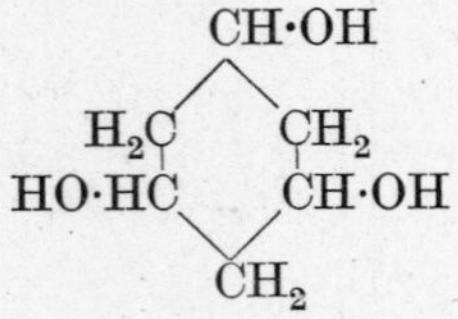

$C_6H_{12}O_3$ MW, 132

(α) Cryst. + $2H_2O$ from H_2O. M.p. about 110° decomp. ⟶ solid remelting at 184°. Spar. sol. C_6H_6, Me_2CO.
Triacetyl: m.p. 79°.
Tri-phenylurethane: m.p. 245°.
(β) Cryst. from EtOH. M.p. 145°. Sol. H_2O. Spar. sol. C_6H_6, Me_2CO.
Tri-phenylurethane: m.p. 160°.

Lindemann, Baumann, *Ann.*, 1930, **477**, 78.

Phlorol.
o-Ethylphenol, *q.v.*
Phlorone.
See p-Xylo-*p*-quinone.
Phlorpropiophenone (2 : 4 : 6-*Trihydroxypropiophenone*)

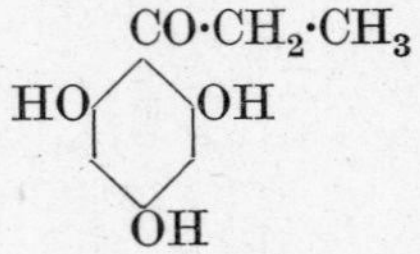

$C_9H_{10}O_4$ MW, 182

Needles + $1H_2O$ from H_2O. M.p. 174–5°. Sol. EtOH, warm H_2O. Alc. $FeCl_3$ ⟶ purple col.
2 : 4-*Di-Me ether*: $C_{11}H_{14}O_4$. MW, 210. Plates from EtOH. M.p. 111°. $FeCl_3$ ⟶ wine-red col.
2 : 6-*Di-Me ether*: prisms from AcOEt. M.p. 180°. No col. with $FeCl_3$. *Acetyl*: plates from EtOH.Aq. M.p. 76°. *Benzoyl*: needles from MeOH. M.p. 103°.
2-*Benzoyl*: prisms from MeOH. M.p. 191–2°. Alc. $FeCl_3$ ⟶ wine-red col.
4-*Benzoyl*: needles from MeOH. M.p. 193°. Alc. $FeCl_3$ ⟶ reddish-brown col.

Canter, Curd, Robertson, *J. Chem. Soc.*, 1931, 1245.
Howells, Little, *J. Am. Chem. Soc.*, 1932, **54**, 2452.

Phlorrhizin.
See Phloridzin.
Phonopyrrole.
Hæmopyrrole, *q.v.*
Phorone (2 : 6-*Dimethyl*-2 : 5-*heptadienone*-4, *di-isopropylideneacetone*)

$$(CH_3)_2C{:}CH{\cdot}CO{\cdot}CH{:}C(CH_3)_2$$
I

$$(CH_3)_2C{:}C{:}C(OH){\cdot}CH{:}C(CH_3)_2$$
II

$C_9H_{14}O$ MW, 138

I.
Yellowish-green prisms. M.p. 28°. B.p. 197·2°/743·3 mm. D_4^{20} 0·8850. n_D^{20} 1·49982.
Oxime: m.p. 48°. B.p. 218°.

II.
(a) B.p. 79·8°/14 mm. $D_4^{18·1}$ 0·8854. $n_D^{18·1}$ 1·48847. (b) B.p. 81·8–82°/14 mm. D_4^{18} 0·8893. n_D^{18} 1·4932.

Auwers, Eisenlohr, *J. prakt. Chem.*, 1911, **84**, 76.
Francis, *J. Chem. Soc.*, 1927, 2898.
I.G., D.R.P., 483,823, (*Chem. Abstracts*, 1930, **24**, 2146).
Sugden, *J. Chem. Soc.*, 1928, 412.
Pereira, *Chem. Abstracts*, 1910, **4**, 2275.
Claisen, *Ann.*, 1876, **180**, 4.

Phoronic Acid (3-*Keto*-1 : 1 : 5 : 5-*tetramethylpimelic acid*)

$(CH_3)_2C·COOH$
CH_2
CO
CH_2
$(CH_3)_2C·COOH$

$C_{11}H_{18}O_5$ MW, 230

Prisms from EtOH.Aq. M.p. 184° decomp. Sol. EtOH. Spar. sol. hot H_2O.
Me ester: $C_{12}H_{20}O_5$. MW, 244. Prisms from MeOH. M.p. 105–6°.
Di-Me ester: $C_{13}H_{22}O_5$. MW, 258. Prisms from pet. ether. M.p. 32°.
Di-Et ester: $C_{15}H_{26}O_5$. MW, 286. M.p. 33° (125°).
Di-lactone (*anhydride*): $C_{11}H_{16}O_4$. MW, 212. M.p. 138° (132°).

Toivonen, *Chem. Zentr.*, 1928, II, 39.
Milikan, *Rec. trav. chim.*, 1912, **31**, 287.

Phosgene.
See Carbonyl chloride.
Phosphaniline.
See Phenylphosphine.
Phosphinobenzene.
See under Phenylphosphorous Acid.
Phosphobenzene (*Diphosphenyl*)

$C_6H_5·P:P·C_6H_5$

$C_{12}H_{10}P_2$ MW, 216

Yellow powder. M.p. 149–50°. Sol. hot C_6H_6. Insol. EtOH, Et_2O, hot H_2O.

Köhler, Michaelis, *Ber.*, 1877, **10**, 812.

Phosphoric Acid. *Organic derivatives.*
Tri-Me ester: $C_3H_9O_4P$. MW, 140. B.p. 197°, 97°/36 mm., 85°/24 mm. D^{22} 1·200.
Tri-Et ester: $C_6H_{15}O_4P$. MW, 182. B.p. 215°, 190°/445 mm., 161°/188 mm., 146°/112 mm., 123°/50 mm., 103°/25 mm., 98–98·5°/8–10 mm. D_0^{19} 1·0725. $n_D^{17·1}$ 1·40674.
Tripropyl ester: $C_9H_{21}O_4P$. MW, 224. B.p. 138°/47 mm., 133·5°/22 mm., 120·5–121·5°/8–10 mm. D^{22} 1·007.
Tri-isopropyl ester: b.p. 218–20°/763 mm., 136°/68 mm., 95–6°/8–10 mm.
Tributyl ester: $C_{12}H_{27}O_4$. MW, 266. B.p. 160–2°/15 mm.
Tri-isobutyl ester: b.p. 192°, 119–29°/8–12 mm. D^{22} 0·965.
Tri-n-amyl ester: $C_{15}H_{33}O_4P$. MW, 308. B.p. 158–63°/6 mm.
Monohexadecyl ester: $C_{16}H_{35}O_4P$. MW, 322. M.p. 74°.
Triallyl ester: $C_9H_{15}O_4P$. MW, 218. B.p. 157°/44 mm.
Phenyl ester: *see* Diphenyl phosphate, Triphenyl phosphate, *and under* Phenol.
Naphthyl ester: *see under* Naphthol.
Dibenzyl ester: $C_{14}H_{15}O_4P$. MW, 278. M.p. 78–9°.
Tribenzyl ester: $C_{21}H_{21}O_4P$. MW, 368. M.p. 64°.
Dianilide: m.p. 214–16°.
Trianilide: m.p. 212–13° (208–10°).
Di-o-toluidide: m.p. 120°.
Di-p-toluidide: m.p. 195°.
Tri-o-toluidide: m.p. 236°.
Tri-p-toluidide: m.p. 192–4°.
Tri-benzylamide: m.p. 98°.
Tri-1-naphthylamide: m.p. 216°.
Tri-2-naphthylamide: m.p. 170°.

Adler, Gottlieb, U.S.P., 1,983,588, (*Chem. Abstracts*, 1935, **29**, 817).
Harlay, *Chem. Abstracts*, 1935, **29**, 2506.
Chem. Fabrik v. Heyden, E.P., 398,659, (*Chem. Abstracts*, 1934, **28**, 1362).
Noller, Dutton, *J. Am. Chem. Soc.*, 1933, **55**, 424.

Phosphorus triethyl.
See Triethylphosphine.
Phrenosin.
See Cerebron.
***o*-Phthalaldehyde** (1 : 2-*Dialdehydobenzene*)

$C_8H_6O_2$ MW, 134

(1) Cryst. from ligroin. M.p. 53·2°.
(2) Yellow cryst. M.p. 56–7°.
Sol. H_2O, ord. org. solvents. Spar. sol. pet. ether. Volatile in steam. $CrO_3 \longrightarrow$ phthalic acid.
Di-phenylhydrazone: m.p. 190–1°.

Tetra-acetate : m.p. 126–7°.

Thiele, Günther, *Ann.*, 1906, **347**, 107.
Seekles, *Rec. trav. chim.*, 1923, **42**, 706.
Bayer, D.R.P., 121,788, (*Chem. Zentr.*, 1901, II, 70).

***m*-Phthalaldehyde.**
See Isophthalaldehyde.

***p*-Phthalaldehyde.**
See Terephthalaldehyde.

***o*-Phthalaldehydic Acid.**
See *o*-Aldehydobenzoic Acid.

Phthalamic Acid (*Phthalic acid monoamide,* o-*carbamylbenzoic acid*)

$C_8H_7O_3N$ MW, 165

Prisms. M.p. 148–9°. Mod. sol. EtOH, hot H_2O. Spar. sol. Et_2O, C_6H_6. Insol. ligroin. Heat of comb. C_p 850·7 Cal. $k = 1{\cdot}6 \times 10^{-4}$ at 25°. Heat at 155° ⟶ phthalimide.

2 : 4-*Dinitrophenylhydrazone* : m.p. 298–9°.

Fodor, F.P., 636,846, (*Chem. Abstracts*, 1929, **23**, 608).
Chesnais, Canadian P., 282,407, (*Chem. Abstracts*, 1928, **22**, 4133).
Aschan, *Ber.*, 1886, **19**, 1402.

Phthalamide (*Phthalic acid diamide*)

$C_8H_8O_2N_2$ MW, 164

Cryst. M.p. 219–20° slow heat. ⟶ phthalimide + NH_3. Spar. sol. H_2O, EtOH. Heat of comb. C_p 291·7 Cal.

Hoogewerff, van Dorp, *Rec. trav. chim.*, 1892, **11**, 100.
Aschan, *Ber.*, 1886, **19**, 1399.

Phthalan (o-*Xylylene oxide,* 2 : 5-*dihydro*-3 : 4-*benzfuran, isocoumaran*)

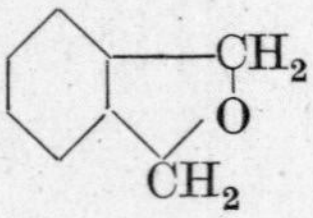

C_8H_8O MW, 120

Oil with odour of benzaldehyde. B.p. 192°. Volatile in steam. D_4^0 1·098. Alk. $KMnO_4$ ⟶ phthalic acid.

Ludwig, *Ber.*, 1907, **40**, 3062.

Phthalanil (N-*Phenylphthalimide*)

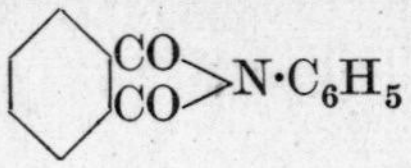

$C_{14}H_9O_2N$ MW, 223

Needles from EtOH. M.p. 210° (208°, 206°, 203°). Sol. $CHCl_3$. Insol. H_2O. Sublimes.

Cornillot, *Ann. chim.*, 1927, **8**, 177.
Jolles, *Gazz. chim. ital.*, 1935, **65**, 1224.
Warren, Briggs, *Ber.*, 1931, **64**, 29.
Das, Sarker, *J. Indian Chem. Soc.*, 1934, **11**, 709.
Poraĭ-Koshitz, *Chem. Abstracts*, 1935, **29**, 131, 6590.
See also Sherrill, Schaeffer, Shoyer, *J. Am. Chem. Soc.*, 1928, **50**, 477.

Phthalanilic Acid (*Phthalicacid monoanilide*)

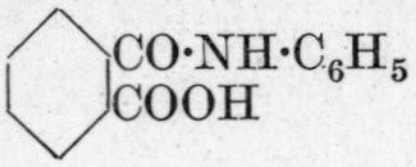

$C_{14}H_{11}O_3N$ MW, 241

Needles from EtOH. M.p. 170° ⟶ phthanil.

Anhydride : *see* Phthalanil.

See last four references above.

Phthalanilide (N : N′-*Diphenylphthalamide, phthalic acid dianilide*)

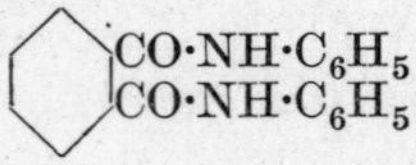

$C_{20}H_{16}O_2N_2$ MW, 316

Needles from EtOH. M.p. 251° (245–50°, 231° decomp.). Spar. sol. EtOH, Et_2O, C_6H_6, $CHCl_3$, AcOH. Heat of comb. C_p 2383·2 Cal.

Tingle, Cram, *Am. Chem. J.*, 1907, **37**, 603.

Phthalanone.
See Phthalide.

Phthalazine (4 : 5-*Benzdiazine,* β-*phenodiazine*)

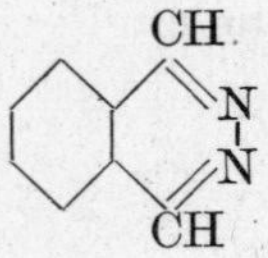

$C_8H_6N_2$ MW, 130

Needles from Et_2O. M.p. 90–1°. B.p. about 315–17° decomp., 189°/29 mm., 175°/17 mm. Sol. H_2O, EtOH, C_6H_6. Spar. sol. Et_2O. Insol. ligroin.

B,HCl : m.p. 231° decomp.
B,HI : m.p. 203°.
B,HAuCl$_4$: m.p. 200°.

Methiodide : m.p. 235–40°.
Ethiodide : m.p. 204–10°.
Benzylchloride : m.p. 97–9°.
Picrate : m.p. 208–10°.

Paul, *Ber.*, 1899, **32**, 2015.

Phthalazone

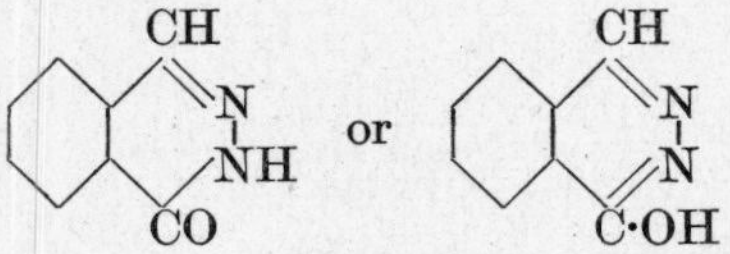

$C_8H_6ON_2$ MW, 146

Needles from H_2O. M.p. 183–4°. B.p. 337°. Sol. H_2O, EtOH, C_6H_6. Sublimes in prisms.
N-*Acetyl* : m.p. 135°.
N-*Me* : $C_9H_8ON_2$. MW, 160. M.p. 114° (111–12°).
O-*Me* : needles. M.p. 60–1°.
N-*Et* : $C_{10}H_{10}ON_2$. MW, 174. M.p. 55° (67–8°). B.p. 295°.
O-*Et* : m.p. 29–31°.

Rothenburg, *J. prakt. Chem.*, 1895, **51**, 147.
Paul, *Ber.*, 1899, **32**, 2020.

Phthalic Acid (*Benzene-o-dicarboxylic acid*)

$C_8H_6O_4$ MW, 166

Plates from hot H_2O. M.p. 231° (rapid heat.), 191° (in sealed tube). Mod. sol. H_2O, EtOH. Spar. sol. Et_2O. Insol. $CHCl_3$. Heat of comb. C_p 771·6 Cal., C_v 779·3 Cal. k (first) = $1{\cdot}3 \times 10^{-3}$ at 25°; (second) = $3{\cdot}9 \times 10^{-6}$ at 18°.
Aniline salt : m.p. 158°.
Pyridine acid salt : m.p. 86°.
Me ester : $C_9H_8O_4$. MW, 180. M.p. 85° (82·5°). $k = 6{\cdot}56 \times 10^{-4}$ at 25°.
Di-Me ester : $C_{10}H_{10}O_4$. MW, 194. B.p. 282°. $D_4^{20\cdot7}$ 1·1905. $n_D^{20\cdot7}$ 1·515. Heat of comb. C_p 1120·4 Cal., C_v 1120·1 Cal.
Me-Et ester : $C_{11}H_{12}O_4$. MW, 208. B.p. 285–7° (281–2°).
Et ester : $C_{10}H_{10}O_4$. MW, 194. M.p. 2°. D_4^{22} 1·1877. n_D^{22} 1·509. $k = 5{\cdot}51 \times 10^{-4}$ at 25°.
Di-Et ester : *see* Diethyl phthalate.
Dibutyl ester : $C_{16}H_{22}O_4$. MW, 278. B.p. 212–15°. D^{21} 1·043–1·050.
d-*Isobutyl ester* : $C_{12}H_{14}O_4$. MW, 222. M.p. 46–7°. $[\alpha]_D^{20}$ + 38·4° in EtOH.
dl-*Isobutyl ester* : cryst. from pet. ether. M.p. 56–7°.
Di-isobutyl ester : b.p. 182–4°/10 mm.
Dihexadecyl ester : $C_{40}H_{70}O_4$. MW, 614. M.p. 43°.
Cyclohexyl ester : $C_{14}H_{16}O_4$. MW, 248. M.p. 99°.
Di-cyclohexyl ester : $C_{20}H_{26}O_4$. MW, 330. M.p. 66°.
Phenyl ester : $C_{14}H_{10}O_4$. MW, 242. Needles from C_6H_6–ligroin. M.p. 103°.
Diphenyl ester : $C_{20}H_{14}O_4$. MW, 318. Prisms from EtOH. M.p. 73° (70°). B.p. 250–7°/14 mm.
Di-1-naphthyl ester : $C_{28}H_{18}O_4$. MW, 418. M.p. 155°.
Benzyl ester : $C_{15}H_{12}O_4$. MW, 256. M.p. 106–7°.
Dibenzyl ester : $C_{22}H_{18}O_4$. MW, 346. M.p. 42–3°. B.p. 277°/15 mm., 274°/12 mm.
Di-p-nitrobenzyl ester : m.p. 154–5°.
Difluoride : *see* Phthaloyl fluoride.
Dichloride : *see* Phthaloyl chloride.
Monoamide : *see* Phthalamic Acid.
Diamide : *see* Phthalamide.
Mononitrile : *see* *o*-Cyanobenzoic Acid.
Dinitrile : *see* Phthalonitrile.
Monoanilide : *see* Phthalanilic Acid.
Dianilide : *see* Phthalanilide.
Anhydride : *see* Phthalic Anhydride.
Imide : *see* Phthalimide.
Mono-phenylhydrazide : m.p. 165–6°.
Di-phenylhydrazide : m.p. 161°.

Pickard, Kenyon, *J. Chem. Soc.*, 1913, **103**, 1937; 1914, **105**, 1126.
Miller, *Chem. Zentr.*, 1914, I, 790.
Buchsweiler, D.R.P., 232,818, (*Chem. Zentr.*, 1911, I, 1090).
Reid, *J. Am. Chem. Soc.*, 1917, **39**, 1249.
Dennstedt, Hassler, D.R.P., 203,848, (*Chem. Zentr.*, 1908, II, 1750).

Phthalic Anhydride

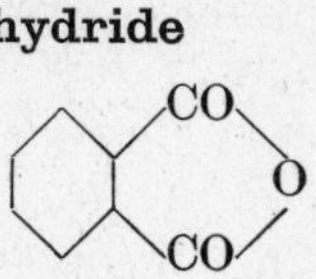

$C_8H_4O_3$ MW, 148

Needles from EtOH or C_6H_6. M.p. 131·61°. B.p. 295·09° (285·1°), 284·54°/751·4 mm., 283·75°/739 mm. Sol. EtOH. Spar. sol. Et_2O, H_2O. Sublimes. Sp. gr. 1·527. Intermediate for dyestuffs of the pyronine or phthalein class (Fluorescein, Rhodamine, Eosine, Phloxine, etc.) and for synthesis of anthraquinones, glyptal resins, and many other industrial products.
Oxime : *see* Phthaloxime.

Mono-2-pyridylhydrazide : m.p. 208°.
Mono-2-quinolylhydrazide : m.p. 236°.

Punnett, U.S.P., 1,978,506, (*Chem. Abstracts*, 1935, **29**, 176).
National Aniline, E.P., 415,748, (*Chem. Abstracts*, 1935, **29**, 819); U.S.P., 2,004,586, (*ibid.*, 5128).
Douglass, Jones, U.S.P., 2,013,727, (*Chem. Abstracts*, 1935, **29**, 6903).
Buylla, Pertierra, *Chem. Abstracts*, 1933, **27**, 1624.
Timmermans, Burrul, *Chimie et industrie*, 1931, Suppl. No., 196.
Marti, *Bull. soc. chim. Belg.*, 1930, **39**, 590.
Andrews, *Ind. Eng. Chem.*, 1921, **13**, 167.
Gibbs, *Ind. Eng. Chem.*, 1920, **12**, 1017 (*Bibl.*).

Phthalidanil.
See N-Phenylphthalimidine.

Phthalide (1-*Phthalanone*, o-*hydroxymethylbenzoic acid lactone*, 1(2)-*isobenzfuranone*, 3 : 4-*benzfuranone*-2)

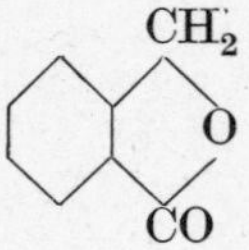

$C_8H_6O_2$ MW, 134

(i) Needles or plates from H_2O. M.p. 75° (73–4°). Stable. (ii) M.p. 65·8° (65°). Labile. Sol. EtOH, Et_2O, hot H_2O. $D_4^{99·1}$ 1·1636. $n_D^{99·1}$ 1·536. Heat of comb. C_p 885·1 Cal., C_v 884·7 Cal.

Jaeger, U.S.P., 1,889,961, (*Chem. Abstracts*, 1933, **27**, 1640).
Kalle, D.R.P., 267,596, (*Chem. Zentr.*, 1914, I, 199).
Gardner, Naylor, *Organic Syntheses*, 1936, XVI, 71.

Phthalide-3-acetic Acid

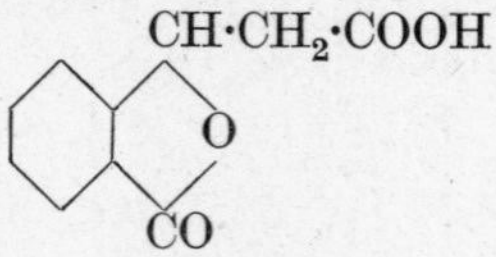

$C_{10}H_8O_4$ MW, 192

Cryst. + $1H_2O$ from H_2O. M.p. 151·5°. Sol. EtOH, hot H_2O.
Me ester : $C_{11}H_{10}O_4$. MW, 206. M.p. 62°.
Et ester : $C_{12}H_{12}O_4$. MW, 220. M.p. 76°.

Gabriel, Michael, *Ber.*, 1877, **10**, 1558.
Roth, *Ber.*, 1914, **47**, 1598.

Phthalide-3-carboxylic Acid

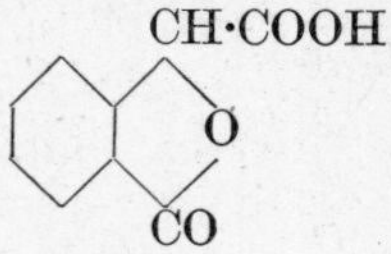

$C_9H_6O_4$ MW, 178

Leaflets from C_6H_6–AcOH. M.p. 153° (151°). Sol. H_2O, EtOH, Et_2O, AcOH.
Me ester : $C_{10}H_8O_4$. MW, 192. Needles from ligroin. M.p. 57° (53–4°).
Amide : $C_9H_7O_3N$. MW, 177. Cryst. from H_2O. M.p. 185·5°.

Fries, *Ann.*, 1904, **334**, 358.
Tscherniac, *J. Chem. Soc.*, 1916, **109**, 1240.
Ruhemann, *J. Chem. Soc.*, 1910, **97**, 2030.

Phthalimide

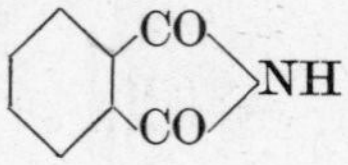

$C_8H_5O_2N$ MW, 147

Needles from H_2O, prisms from AcOH, leaflets by sublimation. M.p. 233–5° (238°). Sol. hot AcOH. Insol. C_6H_6, ligroin. Forms *N*-metallic derivs.
N-*Acetyl* : m.p. 133–5°.
N-*Chloro* : chlorylphthalimide. $C_8H_4O_2NCl$. MW, 181·5. M.p. 183–5°.
N-*Bromo* : $C_8H_4O_2NBr$. MW, 226. Yellow cryst. from C_6H_6. M.p. 206–7°.
N-*Me* : *see N*-Methylphthalimide.
N-*Et* : $C_{10}H_9O_2N$. MW, 175. Needles from EtOH. M.p. 78–9°. B.p. 285°/758 mm.
N-2-*Chloroethyl* : $C_{10}H_8O_2NCl$. MW, 209·5. M.p. 79–81°.
N-2-*Bromoethyl* : $C_{10}H_8O_2NBr$. MW, 254. M.p. 82–83·5°.
N-2-*Iodoethyl* : $C_{10}H_8O_2NI$. MW, 301. M.p. 99–100°.
N-*Propyl* : $C_{11}H_{11}O_2N$. MW, 189. M.p. 66°. B.p. 296·9°/758 mm. (282–3°/756 mm.).
N-2-*Chloropropyl* : $C_{11}H_{10}O_2NCl$. MW, 223·5. M.p. 100–2°.
N-3-*Chloropropyl* : m.p. 67–8°.
N-2 : 3-*Dichloropropyl* : $C_{11}H_9O_2NCl_2$. MW, 258. M.p. 93°.
N-2-*Bromopropyl* : $C_{11}H_{10}O_2NBr$. MW, 268. M.p. 110–11° (105°).
N-3-*Bromopropyl* : m.p. 72–3°.

N-2 : 3-*Dibromopropyl* : $C_{11}H_9O_2NBr_2$. MW, 347. M.p. 113–14°.
N-3-*Iodopropyl* : $C_{11}H_{10}O_2NI$. MW, 315. M.p. 88°.
N-*Isopropyl* : m.p. 85°. B.p. 286°/761 mm.
N-2-*Chloroisopropyl* : m.p. 56–8°.
N-2-*Bromoisopropyl* : m.p. 59–60°.
N-*Butyl* : $C_{12}H_{13}O_2N$. MW, 203. B.p. 311–18°/758 mm.
N-4-*Bromobutyl* : $C_{12}H_{12}O_2NBr$. MW, 282. M.p. 80·5°.
N-4-*Iodobutyl* : $C_{12}H_{12}O_2NI$. MW, 329. M.p. 88–89·5°.
N-*Isobutyl* : m.p. 93°. B.p. 293–5°.
N-*Amyl* : $C_{13}H_{15}O_2N$. MW, 217. M.p. 23°. B.p. 303°. D_4^{25} 1·093. $[\alpha]_D^{25}$ + 7·53°.
N-*Isoamyl* : m.p. 12·5°. B.p. 307–8°.
N-*Octyl* : $C_{16}H_{21}O_2N$. MW, 259. M.p. 48–9°. B.p. about 216°/20 mm.
N-*Cyclopropyl* : $C_{11}H_9O_2N$. MW, 187. M.p. 135–6°.
N-α-*Camphyl* : $C_{18}H_{21}O_2N$. MW, 283. M.p. 54°.
N-*Vinyl* : $C_{10}H_7O_2N$. MW, 173. M.p. 86°.
N-*Propenyl* : $C_{11}H_9O_2N$. MW, 187. Yellow leaflets from EtOH. M.p. 151°.
N-*Isopropenyl* : m.p. 105–6°.
N-*Allyl* : $C_{11}H_9O_2N$. MW, 187. Cryst. from EtOH. M.p. 71°. B.p. 295°.
N-*Phenyl* : *see* Phthalanil.
N-p-*Chlorophenyl* : $C_{14}H_8O_2NCl$. MW, 257·5. M.p. 194–5°.
N-2 : 4-*Dichlorophenyl* : $C_{14}H_7O_2NCl_2$. MW, 292. M.p. 155°.
N-p-*Bromophenyl* : $C_{14}H_8O_2NBr$. MW, 302. M.p. 203–4°.
N-2 : 4-*Dibromophenyl* : $C_{14}H_7O_2NBr_2$. MW, 381. M.p. 153·5°.
N-p-*Iodophenyl* : $C_{14}H_8O_2NI$. MW, 349. M.p. 227–8° (235°).
N-o-*Nitrophenyl* : $C_{14}H_8O_4N_2$. MW, 268. M.p. 202–3°.
N-m-*Nitrophenyl* : m.p. 242–4°.
N-p-*Nitrophenyl* : m.p. 264–6°.
N-*Picryl* : $C_{14}H_6O_8N_4$. MW, 358. M.p. 259°.
N-*Benzyl* : $C_{15}H_{11}O_2N$. MW, 237. M.p. 115–16°.
N-o-*Tolyl* : $C_{15}H_{11}O_2N$. MW, 237. M.p. 182°.
N-m-*Tolyl* : m.p. 170–2°.
N-p-*Tolyl* : m.p. 204°.
N-*Cinnamyl* : $C_{17}H_{13}O_2N$. MW, 263. M.p. 153°.
N-1-*Naphthyl* : $C_{18}H_{11}O_2N$. MW, 273. M.p. 180–1°.
N-2-*Naphthyl* : m.p. 216°.

Herzog, *Z. angew. Chem.*, 1919, **32**, 301.
Tseng, *Chem. Abstracts*, 1934, **28**, 6133.
Inone, Horiguchi, *Chem. Abstracts*, 1933, **27**, 2684.
Jaeger, Daniels, U.S.P., 1,966,068, (*Chem. Abstracts*, 1934, **28**, 5476); U.S.P., 1,914,723, (*Chem. Abstracts*, 1933, **27**, 4243); U.S.P., 1,968,253, (*Chem. Abstracts*, 1934, **28**, 5835).
Manske, *Organic Syntheses*, 1932, XII, 10.
Salzberg, Supniewski, *Organic Syntheses*, 1927, VII, 8.

Phthalimidine (1-*Isoindolenone*, *benzylamine-o-carboxylic lactam*)

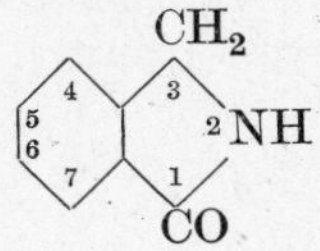

C_8H_7ON MW, 133

Needles from H_2O. M.p. 150° (149°). B.p. 336–7°/730 mm. Sol. EtOH, Et_2O, $CHCl_3$.
B,HCl : m.p. 150° decomp.
N-*Acetyl* : m.p. 151°.
N-*Me* : C_9H_9ON. MW, 147. M.p. 120°. B.p. 300°.
N-*Et* : $C_{10}H_{11}ON$. MW, 161. M.p. 45°. B_2,H_2PtCl_6 : m.p. 145°.
N-*Isobutyl* : $C_{12}H_{15}ON$. MW, 189. B.p. 310–12°/740 mm.
N-*Phenyl* : *see* *N*-Phenylphthalimidine.
N-*Benzyl* : $C_{15}H_{13}ON$. MW, 223. M.p. 90–1°.
N-o-*Hydroxybenzyl* : $C_{15}H_{13}O_2N$. MW, 239. M.p. 159–60°.
N-p-*Hydroxybenzyl* : red needles from H_2O. M.p. 187–98°.
N-o-*Aminobenzyl* : $C_{15}H_{14}ON_2$. MW, 238. M.p. 153–4°.
N-p-*Aminobenzyl* : m.p. 187–8°.
N-*Nitroso* : m.p. 150°.
Picrate : m.p. 140°.

Rupe, Bernstein, *Helv. Chim. Acta*, 1930, **13**, 469.
Sakurai, *Bull. Chem. Soc. Japan*, 1930, **5**, 184.
Packendorff, *Ber.*, 1934, **67**, 907.

Phthaliminoacetic Acid (*Phthaloylglycine*)

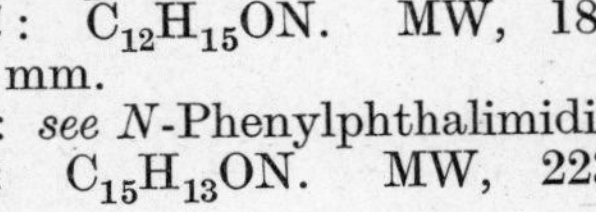

$C_{10}H_7O_4N$ MW, 205

Prisms or needles. From H_2O. M.p. 192–3°. Sol. hot H_2O, hot EtOH. Insol. $CHCl_3$, pet. ether, ligroin. $k = 1 \times 10^{-3}$ at 25°.

Et ester : $C_{12}H_{11}O_4N$. MW, 233. Needles from H_2O. M.p. 104–5° (112–13°).

Chloride : $C_{10}H_5O_3NCl$. MW, 222·5. Needles from ligroin. M.p. 84–5°.

Anhydride : $C_{20}H_{12}O_7N_2$. MW, 392. Needles from $PhNO_2$. M.p. 242°.

Anilide : m.p. 231–2°.

Phenylhydrazide : m.p. 199°.

Johnson, Scott, *J. Am. Chem. Soc.*, 1913, **35**, 1133.
Reise, *Ann.*, 1887, **242**, 1.
Gabriel, *Ber.*, 1907, **40**, 2649.
Scheiber, *Ber.*, 1913, **46**, 1103.

1-Phthaliminopropionic Acid (*N-Phthaloylalanine*)

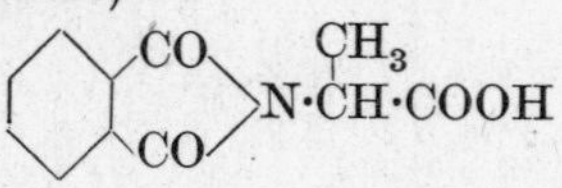

$C_{11}H_9O_4N$ MW, 219

d-.

Et ester : $C_{13}H_{13}O_4N$. MW, 247. Cryst. from ligroin. M.p. 58–61°.

l-.

M.p. 150–1°. Sol. EtOH, Et_2O, Me_2CO. Spar. sol. ligroin. $[\alpha]_D^{20}$ − 17·8° in EtOH.

Et ester : cryst. from ligroin. M.p. 54–6°. $[\alpha]_D^{20}$ − 12·5° in EtOH.

dl-.

Needles from H_2O. M.p. 160–2° (164°). Sol. EtOH, Et_2O, Me_2CO, AcOH, hot H_2O. Insol. pet. ether.

Et ester : plates from CS_2. M.p. 65° (61–3°).

Phenyl ester : $C_{17}H_{13}O_4N$. MW, 295. Needles from EtOH. M.p. 99°. Sol. Et_2O, C_6H_6, AcOH, hot EtOH.

Chloride : $C_{11}H_8O_3NCl$. MW, 237·5. Cryst. from ligroin. M.p. 73° (71°).

Bayer, D.R.P., 209,962, (*Chem. Zentr.*, 1909, I, 1951).
Bachstez, *Ber.*, 1914, **47**, 3166.
Fischer, *Ber.*, 1907, **40**, 498.
Gabriel, *Ber.*, 1905, **38**, 634.

2-Phthaliminopropionic Acid

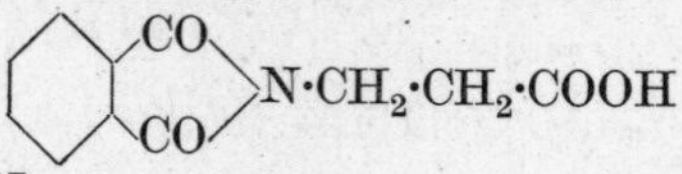

$C_{11}H_9O_4N$ MW, 219

Cryst. from H_2O. M.p. 150–1°. Sol. Et_2O, Me_2CO, AcOH, AcOEt. Spar. sol. H_2O, EtOH, C_6H_6. Insol. ligroin.

Et ester : needles. M.p. 73·5°.

Isoamyl ester : $C_{16}H_{19}O_4N$. MW, 289. M.p. 61°.

Chloride : m.p. 107–8°.

Hale, Britton, *J. Am. Chem. Soc.*, 1919, **41**, 845.

Phthalocyanine

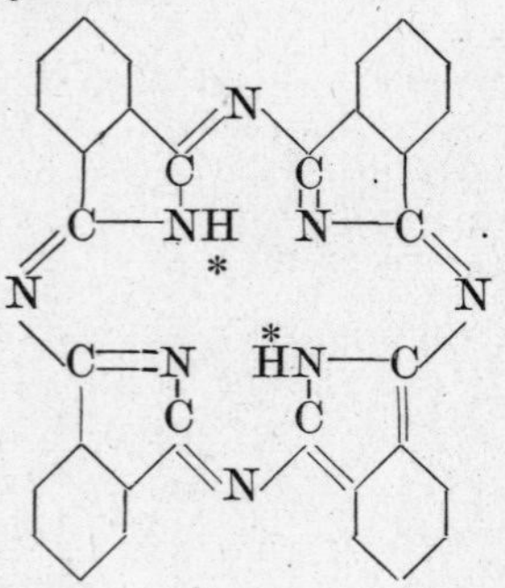

$C_{32}H_{18}N_8$ MW, 514

Greenish-blue needles with purple reflex from quinoline. Sublimes at 550° decomp. under red. press. Sol. benzophenone, naphthalene, cyclohexanol, menthol, quinoline ⟶ blue sols. Sol. aniline and homologues ⟶ green sols. Very stable. Forms metallic derivs. at *N* atoms marked *, of formula $(C_8H_4N_2)_4M$, very stable blue cryst. solids.

Robertson, *J. Chem. Soc.*, 1935, 615.
Linstead, *J. Chem. Soc.*, 1934, 1020, 1035.
Barnett, Dent, Linstead, *J. Chem. Soc.*, 1936, 1719.
Linstead, Robertson, *ibid.*, 1736.

Phthalonic Acid (*o-Carboxybenzoylformic acid*)

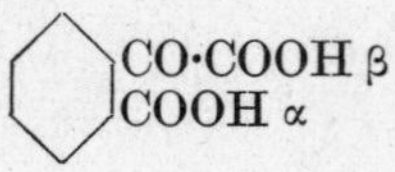

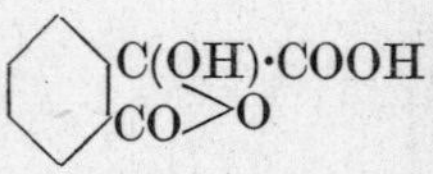

ψ-Form

$C_9H_6O_5$ MW, 194

Cryst. + $2H_2O$ from H_2O. M.p. anhyd. 146°. Sol. EtOH, Et_2O, Me_2CO. Spar. sol. C_6H_6, $CHCl_3$, pet. ether. Ox. ⟶ phthalic acid.

α-Me ester : $C_{10}H_8O_5$. MW, 208. Cryst. + $1H_2O$. M.p. 79–81°. $k = 1{\cdot}5 \times 10^{-4}$ at 25°.

Di-Me ester : $C_{11}H_{10}O_5$. MW, 222. Cryst. from MeOH. M.p. 66–8°.

α-Amide : α-phthalonamic acid. $C_9H_7O_4N$. MW, 193. Prisms + $1\frac{1}{2}H_2O$ from H_2O. M.p. anhyd. 178–9° decomp.

β-Amide : β-phthalonamic acid. M.p. 155° decomp. Sol. H_2O.

Anhydride : $C_9H_4O_4$. MW, 176. Needles

from Ac_2O. M.p. 185–6° (190–1°) decomp. (rapid heat.). Spar. sol. Et_2O.

Anilide: phthalonanilic acid. $C_{15}H_{11}O_4N$. MW, 269. Needles from $CHCl_3$. M.p. 176°.

Dianilide: phthalonanilide. $C_{21}H_{16}O_3N_2$. MW, 344. Needles from EtOH. M.p. 206–8°.

ψ-Acetyl: m.p. 185–6° ⟶ phthalic anhydride + acetic acid.

ψ-Chloride: $C_9H_5O_4Cl$. MW, 212·5. M.p. 133°.

ψ-Dichloride: $C_9H_4O_3Cl_2$. MW, 231. M.p. 70°. B.p. 120°/12 mm.

ψ-Phenylhydrazone: m.p. 171–2°.

Tscherniac, *J. Chem. Soc.*, 1916, **109**, 1236 (*Bibl.*).
Cornillot, *Ann. Chim.*, 1927, **7**, 227; *Compt. rend.*, 1924, **179**, 274.
Kuroda, Perkin, *J. Chem. Soc.*, 1923, **123**, 2106.
Fuson, *J. Am. Chem. Soc.*, 1926, **48**, 1093.
Gabriel, Colman, *Ber.*, 1900, **33**, 999.

Phthalonitrile (*Phthalic acid dinitrile*, o-*dicyanobenzene*)

$C_8H_4N_2$ MW, 128

Needles from H_2O. M.p. 141° (140°). Sol. EtOH, Et_2O, $CHCl_3$, C_6H_6. Spar. sol. H_2O, ligroin. Volatile in steam. Slowly hyd. by hot HCl to the acid.

Braun, Tscherniac, *Ber.*, 1907, **40**, 2710.
I.C.I., E.P., 413,639, (*Chem. Abstracts*, 1935, **29**, 178).

Phthalophenone (*Diphenylphthalide*, *triphenylcarbinol*-o-*carboxylic lactone*)

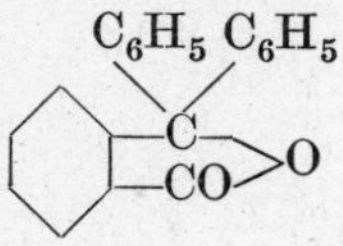

$C_{20}H_{14}O_2$ MW, 286

Leaflets from EtOH. M.p. 115°. B.p. above 400° decomp. H_2SO_4 ⟶ greenish-yellow col. ⟶ violet on heating.

Heller, *Ber.*, 1912, **45**, 667.
Copisarow, *J. Chem. Soc.*, 1917, **111**, 18.
Scheiber, *Ann.*, 1912, **389**, 124.

Phthaloxime (*Isonitrosophthalide*, N-*hydroxyphthalimide*)

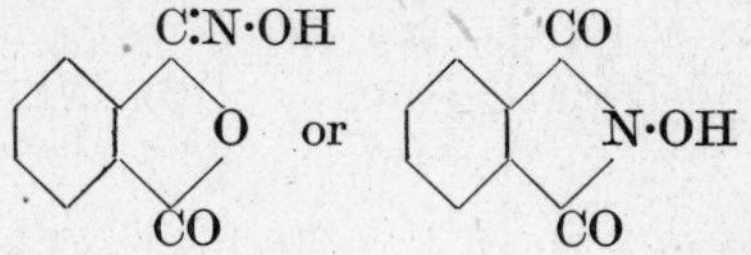

$C_8H_5O_3N$ MW, 163

(i) Needles from EtOH. M.p. 220–6° decomp. (rapid heat. in sealed tube). Sol. hot EtOH, hot Me_2CO. Mod. sol. hot H_2O. Insol. Et_2O, C_6H_6.

Acetyl deriv.: m.p. 183–5°.

Benzoyl deriv.: m.p. 171·5°.

O-*Me*: $C_9H_7O_3N$. MW, 177. Needles from EtOH. M.p. 133°.

O-*Et*: $C_{10}H_9O_3N$. MW, 191. Prisms. M.p. 95–100°.

(ii) Yellow needles from EtOH. M.p. 220–6° decomp. (rapid heat. in sealed tube).

Acetyl and benzoyl derivs., *O*-Me and *O*-Et ethers identical with corresponding derivs. of (i).

Basler Chem. Fabrik, D.R.P., 130,681, (*Chem. Zentr.*, 1902, I, 1184).
Brady, Baker, Goldstein, Harris, *J. Chem. Soc.*, 1928, 538.

Phthaloylacetic Acid (1 : 3-*Diketohydrindene-2-carboxylic acid*)

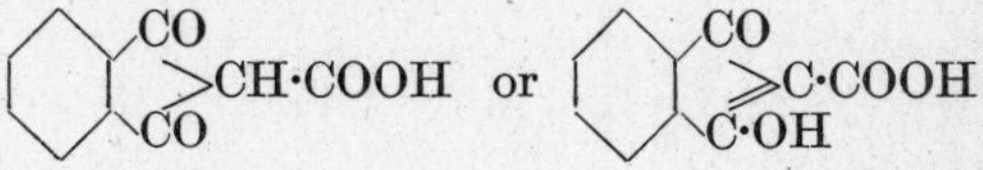

$C_{10}H_6O_4$ MW, 190

Unstable, readily losing CO_2 ⟶ 1 : 3-diketohydrindene.

Et ester: $C_{12}H_{10}O_4$. MW, 218. Yellow needles. M.p. 75–8°. Sol. EtOH, Et_2O, C_6H_6, ligroin. Insol. H_2O. Sol. alkalis ⟶ enol salts. $FeCl_3$ ⟶ red col. with EtOH sol.

Gabriel, Neumann, *Ber.*, 1893, **26**, 953.

Phthaloyl chloride (3 : 3-*Dichlorophthalide*)

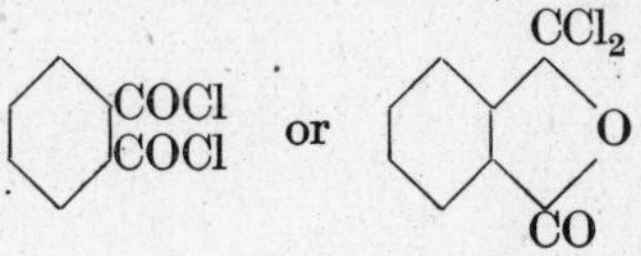

I. II.

$C_8H_4O_2Cl_2$ MW, 203

I.

F.p. 12°. M.p. 15–16°. B.p. 281·1°, 275·4°/726 mm., 47°/130 mm. D_4^{20} 1·4089. $n_D^{15.5}$ 1·571. Heat of comb. C_p 802·03 Cal., C_v 802·05 Cal.

II.
M.p. 88–9°. B.p. 275·2°/719·8 mm.

v. Braun, Kaiser, *Ber.*, 1922, **55**, 1305.
Ott, *Organic Syntheses*, 1931, XI, 88.
Garner, Sugden, *J. Chem. Soc.*, 1927, 2877.
Monsanto, E.P., 418,162, (*Chem. Abstracts*, 1935, **29**, 1436); U.S.P., 1,906,761, (*Chem. Abstracts*, 1933, **27**, 3484).

Phthaloyl fluoride

$C_8H_4O_2F_2$ MW, 170

Plates from pet. ether. M.p. 42–3°. B.p. 224–6°/760 mm., 142°/65 mm., 135°/15 mm. Lachrymatory. $H_2O \longrightarrow$ phthalic anhydride.

Dunn, Davies, Hambly, Paul, Semmens, *J. Chem. Soc.*, 1933, 15.

Phthaloylglycine.
See Phthaliminoacetic Acid.

Phthaloylmalonic Acid (1 : 3-*Diketohydrindene*-2 : 2-*dicarboxylic acid*)

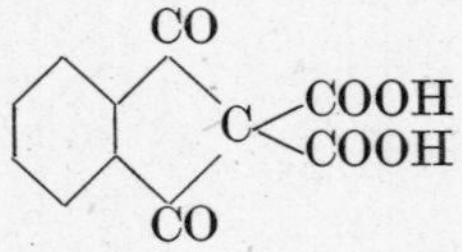

$C_{11}H_6O_6$ MW, 234

Di-Et ester: $C_{15}H_{14}O_6$. MW, 290. M.p. 74–5°. Sol. Et_2O, hot EtOH. $D_4^{83·5}$ 1·1896. $n_D^{84·4}$ 1·541.
Et ester-nitrile: $C_{13}H_9O_4N$. MW, 243. (i) M.p. 190–2°. Spar. sol. $CHCl_3$, C_6H_6. (ii) M.p. 140–1°.

Scheiber, Hofer, *Ber.*, 1920, **53**, 898.

1 : 8-Phthaloylnaphthalene

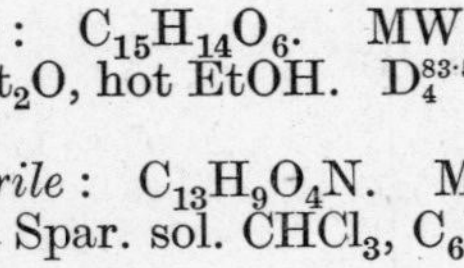

$C_{18}H_{10}O_2$ MW, 258

Needles from EtOH. M.p. 178°. $H_2SO_4 \longrightarrow$ yellow col. with green fluor.
Mono-dinitrophenylhydrazone: m.p. 265°.

Rieche, Sauthoff, Müller, *Ber.*, 1932, **65**, 1380.

1 : 8-Phthaloyl-2-naphthol (1-*Hydroxy*-7 : 12-*dihydropleiadenedione*-7 : 12)

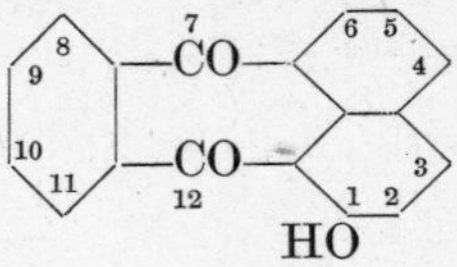

$C_{18}H_{10}O_3$ MW, 274

Yellowish-green needles from chlorobenzene. M.p. 196°. Forms no phenylhydrazone.
Acetyl deriv.: m.p. 216°.
Benzoyl deriv.: m.p. 213°.
7-*Oxime*: m.p. 242°. *Acetyl deriv.*: m.p. 237°.
12-*Oxime*: m.p. 262°. *Acetyl deriv.*: m.p. 155–60°.
Me ether: $C_{19}H_{12}O_3$. MW, 288. M.p. 205°.
Et ether: $C_{20}H_{14}O_3$. MW, 302. Yellow leaflets from Et_2O. M.p. 163·5°.

Riche, Sauthoff, Müller, *Ber.*, 1932, **65**, 1379.

Phthaloyl peroxide

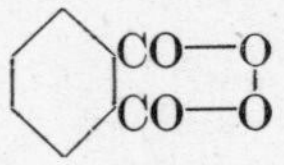

$C_8H_4O_4$ MW, 164

Cryst. M.p. 133·5° decomp. Explodes at 136°. Insol. ord. org. solvents.

Pechmann, Vanino, *Ber.*, 1894, **27**, 1511.
Baeyer, Villiger, *Ber.*, 1901, **34**, 762.

Phthaloylphenylhydrazine (N-*Anilinophthalimide*)

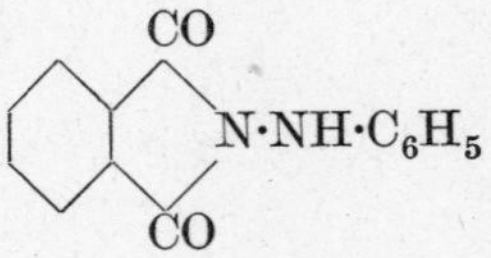

$C_{14}H_{10}O_2N_2$ MW, 238

(i) Yellow prisms from Me_2CO. M.p. 184°. D_4^{15} 1·356.
(ii) Plates from Me_2CO. Does not melt. D_4^{17} 1·354. Heat $\longrightarrow$ (i).
Sol. $CHCl_3$, Me_2CO, hot EtOH, hot. AcOH. Spar. sol. Et_2O, C_6H_6. Insol. H_2O, ligroin.

Scheiber, *Ann.*, 1912, **389**, 152.

Phthaloylpyridine.
See Anthrapyridinequinone.

Phthaloylquinoline.
See Anthraquinolinequinone.

Phthalyl Alcohol (o-*Xylylene glycol*, α:α-o-*ylenediol*, 1 : 2-*di*-(*hydroxymethyl*)-*benzene*, ωω′-*ihydroxy*-o-*xylene*)

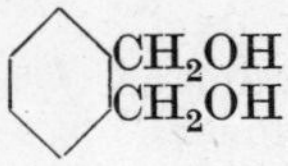

$_8H_{10}O_2$ MW, 138

Plates from Et_2O. M.p. 64·2–64·8° (62·5°). ;ol. H_2O, EtOH, Et_2O. Spar. sol. C_6H_6.

Diacetyl : m.p. 37°.

Di-Et ether : $C_{12}H_{18}O_2$. MW, 194. Oil. B.p. :46–8°/738 mm.

Perkin, *J. Chem. Soc.*, 1888, **53**, 7.
Wislicenus, Penndorf, *Ber.*, 1910, **43**, 1837.

Phthiocol (3-*Hydroxy*-2-*methyl*-1 : 4-*naphtho*-*uinone*)

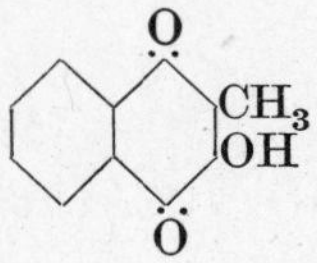

$_{11}H_8O_3$ MW, 188

Pigment from tubercle bacilli. Yellow prisms rom MeOH.Aq. M.p. 173–4°. Volatile in steam. ;ol. dil. alkalis with intense red col. Ox. ⟶ ›hthalic acid.

Acetyl deriv. : m.p. 106–7°. Sol. alkalis to ›right red sols.

Monoxime : m.p. 199–200°.

Di-nitrophenylhydrazone : does not melt below :70°.

Me ether : $C_{12}H_{10}O_3$. MW, 202. M.p. 93°.

Madinaveitia, *Chem. Abstracts*, 1935, **29**, 5438.
Newman, Crowder, Anderson, *J. Biol. Chem.*, 1934, **105**, 279.
Ball, *J. Biol. Chem.*, 1934, **106**, 515.
Anderson, Newman, *J. Biol. Chem.*, 1934, **103**, 405.

Phthioic Acid

$C_{25}H_{51}·COOH$

$_{26}H_{52}O_2$ MW, 396

Obtained from human tubercle bacilli. M.p. :0–1°. D_4^{25} 0·8763. n_D^{25} 1·4628. $[\alpha]_D$ + 12·56°. The hydrocarbon chain is branched.

Me ester : $C_{27}H_{54}O_2$. MW, 410. B.p. 175–;°/0·05 mm., 158°/0·03 mm. D_4^{25} 0·8620. n_D^{25} ·4550. $[\alpha]_D^{22}$ + 12·2°.

Amide : $C_{26}H_{53}ON$. MW, 395. Plates from EtOH. M.p. 45°.

Methylamide : $C_{27}H_{55}ON$. MW, 409. M.p. 27°.

Spielman, Anderson, *J. Biol. Chem.*, 1936, **112**, 759 (*Bibl.*).

Phyllodulcin (8 : 3′-*Dihydroxy*-4′-*methoxy*-3-*phenyl*-3 : 4-*dihydroisocoumarin*)

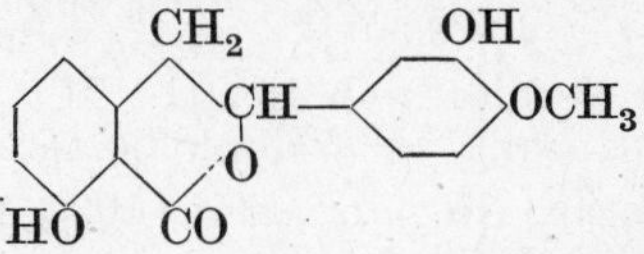

$C_{16}H_{14}O_5$ MW, 286

d-.

Occurs in leaves of *Hydrangea thumbergii*, Sieb. M.p. 120°. $[\alpha]_D$ + 67·7 to 69·7°. It was originally thought that a natural preparation consisted of a mixture of *d*-phyllodulcin + another compound which was given the name *d*-isophyllodulcin. The mixture has now been shown to consist of *d*- + *dl*-phyllodulcin and accordingly isophyllodulcin does not exist.

Diacetyl deriv. : m.p. 148–9°.

Dibenzoyl deriv. : m.p. 183–183·5°.

dl-.

M.p. 131°.

Di-Me ether : $C_{18}H_{18}O_5$. MW, 314. (i) Needles from EtOH. M.p. 105°. Labile. (ii) M.p. 125°. Stable.

Maniwa, *Chem. Abstracts*, 1924, **18**, 2694.
Asahina, Asano, *Ber.*, 1931, **64**, 1253.

Phyllomerol (6 : 7-*Dihydroxy*-2-*methyl*-*naphthalene*)

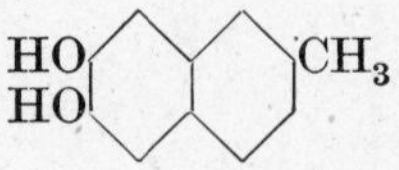

$C_{11}H_{10}O_2$ MW, 174

Cryst. M.p. 161–2°. $FeCl_3$ ⟶ green col. in MeOH.

Me ether : $C_{12}H_{12}O_2$. MW, 188. M.p. 119–22°.

Di-Me ether : $C_{13}H_{14}O_2$. MW, 202. Needles. M.p. 98–100°. *Picrate* : m.p. 120–1°.

Methylene ether : *see* Podophyllomerol.

Borsche, Niemann, *Ber.*, 1932, **65**, 1633; *Ann.*, 1933, **502**, 268.

Phyllomeronic Acid (6 : 7-*Dihydroxy*-2-*methylnaphthalene*-3-*carboxylic acid*, *phyllomerol*-3-*carboxylic acid*, 6 : 7-*dihydroxy*-3-*methyl*-2-*naphthoic acid*)

$C_{12}H_{10}O_4$ MW, 218

Leaflets from MeOH. M.p. 243–4°. $FeCl_3$ ⟶ deep blue col.

6 : 7-*Diacetyl* : m.p. 220°.

Me ester : $C_{13}H_{12}O_4$. MW, 232. Needles from MeOH. M.p. 186–7°. $FeCl_3$ ⟶ green col.

Di-Me ether : $C_{14}H_{14}O_4$. MW, 246. Needles from MeOH. M.p. 223–5°. *Me ester* : $C_{15}H_{16}O_4$. MW, 260. Needles from MeOH. M.p. 125–6°.

Methylene ether : *see* Podophyllomeronic Acid.

Borsche, Niemann, *Ber.*, 1932, **65**, 1633; *Ann.*, 1932, **499**, 68.

Phyllopyrrole (2 : 3 : 5-*Trimethyl-4-ethylpyrrole*)

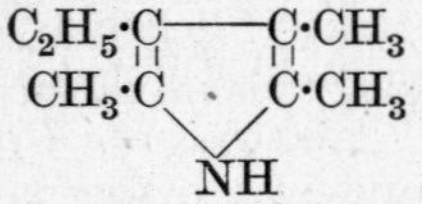

$C_9H_{15}N$ MW, 137

Leaflets from Et_2O. M.p. 66–7°. B.p. 213°/725 mm., 110–12°/35 mm., 92–3°/12 mm. Turns oily then resinous in air.

Picrate : m.p. 101–3°.

Siedel, *Z. physiol Chem.*, 1935, **231**, 167.
Signaigo, Adkins, *J. Am. Chem. Soc.*, 1936, **58**, 712.
Colacicchi, *Atti accad. Lincei*, 1913, **21**, i, 489.

Phyllopyrrolidine (*Tetrahydrophyllopyrrole*)

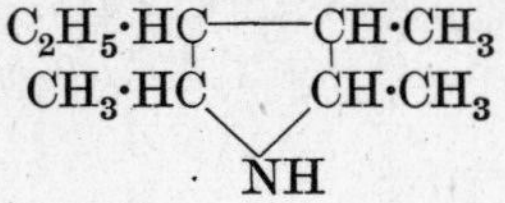

$C_9H_{19}N$ MW, 141

B.p. 160–4°. D_4^{20} 0·824.

1-*Naphthylurea* : m.p. 145°.

Willstätter, Asahina, *Ann.*, 1911, **385**, 215.

Physalien (*Zeaxanthin dipalmitate, physalin, physaliene*)

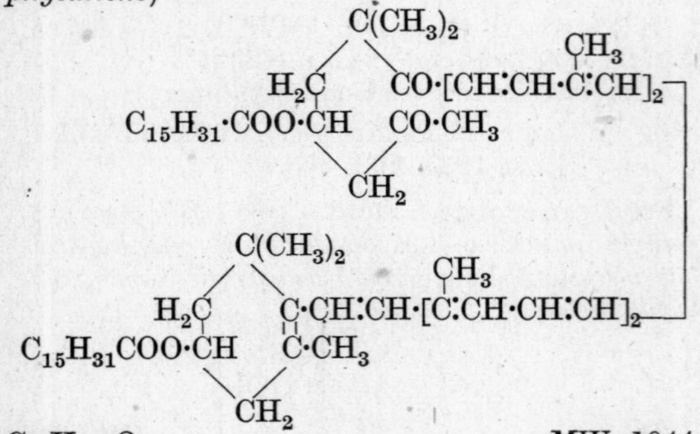

$C_{72}H_{116}O_4$ MW, 1044

Occurs in berries of *Physalis* species. Re cryst. from C_6H_6–MeOH. M.p. 98·5–99·5°.

Winterstein, Ehrenberg, *Z. physiol.Chem.* 1932, **207**, 25.
Kuhn, Grundmann, *Ber.*, 1934, **67**, 596.
Karrer, Solmssen, Walker, *Helv. Chim Acta*, 1934, **17**, 417.
Cholnoky, *Z. physiol. Chem.*, 1930, **189** 159.
Kylin, *Z. physiol. Chem.*, 1927, **163**, 229.
Kuhn, Wiegand, *Helv. Chim. Acta*, 1929 **12**, 499.

Physciaic Acid.

See Physcione.

Physcione (*Physciaic acid, parietin, chrysophyscin, rheumemodin methyl ether, frangula-emodin methyl ether, rheochrysidine*)

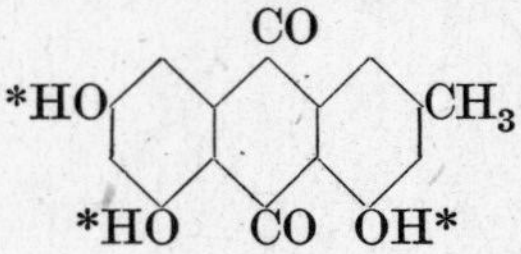

$C_{16}H_{12}O_5$ MW, 284

Occurs in chrysarobin, rhubarb root and lichens. M.p. 207°. Sol. C_6H_6, $CHCl_3$, Py, toluene. Spar. sol. AcOH, AcOEt. Insol EtOH, MeOH, Et_2O, Me_2CO.

Tutin, Clewer, *J. Chem. Soc.*, 1912, **101**, 294.
Eder, Hauser, *Helv. Chim. Acta*, 1925, **8**, 140 (*Bibl.*).
Hesse, *Ann.*, 1917, **413**, 368.

* One of these groups is OCH_3 but which one is not known.

Physodalic Acid.

See Physodic Acid.

Physodic Acid (*Physodalic acid*)

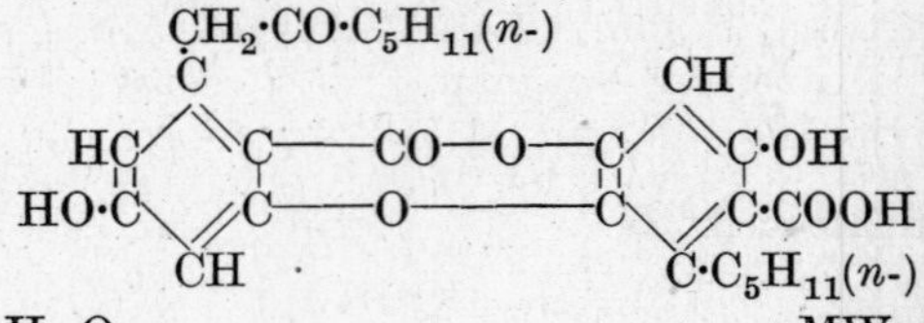

$C_{26}H_{30}O_8$ MW, 470

Occurs in *Parmelia physodes*, and *Cetraria islandica*. Needles from MeOH.Aq. M.p. 205°. $FeCl_3$ ⟶ violet col. Zn + NaOH ⟶ atranol + orcinol.

Diacetyl deriv. : m.p. 153–153·5°.

Oxime : m.p. 209–10°.

Phenylhydrazone : m.p. 265° decomp.

Me ester : $C_{27}H_{32}O_8$. MW, 484. Prisms from EtOH. M.p. 156–7°. *Me ether* : $C_{28}H_{34}O_8$.

MW, 498. Leaflets from AcOH. M.p. 117–19°.
Diacetyl deriv. : m.p. 114–15°.
  Anilide : m.p. 260° decomp.

  Asahina, Nogami, *Ber.*, 1935, **68**, 1500;
    1934, **67**, 805.
  Koller, Locker, *Monatsh.*, 1931, **58**, 209.

Note.—Some doubt exists as to the identity
of physodic with physodylic acid, *q.v.* Hesse,
J. prakt. Chem., 1915, **92**, 439, identifies it with
capraric acid.

Physodylic Acid (*Isidic Acid*)

$C_{23}H_{24}O_6$ MW, 396
  Occurs in *Evernia furfuracea*, Linn. Needles
from AcOH. M.p. 196° (169–70°). Spar. sol.
Et_2O.

  Hesse, *J. prakt. Chem.*, 1915, **92**, 437.

Physostigmine.
See Eserine.

Physostigmine oxide.
See Geneserine.

Physostigmol   (5-*Hydroxy*-1 : 3-*dimethyl*-
indole)

HO⟨⟩C·CH₃
        CH
      N·CH₃

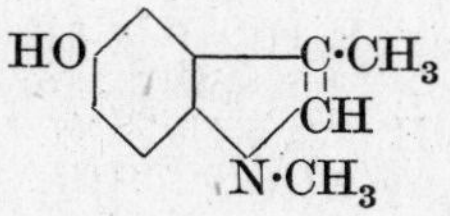

$C_{10}H_{11}ON$ MW, 161
  Needles by sublimation, m.p. 114° (100°).
Plates by cryst., m.p. indefinite.
  Me ether : $C_{11}H_{13}ON$. MW, 175. Leaflets
from MeOH. M.p. 60–1°.
  Et ether : $C_{12}H_{15}ON$. MW, 189. M.p. 86°
(85°). *Picrate* : m.p. 95°.

  Stedman, *J. Chem. Soc.*, 1924, **125**, 1373.
  Julian, Pikl, *J. Am. Chem. Soc.*, 1935,
    57, 566.
  Keimatsu, Sugasawa, *Chem. Abstracts*,
    1928, **22**, 3163.
  Straus, *Ann.*, 1914, **406**, 337.

Phytane (3 : 7 : 11 : 15-*Tetramethylhexadecane*)
  $CH_3 \cdot CH_2 \cdot [CH(CH_3) \cdot CH_2 \cdot CH_2 \cdot CH_2]_3 \cdot CH(CH_3)_2$
$C_{20}H_{42}$ MW, 282
  B.p. 179·5°/15 mm., 169·5°/9·5 mm. Sol.
pet. ether, hot EtOH, hot AcOH. D_4^0 0·803.

  Karrer, *Helv. Chim. Acta*, 1929, **12**, 906.

Phytol (3 : 7 : 11 : 15-*Tetramethyl-2-hexadece-*
nol)

          CH₃   CH₃
CH₂·CH₂·CH·CH₂·CH₂·CH₂·CH·CH₃
CH₂·CH·CH₂·CH₂·CH₂·C:CH·CH₂OH
    CH₃   CH₃

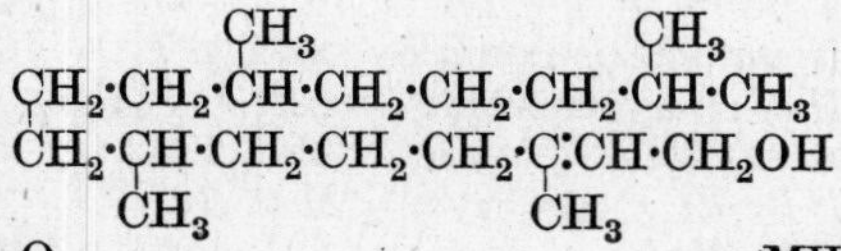

$C_{20}H_{40}O$ MW, 296

Decomp. product of chlorophyll. B.p. 202·5–
204°/10 mm. Sol. ord. org. solvents. D_4^{25} 0·8497.
n_D^{25} 1·4595.
  Urethane : m.p. 25·8–28·9°.
  Acid phthalate : *Ag salt*, m.p. 117–19°.
  Pyruvate : *semicarbazone*, needles from MeOH.
M.p. 72–5°.

  Fischer, Löwenberg, *Ann.*, 1929, **475**, 183.

Phytosterol.
  Generic name for the plant sterols. *See e.g.*,
Fucosterol, Sitosterol, *and* Stigmasterol.

Piaselenole

⟨⟩N=Se
      N

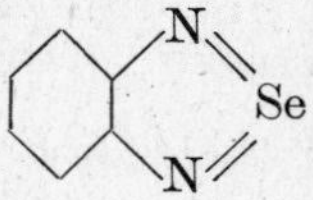

$C_6H_4N_2Se$ MW, 183
  Needles with odour of quinoline. M.p. 76°.
B.p. 246°. Sol. ord. org. solvents. Spar. sol.
H_2O.
  $B,HClO_4$: canary-yellow cryst. from conc.
$HClO_4$. Hyd. by H_2O.

  Battegay, Véchot, *Bull. soc. chim.*, 1925,
    37, 1281.
  Heinemann, E.P., 3,042; D.R.P., 261,412,
    (*Chem. Abstracts*, 1913, **7**, 3200).
  Hinsberg, *Ber.*, 1889, **22**, 2897; *J. prakt.
    Chem.*, 1916, **94**, 182.

Picamar   (4-*Propyl*-2 : 6-*dimethoxyphenol*,
5-*propylpyrogallol*-1 : 3-*dimethyl ether*, 4-*hydroxy*-
3 : 5-*dimethoxy-propylbenzene*)

          $CH_2 \cdot CH_2 \cdot CH_3$
CH_3O⟨⟩OCH_3
          OH

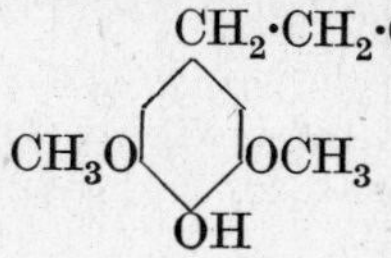

$C_{11}H_{16}O_3$ MW, 196
  Oil. B.p. 285°.
  Acetyl : cryst. from EtOH. M.p. 87°. Br
in $CCl_4 \longrightarrow$ dibromo deriv., m.p. 101–2°.

  Mauthner, *J. prakt. Chem.*, 1921, **102**, 37.

Picein.
See Piceoside.

Picene (1 : 2 : 7 : 8-*Dibenzphenanthrene*, β : β-
dinaphthylene-ethylene)

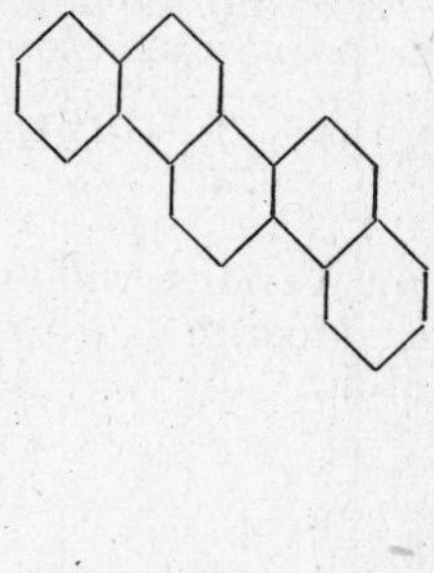

$C_{22}H_{14}$ MW, 278

Colourless cryst. from Py or boiling xylene. M.p. 365–6°. B.p. 518–20°. Sublimes. Spar. sol. boiling C_6H_6, $CHCl_3$, AcOH. Fluoresces pale blue in ultra-violet light. Sol. conc. H_2SO_4 ⟶ intense green col.

Dibromide : m.p. 295°.

2 : 7-*Dinitroanthraquinone add. comp.* : m.p. 299–300°.

Ruzicka *et al.*, *Helv. Chim. Acta*, 1934, **17**, 200, 470.
Winterstein, Schön, Vetter, *Z. physiol. Chem.*, 1934, **230**, 158.
Friedmann, *Ber.*, 1916, **49**, 277.
Meyer, Hofmann, *Monatsh.*, 1916, **37**, 715.
Bamberger, Chattaway, *Ann.*, 1895, **284**, 60.

Picenequinone

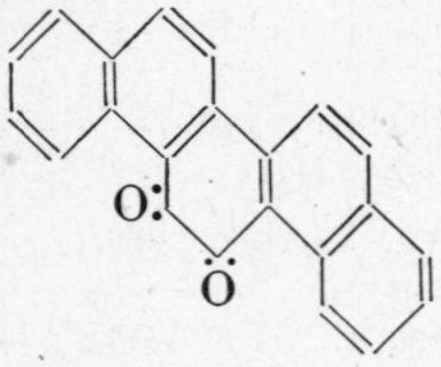

$C_{22}H_{12}O_2$ MW, 308

Red needles or leaflets from boiling AcOH. Sublimes on slow heating. Decomp. on rapid heating. Dist. with Zn dust ⟶ picene. Dist. over lead foil in vacuo ⟶ picylene ketone.

Meyer, Hofmann, *Monatsh.*, 1916, **37**, 681, 721.

Picenic Acid (2-β-*Naphthyl*-1-*naphthoic acid*, 2 : 2′-*dinaphthyl*-1-*carboxylic acid*)

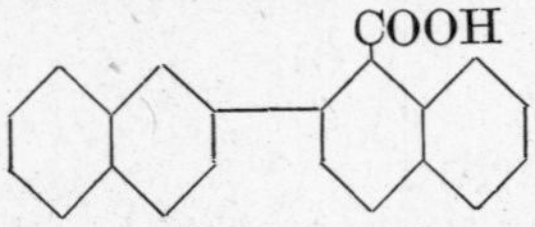

$C_{21}H_{14}O_2$ MW, 298

Cryst. from EtOH. M.p. 201°. Sol. EtOH, C_6H_6, $CHCl_3$. Conc. H_2SO_4 ⟶ picylene ketone. Dist. with CaO ⟶ 2 : 2′-dinaphthyl.

Bamberger, Chattaway, *Ann.*, 1895, **284**, 71.

Piceoside (*Ameliaroside*, p-*hydroxyacetophenone*-β-*glucoside*, *picein*, *salinigrin*)

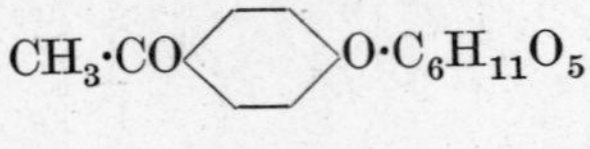

$C_{14}H_{18}O_7$ MW, 298

Constituent of various willow barks, *Amelanchier vulgaris*, Moench., *Picea excelsa*, Link., *Salix discolor*, Muhl. Cryst. + $1H_2O$ from H_2O. M.p. 195°. $[\alpha]_D$ −86·5°. Sol. EtOH, Et_2O, AcOH. Spar. sol. H_2O. Dil. acids or emulsin ⟶ *p*-hydroxyacetophenone + glucose.

Tetra-acetyl : m.p. 172–3°.

Oxime : m.p. 228°.

Phenylhydrazone : m.p. 185°.

Semicarbazone : m.p. 220°.

Ramart-Lucas, Rabaté, *Compt. rend.*, 1933, **196**, 1493.
Jowett, *J. Chem. Soc.*, 1932, 721.
Rabaté, *Bull. soc. chim. biol.*, 1930, **12**, 146, 332, 441, 965.
Bargellini, Leone, *Atti accad. Lincei*, 1925, **2**, 35.
Mauthner, *J. prakt. Chem.*, 1913, **88**, 764.

Picolide (1 : 3-*Diacetoindolizine*, 1 : 3-*diacetopyrrocolin*, 1 : 3-*diacetopyrindole*)

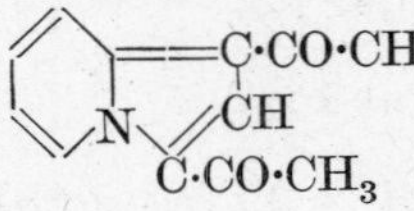

$C_{12}H_{11}O_2N$ MW, 201

Needles from H_2O. M.p. 176°. B.p. 360° (slight decomp.). Sol. $CHCl_3$, AcOH, Py. Mod. sol. cold EtOH. Insol. Et_2O. Sol. in conc. HCl re-ppd. by H_2O. $CHCl_3$ sol. adds Br. Decolourises $KMnO_4$.Aq. Heat with 25% HCl ⟶ pyrrocolin.

Monoxime : needles from EtOH or H_2O. M.p. 244°.

Monophenylhydrazone : yellow needles from EtOH.Aq. M.p. 168°.

Monosemicarbazone : yellow plates from EtOH. M.p. 233°.

Tschitschibabin, Stepanow, *Ber.*, 1929, **62**, 1068.

α-Picoline (2-*Methylpyridine*)

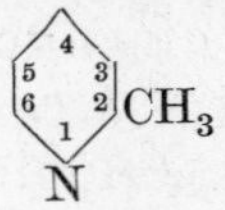

C_6H_7N MW, 93

Oil with strong unpleasant odour. B.p. 129°. D_4^{15} 0·9497. n_D^{17} 1·5029. Misc. with most solvents. Heat of comb. C_v 815·4 Cal. $k = 3{\cdot}2 \times 10^{-8}$ at 25°. Oxidised by boiling $KMnO_4$.Aq. or SeO_2 ⟶ picolinic acid. Reduced by Na in EtOH or by H (+ Pd or Pt) ⟶ α-pipecoline. Forms numerous complex salts.

B,HCl : hygroscopic cryst. + $\frac{1}{2}H_2O$. M.p. anhyd. 200°.

B,HBr,Br : red cryst. M.p. 76°.

B,HBr,HgBr$_2$: needles. M.p. 88°.

B,HI,I_2 : dark brown cryst. M.p. 44°.
$B,HAuCl_4$: cryst. M.p. 183–4° (167–8°).
$B_2,3HgCl_2$: needles. M.p. 170–2°.
$B,HCl,2HgCl_2$: prisms from H_2O. M.p. 154°.
B_2,H_2PtCl_6 : cryst. M.p. 216–17° (195°) decomp.
Methiodide : needles from EtOH. M.p. 226–8°. *Chloroplatinate* : m.p. 225–6°.
Ethobromide : m.p. 97°.
Ethiodide : m.p. 123°.
Picrate : needles. M.p. 169–71° (163°).
Styphnate : m.p. 180°.

Cartwright, Errera, *Compt. rend.*, 1935, **200**, 914.
Henze, *Ber.*, 1934, **67**, 750.
Tartarini, Samaja, *Ann. chim. applicata*, 1933, **23**, 351.
Borisov, *Ber.*, 1930, **63**, 2278.
I.G., E.P., 283,163, (*Chem. Abstracts*, 1928, **22**, 3892).
Wilkie, Shaw, *J. Soc. Chem. Ind.*, 1927, **46**, 469T.
Heap, Jones, Speakman, *J. Am. Chem. Soc.*, 1921, **43**, 1936.

β-Picoline (3-*Methylpyridine*).

Oil with sweetish odour. B.p. 143·8°. D_4^{25} 0·9515. n_D^{24} 1·5043. Misc. with most solvents. Heat of comb. C_v 812·4 Cal. $k = 1{\cdot}1 \times 10^{-8}$ at 25°. Forms numerous complex salts. $KMnO_4 \longrightarrow$ nicotinic acid. Red. $\longrightarrow$ β-pipecoline. $NaNH_2$ in boiling xylene $\longrightarrow$ 1-amino-β-picoline, m.p. 24°. Br in $CCl_4 \longrightarrow$ complex salt of bromopicoline, m.p. 200°.
$B,HCl,2HgCl_2$: cryst. from EtOH. M.p. 147–9°.
$B_2,ZnCl_2$: needles. M.p. 158°.
$B,HAuCl_4$: needles. M.p. 182–4°.
B_2,H_2PtCl_6 : prisms + H_2O. M.p. anhyd. 202°.
Methiodide + 2I : light brown leaflets from EtOH. M.p. 36°.
Picrate : m.p. 149–50°.
Styphnate : m.p. 153–4°.

Aldred, Lyons, *Chem. Abstracts*, 1931, **25**, 3345.
See also second and last references above.

γ-Picoline (4-*Methylpyridine*).

B.p. 143·1°. D_4^{15} 0·9571. n_D^{19} 1·5064. Heat of comb. C_v 816 Cal. $k = 1{\cdot}1 \times 10^{-8}$ at 25°. $KMnO_4 \longrightarrow$ isonicotinic acid. Red. $\longrightarrow$ γ-pipecoline.
$B,2HgCl_2$: needles. M.p. 128–9°.
$B,HAuCl_4$: prisms from H_2O. M.p. 205° decomp.
B_2,H_2PtCl_6 : leaflets. M.p. 231–44° according to rate of heating.
Methiodide + 2I : light brown plates from EtOH. M.p. 101°.
Methiodide + 4I : steel-blue needles. M.p. 63°.
Methiodide + 6I : dark green needles. M.p. 81·5°.
Picrate : m.p. 167°.

Bailey, McElvain, *J. Am. Chem. Soc.*, 1930, **52**, 1633.
I.G., E.P., 283,163, (*Chem. Abstracts*, 1928, **22**, 3892).
Meisenheimer, *Ann.*, 1920, **420**, 197.

α-Picoline-betaïne

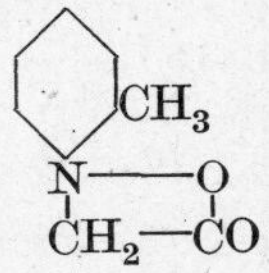

$C_8H_9O_2N$ MW, 151

Needles from EtOH–Et_2O. Decomp. at 162° (turns brown above 100°). Very hygroscopic. Sol. EtOH. H_2O sol. reacts neutral.
B,HCl : m.p. 188° decomp.
B_2,H_2PtCl_6 : prisms + $2H_2O$ from HCl.Aq. M.p. 212° decomp.

Kirpal, *Monatsh.*, 1910, **31**, 976.

β-Picoline-betaïne.

Leaflets + $1H_2O$ from EtOH–Et_2O. Sol. H_2O, EtOH.
B,HCl : prisms. M.p. 189° decomp.
B_2,H_2PtCl_6 : plates from H_2O. Decomp. at 222°.

Krüger, *J. prakt. Chem.*, 1891, **43**, 364, 370.

Picoline-carboxylic Acid.

See Homonicotinic Acid, Methylnicotinic Acid, *and* Methylpicolinic Acid.

Picoline-dicarboxylic Acid.

See 2-Methylcinchomeronic Acid *and* Uvitonic Acid.

α-Picoline-3 : 4 : 6-tricarboxylic Acid (6-*Methylberberonic acid*, 2-*methylpyridine*-3 : 4 : 6-*tricarboxylic acid*)

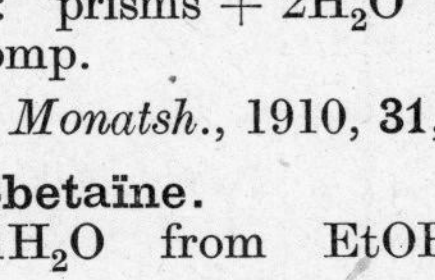

$C_9H_7O_6N$ MW, 225

Prisms or plates + $3H_2O$ from H_2O. M.p. anhyd. 226° decomp. (sealed tube). Very sol.

hot H_2O. Sol. EtOH, AcOH. Spar. sol. Et_2O, C_6H_6, ligroin. On standing several days with AcOH ⟶ α-picoline-3 : 4-dicarboxylic acid. Conc. aq. sol. + ferrous ammonium sulphate ⟶ dark red col. + ppt. Warmed with Cu acetate ⟶ bluish-green ppt.

Anilide-phenylimide : $C_{21}H_{15}O_3N_3$. MW, 357. Needles. M.p. 237°.

Lawson, Perkin, Robinson, *J. Chem. Soc.*, 1924, **125**, 631, 638.
Cf. Mumm, Hüneke, *Ber.*, 1918, **51**, 155.

α-Picoline-3 : 5 : 6-tricarboxylic Acid (2-*Methylpyridine*-3 : 5 : 6-*tricarboxylic acid*, 6-*methylcarbodinicotinic acid*).

Cryst. + $1H_2O$ from H_2O. Turns yellow at 170°. M.p. 226° decomp. The acid or its K salt on heating to 150° ⟶ α-picoline-3 : 5-dicarboxylic acid. $FeCl_3$.Aq. ⟶ yellow ppt.

Weber, *Ann.*, 1887, **241**, 6.

α-Picoline-4 : 5 : 6-tricarboxylic Acid (2-*Methylpyridine*-4 : 5 : 6-*tricarboxylic acid*, 6-*methylcarbocinchomeronic acid*).

Prisms or plates from H_2O. Decomp. slowly on heating (turns yellow at 210°, dark brown to black at 280°). Sol. H_2O. Very spar. sol. EtOH, Et_2O. Stable to boiling AcOH. $FeSO_4$.Aq. ⟶ red col.

Mumm, Hüneke, *Ber.*, 1918, **51**, 157.

β-Picoline-2 : 4 : 5-tricarboxylic Acid (3-*Methylberberonic acid*, 3-*methylpyridine*-2 : 4 : 5-*tricarboxylic acid*)

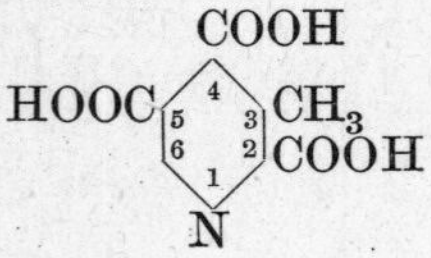

$C_9H_7O_6N$ MW, 225

Prisms + $1H_2O$. M.p. 208°. Sol. EtOH. Spar. sol. cold H_2O. Insol. Et_2O, $CHCl_3$, C_6H_6. $FeSO_4$.Aq. ⟶ weak reddish-brown col.

Dobbie, Lauder, *J. Chem. Soc.*, 1902, **81**, 151.
Dobbie, Marsden, *J. Chem. Soc.*, 1897, **71**, 663.

Picolinic Acid (*Pyridine-2-carboxylic acid*)

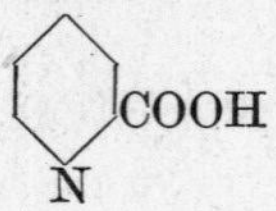

$C_6H_5O_2N$ MW, 123

Needles from H_2O, EtOH or C_6H_6. M.p. 136–7°. Sublimes. Very sol. AcOH. Sol. H_2O. Mod. sol. EtOH. Spar. sol. C_6H_6. Insol. Et_2O, $CHCl_3$, CS_2. Na in boiling EtOH ⟶ hexahydropicolinic acid. NaHg in H_2O ⟶ 1-hydroxyadipic acid. Conc. alc. KOH at 240° ⟶ pyridine. Zn dust + AcOH ⟶ α-picoline.

Me ester : $C_7H_7O_2N$. MW, 137. Hygroscopic cryst. M.p. 14°. B.p. 232°.

Et ester : $C_8H_9O_2N$. MW, 151. B.p. 243°, 122°/13 mm.

Phenyl ester : $C_{12}H_9O_2N$. MW, 199. M.p. 82°.

Anhydride : m.p. 124° (sealed tube).

Chloride : C_6H_4ONCl. MW, 141·5. M.p. 46°. B.p. 160° (slight decomp.)/10 mm.

Amide : $C_6H_6ON_2$. MW, 122. M.p. 106·5°.

Anilide : m.p. 76°.

p-*Toluidide* : m.p. 104°.

Nitrile : *see* 2-Cyanopyridine.

N-*Me-betaïne* : *see* Homarine.

Aurichloride : m.p. 200° (204° decomp.).

Platinichloride : cryst. + $2H_2O$. M.p. 215–16°.

Brode, Bremer, *J. Am. Chem. Soc.*, 1934, **56**, 993.
Hoppe-Seyler, *Z. physiol. Chem.*, 1933, **222**, 105.
Meyer, *Rec. trav. chim.*, 1925, **44**, 323.
Hess, Leibbrandt, *Ber.*, 1917, **50**, 385.
Ley, Ficken, *ibid.*, 1132.

Picramic Acid (4 : 6-*Dinitro-2-aminophenol*)

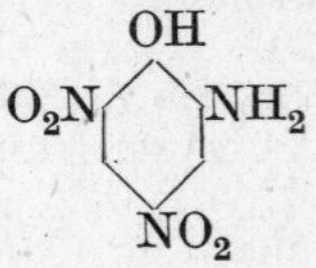

$C_6H_5O_5N_3$ MW, 199

Dark red needles from EtOH, prisms from $CHCl_3$. M.p. 169°. Sol. C_6H_6, AcOH. Mod. sol. EtOH. Spar. sol. Et_2O, $CHCl_3$. Sol. to 0·14% in H_2O at 22°. Sol. alkalis ⟶ reddish-brown col. Colourless sol. in conc. HCl. $k = 2{\cdot}5 \times 10^{-5}$ at 0°, $1{\cdot}1 \times 10^{-4}$ at 65°. Forms salts with acids and bases. More toxic than picric acid. Intermediate for azo dyestuffs. Gives colour reactions with proteins, amino-acids and amines, but not with their salts.

N-*Acetyl* : needles from H_2O. M.p. 201°.

N-*Benzoyl* : greenish-yellow needles from AcOH or xylene. M.p. 299–30°.

N-p-*Toluenesulphonyl* : m.p. 191°. *Py salt* : m.p. 203°.

O-*Acetyl* : m.p. 193°.

O-*Benzoyl* : leaflets. M.p. 218–19°.

N-*Benzyl* : ochre prisms. M.p. 139–40°.

N-*Me*: orange scales from dil. EtOH. M.p. 144–5°.

N-*di-Me*: yellow micro-cryst. from AcOH. M.p. 218–20°.

O-*Me ether*: 4 : 6-dinitro-2-aminoanisole. $C_7H_7O_5N_3$. MW, 213. Violet needles from EtOH. Insol. H_2O.

Clayton, *J. Soc. Dyers Colourists*, 1930, **46**, 365, (*Chem. Abstracts*, 1931, **25**, 926).

Seyewetz, Blanc, *Chimie et Industrie*, 1930, **25**, 605.

Dehn, U.S.P., 1,472,791, (*Chem. Abstracts*, 1924, **18**, 400).

Pomeranz, *Chem.-Ztg.*, 1921, **45**, 865, (*Chem. Abstracts*, 1922, **16**, 163).

Egerer, *J. Biol. Chem.*, 1918, **35**, 565.

Aloy, Frébault, *Bull. soc. chim.*, 1904, **33**, 496.

Hofer, Jakob, *Ber.*, 1908, **41**, 3198.

Kym, *Ber.*, 1899, **32**, 1429.

Picramide (2 : 4 : 6-*Trinitroaniline*)

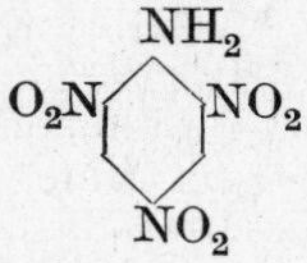

$C_6H_4O_6N_4$ MW, 228

Prisms from AcOH. M.p. 188° (192–5°). Sol. Me_2CO, AcOEt, C_6H_6. Spar. sol. EtOH, Et_2O. Hot KOH ⟶ NH_3 + picric acid.

N-*Acetyl*: 2 : 4 : 6-trinitroacetanilide. Needles from AcOH.Aq. M.p. about 230°.

N-*Benzoyl*: 2 : 4 : 6-trinitrobenzanilide. Needles from EtOH. M.p. 195–6°.

N-*Me*: $C_7H_6O_6N_4$. MW, 242. Yellow needles from EtOH. M.p. 114·8°.

N-*Di-Me*: $C_8H_8O_6N_4$. MW, 256. Yellow plates from C_6H_6. M.p. 138°.

N-*Et*: $C_8H_8O_6N_4$. MW, 256. Cryst. from C_6H_6. M.p. 84°.

N-*Di-Et*: $C_{10}H_{12}O_6N_4$. MW, 284. Prisms from C_6H_6. M.p. 163°.

N-*Propyl*: $C_9H_{10}O_6N_4$. MW, 270. Yellow needles. M.p. 59°.

N-*Dipropyl*: $C_{12}H_{16}O_6N_4$. MW, 312. Orange-red cryst. from Me_2CO–$CHCl_3$. M.p. 38°.

N-*Isopropyl*: yellow needles from EtOH–AcOH. M.p. 106–7°.

N-*Phenyl*: *see* 2 : 4 : 6-Trinitrodiphenylamine.

Hollemann, *Rec. trav. chim.*, 1930, **49**, 112.

James, Jones, Lewis, *J. Chem. Soc.*, 1920, **117**, 1273.

Weiss, Abeles, *Monatsh.*, 1932, **59**, 238.

Picric Acid (2 : 4 : 6-*Trinitrophenol*)

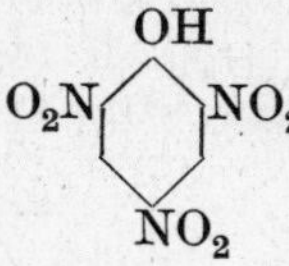

$C_6H_3O_7N_3$ MW, 229

Yellow leaflets from H_2O, prisms from Et_2O, plates from EtOH. Colourless cryst. from hot ligroin or conc. HCl. M.p. 122·5°. Sublimes with slow heat, deflagrates with rapid heat. Explosive, but salts are more so. Very bitter taste. Toxic.

Percentage solubilities:—H_2O, 0·98 at 9°, 2·33 at 50°, 7·6 at 100°; MeOH, 16 at 16°, 40·2 at 50°; EtOH, 6·8 at 16°, 19·7 at 50°; AcOEt, 39·4 at 16°, 68·5 at 50°; Me_2CO, 123·3 at 16°, 220·5 at 50°; Et_2O, 2·64 at 16°, 4·0 at 50°; $CHCl_3$, 2·0 at 16°, 5·7 at 50°; C_6H_6, 7·5 at 16°, 29·5 at 50°; toluene, 12·2 at 16°, 27·8 at 50°; CCl_4, 0·06 at 16°, 0·35 at 50°; CS_2, 0·11 at 16°, 0·18 at 34°; Py, 27·62 at 16°, 58·9 at 50°. Forms add. comp. with 2Py, m.p. 144–5°. Stable to hot conc. H_2SO_4 or HCl. Red. ⟶ picramic acid ⟶ 2 : 6-diamino-4-nitrophenol ⟶ 2 : 4 : 6-triaminophenol. Cl or *aqua regia* or $KClO_3$ + HCl ⟶ chloranil + chloropicrin. PCl_5 ⟶ picryl chloride. Forms cryst. add. comps. with many bases, phenols, hydrocarbons, etc.

Molnar, *Compt. rend.*, 1935, **201**, 59.

Haid, Koenen, *Chem. Abstracts*, 1934, **28**, 2907.

I.C.I., E.P., 370,436, (*Chem. Abstracts*, 1933, **27**, 2965).

Muraour, *Bull. soc. chim.*, 1932, **51**, 1152.

Desvergnes, *Chimie et Industrie*, 1929, **22**, 451.

Benedict, *J. Biol. Chem.*, 1929, **82**, 1.

Olsen, Goldstein, *Ind. Eng. Chem.*, 1924, **16**, 66.

Robertson, Garner, *Proc. Roy. Soc.*, 1923, **103A**, 539.

Holliday, Badier, U.S.P., 1,413,914, (*Chem. Abstracts*, 1922, **16**, 2150).

Marqueyrol, Loriette, *Bull. soc. chim.*, 1919, **25**, 376.

Me ether: 2 : 4 : 6-trinitroanisole. $C_7H_5O_7N_3$. MW, 243. Colourless plates or leaflets from EtOH. M.p. 68°.

Et ether: 2 : 4 : 6-trinitrophenetole. $C_8H_7O_7N_3$. MW, 257. Colourless needles from EtOH. M.p. 78·5°. Sol. Et_2O, CS_2, C_6H_6. Spar. sol. hot H_2O.

Phenyl ether: *see* 2 : 4 : 6-Trinitrodiphenyl Ether.

Benzyl ether: $C_{13}H_9O_7N_3$. MW, 319. Colourless prisms from C_6H_6. M.p. 147°.

Acetyl: colourless cryst. from Et_2O. M.p. 75–6°.

Tommasi, David, *Ann.*, 1873, **169**, 167; *Compt. rend.*, 1873, **77**, 207.
Kumpf, *Ann.*, 1884, **224**, 131.
Jackson, Gazzolo, *Am. Chem. J.*, 1900, **23**, 384.
Buttle, Hewitt, *J. Chem. Soc.*, 1909, **95**, 1759 (*Footnote*).
Jackson, Earle, *Am. Chem. J.*, 1903, **29**, 104.
Blanksma, *Chem. Zentr.*, 1909, I, 1809.
Marqueyrol, Scohy, *Bull. soc. chim.*, 1920, **27**, 105.
Guastalla, Racciu, *Industria chimica*, 1933, **8**, 1370.

Picrocrocin

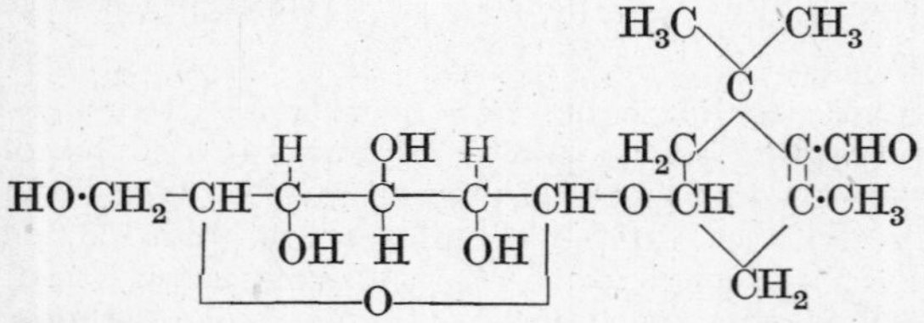

$C_{16}H_{26}O_7$ MW, 330

Terpene-glucoside, bitter principle from *Safran aquila* (*Safran electus*). Stout colourless prisms from $MeOH–CHCl_3–Et_2O$. M.p. 156°. Acid or alk. hyd. ⟶ *d*-glucose + safranal.

Tetra-acetate: needles from pet. ether. M.p. 143°. *Semicarbazone*: m.p. 106°.

Kuhn, Winterstein, *Ber.*, 1934, **67**, 344.
Cf. Lutz, *Biochem. Z.*, 1930, **226**, 97.

Picrolonic Acid (4-*Nitro*-3-*methyl*-1-p-*nitrophenylpyrazolone*-5)

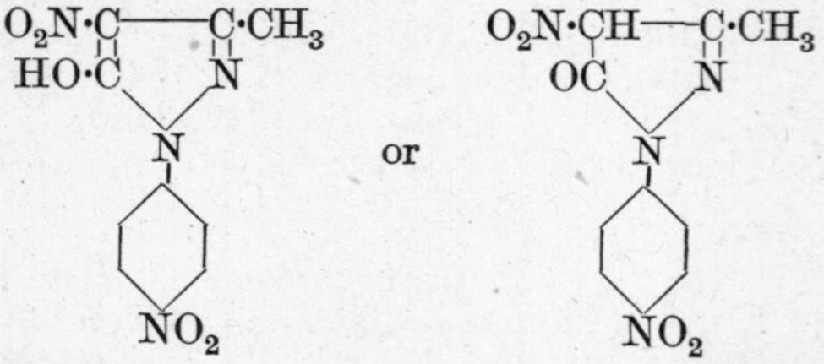

$C_{10}H_8O_5N_4$ MW, 264

Yellow cryst. M.p. 116·5° (decomp. at 125°). Sol. H_2O to 0·12% at 17°. Very spar. sol. EtOH. Org. bases ⟶ cryst. add. comps. of definite m.p. Forms very insol. salts of Ca, Cu, Pb, hence used in detection of these metals.

Hugounenq, Florence, Couture, *Bull. soc. chim. biol.*, 1925, **7**, 58.

Picropodophyllin

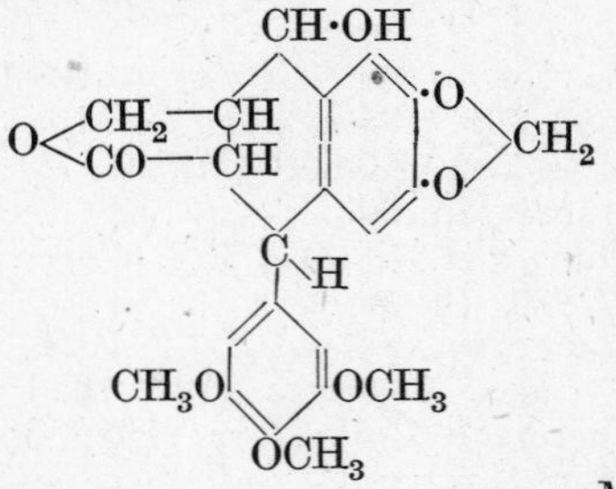

$C_{22}H_{22}O_8$ MW, 414

Constituent of purgative resin from various species of *Podophyllum*. Isomeric with podophyllotoxin but physiologically inactive. Colourless needles from MeOH or C_6H_6. Cryst. + 1 mol. solvent from MeOH or EtOH. M.p. 228°. $[\alpha]_D^{20}$ + 9·38° in $CHCl_3$. Fuming HCl at 110° in sealed tube ⟶ pyromellitic acid. Alk. $KMnO_4$ ⟶ gallic acid trimethyl ether + oxalic acid. Zn dust dist. ⟶ 1 : 6-dimethylnaphthalene.

Acetyl: $C_{24}H_{24}O_9$. MW, 456. M.p. 215–16°. $[\alpha]_D^{16}$ + 17·7° in $CHCl_3$.

Späth, Wesseleý, Nadler, *Ber.*, 1933, **66**, 125.

Picrorocellin

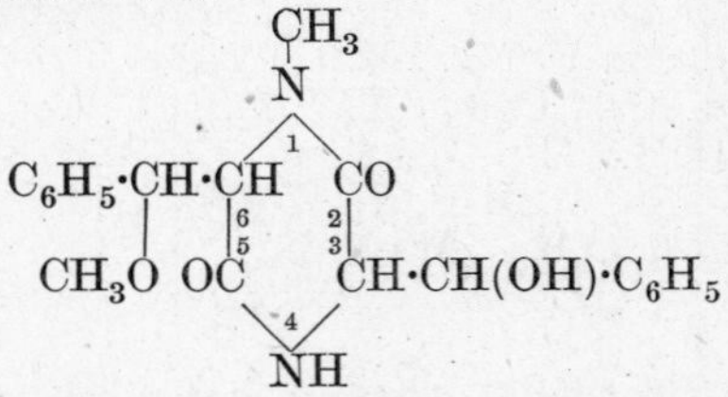

(An alternative structure has H at 1 and CH_3 at 4)

$C_{20}H_{22}O_4N_2$ MW, 354

Constituent of lichen *Rocella fuciformis*. Massive prisms from boiling EtOH. M.p. 190–220° according to rate of heating (192–4°). Insol. cold dil. aq. acids and alkalis. $[\alpha]_D^{18}$ + 12·5° in $CHCl_3$. Heat alone or with boiling NaOH.Aq. ⟶ anhydropicrorocellin.

O : *N*-*Di*-*Me*: dimethylpicrorocellin. $C_{22}H_{26}O_4N_2$. MW, 382. Prisms from boiling EtOH. M.p. 229°. Optically inactive. HI at 140° ⟶ 2 : 5-diketo-3 : 6-dibenzyl-1 : 6-dimethylpiperazine.

Anhydropicrorocellin: $C_{20}H_{20}O_3N_2$. MW, 336. Needles. M.p. 155°. $[\alpha]_D^{18}$ − 463·7° in $CHCl_3$. *Me ether*: prisms from EtOH–C_6H_6–pet. ether. M.p. 139°. $[\alpha]_D^{18}$ − 661·2° in $CHCl_3$.

Forster, Saville, *J. Chem. Soc.*, 1922, **121**, 816.

Picrotin

$C_{15}H_{18}O_7$ MW, 310

Di-lactone constituent of the molecular comp. picrotoxin. Colourless rods from H_2O. M.p. 255° (252°). $[\alpha]_D^{16}$ − 70° in EtOH. Baryta-water or 0·1*N*-KOH in sealed tube ⟶ acetone + a lactone $C_{12}H_{14}O_2$. Alk. $KMnO_4$ ⟶ α- and β-picrotinic acids. $MnO_2 + H_2SO_4$.Aq. ⟶ 1 : 1-dimethylphthalide-3 : 4-dicarboxylic acid. HCl at 180° ⟶ a chloroketone, $C_{14}H_{15}O_3Cl$.

Mercer, Robertson, *J. Chem. Soc.*, 1936, 291; 1935, 997.
Clark, *J. Am. Chem. Soc.*, 1935, **57**, 1111.
Horrmann, *Ann.*, 1916, **411**, 273.

α-Picrotinic Acid

$C_{14}H_{19}O_6 \cdot COOH$

$C_{15}H_{20}O_8$ MW, 328

Main product of prolonged hyd. of picrotin by dil. min. acids. Formed as ester together with K salt of β-picrotinic acid by action of MeOH–KOH on picrotin. Cryst. from AcOEt. M.p. 258° decomp. $[\alpha]_D^{18}$ + 71° 53′ in EtOH. Very sol. H_2O, EtOH, MeOH, Me_2CO, AcOH. Insol. $CHCl_3$, C_6H_6, ligroin. Heat in vacuo above m.p. ⟶ picrotinlactone + picrotoxic acid. 40% H_2SO_4 ⟶ picrotonol.

Me ester: $C_{16}H_{22}O_8$. MW, 342. Needles from H_2O. M.p. 239°. $[\alpha]_D^{18}$ + 77° 11′ in EtOH.

Et ester: $C_{17}H_{24}O_8$. MW, 356. Needles from H_2O. M.p. 199°. $[\alpha]_D^{18}$ + 74° 25′ in EtOH.

Horrmann, *Ann.*, 1916, **411**, 284, 298.
Horrmann, Seydel, *Ber.*, 1912, **45**, 3084.

β-Picrotinic Acid

$C_{14}H_{19}O_6 \cdot COOH$

$C_{15}H_{20}O_8$ MW, 328

Stout cryst. from H_2O. Decomp. at 204–5°. Sol. EtOH, MeOH, AcOH. Spar. sol. AcOEt, Me_2CO. Insol. $CHCl_3$, C_6H_6, ligroin. $[\alpha]_D^{18}$ + 4° 23′ in EtOH. Hot KOH.Aq. ⟶ picrotin-dicarboxylic acid.

K salt: cryst. from MeOH. Sinters at 245–7°, decomp. at 260°. $[\alpha]_D^{18}$ − 3° 57′ in H_2O.

Me ester: $C_{16}H_{22}O_8$. MW, 342. M.p. 231°.

See previous references.

Picrotoxic Acid

$C_{15}H_{18}O_7$ MW, 310

Needles + $2H_2O$ from H_2O. M.p. anhyd. 232°. Very sol. MeOH, EtOH, AcOH. Sol. Me_2CO, AcOEt, H_2O. Insol. C_6H_6, $CHCl_3$, ligroin. $[\alpha]_D^{18}$ + 81° 7′ in EtOH. Decolourises bromine water. Reduces $AgNO_3$ and Fehling's. H ⟶ dihydro-acid.

Me ester: $C_{16}H_{20}O_7$. MW, 324. M.p. 171·5°. $[\alpha]_D^{18}$ + 87° 32′ in EtOH.

Et ester: $C_{17}H_{22}O_7$. MW, 338. M.p. 143·5°. $[\alpha]_D^{18}$ + 81° 12′ in EtOH.

Mercer, Robertson, *J. Chem. Soc.*, 1936, 293.
Horrmann, *Ber.*, 1916, **49**, 1554; *Ann.*, 1916, **411**, 300.

Picrotoxin

$C_{30}H_{34}O_{13}$ MW, 602

Bitter principle from berries of shrubs of *Anamirta cocculus*, *Menispermum cocculus*, and other species. Is an equimolecular comp. of picrotin and picrotoxinin. Prisms from H_2O or EtOH. M.p. 203–4° (199–200°). $[\alpha]_D^{12}$ − 30° in H_2O. Br.Aq. ⟶ monobromopicrotoxinin + picrotin. $MnO_2 + H_2SO_4$.Aq. ⟶ 1 : 1-dimethylphthalide-dicarboxylic acid.

Horrmann, Thilo, *Chem. Zentr.*, 1936, I, 2954.
Mercer, Robertson, *J. Chem. Soc.*, 1936, 291.
Clark, *J. Am. Chem. Soc.*, 1935, **57**, 1111.
Sielisch, *Ann.*, 1912, **391**, 1.

α-Picrotoxinic Acid

$C_{14}H_{17}O_5 \cdot COOH$

$C_{15}H_{18}O_7$ MW, 310

Lactone-acid. Cubes from H_2O. M.p. 209° decomp. Very sol. MeOH, Me_2CO. Sol. EtOH, AcOEt. Insol. C_6H_6, $CHCl_3$. $[\alpha]_D^{18}$ − 5° in EtOH. Reduces cold $KMnO_4$.Aq., NH_3.$AgNO_3$ and Fehling's on warming. Decolourises bromine water. H ⟶ dihydro-deriv. Hot alkalis ⟶ picrotoxinin-dicarboxylic acid. Refluxed 15 mins. with 2*N*-H_2SO_4 ⟶ β-picrotoxinic acid.

Me ester: $C_{16}H_{20}O_7$. MW, 324. Prisms from H_2O. M.p. 182°. $[\alpha]_D^{18}$ − 9° 44′ in EtOH.

Et ester: $C_{17}H_{22}O_7$. MW, 338. Needles from H_2O. M.p. 159°. $[\alpha]_D^{18}$ − 8° 4′ in EtOH.

Horrmann, *Ber.*, 1913, **46**, 2793.
Meyer, Bruger, *Ber.*, 1898, **31**, 2958.

β-Picrotoxinic Acid

$C_{14}H_{17}O_5 \cdot COOH$

$C_{15}H_{18}O_7$ MW, 310

Needles from H_2O. M.p. 235° decomp. Very sol. MeOH, EtOH, Me_2CO, AcOH. Sol. Et_2O, $CHCl_3$. Insol. C_6H_6, ligroin. $[\alpha]_D^{18} - 48°$ in EtOH. Stable in cold to Br.Aq. and $KMnO_4$.Aq. Non-reducing.

Me ester: prisms from EtOH. M.p. 204°. $[\alpha]_D^{18} - 50 \cdot 3°$ in EtOH.

Et ester: prisms from H_2O. M.p. 198°. $[\alpha]_D^{18} - 49° 57'$ in EtOH.

See previous references.

Picrotoxinin

$C_{15}H_{16}O_6$ MW, 292

Di-lactone constituent of the molecular comp. picrotoxin, of which it is the physiologically active (neurophilic) component. Colourless rods from H_2O. M.p. 209·5°. Reduces $AgNO_3$ and Fehling's. Decolourises bromine water. HCl at 180° ⟶ a chloroketone, $C_{14}H_{15}O_3Cl$. Heat with 10% alkali ⟶ acetone + a lactone, $C_{12}H_{14}O_2$. Refluxed with 1% H_2SO_4 for 24 hours ⟶ picrotoxic acid. O_3 in AcOEt ⟶ H·CHO + α-picrotoxinone. H(+ Pd) in AcOEt ⟶ β-dihydropicrotoxinin, m.p. 256–7°. H(+Pt) in AcOH ⟶ α-dihydro comp., m.p. 252°.

Mercer, Robertson, *J. Chem. Soc.*, 1936, 291; 1935, 997.

Clark, *J. Am. Chem. Soc.*, 1935, **57**, 1111.

Picrylaniline.

See 2 : 4 : 6-Trinitrodiphenylamine.

Picryl bromide (2-*Bromo*-1 : 3 : 5-*trinitrobenzene*, 2 : 4 : 6-*trinitrobromobenzene*)

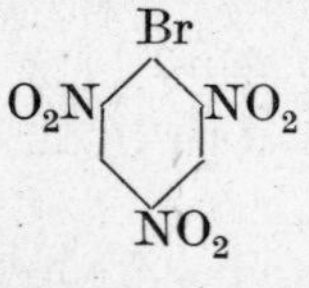

$C_6H_2O_6N_3Br$ MW, 292

Yellowish plates from EtOH–C_6H_6. M.p. 122–3°. Sol. EtOH, $CHCl_3$, AcOH, C_6H_6. Insol. H_2O. Hot NaOH.Aq. ⟶ picric acid. NaOMe ⟶ 2 : 4 : 6-trinitroanisole.

Hertel, Römer, *Z. physik. Chem.*, 1933, 22B, 267.

Picryl chloride (2-*Chloro*-1 : 3 : 5-*trinitrobenzene*, 2 : 4 : 6-*trinitrochlorobenzene*)

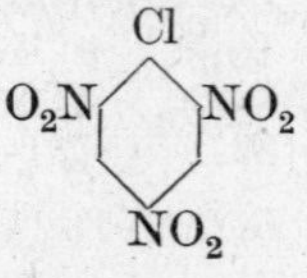

$C_6H_2O_6N_3Cl$ MW, 247·5

Needles or plates from $CHCl_3$ or EtOH–ligroin. M.p. 83°. D^{20} 1·797. Very sol. hot $CHCl_3$, C_6H_6. Sol. boiling EtOH. Spar. sol. Et_2O, hot ligroin. Insol. H_2O. Sn + HCl ⟶ 1 : 3 : 5-triaminobenzene. NH_3.Aq. ⟶ 2 : 4 : 6-trinitroaniline.

Desvergnes, *Chimie et Industrie*, 1931, **25**, 3, 291

See also previous reference.

Picryl iodide (2-*Iodo*-1 : 3 : 5-*trinitrobenzene*, 2 : 4 : 6-*trinitroiodobenzene*)

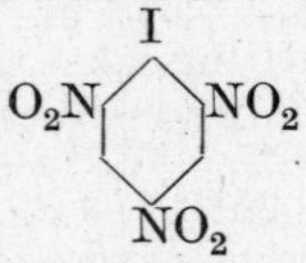

$C_6H_2O_6N_3I$ MW, 339

Golden-yellow tetragonal cryst. from C_6H_6. M.p. 164–5°. D^{22} 2·285. Hot NaOH.Aq. ⟶ picric acid.

Hertel, Römer, *Z. physik. Chem.*, 1933, 22B, 267.

***N*-Picryl-1-naphthylamine** (2 : 4 : 6-*Trinitrophenyl*-1-*naphthylamine*)

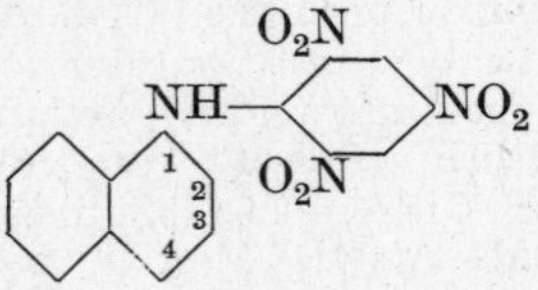

$C_{16}H_{10}O_6N_4$ MW, 354

Red plates from AcOH, needles from EtOH. M.p. 198–9°. Insol. cold EtOH.

N-*Me*: $C_{17}H_{12}O_6N_4$. MW, 368. Plates from AcOH. M.p. 247° (245°). Sol. hot C_6H_6, AcOH. Spar. sol. hot EtOH.

Wedekind, *Ber.*, 1900, **33**, 435.

Busch, Kögel, *Ber.*, 1910, **43**, 1560.

***N*-Picryl-2-naphthylamine** (2 : 4 : 6-*Trinitrophenyl*-2-*naphthylamine*).

Red prisms from AcOH. M.p. 233–233·5°. Mod. sol. most org. solvents.

Bamberger, Müller, *Ber.*, 1900, **33**, 107.

Picrylnitramine (2 : 4 : 6-*Trinitrophenylnitramine*, N : 2 : 4 : 6-*tetranitroaniline*)

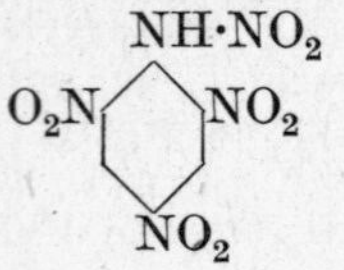

$C_6H_3O_8N_5$ MW, 273

Yellow cryst. from Me_2CO–$CHCl_3$. Deflagrates at 80–110°.

N-*Me* : *see* Tetryl.

N-*Et* : ethylpicrylnitramine. $C_8H_7O_8N_5$. MW, 301. Pale yellow plates from EtOH. M.p. 96°. D^{10} 1·644. Sol. $CHCl_3$, C_6H_6. Red. ⟶ 2 : 4 : 6-triaminophenol. Alkalis or NH_3 ⟶ intense red col.

N-*Propyl* : propylpicrylnitramine. $C_9H_9O_8N_5$. MW, 315. Colourless plates from EtOH. M.p. 98°. Alkalis or NH_3 ⟶ red col.

N-*Isopropyl* : isopropylpicrylnitramine. Pale yellow needles from EtOH. M.p. 108°. Sol. EtOH. D^{10} 1·563.

N-*Butyl* : butylpicrylnitramine. $C_{10}H_{11}O_8N_5$. MW, 329. Colourless plates from EtOH. M.p. 98–9°.

N-*Isobutyl* : isobutylpicrylnitramine. Needles from EtOH. M.p. 110°.

Jones, Willson, *J. Chem. Soc.*, 1930, 2277.
Duin, *Rec. trav. chim.*, 1917, **37**, 112.
Franchimont, *Rec. trav. chim.*, 1910, **29**, 300.
Romburgh, *Rec. trav. chim.*, 1885, **41**, 191.

Picylene-carbinol

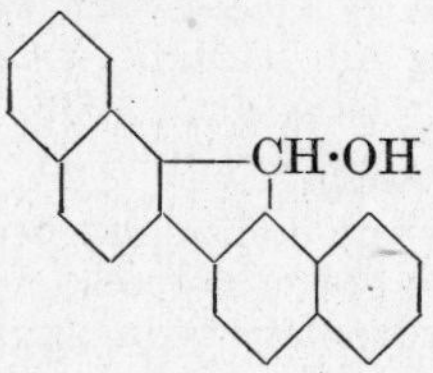

$C_{21}H_{14}O$ MW, 282

Pearly leaflets from $CHCl_3$. M.p. 230°. Sol. hot EtOH, AcOH, $CHCl_3$, C_6H_6. Spar. sol. Et_2O. Sol. in hot conc. H_2SO_4 ⟶ blue col.

Acetate : needles. M.p. 159°.

Bamberger, Chattaway, *Ann.*, 1895, **284**, 69.
Cf. Schmidlin, Hüber, *Ber.*, 1910, **43**, 2824.

Picylene-ketone

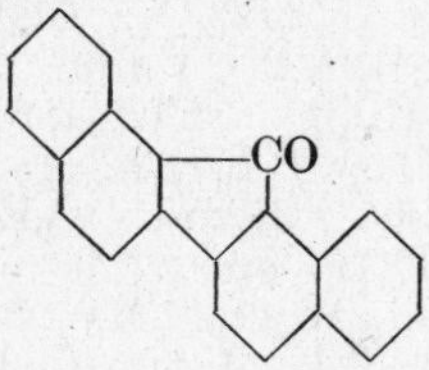

$C_{21}H_{12}O$ MW, 280

Golden-yellow cryst. from xylene. M.p. 185·5°. Sublimes on slow heating. Sol. AcOH, $CHCl_3$, C_6H_6, boiling EtOH. Sol. in conc. H_2SO_4 ⟶ violet col. NaHg ⟶ picylene-carbinol.

See first reference above.

Pilocarpidine

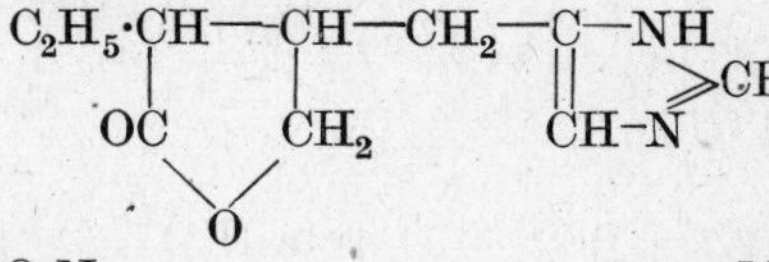

$C_{10}H_{14}O_2N_2$ MW, 194

Alkaloid occurring in leaves of *Pilocarpus Jaborandi*, Holmes. Physiological action similar to pilocarpine, but weaker.

Natural product.

Syrup. Decomp. on dist. Sol. H_2O. $[\alpha]_D^{20}$ + 81·3° in H_2O, + 35·2° in presence of alkali. Salts heated with alkali split off $NHMe_2$. NaOEt ⟶ isopilocarpidine. MeI ⟶ pilocarpine methiodide.

B,HCl : $[\alpha]_D^{20}$ + 72° in H_2O.

B,HNO_3 : prisms from H_2O. M.p. 137°. $[\alpha]_D^{20}$ + 73·2° in H_2O. Mod. sol. EtOH.

B,$HAuCl_4$: needles from AcOH. M.p. 125°.

B_2,H_2PtCl_6 : leaflets + $4H_2O$ from H_2O. M.p. anhyd. 187° decomp.

Synthetic product.

Racemic base : colourless cryst. M.p. 128–9°. Sol. $CHCl_3$.

Preobrashenski *et al.*, *Ber.*, 1936, **69**, 1837 ; 1933, **66**, 1537.
Späth, Kunz, *Ber.*, 1925, **58**, 513.

Pilocarpine

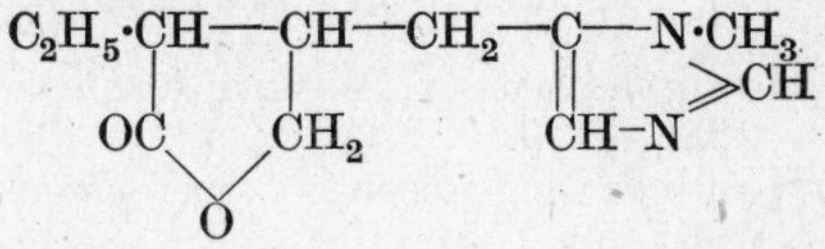

$C_{11}H_{16}O_2N_2$ MW, 208

Alkaloid from leaves of various species of *Pilocarpus*. Colourless oil. B.p. 260°/5 mm. (part. isomerisation). $[\alpha]_D^{20}$ + 100·5° (lowered in presence of alkali). Sol. alkalis ⟶ unstable salts (" pilocarpates "). Heat alone or with alkali ⟶ isopilocarpine.

B,HCl : m.p. 204–5°.

B,HNO_3 : *d*- ; m.p. 178° ; racemic, m.p. 139–40°.

B,$HAuCl_4$: m.p. anhyd. 130°.

Picrate : m.p. 147°.

Styphnate : m.p. 183°.

Preobrashenski *et al.*, *Ber.*, 1936, **69**, 1835 ; 1933, **66**, 1536, 1187 ; 1930, **63**, 460.

Pilopic Acid (*Ethylparaconic acid, 2-keto-3-ethyltetrahydrofuran-4-carboxylic acid*)

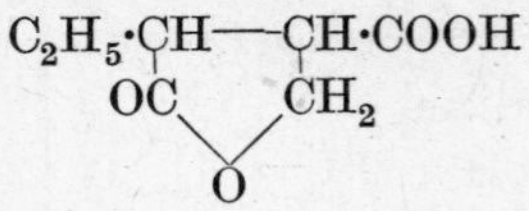

$C_7H_{10}O_4$ MW, 158

d-.
M.p. 122°. $[\alpha]_D^{18}$ + 54·6° in H_2O.

l-.
M.p. 122°. $[\alpha]_D^{18}$ − 54° in H_2O.

dl-.
Needles from H_2O. M.p. 90–1° (86–7°). B.p. 210–15°/18 mm., 189–92°/7 mm. slight decomp. Sol. ord. org. solvents.
Et ester: $C_9H_{14}O_4$. MW, 186. Needles from EtOH.Aq. M.p. 49°. B.p. 283°/751 mm. D^{20} 1·1085. Sol. EtOH, Et_2O. Insol. H_2O.

Preobrashenski *et al.*, *Ber.*, 1935, **68**, 847; 1930, **63**, 460.
Welch, *J. Chem. Soc.*, 1931, 1370.

Pimanthrene (1 : 7-*Dimethylphenanthrene*)

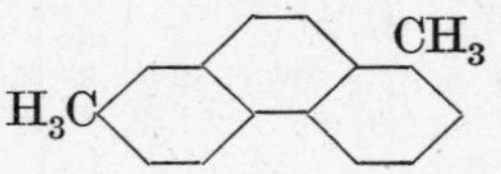

$C_{16}H_{14}$ MW, 206

Plates from EtOH. M.p. 86°.
Picrate: needles from MeOH. M.p. 132°.
Styphnate: needles from MeOH. M.p. 159°.

Haworth, Letsky, Mavin, *J. Chem. Soc.*, 1932, 1789.
Hosking, McFadyen, *J. Soc. Chem. Ind.*, 1934, **53**, 195T.

Pimanthrenequinone (1 : 7-*Dimethylphenanthraquinone*)

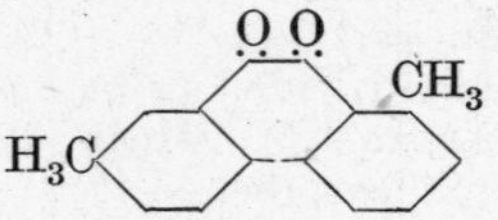

$C_{16}H_{12}O_2$ MW, 236

Plates from EtOH. M.p. 165°.
Quinoxaline deriv.: needles from $CHCl_3$–EtOH. M.p. 194–5°.

See first reference above and also
Ruzicka, Waldmann, *Helv. Chim. Acta*, 1932, **15**, 913.

***d*-Pimaric Acid** (*Dextropimaric acid*)

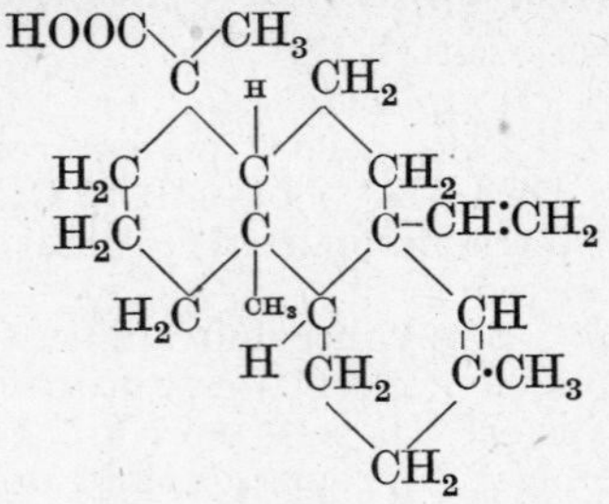

Suggested structure

$C_{20}H_{30}O_2$ MW, 302

Present in French colophony, etc. Prisms from EtOH. M.p. 218–19° (211°). $[\alpha]_D^{20}$ + 87·3° in $CHCl_3$. Stable to heat and min. acids. Dehydrogenation ⟶ pimanthrene.
Me ester: $C_{21}H_{32}O_2$. MW, 316. B.p. 149–50°/0·03 mm. D_4^{19} 1·030. n_D^{19} 1·52.
Et ester: $C_{22}H_{34}O_2$. MW, 330. B.p. 169–70°/0·2 mm. D_4^{14} 1·013. n_D^{14} 1·5151.

Palkin, Harris, *J. Am. Chem. Soc.*, 1933, **55**, 3677.
Ruzicka, Balas, *Helv. Chim. Acta*, 1923, **6**, 677.
Haworth, *J. Chem. Soc.*, 1932, 2717.
Ruzicka, de Graaff, Goldberg, Frank, *Helv. Chim. Acta*, 1932, **15**, 915.

***l*-Pimaric Acid.**
Note.—Since the compound usually described by this name is not a stereoisomer of *d*-pimaric acid, it has recently been suggested that it should be renamed *l*-sapietic acid, *q.v.*

Pimelic Acid (*Pentane*-1 : 5-*dicarboxylic acid*)

$HOOC{\cdot}CH_2{\cdot}[CH_2]_3{\cdot}CH_2{\cdot}COOH$

$C_7H_{12}O_4$ MW, 160

Prisms from H_2O. M.p. 104–5°. B.p. 212°/10 mm. Sol. H_2O, EtOH, hot C_6H_6. Insol. cold C_6H_6. Non-volatile in steam.
Me ester: $C_8H_{14}O_4$. MW, 174. B.p. 181–2°/18 mm. *Chloride*: $C_8H_{13}O_3Cl$. MW, 192·5. B.p. 135–6°/17 mm.
Di-Me ester: $C_9H_{16}O_4$. MW, 188. B.p. 130–5°/17 mm., 121–2°/11 mm.
Et ester: $C_9H_{16}O_4$. MW, 188. Cryst. from Et_2O. M.p. 10°. B.p. 182°/18 mm., 162°/6 mm. n_D^{20} 1·4415. *Chloride*: $C_9H_{15}O_3Cl$. MW, 206·5. B.p. 139°/17 mm.
Di-Et ester: $C_{11}H_{20}O_4$. MW, 216. B.p. 252–5°/748 mm., 153–6°/24 mm., 139–41°/15 mm. D_4^{20} 0·99448.
Diphenacyl ester: cryst. from EtOH. M.p. 72·4°.

Di-p-bromophenacyl ester: cryst. from EtOH. M.p. 136·6°.

Dichloride: $C_7H_{10}O_2Cl_2$. MW, 197. Oil. B.p. 137°/15 mm.

Dinitrile: $C_7H_{10}N_2$. MW, 122. B.p. 175–6°/14 mm. D^{18} 0·949. Solidifies to a glass. Insol. H_2O.

Anilide: cryst. from H_2O. M.p. 108–9°.

Dianilide: cryst. from MeOH.Aq. M.p. 155–6°.

Meyer, *Helv. Chim. Acta*, 1933, **16**, 1292.
Müller, *Monatsh.*, 1934, **65**, 18.
Müller, Rölz, *Organic Syntheses*, 1931, XI, 42.

Pimelic Dialdehyde (*Heptandial*-1 : 7)

$OHC{\cdot}CH_2{\cdot}[CH_2]_3{\cdot}CH_2{\cdot}CHO$

$C_7H_{12}O_2$ MW, 128

Viscous oil with odour resembling tobacco. Very sol. H_2O. Readily polymerises to a white solid insol. H_2O or org. solvents.

Dioxime: cryst. from MeOH. M.p. 153°.

Disemicarbazone: cryst. from EtOH. M.p. 244° decomp.

Weil, Traun, Marcel, *Ber.*, 1922, **55**, 2674.
Fischer, Düll, Ertel, *Ber.*, 1932, **65**, 1472.

Pimelin-ketone.
See Cyclohexanone.

Pinacol (*Pinacone, dimethyl-ψ-butylene glycol, tetramethylethylene glycol*, 2 : 3-*dihydroxy*-2 : 3-*dimethylbutane*)

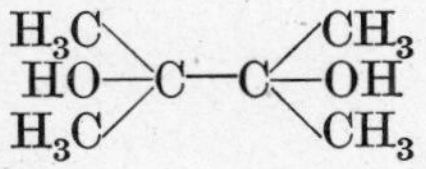

$C_6H_{14}O_2$ MW, 118

Cryst. from Et_2O, m.p. 38° : cryst. + $6H_2O$ from H_2O, m.p. 47°. B.p. 175°. Sol. EtOH, Et_2O, hot H_2O. Spar. sol. CS_2, cold H_2O.

Monoformyl: b.p. about 90°/20 mm.

Diacetyl: m.p. 65°. Sol. EtOH, Et_2O, $CHCl_3$.

Adams, Adams, *Organic Syntheses*, Collective Vol. I, 448.
Friedel, Silva, *Ber.*, 1873, **6**, 267.

Pinacolin (*Pinacolone, methyl* tert.-*butyl ketone*, 1 : 1 : 1-*trimethylacetone*)

$CH_3{\cdot}CO{\cdot}C(CH_3)_3$

$C_6H_{12}O$ MW, 100

B.p. 103–6°/746 mm. D^0 0·8265, D^{16} 0·7999.

Oxime: needles from EtOH.Aq. M.p. 74–5°. B.p. 171·6°/748 mm.

Phenylhydrazone: oil. B.p. 165°/32 mm.

2 : 4-*Dinitrophenylhydrazone*: yellow cryst. from EtOH. M.p. 125°.

Azine: b.p. 213–16°, 103°/17 mm.

Hill, Flosdorf, *Organic Syntheses*, Collective Vol. I, 451.
Badertscher, Whitmore, *J. Am. Chem. Soc.*, 1932, **54**, 825.

Pinacolin Alcohol.
See Methyl-*tert.*-butylcarbinol.

Pinacolone.
See Pinacolin.

Pinacone.
See Pinacol.

Pinane

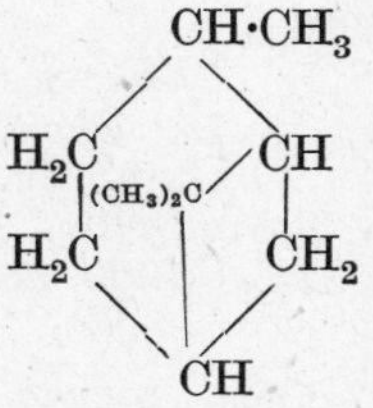

$C_{10}H_{18}$ MW, 138

Two stereoisomeric forms are possible but the homogeneity of any of the forms described has not been established.

d-. α-Pinane.

B.p. 166–166·5°/762 mm. D_4^{20} 0·8560. n_D^{20} 1·4630. $[\alpha]_D^{20}$ + 22·83°.

l-. β-Pinane.

B.p. 167·5–168°/748 mm. D_4^{20} 0·8567. n_D^{20} 1·4605. $[\alpha]_D$ − 19·84.°

dl-. *Inactive* Pinane, pinocamphane.

B.p. 164·5–165°. D_4^{20} 0·8551. n_D^{20} 1·4609.

Rule, Chambers, *J. Chem. Soc.*, 1937, 151.
Lipp, *Ber.*, 1923, **56**, 2098.
Vavon, *Compt. rend.*, 1910, **150**, 1127
Nametkin, Jarzeff, *Ber.*, 1923, **56**, 833.

α-Pinene

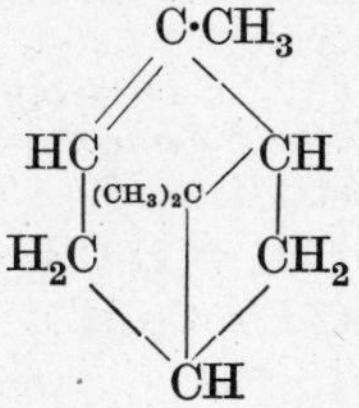

$C_{10}H_{16}$ MW, 136

Constituent of essential oils of Coniferæ. Main constituent of oil of turpentine.

d-. Australene.

M.p. − 50°. B.p. 155–6°, 47–50°/10 mm. D_{15}^{20} 0·862. n_D^{15} 1·4685. $[\alpha]_D$ + 48·3°.

Nitrosochloride: m.p. 81–81·5°. $[\alpha]_D$ + 322°.

l-. Firpene, terebenthene.

B.p. 155–6°. D^{20} 0·8595. n_D^{20} 1·47299. $[\alpha]_D$ − 47·2°.

Nitrosochloride: needles from EtOH–Et_2O. M.p. 81–81·5°. $[\alpha]_D$ − 322° in EtOH or $CHCl_3$.

dl-.

Colourless oil. B.p. 156·2°. D_4^{20} 0·8582. n_D^{20} 1·4658. Heat at 250–70° ⟶ dipentene. Dry HCl ⟶ bornyl chloride.

Nitrosochloride: leaflets from $CHCl_3$–MeOH. M.p. 103°.

Nitrosobromide: cryst. from $CHCl_3$–MeOH. M.p. 91–2° decomp.

Lynn, *J. Am. Chem. Soc.*, 1919, **41**, 361.
Schorger, *J. Am. Chem. Soc.*, 1917, **39**, 1042.
Semmler, Bartelt, *Ber.*, 1907, **40**, 1368.
Wallach, *Ann.*, 1909, **368**, 2; 1890, **258**, 344.

β-Pinene (*Nopinene, pseudopinene*)

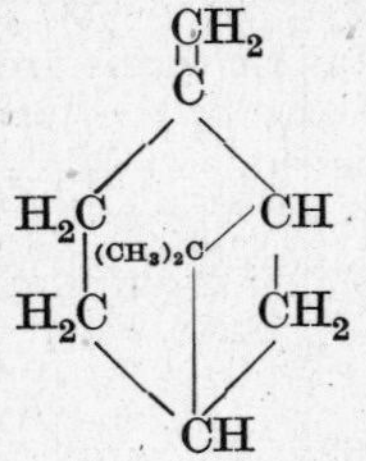

$C_{10}H_{16}$ MW, 136

Constituent of oil of turpentine. B.p. 163–4°. D^{22} 0·8675. n_D^{22} 1·4749. $[\alpha]_D$ − 22°. Dry HCl ⟶ bornyl chloride + dipentene dihydrochloride.

Vavon, *Compt. rend.*, 1910, **150**, 1129.

Pinene Hydrate.

See Methylnopinol.

"Pinene hydrochloride."

See Bornyl chloride.

Pinic Acid (2 : 2-*Dimethyl*-3-*carboxycyclobutylacetic acid*, 2 : 2-*dimethyl*-3-*carboxymethylcyclobutane*-1-*carboxylic acid*)

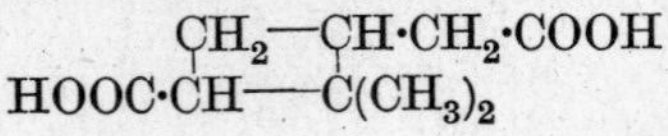

$C_9H_{14}O_4$ MW, 186

d-.

Prisms from Et_2O–pet. ether. M.p. 135–6°. B.p. 212–16°/10 mm. Very sol. H_2O, Et_2O. Sol. Me_2CO. Spar. sol. $CHCl_3$, C_6H_6. Insol. pet. ether. $[\alpha]_D$ + 7·1° in Me_2CO.

Di-Me ester: $C_{11}H_{18}O_4$. MW, 214. Liq. B.p. 128–30°/9 mm. D^{20} 1·0548. n_D^{20} 1·4487. $[\alpha]_D$ + 13·8°.

Di-Et ester: $C_{13}H_{22}O_4$. MW, 242. Liq. B.p. 142–6°/10 mm. D^{20} 1·0104. n_D 1·44962. $[\alpha]_D$ + 8·0°.

l-.

Needles from H_2O. M.p. 135–6°. $[\alpha]_D$ − 7·1° in Me_2CO.

dl-.

Prisms from H_2O. M.p. 101–102·5°. B.p. 214–16°/9 mm. Spar. sol. cold H_2O.

Di-Me ester: liq. B.p. 134–8°/17·5 mm. D^{20} 1·053. n_D^{20} 1·4490.

Di-Et ester: liq. B.p. 145–7°/10 mm. D^{20} 1·0093. n_D 1·44662.

Semmler, Mayer, *Ber.*, 1911, **44**, 3665.
Barbier, Grignard, *Bull. soc. chim.*, 1910, **7**, 548.
Baeyer, *Ber.*, 1896, **29**, 326.

Pinite.

See under Inositol.

Pinitol.

See under Inositol.

Pinocampheol

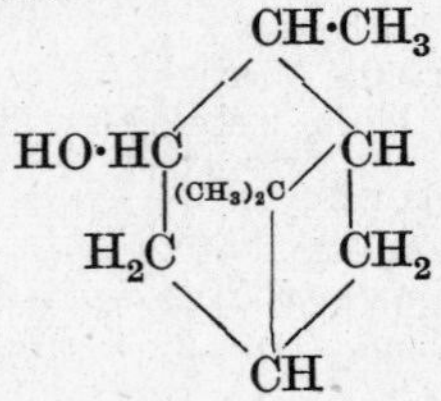

$C_{10}H_{18}O$ MW, 154

Cis:

d-.

M.p. 57°. B.p. 219°. $[\alpha]_D$ + 37°. D^{15} 0·973.

Phthalate: m.p. 126°.

l-.

M.p. 57°. B.p. 219°. $[\alpha]_D$ −36°. D^{15} 0·973.

Phthalate: m.p. 126°.

Naphthylurethane: m.p. 88°.

dl-.

M.p. 42°. B.p. 219°. D^{15} 0·973.

Trans:

d-.

M.p. 67°. B.p. 217°. D^{15} 0·968. n_D^{20} 1·48330. $[\alpha]_D$ + 55°.

Phenylurethane: m.p. 77°.

l-.

M.p. 67°. B.p. 217°. D^{15} 0·968. n_D^{20} 1·48335. $[\alpha]_D$ − 55°.

Phthalate: m.p. 107°.

Phenylurethane: m.p. 77°.

Naphthylurethane: m.p. 91°.

dl-.

M.p. 36°. B.p. 217°. D^{15} 0·968.

Phthalate : m.p. 113°.

Phenylurethane : m.p. 99°.

Schmidt, Schulz, *Chem. Zentr.*, 1934, II, 2077.

Pinocarveol (*Pinyl alcohol, isocarveol*)

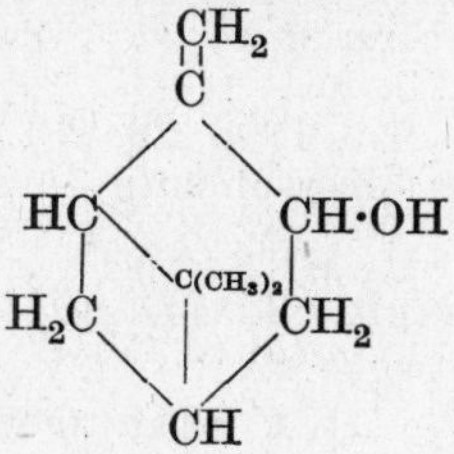

$C_{10}H_{16}O$ MW, 152

d-.

M.p. 7°. B.p. 208–9°/750 mm. D^{20} 0·9815. n_D^{20} 1·4993. $[\alpha]_D + 59°$.

Hydrate : m.p. 190–1°. $[\alpha]_D^{20} + 31°$ in H_2O.

Phenylurethane : m.p. 88–9°.

l-.

Occurs in oil from *Eucalyptus globulus*. M.p. 7°. B.p. 208–9°/750 mm. D^{20} 0·981. n_D^{20} 1·4996. $[\alpha]_D$ −62·19°.

Acetyl : b.p. 227–8°. D^{20} 0·997. $[\alpha]_D$ + 15·8°.

1-*Naphthylurethane* : m.p. 95°.

dl-.

B.p. 215–18°. D^{22} 0·978. n_D^{22} 1·4979. H_2SO_4 or $KHSO_4 \longrightarrow$ *p*-cymene.

Hydrate : m.p. 176–7°.

Phenylurethane : m.p. 95–6°.

Schmidt, *Ber.*, 1929, **62**, 2945; 1930, **63**, 1129.
Wallach, *Ann.*, 1893, **277**, 149; 1906, **346**, 222.

Pinocarvone (*Isocarvone*)

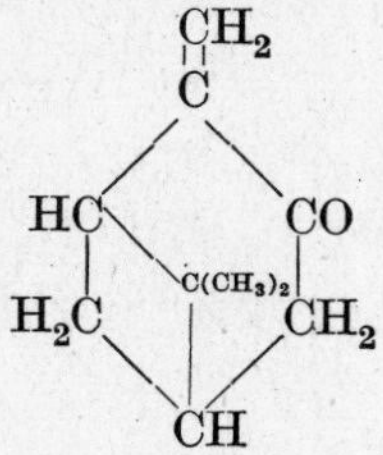

$C_{10}H_{14}O$ MW, 150

d-.

Oil. B.p. 222–3°. D^{20} 0·9881. n_D^{20} 1·50373. $[\alpha]_D$ + 13°.

Oxime : needles from MeOH.Aq. M.p. 68–9°.

Semicarbazone : needles. M.p. 212–15°.

l-.

Oil. B.p. 222–3°. D^{20} 0·987. n_D^{20} 1·50390. $[\alpha]_D$ −15°.

Oxime : needles from MeOH.Aq. M.p. 68–9°.

Semicarbazone : two forms. (i) Needles. M.p. 212–15°. (ii) M.p. 320°.

dl-.

Oil with peppermint odour. B.p. 222–4°, 95°/12 mm. D^{19} 0·989. n_D^{19} 1·5067. Forms add. comp. with H_2S. $NaHSO_3 \longrightarrow$ unstable add. comp.

Oxime : m.p. 98°.

Semicarbazone : m.p. 204°.

Schmidt, *Ber.*, 1930, **63**, 1131.
Wallach, *Ann.*, 1906, **346**, 222.

Pinol

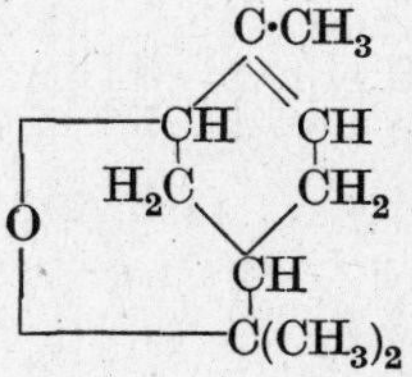

$C_{10}H_{16}O$ MW, 152

Liq. with odour resembling cineol. B.p. 183–4°, 76–7°/14 mm. D^{20} 0·953. n_D^{20} 1·4695. $KMnO_4 \longrightarrow$ terpenylic acid.

Nitrosochloride : m.p. 103°.

Neave, *J. Chem. Soc.*, 1912, **101**, 514.
Wallach, *Ann.*, 1896, **291**, 349.
Wagner, *Ber.*, 1894, **27**, 1644.

Pinol Glycol

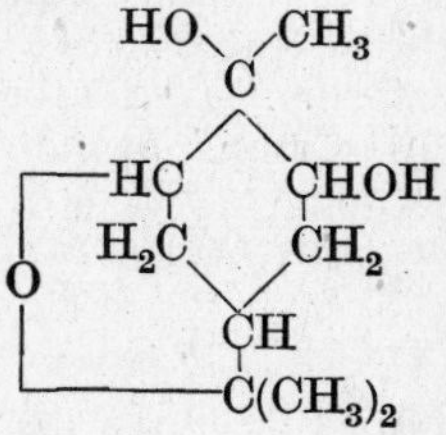

$C_{10}H_{18}O_3$ MW, 186

Cis :

Needles from $CHCl_3$. M.p. 125°. B.p. 157°/12 mm.

Di-Et ether : $C_{14}H_{26}O_3$. MW, 242. Needles from Et_2O. M.p. 52–3°.

Diacetyl : needles from H_2O. M.p. 97–8°.

Trans :

Two forms :

(i) *Active*. M.p. 74°.

(ii) *Inactive*. Plates from H_2O. M.p. 128–9°. B.p. 157–8°/12 mm.

Diacetyl : m.p. 37–8°. B.p. 165–7°/17 mm.

Wallach, *Ann.*, 1892, **268**, 223; 1890, **259**, 311.
Wagner, Slawinski, *Ber.*, 1899, **32**, 2066; 1894, **27**, 1644.

Pinol Hydrate (dl-Δ^1-p-*Menthenediol*-6 : 8)

$$C \cdot CH_3$$
$$HO \cdot HC \qquad CH$$
$$H_2C \qquad CH_2$$
$$CH$$
$$HO \cdot C(CH_3)_2$$

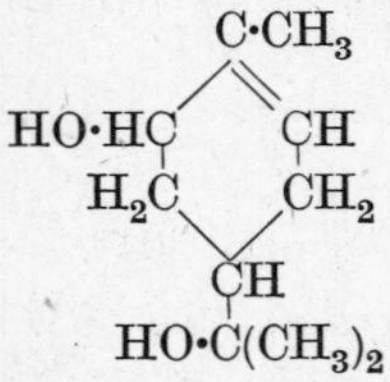

$C_{10}H_{18}O_2$ MW, 170

Plates or needles. M.p. 131°. B.p. 270–1°. Sol. H_2O, EtOH, Et_2O. $H_2SO_4 \longrightarrow$ red col.
Diacetyl : b.p. 159–161·5°. D_0^{18} 1·0385.

Wallach, *Ann.*, 1896, **291**, 351.
Henderson, Agnew, *J. Chem. Soc.*, 1909, **95**, 291.

Pinonene.
*See d-*Δ^4-*Carene.*
Pinonic Acid (2 : 2-*Dimethyl-3-acetocyclo-butylacetic acid*)

$$H_2C - CH \cdot CH_2 \cdot COOH$$
$$CH_3 \cdot CO \cdot HC - C(CH_3)_2$$

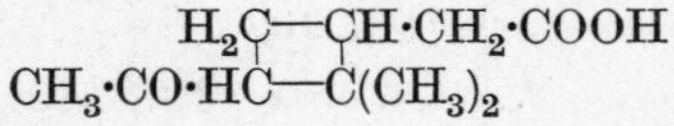

$C_{10}H_{16}O_3$ MW, 184

d-.
Cryst. from pet. ether. M.p. 69°. B.p. 168°/12 mm. $[\alpha]_D^{24} + 88 \cdot 27°$ in $CHCl_3$.
Oxime : two forms. (i) Plates from MeOH. M.p. 129°. (ii) Cryst. from AcOH. M.p. 190–1°.
Semicarbazone : cryst. from EtOH. M.p. 204°.

l-.
Prisms from H_2O or C_6H_6–pet. ether. M.p. 68–9°. $[\alpha]_D^{22} - 90 \cdot 6°$ in $CHCl_3$.
Oxime : two forms. (i) Plates from Et_2O–pet. ether. M.p. 129°. (ii) Cryst. from AcOH.Aq. M.p. 204°.

dl-.
Plates or prisms from MeOH. M.p. 103–5°. B.p. 180–7°/14 mm. Sol. $CHCl_3$.
Oxime : prisms from MeOH. M.p. 150°.
Semicarbazone : m.p. 206–7°.
Me ester : $C_{11}H_{18}O_3$. MW, 198. B.p. 254–5°/755 mm., 128°/11 mm. n_D^{17} 1·4558.

Note.—Numerous oily forms are known which are mixtures of stereoisomers.

Schmidt, *Z. angew. Chem.*, 1929, **42**, 126.
Ruzicka, Trebler, *Helv. Chim. Acta*, 1920, **3**, 762.
Barbier, Grignard, *Bull. soc. chim.*, 1910, **7**, 553.
Tiemann, Semmler, *Ber.*, 1896, **29**, 532.
Perkin, Simonsen, *J. Chem. Soc.*, 1909, **95**, 1175.
Baeyer, *Ber.*, 1896, **29**, 23, 2786.
Tiemann, Kerschbaum, *Ber.*, 1900, **33**, 2664.

Pinononic Acid (2 : 2-*Dimethyl-3-acetocyclo-butane*-1-*carboxylic acid*)

$$H_2C - CH \cdot COOH$$
$$CH_3 \cdot CO \cdot HC - C(CH_3)_2$$

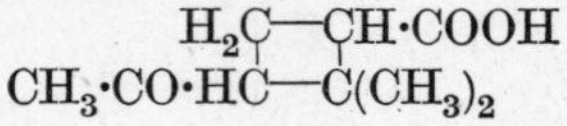

$C_9H_{14}O_3$ MW, 170

d-.
Prisms from H_2O. M.p. 129°. $[\alpha]_D + 40 \cdot 2°$ in Et_2O.
Semicarbazone : m.p. 212° (204°).

l-.
Prisms from $CHCl_3$. M.p. 129°.
Oxime : prisms from Et_2O. M.p. 178–80°.
Me ester : $C_{10}H_{16}O_3$. MW, 184. B.p. 127°/13 mm.

Guha, Ganapathi, *Chem. Abstracts*, 1935, **29**, 5818.
Blumann, Zeitschel, *Ber.*, 1913, **46**, 1189.
Kerschbaum, *Ber.*, 1900, **33**, 891.
Wagner, Ertschikowsky, *Ber.*, 1896, **29**, 881.

α-Pipecolein.
See 6-Methyl-1 : 2 : 3 : 4-tetrahydropyridine.
Pipecolic Acid.
See Hexahydropicolinic Acid.
α-Pipecoline (2-*Methylpiperidine, hexahydro-α-picoline*)

$$CH_2$$
$$H_2C^5 \quad {}^3CH_2$$
$$H_2C_6 \quad {}_2CH \cdot CH_3$$
$$NH$$

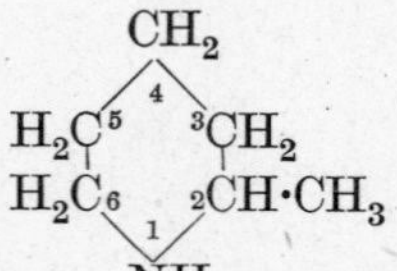

$C_6H_{13}N$ MW, 99

d-.
B.p. 117–117·5°. $[\alpha]_D^{15} + 18 \cdot 7°$ in $CHCl_3$. n_D^{15} 1·44983.
B,HCl : m.p. 210°.
B,HAuCl$_4$: m.p. 131–2°.
B$_2$,H$_2$PtCl$_6$: m.p. 194°.
Picrate : m.p. 116–17°.

d-*Tartrate* : m.p. anhyd. 110–12°.
l-*Tartrate* : m.p. anhyd. 126°.
N-*Me* : $C_7H_{15}N$. MW, 113. B.p. 127°. D^{16} 0·825. $[\alpha]_D^{15} + 68{\cdot}8°$. *Picrate* : cryst. from MeOH. M.p. 240° decomp.

l-.
B,HCl : m.p. 190°.
B,HAuCl₄ : m.p. 131–2°.
B_2,H_2PtCl_6 : m.p. 194°.
Picrate : m.p. 116–17°.
d-*Tartrate* : m.p. anhyd. 126°.
l-*Tartrate* : m.p. anhyd. 111–12°.
N-*Me* : $[\alpha]_D - 33{\cdot}6°$.

dl-.
Liq. resembling piperidine in odour. B.p. 117–18°/747 mm. $D_4^{23\cdot6}$ 0·8436. $n_D^{23\cdot6}$ 1·4464. Sol. H_2O, EtOH, Et_2O.
B,HCl : prisms from H_2O. M.p. 210°.
B,HBr : needles. M.p. 189°.
$B,HAuCl_4$: yellow prisms. M.p. 127° (118–19°).
B_2,H_2PtCl_6 : m.p. 202°.
Picrate : yellow needles. M.p. 134–5°.
N-p-*Toluenesulphonyl* : cryst. from ligroin. M.p. 54·5–55°.
N-*Benzoyl* : cryst. from EtOH. M.p. 44–5°.
N-*Me* : b.p. 126–7°/742 mm. D_4^{15} 0·824. $n_\alpha^{7\cdot4}$ 1·4533. Sol. EtOH, Et_2O, CS_2. Sol. 10–12 parts cold H_2O. *Picrate* : m.p. 240–1°. *B,HCl* : prisms from EtOH. M.p. 258–9°. $B,HAuCl_4$: m.p. 215–16°. B_2,H_2PtCl_6 : m.p. 194–5°.
N-*Et* : $C_8H_{17}N$. MW, 127. B.p. 147–8°. $D^{17\cdot5}$ 0·8368. $n_D^{24\cdot5}$ 1·4480. Sol. EtOH, Et_2O, $CHCl_3$. Spar. sol. H_2O. $B,HAuCl_4$: plates from EtOH.Aq. M.p. 108°.
N-*Propyl* : $C_9H_{19}N$. MW, 141. B.p. 167–167·5°. D^{20} 0·8296. *Picrate* : m.p. 113°.
N-*Phenyl* : b.p. 256·5–257°/710 mm. *Picrate* : prisms from H_2O. M.p. 167–8°.
N-*Benzyl* : b.p. 267°, 160–2°/47 mm.
N-*Nitroso* : b.p. 123°/31 mm.

Borissow, *Ber.*, 1930, **63**, 2278.
Adkins, Kuick, Farlow, Wojcik, *J. Am. Chem. Soc.*, 1934, **56**, 2425.
Skita, Brunner, *Ber.*, 1916, **49**, 1601.
Ladenburg, *Ber.*, 1898, **31**, 291.
Lipp, *Ann.*, 1896, **289**, 225.
Leithe, *Ber.*, 1930, **63**, 805.

β-Pipecoline (3-*Methylpiperidine, hexahydro-β-picoline*).

d-.
d-*Tartrate* : m.p. 76–8°.
l-*Tartrate* : m.p. 170°.

l-.
B.p. 124°. $[\alpha]_D^{25} - 4°$.
d-*Tartrate* : needles. M.p. 170–2°.

dl-.
Liq. resembling piperidine in odour. B.p. 125–6°/763 mm. $D_4^{24\cdot3}$ 0·8446. $n_D^{24\cdot3}$ 1·4463. Very sol. H_2O.
B,HCl : needles from C_6H_6. M.p. 171–2°.
B,HI : needles from C_6H_6. M.p. 158–9°.
$B,HAuCl_4$: m.p. 130–1°.
B_2,H_2PtCl_6 : red prisms from H_2O. M.p. 207°.
Picrate : yellow prisms. M.p. 136–8°.
d-*Tartrate* : m.p. 144–6°.
N-*Me* : oil. B.p. 124–6°. D^{15} 0·818. B_2,H_2PtCl_6 : orange prisms. M.p. 156–8°. *Methiodide* : cryst. from EtOH. M.p. 196–7°.
N-*Et* : b.p. 145·5–146·5°.
N-p-*Nitrophenyl* : leaflets from EtOH. M.p. 61°.
N-2 : 4-*Dinitrophenyl* : yellow needles. M.p. 67°.

Franke, Kohn, *Monatsh.*, 1879, **23**, 878, 883.
Ladenburg, Hesekiel, *Ann.*, 1888, **247**, 67.
Ladenburg, *Ber.*, 1894, **27**, 75.

γ-Pipecoline (4-*Methylpiperidine, hexahydro-γ-picoline*).
Liq. which fumes in air. B.p. 126·5–129°. D^0 0·8674. Sol. H_2O.
Chloroaurate : yellow needles from H_2O. M.p. 125–7°.

Ladenburg, *Ann.*, 1888, **247**, 69.

Piperazine (*Diethylenediamine, hexahydropyrazine*)

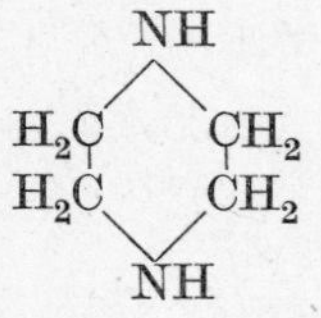

$C_4H_{10}N_2$ MW, 86

Hygroscopic plates from EtOH. M.p. 104°. B.p. 140°.
Hydrate : cryst. + $6H_2O$. M.p. 44°. B.p. 125–30°. Sol. H_2O, EtOH. Insol. Et_2O. $k = 6{\cdot}4 \times 10^{-5}$ at 25°. Aq. sol. reacts strongly alkaline. Dist. with Zn ⟶ pyrazine.
$B,2C_6H_5OH$: prisms from EtOH. M.p. 99–101°.
Picrate : yellow needles from H_2O. M.p. 280° decomp.
N-*Me* : $C_5H_{12}N_2$. MW, 100. B.p. 134–6°.

B,2HCl,H$_2$O : cryst. M.p. 242–3°. *Dipicrate* : m.p. 272° decomp.

N : N-*Di-Me* : $C_6H_{14}N_2$. MW, 114. B.p. 131–2°. D_4^{20} 0·8600. n_a^{20} 1·4474.

N : N-*Di-Et* : $C_8H_{18}N_2$. MW, 142. B.p. 169–71° (165°). *B,2HCl* : needles from EtOH. M.p. 277° decomp.

N : N-*Dipropyl* : $C_{10}H_{22}N_2$. MW, 170. B.p. 206°. *Dipicrate* : m.p. 258° decomp.

N-*Phenyl* : *see* N-Phenylpiperazine.

N : N-*Diphenyl* : *see* N : N-Diphenylpiperazine.

N : N-*Di-o-tolyl* : $C_{18}H_{22}N_2$. MW, 266. Needles from EtOH. M.p. 174°.

N : N-*Di-m-tolyl* : plates from EtOH. M.p. 126°.

N : N-*Di-p-tolyl* : prisms from pet. ether. M.p. 189–90°.

N : N-*Dibenzyl* : $C_{18}H_{22}N_2$. MW, 266. Needles from EtOH. M.p. 92°.

N-*Acetyl* : m.p. 52°. *B,HCl* : m.p. 181°.

N : N-*Diacetyl* : hygroscopic needles or plates from pet. ether. M.p. 144° (138°).

N-*Benzoyl* : m.p. 75°. *B,HCl* : m.p. 274°.

N : N-*Dibenzoyl* : m.p. 196°.

N : N-*Dibenzenesulphonyl* : cryst. from AcOH. M.p. 282–3°.

N-p-*Toluenesulphonyl* : m.p. 173° after sintering at 168°.

N : N-*Dinitroso* : yellow plates from H$_2$O. M.p. 158°.

Garelli, Racciu, *Angew. Chem.*, 1934, **47**, 366.
Abderhalden, Klarmann, Schwab, *Z. physiol. Chem.*, 1924, **135**, 180.
Pratt, Young, *J. Am. Chem. Soc.*, 1918, **40**, 1429.
Prelog, Stepán, *Chem. Abstracts*, 1935, **29**, 4013.
Jacobi, *Ber.*, 1933, **66**, 113.
Abderhalden, Haas, *Z. physiol. Chem.*, 1925, **148**, 245.

Piperazine-N-carboxylic Acid

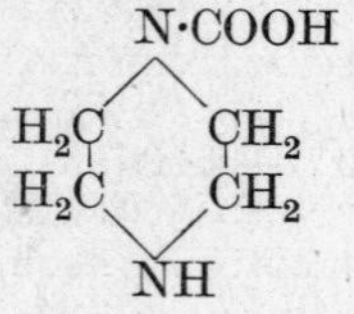

$C_5H_{10}O_2N_2$ MW, 130

Cryst. M.p. 162–5° (sealed tube).

Et ester : $C_7H_{14}O_2N_2$. MW, 158. B.p. 237°, 116–17°/12 mm. *Hydrochloride* : m.p. 145°.

N′-*Benzoyl* : cryst. from ligroin. M.p. 82°.

N′-p-*Toluenesulphonyl* : cryst. from C_6H_6–ligroin. M.p. 121°.

Moore, Boyle, Thorn, *J. Chem. Soc.*, 1929, 39.
Rosdalsky, *J. prakt. Chem.*, 1896, **53**, 24.

Piperazine-N : N′-dicarboxylic Acid

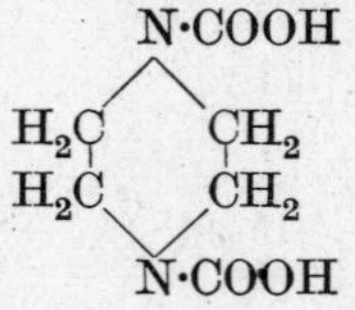

$C_6H_{10}O_4N_2$ MW, 174

Free acid unknown.

Di-Me ester : $C_8H_{14}O_4N_2$. MW, 202. Cryst. from H$_2$O. M.p. 81°.

Di-Et ester : $C_{10}H_{18}O_4N_2$. MW, 230. Needles from ligroin. M.p. 45°.

Diphenyl ester : $C_{18}H_{18}O_4N_2$. MW, 326. Prisms. M.p. 177–8°.

Di-1-naphthyl ester : $C_{26}H_{22}O_4N_2$. MW, 426. M.p. 190–1°.

Di-2-naphthyl ester : m.p. 220°.

Dinitrile : $C_6H_8N_4$. MW, 136. Cryst. from EtOH. M.p. 168°.

van Dorp, *Rec. trav. chim.*, 1909, **28**, 75.
Cazeneuve, Moreau, *Compt. rend.*, 1897, **125**, 1183.

Piperic Acid (4-[3 : 4-*Methylenedioxyphenyl*]-1 : 4-*butadiene-1-carboxylic acid*, 3-*piperonylidenecrotonic acid*, 4-[3 : 4-*methylenedioxyphenyl*]-*vinylacrylic acid*)

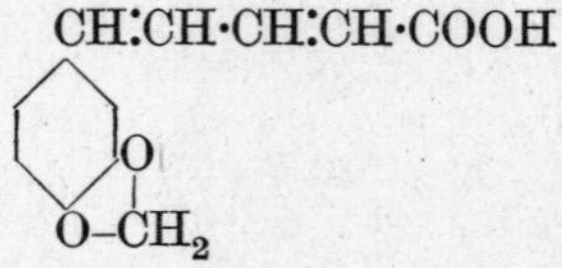

$C_{12}H_{10}O_4$ MW, 218

Colourless needles from EtOH, turning yellow in light. M.p. 215°. Sol. hot EtOH. Spar. sol. Et$_2$O, C_6H_6. Insol. H$_2$O. Sublimes in yellow needles. $H_2SO_4 \longrightarrow$ bluish-violet col. KMnO$_4$ at 3° $\longrightarrow$ piperonal.

Me ester : $C_{13}H_{12}O_4$. MW, 232. Yellow plates from MeOH. M.p. 146°.

Et ester : $C_{14}H_{14}O_4$. MW, 246. Plates from EtOH. M.p. 78°.

p-*Nitrobenzyl ester* : cryst. from 80% EtOH. M.p. 145°.

Ladenburg, Scholtz, *Ber.*, 1894, **27**, 2959.
Babo, Keller, *J. prakt. Chem.*, 1857, **72**, 56.
Fittig, Mielch, *Ann.*, 1869, **152**, 27.

Δ^2-Piperideine.
See 1 : 2 : 3 : 4-Tetrahydropyridine.

Piperidine (*Hexahydropyridine, pentamethyleneimine*)

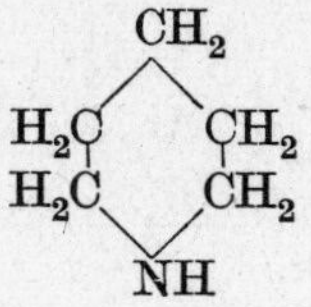

$C_5H_{11}N$ MW, 85

Occurs in form of piperine in black pepper (*Piper nigrum, P. longum, P. officinarum*). Colourless liq. with characteristic odour. M.p. − 9°. B.p. 106·0°, 52·6°/170 mm., 17·7°/20 mm. D_4^{20} 0·8606, D_4^{50} 0·8336, D_4^{80} 0·8033. n_D^{20} 1·4530. Heat of comb. C_v 825 Cal. $k = 1{\cdot}58 \times 10^{-3}$ at 25°. Misc. with H_2O in all proportions. Pyrolysis ⟶ pyrrole. Forms a hydrate, m.p. − 14°. Forms complexes with heavy metal salts.

B,HCl : prisms from EtOH. M.p. 244–5°.
B,HBr : prisms from $CHCl_3$. M.p. 235°.
B,HNO₂ : plates. M.p. 110°.
Acetate : m.p. 106°.
Picrate : yellow needles from H_2O. M.p. 151–2°.
Styphnate : m.p. 231–2°.
B,HAuCl₄ : plates from EtOH. M.p. 204°.
N-*Me* : *see* *N*-Methylpiperidine.
N-*Et* : *see* *N*-Ethylpiperidine.
N-*Propyl* : $C_8H_{17}N$. MW, 127. B.p. 149–50°. *Methiodide* : m.p. 181–2°. *Ethiodide* : m.p. 276·5°.
N-*Isopropyl* : b.p. 149–50°.
N-*Butyl* : $C_9H_{19}N$. MW, 141. B.p. 175–6°. *Methiodide* : m.p. 198°.
N-*Amyl* : $C_{10}H_{21}N$. MW, 155. B.p. 196°. *Picrate* : m.p. 107°.
N-*Isoamyl* : b.p. 188°. *Methiodide* : m.p. 195°.
N-*Allyl* : $C_8H_{15}N$. MW, 125. B.p. 151–2°. D^{19} 0·8445.
N-*Benzyl* : $C_{12}H_{17}N$. MW, 175. B.p. 245°, 119°/13 mm. *B_2,H_2PtCl_6* : m.p. 191–3°.
N-*Phenyl* : *see* *N*-Phenylpiperidine.
N-*Picryl* : yellow prisms from EtOH. M.p. 104–6°.
N-*Triphenylmethyl* : needles from EtOH. M.p. 153°.
N-*Formyl*: piperidine-*N*-aldehyde. $C_6H_{11}ON$. MW, 113. B.p. 222°. *B,HBr* : m.p. 103·5°.
N-*Acetyl* : b.p. 226–7°. *B,H_2PtCl_6* : red cryst. M.p. 107–9°.
N-*Benzoyl* : m.p. 48°. B.p. 320–1°, 108–4°/20 mm.
N-p-*Bromobenzoyl* : plates from EtOH. M.p. 95°.
N-p-*Nitrobenzoyl* : yellow cryst. from EtOH. M.p. 120·5°.
N-3 : 5-*Dinitrobenzoyl* : cryst. from EtOH. M.p. 147°.
N-*Benzenesulphonyl* : prisms. M.p. 93–4°.
N-p-*Toluenesulphonyl* : m.p. 95–6° (103°).
N-*Nitroso* : yellow oil. B.p. 218°, 109°/20 mm.

Marvel, Lazier, *Organic Syntheses*, Collective Vol. I, 93.
Skita, Brunner, *Ber.*, 1916, **49**, 1600.
Babo, Keller, *J. prakt. Chem.*, 1857, **72**, 55.
Marie, Lejeune, *J. chim. phys.*, 1925, **22**, 59.
Skita, Meyer, *Ber.*, 1912, **45**, 3592.
Wojcik, Adkins, *J. Am. Chem. Soc.*, 1934, **56**, 2419.
Staudinger, Müller, *Ber.*, 1923, **56**, 711.
Ouchakof, Lifchitz, Jdanova, *Bull. soc. chim.*, 1935, **2**, 573.

Piperidine-2-aldehyde (2-*Formylpiperidine, 2-aldehydopiperidine*)

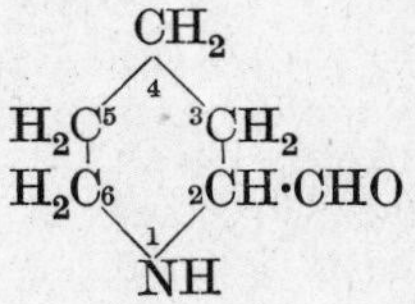

$C_6H_{11}ON$ MW, 113

Di-Et acetal : $C_{10}H_{21}O_2N$. MW, 187. B.p. 95–105°/14 mm.
p-*Nitrophenylhydrazone hydrochloride* : yellow cryst. M.p. 228° decomp.

Harries, Lénart, *Ann.*, 1915, **410**, 105.

Piperidine-3-aldehyde (3-*Formylpiperidine, 3-aldehydopiperidine*).
N-*Et* : $C_8H_{15}ON$. MW, 141. B.p. 40°/0·2 mm. *Di-Et acetal* : $C_{12}H_{25}O_2N$. MW, 215. B.p. 63–5°/0·04 mm.
Di-Et acetal : b.p. 104°/9 mm.
m-*Nitrophenylhydrazone hydrochloride* : yellow cryst. M.p. 232–3° decomp.

Wohl, Losanitsch, *Ber.*, 1907, **40**, 4695.

Piperidine-*N*-aldehyde.
See under Piperidine.

Piperidine-carboxylic Acid.
See Hexahydroisonicotinic Acid, Hexahydronicotinic Acid, *and* Hexahydropicolinic Acid.

Piperidine-N-carboxylic Acid

$$CH_2$$
$$H_2C \quad CH_2$$
$$H_2C \quad CH_2$$
$$N \cdot COOH$$

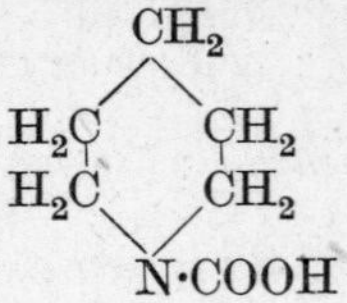

$C_6H_{11}O_2N$ MW, 129

Free acid unknown.

Me ester : $C_7H_{13}O_2N$. MW, 143. B.p. 201°.

Et ester : piperidylurethane, pentamethylene-urethane. $C_8H_{15}O_2N$. MW, 157. B.p. 211–12°, 103°/20 mm.

Phenyl ester : $C_{12}H_{15}O_2N$. MW, 205. Plates from EtOH. M.p. 80°.

2-Naphthyl ester : $C_{16}H_{17}O_2N$. MW, 255. Needles from EtOH. M.p. 107°.

Chloride : $C_6H_{10}ONCl$. MW, 147·5. B.p. 237–8°, 112°/13 mm.

Amide : piperidylurea. $C_6H_{12}ON_2$. MW, 128. Needles from EtOH. M.p. 105–6°.

Nitrile : N-cyanopiperidine. $C_6H_{10}N_2$. MW, 110. B.p. 124°/30 mm., 102°/10 mm.

> Schotten, *Ber.*, 1883, **16**, 647.
> Bouchetal, la Roche, *Bull. soc. chim.*, 1903, **29**, 753 ; 1902, **27**, 451.

Piperidine-3 : 4-dicarboxylic Acid.

See Hexahydrocinchomeronic Acid.

Piperidinic Acid.

See 3-Amino-n-butyric Acid.

Piperidinoacetaldehyde

$$CH_2$$
$$H_2C \quad CH_2$$
$$H_2C \quad CH_2$$
$$N \cdot CH_2 \cdot CHO$$

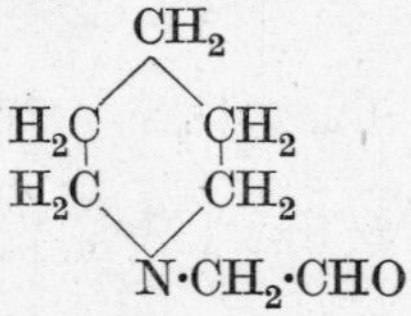

$C_7H_{13}ON$ MW, 127

Not known in free state.

B,HCl : cryst. from Et_2O. M.p. 103°. Decomp. on standing in air.

Chloroaurate : yellow cryst. M.p. 109–11°.

Chloroplatinate : orange-yellow needles. M.p. 121–2°.

Oxime : cryst. from EtOH–Et_2O. M.p. 135–6°.

Semicarbazone : cryst. M.p. 76°.

Acetal : $C_{11}H_{23}O_2N$. MW, 201. Liq. B.p. 219–21°. *B,HAuCl$_4$* : yellow plates. M.p. 96°. *B$_2$,H$_2$PtCl$_6$* : orange needles. M.p. 134°. *Methiodide* : cryst. M.p. 121°. *Ethiodide* : cryst. from C_6H_6. M.p. 123° (105°). *Picrate* : yellow needles. M.p. 67°.

> Stoermer, *Ber.*, 1898, **31**, 2542.
> Stoermer, Burkert, *Ber.*, 1894, **27**, 2016.

Piperidinoacetic Acid (*Piperidine-1-acetic acid, pentamethyleneglycine*)

$$CH_2$$
$$H_2C \quad CH_2$$
$$H_2C \quad CH_2$$
$$N \cdot CH_2 \cdot COOH$$

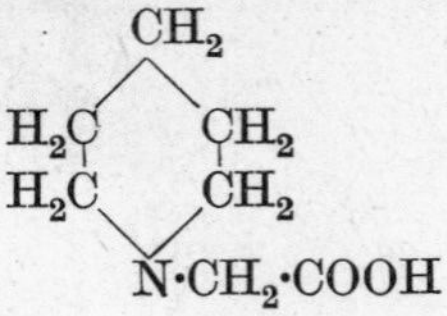

$C_7H_{13}O_2N$ MW, 143

Prisms + $1H_2O$ from EtOH. M.p. anhyd. 215–17°. Sol. H_2O, EtOH, $CHCl_3$. Spar. sol. Et_2O, Me_2CO, ligroin, C_6H_6. Sublimes.

B,HCl : leaflets from EtOH–Et_2O. M.p. 215–16°.

Methochloride : m.p. 213° decomp.

Methochloroaurate : needles from H_2O. M.p. 178–9°.

Methochloroplatinate : orange cryst. M.p. 219°.

Me ester : $C_8H_{15}O_2N$. MW, 157. Oil. B.p. 205–7°.

Et ester : $C_9H_{17}O_2N$. MW, 171. Oil. B.p. 209°/732 mm. *B,HCl* : m.p. 130–1°. *Methochloride* : m.p. 189°. Hygroscopic. *Methiodide* : cryst. from EtOH. M.p. 158–9°. *Methochloroplatinate* : orange cryst. M.p. 225°.

Nitrile : $C_7H_{12}N_2$. MW, 124. Cryst. M.p. 19°. B.p. 210°, 99–100°/15 mm. *Methiodide* : leaflets. M.p. 192–3°.

> Ley, *Ber.*, 1909, **42**, 367.
> Wedekind, *Ber.*, 1902, **35**, 182 ; 1899, **32**, 724.
> Bischoff, *Ber.*, 1898, **31**, 2840.
> Kraut, *Ann.*, 1871, **157**, 66.

Piperidinoacetone (N-*Acetonylpiperidine*)

$$CH_2$$
$$H_2C \quad CH_2$$
$$H_2C \quad CH_2$$
$$N \cdot CH_2 \cdot CO \cdot CH_3$$

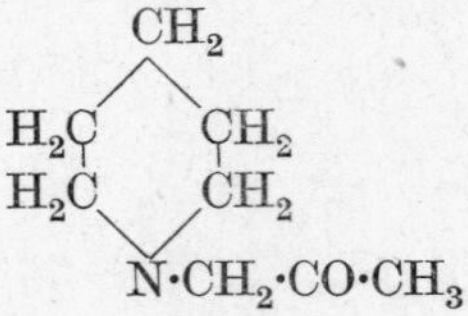

$C_8H_{15}ON$ MW, 141

Liq. B.p. 195–7°. Misc. with H_2O and common org. solvents.

B,HAuCl$_4$: yellow plates. M.p. 107–8°.

B$_2$,H$_2$PtCl$_6$: orange prisms. M.p. 192–3°.

Methiodide : cryst. from EtOH. M.p. 126°.

Methochloroaurate : cryst. M.p. 85°.

Methochloroplatinate : orange cryst. from EtOH. M.p. 218–19°.

Oxime : needles from H_2O, plates from pet. ether. M.p. 104–5° (123°).

Phenylhydrazone: yellow leaflets from EtOH.Aq. M.p. 59–62°.
2 : 4-*Dinitrophenylhydrazone*: yellow needles from MeOH. M.p. 120–2°.

Matthaiopoulos, *Ber.*, 1898, **31**, 2398.
Stoermer, Burkert, *Ber.*, 1895, **28**, 1250.

1-Piperidinoanthraquinone

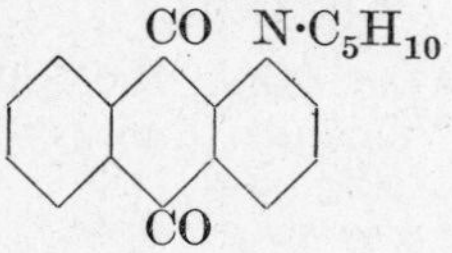

$C_{19}H_{17}O_2N$ MW, 291

Orange leaflets. M.p. 115°. Sol. conc. H_2SO_4 ⟶ yellow sol. Sol. $CHCl_3$–AcOH ⟶ purple sol.

Bayer, D.R.P., 136,777, (*Chem. Zentr.*, 1902, II, 1372).

α-Piperidone (*Valerolactam, 2-ketopiperidine*)

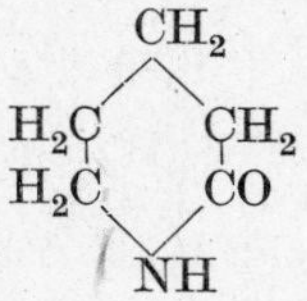

C_5H_9ON MW, 99

Hygroscopic cryst. M.p. 39–40°. B.p. 256°, 137°/14 mm., 64–5°/0·4 mm. Sol. EtOH, Et_2O, H_2O. Sol. dil. min. acids. Insol. alkalis.
B,HCl: cryst. from EtOH–Et_2O. M.p. 182–3°.
B,HgCl₂: needles + $1H_2O$. M.p. 187° decomp.
N-*Me*: $C_6H_{11}ON$. MW, 113. Hygroscopic liq. B.p. 104°/14 mm. *B,HCl*: cryst. from EtOH–Et_2O. M.p. 104°. *B,HgCl₂*: needles + $1H_2O$. M.p. 119–20°.
N-*Et*: $C_7H_{13}ON$. MW, 127. Liq. B.p. 109°/12 mm. *B,HCl*: hygroscopic needles from EtOH–Et_2O. M.p. 108°. *B,HgCl₂*: needles + $1H_2O$. M.p. 113°.
N-*Propyl*: $C_8H_{15}ON$. MW, 141. Liq. B.p. 121°/14 mm. *B,HCl*: m.p. 112°.
N-*Isopropyl*: liq. B.p. 127–8°/15 mm. *B,HCl*: needles from EtOH–Et_2O. M.p. 118°. *B,HgCl₂*: m.p. 140–1°.
N-*Butyl*: $C_9H_{17}ON$. MW, 155. Liq. B.p. 130–1°/11 mm.
N-*Octyl*: $C_{13}H_{25}ON$. MW, 211. Liq. B.p. 172°/10 mm.
N-*Benzyl*: $C_{12}H_{15}ON$. MW, 189. Liq. B.p. 193°/8 mm.
N-*Acetyl*: liq. B.p. 238°.
N-*Benzoyl*: leaflets from EtOH. M.p. 112°.
N-m-*Nitrobenzoyl*: yellow leaflets from EtOH.Aq. M.p. 114°.

Räth, *Ann.*, 1931, **489**, 111.
Ruzicka, *Helv. Chim. Acta*, 1921, **4**, 474.
Fischer, Zemplén, *Ber.*, 1909, **42**, 4886.
Fischer, Bergmann, *Ann.*, 1913, **398**, 114.
Wallach, *Ann.*, 1900, **312**, 179; 1902, **324**, 285.

γ-Piperidone (4-*Ketopiperidine*)

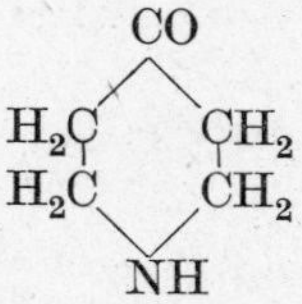

or

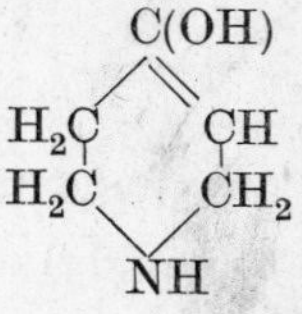

C_5H_9ON MW, 99

Yellow oil which cannot be distilled. Heat. ⟶ condensation products.
B,HCl: cryst. + 1½EtOH from EtOH–Et_2O. M.p. 139–41°. M.p. (solvent free) 147–9°. Cryst. + $1H_2O$ from H_2O. M.p. 94–6°.
N-*Me*: $C_6H_{11}ON$. MW, 113. *B,HCl*: cryst. from EtOH–Et_2O. M.p. 94–5°.
N-*Et*: $C_7H_{13}ON$. MW, 127. *B,HCl*: cryst. from EtOH–Et_2O. M.p. 105–6°.
N-*Propyl*: $C_8H_{15}ON$. MW, 141. *B,HCl*: cryst. from EtOH–Et_2O. M.p. 117–18°.
N-*Butyl*: $C_9H_{17}ON$. MW, 155. *B,HCl*: cryst. from EtOH–Et_2O. M.p. 178–80°.
N-*Phenyl*: $C_{11}H_{13}ON$. MW, 175. *B,HCl*: cryst. from EtOH–Et_2O. M.p. 145–7°.
N-*Benzyl*: $C_{12}H_{15}ON$. MW, 189. *B,HCl*: cryst. from EtOH–Et_2O. M.p. 159–61°.
O-*Me*: b.p. 190·5–191°/738 mm. Volatile in steam. Strongly alkaline. *B,HgCl₂*: needles from H_2O. M.p. 191°.
O-*Et*: b.p. 96°/15 mm. Misc. with EtOH. Insol. H_2O.
O-*Propyl*: b.p. 218–20°/742 mm. *B,HCl*: needles from EtOH–Et_2O. M.p. 156–7°. *Picrate*: prisms from EtOH. M.p. 120–4°.

Kuettel, McElvain, *J. Am. Chem. Soc.*, 1931, **53**, 2696.
Bolyard, *J. Am. Chem. Soc.*, 1930, **52**, 1032.
McElvain, Bolyard, *J. Am. Chem. Soc.*, 1929, **51**, 924.
Ruzicka, Fornasir, *Helv. Chim. Acta*, 1920, **3**, 806.
Koenigs, Neumann, *Ber.*, 1915, **48**, 960.

2-Piperidylacetic Acid (2-*Piperidineacetic acid*)

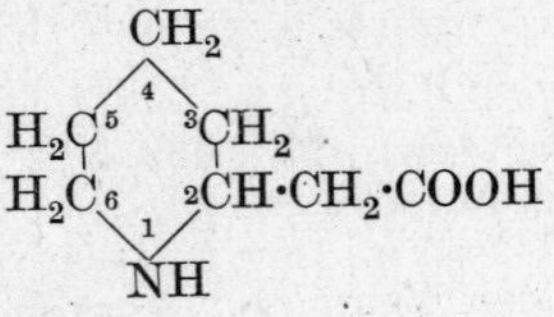

$C_7H_{13}O_2N$ MW, 143

Needles from EtOH. M.p. 214°.
B,HCl: cryst. from EtOH. M.p. 180–2°.
B,HAuCl$_4$: yellow needles. M.p. 171–2° decomp.
Chloroplatinate: yellow cryst. powder. M.p. 203° decomp.

Königs, Happe, *Ber.*, 1903, **36**, 2906; 1902, **35**, 1348.

3-Piperidylacetic Acid (3-*Piperidineacetic acid*).
Et ester: $C_9H_{17}O_2N$. MW, 171. Liq. B.p. 101–3°/6 mm. D_4^{25} 1·0131. n_D^{25} 1·4643. *B_2,H_2PtCl_6*: m.p. 181°.
Nitrile: $C_7H_{12}N_2$. MW, 124. N-*Benzoyl*: Liq. B.p. 165–75°/0·1 mm. D_4^{20} 1·1056. n_D^{20} 1·5602.

Merchant, Marvel, *J. Am. Chem. Soc.*, 1928, **50**, 1199.

2-Piperidylacetone.
See Isopelletierine.
Piperidylethylene.
See Vinylpiperidine.
Piperidylpyridine.
See Pyridylpiperidine, Anabasine, Isonicotine, *and* Isoneonicotine.
Piperidylurea.
See under Piperidine-*N*-carboxylic Acid.
Piperidylurethane.
See under Piperidine-*N*-carboxylic Acid.
Piperil (3 : 4 : 3′ : 4′-*Dimethylenedioxy-benzil, dimethylene ether of veratril*)

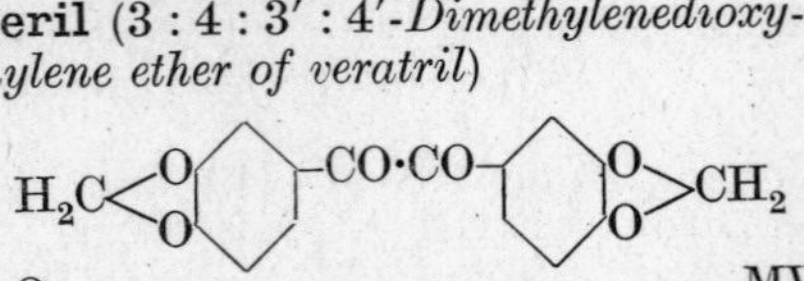

$C_{16}H_{10}O_6$ MW, 298

Yellow needles from C_6H_6–EtOH. M.p. 171·5°. Sol. AcOH, $CHCl_3$, C_6H_6. Spar. sol. EtOH. Insol. ligroin. Alkalis ⟶ piperonylic acid.
Monoxime: cryst. from EtOH. M.p. 199°.
Dioxime: prisms from EtOH. M.p. 244° decomp.
Disemicarbazone: leaflets from AcOH. M.p. 250°.
Diphenylhydrazone: two forms. (i) Yellow needles from C_6H_6–EtOH. M.p. 183–4° decomp. (ii) Yellow needles. M.p. 219–20°.
Di-o-tolylhydrazone: yellow cryst. from C_6H_6–EtOH. M.p. 206·5°.
Di-m-tolylhydrazone: yellow needles from C_6H_6–EtOH. M.p. 187°.
Di-p-tolylhydrazone: yellow needles from C_6H_6–EtOH. M.p. 215°.

Biltz, Arnd, *Ann.*, 1905, **339**, 272.
Biltz, Wienands, *Ann.*, 1899, **308**, 11.

Piperine (*Piperylpiperidine*)

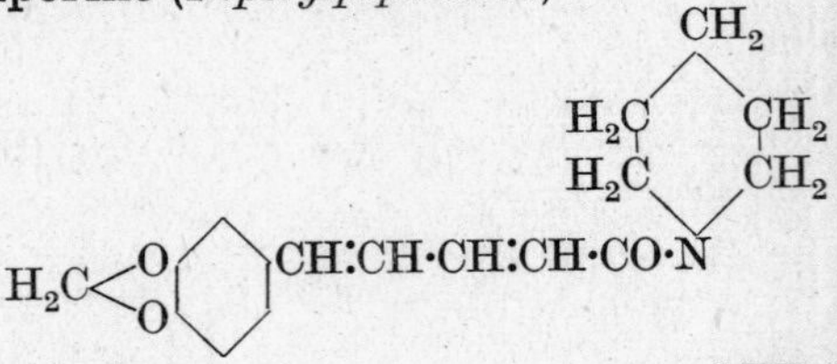

$C_{17}H_{19}O_3N$ MW, 285

Constituent of pepper (*Piper nigrum*, *Piper longum*, *Piper Clusii*, etc.). Columns from EtOH, cryst. from C_6H_6–ligroin. M.p. 129·5°. Sol. AcOH, EtOH, $CHCl_3$, C_6H_6. Spar. sol. Et_2O. Insol. cold H_2O, pet. ether, dil. min. acids. Cryst. substance is prac. tasteless but alc. sols. have sharp burning taste. Alc. KOH ⟶ piperidine and piperic acid. Conc. H_2SO_4 ⟶ red col.
B,HBr: yellow cryst. powder. M.p. about 170°.
B_2,H_2SnBr_6: yellow cryst. M.p. 182–4° decomp.

Rügheimer, *Ber.*, 1882, **15**, 1391.
Cazeneuve, Caillot, *Bull. soc. chim.*, 1877, **27**, 291.
Dauber, *Ann.*, 1850, **74**, 204.
Peinemann, *Arch. pharm.*, 1896, **234**, 245.

Piperitol (Δ^1-p-*Menthenol*-3, 3-*carvomenthenol*, 1-*methyl*-4-*isopropylcyclohexenol*-3)

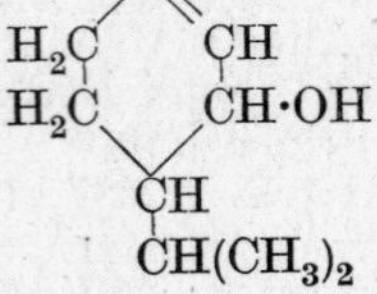

$C_{10}H_{18}O$ MW, 154

Constituent of essential oils of peppermint group of eucalyptus.

d-.

Liq. B.p. 165–70°/200 mm. D_{30}^{30} 0·911. n_D^{30} 1·474. $[\alpha]_D + 46·0°$.

l-.

Liq. B.p. 95–6°/10 mm. D^{22} 0·923. n_D^{22} 1·476. $[\alpha]_D - 34·1°$.

dl-.

Viscous oil with pleasant odour. B.p. 100–6°/19·5 mm. n_D^{18} 1·477.

Read, Walker, *J. Chem. Soc.*, 1934, 308.
Read, Storey, *J. Chem. Soc.*, 1930, 2772, 2779.

Piperitone (Δ^1-p-*Menthenone*-3, 1-*methyl*-4-*isopropylcyclohexenone*-3)

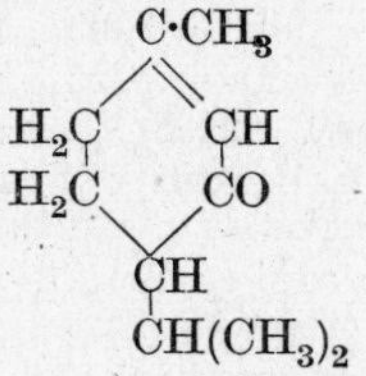

$C_{10}H_{16}O$ MW, 152

d-.

Constituent of Japanese peppermint oil, essential oil from *Andropogon Jwarancusa* and *Cymbopogon sennarensis*. Colourless oil with camphoraceous odour. Turns yellow on standing in air. B.p. 116–118·5°/20 mm. D_4^{20} 0·9344. n_D^{20} 1·4848. $[\alpha]_D^{20} + 49·13°$.

Semicarbazone: m.p. 193–4°. $[\alpha]_D - 216·8°$.

l-.

Occurs in essential oil of *Eucalyptus Dives*. B.p. 109·5–110·5°/15 mm. D_4^{20} 0·9324. n_D^{20} 1·4848. $[\alpha]_D^{20} - 51·53°$.

Oxime: oil. $[\alpha]_D + 238·1°$.

dl-.

Constituent of *Eucalyptus Dives* oil. B.p. 232–3°/769 mm., 113°/18 mm. D_4^{20} 0·9331. n_D^{20} 1·4845.

Oxime: two forms. (i) Cryst. from EtOH. M.p. 118–19°. (ii) M.p. 88–9°.

Semicarbazone: two forms. (i) M.p. 224–6°. (ii) M.p. 171–2°.

Walker, *J. Chem. Soc.*, 1935, 1585.
Read, Walker, *J. Chem. Soc.*, 1934, 308.
Howard, E.P., 410,813, (*Chem. Abstracts*, 1934, 6446).
Stephan, Düker, *J. prakt. Chem.*, 1931, **129**, 145.
Read, Smith, *J. Chem. Soc.*, 1923, **123**, 2268.
Simonsen, *J. Chem. Soc.*, 1921, **119**, 1646.

Piperoin (*Piperonyloin, piperonoin*, 3 : 4 : 3′ : 4′-*dimethylenedioxybenzoin*)

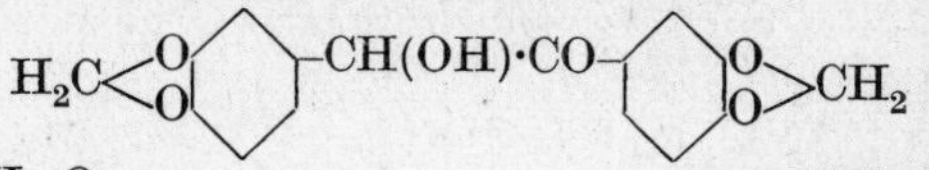

$C_{16}H_{12}O_6$ MW, 300

Needles from EtOH. M.p. 120°. Sol. EtOH, $CHCl_3$. Spar. sol. Et_2O. Fehling's ⟶ piperil.

Benzoyl: prisms from AcOH. M.p. 169°.

Oxalyl: crystals from $PhNO_2$. M.p. 169°.

Greene, Robinson, *J. Chem. Soc.*, 1922, **121**, 2187.
Smith, *Ann.*, 1896, **289**, 324.
Perkin, *J. Chem. Soc.*, 1891, **59**, 164.

2-Piperolidine.

See δ-Coniceine.

Piperonal (*Heliotropin, piperonyl aldehyde*, 3 : 4-*methylenedioxybenzaldehyde, methylene ether of protocatechuic aldehyde*)

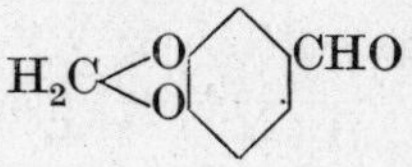

$C_8H_6O_3$ MW, 150

Occurs in *Robinia pseudoacacia*. Cryst. from H_2O. M.p. 37°. B.p. 263°, 185°/78 mm., 140°/15 mm.

$2C_8H_6O_3,3H_2SO_4$: plates. M.p. 70–9°.

$2C_8H_6O_3,SnCl_4$: yellow cryst. powder. Decomp. about 130°.

$2C_8H_6O_3,SnBr_4$: m.p. 150°.

$C_6H_3(NO_3)_2$-1 : 3 : 5 *add. comp.*: golden-yellow plates. M.p. 79°.

Oxime: *syn*-, cryst. from MeOH. M.p. 146°. *Acetyl*: m.p. 99°. *Benzoyl*: m.p. 168°. *Anti*-, needles from H_2O. M.p. 112°. *Acetyl*: m.p. 86°.

Di-Me acetal: $C_{10}H_{12}O_4$. MW, 196. Liq. B.p. 267–9°. D^{15} 1·206.

Di-Et acetal: $C_{12}H_{16}O_4$. MW, 224. Liq. B.p. 279–81°, 153–4°/11 mm. D^{15} 1·129.

Imide: $C_8H_7O_2N$. MW, 149. *B,HCl*: needles from C_6H_6. M.p. about 229–30°.

Methylimide: $C_9H_9O_2N$. MW, 163. M.p. 46°. B.p. 148°/16 mm. *B,HCl*: m.p. 220°.

Cyanhydrin: *see under* 3 : 4-Methylenedioxymandelic Acid.

Anil: piperonylideneaniline. $C_{14}H_{11}O_2N$. MW, 225. Needles from ligroin. M.p. 65°.

Diacetyl: cryst. from EtOH. M.p. 80° (51°).

Semicarbazone: leaflets. M.p. 230–3°.

Phenylhydrazone: needles from EtOH. M.p. 106°.

p-*Bromophenylhydrazone*: leaflets from EtOH, AcOH or C_6H_6. M.p. 155° decomp.

p-*Nitrophenylhydrazone* : red cryst. M.p. 199–200°.
2 : 4-*Dinitrophenylhydrazone* : purplish-red cryst. M.p. 265°.

McLang, *Chem. Abstracts*, 1927, **21**, 77.
Fritzsche, D.R.P., 207,702, (*Chem. Zentr.*, 1909, I, 1207).
Ciamician, Silber, *Ber.*, 1890, **23**, 1160.

Piperonylacetic Acid (3 : 4-*Methylenedioxyhydrocinnamic acid*)

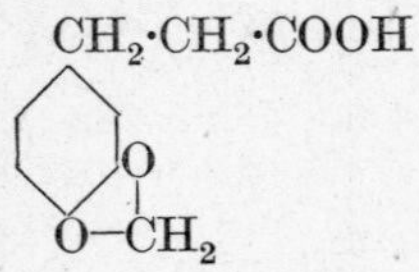

$C_{10}H_{10}O_4$ MW, 194

Needles from H_2O. M.p. 87–8°. B.p. 171–2°/11–12 mm. Red sol. in H_2SO_4. $P_2O_5 \longrightarrow$ methylenedioxyhydrindone.
Et ester : $C_{12}H_{14}O_4$. MW, 222. Liq. B.p. 303°.
Chloride : $C_{10}H_9O_3Cl$. MW, 212·5. Yellow oil. Dist. under diminished pressure $\longrightarrow$ 5 : 6-methylenedioxyhydrindone.
Amide : $C_{10}H_{11}O_3N$. MW, 193. Cryst. from H_2O or ligroin. M.p. 123·5°.
Methylamide : $C_{11}H_{13}O_3N$. MW, 207. Needles from Et_2O. M.p. 134°.
Anilide : needles. M.p. 122–3°.

Perkin, Robinson, *J. Chem. Soc.*, 1907, **91**, 1084.
Lorenz, *Ber.*, 1880, **13**, 758.
Regel, *Ber.*, 1887, **20**, 419.
Piccinini, *Chem. Zentr.*, 1904, I, 879.
Brochet, Bauer, *Bull. soc. chim.*, 1915, **17**, 52.
Decker, *Ann.*, 1913, **395**, 289.
Borsche, Eberlein, *Ber.*, 1914, **47**, 1470.

Piperonylacetone (3 : 4-*Methylenedioxybenzylacetone, methyl* 3 : 4-*methylenedioxyphenylethyl ketone,* 3 : 4-*methylenedioxy*-1-γ-*ketobutylbenzene*)

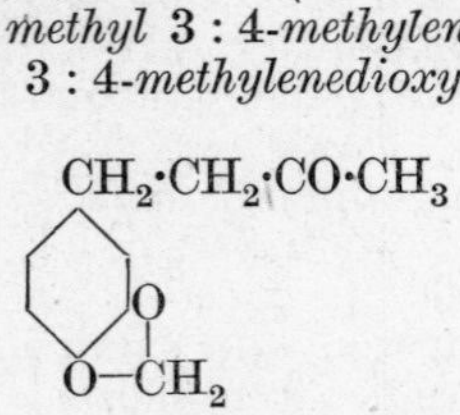

$C_{11}H_{12}O_3$ MW, 192

Leaflets from EtOH or pet. ether. M.p. 55°. B.p. 176·5°/15 mm., 164–5°/12 mm. Sol. most org. solvents.
Oxime : cryst. from EtOH or Et_2O. M.p. 98°.
Semicarbazone : needles. M.p. 166°.

Vavon, Faillebin, *Compt. rend.*, 1919, **169**, 66.
Kaufmann, Radosević, *Ber.*, 1916, **49**, 679.
Brochet, Cabaret, *Compt. rend.*, 1914, **159**, 328.

Piperonyl Alcohol (3 : 4-*Methylenedioxybenzyl alcohol*)

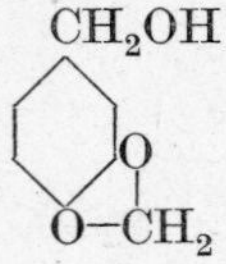

$C_8H_8O_3$ MW, 152

Needles from pet. ether. M.p. 58°. Sol. EtOH, Et_2O. Spar. sol. cold H_2O. Dist. $\longrightarrow$ piperonal. Conc. $H_2SO_4 \longrightarrow$ 2 : 3 : 6 : 7-dimethylenedioxy-9 : 10-dihydroanthracene.
Acetyl : two forms. (i) Cryst. from CCl_4 or pet. ether. M.p. 51°. (ii) Liq. B.p. 153–4°/14 mm. D_4^{18} 1·240. n_D^{18} 1·528.
Benzoyl : needles from EtOH. M.p. 66°.
Phenylurethane : m.p. 102·5°.
Allophanate : m.p. 176·5° decomp.

Carothers, Adams, *J. Am. Chem. Soc.*, 1924, **46**, 1681.
Davidson, Bogert, *J. Am. Chem. Soc.*, 1935, **57**, 905.
Tiffeneau, Führer, *Bull. soc. chim.*, 1914, **15**, 172.
Barger, *J. Chem. Soc.*, 1908, **93**, 567.
Fittig, Remsen, *Ann.*, 1871, **159**, 130, 138.
Decker, Koch, *Ber.*, 1905, **38**, 1741.
Vavon, *Compt. rend.*, 1912, **154**, 361.

Piperonylic Acid (3 : 4-*Methylenedioxybenzoic acid*)

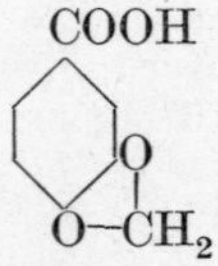

$C_8H_6O_4$ MW, 166

Needles from EtOH, cryst. from H_2O. M.p. 229°. Spar. sol. cold EtOH, Et_2O. Insol. cold H_2O, $CHCl_3$. Sublimes in prisms.
Me ester : $C_9H_8O_4$. MW, 180. Needles or leaflets from pet. ether. M.p. 53°. B.p. 273–4° (part. decomp.). Sol. MeOH, EtOH, Et_2O. Volatile in steam.
Et ester : $C_{10}H_{10}O_4$. MW, 194. Prisms. M.p. 18·5°. B.p. 285°. Sol. EtOH, Et_2O, pet. ether. Insol. H_2O.
Amide : $C_8H_7O_3N$. MW, 165. Prisms or

needles from H_2O. M.p. 169°. Sol. EtOH, Et_2O. Spar. sol. H_2O. Insol. pet. ether.

Chloride: $C_8H_5O_3Cl$. MW, 184·5. Cryst. M.p. 80°. B.p. 155°/25 mm., 149–50°/12 mm.

Nitrile: $C_8H_5O_2N$. MW, 147. Needles from H_2O. M.p. 95°. Sol. EtOH, Et_2O, C_6H_6.

Shriner, Kleiderer, *Organic Syntheses*, 1930, X, 82.
Barger, *J. Chem. Soc.*, 1908, **93**, 567.
Linge, *Rec. trav. chim.*, 1897, **16**, 47.
Rupe, Majewski, *Ber.*, 1900, **33**, 3403.

Piperonylidene-acetaldehyde.
See 3 : 4-Methylenedioxycinnamaldehyde.

Piperonylidene-acetic Acid.
See 3 : 4-Methylenedioxycinnamic Acid.

Piperonylideneacetone (*Methyl 3 : 4-methylenedioxystyryl ketone, 3 : 4-methylenedioxy-1-γ-keto-α-butenylbenzene*)

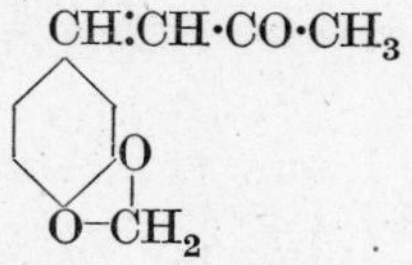

$C_{11}H_{10}O_3$ MW, 190

Cis:
Yellow cryst. M.p. 110–11°.

Trans:
Colourless cryst. M.p. 110–11°.

Sol. most org. solvents. Spar. sol. boiling H_2O. Volatile in steam.

Oxime: white cryst. from EtOH. M.p. about 186°.

Semicarbazone: two forms. (i) Given by *cis-* and *trans-*forms. Colourless cryst. from $CHCl_3$. M.p. 217°. Ultra-violet light ⟶ (ii). (ii) Yellow cryst. from C_6H_6–pet. ether. M.p. 168°.

Phenylhydrazone: prisms. M.p. about 166°.

Note.—The configuration of the above three derivatives is not known.

McGookin, Heilbron, *J. Chem. Soc.*, 1924, **125**, 2101.
Vavon, Faillebin, *Compt. rend.*, 1919, **169**, 67.
Wilson, Heilbron, Sutherland, *J. Chem. Soc.*, 1914, **105**, 2895.
Haber, *Ber.*, 1891, **24**, 620.
Nomura, Mozawa, *Chem. Abstracts*, 1919, **13**, 118.

ω-Piperonylideneacetophenone.
See 3 : 4-Methylenedioxychalkone.

Piperonylideneaniline.
See under Piperonal.

Piperonyloin.
See Piperoin.

Piperylene.
See 1 : 3-Pentadiene.

Piperylpiperidine.
See Piperine.

Pipitzahoic Acid.
See Perezone.

Pivalic Acid (*Trimethylacetic acid*)

$(CH_3)_3C·COOH$

$C_5H_{10}O_2$ MW, 102

M.p. 35·3–35·5°. B.p. 163·7–163·8°, 75–8°/20 mm. D^{50} 0·905.

Mercuric salt: needles from $CHCl_3$. M.p. 235°.

Me ester: $C_6H_{12}O_2$. MW, 116. B.p. 100–2°. D_4^0 0·891.

Et ester: $C_7H_{14}O_2$. MW, 130. B.p. 118·5°. D^0 0·875.

p-*Bromophenacyl ester*: m.p. 76·5°.

Anhydride: $C_{10}H_{18}O_3$. MW, 186. B.p. 190°.

Chloride: C_5H_9OCl. MW, 120·5. B.p. 105–6°.

Amide: $C_5H_{11}ON$. MW, 101. Needles or plates. M.p. 153–4°. B.p. about 212°.

Nitrile: C_5H_9N. MW, 83. Cryst. M.p. 15–16°. B.p. 105–6°.

Anilide: m.p. 127–9°.

Hardy, *J. Chem. Soc.*, 1936, 364–5.
du Pont, U.S.P., 1,995,930, (*Chem. Zentr.*, 1935, II, 594).
Sandborn, Bousquet, *Organic Syntheses*, 1928, VIII, 108.
Puntambeker, Zoellner, *ibid.*, 104.
Butlerow, *Ann.*, 1874, **173**, 355; 1873, **170**, 158.

Pivalic Aldehyde (*Trimethylacetaldehyde*)

$(CH_3)_3C·CHO$

$C_5H_{10}O$ MW, 86

Constituent of wood spirit. Liq. Solidifies on cooling. M.p. 6°. B.p. 74–6°. D^{17} 0·7923. Oxidises in air. Decomp. in daylight.

Trimer: $C_{15}H_{30}O_3$. MW, 258. Needles from EtOH. M.p. 82°.

Di-Et acetal: $C_9H_{20}O_2$. MW, 160. Liq. B.p. 146–8°/742 mm. D_4^{25} 0·8192. n_D 1·3942.

Oxime: m.p. 41°. B.p. 65°/20 mm.

Semicarbazone: m.p. 191°.

Anil: b.p. 101–2°/20 mm.

Azine: m.p. 79°.

Dunbar, Adkins, *J. Am. Chem. Soc.*, 1934, **56**, 444.
Conant, Webb, Mendum, *J. Am. Chem. Soc.*, 1929, **51**, 1250.

Pivalone (*Hexamethylacetone, di-*tert.*-butyl ketone*, 2 : 2 : 4 : 4-*tetramethylpentanone*-3)

$(CH_3)_3C{\cdot}CO{\cdot}C(CH_3)_3$

$C_9H_{18}O$ MW, 142

Liq. B.p. 152°, 70°/43 mm. D^{18} 0·824. n_D^{18} 1·4195. Does not react with usual ketonic reagents.

Vavon, Ivanoff, *Compt. rend.*, 1923, **177**, 453.
Haller, Bauer, *Compt. rend.*, 1910, **150**, 584.
Henderson, Henderson, Heilbron, *Ber.*, 1914, **47**, 887.

Pivalophenone.
See tert.-Butyl phenyl Ketone.

Plasmoquin (*Plasmochin*, N-(4-*diethylamino*-1-*methylbutyl*)-6-*methoxy*-8-*aminoquinoline*)

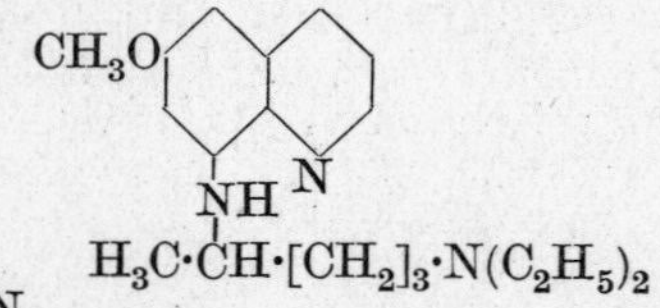

$C_{19}H_{29}ON_3$ MW, 315

Used as an antimalarial.

Knunyantz, Topchiev, Chelintzev, *Chem. Abstracts*, 1934, **28**, 4837.

Platyphylline

$C_{18}H_{25}O_5N$ MW, 335

Alkaloid from *Senecio platyphyllus* D.C. Needles from H_2O. M.p. 124–5°. Very sol. $CHCl_3$. Sol. EtOH, Me_2CO, Et_2O, C_6H_6. Spar. sol. hot H_2O, pet. ether. $[\alpha]_D$ — 45·09°.

Perchlorate: prisms from H_2O. M.p. 222–3° decomp.

B,HAuCl₄: yellow needles $+ \frac{1}{2}H_2O$ from EtOH.Aq. M.p. 200–1° decomp.

Methiodide: needles from EtOH. M.p. 216–17°. $[\alpha]_D$ — 31·27°.

Picrolonate: dark yellow needles from EtOH. M.p. 205–6° decomp.

Orechoff, Konowalowa, Tiedebel, *Ber.*, 1935, **68**, 1886.
Orechoff, *ibid.*, 653.

Plumbagin (5-*Hydroxy*-2-*methyl*-1 : 4-*naphthoquinone*)

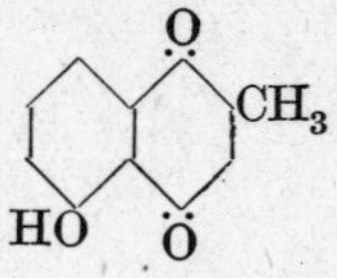

$C_{11}H_8O_3$ MW, 188

Constituent of various species of *Plumbago*. Yellow needles from EtOH.Aq. M.p. 78–9°. Sol. Et_2O, Me_2CO, AcOH, $CHCl_3$, C_6H_6. Insol. cold H_2O. Volatile in steam. Sublimes.

Dioxime: yellow needles from EtOH. M.p. 220°.

Semicarbazone: light brown needles from Py–EtOH. M.p. above 280°.

Phenylhydrazone: reddish-brown needles from EtOH. M.p. 198°.

Acetyl: yellow needles. M.p. 117–18° (138°).

Benzoyl: yellow prisms from EtOH.Aq. M.p. 147°.

Fieser, Dunn, *J. Am. Chem. Soc.*, 1936, **58**, 572.
Buruaga, Verdú, *Chem. Zentr.*, 1935, I, 3146.
Roy, Dutt, *J. Indian Chem. Soc.*, 1928, **5**, 419.

Podocarpic Acid (1 : 2 : 3 : 4 : 4*a* : 9 : 10 : 10*a*-*Octahydro* - 5 - *hydroxy* - 8 : 10*a* - *dimethylphenanthrene*-4-*carboxylic acid*)

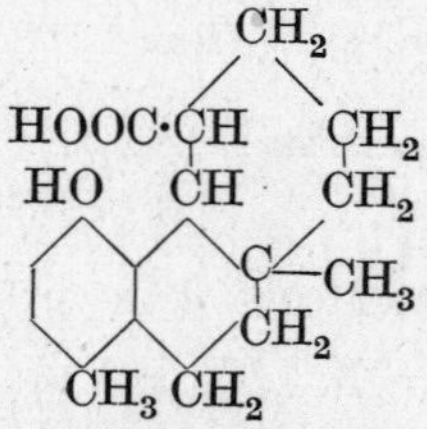

Probable structure

$C_{17}H_{22}O_3$ MW, 274

Occurs in *Podocarpus cupressina, var. imbricata.* Plates from EtOH.Aq. M.p. 193·5°. Sol. EtOH, Et_2O, AcOH. Insol. H_2O, $CHCl_3$, CS_2, C_6H_6. $[\alpha]_{5461}$ + 165° in EtOH.

Me ester: $C_{18}H_{24}O_3$. MW, 288. Cryst. from EtOH. M.p. 208°. *Me ether*: m.p. 128°. *Benzoyl*: m.p. 143°.

Et ester: $C_{19}H_{26}O_2$. MW, 302. Needles. M.p. 161°.

p-*Nitrobenzyl ester*: m.p. 204°.

Me ether: $C_{18}H_{24}O_3$. MW, 288. M.p. 157–8°.

Acetyl: sinters at 100°. M.p. 152°.

Sherwood, Short, *Chem. Abstracts*, 1934, **28**, 6435.
Oudemans, *Ann.*, 1873, **170**, 214.

Podophyllic Acid

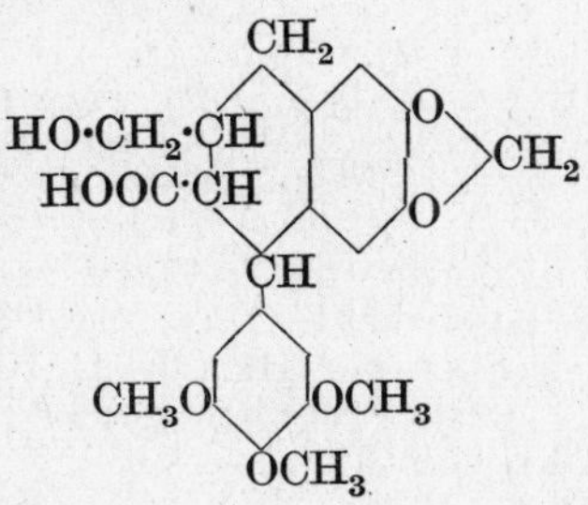

$C_{22}H_{24}O_9$ MW, 432

Needles from $CHCl_3$ or EtOH–C_6H_6. M.p. 163–5°. Sol. EtOH. Spar. sol. H_2O, Et_2O, AcOEt, $CHCl_3$, CCl_4, C_6H_6. $[\alpha]_D^{16}$ −102·8° in EtOH.
Hydrazide: plates from H_2O. M.p. 155–60°.

Borsche, Niemann, *Ann.*, 1932, **494**, 136.
Mellanoff, Schaeffer, *Chem. Zentr.*, 1927, II, 1589.

Podophyllomerol (6 : 7-*Methylenedioxy*-2-*methylnaphthalene*)

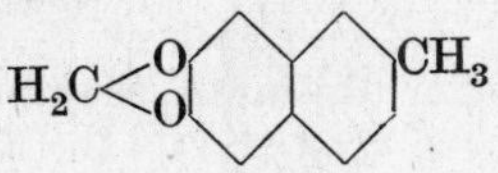

$C_{12}H_{10}O_2$ MW, 186

Plates from MeOH. M.p. 129–129·5°.
Picrate: orange-red needles. M.p. 133–4°.

Borsche, Niemann, *Ann.*, 1932, **499**, 67.

Podophyllomeronic Acid (*Methylene ether of phyllomeronic acid*, 6 : 7-*methylenedioxy*-3-*methyl*-2-*naphthoic acid*)

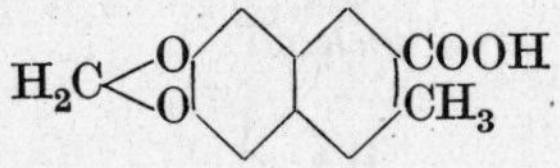

$C_{13}H_{10}O_4$ MW, 230

Plates from AcOH. M.p. 239–40°.
Me ester: $C_{14}H_{12}O_4$. MW, 244. Needles from MeOH. M.p. 125–6°.

Borsche, Niemann, *Ann.*, 1932, **494**, 141; 1932, **499**, 67.
Späth, Wesselý, Kornfeld, *Ber.*, 1932, **65**, 1547.

Podophyllotoxin

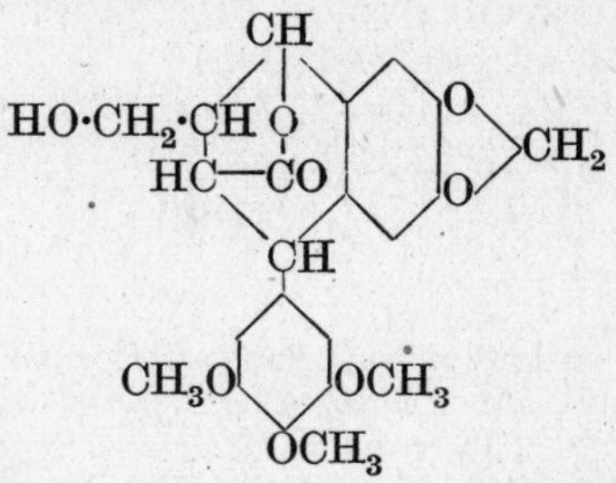

$C_{22}H_{22}O_8$ MW, 414

Occurs in *Podophyllum*. Needles from Me_2CO.Aq. or MeOH. M.p. 114–18°. (M.p. anhyd. 157°.) Sol. EtOH, Me_2CO, AcOH, $CHCl_3$, hot C_6H_6. Spar. sol. EtOH.Aq. Insol. H_2O, Et_2O, ligroin, C_6H_6. $[\alpha]_D^{14}$ −101·3° in EtOH.
Acetyl: needles from MeOH. M.p. 204°. $[\alpha]_D^{16}$ −134·9° in $CHCl_3$.

Späth, Wesselý, Kornfeld, *Ber.*, 1932, **65**, 1542.
Borsche, Niemann, *Ann.*, 1932, **494**, 131; 1932, **499**, 63.
Mellanoff, Schaeffer, *Chem. Zentr.*, 1927, II, 1589.

μ-Polychloroprene.
See under Chloroprene.
Polyoxymethylene.
See under Formaldehyde.
Polyporic Acid (3 : 6-*Dihydroxy*-2 : 5-*diphenyl*-p-*benzoquinone*)

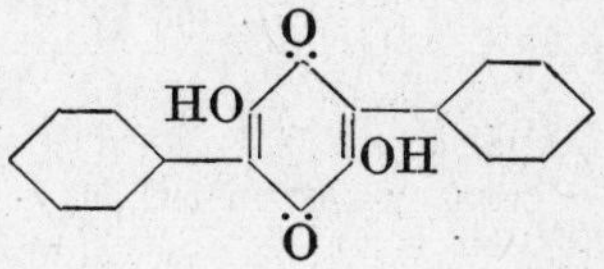

$C_{18}H_{12}O_4$ MW, 292

Occurs in *Polyporus*. Bronze plates from toluene. M.p. 305°. Spar. sol. EtOH, $CHCl_3$. Insol. H_2O, Et_2O, CS_2, C_6H_6. Sublimes.
Di-Me ether: $C_{20}H_{16}O_4$. MW, 320. Red cryst. from EtOH. M.p. 187°.
Di-Et ether: $C_{22}H_{20}O_4$. MW, 348. Yellow needles or orange-red prisms from EtOH. M.p. 134°.
Diacetyl: needles from *n*-butyl alcohol. M.p. 246° (209°).

Shildneck, Adams, *J. Am. Chem. Soc.*, 1931, **53**, 2377.
Kögl, *Ann.*, 1926, **447**, 78.
Stahlschmidt, *Ann.*, 1877, **187**, 177.

Polystichocitrin.
See Flavaspidic Acid.

Populin (6-*Benzoylsalicin*)

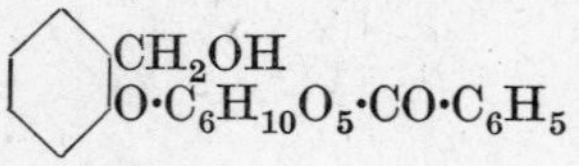

$C_{20}H_{22}O_8$ MW, 390

Occurs in leaves and bark of *Populus tremula* and in buds of *P. nigra*, *P. pyramidalis*, etc. Needles + $2H_2O$ from H_2O, prisms from EtOH. M.p. 180°. Sol. hot H_2O, EtOH. Spar. sol. cold H_2O. $[\alpha]_D$ −53°, −2·0° in Py. Conc. H_2SO_4 ⟶ red col. $Ba(OH)_2$ ⟶ salicin.

Tetra-Me ether: $C_{24}H_{30}O_8$. MW, 446. Needles from Et_2O–ligroin. M.p. 134–5°. $[\alpha]_D$ −31·7° in $CHCl_3$.

Richtinger, Yeakel, *J. Am. Chem. Soc.*, 1934, **56**, 2495.

Porphyroxine

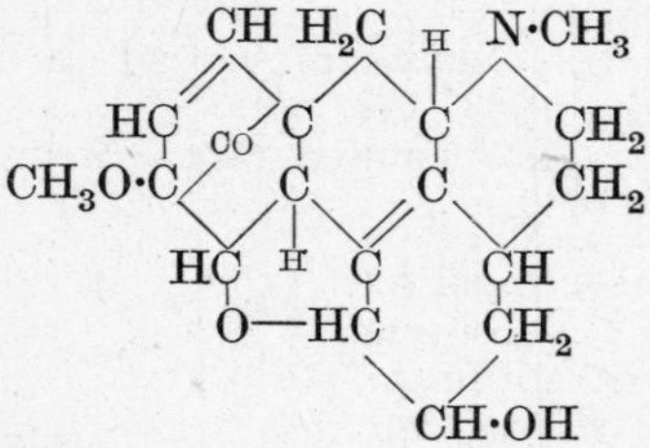

$C_{19}H_{23}O_4N$ MW, 329

Prisms from ligroin. M.p. 134–5°. Sol. $CHCl_3$, Me_2CO, AcOH, CS_2. Mod. sol. MeOH, AcOEt, CCl_4, C_6H_6. Spar. sol. H_2O. $[\alpha]^{32}$ −139·9° in $CHCl_3$.

B,HCl: needles from H_2O. M.p. 155°. $[\alpha]^{32}$ −118·8° in H_2O.

B,HBr: needles. M.p. 148–50°. $[\alpha]^{32}$ −90·6° in H_2O.

B,HI: decomp. at 115°. $[\alpha]^{32}$ −77·8° in H_2O.

B_2,H_2SO_4: plates from H_2O. M.p. 193°.

Methiodide: m.p. 150–2°.

Methosulphate: needles from MeOH. M.p. 205° decomp.

Oxime: m.p. 198° decomp.

Phenylhydrazone: m.p. 150° decomp.

Semicarbazone: decomp. at 244°.

Acetyl: m.p. 125°. *B,HCl*: needles. M.p. 126° decomp. *B,HBr*: m.p. 155° decomp. *B_2,H_2SO_4*: m.p. 190° decomp.

Me ether: $C_{20}H_{25}O_4N$. MW, 343. Cryst. from pet. ether. M.p. 125–6°. *Oxime*: needles from MeOH. M.p. 185–6°. *Phenylhydrazone*: m.p. 189° decomp. *Semicarbazone*: cryst. from EtOH. M.p. 217°.

Rakshit, *J. Chem. Soc.*, 1919, **115**, 455; *Ber.*, 1926, **59**, 2473.

Pratol (7-*Hydroxy-4′-methoxyflavone*)

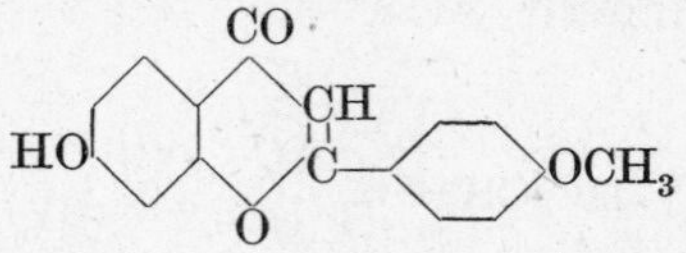

$C_{16}H_{12}O_4$ MW, 268

Occurs in flowers of *Trifolium* species. Pale yellow needles from EtOH. M.p. 263–4°. Sol. hot EtOH. Spar. sol. H_2O, Et_2O, $CHCl_3$, C_6H_6.

Acetyl: needles or hexagonal plates from EtOH. M.p. 176–7°.

Baker, *J. Chem. Soc.*, 1933, 1386.
Power, Salway, *J. Chem. Soc.*, 1910, **97**, 233, 1008.

Pregnandiol

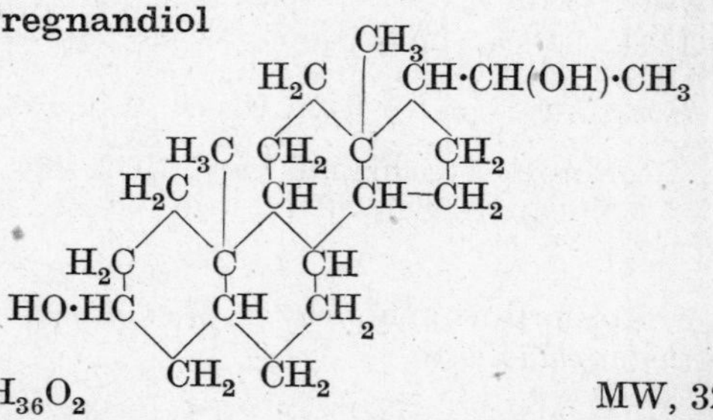

$C_{21}H_{36}O_2$ MW, 320

Isolated from urine of pregnancy. Plates from EtOH or Me_2CO. M.p. 234–5°. Spar. sol. most org. solvents. Gives none of recognised sterol colour reactions.

20-*Acetyl*: cryst. from EtOH or Me_2CO.Aq. M.p. 170·5°.

Diacetyl: needles from EtOH. M.p. 180°.

Butenandt, Schmidt, *Ber.*, 1934, **67**, 1895.
Butenandt, Hildebrandt, Brücher, *Ber.*, 1931, **64**, 2529.
Butenandt, *Ber.*, 1930, **63**, 661.
Marrian, *Biochem. J.*, 1929, **23**, 1090.

Pregnane

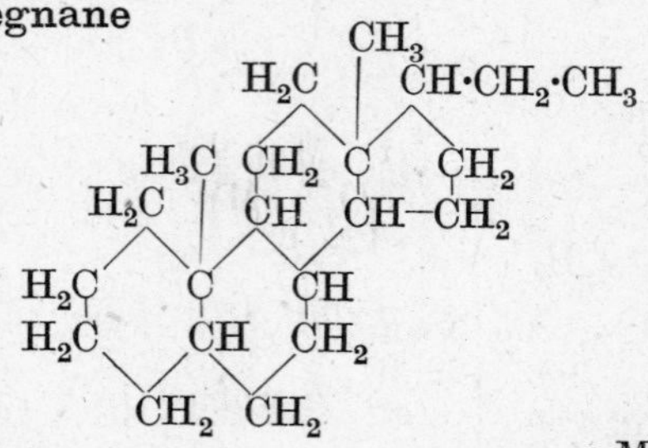

$C_{21}H_{36}$ MW, 288

Cryst. from MeOH. M.p. 83·5°. $[\alpha]_D^{20}$ + 21·2° in $CHCl_3$.

Butenandt, Hildebrandt, Brücher, *Ber.*, 1931, **64**, 2538.

Prehnidine (2 : 3 : 4 : 5-*Tetramethylaniline*, 5-*amino*-1 : 2 : 3 : 4-*tetramethylbenzene*, 5-*amino-prehnitene*)

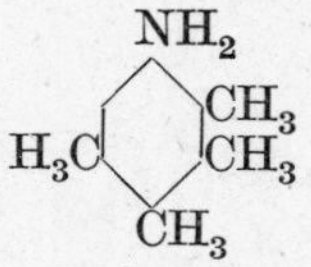

$C_{10}H_{15}N$ MW, 149

Leaflets from H_2O. M.p. 70° (64–6°). B.p. 259–60°. Sol. EtOH, Et_2O, pet. ether. Mod. sol. hot H_2O.

N-*Formyl* : needles from H_2O. M.p. 143–4°.

N-*Acetyl* : needles from EtOH.Aq. M.p. 172° (169·5°).

Limpach, *Ber.*, 1888, **21**, 644.
Töhl, *ibid.*, 905.

Prehnitene (*Prehnitol*, 1 : 2 : 3 : 4-*tetramethyl-benzene*)

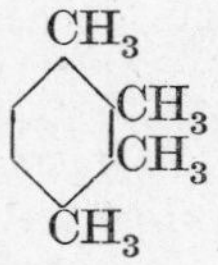

$C_{10}H_{14}$ MW, 134

Liq. Solidifies on cooling. M.p. — 6·4°. B.p. 203–4°, 96·4°/25 mm., 75–75·5°/6·5 mm. D_4^{20} 0·901. n_D^{25} 1·5196.

Picrate : yellow prisms from EtOH. M.p. 92–5°.

Smith, Cass, *J. Am. Chem. Soc.*, 1932, **54**, 1620.
Baril, Hauber, *J. Am. Chem. Soc.*, 1931. **53**, 1089.

Prehnitenol (2 : 3 : 4 : 5-*Tetramethylphenol*, 5-*hydroxyprehnitene*, 5-*hydroxy*-1 : 2 : 3 : 4-*tetra-methylbenzene*)

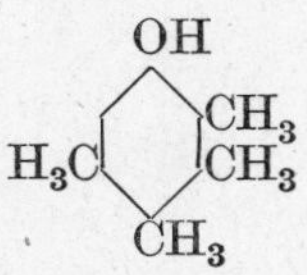

$C_{10}H_{14}O$ MW, 150

Needles from EtOH.Aq. or ligroin. M.p. 86–7°. B.p. 266°. Very sol. EtOH, Et_2O. Spar. sol. H_2O, ligroin. Volatile in steam.

Acetyl : prisms from ligroin. M.p. 56–7°.

Bamberger, Blangey, *Ann.*, 1911, **384**, 307.
Töhl, *Ber.*, 1888, **21**, 907.

Prehnitic Acid (*Benzene*-1 : 2 : 3 : 4-*tetra-carboxylic acid*)

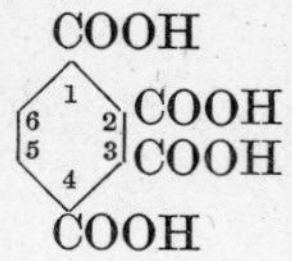

$C_{10}H_6O_8$ MW, 254

Prisms from H_2O. M.p. 238°.

1 : 4-*Di-Me ester* : $C_{12}H_{10}O_8$. MW, 282. M.p. 176–7°.

Tetra-Me ester : $C_{14}H_{14}O_8$. MW, 310. M.p. 133–5°.

Smith, Byrkil, *J. Am. Chem. Soc.*, 1933, **55**, 4305.
Doebner, *Ann.*, 1900, **311**, 143.
Baeyer, *Ann.*, 1873, **166**, 325.
Meyer, Sudborough, *Ber.*, 1894, **27**, **1591**

Prehnitylic Acid (2 : 3 : 4-*Trimethylbenzoic acid*)

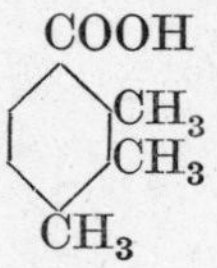

$C_{10}H_{12}O_2$ MW, 164

Prisms from EtOH. M.p. 167·5°. $k = 3{\cdot}49 \times 10^{-5}$ at 25°. Mod. volatile in steam.

Jacobsen, *Ber.*, 1886, **19**, 1214.
Lapworth, Chapman, *J. Chem. Soc.*, 1900, **77**, 316.

Primetin (5 : 6-*Dihydroxyflavone*)

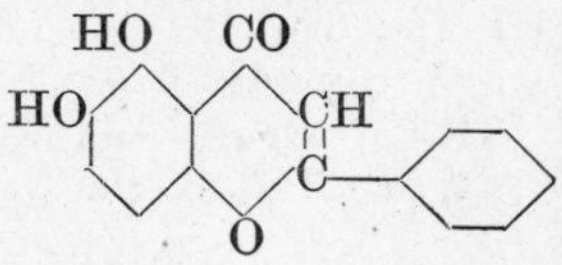

$C_{15}H_{10}O_4$ MW, 254

Obtained from *Primula modesta*. Yellow prisms from EtOH. M.p. 230–1°. Alc. $FeCl_3$ ⟶ green col. Sol. alkalis ⟶ red sols. Sol. conc. H_2SO_4 ⟶ yellow sol.

Mono-Me ether : $C_{16}H_{12}O_4$. MW, 268. Needles from EtOH. M.p. 211–12°. Insol. alkalis. $FeCl_3$ ⟶ brownish-violet col. *Acetyl* : needles from EtOH. M.p. 176–7°.

Diacetyl : needles from EtOH. M.p. 189°.

Nagai, Hatori, *Chem. Zentr.*, 1930, II, 409.

Primeverin

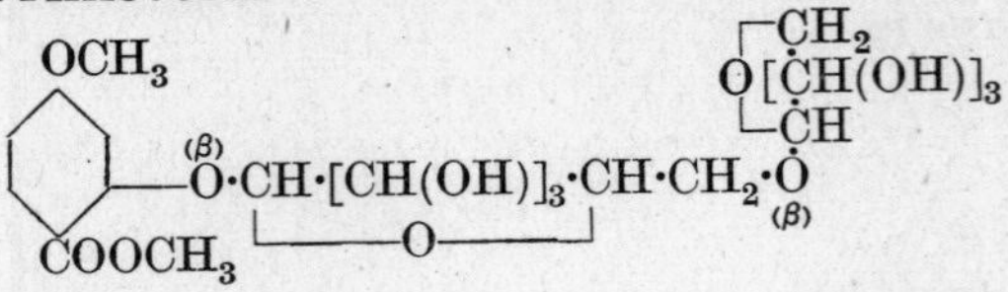

$C_{20}H_{28}O_{13}$ MW, 476

A glucoside from the roots of *Primula officinalis*. Needles from MeOH or EtOH. M.p. 205°. $[\alpha]_D^{20}$ − 76·75° in H_2O. Hyd. ⟶ 4-methoxysalicylic acid + xylose + glucose.

Hexa-acetyl: needles from dil. MeOH or dil. EtOH. M.p. 125°.

Jones, Robertson, *J. Chem. Soc.*, 1933, 1618.

Primeverose (*Glucose*-6-β-d-*xyloside*)

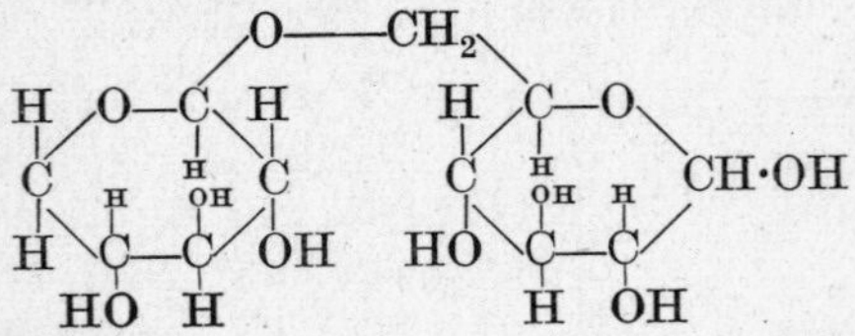

$C_{11}H_{20}O_{10}$ MW, 312

Obtained from various glucosides *e.g.* primeverin and primulaverin from *Primula officinalis*, genticaulin from *Gentiana lutea*, rhamnicosin from *Rhamnus catharticus*. Cryst. M.p. 210° (208°). Sweet taste. Sol. H_2O. Spar. sol. EtOH. $[\alpha]_D^{20}$ + 23·8° ⟶ − 3·4° in H_2O. Reduces Fehling's. Dil. acids ⟶ xylose + *d*-glucose. Br water ⟶ primeverobionic acid.

Phenylosazone: yellow needles from H_2O. M.p. 220°. Sol. EtOH, Me_2CO. Insol. Et_2O, $CHCl_3$. $[\alpha]_D^{19}$ − 109·7° in Py.

β-*Hepta-acetyl*: needles from EtOH. M.p. 216°. Sol. $CHCl_3$. Spar. sol. EtOH, Et_2O. Insol. H_2O. $[\alpha]_D^{20}$ − 23·5° in $CHCl_3$.

Helferich, Rauch, *Ann.*, 1927, **455**, 168.
Goris, Vischniac, *Compt. rend.*, 1919, **169**, 871, 975.
Bridel, *Compt. rend.*, 1925, **180**, 1421.

Primulaverin

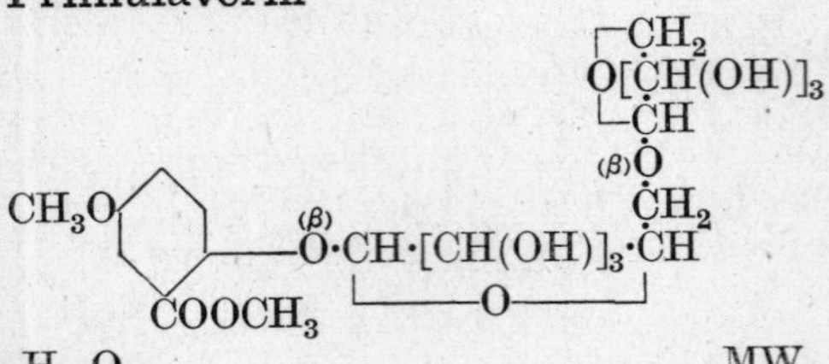

$C_{20}H_{28}O_{13}$ MW, 476

M.p. 163°. $[\alpha]_D$ − 66·51°. Hyd. ⟶ 5-methoxysalicylic acid + xylose + glucose.

Goris, Vischniac, *Bull. soc. chim.*, 1920, **27**, 262.

Primulin chloride
See Œnin chloride.

Procaine.
See Novocaine.

Prodigiosine

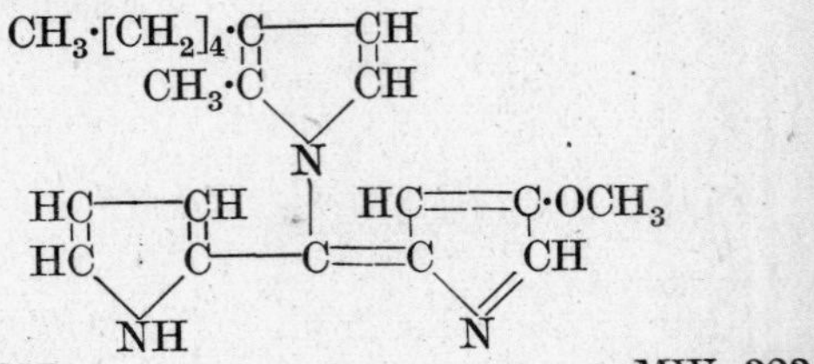

$C_{20}H_{25}ON_3$ MW, 323

Red pigment of *Bacillus prodigiosus*. Brittle solid. Sinters at 70–80°. No definite m.p. Sol. most org. solvents. Insol. H_2O.

B,HClO₄: needles with metallic lustre from EtOH. Sinters at 226°. M.p. 228°.

Monobenzoyl deriv.: needles from EtOH.Aq. M.p. 170°.

Monosalicyloyl deriv.: needles from EtOH.Aq. M.p. 178°.

Picrate: needles from EtOH. M.p. 176°.

Wrede, Rothhaas, *Z. physiol. Chem.*, 1934, **226**, 95.
Wrede, Hettche, *Ber.*, 1929, **62**, 2678.

Proflavine.
See under 2 : 8-Diaminoacridine.

Progesterone (*Progestine*)

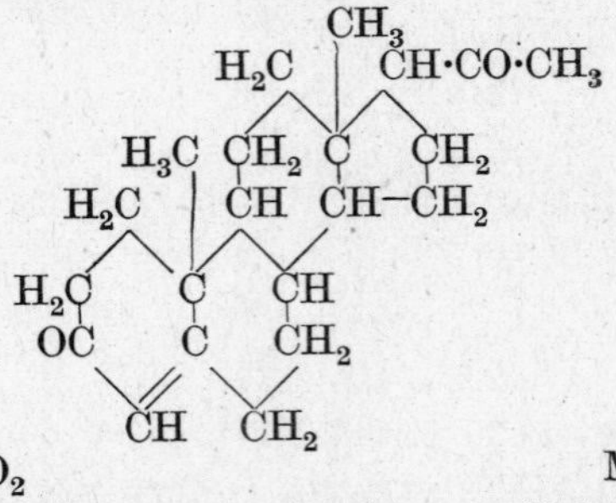

$C_{21}H_{30}O_2$ MW, 314

Obtained from *Corpus luteum*. Exists in two forms of the same physiological activity. (α) Prisms from EtOH. M.p. 128·5°. (β) Needles from pet. ether. M.p. 121–2°.

Readily sol. most org. solvents. Spar. sol. H_2O. $[\alpha]_D$ + 192°. Absorption maximum at 240 mμ. Induces proliferation of uterine mucon.

Dioxime : cryst. from EtOH.Aq. M.p. 243°.

Butenandt, Westphal, Hohlweg, *Z. physiol. Chem.*, 1934, **227**, 84.
Wintersteiner, Allen, *J. Biol. Chem.*, 1934, **107**, 321.
Fieser, *Chemistry of Natural Products Related to Phenanthrene*, p. 188. (Reinhold Publishing Corporation, New York.)

Progestine.
See Progesterone.

Progynon.
See Œstrone.

Proline (*Pyrrolidine-2-carboxylic acid*)

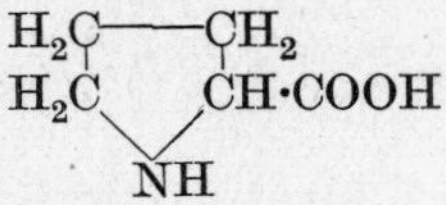

$C_5H_9O_2N$ MW, 115

d-.

Hygroscopic prisms from $EtOH-Et_2O$. M.p. 215–20° decomp. $[\alpha]_D^{20} + 81{\cdot}9°$ in H_2O.

Me ester : $C_6H_{11}O_2N$. MW, 129. $[\alpha]_D^{25} + 34°$.

N-p-*Toluenesulphonyl* : m.p. 130–3°.

N-m-*Nitrobenzoyl* : prisms from H_2O. M.p. 137–40°. $[\alpha]_D^{20} + 120°$ in *N*-NaOH.

l-.

Cryst. from $EtOH-Et_2O$. Decomp. at 220–2°. $[\alpha]_D^{20} - 80{\cdot}9°$ in H_2O.

Amide : $C_5H_{10}ON_2$. MW, 114. N-*Acetyl* : m.p. 178–80°.

Anhydride : $C_{10}H_{14}O_2N_2$. MW, 194. M.p. 149°. $[\alpha]_D^{19} - 147{\cdot}2°$.

N-2 : 4-*Dinitrophenyl* : m.p. 136°.

N-p-*Toluenesulphonyl* : m.p. 130–3°.

Picrate : m.p. 153–4°.

dl-.

Hygroscopic needles from $EtOH-Et_2O$. M.p. 205° decomp.

Hydrate : $C_{10}H_{18}O_4N_2$, H_2O. M.p. 190–1°. Sol. H_2O, EtOH. Spar. sol. Me_2CO, $CHCl_3$, C_6H_6. Insol. Et_2O.

B,HCl : cryst. from H_2O. M.p. 158–9°.

Et ester : $C_7H_{13}O_2N$. MW, 143. Oil. B.p. 80°/13 mm.

Amide : cryst. from C_6H_6. M.p. 93°. Sol. EtOH, AcOEt, $CHCl_3$.

Anhydride : needles. M.p. 183–4°.

Anilide : cryst. from Me_2CO. M.p. 170°.

N-*Me* : *see* Hygric Acid.

N-m-*Nitrobenzoyl* : prisms from H_2O. M.p. 90–2°.

Picrate : cryst. from EtOH. M.p. 135–7°.

Signaigo, Adkins, *J. Am. Chem. Soc.*, 1936, **58**, 1122.
Fischer, Zemplén, *Ber.*, 1909, **42**, 2997.
Kapfhammer, Eck, *Z. physiol. Chem.*, 1927, **170**, 294.
Kapfhammer, Matthes, *Z. physiol. Chem.*, 1933, **223**, 43.
Jacobs, Craig, *J. Biol. Chem.*, 1935, **110**, 521.
Grassmann, Armin, *Ann.*, 1935, **519**, 192.
Putochin, *Ber.*, 1926, **59**, 1987; 1923, **56**, 2213.
Abderhalden, Sickel, *Z. physiol. Chem.*, 1926, **159**, 163.

Prominal (1-*Methyl*-5-*ethyl*-5-*phenylbarbituric acid*)

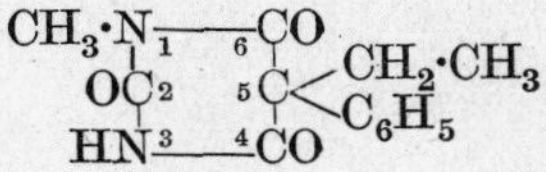

$C_{13}H_{14}O_3N_2$ MW, 246

M.p. 176°.

I.G., F.P., 753,178, (*Chem. Zentr.*, 1934, I, 895).

Prontosil (4′-*Sulphamido*-2 : 4-*diaminoazobenzene hydrochloride, Streptozon, Rubiazol, Prontosil Red*)

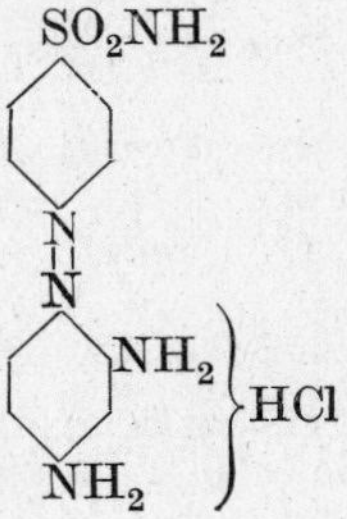

$C_{12}H_{13}O_2N_5$ MW, 259

Cryst. powder. M.p. 247–51°. Sol. 400 parts H_2O. One of a series of substances possessing strong bactericidal properties. Used for treatment of streptococcal and staphylococcal infections, especially erysipelas.

p-Aminobenzenesulphonamide, possessing similar physiological properties, is sometimes referred to as "Prontosil."

Domagk, *Angew. Chem.*, 1935, **48**, 660.
Goissedet, Despois, Gaillot, Mayer, *Compt. Rend. Societé Biologique*, 1936, **121**, 1082.

Propadiene.
See Allene.

Propæsin (p-*Aminobenzoic acid propyl ester*)

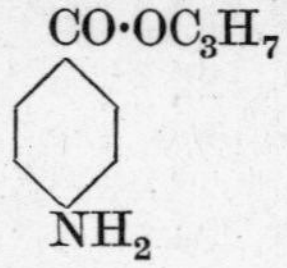

$C_{10}H_{13}O_2N$ MW, 179

Prisms. M.p. 73–4°. Sol. EtOH, Et_2O, C_6H_6. Spar. sol. H_2O. Local anæsthetic.

Fritzsche, D.R.P., 213,459, (*Chem. Zentr.*, 1909, II, 1025).

Propaldehyde.
See Propionaldehyde.

Propanal.
See Propionaldehyde.

Propanalone.
See Pyruvic Aldehyde.

Propandial-1 : 3.
See Glutaraldehyde.

Propane

$CH_3·CH_2·CH_3$

C_3H_8 MW, 44

Occurs in petroleum gas. F.P. — 189·9°. B.p. — 44·5°, — 124·2°/3 mm. D^0 0·536, $D^{15·9}$ 0·515. Heat of comb. C_p 529·21 Cal. (528·4 Cal.).

Maass, Wright, *J. Am. Chem. Soc.*, 1921, **43**, 1098.
Spencer, Price, *J. Chem. Soc.*, 1910, **97**, 388.
Wolkow, Menschutkin, *Chem. Zentr.*, 1900, II, 42.
Timmermans, *Compt. rend.*, 1914, **158**, 790.
Meyer, *Ber.*, 1893, **26**, 2071.

Propane-dicarboxylic Acid.
See Ethylmalonic Acid, Methylsuccinic Acid, *and* Glutaric Acid.

Propane 2 : 2-diethyl disulphone.
See Sulphonal.

Propane-1 : 1-disulphonic Acid (*Ethylmethionic acid*)

$CH_3·CH_2·CH(SO_3H)_2$

$C_3H_8O_6S_2$ MW, 204

Diphenyl ester : $C_{15}H_{14}O_6S_2$. MW, 354. Oil. B.p. 200°/0·005 mm.
Diamide : $C_3H_{10}O_4N_2S_2$. MW, 202. M.p. 169–70°.
Di-trimethylamide : cryst. from Et_2O. M.p. 133°.
Dianilide : cryst. from EtOH. M.p. 151–2°.
Di-[N-*Et*]*-anilide* : ethylmethionide. Prisms from EtOH. M.p. 128–9°.
Di-[N-*Et*]*-phenetidide* : needles from C_6H_6–pet. ether. M.p. 93·5–94·5°.

Schroeter, *Ann.*, 1918, **418**, 230.
Klaver, *Rec. trav. chim.*, 1935, **54**, 208.

Propane-1 : 2-disulphonic Acid

$CH_3·CH·SO_3H$
$\quad\quad CH_2·SO_3H$

$C_3H_8O_6S_2$ MW, 204

Syrup. Sol. H_2O, EtOH.
Dichloride : $C_3H_6O_4S_2Cl_2$. MW, 241. Plates from pet. ether. M.p. 48°.

Autenrieth, Rudolph, *Ber.*, 1901, **34**, 3477.
Buckton, Hofmann, *Ann.*, 1856, **100**, 153.
Clutterbuck, Cohen, *J. Chem. Soc.*, 1922, **121**, 120.

Propane-1 : 3-disulphonic Acid

$HO_3S·CH_2·CH_2·CH_2·SO_3H$

$C_3H_8O_6S_2$ MW, 204

Needles. Decomp. without melting. Sol. H_2O, EtOH.
Dichloride : m.p. 45°.
Diamide : cryst. from H_2O or EtOH. M.p. 169°.
Dianilide : m.p. 129°.
Dihydrazide : needles from EtOH. M.p. 105°.
Di-phenylhydrazide : needles from Me_2CO.Aq. M.p. 177° decomp.

See last reference above and also
Autenrieth, Bernheim, *Ber.*, 1904, **37**, 3808.

Propane-2 : 2-disulphonic Acid (*Dimethylmethionic acid*)

$(CH_3)_2C(SO_3H)_2$

$C_3H_8O_6S_2$ MW, 204

Diphenyl-ester : m.p. 96°.
Di - [N - *Et*] - *anilide* : dimethylmethionide. Cryst. from EtOH. M.p. 130–2°.
Di-[N-*Me*]*-phenetidide* : m.p. 114–15°.
Di-[N-*Et*]*-phenetidide* : m.p. 109°.

Schroeter, *Ann.*, 1919, **418**, 233.
Klaver, *Rec. trav. chim.*, 1935, **54**, 208.

Propane-1-sulphonic Acid

$CH_3·CH_2·CH_2·SO_3H$

$C_3H_8O_3S$ MW, 124

Chloride : $C_3H_7O_2SCl$. MW, 142·5. B.p. 180° decomp., 77·3–78°/13 mm. D_4^{15} 1·2826.

Amide: $C_3H_9O_2NS$. MW, 123. Prisms from Et_2O. M.p. 52°. Sol. H_2O, EtOH.

Duguet, *Rec. trav. chim.*, 1902, **21**, 77.
Wagner, Reid, *J. Am. Chem. Soc.*, 1931, **53**, 3411.

Propane-2-sulphonic Acid

$(CH_3)_2CH{\cdot}SO_3H$

$C_3H_8O_3S$ MW, 124

Chloride: oil. B.p. 79°/18 mm.
Amide: cryst. from Et_2O–pet. ether. M.p. 60°. Sol. EtOH, Et_2O. Insol. C_6H_6.

See last reference above and also
Claus, *Ber.*, 1872, **5**, 660; 1875, **8**, 532.
Duguet, *Rec. trav. chim.*, 1906, **25**, 215.

Propane-1 : 2 : 3-tricarboxylic Acid.
See Tricarballylic Acid.
Propanol.
See Propyl Alcohol *and* Isopropyl Alcohol.
Propanolamine.
See 3-Aminopropyl Alcohol.
Propargyl Alcohol (3-*Hydroxyallylene, hydroxymethylacetylene, acetylenylcarbinol*)

$CH{\vdots}C{\cdot}CH_2OH$

C_3H_4O MW, 56

Volatile liq. B.p. 114–15°. D_4^{20} 0·9715. n_D^{20} 1·43064.
Me ether: *see* Methyl propargyl Ether.
Et ether: C_5H_8O. MW, 84. B.p. 82°. D_4^{25} 0·8324. n_D^{20} 1·40390.
Isoamyl ether: $C_8H_{14}O$. MW, 126. B.p. 140°. $D^{12·8}$ 0·84.
Phenyl ether: C_9H_8O. MW, 132. Liq. Decomp. at 210°. D^6 1·246. Insol. H_2O.
Acetyl: b.p. 124–5°. D_4^{20} 1·0052. n_D^{20} 1·42047.
Phenylurethane: m.p. 63°.

Henry, *Ber.*, 1873, **6**, 729.
Lespieau, *Ann. chim. phys.*, 1912, **27**, 158.
Paal, Heupel, *Ber.*, 1891, **24**, 3039.
Liebermann, Kretschmer, *Ann.*, 1871, **158**, 230.

Propargylamine (3-*Aminoallylene, 3-aminopropine*)

$CH{\vdots}C{\cdot}CH_2NH_2$

C_3H_5N MW, 55

B,HCl: unstable. Sol. H_2O, EtOH.
B,HBr: unstable. M.p. 171°.
B,HI: unstable. M.p. 205°.
B,$(COOH)_2$: m.p. 143°. Sol. H_2O. Insol. EtOH.

N-*Me*: C_4H_7N. MW, 69. *B,HI*: m.p. 83°. *Oxalate*: m.p. 141°.
Picrate: plates. M.p. 189°.

Paal, Hermann, *Ber.*, 1889, **22**, 3080.
Paal, Heupel, *Ber.*, 1891, **24**, 3040.

Propargyl bromide (3-*Bromoallylene, 3-bromopropine*)

$CH{\vdots}C{\cdot}CH_2Br$

C_3H_3Br MW, 119

B.p. 88–90° (82°), 35°/130 mm. D^{19} 1·579. n_D^{19} 1·4942.

Henry, *Ber.*, 1874, **7**, 761.
Kinmann, *Bull. soc. chim.*, 1926, **39**, 698.
v. Braun, Kühn, Siddiqui, *Ber.*, 1926, **59**, 1086.

Propargyl chloride (3-*Chloroallylene, 3-chloropropine*)

$CH{\vdots}C{\cdot}CH_2Cl$

C_3H_3Cl MW, 74·5

Liq. B.p. 65°. D^5 1·0454.

Henry, *Ber.*, 1875, **8**, 398.

Propargylic Acid.
See Propiolic Acid.
Propargylic Aldehyde.
See Propiolic Aldehyde.
Propene.
See Propylene.
Propenylacetic Acid.
See 2-Ethylidenepropionic Acid.
2-Propenylacrylic Acid.
See Sorbic Acid.
3-Propenylallyl Alcohol.
See 2 : 4-Hexadienol-1.
Propenylallylcarbinol (1 : 5-*Heptadienol*-4, 4-*hydroxy*-1 : 5-*heptadiene*)

$CH_3{\cdot}CH{\vdots}CH{\cdot}CH(OH){\cdot}CH_2{\cdot}CH{\vdots}CH_2$

$C_7H_{12}O$ MW, 112

B.p. 156–7° decomp./735 mm., 68–9°/24 mm., 54–5°/6 mm. D_4^{20} 0·8612. $n_D^{13·7}$ 1·45527. Heat with $KHSO_4 \longrightarrow$ 1 : 3 : 5-heptatriene. Oxidises in air.

Auwers, *J. prakt. Chem.*, 1923, **105**, 373.
Enklaar, *Ber.*, 1916, **49**, 211.
I.G., D.R.P., 544,388, (*Chem. Zentr.*, 1932, II, 3156).

Propenylanisole.
See Anethole *and under* Propenylphenol.
Propenylbenzene.
See β-Methylstyrene.

Propenyl bromide (1-*Bromopropylene*)

$CH_3{\cdot}CH{:}CHBr$

C_3H_5Br MW, 121

B.p. 58–60°/747 mm. D_4^{20} 1·4133. n_D^{20} 1·45193. Insol. H_2O. Alc. KOH ⟶ allylene.

Juvala, *Ber.*, 1930, **63**, 1994.
Bachman, *J. Am. Chem. Soc.*, 1933, **55**, 4282.
Schmidt, Kleine, *Ann.*, 1904, **337**, 86.

1-Propenyl-1-butylene.
See 2 : 4-Heptadiene.

Propenylbutyric Acid.
See 4-Heptenic Acid *and* 2-Methyl-3-heptenic Acid.

Propenylcarbinol.
See Crotonyl Alcohol.

Propenyl chloride (1-*Chloropropylene*)

$CH_3{\cdot}CH{:}CHCl$

C_3H_5Cl MW, 76·5

Cis :
F.p. — 134·8°. B.p. 32·8°.

Trans :
F.p. — 99°. B.p. 37·4°.

Wislicenus, *Ann.*, 1888, **248**, 297.
Timmermans, *Bull. soc. chim. Belg.*, 1927, **36**, 502.
Reboul, *Ann. chim. phys.*, 1878, **14**, 462.

3-Propenyl-*o*-cresol (1-[2-*Hydroxy*-m-*tolyl*]-*propylene*)

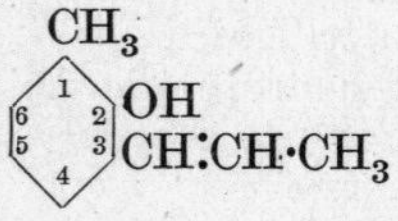

$C_{10}H_{12}O$ MW, 148

Needles from pet. ether. M.p. 41–2°. B.p. 113–15°/12 mm. Sol. most org. solvents, NaOH.

Auwers, Wittig, *Ber.*, 1924, **57**, 1273.

5-Propenyl-*o*-cresol (1-[4-*Hydroxy*-m-*tolyl*]-*propylene*).

Me ether : $C_{11}H_{14}O$. MW, 162. B.p. 121–3°/14 mm. D_4^{16} 0·9844. n_D^{17} 1·5570. *Nitrosochloride* : m.p. 117°.

Klages, *Ber.*, 1904, **37**, 3992.

6-Propenyl-*m*-cresol (1-[4-*Hydroxy*-o-*tolyl*]-*propylene*)

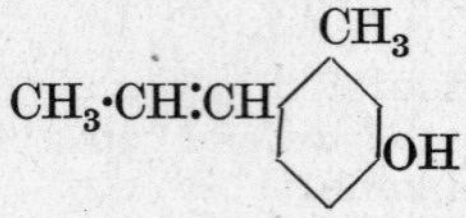

$C_{10}H_{12}O$ MW, 148

Me ether : $C_{11}H_{14}O$. MW, 162. Oil. B.p. 119–21°/13 mm. D_4^{15} 0·9849. n_D^{15} 1·5555. *Nitrosochloride* : needles. M.p. 108°. Spar. sol. Et_2O.

Klages, *Ber.*, 1904, **37**, 3994.

3-Propenyl-*p*-cresol (1-[6-*Hydroxy*-m-*tolyl*]-*propylene*)

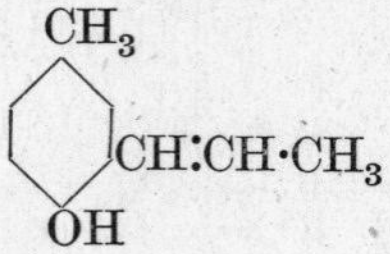

$C_{10}H_{12}O$ MW, 148

B.p. 126–8°/14 mm., 120–4°/11 mm. D_4^{20} 1·019. n_D^{20} 1·5727.

Me ether : $C_{11}H_{14}O$. MW, 162. B.p. 127·5–128°/19 mm. D_4^{20} 0·979. n_D^{20} 1·5522.

Auwers, *Ann.*, 1917, **413**, 299.

2-Propenylcrotonic Acid.
See 2-Methylsorbic Acid.

Propenylethylidenepropane.
See 2 : 6-Octadiene.

Propenylguaiacol.
See Isochavibetol *and* Isoeugenol.

***o*-Propenylphenol** (o-*Hydroxy*-β-*methylstyrene*)

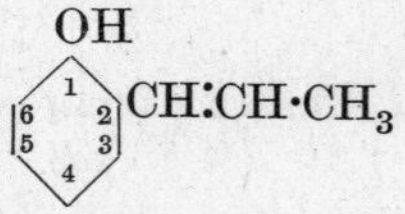

$C_9H_{10}O$ MW, 134

Needles from ligroin. M.p. 37–8°. B.p. 230–1°, 112–13°/12 mm. $D_4^{13·9}$ 1·0441. $n_D^{14·2}$ 1·584.

Me ether : *o*-propenylanisole. $C_{10}H_{12}O$. MW, 148. Volatile oil. B.p. 223–4°/751 mm., 104–5°/13 mm. D_4^{15} 0·9962. n_D^{15} 1·560.

Et ether : *o*-propenylphenetole. $C_{11}H_{14}O$. MW, 162. Oil. B.p. 230–1°/757 mm., 120–1°/17 mm. D_4^{24} 0·97307. n_D^{24} 1·544.

Claisen, *Ann.*, 1919, **418**, 86.
Pauly, v. Buttlar, *Ann.*, 1911, **383**, 280.
Klages, *Ber.*, 1904, **37**, 3987.

***m*-Propenylphenol** (m-*Hydroxy*-β-*methylstyrene*).

Me ether : *m*-propenylanisole. Liq. B.p. 226–9°. D^0 1·0013.

Et ether : *m*-propenylphenetole. Volatile oil. B.p. 124–6°/16 mm. D_4^{22} 0·9782. n_D^{22} 1·542. *Nitrosochloride* : m.p. 122–3°.

Moureu, *Bull. soc. chim.*, 1896, **15**, 1024.
Klages, *Ber.*, 1904, **37**, 3989.

p-**Propenylphenol**.
See Anol.

Propenylphenylcarbinol (1-*Phenyl-2-but-enol*-1, α-*propenylbenzyl alcohol*, 1-*phenylcrotonyl alcohol*)

$$CH_3 \cdot CH:CH \cdot CH(OH) \cdot C_6H_5$$

$C_{10}H_{12}O$ MW, 148

B.p. 121·5–123·5°/14 mm., 88–90°/1 mm. n_D^{18} 1·5412.
Succinate : m.p. 72–80°.
Acid succinate : m.p. 76–8°.

> Ingold, Wilson, *J. Chem. Soc.*, 1933, 1497.
> Burton, *J. Chem. Soc.*, 1929, 457.

2-Propenylpiperidine.
See β-Coniceine.
2-Propenylpropylene.
See 2-Methyl-1 : 3-pentadiene.
2-Propenylpyridine

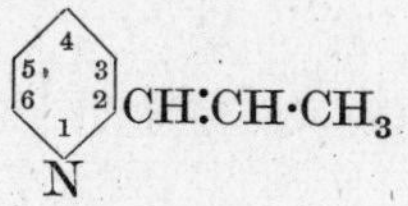

C_8H_9N MW, 119

Liq. B.p. 189–90°. D^0 0·9595. Spar. sol. H_2O. Volatile in steam.
$B,HAuCl_4$: needles from HCl.Aq. M.p. 135–6°.
B_2,H_2PtCl_6 : needles. M.p. 185–6° decomp.

> Ladenburg, *Ann.*, 1888, **247**, 26.

Note.—This compound is referred to in the above reference as α-allylpyridine.

4-Propenylpyridine
Liq. B.p. 200–2°. Volatile in steam.
B,HCl : cryst. M.p. 247°.
$B,HAuCl_4$: yellow needles from HCl.Aq. M.p. 174° decomp.
$B,HCl,HgCl_2$: needles from H_2O. M.p. 150°.
B_2,H_2PtCl_6 : needles. M.p. 206° decomp.
Picrate : yellow needles from H_2O. M.p. 169–70° decomp.

> Ahrens, *Ber.*, 1905, **38**, 157.

4-Propenylveratrol.
See under Isoeugenol.
Propine.
See Allylene.
Propine-1 : 3-dicarboxylic Acid.
See Glutinic Acid.

α-**Propiobetaine** (*Homobetaine, alanine-betaine, methylbetaine*)

$$(CH_3)_3N\!\!-\!\!\!-\!\!CH \cdot CH_3$$
$$\quad\quad O\!\!-\!\!\!-\!\!CO$$

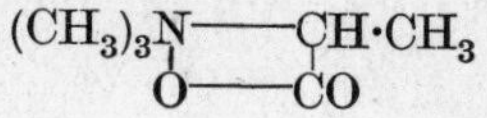

$C_6H_{13}O_2N$ MW, 131

l-.
Plates from EtOH–Et_2O. Decomp. at 242°. $[\alpha]_D^{20} - 19.7°$ in H_2O.
$B,HAuCl_4$: dimorphous. (i) Yellow plates from dil. HCl. M.p. 259° decomp. (ii) Cryst. from H_2O. M.p. 226° decomp.

dl-.
Cryst.
$B,HAuCl_4$: needles from 1% HCl. M.p. 240°.
B_2,H_2PtCl_6 : orange plates + $2H_2O$ from H_2O. M.p. 210–12° decomp.

> Fischer, *Ber.*, 1907, **40**, 5002.
> Kossel, Edlbacher, *Z. physiol. Chem.*, 1919, **107**, 45.

Propiodinitrile (*Dipropionitrile, 2-imino-1-methyl-n-valeronitrile*)

$$CH_3 \cdot CH_2 \cdot C(:NH) \cdot CH(CH_3) \cdot CN$$

$C_6H_{10}N_2$ MW, 110

M.p. 47–8°. B.p. 257–8°. Sol. EtOH, Et_2O. Spar. sol. H_2O. At 330° $\longrightarrow$ propionitrile. Na in EtOH $\longrightarrow$ propylamine. Gradually decomp. by hot H_2O.

> v. Meyer, *J. prakt. Chem.*, 1888, **38**, 338.

Propioin.
See Diethylketol.
Propiolic Acid (*Acetylene-carboxylic acid, propargylic acid*)

$$CH:C \cdot COOH$$

$C_3H_2O_2$ MW, 70

Liq. with odour resembling acetic acid. M.p. 18°; monohydrate cryst. felted mass, m.p. 0·3°; $3C_3H_2O_2 + 1H_2O$, needles, m.p. 10°. B.p. 144° decomp., 102°/200 mm., 83–4°/50 mm. Misc. with H_2O, EtOH, Et_2O, $CHCl_3$. D_4^{20} (anhyd.) 1·1380. n_a^{20} 1·43064. Red. $\longrightarrow$ propionic acid. HCl, HBr, HI $\longrightarrow$ β-halogen-acrylic acid. Reduces $AgNO_3$ and $HgCl_2$ and platinic chloride sols. in warm. Forms explosive Ag and Cu comps. Cu_2Cl_2 $\longrightarrow$ cryst. add. comp.
K salt : cryst. + $1H_2O$. Decomp. at 105°. Very sol. H_2O.

Aniline salt: prisms + $\frac{1}{2}H_2O$ from EtOH.Aq. M.p. 71–2°.

Me ester: $C_4H_4O_2$. MW, 84. B.p. 102°/742 mm. Lachrymatory.

Et ester: $C_5H_6O_2$. MW, 98. B.p. 119°/745 mm. D_{25}^{25} 0·9583. n_a^{15} 1·4133. Red. ⟶ ethyl propargyl ether. $NH_2{\cdot}NH_2$ ⟶ pyrazolone.

Anhydride: $C_6H_2O_3$. MW, 122. B.p. 56°/16 mm. D_4^{21} 1·1432. $n_D^{23{\cdot}4}$ 1·4358. Spar. sol. ligroin.

Nitrile: C_3HN. MW, 51. M.p. 5°. B.p. 42·5°. D_4^{17} 0·8159. n_D^{17} 1·38699. Spar. sol. H_2O. Sols. rapidly decompose. Decomp. by air and light. KOH ⟶ resin. $AgNO_3$ ⟶ white ppt. Vapour affects mucous membrane.

Amide: C_3H_3ON. MW, 69. Needles or plates from Et_2O. M.p. 61–2°. Very sol. H_2O, EtOH, Et_2O. Spar. sol. $CHCl_3$, cold C_6H_6, CS_2.

Anilide: needles from H_2O. M.p. 86–7°.

Backer, Beute, *Rec. trav. chim.*, 1935, **54**, 168.
Chéou, *Chem. Abstracts*, 1935, 2513.
Straus, Heyn, Schwener, *Ber.*, 1930, **63**, 1090.
Straus, Voss, *Ber.*, 1926, **59**, 1685.
Moureu, André, *Compt. rend.*, 1913, **157**, 897.
Moureu, Bongrand, *Compt. rend.*, 1910, **151**, 946.
Perkin, Simonsen, *J. Chem. Soc.*, 1907, **91**, 834.
Baeyer, *Ber.*, 1885, **18**, 677.

Propiolic Aldehyde (*Propargylic aldehyde*)

CH⋮C·CHO

C_3H_2O MW, 54

Thin oil. B.p. 59–61°. Misc. with H_2O. Affects eyes and mucous membranes. $NH_3.AgNO_3$ ⟶ white ppt. $NH_3{\cdot}CuCl_2$ ⟶ yellowish-red ppt. Dil. alkalis ⟶ acetylene + formic acid. NH_2OH ⟶ isoxazole.

Di-Me acetal: $C_5H_8O_2$. MW, 100. B.p. 110°.

Di-Et acetal: $C_7H_{12}O_2$. MW, 128. B.p. 139–41°. NH_2OH ⟶ isoxazole. $NH_2{\cdot}NH_2$ ⟶ pyrazole. *Cu deriv.*: m.p. 160°.

Grard, *Ann. chim.*, 1930, **13**, 336.
Claisen, *Ber.*, 1903, **36**, 3667; 1898, **31**, 1022.

Propionaldehyde (*Propanal, propaldehyde, propionic aldehyde*)

$CH_3{\cdot}CH_2{\cdot}CHO$

C_3H_6O MW, 58

Liq. with suffocating odour. F.p. − 81°. B.p. 47·5–49°. Sol. 5 parts H_2O at 20°. D_{25}^{25} 0·79664. n_D^{20} 1·3636. Heat of comb. C_p 434·35 Cal., C_v 433·8 Cal. HCl ⟶ metapropionaldehyde and parapropionaldehyde. KOH ⟶ propionaldol. Red. ⟶ propyl alcohol. *m*-Dinitrobenzene + KOH ⟶ greenish-brown col. Sodium nitroprusside and piperidine ⟶ blue col. (green to blue in dil. sol.). Forms bisulphite comp.

Metapropionaldehyde: $(C_3H_6O)_n$. Cryst. M.p. 180°. Insol. H_2O. Spar. sol. EtOH. Sublimes. Dist. with little HCl ⟶ propionaldehyde.

Parapropionaldehyde: $C_9H_{18}O_3$. MW, 174. F.p. − 20° to needles. B.p. 172–3°/773 mm., 85–6°/50 mm. Misc. with EtOH, Et_2O. Spar. sol. H_2O. D_{16}^{16} 0·9445. Dist. with little HCl or H_2SO_4 ⟶ propionaldehyde.

Propionaldehyde-ammonia: C_3H_9ON. MW, 75. Flocculent ppt. Mod. sol. EtOH, Et_2O. Spar. sol. ligroin. Gradually decomp. at room temp.

Bisulphite comp.: cryst. + $1H_2O$. Spar. sol. EtOH.

Oxime: C_3H_7ON. MW, 73. M.p. 40°. B.p. 130–2°, 77°/100 mm. D_4^{20} 0·9258. n_D^{20} 1·4287.

Semicarbazone: two forms. (i) Needles from C_6H_6–ligroin. M.p. 88–90°. Very easily sol. H_2O, hot C_6H_6. (ii) Plates from H_2O. M.p. 154°. Mod. sol. C_6H_6.

Phenylhydrazone: oil. B.p. 205°/108 mm. Becomes red in air. *Picrate*: pale yellow needles from EtOH. M.p. 156–7°.

Diphenylhydrazone: needles from EtOH.Aq. M.p. 20–1°.

Methylphenylhydrazone: yellow oil. B.p. 198°/170 mm.

o-*Nitrophenylhydrazone*: orange needles from EtOH.Aq. M.p. 72°.

m-*Nitrophenylhydrazone*: orange-yellow plates from EtOH.Aq. M.p. 83°.

p-*Nitrophenylhydrazone*: orange-yellow needles from EtOH.Aq. M.p. 125°.

o-*Tolylsemicarbazone*: plates. M.p. 129–30°.

p-*Tolylsemicarbazone*: plates. M.p. 135–7°.

Benzoylhydrazone: prisms from hot H_2O. M.p. 117°. Very sol. EtOH, Et_2O, $CHCl_3$. Easily decomp. by acids and alkalis.

Cyanhydrin: *see under* 1-Hydroxybutyric Acid.

Di-Me acetal: $C_5H_{12}O_2$. MW, 104. B.p. 89°. D^{21} 0·849. n^{21} 1·3799.

Di-Et acetal: $C_7H_{16}O_2$. MW, 132. B.p. 123°. D^0 0·8825.

Anil: propylideneaniline. Dimer. $C_{18}H_{22}N_2$. Needles from EtOH. M.p. 103–4°. Sol. Et_2O, C_6H_6. Spar. sol. cold EtOH.

Sah, Shih, *J. Chinese Chem. Soc.*, 1935, **3**, 246.
Bauer, Strauss, *Ber.*, 1932, **65**, 311.
Hurd, Meinert, *Organic Syntheses*, 1932, XII, 64.
I.G., B.P., 354,388, (*Chem. Zentr.*, 1931, II, 2932).
Kirrmann, *Ann. chim.*, 1929, **11**, 223.
Wood, Comley, *J. Soc. Chem. Ind.*, 1923, **42**, 429T.
Harries, Oppenheim, *Chem. Zentr.*, 1916, II, 992.
Nef, *Ann.*, 1904, **335**, 202.

Propionamide

$CH_3 \cdot CH_2 \cdot CONH_2$

C_3H_7ON MW, 73

Plates from C_6H_6. M.p. 81·3°. B.p. 213°. Sol. H_2O, EtOH, Et_2O, $CHCl_3$. Volatile in steam. Heat of comb. C_p 439·8 Cal. Combines with min. acids, Na and K. Na ⟶ sodium dipropionamide. Red. ⟶ propylamine and dipropylamine.

Hg comp.: plates. M.p. 202°. Spar. sol. cold H_2O.

N-*Formyl*: needles from C_6H_6. M.p. 65°. Sol. H_2O, EtOH, Et_2O.

N-*Acetyl*: *see* N-Acetylpropionamide.

N-*Benzoyl*: needles or prisms. M.p. 98°.

N-*Di-Me*: $C_5H_{11}ON$. MW, 101. B.p. 165–78°.

N-*Di-Et*: $C_7H_{15}ON$. MW, 129. B.p. 191°. Sol. H_2O, acids.

N-*Chloro*: cryst. from C_6H_6. M.p. 34°.

N-*Bromo*: needles. M.p. 80°. Sol. H_2O, EtOH, Et_2O, Me_2CO, $CHCl_3$. Spar. sol. cold C_6H_6, pet. ether.

N-*Iodo*: m.p. 128° decomp. Sol. EtOH, Me_2CO. Mod. sol. AcOH. Spar. sol. C_6H_6, pet. ether.

Mitchell, Reid, *J. Am. Chem. Soc.*, 1931, **53**, 1881.
Soc. Française de Catalyse Généralisée, F.P., 701,579, (*Chem. Zentr.*, 1931, II, 1193).
Hoffmann, *Ber.*, 1882, **15**, 981.

Propionaphthone.

See Ethyl naphthyl Ketone.

Propione.

See Diethyl Ketone.

Propionic Acid

$CH_3 \cdot CH_2 \cdot COOH$

$C_3H_6O_2$ MW, 74

Colourless liq. with acrid odour. F.p. −19·7°. B.p. 141·35°. D_{15}^{15} 0·99874. n_D^{22} 1·3859. Misc. in all proportions with H_2O. Heat of comb. 367·4 Cal. Mol. b.p. elevation 35·1. $k = 1 \cdot 22 \times 10^{-5}$ at 25°. Most salts sol. H_2O.

NH_4 salt: very hygroscopic cryst. M.p. 45°. Sol. H_2O, EtOH, AcOH.

K salt: plates + $1H_2O$ from EtOH.Aq. Becomes anhyd. at 120° and does not melt below 300°.

Me ester: *see* Methyl propionate.

Et ester: $C_5H_{10}O_2$. MW, 102. F.p. − 72·6°. B.p. 99·1°. D_4^{25} 0·8830. n_D^{20} 1·38385.

Propyl ester: $C_6H_{12}O_2$. MW, 116. B.p. 122°. D^{20} 0·8809.

Isopropyl ester: b.p. 109–11°/750 mm. D^0 0·8931.

Butyl ester: *see* Butyl propionate.

Isobutyl ester: *see* Isobutyl propionate.

n-*Amyl ester*: $C_8H_{16}O_2$. MW, 144. F.p. − 73·1°. B.p. 168·65°. D_4^{15} 0·8761. n_D^{15} 1·4096.

Isoamyl ester: *see* Isoamyl propionate.

tert.-*Amyl ester*: *see tert.*-Amyl propionate.

Decyl ester: $C_{13}H_{26}O_2$. MW, 214. B.p. 124°/8 mm. D_4^{20} 0·8639. n_D^{20} 1·42907.

Glycerol mono-ester: *see* Propionin.

Glycerol di-ester: dipropin. $C_9H_{16}O_5$. MW, 204. B.p. 170–3°/10 mm.

Glycerol tri-ester: tripropin. $C_{12}H_{20}O_6$. MW, 260. B.p. 177–82°/20 mm., 130–2°/3 mm. D_{18}^{20} 1·100. n_D^{19} 1·43175.

Phenyl ester: $C_9H_{10}O_2$. MW, 150. Prisms. M.p. 20°. B.p. 211°.

Benzyl ester: $C_{10}H_{12}O_2$. MW, 164. B.p. 222°.

Chloride: propionyl chloride. C_3H_5OCl. MW, 92·5. B.p. 80°. D_4^{20} 1·0646. n_D^{20} 1·40507.

Bromide: propionyl bromide. C_3H_5OBr. MW, 137. B.p. 103–103·6°/770 mm. $D^{16 \cdot 4}$ 1·5210. $n_D^{16 \cdot 4}$ 1·45783.

Amide: *see* Propionamide.

Anhydride: $C_6H_{10}O_3$. MW, 130. B.p. 168·4–168·8°/780 mm., 67·5°/18 mm. D^{15} 1·0169.

Nitrile: propionitrile, ethyl cyanide. C_3H_5N. MW, 55. Liq. with ethereal odour. F.p. − 103·5°. B.p. 97°. D_4^{25} 0·7770. n_D^{25} 1·3659. Part misc. with H_2O. Mol. b.p. elevation 22·6. Heat of comb. C_v 446·7 Cal. Na, K ⟶ di- and tri-molecular comps. AcOH ⟶ N-acetylpropionamide. Extremely poisonous.

Hydrazide: cryst. M.p. 40°. B.p. 130°/16 mm. Sol. H_2O. Spar. sol. Et_2O.

Anilide: propionanilide. Plates from EtOH.Aq., Et_2O, or C_6H_6. M.p. 105–6°. Mod. sol. hot H_2O, EtOH, Et_2O. Spar. sol. cold H_2O. Heat of comb. C_p 1168·0 Cal.

o-*Nitroanilide*: lemon-yellow cryst. from EtOH. M.p. 63°. Sol. boiling H_2O, EtOH, Et_2O, C_6H_6.

p-*Nitroanilide*: yellowish-brown plates from Ac_2O. M.p. 182°.

o-*Toluidide*: cryst. M.p. 18°. B.p. 144–5°/11 mm.

m-*Toluidide*: needles from Et_2O. M.p. 81°. Sol. EtOH, Et_2O, ligroin.

p-*Toluidide*: plates from C_6H_6. M.p. 126°. Sol. EtOH, Et_2O, Me_2CO, AcOH, $CHCl_3$, C_6H_6. Spar. sol. cold H_2O, ligroin.

1-*Naphthylamide*: cryst. from EtOH. M.p. 116°.

Hardy, *J. Chem. Soc.*, 1936, 361, 365.
du Pont, U.S.P., 2,015,065, (*Chem. Zentr.*, 1936, I, 1310); U.S.P., 1,979,717, (*Chem. Abstracts*, 1935, **29**, 181).
I.G., U.S.P., 2,005,183, (*Chem. Abstracts*, 1935, **29**, 5125).
Werkmann, Rayburn, Hixon, U.S.P., 1,991,993, (*Chem. Abstracts*, 1935, **29**, 2298).
Timmermans, Hennaut-Roland, *J. chim. phys.*, 1930, **27**, 401.
Pierre, Puchot, *Ann. chim.*, 1873, **28**, 75.
Auger, *Compt. rend.*, 1907, **145**, 1289.
Hanriot, Bouveault, *Bull. soc. chim.*, 1889, **1**, 171.
Simons, *J. Am. Chem. Soc.*, 1926, **48**, 1993.

Propionin (*Monopropin, glycerol α-propionate*)

$CH_2·O·CO·CH_2·CH_3$
$CHOH$
CH_2OH

$C_6H_{12}O_4$ MW, 148

B.p. 132–4°/3 mm. D_4^{20} 1·1537.

Diacetyl: $C_{10}H_{16}O_6$. MW, 232. B.p. 150°/12 mm.

Eastman Kodak, U.S.P., 2,005,371, (*Chem. Zentr.*, 1935, II, 2446).
Schuette, Hale, *J. Am. Chem. Soc.*, 1930, **52**, 1979.
Abderhalden, Eichwald, *Ber.*, 1914, **47**, 1859.

Propionitrile.
See under Propionic Acid.

Propionoin.
See Diethylketol.

Propionylacetamide.
See Acetylpropionamide.

Propionylacetic Acid (2-*Keto*-n-*valeric acid*)

$CH_3·CH_2·CO·CH_2·COOH$

$C_5H_8O_3$ MW, 116

Et ester: $C_7H_{12}O_3$. MW, 144. B.p. 191°, 75–8°/9 mm. Alc. $FeCl_3$ ⟶ red. col. Forms bisulphite comp.

Nitrile: C_5H_7ON. MW, 97. B.p. 164–5°. D^9 0·976. Insol. H_2O.

Cu deriv.: green cryst. M.p. 144–5°.

Décombe, *Ann. chim.*, 1932, **18**, 81.
I.C.I., F.P., 666,703, (*Chem. Abstracts*, 1930, **24**, 1120).
Breckport, *Chem. Abstracts*, 1924, **18**, 816.
Wahl, *Compt. rend.*, 1911, **152**, 97.
Dupont, *Compt. rend.*, 1909, **148**, 1524.
Reymenant, *Chem. Zentr.*, 1901, I, 95.

Propionylacetone (*Acetylpropionylmethane, hexandione-2 : 4, 2 : 4-diketohexane*)

$CH_3·CH_2·CO·CH_2·CO·CH_3$

$C_6H_{10}O_2$ MW, 114

Oil. B.p. 158°. D_4^{20} 0·959. n_D^{20} 1·4516.

Cu deriv.: blue needles. M.p. 197–8° (179°).

Powell, Seymour, *J. Am. Chem. Soc.*, 1931, **53**, 1049.
Fittig, *Ann.*, 1907, **353**, 24.
Claisen, Ehrhardt, *Ber.*, 1889, **22**, 1014.

Propionylanisole.
See under 2-, *and* 4-Hydroxypropiophenone.

Propionylbenzene.
See Propiophenone.

2-Propionylbenzoic Acid.
See Propiophenone-*o*-carboxylic Acid.

3-Propionyl-*sec.*-*n*-butyl Alcohol.
See 3-Methyl-2-hexanolone-4.

4-Propionyl-1-butylene.
See 1-Heptenone-5.

2-Propionyl-2-butylene.
See 3-Methyl-2-hexenone-4.

3-Propionylbutyric Acid.
See 4-Keto-*n*-heptylic Acid.

Propionylbutyryl.
See Heptandione-3 : 4.

Propionylbutyrylmethane.
See Octandione-3 : 5.

5-Propionyl-*n*-caproic Acid.
See 6-Ketopelargonic Acid.

Propionylcaproyl (*Nonandione*-3 : 4, *ethyl* n-*amyl diketone*, 3 : 4-*diketononane*)

$$CH_3{\cdot}[CH_2]_4{\cdot}CO{\cdot}CO{\cdot}CH_2{\cdot}CH_3$$

$C_9H_{16}O_2$ MW, 156

B.p. 77–80°/10 mm. D_4^0 0·927.

3-*Oxime*: needles. M.p. 33–4°. B.p. 131–2°/9 mm. Spar. sol. most org. solvents.

Dioxime: needles from boiling C_6H_6. M.p. 158°. Sol. EtOH, Et_2O. Spar. sol. pet. ether. Sublimes.

Locquin, *Bull. soc. chim.*, 1904, **31**, 1176.

7-Propionylcaprylic Acid.

See 8-Ketoundecylic Acid.

Propionylcarbinol (*Ethylketol*, 2-*keto*-n-*butyl alcohol*, *hydroxymethyl ethyl ketone*, 1-*butanolone*-2)

$$CH_3{\cdot}CH_2{\cdot}CO{\cdot}CH_2OH$$

$C_4H_8O_2$ MW, 88

Colourless liq. B.p. 160°. Misc. with H_2O, EtOH, Et_2O. D_{15}^{15} 1·0365. $n_D^{14\cdot5}$ 1·4315. Reduces Fehling's. Acid $KMnO_4$ $\longrightarrow$ propionic acid. Forms bisulphite comp.

Formyl: $C_5H_8O_3$. MW, 116. B.p. 176–8°. D_{17}^{17} 1·0946. n_D^{17} 1·424. *Semicarbazone*: cryst. from $CHCl_3$ or C_6H_6. M.p. 115°.

Me ether: $C_5H_{10}O_2$. MW, 102. B.p. 130–1°/729 mm. *Phenylhydrazone*: yellow oil. B.p. 170°/18 mm.

Et ether: $C_6H_{12}O_2$. MW, 116. Colourless oil turning yellow in air. B.p. 146°, 55°/24 mm. D_4^{16} 0·914. *Semicarbazone*: m.p. 87°.

Isobutyl ether: $C_8H_{16}O_2$. MW, 144. B.p. 68–9°/13 mm. *Semicarbazone*: m.p. 72°.

Oxime: cryst. from $CHCl_3$. M.p. 60–1°.

Semicarbazone: cryst. from EtOH. M.p. 136–8°. Spar. sol. H_2O.

Sommelet, *Bull. soc. chim.*, 1911, **9**, 35.
Kling, *Compt. rend.*, 1905, **140**, 1345.

Propionylcresol.

See Hydroxymethylpropiophenone.

Propionyl cyanide.

See under 1-Ketobutyric Acid.

Propionylcyclohexane.

See Hexahydropropiophenone.

Propionylethylene.

See Ethyl vinyl Ketone.

Propionylformic Acid.

See 1-Ketobutyric Acid.

2-Propionylheptane.

See 4-Methylnonanone-3.

6-Propionyl-*n*-heptylic Acid.

See 7-Ketocapric Acid.

Propionyl hydroperoxide.

See Perpropionic Acid.

1-Propionylisobutylene.

See 2-Methyl-2-hexenone-4.

Propionylnaphthalene.

See Ethyl naphthyl Ketone.

2-Propionyl-1-naphthol.

See Ethyl 1-hydroxy-2-naphthyl Ketone.

***p*-Propionylphenetole.**

See under 4-Hydroxypropiophenone.

Propionylphenol.

See 2-, *and* 4-Hydroxypropiophenone.

3-Propionylpropanol-1.

See 1-Hexanolone-4.

1-Propionylpropionic Acid (1-*Methylpropionylacetic acid*, 2-*keto*-1-*methyl*-n-*valeric acid*)

$$CH_3{\cdot}CH_2{\cdot}CO{\cdot}\underset{}{\overset{CH_3}{\overset{|}{C}H}}{\cdot}COOH$$

$C_6H_{10}O_3$ MW, 130

Me ester: $C_7H_{12}O_3$. MW, 144. Liq. with aromatic odour. B.p. 187°, 80°/12 mm.

Et ester: $C_8H_{14}O_3$. MW, 158. Oil. B.p. 199°, 87–8°/16 mm. D^{15} 0·9827. Forms Na deriv. Red. $\longrightarrow$ 2-hydroxy-1-methyl-*n*-valeric acid. NaOH $\longrightarrow$ diethyl ketone. $C_6H_5{\cdot}NH{\cdot}NH_2$ $\longrightarrow$ 4-methyl-3-ethyl-1-phenylpyrazolone-5. *Di-Et-acetal*: b.p. 223–6°.

Isobutyl ester: $C_{10}H_{18}O_3$. MW, 186. B.p. 99–100°/11 mm.

Amide: $C_6H_{11}O_2N$. MW, 129. Hygroscopic cryst. M.p. 82°. Sol. H_2O.

Nitrile: C_6H_9ON. MW, 111. Oil with sweet odour. B.p. 193·5°. D^0 0·9728.

Schroeter, *Ber.*, 1916, **49**, 2719.
Pingel, *Ann.*, 1888, **245**, 84.
Hantzsch, Wohlbrück, *Ber.*, 1887, **20**, 1320.

2-Propionylpropionic Acid.

See 3-Keto-*n*-caproic Acid.

3-Propionyl-*n*-propyl Alcohol.

See 1-Hexanolone-4.

Propionylpropylene.

See 1-Hexenone-4, 2-Hexenone-4, *and* 2-Methyl-1-pentenone-3.

β-Propionylstyrene.

See Ethyl styryl Ketone.

Propionylthiophene.

See Propiothienone.

Propionyltoluene.

See Ethyl tolyl Ketone.

4-Propionyl-*n*-valeric Acid.

See 5-Keto-*n*-caprylic Acid.

Propionylvaleryl.

See Octandione-3 : 4.

Propiophenone (*Ethyl phenyl ketone, propionylbenzene*)

$C_6H_5{\cdot}CO{\cdot}CH_2{\cdot}CH_3$

$C_9H_{10}O$ MW, 134

Plates. M.p. 19–20°. B.p. 218°/764 mm., 115–20°/21 mm., 75°/3 mm. D_{25}^{25} 1·0087. n_D^{20} 1·534. CrO_3 ⟶ benzoic and acetic acids. Na in EtOH ⟶ ethylphenylcarbinol. Zn + HCl or H (+ Ni) ⟶ propylbenzene.

Oxime: plates from pet. ether. M.p. 53–4°. B.p. 245–6° (decomp.), 165°/38 mm.

2 : 4-*Dinitrophenylhydrazone*: red leaflets from EtOH. M.p. 187–9°.

Semicarbazone: needles from EtOH. M.p. 182 (173°). Spar. sol. EtOH, Et_2O.

Di-Me acetal: $C_{11}H_{16}O_2$. MW, 180. Oil. B.p. 206–8°, 92–3°/18 mm. D_4^{15} 0·9888.

Imide: b.p. 102°/13 mm.

Azine: yellow needles. M.p. 79–80°. Sol. EtOH.

Anil: pale yellow needles from hexane. M.p. 50°. B.p. 169°/11 mm. Spar. sol. pet. ether.

Thompson, Stevens, *J. Chem. Soc.*, 1932, 2611.
Shriner, Turner, *J. Am. Chem. Soc.*, 1930, **52**, 1267.
Straus, Berkov, *Ann.*, 1913, **401**, 140.
Auwers, *Ber.*, 1912, **45**, 996.

Propiophenone-*o*-carboxylic Acid (2-*Propionylbenzoic acid*)

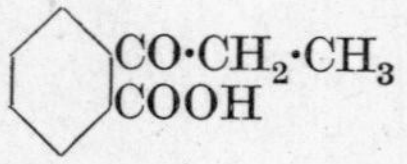

$C_{10}H_{10}O_3$ MW, 178

Needles from EtOH.Aq., or C_6H_6. M.p. 93° (97°). NaHg ⟶ 3-ethylphthalide.

Me ester: $C_{11}H_{12}O_3$. MW, 192. B.p. 157–8°/19 mm. $D_4^{16\cdot4}$ 1·1274. $n_D^{16\cdot4}$ 1·5197.

Amide: $C_{10}H_{11}O_2N$. MW, 177. Needles from H_2O. Sinters at 150°. M.p. 159°. Spar. sol. $CHCl_3$, ligroin, C_6H_6, CS_2.

Anilide: cryst. M.p. 160°. Insol. H_2O.

Auwers, Heinze, *Ber.*, 1919, **52**, 590.

Propiopiperone (3 : 4-*Methylenedioxypropiophenone*)

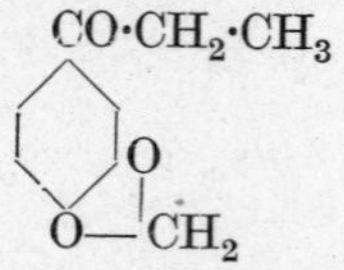

$C_{10}H_{10}O_3$ MW, 178

Needles. M.p. 39°. B.p. 153–4°/13 mm. D^{20} 1·210.

Oxime: prisms. M.p. 104°.

Semicarbazone: m.p. 187–8°.

Phenylhydrazone: yellow needles. M.p. 97°.

Foulds, Robinson, *J. Chem. Soc.*, 1914, **105**, 1972.
Schimmel, *Chem. Zentr.*, 1905, I, 1470.
Wallach, Pond, *Ber.*, 1895, **28**, 2719.

Propiothienone (2-*Propionylthiophene, ethyl 1-thienyl ketone*)

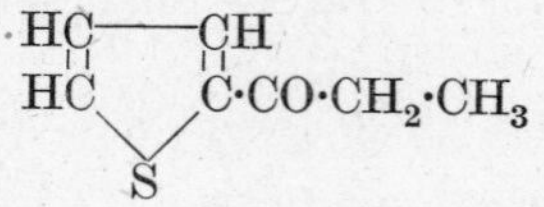

C_7H_8OS MW, 140

Pale yellow oil. B.p. 228°, 100–1°/11 mm. Ox. ⟶ thiophene-2-carboxylic acid.

Oxime: plates. M.p. 55–6°.

Semicarbazone: plates from C_6H_6. M.p. 167°. Sol. hot H_2O, Me_2CO, C_6H_6. Spar. sol. Et_2O. Insol. pet. ether.

Steinkopf, Schubart, *Ann.*, 1921, **424**, 8.
Thomas, Couderc, *Bull. soc. chim.*, 1918, **23**, 288.

Proponal (5 : 5-*Dipropylbarbituric acid*)

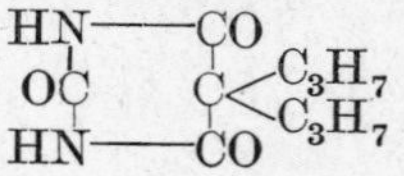

$C_{10}H_{16}O_3N_2$ MW, 212

Colourless plates from H_2O. M.p. 146° (166°). Aq. sol. has bitter taste. Sol. 1640 parts H_2O at 20°, 70 parts at 100°. Very sol. EtOH, Et_2O, AcOEt, $CHCl_3$, C_6H_6, alkalis. Forms mono-Na salt. Hypnotic.

Quinine comp.: needles. M.p. 127–8°. Very sol. EtOH, Me_2CO. Sol. Et_2O, $CHCl_3$, hot H_2O, hot C_6H_6, hot ligroin.

Itallie, Steenhauer, *Pharm. Weekblad*, 1930, **67**, 977, (*Chem. Zentr.*, 1931, I, 823).
Merck, D.R.P., 249,908, (*Chem. Zentr.*, 1912, II, 777); D.R.P., 146,496, (*Chem. Zentr.*, 1903, II, 1483).
Conrad, *Ann.*, 1905, **340**, 321.
Fischer, Dilthey, *Ann.*, 1904, **335**, 344.

***N*-Propylacetamide.**
See under Propylamine.

Propylacetanilide.
See under Aminopropylbenzene.

1-Propylacetoacetic Acid.
See 1-Aceto-*n*-valeric Acid.

Propylacetonylcarbinol.
See 4-Heptanolone-2.

Propyl acetonyl Ether.
See under Hydroxyacetone.

p-Propylacetophenone (p-*Acetopropylbenzene*)

$$CH_3 \cdot CH_2 \cdot CH_2 \langle\ \rangle CO \cdot CH_3$$

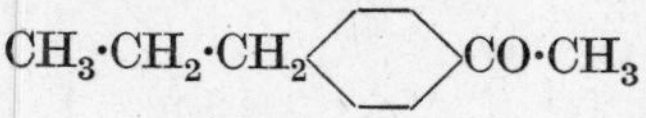

$C_{11}H_{14}O$ MW, 162

Oil. B.p. 252°. D^{15} 0·9785. Ox. $\longrightarrow$ p-propylbenzoic acid.

Oxime : plates from pet. ether. M.p. 43–4°.

Phenylhydrazone : yellowish-white hexagonal plates from pet. ether. M.p. 92°. Very sol. warm pet. ether. Very unstable.

Widman, *Ber.*, 1888, **21**, 2224.

n-Propylacetylene.
See 1-Pentine.

2-Propylacrolein (2-*Hexenal*-1, 1-*hexylene aldehyde, hexenic aldehyde*)

$$CH_3 \cdot CH_2 \cdot CH_2 \cdot CH{:}CH \cdot CHO$$

$C_6H_{10}O$ MW, 98

Constituent of leaves of green plants. Colourless oil. B.p. 150°, 49·5°/18·5 mm. D_4^{13} 0·861. n_D^{13} 1·4470.

Semicarbazone : m.p. 175–6°.
p-*Nitrophenylhydrazone* : m.p. 139°.

Delaby, Guillot-Allègre, *Bull. soc. chim.*, 1933, **53**, 301.
Curtius, Franzen, *Ann.*, 1914, **404**, 93 ; 1912, **390**, 89.

1-Propylacrylic Acid (α-*Amylene*-β-*carboxylic acid*, 1-*methylene*-n-*valeric acid*, 1-*pentene*-2-*carboxylic acid*)

$$CH_3 \cdot CH_2 \cdot CH_2 \cdot \overset{\overset{\textstyle CH_2}{\|}}{C} \cdot COOH$$

$C_6H_{10}O_2$ MW, 114

Prisms. M.p. 24·4°. B.p. 213°/750 mm. D_{25}^{25} 0·9812. Sol. Et_2O, $CHCl_3$, CS_2, C_6H_6. Spar. sol. H_2O. Heat of comb. C_v 795·7 Cal. $k = 0·97 \times 10^{-5}$ at 25°. Gives spar. sol. Ca salt, cryst. Ag salt.

Et ester : $C_8H_{14}O_2$. MW, 142. B.p. 167–8°.

Lieben, Zeisel, *Monatsh.*, 1883, **4**, 46.

2-Propylacrylic Acid (1-*Hexenic acid*, 1 : 2-*hexenoic acid*, α-*amylene*-α-*carboxylic acid*, 1-*pentene*-1-*carboxylic acid, butylideneacetic acid, isohydrosorbic acid*)

$$CH_3 \cdot CH_2 \cdot CH_2 \cdot CH{:}CH \cdot COOH$$

$C_6H_{10}O_2$ MW, 114

Needles from H_2O or EtOH. M.p. 33°. B.p. 216–17°, 118°/19 mm. $k = 1·98 \times 10^{-5}$ at

25°. Br $\longrightarrow$ 1 : 2-dibromocaproic acid. HBr $\longrightarrow$ 2-bromocaproic acid. $AgClO_3 \longrightarrow$ 1 : 2-dihydroxycaproic acid.

Et ester : $C_8H_{14}O_2$. MW, 142. B.p. 174–5°, 80°/22 mm. D_4^{20} 0·8986. n_D^{20} 1·4348.

Chloride : C_6H_9OCl. MW, 132·5. B.p. 70°/23 mm.

Anilide : needles. M.p. 109–10°.

Fittig, Baker, *Ann.*, 1894, **283**, 118.
Goldberg, Linstead, *J. Chem. Soc.*, 1928, 2351.
Boxer, Linstead, *J. Chem. Soc.*, 1931, 740.
Delaby, Guillot-Allègre, *Compt. rend.*, 1931, **192**, 1467.

1-Propyladipic Acid.
See Heptane-1 : 4-dicarboxylic Acid.

2-Propyladipic Acid

$$\begin{array}{l} \qquad CH_2 \cdot COOH \\ C_3H_7 \cdot CH \\ \qquad CH_2 \\ \qquad CH_2 \cdot COOH \end{array}$$

$C_9H_{16}O_4$ MW, 188

Sinters at 45°. M.p. 49°. B.p. 184–6°/0·1 mm.

Dinitrile : $C_9H_{14}N_2$. MW, 150. B.p. 174–6°/12 mm.

v. Braun, Keller, Weissbach, *Ann.*, 1931, **490**, 182.

Propyl Alcohol (*Propanol*-1)

$$CH_3 \cdot CH_2 \cdot CH_2OH$$

C_3H_8O MW, 60

B.p. 97·4°, 79–80°/374·6 mm., 65·94°/198·8 mm., 49·92°/90 mm., 30·35°/28·5 mm. D_4^{15} 0·80753, D_4^{20} 0·8035, D_4^{25} 0·7993. n_D^{20} 1·38499, n_D^{25} 1·3833. Misc. with H_2O, EtOH, Et_2O. Crit. temp. 263·7°. KOH at 240–50° $\longrightarrow$ propionic acid + propylene. Br $\longrightarrow$ 1 : 1-dibromopropionaldehyde + propyl bromide. I + KOH $\longrightarrow$ iodoform.

Nitrite : see Propyl nitrite.
Nitrate : see Propyl nitrate.
Phosphate : *see under* Phosphoric Acid.
Acetyl : propyl acetate. B.p. 101·67°. D_4^{20} 0·88630, D_4^{40} 0·86390. n_D^{20} 1·38422.
Benzoyl : propyl benzoate. F.p. — 51·6°. B.p. 230·6–230·9°. D_4^{15} 1·0274. n_D^{15} 1·50139. Heat of comb. C_p 1255·010 Cal.
3 : 5-*Dinitrobenzoyl* : m.p. 73°.
Acid phthalate : m.p. 54–5°.
Phenylurethane : m.p. 58°.
p-*Nitrophenylurethane* : m.p. 115°.

1-*Naphthylurethane* : m.p. 105°.

Dreyfus, U.S.P., 1,996,101, (*Chem. Abstracts*, 1935, **29**, 3349).
du Pont, U.S.P., 2,014,740, (*Chem. Abstracts*, 1935, **29**, 7342).
Schüpphaus, *J. Am. Chem. Soc.*, 1892, **14**, 53.
Crismer, *Chem. Zentr.*, 1904, I, 1480.
Shriner, Cox, *J. Am. Chem. Soc.*, 1931, **53**, 1602.

Propylallene.
See 1 : 2-Hexadiene.

3-Propylallyl Alcohol.
See 2-Hexenol-1.

Propylallylamine

$CH_2:CH\cdot CH_2\cdot NH\cdot CH_2\cdot CH_2\cdot CH_3$

$C_6H_{13}N$ MW, 99

B.p. 110–14°. D^{18} 0·7708. Sol. 15–20 parts H_2O.

Liebermann, Paal, *Ber.*, 1883, **16**, (I), 526.

Propylallylcarbinol.
See 1-Heptenol-4.

Propyl allyl Ether

$CH_2:CH\cdot CH_2\cdot O\cdot CH_2\cdot CH_2\cdot CH_3$

$C_6H_{12}O$ MW, 100

B.p. 90–2°. D^{20} 0·7764.

Deulofeu, *Chem. Zentr.*, 1928, II, 2547.
Lippert, *Ann.*, 1893, **276**, 192.

Propyl allyl Ketone.
See 1-Heptenone-4.

Propylamine (1-*Aminopropane*)

$CH_3\cdot CH_2\cdot CH_2NH_2$

C_3H_9N MW, 59

B.p. 49°. D_4^4 0·7330, D_4^{25} 0·714. $n_D^{16\cdot 6}$ 1·39006, $n_D^{23\cdot 5}$ 1·3873. Heat of comb. C_p (vapour) 575·74 Cal., C_p (liq.) 560·3 Cal., C_v (liq.) 559·4 Cal. $k = 4\cdot 7 \times 10^{-4}$ at 25°.

B,HCl : m.p. 157–8°.
B,HAuCl₄ : m.p. 169°.
B_2,H_2PtCl_6 : m.p. 214°.
B_2,H_2PtBr_6 : red leaflets. M.p. 257–8° decomp.
Picrate : m.p. 135°.
N-*Acetyl* : *N*-propylacetamide. $C_5H_{11}ON$. MW, 101. B.p. 222–5°. *B,HCl* : needles. M.p. 47°.
N-*Benzoyl* : *N*-propylbenzamide. Cryst. from EtOH or C_6H_6. M.p. 84·5°. B.p. 294–5°/750 mm. slight decomp.

Neogi, Chowdhuri, *J. Chem. Soc.*, 1917, **111**, 902.
Rakshit, *J. Am. Chem. Soc.*, 1913, **35**, 445.
Hofmann, *Ber.*, 1882, **15**, 769.
Linnemann, *Ann.*, 1872, **161**, 44.

2-Propylaminoethyl Alcohol (N-2-*Hydroxyethylpropylamine, propylethanolamine*)

$CH_3\cdot CH_2\cdot CH_2\cdot NH\cdot CH_2\cdot CH_2OH$

$C_5H_{13}ON$ MW, 103

Oil. B.p. 182°/746 mm. D_4^{20} 0·9005. n_D^{20} 1·4428. Sol. H_2O, EtOH, Et_2O. Strongly basic.

$B,HAuCl_4$: plates from H_2O. M.p. 85°.
Picrate : yellowish-brown prisms from H_2O. M.p. 129°. Sol. H_2O, EtOH.
Picrolonate : brownish-red prisms from EtOH.Aq. M.p. 238° decomp.

Matthes, *Ann.*, 1901, **315**, 110.

γ-Propylaminopropylbenzene.
See under 3-Phenylpropylamine.

Propyl-*n*-amylcarbinol (*Nonanol*-4)

$CH_3\cdot [CH_2]_3\cdot CH_2\cdot CH(OH)\cdot CH_2\cdot CH_2\cdot CH_3$

$C_9H_{20}O$ MW, 144

B.p. 192–3°. D^{20} 0·8282. n_D 1·41971. Insol. H_2O.

Acetyl : b.p. 199–200°. D^{20} 0·8282.

Pexters, *Chem. Zentr.*, 1907, I, 1398.

***n*-Propyl-*tert*.-amylcarbinol.**
See 3 : 3-Dimethylheptanol-4.

Propyl *n*-amyl Ketone (*Nonanone*-4)

$CH_3\cdot CH_2\cdot CH_2\cdot CH_2\cdot CH_2\cdot CO\cdot CH_2\cdot CH_2\cdot CH_3$

$C_9H_{18}O$ MW, 142

B.p. 187–8°, 75–6°/20 mm., 70·5–71·5°/10 mm. D_4^0 0·837.

Semicarbazone : cryst. from EtOH. M.p. 73–4° (rapid heat.) (67°, 145°).
p-*Nitrophenylhydrazone* : yellow cryst. from EtOH. M.p. 84–5°.

Karrer, Wettstein, Fröwis, Morf, *Helv. Chim. Acta*, 1932, **15**, 231.
Bryant, Clemo, *J. Chem. Soc.*, 1931, 2080.

***N*-Propylaniline**

$C_6H_5\cdot NH\cdot CH_2\cdot CH_2\cdot CH_3$

$C_9H_{13}N$ MW, 135

Pale yellow oil. B.p. 222°. D^{18} 0·949.

Hydrochloride: needles. M.p. 150°.
Oxalate: plates from H_2O. M.p. 152°.

Voss, Blanke, *Ann.*, 1931, **485**, 280.
Hickinbottom, *J. Chem. Soc.*, 1930, 992.

Propylaniline.
See Aminopropylbenzene.

Propylanisole.
See under Propylphenol.

***N*-Propylbenzamide.**
See under Propylamine.

Propylbenzene (1-*Phenylpropane*)

$C_6H_5 \cdot CH_2 \cdot CH_2 \cdot CH_3$

C_9H_{12} MW, 120

M.p. −99·2°. B.p. 159·45°. D_0^0 0·87864, D_4^{20} 0·8617. n_D^{20} 1·4925. Heat of comb. C_v 1244·6 Cal. $K_2Cr_2O_7 + H_2SO_4 \longrightarrow$ benzoic acid.
Picrate: yellow cryst. M.p. 103·5°.

Gilman, Catlin, *Organic Syntheses*, Collective Vol. I, 458.
Auwers, *Ann.*, 1919, **419**, 92.
Baril, Hauber, *J. Am. Chem. Soc.*, 1931, **53**, 1087.

***o*-Propylbenzoic Acid**

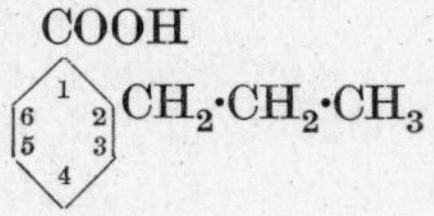

$C_{10}H_{12}O_2$ MW, 164

Leaflets from EtOH.Aq. M.p. 58°. B.p. 272°/739 mm.
Et ester: $C_{12}H_{16}O_2$. MW, 192. B.p. 244–7°/785 mm. D_{15}^{15} 1·003.
Chloride: $C_{10}H_{11}OCl$. MW, 182·5. Yellow liq. B.p. 236°.
Amide: $C_{10}H_{13}ON$. MW, 163. Needles from H_2O. M.p. 127–8°. Sol. EtOH, Et_2O, AcOH, C_6H_6.
Nitrile: $C_{10}H_{11}N$. MW, 145. B.p. 227–9°/758 mm.

Gabriel, Michael, *Ber.*, 1878, **11**, 1014.
Gottlieb, *Ber.*, 1899, **32**, 961.

***p*-Propylbenzoic Acid.**
Prisms or leaflets from H_2O. M.p. 141°. Sol. EtOH, Et_2O, $CHCl_3$, CS_2, C_6H_6. Spar. sol. boiling H_2O. Volatile in steam. $KMnO_4 \longrightarrow$ terephthalic acid.
Nitrile: b.p. 227°.

Widman, *Ber.*, 1889, **22**, 2278.
Francksen, *Ber.*, 1884, **17**, 1229.

α-Propylbenzyl Alcohol.
See Propylphenylcarbinol.

Propylbenzylcarbinol (1-*Phenylpentanol*-2, 1-*phenyl*-sec.-n-*amyl alcohol*, β-*hydroxy*-n-*amylbenzene*)

$CH_3 \cdot CH_2 \cdot CH_2 \cdot CH(OH) \cdot CH_2 \cdot C_6H_5$

$C_{11}H_{16}O$ MW, 164

B.p. 127°/15 mm. D_4^{25} 0·9579. n_{5875}^{25} 1·51017.
Phenylurethane: needles from pet. ether. M.p. 80°.

Roblin, Davidson, Bogert, *J. Am. Chem. Soc.*, 1935, **57**, 151.

Propylbenzylethylene.
See 1-Phenylhexene-2.

Propyl benzyl Ketone (ω-*Butyryltoluene*, β-*ketoamylbenzene*, 1-*phenylpentanone*-2)

$C_6H_5 \cdot CH_2 \cdot CO \cdot CH_2 \cdot CH_2 \cdot CH_3$

$C_{11}H_{14}O$ MW, 162

B.p. 244°. D_4^0 0·984.
Semicarbazone: m.p. 84°.

Senderens, *Ann. chim.*, 1913, **28**, 321.
Ludlam, *J. Chem. Soc.*, 1902, **81**, 1189.

Propyl bromide (1-*Bromopropane*)

$CH_3 \cdot CH_2 \cdot CH_2Br$

C_3H_7Br MW, 123

B.p. 71°. Spar. sol. H_2O. D_4^{20} 1·3529. n_D^{20} 1·43414. Heat of comb. C_p 499·3 Cal. Heat with $AlBr_3 \longrightarrow$ isopropyl bromide.

Karvonen, *Chem. Abstracts*, 1920, **14**, 2176.
Tseng, Hou, *J. Chinese Chem. Soc.*, 1934, **2**, 57.
Bodroux, *Compt. rend.*, 1915, **160**, 205.
Norris, *Am. Chem. J.*, 1907, **38**, 640.

3-Propylbutanone.
See 3-Methylhexanone-2.

3-Propyl-*sec.*-*n*-butyl Alcohol.
See 3-Methylhexanol-2.

Propyl-*n*-butylcarbinol (*Octanol*-4, 4-*hydroxyoctane*)

$CH_3 \cdot [CH_2]_3 \cdot CH(OH) \cdot CH_2 \cdot CH_2 \cdot CH_3$

$C_8H_{18}O$ MW, 130

d-.
B.p. 79°/16 mm. D_4^{22} 0·818. $[\alpha]_D^{22}$ + 0·74°.

dl-.
B.p. 71°/10 mm. D_4^0 0·838.

Levene, Marker, *J. Biol. Chem.*, 1931, **91**, 405.
Bouveault, Locquin, *Bull. soc. chim.*, 1906, **35**, 644, 646.

Propyl-*sec*.-*n*-butylcarbinol (3-*Methylheptanol*-4)

$$CH_3{\cdot}CH_2{\cdot}CH(CH_3){\cdot}CH(OH){\cdot}CH_2{\cdot}CH_2{\cdot}CH_3$$

$C_8H_{18}O$ MW, 130

$D^{22\cdot2}$ 0·8272. n_D^{25} 1·4286.

Bridgman, *Chem. Zentr.*, 1933, II, 348.

Propyl-*tert*.-butylcarbinol.
See 2 : 2-Dimethylhexanol-3.

Propylbutylene.
See 3-Methyl-1-hexene *and* 3-Methyl-2-hexene.

Propyl *n*-butyl Ether

$$CH_3{\cdot}[CH_2]_2{\cdot}CH_2{\cdot}O{\cdot}CH_2{\cdot}CH_2{\cdot}CH_3$$

$C_7H_{16}O$ MW, 116

B.p. 117·1°. D^0 0·7773.

Dobriner, *Ann.*, 1888, **243**, 7.

Propyl *tert*.-butyl Ether

$$(CH_3)_3C{\cdot}O{\cdot}CH_2{\cdot}CH_2{\cdot}CH_3$$

$C_7H_{16}O$ MW, 116

B.p. 97·4°. D_4^{25} 0·7472. n_D^{25} 1·3830.

Norris, Rigby, *J. Am. Chem. Soc.*, 1932, **54**, 2088.

1-Propyl-2-butylethylene.
See 4-Nonene.

Propyl butyl Ketone (4-*Keto-octane, octanone*-4)

$$CH_3{\cdot}[CH_2]_3{\cdot}CO{\cdot}CH_2{\cdot}CH_2{\cdot}CH_3$$

$C_8H_{16}O$ MW, 128

B.p. 165–8°.
Oxime: b.p. 116–17°/20 mm.

Bouveault, Locquin, *Bull. soc. chim.*, 1906, **35**, 648.

2-Propylbutyraldehyde.
See 2-Methylcaproic Aldehyde.

2-Propylbutyric Acid.
See 2-Methylcaproic Acid.

Propylcarbamic Acid.
Et ester, *see* Propylurethane: Amide, *see* Propylurea.

Propylcarbylamine.
See Propyl isocyanide.

Propylcatechol.
See 2 : 3-Dihydroxy-1-propylbenzene *and* 3 : 4-Dihydroxy-1-propylbenzene.

Propyl chloride (1-*Chloropropane*)

$$CH_3{\cdot}CH_2{\cdot}CH_2Cl$$

C_3H_7Cl MW, 78·5

M.p. — 122·8°. B.p. 46·60°. D_4^{15} 0·89694, D_4^{20} 0·8910. n_D^{20} 1·38838. Heat of comb. C_p (vapour) 492·38 Cal.

Norris, Taylor, *J. Am. Chem. Soc.*, 1924, **46**, 756.
Dehn, Davis, *J. Am. Chem. Soc.*, 1907, **29**, 1329.

3-Propylcrotonaldehyde.
See 1-Heptenal.

2-Propylcrotonic Acid.
See 2-Methyl-1-hexenic Acid.

Propyl cyanide.
See under n-Butyric Acid.

Propylcyanoacetic Acid.
See under Propylmalonic Acid.

1-Propyl-1-cyanoisovaleric Acid.
See under Propylisopropylmalonic Acid.

Propylcyclohexane (*Hexahydropropylbenzene*)

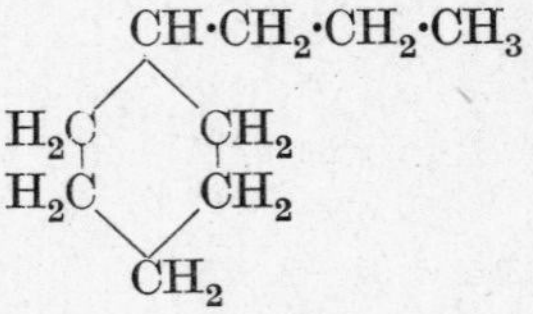

C_9H_{18} MW, 126

Liq. with odour resembling petrol. B.p. 154·5–155·5°/756 mm. $D_4^{20\,vac.}$ 0·7898. n_D^{21} 1·437.

Eisenlohr, *Chem. Abstracts*, 1926, **20**, 171.
Bourguel, *Bull. soc. chim.*, 1927, **41**, 1475.

1-Propylcyclohexanol (1-*Propylhexahydrophenol*)

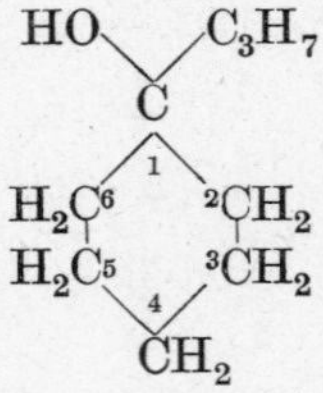

$C_9H_{18}O$ MW, 142

Liq. with odour resembling camphor. B.p. 180° decomp., 85°/20 mm. D_0^0 0·945, D_4^{12} 0·934. n_D^{12} 1·468. Insol. H_2O.

Sabatier, Mailhe, *Bull. soc. chim.*, 1905, **33**, 75.

2-Propylcyclohexanol (2-*Propylhexahydrophenol*).

Cis:
B.p. 84°/10 mm. D_4^{11} 0·9247. n_D^{11} 1·4688.
Isovaleryl: b.p. 138–9°/18 mm. D_4^{11} 0·914. n_D^{11} 1·450.

Acid succinate: cryst. from AcOH.Aq. M.p. 31–2°.
Benzoyl: b.p. 177–8°/14 mm. D_4^{16} 1·0262. n_D^{16} 1·5150.
Acid phthalate: cryst. from EtOH.Aq. M.p. 107–8°.
Phenylurethane: cryst. from pet. ether. M.p. 97–97·5°.

Trans:
B.p. 90°/14 mm. D_4^{11} 0·9160. n_D^{11} 1·4668.
Isovaleryl: b.p. 129–30°/13 mm. D_4^{11} 0·9131. n_D^{11} 1·4490.
Acid succinate: m.p. 48–9°.
Benzoyl: b.p. 179–80°/15 mm. D_4^{16} 1·0154. n_D^{16} 1·513.
Acid phthalate: plates from EtOH.Aq. M.p. 120–1°.
Phenylurethane: m.p. 69–70°.

Vavon, Anziani, *Bull. soc. chim.*, 1927, **41**, 1638.

2-Propylcyclohexanone

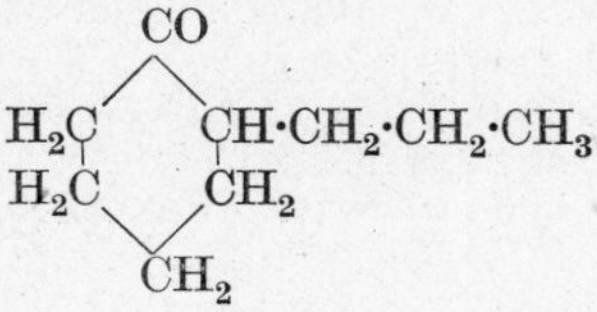

$C_9H_{16}O$ MW, 140

B.p. 198–9°/748 mm., 83–4°/13 mm. D_4^{13} 0·9145. n_D^{13} 1·4558.
Oxime: cryst. from EtOH.Aq. M.p. 67–8°.
Semicarbazone: cryst. from EtOH.Aq. M.p. 133·5–134° decomp.

See previous reference.

N-Propylcyclohexylamine (*Hexahydro*-N-*propylaniline*)

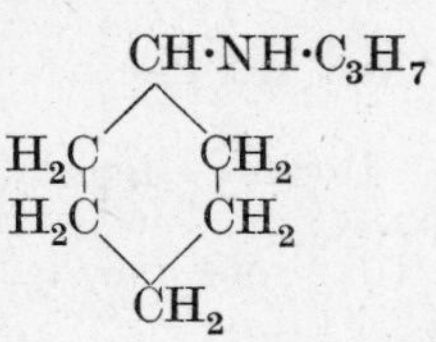

$C_9H_{19}N$ MW, 141

B.p. 185°.
Hydrochloride: m.p. 248–50°.
Phenylurea deriv.: needles from EtOH. M.p. 122–3°.

Skita, Keil, *Monatsh.*, 1929, **53** and **54**, 759.

2-Propylcyclohexylamine

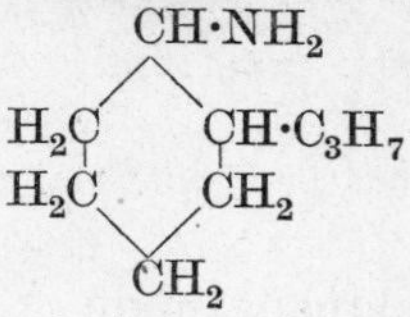

$C_9H_{19}N$ MW, 141

B.p. 60°/14 mm. D_4^{19} 0·8752.
N-*Benzenesulphonyl*: m.p. 131–2°.
Methiodide: m.p. 208–10°.

v. Braun, Bayer, *Ber.*, 1925, **58**, 390.

Propyl cyclohexyl Ketone.
See Hexahydrobutyrophenone.

Propylcyclopentane

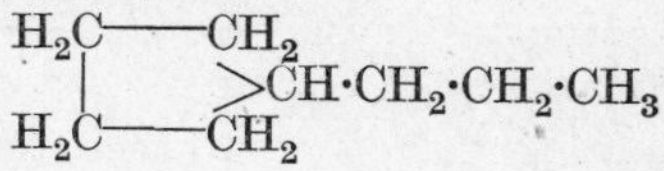

C_8H_{16} MW, 112

M.p. — 120·3°. B.p. 131·3–131·5°, 126–8°/739 mm. D_4^{15} 0·7814, D_4^{20} 0·7772. n_D^{20} 1·4266.

Chavanne, Becker, *Bull. soc. chim. Belg.*, 1927, **36**, 591.
Zelinskiĭ, Kazanskiĭ, *Chem. Abstracts*, 1935, **29**, 153.

1-Propylcyclopentanol

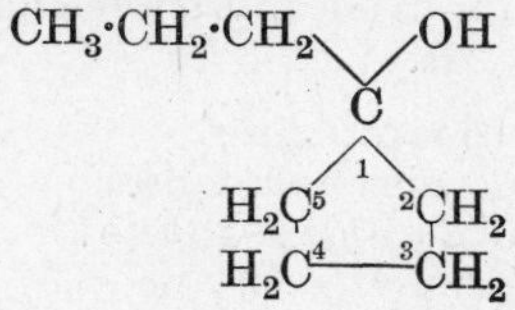

$C_8H_{16}O$ MW, 128

B.p. 175·2–175·7°. D_4^{15} 0·9083, D_4^{20} 0·9044. n_D^{20} 1·4540.
Allophanate: m.p. 178°.

See first reference above.

2-Propylcyclopentanol.

Cis:
B.p. 79–80°/12 mm. D_9^{9} 0·9165. n_D^{9} 1·4600.
Acid succinate: m.p. 27–8°.
3 : 5-*Dinitrobenzoyl*: cryst. from EtOH. M.p. 70–1°.
Acid phthalate: needles. M.p. 95–6°.
Phenylurethane: m.p. 83–4°.

Trans:
B.p. 78–9°/10 mm. D_9^{9} 0·9018. n_D^{9} 1·4565.
Acid succinate: viscous oil. D_{16}^{16} 1·0686. n_D^{16} 1·4605.
3 : 5-*Dinitrobenzoyl*: plates from EtOH. M.p. 30–1°.

Acid phthalate: cryst. from EtOH.Aq. M.p. 68°.

Phenylurethane: cryst. from EtOH.Aq. M.p. 61–2°.

Vavon, Flurer, *Bull. soc. chim.*, 1929, **45**, 756.

2-Propylcyclopentanone

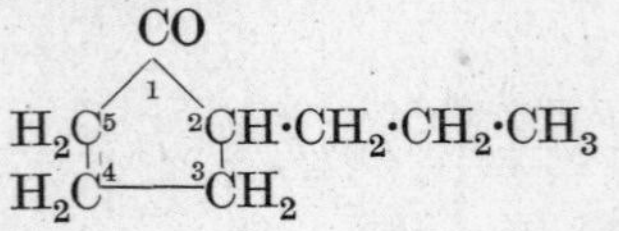
CO
1
H_2C^5
$^2CH \cdot CH_2 \cdot CH_2 \cdot CH_3$
H_2C^4
$^3CH_2$

$C_8H_{14}O$ MW, 126

B.p. 183·1–183·2°, 70·2°/15 mm., 59·4°/8 mm. D_4^{20} 0·9017. n_D^{20} 1·4429.

Oxime: b.p. 109–11°/9 mm.

Semicarbazone: cryst. from EtOH. M.p. 214° decomp.

Chiurdoglu, *Bull. soc. chim. Belg.*, 1934, **43**, 35.
Vavon, Flurer, *Bull. soc. chim.*, 1929, **45**, 754.

3-Propylcyclopentanone.

B.p. 190–1°. D_4^{20} 0·9041. n_D^{12} 1·4456.

Oxime: b.p. 121–2°/12 mm.

Semicarbazone: cryst. from MeOH. M.p. 178–9°.

v. Braun, Keller, Weissbach, *Ann.*, 1931, **490**, 181.

Propyldichloroamine.

See N-Dichloropropylamine.

α-Propyldiphenylmethane.

See 1 : 1-Diphenyl-*n*-butane.

Propylene (*Propene*)

$CH_3 \cdot CH : CH_2$

C_3H_6 MW, 42

Colourless gas. M.p. − 185·2°. B.p. − 47·8°/750 mm. n_{5876} 1·001. Crit. temp. 92·1°. Liquefies under 7–8 atms. press. Heat of comb. C_p 499·3 Cal. Abs. EtOH absorbs 12–13 vols. Absorbed quantitatively by solutions of mercuric nitrate and sulphate.

Nitrosite: prisms. M.p. 119–20°. Sn + HCl ⟶ propylenediamine.

Ipat'ev, *Ber.*, 1934, **67**, 1061.
Goudet, Schenker, *Helv. Chim. Acta*, 1927, **10**, 135.
Rosenthal, U.S.P., 1,939,084, (*Chem. Abstracts*, 1934, **28**, 1364).
Maximoff, U.S.P., 1,870,859, (*Chem. Zentr.*, 1932, II, 3013).
Senderens, Aboulenc, *Chem. Zentr.*, 1936, I, 3818.

Propylene bromide.

See 1 : 2-Dibromopropane.

Propylene-carboxylic Acid.

See Crotonic Acid, Isocrotonic Acid, 1-Methylacrylic Acid, *and* Vinylacetic Acid.

Propylene chloride.

See 1 : 2-Dichloropropane.

Propylene chlorohydrin.

See 2-Chloropropyl Alcohol *and* 1-Chloroisopropyl Alcohol.

Propylene chloroiodide.

See 2-Chloro-1-iodopropane.

Propylene cyanide.

See under Methylsuccinic Acid.

Propylene-1 : 3-dialdehyde.

See Glutacondialdehyde.

Propylenediamine (1 : 2-*Diaminopropane*)

$CH_3 \cdot CH(NH_2) \cdot CH_2NH_2$

$C_3H_{10}N_2$ MW, 74

d-.

B.p. 120·5°. D_4^{25} 0·8584. $[\alpha]_D^{25}$ + 29·78°.

Di-l-*tartrate*: m.p. 143°.

l-.

B.p. 120·5°. D_4^{25} 0·8588. Sol. H_2O, $CHCl_3$. Insol. Et_2O. $[\alpha]_D^{25}$ − 29·70°. ($[\alpha]_D^{24 \cdot 3}$ − 20·957°).

B,2HCl: m.p. 240°. $[\alpha]_D^{25}$ − 4·04° in H_2O.

Di-d-tartrate: m.p. 143°.

Picrate: yellow cryst. M.p. 237°.

dl-.

B.p. 119–20°. D^{15} 0·878. Forms hydrate with $\frac{1}{2}H_2O$.

B,2HCl: m.p. 220°.

1-N-*Di-Et*: $C_7H_{18}N_2$. MW, 130. B.p. 152°.

1 : 2-N-*Diacetyl*: needles from C_6H_6. M.p. 138–9°. B.p. 190°/18 mm. Very sol. H_2O, EtOH, $CHCl_3$. Spar. sol. C_6H_6. Insol. Et_2O, ligroin.

1 : 2-N-*Dipropionyl*: needles. M.p. 165°. B.p. 190°/56 mm.

1 : 2-N-*Dibenzoyl*: needles from C_6H_6. M.p. 192–3°.

Dipicrate: yellow needles from H_2O. M.p. 137°.

Windaus, Dorries, Jensen, *Ber.*, 1921, **54**, 2750.
I.G., D.R.P., 551,436, (*Chem. Zentr.*, 1932, II, 740).
Hofmann, *Ber.*, 1873, **6**, 308.
Tsugajew, Sokolow, *Ber.*, 1909, 42, 56.

Propylene dibromide.

See 1 : 2-Dibromopropane.

Propylene-dicarboxylic Acid.

See Glutaconic Acid *and* Itaconic Acid.

Propylene dichloride.

See 1 : 2-Dichloropropane.

Propylene Glycol (1 : 2-*Dihydroxypropane*, α-*propylene glycol*)

$$CH_3 \cdot CH(OH) \cdot CH_2OH$$

$C_3H_8O_2$ MW, 76

d-.

B.p. 95°/15 mm. $[\alpha]_D^{18}$ + 13·71° in H_2O. Readily racemises in H_2O.

Dibutyryl: b.p. 95–105°/15 mm. $[\alpha]_D^{18}$ + 2·05°.

l-.

B.p. 85–91°/12 mm. $[\alpha]_D^{20}$ − 9·8° in H_2O.

Di-phenylurethane: m.p. 146–7°. $[\alpha]_D^{20}$ + 13·3° in EtOH.

dl-.

Viscous oil with sweet taste. B.p. 188–9°, 96–8°/21 mm. $D^{19·4}$ 1·0403. Misc. with H_2O and EtOH in all proportions. Conc. HI ⟶ isopropyl iodide. $ZnCl_2$ or 50% H_2SO_4 ⟶ propionaldehyde. H_2O_2 + $FeSO_4$ ⟶ acetone + propionaldehyde.

Diacetyl: b.p. 190–1°/762 mm. D_4^{20} 1·059. n_D^{20} 1·4173.

Di-phenylurethane: m.p. 152·5–153·5°.

Dinitrite: b.p. 108–10°. Insol. H_2O.

Monopalmitate: plates from EtOH. M.p. 54·3°.

Dipalmitate: plates from EtOH. M.p. 68·8°.

Monostearate: plates from EtOH. M.p. 59·5°.

Distearate: plates from EtOH. M.p. 72·3°.

1-*Me ether*: $C_4H_{10}O_2$. MW, 90. B.p. 126–7°. D_4^{20} 0·9260. n_D^{20} 1·4070. *Acetyl*: b.p. 147°/762 mm. D_4^{20} 0·9709. n_D^{20} 1·4045.

1-*Et ether*: $C_5H_{12}O_2$. MW, 104. B.p. 136°. D_4^{20} 0·9028. n_D^{20} 1·4. *Acetyl*: b.p. 158–60°. D_4^{20} 0·9461. n_D^{20} 1·4097.

2-*Et ether*: b.p. 140–1°. D_4^{20} 0·9044. n_D^{20} 1·4122. Sol. H_2O.

Morley, Green, *J. Chem. Soc.*, 1885, **47**, 132.

Nef, *Ann.*, 1904, **335**, 291.

Ochiai, Miyaki, *Biochem. Z.*, 1935, **282**, 293.

Klebanskiï, Dolgopol'skiï, *Chem. Abstracts*, 1935, **29**, 5814.

du Pont, U.S.P., 1,963,997, (*Chem. Zentr.*, 1934, II, 3314).

Matignon, Moureu, Dodé, *Chem. Zentr.*, 1933, II, 646.

Levene, Walti, *J. Biol. Chem.*, 1926, **68**, 415.

Dewael, *Bull. soc. chim. Belg.*, 1930, **39**, 395.

Abderhalden, Eichwald, *Ber.*, 1918, **51**, 1319.

Howe, *Chem. Abstracts*, 1919, **13**, 1843.

β-Propylene Glycol.
See Trimethylene Glycol.

Propyleneimine

$$H_2C \overline{\qquad} CH \cdot CH_3$$
$$\diagdown \diagup$$
$$NH$$

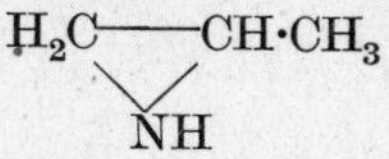

C_3H_7N MW, 57

Oil. B.p. 66–7°/751 mm. D^{16} 0·812. Fumes in air. Decomp. in aq. or HCl sol. Evaporate with HCl ⟶ 2-chloroisopropylamine.

Gabriel, v. Hirsch, *Ber.*, 1896, **29**, 2747.

Gabriel, Ohle, *Ber.*, 1917, **50**, 815.

Propylene iodohydrin.
See 1-Iodoisopropyl Alcohol.

Propylene oxide

$$H_2C \overline{\qquad} CH \cdot CH_3$$
$$\diagdown \diagup$$
$$O$$

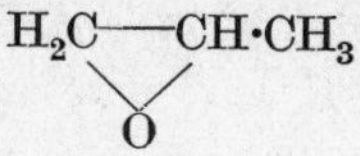

C_3H_6O MW, 58

dl-.

Liq. with odour resembling ether. B.p. 35°. D^0 0·859. Misc. with H_2O, EtOH, Et_2O. Al_2O_3 at 250–60° ⟶ propionaldehyde + a little acetone. Ag_2O ⟶ acetic acid. NaHg + H_2O ⟶ isopropyl alcohol. Hot H_2O ⟶ propylene glycol. C_2H_5MgI in Et_2O ⟶ methylpropylcarbinol.

d-.

B.p. 36·5–38°. $[\alpha]_D^{18}$ + 12·72°. Part. racemises with hot H_2O.

l-.

$[\alpha]_D^{18}$ − 8·26°. Part. racemises with hot H_2O.

I.G., E.P., 292,066, (*Chem. Abstracts*, 1929, **23**, 1415).

Abderhalden, Eichwald, *Ber.*, 1918, **51**, 1318.

Krassuski, *Chem. Zentr.*, 1902, II, 19.

Henry, *Chem. Zentr.*, 1903, II, 486.

Propylene oxide carboxylic Acid.
See Methylglycidic Acid.

Propylene-tricarboxylic Acid.
See Aconitic Acid *and* Isaconitic Acid.

Propylethanolamine.
See Propylaminoethyl Alcohol.

Propyl *p*-ethoxyphenyl Ketone.
See under *p*-Hydroxybutyrophenone.

Propylethylene.
See 1-Pentene.

Propyl fluoride (1-*Fluoropropane*)

$$CH_3 \cdot CH_2 \cdot CH_2F$$

C_3H_7F MW, 62

Gas. Liq. at $-3°$. Burns with bright flame.

Meslans, *Ann. chim. phys.*, 1894, **1**, 363.
du Pont, E.P., 406,284, (*Chem. Zentr.*, 1934, II, 132).

Propylfumaric Acid (1-*Pentene*-1 : 2-*dicarboxylic acid, α-amylene-αβ-dicarboxylic acid, ethylmesaconic acid*)

$$\begin{array}{l} CH_3{\cdot}CH_2{\cdot}CH_2{\cdot}C{\cdot}COOH \\ \qquad\qquad\quad HOOC{\cdot}CH \end{array}$$

$C_7H_{10}O_4$ MW, 158

Leaflets. M.p. 174–5° (172·5–173°). Very sol. EtOH, Et_2O. Spar. sol. $CHCl_3$. Very spar. sol. C_6H_6, CS_2. Sol. 90 parts H_2O at ord. temp. $k = 9{\cdot}3 \times 10^{-4}$ at 25°. CH_3COCl at 105–10° $\longrightarrow$ ethylcitraconic anhydride.

Et ester-amide: $C_9H_{15}O_3N$. MW, 185. Needles. M.p. 78–9°.

Diamide: $C_7H_{12}O_2N_2$. MW, 156. M.p. 214–15° decomp.

Demarçay, *Ann. chim. phys.*, 1880, **20**, 489.
Walden, *Ber*, 1891, **24**, 2035.
Ssemenow, *Chem. Zentr.*, 1899, I, 783.

1-Propylglutaric Acid (*Hexane*-1 : 3-*dicarboxylic acid*)

$$\begin{array}{l} CH_3{\cdot}CH_2{\cdot}CH_2{\cdot}CH{\cdot}COOH \\ \qquad\qquad\qquad\quad CH_2 \\ \qquad\qquad\qquad\quad CH_2{\cdot}COOH \end{array}$$

$C_8H_{14}O_4$ MW, 174

Cryst. from H_2O. M.p. 66–8°. $k = 5{\cdot}86 \times 10^{-5}$ at 24·4°.

Mellor, *J. Chem. Soc.*, 1901, **79**, 129.

2-Propylglutaric Acid

$$\begin{array}{l} \qquad\qquad\qquad CH_2{\cdot}COOH \\ CH_3{\cdot}CH_2{\cdot}CH_2{\cdot}CH \\ \qquad\qquad\qquad CH_2{\cdot}COOH \end{array}$$

$C_8H_{14}O_4$ MW, 174

Needles from HCl. M.p. 52°. Sol. H_2O and most org. solvents. k (first) $= 0{\cdot}487 \times 10^{-4}$ at 25° : (second) $= 4{\cdot}11 \times 10^{-7}$ at 25°.

Di-Et ester: $C_{12}H_{22}O_4$. MW, 230. B.p. 132°/10 mm.

Anhydride: $C_8H_{12}O_3$. MW, 156. Mobile oil. B.p. 180°/20 mm.

Monoanilide: plates from C_6H_6. M.p. 128°.

Day, Thorpe, *J. Chem. Soc.*, 1920, **117**, 1471.

1-Propylglyceric Acid (1 : 2-*Dihydroxypentane-2-carboxylic acid*)

$$\begin{array}{l} \qquad\qquad\quad C_3H_7 \\ OH{\cdot}CH_2{\cdot}C(OH){\cdot}COOH \end{array}$$

$C_6H_{12}O_4$ MW, 148

M.p. 94–5°. Sol. Et_2O.

Ssemenow, *Chem. Zentr.*, 1899, I, 1071.

2-Propylglyceric Acid (1 : 2-*Dihydroxycaproic acid*, 1 : 2-*dihydroxypentane*-1-*carboxylic acid*)

$$CH_3{\cdot}CH_2{\cdot}CH_2{\cdot}CH(OH){\cdot}CH(OH){\cdot}COOH$$

$C_6H_{12}O_4$ MW, 148

Exists in two forms:

(i) Cryst. from AcOEt. M.p. 108·5°. Sol. hot H_2O. Mod. sol. Et_2O. Insol. $CHCl_3$.

Phenylhydrazide: m.p. 141·5–142°.

(ii) Cryst. from AcOEt. M.p. 99·5°. Sol. EtOH, hot H_2O. Mod. sol. Et_2O. Insol. $CHCl_3$.

Phenylhydrazide: m.p. 120–1°.

Braun, *J. Am. Chem. Soc.*, 1930, **52**, 3190.

1-Propylglycerol.
See Hexantriol-1 : 2 : 3.

Propylglyoxal (1-*Ketovaleraldehyde*, 1-*pentanalone*-2)

$$CH_3{\cdot}CH_2{\cdot}CH_2{\cdot}CO{\cdot}CHO$$

$C_5H_8O_2$ MW, 100

Greenish liq. with strong odour. B.p. 36°/16 mm. Reduces $NH_3.AgNO_3$. Colours Schiff's reagent. Polymerises.

Disemicarbazone: plates + 1AcOH from AcOH.Aq. M.p. 250°.

Osazone: needles from AcOH. M.p. 105°.

Di-Me acetal: $C_7H_{14}O_3$. MW, 146. B.p. 65–6°/14 mm. Reduces $NH_3.AgNO_3$ but not Fehling's.

Blaise, *Compt. rend.*, 1922, **175**, 1216.

Propylguaiacol.
See Cœrulignol *and under* 2 : 3-Dihydroxy-1-propylbenzene.

1-Propylguanidine

$$\begin{array}{l} \quad\; NH \\ H_2N{\cdot}C{\cdot}NH{\cdot}CH_2{\cdot}CH_2{\cdot}CH_3 \end{array}$$

$C_4H_{11}N_3$ MW, 101

B_2,H_2SO_4: m.p. 220° decomp.

$B,HAuCl_4$: red needles from EtOH. M.p. 200° decomp.

B_2,H_2PtCl_6: yellow prisms. M.p. 195° decomp.

Picrate: yellow needles from EtOH. M.p. 177–8°.

Piovano, *Gazz. chim. ital.*, 1928, **58**, 245.

4-Propyl-1-heptenol-4.
See Dipropylallylcarbinol.

Propyl heptyl Ketone (*Undecanone*-4)

$CH_3\cdot[CH_2]_5\cdot CH_2\cdot CO\cdot CH_2\cdot CH_2\cdot CH_3$

$C_{11}H_{22}O$ MW, 170

Oil with characteristic fruity odour. M.p. 4–5°. B.p. 106–7°/13 mm. D^{25} 0·8274. n_D^{24} 1·4248.

Oxime: b.p. 141°/13 mm.

Semicarbazone: plates from EtOH. M.p. 54–6°.

v. Braun, Kröper, *Ber.*, 1929, **62**, 2882.

Propylhexahydrocresol.
See Methylpropylcyclohexanol.

Propylhexahydrophenol.
See Propylcyclohexanol.

Propylhexahydrotoluene.
See Methylpropylcyclohexane.

3-Propylhexanol-3.
See Ethyldipropylcarbinol.

Propyl hexyl Ketone (*Decanone*-4)

$CH_3\cdot[CH_2]_5\cdot CO\cdot CH_2\cdot CH_2\cdot CH_3$

$C_{10}H_{20}O$ MW, 156

M.p. −9°. B.p. 206–7°, 87–9°/11 mm. $D_0^{20\cdot5}$ 0·824. Does not form bisulphite comp.

Semicarbazone: m.p. 51–2°.

Karrer, Shibata, Wettstein, Jacubowicz, *Helv. Chim. Acta*, 1930, **13**, 1300.

Propylhydrazine

$CH_3\cdot CH_2\cdot CH_2\cdot NH\cdot NH_2$

$C_3H_{10}N_2$ MW, 74

B.p. 119°. Reduces $NH_3.AgNO_3$ and Fehling's in the cold.

Stolle, Bernath, *J. prakt. Chem.*, 1904, **70**, 280.

Propylhydroquinone.
See 2 : 5-Dihydroxy-1-propylbenzene.

Propylhydroxylamine (1-*Hydroxylaminopropane*)

$CH_3\cdot CH_2\cdot CH_2\cdot NH\cdot OH$

C_3H_9ON MW, 75

Needles from Et_2O. M.p. 77° (about 46°). Very volatile. Spar. sol. ligroin. Reacts basic. Reduces Fehling's.

Pierron, *Bull. soc. chim.*, 1899, **21**, 784.
Kjellin, *Ber.*, 1897, **30**, 1892.

Propyl hydroxynaphthyl Ketone.
See Hydroxybutyronaphthone.

Propyl hydroxyphenyl Ketone.
See o-, m-, *and* *p*-Hydroxybutyrophenone.

Propyl *p*-hydroxyphenyl sulphide.
See under Thiohydroquinone.

Propyl 1-hydroxypropyl Ketone.
See 3-Heptanolone-4.

Propyl hydroxytolyl Ketone.
See Hydroxy-methylbutyrophenone.

Propylideneacetic Acid.
See 2-Ethylacrylic Acid.

Propylideneacetone.
See 3-Hexenone-2.

Propylideneaniline.
See under Propionaldehyde.

2-Propylidenebutane.
See 3-Methyl-3-hexene.

Propylidenebutylene.
See 1 : 4-Heptadiene, 2 : 4-Heptadiene, *and* 3-Methyl-1 : 3-pentadiene.

2-Propylidenebutyric Acid.
See 2-Methylhydrosorbic Acid.

Propylidene chloride.
See 1 : 1-Dichloropropane.

Propylidene chlorobromide.
See 1-Chloro-1-bromopropane.

α-Propylidenediphenylmethane.
See 1 : 1-Diphenylbutylene-1.

2-Propylidene-ethyl Alcohol (2-*Pentenol*-1, 3-*ethylallyl alcohol*, α-*butenylcarbinol*)

$CH_3\cdot CH_2\cdot CH{:}CH\cdot CH_2OH$

$C_5H_{10}O$ MW, 86

Liq. B.p. 141–2° (138–9°). D_4^0 0·8645, D_4^{20} 0·8468. n_D^{20} 1·4299.

Acetyl: b.p. 149–51°. D^{22} 0·9019. n_D^{22} 1·4219.

Bouis, *Ann. chim.*, 1928, **9**, 402.
Prévost, *Ann. chim.*, 1928, **10**, 113.
Delaby, *Ann. chim.*, 1923, **20**, 196.

Propylidene-ethylene.
See 1 : 2-Pentadiene.

3-Propylideneisobutane.
See 2-Methyl-3-hexene.

1-Propylideneisobutyric Acid.
See 1-Methylhydrosorbic Acid.

2-Propylidenepropane.
See 2-Methyl-2-pentene.

2-Propylidenepropionaldehyde.
See 1-Methyl-2-ethylacrolein.

1-Propylidenepropionic Acid.
See 1-Methyl-2-ethylacrylic Acid.

2-Propylidenepropionic Acid.
Hydrosorbic Acid, *q.v.*

Propylidenepropyl Alcohol.
See 3-Hexenol-1 *and* 2-Methyl-2-pentenol-1.

3-Propylidene-propylene.
See 1 : 3-Hexadiene.

Propylidenesuccinic Acid (*Ethylitaconic acid, 2-pentene-1 : 2-dicarboxylic acid*)

$$CH_3{\cdot}CH_2{\cdot}CH{:}\underset{\displaystyle CH_2{\cdot}COOH}{C}{\cdot}COOH$$

$C_7H_{10}O_4$ MW, 158

Prisms from H_2O. M.p. 164–5° (163–7° decomp.). Spar. sol. $CHCl_3$, cold H_2O. Very spar. sol. Et_2O, C_6H_6, ligroin. $k = 3{\cdot}56 \times 10^{-5}$ at 25°.

Fichter, Probst, *Ann.*, 1910, **372**, 76.

Propyl iodide (1-*Iodopropane*)

$$CH_3{\cdot}CH_2{\cdot}CH_2I$$

C_3H_7I MW, 170

B.p. 102·5°. D_4^{20} 1·7471. n_D^{20} 1·50546. Heat of comb. C_p 514·3 Cal., C_v 512·3 Cal.

Adams, Voorhees, *J. Am. Chem. Soc.*, 1919, **41**, 797.
Hirao, *J. Chem. Soc. Japan*, 1931, **52**, 269.

1-Propylisoamyl Alcohol.
See Propylisobutylcarbinol.

Propylisoamylamine

$$(CH_3)_2CH{\cdot}CH_2{\cdot}CH_2{\cdot}NH{\cdot}CH_2{\cdot}CH_2{\cdot}CH_3$$

$C_8H_{19}N$ MW, 129

Liq. B.p. 148–9° (141°).

Sabatier, Mailhe, *Compt. rend.*, 1909, **148**, 900.
Freundler, Juillard, *ibid.*, 290.

Propylisoamylcarbinol (2-*Methyloctanol*-5, 1-*propylisohexyl alcohol*)

$$(CH_3)_2CH{\cdot}CH_2{\cdot}CH_2{\cdot}CH(OH){\cdot}CH_2{\cdot}CH_2{\cdot}CH_3$$

$C_9H_{20}O$ MW, 144

B.p. 184–6°. D_4^0 0·8335, D_4^{16} 0·8199.

Douris, *Compt. rend.*, 1913, **157**, 57.

Propyl isoamyl Ketone (2-*Methyloctanone*-5)

$$(CH_3)_2CH{\cdot}CH_2{\cdot}CH_2{\cdot}CO{\cdot}CH_2{\cdot}CH_2{\cdot}CH_3$$

$C_9H_{18}O$ MW, 142

B.p. 177–9°. D_4^0 0·8362, D_4^{21} 0·8205.
Semicarbazone : m.p. 107° (102°).

Douris, *Compt. rend.*, 1913, **157**, 56.

Propylisobutylacetic Acid.
See 1-Propylisocaproic Acid.

1-Propylisobutyl Alcohol.
See Propylisopropylcarbinol.

Propylisobutylamine

$$(CH_3)_2CH{\cdot}CH_2{\cdot}NH{\cdot}CH_2{\cdot}CH_2{\cdot}CH_3$$

$C_7H_{17}N$ MW, 115

Liq. with odour resembling fusel-oil. B.p. 123–5°. Spar. sol. H_2O.
B,HCl : plates from EtOH–Et_2O. M.p. 135°.
Acid oxalate : needles. M.p. 224°.
B,HAuCl$_4$: m.p. 187–8°. Very sol. EtOH.
B$_2$,H$_2$PtCl$_6$: orange cryst. M.p. 187–8°. Sol. EtOH, hot H_2O.

Paal, Heupel, *Ber.*, 1891, **24**, 3048.
Pope, Read, *J. Chem. Soc.*, 1912, **101**, 522.

Propylisobutylcarbinol (2-*Methylheptanol*-4, 1-*propylisoamyl alcohol*)

$$(CH_3)_2CH{\cdot}CH_2{\cdot}CH(OH){\cdot}CH_2{\cdot}CH_2{\cdot}CH_3$$

$C_8H_{18}O$ MW, 130

Somewhat viscous pleasant-smelling liq. B.p. 164° (160°). D^{20} 0·8207. n_D 1·42031. Sol. most org. solvents. Insol. H_2O.

Clarke, *J. Am. Chem. Soc.*, 1909, **31**, 114.
Muset, *Chem. Zentr.*, 1907, I, 1313.

Propyl isobutyl Ether

$$(CH_3)_2CH{\cdot}CH_2{\cdot}O{\cdot}CH_2{\cdot}CH_2{\cdot}CH_3$$

$C_7H_{16}O$ MW, 116

B.p. 106°/720 mm. D^{15} 0·7549. $n_{5461}^{24{\cdot}9}$ 1·3852. Very spar. sol. H_2O.

Henstock, *J. Chem. Soc.*, 1931, 371.

Propyl isobutyl Ketone (2-*Methylheptanone*-4)

$$(CH_3)_2CH{\cdot}CH_2{\cdot}CO{\cdot}CH_2{\cdot}CH_2{\cdot}CH_3$$

$C_8H_{16}O$ MW, 128

B.p. 155°/750 mm. D_0^{22} 0·813. Does not form bisulphite comp.
Semicarbazone : m.p. 123–4°.

Fournier, *Bull. soc. chim.*, 1910, **7**, 839.

Propylisobutylmalonic Acid (2-*Methylheptane*-4 : 4-*dicarboxylic acid*)

$$\begin{matrix}CH_3{\cdot}CH_2{\cdot}CH_2\\(CH_3)_2CH{\cdot}CH_2\end{matrix}\!\!>\!C\!<\!\!\begin{matrix}COOH\\COOH\end{matrix}$$

$C_{10}H_{18}O_4$ MW, 202

Prisms or plates from H_2O. M.p. 147–9° decomp. Sol. EtOH, Et_2O. Spar. sol. C_6H_6, cold H_2O.
Di-Et ester : $C_{14}H_{26}O_4$. MW, 258. B.p. 126°/9·5 mm.

Fischer, Holzapfel, v. Gwinner, *Ber.*, 1912, **45**, 252.

1-Propylisocaproic Acid (*2-Methylheptane-4-carboxylic acid, propylisobutylacetic acid*)

$$(CH_3)_2CH{\cdot}CH_2{\cdot}\underset{}{\overset{C_3H_7}{CH}}{\cdot}COOH$$

$C_9H_{18}O_2$ MW, 158

d-.

Oil. B.p. about 100°/0·5 mm. D^{22} 0·8876. $[\alpha]_D^{22}$ + 9·80°.

dl-.

B.p. 125–7°/12 mm., 122°/8·5 mm. D^{20} 0·8928. Sol. EtOH, Et_2O. Very spar. sol. H_2O.

Fischer, Holzapfel, v. Gwinner, *Ber.*, 1912, **45**, 253.

Propyl isocyanide (*Propylcarbylamine*)

$$CH_3{\cdot}CH_2{\cdot}CH_2{\cdot}NC$$

C_4H_7N MW, 69

B.p. 99·5°. Heat of comb. C_p 638·9 Cal.

Guillemard, *Ann. chim. phys.*, 1908, **14**, 412.

1-Propylisohexyl Alcohol.
See Propylisoamylcarbinol.

Propylisopropylacetic Acid.
See 2-Methylhexane-3-carboxylic Acid.

Propylisopropylcarbinol (*2-Methylhexanol-3, 1-propylisobutyl alcohol*)

$$(CH_3)_2CH{\cdot}CH(OH){\cdot}CH_2{\cdot}CH_2{\cdot}CH_3$$

$C_7H_{16}O$ MW, 116

d-.

B.p. 145–6°. $D_4^{16\cdot7}$ 0·8266. $[\alpha]_D^{20}$ + 21·25°.
Acid phthalate: m.p. 79–80°. $[\alpha]_D$ + 8·36° in EtOH.

dl-.

Pleasant-smelling liq. with burning taste. B.p. 141–2°/765 mm. D^{17} 0·821. n_D 1·41493. Insol. H_2O.
Acid phthalate: m.p. 59–60°.

Muset, *Chem. Zentr.*, 1907, I, 1313.
Pickard, Kenyon, *J. Chem. Soc.*, 1912, **101**, 633.

Propyl isopropyl Ether

$$(CH_3)_2CH{\cdot}O{\cdot}CH_2{\cdot}CH_2{\cdot}CH_3$$

$C_6H_{14}O$ MW, 102

B.p. 83°. D_4^0 0·7597, $D_4^{12\cdot5}$ 0·7474. n_D^{21} 1·376.

Bennett, Philip, *J. Chem. Soc.*, 1928, 1930.
Truchet, Graves, *Bull. soc. chim.*, 1932, **51**, 686.

Propyl isopropyl Ketone (*2-Methylhexanone-3*)

$$(CH_3)_2CH{\cdot}CO{\cdot}CH_2{\cdot}CH_2{\cdot}CH_3$$

$C_7H_{14}O$ MW, 114

Oil with peppermint odour. B.p. 135–6° (129–30°).
Semicarbazone: m.p. 119°.

Meerwein, *Ann.*, 1919, **419**, 138.

Propylisopropylmalonic Acid (*2-Methylhexane-3 : 3-dicarboxylic acid*)

$$\begin{matrix}CH_3{\cdot}CH_2{\cdot}CH_2\\(CH_3)_2CH\end{matrix}>C<\begin{matrix}COOH\\COOH\end{matrix}$$

$C_9H_{16}O_4$ MW, 188

d-.

Mononitrile: cryst. M.p. 94–5°. $[\alpha]_D^{20}$ + 11·5° in toluene.

l-.

Mononitrile: cryst. from Et_2O. M.p. 90°. $[\alpha]_D^{20}$ − 10·5° in toluene.

dl-.

Di-Et ester: $C_{13}H_{24}O_4$. MW, 244. B.p. 143°/42 mm. D_{25}^{25} 0·9803. n^{25} 1·4239.
Monoamide: $C_9H_{17}O_3N$. MW, 187. Prisms from H_2O. M.p. 137° decomp. Sol. EtOH, Me_2CO. Spar. sol. ligroin, cold H_2O.
Mononitrile: 1-isopropyl-1-cyanovaleric acid, 1-propyl-1-cyanoisovaleric acid. $C_9H_{15}O_2N$. MW, 169. M.p. 40–8°. B.p. 168–9°/13 mm. Very spar. sol. H_2O. *Et ester*: $C_{11}H_{19}O_2N$. MW, 197. B.p. 242–3°/749 mm., 113–14°/11–12 mm. D^{20} 0·943.

Shonle, Moment, *J. Am. Chem. Soc.*, 1923, **45**, 248.
Fischer, Flatau, *Ber.*, 1909, **42**, 2984.

1-Propyl-2-isopropylsuccinic Acid (*2-Methylheptane-3 : 4-dicarboxylic acid*)

$$\begin{matrix}CH_3{\cdot}CH_2{\cdot}CH_2{\cdot}CH{\cdot}COOH\\(CH_3)_2CH{\cdot}CH{\cdot}COOH\end{matrix}$$

$C_{10}H_{18}O_4$ MW, 202

Cis:

Plates from $CHCl_3$–pet. ether. M.p. 151–2°. $k = 2{\cdot}95 \times 10^{-4}$ at 25°. HCl at 200° ⟶ part. to *trans* form.
Anhydride: $C_{10}H_{16}O_3$. MW, 184. B.p. 265–75°/742 mm.

Trans:

Cryst. from C_6H_6–pet. ether. M.p. 192–4°. $k = 1{\cdot}47 \times 10^{-4}$ at 25°. HCl at 200° ⟶ part. to *cis* form.

Bone, Sprankling, *J. Chem. Soc.*, 1900, **77**, 660.

1-Propylisoquinoline

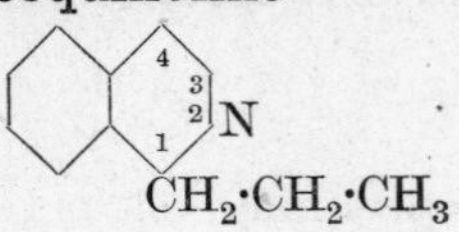

$C_{12}H_{13}N$ MW, 171

B.p. 140–60°/10 mm.
Picrate : m.p. 200–1°.

Späth, Berger, Kuntara, *Ber.*, 1930, **63**, 138.

3-Propylisoquinoline.

Oil with characteristic odour. B.p. 271°. D^{24} 1·0156.

B,HAuCl$_4$: yellow needles. M.p. 118° decomp.

B$_2$,H$_2$PtCl$_6$: yellow needles. Decomp. at 189° without melting.

Picrate : m.p. 161°.

Albahary, *Ber.*, 1896, **29**, 2397.

Propyl isothiocyanate

$CH_3{\cdot}CH_2{\cdot}CH_2{\cdot}N{:}CS$

C_4H_7NS MW, 101

B.p. 152·7°/743 mm. D_4^{16} 0·9781. n_D^{16} 1·5085.

Delépine, *Ann. chim. phys.*, 1912, **25**, 560.

1-Propylisovaleric Acid.

See 2-Methylhexane-3-carboxylic Acid.

2-Propylkairoline.

See under 2-Propyl-1 : 2 : 3 : 4-tetrahydroquinoline.

Propylmaleic Acid (*Ethylcitraconic acid, 1-pentene-1 : 2-dicarboxylic acid*)

$CH_3{\cdot}CH_2{\cdot}CH_2{\cdot}C{\cdot}COOH$
$HC{\cdot}COOH$

$C_7H_{10}O_4$ MW, 158

Prisms from H_2O, needles from Et_2O–ligroin. M.p. 93–5° (92–4°). Sol. H_2O, Et_2O, $CHCl_3$, C_6H_6. Spar. sol. ligroin. Heat ⟶ propylmaleic anhydride. H_2O at 135–50° ⟶ mainly propylidene-succinic acid. NaHg ⟶ propylsuccinic acid. Ag salt spar. sol. H_2O. Ba salt less sol. hot H_2O than cold.

Anhydride : $C_7H_8O_3$. MW, 140. Oil. B.p. 152–3°/68 mm.

Fittig, Glaser, *Ann.*, 1899, **304**, 184.

Propylmalonic Acid (*Butane-1 : 1-dicarboxylic acid*)

$CH_3{\cdot}CH_2{\cdot}CH_2{\cdot}CH{<}{COOH \atop COOH}$

$C_6H_{10}O_4$ MW, 146

Plates from C_6H_6. M.p. 96°. Sol. to 45·6 parts in 100 parts H_2O at 0°. $k = 1{\cdot}13 \times 10^{-3}$ at 25°. At 180° ⟶ *n*-valeric acid.

Di-Me ester : $C_8H_{14}O_4$. MW, 174. B.p. 203°/756 mm. D_4^{20} 1·0398. n_D^{20} 1·42155.

Di-Et ester : $C_{10}H_{18}O_4$. MW, 202. B.p. 221° (222–7°/750 mm.), 193·5–194·5°/330 mm. D_{15}^{15} 0·99309, D_{25}^{25} 0·98541.

Diamide : $C_6H_{12}O_2N_2$. MW, 144. Cryst. from H_2O. M.p. 184°. Spar. sol. EtOH, cold H_2O. Insol. Et_2O, $CHCl_3$.

Mononitrile : 1-cyano-*n*-valeric acid, propylcyanoacetic acid. $C_6H_9O_2N$. MW, 127. Oil. B.p. 125–30°/0·2 mm. *Et ester* : $C_8H_{13}O_2N$. MW, 155. B.p. 218–19°/755 mm., 105–10°/15 mm. D^{32} 0·972. *Amide* : 1-cyano-*n*-valeramide, propylcyanoacetamide. $C_6H_{10}ON_2$. MW, 126. Prisms from Et_2O. M.p. 124–124·5° (118°). B.p. 281°. Sol. Et_2O, $CHCl_3$. Mod. sol. hot H_2O. *Anilide* : m.p. 88–9°.

Dinitrile : $C_6H_8N_2$. MW, 108. Oil. B.p. 210°/750 mm. D^{18} 0·9224.

Monohydrazide : $C_6H_{12}O_3N_2$. MW, 160. Cryst. from H_2O. M.p. 139° decomp. *K salt* : m.p. 120°. Very hygroscopic.

Dihydrazide : $C_6H_{14}O_2N_4$. MW, 174. Prisms from EtOH. M.p. 158°. *B,2HCl* : m.p. 180°. N : N′-*Diacetyl* : m.p. 245°.

Dianilide : prisms. M.p. 198°.

Di-p-toluidide : prisms. M.p. 186°.

Fürth, *Monatsh.*, 1888, **9**, 309.
Bischoff, *Ber.*, 1895, **28**, 2619.
Fischer, Brieger, *Ber.*, 1915, **48**, 1520.
Henry, *Jahresber. Fortschr. Chem.*, 1889, 638.
Vogel, *J. Chem. Soc.*, 1934, 333.
Curtius, Lehmann, *J. prakt. Chem.*, 1930, **125**, 224.

Propyl Mercaptan (*1-Mercaptopropane, thiopropyl alcohol*)

$CH_3{\cdot}CH_2{\cdot}CH_2SH$

C_3H_8S MW, 76

M.p. − 113·3°. B.p. 67°. D_4^0 0·86169, D_4^{25} 0·83572. n_D^{25} 1·4351.

3 : 5-*Dinitrobenzoyl* : cryst. from AcOH.Aq. M.p. 51–2°.

Acid 3-nitrophthalate : cryst. from AcOH.Aq. M.p. 136–7°.

Hg(S·C$_3$H$_7$)$_2$: leaflets. M.p. 71–2°.

Ellis, Reid, *J. Am. Chem. Soc.*, 1932, **54**, 1674.
Wertheim, *J. Am. Chem. Soc.*, 1929, **51**, 3661.

Propyl p-methoxyphenyl Ketone.

See under p-Hydroxybutyrophenone.

Propyl p-methoxyphenyl sulphide.

See under Thiohydroquinone.

1-Propylnaphthalene

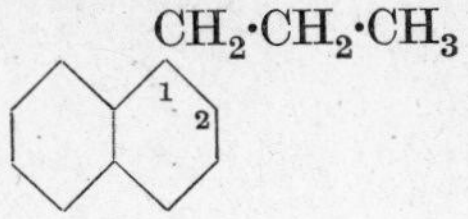

$C_{13}H_{14}$ MW, 170

B.p. 274–5°.
Picrate : yellow needles. M.p. 140–1°.

Bargellini, Melacini, *Gazz. chim. ital.*, 1908, **38**, ii, 570.

2-Propylnaphthalene.
B.p. 277–9°.
Picrate : yellow needles. M.p. 89–90°.

See previous reference.

Note.—Roblin, Davidson, Bogert, *J. Am. Chem. Soc.*, 1935, **57**, 158, claim that the data for the above two compounds should be interchanged.

Propyl naphthyl Ether.
See under Naphthol.

Propyl 1-naphthyl Ketone (*α-Butyronaphthone*)

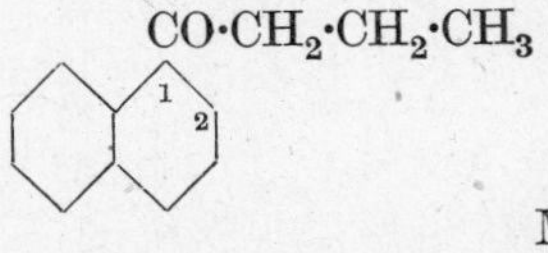

$C_{14}H_{14}O$ MW, 198

Yellow oil. B.p. 316–18°. D^{0} 1·0861. n_{D}^{27} 1·596. Very sol. most org. solvents.
Oxime : liq. B.p. 206–8°/13 mm.

Rousset, *Bull. soc. chim.*, 1896, **15**, 65.

Propyl 2-naphthyl Ketone (*β-Butyronaphthone*).
Prisms. M.p. 52°. B.p. 322–4°, 184–5°/16 mm.
Oxime : needles. M.p. 89°.
Azine : yellow needles. M.p. 130°.
Picrate : needles. M.p. 68–9°.
Comp. with $AlCl_3$: dark green needles. M.p. 92–5°.

Barbot, *Bull. soc. chim.*, 1930, **47**, 1314.
Perrier, *Bull. soc. chim.*, 1896, **15**, 322.
Rousset, *Bull. soc. chim.*, 1896, **15**, 66.

Propylnitramine (N-*Nitropropylamine*, 1-*nitraminopropane*)

$CH_3·CH_2·CH_2·NH·NO_2$

$C_3H_8O_2N_2$ MW, 104

Colourless liq. Cryst. on cooling. M.p. — 21°. B.p. 128–9°/40 mm. D^{15} 1·1046. Misc. with EtOH, Et_2O. Spar. sol. H_2O ⟶ acid sol.

Umbgrove, Franchimont, *Rec. trav. chim.*, 1898, **17**, 272.

Propyl nitrate

$CH_3·CH_2·CH_2·O·NO_2$

$C_3H_7O_3N$ MW, 105

B.p. 110·5°. D_4^{20} 1·0548. n_D^{20} 1·3979.

Cowley, Partington, *J. Chem. Soc.*, 1933, 1252.
Wallach, Schulze, *Ber.*, 1881, **14**, 421.

Propyl nitrite

$CH_3·CH_2·CH_2·O·NO$

$C_3H_7O_2N$ MW, 89

B.p. 46–8° (57°). D_4^{20} 0·8861. n_D^{20} 1·3604. H (+ Ni) at 130° ⟶ propylamine; at 200° ⟶ a mixture of mono-, di- and tri-propylamines.

Cowley, Partington, *J. Chem. Soc.*, 1933, 1253.

Propyl pentadecyl Ketone (*Nonadecanone*-4)

$CH_3·[CH_2]_{14}·CO·CH_2·CH_2·CH_3$

$C_{19}H_{38}O$ MW, 282

M.p. 50·5°. B.p. 211°/11 mm., part. decomp. Spar. sol. EtOH.
Oxime : exists in two forms. (i) M.p. 25·5–26·5°. (ii) M.p. 43·5–44·5°.

Bertrand, *Bull. soc. chim.*, 1896, **15**, 766.
Furukawa, *Chem. Abstracts*, 1933, **27**, 2131.

2-Propyl-2-pentene.
See 4-Methyl-3-heptene.

1-Propylphenanthraquinone

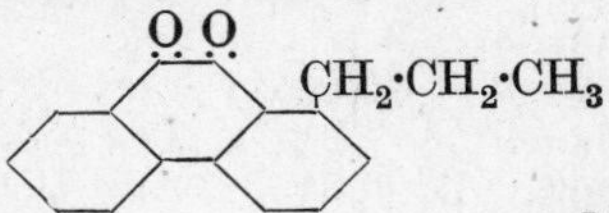

$C_{17}H_{14}O_2$ MW, 250

Orange plates from EtOH. M.p. 139–40°.
Quinoxaline deriv. : pale yellow needles from AcOH. M.p. 144–5°.

Haworth, Mavin, Sheldrick, *J. Chem. Soc.*, 1934, 460.

1-Propylphenanthrene

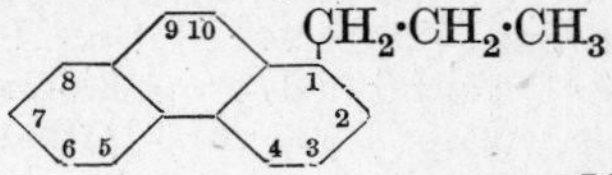

$C_{17}H_{16}$ MW, 220

Plates from MeOH. M.p. 34–5°.

Picrate: yellow needles from MeOH. M.p. 100–1°.

See previous reference.

9-Propylphenanthrene.

Plates from EtOH. M.p. 74°. B.p. 265–70°/22 mm.

Picrate: yellow needles from EtOH. M.p. 134°.

Miller, Bachman, *J. Am. Chem. Soc.*, 1935, **57**, 768.

Propylphenetole.

See under Propylphenol.

***o*-Propylphenol** (2-*Hydroxy*-1-*propylbenzene*)

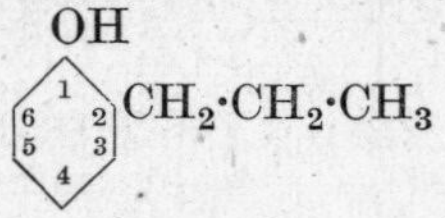

$C_9H_{12}O$ MW, 136

Oil. B.p. 220–220·5°. D_{15}^{15} 1·000.

Me ether: 2-methoxy-1-propylbenzene, *o*-propylanisole. $C_{10}H_{14}O$. MW, 150. B.p. 207–9°/757·7 mm. D^0 0·96944.

Et ether: 2-ethoxy-1-propylbenzene, *o*-propylphenetole. B.p. 213°/754 mm., 99–100°/16 mm. D_4^{26} 0·92396. n_D^{26} 1·494.

Propionyl: b.p. 245°.

Phenylurethane: needles from formic acid. M.p. 111°.

Claisen, *Ann.*, 1919, **418**, 87.
Farinholt, Harden, Twiss, *J. Am. Chem. Soc.*, 1933, **55**, 3386.

***m*-Propylphenol** (3-*Hydroxy*-1-*propylbenzene*).

B.p. 228°. Spar. sol. H_2O. $FeCl_3 \longrightarrow$ green col. in EtOH, bluish col. in H_2O.

Me ether: 3-methoxy-1-propylbenzene, *m*-propylanisole. B.p. 212–13°.

Et ether: 3-ethoxy-1-propylbenzene, *m*-propylphenetole. B.p. 220–4°/753 mm., 109–10°/15 mm. D_4^{20} 0·94558. n_D^{20} 1·5025.

Henrard, *Chem. Zentr.*, 1907, II, 1512.
Ciamician, Silber, *Ber.*, 1890, **23**, 1162.

***p*-Propylphenol** (4-*Hydroxy*-1-*propylbenzene*).

Cryst. M.p. 21–2°. B.p. 230–2°, 120°/19 mm. D_4^0 1·089.

Me ether: 4-methoxy-1-propylbenzene, *p*-propylanisole, dihydroanethole. B.p. 215–16°, 86·5°/10 mm. D_4^{20} 0·94718. n_D^{20} 1·5045.

Et ether: 4-ethoxy-1-propylbenzene, *p*-propylphenetole. B.p. 223–30°, 108–10°/13 mm. D_4^{15} 0·94.

Acetyl: b.p. 245–6°/745 mm. D^0 1·02904.

Propionyl: b.p. 254–6°.

Benzoyl: m.p. 37–8°.

Salicyloyl: m.p. 57°.

Phenylurethane: cryst. from EtOH. M.p 128·5–129°.

Farinholt, Harden, Twiss, *J. Am. Chem. Soc.*, 1933, **55**, 3386.
Baranger, *Bull. soc. chim.*, 1931, **49**, 1213.
Albright, *J. Am. Chem. Soc.*, 1914, **36**, 2197.
Clemmensen, *Ber.*, 1914, **47**, 53.
Ipatjew, *Ber.*, 1913, **46**, 3590.

1-Propyl-1-phenylbutylene-1.

See 4-Phenyl-3-heptene.

Propylphenylcarbinol (1-*Phenyl*-n-*butyl alcohol*, α-*hydroxybutylbenzene*, α-*propylbenzyl alcohol*)

$CH_3{\cdot}CH_2{\cdot}CH_2{\cdot}CH(OH){\cdot}C_6H_5$

$C_{10}H_{14}O$ MW, 150

d-.

M.p. 49°. B.p. 115°/14 mm. $[\alpha]_{5461} + 52{\cdot}2°$ in C_6H_6.

Acetyl: b.p. 125°/16 mm. $n_D^{20{\cdot}5}$ 1·4889.

Acid phthalate: m.p. 53–4°. $[\alpha]_{5461} + 11{\cdot}5°$ in Et_2O.

l-.

M.p. 48–9°. $[\alpha]_{5461} - 53{\cdot}5°$ in C_6H_6.

Acid phthalate: m.p. 52–3°. $[\alpha]_{5461} - 11{\cdot}0°$ in Et_2O.

dl-.

Oil with aromatic odour. B.p. 168–70°/100 mm., 113–15°/10 mm. $D_4^{13{\cdot}7}$ 0·9861. $n_D^{13{\cdot}7}$ 1·51914.

Acetyl: b.p. 117–18°/8 mm.

Acid phthalate: m.p. 90–1°.

Grignard, *Ann. chim. phys.*, 1901, **24**, 466.
Kenyon, Partridge, *J. Chem. Soc.*, 1936, 128.
Klages, *Ber.*, 1904, **37**, 2312.

Propyl-phenylethyl-carbinol.

See 1-Phenylhexanol-3 *and* 2-Phenylhexanol-3.

Propyl phenylethyl Ketone.

See 1-Phenylhexanone-3 *and* 2-Phenylhexanone-3.

Propylphenylglycollic Acid.

See 1-Hydroxy-1-phenylbutyric Acid.

3-Propyl-3-phenylhexane.

See 4-Ethyl-4-phenylheptane.

Propyl phenyl Ketone.

See Butyrophenone.

Propylphenylpropylene.

See 1-Phenylhexene-2.

Propyl phenyl sulphone

$C_6H_5 \cdot SO_2 \cdot CH_2 \cdot CH_2 \cdot CH_3$

$C_9H_{12}O_2S$ MW, 184

Plates from ligroin. M.p. 46° (44°). Sol. EtOH, Et_2O, $CHCl_3$, C_6H_6. Spar. sol. boiling H_2O.

Baldwin, Robinson, *J. Chem. Soc.*, 1932, 1448.

3-Propylphthalide

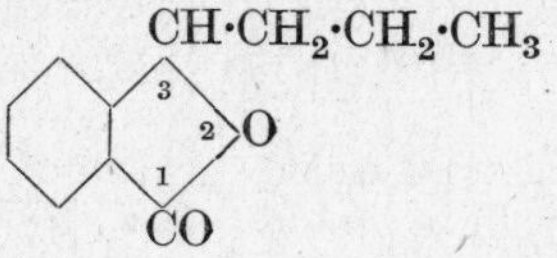

$C_{11}H_{12}O_2$ MW, 176

Oil with odour of celery. M.p. 20°. B.p. 293–7°/735 mm. decomp., 243–7°/220 mm., 150°/14 mm. D_{15}^{15} 1·1073. $n_D^{17.5}$ 1·5327. Volatile in steam. NaOH fusion ⟶ butyric and benzoic acids.

Tasman, *Rec. trav. chim.*, 1927, **46**, 653.

***N*-Propylphthalimide.**
See under Phthalimide.

***N*-Propylpiperidine** (*Propylpiperidylamine*)

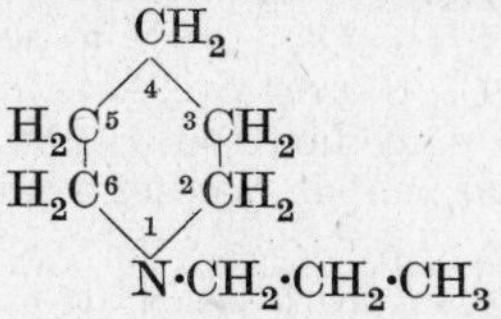

$C_8H_{17}N$ MW, 127

B.p. 149–50°.
B,HCl: m.p. 212–13°. Hygroscopic.
Chloroplatinate: m.p. 179°.
Picrate: yellow needles. M.p. 121° (108°).
Methiodide: m.p. 181–2°.
Ethiodide: m.p. 276·5°.

v. Braun, *Ber.*, 1909, **42**, 2048.
Auerbach, Wolffenstein, *Ber.*, 1899, **32**, 2511.
Ladenburg, *Ber.*, 1881, **14**, 1348.

2-Propylpiperidine.
See Coniine.

3-Propylpiperidine.

d-.
$[\alpha]_D^{16} + 5.9°$.
B,HCl: cryst. from Me_2CO. M.p. 147°. Very sol. H_2O, EtOH.
l-*Tartrate*: cryst. from H_2O. M.p. 161°.

l-.
B.p. 174°/752·5 mm. D_4^{19} 0·8517. $[\alpha]_D^{16}$ — 6·6°.
B,HCl: needles from Me_2CO. M.p. 147°. Very sol. H_2O, EtOH.
d-*Tartrate*: cryst. from H_2O. M.p. 161°.

dl-.
Liq. with odour resembling coniine. B.p. 174°/758 mm. D_4^{26} 0·8475. Sol. in about 80 parts H_2O at ord. temp. Turns brown in air.
B,HCl: prisms or needles from H_2O. M.p. 127–9°. Sol. H_2O, EtOH. Insol. Et_2O.
B,HAuCl₄: lemon-yellow needles from H_2O. M.p. 95–8°.
B₂,H₂PtCl₆: orange-yellow needles. M.p. 94° (slow heat.), 134° (rapid heat.).
Picrate: yellow needles. M.p. 121·5°.

Granger, *Ber.*, 1895, **28**, 1203; 1897, **30**, 1060.

4-Propylpiperidine.
Liq. with odour resembling coniine. B.p. 178–80°.

Ahrens, *Ber.*, 1905, **38**, 159.

Propylpiperidylamine.
See *N*-Propylpiperidine.

Propylpropenylcarbinol.
See 2-Heptenol-4.

Propylpropenylethylene.
See 2 : 4-Octadiene.

Propyl propenyl Ketone.
See 2-Heptenone-4.

Propylpropiolic Acid (1-*Pentine*-1-*carboxylic acid*)

$CH_3 \cdot CH_2 \cdot CH_2 \cdot C \vdots C \cdot COOH$

$C_6H_8O_2$ MW, 112

Feathery cryst. M.p. 27°. B.p. 126–7°/24 mm., 119–21°/16 mm. Sol. EtOH, Et_2O, ligroin. Somewhat difficultly sol. H_2O. Dist. at atmospheric press. ⟶ propylacetylene. Hot KOH.Aq. ⟶ methyl propyl ketone. Hot alc. KOH ⟶ butyrylacetic acid.
Me ester: $C_7H_{10}O_2$. MW, 126. B.p. 80–2°/23 mm. D^0 0·9648.
Et ester: $C_8H_{12}O_2$. MW, 140. B.p. 93–4°/24 mm. D^0 0·9468.
Isoamyl ester: $C_{11}H_{18}O_2$. MW, 182. B.p. 127–8°/22 mm. D^0 0·9207.

Moureu, Delange, *Bull. soc. chim.*, 1903, **29**, 652.

Propylpropionylcarbinol.
See 4-Heptanolone-3.

2-Propylpropylene.
See 2-Methyl-1-pentene.

2-Propylpyridine.
See Conyrine.

3-Propylpyridine

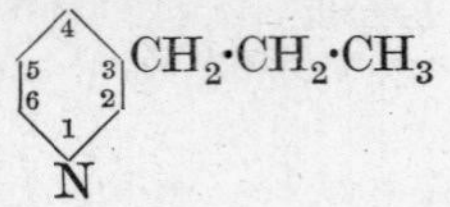

$C_8H_{11}N$ MW, 121

B.p. 170°. Ox. ⟶ nicotinic acid.

Cahours, Étard, *Compt. rend.*, 1881, **92**, 1082.

4-Propylpyridine.

B.p. 184–6°. D^{15} 0·9381. Sol. EtOH, Et_2O. Spar. sol. H_2O.

B,HCl : needles from EtOH.Aq. M.p. 215°.

$B,HAuCl_4$: yellow cryst. M.p. 113–15°.

B_2,H_2PtCl_6 : brownish-yellow cryst. M.p. 204°.

Picrate : needles from EtOH. M.p. 153°.

Koenigs, Jaeschke, *Ber.*, 1921, **54**, 1355.

Propyl 2-pyridyl Ketone (2-*Butyrylpyridine*)

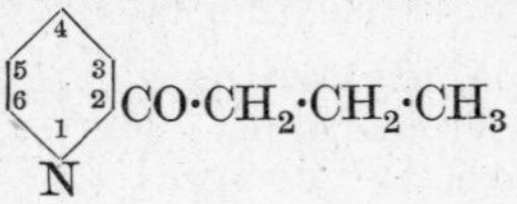

$C_9H_{11}ON$ MW, 149

Oil with characteristic odour. B.p. 217–18° (216–20°). Sol. acids.

Oxime : needles from pet. ether. M.p. 48°.

Benzoyl : yellow leaflets from C_6H_6. M.p. 56–7°.

Phenylhydrazone : yellowish needles from EtOH. M.p. 82°. Unstable.

p-*Sulphophenylhydrazone* : yellow needles. M.p. 251°.

Picrate : yellow needles from H_2O. M.p. 75°.

Methiodide : yellow needles from EtOH–Et_2O. M.p. 79°.

Engler, Majmon, *Ber.*, 1891, **24**, 2536.
Pinner, *Ber.*, 1901, **34**, 4243.

Propyl 3-pyridyl Ketone (3-*Butyrylpyridine*).

Liq. with odour resembling coniine. B.p. 246–52°. Sol. EtOH, Et_2O, acids.

Phenylhydrazone : yellow cryst. M.p. 182° (129–30°).

Semicarbazone : m.p. 169–70°.

Ethiodide : yellow cryst. M.p. 192°.

La Forge, *J. Am. Chem. Soc.*, 1928, **50**, 2477.
Engler, *Ber.*, 1891, **24**, 2541.

Propyl 4-pyridyl Ketone (4-*Butyrylpyridine*).

B.p. 229–31°.

Picrate : yellow needles from H_2O. M.p. 96°.

Pinner, *Ber.*, 1901, **34**, 4252.

Propylpyrogallol dimethyl Ether.

See Picamar.

***N*-Propylpyrrolidine**

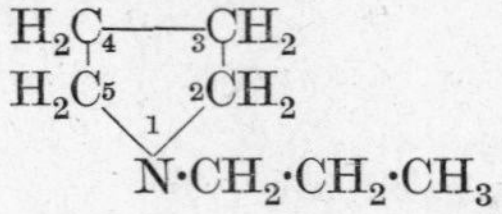

$C_7H_{15}N$ MW, 113

B.p. 130°. D_4^{20} 0·8171. n_D^{20} 1·4389. Sol. H_2O.

B_2,H_2PtCl_6 : red cryst. Decomp. at 184–90°.

Picrate : yellow plates. M.p. 105° (101°).

v. Braun, *Ber.*, 1911, **44**, 1254.
Jurjew, Schenjan, *Chem. Zentr.*, 1936, I, 4293.

2-Propylpyrrolidine.

Oil with odour resembling piperidine. B.p. 145–50°/765 mm. Sol. H_2O with alk. reaction.

Chloroaurate : yellow needles or leaflets. M.p. 120°.

Chloroplatinate : m.p. anhyd. 135°.

Picrate : m.p. 104–104·5°.

N-*Me* : $C_8H_{17}N$. MW, 127. B.p. 146–7°. D^{15} 0·815. *$B,HAuCl_4$* : yellow leaflets. M.p. 76°. *B_2,H_2PtCl_6* : orange leaflets. M.p. 145–6°. *Picrate* : yellow needles from EtOH. M.p. 124°.

N-*Benzenesulphonyl* : needles from 80% EtOH. M.p. 66–67·5°.

Hess, *Ber.*, 1913, **46**, 4110.
Löffler, *Ber.*, 1910, **43**, 2039.
Gabriel, *Ber.*, 1909, **42**, 1264.

3-Propylpyrrolidine.

Oil with odour resembling piperidine. B.p. 158–60°/746 mm. D_4^{20} 0·8450. n_D^{20} 1·4469. Fumes in air. Absorbs H_2O and CO_2 from the air.

Longinow, *Chem. Zentr.*, 1915, I, 982.

Propyl 2-pyrryl Ketone (2-*Butyrylpyrrole*)

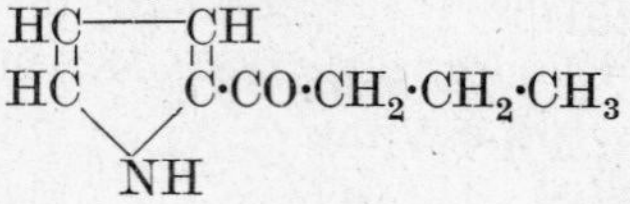

$C_8H_{11}ON$ MW, 137

Cryst. from H_2O. M.p. 48·5°. B.p. 235°. Sol. EtOH, Et_2O, C_6H_6, pet. ether, KOH.Aq.

Phenylhydrazone : yellow cryst. from pet. ether. M.p. 80·5°.

Semicarbazone : needles from H_2O. M.p. 131°.

Tschelinzeff, Terentjeff, *Ber.*, 1914, **47**, 2650.
Oddo, *Ber.*, 1910, **43**, 1016.

2-Propylquinoline

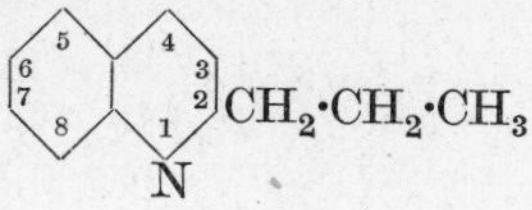

$C_{12}H_{13}N$ MW, 171

Pale yellowish-green oil. B.p. 142–5°/13 mm., 130–1°/10 mm. D_4^{17} 1·038. n_D^{23} 1·5886.
Chloromercurate : m.p. 112°.
Methiodide : m.p. 184°.
Picrate : yellow needles or leaflets from EtOH. M.p. 163–4°.
Methopicrate : yellow needles. M.p. 118°.

Freund, Kessler, *J. prakt. Chem.*, 1918, **98**, 233.
Meisenheimer, Schütze, *Ber.*, 1923, **56**, 1353.
Delaby, Hiron, *Compt. rend.*, 1930, **191**, 845.

4-Propylquinoline.
Liq. with odour resembling quinoline. B.p. 159°/16 mm.
Hydrochloride : m.p. 156–7°.
B,HBr,$CdBr_2$: cryst. from EtOH. M.p. 148°.
B_2,2HCl,$HgCl_2$: cryst. from EtOH. M.p. 148°.
B_2,H_2PtCl_6 : cryst. from conc. HCl. M.p. 198° decomp.
Picrate : yellow needles from EtOH. M.p. 204°.

Koenigs, *Ber.*, 1898, **31**, 2376.
Blaise, Maire, *Bull. soc. chim.*, 1908, **3**, 667.

8-Propylquinoline.
Pale yellow liq. B.p. 142°/15 mm.
B_2,H_2PtCl_6 : m.p. 196°. Very spar. sol. hot H_2O.
Picrate : yellowish-red needles from EtOH. M.p. 142°.
Methiodide : m.p. 136°.

v. Braun, Heider, Wyczatkowska, *Ber.*, 1918, **51**, 1215.

Propylresorcinol.
See 2 : 4-Dihydroxy-1-propylbenzene.

Propylsuccinic Acid (*Pentane*-1 : 2-*dicarboxylic acid*)

$$CH_3{\cdot}CH_2{\cdot}CH_2{\cdot}CH{\cdot}COOH$$
$$CH_2{\cdot}COOH$$

$C_7H_{12}O_4$ MW, 160

d-.
M.p. 93·9°. $[\alpha]_D + 9{\cdot}6°$.

dl-.
Cryst. from H_2O or C_6H_6. M.p. 100·5° (92–3°). 2·83 parts sol. 100 parts cold $CHCl_3$. *k* (first) = $8{\cdot}9 \times 10^{-5}$ at 25°; (second) = $1{\cdot}2 \times 10^{-6}$ at 100°.
Di-Me ester : $C_9H_{16}O_4$. MW, 188. B.p. 112°/15 mm., 107°/11 mm.
Di-Et ester : $C_{11}H_{20}O_4$. MW, 216. B.p. 132–4°/25 mm.
Diamide : $C_7H_{14}O_2N_2$. MW, 158. Needles from EtOH. M.p. 234–5°. Spar. sol. EtOH.
Anhydride : $C_7H_{10}O_3$. MW, 142. Viscous liq. B.p. 145–55°/20 mm.
Dihydrazide : powder from EtOH. M.p. 176°.

Locquin, *Bull. soc. chim.*, 1909, **5**, 1073.
Fittig, Glaser, *Ann.*, 1899, **304**, 188.
Timmermans, van der Haegen, *Bull. soc. chim. Belg.*, 1933, **42**, 448.
Scheibler, Schmidt, *Ber.*, 1921, **54**, 153.

2-Propyl-1 : 4 : 5 : 6-tetrahydropyridine.
See γ-Coniceine.

***N*-Propyl-1 : 2 : 3 : 4-tetrahydroquinoline**

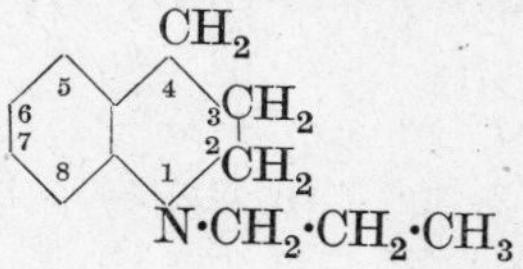

$C_{12}H_{17}N$ MW, 175

Colourless liq. B.p. 146°/16 mm. Gradually turns reddish-brown.
B,HCl : m.p. 162°.
B,HBr : m.p. 177°. Somewhat difficultly sol. cold H_2O.
B,HI : needles. M.p. 178°. Insol. cold H_2O.
Picrate : m.p. 73°.
Methiodide : kairoline propiodide. Plates from EtOH–Et_2O. M.p. 135°.

v. Braun, *Ber.*, 1909, **42**, 2222.

2-Propyl-1 : 2 : 3 : 4-tetrahydroquinoline.
Oil with faint violet fluor. B.p. 258°/746 mm., 152°/20 mm., 140–1°/10 mm. D^{17} 0·959. $n_D^{14\cdot5}$ 1·5673.
B,HCl : m.p. 221°. Spar. sol. EtOH, hot H_2O. Sublimes.
Picrate : orange plates from EtOH or Et_2O. M.p. 125°.
N-*Me* : 2-propylkairoline. $C_{13}H_{19}N$. MW, 189. B.p. 272–6°, 151–7°/20 mm., 144·5°/10 mm. Volatile in steam. *Picrate* : yellow leaflets from EtOH. M.p. 123° (120°). *Methiodide* : melts between 180–200° ⟶ its components.

N-*Benzoyl* : leaflets from EtOH or Et_2O. M.p. 102° (97°).

v. Braun, Gmelin, Petzold, *Ber.*, 1924, **57**, 382.
Tröger, Ungar, *J. prakt. Chem.*, 1926, **112**, 254.
Meisenheimer, Schütze, *Ber.*, 1923, **56**, 1357.

2-Propyl-5 : 6 : 7 : 8-tetrahydroquinoline

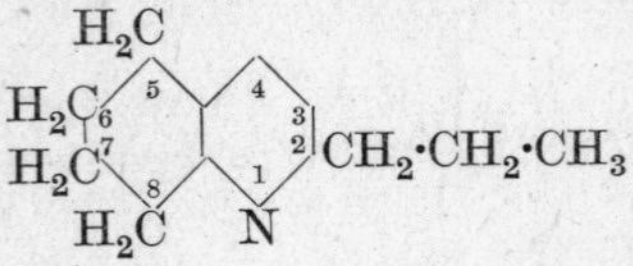

$C_{12}H_{17}N$ MW, 175

B.p. 130–2°/11 mm.
B_2,H_2PtCl_6 : decomp. at 62°.
Picrate : yellow cryst. from EtOH. M.p. 119°.

See first reference above.

1-Propyltetramethylene Glycol.
See Heptandiol-1 : 4.

2-Propylthiophene

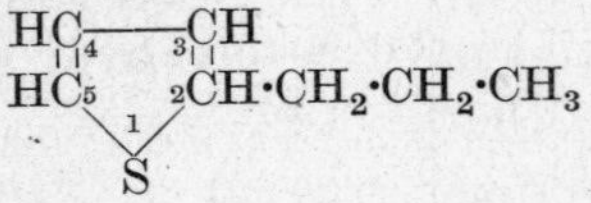

$C_7H_{10}S$ MW, 126

B.p. 157–60°. D_{20}^{20} 0·9700, D_4^{20} 0·9683. n_D^{20} 1·5048.

Scheibler, Schmidt, *Ber.*, 1921, **54**, 149.
Steinkopf, Schubart, *Ann.*, 1921, **424**, 21.

3-Propylthiophene.
B.p. 160–2°. D_{20}^{20} 0·9733, D_4^{20} 0·9716. n_D^{20} 1·5057. Isatin + $H_2SO_4 \longrightarrow$ blue col.

Scheibler, Schmidt, *Ber.*, 1921, **54**, 153.

Propylthiourea

$H_2N\cdot CS\cdot NH\cdot CH_2\cdot CH_2\cdot CH_3$ (positions 3, 2, 1)

$C_4H_{10}N_2S$ MW, 118

Needles from EtOH. M.p. 110°. Sol. EtOH. Mod. sol. H_2O.
3-N-*Me* : plates from EtOH.Aq. M.p. 79°. Sol. EtOH, Me_2CO, $CHCl_3$. Mod. sol. H_2O. Insol. ligroin.
3-N-*Et* : plates from EtOH. M.p. 52°.

Hecht, *Ber.*, 1890, **23**, 283.

***o*-Propyltoluene** (2-*Methylpropylbenzene*)

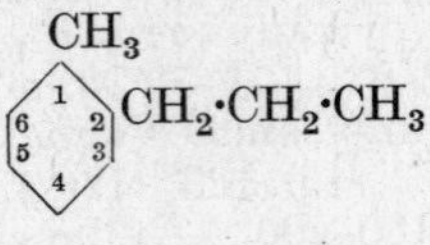

$C_{10}H_{14}$ MW, 134

B.p. 184°, 65–8°/14 mm. D_4^{19} 0·8747. n_D^{20} 1·4995.

Claus, Hansen, *Ber.*, 1880, **13**, 897.
Auwers, *Ann.*, 1919, **419**, 111.
Kuhn, Deutsch, *Ber.*, 1932, **65**, 48.

***m*-Propyltoluene** (3-*Methylpropylbenzene*).
B.p. 181·5–182·5°. D_4^{17} 0·8648, D_4^{20} 0·862. n_D^{20} 1·4951.

See second reference above and also
Claus, Stüsser, *Ber.*, 1880, **13**, 899.

***p*-Propyltoluene** (4-*Methylpropylbenzene*).
B.p. 183–4°. $D_4^{15\cdot 4}$ 0·8642. n_D^{22} 1·4823.

Bayrac, *Bull. soc. chim.*, 1895, **13**, 894.
Auwers, *Ann.*, 1919, **419**, 112.
Ipat'ev, Orlov, Petrov, *Chem. Abstracts*, 1931, **25**, 4540.

3-Propyl-*p*-toluic Acid (4-*Methyl*-2-*propylbenzoic acid*)

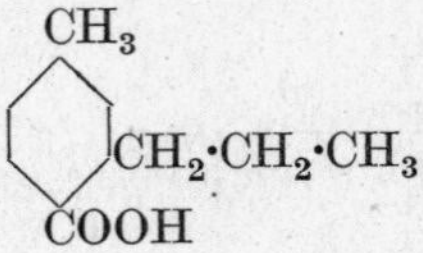

$C_{11}H_{14}O_2$ MW, 178

Needles from H_2O. M.p. 75–6°. Volatile in steam.

Claus, *J. prakt. Chem.*, 1892, **46**, 495.

***N*-Propyl-*o*-toluidine**

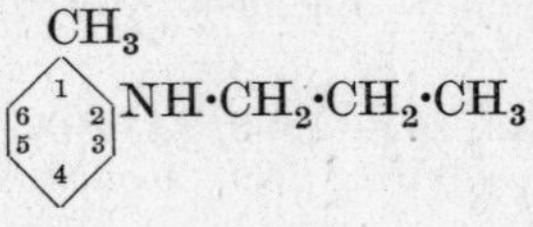

$C_{10}H_{15}N$ MW, 149

Oil. B.p. 230°.

Bischoff, Mintz, *Ber.*, 1892, **25**, 2319.

***N*-Propyl-*p*-toluidine.**
Oil with odour of carraway. B.p. 235°/761 mm. D^{20} 0·9243, D^{35} 0·9172. n_D 1·5367.
B,HCl : needles. M.p. 150–1°.
$B_2,(COOH)_2$: cryst. M.p. 116–17°.
$B,(COOH)_2$: m.p. 172–3° decomp.

Hori, Morley, *J. Chem. Soc.*, 1891, **59**, 35.
Bischoff, Mintz, *Ber.*, 1892, **25**, 2321.

3-Propyl-*p*-toluidine (4-*Methyl*-2-*propylaniline*)

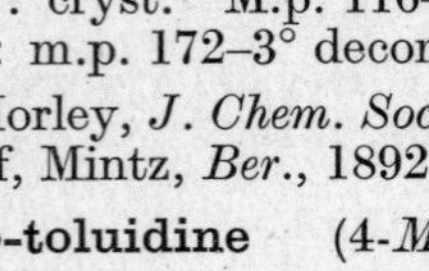

$C_{10}H_{15}N$ MW, 149

B.p. 98–9°/13 mm. D_4^{22} 0·9666.
B,HCl : cryst. from H_2O. M.p. 195°.
N-*Benzoyl* : m.p. 174·5°.
Picrate : cryst. from EtOH. M.p. 201°.

v. Braun, Bayer, Blessing, *Ber.*, 1924, **57**, 402.

Propyl tolyl Ether.
See under Cresol.

Propyl o-tolyl Ketone (*2-Methylbutyrophenone*)

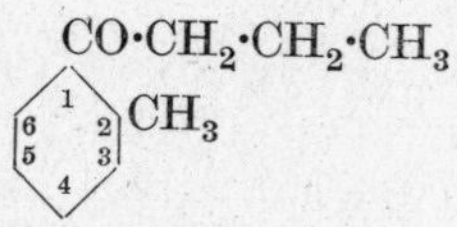

$C_{11}H_{14}O$ MW, 162

B.p. 238·5°/758 mm. D_4^0 0·9936.
Semicarbazone : m.p. 176°.

Senderens, *Bull. soc. chim.*, 1911, **9**, 949.

Propyl m-tolyl Ketone (*3-Methylbutyrophenone*).
B.p. 247°/758 mm. D_4^0 0·9882.
Semicarbazone : m.p. 152°.

See previous reference.

Propyl p-tolyl Ketone (*4-Methylbutyrophenone*).
B.p. 251·5°/758 mm. Sol. EtOH, Et_2O.
Semicarbazone : m.p. 190° (232°).
Phenylhydrazone : m.p. 73°.

See previous reference and also
Willgerodt, Hambrecht, *J. prakt. Chem.*, 1910, **81**, 78.
Blaise, *Compt. rend.*, 1901, **133**, 1217.

1-Propyltricarballylic Acid.
See Hexane-1 : 2 : 3-tricarboxylic Acid.

Propylurea

$$H_2N{\cdot}CO{\cdot}NH{\cdot}CH_2{\cdot}CH_2{\cdot}CH_3$$
(3 2 1)

$C_4H_{10}ON_2$ MW, 102

Prisms from EtOH. M.p. 110°. Sol. EtOH. Mod. sol. H_2O.
3-*Acetyl* : plates from CS_2. M.p. 115°. Mod. sol. H_2O, EtOH, Et_2O, $CHCl_3$, C_6H_6.

Hecht, *Ber.*, 1890, **23**, 283.
Mauguin, *Ann. chim. phys.*, 1911, **22**, 343.

Propylurethane (*Ethyl propylaminoformate, ethyl propylcarbamate*)

$$CH_3{\cdot}CH_2{\cdot}CH_2{\cdot}NH{\cdot}CO{\cdot}OC_2H_5$$

$C_6H_{13}O_2N$ MW, 131

B.p. 191·5–192·5°/758 mm.

Schreiner, *J. prakt. Chem.*, 1880, **21**, 125.
Nirdlinger, Acree, *Am. Chem. J.*, 1910, **43**, 378.

1-Propylvaleric Acid.
Dipropylacetic Acid, *q.v.*

3-Propylvaleric Acid.
See 3-Methyl-*n*-heptylic Acid.

Propylveratrol.
See under Cœrulignol *and under* 2 : 3-Dihydroxy-1-propylbenzene.

Propylvinylcarbinol.
See 1-Hexenol-3.

Propyl vinyl Ketone.
See 1-Hexenone-3.

Prothebenine.
See under Thebenine.

Protocatechuic Acid (*3 : 4-Dihydroxybenzoic acid, catechol-4-carboxylic acid*)

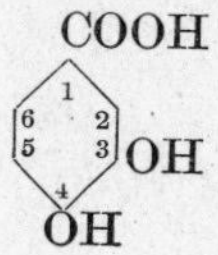

$C_7H_6O_4$ MW, 154

Needles + $1H_2O$ from H_2O. M.p. 199°. Sol. EtOH. Mod. sol. H_2O. Insol. C_6H_6. $k = 3{\cdot}3 \times 10^{-5}$ at 25°. Aq. sol. with $FeCl_3$ ⟶ green col. ⟶ dark red with $NaHCO_3$.
3-*Me ether* : *see* Vanillic Acid.
4-*Me ether* : *see* Isovanillic Acid.
Di-Me ether : *see* Veratric Acid.
Di-Et ether : 3 : 4-diethoxybenzoic acid. $C_{11}H_{14}O_4$. MW, 210. Needles from EtOH. M.p. 165–6°. $k = 3{\cdot}4 \times 10^{-5}$ at 25°. *Et ester* : $C_{13}H_{18}O_4$. MW, 238. Cryst. from EtOH. M.p. 56–7°.

Me ester : $C_8H_8O_4$. MW, 168. Needles from H_2O. M.p. 134·5°. Sol. EtOH. Spar. sol. H_2O. Has antimicrobic properties. 3-*Benzoyl* : m.p. 153·5–155°. 3-*Acetyl-4-benzoyl* : cryst. from MeOH. M.p. 102–3°. 4-*Acetyl-3-benzoyl* : prisms. M.p. 54–5°.

Et ester : $C_9H_{10}O_4$. MW, 182. Prisms from H_2O. M.p. 133–4°. Sol. EtOH.

Phenyl ester : $C_{13}H_{10}O_4$. MW, 230. Cryst. from EtOH.Aq. M.p. 189°. $FeCl_3$ ⟶ green col.

Amide : $C_7H_7O_3N$. MW, 153. Cryst. from H_2O. M.p. 212°.

Nitrile : $C_7H_5O_2N$. MW, 135. Needles from H_2O. M.p. 156°. Sol. H_2O, EtOH, Et_2O. Spar. sol. C_6H_6, ligroin, xylene. *Diacetyl* : needles from EtOH. M.p. 87°. *Dibenzoyl* : cryst. from EtOH. M.p. 131°.

Anilide : prisms from EtOH. M.p. 166–7°.
3-*Acetyl* : prisms from H_2O. M.p. 202–3°.
4-*Benzoyl* : cryst. from C_6H_6. M.p. 154–5°.
Diacetyl : cryst. from H_2O. M.p. 157–8°.

3-*Benzoyl*: microneedles. M.p. 225–7°.

Hoesch, Zarzecki, *Ber.*, 1917, **50**, 462.
Fischer, Bergmann, Lipschitz, *Ber.*, 1918, **51**, 45.
Schmidt, E.P., 145,081, (*Chem. Abstracts*, 1920, **14**, 3089); D.R.P., 278,778, (*Chem. Zentr.*, 1914, II, 1080).
Ono, Imoto, *J. Chem. Soc. Japan*, 1935, **56**, 715.
Pratt, Perkins, *J. Am. Chem. Soc.*, 1918, **40**, 224.
Miller, *Ann.*, 1883, **220**, 116.

Protocatechuic Aldehyde (3 : 4-*Dihydroxybenzaldehyde*)

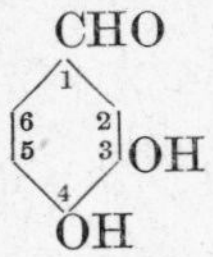

$C_7H_6O_3$ MW, 138

Cryst. from toluene. M.p. 153°.
Oxime: m.p. 157° decomp.
Phenylhydrazone: two forms. (i) M.p. 175–6° decomp. (ii) M.p. 121–8°.
Semicarbazone: decomp. at 230°.
Azine: cryst. from EtOH.Aq. Decomp. about 245°.
2 : 4-*Dinitrophenylhydrazone*: dark red microcryst. from MeOH. M.p. 275° decomp.
3-*Me ether*: *see* Vanillin.
4-*Me ether*: *see* Isovanillin.
Di-Me ether: *see* Veratric Aldehyde.
3-*Et ether*: $C_9H_{10}O_3$. MW, 166. Plates from H_2O. M.p. 77·5°. 4-*Benzyl ether*: cryst. M.p. 57°.
Di-Et ether: $C_{11}H_{14}O_3$. MW, 194. Colourless oil. B.p. 278–80°.
3-*Propyl ether*: $C_{10}H_{12}O_3$. MW, 180. Needles from H_2O. M.p. 82°.
3-*Isobutyl ether*: $C_{11}H_{14}O_3$. MW, 194. Needles from EtOH.Aq. M.p. 94°.
3-*Benzyl ether*: m.p. 113–14°.
4-*Benzyl ether*: plates from EtOH. M.p. 122°.
Methylene ether: *see* Piperonal.
Ethylene ether: $C_9H_8O_3$. MW, 164. Needles from ligroin. M.p. 51·5°. B.p. 299°. *Oxime*: cryst. from EtOH. M.p. 75–75·5°. *Phenylhydrazone*: cryst. from EtOH. M.p. 107–8°. *Azine*: yellow needles from AcOH. M.p. 190–1°.
Carbonate: m.p. 124°. B.p. 289°, 162°/13 mm. Mod. sol. EtOH, Me_2CO, $CHCl_3$, AcOH. Spar. sol. Et_2O, CCl_4.
3-*Acetyl*: plates from C_6H_6. M.p. 109–10°. p-*Nitrophenylhydrazone*: red needles from EtOH. M.p. 195°. 4-*Benzoyl*: needles from EtOH. M.p. 109°. *Phenylhydrazone of* 3-*acetyl*-4-*benzoyl*: needles from EtOH. M.p. 158°.
Diacetyl: cryst. from EtOH. M.p. 54°. *Phenylhydrazone*: needles from EtOH. M.p. 135°. *Semicarbazone*: needles from EtOH. M.p. 200–2° decomp.
3-*Benzoyl*: needles from EtOH. M.p. 136–7°. *Phenylhydrazone*: cryst. from EtOH. M.p. 192°. 4-*Acetyl*: cryst. from EtOH. M.p. 68°. *Phenylhydrazone of 4-acetyl-3-benzoyl*: yellow plates from EtOH. M.p. 166°.
Dibenzoyl: *phenylhydrazone*, yellow plates. M.p. 167°.
Di-carbomethoxyl: m.p. 99–100°. p-*Nitrophenylhydrazone*: m.p. 187–9°.

Gattermann, *Ann.*, 1907, **357**, 374.
Boehringer, D.R.P., 269,544, (*Chem. Zentr.*, 1914, I, 591).
Schmidt, D.R.P., 295,337, (*Chem. Zentr.*, 1917, I, 41).
Hoesch, Zarzecki, *Ber.*, 1917, **50**, 465.
Tiemann, Koppe, *Ber.*, 1881, **14**, 2015.
Pacsu, v. Vargha, *Ber.*, 1926, **59**, 2818.
Fröschl, Bomberg, *Monatsh.*, 1927, **48**, 571.
Roberts, E.P., 417,072, (*Chem. Abstracts*, 1935, **57**, 1099).
Vanillin Fabrik., D.R.P., 591,888, (*Chem. Zentr.*, 1934, I, 2491).

Protocetraric Acid.
See Obtusatic Acid.

Protocotoin

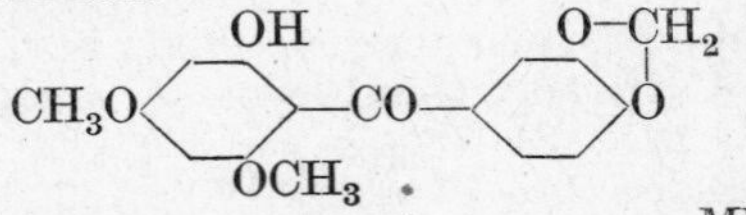

$C_{16}H_{14}O_6$ MW, 302

Occurs in Coto bark. Prisms from MeOH. M.p. 141–2°. Sol. Et_2O, $CHCl_3$, AcOH, C_6H_6. Insol. H_2O. Sol. alkalis with yellow col. 65% $HNO_3 \longrightarrow$ bluish-green col. turning red on warming. $FeCl_3$ in EtOH.Aq. $\longrightarrow$ reddish-brown col. $H_2SO_4 \longrightarrow$ orange col.
Me ether: oxyleukotin, methylprotocotoin. $C_{17}H_{16}O_6$. MW, 316. Prisms from EtOH. M.p. 134–5°. Sol. EtOH, AcOH. Mod. sol. Et_2O, $CHCl_3$, C_6H_6. Insol. H_2O. 65% $HNO_3 \longrightarrow$ green col. turning reddish-brown on warming. $H_2SO_4 \longrightarrow$ orange col. No. col. with $FeCl_3$ in EtOH.Aq. *Phenylhydrazone*: prisms from EtOH. M.p. 211°. *Acetyl*: cryst. from EtOH. M.p. 103°.

Späth, Bretschneider, *Monatsh.*, 1928, **49**, 429.
Houben, Fischer, *J. prakt. Chem.*, 1929 **123**, 89.
Ciamician, Silber, *Ber.*, 1893, **26**, 779; 1891, **24**, 2984.

Protolichesteric Acid

$$HOOC \cdot CH - C{:}CH_2$$
$$CH_3 \cdot [CH_2]_{12} \cdot CH \quad CO$$
$$O$$

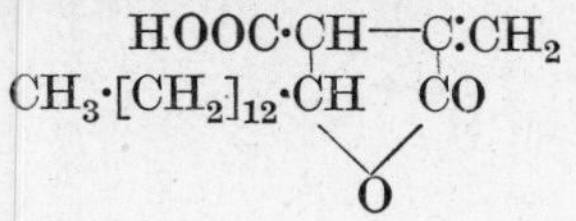

$C_{19}H_{32}O_4$ MW, 324

l-.

Obtained from Japanese sub-alpine moss. Plates from AcOH. M.p. 107·5°. $[\alpha]_D^{27}$ — 12·71°. *Semicarbazone* : m.p. 140°.
Pyrazoline deriv. : plates from pet. ether. M.p. 54–5°. $[\alpha]_D^{18}$ — 183·1°.

d-.

Obtained from European Iceland moss. Plates from AcOH. M.p. 106°. $[\alpha]_D^{20}$ + 12·07°.
Pyrazoline deriv. : plates. M.p. 54–5°. $[\alpha]_D^{18}$ + 190·6°.

l- (Allo-).

Plates from AcOH. M.p. 88°. $[\alpha]_D^{20}$ — 49·53°.
Pyrazoline deriv. : plates from pet. ether. M.p. 68–9°. $[\alpha]_D^{18}$ — 73·69°.

Asahina, Asano, *J. Pharm. Soc. Japan*, 1927, **539**, 1.
Asano, Kanematsu, *Ber.*, 1932, **65**, 1175.
Asahina, Yanagita, *Ber.*, 1936, **69**, 120.

Protopine (*Fumarine*)

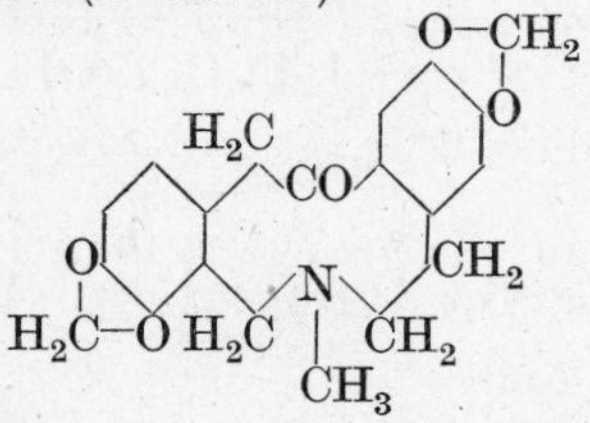

$C_{20}H_{19}O_5N$ MW, 353

Widely distributed in the *Papaveraceæ* and *Fumariaceæ*. Prisms from MeOH. M.p. 208°. Sol. $CHCl_3$. Spar. sol. MeOH, EtOH, Me_2CO, C_6H_6. Insol. H_2O. AcOH sol. $\longrightarrow$ deep bluish-violet col. with H_2SO_4.
Methiodide : cryst. from MeOH. M.p. 217°.
Methosulphate : prisms from MeOH. M.p. 252°.

Perkin, *J. Chem. Soc.*, 1916, **109**, 1023.
Haworth, Perkin, *J. Chem. Soc.*, 1926, 1769.

Prulaurasine (dl-*Mandelonitrile*-d-β-*glucoside, laurocerolin*)

$$C_6H_5 \cdot CH {<}^{O \cdot C_6H_{11}O_5}_{CN}$$

$C_{14}H_{17}O_6N$ MW, 295

Occurs in leaves of common cherry laurel (*Prunus laurocerasus*). Prisms or needles. M.p. 122–122·5°. $[\alpha]_D$ — 54°. Sol. H_2O, MeOH. Insol. Et_2O. Hyd. $\longrightarrow$ *dl*-mandelonitrile + glucose.
Tetra-acetyl : needles. M.p. 120–3°. Sol. EtOH, Me_2CO, $CHCl_3$, AcOEt, C_6H_6. Insol. ligroin.

Hérissey, *Compt. rend.*, 1905, **41**, 959.
Caldwell, Courtauld, *J. Chem. Soc.*, 1907, **91**, 671.
Fischer, Bergmann, *Ber.*, 1917, **50**, 1062.

Prulaurasinic Acid (dl-*Mandelic acid* β-d-*glucoside*)

$$C_6H_5 \cdot CH {<}^{O \cdot C_6H_{11}O_5}_{COOH}$$

$C_{14}H_{18}O_8$ MW, 314

White hygroscopic powder. Cryst. with 1EtOH. $[\alpha]_D^{11}$ — 28·17° to — 33·18°. Hyd. by emulsin. Does not reduce Fehling's.
Tetra-acetyl : needles. M.p. 130–50°. $[\alpha]_D^{15}$ — 36·97° to — 43·46°. *Et ester* : needles from EtOH. M.p. 102–9°. $[\alpha]_D$ — 33° to — 40·1° in C_6H_6. Sol. EtOH, Me_2CO, AcOEt, C_6H_6. Spar. sol. Et_2O, pet. ether.

Karrer, Nägeli, Weidmann, *Helv. Chim. Acta*, 1919, **2**, 257.
Fischer, Bergmann, *Ber.*, 1917, **50**, 1053.

Prunasine (d-*Mandelonitrile*-d-*glucoside*)

$$C_6H_5 \cdot CH {<}^{O \cdot C_6H_{11}O_5}_{CN}$$

$C_{14}H_{17}O_6N$ MW, 295

Occurs in *Prunus laurocerasus*, *P. padus* and *P. cerasus*. Needles from AcOEt. M.p. 147–50°. $[\alpha]_D$ — 27°. Sol. H_2O, MeOH, Me_2CO. Alkalis $\longrightarrow$ prulaurasine. HCl $\longrightarrow$ *d*-mandelic acid.
Tetra-acetyl : needles from EtOH. M.p. 125–6°. $[\alpha]_D^{22}$ — 52·5°.

Fischer, *Ber.*, 1895, **28**, 1508.
Caldwell, Courtauld, *J. Chem. Soc.*, 1907, **91**, 666, 671.
Auld, *J. Chem. Soc.*, 1908, **93**, 1276.
Fischer, Bergmann, *Ber.*, 1917, **50**, 1047.

Note.—All references state prunasine is derived from *l*-mandelonitrile, but see note under Mandelic Acid, Vol. II, p. 535, col. 2.

Prunasinic Acid (d-*Mandelic acid*-β-d-*glucoside*)

$$C_6H_5 \cdot CH {<}^{O \cdot C_6H_{11}O_5}_{COOH}$$

$C_{14}H_{18}O_8$ MW, 314

$[\alpha]_D^{15}$ — 138·6°. Sol. H_2O.

Tetra-acetyl: needles. M.p. 132°. $[\alpha]_D^{15} - 82{\cdot}40°$ in EtOH.

Karrer, Nägeli, Weidmann, *Helv. Chim. Acta*, 1919, 2, 257.
See note under Prunasine.

Prunetin.
See under Genistein.

Prunetol.
See Genistein.

Prunol.
See Ursolic Acid.

Prussic Acid.
See Hydrocyanic Acid.

Pseudaconine.
See ψ-Aconine.

Pseudaconitine.
See ψ-Aconitine.

Psicose (2-*Ketoribohexose*, ψ-*fructose*)

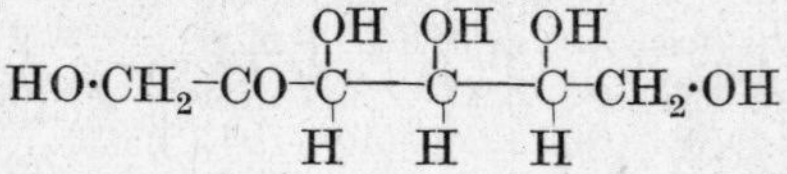

$C_6H_{12}O_6$ MW, 180

d-.
Syrup. Not fermentable. $[\alpha]_D^{20} + 3{\cdot}1°$ in H_2O.
Diacetone deriv.: m.p. 57–58·5°. B.p. 104–5°/0·3 mm. $[\alpha]_D^{20} - 98{\cdot}2°$ in Me_2CO.
Phenylosazone: m.p. 173–4° decomp. (identical with *d*-allosazone). $[\alpha]_D^{20} - 19{\cdot}2°$ in EtOH.

l-.
Syrup. $[\alpha]_D^{20} - 3{\cdot}3°$ in H_2O.
Diacetone deriv.: m.p. 56·5–57°. $[\alpha]_D^{20} + 99°$ in Me_2CO.
Phenylosazone: m.p. 173–4° decomp. (identical with *l*-allosazone). $[\alpha]_D^{20} + 19°$ in EtOH.

Steiger, Reichstein, *Helv. Chim. Acta*, 1935, **18**, 790; 1936, **19**, 184.

Psoralene (*Furo-coumarin*)

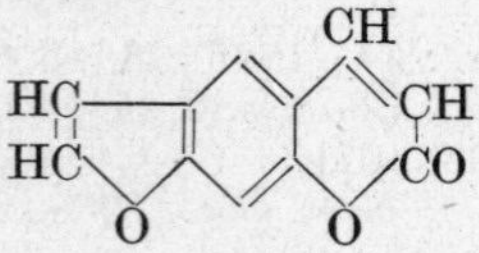

$C_{11}H_6O_3$ MW, 186

Obtained from *Psoralea corylifolia*, Linn. Needles from H_2O. M.p. 171°. Sol. EtOH, $CHCl_3$. Spar. sol. H_2O, Et_2O, pet. ether.

Späth, Manjunath, Pailer, Jois, *Ber.*, 1936, **69**, 1087.
Jois, Manjunath, Rao, *J. Indian Chem. Soc.*, 1933, **10**, 41.

Psychosine.
See under Sphingosine.

Psychotrine

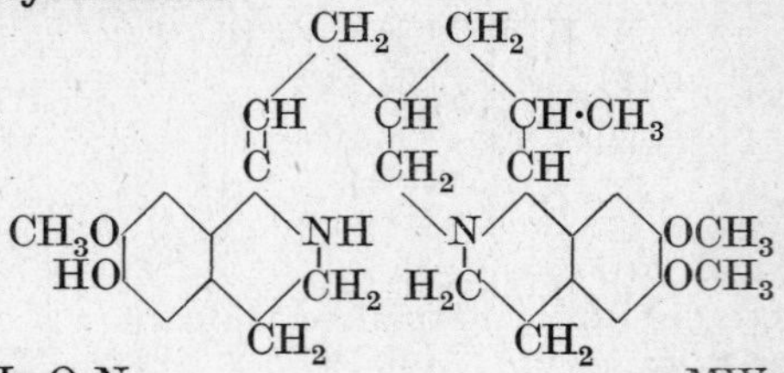

$C_{28}H_{36}O_4N_2$ MW, 464

Obtained from ipecacuanha. Colourless odourless prisms + $4H_2O$ from EtOH.Aq. or Me_2CO.Aq. M.p. anhyd. 122°. Sol. Et_2O. Very sol. EtOH, Me_2CO, $CHCl_3$. Spar. sol. cold H_2O. Insol. cold C_6H_6, ligroin. $[\alpha]_D^{15} + 69{\cdot}3°$ in EtOH. Alc. sol. turns litmus blue. Bitter taste. Blue fluor. in some sols. $FeCl_3 \longrightarrow$ reddish-brown to bluish-black col.

Me ether: prisms from Et_2O. M.p. 123–4°. $[\alpha]_D + 43{\cdot}2°$ in EtOH. *Picrate*: plates from Me_2CO. Softens at 142°. Slowly melts up to 175°. *B,H$_2$SO$_4$*: prisms + $7H_2O$ from H_2O. M.p. 247°. $[\alpha]_D + 44{\cdot}4°$ in H_2O. *B,HBr*: yellow needles from H_2O. M.p. anhyd. 190–200°. $[\alpha]_D$ (anhyd.) + 48·0° in H_2O.

Hydrogen oxalate: needles from EtOH. M.p. 130–45°.

Dibenzoate: amorph. powder. Sinters at 120°. M.p. 132–5°. Very sol. Et_2O, EtOH.

Brindley, Pyman, *J. Chem. Soc.*, 1927, 1067.
Pyman, *J. Chem. Soc.*, 1917, **111**, 431.
Hesse, *Ann.*, 1914, **405**, 34.

Psyllaic Acid.
See Psyllostearic Acid.

Psylla-alcohol.
See Psyllostearyl Alcohol.

Psyllostearic Acid (*Psyllaic acid*)

$C_{33}H_{66}O_2$ MW, 494

Cryst. M.p. 94–5°. Sol. hot EtOH, Et_2O, $CHCl_3$, C_6H_6. Insol. cold H_2O, EtOH, Et_2O.

Sundwik, *Z. physiol. Chem.*, 1911, **72**, 455; 1907, **53**, 365.

Psyllostearyl Alcohol (*Psylla-alcohol*)

$C_{33}H_{68}O$ MW, 480

Obtained with psyllostearic acid by hyd. of wax from *Psylla alni*. Cryst. from Me_2CO. M.p. 69–69·5°. Very sol. hot Me_2CO. Soda-lime at 360–70° $\longrightarrow$ psyllostearic acid.

See previous references.

Pterocarpine

$C_{16}H_{11}O_4(OCH_3)$

$C_{17}H_{14}O_5$ MW, 298

Obtained from red sandalwood. Needles from CCl_4. M.p. 165°. Insol. H_2O, cold EtOH, CS_2, acids, alkalis. Spar. sol. Et_2O. $[\alpha]_D^{20} - 220{\cdot}1°$.

Dinitrophenylhydrazone : dark brown needles. M.p. 305° decomp.

Raudnitz, Perlmann, *Ber.*, 1935, **68**, 1862.
Leonhardt, Fay, *Arch. Pharm.*, 1935, **273**, 53.
Dieterle, Leonhardt, *Arch. Pharm.*, 1929, **267**, 81.

Pukateine

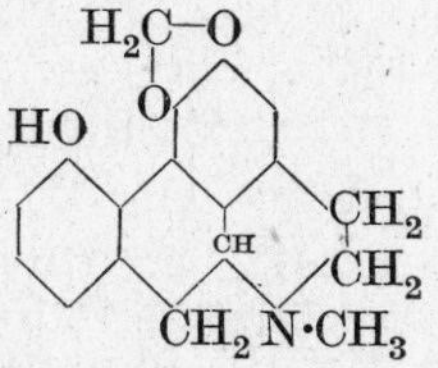

$C_{18}H_{17}O_3N$ MW, 295

l-.

Obtained from the bark of the pukatea (*Laurelia Novae Zealandiae*). Cryst. from Et_2O. M.p. 200°. B.p. 210–15°/2 mm. Sol. EtOH, Et_2O, $CHCl_3$. Very sol. pyridine. Spar. sol. pet. ether. Insol. H_2O. $[\alpha]_D^{15} - 220°$ in EtOH. $H_2SO_4 \longrightarrow$ orange sol. changing to red and violet on warming. $HNO_3 \longrightarrow$ vermilion sol., orange on warming. $K_2Cr_2O_7$ in $H_2SO_4 \longrightarrow$ purple col., excess of reagent $\longrightarrow$ green col. Has an action quantitatively similar to morphine on central nervous system.

Acetyl : *methiodide*, needles from Me_2CO. M.p. 245°.

Me ether : cryst. from dil. EtOH. M.p. 137°. $[\alpha]_D - 261°$. $H_2SO_4 \longrightarrow$ orange to mauve col. $HNO_3 \longrightarrow$ brown sol. *B,HCl* : cryst. from EtOH. M.p. 281°. *B,HBr* : cryst. from EtOH. M.p. 234°. d-*Tartrate* : needles from EtOH.Aq. M.p. 234°. $[\alpha]_D^{20} - 149{\cdot}1°$ in EtOH. *Methiodide* : cryst. M.p. 240–1°.

d-.

Me ether : cryst. from EtOH.Aq. M.p. 136°. $[\alpha]_D^{20} + 256{\cdot}4°$ in EtOH. l-*Tartrate* : cryst. from EtOH. M.p. 225°. $[\alpha]_D^{20} + 147{\cdot}5°$.

Barger, Schlittler, *Helv. Chim. Acta*, 1932, **15**, 381.
Barger, Girardet, *Helv. Chim. Acta*, 1931, **14**, 481.
Aston, *J. Chem. Soc.*, 1910, **97**, 1381.

Pulcheremodin

$C_{15}H_{10}O_5$ MW, 270

From root of *Rumex pulcher*, Linn. Orange needles. M.p. 251°. Readily sol. EtOH, Et_2O, Py. Sol. $CHCl_3$, Me_2CO, AcOH. Mod. sol. MeOH, CS_2. Spar. sol. CCl_4, C_6H_6. $H_2SO_4 \longrightarrow$ red col.

Triacetate : yellow needles. M.p. 194°. Sol. EtOH, AcOH, C_6H_6. $H_2SO_4 \longrightarrow$ carmine red col.

Emmanuel, *Chem. Zentr.*, 1918, I, 564.

Pulegan (1-*Methyl*-3-*isopropylcyclopentane*)

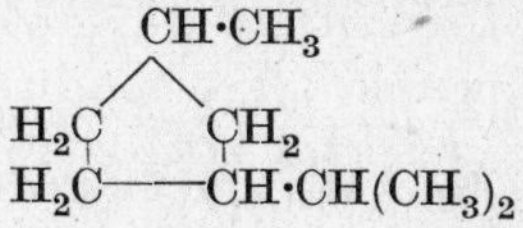

C_9H_{18} MW, 126

Oil with terpene odour. B.p. 142–4°. D^{22} 0·7730. n_D 1·4236.

Wallach, *Ann.*, 1912, **392**, 58.

Puleganic Acid (*Dihydropulegenic acid*, 1-*methyl*-3-*isopropylcyclopentane*-2-*carboxylic acid*)

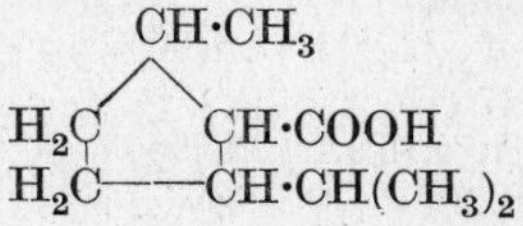

$C_{10}H_{18}O_2$ MW, 170

Colourless viscous oil. F.p. − 18 to − 19°. B.p. 152°/25 mm., 139°/12 mm. D_4^{20} 0·9642. n_D^{24} 1·4524. $[\alpha]_D^{20} - 0{\cdot}36°$.

Me ester : $C_{11}H_{20}O_2$. MW, 184. B.p. 91°/13 mm.

Et ester : $C_{12}H_{22}O_2$. MW, 198. B.p. 145°/4 mm. $D_4^{11\cdot8}$ 0·9178. $n_\alpha^{11\cdot8}$ 1·4405.

Chloride : $C_{10}H_{17}OCl$. MW, 188·5. B.p. 89–90°/11 mm.

Amide : $C_{10}H_{19}ON$. MW, 169. Cryst. from EtOH.Aq. or AcOEt–ligroin. M.p. 150–1°. $[\alpha]_D^{20} + 4{\cdot}8°$ in MeOH.

Nitrile : $C_{10}H_{17}N$. MW, 151. B.p. 103°/13 mm. $D_4^{16\cdot2}$ 0·8814. $n_\alpha^{16\cdot2}$ 1·4475.

Anilide : cryst. from EtOH.Aq. M.p. 149–50°.

Rupe, Schäfer, *Helv. Chim. Acta*, 1928, **11**, 467.
Wallach, *Ann.*, 1918, **414**, 237.

Pulegene (3-*Methyl*-1-*isopropylcyclopentene*)

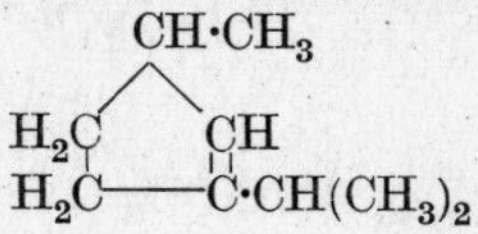

C_9H_{16} MW, 124

Oil. B.p. 138–9°, 39–41°/16 mm. D^{22} 0·791. n_D^{22} 1·4380.

Nitrosochloride: cryst. M.p. 74–5°.

Wallach, Collmann, Thede, *Ann.*, 1903, **327**, 131.

Pulegenic Acid (*1-Methyl-3-isopropylidene-cyclopentane-2-carboxylic acid*)

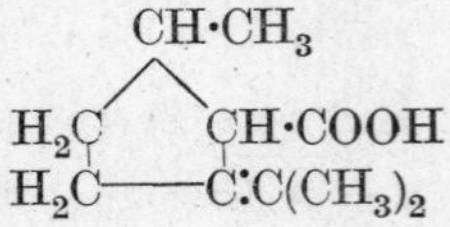

$C_{10}H_{16}O_2$ MW, 168

Pale yellow oil. B.p. 144–6°/12 mm. D_4^{20} 1·0050. n_D^{20} 1·4754. $[\alpha]_D^{20}$ + 48·18°. MeOH–HCl ⟶ hydrochloride of Me ester. Aniline at 200° ⟶ pulegene.

Me ester: $C_{11}H_{18}O_2$. MW, 182. B.p. 98–101°/10 mm. D^{20} 0·97. n_D^{20} 1·4665. *Hydrochloride*: m.p. 15–16°. B.p. 114°/12 mm.

Amide: $C_{10}H_{17}ON$. MW, 167. Needles from H_2O or EtOH.Aq. M.p. 123°. Very sol. EtOH, Et_2O. $[\alpha]_D^{18}$ + 29·05° in MeOH. Red. ⟶ amide of puleganic acid.

Nitrile: $C_{10}H_{15}N$. MW, 149. B.p. 218–20°. n_D^{22} 1·47047.

Anilide: needles from Et_2O–pet. ether. M.p. 124°. B.p. 200°/10 mm. Very sol. EtOH, Et_2O. Spar. sol. pet. ether.

p-*Toluidide*: needles from Et_2O–pet. ether. M.p. 143°.

Rüpe, Schäfer, *Helv. Chim. Acta*, 1928, **11**, 466.
Wallach, *Ann.*, 1918, **414**, 242.

β-Pulegenic Acid (*Isopulegenic acid*).

Differs from pulegenic acid in position of double bond. Oil. B.p. 142–5°/11 mm. D^{20} 0·9975. n_D 1·4747. $[\alpha]_D^{22}$ + 32·7° in Et_2O.

Amide: $C_{10}H_{17}ON$. MW, 167. Needles from MeOH.Aq. M.p. 152°. Red. ⟶ amide of puleganic acid.

See last reference above.

Pulegenol (*Enol form of pulegone*, $\Delta^{2,4(8)}$-p-*menthadienol*-3)

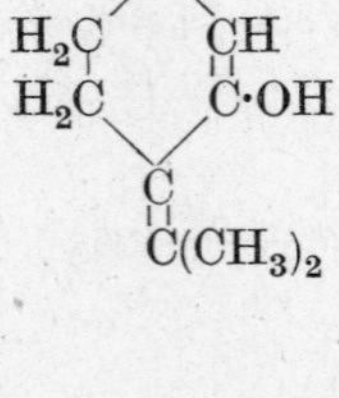

$C_{10}H_{16}O$ MW, 152

Oil. B.p. 85°/6 mm. D_4^{13} 0·916. n_D^{20} 1·48312. $[\alpha]_D$ + 24·6°. Dist. in steam or action of alkalis ⟶ pulegone.

Acetate: oil.

Benzoate: cryst. M.p. 230°.

Et ether: $C_{12}H_{20}O$. MW, 180. B.p. 97–97·5°/12 mm. D_0^{20} 0·9047.

Grignard, Blanchon, *Bull. soc. chim.*, 1931, **49**, 23.
Grignard, Savard, *Bull. soc. chim. Belg.*, 1927, **36**, 97; *Compt. rend.*, 1924, **179**, 1573.

Pulegenone (4-*Methyl*-1-*isopropylcyclopentenone*-5)

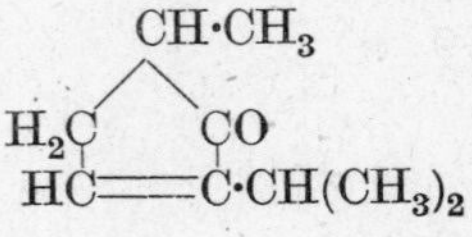

$C_9H_{14}O$ MW, 138

Oil. B.p. 188·5–189°. D_0^{20} 0·9144. n_D^{20} 1·4660.

Oxime: b.p. 237–42°, 123–6°/15 mm. *Benzoate*: cryst. from MeOH. M.p. 104–5°.

Semicarbazone: cryst. from MeOH. M.p. 183–4°.

Wallach, Grote, *Ann.*, 1919, **418**, 50.

Pulegol ($\Delta^{4(8)}$-p-*Menthenol*-3, 1-*methyl*-4-*isopropylidenecyclohexanol*-3)

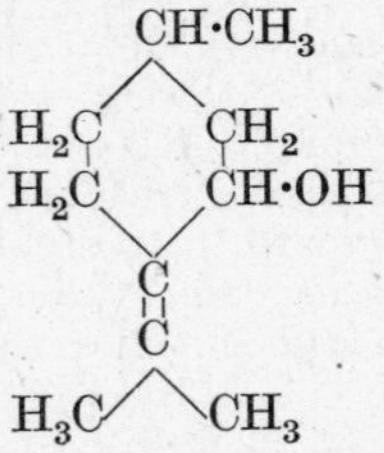

$C_{10}H_{18}O$ MW, 154

Two forms are described. (i) Obtained by Na–EtOH reduction of pulegone. Needles. M.p. 46–7°. B.p. 209–10°. $[\alpha]_D$ − 54·1° in EtOH. *Hydrogen phthalate*: needles from pet. ether. M.p. 212°. $[\alpha]_D$ − 86·8° in EtOH. (ii) Obtained by reduction of pulegone with aluminium isopropylate. B.p. 91·5°/12 mm. D_4^{18} 0·909. n_D^{18} 1·4714. $[\alpha]_{5461}^{18}$ + 80·09°.

Doeuvre, Perret, *Bull. soc. chim.*, 1935, **2**, 298.
Paolini, *Atti accad. Lincei*, 1919, **28**, 190, 236.

β-Pulegomenthol.
See Neomenthol.

Pulegone ($\Delta^{4(8)}$-p-*Menthenone*-3)

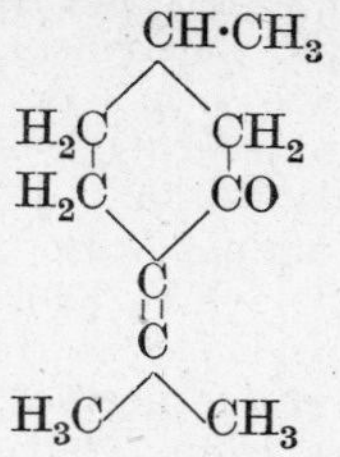

$C_{10}H_{16}O$ MW, 152

In oils from *Mentha pulegium*, *Hedeoma pulegoides*, *Mentha sylvestris*, etc. Colourless oil with pleasant peppermint odour. B.p. 224°, 151–3°/100 mm., 103°/17 mm. D_4^{19} 0·937. n_D^{19} 1·4880. $[\alpha]_{5461}^{20}$ + 28·23°. Heat of comb. C_v 1411·6 Cal. Readily purified through $NaHSO_3$ comp. Ox. ⟶ acetone + *d*-2-methyladipic acid. $NH_2 \cdot NH_2$ ⟶ *d*-isopulegone oxime.

Hydrochloride: cryst. from ligroin. M.p. 24–5°.

Hydrobromide: cryst. from EtOH.Aq. M.p. 40·5°. Very sol. EtOH, Et_2O. $[\alpha]_D$ − 33·88° in EtOH.

Nitrosite: needles from EtOH. M.p. 68–9°. Sol. EtOH, AcOH, $CHCl_3$.

Dinitroso deriv.: m.p. 81·5°.

2 : 4-*Dinitrophenylhydrazone*: red plates from pet. ether. M.p. 142°.

Semicarbazone: prisms from EtOH. M.p. 174°. Mod. sol. EtOH.

Phenylsemicarbazone: needles from EtOH. M.p. 132–3°.

Doeuvre, Perret, *Bull. soc. chim.*, 1935, 2, 298.
Kon, *J. Chem. Soc.*, 1930, 1616.
Baeyer, Henrich, *Ber.*, 1895, **28**, 652.

Pulenene (1 : 4 : 4-*Trimethylcyclohexene*)

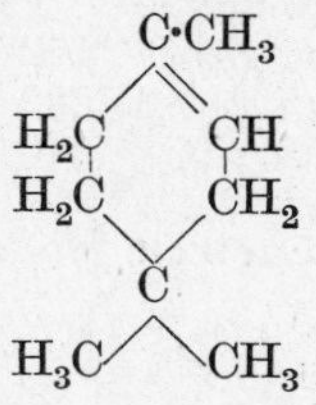

C_9H_{16} MW, 124

Liq. with pleasant odour. B.p. 139·5–140·5°, 36·3–37·3°/14 mm. $D_4^{18 \cdot 8}$ 0·8032. $n_D^{23 \cdot 2}$ 1·444. Ox. ⟶ 2 : 2-dimethyl-4-acetyl-*n*-valeric acid. H_2SO_4 ⟶ reddish-blue col.

Nitrosochloride: rhombohedra from EtOH, needles from AcOEt. M.p. 118–22°.

Other pulenenes are described in the literature. Little data is given and they are of doubtful purity.

Auwers, Lange, *Ann.*, 1915, **409**, 167.
Wallach, Kempe, *Ann.*, 1903, **329**, 89.

βγ-Pulenenol (3 : 3 : 6-*Trimethylcyclohexenol*-4)

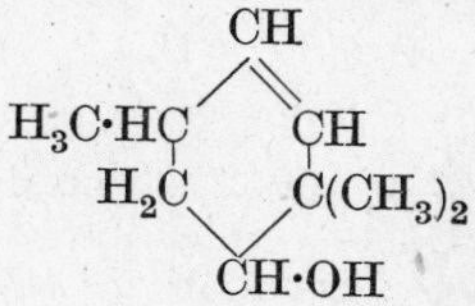

$C_9H_{16}O$ MW, 140

Oil with peppermint odour. B.p. 189°/754 mm., 82–5°/15 mm. $D_4^{18 \cdot 5}$ 0·9209. $n_D^{18 \cdot 5}$ 1·47398.

Auwers, Hessenland, *Ber.*, 1908, **41**, 1807.

αβ-Pulenenone (1 : 4 : 4-*Trimethylcyclohexen-one*-3)

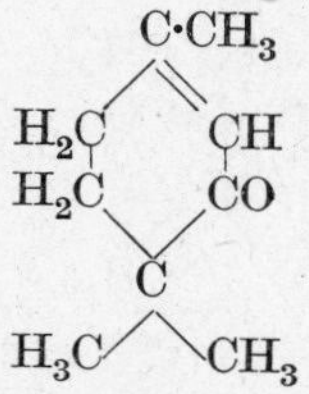

$C_9H_{14}O$ MW, 138

Oil with pleasant odour. B.p. 208°/753 mm., 86–8°/15 mm. $D_4^{16 \cdot 5}$ 0·9317. $n_D^{16 \cdot 5}$ 1·47958. Na–EtOH ⟶ pulenol.

Semicarbazone: prisms from MeOH. M.p. 200–1°. Very sol. hot MeOH. Mod. sol. cold MeOH.

Auwers, Hessenland, *Ber.*, 1908, **41**, 1812.

βγ-Pulenenone (3 : 3 : 6-*Trimethylcyclohexen-one*-4)

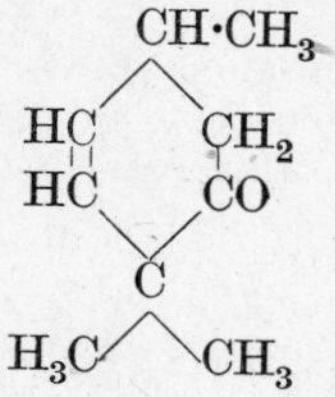

$C_9H_{14}O$ MW, 138

Oil with peppermint odour. B.p. 172–4°, 63–5°/16 mm. $D_4^{17 \cdot 7}$ 0·9055. $n_D^{17 \cdot 7}$ 1·45582.

Dichloride: oil. B.p. 121–122·5°/13 mm. D_4^{22} 1·2008. n_D^{22} 1·50002.

Semicarbazone: needles from MeOH.Aq. or C_6H_6–ligroin. M.p. 127°.

See previous reference.

Pulenol (2 : 2 : 5-*Trimethylcyclohexanol*)

$$CH \cdot CH_3$$
$$H_2C \quad CH_2$$
$$H_2C \quad CHOH$$
$$C$$
$$H_3C \quad CH_3$$

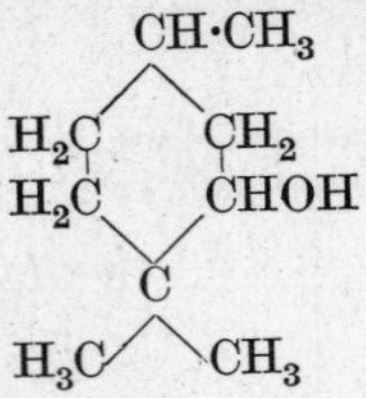

$C_9H_{18}O$ MW, 142

Oil. B.p. 187–9°, 90–2°/23 mm. D^{20} 0·8955. n_D^{20} 1·4569. $CrO_3 \longrightarrow$ pulenone.
Phenylurethane : cryst. from EtOH.Aq. M.p. 92° (82–5°).

Auwers, Hessenland, *Ber.*, 1908, **41**, 1814.
Wallach, Kempe, *Ann.*, 1903, **329**, 87.

Pulenone (2 : 2 : 5-*Trimethylcyclohexanone*)

$$CH \cdot CH_3$$
$$H_2C \quad CH_2$$
$$H_2C \quad CO$$
$$C$$
$$H_3C \quad CH_3$$

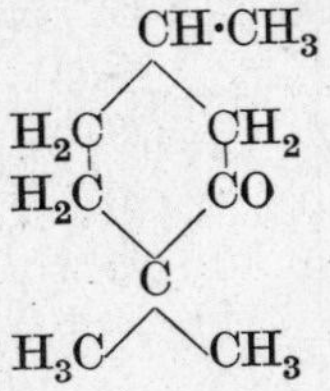

$C_9H_{16}O$ MW, 140

d-.
B.p. 183°. Spar. sol. H_2O. D^{21} 0·8925. n_D^{21} 1·44506. Strongly dextrorotatory.
Oxime : needles. M.p. 94–5°. B.p. 117°/ 12 mm.
Semicarbazone : m.p. 169–70°.

dl-.
B.p. 182–4°, 90–2°/39 mm. D^{24} 0·8871. n_D^{24} 1·4432.
Oxime : cryst. from EtOH. M.p. 93·5°.
Semicarbazone : m.p. 176–7° (169–70°).

See first reference above and also
Wallach, Kempe, *Ann.*, 1903, **329**, 86.
Cornubert, Humeau, *Bull. soc. chim.*, 1931, **49**, 1469.

Pulvinic Acid (*Pulvic acid*)

$$C_6H_5 \cdot HC-CO-C \colon C {<} ^{C_6H_5}_{COOH}$$
$$OC \qquad\qquad O$$

or

$$C_6H_5 \cdot C \colon C(OH)-C \colon C {<} ^{C_6H_5}_{COOH}$$
$$OC \qquad\qquad O$$

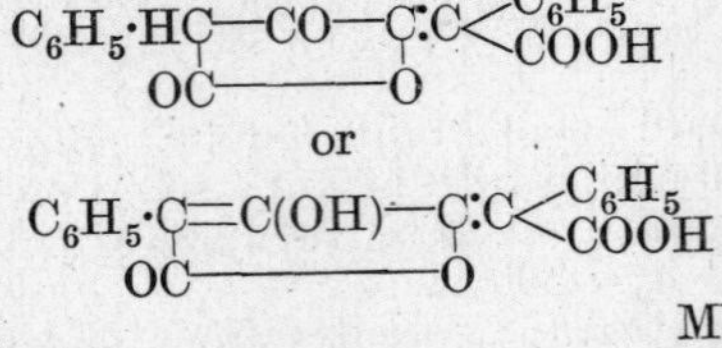

$C_{18}H_{12}O_5$ MW, 308

Orange powder from Et_2O or $CHCl_3$, prisms from C_6H_6, yellow cryst. + 1MeOH from MeOH,

yellowish-red cryst. + 1EtOH from EtOH. M.p. 216–17°. Very sol. EtOH, hot AcOH. Sol. H_2O and pptd. by acids. Spar. sol. Et_2O, $CHCl_3$, C_6H_6. Heat. above m.p., or with Ac_2O or $CH_3COCl \longrightarrow$ lactone. Ox. $\longrightarrow$ oxalic and benzoylformic acids.

Me ester : *see* Vulpinic Acid.
Et ester : $C_{20}H_{16}O_5$. MW, 336. Yellow tablets from EtOH. M.p. 127–8°. Heat above m.p. $\longrightarrow$ lactone. *Acetyl* : needles. M.p. 143–4°. *Me ether* : needles from EtOH. Prisms from AcOH. M.p. 150–1°.
Propyl ester : $C_{21}H_{18}O_5$. MW, 350. Yellow needles or plates from $CHCl_3$. M.p. 134°. Very sol. $CHCl_3$, C_6H_6. Spar. sol. EtOH. *Me ether* : needles. M.p. 121–2°.
Amide : $C_{18}H_{13}O_4N$. MW, 307. Yellow prisms from C_6H_6, yellow plates from AcOH. Sinters at 220–1°, m.p. 226°. Very sol. Me_2CO. Mod. sol. Et_2O, C_6H_6. Spar. sol. EtOH. Insol. H_2O. NH_4 *salt* : needles. M.p. 218°. Very sol. EtOH. Spar. sol. cold H_2O. *Me ether* : cryst. from MeOH. M.p. 216–17°.
Methylamide : plates from EtOH–C_6H_6. M.p. 237°.
Dimethylamide : prisms. M.p. 211°.
Nitrile : $C_{18}H_{11}O_3N$. MW, 289. Reddish-yellow needles from EtOH. Sinters at 190°, m.p. 193–4°. *Acetyl* : yellow needles from EtOH. M.p. 141–2°. Very sol. Et_2O. *Benzoyl* : pale yellow needles from EtOH. M.p. 168–168·5°. Insol. H_2O.
Anilide : cryst. from AcOH. M.p. 187–8°.
1-Naphthylamide : reddish-yellow plates from toluene. M.p. 211–12°.
2-Naphthylamide : reddish-yellow cryst. from toluene. M.p. 192°.

Asano, Yameda, *Ber.*, 1935, **68**, 1569.
Koller, Pfeiffer, *Monatsh.*, 1933, **62**, 164.
Karrer, Gehrekens, Heuss, *Helv. Chim. Acta*, 1926, **9**, 456.
Mazza, *Chem. Zentr.*, 1926, II, 1037.
Volhard, *Ann.*, 1894, **282**, 14.
Schenck, *ibid.*, 39.

Pulvinic Acid Lactone (*Pulvic acid lactone*)

$$C_6H_5 \cdot C {=\!=\!=} C-O-CO$$
$$OC-O-C {=\!=\!=} C \cdot C_6H_5$$

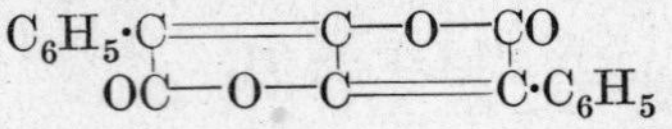

$C_{18}H_{10}O_4$ MW, 290

Found in *Sticta aurata* Ach, *Candelaria medians*, etc. Pale yellow needles from C_6H_6 or AcOH. M.p. 222–4°. Sol. hot $CHCl_3$, C_6H_6, AcOH, Me_2CO. Spar. sol. hot EtOH. Insol. H_2O. Insol. cold aq. alkalis. Sublimes in needles. Hyd. ⟶ pulvinic acid. NH_4OH ⟶ NH_4 salt of pulvinic acid amide. KOH–MeOH ⟶ vulpinic acid. Aniline ⟶ pulvinic acid anilide.

A second lactone of pulvinic acid is described in the literature. Cryst. from AcOH. M.p. 124–5°.

See previous references.

Purine

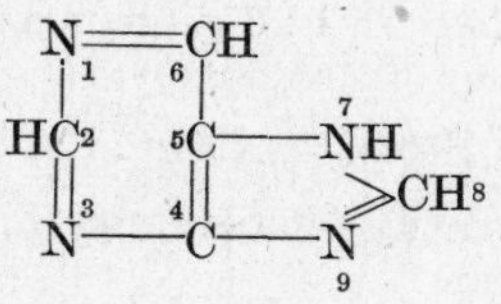

$C_5H_4N_4$ MW, 120

Microscopic needles from EtOH or toluene. M.p. 216–17°. Very sol. H_2O, hot EtOH. Mod. sol. hot AcOEt, Me_2CO. Spar. sol. Et_2O, $CHCl_3$. Amphoteric. Very stable to ox. agents. Gives cryst. hydrochloride and cryst. metallic salts. Forms insol. Zn salt.

B,HNO₃ : cryst. from H_2O. M.p. 205° decomp. Very sol. hot H_2O. Spar. sol. hot EtOH.

Picrate : plates from hot H_2O. M.p. 208°.

7-*Me* : $C_6H_6N_4$. MW, 134. Needles from EtOH. M.p. 184°. Insol. alkalis. Sol. H_2O, boiling EtOH. Spar. sol. C_6H_6. Heat of comb. C_v 820·6 Cal. Hydrochloride, nitrate, sulphate, very sol. H_2O. Forms cryst. Pt, Ag, Au salts. *$HgCl_2$ salt* : prisms from H_2O. M.p. 252°. *Methiodide* : yellow needles from MeOH. M.p. 231–2°. Very sol. H_2O.

9-*Me* : needles from toluene. M.p. 162–3°. Very sol. H_2O, EtOH. Sol. toluene. Sublimes.

Montequi, *Chem. Abstracts*, 1927, **21**, 3353.
Fischer, *Ber.*, 1899, **32**, 493; 1898, **31**, 2564.

Purpuric Acid

$C_8H_5O_6N_5$ MW, 267

Not known in free state. Acidification of salt sols. ⟶ uramil and alloxan.

NH_4 salt : *see* Murexide.

A,CH_3·NH_2 : cryst. + $1H_2O$. Anhyd. at 110°, decomp. at 210°. Mod. sol. H_2O. Spar. sol. Py. Insol. Et_2O, C_6H_6.

A,CH_3·CH_2·NH_2 : red prisms + $1H_2O$. Anhyd. at 110°, decomp. at 205°.

Hantzsch, Robison, *Ber.*, 1910, **43**, 92.
Möhlau, Litter, *J. prakt. Chem.*, 1906, **73**, 449.

Purpurin (1 : 2 : 4-*Trihydroxyanthraquinone*)

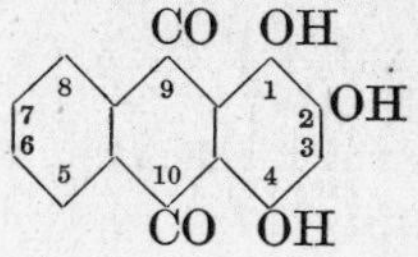

$C_{14}H_8O_5$ MW, 256

As glucoside in madder root. Long orange-red or orange-yellow needles + H_2O from EtOH.Aq.; dark red needles from EtOH. Anhyd. at 100°, m.p. 259° (253°). Very sol. boiling AcOH, boiling C_6H_6, EtOH. Spar. sol. boiling H_2O. Sol. Et_2O ⟶ deep yellow fluorescent sol. Sol. CS_2. Sol. H_2SO_4 ⟶ red. sol. Sol. alkalis ⟶ red. sols. Ox. ⟶ phthalic acid. H_2SO_4 ⟶ purpurin-3-sulphonic acid. Red. ⟶ purpuroxanthin. Br ⟶ 3-bromo deriv. NH_3 ⟶ 4-aminopurpuroxanthin. Gives cryst. Na, K, Pb salts.

2-*Me ether* : $C_{15}H_{10}O_5$. MW, 270. Brick-red needles from C_6H_6. M.p. 232–3° (240–2°). Insol. carbonate sols. Sol. alkalis ⟶ bluish-red col. Very sol. EtOH, C_6H_6. 1-*Acetyl* : yellow needles from Me_2CO. M.p. 224–5°. 1 : 4-*Diacetyl* : yellow needles. M.p. 170–2°.

2 : 4-*Di-Me ether* : $C_{16}H_{12}O_5$. MW, 284. Orange needles. M.p. 186–9°. *Acetyl* : lemon-yellow needles from EtOH. M.p. 189–90°.

2-*Acetyl* : orange needles from EtOH. M.p. 179–80°. Sol. hot C_6H_6, hot AcOH. Spar. sol. EtOH to fluorescent sol.

Triacetyl : pale yellow needles. Sinters at 193°, m.p. 198–200°.

du Pont, U.S.P., 1,985,452, (*Chem. Zentr.*, 1935, II, 439).
Newport Chem. Corp., U.S.P., 1,790,932, (*Chem. Abstracts*, 1931, **25**, 1539).
Marshall, *J. Chem. Soc.*, 1931, 3206.
Perkin, Storey, *J. Chem. Soc.*, 1928, 238.

Purpurin-3-carboxylic Acid (*Pseudopurpurin*, 1 : 3 : 4-*trihydroxyanthraquinone-2-carboxylic acid*)

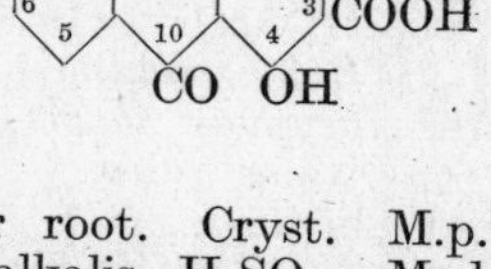

$C_{15}H_8O_7$ MW, 300

In madder root. Cryst. M.p. 222–4° decomp. Sol. alkalis, H_2SO_4. Mod. sol. boiling C_6H_6, $CHCl_3$. Sol. hot H_2O ⟶ orange-red sol.

Insol. cold H_2O, EtOH. At 180–95° ⟶ purpurin. Ac_2O at 180° ⟶ triacetylpurpurin.

Baeyer, D.R.P., 272,301, (*Chem. Zentr.*, 1914, I, 1474).
Liebermann, Plath, *Ber.*, 1877, **10**, 1618.

Purpurogallin

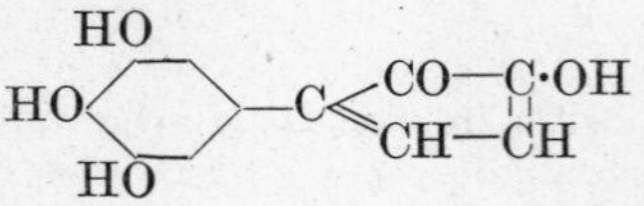

$C_{11}H_8O_5$ MW, 220

In gall of *Dryophanta divisa* as glucoside. Yellow or dark red needles from AcOH. M.p. 274° (rapid heat.). Decomp. without melting when slowly heated. Sol. Et_2O, $CHCl_3$. Mod. sol. EtOH. Spar. sol. H_2O. Reduces Au, Ag and alk. Cu sols. Characteristic col. with alkalis, orange-red ⟶ blue ⟶ green ⟶ dark yellow. H_2SO_4 ⟶ orange-red col. Gives spar. sol. Ba salt.

Tetra-acetyl: colourless plates from EtOH or C_6H_6. M.p. 182–3°. Sol. EtOH, Et_2O. Insol. H_2O.

Tribenzoyl: colourless prisms. M.p. 212–13°. Insol. EtOH.

Tri-Me ether: $C_{14}H_{14}O_5$. MW, 262. Orange needles from AcOEt. M.p. 174–7°. Spar. sol. EtOH. Insol. aq. alkalis. *Acetyl*: needles from EtOH. M.p. 140–3°. Spar. sol. EtOH.

Tetra-Me ether: $C_{15}H_{16}O_5$. MW, 276. Prisms from EtOH. M.p. 93–4°. Sol. EtOH.

Evans, Dehn, *J. Am. Chem. Soc.*, 1930, **52**, 3649.
Wilstätter, Heiss, *Ann.*, 1923, **433**, 17.
Nierenstein, *J. Chem. Soc.*, 1919, **115**, 1331.
Perkin, Steven, *J. Chem. Soc.*, 1903, **83**, 194.

Purpuroxanthin (1 : 3-*Dihydroxyanthraquinone, xanthopurpurin*)

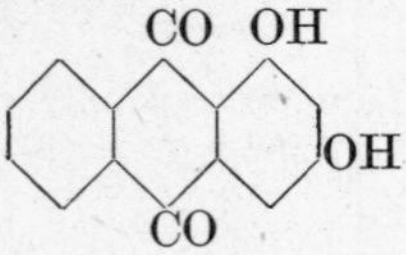

$C_{14}H_8O_4$ MW, 240

Yellow needles or leaflets. M.p. 268–70° (264°). Sol. Me_2CO, AcOH, $PhNO_2$. Mod. sol. EtOH, C_6H_6. Sol. alkalis ⟶ red. sols. Sublimes. Alk. fusion or $H_2SO_4 + MnO_2$ ⟶ purpurin. Zn dust dist. ⟶ anthracene. HNO_3 ⟶ phthalic acid.

1-*Acetyl*: orange-yellow needles from MeOH. M.p. 231–5°. Very sol. Me_2CO.

3-*Acetyl*: yellow needles from EtOH. M.p. 144°.

Diacetyl: pale yellow needles. M.p. 183–4°.

1-*Me ether*: $C_{15}H_{10}O_4$. MW, 254. Yellow leaflets from Me_2CO. M.p. 311–13°. *Acetyl*: yellow leaflets from EtOH. M.p. 154–5°.

3-*Me ether*: pale yellow needles from AcOH. M.p. 193°.

Di-Me ether: $C_{16}H_{12}O_4$. MW, 268. Yellow needles. M.p. 151–3°.

Di-phenyl ether: 1 : 3-diphenoxyanthraquinone. Yellow needles from AcOH. M.p. 167°.

Perkin, Story, *J. Chem. Soc.*, 1929, 1399.

Purpuroxanthin-2-carboxylic Acid.
See Munjistin.

Putrescine (*Tetramethylenediamine*, 1 : 4-*diaminobutane*)

$$H_2N{\cdot}CH_2{\cdot}CH_2{\cdot}CH_2{\cdot}CH_2{\cdot}NH_2$$

$C_4H_{12}N_2$ MW, 88

Product of decomp. of excreta, dead animal matter, etc. Cryst. with strong odour. M.p. 27–8° (24°). B.p. 158–9°. D_4^{25} 0·877. Sol. H_2O. Absorbs CO_2. $k = 5{\cdot}1 \times 10^{-4}$ at 25°. Salts are not poisonous.

B,2HCl: needles from H_2O. Does not melt below 290°. Very sol. H_2O. Insol. MeOH.

B,2HAuCl$_4$: cryst. + $2H_2O$. M.p. 235–40°.

B,H$_2$PtCl$_6$: darkens at 230°. Does not melt below 275°. Spar. sol. cold H_2O. Insol. EtOH.

N : N′-*Diacetyl*: m.p. 137°. Sol. H_2O, EtOH.

Monobenzoyl: colourless viscous oil. B.p. 176–8°/0·1 mm. *Hydrochloride*: m.p. 167°. N′-*Acetyl*: m.p. 143°. *Picrate*: m.p. 168–70°.

N : N′-*Dibenzoyl*: m.p. 177°.

N : N′-*Di*-m-*nitrobenzoyl*: m.p. 246°.

Picrate: pale yellow prisms. Turns brown at 250°. Decomp. at 250–5°.

N : N′-*Di-Me*: $C_6H_{16}N_2$. MW, 116. B.p. 168°. *Di*-m-*nitrobenzoyl*: cryst. from MeOH. M.p. 118°.

N : N′-*Tetra-Me*: $C_8H_{20}N_2$. MW, 144. Colourless liq. B.p. 168°. Misc. with hot H_2O. Sol. EtOH, Et_2O. $D_4^{18\cdot9}$ 0·8041. $n_a^{18\cdot9}$ 1·4316. Volatile in steam. *B,2HCl*: prisms from EtOH. M.p. 273° decomp. *B,2HAuCl$_4$*: yellow prisms from hot H_2O. Sinters at 200°. Decomp. at 206–7°. *B,H$_2$PtCl$_6$*: prisms + $2H_2O$. M.p. 234° decomp. *Picrate*: m.p. 198–9°.

Braun, Pirkernelle, *Ber.*, 1934, **67**, 1056.
Keil, *Z. physiol. Chem.*, 1931, **196**, 81.
Wrede, Fanselow, Strack, *Z. physiol. Chem.*, 1927, **163**, 219.
Keil, *Ber.*, 1926, **59**, 2816.

Pyocyanine

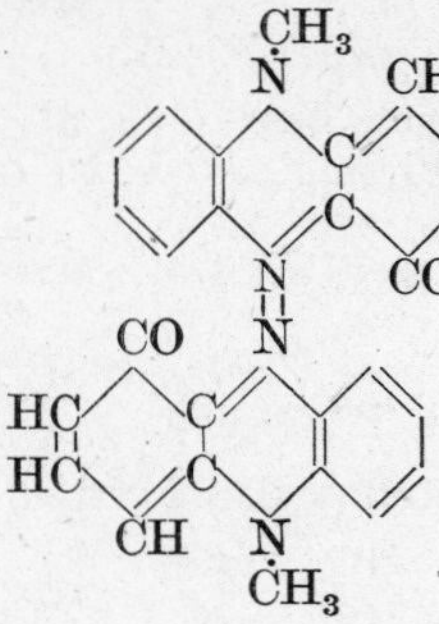

$C_{26}H_{20}O_2N_4$ MW, 420

Pigment of *Bacillus pyocyaneus*. Blue needles from $CHCl_3$–pet. ether. M.p. 133°. Sol. $CHCl_3$, Me_2CO, AcOEt, hot H_2O. Insol. Et_2O, C_6H_6, pet. ether, CCl_4, CS_2. Hyd. $\longrightarrow$ 2 mols. hemipyocyanine. Acetylation or benzoylation $\longrightarrow$ hemipyocyanine acetate or benzoate. Increases respiration of living cells.

Perchlorate: red needles. M.p. 221–3° decomp.

Picrate: red leaflets + 2MeOH from MeOH, or violet leaflets + 1EtOH from EtOH. M.p. 194–5° decomp.

Picrolonate: reddish-black cryst. + 1EtOH. M.p. 195–6°.

Wrede, Strack, *Z. physiol. Chem.*, 1929, **181**, 58; *Ber.*, 1929, **62**, 2051.
McCombie, Scarborough, *J. Chem. Soc.*, 1923, **123**, 3279.

Pyramidone (4-*Dimethylaminoantipyrine, amidopyrine*)

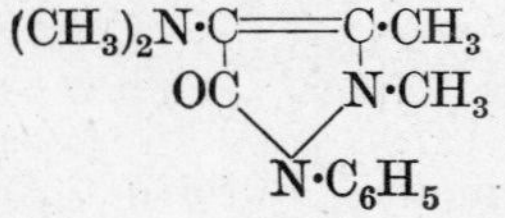

$C_{13}H_{17}ON_3$ MW, 231

Cryst. powder. M.p. 108°. Sol. H_2O, EtOH, Et_2O, C_6H_6. $FeCl_3 \longrightarrow$ bluish-violet col. Antipyretic. Less toxic and more powerful than antipyrine.

B,HBr: pyrobromone. Needles. M.p. 190°. Sol. H_2O, EtOH. Insol. Et_2O, C_6H_6.

B,HI: pyro-iodone. M.p. 196–7°.

Citrate: cryst. from EtOH.Aq. M.p. 85°.

B,HAu(CN)₄: plates. M.p. 183–5°.

Methobromide: decomp. at 212°.

Methiodide: decomp. about 220°. Sol. H_2O.

Picrate: m.p. 168–70°.

Styphnate: yellow needles from EtOH. M.p. 191.°

Rodionov, *Bull. soc. chim.*, 1926, **39**, 305.
Klebanskiĭ, Lemke, *Chem. Abstracts*, 1935, **29**, 6891.
Reuter, U.S.P., 2,005,506, (*Chem. Abstracts*, 1935, **29**, 5130).
I.G., D.R.P., 617,237, (*Chem. Zentr.*, 1935, II, 3949).
Knorr, Stolz, *Ann.*, 1896, **293**, 66.

Pyranthridine

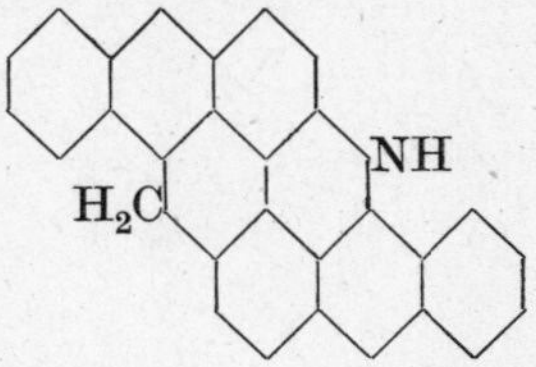

$C_{29}H_{17}N$ MW, 379

Reddish-brown leaflets from xylene. M.p. 370°. Conc. $H_2SO \longrightarrow$ dark blue salt.

Scholl, Dischendorfer, *Ber.*, 1918, **51**, 441.

Pyranthridone

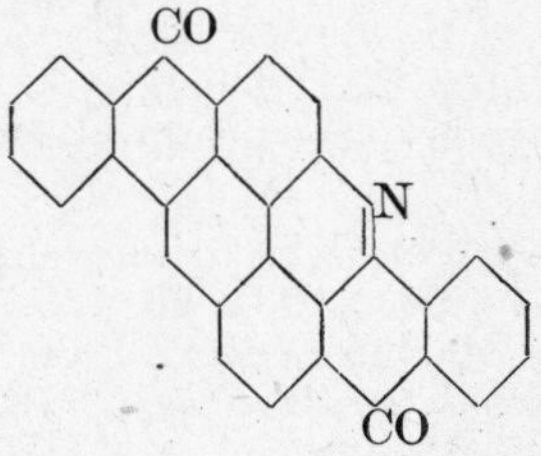

$C_{29}H_{13}O_2N$ MW, 407

Brownish-yellow needles from quinoline. Does not melt below 500°. Sublimes. Sol. conc. H_2SO_4 with red col. Insol. most org. solvents. Gives violet-blue vat.

See previous reference and also
Scholl, D.R.P., 307,390, (*Chem. Zentr.*, 1918, II, 495).

Pyranthrone

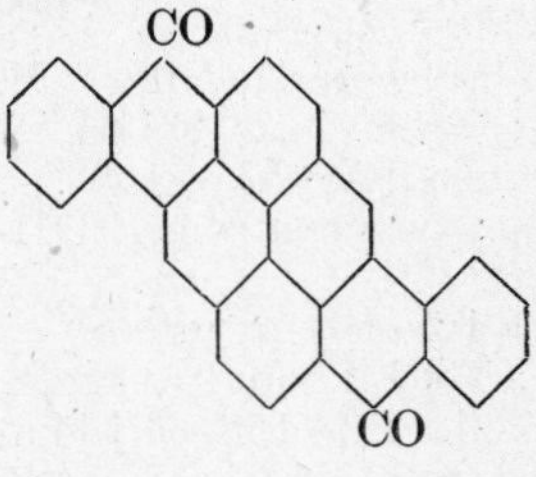

$C_{30}H_{14}O_2$ MW, 406

Brown cryst. Sol. hot $PhNO_2$, hot aniline. Sol. conc. H_2SO_4 with blue col. Well known orange vat dyestuff.

Scholl, *Ber.*, 1910, **43**, 350; D.R.P., 239,761, (*Chem. Zentr.*, 1911, II, 1498).
Badische, D.R.P., 175,067, (*Chem. Zentr.*, 1906, II, 1537).
Gallotti, *Chem. Abstracts*, 1934, **28**, 5063.
See also Colour Index, No. 1096.

Pyrantin.
See under Succinimide.

Pyrazine (1 : 4-*Diazine*)

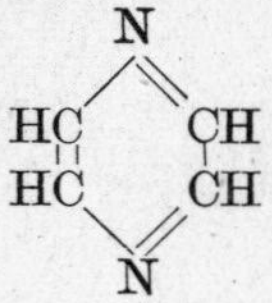

$C_4H_4N_2$ MW, 80

Prisms from H_2O. M.p. 47°. B.p. 115·5–115·8°/768·4 mm. $D_4^{60·9}$ 1·0311. $n_D^{60·9}$ 1·4953. Sol. H_2O, EtOH, Et_2O. Volatile in steam.

B,H_2SO_4 : m.p. 136–7°.

$B,HAuCl_4$: yellow plates from HCl. M.p. 245° decomp.

$B,AuCl_3$: m.p. 202–3°.

$B,HgCl_2$: m.p. 273° decomp.

Picrate : yellow needles from EtOH. M.p. 157°.

Aston, Peterson, Holowchzk, *J. Am. Chem. Soc.*, 1934, **56**, 153.
Wolff, Marburg, *Ann.*, 1906, **363**, 215.
Stoehr, *J. prakt. Chem.*, 1894, **49**, 392; 1895, **51**, 449.
Gabriel, Pinkus, *Ber.*, 1893, **26**, 2207.

Pyrazole (1 : 2-*Diazole*)

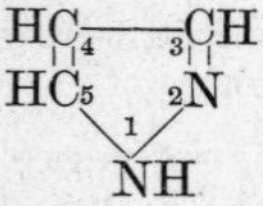

$C_3H_4N_2$ MW, 68

Needles or prisms from ligroin. M.p. 69·5–70°. B.p. 186–8°/757·9 mm. Sol. H_2O, EtOH, Et_2O, C_6H_6. $k = 3{\cdot}0 \times 10^{-12}$ at 25°.

B,HCl : hygroscopic needles. M.p. 104°.

B_2,H_2SO_4 : cryst. from EtOH. M.p. 134°.

B,HNO_3 : needles. M.p. 148°.

$B,(COOH)_2$: needles from EtOH–Et_2O. M.p. 192° decomp.

N-*Me* : *see* 1-Methylpyrazole.

N-*Phenyl* : *see* 1-Phenylpyrazole.

N-*Acetyl* : oil. B.p. 155–6°/744 mm. *Picrate* : yellow prisms from EtOH. M.p. 170–1°.

N-*Benzoyl* : oil. B.p. 281°/747 mm., 220–5°/60 mm.

Picrate : yellow needles. M.p. 160°.

v. Pechmann, *Ber.*, 1898, **31**, 2950.
Curtius, Wirsing, *J. prakt. Chem.*, 1894, **50**, 544.
Dains, Harger, *J. Am. Chem. Soc.*, 1918, **40**, 562.
Mingoia, *Chem. Zentr.*, 1931, II, 2324.
Knorr, D.R.P., 74,619.

Pyrazole-1-carboxylic Acid

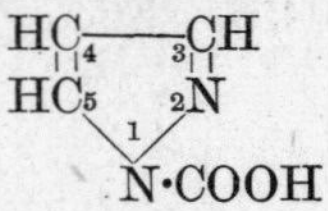

$C_4H_4O_2N_2$ MW, 112

M.p. 102–3° decomp. Boil with $H_2O \longrightarrow$ pyrazole.

Et ester : $C_6H_8O_2N_2$. MW, 140. Oil. B.p. 213°/741 mm., 120–3°/42 mm.

Amide : $C_4H_5ON_3$. MW, 111. Cryst. from EtOH. M.p. 136·5°.

Mingoia, *Chem. Zentr.*, 1931, II, 2324.
Knorr, *Ber.*, 1895, **28**, 716.

Pyrazole-3-carboxylic Acid.

Prisms from H_2O. M.p. 210–12°. Sol. H_2O, EtOH. Mod. sol. Et_2O, AcOH. Insol. $CHCl_3$, C_6H_6.

Me ester : $C_5H_6O_2N_2$. MW, 126. Cryst. from C_6H_6. M.p. 139–40°. Sol. MeOH. Spar. sol. ligroin.

N-*Me* : $C_5H_6O_2N_2$. MW, 126. Cryst. M.p. 222°. Mod. sol. hot H_2O.

N-*Phenyl* : *see* 1-Phenylpyrazole-3-carboxylic Acid.

Auwers, Breyhan, *J. prakt. Chem.*, 1935, **143**, 274.
Auwers, Cauer, *J. prakt. Chem.*, 1930, **126**, 187.
v. Pechmann, Burkhard, *Ber.*, 1900, **33**, 3595.
Buchner, Kachumian, *Ber.*, 1902, **35**, 41.
Knorr, Macdonald, *Ann.*, 1894, **279**, 231.
Jowett, Potter, *J. Chem. Soc.*, 1903, **83**, 469.

Pyrazole-4-carboxylic Acid.

Needles from H_2O. M.p. 219–20° (decomp. at 275°). Sol. EtOH. Mod. sol. H_2O, Et_2O. Sublimes.

N-*Phenyl* : *see* 1-Phenylpyrazole-4-carboxylic Acid.

Knorr, Laubmann, *Ber.*, 1889, **22**, 180.
Behagel, Buchner, *Ber.*, 1902, **35**, 35.

Pyrazole-3 : 5-dicarboxylic Acid

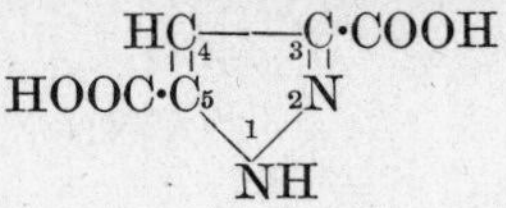

$C_5H_4O_4N_2$ MW, 156

Needles. M.p. 287–90° decomp. $D^{22\cdot5}$ 1·626. Spar. sol. H_2O, EtOH, Et_2O. Very spar. sol. $CHCl_3$, ligroin.

Di-Me ester : $C_7H_8O_4N_2$. MW, 184. Plates from Et_2O. M.p. 151·5°. Sol. EtOH. Spar. sol. ligroin. N-*Me* : needles from ligroin. M.p. 72–73·5°. N-*Acetyl* : plates from EtOH. M.p. 84·5–85°.

N-*Phenyl* : *see* 1-Phenylpyrazole-3 : 5-dicarboxylic Acid.

Auwers, Cauer, *J. prakt. Chem.*, 1930, **126**, 196.
Gray, *Ber.*, 1900, **33**, 1223.
Knorr, Macdonald, *Ann.*, 1894, **279**, 218 (*Footnote*).

Pyrazole-4 : 5-dicarboxylic Acid.

Needles + $1H_2O$ from dil. HNO_3. M.p. 260° decomp. Sol. EtOH. Spar. sol. Et_2O. Insol. $CHCl_3$.

Di-Me ester : needles from H_2O. M.p. 141°.

N-*Phenyl* : *see* 1-Phenylpyrazole-4 : 5-dicarboxylic Acid.

v. Pechmann, *Ber.*, 1900, **33**, 630.
v. Pechmann, Sell, *Ber.*, 1899, **32**, 2299.

2-Pyrazoline (4 : 5-*Dihydropyrazole*)

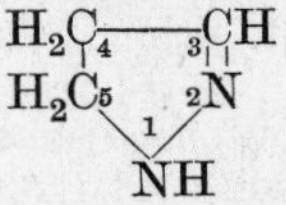

$C_3H_6N_2$ MW, 70

Colourless liq. B.p. 144°. D_4^{20} 1·017. n_{He}^{20} 1·478. Misc. with H_2O, EtOH. Volatile in steam and ether.

N-o-*Tolyl* : liq. B.p. 271°/759·5 mm. D_0^0 1·084.

N-p-*Tolyl* : needles from EtOH.Aq. M.p. 60·5°. B.p. 281–2°/758 mm.

Auwers, Heimke, *Ann.*, 1927, **458**, 180.

5-Pyrazolone

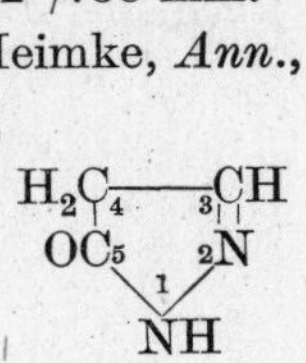

$C_3H_4ON_2$ MW, 84

Needles from toluene. M.p. 165°. Sol. H_2O, EtOH. Spar. sol. Et_2O.

4-*Isonitroso* : needles from H_2O. M.p. 180–1°.

Ruhemann, Morrel, *Ber.*, 1895, **28**, 988.
Knorr, *Ber.*, 1896, **29**, 253.
Dains, O'Brien, Johnson, *J. Am. Chem. Soc.*, 1916, **38**, 1510.

Pyrene

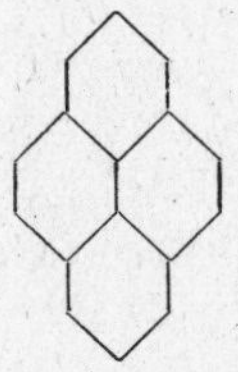

$C_{16}H_{10}$ MW, 202

Constituent of coal tar. Pale yellow plates by cryst. or sublimation. M.p. 149–50°. Does not boil below 360°. Sol. Et_2O, CS_2, C_6H_6, toluene. Sols. show blue fluor. $CrO_3 \longrightarrow$ pyrenequinone $\longrightarrow$ pyrenic acid.

Picrate : red needles from EtOH. M.p. 222°. Mod. sol. hot EtOH. Sol. CS_2, C_6H_6.

Clar, *Ber.*, 1936, **69**, 1683.
Fleischer, Retze, *Ber.*, 1922, **55**, 3280.
Weitzenböck, *Monatsh.*, 1913, **34**, 221.
Graebe, *Ann.*, 1871, **158**, 285.

Pyrene-3 : 8-quinone

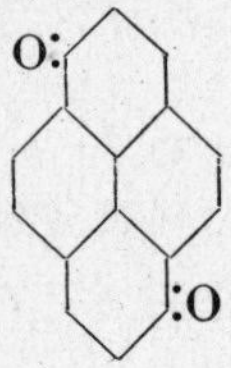

$C_{16}H_8O_2$ MW, 232

Yellow needles from $PhNO_2$. M.p. 309° (rapid heat.); darkens at 290° (slow heat.). Sol. conc. H_2SO_4 with yellowish-orange col. Sol. $PhNO_2$. Spar. sol. EtOH, Et_2O, CS_2, C_6H_6.

Vollmann, Becker, Corell, Streeck, *Ann.*, 1937, **531**, 1.
Goldschmiedt, *Monatsh.*, 1883, **4**, 310.
Griebe, *Ann.*, 1871, **158**, 295.
See also Scholl, Seer, *Ann.*, 1912, **394**, 125.

Pyrene-3 : 10-quinone

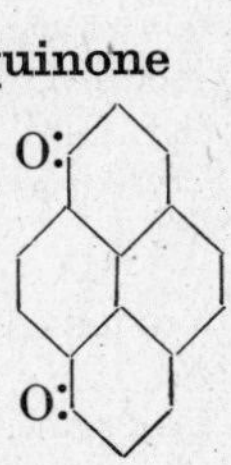

$C_{16}H_8O_2$ MW, 232

Brownish-red needles from AcOH. M.p. 270°. Sol. conc. H_2SO_4 with olive-green col.

See first reference above.

Pyrenic Acid

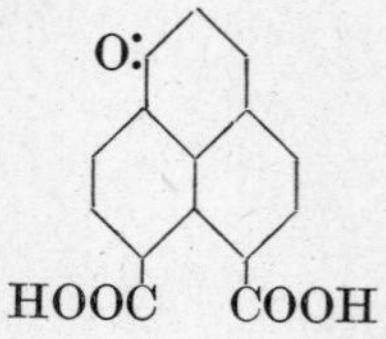

$C_{15}H_8O_5$ MW, 268

Pale yellow plates.

α-Me ester: $C_{16}H_{10}O_5$. MW, 282. Yellow needles from MeOH. Decomp. at 275°. Sol. boiling EtOH to 0·5%.

β-Me ester: yellowish-green needles from MeOH. Sol. boiling EtOH to 1·06%.

Anhydride: $C_{15}H_6O_4$. MW, 250. Needles. Decomp. at 260°.

Imide: $C_{15}H_{11}O_2N$. MW, 237. Yellow plates. Insol. cold alkalis, sol. hot alkalis ⟶ red sols.

Bamberger, Philip, *Ann.*, 1887, **240**, 168.
Langstein, *Monatsh.*, 1910, **31**, 863.

Pyrethrolone

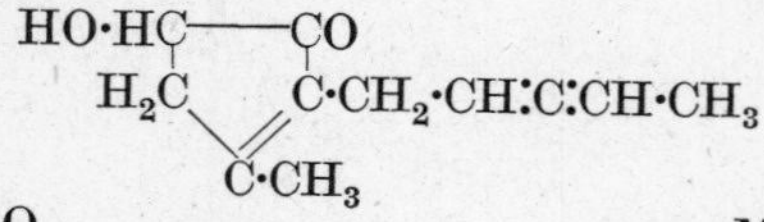

$C_{11}H_{14}O_2$ MW, 178

Viscous oil. B.p. 115–18°/0·125 mm., 111–12°/0·05 mm. Reduces $KMnO_4$ instantly, warm Fehling's, and $NH_3.AgNO_3$ in the cold.

Semicarbazone: cryst. from MeOH. M.p. 200° decomp.

p-*Nitrophenylosazone*: brown microcryst. powder. Decomp. above 350°.

Acetyl: viscous oil. B.p. 104–5°/0·5 mm. $[\alpha]_D^{15}$ − 23·79°. *Semicarbazone*: m.p. 143–5°.

Me ether: $C_{12}H_{16}O_2$. MW, 192. B.p. 82–3°/0·25 mm. *Semicarbazone*: cryst. from MeOH. M.p. 183° decomp.

Et ether: $C_{13}H_{18}O_2$. MW, 206. B.p. 102–3° in high vacuo. *Semicarbazone*: cryst. from MeOH. M.p. 179–80°.

Staudinger, Ruzicka, *Helv. Chim. Acta*, 1924, **7**, 215.
La Forge, Haller, *J. Am. Chem. Soc.*, 1936, **58**, 1061.

Pyridanthrone (*Anthrapyridone*)

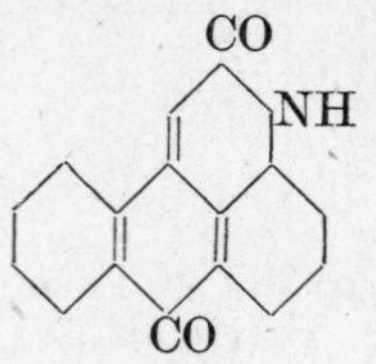

$C_{16}H_9O_2N$ MW, 247

Cryst. from $PhNO_2$. M.p. 406–8°. Sol. conc. H_2SO_4 with yellow col. and yellow fluor.

N-*Me*: $C_{17}H_{11}O_2N$. MW, 261. Cryst. from $PhNO_2$. M.p. 267–8°.

Seka, Schreckental, Heilperin, *Monatsh.*, 1929, **53** and **54**, 478.
Höchst, D.R.P., 250,885, (*Chem. Zentr.*, 1912, II, 1319).
Bayer, D.R.P., 209,033, (*Chem. Zentr.*, 1909, I, 1680).
Badische, D.R.P., 216,597, (*Chem. Zentr.*, 1910, I, 68).

Pyridazine (1 : 2-*Diazine, orthodiazine*)

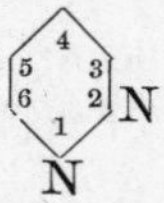

$C_4H_4N_2$ MW, 80

Liq. F.p. − 8°. B.p. 208°. $D_4^{23·5}$ 1·1035. $n_D^{23·5}$ 1·5231. Very sol. H_2O. Sol. EtOH, Et_2O, C_6H_6. Insol. pet. ether. Na + EtOH ⟶ putrescine.

B,AuCl_3: yellow needles from H_2O. M.p. 170° decomp. Insol. cold H_2O.

Chloroaurate: yellow cryst. M.p. 110°.

B_2,H_2PtCl_6: orange prisms. Decomp. at 218°. Sol. H_2O.

Picrate: yellow needles from H_2O or EtOH. M.p. 169° decomp.

Wohl, Bernreuther, *Ann.*, 1930, **481**, 12.
Gabriel, *Ber.*, 1909, **42**, 658.

Pyridine

C_5H_5N MW, 79

Occurs in coffee oil. Extracted in quantity from coal tar. Colourless liq. with characteristic odour. F.p. − 42°. B.p. 115·5°. Forms azeotropic mixture with 3 mols. H_2O, b.p. 92–3°. Very hygroscopic. Misc. with H_2O in all proportions. Volatile in steam. D_4^{25} 0·97796. n_D^{21} 1·5092. $k = 2{\cdot}4 \times 10^{-9}$ at 25°. Heat of comb. C_v 664·7 Cal., C_p 675·1 Cal. Latent heat of vap. 101·4 Cal. per kilogram at 115·5°. Sp. heat (21°) 0·391. Crit. temp. about 344°. F.p. depression 4·97 per kilogram. B.p. elevation 2·69 per kilogram. Red heat ⟶ 2 : 4′-dipyridyl. Red. ⟶ piperidine. H_2SO_4 ⟶ 3-sulphonic acid. $NaNH_2$ ⟶ 2-aminopyridine. MeOH–HCl ⟶ pyridine methochloride. $ClCH_2{\cdot}COOEt$ ⟶ pyridine-betaine hydrochloride. Used for denaturing industrial spirit. Powerful solvent.

B,HCl : hygroscopic plates from EtOH. M.p. 82°. B.p. 218–19°. Sol. H_2O, EtOH, $CHCl_3$. Insol. Et_2O.

B,2HCl : prisms. M.p. 46–7°.

B,HBr : reddish-yellow plates. M.p. 213°. Sol. H_2O, EtOH, $CHCl_3$. Insol. Et_2O.

B,HI : cryst. + $1H_2O$ from H_2O. M.p. 268° decomp.

B,HClO₃ : cryst. from EtOH. M.p. 147° decomp.

B,(COOH)₂ : m.p. 151–2°.

Phthalate : cryst. M.p. 109°.

Tartrate : m.p. 154°.

Citrate : m.p. 123°.

3 : 5-*Dinitrobenzoate* : yellow needles. M.p. 162°.

B,HAuCl₄ : yellow needles from H_2O or EtOH. M.p. 329° (304°). Spar. sol. hot H_2O.

B,H₂PtCl₆ : reddish-yellow needles. M.p. 262–4° decomp. Very sol. H_2O. Insol. EtOH.

B₂,HgCl₂ : needles from Py. M.p. 108°.

B,HgCl₂ : needles from H_2O or EtOH. M.p. 180°.

Methiodide : needles or prisms from EtOH or Me_2CO. Very hygroscopic. Yellows at 100°. M.p. 118°. Very sol. H_2O. Sol. EtOH, $CHCl_3$, AcOH, Me_2CO. Insol. Et_2O, C_6H_6, CS_2.

Ethobromide : cryst. from EtOH. M.p. 111–12°. Sol. H_2O, EtOH. Insol. Et_2O.

Ethiodide : plates from EtOH–Et_2O. M.p. 90·5°. Sol. H_2O, EtOH, AcOH, Me_2CO. Insol. Et_2O, $CHCl_3$, C_6H_6, CS_2.

Propiodide : plates from EtOH. M.p. 52–3°. Sol. H_2O, EtOH, AcOEt, C_6H_6. Insol. Et_2O, $CHCl_3$.

Isopropiodide : cryst. from EtOH. M.p. 114–15°. Sol. H_2O, EtOH, AcOEt. Insol. Et_2O.

Phenochloride : needles. M.p. 105–6°. Very sol. H_2O. Sol. EtOH. Insol. Et_2O.

Phenobromide : m.p. 155°.

Pheniodide : pale yellow cryst. M.p. 207°.

Picrate : yellow needles. M.p. 165–6°.

Styphnate : cryst. from EtOH. M.p. 184·5–185·5°.

Ma, Hsia, Sah, *Chem. Abstracts*, 1934, **28**, 3692.
Ferns, Lapworth, *J. Chem. Soc.*, 1912, **101**, 283.
Decker, Kaufmann, *J. prakt. Chem.*, 1911, **84**, 436.

Pyridine-betaine (*Anhydride or lactone of N-carboxymethylpyridinium hydroxide*)

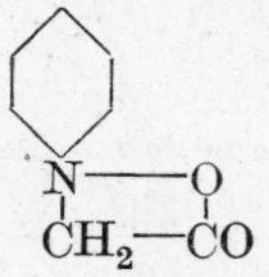

$C_7H_7O_2N$ MW, 137

Hygroscopic plates + $1H_2O$. Anhyd. at 100°. M.p. 150° decomp. Very sol. H_2O, hot EtOH. Insol. Et_2O.

B₂,HCl,H₂O : prisms from EtOH. M.p. 159° decomp. Very sol. H_2O. Insol. EtOH, Et_2O.

B,HCl : plates from H_2O or EtOH. M.p. 202–5°. Very sol. H_2O. Sol. hot EtOH. Spar. sol. cold EtOH. Insol. Et_2O.

B₂,HBr,H₂O : plates or prisms from EtOH. Decomp. at 170°.

B,HBr : plates from EtOH.Aq. Decomp. at 198–200°.

B₂,HI : needles from EtOH. Blackens at 175–80°. M.p. 250–2° decomp. Very sol. H_2O. Sol. warm EtOH. Insol. Et_2O.

B₂,H₂SO₄ : plates. Decomp. at 175°.

B,HNO₃ : plates from EtOH.Aq. M.p. 145° decomp.

B₂,H₂PtCl₆ : orange-red cryst. M.p. 215°. Sol. H_2O. Insol. EtOH.

Chloroaurate : m.p. 165°.

B,AgNO₃ : plates. Decomp. at 171·5°.

B₂,(HgCl₂)₄,HCl : plates + $1H_2O$ from H_2O. M.p. 134°.

Picrate : yellow prisms from EtOH.Aq. M.p. 142–3°.

Chattaway, Garton, *J. Chem. Soc.*, 1924, **125**, 187.
Krüger, *J. prakt. Chem.*, 1891, **43**, 287.
Vongerichten, *Ber.*, 1882, **15**, 1251.

Pyridine-carboxylic Acid.

See Picolinic Acid, Nicotinic Acid, *and* Isonicotinic Acid.

Pyridine-choline (N-β-*Hydroxyethylpyridinium hydroxide*)

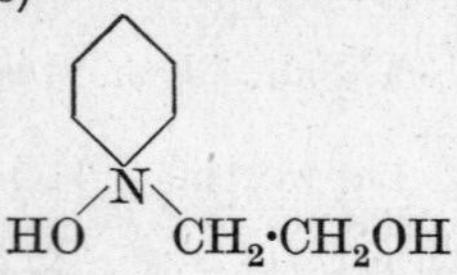

$C_7H_{11}O_2N$ MW, 141

Chloride: β-hydroxyethylpyridinium chloride. $C_7H_{10}ONCl$. MW, 159·5. Hygroscopic prisms from EtOH. Very sol. H_2O, EtOH. Insol. Et_2O. $Ag_2O \longrightarrow$ free base. $CrO_3 \longrightarrow$ pyridine-betaine hydrochloride. *B,AuCl$_3$*: needles or plates. M.p. 117°. Very sol. boiling H_2O. *B$_2$,PtCl$_4$*: orange-yellow plates from EtOH. M.p. 179°. Very sol. H_2O. Insol. cold EtOH.

Schmidt, *Arch. Pharm.*, 1913, **251**, 205.

Pyridine-2 : 3-dicarboxylic Acid.
See Quinolinic Acid.
Pyridine-2 : 4-dicarboxylic Acid.
See Lutidinic Acid.
Pyridine-2 : 5-dicarboxylic Acid.
See Isocinchomeronic Acid.
Pyridine-2 : 6-dicarboxylic Acid.
See Dipicolinic Acid.
Pyridine-3 : 4-dicarboxylic Acid.
See Cinchomeronic Acid.
Pyridine-3 : 5-dicarboxylic Acid.
See Dinicotinic Acid.

Pyridine-neurine (N-*Vinylpyridinium hydroxide*)

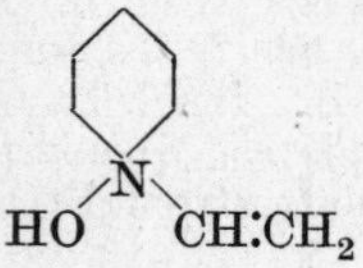

C_7H_9ON MW, 123

Chloride: vinylpyridinium chloride. C_7H_8NCl. MW, 141·5. *B,AuCl$_3$*: yellow needles from H_2O. M.p. 178°. *B$_2$,PtCl$_4$*: yellowish-red plates from H_2O. M.p. 193° decomp.

Schmidt, *Arch. Pharm.*, 1913, **251**, 206.

Pyridine-2-sulphonic Acid

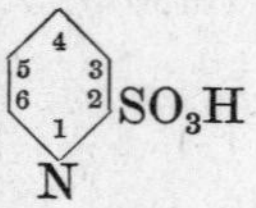

$C_5H_5O_3NS$ MW, 159

Needles from EtOH. M.p. 247–8°. Very sol. H_2O.

NH$_4$ salt: m.p. 274–5°.

Ag salt: yellow cryst. from H_2O. M.p. 290° decomp. Very sol. hot H_2O.

Plazek, Marcinków, *Chem. Abstracts*, 1935, **29**, 2535.
Gastel, Wibaut, *Rec. trav. chim.*, 1934, **53**, 1031.
Marckwald, Klemm, Trabert, *Ber.*, 1900, **33**, 1560.

Pyridine-3-sulphonic Acid.

Needles or plates. M.p. 357°. Very sol. H_2O. Spar. sol. EtOH. Insol. Et_2O. Dry dist. $\longrightarrow$ 3 : 3′-dipyridyl. KOH fusion $\longrightarrow$ 3-hydroxypyridine.

NH$_4$ salt: cryst. M.p. 243°.

Betaine: $C_6H_7O_3NS$. MW, 173. Cryst. from H_2O. M.p. 130°.

See second reference above and also
I.G., F.P., 685,062, (*Chem. Abstracts*, 1930, **24**, 5307).
Fischer, *Ber.*, 1882, **15**, 62.

Pyridine-4-sulphonic Acid.

Needles from EtOH. M.p. 134–5°.

Koenigs, Kinne, *Ber.*, 1921, **54**, 1357.

Pyridine-2 : 3 : 4-tricarboxylic Acid (*Carbocinchomeronic acid*)

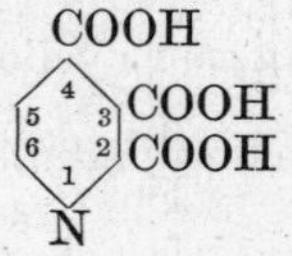

$C_8H_5O_6N$ MW, 211

Cryst. + $1\frac{1}{2}H_2O$ from H_2O. M.p. anhyd. 249–50° (rapid heat.). Sol. hot H_2O. Mod. sol. hot EtOH. Insol. Et_2O, C_6H_6. Heat at 170–80° or boiling AcOH $\longrightarrow$ cinchomeronic acid.

Tri-Me ester: $C_{11}H_{11}O_6N$. MW, 253. Needles. M.p. 102°. *Hydrochloride*: m.p. 68°.

3 : 4-*Di-Et ester*: $C_{12}H_{13}O_6N$. MW, 267. M.p. 118°. Sol. most ord. org. solvents. *Hydrochloride*: m.p. 142°.

Tri-Et ester: $C_{14}H_{17}O_6N$. MW, 295. B.p. 300–5°. *Hydrochloride*: m.p. 61°.

Mumm, Hüneke, *Ber.*, 1918, **51**, 159.
Eckert, Lorià, *Monatsh.*, 1917, **38**, 244.

Pyridine-2 : 3 : 5-tricarboxylic Acid (*Carbodinicotinic acid*).

Cryst. + $1\frac{1}{2}H_2O$ from H_2O. M.p. 323°. Sol. hot H_2O, EtOH.

Weber, *Ann.*, 1887, **241**, 11.

Pyridine-2 : 3 : 6-tricarboxylic Acid.

Needles or plates + $2H_2O$ from H_2O or EtOH.Aq. M.p. 130°. Very sol. H_2O, EtOH.Aq.

Spar. sol. EtOH, Et_2O, AcOH. Heat above m.p. ⟶ pyridine-2 : 5-dicarboxylic acid. Gives cryst. spar. sol. Ca salt.

Eckert, Lorià, *Monatsh.*, 1917, **38**, 241.
Miller, *Ber.*, 1891, **24**, 1916.

Pyridine-2 : 4 : 5-tricarboxylic Acid.
See Berberonic Acid.

Pyridine - 3 : 4 : 5 - tricarboxylic Acid. (β-*Carbocinchomeronic acid*).

Cryst. in leaflets + $3H_2O$ from H_2O. Chars at 261°. Sol. hot H_2O.

Weber, *Ann.*, 1887, **241**, 16.

Pyridinoanthracene.
See Anthraquinoline.

Pyridinoanthraquinone.
See Anthraquinolinequinone.

Pyridinostyrene.
See Stilbazole.

Pyridoin (α-*Hydroxy*-β-*keto-dipyridylethane*)

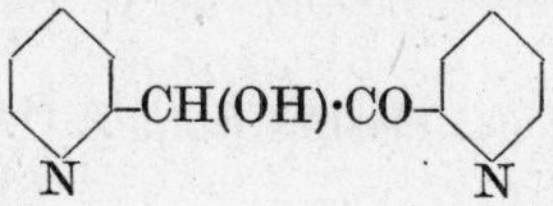

$C_{12}H_{10}O_2N_2$ MW, 214

Yellow needles from EtOH. M.p. 156°. Sol. hot EtOH, Me_2CO, AcOEt, $CHCl_3$, C_6H_6. Insol. H_2O. Dil. AcOH ⟶ red col. Reduces Fehling's.

Harries, Lénárt, *Ann.*, 1915, **410**, 108.

Pyridone.
See Hydroxypyridine.

Pyridopyridine.
See Naphthyridine.

2-Pyridylacetic Acid

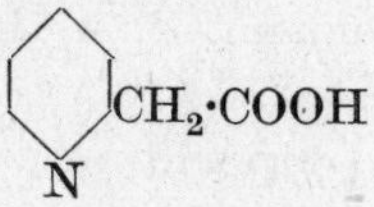

$C_7H_7O_2N$ MW, 137

Cryst. M.p. 98°. Boiling aq. sol. ⟶ α-picoline.

Me ester : $C_8H_9O_2N$. MW, 151. B.p. 123°/12 mm.

Anilide : m.p. 134°.

Picrate : m.p. 142°.

Oparina, *Chem. Zentr.*, 1935, I, 2536.

2-α-Pyridylacrylic Acid

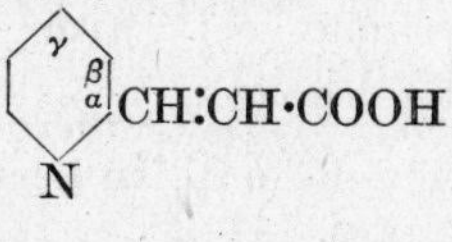

$C_8H_7O_2N$ MW, 149

Needles from H_2O. M.p. 202–3° decomp. Very sol. EtOH. Insol. cold H_2O. Red. ⟶ 2-α-pyridylpropionic acid.

Me ester : $C_9H_9O_2N$. MW, 163. *B,HCl* : cryst. from MeOH. M.p. 185–6°.

Et ester : $C_{10}H_{11}O_2N$. MW, 177. F.p. 4°. B.p. 161°/25 mm. *B,HAuCl₄* : yellow needles. M.p. 149°. *B₂,H₂PtCl₆* : yellow needles. M.p. 114°.

B,HCl : cryst. from EtOH. M.p. 220° decomp.

B,HBr : cryst. from AcOH. M.p. 222–3°.

B,HAuCl₄ : yellow needles from H_2O. M.p. 194–5°.

B₂,H₂PtCl₆ : reddish-yellow prisms. M.p. 213° decomp.

Methobromide : cryst. from AcOH. M.p. 242°. Very sol. H_2O. Spar. sol. AcOH. Insol. EtOH.

Methiodide : yellow needles from EtOH.Aq. M.p. 219–20° decomp.

Einhorn, *Ann.*, 1891, **265**, 221.
Einhorn, Liebrecht, *Ber.*, 1887, **20**, 1593.

2-γ-Pyridylacrylic Acid.

Reddish-brown cryst. from AcOEt. M.p. 296° decomp. Very sol. acids, alkalis. Spar. sol. H_2O. $KMnO_4$ ⟶ isonicotinic acid.

B,HCl : brown cryst. + $1H_2O$. M.p. 243–4°. Very sol. H_2O. Sol. EtOH. Spar. sol. Et_2O.

Acetate : cryst. from AcOH. M.p. 287–8°.

B,HAuCl₄ : yellow needles. M.p. 235° decomp. Spar. sol. H_2O, EtOH. Insol. Et_2O.

Alberts, Bachmann, *J. Am. Chem. Soc.*, 1935, **57**, 1285.
Rabe, Kindler, *Ber.*, 1919, **52**, 1842.

Pyridylamine.
See Aminopyridine.

Pyridylbenzene.
See Phenylpyridine.

2-Pyridylcarbinol (ω-*Hydroxy*-α-*picoline*, 2-*hydroxymethylpyridine*)

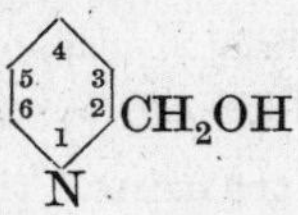

C_6H_7ON MW, 109

Viscous oil with odour of pyridine. B.p. 112–13°/16 mm. Misc. with H_2O and most org. solvents.

B₂,H₂PtCl₆ : reddish-yellow needles from EtOH. M.p. 179° decomp. Very sol. H_2O. Spar. sol. EtOH.

Picrate: yellow cryst. from EtOH. M.p. 159°. Spar. sol. cold EtOH.

Harries, Lénárt, *Ann.*, 1915, **410**, 107.

3-Pyridylcarbinol (ω-*Hydroxy-β-picoline, 3-hydroxymethylpyridine*).

B,HAuCl$_4$: yellow needles from H_2O. M.p. 136–7°.

B$_2$*,H*$_2$*PtCl*$_6$: brownish-red plates + $1H_2O$ from H_2O. M.p. 193–5°.

Picrate: yellow needles from H_2O. M.p. 128°. Very sol. boiling H_2O, Me_2CO.

Dehnel, *Ber.*, 1900, **33**, 3498.

Pyridyl-2 : 6-diacetic Acid (2 : 6-*Di-[carboxymethyl]-pyridine*)

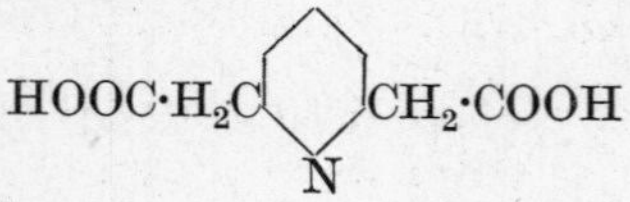

$C_9H_9O_4N$ MW, 195

Cryst. + $1H_2O$. M.p. 140°.

Di-Me ester: $C_{11}H_{13}O_4N$. MW, 223. M.p. 64°.

Dianilide: m.p. 198°. *B*$_2$*,H*$_2$*PtCl*$_6$: M.p. 216°.

Oparina, *Chem. Zentr.*, 1935, I, 2536.

Pyridylethylene.
See Vinylpyridine.

Pyridyl Mercaptan.
See Mercaptopyridine.

Pyridyl-2-nitramine (N-*Nitro-2-amino-pyridine, 2-nitraminopyridine*)

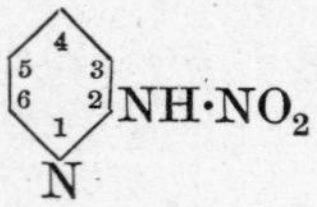

$C_5H_5O_2N_3$ MW, 139

Needles from H_2O. Decomp. at 184°. Sol. EtOH, hot H_2O, AcOEt. Sol. dil. alkalis. Spar. sol. strong min. acids. Insol. C_6H_6, ligroin.

Tschitschibabin, Rasorenow, *J. Russ. Phys.-Chem. Soc.*, 1915, **47**, 1290.

Pyridyl-3-nitramine (N-*Nitro-3-amino-pyridine, 3-nitraminopyridine*).

Small needles from H_2O. Decomp. at 170–5°. Sol. hot H_2O. Insol. C_6H_6. Aq. sol. reacts acid to litmus, neutral to Congo Red. Sol. dil. min. acids.

Tschitschibabin, Kirssanow, *Ber.*, 1927, **60**, 2435.

2-[2-Pyridyl]-piperidine (2-[2-*Piperidyl*] *pyridine*)

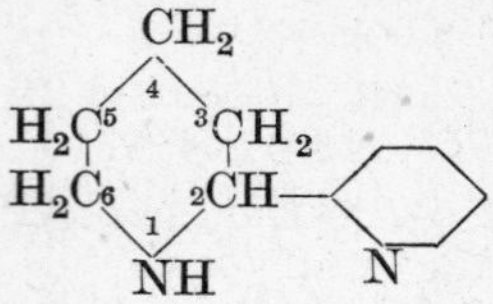

$C_{10}H_{14}N_2$ MW, 16

B.p. 265–6°/756 mm. Sol. H_2O, org. solvents

Picrate: prisms from H_2O. M.p. 187°.

Smith, *J. Am. Chem. Soc.*, 1931, **53**, 281

3-[2-Pyridyl]-piperidine.
See Isoneonicotine.

2-[3-Pyridyl]-piperidine.
See Anabasine.

3-[3-Pyridyl]-piperidine.
See Nicotidine.

4-[3-Pyridyl]-piperidine (3-[4-*Piperidyl*] *pyridine*).

Oil.

Picrate: long needles from H_2O. M.p. 240° slight decomp.

Smith, *J. Am. Chem. Soc.*, 1931, **53**, 282

1-[4-Pyridyl]-piperidine (4-[1-*Piperidyl*] *pyridine*).

Yellow cryst. M.p. 80°. B.p. 164°/13 mm Sol. EtOH, Et_2O, $CHCl_3$, C_6H_6, dil. min. acids Volatile in steam. Sublimes in vacuo at low temps.

B,HAuCl$_4$: orange plates. M.p. 161–3°.

Picrate: leaflets. M.p. 142°.

Methiodide: yellow cryst. from MeOH. M.p 159°.

Graf, Lehmann, *J. prakt. Chem.*, 1933, **138**, 242.

4-[4-Pyridyl]-piperidine.
See Isonicotine.

1-[2-Pyridyl]-pyrrole

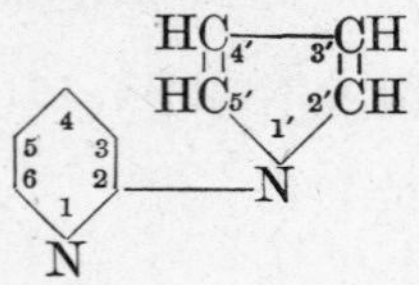

$C_9H_8N_2$ MW, 144

M.p. 17°. B.p. 250°/748 mm., 123°/11 mm. Gives intense blue col. with pine splinter moistened with HCl.

Chloroplatinate: yellow microcryst. powder + $2H_2O$. Slowly decomp. on heating.

Methiodide: m.p. 141–2°.

Picrate : m.p. 143°.

Tschitschibabin, Bylinkin, *Ber.*, 1923, **56**, 1745.
Wibaut, Dingemanse, *Chem. Abstracts*, 1923, **17**, 3873.

2-[2-Pyridyl]-pyrrole.
Cryst. from ligroin. M.p. 90° (87–8°). Intense blue col. with pine splinter moistened with HCl.
Methiodide : m.p. 188°.
Picrate : yellow cryst. M.p. 221° (143°).
N-*Me* : *see* 2 : 2′-Nicotyrine.

See first reference above and also
Wibaut, *Chem. Abstracts*, 1927, **21**, 3362.
Wibaut, *Rec. trav. chim.*, 1926, **45**, 657.

3-[2-Pyridyl]-pyrrole.
M.p. 132°.
Methiodide : m.p. 146°.
Picrate : m.p. 193°.

See last two references above.

2-[3-Pyridyl]-pyrrole (*Nornicotyrine*).
Needles from ligroin-C_6H_6. M.p. 100–2°. Very sol. EtOH, Et_2O, $CHCl_3$, C_6H_6. Spar. sol. ligroin, H_2O. EtOH, Et_2O sols. show blue fluor. $FeCl_3$ ⟶ orange-red col. Gives cryst. K salt.
B,HgCl₂ : m.p. 178–9°.
B₂,H₂PtCl₆ : yellow needles + $2H_2O$ from H_2O. Decomp. at 150°.
Methiodide : pale yellow needles from EtOH. M.p. 170–1°.
Picrate : yellow prisms from H_2O or EtOH. M.p. 202–3° (182°).
N-*Me* : *see* 3 : 2′-Nicotyrine.

Ehrenstein, *Arch. Pharm.*, 1931, **269**, 650.
Pictet, *Compt. rend.*, 1903, **137**, 861.
Pictet, Crépieux, *Ber.*, 1895, **28**, 1909.

2-[2-Pyridyl]-pyrrolidine (*α-Nornicotine*)

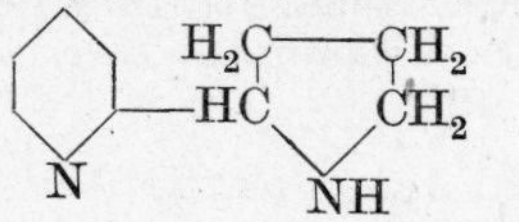

$C_9H_{12}N_2$ MW, 148

Oil. B.p. 120°/12 mm. Misc. with H_2O in all proportions. Sol. most org. solvents.
Picrate : cryst. from EtOH. M.p. 166°.
N-*Me* : α-nicotine. $C_{10}H_{14}N_2$. MW, 162. Oil. B.p. 122°/25 mm. Completely misc. with H_2O and most org. solvents. *Picrate* : cryst. from EtOH. M.p. 169°.

Craig, *J. Am. Chem. Soc.*, 1934, **56**, 1146.

2-[3-Pyridyl]-pyrrolidine.
See Nornicotine.

Pyrimidine (1 : 3-*Diazine*)

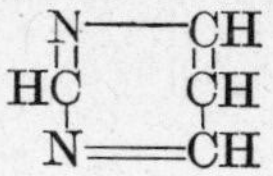

$C_4H_4N_2$ MW, 80

Cryst. mass. M.p. 21°. B.p. 123·5–124°. Misc. with H_2O ⟶ neutral sol.
B,AuCl₃ : needles. M.p. 226°.
Picrate : yellow needles. M.p. 156°.

Emery, *Ber.*, 1901, **34**, 4180.

Pyrindole.
See Indolizine.
Pyrobromone.
See under Pyramidone.
Pyrocatechol.
See Catechol.
Pyrocoll

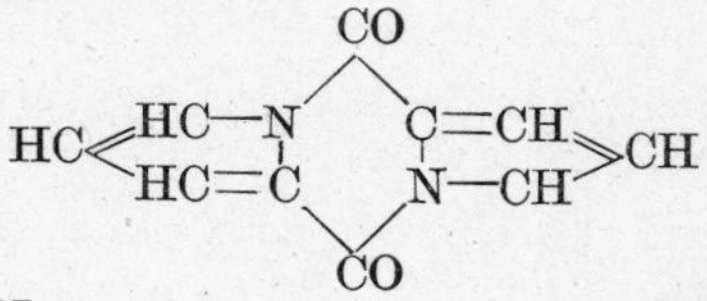

$C_{10}H_6O_2N_2$ MW, 186

From gelatine. Plates from AcOH. M.p. 268°. Sol. AcOEt, $CHCl_3$. Spar. sol. cold EtOH, Et_2O, C_6H_6, AcOH. Insol. H_2O. KOH ⟶ pyrrole-2-carboxylic acid.

Hale, Hoyt, *J. Am. Chem. Soc.*, 1916, **38**, 1065.
Ciamician, Silber, *Ber.*, 1884, **17**, 105.
Weidel, Ciamician, *Monatsh.*, 1880, **1**, 279.

Pyrogallic Acid.
See Pyrogallol.
Pyrogalline

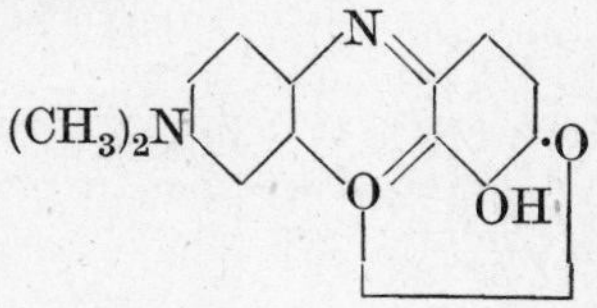

$C_{14}H_{12}O_3N_2$ MW, 256

Cryst. with greyish-green reflex from xylene. M.p. 240–1°. Sol. hot H_2O ⟶ bluish-violet sol. Sol. alkalis ⟶ reddish-violet sols. H_2SO_4 ⟶ red sol. HCl ⟶ blue sol. AcOH ⟶ blue sol.
Me ether : $C_{15}H_{14}O_3N_2$. MW, 270. Metallic green prisms from C_6H_6. M.p. 199–200°. Spar. sol. H_2O ⟶ blue sol. Gives cryst. salts with strong acids.

Kehrmann, Beyer, *Ber.*, 1912, **45**, 3341.

Pyrogallitol (1 : 2 : 3-*Trihydroxycyclohexane, hexahydropyrogallol*)

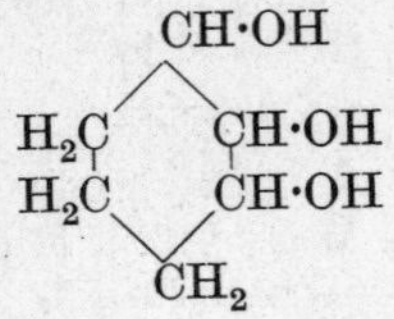

$C_6H_{12}O_3$ MW, 132

Three forms are known :

α-.
Needles from AcOEt or Me_2CO. M.p. 108°.
Tribenzoyl : needles from EtOH. M.p. 142°.

β-.
Cryst. from AcOEt. M.p. 124–5°.
Tribenzoyl : cryst. from AcOH. M.p. 184°.

γ-.
Cryst. from AcOH. M.p. 148°.
Tribenzoyl : cryst. from EtOH. M.p. 142°.

Lindemann, de Lange, *Ann.*, 1930, **483**, 31.

Pyrogallol (*Pyrogallic acid*, 1 : 2 : 3-*trihydroxybenzene*)

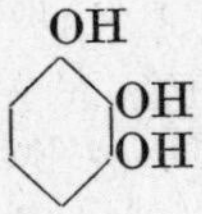

$C_6H_6O_3$ MW, 126

Plates and needles. M.p. 132·5–133·5°. B.p. 309°, 171·5°/12 mm. Sol. 2·25 parts.H_2O at 13°. Sol. EtOH, Et_2O. Bitter taste. Heat of comb. 639 Cal. Rapidly absorbs O, turning brown. Reduces Pt, Au, Ag, Hg salts. Aq. sol. + Pd or enzymes ⟶ purpurogallin. Aq. sol. + $(NH_4)_2CO_3$ ⟶ pyrogallol-4-carboxylic acid and pyrogallol-4 : 6-dicarboxylic acid. Red. ⟶ 1 : 2 : 3-cyclohexantriol. CH_3COCl ⟶ triacetyl deriv. Alk. sol. + $FeCl_3$ ⟶ deep red col. H·CHO + HCl ⟶ bright red col., ppt. on boiling. Used as developer in photography, in medicine, and for gas analysis. Is a blood poison.

Monoacetyl : viscous oil. B.p. 185°/25 mm.
Diacetyl : m.p. 110–11°. Sol. alkalis.
Triacetyl : m.p. 165°.
Monobenzoyl : prisms from AcOH or $CHCl_3$. M.p. 140°. Very sol. EtOH, Et_2O. Insol. H_2O. $FeCl_3$ ⟶ green col.
Dibenzoyl : needles from toluene. M.p. 108°. Very sol. EtOH, Et_2O. Insol. H_2O. No col. with $FeCl_3$.
Tribenzoyl : prisms from EtOH. M.p. 89–90°.
Tri-phenylurethane : needles from EtOH–Et_2O. M.p. 173°. Very sol. EtOH. Spar. sol. Et_2O, $CHCl_3$, C_6H_6.
Tri-diphenylurethane : m.p. 211·5–212·5°.
Tricinnamoyl : cryst. from EtOH. M.p. 136°.
$C_6H_6O_3,C_6H_3(NO_2)_3$-1 : 3 : 5 : yellow needles. M.p. 163°.
1-*Me ether* : $C_7H_8O_3$. MW, 140. Needles. M.p. 38–41°. B.p. 129°/10 mm. *Diacetyl* : plates from EtOH. M.p. 91–3°. Spar. sol. EtOH. *Dibenzoyl* : cryst. from EtOH. M.p. 156–8°.
2-*Me ether* : cryst. from C_6H_6. M.p. 85–7°. B.p. 154–5°/24 mm. *Diacetyl* : plates from EtOH. M.p. 51–4°.
1 : 2-*Di-Me ether* : $C_8H_{10}O_3$. MW, 154. Clear oil. B.p. 233–4°, 124–5°/17 mm. *Benzoyl* : needles from pet. ether. M.p. 55–7°.
1 : 3-*Di-Me ether* : prisms from H_2O. M.p. 55–6°. B.p. 262–7°. Sol. 57 parts H_2O at 13°. *Acetyl* : cryst. from EtOH.Aq. M.p. 53·5°. *Benzoyl* : prisms. M.p. 118°.
Tri-Me ether : $C_9H_{12}O_3$. MW, 168. Needles from EtOH.Aq. M.p. 47°. B.p. 241°. D_{45}^{45} 1·1118. Very sol. EtOH, Et_2O, C_6H_6. $C_9H_{12}O_3,C_6H_3(NO_2)_3$-1 : 3 : 5 : yellow prisms. M.p. 81°.
Mono-Et ether : $C_8H_{10}O_3$. MW, 154. Needles. M.p. 95° (102–4°). Very sol. EtOH, Et_2O. Spar. sol. cold H_2O, C_6H_6.
1 : 3-*Di-Et ether* : $C_{10}H_{14}O_3$. MW, 182. Needles. M.p. 79–80°. B.p. 263–5°. Very sol. C_6H_6. Spar. sol. cold EtOH.Aq.
Tri-Et ether : $C_{12}H_{18}O_3$. MW, 210. Cryst. from EtOH.Aq. M.p. 39°. Insol. alkalis.
Triallyl ether : m.p. 3·5–4°. D_4^{20} 1·04. n_D^{20} 1·5265.

Marks, E.P., 140,694, (*Chem. Abstracts*, 1920, **14**, 2203).
Ullmann, *Ann.*, 1903, **327**, 116.
Einhorn, Hollandt, *Ann.*, 1898, **301**, 106.
Luynes, Esperandieu, *Compt. rend.*, 1865, **61**, 487.

Pyrogallol-dicarboxylic Acid.
See 4 : 5 : 6-Trihydroxyisophthalic Acid *and* 3 : 4 : 5-Trihydroxyphthalic Acid.

Pyroglutamic Acid.
See Glutiminic Acid.

Pyroguaiacin (6-*Hydroxy*-7-*methoxy*-2 : 3-*dimethylnaphthalene*)

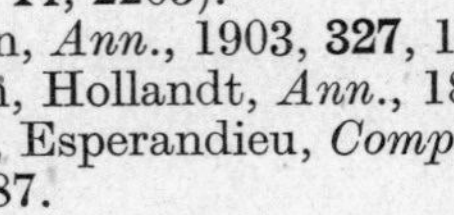

$C_{13}H_{14}O_2$ MW, 202

Plates from EtOH. M.p. 183°. Mod. sol. Et_2O. Spar. sol. boiling H_2O, EtOH. Sublimes.

Zn dust. dist. ⟶ 2 : 3-dimethylnaphthalene. H_2SO_4 ⟶ dark blue col. Gives cryst. Na and K salts.

Acetyl: needles from EtOH. M.p. 122–4°.

Benzoyl: cryst. from AcOH. M.p. 179°.

6-*Me ether*: 6 : 7-dimethoxy-2 : 3-dimethylnaphthalene. $C_{14}H_{16}O_2$. MW, 216. Plates from EtOH or formic acid, needles from ligroin. M.p. 149–50°. Spar. sol. EtOH, formic acid. Ox. ⟶ 6 : 7-dimethoxy-2 : 3-dimethyl-1 : 4-naphthoquinone. *Picrate*: red needles from MeOH. M.p. 130–1°.

Haworth, Mavin, *J. Chem. Soc.*, 1932, 1488.
Schroeter, Lichtenstadt, Irineu, *Ber.*, 1918, **51**, 1604.

Pyrohypaconitine.
See under Hypaconitine.

Pyroiodone.
See under Pyramidone.

Pyromeconic Acid (3-*Hydroxy-γ-pyrone*)

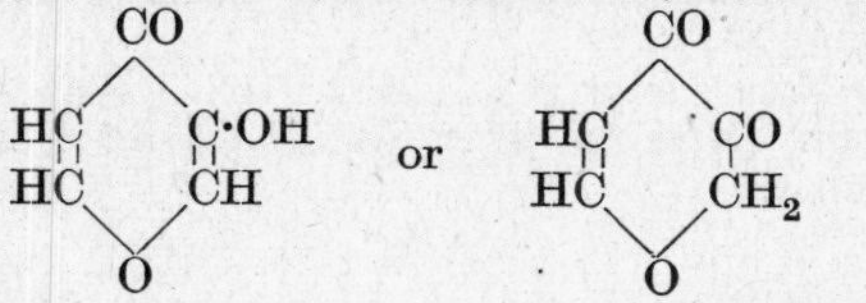

$C_5H_4O_3$ MW, 112

Colourless prisms from H_2O or EtOH. M.p. 117°. B.p. 227–8°. Very sol. H_2O, EtOH. Sol. $CHCl_3$. Spar. sol. Et_2O. Possesses slight acid properties. Sublimes. $FeCl_3$ ⟶ blood-red col. Forms unstable salts decomp. by H_2O. Does not combine with hydroxylamine. Gives cryst., spar. sol. ferric salt. Gives unstable hydrochloride. Red. ⟶ 3 : 4-dihydroxytetrahydropyran.

Acetyl: prisms from EtOH. M.p. 91°. Very sol. H_2O, EtOH, $CHCl_3$. No col. with $FeCl_3$.

Me ether: $C_6H_6O_2$. MW, 126. Cryst. from C_6H_6–ligroin. M.p. 85°. Sol. boiling ligroin. Very sol. cold H_2O, hot C_6H_6, Et_2O. Sublimes in vacuo.

Et ether: $C_7H_8O_3$. MW, 140. Colourless oil. B.p. 220–1°.

Borsche, *Ber.*, 1916, **49**, 2544.
Ost, *J. prakt. Chem.*, 1879, **19**, 183.

Pyromellitic Acid (*Benzene*-1 : 2 : 4 : 5-*tetracarboxylic acid*)

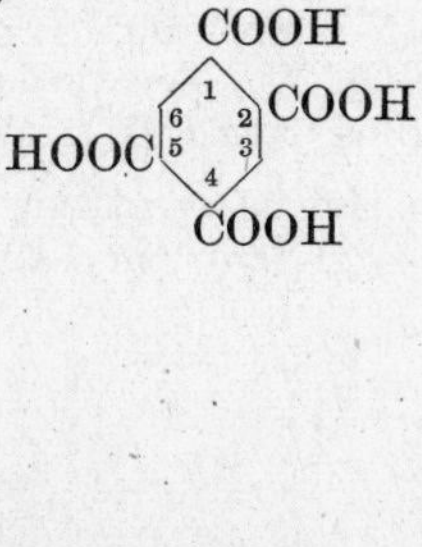

$C_{10}H_6O_8$ MW, 254

Prisms + $2H_2O$ from H_2O. M.p. anhyd. 275°.

1 : 4-*Di-Me ester*: $C_{12}H_{10}O_8$. MW, 282. M.p. 176–7°.

Tetra-Me ester: $C_{14}H_{14}O_8$. MW, 310. Leaflets from MeOH. M.p. 141·5°.

Tetra-Et ester: $C_{18}H_{22}O_8$. MW, 366. M.p. 54°.

Di-anhydride: $C_{10}H_2O_6$. MW, 218. Needles. M.p. 286°. Sol. Me_2CO, AcOEt. Insol. Et_2O, $CHCl_3$, ligroin. Sublimes.

Philippi, Thelen, *Organic Syntheses*, 1930, X, 90.
v. Braun, Lemke, *Ber.*, 1924, **57**, 682.
de Diesbach, Guhl, *Helv. Chim. Acta*, 1927, **10**, 448.
Schroeter, *Ber.*, 1924, **57**, 2023.
Fieser, Herschberg, *J. Am. Chem. Soc.*, 1935, **57**, 1508.
I.G., D.R.P., 563,129, (*Chem. Abstracts*, 1933, **27**, 1008).
Feist, *Ber.*, 1911, **44**, 137.
Silberrad, *J. Chem. Soc.*, 1906, **89**, 1795.

Pyromucic Acid (*Furan-2-carboxylic acid*, *α-furoic acid*)

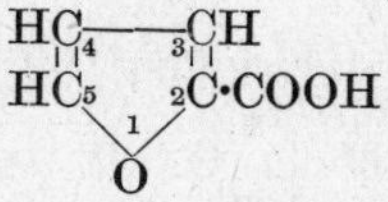

$C_5H_4O_3$ MW, 112

Leaflets from H_2O. M.p. 133–4°. B.p. 230–2°, 141–4°/20 mm. Part. sublimes at 100°, easily at 130–40°/50–60 mm. Sol. to 2·7% in H_2O at 0°. Sol. 28 parts H_2O at 15°, 4 parts at boil. Sol. EtOH, Et_2O. $k = 7{\cdot}6\ (7{\cdot}07) \times 10^{-4}$ at 25°. Heat of comb. C_v 494·4 Cal. At 275° under press. quantitatively ⟶ furan + CO_2. MnO_2 + conc. HCl ⟶ mucochloric acid.

Me ester: $C_6H_6O_3$. MW, 126. B.p. 181·3°. $D_4^{21\cdot4}$ 1·1786. n_D^{20} 1·4860.

Et ester: $C_7H_8O_3$. MW, 140. Leaflets. M.p. 34°. B.p. 195°/766 mm., 128°/95 mm. $D_4^{20\cdot8}$ 1·1174, D_4^{40} 1·0974. $n_D^{20\cdot8}$ 1·4797.

Propyl ester: $C_8H_{10}O_3$. MW, 154. B.p. 210·9°. $D_4^{25\cdot9}$ 1·0745. $n_D^{25\cdot9}$ 1·4737.

Isopropyl ester: b.p. 198·6°. $D_4^{23\cdot7}$ 1·0655. $n_D^{23\cdot7}$ 1·4682.

Butyl ester: $C_9H_{12}O_3$. MW, 168. B.p. 83–4°/1 mm. D_4^{20} 1·0555.

Isobutyl ester: b.p. 220·8–222·6°. $D_4^{27\cdot5}$ 1·0383. $n_D^{27\cdot5}$ 1·4676.

n-*Amyl ester*: $C_{10}H_{14}O_3$. MW, 182. B.p. 95–7°/1 mm. D_4^{20} 1·0335.

n-*Hexyl ester*: $C_{11}H_{16}O_3$. MW, 196. B.p. 105–7°/1 mm. D_4^{20} 1·0170.

n-*Heptyl ester*: $C_{12}H_{18}O_3$. MW, 210. B.p. 116–17°/1 mm. D_4^{20} 1·0005.

Phenyl ester: $C_{11}H_8O_3$. MW, 188. Prisms from EtOH. M.p. 42°.

p-*Nitrobenzyl ester*: cryst. from 70% EtOH. M.p. 133·5°.

Anhydride: $C_{10}H_6O_5$. MW, 206. Needles from EtOH. M.p. 73°. B.p. 325° part. decomp.

Chloride: $C_5H_3O_2Cl$. MW, 130·5. M.p. — 2°. B.p. 173°, 66°/10 mm. Stable to H_2O.

Amide: $C_5H_5O_2N$. MW, 111. M.p. 142–3°. Part. sublimes at 100°.

Methylamide: $C_6H_7O_2N$. MW, 125. Cryst. from ligroin. M.p. 64°. B.p. 250–3°.

Ethylamide: $C_7H_9O_2N$. MW, 139. B.p. 258°.

Nitrile: C_5H_3ON. MW, 93. B.p. 146°/738 mm. D_4^{20} 1·0822. n_D^{20} 1·4798.

Anilide: prisms from C_6H_6. M.p. 123·5°.

o-*Toluidide*: prisms from EtOH. M.p. 62°.

m-*Toluidide*: prisms from EtOH. M.p. 87°.

p-*Toluidide*: prisms from EtOH. M.p. 107·5°.

Wilson, *Organic Syntheses*, Collective Vol. I, 270.
Gennari, *Gazz. chim. ital.*, 1894, **24**, ii, 249.
Hughes, Johnson, *J. Am. Chem. Soc.*, 1931, **53**, 744.
Trickey, Miner, U.S.P., 1,665,236, (*Chem. Abstracts*, 1928, **22**, 1783).
Zanetti, Beckmann, *J. Am. Chem. Soc.*, 1926, **48**, 1068.

Pyromucylacetic Acid.
See α-Furoylacetic Acid.

Pyromucylformic Acid.
See α-Furoylformic Acid.

α-Pyrone.
See Coumalin.

γ-Pyrone

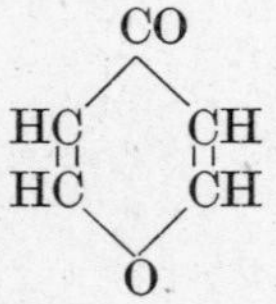

$C_5H_4O_2$ MW, 96

Hygroscopic cryst. M.p. 32·5°. B.p. 215°, 105°/23 mm., 97°/13 mm. Very sol. H_2O, Et_2O, $CHCl_3$, AcOH. Sol. C_6H_6. Spar. sol. pet. ether, CS_2. Sol. KOH.Aq. with yellow col. Non-volatile in steam. NH_3 at 120–40° ⟶ 4-hydroxypyridine.

$C_5H_4O_2,HCl$: prisms from EtOH. M.p. 139°.

$C_5H_4O_2,(COOH)_2$: plates. M.p. 136·5°.

$3C_5H_4O_2,(COOH)_2$: prisms. M.p. 139°.

$3C_5H_4O_2,HAuCl_4$: leaflets. M.p. 116·5°.

Picrate: needles from H_2O or EtOH. M.p. 129°.

Willstätter, Pummerer, *Ber.*, 1904, **37**, 3745; 1905, **38**, 1465.
Ost, *J. prakt. Chem.*, 1884, **29**, 63.

α-Pyrone-5-carboxylic Acid.
See Coumalic Acid.

α-Pyrone-6-carboxylic Acid

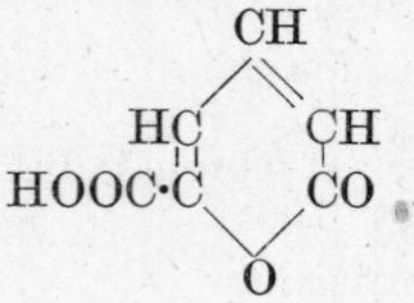

$C_6H_4O_4$ MW, 140

Prisms from H_2O. M.p. 228°. Sublimes in needles. Spar. sol. EtOH, Me_2CO, hot H_2O. Insol. $CHCl_3$, C_6H_6, pet. ether. Reduces $NH_3.AgNO_3$.

Et ester: $C_8H_8O_4$. MW, 168. Plates from ligroin. M.p. 59–60°. Sol. H_2O and most org. solvents.

Lapworth, *J. Chem. Soc.*, 1901, **79**, 1280.
Gault, *Compt. rend.*, 1914, **159**, 73.

γ-Pyrone-2-carboxylic Acid.
See Comanic Acid.

γ-Pyrone-2 : 6-dicarboxylic Acid.
See Chelidonic Acid.

Pyroracemic Acid.
See Pyruvic Acid.

Pyroracemic Alcohol.
See Hydroxyacetone.

Pyroracemic Aldehyde.
See Pyruvic Aldehyde.

Pyrotartaric Acid.
See Methylsuccinic Acid.

Pyroterebic Acid (3-*Methyl*-2-*butylene*-1-*carboxylic acid*, 2-*isopropylidene-propionic acid*)

$$(CH_3)_2C{:}CH{\cdot}CH_2{\cdot}COOH$$

$C_6H_{10}O_2$ MW, 114

Oil with somewhat sharp odour. B.p. 207–8°, 111°/22 mm. Readily converted to isocaprolactone. $k = 2{\cdot}51 \times 10^{-5}$ at 25°.

Et ester: $C_8H_{14}O_2$. MW, 142. B.p. 58°/11 mm. D_4^{17} 0·9134. n_D^{17} 1·4329.

Nitrile: C_6H_9N. MW, 95. B.p. 166°, 65°/20 mm. Fuming HCl ⟶ isocaprolactone.

Anilide: needles from C_6H_6. M.p. 106°.

Fittig, Geisler, *Ann.*, 1881, **208**, 39.
Linstead, *J. Chem. Soc.*, 1929, 2506.

Pyrotritaric Acid (*Uvinic acid, 2 : 5-dimethyl-furan-3-carboxylic acid, 2 : 5-dimethyl-β-furoic acid*)

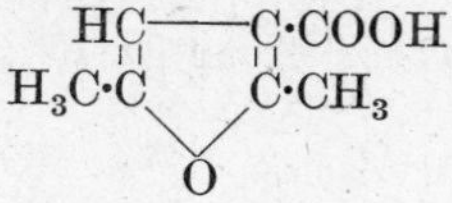

$C_7H_8O_3$ MW, 140

Needles from hot H_2O. M.p. 135°. Sol. EtOH, Et_2O. Mod. sol. hot H_2O. Sublimes. Volatile in steam. Chromic mixture $\longrightarrow CO_2 +$ $CH_3 \cdot COOH$. Dil. $HNO_3 \longrightarrow CO_2 +$ oxalic acid.

Me ester: $C_8H_{10}O_3$. MW, 154. B.p. 198°.

Et ester: $C_9H_{12}O_3$. MW, 168. Oil. B.p. 208–9°, 99–101°/14 mm., 83–5°/6 mm. $D_4^{23 \cdot 1}$ 1·0478. $n_D^{23 \cdot 1}$ 1·4686.

Hydrazide: cryst. from H_2O. M.p. 136°.

Gilman, Burtner, *Rec. trav. chim.*, 1932, **51**, 667.
Scott, Johnson, *J. Am. Chem. Soc.*, 1932, **54**, 2555.

Pyrrocoline.
See Indolizine.

Pyrrodiazole.
See 1 : 2 : 4-Triazole.

Pyrrole

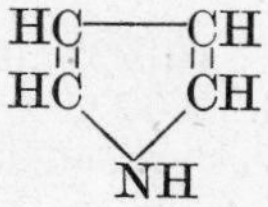

C_4H_5N MW, 67

Present in coal tar. Colourless liq. with characteristic odour. B.p. 130–1°/761 mm. D_4^{20} 0·9691. n_D^{20} 1·5085. Heat of comb. C_v 567·5 Cal. Sol. EtOH, Et_2O. Spar. sol. H_2O. Turns brown in air. Forms metallic salts. $CrO_3 +$ $H_2SO_4 \longrightarrow$ maleinimide. Polymerises with HCl to a trimer.

N-*Me*: *see N*-Methylpyrrole.

N-*Et*: C_6H_9N. MW, 95. Liq. with odour resembling pyrrole. B.p. 131°. D^{16} 0·8881. Misc. with EtOH, Et_2O.

N-*Propyl*: $C_7H_{11}N$. MW, 109. B.p. 146·5–147·5°. D_4^{20} 0·8833.

N-*Butyl*: $C_8H_{13}N$. MW, 123. B.p. 165–80°.

N-*Isoamyl*: $C_9H_{15}N$. MW, 137. B.p. 180–4°. D^{10} 0·8786.

N-*Allyl*: C_7H_9N. MW, 107. B.p. 105°/48 mm. Unstable in air. Volatile in steam.

N-*Phenyl*: *see* 1-Phenylpyrrole.

N-o-*Tolyl*: oil. B.p. 246°. Spar. sol. boiling H_2O. Volatile in steam.

N-p-*Tolyl*: leaflets from EtOH. M.p. 82°. B.p. 252°/728·5 mm. Very sol. EtOH, $CHCl_3$, C_6H_6, pet. ether. Spar. sol. boiling H_2O. Volatile in steam.

N-*Benzyl*: b.p. 245–6°, 138–9°/27 mm. Sol. EtOH, Et_2O. Insol. H_2O. Turns yellow in light and air.

N-1-*Naphthyl*: needles from EtOH.Aq. M.p. 42°. B.p. above 360°. Volatile in steam.

N-2-*Naphthyl*: cryst. from EtOH.Aq. M.p. 107°. B.p. above 360°. Volatile in steam.

N-*Formyl*: b.p. 39°/22 mm.

N-*Acetyl*: b.p. 181–2°. Insol. H_2O.

N-*Propionyl*: yellowish oil. B.p. 192–4°.

N-*Benzoyl*: yellowish oil. B.p. 276°/715 mm. Sol. EtOH, Et_2O, $CHCl_3$, AcOH, C_6H_6, pet. ether. Insol. H_2O. Volatile in steam.

Picrate: orange-red cryst. M.p. 69° decomp.

McElvain, Bolliger, *Organic Syntheses*, Collective Vol. I, 461.
Pictet, *Ber.*, 1904, **37**, 2792.
Jurjew, *Ber.*, 1936, **69**, 440.
Jurjew, Schenjan, *Chem. Zentr.*, 1936, **I**, 4293.
Fischer, Orth, *Die Chemie des Pyrrols*, Vol. I (1934).

Pyrrole-2-aldehyde (2-*Formylpyrrole*)

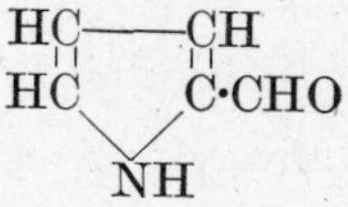

C_5H_5ON MW, 95

Prisms from pet. ether. M.p. 46–7°. B.p. 217–19°, 114°/15 mm. n_D^{16} 1·5939. Heat of comb. C_p 616·7 Cal. Volatile in steam. Does not oxidise in air.

Oxime: needles from $CHCl_3$ or C_6H_6. M.p. 164·5°.

Phenylhydrazone: needles from ligroin. M.p. 139–139·5°.

p-*Nitrophenylhydrazone*: red needles from xylene. M.p. 182·5–183°.

Semicarbazone: leaflets from H_2O. M.p. 183·5°.

N-*Me*: *see N*-Methylpyrrole-2-aldehyde.

N-*Butyl*: $C_9H_{13}ON$. MW, 151. B.p. about 75°/2 mm. *Semicarbazone*: cryst. from EtOH.Aq. M.p. 146–147·5°.

N-*Isoamyl*: $C_{10}H_{15}ON$. MW, 165. B.p. about 90°/2 mm. *Semicarbazone*: cryst. from EtOH.Aq. M.p. 155–7°.

N-*Phenyl*: m.p. 120°. Decomp. in sunlight.

N-*Benzoyl*: cryst. from ligroin. M.p. 90°.

Phenylhydrazone : greenish-yellow plates from EtOH. M.p. 154°.

Emmert, Diehl, Gollwitzer, *Ber.*, 1929, **62**, 1737.
Putochin, *Ber.*, 1926, **59**, 1992.
Emmert, Diehl, *Ber.*, 1931, **64**, 131.
Reichstein, *Helv. Chim. Acta*, 1930, **13**, 352.
Alessandri, Passerini, *Gazz. chim. ital.*, 1921, **51**, 262.

Pyrrole-*N*-carboxylic Acid (*Pyrrole*-1-*carboxylic acid*)

$$\begin{array}{c} \text{HC}_4\text{———}_3\text{CH} \\ \text{HC}_5\text{———}_2\text{CH} \\ \text{N·COOH} \end{array}$$

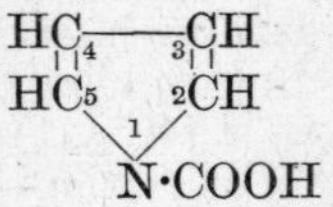

$C_5H_5O_2N$ MW, 111

Prisms from Et_2O. M.p. 95° decomp. Sol. EtOH, Et_2O. Mod. sol. $CHCl_3$. Spar. sol. H_2O, C_6H_6, ligroin. At m.p. decomp. quantitatively into pyrrole + CO_2. Resinifies with min. acids.

Et ester : $C_7H_9O_2N$. MW, 139. Liq. with characteristic odour. B.p. 180°/770 mm. Insol. H_2O.

Amide : $C_5H_6ON_2$. MW, 110. Leaflets from H_2O. M.p. 166°. Sublimes.

Tschelinzeff, Maxoroff, *Ber.*, 1927, **60**, 196.
Ciamician, Magnaghi, *Ber.*, 1885, **18**, 416.

Pyrrole-2-carboxylic Acid (*Pyrrole*-α-*carboxylic acid*).

Leaflets from H_2O. M.p. 208·5 (192°) decomp. ⟶ pyrrole + CO_2. Sol. H_2O, EtOH, Et_2O. k (acid) = $4·0 \times 10^{-5}$ at 25° : k (base) = 3×10^{-13}. Isoelectric point 2·9. The esters possess marked local anæsthetic properties.

Me ester : $C_6H_7O_2N$. MW, 125. Needles from pet. ether. M.p. 73°. B.p. 220–3°/740 mm., 120–30°/20–30 mm., 115–20°/12–16 mm. Sol. EtOH, Et_2O. Spar. sol. H_2O, pet ether.

Et ester : $C_7H_9O_2N$. MW, 139. Cryst. M.p. 39°. B.p. 230–2°. Very sol. EtOH, Et_2O, C_6H_6, pet. ether. Very spar. sol. H_2O.

Propyl ester : $C_8H_{11}O_2N$. MW, 153. B.p. 164–7°/50 mm.

Butyl ester : $C_9H_{13}O_2N$. MW, 167. M.p. 36–8°. B.p. 255–60°/740 mm.

Isobutyl ester : m.p. 68–9°. B.p. 250–5°/740 mm., 119–22°/70 mm.

Isoamyl ester : $C_{10}H_{15}O_2N$. MW, 181. B.p. 186–90°/100 mm.

Chloride : α-pyrroyl chloride. C_5H_4ONCl. MW, 127·5. Cryst. from Et_2O–ligroin. Sinters

at 110°, decomp. at higher temps. Very sol· Et_2O, $CHCl_3$. Decomp. rapidly in moist air.

Amide : $C_5H_6ON_2$. MW, 110. Plates from H_2O or EtOH. M.p. 176°. Sweet taste.

Anilide : prisms from EtOH.Aq. M.p 153–4°.

N-Me : $C_6H_7O_2N$. MW, 125. M.p. 135°. *Methylamide* : prisms. M.p. 89–90°. Volatile in steam.

N-Et : $C_7H_9O_2N$. MW, 139. Needles from H_2O. M.p. 78°. *Ethylamide* : prisms from H_2O. M.p. 43–4°. B.p. 269–70°.

N-Phenyl : see 1-Phenylpyrrole-2-carboxylic Acid.

Hydrazide : cryst. from EtOH.Aq. M.p. 231–2° decomp.

Azide : cryst. M.p. 105° decomp.

Oddo, *Chem. Abstracts*, 1925, **19**, 2492.
Blicke, Blake, *J. Am. Chem. Soc.*, 1930, **52**, 238.
Schwanert, *Ann.*, 1860, **116**, 272.
Ciamician, Silber, *Ber.*, 1884, **17**, 104, 1152.
Bell, *Ber.*, 1877, **10**, 1866.
Fischer, van Slyke, *Ber.*, 1911, **44**, 3169.
Oddo, Moschini, *Gazz. chim. ital.*, 1912, **42**, ii, 254.

Pyrrole-3-carboxylic Acid (*Pyrrole*-β-*carboxylic acid*).

Needles. M.p. 161–2° decomp. Heat in vacuo ⟶ pyrrole + CO_2.

Me ester : needles or leaflets. M.p. 129°. Sol. EtOH, Et_2O. Spar. sol. pet. ether.

Dennstedt, Zimmermann, *Ber.*, 1887, **20**, 855.
Ciamician, Silber, *Ber.*, 1884, **17**, 1438.
Oddo, Moschini, *Gazz. chim. ital.*, 1912, **42**, ii, 255.

Pyrrole-2 : 5-dicarboxylic Acid

$$\begin{array}{c} \text{HC———CH} \\ \text{HOOC·C}\quad\text{C·COOH} \\ \text{NH} \end{array}$$

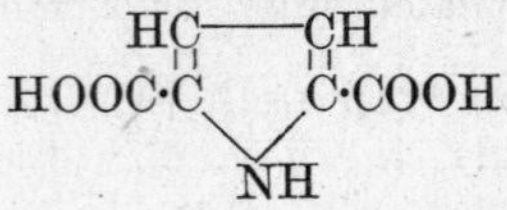

$C_6H_5O_4N$ MW, 155

Needles from EtOH.Aq. Decomp. about 260°, part. ⟶ pyrrole + CO_2. Sol. Et_2O, Me_2CO. Insol. $CHCl_3$, AcOEt, C_6H_6, pet. ether.

Me ester : $C_7H_7O_4N$. MW, 169. M.p. 243°.

Di-Me ester : $C_8H_9O_4N$. MW, 183. Needles from H_2O. M.p. 132°. Sol. EtOH, Et_2O, C_6H_6.

Di-Et ester : $C_{10}H_{13}O_4N$. MW, 211. Needles. M.p. 82°.

N-Me : $C_7H_7O_4N$. MW, 169. Cryst. from H_2O. Sinters and sublimes with part. decomp.

about 275°. *Di-Me ester*: $C_9H_{11}O_4N$. MW, 197. Needles from EtOH.Aq. M.p. 80–1°.

N-*Et*: $C_8H_9O_4N$. MW, 183. Needles from EtOH.Aq. Decomp. at 250° without melting ⟶ *N*-ethylpyrrole + CO_2. Insol. H_2O. *Diethylamide*: needles. M.p. 229–30°.

N-*Phenyl*: $C_{12}H_9O_4N$. MW, 231. Cryst. from H_2O. M.p. 235–40° ⟶ *N*-phenylpyrrole + CO_2. Sol. EtOH, Et_2O, $CHCl_3$, AcOH, C_6H_6. Insol. pet. ether.

Ciamician, Silber, *Ber.*, 1887, **20**, 2595; 1886, **19**, 1960.
Tschelinzew, Maxorow, *Chem. Zentr.*, 1923, I, 1507.
Bell, *Ber.*, 1877, **10**, 1864.

Pyrrolidine (*Tetrahydropyrrole, tetramethyleneimine*)

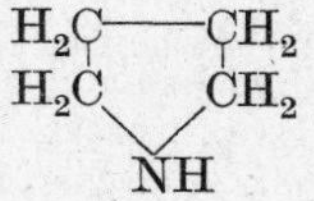

C_4H_9N MW, 71

Present in tobacco leaves. Liq. with odour resembling piperidine. B.p. 88·5–89°. $D^{22·5}$ 0·8520. n_D^{15} 1·4270. Fumes in air. Misc. with H_2O. Strongly alkaline.

B,HAuCl$_4$: yellow cryst. from H_2O. M.p. 206° decomp.

B$_2$,2HI,CdI$_2$: leaflets or needles from H_2O. M.p. 217–19° (200–2°).

B$_2$,H$_2$PtCl$_6$: orange prisms from EtOH.Aq. M.p. about 200° decomp.

Picrate: (i) *B,C$_6$H$_3$O$_7$N$_3$*: yellow needles from EtOH. M.p. 112°. (ii) *B$_2$,C$_6$H$_3$O$_7$N$_3$*: dark red cryst. M.p. 163–4°.

N-*Me*: *see N*-Methylpyrrolidine.

N-*Et*: $C_6H_{13}N$. MW, 99. B.p. 104°. D_4^{20} 0·8156. n_D^{15} 1·4113. *Picrate*: leaflets. M.p. 186°.

N-*Propyl*: $C_7H_{15}N$. MW, 113. B.p. 130°. D_4^{20} 0·8171. n_D^{20} 1·4389. Sol. H_2O. *Picrate*: m.p. 105° (101°).

N-*Butyl*: $C_8H_{17}N$. MW, 127. Slightly sol. H_2O. *Chloroaurate*: yellow leaflets from H_2O. M.p. 78°. *Picrate*: m.p. 124°.

N-*Amyl*: $C_9H_{19}N$. MW, 141. B.p. 179°, 89–94°/28 mm. D_4^{20} 0·8216. n_D 1·44276. *Chloroplatinate*: prisms from EtOH. M.p. 145°. *Picrate*: reddish-yellow needles from EtOH. M.p. 118–19°. *Methiodide*: m.p. 169–70°.

N-*Isoamyl*: b.p. 78°/32 mm. D_4^{20} 0·8137. n_D 1·43994. *Chloroaurate*: m.p. 158°.

N-*Allyl*: $C_7H_{12}N$. MW, 110. Volatile in steam and ether vapour. *Chloroaurate*: m.p. 97–8°. *Chloroplatinate*: m.p. 205°.

N-*Benzyl*: $C_{11}H_{15}N$. MW, 161. B.p. 237°. Sol. EtOH, Et_2O. Absorbs CO_2 and H_2O from the air. *B,HAuCl$_4$*: yellow prisms. M.p. 120° decomp. *B$_2$,H$_2$PtCl$_6$*: yellowish-red needles. M.p. 156° decomp. *Picrate*: m.p. 128°.

N-*Phenyl*: *see* 1-Phenylpyrrolidine.

N-*Benzoyl*: viscous liq. B.p. 190–1°/12 mm. Insol. H_2O and dil. acids. Dist. with PCl_5 ⟶ benzonitrile + 1 : 4-dichlorobutane.

N-*Nitroso*: yellow oil. B.p. 214° decomp.

N-p-*Toluenesulphonyl*: cryst. from EtOH. M.p. 123°.

Schlinck, *Ber.*, 1899, **32**, 951.
v. Braun, Beschke, *Ber.*, 1906, **39**, 4121.
Ladenburg, *Ber.*, 1887, **20**, 442.
v. Braun, *Ber.*, 1911, **44**, 1252; 1916, **49**, 2642.
de Jong, Wibaut, *Rec. trav. chim.*, 1930, **49**, 237.
Yur'ev, Shen'yan, *Chem. Abstracts*, 1935, **29**, 3335.
Ochiai, Tsuda, *Ber.*, 1934, **67**, 1017.

Pyrrolidine-2-carboxylic Acid.
See Proline.

2-Pyrrolidone (2-*Ketopyrrolidine, butyrolactam, anhydride or lactam of piperidinic acid*)

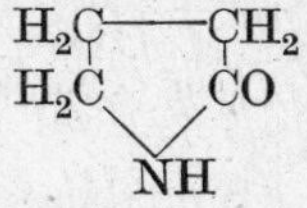

C_4H_7ON MW, 85

Cryst. from pet. ether. M.p. 24·6°. B.p. 245°, 133°/12 mm. (114°/14 mm.). D_4^{20} 1·120, D_4^{40} 1·097. Spar. volatile in steam. Aq. sol. reacts neutral to litmus. Very sol. H_2O, EtOH, Et_2O, $CHCl_3$, AcOEt, CS_2, C_6H_6. Spar. sol. pet. ether. In moist air ⟶ a monohydrate.

B,H$_2$O: plates. M.p. 35° (29·7–29·9°).

B$_2$,HCl: cryst. from Me_2CO. M.p. 86–8°.

B,HCl: cryst. from Me_2CO. M.p. 128–31°.

B$_2$,HBr: cryst. from $CHCl_3$ or Me_2CO. M.p. 135–7°.

B,HBr: cryst. M.p. 108–21°.

B$_2$,HAuCl$_4$: yellow cryst. from H_2O. M.p. 82°.

N-*Me*: *see N*-Methyl-2-pyrrolidone.

N-*Et*: $C_6H_{11}ON$. MW, 113. Oil. B.p. 218°/751 mm.

N-*Isopropyl*: $C_7H_{13}ON$. MW, 127. Oil with peppermint odour. B.p. 221–2°/736 mm. Volatile.

N-*Phenyl*: *see* 1-Phenylpyrrolidone-2.

N-p-*Tolyl*: needles from H_2O. M.p. 88·5°. B.p. 189°/13 mm.

N-*Acetyl*: b.p. 231°/737 mm.

Tafel, Stern, *Ber.*, 1900, **33**, 2226.
Gabriel, *Ber.*, 1889, **22**, 3338.
Späth, Breusch, *Monatsh.*, 1928, **50**, 356.

2-Pyrrolidone-5-carboxylic Acid.
See Glutiminic Acid.

3-Pyrroline (*Dihydropyrrole*)

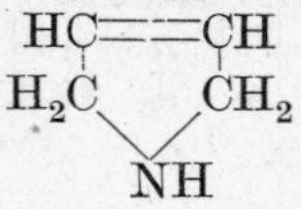

C_4H_7N MW, 69

Liq. Fumes in air. B.p. 90–1°/750·5 mm. D_4^{20} 0·9097. n_D^{20} 1·4664. Sol. H_2O. Absorbs CO_2 and H_2O from the air.

B,HCl: prisms from EtOH. M.p. 173–4°.

B,HAuCl$_4$: yellow prisms from H_2O. M.p. 152°.

B$_2$,*H*$_2$*PtCl*$_6$: orange-red cryst. from H_2O. M.p. 182°.

Picrolonate: yellow plates from EtOH. M.p. 260°.

N-*Me*: present in tobacco leaves. Oil with ammoniacal odour. B.p. 79–80°. Misc. with H_2O. *B,HAuCl*$_4$: yellow leaflets from dil. HCl. M.p. 190–1°. *Picrolonate*: yellow prisms from H_2O. M.p. 222° decomp. *Methiodide*: cryst. from EtOH. M.p. 286°.

N-2 : 4-*Dinitrophenyl*: yellow needles from EtOH. M.p. 124·5°.

N-*Benzyl*: oil. B.p. about 150°.

N-*Benzoyl*: oil. B.p. 160–1°/2 mm.

N-*Nitroso*: needles from pet. ether. M.p. 37–8°.

Treibs, Dinelli, *Ann.*, 1935, **517**, 172.
Ciamician, Dennstedt, *Ber.*, 1883, **16**, 1536.
Knorr, Rabe, *Ber.*, 1901, **34**, 3497.
Dennstedt, D.R.P., 127,086, (*Chem. Zentr.*, 1902, I, 338).

Pyrrone.
See 2 : 2′-Dipyrryl Ketone.

Pyrrotriazole.
See 1 : 2 : 3 : 4-Tetrazole.

1-Pyrrylisopropyl Alcohol.
See 2-β-Hydroxypropylpyrrole.

Pyruvic Acid (1-*Ketopropionic acid, pyroracemic acid*)

$$CH_3{\cdot}CO{\cdot}COOH$$

$C_3H_4O_3$ MW, 88

Liq. with odour resembling acetic acid. M.p. about 13·6°. B.p. 165° part. decomp., 75–80°/25 mm., 65°/10 mm. $D_4^{15\cdot3}$ 1·2668. $n_D^{15\cdot3}$ 1·43025. Misc. in all proportions with H_2O, EtOH, Et_2O. Scratched with Pt wire ⟶ a trimer, m.p 92°. Warm conc. HNO_3 ⟶ oxalic acid. CrO_3 ⟶ acetic acid. Reduces $NH_3.AgNO_3$ and $HgCl_2$. $k = 3{\cdot}2 \times 10^{-3}$ at 25°.

Oxime: 1-isonitrosopropionic acid. Decomp. at 180–1° (177°). $k = 5{\cdot}14\ (4{\cdot}7) \times 10^{-4}$ at 25°. *Acetate*: cryst. M.p. 60° decomp.

Semicarbazone: needles from H_2O. M.p. about 200° decomp.

Phenylhydrazone: needles from H_2O. M.p. 192°.

o-*Nitrophenylhydrazone*: yellow needles from EtOH. M.p. 221°.

p-*Nitrophenylhydrazone*: yellow cryst. from EtOH. M.p. 220°.

2 : 4-*Dinitrophenylhydrazone*: yellow cryst. from AcOH. M.p. 218° (213°).

p-*Bromophenylhydrazone*: yellow needles from AcOH. M.p. 184°.

m-*Nitrobenzoylhydrazone*: m.p. 185·5–186·5°.

Me ester: $C_4H_6O_3$. MW, 102. B.p. 134–7°. D^0 1·154. *Oxime*: needles from Et_2O. M.p. 69°. B.p. 122–3°/14 mm. *Oxime acetate*: m.p. 42°. B.p. 126°/14 mm. 2 : 4-*Dinitrophenylhydrazone*: m.p. 186·5–187·5°. *Di-Me acetal*: b.p. 66–66·5°/16 mm. $D_4^{17\cdot6}$ 1·0678. $n_D^{17\cdot6}$ 1·412.

Et ester: $C_5H_8O_3$. MW, 116. B.p. 155° (144°), 55°/17 mm. $D_4^{15\cdot6}$ 1·0596. $n_D^{15\cdot6}$ 1·408. *Oxime*: prisms or needles. M.p. 97°. B.p. 213° slight decomp. *Semicarbazone*: m.p. 206° decomp. *Phenylhydrazone*: two forms. (i) M.p. 117–18°. (ii) M.p. 31–2°. p-*Nitrophenylhydrazone*: yellow cryst. from EtOH. M.p. 187°. 2 : 4-*Dinitrophenylhydrazone*: yellow cryst. from dioxan–EtOH. M.p. 154·5–155°. *Di-Et acetal*: b.p. 190–1° slight decomp., 81·5–82·5°/15 mm. $D_4^{18\cdot2}$ 0·9783. $n_D^{17\cdot1}$ 1·415.

Propyl ester: $C_6H_{10}O_3$. MW, 130. B.p. 166°. *Semicarbazone*: m.p. 178°. 2 : 4-*Dinitrophenylhydrazone*: m.p. 119–20°.

d-*Amyl ester*: $C_8H_{14}O_3$. MW, 158. B.p. 185–6°. 85–6°/16 mm., 81–2°/10 mm. D_4^{18} 0·9724. n_D^{18} 1·4206. $[\alpha]_D^{15}$ + 3·25°.

Isoamyl ester: b.p. 185°, 86°/14 mm. D^{17} 0·978.

Hexadecyl ester: $C_{19}H_{36}O_3$. MW, 312. M.p. 26·5–27·5°. *Semicarbazone*: m.p. 140–1°.

Allyl ester: $C_6H_8O_3$. MW, 128. B.p. 165°, 65°/14 mm. $D_4^{17\cdot5}$ 1·082.

l-*Menthyl ester*: oil. B.p. 136–40°/22 mm., 131–2°/10 mm. $D_4^{19\cdot6}$ 0·9852. $[\alpha]_D^{20}$ − 82·00° in $CHCl_3$.

Benzyl ester: b.p. 207–8°, 103–4°/36 mm. D^{14} 1·090. *Semicarbazone*: m.p. 176°.

Amide: $C_3H_5O_2N$. MW, 87. Prisms or plates from EtOH. M.p. 124–5°. Sol. H_2O,

$CHCl_3$, hot C_6H_6. *Oxime*: plates or prisms from H_2O. M.p. 178·5° decomp. *Semicarbazone*: m.p. 230° decomp.

Nitrile: acetyl cyanide. C_3H_3ON. MW, 69. Liq. with characteristic odour. B.p. 93°. D_4^{20} 0·9745. n^{20} 1·3743. *Phenylhydrazone*: leaflets from C_6H_6. M.p. 150–1°. *Semicarbazone*: m.p. 215° decomp.

Anil: 1-phenyliminopropionic acid, anil-pyruvic acid. M.p. 127–8° decomp. Sol. H_2O, EtOH. Spar. sol. AcOEt, C_6H_6. Very spar. sol. $CHCl_3$. Sol. conc. H_2SO_4 with wine-red col.

o-*Tolylimide*: m.p. 146° decomp.

p-*Tolylimide*: m.p. 127°.

Anilide: needles from H_2O or EtOH. M.p. 104°. Sublimes. *Oxime*: yellowish plates from EtOH. M.p. 119°.

N-*Me-anilide*: cryst. from H_2O. M.p. 152–3°.

o-*Toluidide*: needles from EtOH. M.p. 70–1°.

p-*Toluidide*: plates from C_6H_6. M.p. 109°. *Oxime*: leaflets from EtOH. M.p. 130°.

Howard, Fraser, *Organic Syntheses*, Collective Vol. I, 462.
Fernbach, Strange, E.P., 14,607, (*Chem. Abstracts*, 1919, **13**, 1595).
Boehringer Sohn, D.R.P., 523,190, (*Chem. Zentr.*, 1931, II, 496).
Tschelinzeff, Schmidt, *Ber.*, 1929, **62**, 2211.

Pyruvic Alcohol.
See Hydroxyacetone.

Pyruvic Aldehyde (1-*Ketopropionaldehyde, methylglyoxal, pyroracemic aldehyde, propanalone*)

$CH_3{\cdot}CO{\cdot}CHO$

$C_3H_4O_2$ MW, 72

Yellow liq. with pungent odour. Begins to boil at 72° ⟶ a yellowish-green vapour. Liq. at room temp. is bimolecular, rapidly polymerising to an amorphous glassy mass of unknown MW. Latter at 50° ⟶ bimolecular liq. or monomolecular vap.

Oxime: *see* Isonitrosoacetone.

Dioxime: *see* Methylglyoxime.

Phenylosazone: m.p. 145° (154·8°).

Disemicarbazone: m.p. 254°.

o-*Nitrophenylhydrazone*: yellow needles from EtOH. M.p. 128°.

m-*Nitrophenylhydrazone*: pale yellow needles from EtOH. M.p. 152°.

p-*Nitrophenylhydrazone*: yellow needles from EtOH. M.p. 217°.

Di-p-*nitrophenylhydrazone*: m.p. 302–4°.

Di-2 : 4-*dinitrophenylhydrazone*: reddish-orange cryst. from $PhNO_2$. M.p. 299–300°.

Di-m-*nitrobenzoylhydrazone*: m.p. 288·5°.

Dihydrazone: cryst. from EtOH. M.p. 93–4°.

Di-Me acetal: b.p. 143–7°.

Di-Et acetal: liq. with odour resembling acetone. B.p. 161·7–161·8°/761 mm., 54–5°/13–15 mm.

Tetra-Et acetal: b.p. 192°.

Diacetate: pale yellow liq. B.p. 115–16°/13 mm.

Meisenheimer, *Ber.*, 1912, **45**, 2637.
Neuberg, Färber, Levite, Schwenk, *Biochem. Z.*, 1917, **83**, 264.
Dakin, Dudley, *J. Biol. Chem.*, 1913, **15**, 130.
Neuberg, Dalmer, *Biochem. Z.*, 1925, **162**, 488.
Fischer, Taube, *Ber.*, 1924, **57**, 1506.
Henze, Müller, *Z. physiol. Chem.*, 1933, **214**, 281.

Pyruvil (5-*Methylallantoin*)

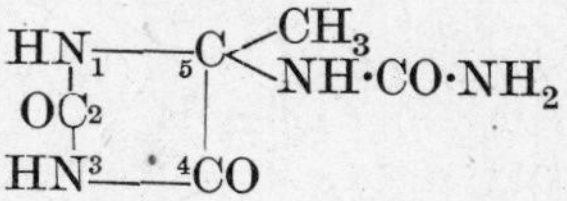

$C_5H_8O_3N_4$ MW, 172

Plates from H_2O. Insol. EtOH, Et_2O. Heat of comb. 567·7 Cal.

Davidson, *J. Am. Chem. Soc.*, 1925, **47**, 255.
Simon, *Compt. rend.*, 1901, **133**, 587.

Pyruvylformic Acid.
See Diketobutyric Acid.

Q

p-Quaterphenyl.
Benzerythrene, *q.v.*

Quebrachamine

$C_{19}H_{26}N_2$ MW, 282

Isolated from quebracho bark. Leaflets from EtOH or C_6H_6. M.p. 147°. $[\alpha]_D$ − 109·5° in Me_2CO. Weak tertiary base. Sol. Me_2CO. Mod. sol. EtOH, Et_2O, C_6H_6. Insol. H_2O.

B,H₂SO₄,2H₂O : prisms. Spar. sol. cold H_2O.

B,(COOH)₂ : prisms from EtOH. M.p. 217°.

Picrate : scarlet needles from EtOH. M.p. 195–6°.

Methiodide : cream-coloured prisms from MeOH. M.p. 234°. Sol. EtOH, Me_2CO. Insol. Et_2O, C_6H_6.

Methosulphate : prisms. M.p. 235°. Sol. EtOH. Mod. sol. H_2O.

Hesse, *Ann.*, 1882, **211**, 249.
Field, *J. Chem. Soc.*, 1924, **125**, 1444.

Quebrachine.
See Yohimbine.

Quebrachitol.
See under Inositol.

Quercetagetin (3 : 5 : 6 : 7 : 3′ : 4′-*Hexahydroxyflavone*)

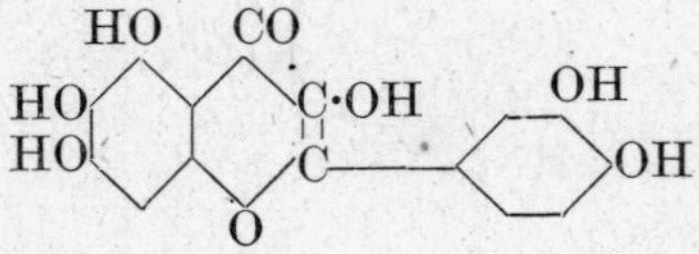

$C_{15}H_{10}O_8$ MW, 318

Isolated from flowers of African marigold (*Tagetes patula*). Cryst. + $2H_2O$ from dil. EtOH. Pale yellow needles or leaflets. M.p. 318–20°. Sol. hot EtOH, dil. alkalis. Spar. sol. boiling H_2O. Ox. by air becoming olive-green and finally brown. $FeCl_3$ in EtOH ⟶ olive-green col. Lead acetate in EtOH ⟶ orange-red ppt. KOH fusion ⟶ protocatechuic acid. Forms oxonium salts with min. acids.

$C_{15}H_{10}O_8,H_2SO_4$: orange needles. Hyd. by H_2O.

Hexacetyl : needles from EtOH–AcOH. M.p. 209–11° (203–5°).

Penta-Me ether : pale yellow needles from EtOH. M.p. 161–2°. *Acetyl* : m.p. 161–3°.

Hexa-Me ether : colourless needles from Me_2CO. M.p. 157–8°.

Hexa-Et ether : cryst. from EtOH. M.p 139–41°.

Latour, Magnier de la Source, *Bull. soc. chim.*, 1877, **28**, 337.
Perkin, *J. Chem. Soc.*, 1913, **103**, 209.
Baker, Nodzu, Robinson, *J. Chem. Soc.*, 1929, 74.

Quercetin (*Meletin, sophoretin, quercitin*, 3 : 5 : 7 : 3′ : 4′-*pentahydroxyflavone*)

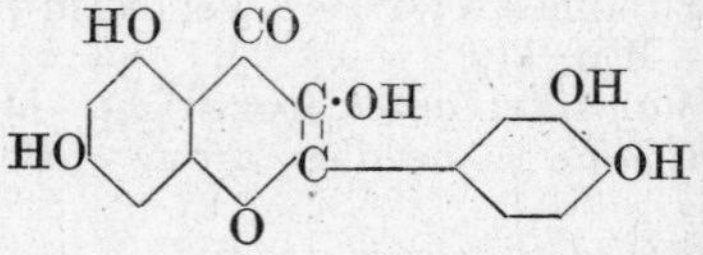

$C_{15}H_{10}O_7$ MW, 302

Found in rind of many fruits. Yellow needles + $2H_2O$ from EtOH.Aq. M.p. anhyd. 313–14°. Very sol. aq. alkalis with golden-yellow col. Sol. AcOH, boiling EtOH. Spar. sol. hot H_2O. Conc. H_2SO_4 ⟶ yellow sol. with faint green fluor. Reduces $NH_3.AgNO_3$ in cold and Fehling's on heating. Tasteless.

7-*Me ether* : *see* Rhamnetin.

3′-*Me ether* : *see* Isorhamnetin.

7 : 3′-*Di-Me ether* : *see* Rhamnazin.

5-*Me ether* : $C_{16}H_{12}O_7$. MW, 316. Prismatic needles from EtOH. M.p. 305–8°. Alkalis ⟶ orange sols. *Tetra-acetyl* : needles from Me_2CO. M.p. 202–4°.

3 : 3′ : 4′-*Tri-Me ether* : $C_{18}H_{16}O_7$. MW, 344. Pale yellow needles from AcOEt. M.p. 240–5°. Alc. $FeCl_3$ ⟶ intense greenish-brown col. Conc. H_2SO_4 ⟶ yellow sol. with weak green fluor. *Diacetyl* : needles from EtOH. M.p. 159–60°.

3 : 5 : 3′ : 4′-*Tetra-Me ether* : $C_{19}H_{18}O_7$. MW, 358. Needles from EtOH. M.p. 284–5°. Spar. sol. EtOH. Alkalis ⟶ pale yellow sols. *Acetyl* : needles. M.p. 174–6°.

3 : 7 : 3′ : 4′-*Tetra-Me ether* : pale yellow needles from EtOH. M.p. 159–60° (155°). Spar. sol. EtOH. Alc. KOH ⟶ bright yellow col. *Acetyl* : needles from EtOH. M.p. 169–70°. Spar. sol. cold EtOH.

5 : 7 : 3′ : 4′-*Tetra-Me ether* : needles from EtOH. M.p. 197–8°. Conc. H_2SO_4 ⟶ yellow sol. with green fluor. *Acetyl* : needles from EtOH. M.p. 160–3°.

Penta-Me ether : $C_{20}H_{20}O_7$. MW, 372.

Needles from EtOH or AcOEt. M.p. 151–2°. Gives no col. with alc. KOH.

7 : 3′ : 4′-*Tri-Et ether* : $C_{21}H_{22}O_7$. MW, 386. Yellow needles from EtOH. M.p. 123–4°.

3 : 7 : 3′ : 4′-*Tetra-Et ether* : $C_{23}H_{26}O_7$. MW, 414. Yellow needles. M.p. 121–2°. Mod. sol. cold EtOH. Insol. H_2O. *Acetyl* : needles from 70% EtOH. M.p. 152–3°. Mod. sol. cold EtOH. Dil. alc. sol. shows faint blue fluor.

Penta-Et ether : $C_{25}H_{30}O_7$. MW, 442. Needles M.p. 116–18°.

3 : 7 : 3′ : 4′-*Tetra-acetyl* : needles. M.p. 193–4°.

Penta-acetyl : needles from EtOH or C_6H_6. M.p. 193·5° (190–1°).

Pentachloroacetyl : needles. M.p. 180°.

Pentabenzoyl : needles from hot Me_2CO. M.p. 188–90°.

3-*Glucoside* : *see* Isoquercitrin.

7-*Glucoside* : *see* Quercimeritrin.

3-*Rhamnoside* : *see* Quercitrin.

3-*Rutinoside* : *see* Rutin.

?-*Glucoside* : incarnatrin. $C_{21}H_{20}O_{12}$. MW, 464. In flowers of *Trifolium incarnatum*, Linn. Yellow needles + $3H_2O$ from H_2O. Softens at 165°, decomp. at 242–5°. Position of glucose not known.

Perkin, Pate, *J. Chem. Soc.*, 1895, **67**, 646.
v. Kostanecki, Lampe, Tambor, *Ber.*, 1904, **37**, 1404.
Herzig, *Monatsh.*, 1888, **9**, 541 ; 1912, **33**, 690.
Attree, Perkin, *J. Chem. Soc.*, 1927, **239**.
Allan, Robinson, *J. Chem. Soc.*, 1926, 2336.
Kubota, Perkin, *J. Chem. Soc.*, 1925, 1894.
Rogerson, *J. Chem. Soc.*, 1910, **97**, 1004.

Quercimeritrin (*Quercetin 7-glucoside*)

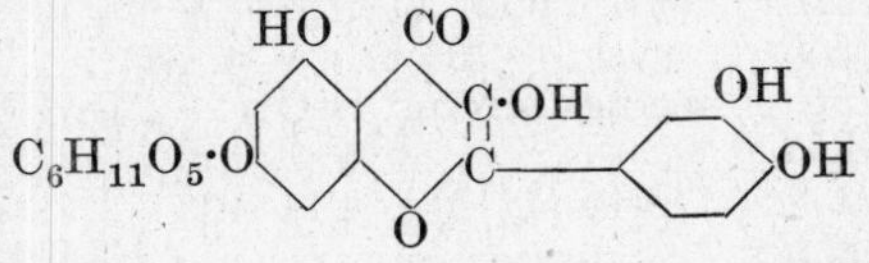

$C_{21}H_{20}O_{12}$ MW, 464

Isolated from cotton flowers, leaves of *Gossypium hirsutum*, *Helianthus annus*, and from bark of *Prunus seratina*, Ehrh. Yellow plates. M.p. 247–9°. Yellow needles + $3H_2O$ from Aq.Py. M.p. 246–8°. Loses H_2O at 100°. Prac. insol. hot H_2O. Hyd. ⟶ quercetin + glucose.

Octa-acetyl : m.p. 216–17° (214–16°).

Penta-Me ether : cryst. + $2H_2O$. Sinters at 197°. M.p. 203–5°.

Perkin, *J. Chem. Soc.*, 1909, **96**, 2185.
Sando, *J. Biol. Chem.*, 1925, **64**, 71 ; 1926, **68**, 407.
Attree, Perkin, *J. Chem. Soc.*, 1927, 237.
Neelakantan, Rao, Seshadri, *Chem. Zentr.*, 1936, I, 3518.

Quercin.
See Scyllitol.

Quercitin.
See Quercetin.

***d*-Quercitol** (*Pentahydroxycyclohexane*)

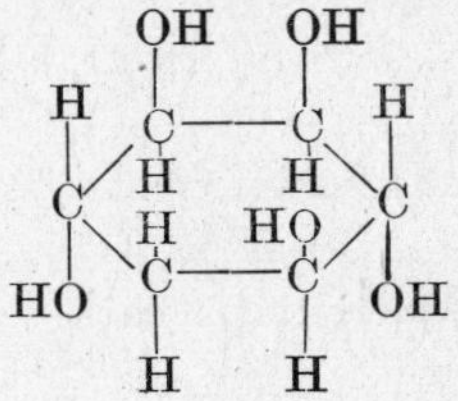

$C_6H_{12}O_5$ MW, 164

Occurs in acorns, oak bark, leaves of *Chamærops humilis*, Linn., seeds of *Mimusops elengi*, and *Achras sapota*, Linn. Prisms from H_2O or dil. EtOH. M.p. 234° (232°, 235–7°). Sol. H_2O. Insol. cold EtOH, Et_2O. $[\alpha]_D^{15}$ + 24·37° in H_2O, $[\alpha]_D^{20}$ + 25·6° in H_2O. Non-fermentable. HNO_3 ⟶ mucic acid. $KMnO_4$ ⟶ oxalic and malonic acids. *d*- and *l*-quercitol are not optical antipodes.

Monoacetyl : cryst. Sol. Et_2O.

Diacetyl : hard friable mass. Sol. EtOH.

Triacetyl : amorph. Sol. EtOH, Et_2O. Insol. H_2O.

Tetra-acetyl : amorph. brittle mass. Hygroscopic.

Penta-acetyl : amorph. Sol. Et_2O. Mod. sol. EtOH. Spar. sol. H_2O.

Pentacarbanilate : amorph. M.p. 120–40°. Insol. ligroin.

Prunier, *Ann. chim. phys.*, 1878, **15**, 9.
Kiliani, Schäfer, *Ber.*, 1896, **29**, 1762.
Missenden, *Chem. News*, 1922, **125**, 120.
Karrer, *Helv. Chim. Acta*, 1926, **9**, 116.
Kiliani, *Ber.*, 1931, **64**, 2473.
Posternak, *Helv. Chim. Acta*, 1932, **15**, 948.

***l*-Quercitol** (*Pentahydroxycyclohexane*)

$$HO\cdot CH\Big<\begin{matrix}CH\cdot OH - CH\cdot OH\\ CH_2 \text{———} CH\cdot OH\end{matrix}\Big>CH\cdot OH$$

$C_6H_{12}O_5$ MW, 164

Occurs in leaves of *Gymnema sylvestre*, R.Br. Prisms + H_2O from H_2O or needles from EtOH. M.p. 174°. $[\alpha]_D^{20}$ − 73·9° in H_2O. Sol. H_2O. Prac. insol. EtOH.

Penta-acetyl: needles from dil. EtOH, m.p. 124–5°: cryst. + C_6H_6 from C_6H_6, m.p. 87–97°. $[\alpha]_D$ − 26·0° in $CHCl_3$.

Pentabenzoyl: amorph. from EtOH, m.p. 133°: needles + EtOH from pet. ether–AcOEt–EtOH, m.p. 116°. $[\alpha]_D$ − 79° in $CHCl_3$.

Power, Tutin, *J. Chem. Soc.*, 1904, **85**, 624.

Quercitrin (*Quercetin 3-rhamnoside*)

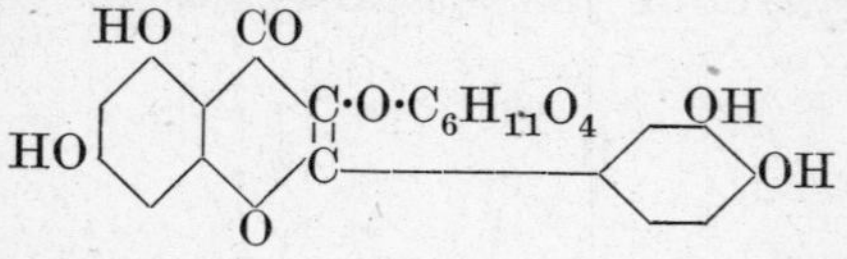

$C_{21}H_{20}O_{11}$ MW, 448

Occurs in quercitron bark. Pale yellow leaflets + $2H_2O$. M.p. 182–5° (air dried), 250–2° anhyd. Sol. EtOH. Insol. cold H_2O. Gives yellow ppt. with aq. lead acetate. Hyd. ⟶ quercetin + rhamnose.

Hepta-acetyl: powder. $[\alpha]_D^{24}$ − 165·6° in $CHCl_3$. Sol. EtOH, Me_2CO, $CHCl_3$, C_6H_6. Insol. H_2O, Et_2O, pet. ether.

Zwenger, Dronke, *Ann.*, *Suppl.*, 1861, **1**, 267.

Liebermann, Hamburger, *Ber.*, 1879, **12**, 1179.

Zemplén, Csürös, Gerecs, Aczél, *Ber.*, 1928, **61**, 2486.

Quinacetophenone (*Acetohydroquinone*, 2:5-*dihydroxyacetophenone*)

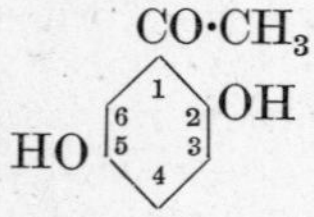

$C_8H_8O_3$ MW, 152

Yellowish-green cryst. from H_2O. M.p. 202°. Sol. EtOH. Spar. sol. Et_2O, C_6H_6. Prac. insol. cold H_2O. Sol. alkalis with yellow col. $FeCl_3$ ⟶ transient blue col. Sublimes.

5-*Me ether*: $C_9H_{10}O_3$. MW, 166. Yellow prisms from dil. EtOH. M.p. 52°.

2 : 5-*Di-Me ether*: $C_{10}H_{12}O_3$. MW, 180. Cryst. M.p. 20–2°. B.p. 155–8°/14 mm. D_4^{20} 1·1385. *Semicarbazone*: needles from dil. EtOH. M.p. 181–2°. *Phenylhydrazone*: yellow prisms from EtOH. M.p. 99–100°.

5-*Et ether*: $C_{10}H_{12}O_3$. MW, 180. Yellow prisms from EtOH. M.p. 57°.

2 : 5-*Di-Et ether*: $C_{12}H_{16}O_3$. MW, 208. Cryst. from EtOH. M.p. 42°.

5(?)-*Acetyl*: yellow needles from AcOH. M.p. 91°. *Phenylhydrazone*: needles from dil. EtOH or C_6H_6. M.p. 147°.

2 : 5-*Diacetyl*: needles from AcOH. M.p. 68°.

2 : 5-*Dibenzoyl*: prisms from EtOH–C_6H_6. M.p. 113°. *Phenylhydrazone*: yellow needles from dil. EtOH. M.p. 148°.

Oxime: plates from toluene. M.p. 149–50°.

Nencki, Schmid, *J. prakt. Chem.*, 1881, **23**, 546.

Klinger, Kolvenbach, *Ber.*, 1898, **31**, 1214.

Kostanecki, Lampe, *Ber.*, 1904, **37**, 774 (*Footnote*).

Kauffmann, Beisswenger, *Ber.*, 1905, **38**, 791.

Quinaform.

See under Quinine.

Quinaldic Acid.

See Quinaldinic Acid.

Quinaldine (2-*Methylquinoline*)

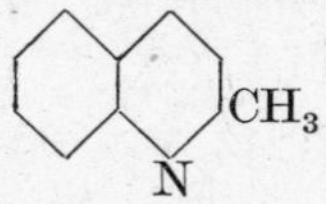

$C_{10}H_9N$ MW, 143

Present in coal tar. F.p. − 2° to − 1°. B.p. 247·6°/760 mm., 238–9°/716 mm., 135·5°/26 mm., 118°/10 mm. D_4^{20} 1·0585. n_D^{20} 1·6126. Heat of comb. C_v 1286·27 Cal. $k = 3{\cdot}6 \times 10^{-9}$ at 14°, $7{\cdot}4 \times 10^{-9}$ at 25°. CrO_3 ⟶ quinaldinic acid. $KMnO_4$ ⟶ acetylanthranilic acid. Sn + HCl ⟶ 1 : 2 : 3 : 4-tetrahydroquinaldine. Conc. HNO_3 ⟶ nitroquinaldinic acid. HNO_3 + H_2SO_4 ⟶ 5- and 8-nitroquinaldines. H_2SO_4 ⟶ quinaldine-5-, -6-, and -8-sulphonic acids. SeO_2 ⟶ quinoline-2-aldehyde and quinaldinic acid.

B,HCl: needles from EtOH–Et_2O. M.p. 224°.

B,2HCl: m.p. about 31°.

B_2,HBr: cryst. + $3H_2O$. M.p. 54°.

B,HI: needles from EtOH. M.p. 186°. Sol. H_2O.

B,H_2SO_4: prisms. M.p. 211–13°.

B_2,H_2PtCl_6: orange-red prisms from H_2O. M.p. 228–9° (226°, 230–41°). Less sol. hot H_2O than quinoline chloroplatinate.

$B_2,H_2Cr_2O_7$: yellowish-red needles. Sol. hot H_2O. Also yellow needles + $3H_2O$ for H_2O. M.p. 110°.

$B_2,2HCl,ZnCl_2$: decomp. at 245°.

$B,HCl,HgCl_2$: needles. M.p. 165·5°.

$B_2,2HCl,CuCl_2$: orange tablets. M.p. 175–8° decomp.

Picrate: yellow needles. M.p. 194° (191°). par. sol. H_2O, cold EtOH.

Styphnate: m.p. 213–14°.

N-*Oxide*: needles + H_2O (or $\frac{1}{2}H_2O$) from H_2O. M.p. 77–8°. Decomp. at 200°. Sol. most org. solvents and acids. Insol. alkalis. B_4,H_2PtCl_6: yellow prisms + $2H_2O$. M.p. 207° decomp. *Picrate*: yellow cryst. from EtOH. M.p. about 173°.

Methiodide: yellow needles from EtOH. M.p. 195°. Sol. H_2O. Insol. Et_2O.

Ethiodide: yellow needles from EtOH. M.p. 233–4°. Sol. H_2O. Spar. sol. EtOH. Insol. Et_2O.

Propiodide: greenish-yellow prisms from EtOH. M.p. 166–7° decomp.

Isobutyliodide: yellow plates from EtOH. M.p. 172°.

Isoamyliodide: yellow prisms from EtOH. M.p. 175°. Sol. H_2O. Spar. sol. cold EtOH.

Methyl-p-*toluenesulphonate*: cryst. M.p. 134°.

Ethyl-benzenesulphonate: cryst. M.p. 105°.

Methoperchlorate: prisms from MeOH. M.p. 254°. Mod. sol. cold H_2O.

Doebner, v. Miller, *Ber.*, 1883, **16**, 2465.
Skraup, *Ber.*, 1882, **15**, 897.
Schering, D.R.P., 24,317.
Mills, Harris, Lambourne, *J. Chem. Soc.*, 1921, **119**, 1297.
Basu, *Ann.*, 1934, **512**, 134.
Rabinovich, Dzirkal, *Chem. Abstracts*, 1934, **28**, 3725.
Tseou Heou-Feo, *Bull. soc. chim.*, 1935, **2**, 90.

Quinaldine-5-aldehyde (2-*Methylquinoline*-5-*aldehyde*, 5-*aldehydoquinaldine*)

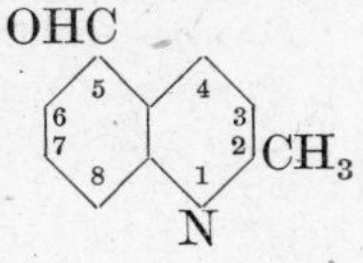

$C_{11}H_9ON$ MW, 171

Cryst. + H_2O from H_2O. M.p. 73°, anhyd. 81°. Sol. EtOH, Et_2O, Me_2CO, C_6H_6, dil. min. acids. Spar. sol. hot H_2O, pet. ether. Volatile in steam. $Ag_2O \longrightarrow$ quinaldine-5-carboxylic acid.

B_2,H_2PtCl_6: orange-yellow plates from alc. HCl. M.p. 211°. Spar. sol. hot EtOH.

Picrate: needles from EtOH. M.p. 182° decomp.

Eckhardt, *Ber.*, 1889, **22**, 277.
See also Decker, Remfry, *Ber.*, 1905, **38**, 2775.

Quinaldine-6-aldehyde (2-*Methylquinoline*-6-*aldehyde*, 6-*aldehydoquinaldine*).

Needles from H_2O, plates from C_6H_6–pet. ether, m.p. 106°. Sol. EtOH, Et_2O, C_6H_6, min. acids. Mod. sol. hot H_2O, pet. ether.

Phenylhydrazone: golden-yellow prisms from EtOH. M.p. 160°.

B_2,H_2PtCl_6: orange prisms + $2H_2O$.

v. Miller, Kinkelin, *Ber.*, 1885, **18**, 3237.

Quinaldine-3-carboxylic Acid (2-*Methylquinoline*-3-*carboxylic acid*)

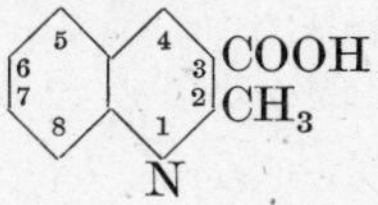

$C_{11}H_9O_2N$ MW, 187

Needles from EtOH or C_6H_6. M.p. 238° (235° decomp., 251° decomp.). Spar. sol. most solvents. Prac. insol. H_2O. Heat $\longrightarrow$ quinaldine.

Me ester: $C_{12}H_{11}O_2N$. MW, 201. Needles from EtOH. M.p. 72°. *Methiodide*: yellow needles or plates from H_2O. M.p. 200° decomp. Sol. H_2O, hot EtOH. Insol. Et_2O. *Ethochloride*: needles from EtOH–Et_2O. M.p. 150° decomp. *Ethobromide*: prisms from H_2O. M.p. 154°. *Ethiodide*: yellow plates from H_2O or EtOH. M.p. 210° decomp.

Et ester: $C_{13}H_{13}O_2N$. MW, 215. Needles from dil. EtOH. M.p. 71°. *Methochloride*: yellow plates or needles from H_2O or EtOH. M.p. 158° decomp. *Methiodide*: yellow plates or needles from H_2O or EtOH. M.p. 208° decomp. Spar. sol. cold H_2O, EtOH. *Ethochloride*: needles from EtOH–Et_2O. M.p. 146° decomp. *Ethobromide*: prisms from H_2O. M.p. 217°. *Ethiodide*: orange needles from EtOH. M.p. 236° decomp.

Propyl ester: $C_{14}H_{15}O_2N$. MW, 229. Prisms or needles from EtOH. M.p. 51°. *Methiodide*: yellow needles. M.p. 186° decomp.

Benzyl ester: $C_{18}H_{15}O_2N$. MW, 277. Prisms. M.p. 82°. *Methiodide*: yellow needles from H_2O. M.p. 172°.

Amide: $C_{11}H_{10}ON_2$. MW, 186. Cryst.

Nitrile: 3-cyanoquinaldine. $C_{11}H_8N_2$. MW, 168. Prisms from H_2O or needles from EtOH. M.p. 131° (125–7°).

Friedländer, Gohring, *Ber.*, 1883, **16**, 1836.
Hantzsch, *Ber.*, 1886, **19**, 37.
Claus, Steinitz, *Ann.*, 1894, **282**, 117 (*Footnote*).
Rohde, *Ber.*, 1889, **22**, 267.
v. Walther, *J. prakt. Chem.*, 1903, **67**, 509.
v. Meyer, *J. prakt. Chem.*, 1914, **90**, 27.

Quinaldine-4-carboxylic Acid (*2-Methylquinoline-4-carboxylic acid, 2-methylcinchoninic acid, aniluvitonic acid*).

Yellow cryst. + $1H_2O$ from hot H_2O. M.p. 244° (242°, 246° decomp.). Sol. hot EtOH, AcOH, dil. acids. Spar. sol. Et_2O, C_6H_6. Insol. $CHCl_3$, pet. ether. Sublimes. Heat ⟶ quinaldine. Alk. $KMnO_4$ ⟶ 6-methylpyridine-2 : 3 : 4-tricarboxylic acid. Acid $KMnO_4$ ⟶ acetylanthranilic acid.

Me ester: m.p. 61–2°. Sol. EtOH, Et_2O, $CHCl_3$, C_6H_6. Part. decomp. on dist.

Et ester: prisms from pet. ether. M.p. 77°. Sol. EtOH, Et_2O, Me_2CO, C_6H_6. *Picrate*: yellow needles from EtOH. M.p. 156°. B_2,H_2PtCl_6: yellow needles + $2H_2O$. M.p. 203° decomp.

Amide: needles from H_2O. M.p. 239°. Sol. hot EtOH. Spar. sol. cold H_2O, Et_2O. Br + NaOH ⟶ 4-aminoquinaldine. *Picrate*: m.p. 239° (231–2° decomp.).

B_2,H_2PtCl_6: yellow needles + $2H_2O$. M.p. 220° decomp.

Picrate: greenish-yellow needles from EtOH. M.p. 191°.

v. Miller, *Ber.*, 1891, **24**, 1918.
Böttinger, *Ann.*, 1878, **191**, 321.
Simon, *Ann. chim. phys.*, 1896, **9**, 466.
Beyer, *J. prakt. Chem.*, 1886, **33**, 411.
Pfitzinger, *J. prakt. Chem.*, 1886, **33**, 100; 1888, **38**, 582; 1897, **56**, 284.
Bayer, D.R.P., 290,703, (*Chem. Zentr.*, 1916, I, 645).
Knövenagel, Bähr, *Ber.*, 1922, **55**, 1927.

Quinaldine-5-carboxylic Acid (*2-Methylquinoline-5-carboxylic acid*).

Needles from EtOH. M.p. 285° decomp. Sol. cold NH_3 and warm dil. acids. Mod. sol. EtOH. Prac. insol. H_2O. Insol. Et_2O, $CHCl_3$, C_6H_6, ligroin.

Nitrile: 5-cyanoquinaldine. Needles + $2H_2O$ from H_2O. M.p. 82°, anhyd. 104°. Sol. EtOH, Et_2O, C_6H_6, hot H_2O. Volatile in steam.

Doebner, v. Miller, *Ber.*, 1884, **17**, 941.
Eckhardt, *Ber.*, 1889, **22**, 281.
v. Miller, *Ber.*, 1890, **23**, 2263.
Richard, *ibid.*, 3489.
Rist, *ibid.*, 3486.

Quinaldine-6-carboxylic Acid (*2-Methylquinoline-6-carboxylic acid*).

Needles from EtOH. M.p. 261–2° (259°, 256°). Sol. hot EtOH. Spar. sol. hot H_2O. Sublimes.

Doebner, v. Miller, *Ber.*, 1884, **17**, 939.
v. Miller, *Ber.*, 1890, **23**, 2263.
I.G., D.R.P., 567,273, (*Chem. Zentr.*, 1933, I, 1687).

Quinaldine-8-carboxylic Acid (*2-Methylquinoline-8-carboxylic acid*).

Needles + $\frac{1}{2}H_2O$ from H_2O. M.p. 151°. Sol. H_2O, EtOH, acids, alkalis. Part. decomp. on heating ⟶ quinaldine.

Doebner, v. Miller, *Ber.*, 1884, **17**, 943.
v. Miller, *Ber.*, 1890, **23**, 2259.

Quinaldine-3 : 4-dicarboxylic Acid (*2-Methylquinoline-3 : 4-dicarboxylic acid*)

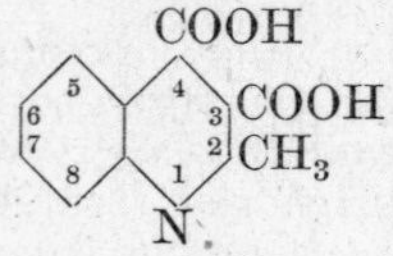

$C_{12}H_9O_4N$ MW, 231

Needles + H_2O from H_2O. M.p. 238–9° (236–7°) (slow heat.), about 245° (rapid heat.). Prac. insol. H_2O.

Di-Et ester: $C_{16}H_{17}O_4N$. MW, 287. M.p. 88–9°. Sol. Et_2O, C_6H_6. Spar. sol. EtOH.

Anhydride: $C_{12}H_7O_3N$. MW, 213. M.p. 218°.

Imide: $C_{12}H_8O_2N_2$. MW, 212. Yellow needles from AcOEt. M.p. 257°.

3-*Nitrile*: 3-cyanoquinaldine-4-carboxylic acid, 2-methyl-3-cyanocinchoninic acid. Plates from EtOH. M.p. 238° decomp. Sol. NaOH. Heat ⟶ 3-cyanoquinaldine.

v. Walther, *J. prakt. Chem.*, 1903, **67**, 504.
Pfitzinger, *J. prakt. Chem.*, 1897, **56**, 316.
Engelhard, *J. prakt. Chem.*, 1898, **57**, 479.
Schering, D.R.P., 275,963, (*Chem. Zentr.*, 1914, II, 182).
Lawson, Perkin, Robinson, *J. Chem. Soc.*, 1924, **125**, 634.

Quinaldine-4 : 6-dicarboxylic Acid (*2-Methylquinoline-4 : 6-dicarboxylic acid*).

Powder. Sinters at 160°.

v. Miller, *Ber.*, 1890, **23**, 2262.

Quinaldinic Acid (*Quinaldic acid, quinoline-2-carboxylic acid*).

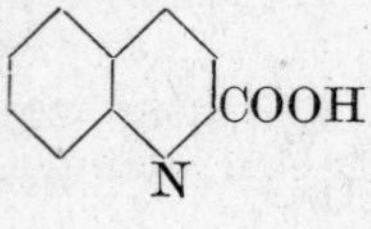

$C_{10}H_7O_2N$ MW, 17

Needles + $2H_2O$ from H_2O. Loses H_2O at 100°. M.p. anhyd. 157°. Sol. hot H_2O, C_6H_6. Mod. sol. cold H_2O. k (acid) $= 1{\cdot}2 \times 10^{-5}$ at 25°. Gives reddish-yellow col. with $FeSO_4$. Heat ⟶ quinoline. Alk. $KMnO_4$ ⟶ pyridine-2 : 3 : 6-tricarboxylic acid. HNO_3 at 60–70° ⟶ 5- and 8-nitroquinaldinic acids. Used in estimation of Zn, Cu, Cd, UO_2, and for separation of Cu from Cd, P, As, Pb, Ni, CO, Mn, etc.

Me ester: $C_{11}H_9O_2N$. MW, 187. Needles from ligroin. M.p. 86° (85°, 78°). *Methiodide*: orange cryst. M.p. 122–9° decomp. *Methochloride*: m.p. 158–65° decomp. *Methonitrate*: m.p. 138° decomp.

Et ester: $C_{12}H_{11}O_2N$. MW, 201. Needles. M.p. 36°.

Nitrile: 2-cyanoquinoline. $C_{10}H_6N_2$. MW, 154. Needles. M.p. 94°. Sol. EtOH, C_6H_6, Et_2O.

Amide: $C_{10}H_8ON_2$. MW, 172. Needles from dil. EtOH. or C_6H_6–ligroin. M.p. 133° (123°). Sol. EtOH, C_6H_6, $CHCl_3$, AcOH. Spar. sol. Et_2O, ligroin, hot H_2O. Sol. dil. HCl.

Chloride: $C_{10}H_6ONCl$. MW, 191·5. Exists in two forms. (i) M.p. 175–6°: (ii) m.p. 97°.

N-*Oxide*: needles from H_2O. M.p. 171° decomp. (167° decomp.). Sol. Me_2CO, EtOH, C_6H_6. Spar. sol. Et_2O, ligroin.

Picrate: yellow needles from H_2O. Sol. hot H_2O, EtOH.

Doebner, v. Miller, *Ber.*, 1883, **16**, 2472.
Besthorn, Ibele, *Ber.*, 1906, **39**, 2329.
v. Miller, Krämer, *Ber.*, 1891, **24**, 1915.
Besthorn, *Ber.*, 1909, **42**, 2698.
Meyer, *Monatsh.*, 1904, **25**, 1199.
Mills, Hamer, *J. Chem. Soc.*, 1922, **121**, 2008.
Taylor, *J. Chem. Soc.*, 1929, 1110.
Hammick, *J. Chem. Soc.*, 1923, **123**, 2882.
Hammick, Dickinson, *J. Chem. Soc.*, 1929, 214.
Kaufmann, Dändliker, *Ber.*, 1913, **46**, 2928.

γ-Quinaldone

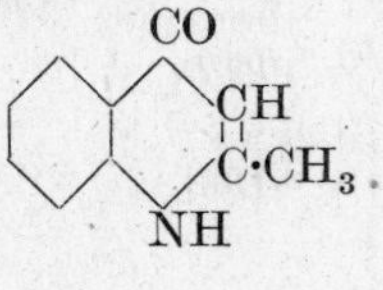

$C_{10}H_9ON$ MW, 159

The compound of the above formula described by Heller and Sourlis (*Ber.*, 1908, **41**, 2696) has been shown by Meisenheimer and Stotz (*Ber.*, 1925, **58**, 2334) to be quinaldine *N*-oxide.

N-*Me*.: 1 : 2-dimethyl-γ-quinolone. Needles from C_6H_6. M.p. 176°. Sol. H_2O, EtOH, hot C_6H_6. *B,HCl*: prisms + H_2O. M.p. anhyd. 217°. *B,HI*: needles + H_2O from H_2O. M.p. anhyd. 201°. *B_2,H_2PtCl_6*: yellow cryst. from H_2O. M.p. 240° decomp. Sol. hot H_2O. *Picrate*: decomp. at 233°.

Conrad, Limpach, *Ber.*, 1887, **20**, 956.
Conrad, Eckhardt, *Ber.*, 1889, **22**, 76.
Knorr, *Ber.*, 1897, **30**, 925.

2-[5-Quinaldyl]-acrylic Acid

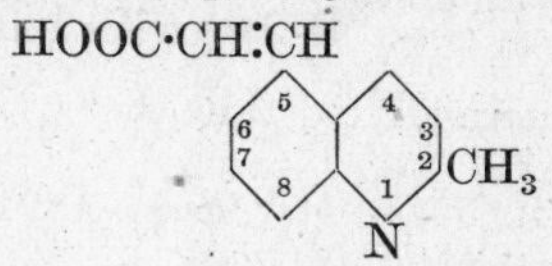

$C_{13}H_{11}O_2N$ MW, 213

Prisms from EtOH. M.p. 246° decomp. Mod. sol. EtOH, Me_2CO, C_6H_6. Prac. insol. Et_2O, $CHCl_3$, ligroin. $KMnO_4$ ⟶ quinaldine-5-aldehyde.

Ag salt: cryst. + 2 or $4H_2O$.
B,HCl: needles + H_2O.
B,HNO_3: needles + H_2O.
B_2,H_2PtCl_6: yellow plates + $2H_2O$.
Picrate: needles + H_2O from EtOH. M.p. 150–2°. Sol. hot H_2O, EtOH, Me_2CO. Prac. insol. Et_2O.

Eckhardt, *Ber.*, 1889, **22**, 272.
See also Decker, Remfry, *Ber.*, 1905, **38**, 2775.

2-[6-Quinaldyl]-acrylic Acid.

Needles from EtOH. M.p. 240–50°. Spar. sol. cold EtOH. Prac insol. H_2O. Sol. dil. alkalis. Spar. sol. dil. acids. $KMnO_4$ ⟶ quinaldine-6-aldehyde.

B,HCl: prisms + H_2O from dil. HCl. Sol. H_2O.
B,HNO_3: prisms + H_2O. Spar. sol. dil. HNO_3.
B_2,H_2PtCl_6: reddish-yellow prisms + $2H_2O$.

v. Miller, Kinkelin, *Ber.*, 1885, **18**, 3235.

2-[7-Quinaldyl]-acrylic Acid.

Cryst. + $\frac{1}{2}$EtOH from EtOH. M.p. 204°.

Eckhardt, *Ber.*, 1889, **22**, 273.

Quinalizarin (1 : 2 : 5 : 8-*Tetrahydroxyanthraquinone*)

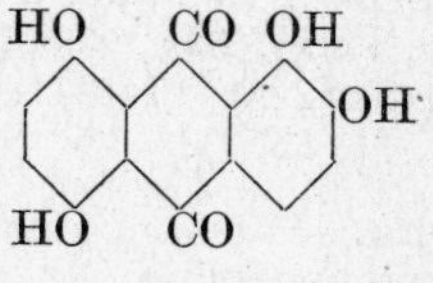

$C_{14}H_8O_6$ MW, 272

Red needles with green metallic lustre from $PhNO_2$. Does not melt below 275°. Very spar. sol. most solvents. Sublimes. Sol. alkalis with reddish-violet col. Sol. conc. H_2SO_4 with bluish-violet col. Zn fusion ⟶ anthracene.

Tetra-acetyl: needles from EtOH–$CHCl_3$. M.p. 201°.

1 : 2-*Di-Me ether*: $C_{16}H_{12}O_6$. MW, 300. Brownish-red plates from EtOH or C_6H_6. M.p. 225–30°. Mod. sol. boiling AcOH. Spar. sol. hot EtOH, hot C_6H_6. Sol. alkalis with bluish-violet col. Sol. conc. H_2SO_4 with blue col.

Liebermann, Kostanecki, *Ann.*, 1887, **240**, 301.
Schmidt, *J. prakt. Chem.*, 1891, **43**, 239.
Gattermann, *ibid.*, 249.
Graebe, *Ber.*, 1890, **23**, 3739.

Quinanisole.
See under 6-Hydroxyquinoline *and* 8-Hydroxyquinoline.

Quinazoline (5 : 6-*Benzpyrimidine, phenmiazine*)

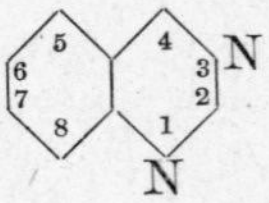

$C_8H_6N_2$ MW, 130

Yellow plates from pet. ether. M.p. 48–48·5°. B.p. 243°/772·5 mm. (241·5°/764 mm.). Sol. H_2O with neutral reaction. Sol. usual solvents. Odour resembles naphthalene. Alk. $KMnO_4$ ⟶ pyrimidine-4 : 5-dicarboxylic acid + 4-hydroxyquinazoline.

B,HAuCl$_4$: orange-red cryst. + H_2O. M.p. 185°.

B$_2$,*H*$_2$*PtCl*$_6$: orange-yellow prisms. Does not melt below 250°.

Picrate: needles. M.p. 188–90°.

3-*Methohydroxide*: prisms from H_2O. M.p. 163–5°. Spar. sol. H_2O, Et_2O, C_6H_6, HCl.

3-*Methochloride*: needles. Sinters at 165–6°, m.p. 171–2°. Sol. H_2O.

3-*Methobromide*: m.p. 150–2°. Sol. H_2O.

3-*Methiodide*: yellow prisms + MeOH. M.p. 125–7°. Sol. H_2O.

3-*Ethohydroxide*: m.p. 145–6°. Sol. hot H_2O.

3-*Ethochloride*: m.p. 150–1°. Sol. H_2O.

Gabriel, *Ber.*, 1903, **36**, 808.
Bischer, Lang, *Ber.*, 1895, **28**, 292.
Riedel, D.R.P., 174,941, (*Chem. Zentr.*, 1906, II, 1372).

Quinazolone.
See Hydroxyquinazoline.

Quindoline

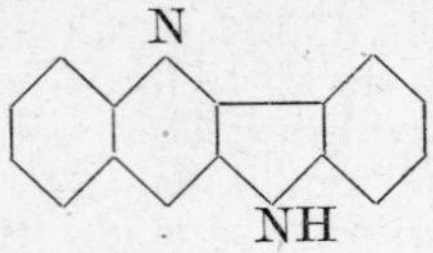

$C_{15}H_{10}N_2$ MW, 218

Needles from EtOH. M.p. 247–8°. Sol. EtOH, Et_2O with blue fluor. Insol. H_2O. Sol. hot dil. HCl, conc. H_2SO_4 with blue fluor. Sublimes with part. decomp.

B,HCl: yellow cryst. Sol. H_2O, EtOH.

B,HI: yellow cryst. Sol. H_2O, EtOH.

B,HNO$_3$: yellow cryst. Sol. H_2O, EtOH.

Picrate: yellow cryst. Sol. EtOH.

Methochloride: yellow cryst. M.p. 273° decomp.

Methiodide: yellow needles from H_2O.

Methosulphate: orange-yellow needles. M.p. 242–5°.

Ethiodide: yellow needles from H_2O or EtOH. M.p. 222–3°.

Acetyl: yellow needles from EtOH. M.p. 177–8°.

Fichter, Boehringer, *Ber.*, 1906, **39**, 3940.
Fichter, Rohner, *Ber.*, 1910, **43**, 3490.
Noelting, Steuer, *ibid.*, 3512.
Armit, Robinson, *J. Chem. Soc.*, 1922, **121**, 836.

Quindoline-10-carboxylic Acid (*Flavindin*)

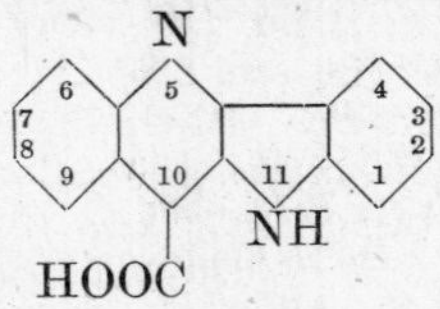

$C_{16}H_{10}O_2N_2$ MW, 262

Yellow ppt. NaHg or Zn ⟶ quindoline.

Giraud, *Compt. rend.*, 1879, **89**, 104; 1880, **90**, 1429.
Noelting, Steuer, *Ber.*, 1910, **43**, 3512.
Fichter, Rohner, *ibid.*, 3489.
Armit, Robinson, *J. Chem. Soc.*, 1922, **121**, 836.

Quinene (*Quinenine*)

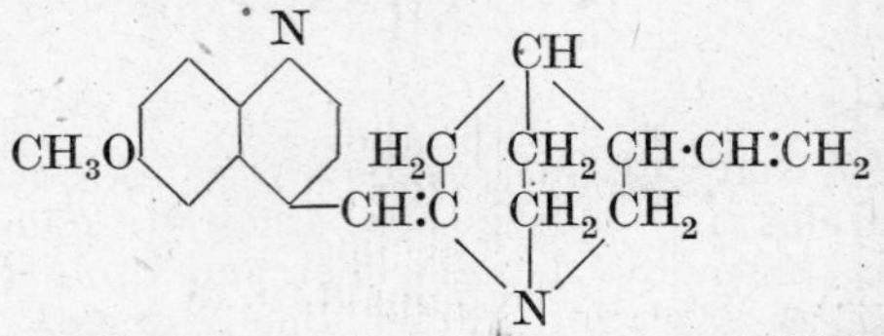

$C_{20}H_{22}ON_2$ MW, 306

Rhombic cryst. + $2H_2O$ from Et_2O or ligroin. Sinters at 75°, m.p. 81–2°. Loses H_2O at 100°. 25% H_3PO_4 at 170–80° ⟶ 6-methoxylepidine + meroquinene. HBr (D 1·49) at 190° ⟶ apoquinene. Br in $CHCl_3$ ⟶ quinene dibromide. Fluoresces in dil. H_2SO_4. Gives thalleioquin reaction.

B,2HCl : yellow needles + H_2O from EtOH. M.p. 180–5°. $[\alpha]_D^{24}$ (anhyd.) + 18·4° in H_2O.

B,2HCl,CuCl₂ : yellowish-green cryst. Decomp. at 125–30°.

Comstock, Koenigs, *Ber.*, 1884, **17**, 1989; 1885, **18**, 1223.
Heidelberger, Jacobs, *J. Am. Chem. Soc.*, 1920, **42**, 1501.
Cohen, *J. Chem. Soc.*, 1933, 996.

Quinenine.
See Quinene.

Quinhydrone (*Molecular comp. of* p-*benzoquinone and hydroquinone*)

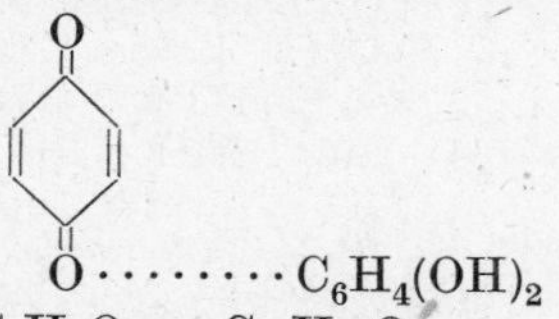

$C_6H_4O_2 + C_6H_6O_2 = C_{12}H_{10}O_4$ MW, 218

Reddish-brown needles with green lustre. M.p. 171°. Sol. EtOH, Et_2O with yellow col. Spar. sol. cold H_2O. Insol. pet. ether, ligroin. Sol. NH_3 with green col. D^{20} 1·401. Sublimes. Boiling H_2O ⟶ quinone + hydroquinone.

Bamberger, Czerkis, *J. prakt. Chem.*, 1903, **68**, 486.
Wöhler, *Ann.*, 1844, **51**, 153.
Torrey, Hardenbergh, *Am. Chem. J.*, 1905, **33**, 168.
Clark, *Am. Chem. J.*, 1892, **14**, 571.
Michael, Cobb, *J. prakt. Chem.*, 1910, **82**, 304.
Evans, Dehn, *J. Am. Chem. Soc.*, 1930, **52**, 3204.
Müller, *Chem. Abstracts*, 1929, **23**, 5471.
Trénel, Bischoff, *Z. angew. Chem.*, 1929, **42**, 288.

Quinic Acid (1 : 3 : 4 : 5-*Tetrahydroxycyclohexane*-1-*carboxylic acid*, 1 : 3 : 4 : 5-*tetrahydroxyhexahydrobenzoic acid*)

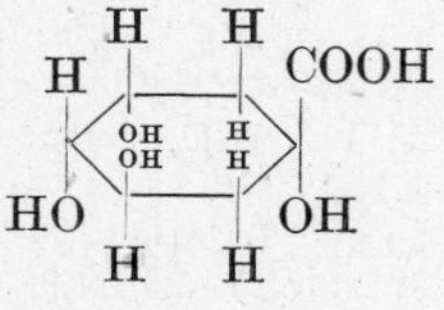

$C_7H_{12}O_6$ MW, 192

l-.

Occurs in cinchona bark, coffee beans, bilberries, sugar beet, etc. Prisms from H_2O. M.p. 162°. Sol. 2·5 parts H_2O at 9°. $[\alpha]_D^{15}$ −43·84° in H_2O, $[\alpha]_D^{20}$ − 44·03° in H_2O, $[\alpha]_D^{25\cdot5}$ −42·1° in H_2O. Triboluminescent. Heat at 200–50° ⟶ γ-lactone (quinide). $KMnO_4$ ⟶ *p*-benzoquinone. PbO_2 ⟶ hydroquinone. KOH fusion ⟶ protocatechuic acid. HI at 115–20° ⟶ benzoic acid.

NH_4 salt : cryst. from H_2O. M.p. 179°.

Na Salt : prisms or plates + $2H_2O$. Sol. ½ part H_2O at 15°.

Tetra-acetyl : cryst. M.p. 132 6°. Sol. EtOH, Et_2O, alkalis. Mod. sol. H_2O. Spar. sol. CS_2. Insol. ligroin. $[\alpha]_D^{20}$ − 22·50° in EtOH.

Tetrabenzoyl : amorph. + $2H_2O$. M.p. 137–8°. Sol. EtOH, Et_2O. Insol. H_2O.

Me ester : $C_8H_{14}O_6$. MW, 206. Needles from MeOH. M.p. 120° (126° to a milky liquid becoming clear at 142–3°). Sol. H_2O, EtOH. Insol. Et_2O, C_6H_6, pet. ether. *Tetra-Me ether* : m.p. 56–8°. $[\alpha]_D$ − 18·5° in C_6H_6.

Et ester : $C_9H_{16}O_6$. MW, 220. Viscous mass. Sol. H_2O, EtOH. Less sol. Et_2O. *Tetra-acetyl* : plates from H_2O. M.p. 135–6°. Mod. sol. EtOH, Et_2O. Spar. sol. H_2O: Sublimes.

Phenyl ester : $C_{13}H_{16}O_6$. MW, 268. *Tetra-acetyl* : cryst. from dil. EtOH. M.p. 167°. Sol hot EtOH, AcOH. Insol. cold H_2O, Et_2O.

Amide : $C_7H_{13}O_5N$. MW, 191. Cryst. M.p. 132°. Sol. H_2O, EtOH. Insol. Et_2O, C_6H_6. *Tetra-acetyl* : m.p. 186–7° decomp. $[\alpha]_D^{21}$ − 28·6° in tetrachloroethane. *Tetra-Me ether* : m.p. 115–16°.

Nitrile : $C_7H_{11}O_4N$. MW, 173. *Tetra-acetyl* : m.p. 161–2°. $[\alpha]_D^{18}$ − 29·9° in $CHCl_3$.

γ-Lactone : *see* Quinide.

d-.

Prisms. M.p. 164°. Sol. hot H_2O. Spar. sol. EtOH. Prac. insol. Et_2O. $[\alpha]_D^{20}$ + 44° in H_2O.

dl-.

Cryst. $k = 2{\cdot}2 \times 10^{-4}$ at 9°.

Fischer, Dangschat, *Ber.*, 1932, **65**, 1009.
Karrer, Widmer, Riso, *Helv. Chim. Acta*, 1925, **8**, 195.
Herzig, Ortony, *Arch. Pharm.*, 1920, **258**, 91.
Gorter, *Ann.*, 1908, **358**, 329; 1908, **359**, 221.
Erwig, Koenigs, *Ber.*, 1889, **22**, 1461.
Echtermeier, *Arch. Pharm.*, 1906, **244**, 42.
v. Lippemann, *Ber.*, 1901, **34**, 1159.
Hesse, *Ann.*, 1859, **110**, 333.
Zwenger, *Ann.*, 1860, **115**, 108.

Quinicine (*Quinotoxine*)

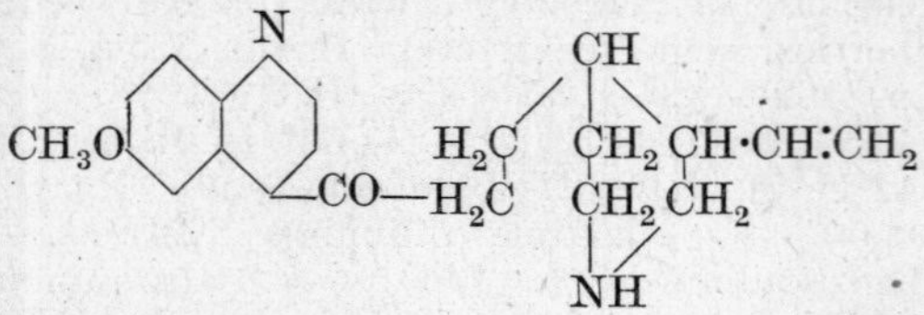

$C_{20}H_{24}O_2N_2$ MW, 324

One of the cinchona alkaloids. Isomeric with quinine. Reddish-yellow amorph. mass. M.p. about 60°. Sol. EtOH, Et_2O, $CHCl_3$. Prac. insol. H_2O. Sol. in EtOH absorbs CO_2. Forms stable salts. Pptd. from sol. by excess KCNO. $[\alpha]_D^{15}$ + 44·1° in $CHCl_3$. Shows no fluor. in dil. H_2SO_4. Gives thalleioquin reaction.

B,HCl : leaflets. M.p. 180–2° (179–80°). $[\alpha]_D^{13\cdot7}$ + 16·26° in H_2O.

B_2,(COOH)$_2$: prisms + $9H_2O$. M.p. 149°.

Oxime : m.p. 112–16°.

p-*Bromophenylhydrazone* : yellow cryst. M.p. 141°.

N-*Me* : yellow oil. *B,2HCl* : cryst. + H_2O. M.p. 153–5°. $[\alpha]_D^{23}$ + 16·6° in H_2O.

N-*Et* : yellow oil. *B,HCl* : yellow cryst. from 95% EtOH. M.p. 202–4°. $[\alpha]_D^{23}$ + 68·1° in H_2O.

Dihydride : *see* Quinoticine.

v. Miller, Rohde, Fussenegger, *Ber.*, 1900, **33**, 3228.
Howard, *J. Chem. Soc.*, 1871, **24**, 61; 1872, **25**, 101.
Hesse, *Ann.*, 1875, **178**, 244.
Fränkel, Diamant, *Ber.*, 1925, **58**, 554.
Heidelberger, Jacobs, *J. Am. Chem. Soc.*, 1919, **41**, 832; 1922, **44**, 1093.

Quinide (*γ-Lactone of quinic acid*)

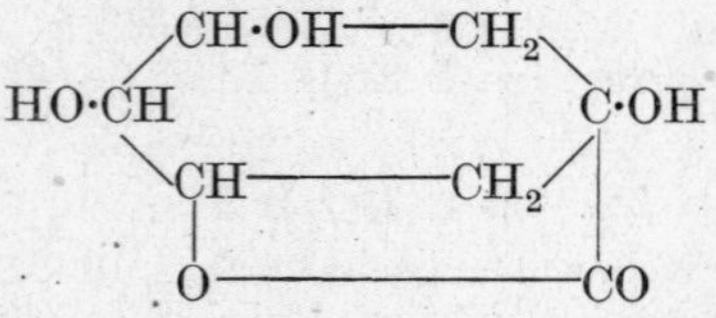

$C_7H_{10}O_5$ MW, 174

dl-.

Cryst. from H_2O or EtOH. M.p. 200° (198°). Sol. H_2O. Spar. sol. dil. EtOH. Neutral reaction.

l-.

M.p. 187°. $[\alpha]_D^{17}$ − 17·13° in H_2O.

Triacetyl : prisms from EtOH. M.p. 133–4°. $[\alpha]_D^{15}$ − 13·4° in Me_2CO.

Tribenzoyl : cryst. from EtOH. M.p. 148°.

Erwig, Koenigs, *Ber.*, 1889, **22**, 1458.
Hesse, *Ann.*, 1859, **110**, 335.
v. Lippmann, *Ber.*, 1901, **34**, 1159.
Echtermier, *Arch. Pharm.*, 1906, **244**, 53.
Gorter, *Ann.*, 1908, **359**, 223.
Fischer, *Ber.*, 1921, **54**, 781.

Quinidine (*Conquinine, conchinine*)

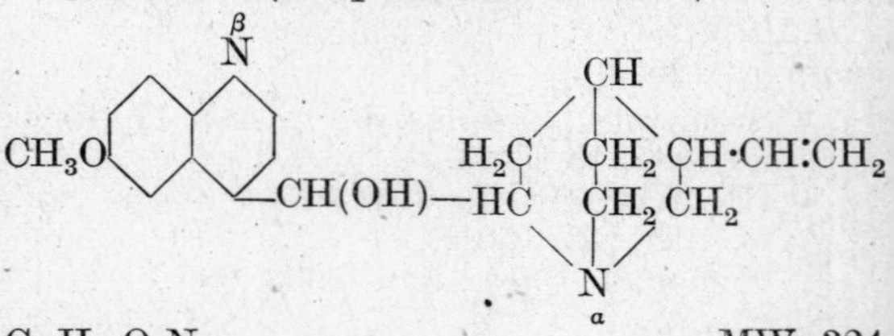

$C_{20}H_{24}O_2N_2$ MW, 324

One of the cinchona alkaloids. Stereoisomeric with quinine. Cryst. + $2\frac{1}{2}H_2O$ from dil. EtOH. Loses $\frac{1}{2}H_2O$ on exposure to air. Cryst. + EtOH from EtOH. Loses EtOH at 100°. M.p. anhyd. 174–5° (171·5°, 170–1°, 168°). $[\alpha]_D$ + 262° (251°) in EtOH, $[\alpha]_D^{15}$ + 236·8° in 97% EtOH, + 243·5° in 99% EtOH. $[\alpha]_D$ + 230° in $CHCl_3$. Sol. 6900 parts H_2O at 25°, 750 parts at 100°. Sol. 26 parts EtOH, 22 parts Et_2O at 20°. Anhyd. quinidine sol. 4950 parts H_2O, 129 parts Et_2O, 57 parts AcOEt, 177 parts CCl_4, 41 parts C_6H_6 at 18–22°. The salts of quinidine, with the exception of the hydriodide, are more sol. than those of quinine. Quinidine forms add. comps. with alcohols, acetone, benzene, etc. Cold acid $KMnO_4$ ⟶ quitenidine + formic acid. Hot alk. $KMnO_4$ ⟶ pyridine-2 : 3 : 4-tricarboxylic acid, oxalic acid, CO_2, and NH_3. CrO_3 ⟶ quininone + quininic acid. PCl_5 ⟶ quinidine chloride. Gives thalleioquin reaction. 60% H_2SO_4 ⟶ cupreidine + isocupreidine.

B_2,H_2SO_4 : needles or prisms + $2H_2O$ from hot H_2O. Loses H_2O at 120°. Sol. 108 parts H_2O at 10°, 100 parts H_2O at 15°, 7 parts H_2O at 100°. Sol. 20 parts $CHCl_3$ at 15°. Sol. EtOH. Insol. Et_2O. $[\alpha]_D^{17}$ + 211·5° in EtOH. $[\alpha]_D^{15}$ + 218·2° in 80% EtOH, $[\alpha]_D^{15}$ + 179·5° in H_2O, $[\alpha]_D$ + 184·17° in $CHCl_3$.

B,H_2SO_4 : prisms + $4H_2O$. Sol. 8·7 parts H_2O at 10° with blue fluor.

B,HCl : prisms + H_2O. Sol. hot H_2O, EtOH. Prac. insol. Et_2O. $[\alpha]_D^{15}$ + 200·9° (+ 195·8°) in H_2O. Also needles + $2H_2O$, m.p. anhyd. 258–9° Sol. 75 parts H_2O at 15°. $[\alpha]_D$ + 212° in EtOH, $[\alpha]_D^{20}$ + 200° in H_2O.

B,2HCl : prisms + H_2O. Sol. EtOH. Spar. sol. $CHCl_3$. $[\alpha]_D^{15}$ + 250·3° in H_2O.

B,HBr : sol. 200 parts H_2O at 14°.
B,HI : prisms. Sol. 1270 parts H_2O at 15°. Prac. insol. EtOH.
B,2HI : golden prisms + $3H_2O$. Sol. 90 parts H_2O at 15°.
B,HNO₃ : prisms. Sol. 85 parts H_2O at 15°.
B,H₃PO₄ : prisms. Sol. 131 parts H_2O at 10°. Mod. sol. EtOH.
B₂,H₂CrO₄ : yellow plates + $6H_2O$.
B₂,H₂PtCl₆ : orange needles + $3H_2O$.
B,2HCl,CuCl₂ : orange plates. M.p. 208–9° decomp.
B₂,(COOH)₂ : cryst. + H_2O from H_2O. Sol. 151 parts H_2O at 15°. $[\alpha]_D^{15}$ + 186·8° in $CHCl_3$–EtOH.
Benzoate : cryst. + H_2O. Sol. EtOH.
Salicylate : sol. 1650 parts H_2O at 25°.
Acetyl : amorph. Sol. Et_2O. $[\alpha]_D^{15}$ + 128° in EtOH. *B,HAuCl₄* : yellow amorph. + $2H_2O$. *B,H₂PtCl₆* : yellow cryst. + $3H_2O$. Spar. sol. H_2O.
Salicyloyl : powder. Sol. EtOH, Et_2O, $CHCl_3$, C_6H_6. *Salicylate* : needles from EtOH. M.p. 168°.
α-Methiodide : needles + H_2O. M.p. 248° decomp. Sol. hot H_2O, EtOH.
Dimethiodide : yellow plates + $1\frac{1}{2}H_2O$. M.p. 156° decomp. More sol. H_2O and less sol. EtOH than monomethiodide.
α-Ethiodide : m.p. anhyd. 248° decomp. Sol. hot H_2O, EtOH.
Diethiodide : yellow prisms + $3H_2O$ from dil. EtOH. M.p. anhyd. 205° decomp. Sol. hot H_2O. Less sol. EtOH.

Hesse, *Ann.*, 1874, **174**, 337 ; *Ber.*, 1882, **15**, 3008.
Butler, Cretcher, *J. Am. Pharm. Assocn.*, 1933, **22**, 414.
Cohen, *J. Chem. Soc.*, 1933, 999.

Quininal

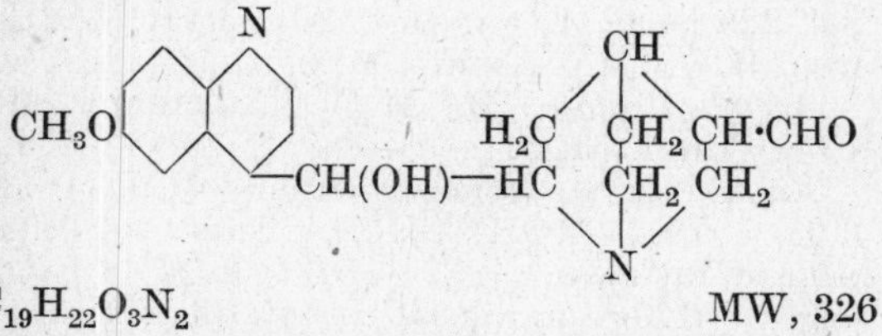

$C_{19}H_{22}O_3N_2$ MW, 326

Cryst. M.p. 160°. $[\alpha]_D^{19}$ − 30° in $CHCl_3$.
Phenylhydrazone : m.p. 145–7°.
p-*Bromophenylhydrazone* : m.p. 148–50°.
Acetyl : m.p. about 120° decomp. $[\alpha]_D^{22}$ − 63·5° in $CHCl_3$.
Benzoyl : m.p. 126°. $[\alpha]_D^{22·4}$ + 79·4° in $CHCl_3$.
Chloropicrate : m.p. 130°.
Dichloropicrate : m.p. 126° decomp.

Seekles, *Rec. trav. chim.*, 1923, **42**, 99.

Quinindoline

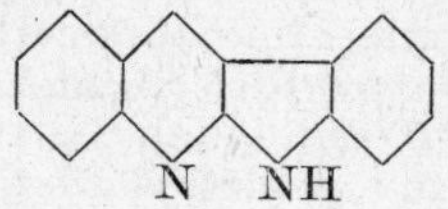

$C_{15}H_{10}N_2$ MW, 218

Yellow needles or leaflets from $PhNO_2$. M.p. 346° (342–3°). Sol. boiling $PhNO_2$, aniline. Prac. insol. hot C_6H_6, AcOEt, EtOH, $CHCl_3$, Et_2O. Sublimes. Sol. H_2SO_4 with violet fluor.
B,HCl : yellow needles. M.p. about 280° decomp.
B₂,H₂PtCl₆ : yellow cryst.
Acetyl : needles. M.p. 185°. Sol. C_6H_6. Spar. sol. MeOH.

Gabriel, Eschenbach, *Ber.*, 1897, **30**, 3020.
Lawson, Perkin, Robinson, *J. Chem. Soc.*, 1924, **125**, 634.
Friedländer, Sander, *Ber.*, 1924, **57**, 652.

Quinine

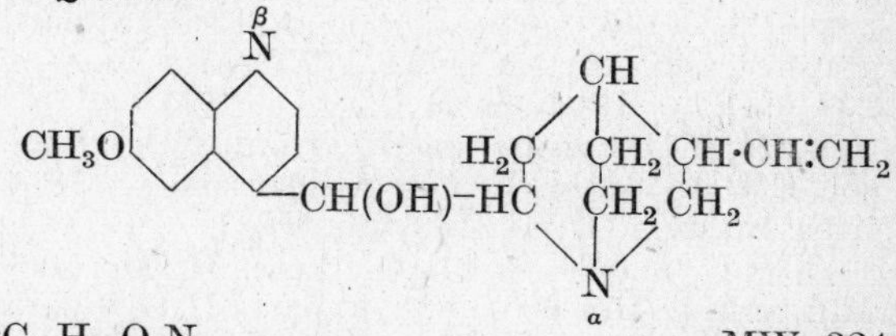

$C_{20}H_{24}O_2N_2$ MW, 324

The most important of the cinchona alkaloids. Stereoisomeric with quinidine. Cryst. + $3H_2O$ from Et_2O below 10°, or needles + $3H_2O$ from EtOH. Loses $1H_2O$ above 15°, $2H_2O$ over H_2SO_4, and $3H_2O$ at 125°. The commercial product is usually a microcryst. powder + $2H_2O$. *Trihydrate* : m.p. 57° : sol. 1670 parts H_2O at 15°, 0·8 part EtOH, 1·1 parts $CHCl_3$, 1·9 parts Et_2O, 212 parts glycerol and 166 parts C_6H_6 at 25°. $[\alpha]_D^{15}$ − 145·2° in EtOH. *Anhydrous* : m.p. 177° (176°, 174·9°, 172·8°) : sol. 1960 parts H_2O at 15°, 760 parts H_2O at 100°, 1·1 parts EtOH, 22·6 parts Et_2O, 1·9 parts $CHCl_3$, 200 parts C_6H_6, 189 parts CCl_4 at 18–22°, 3450 parts 5% KOH and 1890 parts 10% NH_3 at 25°. Sol. dil. H_2SO_4 with blue fluor. $[\alpha]_D^{15}$ − 158·7° in Et_2O, − 169·3° in 97% EtOH. $[\alpha]_D^{17}$ − 167·5° in EtOH, − 117° in $CHCl_3$. Bitter taste. Gives thalleioquin reaction. Acid $KMnO_4$ in cold ⟶ quitenine + formic acid. Alk. $KMnO_4$ ⟶ pyridine-2 : 3 : 4-tricarboxylic acid. CrO_3 ⟶ quininone + quininic acid. PCl_5

⟶ quinine chloride. Boiling AcOH ⟶ quinicine. Red. ⟶ hydroquinine. Br ⟶ quinine dibromide. HCl ⟶ apoquinine. HNO_3 ⟶ cinchomeronic acid. KOH fusion ⟶ 6-methoxylepidine + 6-methoxyquinoline. Forms add. comps. with C_6H_6 and other aromatic compounds. (*Note*: quinine is the Me ether of cupreine, but on demethylation apoquinine is formed, which is also obtained when cupreine is treated with hydrogen halides.)

B_2,H_2SO_4: silky needles + $8H_2O$. Bitter taste. Loses $6H_2O$ on exposure to air giving dihydrate, m.p. 205°. Dehydrated completely at 100°. Sol. 740 parts H_2O at 13°, 30 parts H_2O at 100°, 65 parts EtOH at 15°, 24 parts glycerol at 15°, 1000 parts $CHCl_3$ at 15°. Readily sol. $CHCl_3$–EtOH (2 : 1). $[\alpha]_D^{17}$ − 157·4° in EtOH. $[\alpha]_D^{15}$ (anhyd.) − 235° in dil. H_2SO_4. Sol. dil. H_2SO_4 with strong blue fluor. Pptd. by potassium chromate, oxalate or picrate, sodium salicylate, tannic acid, Rochelle salt, etc.

B,H_2SO_4: prisms + $7H_2O$ from H_2O or EtOH. Loses $6H_2O$ over H_2SO_4 and $7H_2O$ at 100°. Softens at 60°, m.p. anhyd. 160°. Bitter taste. Shows strong fluor. in aq. sol. Sol. 11 parts H_2O, 45 parts EtOH at 13°, 18 parts glycerol, 920 parts $CHCl_3$, 1770 parts Et_2O at 25°. $[\alpha]_D^{15}$ − 164·5° in H_2O.

$B,2H_2SO_4$: prisms + $7H_2O$ from H_2O. Spar. sol. EtOH. Insol. Et_2O. Also prisms + $5H_2O$ from EtOH. $[\alpha]_D^{15}$ − 168·4° in H_2O.

B,HCl: needles + $2H_2O$. Loses H_2O at 100°. M.p. anhyd. 158–60°. Sol. 40 parts H_2O, 9 parts $CHCl_3$, 3 parts EtOH at 15°. Sol. 1 part boiling H_2O. $[\alpha]_D^{17}$ − 133·7° in H_2O, − 57·1° in $CHCl_3$. $[\alpha]_D^{15}$ − 145·5° in 97% EtOH.

B,2HCl: needles. Turns brown at 165–75°, m.p. 180–5°. Sol. 0·75 part H_2O, 5 parts EtOH, 7 parts $CHCl_3$ at 15°. Insol. Et_2O. $[\alpha]_D^{17-19}$ − 233° in H_2O.

B,HBr: needles + H_2O. Softens at 152°, melting finally at 200°. Sol. 55 parts H_2O, 7 parts EtOH, 10 parts $CHCl_3$ at 15°. Sol. 1 part boiling H_2O. Spar. sol. Et_2O. Hygroscopic.

B,2HBr: yellow prisms + $3H_2O$. M.p. 81–2°. Sol. 7 parts H_2O at 15°. Sol. EtOH. Insol. Et_2O.

B,HI: yellow needles. Sol. EtOH, Et_2O. Spar. sol. cold H_2O.

B,2HI: yellow prisms + $5H_2O$. M.p. about 100°. Sol. 20 parts H_2O at 15°.

B,HNO_3: cryst. + H_2O from H_2O. Sol. 70 parts H_2O at 25°.

B,H_2CO_3: needles + H_2O. Sol. EtOH.

B_2,H_3PO_4: needles + $8H_2O$ from H_2O. Sol. 784 parts H_2O at 10°.

B,H_3PO_2: sol. 60 parts H_2O at 15°.

B_2,H_2PtCl_6: orange, amorph. + $3H_2O$. Prac insol. cold H_2O.

B,H_2PtCl_6: yellow cryst. + H_2O. Lose H_2O at 100°. Decomp. above 100°.

B_2,H_2CrO_4: yellow cryst. + $2H_2O$. Sol 2400 parts H_2O at 15°, 160 parts H_2O at 100° Sol. EtOH. Insol. Et_2O.

$B,2HCl,CuCl_2$: brick-red needles. M.p. 210 decomp.

Formate: B,H·COOH. Quinaform. Needles M.p. 109° decomp. Sol. 19 parts H_2O at 16° 8 parts H_2O at 32°. $[\alpha]_D^{20}$ − 144·2° in H_2O B,2H·COOH: needles. Decomp. at 50°.

Acetate: B,CH_3COOH. Needles. M.p. 140° Sol. 30 parts H_2O at 15°.

Chloroacetate: cryst. + $2\frac{1}{2}H_2O$. Sol. 64 part H_2O at 21°. Sol. hot EtOH.

Dichloroacetate: needles + $2H_2O$. Sol. 41· parts H_2O at 22°.

Trichloroacetate: needles. M.p. 139–40°. Sol H_2O, EtOH.

Oxalate: $B_2,(COOH)_2$. Prisms + $6H_2O$. Sol 1030 parts H_2O at 10°.

d-*Tartrate*: $B_2,C_4H_6O_6$. Cryst. powde + $2H_2O$. Loses $1H_2O$ at 120° and second H_2O at 140°. Spar. sol. H_2O. $[\alpha]_D^{17}$ − 216·6° in dil HCl. $B,C_4H_6O_6$: cryst. + H_2O. Loses H_2O at 160°. Less sol. H_2O than *l*-tartrate.

l-*Tartrate*: $B,C_4H_6O_6$. Cryst. + H_2O. Lose H_2O at 100°. More sol. H_2O than *d*-tartrate.

Citrate: $B,C_6H_8O_7$: needles from H_2O M.p. 204° part decomp. $B_2,C_6H_8O_7$. Prisms or needles + $7H_2O$. Sol. 930 parts H_2O a 12°. $B_3,2C_6H_8O_7$: cryst.

l-*Lactate*: $B,C_3H_6O_3$. Needles + $\frac{1}{2}H_2O$ from H_2O.

dl-*Lactate*: $B,C_3H_6O_3$. Cryst. + H_2O.

Benzoate: $B,C_7H_6O_2$. Prisms. Sol. 37 parts H_2O at 100°.

Salicylate: $B,C_7H_6O_3$. Prisms from EtOH Sol. 225 parts H_2O at 16°. Also cryst. + $2H_2O$ from H_2O. M.p. about 195°.

Acetylsalicylate: $B,C_9H_8O_4$. Xaxaquin. M.p 157°. Insol. Et_2O.

Acetyl: cryst. from pet. ether. M.p. 116–17° (108°). Sol. EtOH, $CHCl_3$. Spar. sol. Et_2O. Almost tasteless. $[\alpha]_D^{15}$ − 54·3° in 97% EtOH, $[\alpha]_D^{22\cdot 9}$ − 120·8° in dil. HCl. Sol. dil. acids.

Propionyl: prisms from Et_2O. M.p. 129° Sol. $CHCl_3$. Mod. sol. EtOH, Et_2O. Prac. insol. H_2O.

Isovaleryl: amorph. Hygroscopic. Sol EtOH, Et_2O, C_6H_6.

Benzoyl: prisms from Et_2O. M.p. 139° (138°). Sol. EtOH, Et_2O, $CHCl_3$, C_6H_6, pet. ether,

CS_2. Insol. H_2O. Sol. min. acids. $[\alpha]_D^{17} + 121{\cdot}6°$ in EtOH, $[\alpha]_D^{19{\cdot}2} + 119{\cdot}9°$ in EtOH.

Salicyloyl: saloquinine. Cryst. from dil. EtOH or Et_2O. M.p. 140°. Sol. EtOH, Et_2O, $CHCl_3$, C_6H_6. Insol. H_2O. *Salicylate*: $B,C_7H_6O_3$. Rheumatin. Needles. M.p. 179°. Tasteless. Spar. sol. H_2O.

Anisoyl: needles from Et_2O. M.p. 87–8°. Sol. EtOH, $CHCl_3$, C_6H_6.

Cinnamoyl: needles from Et_2O. M.p. 111°. Sol. hot H_2O, EtOH, Et_2O, C_6H_6. Spar. sol. cold H_2O.

α-*Methochloride*: needles + H_2O. M.p. 181–2°. Sol. H_2O, EtOH.

α-*Methobromide*: needles + H_2O. M.p.124–6°. Sol. EtOH. Mod. sol. cold H_2O.

α-*Methiodide*: needles + 1 or $2H_2O$ from H_2O. M.p. 233–6° decomp. Sol. EtOH. Spar. sol. cold H_2O. Prac. insol. Et_2O, $CHCl_3$.

Dimethioidide: yellow plates + $3H_2O$. M.p. 167–8° decomp. (158–62° decomp.). $[\alpha]_D^{18} - 151°$ in $2N.H_2SO_4$.

α-*Ethochloride*: needles + $3H_2O$. $[\alpha]_D - 122°$ in H_2O.

α-*Ethobromide*: cryst. + $2H_2O$. $[\alpha]_D - 117°$ in H_2O.

α-*Ethiodide*: cryst. + H_2O. M.p. anhyd. 210–11°. $[\alpha]_D - 105°$ in EtOH.

β-*Ethiodide*: needles + $3H_2O$. M.p. 93°.

Diethiodide: yellow cryst. + $3H_2O$ from dil. EtOH. M.p. 140°. Sol. hot H_2O, EtOH. Insol. Et_2O.

De Vrij, *Jahresber. Fortschr. Chem.*, 1864, 443.
Hesse, *Ann.*, 1890, **258**, 133.
Grimaux, Arnaud, *Bull. soc. chim.*, 1892, **7**, 306.
Seekles, *Rec. trav. chim.*, 1923, **42**, 72.
Cohen, *J. Chem. Soc.*, 1933, 999.
Kindler, *Chem.-Ztg.*, 1932, **56**, 165.

Quininic Acid (6-*Methoxycinchoninic acid, 6-hydroxyquinoline-4-carboxylic acid methyl ether*)

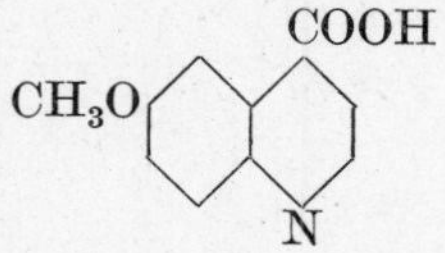

$C_{11}H_9O_3N$ MW, 203

Yellow prisms from dil. HCl. M.p. 280° decomp. Sol. acids with yellow col. Sol. alkalis. Spar. sol. EtOH with blue fluor. destroyed by H_2O or acids. Spar. sol. cold H_2O, Et_2O, C_6H_6. $k = 9 \times 10^{-6}$ at 25°. Alk. $KMnO_4 \longrightarrow$ pyridine-2 : 3 : 4-tricarboxylic acid. Conc. HCl $\longrightarrow$ 6-hydroxycinchoninic acid.

Me ester: $C_{12}H_{11}O_3N$. MW, 217. Prisms from EtOH or Et_2O. M.p. 85°.

Et ester: $C_{13}H_{13}O_3N$. MW, 231. M.p. 69°. Insol. H_2O. *B,HCl*: yellow needles from EtOH. M.p. 160° decomp. B_2,H_2PtCl_6: orange cryst. + $2H_2O$. M.p. 228° decomp.

Amide: $C_{11}H_{10}O_2N_2$. MW, 202. Needles from AcOEt. M.p. 197°. Sol. EtOH. Spar. sol. H_2O, Et_2O. Insol. ligroin, C_6H_6.

Chloride: $C_{11}H_8O_2NCl$. MW, 221·5. *B,HCl*: yellow powder. Decomp. at 186°.

Nitrile: 6 - methoxy - 4 - cyanoquinoline. $C_{11}H_8ON_2$. MW, 184. Yellow needles from C_6H_6. M.p. 157°. Readily sol. EtOH, $CHCl_3$, toluene. Sol. Et_2O, ligroin. Insol. H_2O.

Hydrazide: m.p. 151°.

B,HCl: yellow plates + $2H_2O$. M.p. 225°.

Methochloride: yellow needles. M.p. 215°. Sol. H_2O.

Methiodide: yellow plates or needles from EtOH or H_2O. M.p. 205° decomp. Sol. hot H_2O, EtOH.

Ethobromide: yellow needles from EtOH. M.p. 210°.

Skraup, *Monatsh.*, 1881, **2**, 592.
Hirsch, *Monatsh.*, 1896, **17**, 327.
Koenigs, Schönewald, *Ber.*, 1902, **35**, 2986.
Kaufmann, Peyer, *Ber.*, 1912, **45**, 1805.
John, *Ber.*, 1930, **63**, 2657.
John, Andraschko, *J. prakt. Chem.*, 1930, **128**, 180.
Rabe, Huntenburg, Schultze, Volger, *Ber.*, 1931, **64**, 2492.

Quininone (6-*Methoxycinchoninone*)

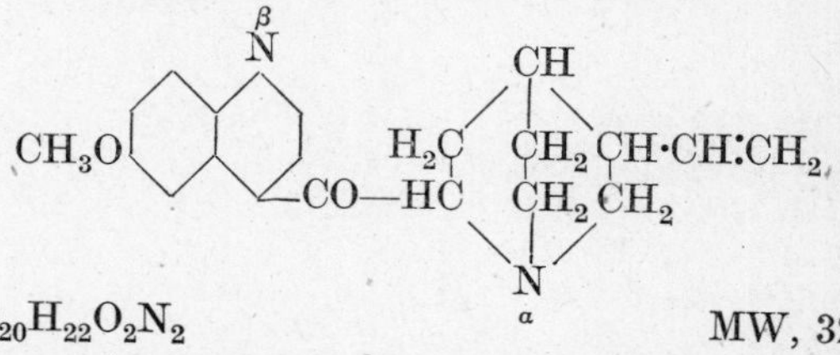

$C_{20}H_{22}O_2N_2$ MW, 322

Needles or leaflets. M.p. 108° (101–8° slow heat.). $[\alpha]_D^{23} + 73{\cdot}8°$ in EtOH. Sol. EtOH, Et_2O, $CHCl_3$, C_6H_6. Spar. sol. ligroin.

B,HCl: hygroscopic cryst. M.p. 210–12°. $[\alpha]_D^{14} + 58{\cdot}7°$ in EtOH.

Oxime: m.p. 113° (not sharp).

Picrate: cryst. from EtOH. M.p. 232–3°.

Picrolonate: yellow needles from EtOH. M.p. 197–8°.

α-Methiodide: cryst. from MeOH. M.p. 213–14°.

Rabe, Kuliga, *Ann.*, 1909, **364**, 346, 349.

Quinisatin (2 : 3 : 4-*Triketotetrahydroquinoline*)

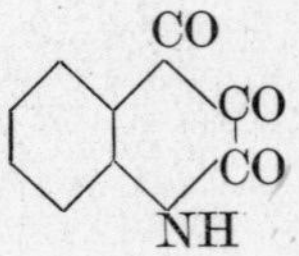

$C_9H_5O_3N$ MW, 175

Yellow prisms + H_2O from H_2O. Loses H_2O at 120–5° turning red. M.p. 255–60°. Mod. sol. cold, sol. hot H_2O. Anhyd. sol. EtOH. Sol. NaOH aq. with yellow col. $NH_2OH \longrightarrow$ 3-oxime.

N-*Me*: reddish-yellow cryst. M.p. 120–2°. Sol. alkalis with yellow col. *Oxime*: red needles from AcOH. Decomp. at 188°. Sol. alkalis with green col.

3-*Oxime*: orange-yellow prisms from EtOH. M.p. 208° decomp. Sol. AcOH. Spar. sol. H_2O, EtOH, Et_2O, $CHCl_3$, C_6H_6. Sol. alkalis with reddish-brown col. Sol. H_2SO_4 with red col. Sn + HCl $\longrightarrow$ 3-amino-2 : 4-dihydroxyquinoline.

Baeyer, Homolka, *Ber.*, 1883, **16**, 2219; 1884, **17**, 985.
Friedländer, Müller, *Ber.*, 1887, **20**, 2015.
See also Kalb, *Ber.*, 1911, **44**, 1460.

Quinitol (*Hexahydrohydroquinone*, *cyclohexandiol*-1 : 4, 1 : 4-*dihydroxycyclohexane*)

$$HO{\cdot}CH\!<\!\begin{matrix}CH_2\text{—}CH_2\\CH_2\text{—}CH_2\end{matrix}\!>\!CH{\cdot}OH$$

$C_6H_{12}O_2$ MW, 116

Cis:

Prisms from Me_2CO. M.p. 102°. Sol. H_2O, EtOH, Me_2CO. Spar. sol. Et_2O, $CHCl_3$. Sublimes in vacuo. Stable to $KMnO_4$.

Diacetyl: cryst. from dil. EtOH. M.p. 34–6°. B.p. 245–50°/710 mm., 145–7°/25 mm.

Dipropionyl: m.p. 39·5–40°.

Dibenzoyl: m.p. 116–17°.

Dicinnamoyl: m.p. 122°.

Me ether: $C_7H_{14}O_2$. MW, 130. B.p. 102–3°/15 mm. n_D^{19} 1·4671. D^{19} 1·023.

Di-Me ether: $C_8H_{16}O_2$. MW, 144. B.p. 67·5–68°/14 mm. n_D^{18} 1·4440. D^{18} 0·9526.

Trans:

Plates from Me_2CO. M.p. 139°. Sol. H_2O, EtOH. Spar. sol. cold Me_2CO. Very spar. sol. Et_2O.

Diacetyl: cryst. from EtOH. M.p. 102–3°. B.p. 245–50°/710 mm., 145–7°/25 mm.

Dipropionyl: m.p. 75·5–76°.

Dibenzoyl: m.p. 151°.

Dicinnamoyl: m.p. 189°.

Me ether: b.p. 102·5–103°/15 mm. n_D^{20} 1·4649. D^{19} 1·021.

Di-Me ether: b.p. 68–9°/15 mm. n_D^{18} 1·4430.

Sabatier, Mailhe, *Ann. chim. phys.*, 1909, **16**, 90.
Leroux, *Ann. chim. phys.*, 1910, **21**, 542.
Baeyer, *Ann.*, 1894, **278**, 92.
Willstätter, Lessing, *Ber.*, 1901, **34**, 507.
Uspenski, Turin, *Chem. Zentr.*, 1923, III, 754.
Palfray, Sabetay, *Bull. soc. chim.*, 1928, **43**, 898.
Palfray, Rothstein, *Bull. soc. chim.*, 1929, **45**, 855.
Rothstein, *Ann. chim.*, 1930, **14**, 486.

Quinizarin (1 : 4-*Dihydroxyanthraquinone*)

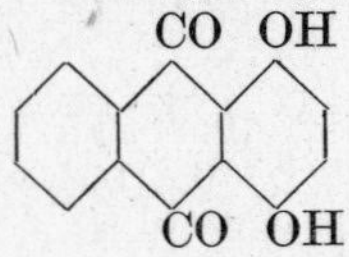

$C_{14}H_8O_4$ MW, 240

Red. cryst. from AcOH, m.p. 200–2°; red cryst. from toluene, m.p. 194°. Sol. 12–13 parts boiling AcOH. Sol. alkalis with violet-blue col. Sol. conc. H_2SO_4 with violet-red col. and greenish-yellow fluor. PbO_2 in AcOH $\longrightarrow$ anthra-1 : 4 : 9 : 10-diquinone. $HNO_3 \longrightarrow$ 2-nitro deriv. $K_3Fe(CN)_6 \longrightarrow$ phthalic acid. Hydrosulphite $\longrightarrow$ leucoquinizarin. Intermediate for dyestuffs.

Me ether: $C_{15}H_{10}O_4$. MW, 254. Yellow needles from MeOH. M.p. 189° (167–8°). Sol. alkalis.

Di-Me ether: $C_{16}H_{12}O_4$. MW, 268. Cryst. from C_6H_6. M.p. 170–1° (143°).

Et ether: $C_{16}H_{12}O_4$. MW, 268. Red needles from EtOH. M.p. 150–1°. Mod. sol. alkalis with reddish-violet col.

Di-Et ether: $C_{18}H_{16}O_4$. MW, 296. Yellow needles. M.p. 176–7°.

Diphenyl ether: 1 : 4-diphenoxyanthraquinone. $C_{26}H_{16}O_4$. MW, 392. Yellow needles from EtOH. M.p. 165°. Sol. boiling EtOH, C_6H_6, AcOH. Spar. sol. boiling MeOH. Insol. ligroin. Sol. conc. H_2SO_4 with bluish-violet col.

Acetyl: orange-yellow needles from C_6H_6. M.p. 186°.

Diacetyl: orange-yellow cryst. from AcOH. M.p. 207–8° (200°). Exists in polymorphic forms.

1-*Acetyl*-4-*benzoyl* : m.p. 195–6°.

Baeyer, Caro, *Ber.*, 1875, **8**, 152.
Liebermann, *Ann.*, 1882, **212**, 10.
Bayer, D.R.P., 229,316, (*Chem. Zentr.*, 1911, I, 181); D.R.P., 255,031, (*Chem. Zentr.*, 1913, I, 354).
M.L.B., D.R.P., 242,379, (*Chem. Zentr.*, 1912, I, 301).
Eckert, Steiner, *Monatsh.*, 1914, **35**, 1145.
Green, *J. Chem. Soc.*, 1926, 1428.
Bigelow, Reynolds, *Organic Syntheses*, Collective Vol. I, 464.
National Aniline and Chemical Co., U.S.P., 1,886,237, (*Chem. Abstracts*, 1933, **27**, 1366).
British Celanese, E.P., 346,355, (*Chem. Abstracts*, 1932, **26**, 1948).
United Alkali, E.P., 245,584, (*Chem. Abstracts*, 1927, **21**, 249).
du Pont, U.S.P., 2,003,859, (*Chem. Abstracts*, 1935, **29**, 4776).

Quinizarin-2-carboxylic Acid (1 : 4-*Dihydroxyanthraquinone-2-carboxylic acid*)

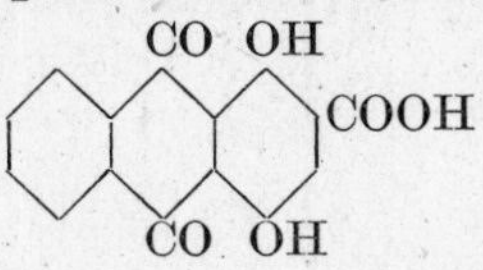

$C_{15}H_8O_6$ MW, 284

Red or yellowish-brown needles from $PhNO_2$. M.p. 249–50° (244–6°). Sol. Me_2CO, warm AcOH, toluene. Spar. sol. EtOH, Et_2O, C_6H_6. Sol. alkalis. Heat ⟶ quinizarin.

Ullmann, Schmidt, *Ber.*, 1919, **52**, 2111.
Bayer, D.R.P., 273,341, (*Chem. Zentr.*, 1914, I, 1719).

Quinol.

See Hydroquinone.

Quinoline (2 : 3-*Benzpyridine*)

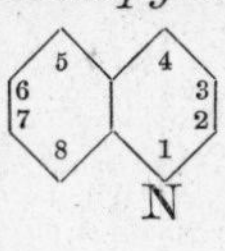

C_9H_7N MW, 129

Occurs in coal-tar and in "stupp" fat. F.p. − 20° (− 15°). B.p. 238·05°/760 mm., 236·9°/749·2 mm., 114°/17 mm. Sol. hot H_2O, dil. acids, EtOH, Et_2O, Me_2CO, CS_2. Mod. sol. cold H_2O. Hygroscopic. Volatile in steam. D_0^0 1·1081, D_0^{20} 1·0947, D_4^{20} 1·0929, D_4^{25} 1·0900 (1·08979), D_4^{50} 1·0699. n_D^{11} 1·6305, n_D^{20} 1·6268, $n_D^{24\cdot9}$ 1·6245, n_D^{29} 1·6218. Heat of comb. C_v 1122·3 Cal. $KMnO_4$ ⟶ quinolinic acid, oxalic acid, NH_3, and CO_2. $HNO_3 + H_2SO_4$ ⟶ 5- + 8-nitroquinolines ⟶ 5 : 7- + 6 : 8-dinitroquinolines. H_2SO_4 at 220° ⟶ quinoline-8-sulphonic acid + a small quantity of quinoline-5-sulphonic acid. H_2SO_4 at 300° ⟶ quinoline-6-sulphonic acid. Sn + HCl or Na + EtOH ⟶ 1 : 2 : 3 : 4-tetrahydroquinoline. HI(+ P) ⟶ hexa- and decahydroquinolines. H(+ Ni) ⟶ 1 : 2 : 3 : 4-tetrahydroquinoline ⟶ decahydroquinoline.

B,HCl : deliquescent prisms + $\frac{1}{2}H_2O$. M.p. 94°, anhyd. 134·5°. Sol. EtOH, $CHCl_3$. Spar. sol. Et_2O–C_6H_6.

B_2,3HCl : m.p. 82°.

B,2HCl : m.p. 46·7° (48·5–57°).

B_2,HBr : cryst. + $2H_2O$. M.p. 41°.

B,HI : yellow needles from EtOH. M.p. 135°.

B,H_2SO_4 : cryst. from EtOH or AcOH. M.p. 163·5–164·5°.

B,HNO_3 : needles from EtOH.

B,$HClO_3$: yellow cryst. M.p. 66–7°. Hygroscopic. Sol. EtOH.

B,HSCN : plates. M.p. 140°. Spar. sol. H_2O, EtOH.

B_2,$H_2Cr_2O_7$: yellow needles from H_2O. M.p. 167° (165–7°). Sol. 282 parts H_2O at 10·5°

B,HCl,$CuCl_2$: brown needles. Decomp. at 185°.

B_2,2HCl,$AuCl_3$: cryst. ppt. M.p. 180°. Decomp. at about 260°.

B,$AuCl_3$: yellow cryst. from EtOH.

B,$HAuCl_4$: yellow needles. M.p. 235–8°. Decomp. at about 260°. Spar. sol. cold H_2O.

B_2,H_2PtCl_6 : orange-yellow needles + $2H_2O$ from dil. HCl. M.p. 227·5° (225°, 226°, 218°).

B_2,H_2PtBr_6 : red prisms or needles. M.p. 254–5°.

Dichloroacetate : cryst. M.p. 63–4°. Sol. H_2O.

Trichloroacetate : cryst. from EtOH. M.p. 100°. Sol. H_2O.

B,$(COOH)_2$: needles from EtOH. M.p. about 105°.

d-*Tartrate* : cryst. + $5H_2O$. M.p. 131°. $[\alpha]_D^{20}$ + 13·2° in H_2O ($[\alpha]_D^{15}$ + 13·5° in H_2O).

Acid d-*Tartrate* : $[\alpha]_D^{15}$ + 14·9° in H_2O.

Acid phthalate : cryst. M.p. 98–9°. Sol. EtOH.

Picrate : yellow needles from C_6H_6. M.p. 203°.

Styphnate : m.p. 207–8°.

Methochloride : cryst. + H_2O from EtOH. M.p. 126°.

Methobromide : needles. M.p. 70°. Sol. H_2O, EtOH, Et_2O, $CHCl_3$. Spar. sol. Me_2CO. Prac. insol. C_6H_6, pet. ether.

Methiodide: orange-red cryst. from EtOH, m.p. 133° (144·5°); yellow cryst. + H_2O from EtOH, m.p. 72°; yellow cryst. + C_6H_6 from C_6H_6, m.p. about 133°.

Methopicrate: yellow needles from H_2O. M.p. 164–5° (169·5°).

Ethochloride: plates + H_2O. M.p. 92·5°, anhyd. 122°.

Ethobromide: plates + H_2O from H_2O or EtOH. M.p. 80°. Loses H_2O at 100°. Sol. $CHCl_3$. Insol. Et_2O.

Ethiodide: yellow prisms from EtOH. M.p. 158° (156–7°). Sol. H_2O, EtOH, $CHCl_3$. Insol. Et_2O.

Propyl chloride: plates + H_2O from H_2O, m.p. 95°. Loses H_2O at 130–5° and melts at 135°. The anhyd. salt is hydroscopic. Cryst. from $CHCl_3$ in prisms + $CHCl_3$, m.p. 79°.

Propyl bromide: hygroscopic cryst. from EtOH, m.p. 148°; plates + $2H_2O$ from H_2O or EtOH, m.p. 66°.

Propyl iodide: yellow cryst. from H_2O or EtOH, m.p. 145°; yellow prisms + $CHCl_3$ from $CHCl_3$.

Isopropyliodide: needles from Me_2CO. M.p. 136°.

Butyl iodide: yellow cryst. from EtOH or prisms from Me_2CO. M.p. 174°.

Isobutyl iodide: yellow cryst. from EtOH or prisms from Me_2CO. M.p. 161°.

Isoamyl bromide: yellow needles + H_2O from EtOH. M.p. 87°, anhyd. 140°.

Isoamyl iodide: yellowish-green cryst. M.p. 184–5°.

Hexadecyl iodide: m.p. 101°.

Allyl iodide: cryst. from H_2O or EtOH. M.p. 177·5°.

Benzyl chloride: plates + $3H_2O$ from H_2O. M.p. 65°, anhyd. 170°. Sol. H_2O, EtOH. Insol. Et_2O. $KMnO_4 \longrightarrow$ 2-benzylaminobenzoic acid.

Benzyl iodide: cryst. M.p. 135°.

N-*Oxide*: needles + $2H_2O$. M.p. 62°.

Picrate: m.p. 143°.

Skraup, *Monatsh.*, 1880, **1**, 316; 1881, **2**, 141.
Walter, *J. prakt. Chem.*, 1894, **49**, 549.
Kneuppel, *Ber.*, 1896, **29**, 704.
Hantzsch, *Ber.*, 1909, **42**, 80.
Barnett, *Chem. News*, 1920, **121**, 205.
König, *Ber.*, 1923, **56**, 1853.
Cohn, Gustavson, *J. Am. Chem. Soc.*, 1928, **50**, 2709.
Cohn, *J. Am. Chem. Soc.*, 1930, **52**, 3685.
Clarke, Davis, *Organic Syntheses*, Collective Vol. I, 466.
Kirkhgof, Fedotov, *Chem. Abstracts*, 1933, **27**, 5331.
Darzens, Delaby, Hiron, *Bull. soc. chim.* 1930, **47**, 227.
Kirchhof, Sassossow, *Chem. Zentr.*, 1935, I, 2371.
Mikhailov, *Chem. Abstracts*, 1934, **28**, 3736.
Dehn, Cope, *J. Am. Chem. Soc.*, 1926, **48**, 2634.

Quinoline-2-aldehyde (2-*Aldehydoquinoline*)

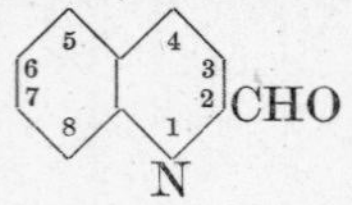

$C_{10}H_7ON$ MW, 157

Prisms or plates from pet. ether, m.p. 71° (70–1°, 67–9°): needles + ?H_2O from H_2O, m.p. 51°. Sol. EtOH, C_6H_6. Spar. sol. H_2O, pet ether. Reduces $NH_3.AgNO_3$.

Oxime: needles. M.p. 189° (184°).

Phenylhydrazone: yellow plates from EtOH. M.p. 204° (195–8°). Spar. sol. cold EtOH. Prac. insol. H_2O, Et_2O.

p-*Nitrophenylhydrazone*: yellow cryst. Sublimes at 225°. M.p. 250°.

Einhorn, *Ber.*, 1886, **19**, 908.
v. Miller, Spady, *Ber.*, 1885, **18**, 3404; 1886, **19**, 132.
Hammick, *J. Chem. Soc.*, 1926, 1303.
Monti, *Chem. Abstracts*, 1934, **28**, 4733.
Cooper, Cohen, *J. Chem. Soc.*, 1932, 723.
Pfitzinger, *J. prakt. Chem.*, 1902, **66**, 264.
Kaufmann, Valette, *Ber.*, 1913, **46**, 57.
Kwartler, Lindwall, *J. Am. Chem. Soc.*, 1937, **59**, 524.

Quinoline-4-aldehyde (4-*Aldehydoquinoline*).

Plates + $1H_2O$, m.p. 84–84·5°. Sol. H_2O, EtOH, Et_2O, toluene. Anhyd. needles from toluene, m.p. 51–3°. Sol. Et_2O, toluene, xylene. Reduces Tollen's.

Oxime: needles from MeOH. M.p. 181–2°.

p-*Nitrophenylhydrazone*: yellow prisms from EtOH. M.p. 261–2°.

See last reference above.

Quinoline-6-aldehyde (6-*Aldehydoquinoline*).

Needles + H_2O from H_2O. M.p. 55°, anhyd. 75–6°.

B_2,H_2PtCl_6: reddish-yellow needles. M.p. 244°.

Anil: needles from dil. EtOH. M.p. 99°.

Oxime: yellow needles from EtOH. M.p. 191°.

Phenylhydrazone: reddish-yellow needles + H_2O from EtOH. M.p. 185°.
Semicarbazone: yellow needles from EtOH. M.p. 239°.
Azine: yellow needles from EtOH. M.p. 261°. Spar. sol. EtOH.
Methiodide: yellow cryst. from EtOH. M.p. 218°. Sol. H_2O.

Howitz, Philipp, *Ann.*, 1913, **396**, 28.

Quinoline-8-aldehyde (8-*Aldehydoquinoline*).

Needles from dil. EtOH. M.p. 94–5°. Sol. hot H_2O, EtOH, Et_2O. Volatile in steam.
B,HCl: cryst. from EtOH. M.p. 213°. Sol. H_2O, EtOH.
B,HI: red cryst. from H_2O. M.p. 228° decomp.
B_2,H_2PtCl_6: reddish-yellow cryst. from alc. HCl. M.p. 250° decomp.
Anil: yellow cryst. from EtOH. M.p. 82°.
Oxime: plates + $\frac{1}{2}H_2O$ from dil. EtOH. M.p. 115°.
Phenylhydrazone: yellow needles from EtOH. M.p. 176°.
Semicarbazone: needles from C_6H_6. M.p. 238–9°.
Azine: yellow needles from C_6H_6. M.p. 248–9°. Spar. sol. C_6H_6.

Howitz, *Ber.*, 1902, **35**, 1274.
Howitz, Schwenk, *Ber.*, 1905, **38**, 1289.
Howitz, Köpke, *Ann.*, 1913, **396**, 39.

2-Quinoline-carbinol.
See 2-Hydroxymethyl-quinoline.

Quinoline-2-carboxylic Acid.
See Quinaldinic Acid.

Quinoline-3-carboxylic Acid

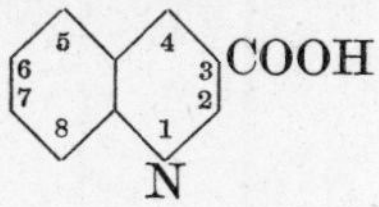

$C_{10}H_7O_2N$ MW, 173

Plates from dil. EtOH. M.p. 275° part. decomp. (271–2°). Sol. hot H_2O, EtOH. Spar. sol. cold H_2O. Alk. $KMnO_4$ ⟶ pyridine-2 : 3 : 5-tricarboxylic acid. Heat with lime ⟶ quinoline.
Me ester: $C_{11}H_9O_2N$. MW, 187. M.p. 76°. *Picrate*: m.p. 187–8°.
Et ester: $C_{12}H_{11}O_2N$. MW, 201. M.p. 65°.
Nitrile: 3-cyanoquinoline. $C_{10}H_6N_2$. MW, 154. M.p. 108°.
Amide: $C_{10}H_8ON_2$. MW, 172. Needles from H_2O. M.p. 198–9° (195°). Mod. sol. EtOH.
Picrate: needles. M.p. 217–18°. Spar. sol. cold EtOH.
B_2,H_2PtCl_6: orange-yellow plates or needles. Sol. hot H_2O.

Doebner, v. Miller, *Ber.*, 1885, **18**, 1644.
Riedel, *Ber.*, 1883, **16**, 1613.
Graebe, Caro, *Ber.*, 1880, **13**, 101.
Mills, Watson, *J. Chem. Soc.*, 1910, **97**, 745.
Koller, Ruppersberg, Strang, *Monatsh.*, 1929, **52**, 66.

Quinoline-4-carboxylic Acid.
See Cinchoninic Acid.

Quinoline-5-carboxylic Acid.

Cryst. from hot AcOH. M.p. 338–40°. Spar. sol. EtOH, H_2O. Insol. Et_2O, C_6H_6, CS_2. Sublimes. Sol. dil. acids and alkalis. Heat with lime ⟶ quinoline.
Nitrile: 5-cyanoquinoline. $C_{10}H_6N_2$. MW, 154. Needles from ligroin, m.p. 89° (87–8°): needles + $1\frac{1}{2}H_2O$ from dil. EtOH, m.p. 70°. Does not boil below 360°. Sol. EtOH, C_6H_6, CS_2. Spar. sol. H_2O, ligroin.
B,HCl: needles or prisms + H_2O. Sol. EtOH.
B_2,H_2PtCl_6: yellow plates or needles. Spar. sol. H_2O.

Bedall, Fischer, *Ber.*, 1881, **14**, 2574; 1882, **15**, 683.
Jakubowski, *Ber.*, 1910, **43**, 3026.
Schlosser, Skraup, *Monatsh.*, 1881, **2**, 519.
Lellmann, Alt, *Ann.*, 1887, **237**, 318.
See also Skraup, Brunner, *Monatsh.*, 1886, **7**, 153, 519.

Quinoline-6-carboxylic Acid.

Prisms, plates or needles. M.p. 291–2° (290–1°). Sol. warm EtOH. Spar. sol. H_2O. Sublimes. Sol. dil. acids and alkalis.
Et ester: $C_{12}H_{11}O_2N$. MW, 201. Needles from dil. EtOH. M.p. 50°. *B,HCl*: needles from EtOH. M.p. 210° decomp. Sol. H_2O.
Amide: $C_{10}H_8ON_2$. MW, 172. Yellow plates from C_6H_6–EtOH. M.p. 174°. *Ethiodide*: red or greenish-yellow cryst. from dil. EtOH. M.p. 229° part. decomp.
Nitrile: cryst. from C_6H_6–ligroin. M.p. 131° (135°). Sublimes. Sol. dil. HCl with red col.
B,HCl: needles + H_2O. Hyd. by H_2O.
B_2,H_2PtCl_6: reddish-yellow plates.

Schlosser, Skraup, *Monatsh.*, 1881, **2**, 526.
v. Georgievics, *Monatsh.*, 1891, **12**, 306.
Biedermann, *Ber.*, 1889, **22**, 2762.
Einhorn, Feibelmann, *Ber.*, 1909, **42**, 4854.
Howitz, Philipp, *Ann.*, 1913, **396**, 29.
I.G., F.P., 727,528, (*Chem. Abstracts*, 1932, **26**, 5104).

Quinoline-7-carboxylic Acid.

Needles from H_2O or EtOH. M.p. 248–9° (248·5–250°, 247°). Sol. EtOH. Spar. sol. hot H_2O. Prac. insol. cold H_2O, C_6H_6. Insol. Et_2O. Sublimes. Heat with lime ⟶ quinoline.

B,HCl : prisms + H_2O from HCl.Aq.

B_2,H_2PtCl_6 : orange prisms or needles.

Skraup, Brunner, *Monatsh.*, 1886, **7**, 142.
Fischer, van Loo, *Ber.*, 1886, **19**, 2473.

Quinoline-8-carboxylic Acid.

Needles from H_2O. M.p. 187° (186–187·5°). Mod. sol. hot H_2O, EtOH. Sol. dil. acids and alkalis. Sublimes. $KMnO_4$ ⟶ quinolinic acid.

Nitrile : 8-cyanoquinoline. Needles from 50% EtOH. M.p. 84°. *B_2,H_2PtCl_6* : orange-yellow needles from H_2O.

B,HCl : prisms from dil. HCl. Sol. H_2O. Spar. sol. dil. EtOH.

B_2,H_2PtCl_6 : orange-yellow needles or red granular cryst. from dil. HCl. Spar. sol. H_2O.

Schlosser, Skraup, *Monatsh.*, 1881, **2**, 530.
Howitz, *Ber.*, 1902, **35**, 1275.
Bedall, Fischer, *Ber.*, 1882, **15**, 683.
Lellmann, Reusch, *Ber.*, 1889, **22**, 1391.
Chakravarti, Granapati, *Chem. Abstracts*, 1935, **29**, 1090.

Quinoline-2 : 3-dicarboxylic Acid (*Acridinic acid*)

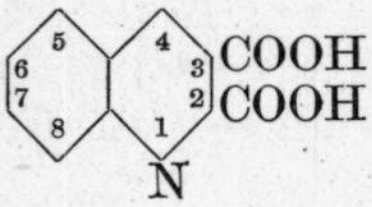

$C_{11}H_7O_4N$ MW, 217

Needles + 2 or $3H_2O$ from hot H_2O or EtOH. Starts to lose CO_2 at 105° leaving residue, m.p. 274°. Sol. EtOH. Spar sol. cold H_2O, Et_2O. Decomp. at 120° ⟶ quinoline-3-carboxylic acid. Does not form salts with acids. Heat with lime ⟶ quinoline. $FeSO_4$ ⟶ reddish-yellow col.

Me ester : $C_{12}H_9O_4N$. MW, 231. M.p. 174–6°.

Di-Me ester : $C_{13}H_{11}O_4N$. MW, 245. Prisms from MeOH or C_6H_6. M.p. 107–8°.

Et ester : $C_{13}H_{11}O_4N$. MW, 245. M.p. 170–2°.

Di-Et ester : $C_{15}H_{15}O_4N$. MW, 273. Prisms from dil. EtOH. M.p. 55–6°.

Anhydride : $C_{11}H_5O_3N$. MW, 199. M.p. 225° (223°).

Amide : $C_{11}H_8O_3N_2$. MW, 216. Cryst. for H_2O or EtOH. M.p. 174–6° decomp.

Diamide : $C_{11}H_9O_2N_3$. MW, 215. Sinters at 250–70° ⟶ imide.

Anilide : m.p. 187° decomp.

Dianilide : sinters at 245°.

Imide : $C_{11}H_6O_2N_2$. MW, 198. M.p. 316° (314–15°).

Phenylimide : m.p. 319–20°.

Graebe, Caro, *Ber.*, 1880, **13**, 100.
Konopnicki, Sucharda, *Chem. Abstracts*, 1928, **22**, 785.
Koller, Strang, *Monatsh.*, 1928, **50**, 48.
Hozer, v. Niementowski, *J. prakt. Chem.*, 1927, **116**, 43.

Quinoline-2 : 4-dicarboxylic Acid.

Needles from H_2O. M.p. 246° decomp. Spar. sol. cold H_2O, EtOH, Et_2O. Insol. $CHCl_3$, C_6H_6, pet. ether. Heat at 240° ⟶ cinchoninic acid. Heat with lime ⟶ quinoline.

2-*Nitrile* : 2-cyanocinchoninic acid. $C_{11}H_6O_2N_2$. MW, 198. Needles. M.p. 226°.

Pfitzinger, *J. prakt. Chem.*, 1897, **56**, 308; 1902, **66**, 264.
Doebner, Peters, *Ber.*, 1889, **22**, 3009.

Quinoline-2 : 6-dicarboxylic Acid.

Cryst. M.p. 275–80° decomp.

v. Miller, *Ber.*, 1890, **23**, 2261.

Quinoline-5 : 6-dicarboxylic Acid.

Plates + H_2O from dil. HCl. M.p. 238–41°. Spar. sol. H_2O, EtOH, Et_2O.

B,HCl : prisms for conc. HCl. Hyd. by H_2O.

B_2,H_2PtCl_6 : brownish-yellow needles. Decomp. above 240°.

Hepner, *Monatsh.*, 1906, 27, 1062.

Quinoline-5 : 8-dicarboxylic Acid.

Needles + $2H_2O$ from dil. HCl. M.p. 268–70°. Prac. insol. cold H_2O. At 270–80° ⟶ quinoline-5- and -8-carboxylic acids.

B,HCl : cryst. + $1\frac{1}{2}H_2O$. Hyd. by H_2O.

B_2,H_2PtCl_6 : yellowish-red cryst. Decomp. by H_2O or EtOH.

Skraup, Brunner, *Monatsh.*, 1886, **7**, 149.

Quinoline-7 : 8-dicarboxylic Acid.

Prisms or needles + H_2O from H_2O. M.p. 206–7° decomp. Spar. sol. hot EtOH, cold H_2O. Part. decomp. on steam dist.

B,HCl : prisms. M.p. 212° decomp. Hyd. by H_2O.

Haid, *Monatsh.*, 1906, **27**, 333.

Quinoline-hydroquinone.

See 5 : 8-Dihydroxyquinoline.

Quinoline-5 : 6-quinone

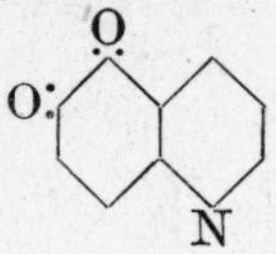

$C_9H_5O_2N$ MW, 159

Prisms. Does not melt below 350°. Sol. AcOH and min. acids. Prac. insol. H_2O and most org. solvents.

5 - *Oxime* : 5 - nitroso - 6 - hydroxyquinoline. Golden-yellow needles from EtOH or AcOH. Chars above 180° without melting. Sol. dil. acids and alkalis. Spar. sol. Et_2O. Insol. H_2O. $HNO_3 \longrightarrow$ 5-nitro-6-hydroxyquinoline. $SnCl_2 \longrightarrow$ 5-amino-6-hydroxyquinoline.

Dioxime : needles from EtOH. Decomp. at 190°.

Mathëus, *Ber.*, 1888, **21**, 1887.
v. Kostanecki, *Ber.*, 1891, **24**, 150.
v. Kostanecki, Reicher, *ibid.*, 158.

Quinoline-5 : 8-quinone

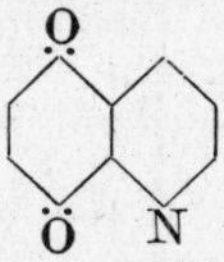

$C_9H_5O_2N$ MW, 159

Greenish needles from EtOH. Decomp. at 110–20°. Very unstable towards alkalis. $SO_2 \longrightarrow$ 5 : 8-dihydroxyquinoline.

5 - *Oxime* : 5 - nitroso - 8 - hydroxyquinoline. Needles from EtOH. Darkens at 220°. Decomp. at 245°. Prac. insol. Et_2O, $CHCl_3$, C_6H_6. Insol. H_2O. Cold HNO_3 or $K_3Fe(CN)_6 \longrightarrow$ 5-nitro-8-hydroxyquinoline. Hot $HNO_3 \longrightarrow$ 5 : 7-dinitro-8-hydroxyquinoline. $SnCl_2 \longrightarrow$ 5-amino-8-hydroxyquinoline.

Dioxime : cryst. from dil. EtOH. Decomp. above 200°. Sol. alkalis with yellow col.

Fischer, Renouf, *Ber.*, 1884, **17**, 1644.
v. Kostanecki, *Ber.*, 1891, **24**, 152.
v. Kostanecki, Reicher, *ibid.*, 157.

Quinoline-2-sulphonic Acid

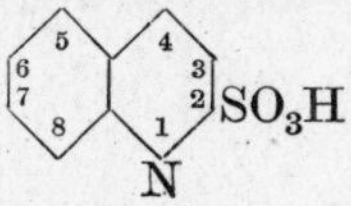

$C_9H_7O_3NS$ MW, 209

Needles from dil. HCl. Does not melt below 270°. Spar. sol. cold H_2O. Boiling $H_2O \longrightarrow$ carbostyril + SO_2. Alkali salts sol. H_2O.

Besthorn, Geisselbrecht, *Ber.*, 1920, **53**, 1021.

Quinoline-3-sulphonic Acid.

Needles + H_2O from H_2O. Loses H_2O at 110°. Does not melt below 270°. Mod. sol. hot H_2O.

Ba salt : needles + H_2O from H_2O. Mod. sol. H_2O.

Besthorn, Geisselbrecht, *Ber.*, 1920, **53**, 1032.

Quinoline-4-sulphonic Acid.

Needles from dil. HCl. Does not melt below 270°. Alkali salts sol. H_2O.

Ca salt : needles + $4H_2O$. Sol. cold H_2O.

Ag salt : needles. Sol. H_2O.

Besthorn, Geisselbrecht, *Ber.*, 1920, **53**, 1023.

Quinoline-5-sulphonic Acid.

Cryst. + H_2O. Sol. H_2O. Sn + HCl $\longrightarrow$ 1 : 2 : 3 : 4 - tetrahydroquinoline - 5 - sulphonic acid. Br in AcOH $\longrightarrow$ 3-bromoquinoline-5-sulphonic acid. Br $\longrightarrow$ 3 : 5 : 8-tribromoquinoline + 3 : 5 : 6 : 8-tetrabromoquinoline. Heat with H_2SO_4 at 250–300° $\longrightarrow$ quinoline-6-sulphonic acid. KOH fusion $\longrightarrow$ 5-hydroxyquinoline.

Ca salt : needles + $5H_2O$ from H_2O or dil. EtOH.

Bedall, Fischer, *Ber.*, 1882, **15**, 684.
Fischer, *Ber.*, 1882, **15**, 1979; 1887, **20**, 731.
Claus, *J. prakt. Chem.*, 1888, **37**, 258.
La Coste, Valeur, *Ber.*, 1887, **20**, 95.
Riemerschmied, *Ber.*, 1883, **16**, 721.

Quinoline-6-sulphonic Acid.

Needles + $1\frac{1}{2}H_2O$. Does not melt below 260°. Spar. sol. cold H_2O, cold EtOH. Br $\longrightarrow$ 3 : 6-dibromoquinoline + 3 : 6 : 8-tribromoquinoline. KOH fusion $\longrightarrow$ 6-hydroxyquinoline. KCN fusion $\longrightarrow$ 6-cyanoquinoline.

Happ, *Ber.*, 1884, **17**, 192.
Fischer, Willmack, *Ber.*, 1884, **17**, 440.
Knueppel, *Ber.*, 1896, **29**, 707.
v. Georgievics, *Monatsh.*, 1887, **8**, 577.

Quinoline-7-sulphonic Acid.

Needles from H_2O. Decomp. above 300°. Sol. H_2O. Spar. sol. EtOH.

Na salt : cryst. + $3H_2O$. Sol. H_2O.

K salt : cryst. + $1\frac{1}{2}$–$2H_2O$.

Ca salt : needles + $4H_2O$. Sol. H_2O.

Ba salt : cryst. + $4H_2O$.

Pb salt : cryst. powder. Sol. H_2O.

Chloride : $C_9H_6O_2NClS$. MW, 227·5. Viscous brown mass. Prac. insol. Et_2O, $CHCl_3$.

Amide : $C_9H_8O_2N_2S$. MW, 208. Cryst. M.p. 119°. Sol. EtOH, Et_2O, $CHCl_3$.

Claus, *J. prakt. Chem.*, 1888, **37**, 261.

Quinoline-8-sulphonic Acid.

Prisms. Spar. sol. H_2O. Dist. ⟶ 3 : 7′- or 4 : 7′-diquinolyl. $KMnO_4$ ⟶ quinolinic acid + 2-amino-3-sulphobenzoic acid. Sn + HCl ⟶ 1 : 2 : 3 : 4-tetrahydroquinoline-8-sulphonic acid. Br ⟶ 3 : 6 : 8-tribromoquinoline + 3 : 5 : 6 : 8-tetrabromoquinoline. KOH fusion ⟶ 8-hydroxyquinoline. H_2SO_4 at 300° ⟶ quinoline-6-sulphonic acid. Fuming HNO_3 at 160° ⟶ 8-nitroquinoline. KCN fusion ⟶ 8-cyano- + 5-cyano-quinolines.

NH_4 salt: plates + H_2O.

Na salt: needles + $5H_2O$.

K salt: prisms + $2H_2O$.

Ca salt: needles + $6H_2O$.

Ba salt: plates + $9H_2O$.

Pb salt: prisms. Spar. sol. H_2O.

Me ester: $C_{10}H_9O_3NS$. MW, 223. Prisms. M.p. 96°. Sol. EtOH, $CHCl_3$. Spar. sol. Et_2O. Prac. insol. ligroin.

Et ester: $C_{11}H_{11}O_3NS$. MW, 237. Cryst. M.p. 73°. Sol. EtOH, Et_2O, $CHCl_3$.

Benzyl ester: $C_{16}H_{13}O_3NS$. MW, 299. Plates or prisms from Et_2O. M.p. 84°. Sol. EtOH, $CHCl_3$. Spar. sol. ligroin.

Chloride: needles. M.p. 124° (122°). Sol. EtOH, Et_2O, $CHCl_3$.

Amide: needles from H_2O. M.p. 183–4°.

Bedall, Fischer, *Ber.*, 1882, **15**, 684.
Fischer, *Ber.*, 1882, **15**, 1979; 1887, **20**, 731.
La Coste, Valeur, *Ber.*, 1887, **20**, 95.
Claus, *J. prakt. Chem.*, 1888, **37**, 258.
v. Georgievics, *Monatsh.*, 1887, **8**, 641.
Claus, Steinitz, *Ann.*, 1894, **282**, 132.
Claus, Küttner, *Ber.*, 1886, **19**, 925.
Hoogewerff, van Dorp, *Rec. trav. chim.*, 1889, **8**, 184.

Quinolinic Acid (*Pyridine*-2 : 3-*dicarboxylic acid*)

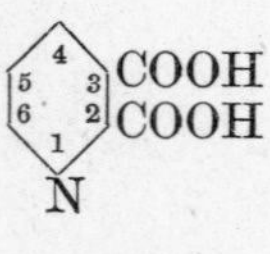

$C_7H_5O_4N$ MW, 167

Prisms from H_2O. M.p. 190–5° decomp. (rapid heat); decomp. at 110° (slow heat). Sol. 183 parts H_2O at 6·5°. Prac. insol. EtOH, Et_2O. Heat ⟶ nicotinic acid.

1-*Me ester*: $C_8H_7O_4N$. MW, 181. Prisms + H_2O from H_2O. M.p. 90°. Obtained anhyd. from AcOEt, m.p. 123°. Sol. hot H_2O, EtOH, Et_2O, $CHCl_3$, C_6H_6.

2-*Me ester*: cryst. from C_6H_6. M.p. 106°. Sol. H_2O and most org. solvents.

1-*Me ester 2-chloride*: $C_8H_6O_3NCl$. MW, 199·5. Needles. M.p. 126°.

Di-Me ester: $C_9H_9O_4N$. MW, 195. Plates from CS_2–ligroin. M.p. 54–5°.

1-*Et ester*: $C_9H_9O_4N$. MW, 195. Plates from C_6H_6. M.p. 132°. Also prisms + H_2O from H_2O.

1-*Et ester 2-chloride*: $C_9H_8O_3NCl$. MW, 213·5. M.p. 163°.

1-*Me* 2-*Et ester*: $C_{10}H_{11}O_4N$. MW, 209. B.p. 250–5° decomp. *B_2,H_2PtCl_6*: orange-red cryst. from alc. HCl. M.p. 165° decomp.

2-*Me* 1-*Et ester*: b.p. 254–8° decomp. *B_2,H_2PtCl_6*: yellow needles from alc. HCl. M.p. 174° decomp.

Di-Et ester: $C_{11}H_{13}O_4N$. MW, 223. B.p. 280–5° part. decomp.

Dichloride: $C_7H_3O_2NCl_2$. MW, 204. B.p. 159°/19 mm.

1-*Amide*: $C_7H_6O_3N_2$. MW, 166. Prisms. M.p. 168·5° decomp. Spar. sol. cold H_2O.

2-*Amide*: prisms. M.p. 160° decomp.

Diamide: $C_7H_7O_2N_3$. MW, 165. Needles from EtOH. M.p. 209° decomp. (190° decomp.). Sol. H_2O, EtOH.

Imide: $C_7H_4O_2N_2$. MW, 148. Needles from EtOH. M.p. 233° (230°). Spar. sol. H_2O, EtOH, AcOH. Insol. C_6H_6, ligroin.

Anhydride: $C_7H_3O_3N$. MW, 149. M.p. 161–2°.

3-*Nitrile*: 3-cyanopicolinic acid. $C_7H_4O_2N_2$. MW, 148. Needles from H_2O. M.p. 175–6°. Sol. EtOH. Spar. sol. Et_2O, $CHCl_3$, pet. ether.

Dihydrazide: needles from EtOH. M.p. 224°. Sol. H_2O. Spar. sol. EtOH.

Me-betaine: plates + H_2O. M.p. 151° decomp. Sol. warm H_2O.

Hoogewerff, van Dorp, *Ber.*, 1879, **12**, 747; *Ann.*, 1880, **204**, 87, 116.
Phillips, *Ann.*, 1895, **288**, 255.
Scheiber, Knothe, *Ber.*, 1912, **45**, 2256.
Kirpal, *Monatsh.*, 1900, **21**, 959; 1901, **22**, 361.
Meyer, *Monatsh.*, 1901, **22**, 580.
Engler, *Ber.*, 1894, **27**, 1787.
Stix, Bulgatsch, *Ber.*, 1932, **65**, 11.
Sucharda, *Ber.*, 1925, **58**, 1727.

α-Quinolone.

See Carbostyril.

γ-Quinolone (*Keto form of* 4-*hydroxyquinoline*)

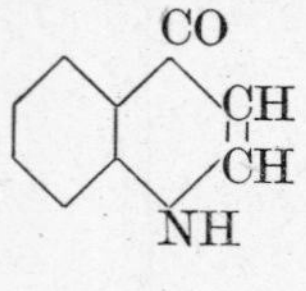

C_9H_7ON MW, 145

Cryst. from EtOH. M.p. 235°.
Acetyl : m.p. 228°.
Phenylhydrazone : needles from dil. EtOH. M.p. 168°.
N-*Me* : see Echinopsine.
N-*Et* : dark resin. Sol. H_2O. Prac. insol. Et_2O. *Chloroaurate* : m.p. 155° decomp.

Reissert, *Ber.*, 1887, **20**, 3109; 1888, **21**, 1376.
Meyer, *Monatsh.*, 1906, **27**, 265.

γ-Quinolone-2-carboxylic Acid (*Keto form of kynurenic acid*).

The compound (m.p. 167°) regarded as γ-quinolone-2-carboxylic acid by Heller and Sourlis (*Ber.*, 1908, **41**, 2699) has been shown by Meisenheimer and Stotz (*Ber.*, 1925, **58**, 2334) to be quinaldinic acid *N*-oxide.

2-Quinolylacetaldehyde

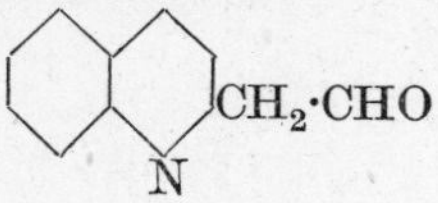

$C_{11}H_9ON$ MW, 171

Cryst. from H_2O or EtOH. M.p. 184° (103–4°). Sol. acids. Reduces $NH_3.AgNO_3$.
Oxime : m.p. 205°.
Phenylhydrazone : yellow needles from EtOH. M.p. 198–9°.
B_2,H_2PtCl_6 : yellow cryst. + $2H_2O$ from dil. HCl.
Semicarbazone : needles from EtOH. M.p. 244° decomp.
Picrate : yellow cryst. from dil. EtOH. M.p. 212°.

Einhorn, *Ber.*, 1886, **19**, 908.
Einhorn, Sherman, *Ann.*, 1895, **287**, 38.
Hupe, Schramme, *Z. physiol. Chem.*, 1928, **177**, 315.
Kenner, Nandi, *Ber.*, 1936, **69**, 639.
Borsche, Manteuffel, *Ann.*, 1936, **526**, 45.

2-Quinolylacetic Acid

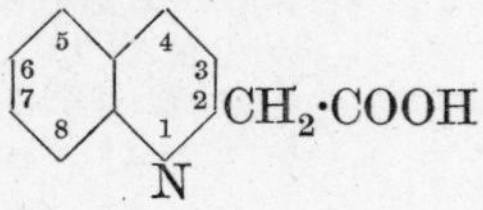

$C_{11}H_9O_2N$ MW, 187

Prisms from MeOH. M.p. 274–5° (271–2°). Sublimes. Ca salt insol. H_2O, EtOH.
Me ester : $C_{12}H_{11}O_2N$. MW, 201. Flakes from ligroin. M.p. 72°.
Et ester : $C_{13}H_{13}O_2N$. MW, 215. Plates from ligroin. M.p. 68–9° (67°). B.p. 240°/16 mm. *Picrate* : m.p. 152°.
Nitrile : $C_{11}H_{10}ON_2$. MW, 186. M.p. 53–4°. B.p. 140°/1 mm. *Picrate* : m.p. 176–7° decomp.
B_2,H_2PtCl_6 : dimorphous. Needles and brownish-red plates. Sol. H_2O.
Picrate : yellow needles from MeOH. M.p. 236–7°.

Einhorn, Sherman, *Ann.*, 1895, **287**, 40.
Kenner, Nandi, *Ber.*, 1936, **69**, 639.
Borsche, Manteuffel, *Ann.*, 1936, **526**, 22.

8-Quinolylacetic Acid.

Free acid not described.
Nitrile : $C_{11}H_8N_2$. MW, 168. Cryst. M.p. 88°.

Claus, D.R.P., 98,272, (*Chem. Zentr.*, 1898, II, 744).
Howitz, Nöther, *Ber.*, 1906, **39**, 2706.

2-[2-Quinolyl]-acrylic Acid

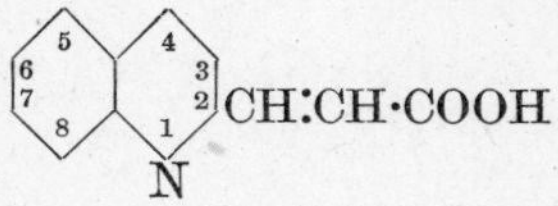

$C_{12}H_9O_2N$ MW, 199

Plates from MeOH. Decomp. at 194–6° (190–5°). $KMnO_4$ (according to conditions) ⟶ either quinoline-2-aldehyde or 1 : 2-dihydroxy-2-[2-quinolyl]-propionic acid. $SnCl_2$ or NaHg ⟶ 2-[2-quinolyl]-propionic acid. Na + EtOH or Sn + HCl ⟶ 2-[2-(1 : 2 : 3 : 4-tetrahydroquinolyl)]-propionic acid.
Et ester : $C_{14}H_{13}O_2N$. MW, 227. Needles from ligroin. M.p. 73°.
Amide : $C_{12}H_{10}ON_2$. MW, 198. Needles from H_2O. M.p. 175–6°. Sol. warm. EtOH, C_6H_6.
B,HCl : m.p. 216–18°.
B,HBr : m.p. 218–20°.
Acetate : m.p. 203°.

Einhorn, *Ber.*, 1886, **19**, 908.
Einhorn, Sherman, *Ann.*, 1895, **287**, 27.
v. Miller, Spady, *Ber.*, 1885, **18**, 3403; 1886, **19**, 130.
Alberts, Bachmann, *J. Am. Chem. Soc.*, 1935, **57**, 1285.

2-[4-Quinolyl]-acrylic Acid.

Needles from EtOH–AcOH. M.p. 250–5° decomp. Spar. sol. EtOH. Prac. insol. H_2O. HI(+ P) in AcOH ⟶ 2-[4-quinolyl]-propionic acid.

B_2,H_2PtCl_6 : yellow needles + $1\frac{1}{2}H_2O$ from H_2O.

Koenigs, Müller, *Ber.*, 1904, **37**, 1338.

Quinolylamine.
See Aminoquinoline.
α-Quinolylcarbinol.
See 2-Hydroxymethyl-quinoline.
Quinolylethylene.
See Vinylquinoline.

2-Quinolylhydrazine (2-*Hydrazinoquinoline*)

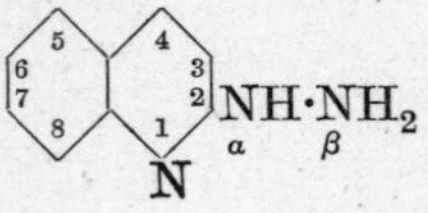

$C_9H_9N_3$ MW, 159

Cryst. from C_6H_6. M.p. 142–3° (134–5°). Sol. EtOH. Spar. sol. Et_2O, ligroin.

B_2,H_2PtCl_6 : cryst. ppt. M.p. 170° decomp.

Picrate : m.p. 187° decomp.

β-N-*Phenyl* : *sym.*-phenylquinolylhydrazine. Needles from EtOH. M.p. 191°. Unstable. Sol. $CHCl_3$, AcOH. Spar. sol. EtOH. Prac. insol. Et_2O.

β-N-*Acetyl* : prisms from EtOH. M.p. 195°.

β-N-*Benzoyl* : needles from Me_2CO. M.p. 204°.

Perkin, Robinson, *J. Chem. Soc.*, 1913, **103**, 1978.
Marckwald, Meyer, *Ber.*, 1900, **33**, 1885.
Ephraim, *Ber.*, 1891, **24**, 2818.
Fargher, Furness, *J. Chem. Soc.*, 1915, **107**, 697.

5-Quinolylhydrazine.
Yellow needles from H_2O. M.p. 150–1°. Sol. EtOH. Spar. sol. C_6H_6. Insol. pet. ether.

B,2HCl : yellow needles. M.p. 248°.

Dufton, *J. Chem. Soc.*, 1892, **61**, 785.

6-Quinolylhydrazine.
Non-crystalline. Readily resinifies.

B,HCl : cryst. from dil. EtOH.

Benzylidene deriv. : yellowish-red needles from H_2O or red cryst. from EtOH. M.p. 203°.

Knueppel, *Ann.*, 1900, **310**, 82.

8-Quinolylhydrazine.
Needles. M.p. 64°.

B,2HCl : yellow prisms.

Dufton, *J. Chem. Soc.*, 1891, **59**, 757.

2-Quinolyl Mercaptan.
See Thiocarbostyril.

2-Quinolylnitramine (2-*Nitraminoquinoline*, N-*nitro-2-aminoquinoline*)

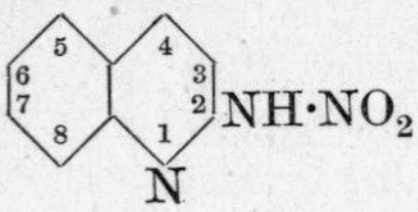

$C_9H_7O_2N_3$ MW, 189

Yellowish needles from AcOH. M.p. 223–5° decomp. Turns red in air.

Tschitschibabin, Witkovsky, Lapschin, *Ber.*, 1925, **58**, 806.

4-Quinolylnitramine (4-*Nitraminoquinoline*, N-*nitro-4-aminoquinoline*).

Yellow needles + H_2O from H_2O. M.p. 207° decomp. Sol. EtOH, hot H_2O.

B_2,H_2PtCl_6 : orange-red cryst. Decomp. at 210°. Hyd. by H_2O.

See previous reference and also
Claus, Frobenius, *J. prakt. Chem.*, 1897, **56**, 202.

2-[2-Quinolyl]-propionic Acid

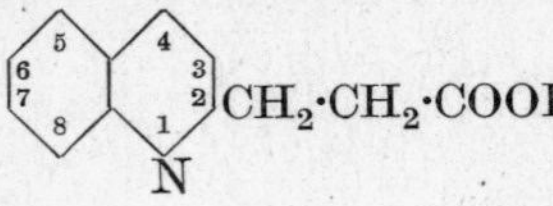

$C_{12}H_{11}O_2N$ MW, 201

Plates from C_6H_6. M.p. 122–3°. Sol. EtOH, Et_2O, C_6H_6, $CHCl_3$, Me_2CO. Insol. H_2O, ligroin.

Amide : $C_{12}H_{12}ON_2$. MW, 200. Needles from C_6H_6. M.p. 149–50°. Sol. hot H_2O, EtOH, C_6H_6. Insol. pet. ether.

Hydrazide : m.p. 165°. Reduces Fehling's and $NH_3.AgNO_3$.

B_2,H_2PtCl_6 : brownish-red plates from dil. HCl. M.p. 197° decomp.

Einhorn, Sherman, *Ann.*, 1895, **287**, 29.
Koenigs, *Ber.*, 1900, **33**, 220.
Kermack, Muir, *J. Chem. Soc.*, 1931, 3092.

2-[4-Quinolyl]-propionic Acid.
Needles from H_2O. M.p. 202–3°. Sol. EtOH, hot H_2O, boiling Me_2CO. Na + EtOH $\longrightarrow$ 2-[4-(1 : 2 : 3 : 4-tetrahydroquinolyl)]-propionic acid.

Koenigs, Müller, *Ber.*, 1904, **37**, 1339.

Quinone.
See *p*-Benzoquinone.
Quinone-anilide.
See 2 : 5-Dianilino-*p*-benzoquinone.
Quinophan.
See 2-Phenylquinoline-4-carboxylic Acid.

Quinophenol.
See 8-Hydroxyquinoline.

Quinophthalone

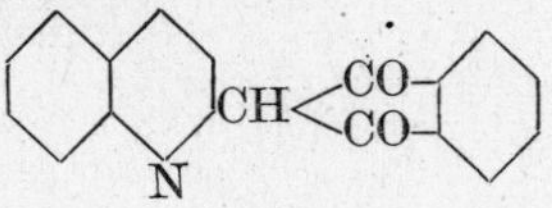

or

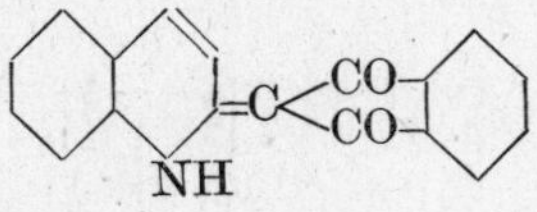

$C_{18}H_{11}O_2N$ MW, 273

Golden-yellow needles from EtOH. M.p. 241° (234°). Sol. hot AcOH, hot Me_2CO, $CHCl_3$, warm C_6H_6, toluene. Prac. insol. EtOH, Et_2O. Sol. conc. HCl and conc. H_2SO_4 with red col. Sublimes. Warm HNO_3 (D 1·2) $\longrightarrow$ quinaldinic + phthalic acids.

Phenylhydrazone: red needles from $CHCl_3$. M.p. 206°.

Anil: red needles from EtOH. M.p. 232°. Sol. $CHCl_3$. Spar sol. EtOH.

N-*Me*: orange-yellow needles or brownish-red prisms. M.p. 249·5°.

Jacobsen, Reimer, *Ber.*, 1883, **16**, 1082.
Eibner, *Ber.*, 1904, **37**, 3606.
Eibner, Lange, *Ann.*, 1901, **315**, 336.
Eibner, Hofmann, *Ber.*, 1904, **37**, 3015, 3018.
Kuhri, Bär, *Ann.*, 1935, **516**, 155.
Weno, Suzuki, *J. Soc. Chem. Ind. Japan*, 1933, **36**, Supplementary binding, 195.

Quinosol.
See under 8-Hydroxyquinoline.

Quinoticine (*Quinotoxine dihydride, quinicine dihydride, hydroquinotoxine, hydroquinicine*)

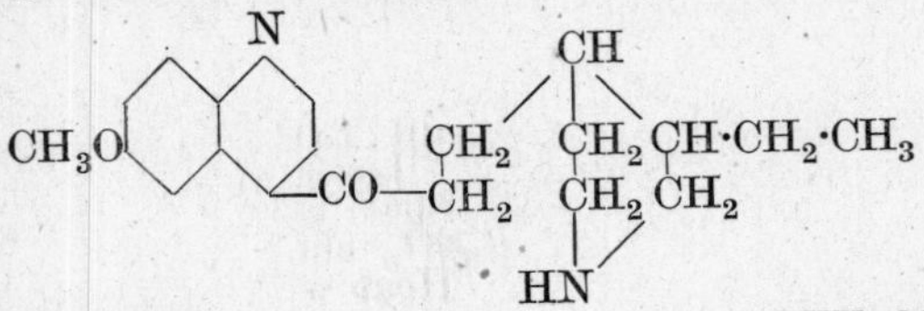

$C_{20}H_{26}O_2N_2$ MW, 326

Yellow cryst. Sol. EtOH, Et_2O, $CHCl_3$, dil. acids. $[\alpha]_D^{15}$ − 17° in HCl. Gives yellow col. in H_2SO_4 but no fluor.

B_2,H_2PtCl_6: orange cryst. + H_2O. Insol. H_2O.

Hesse, *Ann.*, 1887, **241**, 273.
Rabe, Kindler, *Ber.*, 1919, **52**, 1844.
See also Kaufmann, Rothlin, Brunnschweiler, *Ber.*, 1916, **49**, 2303.

Quinotidine.
Hydroquinidine, *q.v.*

Quinotine.
Hydroquinine, *q.v.*

Quinotinone (*Quininone dihydride, hydroquininone*)

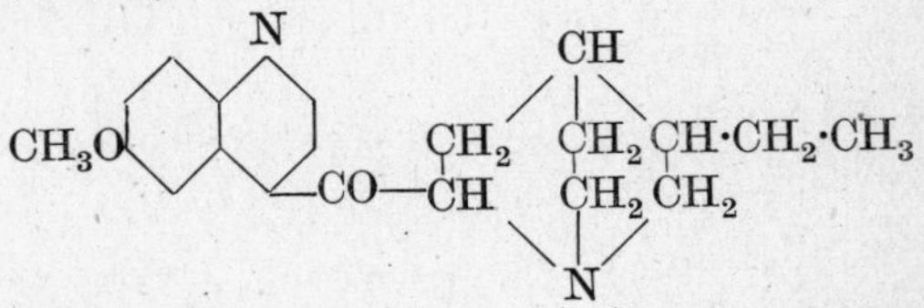

$C_{20}H_{24}O_2N_2$ MW, 324

M.p. 100°. $[\alpha]_D^{19}$ + 73·15° in EtOH, $[\alpha]_D^{20}$ + 65·0° in 96% EtOH.

Rabe, Kindler, *Ber.*, 1919, **52**, 1845.
See also Kaufmann, Rothlin, Brunnschweiler, *Ber.*, 1916, **49**, 2303.

Quinotoxine.
See Quinicine.

Quinovic Acid

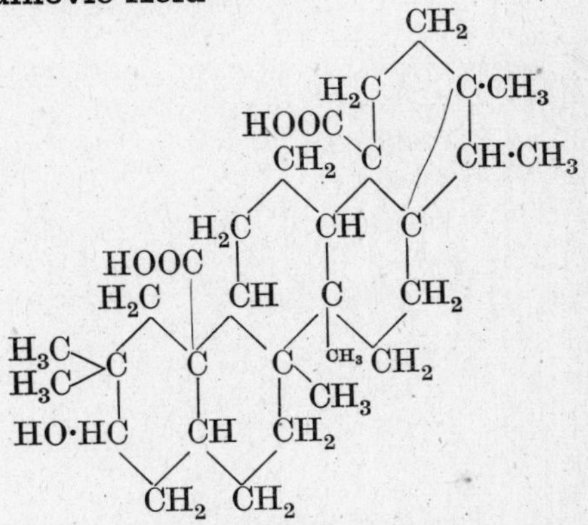

Suggested structure

$C_{30}H_{46}O_5$ MW, 486

Needles. M.p. 298°. Spar. sol. hot EtOH, AcOH. Insol. H_2O. Sol. NH_3 and alkalis. $[\alpha]_D$ + 87–8° in KOH. Decomp. at 300° $\longrightarrow$ pyroquinovic acid. Sol. H_2SO_4 with evolution of CO.

Di-Me ester: $C_{32}H_{50}O_5$. MW, 514. M.p. 173–4°. *Acetyl*: m.p. 208–9°. *Benzoyl*: m.p. 235–6°.

Di-Et ester: $C_{34}H_{54}O_5$. MW, 542. Cryst. M.p. 127–30°. Sol. EtOH, Et_2O.

Acetyl: m.p. 284° decomp.

Benzoyl : m.p. 284° decomp.

Hlasiwetz, *Ann.*, 1851, **79**, 145.
Liebermann, Giesel, *Ber.*, 1883, **16**, 932.
Wieland, Erlenbach, *Ann.*, 1927, **453**, 83.
Wieland, Hoshino, *Ann.*, 1930, **479**, 179.
Wieland, Utzino, *Ann.*, 1931, **488**, 242.
Wieland, Kraus, *Ann.*, 1932, **497**, 140.
Wieland, Hartmann, Dietrich, *Ann.*, 1936, **522**, 191.

Quinovin

$C_{36}H_{56}O_9$ MW, 632

α-.

Occurs with cinchona alkaloids as glucoside. Cryst. powder or needles from EtOH. Sol. EtOH. Spar. sol. Et_2O, $CHCl_3$, C_6H_6. Prac. insol. H_2O. $[\alpha]_D + 59{\cdot}1°$ ($+ 56{\cdot}6°$) in EtOH. Bitter taste. Sol. NH_3 and alkalis. Sol. conc. H_2SO_4 with orange-yellow col. and evolution of CO. Reduces Fehling's. Hyd. $\longrightarrow$ quinovic acid + quinovose (isorhodeose).

β-.

Occurs with alkaloids from the *Remijia* species. Plates from dil. EtOH. M.p. 235° decomp. Sol. EtOH. Insol. Et_2O, AcOEt. $[\alpha]_D + 27{\cdot}9°$ in EtOH.

Hlasiwetz, *Ann.*, 1859, **111**, 182.
Rochleder, *J. prakt. Chem.*, 1867, **102**, 16.
Liebermann, Giesel, *Ber.*, 1883, **16**, 928.

Quinovose (*Chinovose*).

This sugar has been shown to be identical with isorhodeose, (*q.v.*).

See Votoček, Rác, *Chem. Abstracts*, 1929, **23**, 4449; 1932, **26**, 4307.

Quinoxaline (*Benzpyrazine, phenpiazine*)

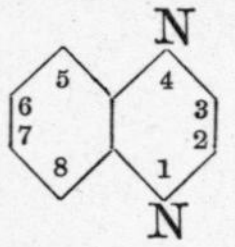

$C_8H_6N_2$ MW, 130

Cryst. M.p. 30·5° (28°). B.p. 225–6° (220–3°, 229·5°/760·3 mm.), 140°/40 mm. D_4^{48} 1·1334. n_D^{48} 1·6231. Sol. H_2O, EtOH, Et_2O, C_6H_6. $KMnO_4 \longrightarrow$ pyrazine-2 : 3-dicarboxylic acid. Na + EtOH $\longrightarrow$ 1 : 2 : 3 : 4-tetrahydroquinoxaline.

B,HCl : needles. Sinters at 170°. Decomp. at 184°. Sol. H_2O, EtOH.

B,H_2SO_4 : plates. M.p. 186–7°. Sol. H_2O. Mod. sol. EtOH.

B_2,H_2PtCl_6 : yellow needles.

Oxalate : needles. M.p. 169°. Spar. sol. H_2O.

Methiodide : reddish-yellow plates from EtOH. M.p. 176° decomp. Sol. H_2O. Mod. sol. EtOH.

Ethiodide : red needles from EtOH. M.p. 146° decomp. Sol. H_2O.

Hinsberg, *Ber.*, 1884, **17**, 320; *Ann.*, 1887, **237**, 334; 1896, **292**, 245.
Merz, Ris, *Ber.*, 1887, **20**, 1194.

Quinoxyl.

See Yatren.

Quinuclidine (*Nuclidine, 1 : 4-ethylenepiperidine*)

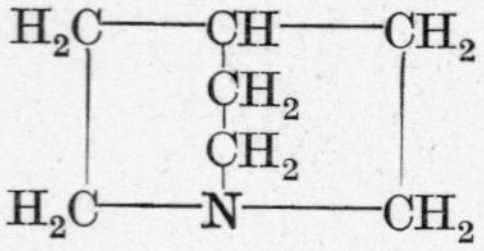

$C_7H_{13}N$ MW, 111

Cryst. M.p. 158° (sealed tube). Very sol. H_2O, org. solvents. Very volatile. Ammoniacal odour. Does not decolourise $KMnO_4$.

$B,HAuCl_4$: leaflets from H_2O. M.p. 271–3° decomp.

B_2,H_2PtCl_6 : leaflets from H_2O. M.p. 238–40° decomp.

Ethiodide : plates from EtOH. M.p. 270–1°. Slightly hygroscopic.

Ethochloroplatinate : leaflets from hot H_2O. M.p. 271–2° (212°) decomp.

Picrate : pale yellow needles from EtOH. M.p. 275–6°. Sol. 35–40 parts hot EtOH.

Meisenheimer, Neresheimer, Schneider, *Ann.*, 1920, **420**, 213.

Quitenine

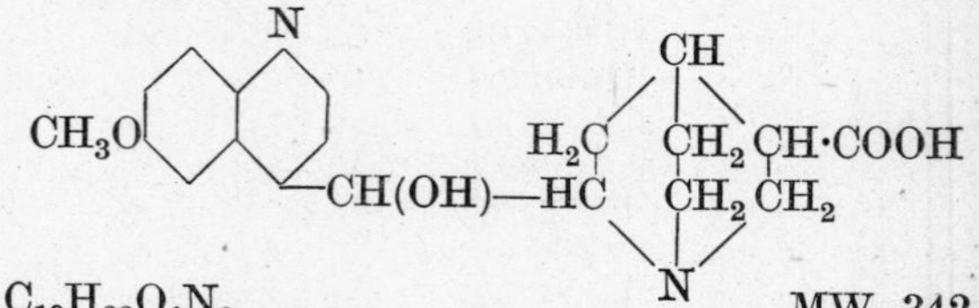

$C_{19}H_{22}O_4N_2$ MW, 342

Prisms + $4H_2O$ from dil. EtOH. M.p. 286° decomp. (228° anhyd.). Loses H_2O at 110°. Sol. acids and alkalis. Spar. sol. H_2O. Insol. Et_2O. Sol. in dil. H_2SO_4 shows blue fluor. $[\alpha]_D - 143°$ in EtOH. Heat with $H_2SO_4 \longrightarrow$ quitenicine. HI $\longrightarrow$ quitenol + CH_3I. Gives thalleioquin reaction.

$B_3,2H_2SO_4$: prisms + $15H_2O$. Sol. H_2O. Spar. sol. EtOH.

B,H_2PtCl_6 : yellow leaflets + $3H_2O$. Spar. sol. H_2O.

Et ester : needles. M.p. 198°. Insol. H_2O.

Ethiodide : prisms. M.p. 210°.

Skraup, *Ann.*, 1879, **199**, 348.
Bucher, *Monatsh.*, 1893, **14**, 598.
Giemsa, Oesterlin, *Ber.*, 1931, **64**, 60.

Quitenol

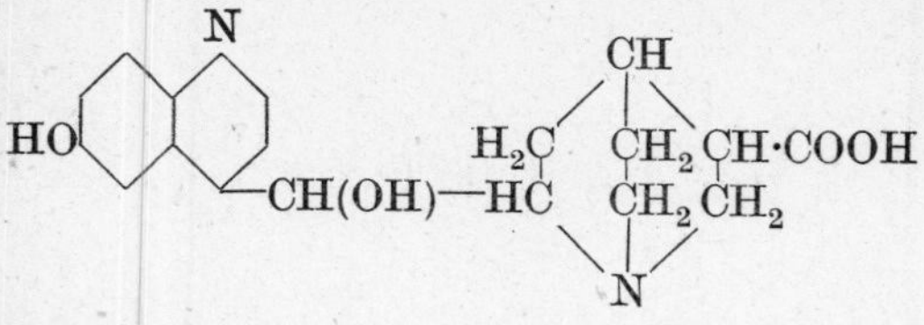

$C_{18}H_{20}O_4N_2$ MW, 328

Needles + H_2O. Decomp. above 270° without melting. Sol. acids, alkalis. Pptd. from alk. sol. by CO_2. Prac. insol. H_2O, EtOH, Et_2O. $FeCl_3$ in dil. HCl gives red col. Gives thalleioquin reaction.

B,2HCl : plates + H_2O.
B_2,H_2PtCl_6 : yellow prisms.
B,H_2SO_4 : yellow plates + H_2O.
Me ether : *see* Quitenine.

Bucher, *Monatsh.*, 1893, **14**, 604.

R

Racemic Acid.
See Tartaric Acid.

R-Acid.
See 2-Naphthol-3 : 6-disulphonic Acid.

Raffinose (*Melitriose, gossypose*)

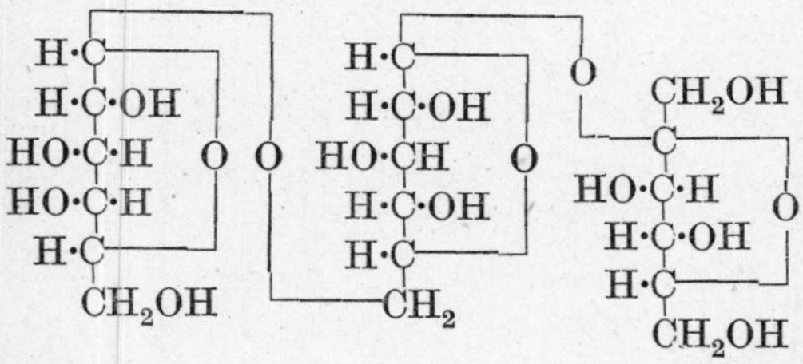

$C_{18}H_{32}O_{16}$ MW, 504

Occurs in sugar beet, cotton seed, manna, etc. White needles or prisms + $5H_2O$. M.p. 80°, anhyd. 118–19°. Slight sweet taste. $[\alpha]_D$ + 104° in H_2O (hydrate), + 123° in H_2O (anhyd.). D^0 1·465. Sol. H_2O. Mod. sol. MeOH. Insol. EtOH, Et_2O. Does not reduce Fehling's. Does not form an osazone. Hyd. by dil. acids ⟶ galactose + glucose + fructose. Emulsin ⟶ sucrose + galactose. Invertase or raffinase ⟶ melibiose + fructose. HNO_3 ⟶ saccharic and mucic acids.

Undeca-acetyl : cryst. from EtOH. M.p. 99–101°. $[\alpha]_D$ + 92·2°. Sol. EtOH, Et_2O, $CHCl_3$, C_6H_6. Spar. sol. CS_2, ligroin.

Octabenzoyl : cryst. from AcOH. M.p. 98°. $[\alpha]_D^{18\cdot5}$ + 155·3° in AcOH.

Undecabenzoyl : m.p. 113°. $[\alpha]_D^{20\cdot5}$ + 106·8°. Sol. $CHCl_3$, AcOEt. Mod. sol. Et_2O, Me_2CO, C_6H_6, hot MeOH, hot EtOH.

*Undeca-*p*-chlorobenzoyl* : m.p. 130–2°. $[\alpha]_D^{18}$ + 96·8°.

*Undeca-*p*-bromobenzoyl* : m.p. 138°. $[\alpha]_D^{20\cdot5}$ + 85·2°.

Undeca-Me ether : b.p. 238–40°/0·02 mm.

Harding, *Sugar*, 1923, **25**, 308.
Englis, Decker, Adams, *J. Am. Chem. Soc.*, 1925, **47**, 2724.
Hudson, Harding, *J. Am. Chem. Soc.*, 1914, **36**, 2110.
Vogel, Pictet, *Helv. Chim. Acta*, 1928, **11**, 898.
Haworth, Charlton, Hickinbottom, *J. Chem. Soc.*, 1927, 1527.
Hungerford, Nees, *Ind. Eng. Chem.*, 1934, **26**, 462.

Ramalic Acid.
See Obtusatic Acid.

Ramalinolic Acid

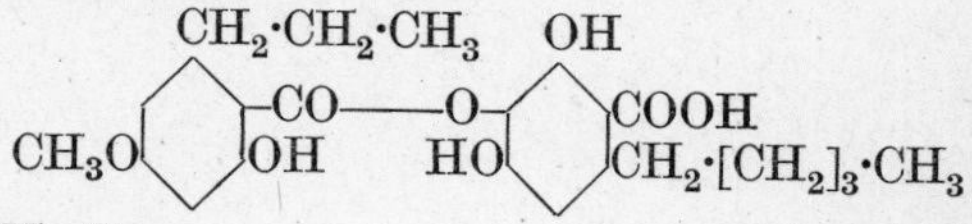

$C_{23}H_{28}O_8$ MW, 432

Prisms from C_6H_6. M.p. 164°. Sol. EtOH, Et_2O, Me_2CO. Spar. sol. C_6H_6, $CHCl_3$. $FeCl_3$ ⟶ violet col. in EtOH.

Tri-Me ether Me ester : $C_{27}H_{36}O_8$. MW, 488. M.p. 75°.

Asahina, Kusaka, *Ber.*, 1936, **69**, 1896.

Ratanhin.
See Surinamine.

Ravenelin (1 : 4 : 5-*Trihydroxy-2-methylxanthone*)

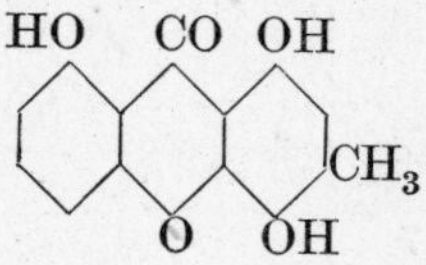

$C_{14}H_{10}O_5$ MW, 258

Found in *Helminthosporium Ravenlii*, C., and *H. Turcicum*, P. Yellow prismatic needles from $Me_2CO–CHCl_3$. M.p. 267–8°. Sol. Py, hot AcOH. Mod. sol. hot EtOH, Me_2CO. Spar. sol. C_6H_6, pet. ether. Hot $Na_2CO_3.Aq.$ ⟶ brownish-yellow sol. NaOH ⟶ yellow sol. ⟶ deep brown on shaking in air. Alc. $FeCl_3$ ⟶ intense greenish-brown col. Conc. H_2SO_4 ⟶ orange-yellow sol. ⟶ orange-brown on heating.

Di-Me ether : $C_{16}H_{14}O_5$. MW, 286. Yellow needles from EtOH. M.p. 285–7°.

Tri-Me ether : $C_{17}H_{16}O_5$. MW, 300. Prisms from EtOH. M.p. 178–9°. Conc. HCl ⟶ intense orange sol. $B,HCl,FeCl_3$: red prisms from AcOH. M.p. 174–5°.

Triacetyl : needles from AcOH. M.p. 204–5°. Sol. hot EtOH, C_6H_6.

Tribenzoyl : prismatic needles from Py. M.p. 255°. Sol. warm Py. Mod. sol. hot AcOH. Spar. sol. boiling EtOH.

Trianisoyl : needles from AcOH. M.p. 216–18°.

> Raistrick, Robinson, White, *Biochem. J.*, 1936, **30**, 1303.

Reductic Acid (1 : 2-*Dihydroxycyclopenten-one*-3)

$$\begin{matrix} H_2C\!\!-\!\!-\!\!-\!\!C\!\cdot\!OH \\ | \quad\quad\quad \| \\ H_2C\quad\quad C\!\cdot\!OH \\ \diagdown\;\;\diagup \\ CO \end{matrix}$$

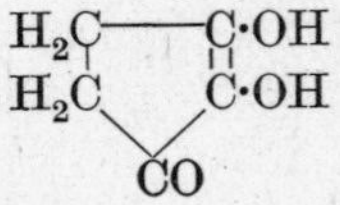

$C_5H_6O_3$ · MW, 114

Yellow cryst. from AcOEt. M.p. 213–213·5°. decomp. (207·5°). Sol. H_2O, EtOH, MeOH. Spar. sol. Et_2O, AcOEt, Me_2CO. Insol. C_6H_6.

Acetyl deriv. : m.p. 195°.

Diacetyl deriv. : oil. B.p. 112°/0·2 mm.

Osazone : m.p. 246°.

Me ether : $C_6H_8O_3$. MW, 128. Needles. M.p. 138°.

Di-Me ether : $C_7H_{10}O_3$. MW, 142. B.p. 120°/12 mm.

> Llgami, *Chem. Abstracts*, 1934, **28**, 7259.
> Reichstein, Oppenauer, *Helv. Chim. Acta*, 1934, **17**, 390.

Regularobufagin

$C_{25}H_{34}O_6$ MW, 430

Prisms from EtOH.Aq. M.p. 235–6°.

Diacetyl deriv. : m.p. 224–5° (196–7°).

> Kotake, *J. Chem. Soc. Japan*, 1934, **55**, 179.
> Jensen, *J. Am. Chem. Soc.*, 1935, **57**, 1765.

Resacetophenone (4-*Acetoresorcinol*, 2 : 4-*di-hydroxyacetophenone*)

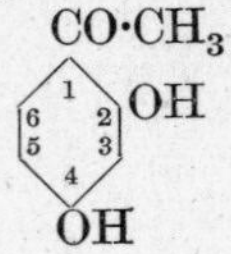

$C_8H_8O_3$ MW, 152

Leaflets or needles. M.p. 147° (145–6°). $FeCl_3$ ⟶ red col.

2-Acetyl : m.p. 119–20°.

4-Acetyl : m.p. 74°. *2-Benzoyl* : m.p. 67°.

Diacetyl : m.p. 38°.

4-Benzoyl : m.p. 106–7°. *2-Anisoyl* : m.p. 109–10°.

Dibenzoyl : m.p. 80–1°.

Dianisoyl : m.p. 118°.

Diveratroyl : m.p. 151–2°.

Dicinnamoyl : m.p. 131°.

Oxime : m.p. 198–200° decomp. *Acetyl* : m.p 174–5° decomp.

Semicarbazone : m.p. 214–20° decomp.

Phenylhydrazone : m.p. 159°.

2-Me ether : *see* Isopæonol (Isopeonol).

4-Me ether : *see* Peonol.

Di-Me ether : 2 : 4-dimethoxyacetophenone, peonol methyl ether, isopeonol methyl ether. $C_{10}H_{12}O_3$. MW, 180. M.p. 44° (40°). *Oxime* : m.p. 125°.

2-Me : *4-Et ether* : isopeonol ethyl ether. $C_{11}H_{14}O_3$. MW, 194. Needles from EtOH. M.p. 49°.

4-Me : *2-Et ether* : peonol ethyl ether. Needles from EtOH. M.p. 70°. $D^{80·2}$ 1·0571. $n_a^{80·2}$ 1·51434.

4-Et ether : $C_{10}H_{12}O_3$. MW, 180. Needles from EtOH. M.p. 49°.

Di-Et ether : 2 : 4-diethoxyacetophenone. $C_{12}H_{16}O_3$. MW, 208. M.p. 74°. *Oxime* : m.p. 122°.

4-Propyl ether : $C_{11}H_{14}O_3$. MW, 194. M.p. 25°.

Dipropyl ether : $C_{14}H_{20}O_3$. MW, 236. M.p. 26°.

4-Butyl ether : $C_{12}H_{16}O_3$. MW, 208. M.p. 43°.

Dibutyl ether : $C_{16}H_{24}O_3$. MW, 264. M.p. 32°.

4-α-Glycerol ether : $C_{11}H_{14}O_5$. MW, 226. M.p. 88°. *Phenylhydrazone* : m.p. 119–20°.

> Robinson, Shah, *J. Chem. Soc.*, 1934, 1494.
> Gulati, Venkataraman, *J. Chem. Soc.*, 1931, 2376.

Kostanecki, Tambor, *Ber.*, 1895, **28**, 2306.
Schaffer, U.S.P., 1,745,507, (*Chem. Abstracts*, 1930, **24**, 1707).
Kondo, Nakagawa, *Chem. Abstracts*, 1931, **25**, 515.
Cox, *Rec. trav. chim.*, 1931, **50**, 850.
Baker, *J. Chem. Soc.*, 1934, 1691.
Nadkarni, Wheeler, *J. Chem. Soc.*, 1936, 589.

Resacetophenone-5-carboxylic Acid (2 : 4-*Dihydroxyacetophenone-5-carboxylic acid*, 2 : 4-*dihydroxy-5-acetobenzoic acid*)

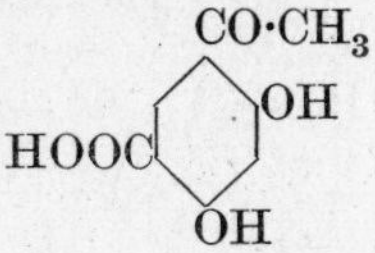

$C_9H_8O_5$ MW, 196

Needles from Me_2CO. M.p. 256° decomp.
Me ester: $C_{10}H_{10}O_5$. MW, 210. Needles from C_6H_6. M.p. 124–5°. *Hydrazone*: (i) m.p. 138°. (ii) M.p. 170°.
Di-Me ether: $C_{11}H_{12}O_5$. MW, 224. Prisms from MeOH. M.p. 231–3°.
Et ester: $C_{11}H_{12}O_5$. MW, 224. M.p. 94°. *Di-Et ether*: $C_{15}H_{20}O_5$. MW, 280. Needles from ligroin. M.p. 96–7°.
p-*Bromophenylhydrazone*: m.p. 243°.

Liebermann, Lindenbaum, *Ber.*, 1908, **41**, 1610.

Resodiacetophenone (4 : 6-*Diacetoresorcinol*)

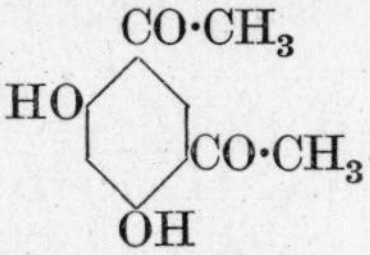

$C_{10}H_{10}O_4$ MW, 194

Needles from EtOH. M.p. 182°. Sol. hot EtOH, hot C_6H_6, warm Et_2O, warm AcOH.
Diacetyl: m.p. 120°.
Dibenzoyl: m.p. 118°.
Dioxime: m.p. 242°.
Phenylhydrazone: m.p. 233°. *Monoacetyl deriv.*: m.p. 191–2°. *Monobenzoyl deriv.*: m.p. 214–15°.
Diphenylhydrazone: m.p. 291°.
Mono-Me ether: $C_{11}H_{12}O_4$. MW, 208. M.p. 121·5°. Diphenylhydrazone: m.p. 245–6°, decomp.
Di-Me ether: $C_{12}H_{14}O_4$. MW, 222. M.p. 171·5°.
Mono-Et ether: $C_{12}H_{14}O_4$. MW, 222. M.p. 109°.
Di-Et ether: $C_{14}H_{18}O_4$. MW, 250. M.p. 156°.
Me-Et ether: $C_{13}H_{16}O_4$. MW, 236. M.p. 152°.
Monopropyl ether: $C_{13}H_{16}O_4$. MW, 236. M.p. 94–5°.
Me-Propyl ether: $C_{14}H_{18}O_4$. MW, 250. M.p. 125·5°.
Et-Propyl ether: $C_{15}H_{20}O_4$. MW, 264. M.p. 95°.
Dipropyl ether: $C_{16}H_{22}O_4$. MW, 278. M.p. 86°.
Monoisopropyl ether: m.p. 97°.
Et-Isopropyl ether: m.p. 101·5°.
Propyl-Isopropyl ether: m.p. 78°.
Di-isopropyl ether: m.p. 126·5°.
Monobutyl ether: $C_{14}H_{18}O_4$. MW, 250. M.p. 63°.
Me-Butyl ether: $C_{15}H_{20}O_4$. MW, 264. M.p. 117°.
Et-Butyl ether: $C_{16}H_{22}O_4$. MW, 278. M.p. 104°.
Propyl-Butyl ether: $C_{17}H_{24}O_4$. MW, 292. M.p. 61·5°.
Isopropyl-Butyl ether: m.p. 76°.
Dibutyl ether: $C_{18}H_{26}O_4$. MW, 306. M.p. 92·5°.
Mono-isobutyl ether: m.p. 88°.
Me-Isobutyl ether: m.p. 102·5°.
Et-Isobutyl ether: m.p. 72°.
Propyl-Isobutyl ether: m.p. 64°.
Isopropyl-Isobutyl ether: m.p. 80°.
Butyl-Isobutyl ether: m.p. 78°.
Di-isobutyl ether: m.p. 99°.

Baker, *J. Chem. Soc.*, 1934, 71 (*Bibl.*); *ibid.*, 1684.

Resoflavin (3 : 4 : 6 : 4′ : 6′-*Pentahydroxydiphenic acid dilactone*)

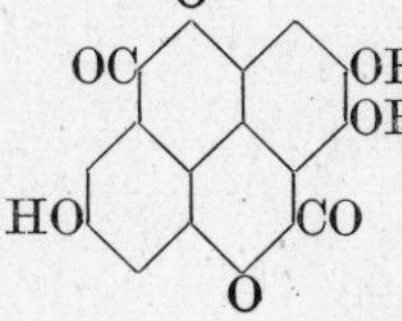

$C_{14}H_6O_7$ MW, 286

Yellow cryst. from EtOH. Decomp. about 380°. Zn dist. ⟶ fluorene.
Triacetyl: m.p. 275–9°.
Tri-Me ether: $C_{17}H_{12}O_7$. MW, 328. M.p. 286–8°.

Badische, D.R.P., 85,390.
Herzig, Tscherne, *Ann.*, 1907, **351**, 30.

Resomorin (3 : 7 : 2′ : 4′-*Tetrahydroxyflavone, 7 : 2′ : 4′-trihydroxyflavonol*)

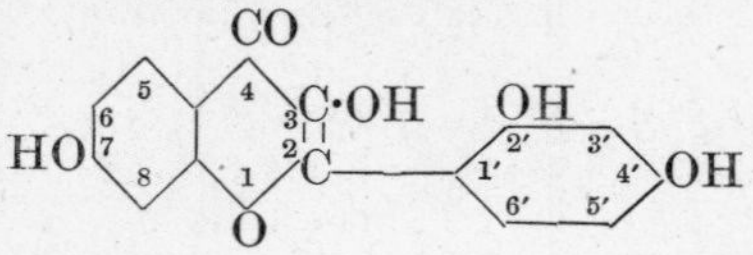

$C_{15}H_{10}O_6$ MW, 286

Cryst. Very sol. EtOH.

7 : 2′ : 4′-*Tri-Me ether* : $C_{18}H_{16}O_6$. MW, 328. Cryst. from C_6H_6 or EtOH. M.p. 205°. Conc. $H_2SO_4 \longrightarrow$ yellowish sol. with intense bluish-green fluor. *Acetyl* : prisms from EtOH.Aq. M.p. 189–91°.

Tetra-acetyl : needles from EtOH.Aq. M.p. 129–30°.

v. Kostanecki, Lampe, Triulzi, *Ber.*, 1906, **39**, 94.

Resorcin-benzein (*Resorcinol-benzein*)

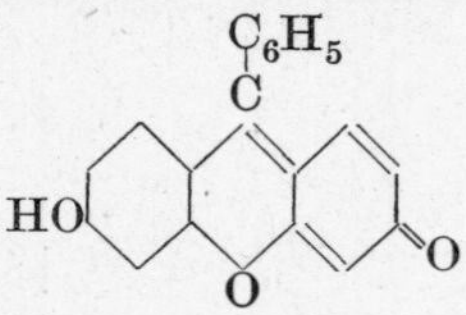

$C_{19}H_{12}O_3$ MW, 288

Red needles from $PhNO_2$. M.p. 330–1°. Sol. EtOH, Me_2CO, $PhNO_2$, aniline, Py. Spar. sol. Et_2O, $CHCl_3$. Sols. fluoresce.

6-*Acetyl* : m.p. 197°.

6-*Me ether* : $C_{20}H_{14}O_3$. MW, 302. Red needles from Et_2O. M.p. 206° (204°).

Liebig, *J. prakt. Chem.*, 1912, **85**, 244.
Gomberg, West, *J. Am. Chem. Soc.*, 1912, **34**, 1568.
Pope, Howard, *J. Chem. Soc.*, 1910, **97**, 1026.
Moir, *Chem. Abstracts*, 1923, **17**, 2283.

Resorcindialdehyde (2 : 4 (or 4 : 6)-*Dihydroxyisophthaldehyde, resorcendialdehyde*)

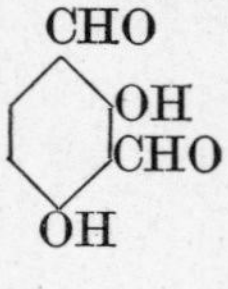

or

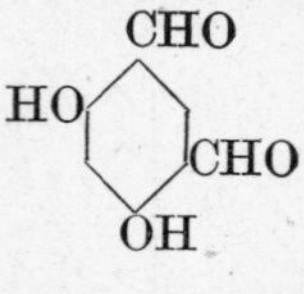

$C_8H_6O_4$ MW, 166

Needles from hot H_2O. M.p. 127°. Sol. EtOH, Et_2O, C_6H_6, $CHCl_3$. Sublimes.

Dioxime : m.p. 209°.

Me ether : $C_9H_8O_4$. MW, 180. (i) Needles from hot H_2O. M.p. 179°. Sol. EtOH, Et_2O, C_6H_6, $CHCl_3$, AcOH. Insol. ligroin. (ii) Needles from hot H_2O. M.p. 88–9°. Sol. EtOH, Et_2O, C_6H_6, ligroin. Spar. sol. H_2O. Both forms volatile in steam.

Tiemann, Lewy, *Ber.*, 1877, **10**, 2211.
Tiemann, Parrisius, *Ber.*, 1880, **13**, 2369.

Resorcinol (1 : 3-*Dihydroxybenzene*)

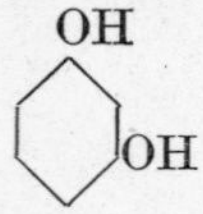

$C_6H_6O_2$ MW, 110

Needles from C_6H_6. Plates from H_2O. (i) M.p. 110°, stable. (ii) M.p. 108–108·5°, labile. B.p. 273° (276·5°/759·7 mm.), 178°/16 mm. Sol. H_2O, EtOH, Et_2O. Mod. sol. $CHCl_3$, CS_2. Spar. sol. C_6H_6. $FeCl_3 \longrightarrow$ violet col. Heat of comb. C_v 683·1 Cal. $k = 3 \cdot 6 \times 10^{-10}$ at 18°. Reduces Tollen's and Fehling's. Sweet taste.

Mono-acetyl : curesol. B.p. 283°.

Diacetyl : b.p. 278°, 273°/708 mm.

Dichloroacetyl : m.p. 71·5–72° (76°). B.p. 191–2°/15 mm.

Di-iodoacetyl : m.p. 59–61°.

Di-1-bromopropionyl : m.p. 66°. B.p. 217–20°/10 mm.

Di-1-bromobutyryl : b.p. 225–7°/19 mm.

Di-1-bromoisobutyryl : b.p. 227–8°/20 mm.

Di-1-bromoisovaleryl : b.p. 222–8°/15 mm.

Penta-acetyl-β-glucoside : m.p. 118–19°. $[\alpha]_D^{18}$ — 40·1° in C_6H_6.

Monobenzoyl : m.p. 135–6° (133°).

Dibenzoyl : m.p. 117°.

Mono-salicyloyl : m.p. 141° (139°).

Disalicyloyl : m.p. 111°.

Di-p-nitrobenzoyl : m.p. 182°.

Dicinnamoyl : m.p. 119·5–120°.

Monohippuryl : *see* Hippurylresorcinol.

Di-benzenesulphonyl : m.p. 69–70°.

Di-p-toluenesulphonyl : m.p. 80–1°.

Di-d-camphor-β-sulphonyl : m.p. 129–30°.

Picrate : m.p. 89–90°.

Mono-Me ether : *m*-hydroxyanisole, *m*-methoxyphenol. $C_7H_8O_2$. MW, 124. B.p. 244°, 144°/25 mm., 102°/5 mm. *Acetyl* : b.p. 254–6°.

Di-Me ether : 1 : 3-dimethoxybenzene. $C_8H_{10}O_2$. MW, 138. M.p. — 52°. B.p. 216·5–217·7°. D_4^4 1·0705.

Mono-Et ether : *m*-hydroxyphenetole, *m*-ethoxyphenol. $C_8H_{10}O_2$. MW, 138. B.p. 246–7°, 117°/5·5 mm.

Di-Et ether : 1 : 3-diethoxybenzene. $C_{10}H_{14}O_2$ MW, 166. M.p. 12·4°. B.p. 234·4–235·2°/756 mm.

Me-Et ether : $C_9H_{12}O_2$. MW, 152. B.p. 216°.

Mono-propyl ether: $C_9H_{12}O_2$. MW, 152. B.p. 120°/5 mm.
Me-Propyl ether: $C_{10}H_{14}O_2$. MW, 166. B.p. 226°.
Dipropyl ether: $C_{12}H_{18}O_2$. MW, 194. B.p. 251°.
Monobutyl ether: $C_{10}H_{14}O_2$. MW, 166. B.p. 130°/5 mm.
Me-Isobutyl ether: $C_{11}H_{16}O_2$. MW, 180. B.p. 234°.
Monoamyl ether: $C_{11}H_{16}O_2$. MW, 180. B.p. 140°/5 mm.
Mono-isoamyl ether: b.p. 138°/5 mm.
Di-isoamyl ether: $C_{16}H_{26}O_2$. MW, 250. M.p. 47°.
Monohexyl ether: $C_{12}H_{18}O_2$. MW, 194. B.p. 145°/5 mm.
Monoheptyl ether: $C_{13}H_{20}O_2$. MW, 208. B.p. 160°/5 mm.
Mono-octyl ether: $C_{14}H_{22}O_2$. MW, 222. B.p. 170°/5 mm.
Mono-nonyl ether: $C_{15}H_{24}O_2$. MW, 236. B.p. 171°/4·5 mm.
Di-trichlorovinyl ether: $C_{10}H_4O_2Cl_6$. MW, 369. M.p. 53–4°.
Phenyl ether: *see* 3-Hydroxydiphenyl Ether.
Diphenyl ether: $C_{18}H_{14}O_2$. MW, 262. M.p. 61·5°.
Di-2 : 4-dinitrophenyl ether: $C_{18}H_{10}O_{10}N_4$. MW, 442. M.p. 184°.
Monobenzyl ether: $C_{13}H_{12}O_2$. MW, 200. M.p. 69·2°. B.p. 200°/5 mm.
Mono-p-chlorobenzyl ether: $C_{13}H_{11}O_2Cl$. MW, 234·5. M.p. 76°. B.p. 235°/13 mm.
Dibenzyl ether: $C_{20}H_{18}O_2$. MW, 290. M.p. 76°.
Mono-phenylethyl ether: $C_{14}H_{14}O_2$. MW, 214. M.p. 44°. B.p. 202°/6 mm.
Mono-phenylpropyl ether: $C_{15}H_{16}O_2$. MW, 228. B.p. 220°/5·5 mm.
Mono-cyclohexyl ether: $C_{12}H_{16}O_2$. MW, 192. B.p. 160°/6 mm.
Me-α-phenylvinyl ether: $C_{15}H_{14}O_2$. MW, 226. B.p. 199–200°/16 mm.

Knoll, D.R.P., 281,099, (*Chem. Zentr.*, 1915, I, 179).
Phillips, Gibbs, *Ind. Eng. Chem.*, 1920, **12**, 857.
Carr, Dahlen, U.S.P., 1,999,955, (*Chem. Abstracts*, 1935, **29**, 4029).
Gallay, U.S.P., 1,956,570, (*Chem. Abstracts*, 1934, **28**, 4073).
Hayashi, *Chem. Abstracts*, 1934, **28**, 1679.
Ruth, *Chem. Abstracts*, 1933, **27**, 5316.
Klarmann, Gatyas, Shternov, *J. Am. Chem. Soc.*, 1931, **35**, 3397.
Fabre, *Ann. chim.*, 1922, **18**, 49.
Dey, *J. Indian Chem. Soc.*, 1935, **12**, 685.

Resorcinol-carboxylic Acid.
See Resorcylic Acid.

Resorcinol-dicarboxylic Acid.
See 4 : 6-Dihydroxyisophthalic Acid *and* 2 : 6-Dihydroxyterephthalic Acid.

Resorcinol-4 : 6-disulphonic Acid

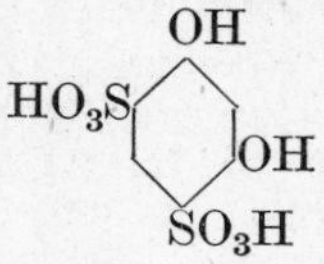

$C_6H_6O_8S_2$ MW, 270

Needles + $2H_2O$. Decomp. at 100°. Sol. H_2O, EtOH. Insol. Et_2O.
Dichloride: $C_6H_4O_6Cl_2S_2$. MW, 307. M.p. 178–9°. *Di-Me ether*: $C_8H_8O_6Cl_2S_2$. MW, 335. Yellow prisms from AcOEt. M.p. 175–8°. Sol. Et_2O, $CHCl_3$, AcOH, CS_2.
Diamide: $C_6H_8O_6N_2S_2$. MW, 268. Does not melt below 300°.
Dianilide: m.p. 262°.

Blumenstock, *Monatsh.*, 1925, **46**, 499.

Resorcinol-4-sulphonic Acid

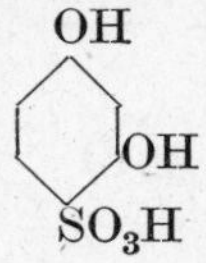

$C_6H_6O_5S$ MW, 190

K salt: prisms + $2H_2O$ from H_2O.
Ba salt: hygroscopic cryst.

Darzens, Dubois, *Bull. soc. chim.*, 1892, **7**, 713.

β-Resorcylcyclohexane.
See 4-Hexahydrobenzoylresorcinol.

α-Resorcylic Acid (3 : 5-*Dihydroxybenzoic acid, resorcinol-5-carboxylic acid*)

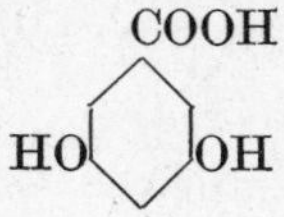

$C_7H_6O_4$ MW, 154

Cryst. + $1\frac{1}{2}H_2O$ from H_2O. M.p. 232–3° (237–40°) anhyd. Sol. EtOH, Et_2O, hot H_2O. $k = 9{\cdot}1 \times 10^{-5}$ at 25°. Oleum or hot conc. $H_2SO_4 \longrightarrow$ 1 : 2 : 4 : 5 : 6 : 8 - hexahydroxy - anthraquinone.
Diacetyl: m.p. 156–7°.
Dicarbomethoxyl: m.p. 161–4°.
Me ester: $C_8H_8O_4$. MW, 168. Leaflets. M.p. 163–5°. *Mono-Me ether*: $C_9H_{10}O_4$. MW, 182. B.p. 375° decomp. *Di-Me ether*:

$C_{10}H_{12}O_4$. MW, 196. M.p. 42–4°. B.p. 298°, 157°/125 mm.

Di-Me ether: *see* 3 : 5-Dimethoxybenzoic Acid.

Di-Et ether: $C_{11}H_{14}O_4$. MW, 210. M.p. 87–8°. *Et ester*: $C_{13}H_{18}O_4$. MW, 238. M.p. 19–20°. B.p. 212°/50 mm.

Zollinger, Roehling, U.S.P., 1,321,271, (*Chem. Abstracts*, 1920, **14**, 186).
Boehringer, D.R.P., 286,266, (*Chem. Zentr.*, 1915, II, 566).
Barth, Senhofer, *Ann.*, 1871, **159**, 222.

β-Resorcylic Acid (2 : 4-*Dihydroxybenzoic acid, resorcinol-4-carboxylic acid*)

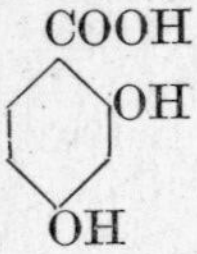

$C_7H_6O_4$ MW, 154

Cryst. from H_2O. M.p. 213° (rapid heat.), (204–6°, 197° decomp.). Sol. EtOH, Et_2O, hot H_2O. $k = 5{\cdot}16 \times 10^{-4}$ at 25°. Heat of comb. C_p 676·9 Cal., C_v 677·2 Cal. Heat ⟶ resorcinol. $FeCl_3$ ⟶ red col. NaOCl ⟶ violet col.

2-*Acetyl*: m.p. 167–8° decomp. (rapid heat.).
4-*Acetyl*: m.p. 152–3°.
Diacetyl: m.p. 136–8°.
2-*Acetyl-4-benzoyl*: m.p. 148–9°.
Di-carbomethoxyl: m.p. 159°. *Chloride*: m.p. 86–7°.
2-*Benzoyl*: m.p. 160–1°. *Carbomethoxyl*: m.p. 148–9°.
4-*Benzoyl*: m.p. 193–4°.
Me ester: $C_8H_8O_4$. MW, 168. M.p. 118–19°.
p-*Nitrobenzyl ester*: $C_{14}H_{11}O_6N$. MW, 289. M.p. 189°.

2-*Me ether*: $C_8H_8O_4$. MW, 168. Leaflets from H_2O. Decomp. at 187–9° (rapid heat.).

4-*Me ether*: 2-hydroxyanisic acid, 4-methoxysalicylic acid. M.p. 157° (about 161°). *Acetyl*: m.p. 145–7°. *Me ester*: $C_9H_{10}O_4$. MW, 182. Primula camphor. Occurs in root of *Primula veris.** Plates from ligroin. M.p. 49°. *Et ester*: $C_{10}H_{12}O_4$. MW, 196. B.p. 272–4°.

Di-Me ether: *see* 2 : 4-Dimethoxybenzoic Acid.

2-*Et ether*: $C_9H_{10}O_4$. MW, 182. Needles from H_2O. M.p. 154°. Sol. EtOH, Et_2O, C_6H_6, hot H_2O.

4-*Et ether*: *Me ester*: $C_{10}H_{12}O_4$. MW, 196. Plates from pet. ether. M.p. 77–9°. *Et ester*: $C_{11}H_{14}O_4$. MW, 210. Needles from EtOH. M.p. 53–4° (45°).

Di-Et ether: $C_{11}H_{14}O_4$. MW, 210. Needles from EtOH.Aq. M.p. 99°. *Me ester*: $C_{12}H_{16}O_4$. MW, 224. Cubes from EtOH.Aq. M.p. 51–4°.

Chloride: $C_7H_5O_3Cl$. MW, 172·5. F.p. — 20°. B.p. 170°/12 mm.

Amide: $C_7H_7O_3N$. MW, 153. M.p. 221–2°.

Nitrile: 4-cyanoresorcinol. $C_7H_5O_2N$. MW, 135. M.p. 175°. Sol. H_2O, EtOH. *Diacetyl*: m.p. 72°.

Anilide: m.p. 126–7°.

Shoesmith, Haldane, *J. Chem. Soc.*, 1924, **125**, 113.
Miksic, *J. prakt. Chem.*, 1928, **119**, 218.
Clibbens, Nierenstein, *J. Chem. Soc.*, 1915, **107**, 1493; *Organic Syntheses*, 1930, X, 94.
Robinson, Shah, *J. Chem. Soc.*, 1934, 1496.
Mauthner, *J. prakt. Chem.*, 1930, **124**, 319.
Bergmann, Dangschat, *Ber.*, 1919, **52**, 371.

**Note.—Primula veris* is the synonym of three different *Primula* species. Since the authority is not given in the original paper it is impossible to assign the correct Index Kewensis name to this plant.

γ-Resorcylic Acid (2 : 6-*Dihydroxybenzoic acid, resorcinol-2-carboxylic acid*)

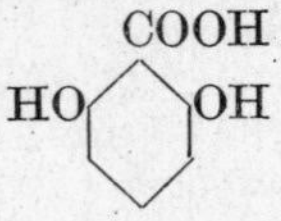

$C_7H_6O_4$ MW, 154

Cryst. + $1H_2O$ from H_2O. M.p. varies from 150 to 170° according to rate of heating ⟶ resorcinol. Sol. EtOH, Et_2O, hot H_2O. $k = 5{\cdot}0 \times 10^{-2}$ at 25°. Reduces warm Fehling's but not Tollen's. $FeCl_3$ ⟶ violet to blue col.

Me ester: $C_8H_8O_4$. MW, 168. M.p. 67–8°.

Me ether: $C_8H_8O_4$. MW, 168. Cryst. from $CHCl_3$–C_6H_6. M.p. 135°.

Di-Me ether: *see* 2 : 6-Dimethoxybenzoic Acid.

Di-Et ether: $C_{11}H_{13}O_2N$. MW, 191. M.p. 122°.

Brunner, *Ann.*, 1907, **351**, 320.
Mauthner, *J. prakt. Chem.*, 1930, **124**, 319.

β-Resorcylic Aldehyde (2 : 4-*Dihydroxybenzaldehyde*)

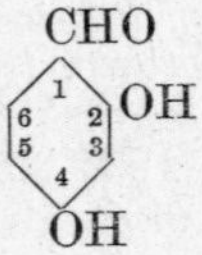

$C_7H_6O_3$ MW, 138

Needles from Et_2O–ligroin. M.p. 135–6°. B.p. 220–8°/22 mm. Sol. H_2O, EtOH, Et_2O, $CHCl_3$, AcOH. Spar. sol. C_6H_6. Gives deep brown col. with $FeCl_3$, yellow ppt. with Schiff's reagent.

Diacetyl: m.p. 69°.

Di-carbomethoxyl: m.p. 72°. *Phenylhydrazone*: m.p. 138°. *Semicarbazone*: m.p. 185°.

Oxime: m.p. 192°.

Semicarbazone: decomp. at 260°.

Phenylhydrazone: m.p. 156–60° decomp.

unsym.-*Me-p-nitrophenylhydrazone*: m.p. 265°.

3 : 4-*Dichloro-6-nitrophenylhydrazone*: m.p. 251°.

Anil: m.p. 125–6°.

2-*Me ether*: $C_8H_8O_3$. MW, 152. M.p. 153°. 4-*Acetyl*: m.p. 86°.

4-*Me ether*: 2-hydroxyanisaldehyde, 4-methoxysalicylaldehyde. M.p. 40–2°.

Di-Me ether: 2-methoxyanisaldehyde. $C_9H_{10}O_3$. MW, 166. M.p. 68–9° (71°). B.p. 165°/10 mm.

4-*Et ether*: 4-ethoxysalicylaldehyde. $C_9H_{10}O_3$. MW, 166. M.p. 35°.

Di-Et ether: $C_{11}H_{14}O_3$. MW, 194. M.p. 71–2°.

Karrer, *Helv. Chim. Acta*, 1919, **2**, 89.
Weil, Traun, Marcel, *Ber.*, 1922, **55**, 2665.
Mitter, Suha, *J. Indian Chem. Soc.*, 1934, **11**, 257.
Hinkel, Ayling, Morgan, *J. Chem. Soc.*, 1932, 2798.
Shoesmith, Haldane, *J. Chem. Soc.*, 1923, **123**, 2704.

γ-Resorcylic Aldehyde (2 : 6-*Dihydroxybenzaldehyde*).

M.p. 155–6°.

Shah, Laiwalla, *Chem. Zentr.*, 1937, I, 1679.

Resorufine (*Azoresorufin, 9-hydroxy-3-isophenoxazone, diazoresorufine*)

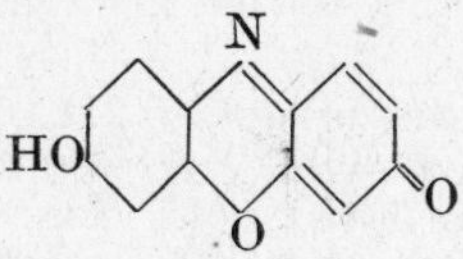

$C_{12}H_7O_3N$ MW, 213

Acetyl deriv.: m.p. 221°.

Et ether: $C_{14}H_{11}O_3N$. MW, 241. Orange-red needles from EtOH. M.p. 225°.

Eichler, *J. prakt. Chem.*, 1934, **139**, 113.

Retene (1-*Methyl-7-isopropylphenanthrene*)

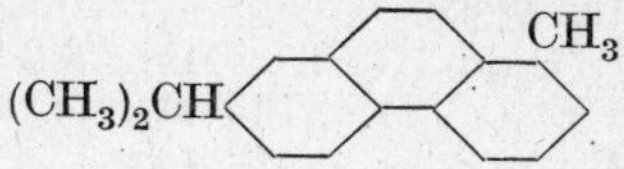

$C_{18}H_{18}$ MW, 234

Plates from EtOH. M.p. 100·5–101° (98–9°). B.p. 390°, 158–65°/0·2 mm. Sol. C_6H_6, ligroin, CS_2, hot EtOH, hot AcOH. Heat of comb. C_p 2326·1 Cal., C_v 2323·6 Cal.

Picrate: m.p. 124–5°.

Styphnate: m.p. 141–2°.

$C_{18}H_{18},C_6H_3(NO_3)_3$-1 : 3 : 5 : m.p. 139–40°.

Cheung, *Chem. Abstracts*, 1929, **23**, 4464, (*Bibl.*).
Haworth, Letsky, Mavin, *J. Chem. Soc.*, 1932, 1791.
Nagel, Körnchen, *Chem. Abstracts*, 1932, **26**, 1808.
Bardhan, Sengupta, *J. Chem. Soc.*, 1932, 2798.
Henke, Etzel, U.S.P., 1,881,565, (*Chem. Abstracts*, 1933, **27**, 516).
Nyman, *Chem. Zentr.*, 1936, I, 2348.
Ruzicka, Waldman, *Helv. Chim. Acta*, 1933, **16**, 847.
Hosking, McFadyen, *J. Soc. Chem. Ind.*, 1934, **53**, 195T.
Darzens, Lévy, *Chem. Zentr.*, 1937, I, 592.
Keimatsu, Ishiguro, *Chem. Abstracts*, 1935, **29**, 7323, (*Refs.*).

Retene-6-carboxylic Acid (1-*Methyl-7-isopropylphenanthrene-6-carboxylic acid*)

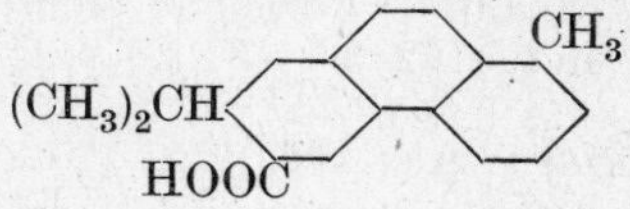

$C_{19}H_{18}O_2$ MW, 278

Needles from C_6H_6. M.p. 241–3° (238–238·5°).

Nyman, *Chem. Zentr.*, 1936, I, 2349.
Adelson, Bogert, *J. Am. Chem. Soc.*, 1936, **58**, 654.

Retene-2(?)-sulphonic Acid

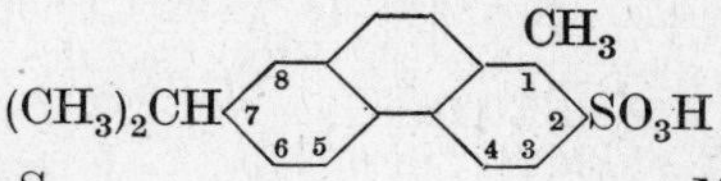

$C_{18}H_{18}O_3S$ MW, 314

M.p. 188–9°.

Me ester: $C_{19}H_{20}O_3S$. MW, 328. M.p. 164–6°.

Et ester: $C_{20}H_{20}O_3S$. MW, 342. M.p. 137·5–138·5°.

Chloride: $C_{18}H_{17}O_2ClS$. MW, 332·5. Yellow scales from Et_2O. M.p. 135–6°.

Komppa, Fogelberg, *J. Am. Chem. Soc.*, 1932, **54**, 2907.

Retene-6-sulphonic Acid.

M.p. 121–3°.

Me ester: m.p. 117–19°.

Et ester: m.p. 114–15°.

Chloride: yellow needles from C_6H_6. M.p. 146–147·5°.

Amide: $C_{18}H_{19}O_2NS$. MW, 313. M.p. 206–207·5°.

See previous reference and also

Hasselstrom, Bogert, *J. Am. Chem. Soc.*, 1935, **57**, 1580.

6-Retenol (6-*Hydroxyretene*)

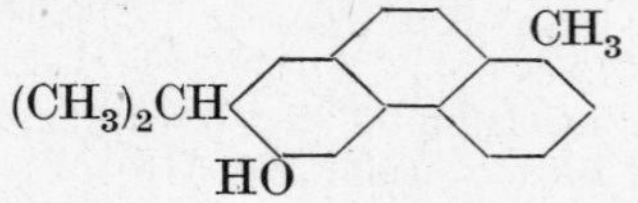

$C_{18}H_{18}O$ MW, 250

Yellow scales from xylene. M.p. 163·5–164·5°.

Acetyl: m.p. 134–5°.

Adelson, Bogert, *J. Am. Chem. Soc.*, 1936, **58**, 653.

Retronecine (*Senecifolinene* ?)

$C_8H_{13}O_2N$ MW, 155

M.p. 121–2°. Sol. H_2O, EtOH. Mod. sol. Me_2CO, $CHCl_3$. Spar. sol. Et_2O. $[\alpha]_D + 50{\cdot}2°$ in EtOH. Alkaline. Forms no picrate.

B,HCl: m.p. 162–3° (161°). $[\alpha]_D^{15} - 16°$ in EtOH.

Aurichloride: m.p. 146°.

Diacetyl deriv.: *picrate*, m.p. 146°. *Methiodide*: m.p. 118–20°.

Barger, Seshadri, Watt, Yabuta, *J. Chem. Soc.*, 1935, 13.

Barger, Blackie, *J. Chem. Soc.*, 1936, 744.

Retrorsine

$C_{18}H_{25}O_6N$ MW, 351

Occurs in *Senecio barbellatus*, D.C. Leaflets from AcOEt. M.p. 214–15° (212°). Sol. EtOH, $CHCl_3$. Spar. sol. H_2O, Et_2O, AcOEt, Me_2CO. $[\alpha]_D^{18} - 17{\cdot}6°$ in EtOH.

$B,HNO_3,\frac{1}{2}EtOH$: m.p. 145°.

Phenylurethane: m.p. 200–2°.

Methiodide: m.p. 260°.

Barger, Seshadri, Watt, Yabuta, *J. Chem. Soc.*, 1935, 11.

Rhababerone (*Isoemodin*, 3 : 5 : 8-*trihydroxy-2-methylanthraquinone*)

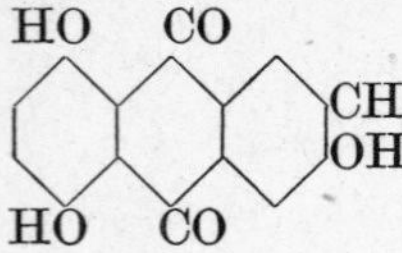

$C_{15}H_{10}O_5$ MW, 270

Occurs in rhubarb. Yellow leaflets from hot EtOH. M.p. 223–4° (212°). Sol. hot. EtOH, hot AcOH. Spar. sol. Et_2O. Insol. H_2O. $FeCl_3 \longrightarrow$ dark brown col. in EtOH. Sol. alkalis $\longrightarrow$ purple-red col.

Keimatsu, Hirano, *Chem. Abstracts*, 1931, **25**, 3647; *Chem. Zentr.*, 1931, I, 3348.

Rhamnazin (3 : 5 : 4′-*Trihydroxy*-7 : 3′-*dimethoxyflavone, quercetin* 7 : 3′-*dimethyl ether*)

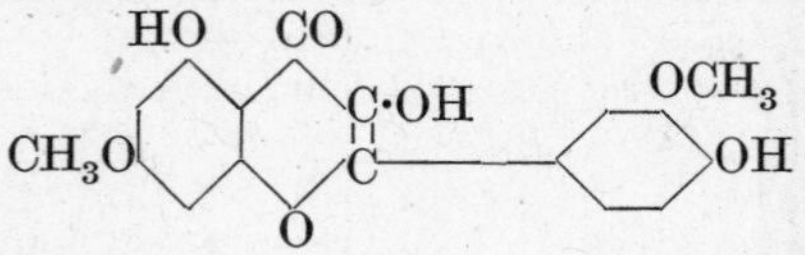

$C_{17}H_{14}O_7$ MW, 330

Found in fruits of *Rhamnus infectoria*, Linn. Pale yellow needles from toluene. M.p. 214–15°. Mod. sol. boiling AcOH, toluene. Spar. sol. EtOH. Alkalis $\longrightarrow$ orange-red sols. $FeCl_3 \longrightarrow$ olive-green col.

Triacetyl: needles from EtOH. M.p. 154–5°.

Tribenzoyl: needles from AcOH. M.p. 204–5°. Spar. sol. AcOH.

Perkin, Allison, *J. Chem. Soc.*, 1902, **81**, 469.

α-Rhamnegin.

See Xanthorhamnin.

Rhamnetidin chloride

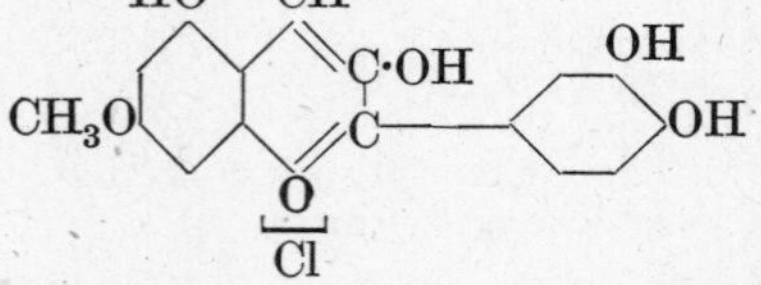

$C_{16}H_{13}O_6Cl$ MW, 336·5

Purplish-brown prisms + $2H_2O$. Orange-red by transmitted light. Green reflex. Sol. EtOH $\longrightarrow$ bluish-red col. Sol. hot HCl $\longrightarrow$ brownish-red col. $Na_2CO_3 \longrightarrow$ blue col. $FeCl_3 \longrightarrow$ blue col. in EtOH, violet in H_2O.

Kondo, Segawa, *Chem. Abstracts*, 1932, **26**, 4333.

Robertson, Robinson, *J. Chem. Soc.*, 1927, 2205.

Rhamnetin (*Quercetin 7-methyl ether, 3 : 5 : 3′ : 4′-tetrahydroxy-7-methoxyflavone, β-rhamnocitrin*)

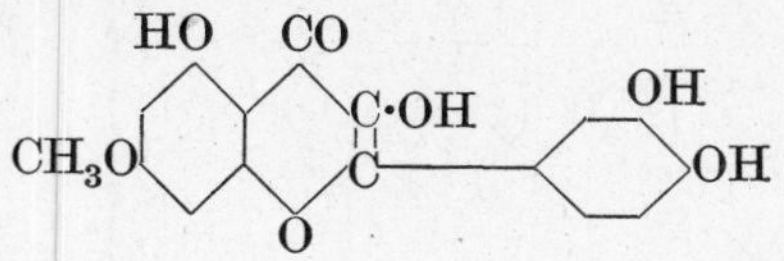

$C_{16}H_{12}O_7$ MW, 316

Occurs in fruit of *Rhamnus cathartica*, Linn., and other species. Yellow needles from EtOH or phenol. Does not melt below 300°. Sol. Me_2CO, hot EtOH. Spar. sol. H_2O. $FeCl_3 \longrightarrow$ brown col. Conc. $H_2SO_4 \longrightarrow$ yellow col. with greenish-blue fluor. Reduces cold Tollen's and warm Fehling's.

Tetra-acetyl : m.p. 190–2°.

Tetra-propionyl : m.p. 158–62°.

Herzig, *Monatsh.*, 1888, **9**, 549.
Liebermann, Hörmann, *Ann.*, 1879, **196**, 313.
Krassowski, *Chem. Zentr.*, 1909, I, 772.
Oesch, Perkin, *J. Chem. Soc.*, 1914, **105**, 2354.

Rhamninose

$C_{18}H_{32}O_{14}$ MW, 472

Obtained from xanthorhamnin present in Persian berries (*Rhamnus infectoria*). Cryst. M.p. 135–40° decomp. Sweet taste. $[\alpha]_D$ $-$ 41·0° in H_2O, $-$ 26·37° in 75% EtOH. Sol. H_2O, EtOH. Insol. Et_2O, Me_2CO, AcOEt. Reduces Fehling's. Hyd. by dil. acids $\longrightarrow$ 2 mols. rhamnose + 1 mol. galactose. NaHg $\longrightarrow$ rhamninitol. Br water $\longrightarrow$ rhamnotrionic acid.

Octa-acetyl : cryst. M.p. 95°. $[\alpha]_D$ $-$ 30·87° in EtOH, $-$ 31·7° in AcOH.

Ter Meulen, *Rec. trav. chim.*, 1923, **42**, 380.
Tanret, Tanret, *Bull. soc. chim.*, 1899, **21**, 1065.

Rhamnitol

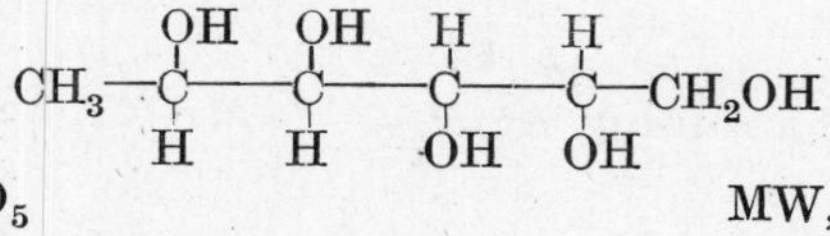

$C_6H_{14}O_5$ MW, 166

d-.

Prisms from Me_2CO. M.p. 123°. Sol. H_2O, EtOH. Spar. sol. $CHCl_3$. Insol. Et_2O. $[\alpha]_D^{20}$ $-$ 12·4° in H_2O.

Dibenzylidene deriv. : m.p. 207°. $[\alpha]_D$ + 60·7° in $CHCl_3$.

l-.

M.p. 121°. $[\alpha]_D^{20}$ + 10·7° in H_2O.

Dibenzylidene deriv. : cryst. M.p. 203°. $[\alpha]_D$ $-$ 55° in $CHCl_3$.

Votoček, Valentin, Rac, *Chem. Abstracts*, 1931, **25**, 84.
Fischer, Piloty, *Ber.*, 1890, **23**, 3103.
de Bruyn, van Ekenstein, *Rec. trav. chim.*, 1899, **18**, 151.

Rhamnocitrin (*Kæmpferol methyl ether*)

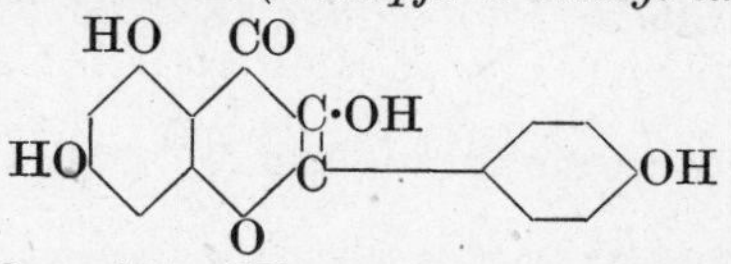

One of the OH groups is methylated

$C_{16}H_{12}O_6$ MW, 300

Occurs in fruits of *Rhamnus cathartica*, Linn. Yellow needles. M.p. 221–2°. Mod. sol. Me_2CO, AcOEt. Spar. sol. hot EtOH. Insol. H_2O, Et_2O, C_6H_6. Conc. $H_2SO_4 \longrightarrow$ green fluor. Reduces Fehling's.

Triacetyl : m.p. 200–1°.

Oesch, Perkin, *J. Chem. Soc.*, 1914, **105**, 2352.

β-Rhamnocitrin.

See Rhamnetin.

Rhamnoheptonic Acid

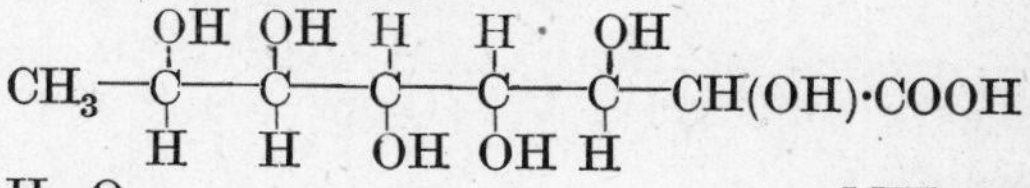

$C_8H_{16}O_8$ MW, 240

Free acid not isolated.

γ-Lactone : $C_8H_{14}O_7$. MW, 222. Needles from EtOH. M.p. 160°. $[\alpha]_D^{20}$ + 55·6° in H_2O. Sol. H_2O. Mod. sol. MeOH, EtOH. Insol Et_2O.

Phenylhydrazide : needles from H_2O. M.p. about 215° decomp. Spar. sol. H_2O, EtOH.

Fischer, Piloty, *Ber.*, 1890, **23**, 3106.

Rhamnoheptose

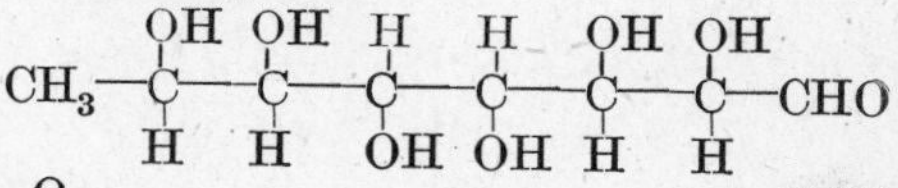

$C_8H_{16}O_7$ MW, 224

Syrup. Sol. H_2O, EtOH. Insol. Et_2O. $[\alpha]_D^{20}$ + 8·4° in H_2O.

Phenylosazone : yellow needles. M.p. 200° decomp.

Anderson, *J. Am. Chem. Soc.*, 1911, **33**. 1514.
Fischer, Piloty, *Ber.*, 1890, **23**, 3107.

α-Rhamnohexitol

$$CH_3-\underset{H}{\overset{OH}{C}}-\underset{H}{\overset{OH}{C}}-\underset{OH}{\overset{H}{C}}-\underset{OH}{\overset{H}{C}}-\underset{H}{\overset{OH}{C}}-CH_2OH$$

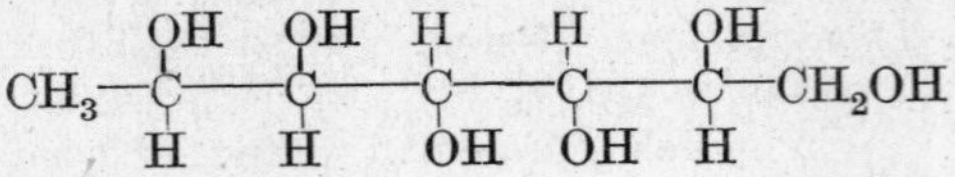

$C_7H_{16}O_6$ MW, 196

Prisms from EtOH. M.p. 173°. $[\alpha]_D + 14°$ in H_2O. Mod. sol. hot MeOH, hot EtOH.

> Fischer, Piloty, *Ber.*, 1890, **23**, 3106.
> Valentin, *Chem. Abstracts*, 1932, **26**, 1578.

α-Rhamnohexonic Acid

$$CH_3-\underset{H}{\overset{OH}{C}}-\underset{H}{\overset{OH}{C}}-\underset{OH}{\overset{H}{C}}-\underset{OH}{\overset{H}{C}}-\underset{H}{\overset{OH}{C}}-COOH$$

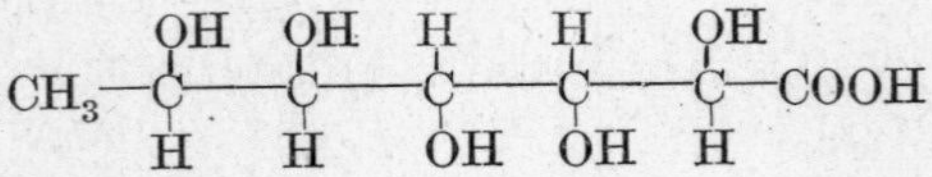

$C_7H_{14}O_7$ MW, 210

M.p. 171°. $[\alpha]_D^{20} + 21·5°$ in H_2O.
NH_4 *salt* : m.p. 151°.
Brucine salt : m.p. 120–3°.
Et ester : $C_9H_{18}O_7$. MW, 238. M.p. 165–6° decomp. $[\alpha]_D^{20} + 12·9°$ in H_2O.
Amide : $C_7H_{15}O_6N$. MW, 209. M.p. 177·5–178° decomp. (194°). $[\alpha]_D^{20} - 19·9°$ in H_2O (− 47·26°).
Nitrile : $C_7H_{13}O_5N$. MW, 191. M.p. 145°. $[\alpha]_D^{20} - 23·47°$.
γ-Lactone : $C_7H_{12}O_6$. MW, 192. Cryst. from Me_2CO. M.p. 171–171·5° (174·5°). $[\alpha]_D^{20} + 87·3°$ in H_2O.
Phenylhydrazide : m.p. 205–6° decomp. $[\alpha]_D^{20} - 5·2°$ in H_2O.

> Brackenbury, Upson, *J. Am. Chem. Soc.*, 1934, **56**, 2659.
> Jackson, Hudson, *ibid.*, 2455.
> Miksic, *Chem. Abstracts*, 1929, **23**, 2942.
> Fischer, Morrell, *Ber.*, 1894, **27**, 386.

β-Rhamnohexonic Acid

$$CH_3-\underset{H}{\overset{OH}{C}}-\underset{H}{\overset{OH}{C}}-\underset{OH}{\overset{H}{C}}-\underset{OH}{\overset{H}{C}}-\underset{OH}{\overset{H}{C}}-COOH$$

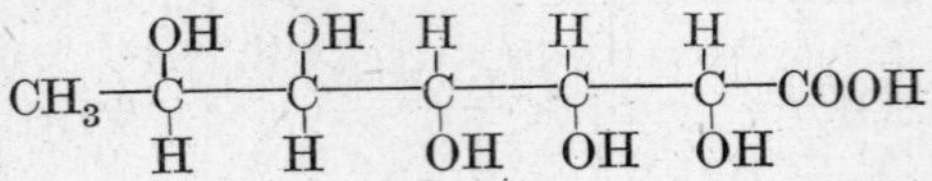

$C_7H_{14}O_7$ MW, 210

Free acid not isolated.
Brucine salt : m.p. 114–18°.
γ-Lactone : plates from Me_2CO. M.p. 134–8°. $[\alpha]_D^{20} + 43·34°$ in H_2O.
Phenylhydrazide : m.p. 170° decomp.

> Fischer, Morrell, *Ber.*, 1894, **27**, 389.

Rhamnohexose

α-
$$CH_3-\underset{H}{\overset{OH}{C}}-\underset{H}{\overset{H}{\underset{|}{C}}}-\underset{OH}{\overset{H}{\underset{|}{C}}}-\underset{OH}{\overset{H}{C}}-\underset{H}{\overset{OH}{C}}-CH·OH$$

β-
$$CH_3-\underset{H}{\overset{OH}{C}}-\underset{H}{\overset{H}{\underset{|}{C}}}-\underset{OH}{\overset{H}{\underset{|}{C}}}-\underset{OH}{\overset{H}{C}}-\underset{OH}{\overset{H}{\underset{|}{C}}}-CH·OH$$

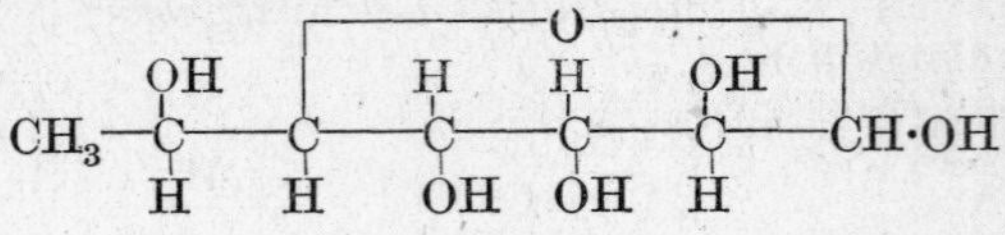

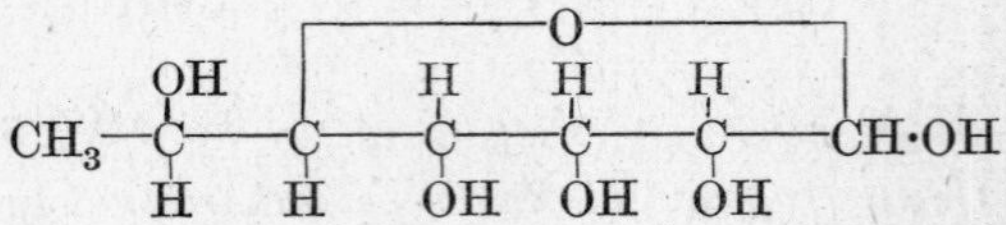

$C_7H_{14}O_6$ MW, 194

α-
l-.
Prisms or plates from hot MeOH. M.p. 180–1°. Sol. H_2O, hot MeOH. Spar. sol. EtOH. $[\alpha]_D^{20}$ − 80° ⟶ − 61·4° in H_2O. Sweet taste. NaHg ⟶ α-rhamnohexitol.
Phenylosazone : yellow needles. M.p. 200° decomp. Sol. hot EtOH. Insol. H_2O.
Benzylphenylhydrazone : m.p. 183–4°.

β-
l-.
Syrup.
Phenylosazone : identical with that of α-form.
Monobenzylidene deriv. : m.p. 233–4°. $[\alpha]_D$ + 50–8° in $CHCl_3$.

> Votoček, Valentin, Leminger, *Chem. Abstracts*, 1931, **25**, 4527.
> Votoček, Valentin, Rac, *ibid.*, 84.
> Anderson, *J. Am. Chem. Soc.*, 1911, **33**, 1514.
> Fischer, Morrell, *Ber.*, 1894, **27**, 391.

Rhamnol (*Cinchol*)

$C_{29}H_{50}O$ MW, 414

Phytosterol occurring in cascara and other barks. M.p. 136–7°. $[\alpha]_D^{16}$ − 33·5° in $CHCl_3$.
Acetyl deriv. : m.p. 123°. $[\alpha]_D^{16}$ − 38·3° in $CHCl_3$.
3 : 5-Dinitrobenzoyl deriv. : m.p. 200–2°. $[\alpha]_D^{16}$ − 10·9° in $CHCl_3$.

> Windaus, Deppe, *Ber.*, 1933, **66**, 1689.

Rhamnolutin.
See Kæmpferol.

Rhamnonic Acid

$$CH_3-\underset{H}{\overset{OH}{C}}-\underset{H}{\overset{OH}{C}}-\underset{OH}{\overset{H}{C}}-\underset{OH}{\overset{H}{C}}-COOH$$

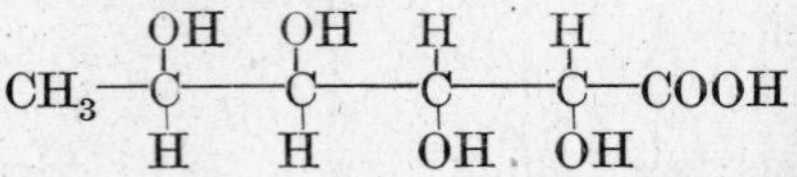

$C_6H_{12}O_6$ MW, 180

l-.
Obtained only in solution. $[\alpha]_D$ − 7·67 ⟶ 29·28° in H_2O.

Brucine salt : m.p. 120–6° (132°).

Quinine salt : m.p. 180–1°.

Nitrile : *tetra-acetyl deriv.* : m.p. 69–70°.

γ-Lactone : $C_6H_{10}O_5$. MW, 162. M.p. 149–51°. $[\alpha]_D^{20} - 39.2°$ in H_2O.

δ-Lactone : m.p. 178–82°. $[\alpha]_D + 98–101°$.

Amide : $C_6H_{13}O_5N$. MW, 179. M.p. 134–134·5°. $[\alpha]_D^{20} + 27.7°$ in H_2O.

Phenylhydrazide : m.p. 195–6°. $[\alpha]_D^{80} + 17.2°$ in H_2O.

> Brackenbury, Upson, *J. Am. Chem. Soc.*, 1933, **55**, 2514.
>
> Isbell, Frush, *Chem. Abstracts*, 1934, **28**, 1667.
>
> Rehorst, *Ann.*, 1933, **503**, 143.

Rhamno-octonic Acid

$$CH_3-\overset{\overset{OH}{|}}{\underset{\underset{H}{|}}{C}}-\overset{\overset{OH}{|}}{\underset{\underset{H}{|}}{C}}-\overset{\overset{H}{|}}{\underset{\underset{OH}{|}}{C}}-\overset{\overset{H}{|}}{\underset{\underset{OH}{|}}{C}}-\overset{\overset{OH}{|}}{\underset{\underset{H}{|}}{C}}\cdot CH(OH)\cdot CH(OH)\cdot COOH$$

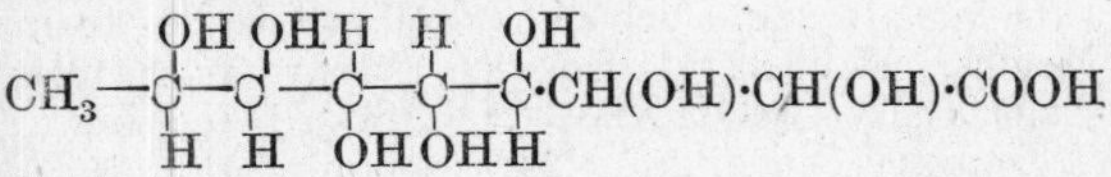

$C_9H_{18}O_9$ MW, 270

Free acid not isolated.

γ-Lactone : $C_9H_{16}O_8$. MW, 252. Needles from H_2O. M.p. 171–2°. $[\alpha]_D^{20} - 50.8°$ in H_2O. Sol. H_2O, EtOH. Spar. sol. Me_2CO. NaHg $\longrightarrow$ rhamno-octose.

Phenylhydrazide : needles from H_2O. M.p. about 220° decomp. Spar. sol. hot H_2O.

> Fischer, Piloty, *Ber.*, 1890, **23**, 3109, 3827.

Rhamno-octose

$$CH_3-\overset{\overset{OH}{|}}{\underset{\underset{H}{|}}{C}}-\overset{\overset{OH}{|}}{\underset{\underset{H}{|}}{C}}-\overset{\overset{H}{|}}{\underset{\underset{OH}{|}}{C}}-\overset{\overset{H}{|}}{\underset{\underset{OH}{|}}{C}}-\overset{\overset{OH}{|}}{\underset{\underset{H}{|}}{C}}-\overset{\overset{OH}{|}}{\underset{\underset{H}{|}}{C}}-CH(OH)\cdot CHO$$

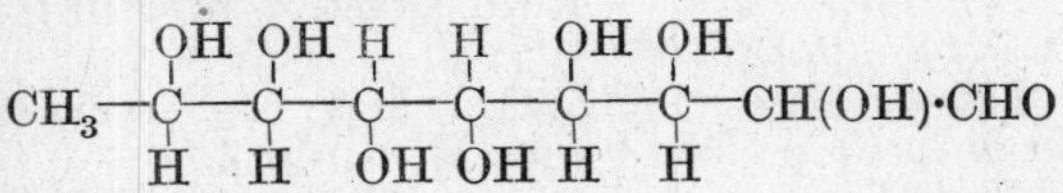

$C_9H_{18}O_8$ MW, 254

Syrup. Sol. H_2O.

Phenylosazone : m.p. 216°.

> Fischer, Piloty, *Ber.*, 1890, **23**, 3110.

Rhamnose

$$CH_3-\overset{\overset{H}{|}}{\underset{\underset{}{|}}{C}}-\overset{\overset{H}{|}}{\underset{\underset{OH}{|}}{C}}-\overset{\overset{OH}{|}}{\underset{\underset{H}{|}}{C}}-\overset{\overset{OH}{|}}{\underset{\underset{H}{|}}{C}}-CH\cdot OH$$

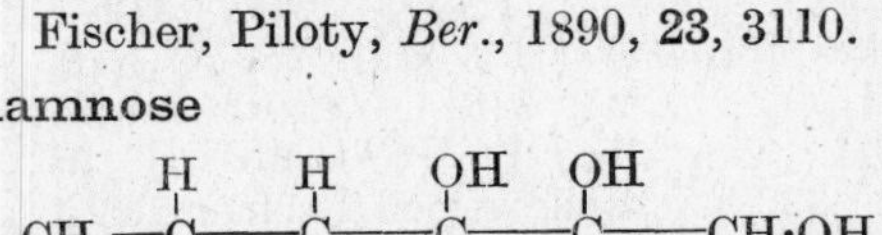

$C_6H_{12}O_5$ MW, 164

d-.

Cryst. $+ H_2O$. Sol. H_2O. Insol. Et_2O. $[\alpha]_D^{16·5} - 8.25°$ in H_2O. Reduces warm Fehling's. NaHg $\longrightarrow$ *d*-rhamnitol.

Phenylosazone : yellow prisms or needles from dil. EtOH. M.p. 191° (185°, 186–7°, 189–90°). $[\alpha]_D^{20} - 95.2°$ in Py. Sol. EtOH, Py. Identical with phenylosazone of *d*-isorhodeose and *d*-isorhamnose.

p-*Bromophenylosazone* : yellow cryst. from dil. EtOH. M.p. 225° (222–3°).

l-.

α-Form :

A constituent of many glucosides. Cryst. $+ H_2O$ from H_2O. M.p. 105° (93–4°). Sweet taste. $[\alpha]_D^{15} + 9.1°$ in H_2O ($[\alpha]_D^{20} - 7.7° \longrightarrow + 8.9°$ in H_2O.) Sol. H_2O, MeOH. Reduces warm Fehling's.

Oxime : plates. M.p. 127–8°. $[\alpha]_D^{20} + 13.70°$ in H_2O (final). Sol. H_2O. Spar. sol. EtOH. Insol. Et_2O.

Semicarbazone : cryst. from dil. EtOH. M.p. 183°. $[\alpha]_D^{20} + 75° \longrightarrow + 57°$ in H_2O.

Phenylhydrazone : laminæ. M.p. 159°. $[\alpha]_D^{20} + 54.2°$ in H_2O, $[\alpha]_D + 27°$ in EtOH. Mod. sol. H_2O, EtOH. Insol. Et_2O.

Diphenylhydrazone : prisms. M.p. 134°. Sol. H_2O, EtOH. Insol. Et_2O.

p-*Nitrophenylhydrazone* : reddish-yellow cryst. M.p. 186° (191–2°). $[\alpha]_D + 21.4° (- 50.3° \longrightarrow - 8.5°)$ in EtOH–Py. Sol. EtOH.

Methylphenylhydrazone : cryst. M.p. 124°. $[\alpha]_D + 0.7°$ in MeOH. Sol. MeOH. Spar. sol. H_2O, EtOH.

Benzylphenylhydrazone : yellow cryst. M.p. 121°. $[\alpha]_D - 6.4°$ in MeOH.

β-Naphthylhydrazone : brown needles. M.p. 170°. $[\alpha]_D + 8.4°$ in MeOH, $- 11.8°$ in AcOH. Sol. MeOH. Spar. sol. H_2O.

Phenylosazone : yellow needles. M.p. 222° (180°, 185°, 186–7°, 182°). $[\alpha]_D^{20} + 93.92°$ (94°) in Py. Sol. hot EtOH, AcOH, Me_2CO. Spar. sol. EtOH, C_6H_6. Insol. H_2O. Reduces boiling Fehling's.

p-*Nitrophenylosazone* : red needles from EtOH. M.p. 208° decomp. Spar. sol. EtOH.

Methylglucoside : cryst. from AcOEt. M.p. 108–9° (109–10°). $[\alpha]_D^{20} - 62.5° (- 25.43°)$ in H_2O. *Tri-Me ether* : b.p. 112°/11 mm., 101°/9 mm. $[\alpha]_D^{20} - 15.54°$ in H_2O. *Triacetyl* : m.p. 86–7°. $[\alpha]_D^{16} - 53.5°$ in $C_2H_2Cl_4$.

2 : 3 : 4-*Tri-Me ether* : syrup. B.p. 141°/19 mm. n_D^{15} 1·4565. $[\alpha]_D^{18} + 24.15° \longrightarrow + 25.44°$ in H_2O, $+ 3.25° \longrightarrow + 5.82°$ in C_6H_6, $- 4.86° \longrightarrow - 9.52°$ in EtOH. *Phenylhydrazone* : yellow prisms. M.p. 126–8° decomp.

Tetranitrate : cryst. from EtOH. M.p. 135° decomp.

β-Form :

Needles from Me_2CO. M.p. 122–6°. $[\alpha]_D + 54.0° \longrightarrow + 8.9°$ in H_2O. Sol. H_2O, EtOH.

Methylglucoside : needles from AcOEt. M.p.

138–40°. $[\alpha]_D^{20}$ + 95·39° in H_2O.   *Triacetyl* :
m.p. 151–2°. $[\alpha]_D^{18}$ + 45·73° in $C_2H_2Cl_4$.
   Triacetyl : plates from Et_2O.   M.p. 96–8°.
$[\alpha]_D^{21}$ + 28·09° $\longrightarrow$ + 18·6° in EtOH.

dl-.
M.p. anhyd. 151·3–153°.

> Votoček, Valentin, Rac, *Chem. Abstracts*
>   1931, **25**, 84.
> Votoček, Valentin, *Compt. rend.*, 1926,
>   **183**, 62.
> Fischer, Zach, *Ber.*, 1912, **45**, 3770.
> Harding, *Sugar*, 1923, **25**, 82.
> Hirst, Macbeth, *J. Chem. Soc.*, 1926, 22.
> Clark, *J. Biol. Chem.*, 1919, **38**, 255.
> Walton, *J. Am. Chem. Soc.*, 1921, **43**, 127.
> Fischer, Bergmann, Rabe, *Ber.*, 1920,
>   **53**, 2362.

Rhamnotetronic Acid (*Methyltetronic acid*)

$$CH_3 - \overset{\displaystyle OH}{\underset{\displaystyle H}{C}} - \overset{\displaystyle OH}{\underset{\displaystyle H}{C}} - \overset{\displaystyle H}{\underset{\displaystyle OH}{C}} - COOH$$

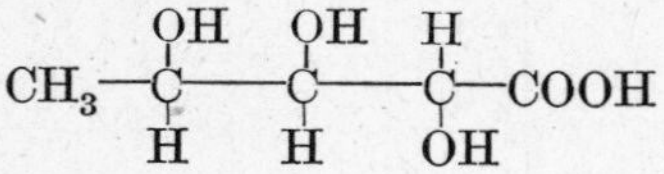

$C_5H_{10}O_5$ MW, 150

l-.
Free acid not isolated.
Brucine salt : needles from EtOH.   M.p.
145–50° decomp.
Amide : $C_5H_{11}O_4N$.   MW, 149.   Plates from
EtOH.   M.p. 135° decomp. $[\alpha]_D$ + 54·8° in
H_2O.
Phenylhydrazide : laminæ from AcOEt.   M.p.
169°.
γ-*Lactone* : $C_5H_8O_4$.   MW, 132.   Needles
from H_2O or EtOH.   M.p. 123° (120–1°). $[\alpha]_D^{20}$
− 47·5° in H_2O.   Sol. EtOH, AcOEt, Et_2O.
Spar. sol. $CHCl_3$, C_6H_6.

> Ruff, *Ber.*, 1902, **35**, 2365.
> Hudson, Chernoff, *J. Am. Chem. Soc.*,
>   1918, **40**, 1005.

Rhamnotetrose (*Methyltetrose*)

$$CH_3 - \overset{\displaystyle OH}{\underset{\displaystyle H}{C}} - \overset{\displaystyle OH}{\underset{\displaystyle H}{C}} - \overset{\displaystyle H}{\underset{\displaystyle OH}{C}} - CHO$$

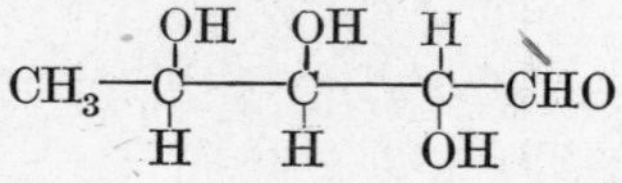

$C_5H_{10}O_4$ MW, 134

l-.
Syrup.   Sol. H_2O, EtOH. $[\alpha]_D^{20}$ − 30·5° $\longrightarrow$
− 16·35° in 96% EtOH.   Reduces Fehling's.
$HNO_3 \longrightarrow$ tartaric acid.
Benzylphenylhydrazone : needles from C_6H_6.
M.p. 96–7°. $[\alpha]^{20}$ − 6·5° in 96% EtOH.   Sol.
EtOH, Et_2O.   Prac. insol. H_2O, C_6H_6.
Phenylosazone : yellow needles from EtOH.

M.p. 172–3°.   Sol. hot EtOH, C_6H_6.   Prac.
insol. H_2O, Et_2O.

> Ruff, *Ber.*, 1902, **35**, 2364.
> Fischer, *Ber.*, 1896, **29**, 1381.

Rhamnoxanthin.
Frangulin, *q.v.*
Rheic Acid.
Chrysophanic Acid, *q.v.*
Rhein (*Chrysazin-3-carboxylic acid*, 4 : 5-*di-
hydroxyanthraquinone-2-carboxylic acid*)

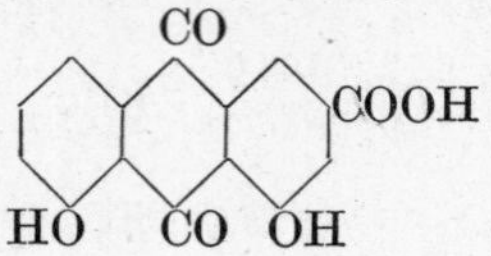

$C_{15}H_8O_6$ MW, 284
   Occurs in senna leaves.   Yellow needles from
MeOH.   M.p. 321°.   Sol. Py.   Spar. sol. EtOH,
Et_2O, C_6H_6, AcOH, Me_2CO, $CHCl_3$, pet. ether.
   Diacetyl : m.p. 258° (246° decomp.).
   Mono-propionyl deriv. : m.p. 223–4°.   *Me
ether* : m.p. 281–2°.
   Dipropionyl : m.p. 223–4°.
   Dibenzoyl : m.p. 262° (253–5°).
   Me ester : $C_{16}H_{10}O_6$.   MW, 298.   Orange
needles from MeOH.   M.p. 174°.
   Et ester : $C_{17}H_{12}O_6$.   MW, 312.   Orange
needles from EtOH.   M.p. 159° (160–1°).
Diacetyl : m.p. 170°.
   Propyl ester : $C_{18}H_{14}O_6$.   MW, 326.   Brown
needles.   M.p. 145°.   *Diacetyl* : m.p. 178°.
   Isopropyl ester : brown cryst.   M.p. 181°.
Diacetyl : m.p. 190°.
   Isobutyl ester : $C_{19}H_{16}O_6$.   MW, 340.   Yellow
needles.   M.p. 153°.   *Diacetyl* : m.p. 109°.
   Phenyl ester : $C_{21}H_{12}O_6$.   MW, 360.   Yellow
needles.   M.p. 215°.   *Diacetyl* : m.p. 170°.
   Benzyl ester : $C_{22}H_{23}O_6$.   MW, 374.   *Diacetyl* :
m.p. 203°.
   Di-Me ether : $C_{17}H_{12}O_6$.   MW, 312.   Brown
needles from EtOH.   M.p. 283–4°.   *Et ester* :
$C_{19}H_{16}O_6$.   MW, 340.   Yellow needles from
AcOH.   M.p. 185–7°.   *Chloride* : $C_{17}H_{11}O_5Cl$.
MW, 330·5.   Yellow prisms from $CHCl_3$–pet.
ether.   M.p. 190°.   *Amide* : $C_{17}H_{13}O_5N$.   MW,
311.   Brownish-yellow plates from AcOEt.   M.p.
287°.

> Oesterle, Haugseth, *Arch. Pharm.*, 1915,
>   **253**, 330.

Rheochrysidine.
See Physcione.
Rheumatin.
See under Quinine.
Rheum-emodin.
Frangula-emodin, *q.v.*

Rhizonaldehyde (2-*Hydroxy*-4-*methoxy*-3 : 6-*nethylbenzaldehyde*, β-*orcylaldehyde* 5-*methyl* *er*)

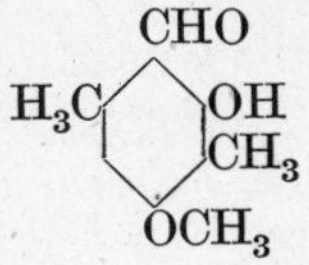

$_0H_{12}O_3$ MW, 180

Prisms from EtOH.Aq. M.p. 136°. Sol. $_2O$, C_6H_6, hot EtOH, hot pet. ether. $FeCl_3$ → reddish-brown col.

Oxime : m.p. 188–9°.
Acetyl : m.p. 71°.
Carbomethoxyl : m.p. 90°.

Sonn, *Ber.*, 1916, **49**, 2591.
Robertson, Stephenson, *J. Chem. Soc.*, 1930, 318.
Pfau, *Helv. Chim. Acta*, 1928, **11**, 873.

Rhizonic Acid (2-*Hydroxy*-4-*methoxy*-3 : 6-*nethylbenzoic acid*)

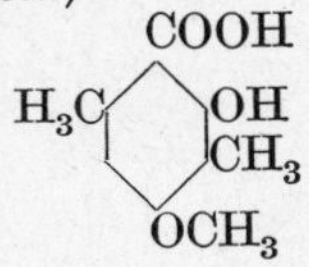

$_0H_{12}O_4$ MW, 196

Occurs in *Evernii prunastri*, and *Rizocarpon ographicum*, Linn. Cryst. from EtOH. M.p. 5° (232°).

Me ester : $C_{11}H_{14}O_4$. MW, 210. Needles om EtOH. M.p. 95°. *Me ether* : $C_{12}H_{16}O_4$. W, 224. B.p. 161–3°/10 mm.
Et ester : $C_{12}H_{16}O_4$. MW, 224. Needles om EtOH. M.p. 82° (81°).
Acetyl : m.p. 146° decomp.
2-*Me ether* : $C_{11}H_{14}O_4$. MW, 210. Prisms om pet. ether. M.p. 104–5°.

Asahina, Akagi, *Ber.*, 1935, **68**, 1132.
Robertson, Stephenson, *J. Chem. Soc.*, 1930, 319.
Sonn, *Ber.*, 1929, **62**, 3012.

Rhodacene (*Quinonoid form of chalkacene*, v.)

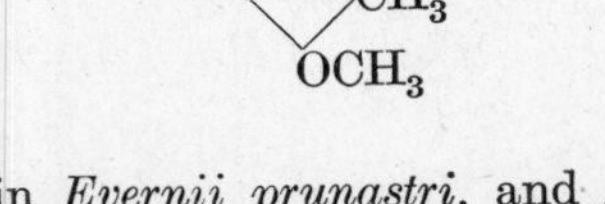

$_{30}H_{16}$ MW, 376

Violet microcryst. M.p. 338–40°. Sol. C_6H_6 ıd homologues with red col. and red fluor.

Dziewoński, Podgorska, Lemberger, Suszka, *Ber.*, 1920, **53**, 2173.

Rhodanic Acid.
See Rhodanine.

Rhodanine (*Rhodanic acid*)

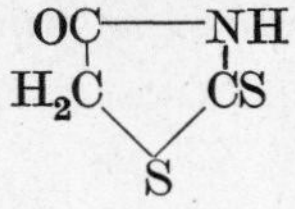

$C_3H_3ONS_2$ MW, 133

Pale yellow prisms from EtOH. M.p. 170°.

Julian, Sturgis, *J. Am. Chem. Soc.*, 1935, **57**, 1126.

Rhodeitol.
See Fucitol.

Rhodeohexonic Acid

α 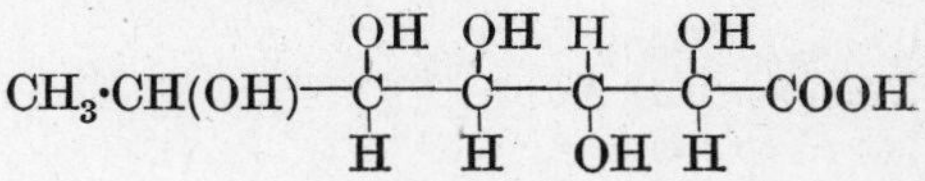

β 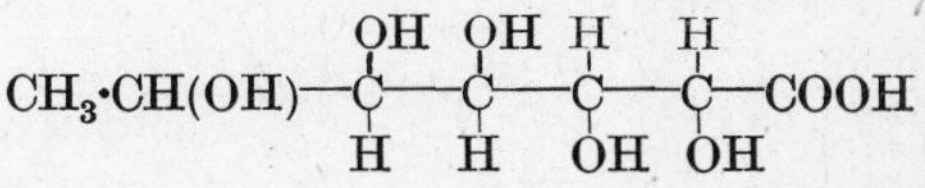

$C_7H_{14}O_7$ MW, 210

α-*Form* :
Syrup rapidly changing to lactone.
γ-*Lactone* : $C_7H_{12}O_6$. MW, 192. Cryst. + $2H_2O$. M.p. 41·5° (129–31°).
Amide : $C_7H_{15}O_6N$. MW, 209. M.p. 206°.
Phenylhydrazide : m.p. 231° decomp.

β-*Form* :
Syrup rapidly changing to lactone.
γ-*Lactone* : m.p. 115°.
Amide : amorph. grey powder. M.p. 197–8°.
Phenylhydrazide : m.p. 211° decomp.

Votoček, *Chem. Abstracts*, 1935, **29**, 2918 ; *Ber.*, 1910, **43**, 469.
Krauz, *Ber.*, 1910, **43**, 482.

Rhodeohexose

α 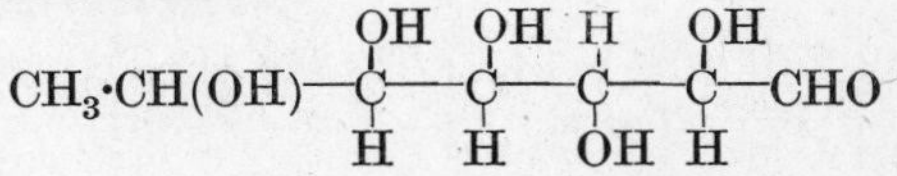

β 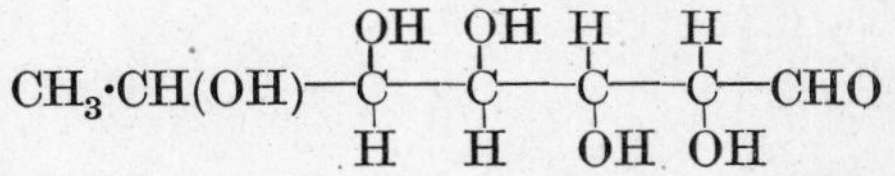

$C_7H_{14}O_6$ MW, 194

α-*Form* :
Cryst. from EtOH. M.p. 125–6°. $[\alpha]_D^{20}$ + 11·96° in H_2O.
Phenylhydrazone : m.p. 150°.
p-*Bromophenylhydrazone* : m.p. 173°.

β-*Form*:
Syrup.
Phenylhydrazone: m.p. 131–7°.
p-*Bromophenylhydrazone*: m.p. 145°.

Krauz, *Chem. Zentr.*, 1911, II, 1216; *Ber.*, 1910, **43**, 482.

Rhodeoretin.
See Convolvulin.
Rhodeose.
See Fucose.
Rhodinal.
See Citronellal.
Rhodinic Acid.
See Citronellic Acid.
Rhodinol.
See Citronellol.
Rhodinolic Acid.
See Citronellic Acid.
Rhodoviolascin

$C_{40}H_{54}(OCH_3)_2$

$C_{42}H_{60}O_2$ MW, 596

Carotinoid pigment from Rhodovibrio bacteria. Cryst. from C_6H_6. M.p. 218°. Contains 13 double bonds.

Karrer, Solmssen, *Helv. Chim. Acta*, 1936, **19**, 3.

Rhodoxanthin

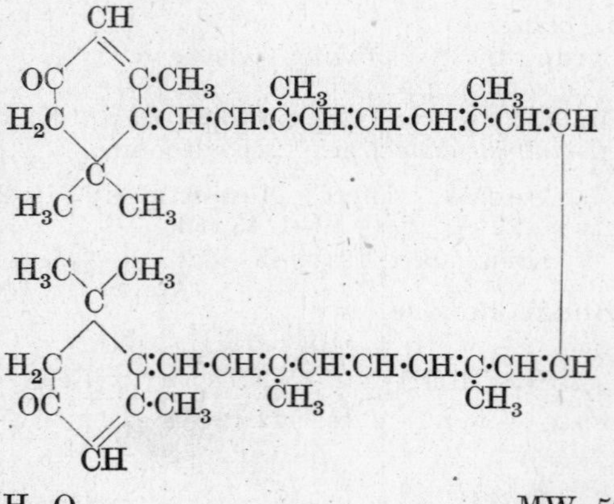

$C_{40}H_{50}O_2$ MW, 562

Pigment occurring in *Taxus baccata*, Linn. (Yew). Bluish-black leaflets from C_6H_6–MeOH. M.p. 219°. Absorption maxima in CS_2 at 564, 525 and 491 mμ.

Dioxime: m.p. 227–8°. Absorption maxima in CS_2 at 516, 483 and 453 mμ.

Kuhn, Brockmann, *Ber.*, 1933, **66**, 828.

2-Ribodesose

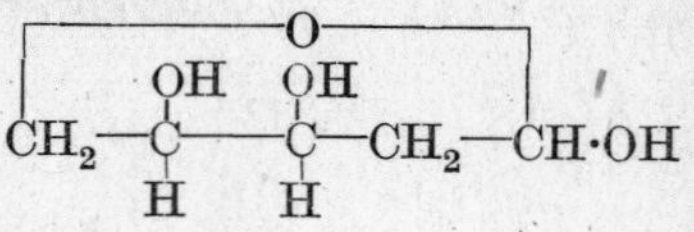

$C_5H_{10}O_4$ MW, 1

Cryst. from propyl alcohol. M.p. 90°. S H_2O. $[\alpha]_D^{23}$ + 2·13° in Py, + 2·88° ⟶ + 2·1 in H_2O. Reduces Fehling's. Sweet taste.

Benzylphenylhydrazone: m.p. 127–9°.

There are described also:

d-2-*Ribodesose* (Thyminose).

Cryst. M.p. 78°. $[\alpha]_D^{25}$ − 90·6° ⟶ 40·0° Py, − 60° ⟶ − 50° in H_2O.

Benzylphenylhydrazone: cryst. M.p. 128 $[\alpha]_D^{25}$ − 17·5° in Py.

l-β-2-*Ribodesose* (*l*-Arabodesose).

Cryst. M.p. 80°. $[\alpha]_D^{25}$ + 91·7° ⟶ + 40· in Py.

Benzylphenylhydrazone: m.p. 125–6°. [α + 17·5° in Py.

Meisenheimer, Jung, *Ber.*, 1927, **60**, 146
Levene, Mori, *J. Biol. Chem.*, 1929, **8** 803.
Levene, Mikeska, Mori, *J. Biol. Chem* 1930, **85**, 785.

Ribonic Acid

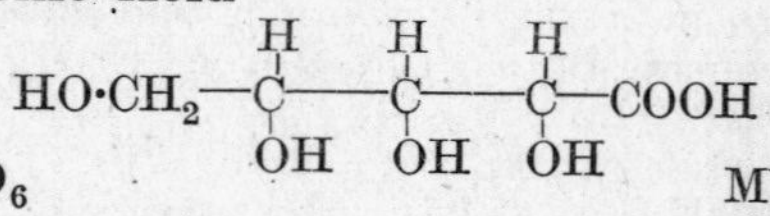

$C_5H_{10}O_6$ MW, 16

d-.

Obtained only in solution. $[\alpha]_D$ + 8·42° i H_2O (final).

γ-Lactone: $C_5H_8O_5$. MW, 148. Cryst. fro AcOEt. M.p. 72–8° (80°). $[\alpha]_D$ + 18·4° i H_2O.

Hydrazide: m.p. 150°. $[\alpha]_D^{15}$ + 27·5°.

l-.

M.p. 104–5°. $[\alpha]_D^{20}$ + 17·6° in H_2O.

γ-Lactone: prisms from AcOEt. M.p. 84–6 (80°, 72–6°). Sol. H_2O, EtOH, Me_2CO. Mod sol. AcOEt. Spar. sol. Et_2O. $[\alpha]_D^{20}$ − 18° in H_2C

Amide: $C_5H_{11}O_5N$. MW, 165. Plate M.p. 136–7°. $[\alpha]_D^{14}$ − 18·7°.

Phenylhydrazide: m.p. 204°. $[\alpha]_D^{18}$ − 33° i H_2O.

Schmidt, Weber-Molster, *Ann.*, 1934 **515**, 43.
Rehorst, *Ann.*, 1933, **503**, 143.
Fischer, Piloty, *Ber.*, 1891, **24**, 4216.
Hasenfratz, *Compt. rend.*, 1927, **184**, 210
v. Ekenstein, Blanksma, *Chem. Zentr.* 1913, II, 1562.

Ribose

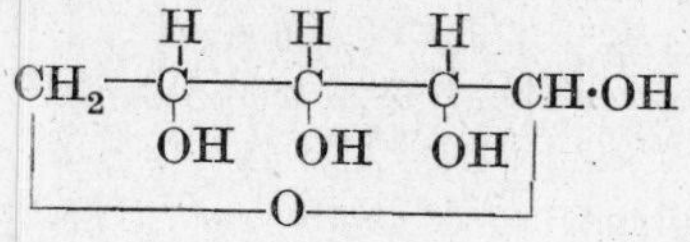

$C_5H_{10}O_5$ MW, 150

d-.

A constituent of many nucleosides and nucleotides. Cryst. M.p. 95° (86–7°). Hygroscopic. $[\alpha]_D - 21{\cdot}5°$ ($-$ 19·5°) in H_2O. Sol. H_2O. Spar. sol. EtOH.

p-*Bromophenylhydrazone*: cryst. M.p. 170° (166–7°). $[\alpha]_D + 5{\cdot}69°$ in EtOH.

Phenylosazone: yellow cryst. from H_2O. M.p. 160° (162–3°, 163–4°). Indentical with phenylosazone of *d*-arabinose.

p-*Bromophenylosazone*: m.p. 180–5°.

β-*Methylglucoside*: m.p. 83–4°. $[\alpha]_D^{20} - 113{\cdot}6°$.

l-.

Cryst. from EtOH. M.p. 87°. $[\alpha]_D + 18{\cdot}8°$ in H_2O. Sol. H_2O. Spar. sol. EtOH. Sweet taste.

Phenylhydrazone: cryst. from EtOH. M.p. 154–5° decomp. Sol. H_2O. Spar. sol. EtOH.

p-*Bromophenylhydrazone*: cryst. from EtOH. M.p. 164–5°. Sol. H_2O.

Phenylosazone: yellow cryst. from Me_2CO or H_2O. M.p. 166°. Identical with phenylosazone of *l*-arabinose. $[\alpha]_D + 1°$ in Py–EtOH, + 18·9° in EtOH. Sol. hot H_2O, EtOH, Me_2CO, Py. Insol. H_2O, Et_2O, C_6H_6, ligroin.

dl-.

M.p. 83–4°.

Phenylosazone: yellow needles or prisms. M.p. 166–8°. Identical with phenylosazone of *dl*-arabinose.

Austin, Humoller, *J. Am. Chem. Soc.*, 1934, **56**, 1152.
Levene, *J. Biol. Chem.*, 1935, **108**, 419.
Steiger, *Helv. Chim. Acta*, 1936, **19**, 189.
Fischer, Piloty, *Ber.*, 1891, **24**, 4220.
Levene, Jacobs, *Ber.*, 1909, **42**, 3247.
v. Ekenstein, Blanksma, *Chem. Zentr.*, 1913, II, 1562; 1914, I, 965.
Minsaas, *Ann.*, 1934, **512**, 286.

Ricinelaidic Acid (*Stereoisomer of ricinoleic acid*)

$CH_3{\cdot}[CH_2]_5{\cdot}CH(OH){\cdot}CH_2{\cdot}CH{:}CH{\cdot}[CH_2]_7{\cdot}COOH$

$C_{18}H_{34}O_3$ MW, 298

Needles from ligroin. M.p. 51–2°. B.p. 240–2°/10 mm. Sol. EtOH. $[\alpha]_D^{20} + 6{\cdot}67°$ in EtOH.

Et ester: $C_{20}H_{38}O_3$. MW, 326. M.p. 16°.

Amide: $C_{18}H_{35}O_2N$. MW, 297. M.p. 91–3°.

Phenylhydrazide: m.p. 110–110·5°.

Mühle, *Ber.*, 1913, **46**, 2096.
Krafft, *Ber.*, 1888, **21**, 2735.

Ricinidine

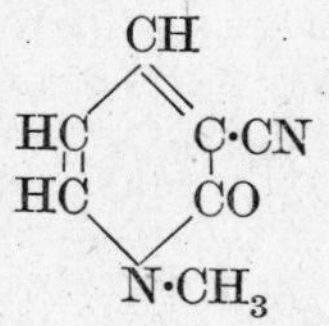

$C_7H_6ON_2$ MW, 134

M.p. 140°. B.p. 243°/28 mm.

Späth, Koller, *Ber.*, 1923, **56**, 886.

Ricinine (4-*Methoxy*-2-*keto*-1-*methyl*-1 : 2-*dihydronicotinonitrile*, 4-*methoxy*-N-*methyl*-3-*cyano*-2-*pyridone*)

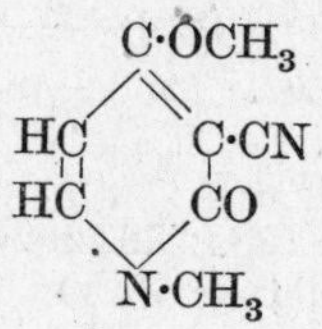

$C_8H_8O_2N_2$ MW, 164

Occurs in castor-oil seeds. Leaflets or prisms from H_2O. M.p. 201·5°. Sol. hot H_2O, hot $CHCl_3$. Spar. sol. EtOH. Insol. pet. ether. Reduces $KMnO_4$.

B,HgCl$_2$: m.p. 204°.

Späth, Koller, *Ber.*, 1925, **58**, 2124.
Schroeter, Seidler, Sulzbacher, Kametz, *Ber.*, 1932, **65**, 432.
Reitmann, *Chem. Abstracts*, 1935, **29**, 4359.

Ricinoleic Acid (*Ricinolic acid*)

$CH_3{\cdot}[CH_2]_5{\cdot}CH(OH){\cdot}CH_2{\cdot}CH{:}CH{\cdot}[CH_2]_7{\cdot}COOH$

$C_{18}H_{34}O_3$ MW, 298

Occurs in castor oil as glyceride. B.p. 226–8°/10 mm. (245°/10 mm.). Sol. EtOH, Et_2O. $[\alpha]_D^{22} + 5{\cdot}05°$. D^{15} 0·9496. n_D^{15} 1·4145.

Me ester: $C_{19}H_{36}O_3$. MW, 312. B.p. 225–7°/15 mm. *Acetyl*: b.p. 210°/13 mm. D^{22} 0·9301. n_D^{22} 1·4570. $[\alpha]_D^{22} + 15{\cdot}25°$. *Propionyl*: b.p. 260°/13 mm. D^{18} 0·9226. n_D^{18} 1·4535. $[\alpha]_D^{18} + 16{\cdot}88°$. *Benzoyl*: b.p. 195–6°/0·08 mm.

Et ester: $C_{20}H_{38}O_3$. MW, 326. B.p. 258°/13 mm. D^{22} 0·9145. n_D^{22} 1·4618. $[\alpha]_D^{22} + 5{\cdot}28°$. *Acetyl*: b.p. 255–6°/13 mm. D^{22} 0·9170. n_D^{22} 1·4540. $[\alpha]_D^{22} + 14{\cdot}85°$. *Propionyl*: b.p. 265°/13 mm. D^{18} 0·9151. n_D^{18} 1·4517. $[\alpha]_D^{18} + 16{\cdot}06°$.

Propyl ester: $C_{21}H_{40}O_3$. MW, 340. B.p. 268°/13 mm. D^{22} 0·9079. n_D^{22} 1·4573. $[\alpha]_D^{22}$ + 4·15°. *Acetyl*: b.p. 260°/13 mm. D^{22} 0·9117. n_D^{22} 1·4513. $[\alpha]_D^{22}$ + 14·40°. *Propionyl*: b.p. 310–20°/645 mm. D^{22} 0·9128. n_D^{22} 1·4498. $[\alpha]_D^{22}$ + 13·61°.

Isopropyl ester: b.p. 210°/10 mm. D^{22} 0·9083. n_D^{22} 1·4583. $[\alpha]_D^{22}$ + 4·04°.

Butyl ester: $C_{22}H_{42}O_3$. MW, 354. B.p. 278°/13 mm. D^{22} 0·9058. n_D^{22} 1·4566. $[\alpha]_D^{22}$ + 3·73°.

Isobutyl ester: b.p. 282°/9 mm. D^{22} 0·9028. n_D^{22} 1·4538. $[\alpha]_D^{22}$ + 4·01°. *Acetyl*: b.p. 255–60°/13 mm. D^{22} 0·9012. n_D^{22} 1·4548. $[\alpha]_D^{22}$ + 9·58°. *Propionyl*: b.p. 325–35°/160 mm. D^{22} 0·9027. n_D^{22} 1·4525. $[\alpha]_D^{22}$ + 9·45°.

Heptyl ester: $C_{25}H_{48}O_3$. MW, 396. B.p. 295°/10 mm. D^{22} 0·8983. n_D^{22} 1·4566. $[\alpha]_D^{22}$ + 3·32°.

Phenylhydrazide: m.p. 63°.

van Alphen, *Rec. trav. chim.*, 1925, **44**, 1064.
Ricler, U.S.P., 1,955,021, (*Chem. Abstracts*, 1934, **28**, 2926).
Straus, Heinze, Salzmann, *Ber.*, 1933, **66**, 631.
Böhme, D.R.P., 592,053, (*Chem. Abstracts*, 1934, **28**, 2725).

Ricinolic Acid.
See Ricinoleic Acid.

Ricinstearolic Acid

$CH_3·[CH_2]_5·CH(OH)·CH_2·C⋮C·[CH_2]_7·COOH$

$C_{18}H_{32}O_3$ MW, 296

Needles from ligroin. M.p. 52°. B.p. 260°/10 mm. Sol. EtOH, Et_2O. Insol. H_2O. $[\alpha]_D$ + 13·67° in H_2O.

A_2,Ba: m.p. 135°.

Me ester: $C_{19}H_{34}O_3$. MW, 310. B.p. 225°/12 mm.

Et ester: $C_{20}H_{36}O_3$. MW, 324. B.p. 230°/12 mm.

Mühle, *Ber.*, 1913, **46**, 2091.

Rissic Acid (4 : 5-*Dimethoxy-2-carboxyphenoxyacetic acid*)

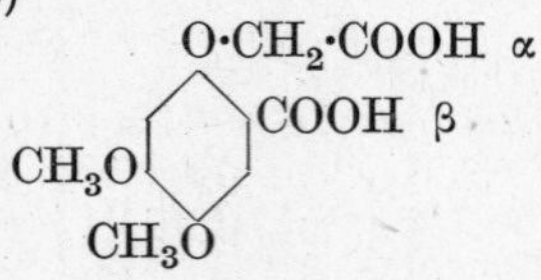

$C_{11}H_{12}O_7$ MW, 256

Needles from hot butyl alcohol. M.p. 262° (256° decomp.).

α : β-Di-Me ester: $C_{13}H_{16}O_7$. MW, 284. M.p. 86°. B.p. 265–70°/0·4 mm.

α-Et ester: $C_{13}H_{16}O_7$. MW, 284. Prisms from EtOH. M.p. 190°.

Robertson, *J. Chem. Soc.*, 1932, 1380.
Butenandt, McCartney, *Ann.*, 1932, **494**, 17.
Clark, *J. Am. Chem. Soc.*, 1931, **53**, 2371; 1932, **54**, 2548.
Takei, Miyajima, Ono, *Ber.*, 1931, **64**, 251; *Chem. Abstracts*, 1932, **26**, 5300.

Robigenin.
See Kæmpferol.

Robinetin (3 : 7 : 3′ : 4′ : 5′-*Pentahydroxyflavone*)

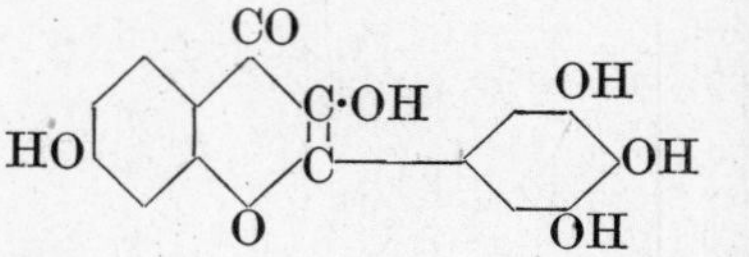

$C_{15}H_{10}O_7$ MW, 302

Found in stem-wood of *Robinia pseudacacia*, Linn., and *Gleditschia monosperma*, Walt. Greenish-yellow needles from AcOH.Aq. Decomp. at 325–30°. Sol. EtOH, Me_2CO, AcOH, AcOEt, Py. Spar. sol. H_2O, Et_2O. Insol. $CHCl_3$, C_6H_6, pet. ether. Conc. H_2SO_4 ⟶ yellow sol. Alkalis ⟶ red sols. Drop of conc. H_2SO_4 in red AcOH sol. gives characteristic intense green col.

3 : 3′ : 4′ : 5′-*Tetra-Me ether*: $C_{19}H_{18}O_2$. MW, 358. Pale yellow cryst. from EtOH. M.p. 250–1°. Alkalis and conc. H_2SO_4 ⟶ yellow sols. *Acetyl*: needles from EtOH. M.p. 149–50°.

Penta-Me ether: $C_{20}H_{20}O_7$. MW, 372. Prisms from MeOH. M.p. 149°. Conc. HCl ⟶ yellow sol.

Penta-acetyl: cryst. from EtOH. M.p. 224°. Sol. EtOH, Me_2CO, C_6H_6.

Charlesworth, Robinson, *J. Chem. Soc.*, 1933, 269.

Rochelle Salt.
See under Tartaric Acid.

Rodinal.
See *p*-Aminophenol.

Rongalite.
See under Formaldehyde.

Rosilic Acid.
9-Hydroxystearic Acid, *q.v.*

Rotenic Acid.
See Isotubaic Acid.

Rotenone

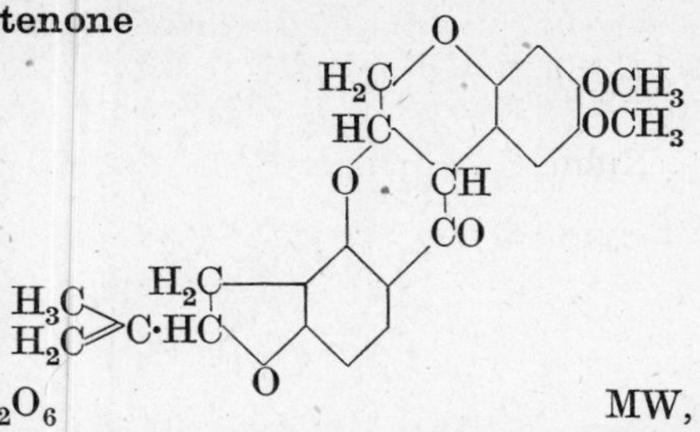

$C_{23}H_{22}O_6$ MW, 394

Occurs in resin from root of *Derris elliptica*, Benth. Needles or plates from Me_2CO.Aq. M.p. 163°. B.p. 210–20°/0·5 mm. Sol. ord. org. solvents. Sol. in EtOH reduces Fehling's and Tollen's. $[\alpha]_D^{29.5}$ — 225·2° in C_6H_6. Powerful contact insecticide and fish poison.

Oxime: (i) m.p. 249°. (ii) M.p. 230°.

Hydrazone: (i) m.p. 258° decomp. (ii) M.p. 229°.

Phenylhydrazone: (i) m.p. 255° (245°). (ii) M.p. 203°.

Takei, Miyajima, Ono, *Sci. Papers Inst. Phys. Chem. Research, Tokyo*, 1932, **19**, 1, (*Review and Bibl.*).

La Forge, Haller, Smith, *Chemical Reviews*, 1933, **12**, 181 (*Review*).

Roteol.

See Isotubanol.

Ruban (2-*Quinuclidyl*-4-*quinolylmethane*)

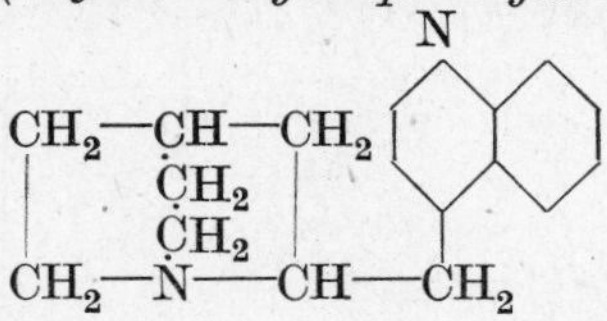

$C_{17}H_{20}N_2$ MW, 252

d-.

Oil. $[\alpha]_D^{16}$ + 80·5°.

l-.

Oil. $[\alpha]_D^{16}$ — 78·4°.

Rabe, Riza, *Ann.*, 1932, **496**, 151.

Rabe, *Ber.*, 1922, **55**, 523, 532.

Rubanol (9-*Hydroxyruban*)

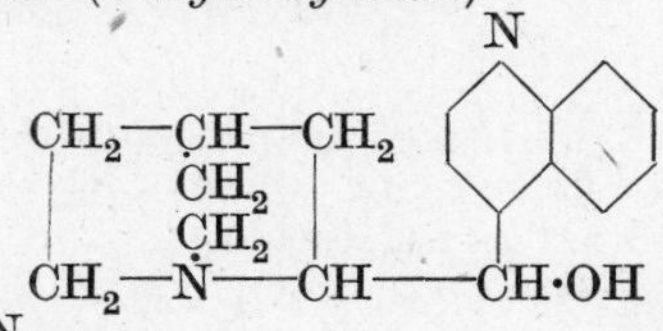

$C_{17}H_{20}ON_2$ MW, 268

d : *d*-.

Cryst. from EtOH. M.p. 229·5–230° decomp. Sol. EtOH. Spar. sol. Et_2O. $[\alpha]_D^{16}$ + 132·5° in EtOH.

l-*Acid tartrate*: m.p. 186–7° decomp. $[\alpha]_D^{15}$ + 84·7° in H_2O.

d : *l*-.

Prisms from Et_2O. M.p. 118–19°. Sol. EtOH, Et_2O. $[\alpha]_D^{16}$ + 14·3° in EtOH.

Di-[dibenzyl]-tartrate: m.p. 189–91° decomp. $[\alpha]_D^{18}$ — 47·9° in MeOH.

l : *d*-.

M.p. 117–18°. $[\alpha]_D^{18}$ — 14·9° in EtOH.

Di-[dibenzyl]-tartrate: m.p. 189–91° decomp. $[\alpha]_D^{22}$ + 48·0° in MeOH.

l : *l*-.

M.p. 228·5–230·5° decomp. $[\alpha]_D^{15}$ — 131·8° in EtOH.

d-*Acid tartrate*: m.p. 186–8° decomp. $[\alpha]_D^{15}$ — 83·9° in H_2O.

Rabe, Riza, *Ann.*, 1932, **496**, 158.

Ruberythric Acid (*Alizarin primveroside*)

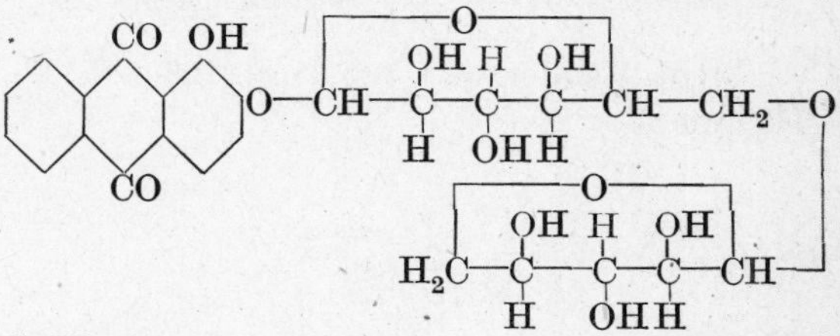

$C_{25}H_{26}O_{13}$ MW, 534

Occurs in *Rubia tinctorum*, Linn. Yellow prisms from H_2O. M.p. 258–60°. Spar. sol. H_2O, EtOH, Et_2O. Insol. C_6H_6. Sol. alkalis ⟶ red col. Hyd. ⟶ alizarin + glucose + xylose.

Octa-acetyl deriv.: m.p. 230°.

Penta-Me ether: $C_{30}H_{38}O_{14}$. MW, 622. Pale yellow needles from MeOH. M.p. 170–80°.

Richter, *J. Chem. Soc.*, 1936, 1701 (*Bibl.*).

Jones, Robertson, *J. Chem. Soc.*, 1933, 1167.

Zemplén, Müller, *Ber.*, 1929, **62**, 2107.

Glaser, Kahler, *Ber.*, 1927, **60**, 1349.

Rubiadin (2-*Methylpurpuroxanthin*, 2-*methylxanthopurpurin*, 1 : 3-*dihydroxy*-2-*methylanthraquinone*)

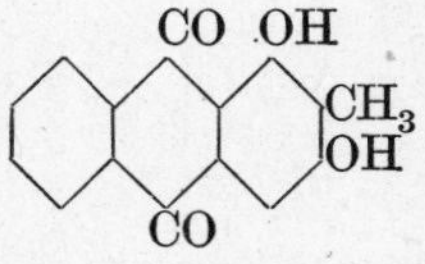

$C_{15}H_{10}O_4$ MW, 254

Occurs in root of *Rubia tinctorum*, Linn. (madder). Yellow plates from AcOH. M.p. 290°.

3-*Acetyl*: m.p. 191°.

Diacetyl: m.p. 225°.

3-β-*Glucoside*: occurs in *Rubia tinctorum*, Linn. $C_{21}H_{20}O_9$. MW, 416. Yellow needles from EtOH. M.p. 270–1°. *Tetra-acetyl*: m.p. 230°.

1 : 3-*Di*-β-*glucoside*: m.p. 248°.

Primveroside: occurs in *Galium verum*, Linn. $C_{26}H_{28}O_{13}$. MW, 548. Yellow plates. M.p. 248–50°. Sol. hot H_2O. Hyd. ⟶ rubiadin-3-glucoside + xylose.

1-*Me ether*: $C_{16}H_{12}O_4$. MW, 268. Yellow needles from EtOH. M.p. 291°. *Acetyl*: m.p. 174°.

3-*Me ether*: yellow plates from AcOH. M.p. 186°. *Acetyl*: m.p. 200°.

Di-Me ether: $C_{17}H_{14}O_4$. MW, 282. Yellow needles from MeOH. M.p. 158°.

Jones, Robertson, *J. Chem. Soc.*, 1930, 1699.
Kusaka, *Chem. Zentr.*, 1935, II, 3381.
Mitter, Biswas, *J. Indian Chem. Soc.*, 1930, **7**, 839.
Hill, Richter, *J. Chem. Soc.*, 1936, 1714.

Rubicene

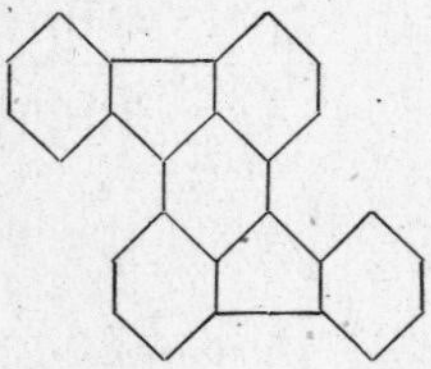

$C_{26}H_{14}$ MW, 326

Red needles from $PhNO_2$. M.p. 306°. Sol. hot $PhNO_2$. Spar. sol. C_6H_6. Insol. EtOH, Et_2O, pet. ether. Dil. sols. show intense yellow fluor.

Scholl, Meyer, *Ber.*, 1932, **65**, 926.
Eckert, *J. prakt. Chem.*, 1929, **121**, 278.
v. Braun, *Ber.*, 1934, **67**, 217.

Rubixanthin

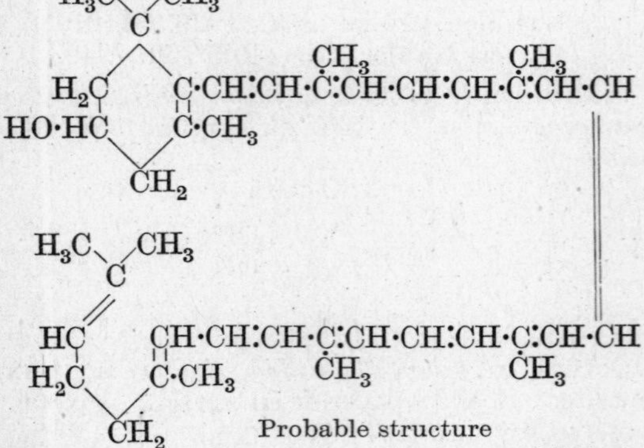

Probable structure

$C_{40}H_{56}O$ MW, 552

Pigment of ripe fruit of *Rosa rubinosa*. Dark red needles from C_6H_6–MeOH. M.p. 160°. Absorption maxima in CS_2 at 533, 494 and 461 mμ.

Kuhn, Grundmann, *Ber.*, 1934, **67**, 339.

Rubrene (5 : 6 : 11 : 12-*Tetraphenylnaphthacene*)

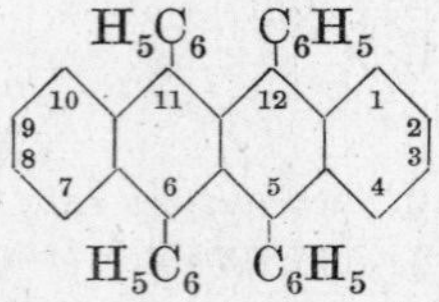

$C_{42}H_{28}$ MW, 532

Red cryst. M.p. 331°. Sol. C_6H_6, CS_2. Sols. are orange when conc., pink with yellow fluor. when dil.

Koblitz, Witmeyer, *Ber.*, 1936, **69**, 1806.
Robin, *Compt. rend.*, 1929, **189**, 337.
Allen, Gilman, *J. Am. Chem. Soc.*, 1936, **58**, 937.
Bergmann, Herlinger, *J. Chem. Physics*, 1936, **4**, 532.
Dufraisse, *Bull. soc. chim.*, 1930, **47**, 216.

Rubreserine

$C_{13}H_{16}O_2N_2$ MW, 232

Oxidation product of eseroline. Red needles $+1H_2O$ from H_2O. M.p. anhyd. 152°. Sol. H_2O, EtOH, $CHCl_3$, hot C_6H_6. Insol. Et_2O, pet. ether.

B,HCl: red cryst. $+ 1H_2O$. M.p. 185° decomp.

B,HAuCl$_4$: decomp. at 190–5°.

Picrate: decomp. at 198°.

Salway, *J. Chem. Soc.*, 1912, **101**, 984.

Rufigallic Acid (*Rufigallol*, 1 : 2 : 3 : 5 : 6 : 7-*hexahydroxyanthraquinone*)

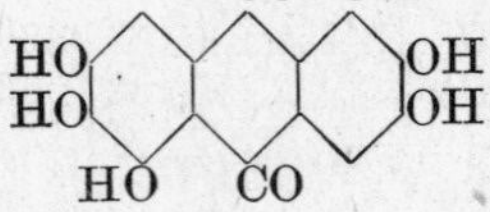

$C_{14}H_8O_8$ MW, 304

Red cryst. Sublimes with decomp. on heating. Sol. EtOH, Et_2O. Sol. alkalis ⟶ violet col. Heat of comb. C_p 1252·4 Cal.

Tetra-Me ether: $C_{18}H_{16}O_8$. MW, 360. Yellow leaflets from AcOEt. M.p. 235–7°. *Diacetyl deriv.*: m.p. 262°. *Monobenzoyl deriv.*: m.p. 190–205°.

Penta-Me ether: $C_{19}H_{18}O_8$. MW, 374. Yellow needles from AcOEt. M.p. 192–4°.

Hexa-Me ether: $C_{20}H_{20}O_8$. MW, 388. Yel-
v needles. M.p. 245° (240°).

Tri-Et ether: $C_{20}H_{20}O_8$. MW, 388. Orange-
l needles from EtOH. M.p. 195°.

Tetra-Et ether: $C_{22}H_{24}O_8$. MW, 416. Red
edles from EtOH. M.p. above 180°. *Di-
etyl deriv.*: m.p. 230–5°.

Hexa-Et ether: $C_{26}H_{32}O_8$. MW, 472. Orange-
llow needles from EtOH.Aq. M.p. above
0°.

Hexa-acetyl: m.p. 282–3°.

Segui, *Chem. Abstracts*, 1934, **28**, 7257.
Fischer, Gross, *J. prakt. Chem.*, 1911, **84**, 369.
Schering, D.R.P., 151,724, (*Chem. Zentr.*, 1904, I, 1586).

Rufigallol.
See Rufigallic Acid.

Rufiopin (1 : 2 : 5 : 6-*Tetrahydroxyanthra-
ıinone*)

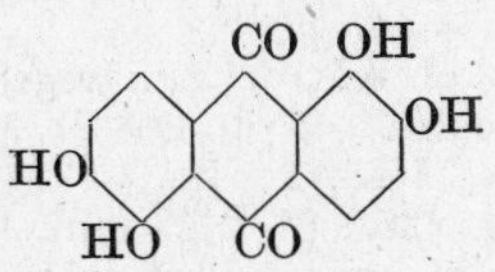

$_{14}H_8O_6$ MW, 272

Orange-red needles from Py. M.p. 340° (316–
°). Sol. hot H_2O. Mod. sol. EtOH, AcOH.
ıar. sol. Et_2O, C_6H_6, $CHCl_3$.

1 : 2 : 6-*Tri-Me ether*: $C_{17}H_{14}O_6$. MW,
4. Orange-red needles from AcOH. M.p.
5–6°.

Tetra-acetyl: m.p. 260–3° decomp. (238°, 260–
° decomp.).

Heller, *Z. angew. Chem.*, 1929, **42**, 170.
Puntambeker, Adams, *J. Am. Chem. Soc.*, 1927, **49**, 487.
Marshall, *J. Chem. Soc.*, 1937, 254.

Rufol.
See 1 : 5-Dihydroxyanthracene.

Rutin (*Eldrin, violaquercitrin, osyritrin, myrticolorin, quercetin rutinoside*)

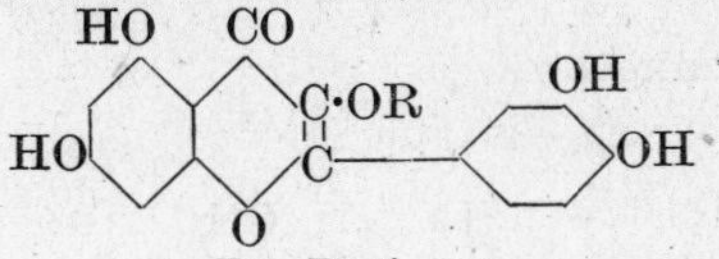

R = Rutinose

$C_{27}H_{30}O_{16}$ MW, 610

Occurs in tomato stems, tobacco leaves, rue leaves and many flowers. Yellow needles $+ 2H_2O$ from H_2O. Softens below 188°, not completely melted at 190°. Sol. hot EtOH. Insol. Et_2O, $CHCl_3$, C_6H_6, CS_2. $FeCl_3 \longrightarrow$ intense green col.

Charaux, *Bull. soc. chim. biol.*, 1924, **6**, 641.
Sanso, Lloyd, *J. Biol. Chem.*, 1924, **58**, 737.
Perkin, *J. Chem. Soc.*, 1900, **97**, 1788.
Zemplén, Gerecs, *Ber.*, 1935, **68**, 1318.

Rutinose

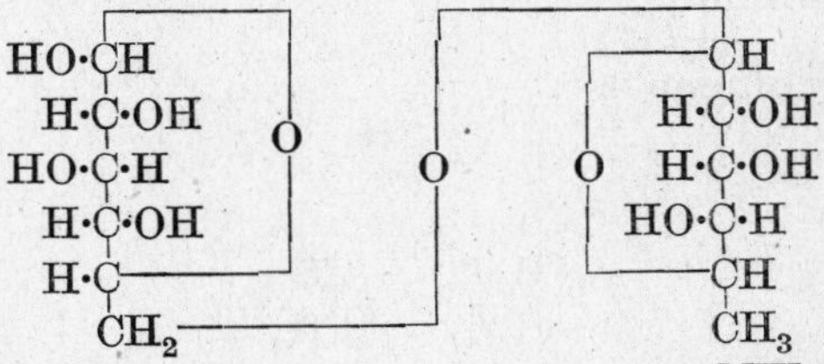

$C_{12}H_{22}O_{10}$ MW, 326

Hygroscopic powder. Softens at 140°, m.p. 189–92° decomp. Sol. H_2O, EtOH. Insol. Et_2O. $[\alpha]_D^{10} + 3{\cdot}24° \longrightarrow - 0{\cdot}81°$ in H_2O, $[\alpha]_D^{20} - 10{\cdot}0°$ in EtOH. Reduces Fehling's.

Hepta-acetyl deriv.: m.p. 168–9°. $[\alpha]_D - 28{\cdot}84°$ in $CHCl_3$. *Me ether*: m.p. 139·5–140°. $[\alpha]_D - 45{\cdot}19°$.

Zemplén, Gerecs, *Ber.*, 1935, **68**, 1319.
Charaux, *Compt. rend.*, 1924, **178**, 1312.

Rutylidene.
See Nonylacetylene.

S

Sabinaketone

$$\begin{array}{c} CO \\ H_2C \quad CH \\ H_2C \quad CH_2 \\ C \\ CH(CH_3)_2 \end{array}$$

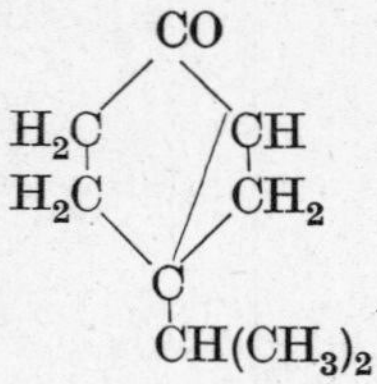

$C_9H_{14}O$ MW, 138

l-.

Prisms from H_2O. M.p. 17°. B.p. 218–19°. D^{20} 0·9555. n_D^{20} 1·4700. Spar. sol. H_2O.
Semicarbazone : cryst. from MeOH. M.p. 141–2°.

Schmidt, *Z. angew. Chem.*, 1929, **42**, 127.
Wallach, *Ann.*, 1908, **359**, 266.

Sabinane.
See Thujane.

Sabinene

$$\begin{array}{c} CH_2 \\ C \\ H_2C \quad CH \\ H_2C \quad CH_2 \\ C \\ CH(CH_3)_2 \end{array}$$

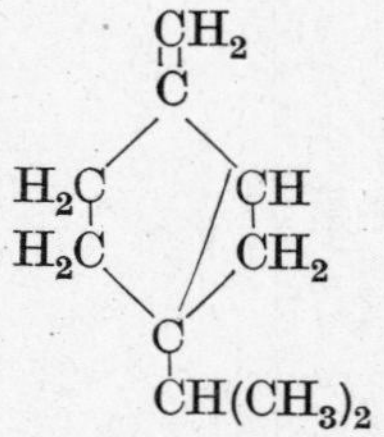

$C_{10}H_{16}$ MW, 136

d-.

Constituent of various essential oils, e.g. *Juniperus sabina.* B.p. 163–5°, 66°/30 mm. D^{20} 0·842. n_D^{20} 1·4678. $[\alpha]_D$ + 80·17° (89·07°).

l-.

B.p. 162–6°. D^{20} 0·8468. $[\alpha]_D^{15}$ − 42·5°.
Hydrate : methylsabinaketol. Cryst. resembling terpineol in odour. M.p. 38–9°. B.p. 195–201° part. decomp. $[\alpha]_D^{15}$ + 53·67° in Et_2O.

Semmler, *Ber.*, 1900, **33**, 1463.
Wallach, *Ann.*, 1907, **357**, 64, 77.

Sabinic Acid (11-*Hydroxylauric acid*)

$$HO \cdot CH_2 \cdot [CH_2]_9 \cdot CH_2 \cdot COOH$$

$C_{12}H_{24}O_3$ MW, 216

Cryst. from C_6H_6 or AcOEt, m.p. 84° : needles from MeOH.Aq, m.p. 78–9°. Sol. EtOH.
Me ester : $C_{13}H_{26}O_3$. MW, 230. M.p. 44·5° (34–5°). B.p. 160°/7 mm. (164–6°/3 mm.).
Phenylurethane : m.p. 64–5°.
Anilide : prisms from pet. ether. M.p. 87°.

Acetyl : m.p. 49–49·2° (43°). B.p. 202–3°.

Chuit, Hausser, *Helv. Chim. Acta*, 192 **12**, 477.
Bhattacharya, Saletore, Simonsen, *Chem. Soc.*, 1928, 2679.
Lycan, Adams, *J. Am. Chem. Soc.*, 192 **51**, 628.

Sabinol

$$\begin{array}{c} CH_2 \\ C \\ HO \cdot HC \quad CH \\ H_2C \quad CH_2 \\ C \\ CH(CH_3)_2 \end{array}$$

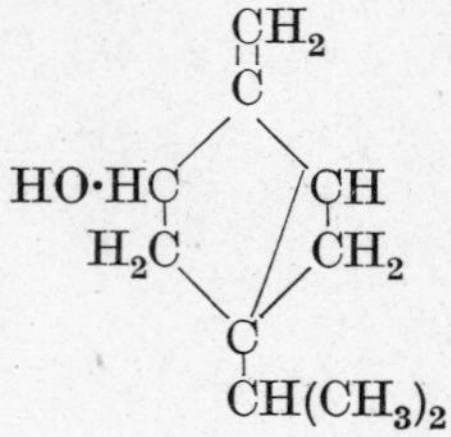

$C_{10}H_{16}O$ MW, 1

Constituent of oils of *Juniperus sabina* an *Sabina officinalis.* B.p. 208°, 77–8°/3 mm D_{15}^{15} 0·9518. n_D^{18} 1·4895. $[\alpha]_D$ + 17·04°.
Acetyl : b.p. 225°, 81–2°/3 mm. D^{15} 0·972.
Acid phthalate : needles from pet. ethe M.p. 94–5°. $[\alpha]_D$ − 14·63°.

Fromm, *Ber.*, 1898, **31**, 2025.

Saccharic Acid (*Tetrahydroxyadipic acid*)

$$\begin{array}{c} \quad OH \quad H \quad OH \quad OH \\ HOOC-C-C-C-C-COOH \\ \quad H \quad OH \quad H \quad H \end{array}$$

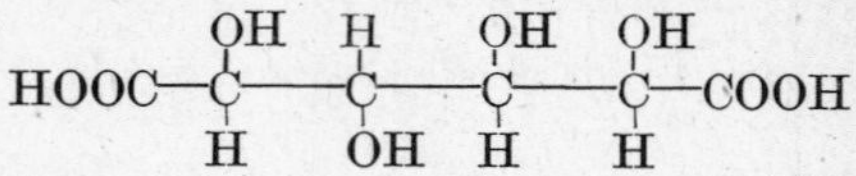

$C_6H_{10}O_8$ MW, 21

d-.

Needles from 95% EtOH. M.p. 125–6 $[\alpha]_D^{19}$ + 6·86° $\longrightarrow$ + 20·60° in H_2O. Sol. H_2O EtOH. Spar. sol. Et_2O. k (first) = 1·0 $\times$ 10^{-5} at 25°. $HNO_3 \longrightarrow$ *d*-tartaric, racemic, an oxalic acids. $KMnO_4 \longrightarrow$ *d*-tartaric and oxal acids.
Cinchonine salt : $2C_{19}H_{22}ON_2,C_6H_{10}O_8$. Cryst from H_2O. Decomp. about 190°. $[\alpha]_D^{20}$ + 149·1 in H_2O.
Quinine salt : $2C_{20}H_{24}O_2N_2,C_6H_{10}O_8$. Needles M.p. 174°.
Di-Me ester : $C_8H_{14}O_8$. MW, 238. *Tetra Me ether* : prisms from Et_2O. M.p. 77–8 (68°). B.p. 150°/1 mm. $[\alpha]_D^{18}$ + 8·88° $\longrightarrow$ + 10·26° in H_2O. Sol. H_2O, Et_2O, $CHCl_3$.
Di-Et ester : $C_{10}H_{18}O_8$. MW, 266. Cryst mass. Sol. H_2O, EtOH. Spar. sol. Et_2O *Tetra-acetyl* : plates from EtOH or prisms from Et_2O. M.p. 61°. Sol. hot EtOH, Et_2O. In sol. H_2O.

Amide: $C_6H_{11}O_7N$. MW, 209. Needles. M.p. 135° decomp. $[\alpha]_D^{19}$ + 22·5° in H_2O. Sol. hot H_2O. Spar. sol. EtOH.
Diamide: $C_6H_{12}O_6N_2$. MW, 208. Cryst. from EtOH. M.p. 172–3°. $[\alpha]_D^{20}$ + 13·3° in H_2O. *Tetra-Me ether*: plates from H_2O. M.p. 237–9°. $[\alpha]_D^{18}$ + 12·22° in H_2O.
γ-Lactone: $C_6H_8O_7$. MW, 192. Cryst. M.p. 130–2°. Sol. H_2O. $[\alpha]_D^{25}$ + 40·8° ⟶ + 22·7° in H_2O.
Diphenylhydrazide: yellow plates. Decomp. at 210°. Insol. H_2O, EtOH, Et_2O.

l-.
Free acid not isolated.
KH salt: needles or prisms from hot H_2O. Mod. sol. H_2O.
Diphenylhydrazide: yellow plates. M.p. 213–14° decomp.

dl-.
Syrup.
KH salt: needles. Mod. sol. H_2O.
Diphenylhydrazide: laminæ. M.p. 209–10° decomp.

Sohst, Tollens, *Ann.*, 1888, **245**, 1.
Henneberg, Tollens, *Ann.*, 1896, **292**, 40.
Fischer, *Ber.*, 1890, **23**, 2621.
Fischer, Stahel, *Ber.*, 1891, **24**, 534.
Kiliani, *Ber.*, 1925, **58**, 2344.
Rehorst, *Ber.*, 1928, **61**, 163.
Haworth, Loach, Long, *J. Chem. Soc.*, 1927, 3154.
Karrer, Peyer, *Helv. Chim. Acta*, 1922, **5**, 577.
Bergmann, *Ber.*, 1921, **54**, 1380, 2653.
Hudson, Komatsu, *J. Am. Chem. Soc.*, 1919, **41**, 1147.

Saccharin (*Benzoic sulphimide, o-sulphobenzoic imide*)

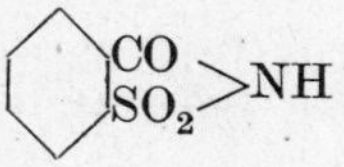

$C_7H_5O_3NS$ MW, 183

Prisms from EtOH, leaflets from H_2O. M.p. 224° decomp. Sol. 250 parts cold H_2O, 40 parts cold EtOH, 221 parts hot C_6H_6. Sublimes in vacuo. Forms salts with NH_3 and org. bases. All salts intensely sweet. Hot alkalis or hot conc. HCl ⟶ *o*-sulphobenzoic acid.
Oxime: m.p. 208–10° decomp. *Acetate*: m.p. 225° decomp. *Benzoate*: m.p. 250° decomp.
N-*Me*: $C_8H_7O_3NS$. MW, 197. Needles from H_2O. M.p. 131–2°. Sol. EtOH, Et_2O. Spar. sol cold H_2O.
N-*Et*: $C_9H_9O_3NS$. MW, 211. Needles from H_2O. M.p. 93–4°. Very sol. EtOH, Et_2O. Mod. sol. hot H_2O.

Zaikov, Sokolov, *Chem. Abstracts*, 1928, **22**, 2933.
Brackett, Hayes, *Am. Chem. J.*, 1887, **9**, 405.
Zil'berg, *Chem. Abstracts*, 1935, **29**, 1794.
Roost, *Chem. Abstracts*, 1928, **22**, 4114.
Orelup, U.S.P. 1,601,505, (*Chem. Zentr.*, 1927, II, 2115).

Saccharose.
See Sucrose.
S-Acid.
See 1-Amino-8-naphthol-4-sulphonic Acid.
2S-Acid.
See 1-Amino-8-naphthol-2 : 4-disulphonic Acid.

Safranal

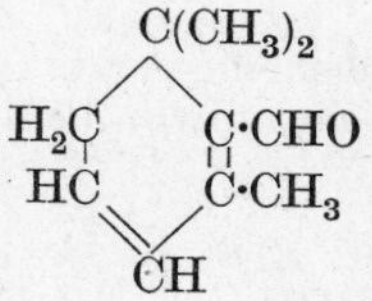

$C_{10}H_{14}O$ MW, 150

Hydrolysis product of picrocrocin. B.p. 70°/1 mm. D_4^{19} 0·9734. n_D^{19} 1·5281.
Oxime: prisms from pet. ether. M.p. 65°.
Semicarbazone: cryst. from MeOH. M.p. 175°.
Thiosemicarbazone: cryst. from C_6H_6. M.p. 199–200°.
2 : 4-*Dinitrophenylhydrazone*: red cryst. from MeOH. M.p. 186°.

Kuhn, Wendt, *Ber.*, 1936, **69**, 1549.
Kuhn, Winterstein, *Ber.*, 1934, **67**, 354.

Safranol

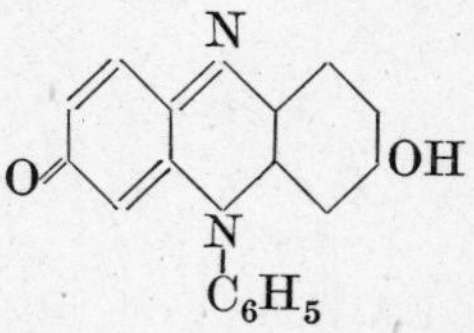

$C_{18}H_{12}O_2N_2$ MW, 288

Needles. Does not melt below 330°. Very spar. sol. Et_2O. Insol. H_2O, EtOH, AcOH. Sol. alkalis.
Me ether: $C_{19}H_{14}O_2N_2$. MW, 302. M.p. 266°.
Et ether: $C_{20}H_{16}O_2N_2$. MW, 316. Bronze prisms from EtOH. M.p. 265° decomp.

Acetyl: red prisms with greenish lustre. M.p. 265–8°.

Jaubert, *Ber.*, 1895, **28**, 273.

Safrol (3 : 4-*Methylenedioxyallylbenzene*)

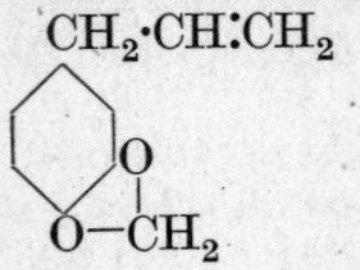

$C_{10}H_{10}O_2$ MW, 162

Constituent of several essential oils, e.g. *Sassafras officinalis*. Monoclinic prisms. Setting-point 11·2°. B.p. 231·5–232°, 104–5°/6 mm. D_4^{20} 1·100. n_D^{20} 1·5383. Sol. EtOH, Et_2O. Insol. H_2O.

Picrate: red cryst. from EtOH. M.p. 75°.

Perkin, Trikojus, *J. Chem. Soc.*, 1927, 1663.

Saiodin.
See under Iodobehenic Acid.

Sakuranin (*Sakuranetin-5-glucoside*)

$C_{22}H_{24}O_{10}$ MW, 448

Constituent of rind of *Prunus yeodensis*. Needles from EtOH or AcOEt. M.p. 212°. Very sol. 60% EtOH, Py. Less sol. EtOH. Insol. H_2O, Et_2O. $[\alpha]_D^{23}$ − 106·6° in Me_2CO. Alkalis ⟶ intense yellow sols. Conc. H_2SO_4 ⟶ intense brown col. ⟶ yellow on adding more acid. Alc. $FeCl_3$ ⟶ yellow col.

Oxime: needles from EtOH. M.p. 110°. Conc. HNO_3 ⟶ green col.

Asahina, *Chem. Zentr.*, 1908, II, 253.
Asahina, Shinoda, Inubuse, *Chem. Zentr.*, 1928, I, 1672.

Sakuranetin (*Naringenin 7-methyl ether, 5:4′-dihydroxy-7-methoxyflavanone*)

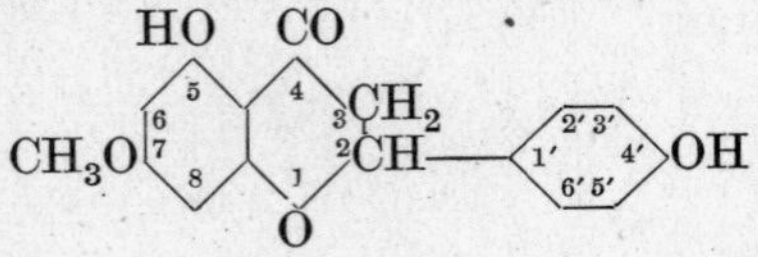

$C_{16}H_{14}O_5$ MW, 286

Needles from EtOH.Aq., dry Et_2O, or C_6H_6. M.p. 150°. Sol. EtOH, Et_2O, C_6H_6, $CHCl_3$, AcOEt, Py. Spar. sol. boiling H_2O. Fuming HNO_3 ⟶ deep indigo-blue col. ⟶ violet on standing. Alkalis ⟶ intense yellow sols. decomp. by CO_2 and weak acids. Mg + alc. HCl ⟶ purplish-red col. KOH fusion ⟶ phloroglucinol + *p*-hydroxybenzoic acid. Tasteless.

4′-Me ether: *see under* Isosakuranetin.
Di-Me ether: *see under* Isosakuranetin.
Oxime: needles + $2H_2O$ from EtOH.Aq., m.p. 120°: needles from AcOH, m.p. 195–6° decomp.
5-Glucoside: *see* Sakuranin.
Diacetyl: m.p. 97°.

Shinoda, Sato, *Chem. Zentr.*, 1929, I, 244.
See also last reference above.

Salacetol (*Acetol salicylate, hydroxyacetone salicylate, β-ketopropyl salicylate*)

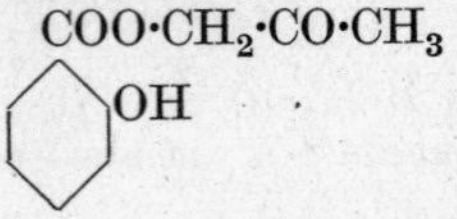

$C_{10}H_{10}O_4$ MW, 194

Needles from EtOH. M.p. 71°. Sol. Et_2O, C_6H_6, hot EtOH. Spar. sol. ligroin. Very spar. sol. hot H_2O. Triboluminescent.

Fritsch, D.R.P., 70,054.

Salazine (*Salicylaldazine, 2 : 2′-dihydroxybenzaldazine*)

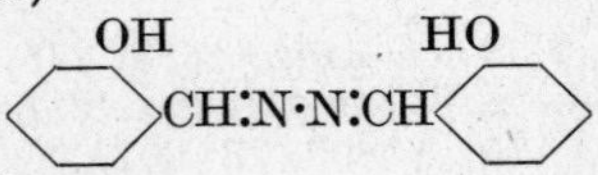

$C_{14}H_{12}O_2N_2$ MW, 240

Yellow needles or leaflets from EtOH. M.p. 214°. Sol. $CHCl_3$, C_6H_6, alkalis. Mod. sol. EtOH. Insol. H_2O. Sublimes.

Di-Me ether: $C_{16}H_{16}O_2N_2$. MW, 268. Yellow needles from EtOH. M.p. 178° (141°).
Di-Et ether: $C_{18}H_{20}O_2N_2$. MW, 296. Yellow cryst. from EtOH. M.p. 136° (130°).
Dibenzyl ether: yellow plates from C_6H_6. M.p. 158°.
Diacetyl: plates from $CHCl_3$. M.p. 191°.
Dibenzoyl: yellow needles from C_6H_6. M.p. 188–9°.

Widman, *Ber.*, 1919, **52**, 1658.
Borsche, *Ber.*, 1901, **34**, 4299; 1921, **54**, 668.
Curtius, Jay, *J. prakt. Chem.*, 1889, **39**, 48.

Salazinic Acid (*Saxatilic acid*)

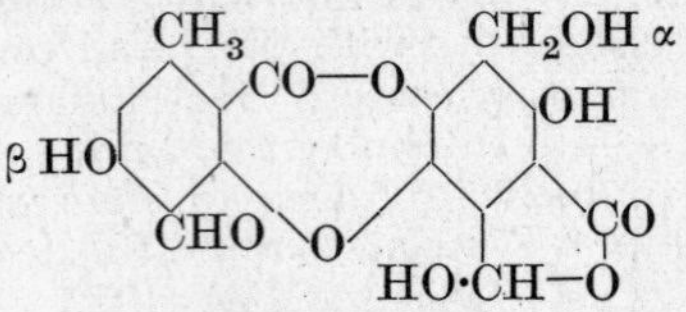

Probable structure

$C_{18}H_{12}O_{10}$ MW, 388

Isolated from *Parmelia conspersa*, Ach. Needles or plates from Me_2CO. M.p. 270° (decomp. at 260°). Sol. Et_2O, $CHCl_3$, C_6H_6. Spar. sol. EtOH, Me_2CO.

α-Me ether: $C_{19}H_{14}O_{10}$. MW, 402. Needles from 80% Me_2CO. M.p. 210° decomp. Sol. EtOH, Me_2CO, AcOH. Spar. sol. Et_2O. Insol. C_6H_6, pet. ether. *Dianil*: yellow prisms from Me_2CO. M.p. 169° decomp.

β-Me ether: needles from 80% Me_2CO. M.p. 250–2° decomp. Sol. EtOH, Me_2CO, AcOH. Insol. Et_2O, C_6H_6, pet. ether. *Penta-acetyl*: plates from Me_2CO. M.p. 228° decomp. *Dianil*: yellow prisms from Me_2CO. M.p. 231° decomp.

α-Acetyl: needles from AcOH. M.p. 275–6° decomp. Sol. EtOH, Me_2CO.

Tetra-acetyl: m.p. 205–6°.

Hexa-acetyl: needles from Me_2CO. M.p. 178°.

Di-phenylhydrazone: yellow prisms. Decomp. at 295°.

Dianil: decomp. at 280°.

Asahina, Tukamoto, *Ber.*, 1934, **67**, 965.
Koller, Kutzelnigg, *Monatsh.*, 1934, **65**, 92.
Asahina, Asano, *Ber.*, 1933, **66**, 895.
Fuzikawa, Ishiguro, *Chem. Zentr.*, 1937, I, 2996.

Salicin (*Saligenin glucoside*)

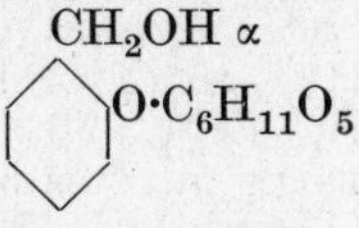

$C_{13}H_{18}O_7$ MW, 286

Glucoside of poplar and willow bark. Needles from H_2O. M.p. 201° (198°). Sol. 24 parts H_2O at 25°. $[\alpha]_D^{20}$ − 62·56° in H_2O. Hydrolysis by emulsin ⟶ glucose + saligenin. H_2SO_4 ⟶ purple col. Possesses burning taste.

Penta-Me ether: $C_{18}H_{28}O_7$. MW, 356. Needles from pet. ether. M.p. 62–4°. $[\alpha]_D$ − 52·1° in MeOH.

Tetra-acetyl: needles from H_2O. M.p. 130° (126°). Insol. pet. ether. *α-Me ether*: plates from EtOH. M.p. 142°. *α-Allyl ether*: needles from EtOH. M.p. 139·5°. *α-Benzyl ether*: plates from EtOH or pet. ether. M.p. 94·5–95°. *α-Phenyl ether*: yellow needles from EtOH. M.p. 161°.

Penta-acetyl: cryst. from EtOH. M.p. 130°. $[\alpha]_D^{23\cdot5}$ − 18·5° in $CHCl_3$.

Benzoyl: *see* Populin.

Kunz, *J. Am. Chem. Soc.*, 1926, **48**, 262.
Zemplén, Braun, *Ber.*, 1925, **58**, 1406.
Irvine, Rose, *J. Chem. Soc.*, 1906, **89**, 814.

Salicyl Alcohol.

See Saligenin.

Salicylaldehyde (o-*Hydroxybenzaldehyde*)

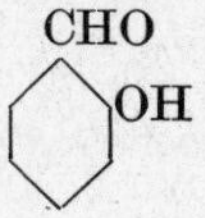

$C_7H_6O_2$ MW, 122

Oil. F.p. − 7°. B.p. 197°, 93°/25 mm., 86°/18 mm. D_4^{20} 1·1674. n_D^{20} 1·574. Heat of comb. C_p 807·3 Cal. Volatile in steam. Does not reduce Fehling's. H_2O_2 ⟶ 2 : 3-dihydroxybenzaldehyde. KOH ⟶ salicylic acid. NaHg ⟶ saligenin. $FeCl_3$ ⟶ violet col. H_2SO_4 ⟶ orange col.

Me ether: *see* o-Methoxybenzaldehyde.

Et ether: o-ethoxybenzaldehyde. $C_9H_{10}O_2$. MW, 150. M.p. 20–2°. B.p. 247–9°, 143–7°/25 mm. *Diacetate*: prisms. M.p. 88–9°. *Oxime*: prisms from pet. ether. M.p. 57–9°. *Semicarbazone*: needles from EtOH. M.p. 219°.

Allyl ether: $C_{10}H_{10}O_2$. MW, 162. B.p. 130°/10 mm.

Benzyl ether: $C_{14}H_{12}O_2$. MW, 212. Prisms from EtOH. M.p. 46°. *Oxime*: plates from pet. ether. M.p. 71·5°.

Acetyl: needles from pet. ether. M.p. 38–9°. B.p. 142°/18 mm. *Semicarbazone*: powder from Me_2CO. M.p. 167°.

Triacetate: o-acetoxybenzylidene diacetate. Prisms from EtOH. M.p. 107°.

Benzoyl: b.p. above 300°.

p-*Nitrobenzoyl*: yellow plates. M.p. 128°.

Oxime: prisms from C_6H_6–pet. ether. M.p. 63° (57°). *Me ether*: (>N·OCH₃). Prisms. M.p. 28°. B.p. 107°/14 mm. *Acetate*: (>N·OCO·CH₃). Needles from pet. ether. M.p. 75° (69°).

Semioxamazone: needles from EtOH.Aq. M.p. 255°.

Semicarbazone: needles from EtOH. M.p. 230°.

Phenylsemicarbazone: needles. M.p. 198–200°.

o-*Tolylsemicarbazone*: needles. M.p. 204·5°.

p-*Tolylsemicarbazone*: needles. M.p. 238–9°.

Thiosemicarbazone: m.p. 231° (sinters at 215°).

Phenylthiosemicarbazone: needles or plates. M.p. 183°.

Hydrazone: plates from EtOH. M.p. 96°.

Phenylhydrazone: needles or plates. M.p. 142–3°. Sensitive to light. *Dibenzoyl*: m.p. 170–1°.

2 : 4 : 6-*Trichlorophenylhydrazone* : needles from EtOH or AcOH. M.p. 98·5–99·5°.
o-*Bromophenylhydrazone* : yellow cryst. M.p. 111–12°.
p-*Bromophenylhydrazone* : yellow plates. M.p. 175·5°.
2 : 4 : 6-*Tribromophenylhydrazone* : needles from EtOH. M.p. 100°.
o-*Nitrophenylhydrazone* : m.p. 193°.
m-*Nitrophenylhydrazone* : m.p. 197°.
p-*Nitrophenylhydrazone* : reddish-brown prisms. M.p. 227°.
2 : 4-*Dinitrophenylhydrazone* : purplish-red needles from EtOH. M.p. 248°.
o-*Tolylhydrazone* : m.p. 111–12°.
1-*Naphthylhydrazone* : yellow plates. M.p. 134°.
2-*Naphthylhydrazone* : yellow needles. M.p. 187°.
Benzoylhydrazone : needles from EtOH.Aq. M.p. 182°.
1-*Naphthoylhydrazone* : needles. M.p. 235°.
Phenylurethane : m.p. 133°.
p-*Toluenesulphonyl* : cryst. from MeOH. M.p. 63–4°.
Glucoside : *see* Helicin.
Azine : *see* Salazine.
Anil : *see* Salicylideneaniline.

Claisen, Eisleb, *Ann.*, 1913, **401**, 95.
Brady, Dunn, *J. Chem. Soc.*, 1914, **105**, 825.
Kawada, Yosida, *Chem. Abstracts*, 1930, **24**, 1040.
Copisarow, *J. Chem. Soc.*, 1929, 588.
B.D.C., E.P., 232,392, (*Chem. Zentr.*, 1925, II, 1226).
Weiss, Donns, U.S.P., 1,380,277, (*Chem. Zentr.*, 1921, IV, 587).

Salicylamine (o-*Hydroxybenzylamine*, ω-*amino*-o-*cresol*)

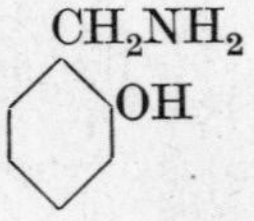

C_7H_9ON MW, 123

Cryst. from EtOH–pet. ether. M.p. 129° after softening at 126°. Sol. H_2O, EtOH, Et_2O. Insol. pet. ether. Sublimes readily. $FeCl_3$ ⟶ violet-blue col. ⟶ red on heating.
Me ether : *o*-methoxybenzylamine. $C_8H_{11}ON$. MW, 137. Liq. B.p. 224°/724 mm. Sol. H_2O, EtOH, Et_2O, C_6H_6. *B,HCl* : prisms from EtOH. M.p. 150°. *B_2,H_2PtCl_6* : yellow plates + $2H_2O$ from H_2O. M.p. 187°.
Et ether : $C_9H_{13}ON$. MW, 151. Oil. *B_2,H_2PtCl_6* : yellow cryst. M.p. 182°.
N-*Acetyl* : *o*-hydroxybenzylacetamide. Plates from $CHCl_3$–pet. ether. M.p. 140°.
Diacetyl deriv. : plates from $CHCl_3$–pet. ether. M.p. 102–3°.
Benzoyl : *o*-hydroxybenzylbenzamide. Plates from $CHCl_3$–pet. ether. M.p. 142° (softens at 140°).
Dibenzoyl deriv. : needles from EtOH–pet. ether. M.p. 142–3° (softens at 137°).
B,HCl : needles from EtOH. Very sol. H_2O.
B,HI : m.p. 184°.
B_2,H_2PtCl_6 : yellow needles + $2H_2O$ from H_2O. M.p. 197° decomp.

Raiford, Clark, *J. Am. Chem. Soc.*, 1923, **45**, 1740.
Löw, *Monatsh.*, 1891, **12**, 397.
Tiemann, *Ber.*, 1890, **23**, 3017.
Goldschmidt, Ernst, *Ber.*, 1890, **23**, 2744.

Salicylic Acid (o-*Hydroxybenzoic acid*)

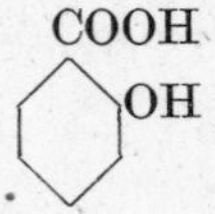

$C_7H_6O_3$ MW, 138

Occurs in form of esters in many essential oils and plant products, *e.g.* oil of wintergreen. Needles from H_2O. M.p. 159°. B.p. 211°/20 mm. Sol. EtOH, Et_2O, Me_2CO. Mod. sol. H_2O, C_6H_6. Volatile in steam. Sublimes in vacuo. Heat of comb. C_p 728·2 Cal. $k = 1{\cdot}06 \times 10^{-3}$ at 25°. Above 200° ⟶ phenol + CO_2 + a little salol. $FeCl_3$ ⟶ violet col. in H_2O. Strong antiseptic.
Me ester : *see* Methyl salicylate.
Et ester : *see* Ethyl salicylate.
Propyl ester : $C_{10}H_{12}O_3$. MW, 180. B.p. 238–40°. D^{20} 1·021.
Isopropyl ester : b.p. 120–2°/18 mm. D^{25} 1·0101. n_D^{25} 1·5003.
Butyl ester : $C_{11}H_{14}O_3$. MW, 194. M.p. 5·9°. B.p. 259–60°.
Isoamyl ester : *see* Isoamyl salicylate.
Allyl ester : $C_{10}H_{10}O_3$. MW, 178. B.p. 247–50°, 105°/5 mm. D^{15} 1·100.
Benzyl ester : $C_{14}H_{12}O_3$. MW, 228. B.p. 208°/26 mm., 186°/10 mm., 170–5°/7 mm. D_4^{20} 1·1799. n_D^{20} 1·5805.
2 : 4-*Dinitrobenzyl ester* : m.p. 168°.
Phenyl ester : *see* Salol.
o-*Tolyl ester* : $C_{14}H_{12}O_3$. MW, 228. M.p. 35°.

m-*Tolyl ester* : m.p. 74°.
p-*Tolyl ester* : m.p. 39°.
Salicyl ester : *see* Diplosal.
Phenacyl ester : m.p. 110°.
1-*Naphthyl ester* : *see under* 1-Naphthol.
2-*Naphthyl ester* : *see under* 2-Naphthol.
Glycerol ester : trisalicylin. Needles. M.p. 79°.
Chloride : *o*-hydroxybenzoyl chloride. $C_7H_5O_2Cl$. MW, 156·5. Needles. M.p. 19–19·5°. B.p. 92°/15 mm.
Amide : $C_7H_7O_2N$. MW, 137. Yellow cryst. M.p. 133°. O-*Benzoyl* : m.p. 144°. N-*Benzoyl* : m.p. 208°.
Nitrile : *o*-cyanophenol. C_7H_5ON. MW, 119. Prisms from C_6H_6–pet. ether. M.p. 98°. $D_4^{99 \cdot 6}$ 1·1052. $n_a^{99 \cdot 6}$ 1·53716. *Benzoyl* : needles from pet. ether. M.p. 106°.
Anilide : prisms from H_2O. M.p. 135°.
Piperidide : plates from EtOH. M.p. 142°.
Me ether : *see o*-Methoxybenzoic Acid.
Et ether : *see o*-Ethoxybenzoic Acid.
Propyl ether : $C_{10}H_{12}O_3$. MW, 180. Plates. M.p. 30°.
Benzyl ether : $C_{14}H_{12}O_3$. MW, 228. M.p. 76–7°.
Phenyl ether : *see o*-Phenoxybenzoic Acid.
Acetyl : *see* Acetylsalicylic Acid.
Benzoyl : needles. M.p. 132°.
p-*Nitrobenzoyl* : yellow cryst. from MeOH. M.p. 205°.

Schott, *Chem. Zentr.*, 1912, I, 754.
Ma, Hoo, Sah, *Chem. Abstracts*, 1934, **28**, 133.
Rosenmund, Harms, *Ber.*, 1920, **53**, 2230.
Pomilio, E.P. 103,739, (*Chem. Abstracts*, 1917, **11**, 1794).

Salicylideneacetone (o-*Hydroxybenzylideneacetone, methyl 2-hydroxystyryl ketone*)

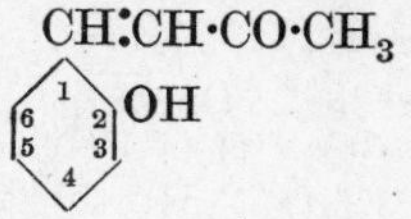

$C_{10}H_{10}O_2$ MW, 162

Needles from ligroin. M.p. 140°. Sol. Et_2O. Spar. sol. cold H_2O.
Me ether : *o*-methoxybenzylideneacetone. $C_{11}H_{12}O_2$. MW, 176. Prisms. M.p. 48–50°. B.p. 180–2°/20 mm. $D_4^{61 \cdot 4}$ 1·0538. $n_D^{61 \cdot 4}$ 1·586. Sol. usual org. solvents.
Oxime : cryst. from C_6H_6–ligroin. M.p. 84–5°. Sol. Et_2O. Spar. sol. EtOH, C_6H_6, ligroin.
Semicarbazone : needles from EtOH. M.p. 206–7° decomp.

Tiemann, Kees, *Ber.*, 1885, **18**, 1966.
Harries, *Ber.*, 1891, **24**, 3180.
Auwers, *Ann.*, 1917, **413**, 279.

ω-Salicylideneacetophenone.
See 2-Hydroxychalkone.

Salicylideneaniline (o-*Hydroxybenzylideneaniline, salicylaldehyde anil*)

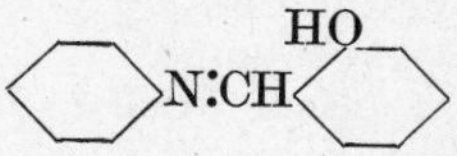

$C_{13}H_{11}ON$ MW, 197

Yellow plates from MeOH. M.p. 51°. Sol. EtOH. Insol. H_2O.
B,HCl : yellow needles. M.p. 91°.
Me ether : *o*-methoxybenzylideneaniline. $C_{14}H_{13}ON$. MW, 211. Needles from EtOH. M.p. 44°. B.p. 330–4°, 235–6°/30 mm.
Picrate : yellow needles. M.p. 153–4°.

Schischkow, *Ann.*, 1857, **104**, 373.
Schiff, *Ann.*, 1869, **150**, 194.
Noelting, *Ann. chim.*, 1910, **19**, 540.

Salicylidene-1-naphthylamine (o-*Hydroxybenzylidene-1-naphthylamine*)

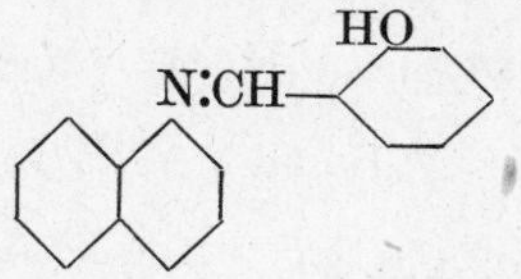

$C_{17}H_{13}ON$ MW, 247

Needles from C_6H_6. M.p. 53° (45·5°). Sol. EtOH, Et_2O, C_6H_6.
B,HCl : m.p. 210° decomp.

Pope, Fleming, *J. Chem. Soc.*, 1908, **93**, 1916.
Senier, Shepheard, *J. Chem. Soc.*, 1909, **95**, 443.

Salicylidene-2-naphthylamine (o-*Hydroxybenzylidene-2-naphthylamine*)

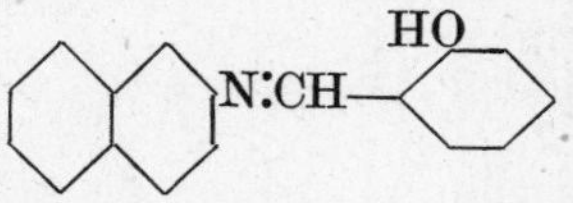

$C_{17}H_{13}ON$ MW, 247

Needles and prisms from EtOH. M.p. 126°. Sol. EtOH, C_6H_6, $CHCl_3$, ligroin. Spar. sol. Et_2O.

Senier, Shepheard, *J. Chem. Soc.*, 1909, **95**, 1950.
Emmerich, *Ann.*, 1887, **241**, 351.

1-Salicylidenepropionic Acid.
See α-Methyl-*o*-coumaric Acid *and* α-Methyl-*o*-coumarinic Acid.

***o*-Salicyloylbenzoic Acid.**
See 2′-Hydroxybenzophenone-2-carboxylic Acid.

Salicyloylglycine.
See 2-Hydroxyhippuric Acid.

Salicyloylsalicylic Acid.
See Diplosal.

β-Salicyloylstyrene.
See 2′-Hydroxychalkone.

Saligenin (*Salicyl alcohol, o-hydroxybenzyl alcohol, ω-hydroxy-o-cresol*)

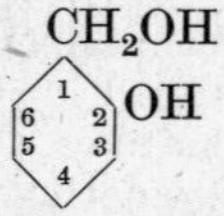

$C_7H_8O_2$ MW, 124

Needles or plates from H_2O or Et_2O. M.p. 87°. D^{25} 1·1613. Sol. EtOH, Et_2O. Mod. sol. H_2O, C_6H_6. Sublimes in plates. $H_2SO_4 \longrightarrow$ red col. $FeCl_3 \longrightarrow$ blue col. Antiseptic.

α-Me ether: $C_8H_{10}O_2$. MW, 138. B.p. 128–30°/40 mm.

2-*Me ether*: *o*-methoxybenzyl alcohol. B.p. 248–50°, 119°/8 mm. D^{17} 1·128. n_D^{17} 1·549. *Acetyl*: b.p. 130°/12 mm. D^{17} 1·117. n_D^{17} 1·515. *Benzoyl*: m.p. 59°.

Di-Me ether: $C_9H_{12}O_2$. MW, 152. B.p. 229–30°.

α-Et ether: $C_9H_{12}O_2$. MW, 152. B.p. 111–13°/20 mm.

2-*Et ether*: b.p. 265°.

2-*Allyl ether*: $C_{10}H_{12}O_2$. MW, 164. B.p. 133–50°/9 mm.

2-*Benzoyl*: needles from C_6H_6–pet. ether. M.p. 66°.

Carothers, Adams, *J. Am. Chem. Soc.*, 1924, **46**, 1680.
Rutovskii, Karolev, *Chem. Abstracts*, 1930, **24**, 24.
Manasse, *Ber.*, 1894, **27**, 2411.
Vavon, *Compt. rend.*, 1912, **154**, 359.
Paal, Senninger, *Ber.*, 1894, **27**, 1084.

Salinigrin.
See Piceoside.

Salipurol.
See Naringenin.

Salipyrine.
See under Antipyrine.

Salol (*Phenyl salicylate*)

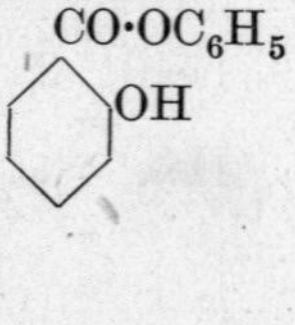

$C_{13}H_{10}O_3$ MW, 214

Plates from MeOH. M.p. 43° (41·7°). B.p. 173°/12 mm. D_4^{50} 1·1553. Sol. MeOH, EtOH, Et_2O. Insol. H_2O. Antiseptic.

Me ether: $C_{14}H_{12}O_3$. MW, 228. Prisms from EtOH. M.p. 59°.

Phenyl ether: *see under* *o*-Phenoxybenzoic Acid.

p-*Nitrobenzyl ether*: cryst. from EtOH.Aq. M.p. 87°.

Chloroformyl: m.p. 90–1°.

Acetyl: cryst. from EtOH. M.p. 98°. B.p. 197–8°/11 mm.

Benzoyl: cryst. from EtOH. M.p. 80·5–81°.

Phosphate: $(HO)_2PO{\cdot}O{\cdot}C_6H_4{\cdot}CO{\cdot}OC_6H_5$. Cryst. M.p. 88°.

Phosphate, hydrate: $(HO)_4P{\cdot}O{\cdot}C_6H_4{\cdot}CO{\cdot}OC_6H_5$. Cryst. from C_6H_6. M.p. 62°. Very sol. H_2O. Sol. $CHCl_3$, AcOH, hot C_6H_6.

Phosphate diethyl ester: $(C_2H_5O)_2OP{\cdot}O{\cdot}C_6H_4{\cdot}CO{\cdot}OC_6H_5$. Oil. B.p. 105–13°/13 mm.

Phosphate diphenyl ester: $(C_6H_5O)_2OP{\cdot}O{\cdot}C_6H_4{\cdot}CO{\cdot}OC_6H_5$. Cryst. from EtOH. M.p. 76–7°.

Seifert, *J. prakt. Chem.*, 1885, **31**, 472.
Graebe, Eichengrün, *Ann.*, 1892, **269**, 324.
Chem. Fabr. v. Heyden, D.R.P., 38,973.
Bayer, D.R.P., 206,055, (*Chem. Zentr.*, 1909, I, 703).

Salophene.
See *p*-Acetylaminophenyl salicylate.

Saloquinine.
See under Quinine.

Salvarsan (*Arsphenamine*, "606," *dihydrochloride of* 3 : 3′-*diamino*-4 : 4′-*dihydroxyarseno benzene*)

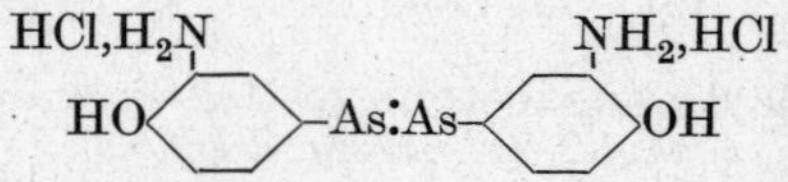

$C_{12}H_{14}O_2N_2Cl_2As_2$ MW, 439

Greyish powder. Decomp. (indefinite) at 180–95°. Sol. hot H_2O. Spar. sol. MeOH, EtOH. Insol. Et_2O, C_6H_6. Used in treatment of protozoal diseases.

Kirchoff, Korsina, Sirkin, D.R.P., 592,870, (*Chem. Zentr.*, 1934, I, 2791).
Christiansen, *J. Am. Chem. Soc.*, 1923, **45**, 1807.
Fargher, Pyman, *J. Chem. Soc.*, 1920, **117**, 376.

Salvianin chloride.
See Monardaein chloride.

Samandarin

$C_{19}H_{31}O_2N$ MW, 305

Secretion of *Salamander maculosa*, *Salamander atra*, etc. Colourless cryst. from EtOH.Aq., Me_2CO, and with 1MeOH from MeOH. M.p. 187–8°. Strongly basic. $[\alpha]_D^{17}$ + 43·7°. HCl ⟶ blue col.

B,HCl : m.p. 321–2°.

N-*Me* : $C_{20}H_{33}O_2N$. MW, 319. *B,HCl* : cryst. from EtOH.Aq. M.p. 300–2° decomp. *Methiodide* : cryst. from H_2O. M.p. 271–2°.

N-*Nitroso* : cryst. from EtOH.Aq. M.p. 164–5°.

Monoformyl deriv. : cryst. from MeOH.Aq. M.p. 148–50°.

Diformyl deriv. : needles from MeOH. M.p. 256–8°.

Diacetyl deriv. : needles from EtOH.Aq. M.p. 167–8°.

Schöpf, Braun, *Ann.*, 1934, **514**, 69.

Sambunigrin (d-*Glucoside of* d-*mandelic acid nitrile*)

$C_6H_5{\cdot}CH(CN){\cdot}O{\cdot}C_6H_{11}O_5$

$C_{14}H_{17}O_6N$ MW, 295

Occurs in black Holunder. Colourless cryst. from C_6H_6–amyl alcohol. M.p. 151–152·5°. $[\alpha]_D^{18}$ − 75·1°. Emulsin ⟶ *d*-mandelonitrile + *d*-glucose.

Tetra-acetyl : needles from EtOH. M.p. 125–6°. $[\alpha]_D^{22}$ − 52·5°.

Fischer, Bergmann, *Ber.*, 1917, **50**, 1063.

Sambunigrinic Acid (β-d-*Glucoside of* d-*mandelic acid*)

$C_6H_5{\cdot}CH(COOH){\cdot}O{\cdot}C_6H_{11}O_5$

$C_{14}H_{18}O_8$ MW, 314

Needles from amyl alcohol, needles + 1EtOH from EtOH, m.p. 175–7°. Sol. H_2O, EtOH, Py. Spar. sol. Et_2O, Me_2O, AcOH, C_6H_6, $CHCl_3$. $[\alpha]_D^{18}$ + 51° in H_2O.

Quinine salt : prisms from H_2O. Sinters at 240°. M.p. 248° decomp. $[\alpha]_D^{20}$ − 70·66°.

Me ester : $C_{15}H_{20}O_8$. MW, 328. Needles from $CHCl_3$–CCl_4. M.p. 88–9°. Sol. H_2O. $[\alpha]_D^{19}$ + 41·2°.

Tetra-acetyl : needles from EtOH.Aq. M.p. 166°. $[\alpha]_D$ − 5·34°.

Fischer, *Z. physiol. Chem.*, 1919, **107**, 176; *Ber.*, 1919, **52**, 200.

Karrer, Nägeli, Weidmann, *Helv. Chim. Acta*, 1919, **2**, 259, 431.

Sanguinarine (ψ-*Chelerythrine*)

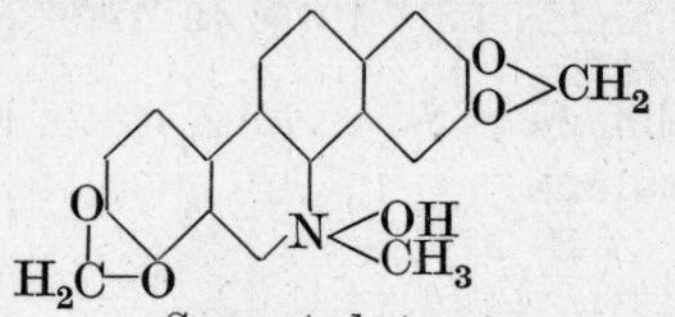

Suggested structure

$C_{20}H_{15}O_5N$ MW, 349

Present in blood-root of *Sanguinaria canadensis*. Cryst. from Et_2O, m.p. 266° (242–3° slow heat.). Cryst. as alcoholate from alcoholic media, m.p. 195–7°. Sol. most org. solvents, sols. showing bluish-violet fluor.

Bruchhausen, Bersch, *Ber.*, 1930, **63**, 2520.

Späth, Kuffner, *Ber.*, 1931, **64**, 370, 1123, 2034.

Sanguisorbigenin

$C_{30}H_{46}O_3$ MW, 454

M.p. 275–6°. Heat ⟶ sanguisorbigenol, a triterpene alcohol.

Me ester : $C_{31}H_{48}O_3$. MW, 468. M.p. 207–9°. *Acetyl* : m.p. 243–5°.

Acetyl : m.p. 324°.

Matsukawa, *Chem. Abstracts*, 1935, **29**, 3346.

Santal

$C_{13}H_{10}O_4$ MW, 230

Plates or needles from EtOH. M.p. 222–3°. Sol. NaOH. $FeCl_3$ ⟶ reddish-violet col.

Di-Me ether : $C_{15}H_{14}O_4$. MW, 258. M.p. 141°.

Diacetyl : colourless cryst. from MeOH. M.p. 152°.

Raudnitz, Perlmann, *Ber.*, 1935, **68**, 1874.

O'Neill, Perkin, *J. Chem. Soc.*, 1918, **113**, 137.

α-Santalene

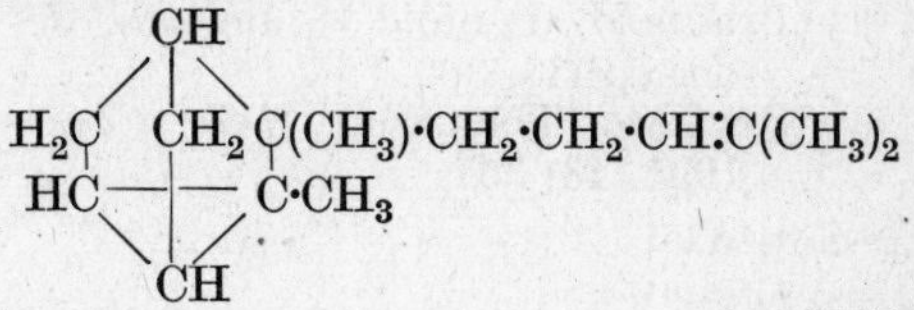

$C_{15}H_{24}$ MW, 204

Constituent of sandalwood oil. B.p. 252°/753 mm., 118–19°/9 mm. D^{20} 0·8984. n_D^{20} 1·491. $[\alpha]_D$ − 15°. S ⟶ eudalene.

Dihydrochloride : b.p. 141–2°/0·5 mm. D^{20} 1·076. n_D^{20} 1·4976. $[\alpha]_D$ + 6°.

Nitrosochloride: m.p. 112–17°.

Semmler, *Ber.*, 1910, **43**, 1898; 1907, **40**, 3322.

Schimmel, *Chem. Zentr.*, 1910, II, 1757.

β-Santalene

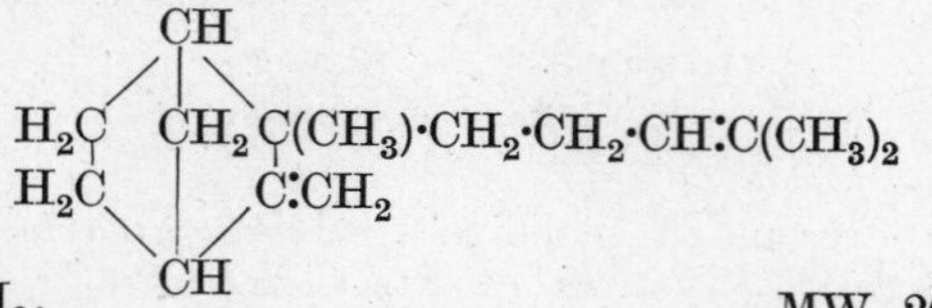

$C_{15}H_{24}$ MW, 204

Constituent of sandalwood oil. Oil with cedar-like odour. B.p. 125–7°/9 mm. D^{20} 0·894. n_D^{20} 1·4946. $[\alpha]_D$ − 35°.

Dihydrochloride: same as from α-santalene (above).

Nitrosochloride: two forms. (i) Plates. M.p. 152°. (ii) Needles. M.p. 106°.

See previous references.

γ-Santalene

$C_{15}H_{24}$ MW, 204

Liq. B.p. 118°/10 mm. D^{20} 0·9355. n_D 1·5042.

Semmler, Bode, *Ber.*, 1907, **40**, 1130.

α-Santalol

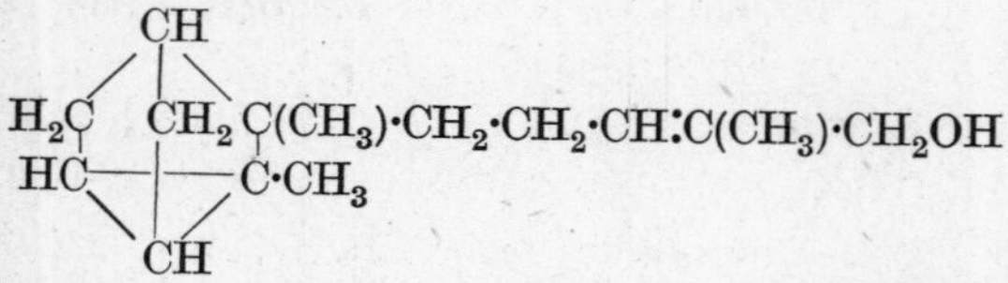

$C_{15}H_{24}O$ MW, 220

Constituent of sandalwood oil. B.p. 166–7°/14 mm., 106°/0·06 mm. D_{25}^{25} 0·9770. n_D^{25} 1·5017. α_{5461} + 10·3°.

Allophanate: needles from MeOH. M.p. 162–3°.

Strychnine salt of hydrogen phthalate: prisms from AcOEt or Me_2CO. M.p. 144–5°. $[\alpha]_{5461}$ − 5·62° in C_6H_6.

Bradfield, Penfold, Simonsen, *J. Chem. Soc.*, 1935, 309.

Ruzicka, Thomann, *Helv. Chim. Acta*, 1935, **18**, 357.

β-Santalol

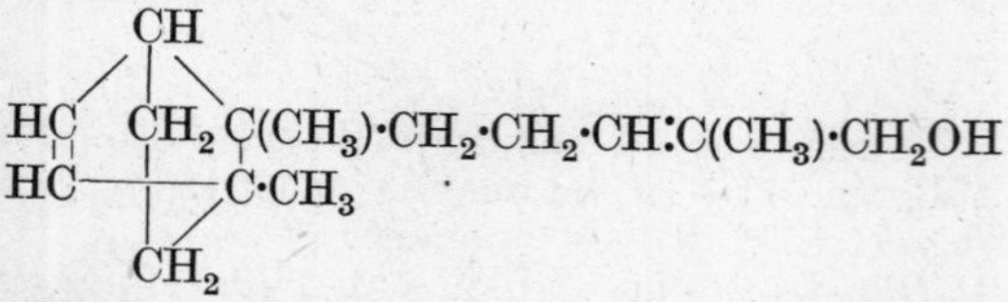

$C_{15}H_{24}O$ MW, 220

Constituent of sandalwood oil. B.p. 177–8°/17 mm., 112°/0·06 mm. D_{25}^{25} 0·9717. n_D^{25} 1·5100. α_{5461} − 87·1°.

Allophanate: needles from MeOH. M.p. 159–60°.

Strychnine salt of hydrogen phthalate: prisms from AcOEt. M.p. 134–5°. $[\alpha]_{5461}$ − 37·5° in C_6H_6.

See previous references.

Santene

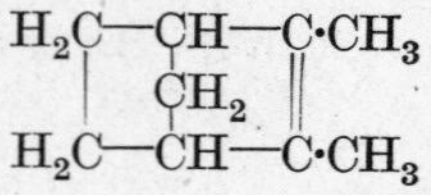

C_9H_{14} MW, 122

Constituent of sandalwood oil and pine-needle oil. Liq. with odour resembling camphene. B.p. 140–1°, 35°/15 mm. D_4^{17} 0·8698. n_D^{17} 1·4688.

Nitrosite: three forms. (i) Blue. M.p. 122–4°. (ii) Colourless. M.p. 104°. (iii) Green. M.p. 127–8° decomp.

Nitrosate: m.p. 216° decomp.

Nitrosochloride: blue. M.p. 109–10°. A white cryst. polymer is also described.

Diels, Alder, *Ann.*, 1931, **486**, 209.

Ruzicka, Liebl, *Helv. Chim. Acta*, 1923, **6**, 271.

Komppa, Hintikka, *Bull. soc. chim.*, 1917, **21**, 14.

Santene Hydrate.

See β-Santenol.

Santenic Acid (1 : 2-*Dimethylcyclopentane*-1 : 3-*dicarboxylic acid*)

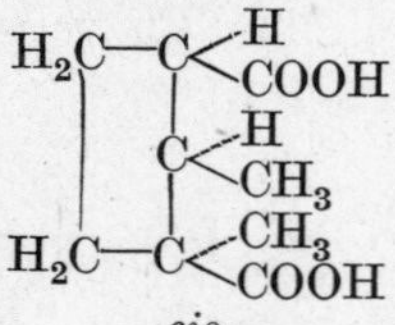

cis-.

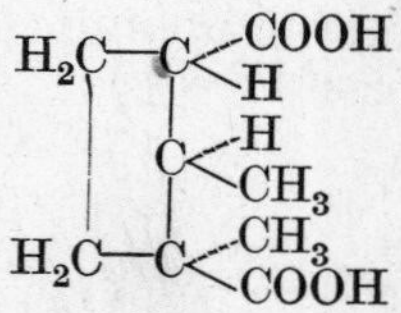

trans-.

Probable configurations

$C_9H_{14}O_4$ MW, 186

Cis:

Acid from natural sources, by oxidation of santenol or santenone. Plates from H_2O. M.p. 170–1°. AcOH–HCl ⟶ *trans*-form.

Di-Me ester: $C_{11}H_{18}O_4$. MW, 214. B.p. 120–3°/9 mm. D^{20} 1·078. n_D^{20} 1·4645.

Di-Et ester: $C_{13}H_{22}O_4$. MW, 242. B.p. 143–4°/14 mm. D_4^{20} 1·0268. n_D^{20} 1·44854.

Anhydride: $C_9H_{12}O_3$. MW, 168. Cryst. M.p. 115–16°.

Anil: $C_{15}H_{17}O_2N$. MW, 243. Cryst. from AcOH.Aq. M.p. 117–18°.

Monoanilide: cryst. from AcOH.Aq. M.p. 205–6°.

Trans:

Cryst. from H_2O. M.p. 166–7°.
Dianilide: needles from EtOH–C_6H_6 or EtOH.Aq. M.p. 221°.

Komppa, *Chem. Zentr.*, 1936, I, 3838; *Ber.*, 1932, **65**, 1708.
Enkvist, *J. prakt. Chem.*, 1933, **137**, 261.
Komppa, Rohrmann, *Ber.*, 1934, **67**, 828.
Komppa, Hintikka, *Bull. soc. chim.*, 1917, **21**, 17.

Santenol.
See under Norborneol.

α-Santenol.
See under Norborneol.

β-Santenol (*Santene hydrate*)

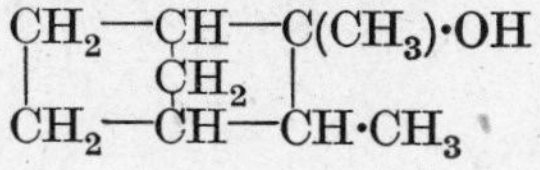

$C_9H_{16}O$ MW, 140

Needles from EtOH. M.p. 101–2°. B.p. 192°. Stereoisomeric with γ-santenol.

Diels, Alder, *Ann.*, 1931, **486**, 205.

γ-Santenol

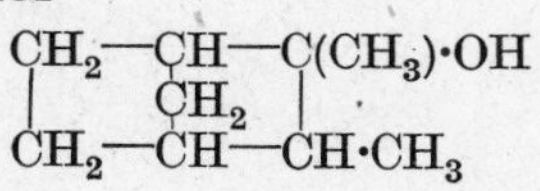

$C_9H_{16}O$ MW, 140

M.p. 63–5°. B.p. 82–4°/15 mm. Stereoisomeric with β-santenol.

Diels, Alder, *Ann.*, 1931, **486**, 209.

Santenone.
See under Norcamphor.

α-Santenone

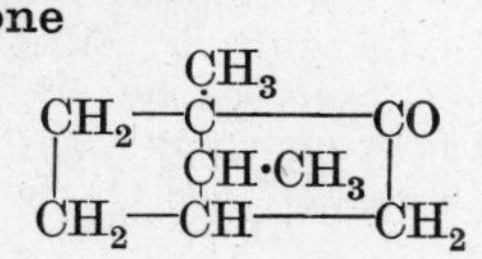

$C_9H_{14}O$ MW, 138

M.p. 55°. B.p. 191°.
Oxime: m.p. 74°.
Semicarbazone: m.p. 236°.

Aschan, *Chem. Abstracts*, 1934, **28**, 2344.
Asahina, Ishidate, *Ber.*, 1935, **68**, 950.

β-Santenone

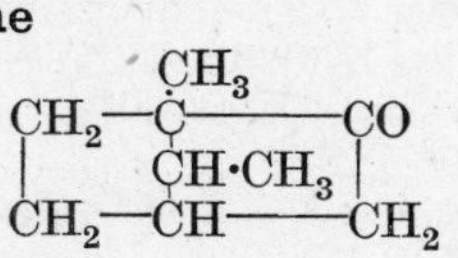

$C_9H_{14}O$ MW, 138

M.p. 46°. B.p. 190°.
Oxime: m.p. 51°.
Semicarbazone: m.p. 222°.

See previous references.

Santenone Alcohol.
See under Norborneol.

Santenylamine.
See under Norbornylamine.

Santonan (*Tetrahydrosantonin*)

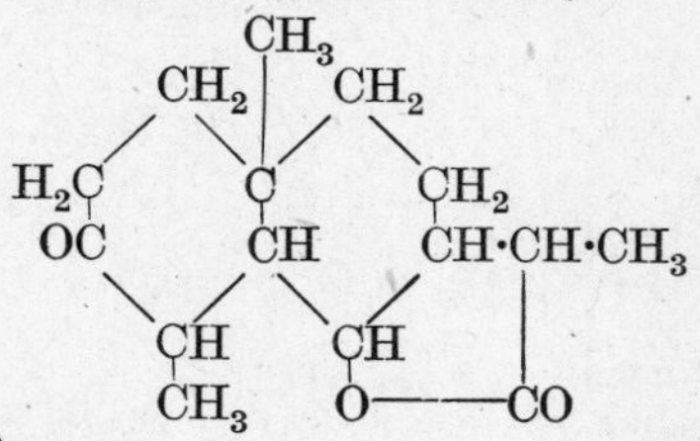

$C_{15}H_{22}O_3$ MW, 250

Two forms.

α-.
Cryst. from EtOH. M.p. 158°. $[\alpha]_D^{18}$ + 17·8° in MeOH.
Oxime: cryst. from EtOH. M.p. 219–20°.
Semicarbazone: powder. M.p. 258° decomp.
Phenylhydrazone: cryst. from EtOH. M.p. 205° decomp.

β-.
Plates from Et_2O. M.p. 105°. $[\alpha]_D^{18}$ + 9·3° in MeOH. More sol. than α-form.
Oxime: m.p. 182°.
Semicarbazone: m.p. 250° decomp.

Clemo, Haworth, *J. Chem. Soc.*, 1930, 2580.
Wedekind, Goost, Jäckh, *Ber.*, 1930, **63**, 50.
Wienhaus, Oettingen, *Ann.*, 1913, **397**, 240.
Asahina, *Ber.*, 1913, **46**, 1776.

Santonanic Acid (*Tetrahydrosantoninic acid*)

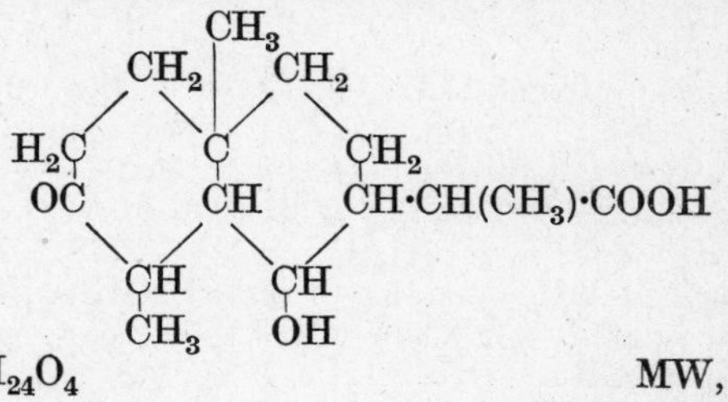

$C_{15}H_{24}O_4$ MW, 268

α-.
Cryst. + $1H_2O$. Sinters at 85°. M.p. 115° decomp. $[\alpha]_D^{18}$ + 20·0°. Heat above m.p. ⟶ α-lactone.

β-.

Cryst. from H_2O. M.p. about 192°. $[\alpha]_D^{18}$ + 2·2°. Heat above m.p. ⟶ β-lactone.

Oxime: m.p. 218–20°.

Wienhaus, Oettingen, *Ann.*, 1913, **397**, 238.

Santonene (*Dihydrosantonin*)

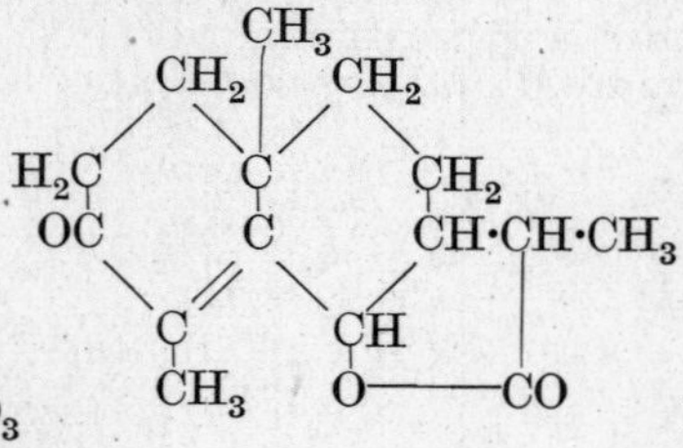

$C_{15}H_{20}O_3$ MW, 248

Two forms.

(i) Prisms or needles from EtOH.Aq. M.p. 105°. $[\alpha]_D^{18}$ + 75·3° in EtOH.

Oxime: prisms from EtOH. M.p. 235° decomp.

Semicarbazone: prisms from EtOH. M.p. 245° decomp.

(ii) Needles from EtOH. M.p. 181–2°. $[\alpha]_D^{25}$ − 280·9°. Insol. Na_2CO_3.

Oxime: needles. M.p. 196°. $[\alpha]_D^{25}$ − 239° in EtOH.

Wedekind, Goost, Jäckh, *Ber.*, 1930, **63**, 53.

Medvedev, Alekseeva, *Chem. Abstracts*, 1928, **22**, 1979.

Santonic Acid

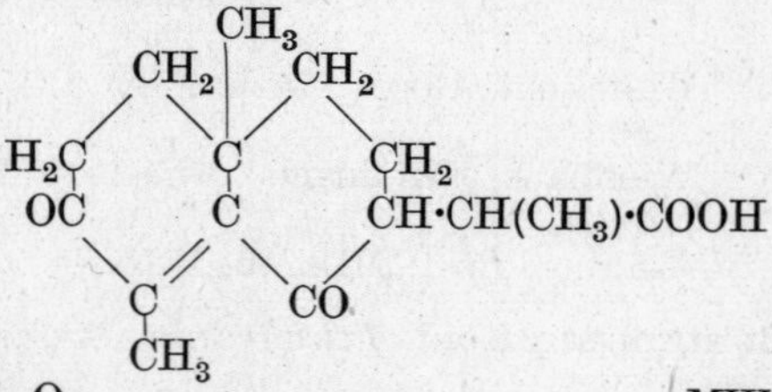

$C_{15}H_{20}O_4$ MW, 264

Cryst. from H_2O or EtOH. M.p. 170–2°. B.p. 285°/15 mm. $[\alpha]_D^{20}$ − 74·0° in $CHCl_3$. Sol. 190 parts H_2O at 17°. Dist. ⟶ meta-santonic acid. H_2SO_4 ⟶ santonin.

Me ester: $C_{16}H_{22}O_4$. MW, 278. Prisms from MeOH, needles from EtOH.Aq. M.p. 86°. $[\alpha]_D^{26}$ − 52·3° in $CHCl_3$. *Oxime*: prisms. M.p. 158–9°.

Et ester: $C_{17}H_{24}O_4$. MW, 292. Prisms from Et_2O. M.p. 94–5°. $[\alpha]_D^{26}$ − 45·4° in $CHCl_3$. *Oxime*: plates from EtOH. M.p. 126°. *Monophenylhydrazone*: yellow plates. M.p. 115°.

Propyl ester: $C_{18}H_{26}O_4$. MW, 306. Syru B.p. 220°/3 mm.

Isobutyl ester: $C_{19}H_{28}O_4$. MW, 320. Needl from Et_2O. M.p. 67°.

Chloride: $C_{15}H_{19}O_3Cl$. MW, 282·5. Prism from EtOH. M.p. 170–1°.

Bromide: $C_{15}H_{19}O_3Br$. MW, 327. M. 145·5°.

Iodide: $C_{15}H_{19}O_3I$. MW, 374. Needl from Et_2O. M.p. 136°.

Oxime: cryst. from EtOH. M.p. 186°.

Dioxime: m.p. 120–5° decomp.

Monosemicarbazone: m.p. 183–5° decomp.

Monophenylhydrazone: yellow needles fro EtOH. M.p. 174°.

Abkin, Medvedev, *Chem. Abstracts*, 193 **29**, 3682.

Harries, Stähler, *Ber.*, 1904, **37**, 259.

Francesconi, *Gazz. chim. ital.*, 1899, 2 224.

Santonin

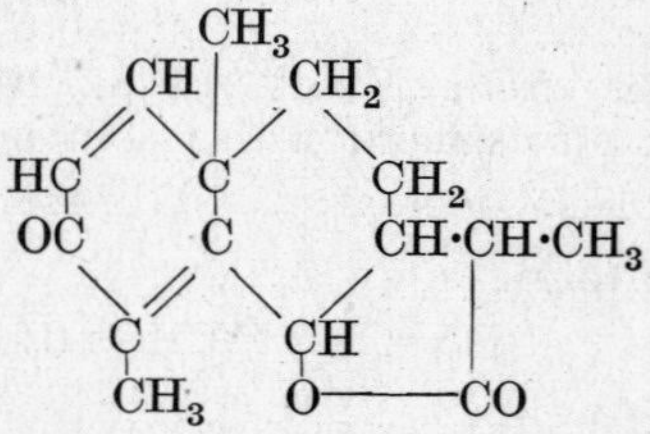

$C_{15}H_{18}O_3$ MW, 24

Widely occurring in plants, especially i *Artemisia*. Colourless cryst. from H_2O, EtO or Et_2O. M.p. 170°. $[\alpha]_D^{18}$ − 173·0° in EtOH Turns yellow in sunlight. Isomerises in sol. i daylight. H_2SO_4 ⟶ blue col. EtOH–KO ⟶ red col. Zn + AcOH ⟶ santonone. Z dust dist. ⟶ 1 : 4-dimethylnaphthalene an 1 : 4-dimethyl-2-naphthol. Alkalis ⟶ salts o santonic acid. Sol. has bitter taste. Used i treatment of nervous complaints.

Oxime: needles + $1H_2O$ from EtOH.Aq M.p. 218°.

Semicarbazone: cryst. from AcOEt. M.p 232° decomp.

Phenylhydrazone: yellow needles. M.p 230–1° decomp.

Clemo, Haworth, *J. Chem. Soc.*, 1930 2579.

Ruzicka, Eichenberger, *Helv. Chim Acta*, 1930, **13**, 1117.

Wedekind, Tettweiler, *Ber.*, 1931, **64** 1796.

Massagetov, *Chem. Abstracts*, 1932, **26** 4413.

β-Santonin

$C_{15}H_{18}O_3$ MW, 246

Stereoisomeric with santonin. Constituent of certain varieties of *Artemisia*. Colourless prisms from EtOH. M.p. 216–18°. $[\alpha]_D^{19}$ — 137·2° in $CHCl_3$.
Oxime: prisms from EtOH. M.p. 224°.

Clemo, *J. Chem. Soc.*, 1934, 1343.

***l*-Sapietic Acid** (l-*Pimaric acid*)

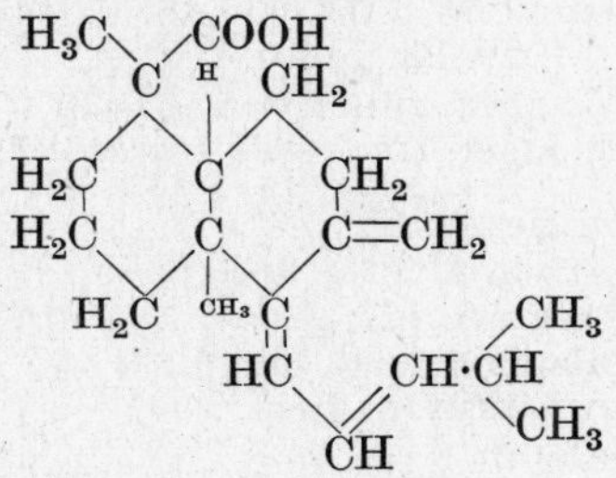

Suggested structure

$C_{20}H_{30}O_2$ MW, 302

Occurs in *Pinus palustris*, etc. Prisms from EtOH. M.p. 152° (148–51°). $[\alpha]_D^{20}$ — 282° in EtOH. Isomerised by hot AcOH to abietic acid. Absorption maximum at 272·5 mμ.
Me ester: $C_{21}H_{32}O_2$. MW, 316. M.p. 57°. B.p. 166–9°/0·5 mm. D_4^{22} 1·0312. n_D^{22} 1·5232. $[\alpha]_D$ — 190·4° in EtOH.
Et ester: $C_{22}H_{34}O_2$. MW, 330. B.p. 175–7°/0·5 mm. D_4^{23} 1·0124. n_D^{23} 1·5153. $[\alpha]_D$ — 170·9° in EtOH.

Hasselstrom, Bogert, *J. Am. Chem. Soc.*, 1935, **57**, 2118.
Palkin, Morris, *J. Am. Chem. Soc.*, 1933, **55**, 3677.
Ruzicka, Balos, Vilim, *Helv. Chim. Acta*, 1924, **7**, 458.

Saponarin (*Vitexin glucoside*)

$C_{21}H_{24}O_{12}$ MW, 468

Occurs in *Saponaria officinalis*, Linn., and other plants. Needles + $2H_2O$ from Py.Aq. M.p. 231–2° decomp. (slow heat), 236° (rapid heat). $[\alpha]_D$ — 7·9° in H_2O. Sol. alkalis with yellow col. Conc. H_2SO_4 ⟶ blue fluor. I ⟶ blue col. which disappears on dilution or addition of EtOH or on warming; reappears on cooling.

Nona-acetyl deriv.: m.p. 183–5°.

Molisch, *Chem. Abstracts*, 1912, **6**, 766.
Barger, Field, *J. Chem. Soc.*, 1912, **101**, 1396.

Sapotalin (1 : 2 : 7-*Trimethylnaphthalene*)

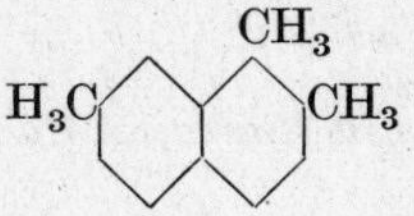

$C_{13}H_{14}$ MW, 170

B.p. 148°/16 mm. D_4^{15} 1·008. n_D^{15} 1·6093.
Picrate: m.p. 129·5–130°.
Styphnate: m.p. 156°.

Spring, Vickerstaff, *J. Chem. Soc.*, 1937, 252.

Sappanin (2 : 4 : 3′ : 4′-*Tetrahydroxydiphenyl*)

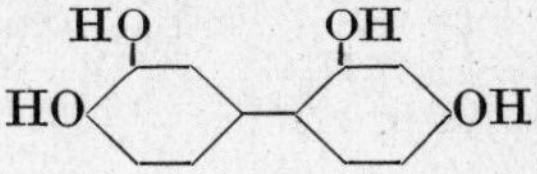

$C_{12}H_{10}O_4$ MW, 218

Occurs in *Cæsalpinia Sappan*, Linn. Leaflets + $2H_2O$ from H_2O. M.p. anhyd. 210–11°. B.p. 230–40°/0·01 mm. Sol. EtOH, Et_2O, hot H_2O. Insol. $CHCl_3$, CS_2, C_6H_6. $FeCl_3$ ⟶ red. col. Reduces Fehling's and Tollen's on warming.
Tetra-Me ether: $C_{16}H_{18}O_4$. MW, 274. Cryst. from MeOH.Aq. M.p. 74–5°.

Späth, Gibian, *Monatsh.*, 1930, **55**, 342.

Sarcine.
See Hypoxanthine.
Sarcolactic Acid.
See under Lactic Acid.
Sarcosine (*Methylaminoacetic acid*, N-*methylglycine*, N-*methylglycocoll*)

$CH_3{\cdot}NH{\cdot}CH_2{\cdot}COOH$

$C_3H_7O_2N$ MW, 89

Cryst. from EtOH. M.p. 212–13° decomp. Heat of comb. C_v 401·2 Cal.
B,HCl: m.p. 168–70°.
B,HBr: m.p. 186–7°.
B,HI: m.p. 152°.
B_2,H_2PtCl_6: m.p. 193–4° decomp.
Et ester: $C_5H_{11}O_2N$. MW, 117. B.p. 43°/10 mm. $D^{15.5}$ 0·971. *Picrate*: m.p. 149·5°.
Nitrile: $C_3H_6N_2$. MW, 70. Viscous liq. *B_2,H_2SO_4*: does not melt below 210°.
N-*Benzoyl*: *N*-methylhippuric acid. M.p. 103·5–104° decomp.

N-*Phenyl*: *see* *N*-Phenylsarcosine.

Baumann, *J. Biol. Chem.*, 1915, **21**, 563.
Cocker, Lapworth, *J. Chem. Soc.*, 1931, 1894.
Johnson, Ambler, *J. Am. Chem. Soc.*, 1914, **36**, 372.

Sarsapic Acid (*Sarsapinic acid*)

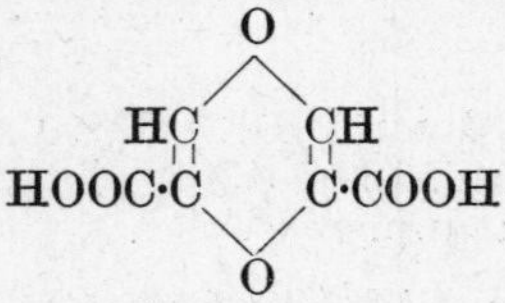

Probable structure

$C_6H_4O_6$ MW, 172

Occurs in sarsaparilla root. Needles from hot H_2O. M.p. 305°. Sol. EtOH. Spar. sol. Et_2O.
Di-Me ester: $C_8H_8O_6$. MW, 200. Leaflets from EtOH. M.p. 121°.

Power, Salway, *J. Chem. Soc.*, 1914, **105**, 205.

Sarsapinic Acid.
See Sarsapic Acid.

Sarsasapogenin (*Parigenin*)

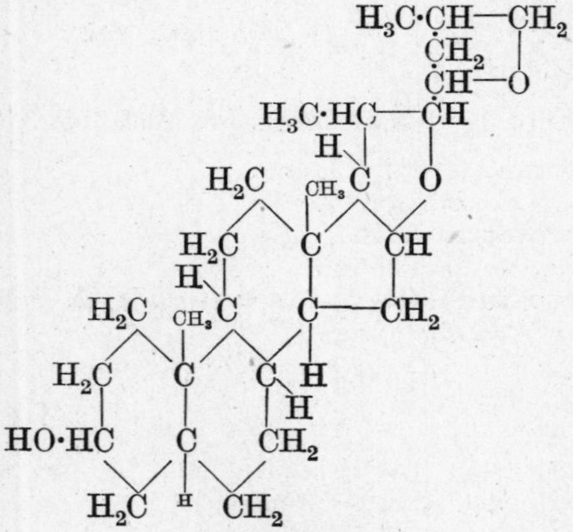

Suggested structure

$C_{27}H_{44}O_3$ MW, 416

Occurs in Vera-Cruz sarsaparilla root. Cryst. from Me_2CO. M.p. 197–8°. $[\alpha]_D^{25}$ − 75° in $CHCl_3$.
Acetyl: m.p. 144–5°. $[\alpha]_D^{25}$ − 70·2° in $CHCl_3$.
Benzoyl: m.p. 170–1°.

Farmer, Kon, *J. Chem. Soc.*, 1937, 414.

Sativic Acid (*Sativinic acid, 8 : 9 : 11 : 12-tetrahydroxystearic acid*)

$$CH_3\cdot[CH_2]_4\cdot[\overset{OH}{C}H]_2\cdot CH_2\cdot[\overset{OH}{C}H]_2\cdot[CH_2]_7\cdot COOH$$

$C_{18}H_{36}O_6$ MW, 348

Occurs in bark of various plants and in human fat. (α) M.p. 153°. (β) M.p. 170°. (γ) M.p. 144–5°. (δ) M.p. 135°.

Zellner, *Monatsh.*, 1925, **46**, 619.
Nicolet, Cox, *J. Am. Chem. Soc.*, 1922, **44**, 144.
Dreyfuss, F.P., 636,488, (*Chem. Abstracts*, 1929, **23**, 1140).
Wagner, *Biochem. Z.*, 1926, **174**, 412.
Reinger, *Chem. Abstracts*, 1922, **16**, 3467

Sativinic Acid.
See Sativic Acid.
Saxatilic Acid.
See Salazinic Acid.
Scammonin.
See Jalapin.
Scatole.
See Skatole.
Schäffer Acid.
See 2-Naphthol-6-sulphonic Acid.
Schöllkopf Acid.
See 1-Naphthylamine-8-sulphonic Acid.
Scillaren-A

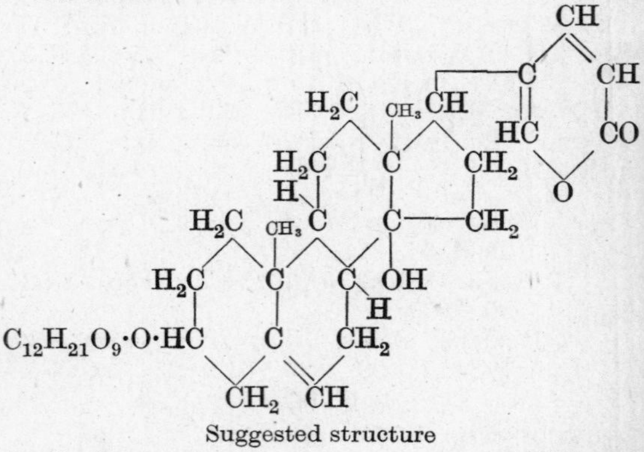

Suggested structure

$C_{36}H_{52}O_{13}$ MW, 692

Occurs in squills. Plates + $1H_2O$ + 1MeOH from MeOH.Aq., m.p. 230–40°; needles from EtOH, m.p. 270°. $[\alpha]_D^{20}$ − 73·8° in EtOH.

Tschesche, Haupt, *Ber.*, 1937, **70**, 44.
Stoll, Hofmann, *Helv. Chim. Acta*, 1935, **18**, 82, 401.
Stoll *et al.*, *Helv. Chim. Acta*, 1933, **16**, 703; 1935, **18**, 649.

Scillaridin-A

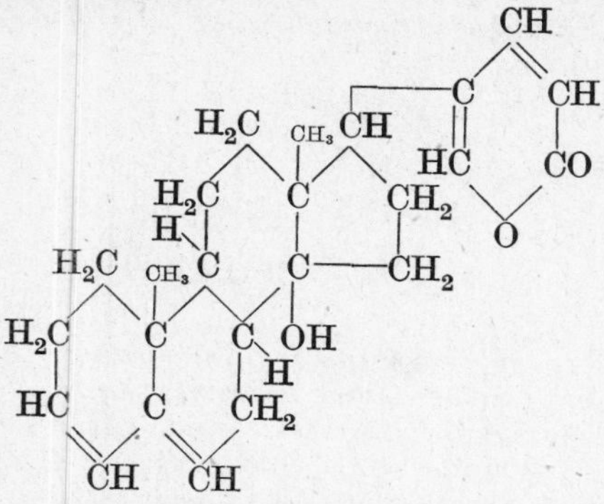

Suggested structure

$C_{24}H_{30}O_3$ MW, 366

Prisms from EtOH. M.p. 245–50°. Spar. sol. EtOH, $CHCl_3$. Insol. H_2O, Et_2O. $[\alpha]_D^{20}$ — 62·6° in MeOH–$CHCl_3$.

See first reference above and also
Stoll *et al.*, *Helv. Chim. Acta*, 1933, **16**, 727; 1935, **18**, 647, 1247.

Scoparin

$C_{22}H_{22}O_{11}$ MW, 462

Occurs in *Cytisus scoparius*, Link. M.p. 202–19° decomp. Sol. hot H_2O, EtOH. Insol. Et_2O, $CHCl_3$, CS_2.

Di-Me ether: $C_{24}H_{26}O_{11}$. MW, 490. Yellow cryst. M.p. 260–5° decomp.

Tri-Me ether: $C_{25}H_{28}O_{11}$. MW, 504. Yellow cryst. M.p. 220–38°.

Octa-Me ether: $C_{29}H_{36}O_{11}$. MW, 560. M.p. 120–30° ⟶ solid, remelting at 229–33°.

Hemmelmayr, Strehly, *Monatsh.*, 1926, **47**, 379.
Herzig, Tiring, *Monatsh.*, 1918, **39**, 253.

Scopine

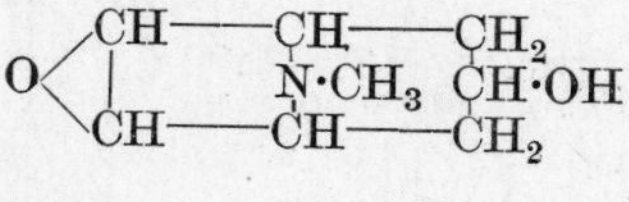

$C_8H_{13}O_2N$ MW, 155

Needles from pet. ether. M.p. 76°.
B,HAuCl$_4$: m.p. 216° decomp.
B$_2$,H$_2$PtCl$_6$: m.p. 219° decomp.
Picrate: leaflets. M.p. 231°.
Tropic ester: *see* Hyoscine.

ψ-Scopine.
M.p. 125–6°.
Benzoyl: m.p. 142°. *B,HCl*: m.p. 216°. *Chloroaurate*: m.p. 220°. *Picrate*: m.p. 204°.

Phenylurethane: m.p. 229°. *B,HAuCl$_4$*: m.p. 210°.

Willstätter, Berner, *Ber.*, 1923, **56**, 1079, 1081.
Polonovski, Polonovski, *Bull. soc. chim.*, 1928, **43**, 590, 594.

Scopolamine.
See Hyoscine.

Scopoletin (*Æsculetin 6-methyl ether, chrysatropic acid, gelseminic acid, 7-hydroxy-6-methoxycoumarin, β-methylæsculetin*)

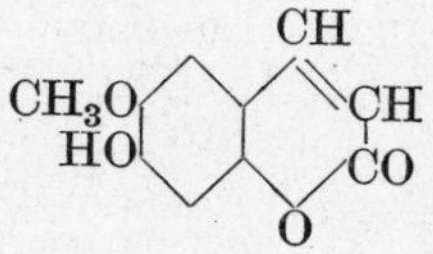

$C_{10}H_8O_4$ MW, 192

Occurs in root of *Gelsemium sempervirens*, Ait., *Atropa belladonna*, Linn., *Convolvulus scammonia*, Linn., *Ipomœa orizabensis*, Ledenois, *Prunus serotina*, Ehrh. and *Fabiana imbricata*, Ruiz & Pav. Needles or prisms. M.p. 204°. Sol. hot EtOH, hot AcOH. Mod. sol. $CHCl_3$. Spar. sol. H_2O. Insol. C_6H_6, CS_2. Blue fluor. in EtOH. Reduces Fehling's and Tollen's. $FeCl_3$ ⟶ green col.

Acetyl: m.p. 177°.
Me ether: 6 : 7-dimethoxycoumarin. $C_{11}H_{10}O_4$. MW, 206. M.p. 145°.
Glucoside: *see* Fabiatrin.

Seka, Kallir, *Ber.*, 1931, **64**, 909 (*Bibl.*).
Head, Robertson, *J. Chem. Soc.*, 1931, 1241 (*Bibl.*).

Scopoligenin.
See Norscopoline.

Scopoline (*Oscine*)

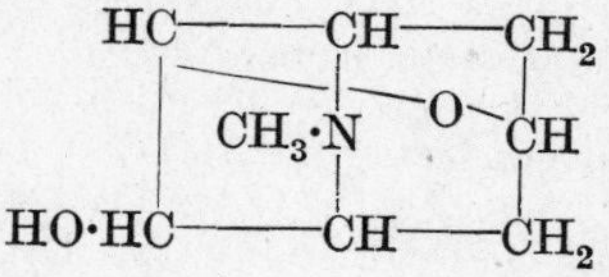

$C_8H_{13}O_2N$ MW, 155

Prisms from Et_2O. M.p. 108–9°. B.p. 248°.
B,HCl: m.p. 270°.
B,HAuCl$_4$: m.p. 220° decomp.
B$_2$,H$_2$PtCl$_6$: m.p. 203° decomp.
Picrate: m.p. 236°.

Willstätter, Berner, *Ber.*, 1923, **56**, 1079.
Polonovski, Polonovski, *Bull. soc. chim.*, 1928, **43**, 590.

Scopolinic Acid (N-*Methylhexahydrodipicolinic acid*, N-*methylpiperidine*-2 : 6-*dicarboxylic acid*)

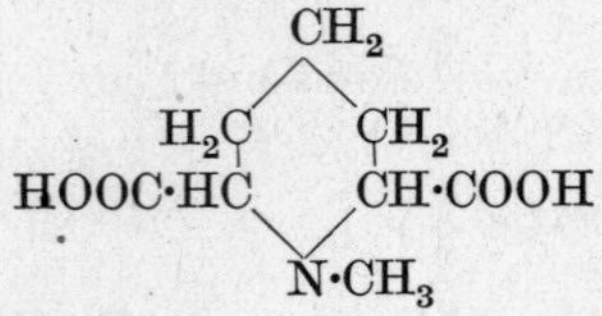

$C_8H_{13}O_4N$ MW, 187

Plates + $1H_2O$. M.p. 225° decomp. (230° anhyd.). Sol. hot H_2O. Spar. sol. Et_2O.

B,HCl : m.p. 225–6° decomp.

Di-Me ester : $C_{10}H_{17}O_4N$. MW, 215. B.p. 140–1°/13 mm.

Schmidt, *Arch. Pharm.*, 1915, **253**, 606.
Hess, Wissing, *Ber.*, 1915, **48**, 1910.
Willstätter, Lessing, *Ber.*, 1902, **35**, 2072.
Hess, Suchier, *Ber.*, 1915, **48**, 2057.

Scopularic Acid.
See Stictic Acid.

Scutellarein (5:6 : 7:4′-*Tetrahydroxyflavone*)

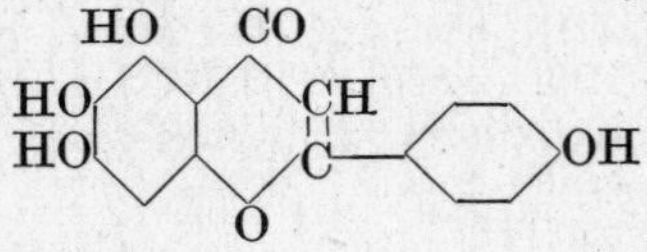

$C_{15}H_{10}O_6$ MW, 286

Yellow leaflets from MeOH. Does not melt below 300°. Sol. boiling MeOH, EtOH, AcOH. Spar. sol. other solvents. Insol. H_2O. KOH ⟶ reddish-yellow sol. Cold $NH_3.AgNO_3$ gives reddish-brown col. and is reduced on heating. Alc. $FeCl_3$ ⟶ reddish-brown col.

6 : 4′-*Di-Me ether* : $C_{17}H_{14}O_6$. MW, 314. Yellow cryst. M.p. 219°. *Diacetyl* : m.p. 149–50°.

6 : 7 : 4′-*Tri-Me ether* : $C_{18}H_{16}O_6$. MW, 328. Yellow microleaflets from AcOEt. M.p. 189–90°. Conc. H_2SO_4 ⟶ greenish-yellow sol. *Acetyl* : microleaflets from AcOEt. M.p. 169°.

Tetra-Me ether : $C_{19}H_{18}O_6$. MW, 342. Exists in two forms. (i) Prisms from EtOH. M.p. 161°. (ii) Cryst. from EtOH. M.p. 142°.

Tetra-acetyl : needles from AcOEt or EtOH. M.p. 235–7°.

Bargellini, *Gazz. chim. ital.*, 1915, **45**, i, 77.
Goldschmiedt, Zerner, *Monatsh.*, 1910, **31**, 464.
Robinson, Schwarzenbach, *J. Chem. Soc.*, 1930, 829.
Wessely, Moser, *Monatsh.*, 1930, **56**, 97.

Scyllitol (*Cocosite, cocositol, quercin, quercinite, hexahydroxycyclohexane, stereoisomer of inositol*)

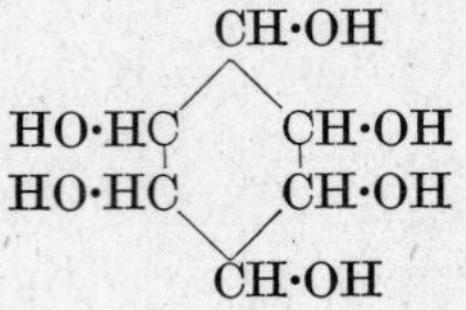

$C_6H_{12}O_6$ MW, 180

Occurs in dogfish (*Scyllium canicula*) and other fish; in *Acanthus vulgaris, Cornus florida*, Linn. (flowering dogwood) and various *Cocos* species. Prisms + $3H_2O$ from H_2O. M.p. 353° decomp. Spar. sol. H_2O. Insol. EtOH, Et_2O, MeOH, C_6H_6, $CHCl_3$.

Hexa-acetyl : m.p. 291°.

Needham, *Biochem. J.*, 1929, **23**, 319.
Hann, Sando, *J. Biol. Chem.*, 1926, **68**, 399.
Goodson, *J. Chem. Soc.*, 1920, **117**, 140.

Scymnol

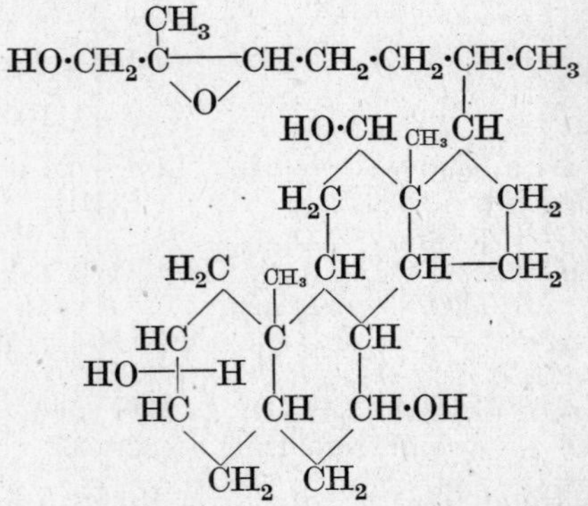

$C_{27}H_{46}O_5$ MW, 450

Occurs as sulphuric ester in bile of shark (*Scymnus borealis*). Cryst. + $2H_2O$ from Me_2CO.Aq., m.p. 115°: anhyd. cubes from AcOEt, m.p. 187°. $[\alpha]_D$ + 38·2° in EtOH.

Hydrochloride : two forms. (i) Needles from MeOH. M.p. 196°. (ii) M.p. 126°. Both forms give scymnol with alkalis.

Tetra-acetyl : plates from MeOH. M.p. 148°. B.p. 280°/0·005 mm.

Tschesche, *Z. physiol. Chem.*, 1931, **203**, 263.
Windaus, Bergmann, König, *Z. physiol Chem.*, 1930, **189**, 148.
Oikawa, *Chem. Abstracts*, 1926, **20**, 401.

Sebacamic Acid.
See under Sebacic Acid.

Sebacanilic Acid (*Sebacic acid monoanilide*)

$HOOC{\cdot}CH_2{\cdot}[CH_2]_6{\cdot}CH_2{\cdot}CO{\cdot}NHC_6H_5$

$C_{16}H_{23}O_3N$ MW, 277

Leaflets from H_2O. M.p. 121–2°.

Me ester: $C_{17}H_{25}O_3N$. MW, 291. Needles from pet. ether. M.p. 67–8°.

Morgan, Walton, *J. Chem. Soc.*, 1936, 905.

Sebacic Acid (*Octane*-1 : 8-*dicarboxylic acid*)

$HOOC{\cdot}CH_2{\cdot}[CH_2]_6{\cdot}CH_2{\cdot}COOH$

$C_{10}H_{18}O_4$ MW, 202

Leaflets. M.p. 134·5° (132–3°). B.p. 294·5°/00 mm., 273°/50 mm., 243·5°/15 mm., 232°/0 mm. Sol. EtOH, Et_2O. Spar. sol. H_2O. Ieat of comb. C_p 1297·3 Cal., C_v 1295·9 Cal. (first) = $2{\cdot}6 \times 10^{-5}$ at 25°; (second) = $2{\cdot}6 \times 0^{-6}$ at 100°.

Me ester: $C_{11}H_{20}O_4$. MW, 216. M.p. 40–1°. .p. 208°/20 mm. *Chloride*: $C_{11}H_{19}O_3Cl$. MW, 34·5. B.p. 177°/23 mm.

Di-Me ester: $C_{12}H_{22}O_4$. MW, 230. M.p. 6·4° (38°). B.p. 293°/754 mm., 175°/20 mm. D_4^{28} 0·98818. n_D^{28} 1·43549.

Et ester: $C_{12}H_{22}O_4$. MW, 230. M.p. 35°. .p. 202–3°/15 mm. $k = 1{\cdot}43 \times 10^{-5}$ at 25°.

Di-Et ester: $C_{14}H_{26}O_4$. MW, 258. M.p. 1·25°. .p. 306°/773 mm., 158–9°/7·5 mm. D_4^{20} 0·96461. n_D^{20} 1·43589.

Dibutyl ester: $C_{18}H_{34}O_4$. MW, 314. B.p. 44–5°. D^{15} 0·9329.

Di-isoamyl ester: $C_{20}H_{38}O_4$. MW, 342. M.p. 8°. B.p. 202–3°/2–3 mm. D_4^{25} 0·9230.

Glycol ester: $C_{12}H_{20}O_4$. MW, 228. M.p. 79°.

Trimethylene glycol ester: $C_{13}H_{22}O_4$. MW, 42. M.p. 14–17°. B.p. 130–3°/2 mm. D_4^{20} 0747. n_D^{20} 1·4719.

Di-p-nitrobenzyl ester: $C_{24}H_{28}O_8N_2$. MW, 472. .p. 72–6°.

Dimenthyl ester: $C_{30}H_{54}O_4$. MW, 478. B.p. 56–8°/20 mm.

Diphenacyl ester: $C_{26}H_{28}O_4$. MW, 404. M.p.)–4°.

Dichloride: $C_{10}H_{16}O_2Cl_2$. MW, 239. B.p. 35–95°/30 mm., 182°/16 mm. $n_D^{18 \cdot 3}$ 1·46836.

Monoamide: sebacamic acid. $C_{10}H_{19}O_3N$. W, 201. M.p. 170°.

Diamide: $C_{10}H_{20}O_2N_2$. MW, 200. M.p. 210° 08°).

Dinitrile: octamethylene dicyanide, sebaco-trile. $C_{10}H_{16}N_2$. MW, 164. B.p. 199–200°/ mm.

Anhydride: $C_{10}H_{16}O_3$. MW, 184. Cryst. om C_6H_6. M.p. 78–9°.

Monoanilide: *see* Sebacanilic Acid.

Dianilide: m.p. 198°.

Dihydrazide: m.p. 184–5°.

Morgan, Walton, *J. Chem. Soc.*, 1936, 903.
Izard, U.S.P., 1,991,391, (*Chem. Abstracts*, 1935, **29**, 2176).
Spanagel, F.P., 796,410, (*Chem. Abstracts*, 1936, **30**, 6138).
Stoll, Rouvé, *Helv. Chim. Acta*, 1936, **19**, 253.
Fischl, Steiner, U.S.P., 1,876,652, (*Chem. Abstracts*, 1933, **27**, 102).
Naegeli, Münzel, D.R.P., 554,700, (*Chem. Abstracts*, 1932, **26**, 5970).
Kao, Ma, *Chem. Abstracts*, 1932, **26**, 4305.
Landa, Kejvan, *Chem. Abstracts*, 1932, **26**, 78.
Montonna, *J. Am. Chem. Soc.*, 1927, **49**, 2114.
Boedtker, *Chem. Abstracts*, 1924, **18**, 3043.

Sedanolic Acid

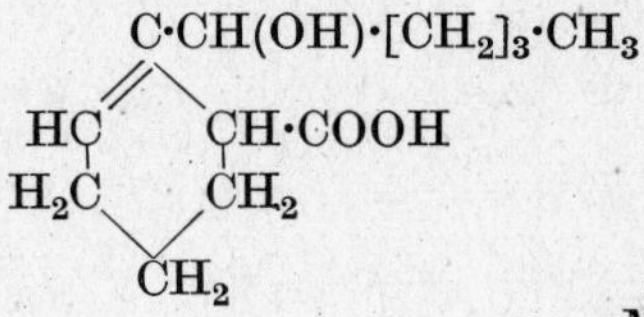

$C_{12}H_{20}O_3$ MW, 212

Needles from C_6H_6. M.p. 88–9°. Sol. Et_2O, C_6H_6, hot pet. ether. Insol. H_2O.

Lactone: sedanolide. $C_{12}H_{18}O_2$. MW, 194. Occurs in celery oil. B.p. 185°/17 mm. $D^{24 \cdot 5}$ 1·0383. $n_D^{24 \cdot 5}$ 1·4923. $[\alpha]_D^{26 \cdot 5}$ − 23·66°.

Ciamician, Silber, *Ber.*, 1897, **30**, 497.

Sedanolide.

See under Sedanolic Acid.

Sedanonic Acid

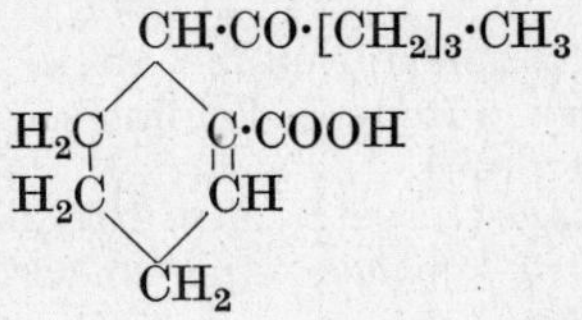

$C_{12}H_{18}O_3$ MW, 210

Saponification product from celery oil. Needles from C_6H_6. M.p. 113°. Sol. EtOH, AcOH. Mod. sol. Et_2O, C_6H_6. Spar. sol. pet. ether. Insol. H_2O.

Oxime: m.p. 128°.

Ciamician, Silber, *Ber.*, 1897, **30**, 500.

Sedoheptitol

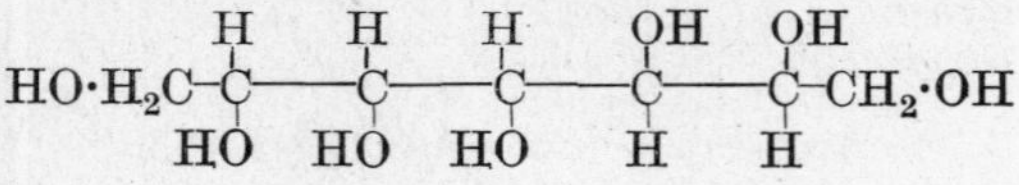

$$HO \cdot H_2C - \overset{\overset{H}{|}}{\underset{\underset{HO}{|}}{C}} - \overset{\overset{H}{|}}{\underset{\underset{HO}{|}}{C}} - \overset{\overset{H}{|}}{\underset{\underset{HO}{|}}{C}} - \overset{\overset{OH}{|}}{\underset{\underset{H}{|}}{C}} - \overset{\overset{OH}{|}}{\underset{\underset{H}{|}}{C}} - CH_2 \cdot OH$$

α-Form

$$HO \cdot H_2C - \overset{\overset{H}{|}}{\underset{\underset{HO}{|}}{C}} - \overset{\overset{H}{|}}{\underset{\underset{HO}{|}}{C}} - \overset{\overset{H}{|}}{\underset{\underset{HO}{|}}{C}} - \overset{\overset{OH}{|}}{\underset{\underset{H}{|}}{C}} - \overset{\overset{H}{|}}{\underset{\underset{HO}{|}}{C}} - CH_2 \cdot OH$$

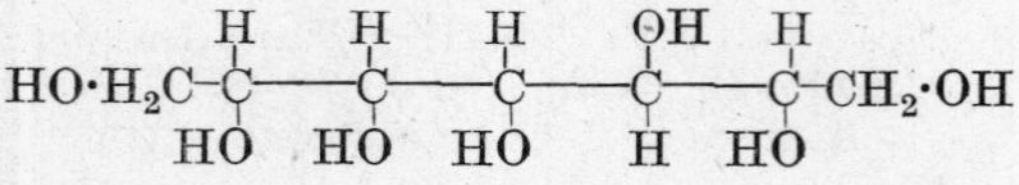

β-Form

$C_7H_{16}O_7$ MW, 212

α-Form : Volemitol, *d*-β-Mannoheptitol.
Occurs in *Lactarius volemus*, etc. Needles from dil. EtOH. M.p. 154–5° (151–2°). $[\alpha]_D^{20}$ + 2·25° in H_2O. Sol. H_2O. Spar. sol. EtOH. Insol. Et_2O.
Triethylidene deriv. : cryst. M.p. 191–4°. $[\alpha]_D$ — 45·55° in $CHCl_3$, $[\alpha]_D^{20}$ — 72·35° in $CHCl_3$, — 117·6° in Py.
Tribenzylidene deriv. : needles. M.p. 214–15° (199–200°). $[\alpha]_D^{20}$ —1·7° in $CHCl_3$, — 48·4° in Py.

β-*Form* :
Plates or needles from dil. EtOH. M.p. 127–8°.
Tribenzylidene deriv. : m.p. 272·5°.

> Bougault, Allard, *Compt. rend.*, 1902, **135**, 796.
> La Forge, Hudson, *J. Biol. Chem.*, 1917, **30**, 68 ; 1928, **79**, 1.
> La Forge, *J. Biol. Chem.*, 1920, **42**, 375.
> Ettel, *Chem. Zentr.*, 1929, II, 714.
> Ettel, *Chem. Abstracts*, 1933, **27**, 1617.

Sedoheptose

$$HO \cdot CH_2 - \overset{\overset{H}{|}}{\underset{\underset{HO}{|}}{C}} - \overset{\overset{H}{|}}{\underset{\underset{HO}{|}}{C}} - \overset{\overset{H}{|}}{\underset{\underset{HO}{|}}{C}} - \overset{\overset{OH}{|}}{\underset{\underset{H}{|}}{C}} - CO \cdot CH_2 \cdot OH$$

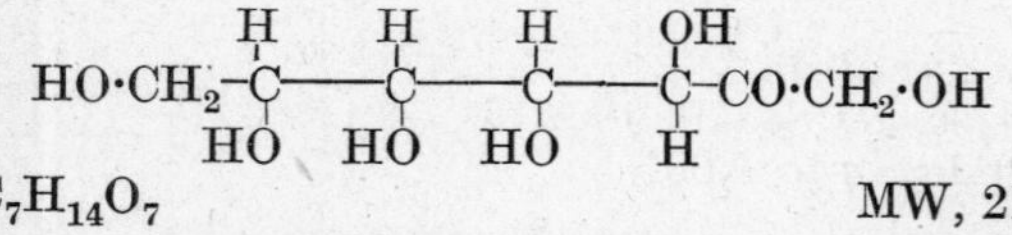

$C_7H_{14}O_7$ MW, 210

Occurs in *Sedum spectabile*. Syrup. Weakly dextrorotatory. Reduces Fehling's. NaHg →
α- + β-sedoheptitol.
Phenylosazone : cryst. M.p. 197° decomp.
p-*Bromophenylosazone* : yellow needles. M.p. 227–8° decomp.

> La Forge, *J. Biol. Chem.*, 1920, **42**, 367.
> La Forge, Hudson, *J. Biol. Chem.*, 1917, **30**, 61.
> See also last reference above.

Selacholeic Acid.
See Nervonic Acid.

Selachyl Alcohol (*Glycerol* 1-*octadecenyl ether*, *α-oleyl glyceryl ether*)

$$CH_2 \cdot O \cdot [CH_2]_8 \cdot CH\colon CH \cdot [CH_2]_7 \cdot CH_3$$
$$CH \cdot OH$$
$$CH_2 \cdot OH$$

$C_{21}H_{42}O_3$ MW, 342

Occurs in liver oil of *Centrophorus granulosus*. B.p. 242°/5 mm. D_4^{15} 0·9206. n_D^{15} 1·4690.

> Davies, Heilbron, Jones, *J. Chem. Soc.*, 1933, 165.

Selenazine (*Phenoselenazine*, *selenodiphenylamine*)

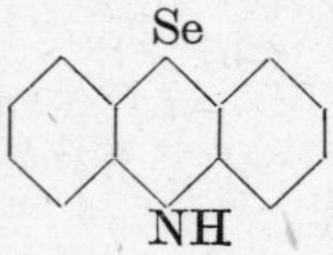

$C_{12}H_9NSe$ MW, 246

Yellow leaflets from C_6H_6. M.p. 195°. Sol. ord. org. solvents. Oxidises in air.
N-*Acetyl :* m.p. 176°.
N-*Me* : $C_{13}H_{11}NSe$. MW, 260. M.p. 138–9°.

> Cornelius, *Chem.-Ztg.*, 1913, **37**, 198.
> Weizmann, Stephen, *Proc. Chem. Soc.*, 1913, **29**, 196.

Selenobenzoic Acid

$$C_6H_5 \cdot COSeH$$

C_7H_6OSe MW, 185

Red cryst. from MeOH. M.p. 133°.
p-*Tolyl ester* : $C_{14}H_{12}OSe$. MW, 275. Prisms from EtOH. M.p. 71–2°. Turns red in air.
p-*Methoxyphenyl ester* : $C_{14}H_{12}O_2Se$. MW, 291. Cryst. from EtOH. M.p. 97°.
p-*Ethoxyphenyl ester* : $C_{15}H_{14}O_2Se$. MW, 305. Needles from ligroin. M.p. 97°.
Amide : C_7H_7NSe. MW, 184. Golden needles from Et_2O. M.p. 126° (115°).

> Mingoia, *Gazz. chim. ital.*, 1926, **56**, 835.
> Becker, Meyer, *Ber.*, 1904, **37**, 2550.

Selenodiphenylamine.
See Selenazine.
Selenofuran.
See Selenophene.
Selenonaphthene (*Benzselenophene*)

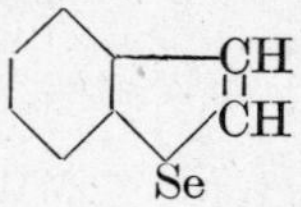

C_8H_6Se MW, 181

Leaflets from MeOH. M.p. 53–4° (50–1°). B.p. 238·5–240°/775 mm. Sol. ord. org. solvents.
Picrate : m.p. 156–7°.
Styphnate : m.p. 146–7°.

Komppa, Nyman, *J. prakt. Chem.*, 1934, **139**, 229.

1-Selenonaphthol

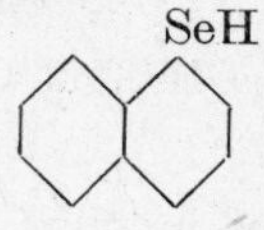

$C_{10}H_8Se$ MW, 207

Red liquid. B.p. 165–7°/20 mm.

Taboury, *Compt. rend.*, 1904, **138**, 982.

Selenophene (*Selenofuran*)

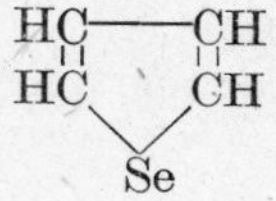

C_4H_4Se MW, 131

Oil. F.p. – 38°. B.p. 109·9–110·1°/752·1 mm. Sol. Me_2CO, C_6H_6, CS_2. Insol. H_2O. D_4^{15} 1·5301. n_D^{15} 1·568. Solvent for S. $H_2SO_4 \longrightarrow$ greenish-black mass.

McMahon, Pearson, Robinson, *J. Chem. Soc.*, 1933, 1644 (*Bibl.*).
Suginome, Umezawa, *Bull. Chem. Soc. Japan*, 1936, **11**, 157 (*Bibl.*).
Day, *Science Progress*, 1929, **23**, 585, (*Review*).
Mazza, Solazzo, *Chem. Abstracts*, 1929, **23**, 2417.

Selenophenol

$C_6H_5{\cdot}SeH$

C_6H_6Se MW, 157

Oil. B.p. 183·6°/760 mm. Sol. Et_2O, CCl_4. Spar. sol. H_2O. D^{15} 1·4865. Oxidises in air to $(C_6H_5)_2Se_2$.

Lesser, Weiss, *Ber.*, 1914, **47**, 2522.
Bayer, D.R.P., 264,940, (*Chem. Abstracts*, 1914, **8**, 1351).

Selenourea

$H_2N{\cdot}CSe{\cdot}NH_2$

CH_4N_2Se MW, 123

Prisms or needles from H_2O. M.p. 200° decomp. (slow heat). Mod. sol. H_2O. Spar. sol. EtOH, Et_2O.

Verneuil, *Ann. chim.*, 1886, **9**, 292.

Selinene

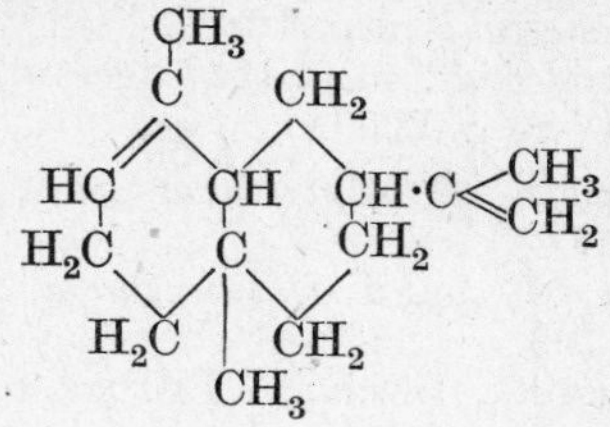

α-.

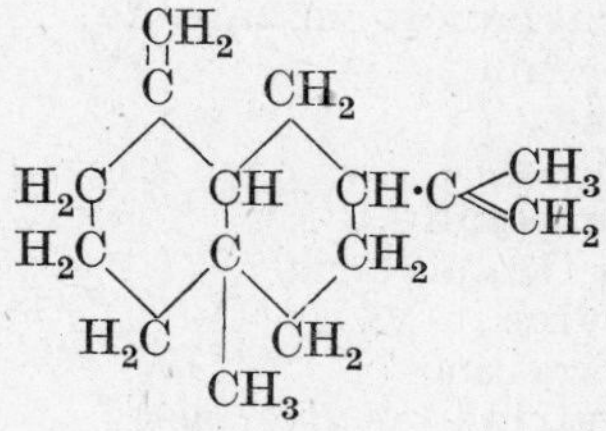

β-.

$C_{15}H_{24}$ MW, 204

α-.
B.p. 268–72°, 128–32°/11 mm. D_{15}^{15} 0·9232. n_{20} 1·5048.

β-.
Occurs in celery oil. B.p. 121–2°/6 mm. D_{15}^{18} 0·9170. n_D^{21} 1·4956. Dihydrochloride + alkali $\longrightarrow$ α-form.

Schimmel, *Chem. Zentr.*, 1910, I, 1719.
Ruzicka, Wind, Koolhaas, *Helv. Chim. Acta*, 1931, **14**, 1138.

Selinenol.
See Eudesmol.

Semicarbazide (*Hydrazinoformamide, carbazinamide*)

$\underset{4}{NH_2}{\cdot}\underset{3}{CO}{\cdot}\underset{2}{NH}{\cdot}\underset{1}{NH_2}$

CH_5ON_3 MW, 75

Prisms from EtOH. M.p. 96°. Reacts with aldehydes and ketones to give characteristic semicarbazones, $R{\cdot}CH{:}N{\cdot}NH{\cdot}CO{\cdot}NH_2$ or $R_2C{:}N{\cdot}NH{\cdot}CO{\cdot}NH_2$.
B,HF : m.p. below 100° decomp.
B,HCl : m.p. 175°.
B,HNO₃ : m.p. 123° decomp.
B,H₂SO₄ : m.p. 145° decomp.
B₂,H₂SO₄ : m.p. 143°.
B,HClO₃ : explodes at 278°.
B,H·COOH : m.p. 128°.
B,(COOH)₂ : m.p. 146° (133° decomp.).
Acid maleate : m.p. 133° decomp.
Maleate : m.p. 100°.
Picrate : m.p. 166° decomp.
1-*Acetyl* : *see* Acetylsemicarbazide.

1-*Chloroacetyl* : m.p. 111–12°.
1-*Dichloroacetyl* : m.p. 108°.
1-*Trichloroacetyl* : m.p. 154° decomp.
1-*Benzoyl* : m.p. 225°.

Audrieth, *J. Am. Chem. Soc.*, 1930, **52**, 1250.
Mistry, Guha, *J. Indian Chem. Soc.*, 1930, I, 793.
Ingersoll, Bircher, Brubaker, *Organic Syntheses*, Collective Vol. I, 472.

3-Semicarbazidobenzamide.
See Kryogenin.

Seminose.
See Mannose.

Semioxamazide.
See under Oxamic Acid.

Sempervine.
See Sempervirine.

Sempervirine (*Sempervine*)

$C_{19}H_{16}N_2$ MW, 272

Occurs in *Gelsemium sempervirens*, Ait. Cryst. + $1H_2O$, m.p. 258–60° : cryst. from $CHCl_3$, m.p. 223° : cryst. from EtOH, m.p. 254°. Sol. EtOH, $CHCl_3$, Py. Insol. Et_2O, C_6H_6.

Hasenfratz, *Compt. rend.*, 1933, **196**, 1530.
Chou, *Chem. Abstracts*, 1931, **25**, 5736.
Stevenson, Sayre, *Chem. Abstracts*, 1916, **10**, 804.

Senecifoline

$C_{18}H_{27}O_8N$ MW, 385

Plates from $CHCl_3$–pet. ether. M.p. 194–5°. Sol. EtOH, Et_2O, $CHCl_3$. Insol. H_2O, pet. ether. $[\alpha]_D + 28{\cdot}8°$ in EtOH.

B,HCl : m.p. 260° decomp. $[\alpha]_D - 20°$ in H_2O.
B,HI : m.p. 248° decomp.
B,HNO_3 : m.p. 240° decomp.
B,$HAuCl_4$: m.p. 220° decomp.

Watt, *J. Chem. Soc.*, 1909, **95**, 469.

Senecifolinene.
See Retronecine.

Senecioic Acid.
See 2 : 2-Dimethylacrylic Acid.

Seneciphylline

$C_{17}H_{23}O_5N$ MW, 321

Occurs in *Senecio platyphyllus*, D.C. Plates from EtOH. M.p. 217–18° decomp. Sol. $CHCl_3$. Mod. sol. EtOH, Me_2CO. Spar. sol. Et_2O, ligroin. $[\alpha]_D - 128{\cdot}04°$ in $CHCl_3$.

Perchlorate : decomp. at 245°.
Aurichloride : m.p. 162–3° decomp.
Platinichloride : decomp. at 240°.
Picrate : m.p. 182–3°.
Methiodide : m.p. 231–2° decomp.

Orechoff, *Ber.*, 1935, **68**, 654.

Sennite.
See under Inositol.

Serine (1-*Aminohydracrylic acid*, 2-*hydroxy*-1-*aminopropionic acid*, 2-*hydroxy*-α-*alanine*)

$$HO{\cdot}CH_2{\cdot}CH(NH_2){\cdot}COOH$$

$C_3H_7O_3N$ MW, 105

Widely distributed in animal proteins.

d-.
Prisms from H_2O. M.p. 228° decomp. $[\alpha]_D^{20} + 6{\cdot}87°$ in H_2O.

l-.
$[\alpha]_D^{20} - 6{\cdot}83°$ in H_2O.
Me ester : *hydrochloride*, m.p. 167°.

dl-.
Leaflets from H_2O. M.p. 246° decomp. Sol. H_2O. Insol. EtOH, Et_2O. $H_2O_2 + FeSO_4 \longrightarrow HO{\cdot}CH_2{\cdot}CHO$. $FeCl_3 \longrightarrow$ red col.
Me ester : $C_4H_9O_3N$. MW, 119. *B,HCl* : m.p. 114°.
N-*Chloroacetyl* : m.p. 122–3°.
N-1-*Bromopropionyl* : m.p. about 143°.
Benzoyl deriv. : decomp. at 149–50°. *B,HCl* : m.p. 185–6°. *Picrate* : m.p. 168–9°.
Phosphoric ester : serine-phosphoric acid. $C_3H_8O_6NP$. Ba salt forms white flocks in hot H_2O.
Et ether : $C_5H_{11}O_3N$. MW, 133. Needles from EtOH. M.p. 256° decomp.
Picrolonate : decomp. at 265°.
Phenylurethane : m.p. 159°.

Leuchs, Geiger, *Ber.*, 1906, **39**, 2645.
Fischer, Jacobs, *ibid.*, 2944.
Mitra, *J. Indian Chem. Soc.*, 1930, **7**, 799.
Dunn, Redemann, Smith, *J. Biol. Chem.*, 1934, **104**, 511 (*Bibl.*).
Levene, Schormüller, *J. Biol. Chem.*, 1934, **106**, 595; **105**, 547.

Serine-phosphoric Acid.
See under Serine.

Sesamin

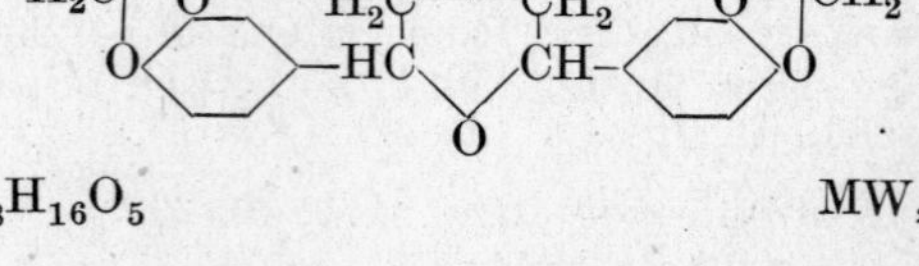

$C_{18}H_{16}O_5$ MW, 312

Occurs in sesame oil. Needles from EtOH. M.p. 123°. Sol. Me_2CO, $CHCl_3$. Spar. sol. Et_2O, pet. ether. $[\alpha]_D^{20} + 68{\cdot}23°$ in $CHCl_3$.

Kreis, *Chem. Abstracts*, 1930, **24**, 2000.
Adriani, *Chem. Abstracts*, 1929, **23**, 2054.
Böeseken, Cohen, *Biochem. Z.*, 1928, **201**, 454.
Bertram, van der Steur, Waterman, *Biochem. Z.*, 1928, **197**, 1.

Sesamol (3 : 4-*Methylenedioxyphenol*, 1 : 2 : 4-*trihydroxybenzene* 1 : 2-*methylene ether*)

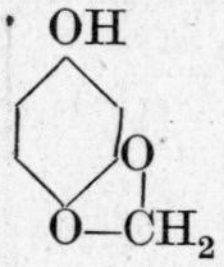

$C_7H_6O_3$ MW, 126

M.p. 65·8°. Sol. EtOH, Et_2O. Spar. sol. H_2O, pet. ether. $FeCl_3$ ⟶ violet-brown col. Colours rapidly in air.

β-*Glucoside*: $C_{13}H_{16}O_8$. Cryst. + $1H_2O$. M.p. 168–9°.

Böeseken, Cohen, Kip, *Rec. trav. chim.*, 1936, **55**, 815.

Sesquicamphene

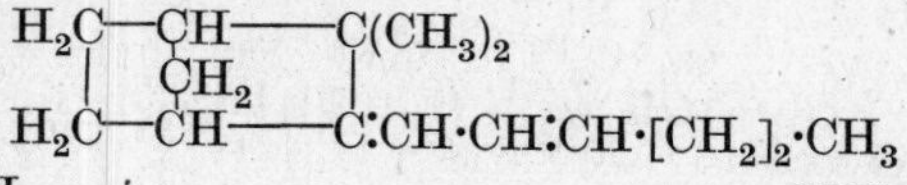

$C_{15}H_{24}$ MW, 204

Occurs in camphor oil. B.p. 255°, 140°/10 mm., 129–33°/8 mm. D^{20} 0·9015. n_D 1·50058. $[\alpha]_D + 73{\cdot}5°$.

Semmler, Rosenberg, *Ber.*, 1913, **46**, 768.
Langlois, *Ann. chim.*, 1919, **12**, 358.

Sesquicitronellene

$C_{15}H_{24}$ MW, 204

Occurs in Java citronella oil. B.p. 138–40°/9 mm. D^{20} 0·8489. n_D 1·53252.

Semmler, Spornitz, *Ber.*, 1913, **46**, 4025.

Sexiphenyl

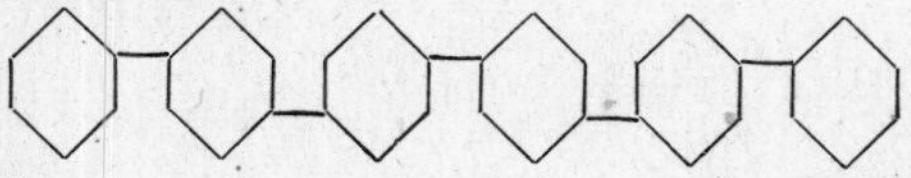

$C_{36}H_{26}$ MW, 458

Cryst. from *o*-dichlorobenzene. M.p. 465°. Sol. quinoline, decahydronaphthalene.

Pummerer, *Ber.*, 1924, **57**, 84; 1933, **66**, 802.

Shikonin (d-*Alkannin*)

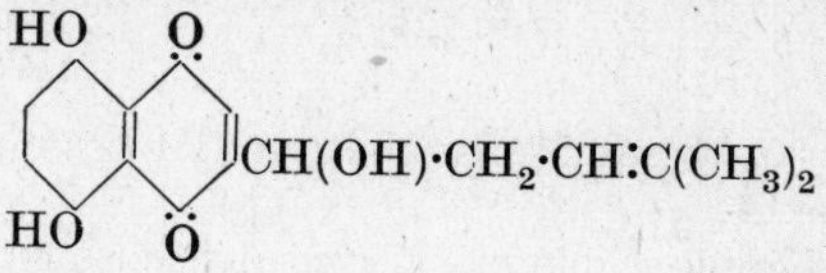

$C_{16}H_{16}O_5$ MW, 288

Occurs in root of *Lithospermum erythrorhizon*, ("shikon"). Brownish-red needles from C_6H_6. M.p. 143°. Reduces Tollen's. $FeCl_3$ ⟶ indigo-blue ppt.

Me ether: $C_{17}H_{18}O_5$. MW, 302. M.p. 105°.

Karoda, Wada, *Chem. Zentr.*, 1937, I, 3156.

Shogaol

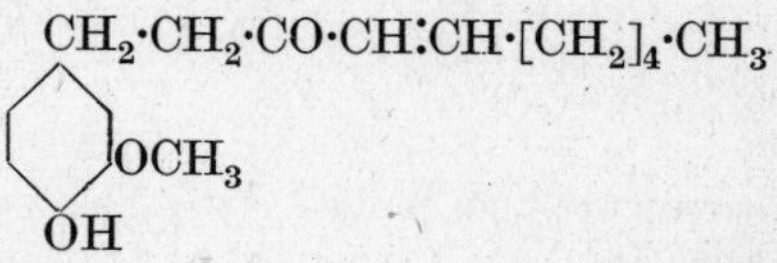

$C_{17}H_{24}O_3$ MW, 276

Occurs in ginger ("shoga"). Pale yellow oil. B.p. 201·3°/2–2·5 mm. Sol. EtOH, AcOH. D_4^{25} 1·0419. n_D^{25} 1·52518. $FeCl_3$ ⟶ green col. Reduces Tollen's.

Acetyl deriv.: b.p. 183–8°/0·6 mm.

Me ether: $C_{18}H_{26}O_3$. MW, 290. Yellow oil. B.p. 160–5°/0·06 mm.

Et ether: $C_{19}H_{28}O_3$. MW, 304. Yellow oil. B.p. 181–6°/0·65 mm.

Nomura, Iwamoto, Murakami, *Chem. Abstracts*, 1930, **24**, 2445.

Shonanic Acid

$C_{10}H_{14}O_2$ MW, 166

Occurs in wood of *Libocedrus formosana*, Florin. Cryst. from pet. ether. M.p. 40–1°. B.p. 264°/754 mm., 134–134·5°/6 mm. D_4^{46} 1·016. n_D^{46} 1·4842. $[\alpha]_D^{18} - 0{\cdot}75°$ in EtOH.

Me ester: $C_{11}H_{16}O_2$. MW, 180. B.p. 222°, 113–14°/20 mm. D_4^{20} 0·9848. n_D^{20} 1·4758. $[\alpha]_D^{28} - 2{\cdot}84°$.

Et ester: $C_{12}H_{18}O_2$. MW, 194. B.p. 228–9°/759 mm., 106–8°/7 mm. D_4^{20} 0·9568. n_D^{20} 1·4674. $[\alpha]_D^{18} - 4{\cdot}24°$.

Chloride: $C_{10}H_{13}OCl$. MW, 184·5. B.p. 215°, 106–7°/20 mm. D_4^{20} 1·0577. n_D^{20} 1·4955.

Amide: $C_{10}H_{15}ON$. MW, 165. M.p. 116–17°.

Anilide: m.p. 111–12°.

Ichikawa, *Bull. Chem. Soc. Japan*, 1936, **11**, 759.

Silicon tetraethyl

$Si(C_2H_5)_4$

$C_8H_{20}Si$ MW, 144

B.p. 152·8–153·2°/758·5 mm. D_4^{25} 0·7620. $n_D^{25\cdot1}$ 1·4246.

Kipping, Lloyd, *J. Chem. Soc.*, 1901, **79**, 456.
Bygden, *Ber.*, 1911, **44**, 2650.

Silvan.
See 2-Methylfuran.

Silvecarvone ($\Delta^{6,8(9)}$-m-*Menthadienone*-2)

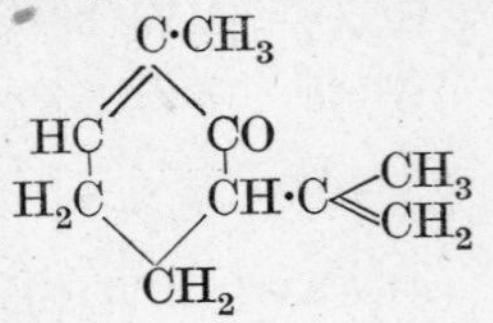

$C_{10}H_{14}O$ MW, 150

Oil.
Semicarbazone : m.p. 175–7°.

Wallach, *Ann.*, 1907, **357**, 74.

Silver Salt.
See under Anthraquinone-2-sulphonic Acid.

Silveterpin (d-m-*Menthandiol*-1 : 8)

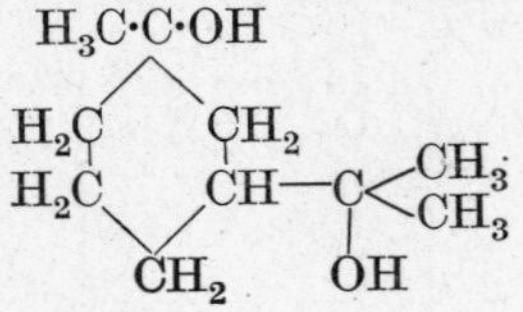

$C_{10}H_{20}O_2$ MW, 172

α-.
M.p. 137–8°. $[\alpha]_D$ + 27·74° in $CHCl_3$. Sublimes.

β-.
M.p. 70–5°. $[\alpha]_D$ + 20·93° in $CHCl_3$.

Haworth, Perkin, Wallach, *J. Chem. Soc.*, 1913, **103**, 1233; *Ann.*, 1913, **399**, 161.

Sinactine (*Tetrahydroepiberberine*)

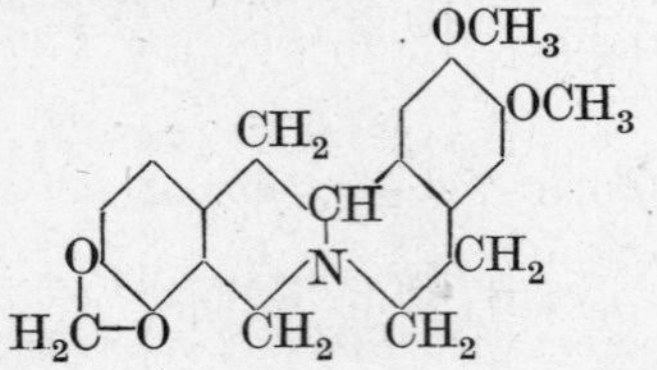

$C_{20}H_{21}O_4N$ MW, 339

l-.
Occurs in *Sinomenium acutum*. Prisms from EtOH. M.p. 175°. Sol. $CHCl_3$. Spar. sol. MeOH, EtOH. Insol. H_2O. $[\alpha]_D$ − 312° in $CHCl_3$.
B,HCl : m.p. about 272° decomp.
B_2,H_2PtCl_6 : m.p. 245–7°.

dl-.
Needles from EtOH. M.p. 168°.
B,HCl : m.p. about 286° decomp.

Goto, Kitasato, *J. Chem. Soc.*, 1930, 1234.

Sinamin.
See Triallyltricyanamide.

Sinapic Acid (*Sinapinic acid*, 4-*hydroxy*-3 : 5-*dimethoxycinnamic acid*)

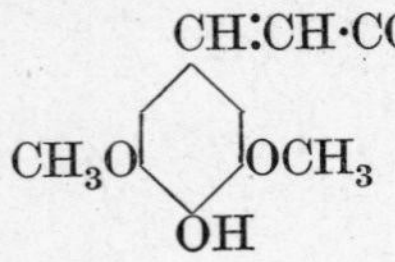

$C_{11}H_{12}O_5$ MW, 224

Yellow needles from EtOH. M.p. 192°. Sol. hot EtOH. Spar. sol. H_2O, Et_2O. Ox. ⟶ 2 : 6-dimethoxy-*p*-benzoquinone. $FeCl_3$ ⟶ red col.
Carbethoxyl : m.p. 174°.
Acetyl : m.p. 188–93°. *Chloride* : m.p. 142–4°.
Me ester : $C_{12}H_{14}O_5$. MW, 238. Cryst. from MeOH.Aq. M.p. 91–2°.
Et ester : $C_{13}H_{16}O_5$. MW, 252. Cryst. + $1H_2O$ from EtOH.Aq. M.p. 80–1°.
Choline ester : *see* Sinapin.
4-*Me ether* : 3 : 4 : 5-trimethoxycinnamic acid. $C_{12}H_{14}O_5$. MW, 238. Needles from H_2O. M.p. 123·5–124·5° (126·8°). Sol. hot H_2O. *Me ester* : $C_{13}H_{16}O_5$. MW, 252. Yellow leaflets from EtOH.Aq. M.p. 91–91·5°.

Späth, *Monatsh.*, 1920, **41**, 271.
Mauthner, *Ber.*, 1908, **41**, 2531.
Bogert, Isham, *J. Am. Chem. Soc.*, 1914, **36**, 519.
Chmielewska, *Chem. Zentr.*, 1937, I, 3156.

Sinapin (4-*Hydroxy*-3 : 5-*dimethoxycinnamic acid choline ester*)

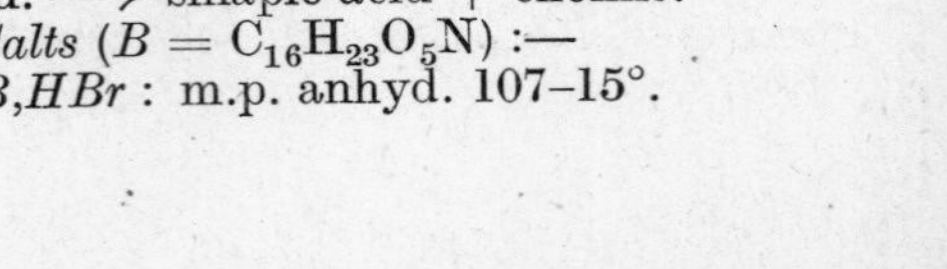

$C_{16}H_{25}O_6N$ MW, 327

Occurs in black mustard seeds. Unstable. Hyd. ⟶ sinapic acid + choline.
Salts ($B = C_{16}H_{23}O_5N$) :—
B,HBr : m.p. anhyd. 107–15°.

B,HI : m.p. 185–6°.
B,H_2SO_4 : m.p. anhyd. 126·5–127·5°.

See first reference above.

Sincalin.
See Choline.

Sinigrin (*Sinigroside, potassium myronate*)

$$KO \cdot SO_2 \cdot OC \cdot N \Big< \begin{array}{l} CH_2 \cdot CH{:}CH_2 \\ S \cdot C_6H_{11}O_5 \end{array}$$

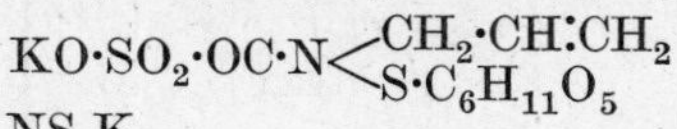

$C_{10}H_{16}O_9NS_2K$ MW, 397

Occurs in black mustard seeds and *Alliaria officinalis*, D.C. M.p. 127–9°. $[\alpha]_D^{18} - 16\cdot4°$ in H_2O.

> Benik, Brauss, *Z. physiol. Chem.*, 1923, **126**, 210.
> Herissey, Boivin, *Chem. Abstracts*, 1928, **22**, 667.
> Schneider, Fischer, Specht, *Ber.*, 1930, **63**, 2789.

Sinigroside.
See Sinigrin.

Sinomenine (*Coculine*)

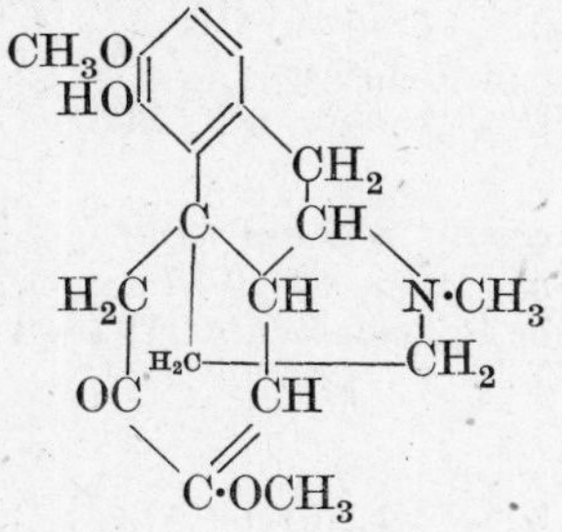

or

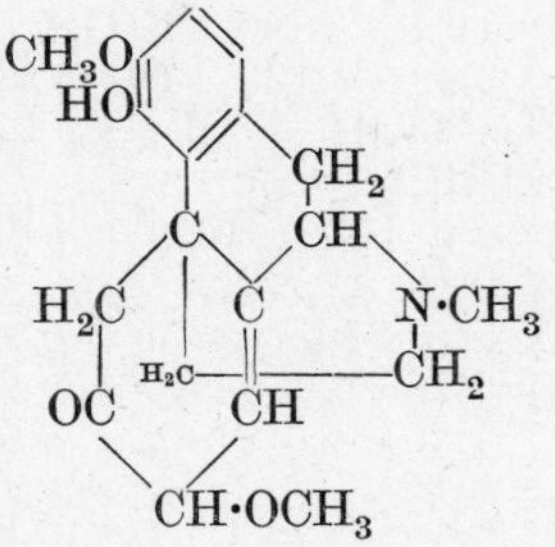

$C_{19}H_{23}O_4N$ MW, 329

Occurs in *Sinomenium acutum*. Needles from C_6H_6. M.p. 162°. Sol. EtOH, $CHCl_3$, Me_2CO, amyl alcohol. Mod. sol. Et_2O, C_6H_6. Spar. sol. H_2O. Insol. pet. ether. $[\alpha]_D^{26} - 70\cdot70°$.

B,HCl : m.p. 231°.
B,HBr : m.p. 231°.
B,HI : m.p. 233°.
B,HNO_3 : m.p. 215° decomp.
Oxime : m.p. 233°.

Picrate : m.p. about 140°.
Methiodide : decomp. at 255°.

> Goto, Michinaki, Shishido, *Ann.*, 1935, **515**, 297.

Sinomenol.
See *under* 2 : 3 : 5 : 6-Tetrahydroxyphenanthrene.

Sitostane

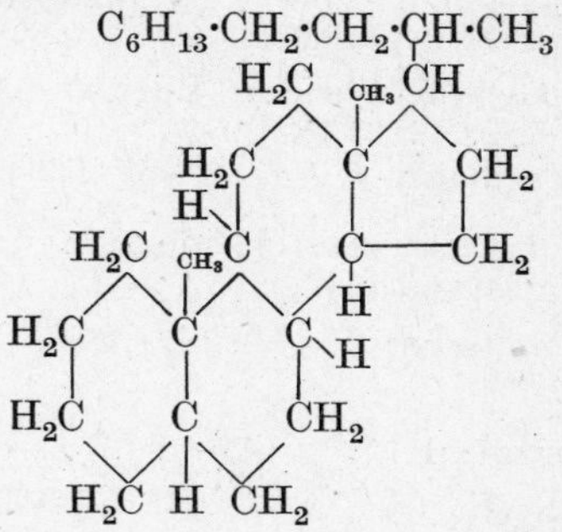

$C_{29}H_{52}$ MW, 400

Derived from β-sitosterol. Cryst. from EtOH. M.p. 84·5–85°. $[\alpha]_D^{20} + 26\cdot9°$ in $CHCl_3$. Sol. EtOH, Et_2O, $CHCl_3$.

> Windaus, Rahlen, *Z. physiol. Chem.*, 1918, **101**, 223.

Note.—According to Bengtsson, *Z. physiol. Chem.*, 1935, **237**, 46, it is highly probable that sitostane is identical with stigmastane.

γ-Sitostane

$C_{29}H_{52}(C_{28}H_{50})$ MW, 400 (386)

Derived from γ-sitosterol. M.p. 87°. $[\alpha]_D^{15} + 20\cdot2°$ in $CHCl_3$.

> Bonstedt, *Z. physiol. Chem.*, 1928, **176**, 279.

Sitostanol (*Dihydrositosterol, ostreastanol*)

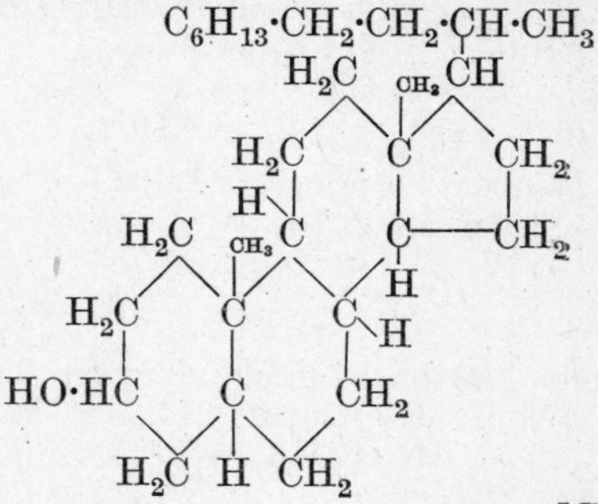

$C_{29}H_{52}O$ MW, 416

Minor constituent of sitosterol complex. Derived from β-sitosterol. Plates from EtOH.

M.p. 139–139·5° (141°). $[\alpha]_D^{20}$ + 25·6° in $CHCl_3$. Sol. common org. solvents.

Acetyl: plates from AcOEt. M.p. 137° (132°). $[\alpha]_D^{20}$ + 15·1° in $CHCl_3$.

Benzoyl: plates from AcOEt. M.p. 137·6–138·6°.

3 : 5-*Dinitrobenzoyl*: plates from AcOEt. M.p. 214–15°. $[\alpha]_D$ + 14·0° in C_6H_6.

Phenylurethane: cryst. from EtOH. M.p. 175°.

Anderson, Shriner, Burr, *J. Am. Chem. Soc.*, 1926, **48**, 2987.
Bergmann, *J. Biol. Chem.*, 1934, **104**, 553.

Note.—For the possible identity of sitostanol with stigmastanol see

Bengtsson, *Z. physiol. Chem.*, 1935, **237**, 46.

γ-Sitostanol

$C_{29}H_{52}O(C_{28}H_{50}O)$ MW, 416 (402)

Plates from EtOH. M.p. 143–4°. $[\alpha]_D^{16·5}$ + 20·8° in $CHCl_3$.

Acetyl: m.p. 144–5°. $[\alpha]_D^{20}$ + 12·4° in $CHCl_3$.

Bonstedt, *Z. physiol. Chem.*, 1928, **176**, 278.

Sitosterol

The phytosterol originally termed sitosterol is a complex mixture separated only with difficulty. Hence the purity of the following fractions must be accepted with reserve.

α_1.

$C_{29}H_{48}O$ MW, 412

Widely distributed in plants in small amounts. Needles from EtOH. M.p. 164–6°. $[\alpha]_D^{28}$ − 1·7° in $CHCl_3$. Precipitated by digitonin.

Acetyl: plates from EtOH. M.p. 137°. $[\alpha]_D^{28}$ + 28·6° in $CHCl_3$.

Benzoyl: needles from EtOH–C_6H_6. M.p. 168–72°. $[\alpha]_D^{27}$ + 41·8° in $CHCl_3$.

3 : 5-*Dinitrobenzoyl*: plates from AcOEt. M.p. 222°. $[\alpha]_D^{24}$ + 37·2° in $CHCl_3$.

Wallis, Fernholz, *J. Am. Chem. Soc.*, 1936, **58**, 2446.

α_2.

$C_{30}H_{50}O$ MW, 426

Widely distributed in plants in small amounts. Cryst. from EtOH–pet. ether. M.p. 156°. $[\alpha]_D^{25}$ + 3·5° in $CHCl_3$. Sol. common org. solvents.

Acetyl: plates from EtOH. M.p. 124–6°. $[\alpha]_D^{27}$ + 16·5° in $CHCl_3$. Spar. sol. MeOH.

Benzoyl: needles from EtOH–C_6H_6. M.p. 164–6°. $[\alpha]_D^{26}$ + 27·4° in $CHCl_3$. Spar. sol. EtOH.

3 : 5-*Dinitrobenzoyl*: needles from Me_2CO. M.p. 206°. $[\alpha]_D^{30}$ + 26·4° in $CHCl_3$.

See previous reference.

β-.

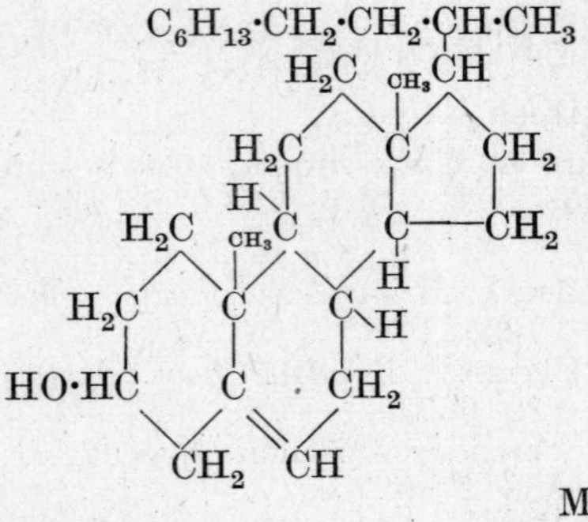

$C_{29}H_{50}O$ MW, 414

Widely distributed in plants. Needles from MeOH. M.p. 136–7°. $[\alpha]_D^{22}$ − 35° in $CHCl_3$.

Acetyl: needles from MeOH. M.p. 134° (128°). $[\alpha]_D^{22}$ − 38·5° in $CHCl_3$.

Benzoyl: m.p. 145·5°.

3 : 5-*Dinitrobenzoyl*: m.p. 203°. $[\alpha]_D^{22}$ − 10·6° in $CHCl_3$.

Anderson, Shriner, Burr, *J. Am. Chem. Soc.*, 1926, **48**, 2987.
Ichiba, *Chem. Zentr.*, 1936, I, 1027.

γ-.

$C_{29}H_{50}O(C_{28}H_{48}O)$ MW, 414 (400)

Plates from EtOH. M.p. 147–8°. $[\alpha]_D$ − 43·13° in $CHCl_3$.

Acetyl: cryst. from EtOH. M.p. 143°. $[\alpha]_D$ − 47·7° in $CHCl_3$. *Dibromide*: needles from C_6H_6–MeOH. M.p. 140–1°. $[\alpha]_D$ − 46·23° in $CHCl_3$.

Benzoyl: m.p. 152°. $[\alpha]_D$ − 19·63° in $CHCl_3$.

Ichiba, *Chem. Zentr.*, 1936, I, 1027.
Sandqvist, Bengtsson, *Ber.*, 1931, **64**, 2167.

δ-.

$C_{29}H_{50}O$ MW, 414

Cryst. from EtOH. M.p. 146–7°. $[\alpha]_D$ − 23·9° in $CHCl_3$.

Acetyl: m.p. 115°. $[\alpha]_D$ − 24·35° in $CHCl_3$.

Benzoyl: m.p. 157–8°. $[\alpha]_D$ − 15·98° in $CHCl_3$.

See first reference above.

ε-.

$C_{29}H_{50}O$ MW, 414

M.p. 143–4°. $[\alpha]_D^{17}$ − 38·7° in $CHCl_3$.

Acetyl: plates from EtOH. M.p. 127–8°. $[\alpha]_D^{17}$ − 44·7° in $CHCl_3$.
3 : 5-*Dinitrobenzoyl*: m.p. 215–17°. $[\alpha]_D^{17}$ − 10° in $CHCl_3$.

Simpson, *J. Chem. Soc.*, 1927, 737.

Skatole (*Scatole*, 3-*methylindole*, β-*methylindole*)

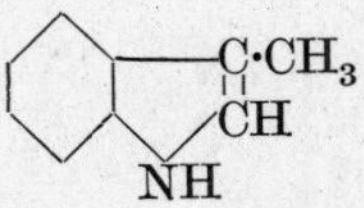

C_9H_9N MW, 131

Occurs in coal tar, beetroot, nectandra wood and fæces. Leaflets from ligroin. M.p. 95°. B.p. 265–6°/755 mm. $K_4Fe(CN)_6 + H_2SO_4 \longrightarrow$ violet col.
B_2,HCl: m.p. 167–8°.
N-*Acetyl*: m.p. 68°.
N-*Propionyl*: m.p. 45°.
Picrate: m.p. 170–1° decomp.
N-*Me*: *see* 1 : 3-Dimethylindole.

Kruber, D.R.P., 515,543, (*Chem. Abstracts*, 1931, **25**, 2443).
King, l'Ecuyer, *J. Chem. Soc.*, 1934, 1903.
Fischer, *Ann.*, 1886, **236**, 138.

Skatole-1-carboxylic Acid (3-*Methylindole*-N-*carboxylic acid*)

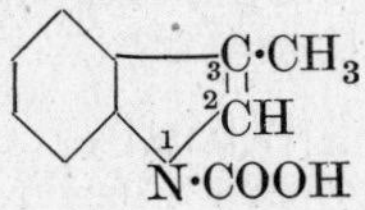

$C_{10}H_9O_2N$ MW, 175

Occurs in beet. Needles. M.p. 162·5°. Sol. EtOH, Et_2O. Spar. sol. H_2O, C_6H_6.

Lippmann, *Ber.*, 1924, **57**, 257.

Skatole-2-carboxylic Acid (3-*Methylindole-2-carboxylic acid*).

Needles from AcOH. M.p. 164–5° (167°). Sol. EtOH, Et_2O, C_6H_6. Spar. sol. H_2O, ligroin. $k = 4{\cdot}7 \times 10^{-6}$ at 25°.
Et ester: $C_{12}H_{13}O_2N$. MW, 203. Needles from EtOH. M.p. 133–4°. Sol. Et_2O, C_6H_6.
Amide: $C_{10}H_{10}ON_2$. MW, 174. Needles from C_6H_6. M.p. 115°.
N-*Me*: $C_{11}H_{11}O_2N$. MW, 189. Cryst. from C_6H_6–EtOH. Decomp. about 213°. Sol. EtOH. Spar. sol. C_6H_6, pet. ether.

Perkin, Kermack, Robinson, *J. Chem. Soc.*, 1921, **119**, 1634.
Oddo, *Gazz. chim. ital.*, 1912, **42**, i, 370.

Smilagenin

$C_{27}H_{44}O_3$ MW, 416

Occurs in Jamaica sarsaparilla root. Needles from Me_2CO. M.p. 183–4°. $[\alpha]_D^{25}$ − 69° in $CHCl_3$.
Acetyl deriv.: m.p. 150–1°. $[\alpha]_D^{25}$ − 59·6°.
Benzoyl deriv.: m.p. 181–181·5°.

Farmer, Kon, *J. Chem. Soc.*, 1937, 414.
Askew, Farmer, Kon, *J. Chem. Soc.*, 1936, 1402.

Sobrerol (Δ^1-p-*Menthenediol*-6 : 8, 1-*methyl*-4-α-*hydroxyisopropylcyclohexenol*-6)

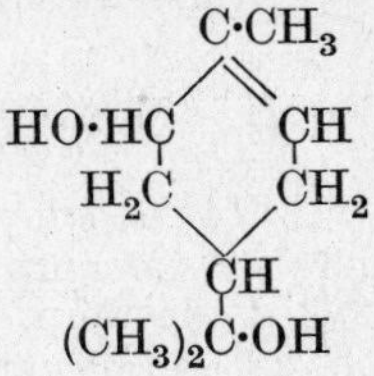

$C_{10}H_{18}O_2$ MW, 170

d-.
Prisms from H_2O, plates from EtOH. M.p. 150° (148–9°). $[\alpha]_D$ + 141° 16′ in EtOH.

l-.
Yellow cryst. M.p. 147–8°.

Dupont, *Chem. Abstracts*, 1922, **16**, 4340.
Gildemeister, Köhler, *Chem. Zentr.*, 1909, II, 2159.
Prilezhaev, Vershuk, *Chem. Abstracts*, 1930, **24**, 607.
Wallach, *Ann.*, 1917, **414**, 196.

Solanidine-S

$C_{18}H_{31}ON$ MW, 277

Occurs in *Solanum sodomæum*, Linn. Needles. M.p. 249–53°.

Rochelmeyer, *Chem. Zentr.*, 1937, I, 1947.
Oddo, Caronna, *Ber.*, 1936, **69**, 283.

Solanidine-T

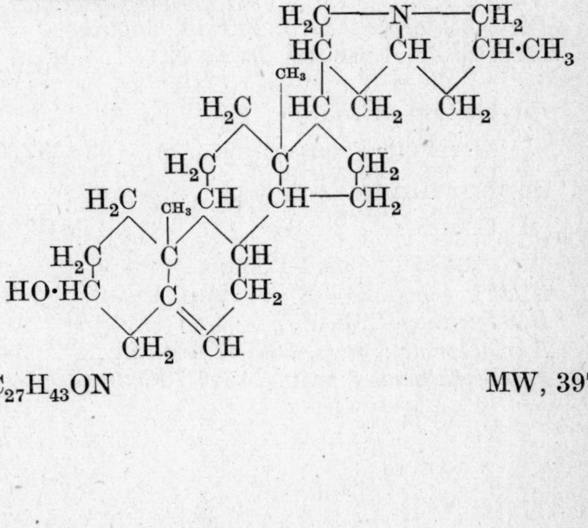

$C_{27}H_{43}ON$ MW, 397

Occurs in *Solanum tuberosum*, Linn. Cryst. from EtOH. M.p. 219° (216°).
Acetyl deriv.: m.p. 204°.

Clemo, Morgan, Raper, *J. Chem. Soc.*, 1936, 1299.
Soltys, Wallenfels, *Ber.*, 1936, **69**, 811.
Heiduschka, Philippi, *Ber.*, 1935, **68**, 669.
Oddo, Caronna, *Ber.*, 1934, **67**, 451.
Dieterle, Rochelmeyer, *Arch. Pharm.*, 1935, **273**, 532.

Solanocarpidine

$C_{26}H_{43}O_3N$ MW, 417

Plates from EtOH. M.p. 197–8°. Sol. ord. org. solvents.
B,HCl: m.p. 313–14° decomp.
B,HBr: m.p. 307–8° decomp.
B,HI: m.p. 283–4° decomp.
B,H_2SO_4: m.p. 293–4° decomp.
B,HNO_3: m.p. 271–2° decomp.
$B,(COOH)_2$: m.p. 238–9° decomp.
Picrate: m.p. 148–9°.

Saiyed, Kanga, *Chem. Zentr.*, 1937, I, 2181.

Solanocarpine

$C_{44}H_{77}O_{19}N$ MW, 923

Occurs in fruit of *Solanum xanthocarpum*, Schrad & Wendl. Needles from EtOH. M.p. 288–9° decomp. Sol. H_2O. Hyd. ⟶ solanocarpidine + glucose + rhamnose + galactose (?)

See previous reference.

Soneryl.
See Neonal.

Sophocarpidine.
Matrine, *q.v.*

Sophocarpine

$C_{15}H_{24}ON_2$ MW, 248

Cryst. + $1H_2O$ from H_2O. M.p. 81–2°, anhyd. 54–5°. $[\alpha]_D^{18}$ − 29·44° in EtOH.
Aurichloride: m.p. 166–7°.
Platinochloride: m.p. 209–12° decomp.
Methiodide: needles from EtOH. M.p. 200–2°.
Picrate: m.p. 155–7°.

Orechoff, Proskurnina, *Ber.*, 1934, **67**, 77.

Sophoramine

$C_{15}H_{20}ON_2$ MW, 244

M.p. 164–5°. $[\alpha]_D$ − 90·85°.
B,HCl: m.p. 247–8° decomp.
B,HI: m.p. 294–6°.
Aurichloride: m.p. 183–4° decomp.
Platinochloride: m.p. 245–7° decomp.
Picrate: m.p. 229–31° decomp.
Picrolonate: m.p. 173–5° decomp.

Orechoff, *Chem. Zentr.*, 1935, II, 2215.
Orechoff, Proskurnina, Konowalowa, *Ber.*, 1935, **68**, 431.

Sophoretin.
See Quercetin.

Sophoricol.
Genistein, *q.v.*

Sophoridine

$C_{15}H_{26}ON_2$ MW, 250

Needles from pet. ether. M.p. 109–10°. $[\alpha]_D$ − 63·57°.
Aurichloride: m.p. 189–90°.
Methiodide: m.p. 234–6°.
Picrolonate: m.p. 226–8° decomp.

Orechoff, *Chem. Zentr.*, 1935, II, 2215.
Orechoff, Proskurnina, Konowalowa, *Ber.*, 1935, **68**, 431.

Sophorine.
See Cytisine.

Sorbic Acid (1 : 3-*Hexadienic acid*, 1 : 3 *pentadiene-1-carboxylic acid*, 2-*propenylacrylic acid*)

$CH_3{\cdot}CH{:}CH{\cdot}CH{:}CH{\cdot}COOH$

$C_6H_8O_2$ MW, 112

Needles from EtOH.Aq. M.p. 132–133·5° (133–4°). B.p. 228° decomp. Sol. EtOH, Et_2O. Mod. sol. hot H_2O. Volatile in steam. Heat of comb. C_p 743·4 Cal., C_v 742·8 Cal. $k = 1{\cdot}73 \times 10^{-5}$ at 25°.
Me ester: $C_7H_{10}O_2$. MW, 126. Leaflets. M.p. 5°. B.p. 180°/759 mm. (174°), 70°/20 mm.
Et ester: $C_8H_{12}O_2$. MW, 140. B.p. 195·5°, 85°/20 mm., 76·5°/12 mm. D_4^{20} 0·9560. n_D^{20} 1·502.
Chloride: C_6H_7OCl. MW, 130·5. B.p. 78°/15 mm.
Amide: C_6H_9ON. MW, 111. Needles from H_2O. M.p. 168°. Sol. H_2O, EtOH.
Nitrile: C_6H_7N. MW, 93. B.p. 72°/20 mm., 50–60°/12 mm.
Anilide: m.p. 153°.
o-*Toluidide*: m.p. 173°.
Phenylhydrazide: m.p. 162–3°.

Philippi, *Monatsh.*, 1929, **51**, 278.
Doebner, Wolff, *Ber.*, 1901, **34**, 2221.
Baumgarten, Glatzel, *Ber.*, 1926, **59**, 2663.

Sorbic Aldehyde (1 : 3-*Hexadienal, sorb-aldehyde*)

$$CH_3 \cdot CH{:}CH \cdot CH{:}CH \cdot CHO$$

C_6H_8O MW, 96

B.p. 173–4°/754 mm., 76°/30 mm., 64–6°/11 mm. $D_4^{2}20 \cdot 9087$. $n_D^{22} 1 \cdot 5372$. Reduces Tollen's rapidly, cold Fehling's slowly.

Oxime : needles from EtOH. M.p. 159·5–160·5° decomp.

Semicarbazone : plates from EtOH. M.p. 206°.

Phenylhydrazone : yellow plates from EtOH. M.p. 101–2°.

Fischer, Wiedemann, *Ann.*, 1934, **513**, 256.

Reichstein, Ammann, Trivelli, *Helv. Chim. Acta*, 1932, **15**, 261.

Kuhn, Hoffer, *Ber.*, 1930, **63**, 2164; 1931, **64**, 1978.

Baumgarten, Glatzel, *Ber.*, 1926, **59**, 2662.

Sorbierite.

See Iditol.

Sorbitol

$$HO \cdot CH_2 \underset{\underset{OH}{|}}{\overset{\overset{H}{|}}{C}} \underset{\underset{H}{|}}{\overset{\overset{OH}{|}}{C}} \underset{\underset{OH}{|}}{\overset{\overset{H}{|}}{C}} \underset{\underset{OH}{|}}{\overset{\overset{H}{|}}{C}} CH_2OH$$

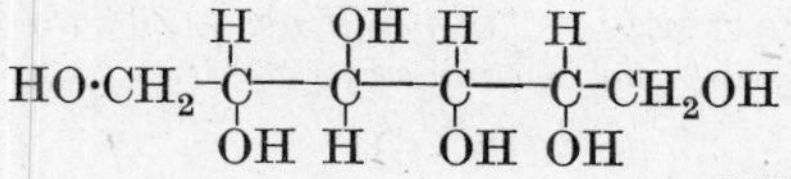

$C_6H_{14}O_6$ MW, 182

d-.

Occurs in ripe mountain ash berries, cherries, plums, pears, apples, medlars, fruit of cherry laurel, etc. Needles + $\frac{1}{2}$ or $1H_2O$. M.p. 110–11° (anhyd.), 75° (hydrate), 87–95° from EtOH. Sweet taste. Sol. H_2O. Spar. sol. cold EtOH. $[\alpha]_D^{15} - 1 \cdot 73°$ in H_2O, $[\alpha]_D^{20} - 2 \cdot 01°$ in H_2O. HI $\longrightarrow$ *sec.-n*-hexyl iodide. Sorbose bacterium $\longrightarrow$ *l*-sorbose.

Hexa-acetyl : cryst. from EtOH. M.p. 99·5° (120°). $[\alpha]_D^{18} + 6 \cdot 8°$ in Me_2CO.

Dibenzoyl deriv. : m.p. 140°. $[\alpha]_D^{18} + 1 \cdot 69 - 1 \cdot 85°$ in Py.

Pentabenzoyl deriv. : m.p. 222°. $[\alpha]_D^{12} + 24 \cdot 54°$ in Py.

Hexabenzoyl : m.p. 129°. $[\alpha]_D^{19} + 24 \cdot 3°$ in Py.

Tetra-Me ether : b.p. 125°/0·4 mm. $n_D 1 \cdot 4568$. $[\alpha]_D - 6 \cdot 2°$ in H_2O.

Penta-Et ether : b.p. 185–90°/10 mm.

Triacetone deriv. : m.p. 46–7°. $[\alpha]_D^{15} + 12 \cdot 7°$ in EtOH.

Benzylidene deriv. : cryst. M.p. 175°. $[\alpha]_D + 6°$ in EtOH.

Dibenzylidene deriv. : cryst. M.p. 163°. $[\alpha]_D + 29°$ in Me_2CO.

o-*Chlorobenzylidene deriv.* : m.p. 170°.

Tri-o-chlorobenzylidene deriv. : m.p. 217°.

2 : 6-*Dichlorobenzylidene deriv.* : m.p. 204·5°.

2-*Nitro-5-chlorobenzylidene deriv.* : m.p. 250·5°.

m-*Nitrobenzylidene deriv.* : m.p. 180°.

Di-m-*Nitrobenzylidene deriv.* : m.p. 228·5°.

Tri-o-nitrobenzylidene deriv. : m.p. 181° (two forms, m.p. 212–15° and 142–6°).

Tri-m-nitrobenzylidene deriv. : m.p. 168°.

l-.

Needles + $\frac{1}{2}H_2O$. M.p. 77°.

Dibenzylidene deriv. : cryst. M.p. 160°. $[\alpha]_D - 28°$.

Boussingault, *Ann. chim. phys.*, 1872, **26**, 376.

Meunier, *Compt. rend.*, 1890, **111**, 49.

Vincent, Delachanal, *ibid.*, 51.

Fischer, *Ber.*, 1890, **23**, 3684.

Fischer, Stahel, *Ber.*, 1891, **24**, 2144.

Lobry de Bruyn, v. Ekenstein, *Rec. trav. chim.*, 1899, **18**, 151; 1900, **19**, 7.

Asahina, Shinoda, *J. Pharm. Soc. Japan*, 1930, **50**, 1.

Davis, Slater, Smith, *Biochem. J.*, 1926, **20**, 1155.

Böeseken, Leefers, *Rec. trav. chim.*, 1935, **54**, 861.

Bleyer, Diemair, Lix, *Chem. Abstracts*, 1933, **27**, 4624.

Sorbose

$$H_2C \underset{\underset{OH}{|}}{\overset{\overset{H}{|}}{C}} \underset{\underset{H}{|}}{\overset{\overset{OH}{|}}{C}} \underset{\underset{OH}{|}}{\overset{\overset{H}{|}}{C}} \underset{}{\overset{\overset{OH}{|}}{C}} CH_2OH$$

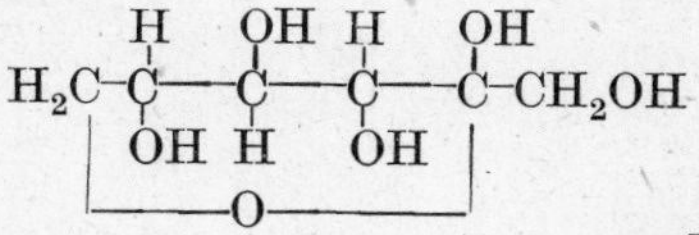

$C_6H_{12}O_6$ MW, 180

d-.

Cryst. M.p. 165°. Sweet taste. Sol. H_2O. Spar. sol. MeOH, EtOH. $[\alpha]_D^{20} + 42 \cdot 9°$ in H_2O. $D^{15} 1 \cdot 654$. Reduces Fehling's. Non-fermentable.

Phenylosazone : m.p. 168° (156°, 160°). Identical with *d*-gulosazone and *d*-idosazone.

β-*Methylglucoside* : cryst. M.p. 119°. $[\alpha]_D + 88 \cdot 5°$ in H_2O.

l-.

Cryst. M.p. 165° (162°, 159–61°). Sweet taste. Sol. H_2O. Spar. sol. EtOH. $[\alpha]_D^{20} - 42 \cdot 9°$ in H_2O ($- 43 \cdot 2°$ in H_2O). $D^{15} 1 \cdot 654$. Reduces Fehling's. Heat of comb. C_v 3714·5 Cal. NaHg $\longrightarrow$ sorbitol + iditol. Non-fermentable.

Phenylosazone : yellow needles. M.p. 168° (164°, 156°). Identical with *l*-gulosazone and *l*-idosazone. p-*Bromophenylosazone* : yellow needles. M.p. 181°.

o-*Nitrophenylosazone* : red powder. M.p. 211–12°.

β-*Methylglucoside* : plates from Me_2CO. M.p. 120–2°. $[\alpha]_D^{20}$ − 88·5° in H_2O.

Penta-acetyl : m.p. 96·5–97·5°. $[\alpha]_D$ + 2·9° in $CHCl_3$.

dl-. β-Acrose.

Laminæ. M.p. 162–3° (154°). D^{17} 1·638 (1·634). Non-fermentable.

Phenylosazone : laminæ from dil. EtOH. M.p. 169–70° decomp.

Schmitz, *Ber.*, 1913, **46**, 2334.
v. Ekenstein, Blanksma, *Rec. trav. chim.*, 1908, **27**, 1.
Schlubach, Vorwerk, *Ber.*, 1933, **66**, 1251.
Maurer, Schiedt, *Biochem. Z.*, 1934, **271**, 61.
Reichstein, Grussner, *Helv. Chim. Acta.*, 1934, **17**, 318.
Talen, *Rec. trav. chim.*, 1925, **44**, 891.
Böeseken, Leefers, *Rec. trav. chim.*, 1935, **54**, 861.
Fischer, Baer, *Helv. Chim. Acta*, 1936, **19**, 519.
Bernhauer, Görlich, *Biochem. Z.*, 1935, **280**, 375.

Sorbyl Alcohol.

See 2 : 4-Hexadienol-1.

Sozoiodolic Acid (2 : 6-*Di-iodophenol*-p-*sulphonic acid*)

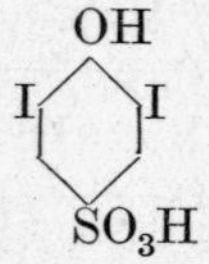

$C_6H_4O_4I_2S$ MW, 426

Prisms + $3H_2O$. M.p. 120–120·5°. Sol. H_2O. $CrO_3 + H_2SO_4 \longrightarrow$ 2 : 6-di-iodo-*p*-benzoquinone.

Et ether : $C_8H_8O_4I_2S$. MW, 454. Cryst. + $2H_2O$. M.p. 108°. Sol. H_2O.

d-*Arginine salt* : decomp. at 213–14°.
Cadaverine salt : decomp. at 242°.
Choline salt : decomp. at 180°.
Creatinine salt : decomp. at 229–31°.
Glucosamine salt : decomp. at 181–2°.
Guanidine salt : decomp. at 247–9°.
Histamine salt : decomp. at 241°.
l-*Histidine salt* : decomp. at 207–8°.
Lysine salt : decomp. at 234–5°.
Putrescine salt : decomp. at 250°.
Urea salt : decomp. at 208°.

Tromsdorff, D.R.P., 45,226.
Rupp, Herrmann, *Arch. Pharm.*, 1916, **254**, 509.
Ackermann, *Z. physiol. Chem.*, 1934, **225**, 46.

Sparassol (*Methyl everninate*, 3-*hydroxy*-*methoxy*-o-*toluic acid methyl ester*)

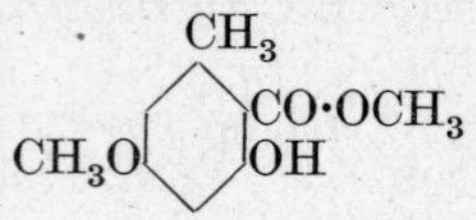

$C_{10}H_{12}O_4$ MW, 1

Occurs in *Evernia prunastri*, Ach., *Sparass ramosa*, Schäff., and *Rhododendron japonicu* C. J. Schneider. M.p. 67–8°. $FeCl_3$ — violet col. in EtOH.

Acetyl : m.p. 41–2°.

3-*Me ether* : $C_{11}H_{14}O_4$. MW, 210. M. 41–2°.

Kinoshita, *Chem. Abstracts*, 1931, 2 1552.
Wedekind, Fleischer, *Ber.*, 1924, **57**, 112
Späth, Jesckki, *ibid.*, 471.
Pfau, *ibid.*, 468.
Falck, *Ber.*, 1923, **56**, 2555.
Koller, Hamburg, *Monatsh.*, 1935, **6** 375.

Sparteine (*Lupinidine*, *hexahydrodeox anagyrine*, *pachycarpine*)

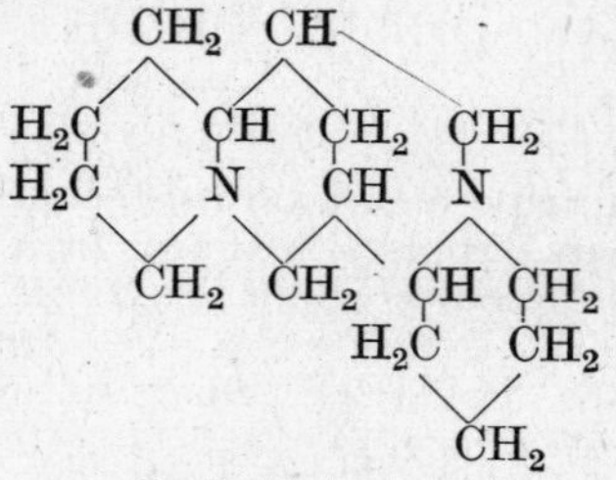

Probable structure

$C_{15}H_{26}N_2$ MW, 23

d-.

Occurs in seeds of *Anagyris fœtida*, Lin *Sophora pachycarpa*, Schrenk, *Thermops lanceolata*, R.Br. B.p. 173–4°/8 mm., 138°/ mm., 133–5°/1 mm. Sol. EtOH, Et_2O, $CHCl$ Insol. H_2O, C_6H_6, ligroin. D_4^{20} 1·027. *n* 1·5312. $[\alpha]_D^{20}$ + 16·1° (+ 5·54°). Volatile i steam. Resinifies in air.

B,2HCl : m.p. 255–7°.
B,HI : m.p. 232–3°.
B,HClO₄ : plates from EtOH. M.p. 171–2°.
B,H₂PtCl₆ : m.p. 240–1° decomp.
Chloroaurate : m.p. 192–3°.
Dipicrate : yellow needles from EtOH–Me_2C M.p. 205–6°.
Methiodide : m.p. 236–8°. $[\alpha]_D$ + 24·5° H_2O.

l-.
B.p. 130–5°/1 mm. $[\alpha]_D - 11{\cdot}3°$ in EtOH.
B,HI : prisms from H_2O. M.p. 231°.
Dipicrate : m.p. 205–6°.

dl-.
Monopicrate : m.p. 134–5°.
Dipicrate : m.p. 205–6°.

Mills, *Ann.*, 1863, **125**, 71.
Clemo, Leitch, Raper, *Ber.*, 1931, **64**, 1520.
Clemo, Raper, *J. Chem. Soc.*, 1933, 644.
Clemo, Raper, Tenniswood, *J. Chem. Soc.*, 1931, 429.
Orechoff, Proskurnina, *Ber.*, 1935, **68**, 1807.

Spermidine (*ω-Aminopropyl-ω-aminobutyl-mine*)

$H_2N{\cdot}CH_2{\cdot}[CH_2]_2{\cdot}NH{\cdot}[CH_2]_3{\cdot}CH_2NH_2$

$_7H_{19}N_3$ MW, 145

Occurs in ox pancreas as phosphate. B.p. 28–30°/14 mm.
$B_2,(H_3PO_4)_3,6H_2O$: plates from EtOH.Aq. I.p. 207–8°. Sol. H_2O.
B,3HAuCl₄ : needles from 1% HCl. M.p. 22°.
Tri-m-*nitrobenzoyl* : m.p. anhyd. 148–50°.
Tripicrate : yellow needles from H_2O. M.p. 11°.

Dudley, Rosenheim, Starling, *Biochem. J.*, 1927, **21**, 97.
v. Braun, Pinkernelle, *Ber.*, 1937, **70**, 1233.

Spermine (*Gerontine, musculamine, neuridine, i-[ω-aminopropyl]-tetramethylenediamine*)

$_2N{\cdot}CH_2{\cdot}[CH_2]_2{\cdot}NH{\cdot}[CH_2]_4{\cdot}NH{\cdot}[CH_2]_2{\cdot}CH_2NH_2$

$_{10}H_{26}N_4$ MW, 202

Occurs as phosphate in semen, ox pancreas, east, etc. Deliquescent cryst. Absorbs CO_2 rom the air.
Phosphate : m.p. 230–4°. Sol. hot H_2O. nsol. EtOH, Et_2O.
Tetrabenzoyl : needles from Me_2CO.Aq. M.p. 55°.
B,4HCl : needles. M.p. 310° decomp.
B,4HAuCl₄ : golden leaflets from 5% HCl. I.p. 226° decomp.
B,2H₂PtCl₆ : m.p. 242–5°.
Tetrapicrate : yellow needles from H_2O. I.p. 248–50°.
Picrolonate : pale yellow needles from H_2O. M.p. 288–9° decomp.

Wrede, Fanselow, Strack, *Z. physiol. Chem.*, 1927, **163**, 219.
Dudley, Rosenheim, Rosenheim, *Biochem. J.*, 1924, **18**, 1263.
Wrede, Strack, Hettche, *Z. physiol. Chem.*, 1928, **173**, 61.
Dudley, Rosenheim, Starling, *Biochem. J.*, 1926, **20**, 1082.

Sphingosine

$CH_3{\cdot}[CH_2]_{12}{\cdot}CH{:}CH{\cdot}CH(NH_2){\cdot}CH(OH){\cdot}CH_2OH$

$C_{18}H_{37}O_2N$ MW, 299

Needles from Et_2O.
B_2,H_2SO_4 : m.p. 233–4° decomp.
Triacetyl deriv. : m.p. 102–3°. $[\alpha]_D^{19} - 24{\cdot}09°$.
Lignoceryl deriv. : m.p. 90–90·5°.
Picrolonate : m.p. 87–9°.
Me ether : *B,HCl*, plates from Me_2CO–EtOH. M.p. 141°.
Di-Me ether : *B,HCl*, plates from Me_2CO–EtOH. M.p. 139° (133–4°).
Di-Et ether : *B,HCl*, plates from Me_2CO. M.p. 113–15°.
Galactoside : psychosine. Cryst. *Sulphate* : m.p. 225° decomp. $[\alpha]_D - 16{\cdot}6°$.

Levene, Jacobs, *J. Biol. Chem.*, 1912, **11**, 547.
Klenk, Diebold, *Z. physiol. Chem.*, 1931, **198**, 25.

Spinacene.
See Squalene.

Spinasterol

$C_{28}H_{46}O$ MW, 398

α-.
Occurs in spinach and senega root. Plates from EtOH. M.p. 172–5° (169–70°). $[\alpha]_D^1 - 3{\cdot}7°$ in $CHCl_3$.
Acetyl : plates from AcOH. M.p. 187° (183–5°). $[\alpha]_D^{23} - 4{\cdot}7°$ in $CHCl_3$.
Propionyl : plates from AcOEt. M.p. 152–3°. $[\alpha]_D^{23} - 5{\cdot}0°$ in $CHCl_3$.
Benzoyl : plates from AcOEt. M.p. 201–2°. $[\alpha]_D^{23} + 2{\cdot}25°$ in $CHCl_3$.
p-*Nitrobenzoyl* : needles from AcOEt. M.p. 217–18°. $[\alpha]_D^{23} + 4{\cdot}5°$ in $CHCl_3$.
Phenylurethane : plates from AcOEt. M.p. 177° (173–4°). $[\alpha]_D^{23} - 2{\cdot}25°$ in $CHCl_3$.

β-.
Occurs in spinach. Cryst. from EtOH. M.p. 145–8°. $[\alpha]_{5461} + 7{\cdot}65°$.
Acetyl : cryst. from AcOH. M.p. 150–4°. $[\alpha]_{5461} + 7{\cdot}2°$.

γ-.
Occurs in spinach. M.p. 159–60°.
Acetyl: m.p. 139·5–140°. $[\alpha]_{5461}$ — 14·1° in $CHCl_3$.
Benzoyl: m.p. 118·5–119°. $[\alpha]_{5461}$ — 10·3° in $CHCl_3$.
p-*Nitrobenzoyl*: m.p. 200°. $[\alpha]_{5461}$ — 8·9° in $CHCl_3$.
Phenylurethane: m.p. 144–5°. $[\alpha]_{5461}$ — 15·9° in $CHCl_3$.

Simpson, *J. Chem. Soc.*, 1937, 730.
Heyl, Larsen, *J. Am. Chem. Soc.*, 1934, **56**, 942, 2664; *Chem. Zentr.*, 1933, II, 2019.
Hart, Heyl, *J. Biol. Chem.*, 1932, **95**, 311.

Squalene (*Spinacene*)

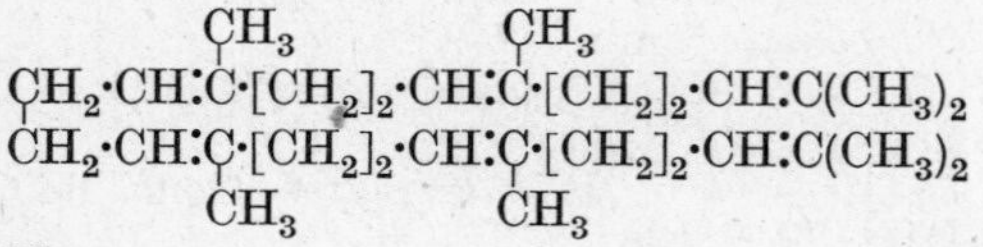

$C_{30}H_{50}$ MW, 410

Occurs in oil of *Centrophorus granulosus*, Müller & Henle, *Scymnorhinus lichio*, *Etmopterus spinan*, *Lepidorhinus squamosus*. F.p. below — 20°. B.p. 284–5°/25 mm., 280°/17 mm., 260–2°/9 mm., 240–2°/4 mm., 105°/0·17 mm. D_{20}^{20} 0·8592. n_D^{20} 1·4990.

Challenger, *Industrial Chemist*, 1928, **4**, 315 (*Bibl.*).
Karrer, Helfenstein, *Helv. Chim. Acta*, 1931, **14**, 78.
Heilbron, Kamm, Owens, *J. Chem. Soc.*, 1926, 1630.

Squamatic Acid

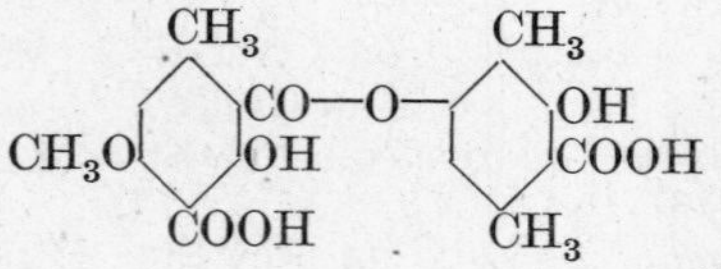

$C_{19}H_{18}O_9$ MW, 390

Occurs in the lichen *Cladonia bellidiflora*. Prisms from AcOH. M.p. 219°. Sol. AcOH, AcOEt. Spar. sol. EtOH, Et_2O, $CHCl_3$.
Di-Me ester: $C_{21}H_{22}O_9$. MW, 418. M.p. 178°. *Di-Me ether*: $C_{23}H_{26}O_9$. MW, 446. Leaflets from MeOH. M.p. 135°.

Asahina, Tanase, *Ber.*, 1937, **70**, 62.
Asahina, Sakurai, *ibid.*, 64.

Stachydrine (*Hygric acid methylbetai*[n]
N-*methylproline methylbetaine*)

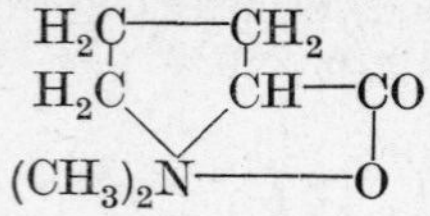

$C_7H_{13}O_2N$ MW, 1

Occurs in *Stachys tuberifera*, Naudin, and fruit of *Citrus grandis*, Hassk, etc. Cry + $1H_2O$. M.p. anhyd. 235° decomp. Sol. H_2 EtOH. Insol. Et_2O, $CHCl_3$. Decomp. in air
B,HCl: cryst. from EtOH. M.p. 23 (211–15°).
B_2,H_2PtCl_6: plates from 50% EtOH. D comp. at 200°.
B,(COOH)₂: needles. M.p. 105–7°.
Picrate: needles. M.p. 195–6°.

Schulze, Trier, *Z. physiol. Chem.*, 191 **67**, 59; *Ber.*, 1909, **42**, 4654.
Steenbock, *J. Biol. Chem.*, 1918, **35**, 1.

Stachyose

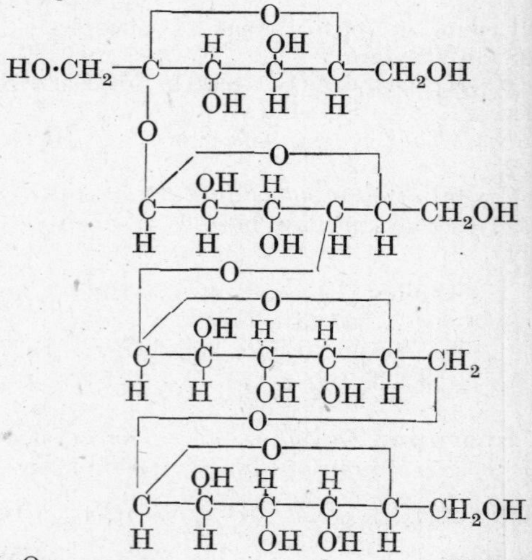

$C_{24}H_{42}O_{21}$ MW, 6

Occurs in ash manna, seeds of *Leguminos* roots and rhizomes of *Labiates*, e.g., *Stach tuberifera*. Plates + $4H_2O$ (or $1\frac{1}{2}H_2O$). Los H_2O at 115° in vacuum. M.p. anhyd. 167–70 Sol. H_2O. Insol. EtOH, Et_2O. Sweet tast $[\alpha]_D^{15}$ + 133·9° in H_2O, + 148·4° (anhyd.) in H_2 Does not reduce Fehling's. Does not form a osazone. Partly fermentable. Hyd. by d acids ⟶ glucose (1 mol.) + galactose (2 mols + fructose (1 mol.). Heat of comb. C_v = 38 Cal. Forms compounds with BaO and SrO.
Tetradeca-acetyl: m.p. 95–6°. $[\alpha]_D^{22·5}$ + 120· in EtOH, $[\alpha]_D^{26}$ + 120·5° in AcOH.

Tetradeca-p-*nitrobenzoyl* : m.p. 166°.
Tetradeca-Me ether : syrup. $[\alpha]_D^{24\cdot5}$ + 133·3° C_6H_6, + 139·2° in $CHCl_3$, + 129·9° in Me_2CO, 135·2° in EtOH, + 137·1° in MeOH, + 120·3° Et_2O.

Tanret, *Compt. rend.*, 1912, **155**, 1526.
Neuberg, Lachmann, *Biochem. Z.*, 1910, **24**, 171.
Onuki, *Chem. Abstracts*, 1932, **26**, 4308; 1933, **27**, 2138.

Starch (*Amylum*)

$_6H_{10}O_5)_n$ MW, $(162)_n$

The main reserve carbohydrate in the vegeble kingdom. Consists of two similarly conituted carbohydrates, amylose and amyloectin, and contains a small percentage of osphorus. White powder. Insol. cold H_2O, tOH, Et_2O. When heated with water swells d gives an opalescent sol. Hyd. by acids ⟶ extrins ⟶ maltose ⟶ glucose. Hyd. by astase ⟶ maltose. Gives blue col. with I l. No generally accepted structure can be ven for starch and its derivatives. The llowing references form a representative selecon, which deals with recent work and reviews.

Haworth, *Chemistry and Industry*, 1935, 859.
Kuhn, Ziese, *Ber.*, 1926, **59**, 2314.
Peiser, *Z. physiol. Chem.*, 1926, **161**, 210; 1927, **167**, 88.
Pringsheim, *Ber.*, 1926, **59**, 3008.
Gray, Staud, *Chem. Reviews*, 1927, **4**, 355 (*Review*).
Hess, Friese, Smith, *Ber.*, 1928, **61**, 1975.
Irvine, *Rec. trav. chim.*, 1929, **48**, 813.
Meyer, Hopff, Mark, *Ber.*, 1929, **62**, 1103.
Baldwin, *J. Am. Chem. Soc.*, 1930, **52**, 2907.
Schoen, *Bull. soc. chim. biol.*, 1930, **12**, 1033 (*Review*).
v. Náray-Szabó, *Z. physik. Chem.*, 1930, **151**, 420.
Freudenberg, *J. Soc. Chem. Ind.*, 1931, **50**, 287T (Review).
Haworth, Percival, *J. Chem. Soc.*, 1931, 1342.
Hirst, Plant, Wilkinson, *J. Chem. Soc.*, 1932, 2375.
Samec, *J. Soc. Chem. Ind.*, 1933, **52**, 389T.
Pringsheim, *Chimie et Industrie* (*Special Number*), April 1934, 996 (*Review*).
Staudinger, Husemann, *Ber.*, 1937, **70**, 1451.

Stearaldehyde.
See Stearic Aldehyde.

Stearamide (*Stearic acid amide*)

$CH_3{\cdot}[CH_2]_{16}{\cdot}CONH_2$

$C_{18}H_{37}ON$ MW, 283

Cryst. from hot EtOH. M.p. 108·5–109°. B.p. 250°/12 mm. (168–9° *in vacuo*). Sol. Et_2O, $CHCl_3$, hot EtOH. Insol. H_2O.

Aschan, *Ber.*, 1898, **31**, 2349.

Stearanilide (*Stearic acid anilide*)

$CH_3{\cdot}[CH_2]_{16}{\cdot}CO{\cdot}NH{\cdot}C_6H_5$

$C_{24}H_{41}ON$ MW, 359

Needles from EtOH. M.p. 94° (88°). B.p. 153·5°/10 mm. Sol. EtOH, Et_2O, C_6H_6, $CHCl_3$, MeOH, Me_2CO, hot AcOH. Spar. sol. pet. ether. Insol. H_2O.

De' Conno, *Gazz. chim. ital.*, 1917, **47**, i, 98.
Nill, U.S.P., 1,659,150, (*Chem Abstracts*, 1928, **22**, 1367).

Stearic Acid (*Octadecylic acid*)

$CH_3{\cdot}[CH_2]_{16}{\cdot}COOH$

$C_{18}H_{36}O_2$ MW, 284

Occurs in moulds, in jalap resin, in fruits of *Citrullus colcynthis*, Schrad., and as esters (glycerides) in fats. Leaflets from EtOH. F.p. 69·41°. M.p. 71·5–72° (69·6°, 69·5°). B.p. 360° decomp., 291°/100 mm., 238°/17 mm., 232°/15 mm., 158–60°/0·25 mm. Mod. sol. hot EtOH. Spar. sol. C_6H_6, CS_2. D_4^{20} 0·9408. n_D^{70} 1·4335. Heat of comb. 2711·8 Cal.

Li salt : m.p. 220–221·5°.
Cu salt : m.p. 115–20°.
Ag salt : m.p. 205°.
Mg salt : m.p. 132°.
Pb salt : m.p. 115·6–115·8° (113–14°).
Co salt : m.p. 73–5°.
Ni salt : m.p. 80–6°.

Me ester : $C_{19}H_{38}O_2$. MW, 298. M.p. 38·5–39·5° (39·7–40°). B.p. 442–3°/747 mm., 214–15°/15 mm.

Et ester : $C_{20}H_{40}O_2$. MW, 312. F.p. 30·92°. (i) M.p. 33·4°. (ii) M.p. 30·9°. B.p. 213–15°/15 mm., 199°/10 mm., 152°/0·18 mm.

2-*Chloroethyl ester* : $C_{20}H_{39}O_2Cl$. MW, 346·5. Leaflets from EtOH. M.p. 49·5°.

2-*Iodoethyl ester* : $C_{20}H_{39}O_2I$. MW, 438. Leaflets from EtOH. M.p. 59·5°.

Propyl ester : $C_{21}H_{42}O_2$. MW, 326. Prisms from pet. ether. M.p. 28·6°.

Isobutyl ester : $C_{22}H_{44}O_2$. MW, 340. M.p. 25°. B.p. 199°/5 mm. D_4^{29} 0·8498. $[\alpha]_D^{20}$ + 9·39° in EtOH.

Isoamyl ester: $C_{23}H_{46}O_2$. MW, 354. M.p. 25·5° (22°).
Hexadecyl ester: $C_{34}H_{68}O_2$. MW, 508. M.p. 55–60°.
Heptadecyl ester: $C_{35}H_{70}O_2$. MW, 522. M.p. 64·7°.
Ethylene glycol di-ester: $C_{38}H_{74}O_4$. MW, 594. M.p. 79° (76°).
Propylene glycol di-ester: $C_{39}H_{76}O_4$. MW, 608. M.p. 40°.
Glycerol ester: *see* Monostearin, Distearin, Tristearin.
Phenyl ester: $C_{24}H_{40}O_2$. MW, 360. M.p. 52°. B.p. 267°/15 mm.
o-*Nitrophenyl ester*: $C_{24}H_{39}O_4N$. MW, 405. M p. 60–1°.
p-*Tolyl ester*: $C_{25}H_{42}O_2$. MW, 374. M.p. 54°. B.p. 276°/15 mm.
Benzyl ester: $C_{25}H_{42}O_2$. MW, 374. M.p. 28°.
1-*Menthyl ester*: $C_{28}H_{54}O_2$. MW, 422. Plates from EtOH. M.p. 39°. $[\alpha]_D^{20}$ — 36·71° in $CHCl_3$.
Chloride: $C_{18}H_{35}OCl$. MW, 302·5. M.p. 23°. B.p. 202–3°/6 mm. (215°/5 mm.).
Amide: *see* Stearamide.
Anhydride: $C_{36}H_{70}O_3$. MW, 550. M.p. 72°.
Nitrile: *see* Stearonitrile.
Anilide: *see* Stearanilide.
o-*Chloroanilide*: m.p. 67–68·5°.
p-*Chloroanilide*: m.p. 101–2°.
p-*Bromoanilide*: m.p. 114°.
2 : 4 : 6-*Tribromoanilide*: m.p. 126°.
p-*Nitroanilide*: m.p. 94·5–95·5°.
o-*Toluidide*: m.p. 97°.
p-*Toluidide*: m.p. 102° (95·5°). B.p. 161·5°/10 mm.
1-*Naphthalide*: m.p. 110·8°. B.p. 205°/10 mm.
2-*Naphthalide*: m.p. 112°. B.p. 239°/10 mm.

Hell, Sadomski, *Ber.*, 1891, **24**, 2388.
Heintz, *J. prakt. Chem.*, 1855, **66**, 22.
Vesely, *Chimie et industrie*, 1929, **22**, 881 (*Bibl.*).
Levene, Taylor, *J. Biol. Chem.*, 1924, **59**, 965.

Stearic Aldehyde (*Stearaldehyde*)

$CH_3 \cdot [CH_2]_{16} \cdot CHO$

$C_{18}H_{36}O$ MW, 268

M.p. 55° (38°). Polymerizes rapidly.
Oxime: needles. M.p. 89°.
Semicarbazone: needles. M.p. 108–9°.
Thiosemicarbazone: needles from EtOH. M.p. 111°.
p-*Nitrophenylhydrazone*: yellow needles fro MeOH. M.p. 101°.

Stephen, *J. Chem. Soc.*, 1925, 1876.
Feulgen, Behrens, *Z. physiol. Chem* 1928, **177**, 221.

Note.—Compounds described in earli literature are polymers.

Stearin.
See Monostearin, Distearin, *and* Tristearin.

Stearolactone.
See under 3-Hydroxystearic Acid.

Stearolic Acid

$CH_3 \cdot [CH_2]_7 C{:}C \cdot [CH_2]_7 \cdot COOH$

$C_{18}H_{32}O_2$ MW, 28

Needles from EtOH.Aq. M.p. 47–8°. Sol Et_2O, hot EtOH. Insol. H_2O. Heat of comb C_v 2624·7 Cal.
Tetrabromide: *see* 8 : 8 : 9 : 9-Tetrabromo stearic Acid.
1-*Glycerol ester*: $C_{21}H_{38}O_4$. MW, 354. Leaf lets from EtOH. M.p. 40·5°.
1 : 2-*Glycerol di-ester*: $C_{39}H_{68}O_5$. MW, 616 M.p. 40°.
1 : 3-*Glycerol di-ester*: m.p. 38·5°.
Glycerol tri-ester: $C_{57}H_{98}O_6$. MW, 878 M.p. 29°.

Hoffmann-La Roche, D.R.P., 243,582 (*Chem. Zentr.*, 1912, I, 695).
Kino, *Chem. Abstracts*, 1930, **24**, 1998 *Chem. Zentr.*, 1936, I, 2531.
See also Posternak, *Compt. rend.*, 1916 **162**, 944.

Stearone (*Di*-n-*heptadecyl ketone, 18-penta tricontanone*)

$CH_3 \cdot [CH_2]_{16} \cdot CO \cdot [CH_2]_{16} \cdot CH_3$

$C_{35}H_{70}O$ MW, 506

Leaflets from ligroin. M.p. 88·4°. Spar. sol hot EtOH, hot Et_2O. Insol. H_2O. D_4^{95} 0·7932.
Oxime: m.p. 62–3°.

Easterfield, Taylor, *J. Chem. Soc.*, 1911, **99**, 2300.
Grün, D.R.P., 296,677, (*Chem. Zentr.*, 1917, I, 611).

Stearonitrile (*Stearic acid nitrile, heptadecyl cyanide*)

$CH_3 \cdot [CH_2]_{16} \cdot CN$

$C_{18}H_{35}N$ MW, 265

M.p. 42·5–43·5°. B.p. 214°/13 mm. (128° *in cuo*). D_4^{41} 0·8178.

Levene, Taylor, *J. Biol. Chem.*, 1924, **59**, 905.
van Epps, Reid, *J. Am. Chem. Soc.*, 1916, **38**, 2125.

Stearoxylic Acid (8 : 9-*Diketostearic acid*)

$CH_3\cdot[CH_2]_7\cdot CO\cdot CO\cdot[CH_2]_7\cdot COOH$

$_{18}H_{32}O_4$ MW, 312

Yellow plates. M.p. 86° (83–4°). Sol. Et_2O, $_6H_6$, hot EtOH. Spar. sol. ligroin.
Monoxime : m.p. 76–81°.
Dioxime : m.p. 153–4°.

Spieckermann, *Ber.*, 1895, **28**, 276.
Böeseken, *Rec. trav. chim.*, 1911, **30**, 146.

Stearyl Alcohol.
See Octadecyl Alcohol.

Stictic Acid (*Scopuloric acid*)

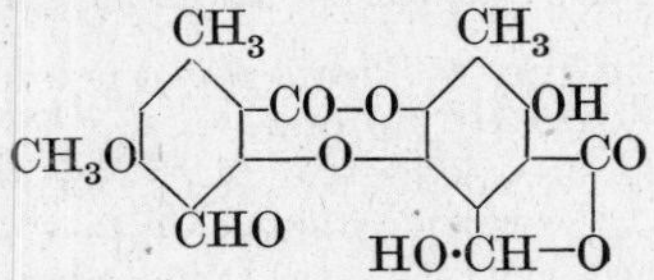

$_{19}H_{14}O_9$ MW, 386

Occurs in lichen *Ramalina scopulorum.* eedles from Me_2CO. M.p. 270°. $FeCl_3 \longrightarrow$ urple $\longrightarrow$ brown col.
Diacetyl deriv. : m.p. 235–6°.
Tetra-acetyl deriv. : m.p. 226–7°.
Di-Me ether : $C_{21}H_{18}O_9$. MW, 414. (i) M.p. 74°. (ii) M.p. 242–3°.

Curd, Robertson, *J. Chem. Soc.*, 1935, 1379.
Asahina *et al.*, *Ber.*, 1933, **66**, 943, 1080; 1936, **69**, 126.

Stigmastane

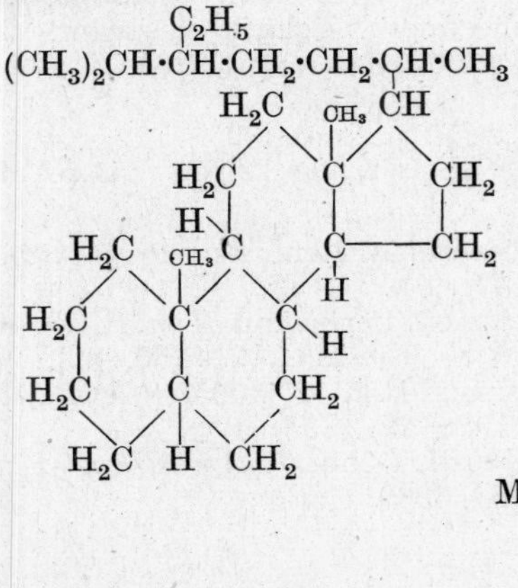

$_{29}H_{52}$ MW, 400

Cryst. from EtOH. M.p. 85·4–85·7°. $[\alpha]_D^{20}$ + 25·4° in $CHCl_3$. Sol. Et_2O. Spar. sol. EOtH.

Windaus, Brunken, *Z. physiol. Chem.*, 1924, **140**, 47.
See also *Note* under Sitostane.

Stigmastanol (*Fucostanol*)

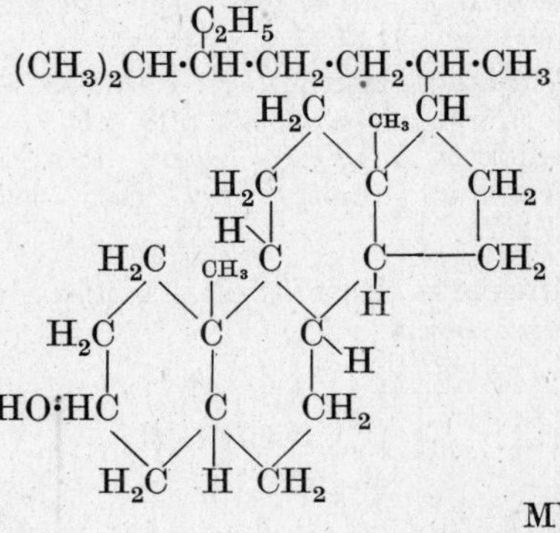

$C_{29}H_{52}O$ MW, 416

Plates from EtOH. M.p. 136–7°. $[\alpha]_D^{20}$ + 24·8° in $CHCl_3$.
Acetyl : needles from EtOH. M.p. 130–1°. $[\alpha]_D^{20}$ + 15·3° in $CHCl_3$.
Benzoyl : plates from AcOEt. M.p. 135·5 137°.
3 : 5-*Dinitrobenzoyl* : plates from AcOEt. M.p. 214–15°. $[\alpha]_D^{20}$ + 13·1° in C_6H_6.

Coffey, Heilbron, Spring, *J. Chem. Soc.*, 1936, 738.
See also previous reference and *Note* under Sitostanol.

Stigmasterol

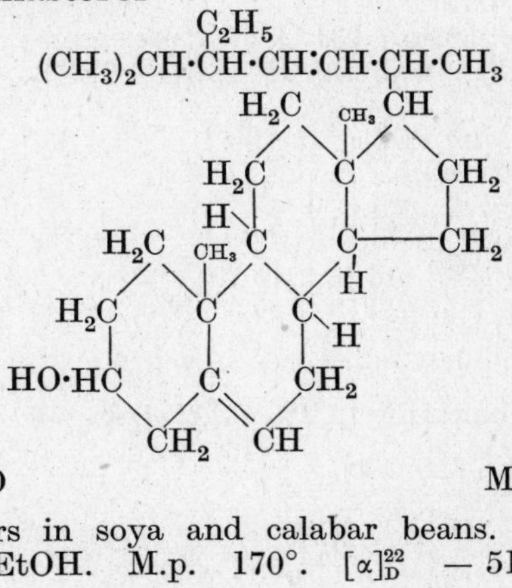

$C_{29}H_{48}O$ MW, 412

Occurs in soya and calabar beans. Cryst. from EtOH. M.p. 170°. $[\alpha]_D^{22}$ − 51·0° in $CHCl_3$.
Acetyl : plates from EtOH. M.p. 144–144·6°. $[\alpha]_D^{20}$ − 55·5° in $CHCl_3$. *Tetrabromide* : plates

from EtOH–$CHCl_3$. M.p. 211–12° (202–3°). $[\alpha]_D^{20}$ − 40°.

Propionyl: prisms from EtOH. M.p. 122°.
Palmityl: m.p. 99°.
Stearyl: m.p. 101°.
Benzoyl: prisms from $CHCl_3$–EtOH. M.p. 160°.
p-*Nitrobenzoyl*: needles from ligroin. M.p. 203°.

Windaus, Hauth, *Ber.*, 1906, **39**, 4378.
Fernholz, *Ann.*, 1933, **508**, 215.
Guiteras, *Z. physiol. Chem.*, 1933, **214**, 89.
Fernholz, Chakravorty, *Ber.*, 1934, **67**, 2021.

α-Stilbazole (2-*Stilbazole*, 2-*styrylpyridine*, β-2-*pyridinostyrene*)

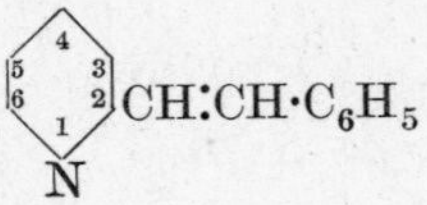

$C_{13}H_{11}N$ MW, 181

Cryst. from EtOH.Aq. M.p. 91°. B.p. 324–5°/750 mm., 194°/14 mm. Sol. Et_2O, CS_2. Mod. sol. EtOH, C_6H_6, ligroin. Insol. H_2O. Volatile in steam. $KMnO_4 \longrightarrow$ benzoic + picolinic acids.

B,HCl,4H₂O: m.p. anhyd. 177°.
$B,HAuCl_4$: m.p. 185°.
$B,HCl,HgCl_2$: m.p. 181–3°.
B,H_2PtCl_6: m.p. 201°.

Wagstaff, *J. Chem. Soc.*, 1934, 277.
Harries, Lenart, *Ann.*, 1915, **410**, 95.

γ-Stilbazole (4-*Stilbazole*, 4-*styrylpyridine*, β-4-*pyridinostyrene*).

Prisms, m.p. 131°: leaflets from EtOH, m.p. 127°. Sol. EtOH, Et_2O, $CHCl_3$. Insol. H_2O.

Hydrochloride: m.p. 204°.
Hydrobromide: m.p. 221°.
Hydriodide: m.p. 174°.
$B,HAuCl_4$: m.p. 201°.
B_2,H_2PtCl_6: m.p. 310°.
Picrate: m.p. 113°.

See first reference above.

α-Stilbazoline (2-*Phenylethylpiperidine*)

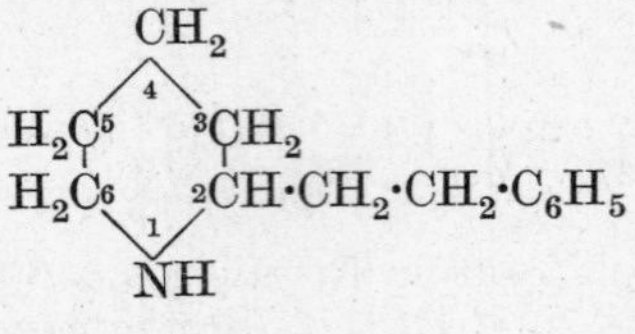

$C_{13}H_{19}N$ MW, 189

d-.
Liq. $[\alpha]_D^{18}$ + 12·16°.
Acid d-*tartrate*: rhombohedra. M.p. 50°.

l-.
Liq. $[\alpha]_D^{18}$ − 11·5°.
B,HCl: needles or prisms from Me_2CO. M.p. 116–17°.
Neutral l-*tartrate*: plates. M.p. 211–12°.
Acid d-*tartrate*: cryst. + H_2O. M.p. 78–80°.

dl-.
Liq. B.p. 288° (277–8°). D_4^0 0·9874. Misc. with EtOH, Et_2O, C_6H_6. Spar. sol. H_2O with strong alk. reaction.
B,HCl: needles from C_6H_6–pet. ether. M.p. 155°.
B,HBr: cryst. from C_6H_6. M.p. 173°.
$B,HAuCl_4$: yellow powder. M.p. 133–4°.
B_2,H_2PtCl_6: yellow powder. M.p. 187–9°.

Ladenburg, *Ber.*, 1904, **37**, 3688.
Baurath, *Ber.*, 1888, **21**, 822.
Bach, *Ber.*, 1901, **34**, 2233.

γ-Stilbazoline (4-*Phenylethylpiperidine*).
Oil. B.p. 200–10°/80 mm.
$B,HAuCl_4$: red leaflets. M.p. 204° decomp.
B_2,H_2PtCl_6: brown leaflets. M.p. about 210°.

Friedländer, *Ber.*, 1905, **38**, 2837.

Stilbene (sym.-*Diphenylethylene*, *toluylene*, *dibenzal*, *dibenzylidene*)

$C_6H_5{\cdot}CH$ / $C_6H_5{\cdot}CH$ — *Cis* (isostilbene)

$C_6H_5{\cdot}CH$ / $HC{\cdot}C_6H_5$ — *Trans* (stilbene)

$C_{14}H_{12}$ MW, 180

Cis:
Yellow oil. B.p. 148–9°/17 mm., 145°/13 mm., 136–7°/10 mm.

Trans:
Cryst. from EtOH. M.p. 124°. B.p. 305°/720 mm., 166–7°/12 mm. Sol. Et_2O, C_6H_6. Shows blue fluor. Volatile in steam. Heat of comb. C_p 1765·7 Cal. n_D^{17} 1·6264.
Picrate: m.p. 94–5°.
$C_{14}H_{12},2SbCl_3$: m.p. 93°.
$C_{14}H_{12},C_6H_3(NO_2)_3$-1 : 3 : 5: m.p. 115–20° (107–10°).

Böeseken, Elsen, *Rec. trav. chim.*, 1928, **47**, 694.
Schenck, Bergmann, *Ann.*, 1928, **463**, 112.
Späth, *Monatsh.*, 1914, **35**, 463.
Corson, E.P., 279,095, (*Chem. Abstracts*, 1928, **22**, 2755).
Ballard, Dehn, *J. Am. Chem. Soc.*, 1932, **54**, 3969.

Stilbene-α-carboxylic Acid.
See α-Phenylcinnamic Acid.

Stilbenediamine (*α : β-Diaminodibenzyl, α : β-diamino*-sym.-*diphenylethane, diphenylethylenediamine*)

$C_6H_5{\cdot}CH(NH_2){\cdot}CH(NH_2){\cdot}C_6H_5$

$C_{14}H_{16}N_2$ MW, 212

d-.
$[\alpha]_D + 134{\cdot}8°$.

Feist, Arnstein, *Ber.*, 1895, **28**, 3169.

l-.
$[\alpha]_D - 128°$.

dl-.
Cryst. from ligroin. M.p. 90–2°.
B,HCl,2H₂O : m.p. 251° decomp.
B,H₂PtCl₆,2H₂O : m.p. 222–5°.
Picrate : m.p. 220°.
N : N′-*Diacetyl* : m.p. above 360°.
N : N′-*Dibenzoyl* : m.p. 287°.
N : N′-*Dibenzylidene* : m.p. 152°.

Meso-.
Leaflets from Et_2O. M.p. 121°.
B,2HCl,2H₂O : m.p. 256° decomp.
B,2HBr : m.p. 276–8°.
B,H₂PtCl₆ : m.p. 265° decomp.
Picrate : m.p. 225°.
Dipicrate : m.p. 239°.
N : N′-*Diformyl* : m.p. 294°.
N-*Acetyl*-N′-*benzoyl* : m.p. 316°.
N : N′-*Dibenzoyl* : m.p. 350°.
N : N′-*Dibenzylidene* : m.p. 164°.

Biltz, Krebs, *Ann.*, 1912, **391**, 208.
Darapsky, Spannagel, *J. prakt. Chem.*, 1915, **92**, 289.

Stilbene dibromide (*α : β-Dibromo*-sym.-*diphenylethane, α : β-dibromodibenzyl*)

$C_6H_5{\cdot}CHBr{\cdot}CHBr{\cdot}C_6H_5$

$C_{14}H_{12}Br_2$ MW, 340

(i) Needles. M.p. 237°. Sol. hot xylene. Mod. sol. Et_2O, CS_2. Spar. sol. EtOH.
(ii) Cryst. from hot EtOH. M.p. 111°. Sol. Et_2O. Spar. sol. EtOH.

Liebermann, *Ber.*, 1910, **43**, 1543.
Pfeiffer, *Ber.*, 1912, **45**, 1818.
Kato, *Chem. Abstracts*, 1932, **26**, 5260.

Stilbene-α : β-dicarboxylic Acid.
See Diphenylfumaric Acid *and* Diphenylmaleic Acid.

Stilbene-2 : 2′-dicarboxylic Acid

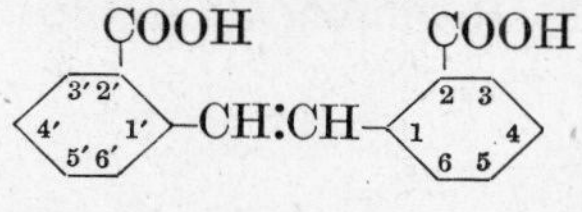

$C_{16}H_{12}O_4$ MW, 268

Needles from dil. AcOH. M.p. 263–4° (rapid heat.), 250° (slow heat.).
Di-Et ester : $C_{20}H_{20}O_4$. MW, 324. Needles. M.p. 79–80°. Sol. Et_2O.

Hasselbach, *Ann.*, 1888, **243**, 258.

Stilbene-4 : 4′-dicarboxylic Acid.
Di-Me ester : $C_{18}H_{16}O_4$. MW, 296. Cryst. from EtOH. M.p. 226–7°. Insol. Et_2O. Sol. in EtOH has bluish-violet fluor.

Meyer, Hofmann, *Monatsh.*, 1917, **38**, 358.

Stilbene dichloride (*α : β-Dichloro*-sym.-*diphenylethane, α : β-dichlorodibenzyl*)

$C_6H_5{\cdot}CHCl{\cdot}CHCl{\cdot}C_6H_5$

$C_{14}H_{12}Cl_2$ MW, 251

(i) Needles from EtOH. M.p. 191–3°. Sol. hot toluene. Spar. sol. EtOH.
(ii) Leaflets. M.p. 93–4°. Sol. ord. org. solvents. Sublimes.

Pfeiffer, Eistert, *J. prakt. Chem.*, 1930, **124**, 168.
Carré, Mauclère, *Compt. rend.*, 1931, **192**, 1567.
Pfeiffer, *Ber.*, 1912, **45**, 1816.

Stilbene oxide.
See 1 : 2-Diphenylethylene oxide.

Stovaine (*1 - Dimethylamino - 2 - methyl - 2 - butanol benzoate*)

$O{\cdot}CO{\cdot}C_6H_5$
$(CH_3)_2N{\cdot}CH_2{\cdot}C{\cdot}CH_2{\cdot}CH_3$
CH_3

$C_{14}H_{21}O_2N$ MW, 235

d-.
M.p. 186–7°. $[\alpha]_D^{20} + 8{\cdot}5°$.

l-.
M.p. 186–7°. $[\alpha]_D^{20} - 8{\cdot}5°$.

dl-.
M.p. 175°. Local anæsthetic.
B,HCl : cryst. from EtOH. M.p. 202°.
Picrate : m.p. 110–12°.

Ribas, Rancaño, *Chem. Abstracts*, 1929, **23**, 2164.
Fourneau, Ribas, *Chem. Abstracts*, 1928, **22**, 761.
Fiore, *Chem. Zentr.*, 1916, I, 1076.
Riedel, D.R.P., 169,746, (*Chem. Zentr.*, 1906, I, 1584).

Note.—Both the free base and its hydrochloride are referred to as "Stovaine."

Strophanthidin

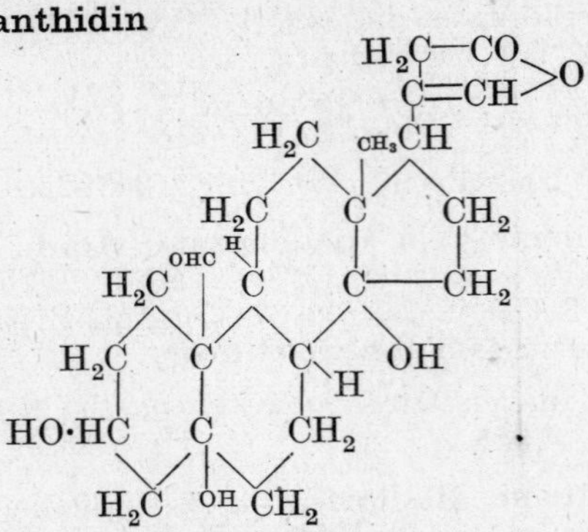

Suggested structure

$C_{23}H_{32}O_6$ MW, 404

Occurs in *Strophanthus kombé*, Oliver. Leaflets + $2H_2O$ from H_2O. M.p. 169–70°, anhyd. 235°. Sol. Et_2O, $CHCl_3$, C_6H_6. Insol. pet. ether. $[\alpha]_D^{25}$ + 43·1° in MeOH.

Oxime: m.p. 270–5°.
Phenylhydrazone: m.p. 230–2°.
p-*Bromophenylhydrazone*: m.p. 200°.
Benzoyl: $[\alpha]_D^{26}$ + 47·8°.
p-*Bromobenzoyl*: m.p. 222–4°.

Lamb, Smith, *J. Chem. Soc.*, 1936, 444.
Jacobs, Elderfield, *J. Biol. Chem.*, 1935, **108**, 497.
Kon, *J. Soc. Chem. Ind.*, 1934, **53**, 956.
Gamble, Kon, *J. Chem. Soc.*, 1935, 443.
Elderfield, *J. Biol. Chem.*, 1936, **113**, 625.

g-Strophanthin.
See Ouabain.

Strychnine

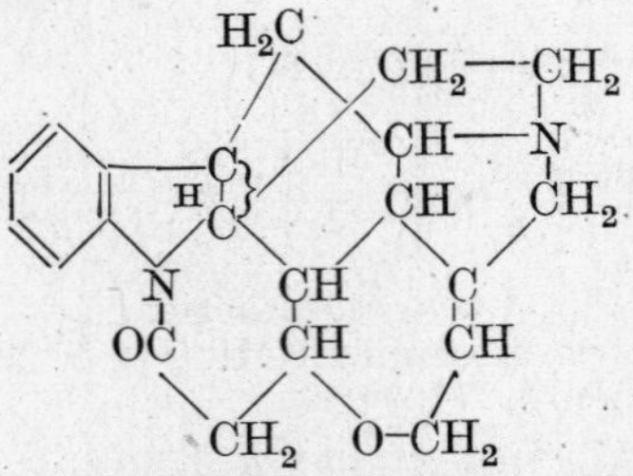

Suggested structure

$C_{21}H_{22}O_2N_2$ MW, 334

Alkaloid occurring in seeds of *Strychnos nux vomica*, Linn., *S. ignatii*, Berg. Prisms from EtOH. M.p. 286–8° (270–1° slow heat.). B.p. 270°/5 mm. $[\alpha]_D^{18}$ − 139·3° in $CHCl_3$, − 104·5° in abs. EtOH. Sol. 6 parts $CHCl_3$, 66·6 parts Py, 165 parts C_6H_6, 6400 parts H_2O at 25°, and 12 parts boiling 90% EtOH. Prac. insol. abs. Et_2O. Cold sol. in H_2SO_4 + an oxidising agent. *e.g.* $K_2C_3O_7$, $KMnO_4$, PbO_2, MnO_2 ⟶ violet-blue col. ⟶ purple ⟶ red ⟶ yellow. Warm in dil. HNO_3 + $K_2Cr_2O_7$ ⟶ intense scarlet col. HNO_3 (D 1·4) ⟶ colourless sol. ⟶ yellow on heating. Bitter taste. Violent tetanic poison. Employed commercially in vermin killers.

B,HCl: needles + $1\frac{1}{2}H_2O$.
B,HBr: needles + H_2O. Spar. sol. H_2O.
B,HI: needles + H_2O. Spar. sol. H_2O.
B,HNO₃: needles. Sol. 42 parts H_2O at 25°, 120 parts EtOH at 25°.
B_2,H_2SO_4: needles + $5H_2O$. M.p. anhyd. 200°. Sol. 48 parts H_2O, 135 parts EtOH.
$B_2,H_2Cr_2O_7$: orange-yellow needles. Sol. 1815 parts H_2O at 25°.
Monopicrate: decomp. at 270°.
Monopicrolonate: decomp. above 290°.
d-*Tartrate*: cryst. + $7H_2O$. M.p. 228°.
l-*Tartrate*: cryst. + $3\frac{1}{2}H_2O$. M.p. 242°.
Benzyl chloride: m.p. 303·5°.
Benzylidene deriv.: m.p. 235–7°.

Robinson, *Annual Report of Biochemistry*, 1935, **4**, 512 (*Bibl.*).
Leuchs, Beyer, *Ber.*, 1935, **68**, 290.
Clemo, *J. Chem. Soc.*, 1936, 1695.
Kotake, Mori, Mitsuwa, *Sci. Papers Inst. Phys. Chem. Research Tokyo*, 1937, **31**, 129.

ψ-Strychnine

$C_{21}H_{23}O_3N_2$ MW, 351

A strychnine alkaloid. Cryst. powder. M.p. 266–8° decomp. Mod. sol. $CHCl_3$. Spar. sol. Me_2CO, C_6H_6. Insol. Et_2O. $[\alpha]_D^{25}$ − 85·9° in $CHCl_3$, − 43·8° in abs. EtOH. H_2SO_4 + $K_2Cr_2O_7$ ⟶ violet col. Not bitter and is less toxic than strychnine. Zn + HCl ⟶ strychnine.

B,HCl: cryst. + $2H_2O$ from H_2O. $[\alpha]_D^{19}$ + 3·9° in H_2O, $[\alpha]_D^{24}$ + 8·3° in 80% EtOH.
B,HNO₃: spar. sol. H_2O. $[\alpha]_D^{28}$ + 7·6° in 80% EtOH.
B,HClO₄: needles from H_2O. Does not melt below 300°.
Ferrichloride: m.p. 234–5°.
Nitroso deriv.: cryst. from 80% EtOH. M.p. 292–4°. Sol. $CHCl_3$. Spar. sol. MeOH, EtOH, Et_2O, C_6H_6. $[\alpha]_D^{19}$ + 223·8° in $CHCl_3$.

Warnat, *Helv. Chim. Acta*, 1931, **14**, 1004.
Blount, Robinson, *J. Chem. Soc.*, 1932, 2305.

Stycerine.
See 1-Phenylglycerol.

Styphnic Acid (2 : 4 : 6-*Trinitroresorcinol*)

$$OH$$
$$O_2N \bighexagon NO_2$$
$$OH$$
$$NO_2$$

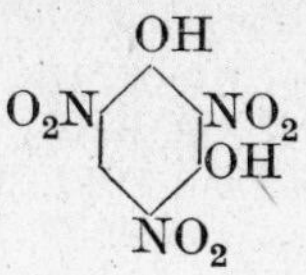

$C_6H_3O_8N_3$ MW, 245

Yellow cryst. from AcOEt. M.p. 179–80° (178°). Explodes on rapid heating. Sol. EtOH, Et_2O. Spar. sol. H_2O. Forms add. comps. with many hydrocarbons.

Di-Me ether : $C_8H_7O_8N_3$. MW, 273. Needles from EtOH. M.p. 124–5°.

Me-Et ether : $C_9H_9O_8N_3$. MW, 287. M.p. 92°.

Di-Et ether : $C_{10}H_{11}O_8N_3$. MW, 301. Leaflets from EtOH. M.p. 121°.

Brass, Fanta, *Ber.*, 1936, **69**, 6 (*Bibl.*).
Sah, *Chem. Abstracts*, 1932, **26**, 5927.
Vermeulen, *Rec. trav. chim.*, 1919, **38**, 107.
Datta, Varma, *J. Am. Chem. Soc.*, 1919, **41**, 2043.

Stypticin.
See under Cotarnine.

Styptol.
See under Cotarnine.

Styracin.
See Cinnamyl cinnamate.

Styracitol (1 : 5-*Anhydro*-d-*sorbitol*)

$$O$$
$$OH\,H \quad OH$$
$$CH_2 - C - C - C - C - CH_2OH$$
$$H \quad OH\,H \quad H$$

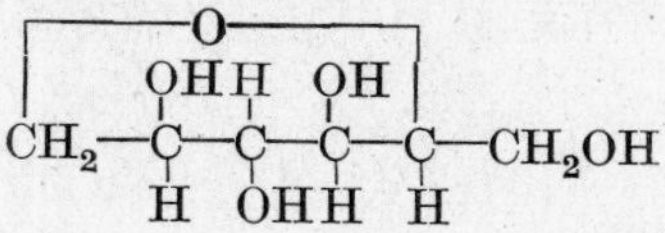

$C_6H_{12}O_5$ MW, 164

Occurs in fruit of *Styrax obassia*. Prisms from 90% EtOH. M.p. 157° (155°). Sol. H_2O. Spar. sol. cold EtOH. Prac. insol. Et_2O, Me_2CO, C_6H_6. Bitter-sweet taste. $[\alpha]_D^{20} - 71.72°$ in H_2O ($[\alpha]_D^{17} - 49.4°$ in H_2O). Does not reduce Fehling's.

Tetra-acetyl : prisms from H_2O, m.p. 66–7° : needles from EtOH, m.p. 58°. B.p. 200°/7 mm. $[\alpha]_D^{22} - 20.86°$ in EtOH.

Tetrabenzoyl : m.p. 142°.

Tetra-Me ether : b.p. 149–51°/24 mm., 143–4°/16 mm. $D_4^{18} 1.1092$. $n_D^{14} 1.4516$. $[\alpha]_D^{14} - 35.63°$.

Diacetone deriv. : m.p. 96–7°. $[\alpha]_D^{17} - 115.24°$ in EtOH.

Dibenzylidene deriv. : (i) m.p. 163–5°. $[\alpha]_D^{25} - 148.73°$ in $CHCl_3$; (ii) m.p. 192–3°. $[\alpha]_D^{25} - 80.47°$ in $CHCl_3$.

Asahina, *Ber.*, 1912, **45**, 2363.
Asahina, Takimoto, *Ber.*, 1931, **64**, 1803.
Zervas, *Ber.*, 1930, **63**, 1689.

Styracol (*Guaiacol cinnamate*)

$$OCH_3$$
$$\bighexagon O \cdot CO \cdot CH:CH \cdot C_6H_5$$

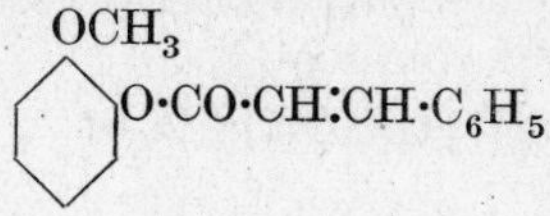

$C_{16}H_{14}O_3$ MW, 254

Needles from EtOH. M.p. 130°.

Knoll, D.R.P., 62,176.

Styrene (*Styrol, styrolene, cinnamol, cinnamene, vinylbenzene, phenylethylene*)

$$C_6H_5 \cdot CH:CH_2$$

C_8H_8 MW, 104

Occurs in storax. F.p. — 33°. M.p. — 33°. B.p. 145–145.8°, 52–3°/28 mm., 48°/20 mm., 40°/14 mm., 33°/10 mm. Sol. EtOH, Et_2O, MeOH, Me_2CO, CS_2. Spar. sol. H_2O. D_4^{20} 0.9090. $n_D^{20} 1.5462$. Polymerises slowly, rapidly in presence of metallic sodium, to

$$\left[-CH_2 \cdot \overset{C_6H_5}{\underset{}{CH}} - \overset{C_6H_5}{\underset{}{CH}} \cdot CH_2 \cdot CH_2 \cdot \overset{C_6H_5}{\underset{}{CH}} - \overset{C_6H_5}{\underset{}{CH}} \cdot CH_2 - \right]_x$$

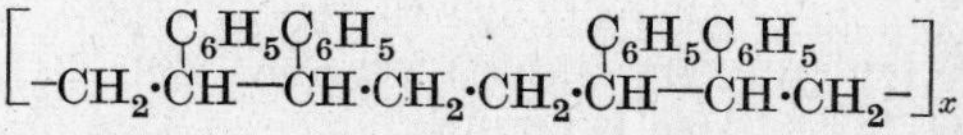

Metastyrene : $(C_8H_8)_x$. MW, $(104)_x$. Amorphous mass. Spar. sol. hot Et_2O. Insol. H_2O, EtOH. Irradiation in C_6H_6 or dist. $\longrightarrow$ styrene.

Polystyrene : a rubber-like substance.

Tetrastyrene : $C_{32}H_{32}$. MW, 416. B.p. 210–17°/0.05 mm.

Naugatuck, D.R.P., 600,268, (*Chem. Abstracts*, 1934, **28**, 6448).
Sontag, *Ann. chim.*, 1934, I, 359.
Zal'kind, Bulavskii, *Chem. Abstracts*, 1936, **30**, 1368.
Gibbons, Smith, U.S.P., 1,938,827, (*Chem. Abstracts*, 1934, **28**, 1367).
Houtz, Adkins, *J. Am. Chem. Soc.*, 1933, **55**, 1609.
Gautier, Gautier, *Bull. soc. chim.*, 1933, **53**, 323.
Midgley, Henne, Leicester, *J. Am. Chem. Soc.*, 1936, **58**, 1961.
Graves, U.S.P., 2,036,410, (*Chem. Abstracts*, 1936, **30**, 3446).
Waterman, Kok, *Rec. trav. chim.*, 1934, **53**, 1133 (*Bibl.*).
I.G., U.S.P., 2,005,295, (*Chem. Abstracts*, 1935, **29**, 5203).
Staudinger, D.R.P., 610,478, (*Chem. Abstracts*, 1935, **29**, 3752).
Hibbert, Burt, *J. Am. Chem. Soc.*, 1925, **47**, 2240.

Styrene bromohydrin (*Phenylethylene bromohydrin, β-bromo-α-hydroxyethylbenzene, bromomethylphenylcarbinol*)

$C_6H_5{\cdot}CH(OH){\cdot}CH_2Br$

C_8H_9OBr MW, 201

B.p. 109–10°/2 mm. n_D^{17} 1·5800. D_4^{20} 1·4994.

Read, Reid, *J. Chem. Soc.*, 1928, 1488.

Styrene chlorohydrin (*Phenylethylene chlorohydrin, β-chloro-α-hydroxyethylbenzene, chloromethylphenylcarbinol*)

$C_6H_5{\cdot}CH(OH){\cdot}CH_2Cl$

C_8H_9OCl MW, 156·5

B.p. 128°/17 mm. D^0 1·225. n^{17} 1·55405.

Detoeuf, *Bull. soc. chim.*, 1922, **31**, 176.

Styrene dibromide (*α : β-Dibromoethylbenzene, phenylethylene dibromide*)

$C_6H_5{\cdot}CHBr{\cdot}CH_2Br$

$C_8H_8Br_2$ MW, 264

Leaflets or needles from EtOH.Aq. M.p. 74–74·5° (72–3°). B.p. 139–41°/15 mm. Sol. EtOH, Et_2O, C_6H_6, AcOH, ligroin.

Evans, Morgan, *J. Am. Chem. Soc.*, 1913, **35**, 56.
Glaser, *Ann.*, 1870, **154**, 154.
Zincke, *Ann.*, 1883, **216**, 288.

Styrene dichloride (*α : β-Dichloroethylbenzene, phenylethylene dichloride*)

$C_6H_5{\cdot}CHCl{\cdot}CH_2Cl$

$C_8H_8Cl_2$ MW, 175

B.p. 233–4°/759 mm., 114·5–115·5°/15 mm. D_4^{15} 1·240. n_D^{15} 1·5544.

Biltz, *Ann.*, 1897, **296**, 275.

Styrene Glycol (*Phenylethylene glycol, α : β-dihydroxyethylbenzene*)

$C_6H_5{\cdot}CH(OH){\cdot}CH_2OH$

$C_8H_{10}O_2$ MW, 138

Needles from ligroin. M.p. 67–8°. B.p. 272–4°/755 mm. Very sol. H_2O, EtOH, Et_2O, $CHCl_3$, AcOH, C_6H_6. Spar. sol. ligroin.

Me ether: $C_9H_{12}O_2$. MW, 152. B.p. 237–8°, 132°/18 mm. D^0 1·080.

Et ether: $C_{10}H_{14}O_2$. MW, 166. B.p. 242–3°. D^0 1·054.

Di-Et ether: $C_{12}H_{18}O_2$. MW, 194. B.p. 105–6°/10 mm. Dil. $H_2SO_4 \longrightarrow$ phenylacetaldehyde.

Diformyl: b.p. 164–5°/25 mm. D^0 1·2091.

Diacetyl: b.p. 274°/755 mm., 183–5°/25 mm.

Dibenzoyl: needles from EtOH or toluene. M.p. 96–7°. Sublimes.

Zincke, *Ann.*, 1883, **216**, 293.
Tiffeneau, *Compt. rend.*, 1907, **145**, 812.
Späth, *Monatsh.*, 1914, **35**, 332.
Balla, *Compt. rend.*, 1934, **198**, 948.

Styrene oxide (*Phenylethylene oxide*)

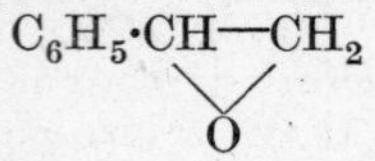

C_8H_8O MW, 120

Liq. with aromatic odour. B.p. 191–2°, 84–5°/15 mm., 77·5–78·5°/12 mm. D_4^{16} 1·0523.

Fourneau, Tiffeneau, *Compt. rend.*, 1905, **140**, 1595; 1908, **146**, 697.
Hibbert, Burt, *Organic Syntheses*, Collective Vol. I, 481.

Styrol.
See Styrene.

Styrolene.
See Styrene.

Styrone.
Cinnamaldehyde, *q.v.*

Styrylacetic Acid (*3-Phenylvinylacetic acid, 2-benzylidenepropionic acid*)

$C_6H_5{\cdot}CH{:}CH{\cdot}CH_2{\cdot}COOH$

$C_{10}H_{10}O_2$ MW, 162

I.

Needles from H_2O. M.p. 87°. B.p. 302°. Sol. EtOH, Et_2O, hot CS_2.

K salt: m.p. 245° decomp.

Me ester: $C_{11}H_{12}O_2$. MW, 176. B.p. 185°/about 20 mm.

Et ester: $C_{12}H_{14}O_2$. MW, 190. B.p. 281–2°/763 mm., 184°/44 mm., 164–5°/25 mm. $D_4^{20·5}$ 1·0340. $n_D^{20·5}$ 1·53271.

Chloride: $C_{10}H_9OCl$. MW, 180·5. M.p. 41–2°. B.p. 106–8°/0·4 mm.

Amide: $C_{10}H_{11}ON$. MW, 161. Needles from C_6H_6. M.p. 130°. Sol. EtOH, $CHCl_3$, hot H_2O. Spar. sol. Et_2O.

Anhydride: $C_{20}H_{18}O_3$. MW, 306. M.p. 120–1°.

Nitrile: cinnamyl cyanide. $C_{10}H_9N$. MW, 143. Leaflets from pet. ether. M.p. 61–2°.

II. *Allo-*.

Amide: needles from C_6H_6–pet. ether. M.p. 85–6°.

Stoermer, Stockmann, *Ber.*, 1914, **47**, 1794.
Borsche, Niemann, Hartman, *Ber.*, 1936, **69**, 1996.
Linstead, Williams, *J. Chem. Soc.*, 1926, 2741.
Fichter, Pfister, *Ber.*, 1904, **37**, 2001.

2-Styrylacrylic Acid (*Cinnamylideneacetic acid, 4-phenyl-1 : 3-butadiene-1-carboxylic acid, 4-phenylvinylacrylic acid*)

$C_6H_5·CH:CH·CH:CH·COOH$

$C_{11}H_{10}O_2$ MW, 174

α-.

Plates from EtOH, prisms from C_6H_6. M.p. 165–6°. Sol. EtOH. Spar. sol. pet. ether. Heat of comb. C_p 1312·7 Cal, C_v 1311·8 Cal.

A,$CH_3·NH_2$: m.p. 142–3°.

A,$C_2H_5·NH_2$: m.p. 117–18°.

A,$(C_2H_5)_2NH$: m.p. about 80°.

Me ester : $C_{12}H_{12}O_2$. MW, 188. M.p. 71°. B.p. 185°/20 mm.

Et ester : $C_{13}H_{14}O_2$. MW, 202. Oil. $D^{79·8}$ 0·9985.

Isopropyl ester : $C_{14}H_{16}O_2$. MW, 216. Yellow oil. B.p. 169°/9 mm. D_4^{18} 1·0256. $n_D^{13·7}$ 1·6066.

Amide : $C_{11}H_{11}ON$. MW, 173. Leaflets from C_6H_6. M.p. 185°. *Acetyl* : m.p. 177–8°.

Methylamide : $C_{12}H_{13}ON$. MW, 187. Needles from C_6H_6–EtOH. M.p. 157°.

Ethylamide : $C_{13}H_{15}ON$. MW, 201. Needles from C_6H_6. M.p. 143–4°.

Diethylamide : $C_{15}H_{19}ON$. MW, 229. M.p. 106°.

Anhydride : $C_{22}H_{18}O_3$. MW, 330. Needles from AcOH. M.p. 152°.

Nitrile : $C_{11}H_9N$. MW, 155. Cryst. from ligroin. M.p. 42°. B.p. 285°, 159°/285 mm.

β-. *Allo-*.

Needles from C_6H_6. M.p. 138°. Sol. Et_2O, CS_2, $CHCl_3$, hot C_6H_6. Heat of comb. C_p 1321·6 Cal, C_v 1320·7 Cal.

Me ester : f.p. — 15°. Decomp. on dist.

Riiber, *Ber.*, 1911, **44**, 2390 ; *Ber.*, 1904, **37**, 2274.
Reynolds, *Am. Chem. J.*, 1911, **46**, 200.
Stobbe, *Ber.*, 1912, **45**, 3408.

Styryl Alcohol.
See Cinnamyl Alcohol.

Styryl bromide.
See β-Bromostyrene.

1-Styryl-1-butylene.
See 1-Phenyl-1 : 3-hexadiene.

Styryl chloride.
See β-Chlorostyrene.

Styryl cyanide.
See under Cinnamic Acid.

2-Styryl-1-cyanoacrylic Acid.
See Cinnamylidenecyanoacetic Acid.

Styrylglycollic Acid (*1-Hydroxy-3-phenylvinylacetic acid, 1-hydroxy-2-benzylidenepropionic acid, benzylidene-lactic acid*)

$C_6H_5·CH:CH·CH(OH)·COOH$

$C_{10}H_{10}O_3$ MW, 178

Needles from H_2O. M.p. 137°. Very sol. boiling H_2O. Spar. insol. H_2O, Et_2O. Insol. CS_2, C_6H_6, ligroin.

Amide : $C_{10}H_{11}O_2N$. MW, 177. Plates from H_2O. M.p. 141·5°. Very sol. EtOH. Sol. hot $CHCl_3$, C_6H_6. Spar. sol. Et_2O, CS_2.

Nitrile : cinnamaldehyde cyanhydrin. $C_{10}H_9ON$. MW, 159. Plates from CS_2. M.p. 74°. *Benzoyl* : cryst. from H_2O. M.p. 72–3°.

Acetyl : needles from H_2O. M.p. 79° (+ $1H_2O$), 90–1° (anhyd.). Very sol. most org. solvents.

Fittig, Ginsberg, Petkow, *Ann.*, 1898, **299**, 20.
Thiele, Sulzberger, *Ann.*, 1901, **319**, 208.
Bougault, *J. pharm. chim.*, 1913, **8**, 404.

Styrylphenol.
See Hydroxystilbene.

2-Styrylpropionic Acid.
See 3-Benzylidenebutyric Acid.

1-Styrylpyridine.
See Stilbazole.

2-Styrylquinoline (*2-Benzylidenequinaldine*, sym.-*phenyl-2-quinolylethylene*, *α-irazole*)

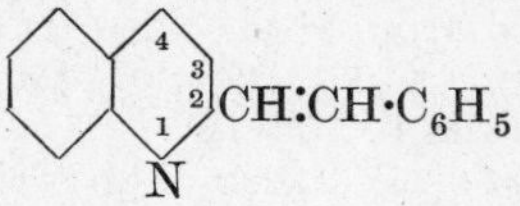

$C_{17}H_{13}N$ MW, 231

Needles from Et_2O–EtOH. M.p. 99–100°. Sol. $CHCl_3$, CS_2, hot EtOH. Insol. H_2O. $CrO_3 \longrightarrow$ benzoic + quinaldinic acids.

Ismailsky, *J. prakt. Chem.*, 1912, **85**, 91.
Noelting, Witte, *Ber.*, 1906, **39**, 2750.

4-Styrylquinoline (*ω-Benzylidenelepidine*, sym.-*phenyl-4-quinolylethylene*).

Cryst. from EtOH. M.p. 92°. Sol. Et_2O. Spar. sol. H_2O. $CrO_3 \longrightarrow$ cinchoninic acid.

Doebner, Miller, *Ber.*, 1885, **18**, 1646.

Suberamic Acid.
See under Suberic Acid.

Suberane.
See Cycloheptane.

Suberanilic Acid.
See under Suberic Acid.

Suberene.
See Cycloheptene.

Suberic Acid (*Hexane*-1 : 6-*dicarboxylic acid*)

$HOOC{\cdot}CH_2{\cdot}CH_2{\cdot}CH_2{\cdot}CH_2{\cdot}CH_2{\cdot}CH_2{\cdot}COOH$

$C_8H_{14}O_4$ MW, 174

Needles from H_2O. M.p. 144° (139–40°). B.p. 279°/100 mm., 258·5°/50 mm., 230°/15 mm., 219·5°/10 mm. Spar. sol. H_2O, Et_2O. Insol. $CHCl_3$. Heat of comb. C_p 982·8 Cal., C_v 988·6 Cal. k (first) $= 2{\cdot}58 \times 10^{-5}$ at 25° ; (second) $= 2{\cdot}5 \times 10^{-6}$ at 100°.

Di-brucine salt : m.p. 102°.

Me ester : $C_9H_{16}O_4$. MW, 188. F.p. about 10°. B.p. 146–50°/1 mm. D^{20} 1·047.

Di-Me ester : $C_{10}H_{18}O_4$. MW, 202. F.p. – 3·1°. B.p. 268°, 174–5°/13–20 mm., 130–1°/9 mm. D_4^{20} 1·0217. n_D^{20} 1·43408.

Et ester : $C_{10}H_{18}O_4$. MW, 202. M.p. 21–2° n5°). B.p. 186–188·5°/16 mm. D^{23} 1·037. 2_D^{23} 1·4412. *Chloride* : $C_{10}H_{17}O_3Cl$. MW, 220·5. B.p. 132°/15 mm. p-*Toluidide* : m.p. 74°.

Di-Et ester : $C_{12}H_{22}O_4$. MW, 230. F.p. 5·9°. B.p. 282°/763 mm., 251–3°/320 mm. D_4^{20} 0·9822. n_D^{20} 1·43278.

Phenacyl ester : $C_{16}H_{20}O_5$. MW, 292. M.p. 102·4°.

p-*Bromophenacyl ester* : $C_{16}H_{19}O_5Br$. MW, 371. M.p. 144·2°.

Dichloride : $C_8H_{12}O_2Cl_2$. MW, 211. B.p. 162–3°/15 mm., 149–50°/12 mm. $D_4^{20\cdot8}$ 1·1718. $n_D^{20\cdot6}$ 1·46847.

Amide : suberamic acid. $C_8H_{15}O_3N$. MW, 173. Cryst. from H_2O. M.p. 125–7°.

Diamide : $C_8H_{16}O_2N_2$. MW, 172. Cryst. from H_2O. M.p. 216–17°.

Anhydride : suberic anhydride. $C_8H_{12}O_3$. MW, 156. Needles from C_6H_6. M.p. 65–6° (63°).

Dinitrile : suberonitrile. $C_8H_{12}M_2$. MW, 136. M.p. – 3·5°. B.p. 185°/15 mm., 176–8°/11 mm.

Anilide : suberanilic acid. M.p. 128°.

Dianilide : m.p. 187° (183°).

Di-p-toluidide : m.p. 218°.

Dihydrazide : m.p. 185–6°.

Green, Hilditch, *J. Chem. Soc.*, 1937, 766.
Rozanov, Belikov, *Chem. Abstracts*, 1930, **24**, 3765.
Verkade, *Rec. trav. chim.*, 1927, **46**, 137.
Arppe, *Ann.*, 1862, **124**, 89.
Dale, Schorlemmer, *Ann.*, 1879, **199**, 145.
Blaise, Koehler, *Bull. soc. chim.*, 1909, **5**, 690.

Suberol.
See Cycloheptanol.

Suberone.
See Cycloheptanone.

Suberyl Alcohol.
See Cycloheptanol.

Suberylamine.
See Cycloheptylamine.

Suberylene.
See Cycloheptene.

Succinaldehydic Acid.
2-Aldehydopropionic Acid, *q.v.*

Succinamic Acid (*Succinic acid monoamide*)

$CH_2{\cdot}CONH_2$
$CH_2{\cdot}COOH$

$C_4H_7O_3N$ MW, 117

Needles from Me_2CO. M.p. 157° (154°). Mod. sol. H_2O, hot Me_2CO. Spar. sol. EtOH, C_6H_6, ligroin. Heat at 200° ⟶ succinimide.

A,$NH_2{\cdot}NH_2$: m.p. 113°.

Me ester : $C_5H_9O_3N$. MW, 131. Plates. M.p. 89–91°. Sol. H_2O, EtOH, Me_2CO. Spar. sol. Et_2O, pet. ether.

Et ester : $C_6H_{11}O_3N$. MW, 145. M.p. 74–5°. B.p. 230–40°.

Amide : *see* Succinamide.

Rubtzov, *Chem. Abstracts*, 1924, **18**, 1472.
Jeffery, Vogel, *J. Chem. Soc.*, 1934, 1103.

Succinamide (*Succinic acid diamide*)

$CH_2{\cdot}CO{\cdot}NH_2$
$CH_2{\cdot}CO{\cdot}NH_2$

$C_4H_8O_2N_2$ MW, 116

Needles from H_2O. M.p. 260° decomp. (242·3°). Sol. hot H_2O. Insol. EtOH, Et_2O. Heat of comb. C_p 509·7 Cal. Heat ⟶ succinimide.

N-d-*Glucoside* : $C_{10}H_{18}O_7N_2$. MW, 278. Prisms + $2H_2O$ from EtOH.Aq. M.p. 88–90° (192° decomp., anhyd.). $[\alpha]_D^{19}$ – 17·40° in H_2O.

Morrell, *J. Chem. Soc.*, 1914, **105**, 2705.

Succinanil (N-*Phenylsuccinimide*)

$CH_2{\cdot}CO$
$CH_2{\cdot}CO$ $>N{\cdot}C_6H_5$

$C_{10}H_9O_2N$. MW, 175

Needles from H_2O. M.p. 156°. Distils at about 400° without decomp. Sol. Et_2O, hot EtOH. Insol. H_2O.

Warren, Briggs, *Ber.*, 1931, **64**, 29.
Ruggli, *Ann.*, 1916, **412**, 4.

Succinanilic Acid (*Succinic acid monoanilide*)

$CH_2{\cdot}CO{\cdot}NH{\cdot}C_6H_5$
$CH_2{\cdot}COOH$

$C_{10}H_{11}O_3N$ MW, 193

Needles from hot H_2O. M.p. 144·5–145·5° (148·5°). Sol. EtOH, Et_2O, hot H_2O. Heat of comb. C_p 1166·5 Cal. $k = 2{\cdot}03 \times 10^{-5}$ at 25°. Heat ⟶ succinanil.

A,CH_3·NH_2: m.p. 115–20°.

Me ester: $C_{11}H_{13}O_3N$. MW, 207. Needles from EtOH. M.p. 97–8°.

Et ester: $C_{12}H_{15}O_3N$. MW, 221. Cryst. from Et_2O–pet. ether. M.p. 56·5–57·5°.

Amide: $C_{10}H_{12}O_2N_2$. MW, 192. Needles from H_2O. M.p. 181°. Heat of comb. C_p 1244·6 Cal.

Anilide: *see* Succinanilide.

Menschutkin, *Ann.*, 1872, **162**, 176.
See also Warren, Briggs, *Ber.*, 1931, **64**, 29.

Succinanilide (*Succinic acid dianilide*, N:N′-*diphenylsuccinamide*)

$$\begin{matrix} CH_2{\cdot}CO{\cdot}NH{\cdot}C_6H_5 \\ | \\ CH_2{\cdot}CO{\cdot}NH{\cdot}C_6H_5 \end{matrix}$$

$C_{16}H_{16}O_2N_2$ MW, 268

Needles from EtOH. M.p. 230°. Sol. Et_2O, hot EtOH. Insol. H_2O. Heat. of comb C_p **1971**·3 Cal. Dist. ⟶ succinanil + aniline.

Morrell, *J. Chem. Soc.*, 1914, **105**, 1736, 2702.
Mistry, Guha, *J. Indian Chem. Soc.*, 1930, I, 797.

Succindialdehyde (*Succinic dialdehyde, succinic aldehyde, dialdehydoethane*)

$$\begin{matrix} CH_2{\cdot}CHO \\ | \\ CH_2{\cdot}CHO \end{matrix}$$

$C_4H_6O_2$ MW, 86

Only polymers produced in preparation. Heated in vacuo ⟶ monomer. B.p. 169–70° decomp., 56·5°/9 mm. D_4^{18} 1·069. n_D^{18} 1·42617.

Monoxime: *Me ether*, b.p. 67°/10 mm.

Dioxime: m.p. 173°.

Di-[di-Me]-acetal: b.p. 201–2°/772 mm., 99°/22 mm., 89°/13 mm. n_D^{20} 1·41555.

Di-[di-Et]-acetal: b.p. 210–15° decomp., 137°/35 mm., 116°/20 mm.

Polymer: m.p. 65°. B.p. 169°.

Harries, *Ann.*, 1913, **395**, 260.
Harries, Hohenemser, *Ber.*, 1908, **41**, 255 (*Footnote* 4).
Schöpf, Lehmann, *Ann.*, 1935, **518**, 1.

Succinic Acid (*Ethane*-1:2-*dicarboxylic acid*)

$$\begin{matrix} CH_2{\cdot}COOH \\ | \\ CH_2{\cdot}COOH \end{matrix}$$

$C_4H_6O_4$ MW, 118

Occurs in fossils, algæ, lichens, fungi, etc. Prisms from H_2O. M.p. 185° (184·5–185°). B.p. 235° ⟶ anhydride. Sol. EtOH, MeOH, Me_2CO, hot H_2O, hot H·COOH. Spar. sol. Et_2O. k (first) $= 6{\cdot}37 \times 10^{-3}$ ($6{\cdot}6 \times 10^{-5}$) at 25°; (second) $= 2{\cdot}54 \times 10^{-6}$ ($2{\cdot}7 \times 10^{-6}$) at 25°.

A,2NH_2OH: m.p. 121° decomp.

Brucine salt: m.p. 216–18°. $[\alpha]_D^{20}$ − 25·4° in H_2O.

Quinine salt: m.p. 198–200°. $[\alpha]_D^{20}$ − 165·5° in H_2O.

Strychnine salt: m.p. 210°. $[\alpha]_D^{20}$ − 25·6° in H_2O.

Me ester: $C_5H_8O_4$. MW, 132. M.p. 58°. B.p. 151°/20 mm., 121–3°/4 mm.

Di-Me ester: *see* Dimethyl succinate.

Et ester: $C_6H_{10}O_4$. MW, 146. M.p. 8°. B.p. 172°/42 mm., 146–9°/17 mm., 119°/3 mm. D^{20} 1·1466. n_D^{20} 1·4327. *Chloride*: $C_6H_9O_3Cl$. MW, 163·5. B.p. 144°/90 mm., 92°/20 mm.

Me-Et ester: $C_7H_{12}O_4$. MW, 160. F.p. below − 20°. B.p. 208·2°.

Di-Et ester: *see* Diethyl succinate.

Di-2-hydroxyethyl ester: $C_8H_{14}O_6$. MW, 206. B.p. 176–80°/0·01 mm. p-*Nitrobenzoyl deriv.*: m.p. 90–1°. *Diphenylurethane*: m.p. 113°.

Di-2-chloroethyl ester: $C_8H_{12}O_4Cl_2$. MW, 243. B.p. 204–5°/30 mm.

Propyl ester: $C_7H_{12}O_4$. MW, 160. M.p. 15°. B.p. 126°/3 mm. D^{20} 1·1071. n_D^{20} 1·4343.

Dipropyl ester: $C_{10}H_{18}O_4$. MW, 202. M.p. − 10·4°. B.p. 250·8° (246–7°/762·2 mm.). D^{20} 1·0011. n_D^{20} 1·4252.

Di-isopropyl ester: b.p. 228°/761 mm.

Butyl ester: $C_8H_{14}O_4$. MW, 174. M.p. 8·6°. B.p. 136·5°/3 mm. D^{20} 1·0732. n_D^{20} 1·4360.

Dibutyl ester: $C_{12}H_{22}O_4$. MW, 230. M.p. − 29·25° (− 37·5°). B.p. 274·5°, 145°/4 mm. D^{20} 0·9652. n_D^{20} 1·4369.

Di-sec. n-*butyl ester*: b.p. 255·5–256·5°/750 mm. D_4^{20} 0·9735.

Di-isobutyl ester: b.p. 264·8–265·8°.

n-*Amyl ester*: $C_9H_{16}O_4$. MW, 188. M.p 17·2°. B.p. 147°/3 mm. D^{20} 1·0460. n_D^{20} 1·4378.

Di-n-amyl. ester: $C_{14}H_{26}O_4$. MW, 258. M.p. − 9°. B.p. 171·5°/16 mm.

Di-active-*amyl ester*: b.p. 175°/20 mm.

Di-isoamyl ester: b.p. 298–9°/765·4 mm., 289·9°/728 mm.

Di-n-heptyl ester: $C_{18}H_{34}O_4$. MW, 314. B.p. 350–1°.

Dihexadecyl ester: $C_{36}H_{70}O_4$. MW, 566. M.p. 58°.

Diallyl ester: $C_{10}H_{14}O_4$. MW, 198. B.p. 249–50°/757·3 mm.

Cyclohexyl ester : $C_{10}H_{16}O_4$. MW, 200. M.p. 44°.

d-*Menthyl ester* : $C_{14}H_{24}O_4$. MW, 256. $[\alpha]_D$ + 55·68° in C_6H_6. *Cinchonidine salt* : m.p. 141–3°. $[\alpha]_D$ − 46·72° in EtOH.

l-*Menthyl ester* : m.p. 64°. $[\alpha]_D$ − 64·00° in $CHCl_3$.

Di-l-*menthyl ester* : $C_{24}H_{42}O_4$. MW, 394. M.p. 63°. $[\alpha]_D^{20}$ − 82·4° in $CHCl_3$.

l-*Bornyl ester* : $C_{14}H_{22}O_4$. MW, 254. M.p. 58°. $[\alpha]_D$ − 35·94° in EtOH.

Di-l-*bornyl ester* : $C_{24}H_{38}O_4$. MW, 390. M.p. 83·7°. $[\alpha]_D$ − 42·39° in EtOH.

Phenyl ester : $C_{10}H_{10}O_4$. MW, 194. M.p. 98°.

Diphenyl ester : $C_{16}H_{14}O_4$. MW, 270. M.p. 121° (118°). B.p. 222·5°/15 mm.

Di-o-*nitrophenyl ester* : $C_{16}H_{12}O_8N_2$. MW, 360. M.p. 162°.

Di-m-*nitrophenyl ester* : m.p. 153°.

Di-p-*nitrophenyl ester* : m.p. 178°.

Di-o-*tolyl ester* : $C_{18}H_{18}O_4$. MW, 298. B.p. 238–40°/5 mm.

Di-m-*tolyl ester* : m.p. 60°.

Di-p-*tolyl ester* : m.p. 121°.

Di-l-*naphthyl ester* : $C_{24}H_{18}O_4$. MW, 370. M.p. 155°.

Di-2-*naphthyl ester* : m.p. 163°.

Benzyl ester : $C_{11}H_{12}O_4$. MW, 208. M.p. 46·5–47° (59°).

Dibenzyl ester : $C_{18}H_{18}O_4$. MW, 298. M.p. 45° (49–50°). B.p. 238°/14 mm.

Amide : see Succinamic Acid.

Diamide : see Succinamide.

Imide : see Succinimide.

Chloride : see Succinyl chloride.

Bromide : see Succinyl bromide.

Anhydride : see Succinic Anhydride.

Nitrile : see 2-Cyanopropionic Acid.

Dinitrile : see Succinonitrile.

Et ester-nitrile : see under 2-Cyanopropionic acid.

Amide-nitrile : see under 2-Cyanopropionic acid.

Anilide : see Succinanilic Acid.

Dianilide : see Succinanilide.

Di-2 : 4-*dichloroanilide* : m.p. 248°.

Mono-o-*nitroanilide* : m.p. 132–132·5°.

Mono-m-*nitroanilide* : m.p. 181–2°.

Mono-p-*nitroanilide* : m.p. 196–7°.

Di-p-*nitroanilide* : m.p. 260°.

Me-*anilide* : m.p. 91–92·5°.

Di-*Me*-*anilide* : m.p. 156·5°.

Et-*anilide* : m.p. 92–3°.

Di-*Et*-*anilide* : m.p. 106°.

o-*Toluidide* : m.p. 97°.

Di-o-*toluidide* : m.p. 100°.

p-*Toluidide* : m.p. 179–80°.

Di-p-toluidide : m.p. 256°.

1-*Naphthalide* : m.p. 171°.

Di-1-*naphthalide* : m.p. 285° decomp.

2-*Naphthalide* : m.p. 190–2°. *Et ester* : m.p. 99–100°.

Di-2-*naphthalide* : m.p. 266°.

Peroxide : see Succinperoxide.

Leffler, Adams, *J. Am. Chem. Soc.*, 1936, **58**, 1553.

I.G., D.R.P., 485,313, (*Chem. Abstracts*, 1930, **24**, 862).

Fourneau, Sabetay, *Bull. soc. chim.*, 1929, **45**, 834.

Zaidan, Kenkyuja, D.R.P., 469,234, (*Chem. Abstracts*, 1929, **23**, 2110).

Conzen-Crowet, *Bull. soc. chim. Belg.*, 1926, **35**, 165.

Succinic Aldehyde.
See Succindialdehyde.

Succinic Anhydride (2 : 5-*Diketotetrahydrofuran*)

$$\begin{array}{c} CH_2 \cdot CO \\ CH_2 \cdot CO \end{array}\!\!\!\!\Big\rangle O$$

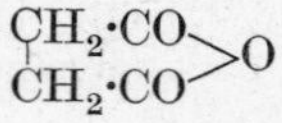

$C_4H_4O_3$ MW, 100

Cryst. from $CHCl_3$. M.p. 119·3–119·6°. B.p. 261°, 189°/100 mm., 169°/50 mm., 139°/15 mm., 131°/10 mm. Sol. $CHCl_3$. Spar. sol. Et_2O. D_4^{20} 1·2340. Heat of comb. C_v 373·1 Cal.

Leffler, Adams, *J. Am. Chem. Soc.*, 1936, **58**, 1551.

Jeffery, Vogel, *J. Chem. Soc.*, 1934, 1103

Shriner, Struck, *Organic Syntheses*, 1932 XII, 66.

Jaeger, Fiedler, U.S.P., 1,929,381, (*Chem. Abstracts*, 1934, **28**, 180).

Succinic Dialdehyde.
See Succindialdehyde.

Succinic Semialdehyde.
See 2-Aldehydopropionic Acid.

Succinimide (2 : 5-*Diketopyrrolidine*)

$$\begin{array}{c} CH_2 \cdot CO \\ CH_2 \cdot CO \end{array}\!\!\!\!\Big\rangle NH$$

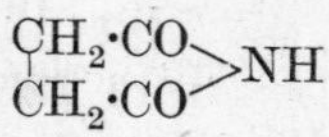

$C_4H_5O_2N$ MW, 99

Plates + $1H_2O$ from EtOH. M.p. 126–7° (125–6°). B.p. 287–8° decomp. Spar. sol. Et_2O. $k = 3 \times 10^{-11}$ at 25°. Forms *N*-metallic derivs.

Oxime : m.p. 197° decomp. *Benzoyl deriv.* : m.p. 184°.

Dioxime : m.p. 207°. *Diacetyl deriv.* : m.p. 170–1°. *Dibenzoyl deriv.* : m.p. 187°.
N-*Acetyl* : b.p. 167°/9·5 mm.
N-*Benzoyl* : m.p. 129–30°.
N-*Me* : *see* *N*-Methylsuccinimide.
N-*Et* : $C_6H_9O_2N$. MW, 127. M.p. 26°. B.p. 236°.
N-2-*Bromoethyl* : $C_6H_8O_2NBr$. 206. M.p. 56–7°.
N-*Propyl* : $C_7H_{11}O_2N$. MW, 141. M.p. 15–16°. B.p. 247–8°/763 mm., 136–7°/27 mm.
N-3-*Bromopropyl* : $C_7H_{10}O_2NBr$. MW, 220. M.p. 52°.
N-*Isopropyl* : m.p. 61°. B.p. 230°/755 mm., 225°/743 mm.
N-sec.-n.-*Butyl* : $C_8H_{13}O_2N$. MW, 155. B.p. 239–40°/758 mm.
N-*Isobutyl* : m.p. 28°. B.p. 247–8°/758 mm.
N-*Isoamyl* : $C_9H_{15}O_2N$. MW, 169, B.p. 261–2°.
N-*Allyl* : $C_7H_9O_2N$. MW, 139. B.p. 249–50°, 244–5°/730 mm., 130–1°/14 mm.
N-*Phenyl* : *see* Succinanil.
N-o-*Nitrophenyl* : $C_{10}H_8O_4N_2$. MW, 220. M.p. 156°.
N-m-*Nitrophenyl* : m.p. 175–6° (172°).
N-p-*Nitrophenyl* : m.p. 208° (203–4°).
N-p-*Hydroxyphenyl* : $C_{10}H_9O_3N$. MW, 191. M.p. 275–6°. *Me ether* : $C_{11}H_{11}O_3N$. MW, 205. M.p. 165°. *Et ether* : pyrantin. $C_{12}H_{13}O_3N$. MW, 219. M.p. 158° (155°). *Propyl ether* : $C_{13}H_{15}O_3N$. MW, 233. M.p. 178°. N-*Benzoyl* : m.p. 215°.
N-o-*Tolyl* : $C_{11}H_{11}O_2N$. MW, 189. M.p. 75°. (101–2°). B.p. 338–40°/733 mm. (339–40°/756 mm.).
N-m-*Tolyl* : m.p. 111–12°. B.p. 340–4°.
N-p-*Tolyl* : m.p. 151°. B.p. 344–5°/733 mm., 212°/13 mm.
N-1-*Naphthyl* : $C_{14}H_{11}O_2N$. MW, 225. M.p. 153°.
N-2-*Naphthyl* : m.p. 183°.
N-*Benzyl* : $C_{11}H_{11}O_2N$. MW, 189. M.p. 98–9° (103°).
N-o-*Nitrobenzyl* : $C_{11}H_{10}O_4N$. MW, 220. M.p. 130°.
N-p-*Nitrobenzyl* : m.p. 150–2°.
N-*Chloro* : cryst. from CCl_4. M.p. 150°.
N-*Bromo* : cryst. from C_6H_6. M.p. 173·5° decomp.

Roeder, *Ber.*, 1913, **46**, 2563.
Ma, Sah, *Chem. Abstracts*, 1934, **28**, 6108.
Fehling, *Ann.*, 1844, **49**, 198.
Tscherniac, *Ber.*, 1901, **34**, 4213.
Swarts, *Am. Chem. J.*, 1897, **19**, 297.

Succinonitrile (*Ethylene dicyanide, succinic acid dinitrile,* sym.-*dicyanoethane*)

$CH_2{\cdot}CN$
$CH_2{\cdot}CN$

$C_4H_4N_2$ MW, 80

F.p. 53°. M.p. 53·7° (54·5°). B.p. 265–7°, 185°/60 mm., 158–60°/20 mm. Sol. H_2O, EtOH, $CHCl_3$. Spar. sol. Et_2O, CS_2.

Fauconnier, *Bull. soc. chim.*, 1888, **50**, 214.

Succinophenone.
See Diphenacyl.

Succinosuccinic Acid (2 : 5-*Diketocyclohexane*-1 : 4-*dicarboxylic acid,* 2 : 5-*diketohexahydroterephthalic acid, succinylsuccinic acid,* 1 : 4-*dihydroxy*-$\Delta^{1,4}$-*cyclohexadiene*-3 : 6-*dicarboxylic acid*).

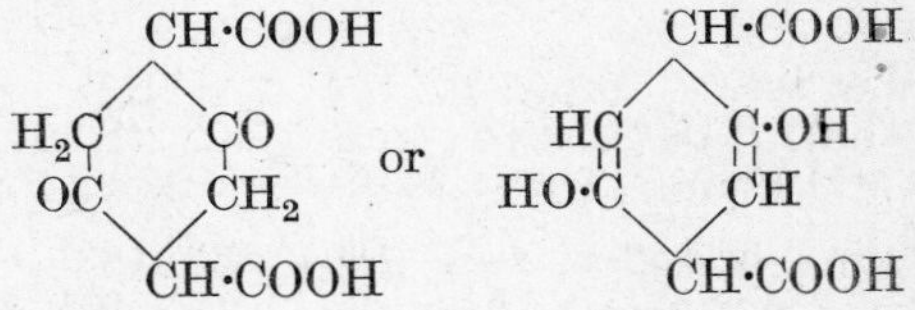

I II

$C_8H_8O_6$ MW, 200

Needles. Spar. sol. H_2O. $FeCl_3 \longrightarrow$ violet col. in EtOH.
Di-Me ester : $C_{10}H_{12}O_6$. MW, 228. Needles from EtOH. M.p. 153°.
Et ester : $C_{10}H_{12}O_6$. MW, 228. M.p. 98° decomp.
Di-Et ester : $C_{12}H_{16}O_6$. MW, 256. (I). M.p. 123°. (II). M.p. 127°.
Propyl ester : $C_{11}H_{14}O_6$. MW, 242. Yellow needles from C_6H_6. M.p. 115° decomp.
Dipropyl ester : $C_{14}H_{20}O_6$. MW, 284. M.p. 91°.
Isobutyl ester : $C_{12}H_{16}O_6$. MW, 256. M.p. 126° decomp.
Di-isobutyl ester : $C_{16}H_{24}O_6$. MW, 312. M.p. 100°.
Diallyl ester : $C_{14}H_{10}O_6$. MW, 274. M.p. 115°.

Liebermann, *Ann.*, 1914, **404**, 287.
Baeyer, Noyes, *Ber.*, 1889, **22**, 2168.
Hantzsch, *Ber.*, 1915, **48**, 772.

Succinperoxide (*Succinic acid peroxide*)

$(HOOC{\cdot}CH_2{\cdot}CH_2{\cdot}CO)_2O_2$

$C_8H_{10}O_8$ MW, 234

Plates. M.p. 128° decomp. Sol. H_2O, EtOH, Me_2CO. Spar. sol. Et_2O. Insol. $CHCl_3$, C_6H_6, ligroin.

Clover, Houghton, *Am. Chem. J.*, 1904, **32**, 55.
Stearns, D.R.P., 170,727, (*Chem. Zentr.*, 1906, II, 79).

Succinyl bromide

$CH_2 \cdot COBr$
$CH_2 \cdot COBr$

$C_4H_4O_2Br_2$ MW, 244

B.p. 105–6°/13 mm.

Hughes, Watson, *J. Chem. Soc.*, 1930, 1735.

Succinyl chloride

$CH_2 \cdot COCl$
$CH_2 \cdot COCl$

$C_4H_4O_2Cl_2$ MW, 155

Leaflets. M.p. 20° (17°). B.p. 190–2° (193·3°), 150–2°/214 mm., 103–4°/25 mm., 88·5°/19 mm. $D_4^{15\cdot2}$ 1·3948. $n_D^{15\cdot2}$ 1·473.

Vorländer, *Ann.*, 1894, **280**, 183.
Morrell, *J. Chem. Soc.*, 1914, **105**, 1733.
Monsanto, E.P., 418,162, (*Chem. Abstracts*, 1935, **29**, 1436).

Sucrol.
See Dulcin.

Sucrose (*Saccharose, cane sugar*)

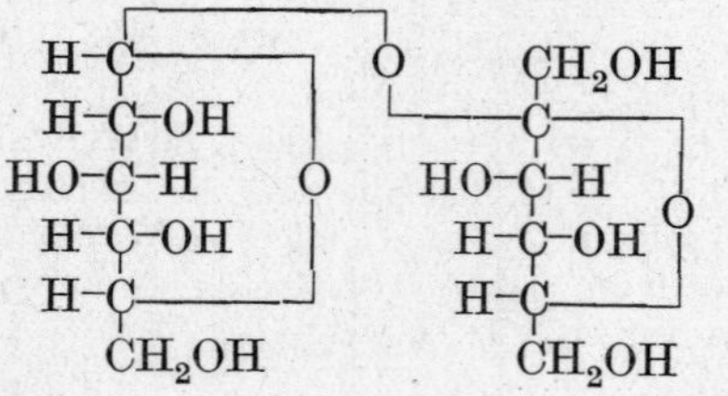

$C_{12}H_{22}O_{11}$ MW, 342

Occurs in ripe fruits, sugar cane, beet, etc. Cryst. M.p. 184–5° from dil. EtOH, 179–80° (174°) from EtOH, 169–70° from MeOH. Sweet taste. 100 parts H_2O dissolve 198·6 parts at 12·5°, 245·0 parts at 45°. Sol. MeOH. Spar. sol. 95% EtOH. Insol. Et_2O. $[\alpha]_D^{20}$ + 66·37° in H_2O. $D^{17\cdot5}$ 1·5805, D^{30} 1·5737 from MeOH, 1·5840 from EtOH. Does not reduce Fehling's. Does not form an osazone. Hyd. by dil. acids or by invertase ⟶ glucose + fructose. Mod. stable to alkalis. Fermentable. $KMnO_4$ ⟶ oxalic acid + CO_2. HNO_3 ⟶ saccharic, tartaric, and oxalic acids. Heat of comb. C_v = 3945·7 Cal. Forms compoun with CaO, BaO and SrO and with halides alkali metals.

Octa-Me ether: syrup. B.p. 176°/0·05 m $[\alpha]_D$ + 69·3° in MeOH, + 66·8° in Me_2C D_4^{20} 1·1406. n_D 1·4588. Hyd. ⟶ 2 : 3 : 4 : tetramethylglucose + 1 : 3 : 4 : 6-tetramethyl-fructose.

Octapropyl ether: m.p. 45·4–45·5°.

Octanitrate: needles. M.p. 85·5°. Decom at 135°. $[\alpha]_D^{20}$ + 55·9° in MeOH. Sol. MeO Et_2O. Spar. sol. EtOH, C_6H_6. Insol. H_2 pet. ether.

Octa-acetyl: needles from EtOH. M.p. 72· (69°, 70°). $[\alpha]_D^{20}$ + 59·6° in $CHCl_3$. Sol. h EtOH, Et_2O, $CHCl_3$, C_6H_6. Prac. insol. h H_2O. Insol. pet. ether.

Hexabenzoyl: cryst. M.p. 109°.

Heptabenzoyl: cryst. M.p. 98°.

Avery, Haworth, Hirst, *J. Chem. So* 1927, 2308.
Josephson, *Ann.*, 1929, **472**, 237.

Sulphanilic Acid.
See Aniline-*p*-sulphonic Acid.

Sulphazone

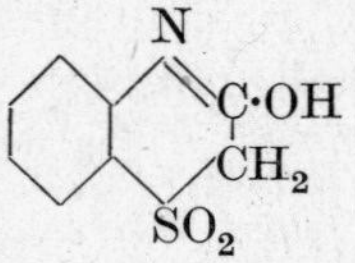

$C_8H_7O_3NS$ MW, 19

Brown leaflets from EtOH.Aq. M.p. 207 8°. Sol. EtOH, Me_2CO, AcOH. Spar. so Et_2O, hot H_2O. Insol. C_6H_6, ligroin.

B,HNO₃: yellow leaflets. Explodes at 172°

Me ether: $C_9H_9O_3NS$. MW, 211. Leafle from MeOH.Aq. M.p. 210°.

Claasz, *Ber.*, 1916, **49**, 614.
M.L.B., D.R.P., 269,428, (*Chem. Abstract* 1914, **8**, 2035).

Sulphoacetic Acid

$HO_3S \cdot CH_2 \cdot COOH$

$C_2H_4O_5S$ MW, 14

Hygroscopic cryst. + $1H_2O$ from H_2O. M. 84–6° (about 75°). Mod. sol. EtOH, Me_2C Insol. Et_2O, $CHCl_3$.

C-*Anilide*: *Na salt*, m.p. 284°. *Anilin salt*, m.p. 229–31°.

C-o-*Toluidide*: *Na salt*, m.p. 223–4 o-*Toluidine salt*: m.p. 189–91°.

C-p-*Anisidide*: p-*anisidine salt*, m.p. 224–7

C-p-*Phenetidide*: *Na salt*, m.p. 270 p-*Phenetidine salt*: m.p. 233–40°.

C-1-*Naphthalide*: *Na salt*, m.p. 285°.

Stillich, *J. prakt. Chem.*, 1906, **73**, 538; 1906, **74**, 53.
Fichter, *Z. Elektrochem*, 1914, **20**, 471.
Lichtenhahn, *Ber.*, 1915, **48**, 1950.

Sulphoalanine.

See Cysteic Acid *and* Isocysteic Acid.

Sulphoanisic Acid.

See under 4-Hydroxysulphobenzoic Acid.

Sulphobenzide.

See Diphenyl sulphone.

***o*-Sulphobenzoic Acid** (*Benzoic acid* o-*sulphonic acid*)

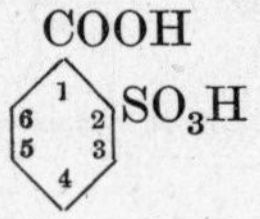

$C_7H_6O_5S$ MW, 202

Needles + $3H_2O$ from H_2O. M.p. 68–9°, anhyd. 134° (141°). Sol. H_2O, EtOH. Insol. Et_2O. Heat ⟶ anhydride.

1-*Me ester*: *chloride*. $C_8H_7O_4ClS$. MW, 234·5. M.p. 64–5°. Sol. EtOH, Et_2O. *Amide*: $C_8H_9O_4NS$. MW, 215. M.p. 125–6°.

1-*Et ester*: *amide*. $C_9H_{11}O_4NS$. MW, 229. M.p. 84°.

Di-Et ester: $C_{11}H_{14}O_5S$. MW, 258. B.p. 212–13°/21 mm.

1-*Phenyl ester*: $C_{13}H_{10}O_5S$. MW, 278. Needles from H_2O. M.p. 277–80°. Sol. H_2O, AcOH. Spar. sol. EtOH. *Chloride*: $C_{13}H_9O_4Cl$. MW, 264·5. Prisms from AcOH. M.p. 103–4°. Sol. EtOH, AcOH. Spar. sol. Et_2O, C_6H_6. *Amide*: $C_{13}H_{11}O_4NS$. MW, 277. Prisms. M.p. 132°.

2-*Phenyl ester*: *amide*. M.p. 95°.

Diphenyl ester: $C_{19}H_{14}O_5S$. MW, 354. Needles from AcOH. M.p. 117·5–118·5°.

1-o-*Tolyl ester*: *chloride*. $C_{14}H_{11}O_4Cl$. MW, 278·5. M.p. 112°. *Amide*: $C_{14}H_{13}O_4NS$. MW, 291. M.p. 152°.

2-*Chloride*: *nitrile*. $C_7H_4O_2NClS$. MW, 201·5. Prisms from Et_2O. M.p. 69–70° (67·5°). Sol. Et_2O, $CHCl_3$, C_6H_6, hot pet. ether.

Dichloride: $C_7H_4O_3Cl_2S$. MW, 239. (i) Needles from pet. ether. M.p. 79°. Sol. Et_2O, $CHCl_3$. Spar. sol. pet. ether. (ii) Plates from Et_2O. M.p. 40°. Sol. Et_2O, $CHCl_3$.

1-*Amide*: $C_7H_7O_4NS$. MW, 201. Prisms + $1H_2O$. M.p. anhyd. 185–6°, (193–4°). Sol. H_2O, EtOH.

2-*Amide*: plates from H_2O. M.p. 165–7° (rapid heat.), 153–5° (slow heat.). Sol. H_2O, EtOH, Et_2O. $k = 2{\cdot}06 \times 10^{-3}$ at 25°. *K deriv.*: m.p. 285–6°. o-*Toluidide*: m.p. 193°. p-*Toluidide*: m.p. 202°. *Hydrazide*: m.p. 182°.

1-*Methylamide*: $C_8H_9O_4NS$. MW, 215. M.p. 126°.

1-*Ethylamide*: $C_9H_{11}O_4NS$. MW, 229. M.p. about 111°.

Imide: *see* Saccharin.

Anhydride: $C_7H_4O_4S$. MW, 184. Plates from C_6H_6. M.p. 129·5° (128°). B.p. 184–6°/18 mm. Sol. Et_2O, C_6H_6, $CHCl_3$, hot H_2O.

Nitrile: *o*-cyanobenzenesulphonic acid. $C_7H_5O_3NS$. MW, 183. Needles from H_2O. M.p. 279–279·5°. Mod. sol. EtOH, hot H_2O. Spar. sol. Et_2O, $CHCl_3$. *Anilide*: m.p. 150–2°.

2-*Anilide*: m.p. 156°.

Dianilide: m.p. 194–5°.

Maarse, *Rec. trav. chim.*, 1914, **33**, 210.
Krannich, *Ber.*, 1900, **33**, 3485.
White, Acree, *Organic Syntheses*, Collective Vol. I, 13, 482.
Auger, Vary, *Bull. soc. chim.*, 1921, **29**, 990.
Ray, Dey, *J. Chem. Soc.*, 1920, **117**, 1406.

***m*-Sulphobenzoic Acid** (*Benzoic acid* m-*sulphonic acid*).

Cryst. + $2H_2O$. M.p. 98°, anhyd. 141°. Sol. H_2O, EtOH. Insol. C_6H_6, $CHCl_3$, pet. ether. Anhyd. acid sol. Et_2O.

1-*Me ester*: $C_8H_8O_5S$. MW, 216. M.p. 65°. *Chloride*: $C_8H_7O_4ClS$. MW, 234·5. M.p. 63–5°.

3-*Me ester*: m.p. 139–40°.

Di-Me ester: $C_9H_{10}O_5S$. MW, 230. M.p. 32–3°. B.p. 198–200°/20 mm.

3-*Chloride*: $C_7H_5O_4ClS$. MW, 220·5. M.p. 133–4°.

Dichloride: $C_7H_4O_3Cl_2S$. MW, 239. M.p. 20·4°.

3-*Amide*: $C_7H_7O_4NS$. MW, 201. M.p. 237–8° (233°). *Nitrile*: $C_7H_6O_2N_2S$. MW, 182. M.p. 151–2°.

Diamide: $C_7H_8O_3N_2S$. MW, 200. M.p. anhyd. 170°.

Offermann, *Ann.*, 1894, **280**, 6.
Maarse, *Rec. trav. chim.*, 1914, **33**, 209.
Nakaseko, *Am. Chem. J.*, 1912, **47**, 448.

***p*-Sulphobenzoic Acid** (*Benzoic acid* p-*sulphonic acid*).

Needles + $3H_2O$. M.p. 94°, anhyd. 259–60°. Sol. H_2O, EtOH. Anhyd. acid sol. Et_2O.

1-*Me ester*: m.p. 99–100°.

4-*Me ester*: m.p. 195–6°.

Di-Me ester: m.p. 88–90°.

1-*Et ester*: *amide.* $C_9H_{11}O_4NS$. MW, 229. M.p. 110–11° ⟶ solid, m.p. 94–5°.

4-*Chloride*: *nitrile.* $C_7H_4O_2NClS$. MW, 201·5. M.p. 111–12°.

Dichloride: m.p. 56–7°.

4-*Amide*: decomp. at 280°. $k = 2{\cdot}56 \times 10^{-4}$ at 25°. N-*Dichloro*: *see* Halazone. *Nitrile*: $C_7H_6O_2N_2S$. MW, 182. M.p. 168–9°.

Diamide: m.p. 236°.

Nitrile: *anilide.* M.p. 112°. m-*Toluidide*: m.p. 128°.

Dianilide: m.p. 252–3° decomp.

Di-m-*toluidide*: m.p. 241–2° decomp.

Heinemann, E.P., 23,575, (*Chem. Abstracts*, 1916, **10**, 1579).
Remsen, *Ann.*, 1875, **178**, 288.
See also second reference above.

Sulphocresotic Acid.
See Hydroxy-sulphotoluic Acid.

Sulphoethylurea.
See Taurocarbamic Acid.

2-Sulphoethyl Alcohol.
See Isethionic Acid.

Sulphonal (*Acetone diethylsulphone, propane-2 : 2-diethyldisulphone*)

$$\begin{matrix}CH_3 \\ CH_3\end{matrix}\!>C<\!\begin{matrix}SO_2{\cdot}C_2H_5 \\ SO_2{\cdot}C_2H_5\end{matrix}$$

$C_7H_{16}O_4S_2$ MW, 228

Prisms from EtOH, microscopic leaflets from Et_2O. M.p. 125·8°. B.p. 300° (slight decomp.). Sublimes (begins at 66°). Volatile in steam. Solubilities (1 gm. in x gms. solvent): H_2O, 422 at 18°, 222 at 37°, 8 at 100°; EtOH, 2 at 78°; Et_2O, 67 at 19°, 79 at 15°; $CHCl_3$, 3·3 at 20°; C_6H_6, 12·7 at 20°; AcOEt, 13·7 at 20°; CCl_4, 110 at 20°. Stable to acids, alkalis, bromine. Hypnotic.

Falck, *Chem. Abstracts*, 1920, **14**, 1002.
Hirayama, Matsuzaki, Okamoto, *Chem. Abstracts*, 1918, **12**, 1586.

Sulphonyldiacetic Acid (*Dimethylsulphone-α : α′-dicarboxylic acid*)

$$HOOC{\cdot}CH_2{\cdot}SO_2{\cdot}CH_2{\cdot}COOH$$

$C_4H_6O_6S$ MW, 182

Plates. M.p. 182°. Decomp. at 200° ⟶ dimethyl sulphone. Very sol. H_2O, EtOH. Mod. sol. H_2SO_4.Aq., Et_2O. k (first) $= 1{\cdot}3 \times 10^{-2}$; (second) $= 4{\cdot}75 \times 10^{-4}$ at 25°. Electrolysis of K salts ⟶ $H_2SO_4 + CO_2$. $NaNO_2$.Aq. ⟶ $CO_2 + HCN + H_2SO_4$.

Fichter, Krummenacher, *Helv. Chim. Acta*, 1918, **1**, 162.
Lovén, *Ber.*, 1884, **17**, 2818.

Sulphonyldiphenylmethane.
See Diphenylmethane sulphone.

3-Sulphophthalic Acid (*Phthalic acid 3-sulphonic acid*)

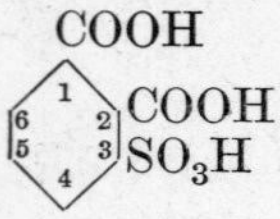

$C_8H_6O_7S$ MW, 24

Prisms + H_2O of cryst. M.p. 62–4°. Ver sol. H_2O, EtOH. Insol. Et_2O.

3-*Amide*: $C_8H_7O_6NS$. MW, 245. Needles + $1H_2O$ from H_2O. M.p. 155° decomp. (soften at 120°). *Di-Me ester*: m.p. 135°. *Di-Et ester* m.p. 102°.

Remsen, Stokes, *Am. Chem. J.*, 1884, **6**, 279.
Moulton, *Am. Chem. J.*, 1891, **13**, 203.
Cf. Rée, *Ann.*, 1886, **233**, 217.

4-Sulphophthalic Acid (*Phthalic acid 4-sulphonic acid*).

Cryst. + $1H_2O$. M.p. 138–40°. Very so H_2O, EtOH. Insol. Et_2O. Fused with NaOH at 220° ⟶ 4-hydroxyphthalic acid. K sal heated with Na formate ⟶ trimellitic acid.

4-*Chloride*: $C_8H_5O_6ClS$. MW, 264·5. Prism from Et_2O. M.p. 167–70° decomp.

4-*Amide*: prisms from H_2O. M.p. 192–200 decomp.

Bentley, Weizmann, *J. Chem. Soc.*, 1907, **91**, 100.
Rée, *Ann.*, 1886, **233**, 219, 228.

Sulphosalicylic Acid.
See 2-Hydroxy-4-sulphobenzoic Acid *and* 6-Hydroxy-3-sulphobenzoic Acid.

4-Sulpho-o-toluic Acid

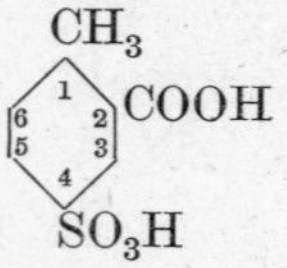

$C_8H_8O_5S$ MW, 21

Fibrous cryst. mass. Very sol. H_2O. Fuse with KOH ⟶ 4-hydroxy-o-toluic acid.

4-*Amide*: $C_8H_9O_4NS$. MW, 215. Needles M.p. 243°.

Jacobsen, Wierss, *Ber.*, 1883, **16**, 1959.
Baudisch, Perkin, *J. Chem. Soc.*, 1909, **95**, 1883.

5-Sulpho-o-toluic Acid.

Mono-NH_4 salt: prisms from H_2O. M.p 284°. Reacts acid.

2-*Amide*: $C_8H_9O_4NS$. MW, 215. Needle

from H_2O. M.p. 217°. *NH_4 salt*: prisms. M.p. 276–8°.

5-*Amide*: m.p. 211°.

Amide-nitrile: $C_8H_8O_2N_2S$. MW, 196. Cryst. M.p. 160°.

Chloride-nitrile: $C_8H_6O_2NClS$. MW, 215·5. Cryst. from ligroin. M.p. 53°.

Nowell, *Am. Chem. J.*, 1912, **48**, 225, 237.

4-Sulpho-*m*-toluic Acid.

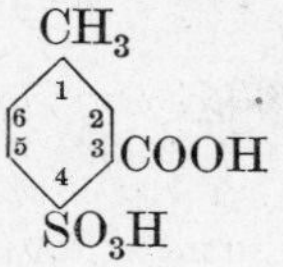

$C_8H_8O_5S$ MW, 216

Fused with KOH ⟶ 4-hydroxy-*m*-toluic acid.

Meldrum, Perkin, *J. Chem. Soc.*, 1909, **95**, 1891.

5-Sulpho-*m*-toluic Acid.

Cryst. + $2H_2O$ from H_2O. M.p. 110°. Fused with KOH ⟶ 5-hydroxy-*m*-toluic acid.

See previous reference.

6-Sulpho-*m*-toluic Acid.

6-*Amide*: needles from H_2O. M.p. 254° (220° slow heat.).

Waters, *Am. Chem. J.*, 1912, **47**, 343, 349.
Meldrum, Perkin, *J. Chem. Soc.*, 1909, **95**, 1891.

2-Sulpho-*p*-toluic Acid

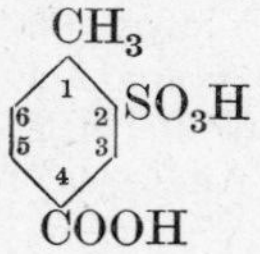

$C_8H_8O_5S$ MW, 216

Cryst. + $1H_2O$ from AcOH, + $3H_2O$ from H_2O.

2-*Amide*: needles from H_2O. M.p. 267°.

Diamide: $C_8H_{10}O_3N_2S$. MW, 214. Needles + $\frac{1}{2}H_2O$ from H_2O. M.p. 228°.

Meldrum, Perkin, *J. Chem. Soc.*, 1908, **93**, 1419.
Weinreich, *Ber.*, 1887, **20**, 981.

3-Sulpho-*p*-toluic Acid.

Cryst. + $3H_2O$. M.p. anhyd. 190° (158°). Sol. H_2O. Spar. sol. Et_2O, $CHCl_3$, C_6H_6. Fused with KOH ⟶ *m*-cresotic acid.

3-*Amide*: cryst. from H_2O. M.p. 185° (181°). *Me ester*: m.p. 145°. *Et ester*: m.p. 95°.

4-*Amide*: *NH_4 salt*, cryst. + $1H_2O$. M.p. 186°.

Amide-nitrile: leaflets from Py. Very spar. sol. H_2O, Et_2O. Sol. alkalis.

Dichloride: $C_8H_6O_3Cl_2S$. MW, 253. Cryst. from pet. ether. M.p. 59°.

Chloride-nitrile: leaflets from ligroin. M.p. 67°.

Weber, *Ber.*, 1892, **25**, 1741.
Randall, *Am. Chem. J.*, 1891, **13**, 258.

Sulphovinic Acid.

See Ethyl hydrogen sulphate.

Sulphuric Ether.

See Diethyl Ether.

Sumatrol

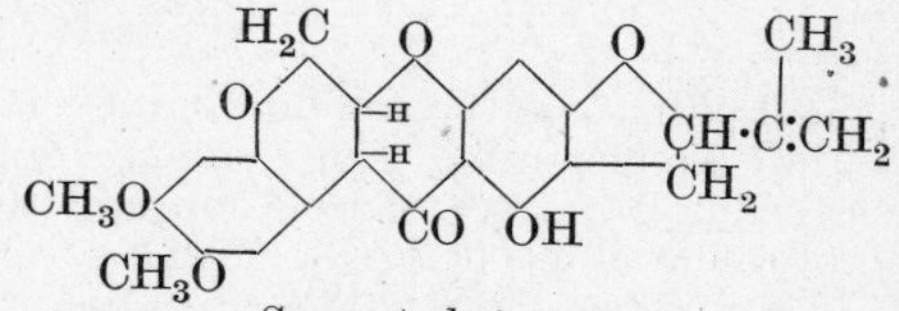

Suggested structure

$C_{23}H_{22}O_7$ MW, 410

Occurs in resin from *Derris* species. Needles from EtOH. M.p. 195–6° (air-dried). Recryst. from Me_2CO, m.p. 183° ⟶ 194° after several days keeping. Sol. $CHCl_3$. Mod. sol. C_6H_6, AcOEt. Spar. sol. MeOH, cold AcOH, 8% NaOH.Aq. $[\alpha]_D$ − 184° in C_6H_6. Alc. $FeCl_3$ ⟶ deep brownish-green col.

Oxime: needles from EtOH.Aq. M.p. 245–7°.

Robertson, Rusby, *J. Chem. Soc.*, 1937, 497.

Superpalite.

See Trichloromethyl chloroformate.

Suprarenin.

See Adrenaline.

Surinamine (*Ratanhin*, *geoffroyin*, *angelin*, *andirin*, N-*methyltyrosine*)

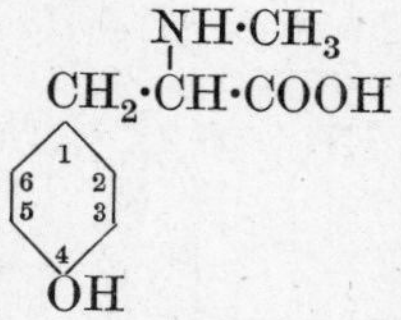

$C_{10}H_{13}O_3N$ MW, 195

Occurs in bark of *Andira retusa*, H.B. and K. Needles. M.p. 257° (decomp. at 280°). $[\alpha]_D^{21}$ + 19·8° in dil. HCl.

Me ester: $C_{11}H_{15}O_3N$. MW, 209. M.p. 111–12° (116–17°).

Me ether-nitrile : $C_{11}H_{14}ON_2$. MW, 190. M.p. 152–3°.

Fischer, Lipschitz, *Ber.*, 1915, **48**, 377.
Winterstein, *Z. physiol. Chem.*, 1919, **105**, 20.
Kanevska, *J. prakt. Chem.*, 1929, **124**, 48.

Sylvan.
See 2-Methylfuran.

Sylvestrene ($\Delta^{1,8(9)}$-m-*Menthadiene*, 1-*methyl*-3-*isopropenylcyclohexene*)

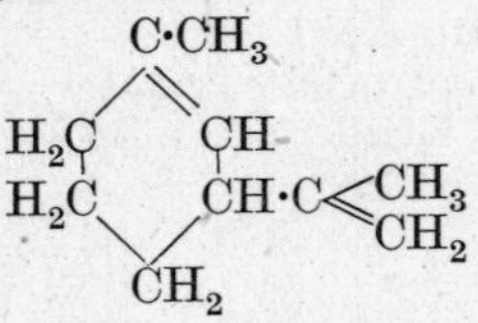

$C_{10}H_{16}$ MW, 136

Terpene hydrocarbon which does not occur in nature, but is generated from *carene* hydrocarbons during processes of isolation and purification of essential oils of *Pinus*. All forms sol. Ac_2O + 1 drop conc. H_2SO_4 ⟶ deep blue col.

d-.
B.p. 175°/751 mm. Polymerises on long heating. D^{18} 0·8479. n_D^{18} 1·4760. $[\alpha]_D^{18}$ + 83·18°. Heat of comb. C_v 1464·2 Cal.
Dihydrochloride : m.p. 72°.
Nitrosochloride : m.p. 106–7°.

l-.
B.p. 176–8°. D^{19} 0·848. n_D^{18} 1·4761. $[\alpha]_D^{18}$ − 68·2° in AcOEt.
Dihydrochloride : m.p. 72°.

dl-. Carvestrene.
B.p. 178°. Resinifies in air.
Dihydrochloride : cryst. from MeOH. M.p. 52°.

Aschan, *Ann.*, 1928, **461**, 1.
Semmler, Schiller, *Ber.*, 1927, **60**, 1591.
Rao, Simonsen, *J. Chem. Soc.*, 1925, 2494.
Haworth, Perkin, Wallach, *J. Chem. Soc.*, 1913, **103**, 2233.

Synthalin (*Decamethylenediguanidine*, 1 : 10-*diguanidino*-n-*decane*)

$H_2N{\cdot}C(\colon NH){\cdot}NH{\cdot}[CH_2]_{10}{\cdot}NH{\cdot}C(\colon NH){\cdot}NH_2$

$C_{12}H_{28}N_6$ MW, 256

Antidiabetic.
B,2HCl : cryst. from EtOH–Et_2O. M.p. 193°.

Kumagai *et al.*, *Sci. Papers Inst. Phys. Chem. Res., Tokyo*, 1928, **9**, 271.
Schering-Kahlbaum A.G., E.P., 285,873, (*Chem. Abstracts*, 1929, **23**, 154).
Ammon, *Chem.-Tech. Rundschau*, 1930, **45**, 406 (*Review*).

Syringa-aldehyde (*Syringic aldehyde*, 4-*hydroxy*-3 : 5-*dimethoxybenzaldehyde*, *gallaldehyde* 3 : 5-*dimethyl ether*)

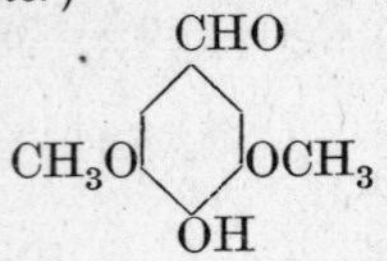

$C_9H_{10}O_4$ MW, 182

M.p. 113°. B.p. 192–3°/14 mm. Sol. EtOH, Et_2O, $CHCl_3$, AcOH, hot C_6H_6. $FeCl_3$.Aq. ⟶ olive-green col. The K and Na salts are yellow.
O-*Carbomethoxyl* : m.p. 98–9°.
Hydrazone : m.p. 208–9°.
p-*Nitrophenylhydrazone* : m.p. 216–17°.
Semicarbazone : m.p. 188°.

Sharp, *J. Chem. Soc.*, 1937, 853.
Mauthner, *J. prakt. Chem.*, 1935, **142**, 26.
McCord, *J. Am. Chem. Soc.*, 1931, **53**, 4181.
Pauly, Strassberger, *Ber.*, 1929, **62**, 2277.
See also references under Gallaldehyde.

Syringetin (5 : 7 : 4′-*Trihydroxy*-3′ : 5′-*dimethoxyflavonol*)

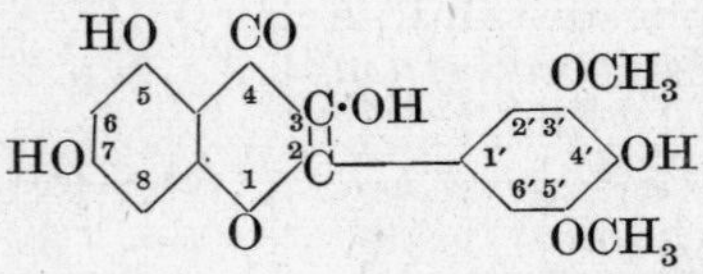

$C_{17}H_{14}O_8$ MW, 346

Pale yellow needles from AcOH. M.p. 288–9° (darkens at 270°). Mod. sol. MeOH, EtOH, Me_2CO, AcOH. Spar. sol. AcOEt, $CHCl_3$. Insol. C_6H_6, pet. ether. Conc. H_2SO_4 ⟶ yellow col. with green fluor. Alk. sols. are intensely deep yellow.
Tetra-acetyl : m.p. 224–6°.
4′-*Benzyl ether* : m.p. 240–1°. *Triacetyl* : m.p. 191–4°.

Heap, Robinson, *J. Chem. Soc.*, 1929, 67.

Syringic Acid (4-*Hydroxy*-3 : 5-*dimethoxybenzoic acid*, *gallic acid* 3 : 5-*dimethyl ether*)

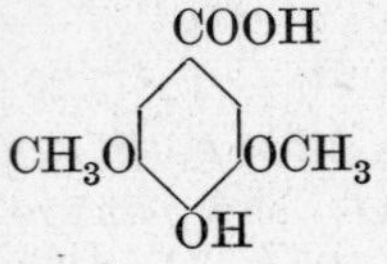

$C_9H_{10}O_5$ MW, 198

Cryst. M.p. 204–5°.
4-*Acetyl* : m.p. 191° (187°).

4-*Benzoyl*: m.p. 229–32°. *Chloride*: m.p. 17–18°. *Anhydride*: m.p. 112–13°.

Me ester: $C_{10}H_{12}O_5$. MW, 212. M.p. 83–4°, hyd. 107°. 4-*Acetyl*: m.p. 131·5°.

Et ester: $C_{11}H_{14}O_5$. MW, 226. M.p. 56°.

4-*Et ether*: 3 : 5-dimethoxy-4-ethoxybenzoic id. $C_{11}H_{14}O_5$. MW, 226. M.p. 123–4°. *Me ter*: m.p. 65°. *Et ester*: m.p. 47°. *Amide*: .p. 155°.

Wassmuth, *Ber.*, 1934, **67**, 701.
Bogert, Coyne, *J. Am. Chem. Soc.*, 1929, **51**, 571.
See also previous reference.

Syringic Aldehyde.
See Syringa-aldehyde.

Syringin (*Methoxyconiferin*)

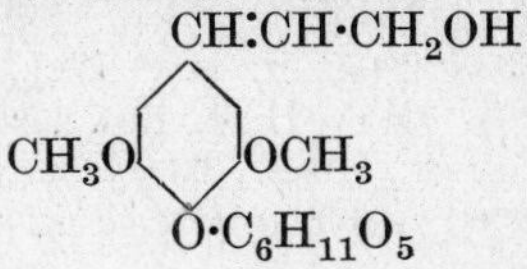

$C_{17}H_{24}O_9$ MW, 372

Glucoside occurring in various species of *Syringa*, *Ligustrum*, and *Jasminum*. Needles + $1H_2O$ from H_2O. M.p. 191–2°. $[\alpha]_D$ − 17·1°. Sol. hot H_2O, EtOH. Very spar. sol. cold H_2O. Insol. Et_2O. Tasteless. Does not reduce Fehling's or Tollen's. No col. with $FeCl_3$. Not pptd. by $Pb(OAc)_2$. Sol. conc. $HNO_3 \longrightarrow$ blood-red col. Sol. conc. $H_2SO_4 \longrightarrow$ dark blue to violet col. Hyd. by emulsin.

Pauly, Strassberger, *Ber.*, 1929, **62**, 2277.

T

Tagatose

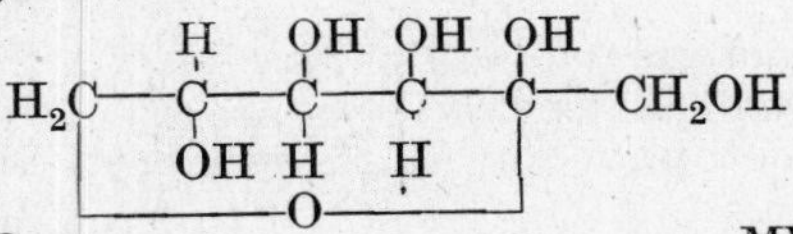

$C_6H_{12}O_6$ MW, 180

d-.

Cryst. M.p. 134–5° (124°). $[\alpha]_D^{22}$ + 1·0° in H_2O ($[\alpha]_D$ − 2·3° in H_2O). Sol. H_2O. Spar. ol. EtOH. Reduces Fehling's. Mod. sweet aste. Non-fermentable.

Phenylosazone: yellow needles. M.p. 193–4°. dentical with *d*-galactosazone.

Diacetone deriv.: m.p. 65–6°. $[\alpha]_D^{20}$ + 81·5° Me$_2$CO, + 71·8° in H_2O.

dl-. Dulcitose.

NaHg $\longrightarrow$ *dl*-talitol.

Methylphenylosazone: needles from Py.Aq. I.p. 148–50°.

de Bruyn, v. Ekenstein, *Rec. trav. chim.*, 1897, **16**, 265.
Neuberg, *Ber.*, 1902, **35**, 2629.
Nef, *Ann.*, 1914, **403**, 341.
Reichstein, Bosshard, *Helv. Chim. Acta*, 1934, **17**, 753.

Triguic Acid.
See Lapachol.

Talitol

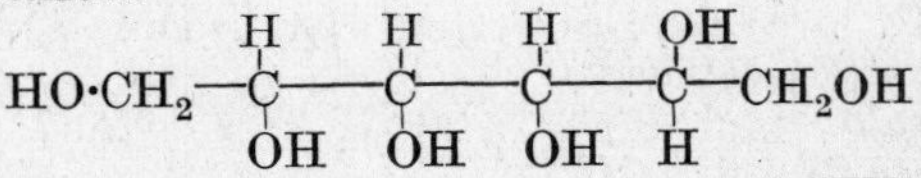

$C_6H_{14}O_6$ MW, 182

d-.

Prisms from EtOH. M.p. 86°. $[\alpha]_D^{18}$ + 3·05° in H_2O, lævorotatory on addn. of borax. Sol. H_2O, EtOH. Prac. insol. Et_2O. Sweet taste.

Tribenzylidene deriv.: needles. M.p. 210°. $[\alpha]_D$ − 40° in $CHCl_3$. Prac. insol. EtOH. Insol. H_2O.

dl-.

Needles from AcOEt. M.p. 66–7°. Sol. H_2O. Mod. sol. EtOH.

Tribenzylidene deriv.: cryst. M.p. 205–6°. Spar. sol. EtOH. Prac. insol. H_2O, Et_2O.

Fischer, *Ber.*, 1894, **27**, 1527.
de Bruyn, v. Ekenstein, *Rec. trav. chim.*, 1899, **18**, 151.
Bertrand, Bruneau, *Compt. rend.*, 1908, **146**, 482.

Talomucic Acid

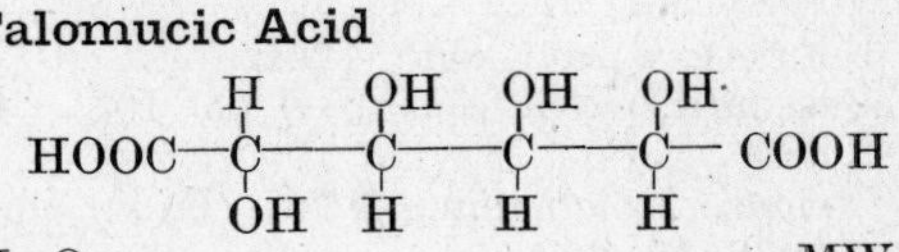

$C_6H_{10}O_8$ MW, 210

d-.

Laminæ from Me₂CO. M.p. 158° decomp. (155–8°). $[\alpha]_D^{20} + 29\cdot4°$ in H_2O ($[\alpha]_D + 29° \longrightarrow + 6\cdot7°$ in H_2O). Sol. H_2O, hot EtOH. Spar. sol. Me₂CO. Prac. insol. Et₂O, CHCl₃, C_6H_6. Partly converted into mucic acid on boiling with Py.Aq.

Diphenylhydrazide : m.p. 185–90°.

l-.

Cryst. from Me₂CO. M.p. 158° decomp. $[\alpha]_D^{20} - 33\cdot9°$ in H_2O.

Diphenylhydrazide : m.p. 185°.

Fischer, *Ber.*, 1891, **24**, 3625.
Fischer, Morrell, *Ber.*, 1894, **27**, 391.
Levene, Jacobs, *Ber.*, 1910, **43**, 3145.
Steiger, Reichstein, *Helv. Chim. Acta*, 1936, **19**, 198.

Talonic Acid

$$HO\cdot CH_2 - \overset{\overset{\textstyle H}{|}}{\underset{\underset{\textstyle OH}{|}}{C}} - \overset{\overset{\textstyle OH}{|}}{\underset{\underset{\textstyle H}{|}}{C}} - \overset{\overset{\textstyle OH}{|}}{\underset{\underset{\textstyle H}{|}}{C}} - \overset{\overset{\textstyle OH}{|}}{\underset{\underset{\textstyle H}{|}}{C}} - COOH$$

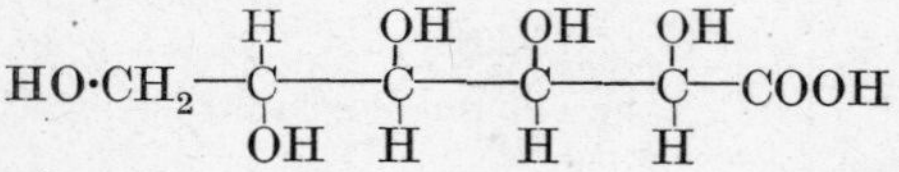

$C_6H_{12}O_7$ MW, 196

d-.

Cryst. $+ H_2O$ from dil. EtOH. M.p. 138–9° (125°). $[\alpha]_D^{25} + 16\cdot73° \longrightarrow - 21\cdot57°$ in H_2O (18·71° in H_2O). Sol. cold H_2O. Dil. $HNO_3 \longrightarrow$ talomucic acid.

K salt : m.p. 171–2° (169°). $[\alpha]_D^{10} + 2\cdot97°$ in H_2O ($[\alpha]_D^{20} + 3°$ in H_2O).

NH₄ salt : m.p. 148°. $[\alpha]_D^{25} + 2\cdot9°$ in H_2O.

Brucine salt : $C_{23}H_{26}O_4N_2, C_6H_{12}O_7$. Needles $+ 3\frac{1}{2}$ (?) H_2O from EtOH. M.p. 95–100°, anhyd. 154–6°. $[\alpha]_D^{20} - 26\cdot15°$ in H_2O.

γ-Lactone : m.p. 135–7° (132–4°). $[\alpha]_D^{25} - 34\cdot65° \longrightarrow - 28\cdot4°$ in H_2O. NaHg $\longrightarrow$ *d*-talose.

Amide : $C_6H_{13}O_6N$. MW, 195. M.p. 121°. $[\alpha]_D^{25} - 13\cdot1° \longrightarrow 0°$ in EtOH.

Phenylhydrazide : prisms from EtOH. M.p. 161–2° (159°). $[\alpha]_D^{20} - 24\cdot75° \longrightarrow 25\cdot1°$ in H_2O ($[\alpha]_D^{25} - 25\cdot43°$ in H_2O).

Hedenburg, Cretcher, *J. Am. Chem. Soc.*, 1927, **49**, 478.
Fischer, *Ber.*, 1891, **24**, 3622.
Fischer, Ruff, *Ber.*, 1900, **33**, 2146.
Cretcher, Renfrew, *J. Am. Chem. Soc.*, 1932, **54**, 1590, 4402.
Brackenbury, Upson, *J. Am. Chem. Soc.*, 1933, **55**, 2512.
Bonnett, Upson, *ibid.*, 1247.
Bosshard, *Helv. Chim. Acta*, 1935, **18**, 485.
Steiger, Reichstein, *Helv. Chim. Acta*, 1936, **19**, 203.

Talose

$$HO\cdot CH_2 - \overset{\overset{\textstyle H}{|}}{C} - \overset{\overset{\textstyle OH}{|}}{\underset{\underset{\textstyle H}{|}}{C}} - \overset{\overset{\textstyle OH}{|}}{\underset{\underset{\textstyle H}{|}}{C}} - \overset{\overset{\textstyle OH}{|}}{\underset{\underset{\textstyle H}{|}}{C}} - CH\cdot OH$$

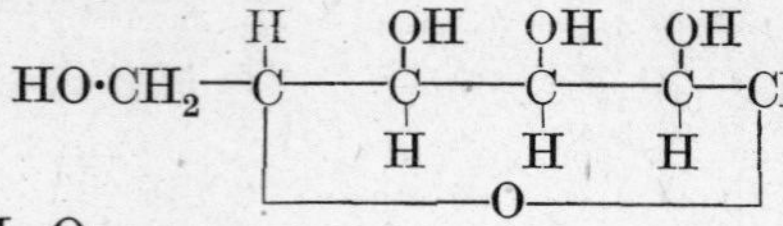

$C_6H_{12}O_6$ MW, 180

d-.

M.p. 128–30°. $[\alpha]_D^{21}$ about 30° $\longrightarrow$ 20·6° in H_2O ($[\alpha]_D^{27} + 78\cdot7° \longrightarrow 46\cdot3°$ in H_2O). Reduces Fehling's. Non-fermentable.

Phenylhydrazone : cryst. M.p. 178° decomp.

p-*Bromophenylhydrazone* : cryst. from EtOH. M.p. 205°.

Phenylosazone : m.p. 202° decomp. (196–7°, 188–91°). Identical with galactosazone.

Methylphenylhydrazone : cryst. from MeOH. M.p. 220–2° (154°).

Benzylphenylhydrazone : yellow laminæ. M.p. 199°.

o-*Nitrophenylhydrazone* : mp. 148·5–149°. $[\alpha]_D^{18} + 88\cdot3°$ in MeOH.

v. Braun, Bayer, *Ber.*, 1925, **58**, 2221.
Blanksma, v. Ekenstein, *Chem. Zentr.*, 1908, II, 1584.
Bosshard, *Helv. Chim. Acta*, 1935, **18**, 482.
Komada, *Chem. Abstracts*, 1932, **26**, 4799.
Levene, *J. Biol. Chem.*, 1931, **93**, 631.

Tanacetone.

See under Thujone.

Tanacetophorone   (1-*Isopropylcyclopenten-one*-3)

$$\begin{array}{c} C\cdot CH(CH_3)_2 \\ H_2C \diagup \quad \diagdown CH \\ H_2C \diagdown \quad \diagup \\ \quad CO \end{array}$$

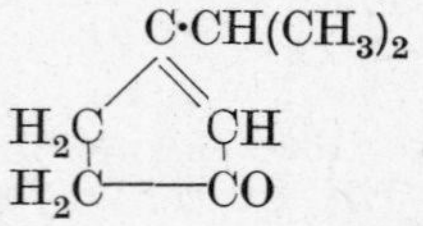

$C_8H_{12}O$ MW, 124

Yellowish-brown oil. B.p. 215–17°, 83·5–84·5°/11 mm. D^{20} 0·9378. n_D^{20} 1·4788. Volatile in steam. Red. $\longrightarrow$ 3-isopropylcyclopentanone.

Semicarbazone : plates from EtOH. M.p. 187–8°.

Pringsheim, Bondi, *Ber.*, 1925, **58**, 1415.
Wallach, *Ann.*, 1918, **414**, 221.

Tanacetyl Alcohol.

See Thujyl Alcohol.

Tangeritin   (3 : 5 : 6 : 7 : 4′ - *Pentamethoxy-flavone*)

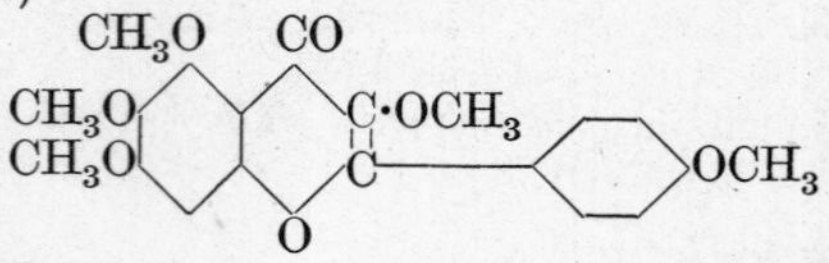

$C_{20}H_{20}O_7$ MW, 372

Constituent of peel of tangerines. Rods or needles from AcOEt. M.p. 154°. Sol. hot EtOH, hot AcOEt, C_6H_6. Spar. sol. pet. ether. Insol. alkalis. Warm conc. $HNO_3 \longrightarrow$ blood-red col. Hyd. $\longrightarrow$ tangeretol + anisic acid. Boiling HI + phenol $\longrightarrow$ 3 : 5 : 6 : 7 : 4′-pentahydroxyflavone.

Robinson, Goldsworthy, *J. Chem. Soc.*, 1937, 46.
Nelson, *J. Am. Chem. Soc.*, 1934, **56**, 1392.

Tannic Acid (*Tannin, gallotannin, Chinese tannin, gallotannic acid, penta-*(m-*digalloyl*)-*glucose*)

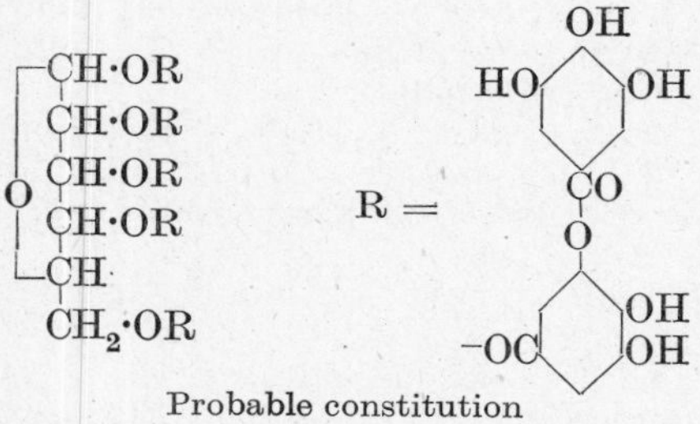

Probable constitution

$C_{76}H_{52}O_{46}$ MW, 1700

Constituent of galls from many species of oak, particularly *Quercus lusitanica*, also in galls from *Rhus semilata*. Commercial product is insol. Et_2O, $CHCl_3$, C_6H_6. Spar. sol. AcOEt. Sol. H_2O, EtOH. Aq. sol. has astringent taste. $FeCl_3 \longrightarrow$ bluish-black col. or ppt. Gives ppts. with most metallic salts, also with many alkaloids, albumen, gelatin, pyridine and quinoline acetate. Optically active with variable dextrorotation. Active principle in several "tannins" used in leather tanning. Has many industrial applications, *e.g.*, as a mordant in the textile industries.

Russell, *Chemical Reviews*, 1935, **17**, 160.
Takino, *Chem. Abstracts*, 1929, **23**, 2707.
Hepworth, *J. Soc. Chem. Ind.*, 1923, **42**, 41T.
Fischer, Bergmann, *Ber.*, 1919, **52**, 829.

Taraxanthin

$C_{40}H_{56}O_4$ MW, 600

Isomeric with violaxanthin. Occurs as ester in flowers of dandelion (*Taraxacum officinale*, Wiggers), yellow coltsfoot (*Tussilago farfara*), buttercup (*Ranunculus acer*), etc. Yellow prisms from MeOH. M.p. 184–5°. $[\alpha]^{20}_{Cd}$ + 200° in AcOEt. Absorption bands in CS_2 at 501, 469 and 441 mμ.

Kuhn, Grundmann, *Ber.*, 1934, **67**, 596.
Karrer, Morf, *Helv. Chim. Acta*, 1932, **15**, 863.
Kuhn, Lederer, *Z. physiol. Chem.*, 1931, **200**, 108.

Tariric Acid (5-*Heptadecine*-1-*carboxylic acid*)

$CH_3\cdot[CH_2]_{10}\cdot C\vdots C\cdot[CH_2]_4\cdot COOH$

$C_{18}H_{32}O_2$ MW, 280

Occurs as glyceride in fruit of *Picramnia-Arten* (Tariri). Cryst. from EtOH. M.p. 50·5°. Red. $\longrightarrow$ stearic acid. Ox. $\longrightarrow$ lauric and glutaric acids. Br in cold $CHCl_3 \longrightarrow$ dibromide. I in AcOH $\longrightarrow$ di-iodide. Gives insol. Ag salt.

Dibromide: cryst. mass. M.p. 32°.
Di-iodide: needles from EtOH. M.p. 48·5°.
Dichloride: brown needles. M.p. about 28°.
Tetrabromide: *see* 5 : 5 : 6 : 6-Tetrabromostearic Acid.

Arnaud, Hasenfratz, *Compt. rend.*, 1911, **152**, 1604.
Arnaud, Posternak, *Compt. rend.*, 1909, **149**, 220.

Taroxylic Acid (5 : 6-*Diketostearic acid*)

$CH_3\cdot[CH_2]_{10}\cdot CO\cdot CO\cdot[CH_2]_4\cdot COOH$

$C_{18}H_{32}O_4$ MW, 312

Pale yellow plates. M.p. 98°. Very sol. boiling EtOH. Spar. sol. cold EtOH. Insol. H_2O. Alkali salts sol. H_2O.

Dioxime: needles. M.p. 166–7°. Very sol. boiling EtOH. Insol. H_2O.

Arnaud, *Compt. rend.*, 1902, **134**, 548.

Tartar emetic (*Potassium antimonyl tartrate*)

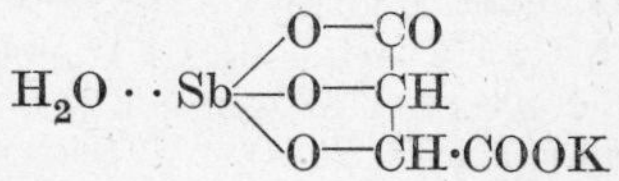

$C_4H_4O_7KSb$ MW, 323

Rhombic cryst. D 2·607. Sol. 3 parts of H_2O at 100°, 25 parts at 15°. One of the few soluble salts of antimony. Used in medicine in small doses: poisonous in larger quantities. Used for mordanting textiles in conjunction with tannic acid.

Reihlen, Hezel, *Ann.*, 1931, **487**, 213.
Chemnitius, *Chem. Abstracts*, 1930, **24**, 2832.

Tartaric Acid (*Dihydroxysuccinic acid*)

d-

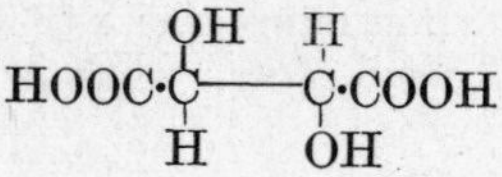

$$HOOC\cdot \overset{\overset{\displaystyle OH}{|}}{\underset{\underset{\displaystyle H}{|}}{C}} \text{——} \overset{\overset{\displaystyle H}{|}}{\underset{\underset{\displaystyle OH}{|}}{C}}\cdot COOH$$

I

l

$$HOOC\cdot \overset{\overset{\displaystyle H}{|}}{\underset{\underset{\displaystyle OH}{|}}{C}} \text{——} \overset{\overset{\displaystyle OH}{|}}{\underset{\underset{\displaystyle H}{|}}{C}}\cdot COOH$$

II

Meso-

$$HOOC\cdot \overset{\overset{\displaystyle OH}{|}}{\underset{\underset{\displaystyle H}{|}}{C}} \text{——} \overset{\overset{\displaystyle OH}{|}}{\underset{\underset{\displaystyle H}{|}}{C}}\cdot COOH$$

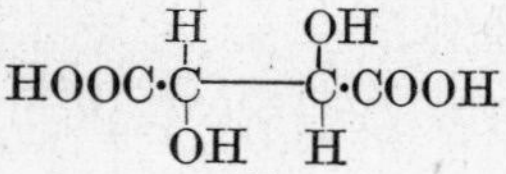

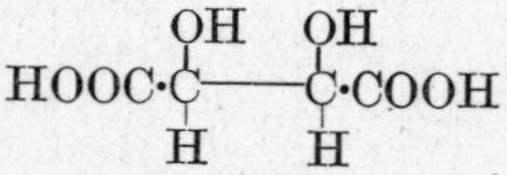

III

Racemic = I + II.

$C_4H_6O_6$ MW, 150

d-.

Ordinary tartaric acid. Occurs in plants, partly free and partly as K, Ca or Mg salts. The KH salt occurs in grape juice. Prisms. M.p. 170° (169°, 168–70°). D_4^7 1·7594, D_4^{18} 1·759, D_4^{20} 1·7598. 100 Parts H_2O dissolve 115·04 parts at 0°, 139·44 parts at 20°, 147·44 parts at 25°, 195·0 parts at 50°, 258·05 parts at 75° and 343·35 parts at 100°. 1 Part dissolves in 2·06 parts 80% EtOH at 15°. 100 Parts 90% EtOH contain 29·146 parts at 15°. 100 Parts abs. EtOH contain 20·385 parts at 15°. 100 Parts Et_2O contain 0·393 parts at 15°. Sol. Me_2CO. $[\alpha]_D^{20} + 11·98°$ (20% sol. in H_2O), $[\alpha]_D^{16} + 13·1°$ (15% sol. in H_2O), $[\alpha]_D + 0·47°$ in MeOH. Heat of comb. C_p 261·75 Cal. k (first) = $1·3 \times 10^{-3}$ at 25° ($1·02 \times 10^{-3}$, $0·97 \times 10^{-3}$); (second) = 69×10^{-6} at 25° (97×10^{-6}, 41×10^{-6}, 45×10^{-6}, $34·3 \times 10^{-6}$). Heat $\longrightarrow$ chars with evolution of CO_2 and CO, and odour of burnt sugar (other products include acetaldehyde, acetone, acetic, formic, and pyruvic acids). On boiling with HCl.Aq. or dil. H_2SO_4 or 30% NaOH it is converted into racemic and meso-tartaric acids. H_2SO_4 at 100° $\longrightarrow$ CO_2, CO and SO_2. H_2O_2 (+ ferrous salt) $\longrightarrow$ dihydroxymaleic acid (Fenton's reaction). $MnO_2 + H_2SO_4$ $\longrightarrow$ $H\cdot COOH + CO_2$. Reacts with cold $KMnO_4$ with difficulty, but rapidly on warming. Reduces $NH_3.AgNO_3$. HI $\longrightarrow$ *d*-malic acid + succinic acid. $HNO_3 + H_2SO_4 \longrightarrow$ di-nitrate of tartaric acid. Prevents the pptn. of CuO and other metallic oxides from alk. sol. Gives yellow col. with $FeCl_3$. Addn. of aq. $CaCl_2$ to neutral sol. pptes. Ca salt, sol. AcOH and cold alkalis.

Mono-NH_4 salt : cryst. Triboluminescent. Sol. 45·6 parts H_2O at 15°. $[\alpha]_D^{15} + 25·55°$ in H_2O.

Di-NH_4 salt : cryst. Triboluminescent. $[\alpha]_D^{15} + 34·6°$ in H_2O. Spar. sol. EtOH.

Mono-Na salt : cryst. + H_2O. Triboluminescent. $[\alpha]_D^{19} + 21·8°$ in H_2O. Sol. H_2O.

Di-Na salt : cryst. + $2H_2O$. Triboluminescent. Sol. 3·46 parts H_2O at 6°, 2·28 parts at 24°, 1·5 parts at 42·5°.

$NaNH_4$ salt : cryst. + $4H_2O$. Triboluminescent. 100 parts aq. sol. at 0° contain 21·2 parts cryst. salt.

Mono-K salt : argol, tartar, cream of tartar (in order of increasing purity). Cryst. Triboluminescent. 100 c.cs. saturated aq. sol. contain 0·370 gm. at 0°, 0·843 gm. at 25°, 1·931 gm. at 50°, 5·850 gm. at 100°.

Di-K salt : cryst. + $\frac{1}{2}H_2O$. Triboluminescent. D_4^{20} 1·984. Sol. 0·75 part H_2O at 2°, 0·66 part at 14°, 0·63 part at 23°, 0·47 part at 64°.

KNH_4 salt : cryst. + $\frac{1}{2}H_2O$. Readily sol. H_2O.

KNa salt : Rochelle Salt. Cryst. + $4H_2O$. Triboluminescent. Sol. 1·70 parts H_2O at 6°.

Potassium antimonyl tartrate : *see* Tartar emetic.

$Ca(C_4H_5O_6)_2$: cryst. + $2H_2O$. 100 parts H_2O dissolve 0·710 part anyhd. salt at 15·6°. More sol. hot H_2O.

$CaC_4H_4O_6$: cryst. + $4H_2O$. Occurs in many plants. 100 gm. H_2O dissolve 0·0185 gm. at 18°, 0·02948 gm. at 25° of hydrated salt. More sol. hot H_2O. Sol. hot alkalis.

$AgC_4H_5O_6$: cryst. + H_2O. Sol. hot aq. tartaric acid.

$Ag_2C_4H_4O_6$: cryst. powder. 100 gm. H_2O dissolve 0·2012 gm. at 18°, 0·2031 gm. at 25°. Insol. EtOH.

Me ester : $C_5H_8O_6$. MW, 164. Prisms + H_2O from H_2O. M.p. 76° (75–7°). 1 part dissolves in 4 parts H_2O at room temp. Sol. AcOEt, Me_2CO. Spar. sol. Et_2O. $[\alpha]_D^{18} + 18·71°$ in H_2O. $k = 4·6 \times 10^{-4}$ at 25°.

Di-Me ester : *see* Dimethyl tartrate.

Et ester : $C_6H_{10}O_6$. MW, 178. Prisms. M.p. about 90°. Deliquescent. Sol. H_2O, EtOH. Insol. Et_2O. $[\alpha]_D + 21·8°$ in H_2O.

Di-Et ester : *see* Diethyl tartrate.

Dipropyl ester : $C_{10}H_{18}O_6$. MW, 234. B.p. 303°, 181°/23 mm., 171–2°/17 mm. (173–4°/ 17 mm.). D^{20} 1·1344, D^{100} 1·0590, D_4^{20} 1·1390. Sol. H_2O and most org. solvents. $[\alpha]_D^{20} + 12·44°$ in H_2O. *Diacetyl* : m.p. 31°. B.p. 313°, 195–7°/13 mm. $[\alpha]_D^{14} + 7·04°$ in EtOH. *Dibenzoyl* :

m.p. 45·5°. B.p. 234°/7 mm. $[\alpha]_{5461}^{17\cdot5}$ − 78·16° in Py.

Di-isopropyl ester: b.p. 275°, 157–8°/16 mm. D^{20} 1·1300, D^{100} 1·0537. $[\alpha]_D^{20}$ + 14·886°. *Diacetyl*: prisms. M.p. 33°. $[\alpha]_D^{20}$ + 5·9° in EtOH.

Dibutyl ester: $C_{12}H_{22}O_6$. MW, 262. Prisms. M.p. 22–22·5°. B.p. 200–3°/18 mm., 178°/12 mm. D^{15} 1·098. $[\alpha]_D^{15}$ + 11·3° in EtOH. *Diacetyl*: b.p. 214°/20 mm. $D^{15\cdot5}$ 1·096. $[\alpha]_D^{22}$ + 8·8° in EtOH. *Dibenzoyl*: m.p. 43°. B.p. 250°/1·3 mm. $[\alpha]_{5461}^{15}$ − 57·62° in Py.

Di-isobutyl ester: m.p. 68°. B.p. 323–5°, 197°/23 mm., 183°/11 mm., 157°/3·5 mm. D^{100} 1·0145. $[\alpha]_D$ + 11·8° in EtOH. *Diacetyl*: b.p. 322–6°, 196–7°/12 mm. $D^{16\cdot5}$ 1·096. $[\alpha]_D^{14}$ + 10·51° in EtOH. *Dibenzoyl*: b.p. about 240°/3 mm. $D^{17\cdot1}$ 1·3360. $[\alpha]_D^{22}$ − 48·86° in EtOH.

Di-d-amyl ester: $C_{14}H_{26}O_6$. MW, 290. B.p. 208°/20 mm. D_4^{20} 1·0636. $[\alpha]_D^{20}$ + 17·73°.

Di-dl-amyl ester: b.p. 208°/20 mm. (215–20°/10–25 mm.). D_4^{20} 1·0637. $[\alpha]_D^{20}$ + 14·10°.

Di-isoamyl ester: b.p. 195°/16 mm.

Diallyl ester: $C_{10}H_{14}O_6$. MW, 230. B.p. 191°/20 mm., 171°/10 mm.

Diphenyl ester: $C_{16}H_{14}O_6$. MW, 302. Needles. M.p. 101–2°. Sol. hot EtOH, Et_2O, glycerol. Insol. H_2O.

Dibenzyl ester: $C_{18}H_{18}O_6$. MW, 330. M.p. about 50°. B.p. 250–70°/4 mm. $D^{72\cdot2}$ 1·2036. *Dibenzoyl*: needles from EtOH. M.p. 76–7°. $[\alpha]_D^{18}$ + 6·2° in Me_2CO, + 41·7° in C_6H_6.

Diphenacyl ester: $C_{20}H_{18}O_8$. MW, 386. M.p. 130°.

Anhydride: $C_4H_4O_5$. MW, 132. *Dibenzoyl*: m.p. 173°. $[\alpha]_D^{20}$ + 141·98° in Me_2CO.

Amide: *see* Tartramidic Acid.

Diamide: *see under* Tartramidic Acid.

Dihydrazide: needles. M.p. 182·5–183°. Sol. H_2O. Spar. sol. EtOH. Insol. Et_2O. $[\alpha]_D^{20}$ + 97·1° in H_2O. *B,2HCl*: cryst. Sol. H_2O. Spar. sol. EtOH. Insol. Et_2O. N : N-*Diacetyl*: needles from dil. EtOH. M.p. 216°. Sol. H_2O, AcOH. Spar. sol. EtOH. Insol. Et_2O.

Di-azide: cryst. M.p. 66° decomp. Sol. H_2O, EtOH, Me_2CO. Mod. sol. Et_2O. Insol. $CHCl_3$, C_6H_6, ligroin.

Anilide: *see* Tartranilic Acid.

Dianilide: *see under* Tartranilic Acid.

Mono-Me ether: $C_5H_8O_6$. MW, 164. Prisms from Et_2O. M.p. 174°. $[\alpha]_D$ + 45·4° in H_2O.

Di-Me ether: *see* Dimethoxysuccinic Acid.

Di-Et ether: *see* Diethoxysuccinic Acid.

Diacetyl: cryst. + $3H_2O$ from Et_2O. M.p. 58°. Sol. H_2O, EtOH. Spar. sol. $CHCl_3$, C_6H_6. $[\alpha]_D^{22}$ − 23·04° in H_2O. Hyd. by warm aq. alkalis.

Dibenzoyl: cryst. + H_2O from H_2O. M.p. 90° (88–9°), anhyd. 138–40°. $[\alpha]_D^{18}$ − 115·78° in EtOH, $[\alpha]_D^{20}$ − 118·51° in MeOH. Sol. EtOH. Less sol. $CHCl_3$. Spar. sol. cold H_2O, C_6H_6.

Dietrich, *Jahresber, Fortschr. Chem.*, 1878, 1136.
Rasch, D.R.P., 92,650, (*Chem. Zentr.*, 1897, II, 655).
Hölbling, *Chem. Zentr.*, 1896, II, 1068.
Gladyss, D.R.P., 116,090, (*Chem. Zentr.*, 1901, I, 69).
McKenzie, *J. Chem. Soc.*, 1915, **107**, 440.
Voss, *Chem.-Ztg.*, 1921, **45**, 309, 335, 360, 411.
Patterson, *J. Chem. Soc.*, 1913, **103**, 173.
Freundler, *Ann. chim. phys.*, 1894, **3**, 445.
Dyson, *Chemist & Druggist*, 1932, **116**, 668.

l-.

Physical properties identical with those of the *d*-acid. $[\alpha]_D$ in H_2O of same magnitude but opposite in sign to that of the *d*-acid.

Di-Me ester: *see* Dimethyl tartrate.

Di-Et ester: *see* Diethyl tartrate.

Dibenzoyl: cryst. + H_2O. M.p. 85°. $[\alpha]_D^{24}$ + 103·7°.

Di-Me ether: *see* Dimethoxysuccinic Acid.

Marckwald, *Ber.*, 1896, **29**, 42.
Ladenburg, *Ann.*, 1909, **364**, 232.
Parck, *Chem. Abstracts*, 1926, **20**, 1219.
Dale, Rice, *J. Am. Chem. Soc.*, 1933, **55**, 4984.
Kiliani, *Ber.*, 1911, **44**, 112 (*Footnote* 3).

dl-. Racemic Acid.

Cryst. anhyd. from H_2O above 73° or from EtOH. M.p. 206° (205–6°). Cryst. + H_2O, m.p. 203–4°. Loses H_2O at 100°. Less sol. H_2O than *d*- and *l*-acids. 100 Parts H_2O dissolve 9·23 parts hydrated acid at 0°, 14·00 parts at 10°, 20·6 parts at 20°, 24·61 parts at 25°, 29·10 parts at 30°, 59·54 parts at 50°, 184·91 parts at 100°. Sol. 48 parts cold EtOH. Sol. in EtOH at 15° to extent of 2·08%, in Et_2O 1·08%. Heat of comb. C_v (hydrated) 278·4 Cal., (anhyd.) 279·5 Cal. k (first) = $10\cdot2 \times 10^{-4}$ at 25° ($10\cdot3 \times 10^{-4}$, 11×10^{-4}, $9\cdot7 \times 10^{-4}$, $9\cdot6 \times 10^{-4}$); (second) = $4\cdot0 \times 10^{-5}$ at 25° ($2\cdot8 \times 10^{-5}$, $3\cdot94 \times 10^{-5}$). Heat with HCl.Aq. at 130–40° or in alk. sol. ⟶ partly to mesotartaric acid.

Mono-NH_4 salt: prisms. Triboluminescent. Sol. 100 parts H_2O at 20°. More sol. boiling H_2O. Insol. EtOH.

Di-NH_4 salt: prisms. Sol. H_2O. Prac. insol. EtOH.

Mono-Na salt: exists hydrated in several modifications. Loses H_2O at 100°. Triboluminescent. Decomp. at 219°. Sol. 11·3 parts H_2O at 19°. More sol. boiling H_2O. Insol. EtOH.

Di-Na salt: prisms. Triboluminescent. Sol. 2·63 parts H_2O at 25°. Insol. EtOH.

$NaNH_4$ salt: prisms + H_2O. Decomposes below 27° into d- and l-*$NaNH_4$* tartrates, and above 35° into Na racemate and NH_4 racemate.

Mono-K salt: prisms. Triboluminescent. Sol. 180 parts H_2O at 19°, 139 parts at 25°, 14·3 parts at 100°.

Di-K salt: plates + $2H_2O$. Sol. 0·97 part H_2O at 25°. Prac. insol. EtOH.

KNa salt: prisms + $3H_2O$. M.p. 100°. 100 gms. of saturated aq. sol. contains 36·66 gms. of anhyd. salt at 9·7°, 47·97 gms. at 29·5°. Also prisms or plates + $4H_2O$.

$CaC_4H_4O_6$: cryst. + $4H_2O$. Loses H_2O at 200°. Prac. insol. cold H_2O. More sol. hot H_2O. Insol. AcOH. Sol. HCl.Aq. but pptd. by NH_3.

Me ester: prisms. Sol. H_2O, EtOH. Spar. sol. Et_2O. Hyd. by boiling H_2O.

Di-Me ester: *see* Dimethyl tartrate.

Et ester: prisms. Sol. H_2O, EtOH. Insol. Et_2O.

Di-Et ester: *see* Diethyl tartrate.

Dipropyl ester: m.p. 25°. B.p. 286°/765 mm., 167°/11 mm. D_4^{20} 1·1256.

Di-isopropyl ester: m.p. 34°. B.p. 275°/765 mm., 154°/12 mm. D_4^{20} 1·1166.

Dibutyl ester: b.p. 320°/765 mm., 185°/12 mm. D_4^{18} 1·0879.

Di-isobutyl ester: m.p. 58°. B.p. 311°/768·5 mm., 195°/13 mm. D_4^{80} 1·0160.

*Di-*d-*amyl ester*: $C_{14}H_{26}O_6$. MW, 290. B.p. 201–2°/16 mm. (215–25°/10–25 mm.). D_4^{20} 1·064. n 1·4501. $[\alpha]_D^{20}$ + 3·37°.

Dibenzoyl: m.p. 112–13°.

Dinitrile: $C_4H_4O_2N_2$. MW, 112. *Diacetyl*: plates or prisms from AcOH. M.p. 97–8°.

Anhydride: *dibenzoyl*, m.p. 182°.

Di-Me ether: *see* Dimethoxysuccinic Acid.

Campbell, Slotin, Johnston, *J. Am. Chem. Soc.*, 1933, **55**, 2604.
Newman, Riley, *J. Chem. Soc.*, 1933, 45.
Hollemann, *Organic Syntheses*, Collective Vol. I, 484.
Pasteur, *Ann. chim. phys.*, 1850, **28**, 79.
Campbell, *J. Chem. Soc.*, 1929, 1111.

Meso-.

Plates + H_2O. M.p. anhyd. 140°. D_4^{20} 1·666. Sol. 0·8 part H_2O at 15°. k (first) = $6{\cdot}0 \times 10^{-4}$ at 25° ($6{\cdot}3 \times 10^{-4}$); (second) = $1{\cdot}4 \times 10^{-5}$ at 25°. Heat with H_2O at 175°, with aq. HCl at 130–40° or with aq. alkalis ⟶ partly to racemic acid.

Mono-K salt: needles. Sol. 8 parts H_2O at 19°.

$CaC_4H_4O_6$: prisms + $3H_2O$. Loses H_2O on standing, second H_2O at 100°, third H_2O at 170°. Sol. 600 parts boiling H_2O. Prac. insol. AcOH.

Di-Me ester: *see under* Dimethyl tartrate.

Di-Et ester: *see under* Diethyl tartrate.

Dibutyl ester: m.p. 48–50°.

*Di-*d-*amyl ester*: b.p. 203–4°/17 mm. D_4^{20} 1·0658. n_D^{20} 1·4530. $[\alpha]_D^{20}$ + 4·77°.

Dinitrile: plates or prisms from Et_2O. M.p. about 131° decomp. Sol. H_2O, EtOH, Et_2O. Spar. sol. $CHCl_3$. Prac. insol. CS_2. Not very stable. *Diacetyl*: prisms from Et_2O or AcOH. M.p. 75–7°.

Anhydride: *dibenzoyl*, m.p. 207–8°.

Di-Me ether: *see* Dimethoxysuccinic Acid.

Winther, *Z. physik. Chem.*, 1906, **56**, 507.
Pollak, *Monatsh.*, 1894, **15**, 469.

Tartramide.

See under Tartramidic Acid.

Tartramidic Acid (*Tartaric monoamide*)

HO·CH·CO·NH_2
HO·CH·COOH

$C_4H_7O_5N$ MW, 149

d-.

Cryst. from H_2O. M.p. 171–2°. $[\alpha]_D^{13}$ + 63·7° in H_2O.

$Ca(C_4H_6O_5N)_2$: cryst. + $6H_2O$. Sol. H_2O. Insol. EtOH. $[\alpha]_D^{18}$ + 59·5° in H_2O.

Et ester: $C_6H_{11}O_5N$. MW, 177. Plates. M.p. 136–7°.

Amide: $C_4H_8O_4N_2$. MW, 148. *d*-Tartramide, diamide of tartaric acid. Cryst. M.p. 195° decomp. Spar. sol. MeOH, EtOH. Insol. Et_2O, C_6H_6. $[\alpha]_D^{20}$ + 106·5° in H_2O, + 144° in MeOH. *Di-Me ether*: *see under* Dimethoxysuccinic Acid. *Dibenzoyl*: needles from EtOH. M.p. 240°.

Di-Me ether: *see under* Dimethoxysuccinic Acid.

Anilide: *see under* Tartranilic Acid.

Weerman, *Rec. trav. chim.*, 1917, **37**, 45.
Grote, *Ann.*, 1864, **130**, 203.
Frankland, Slator, *J. Chem. Soc.*, 1903, **83**, 1354.

Tartranilic Acid (*Tartaric monoanilide*)

HO·CH·CO·NH·C_6H_5
HO·CH·COOH

$C_{10}H_{11}O_5N$ MW, 225

d-.

Plates. M.p. 180° decomp. Mod. sol. H_2O, EtOH. (Needles from AcOH. M.p. 194°.) $[\alpha]_D^{15}$ + 114·7° in MeOH.

NH_4 salt: needles. $[\alpha]_D^{15}$ + 102·2° in H_2O.

Na salt: needles. M.p. 226°. Spar. sol. EtOH. $[\alpha]_D^{15}$ + 101·3° in H_2O.

Aniline salt: cryst. M.p. 149–50°.

Me ester: $C_{11}H_{13}O_5N$. MW, 239. Needles from AcOH. M.p. 175°. Sol. EtOH. Spar. sol. H_2O. $[\alpha]_D^{15}$ + 106° in MeOH.

Et ester: $C_{12}H_{15}O_5N$. MW, 253. Plates from H_2O. M.p. 151–2°. (Needles, m.p. 163°.) Sol. hot H_2O. $[\alpha]_D^{15}$ + 102·4° in MeOH.

Propyl ester: $C_{13}H_{17}O_5N$. MW, 267. Plates from EtOH. M.p. 161°. $[\alpha]_D^{15}$ + 99·1° in MeOH.

Isobutyl ester: $C_{14}H_{19}O_5N$. MW, 281. Needles from EtOH. M.p. 158°. $[\alpha]_D^{15}$ + 92·6° in MeOH.

Isoamyl ester: $C_{15}H_{21}O_5N$. MW, 295. Needles from EtOH. M.p. 139°. $[\alpha]_D^{15}$ + 89·2° in MeOH.

Amide: $C_{10}H_{12}O_4N_2$. MW, 224. Anilide of tartramidic acid. Plates. M.p. 226°. $[\alpha]_D^{15}$ + 139° in H_2O, + 153° in MeOH.

Anilide: $C_{16}H_{16}O_4N_2$. MW, 300. Dianilide of tartaric acid. Prisms from MeOH or needles from EtOH. M.p. 275° (250° decomp., 255–6° decomp., 263–4° decomp.). Sol. Py. Spar. sol. Et_2O, EtOH. Prac. insol. C_6H_6, AcOH. Insol. H_2O. $[\alpha]_D^{15}$ + 259° in Py ($[\alpha]_D^{20}$ + 246·5° in Py), + 206° in MeOH. *Acetyl*: needles from EtOH. M.p. 148°. *Diacetyl*: needles from dil. EtOH. M.p. 214–15°. Sol. EtOH, Et_2O, $CHCl_3$, Me_2CO, C_6H_6. Prac. insol. ligroin. Insol. H_2O. *Tetra-acetyl*: needles + 2EtOH from EtOH. M.p. 137°.

Di-Me ether: *see under* Dimethoxysuccinic Acid.

Di-Et ether: *see under* Diethoxysuccinic Acid.

Tingle, Bates, *J. Am. Chem. Soc.*, 1909, **31**, 1240.
Polikier, *Ber.*, 1891, **24**, 2959.
Bischoff, Nastvogel, *Ber.*, 1890, **23**, 2047.
Arppe, *Ann.*, 1855, **93**, 355.
Casale, *Gazz. chim. ital.*, 1917, **47**, 277.

Tartronic Acid (*Hydroxymalonic acid*)

HO·CH<(COOH)(COOH)

$C_3H_4O_5$ MW, 120

Prisms + H_2O from H_2O. Loses H_2O at 60°. M.p. 160° decomp. (156–8°, 155°, 158–9°). Sol. H_2O, EtOH. Spar. sol. Et_2O. Anhyd. acid sol. Et_2O. Sublimes. k (first) = 5×10^{-3} at 25°. Forms cryst. salts.

Di-Me ester: $C_5H_8O_5$. MW, 148. M.p. 44·5–45°. Sol. $CHCl_3$, Et_2O. Spar. sol. pet. ether.

Di-Et ester: $C_7H_{12}O_5$. MW, 176. F.p. − 2·5°. B.p. 222–5° (218–19°), 120·5–121°/15 mm. D^{15} 1·152. *Et ether*: b.p. 228°. *Acetyl*: b.p. 235–45°, 158–63°/60 mm., 138°/17–18 mm. $D_{15}^{19\cdot5}$ 1·131.

Monoamide: $C_3H_5O_4N$. MW, 119. Needles or prisms from H_2O. M.p. about 160° decomp. Sol. EtOH. Spar. sol. cold H_2O. Prac. insol. Et_2O.

Diamide: $C_3H_6O_3N_2$. MW, 118. Needles from EtOH.Aq. M.p. 195–6° (198°). Mod. sol. hot H_2O. Spar. sol. cold H_2O, EtOH.

Et ether: $C_5H_8O_5$. MW, 148. Prisms from pet. ether. M.p. 123–5°. Decomp. at 135°. Sol. H_2O, EtOH. Spar. sol. C_6H_6, ligroin.

Wislicenus, Münzesheimer, *Ber.*, 1898, **31**, 552.
Conrad, Brückner, *Ber.*, 1891, **24**, 2997.
Behrend, Prüsse, *Ann.*, 1918, **416**, 233.
Filippo, *Rec. trav. chim.*, 1910, **29**, 115.

Tartronylurea.

See Dialuric Acid.

Taurine (*Aminoethylsulphonic acid, amino-ethanesulphonic acid, ethylaminesulphonic acid*)

$H_2N·CH_2·CH_2·SO_3H$ or $H_3N·CH_2·CH_2$ / O——SO_2

$C_2H_7O_3NS$ MW, 125

Occurs mainly combined. Free in lungs and flesh extract of oxen. In shark blood; liver, spleen and kidney of ray; in muscle, oysters, molluscs, etc. Columns from H_2O. Decomp. at 300–5°. Sol. 15·5 parts H_2O at 12°. Insol. EtOH. Neutral in dil. sol. Acid in conc. sol. Heat of comb. C_v 382·2 Cal., C_p 382·9 Cal. Stable to boiling conc. acids. Not esterified readily. Phenol + hypochlorites ⟶ blue col. MeOH + KOH + MeI ⟶ taurobetaine. Hg salt used for identification and separation.

N-*Me*: $C_3H_9O_3NS$. MW, 139. Prisms. M.p. 241–2°. Very sol. H_2O. Insol. EtOH, Et_2O.

N-*Di-Me*: $C_4H_{11}O_3NS$. MW, 153. Prisms from MeOH. M.p. 315–16°. Very sol. H_2O, AcOH. Insol. EtOH, Et_2O.

N-*Et*: $C_4H_{11}O_3NS$. MW, 153. Prisms from H_2O. M.p. 147°.

N-*Di-Et* : $C_6H_{15}O_3NS$. MW, 181. Plates from EtOH. M.p. 151°.

N-*Allyl* : $C_5H_{11}O_3NS$. MW, 165. Prisms from EtOH. M.p. 190–5°.

Cortese, *J. Am. Chem. Soc.*, 1936, **58**, 191.
Teroaka, *Z. physiol. Chem.*, 1925, **145**, 238.
James, *J. prakt. Chem.*, 1885, **31**, 414.

Taurobetaine (*Trimethyltaurine*)

$$(CH_3)_3N\!-\!CH_2\!-\!CH_2$$
$$O\!-\!-\!-\!SO_2$$

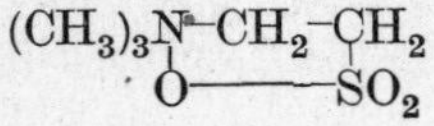

$C_5H_{13}O_3NS$ MW, 167

Prisms from H_2O. Does not melt below 250°. Very sol. H_2O. Insol. EtOH, Et_2O. Neutral reaction. Sweet taste. $Ba(OH)_2 \longrightarrow$ trimethylamine + isethionic acid.

Brieger, *Z. physiol. Chem.*, 1882, **7**, 36.

Taurocarbamic Acid (2-*Ureidoethane*-1-*sulphonic acid, sulphoethylurea*)

$$H_2N\!\cdot\!CO\!\cdot\!NH\!\cdot\!CH_2\!\cdot\!CH_2\!\cdot\!SO_3H$$

$C_3H_8O_4N_2S$ MW, 168

Prisms from EtOH.Aq. M.p. 182° decomp. Very sol. H_2O. Spar. sol. EtOH. Insol. Et_2O. $Ba(OH)_2$ or HCl on heating $\longrightarrow$ taurine. Forms cryst. Ba and Ag salts.

Lippich, *Z. physiol. Chem.*, 1910, **68**, 292.

Taurocholic Acid

$$HO_3S\!\cdot\!CH_2\!\cdot\!CH_2\!\cdot\!NH\!\cdot\!CO\!\cdot\!CH_2\!\cdot\!CH_2\!\cdot\!CH\!\cdot\!CH_3$$

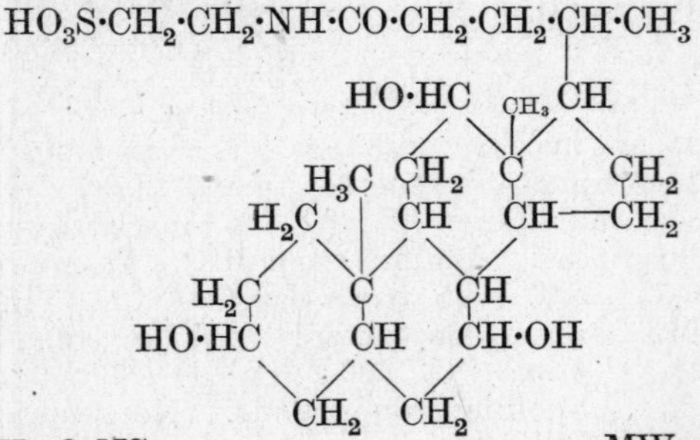

$C_{26}H_{45}O_7NS$ MW, 515

Constituent of bile. Amorph. powder. M.p. about 125° decomp. Very sol. H_2O, hot EtOH. Spar. sol. Et_2O, AcOEt. Very hygroscopic. $[\alpha]_D^{20} + 38\cdot8°$ in EtOH.Aq.

Na salt : needles or plates $+ 1\frac{1}{2}H_2O$ from H_2O. M.p. anhyd. 180°. Boiling $H_2O \longrightarrow$ isomeric form, cryst. $+ 2H_2O$, m.p. 235°. Both forms have identical solubilities and rotations.

Ba salt : plates or needles $+ 5H_2O$ from H_2O.

M.p. 225–7° decomp. Very sol. H_2O, hot EtOH. Spar. sol. Et_2O, AcOEt. $[\alpha]_D^{20} + 25\cdot6°$.

Kazuno, Yamasaki, *Z. physiol. Chem.*, 1934, **224**, 160.
Tanaka, *Z. physiol. Chem.*, 1933, **220**, 39.
Hammarsten, *Z. physiol. Chem.*, 1904, **43**, 127.

Tazettine (*Ungernine*)

$C_{18}H_{21}O_5N$ MW, 331

Constituent of bulbs of *Narcissus tazetta*. After high vac. sublimation, m.p. 210–11°. Sol. EtOH. Spar. sol. Et_2O. $[\alpha]_D^{16} + 150\cdot4$ in $CHCl_3$. $H_2SO_4 \longrightarrow$ brownish-red col. Zn dust dist. $\longrightarrow$ phenanthridine. $KMnO_4 \longrightarrow$ hydrastic acid.

Acetyl deriv. : cryst. from Et_2O–pet. ether. M.p. 125–126·5°.

Methiodide : m.p. 220° decomp.

Picrate : yellow cryst. from EtOH. M.p. 205–8° decomp.

Perchlorate : m.p. 105–8° decomp. $[\alpha]_D^{15} + 109\cdot6°$ in MeOH.

Robinson, *Ann. Rev. Biochem.*, 1935, **4**, 507.
Späth, Kahovec, *Ber.*, 1934, **67**, 1501.
Norkina, Orechoff, *Ber.*, 1936, **69**, 500.
Späth, Orechoff, Kuffner, *ibid.*, 2446.

Tecomin.
See Lapachol.

Tectochrysin.
See under Chrysin.

Tectoquinone.
See under 2-Methylanthraquinone.

Teloidine (3 : 6 : 7-*Trihydroxytropane*, *tropantriol*-3 : 6 : 7)

$$HO\!\cdot\!HC\!-\!CH\!-\!-\!-\!CH_2$$
$$N\!\cdot\!CH_3 \quad CH\!\cdot\!OH$$
$$HO\!\cdot\!HC\!-\!CH\!-\!-\!-\!CH_2$$

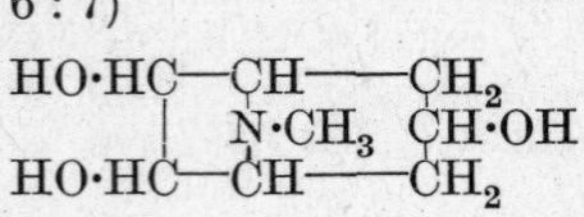

$C_8H_{15}O_3N$ MW, 173

Needles $+ 1H_2O$ from $Me_2CO.Aq$. M.p. 168–9°. Very sol. H_2O, EtOH. Spar. sol. most cold org. solvents.

B,HCl : prisms from EtOH. Does not melt below 300°.

B,HBr : plates and needles from EtOH. M.p. 295° decomp.

B,HAuCl$_4$: yellow plates $+ \frac{1}{2}H_2O$ from H_2O. M.p. 225° decomp.

King, *J. Chem. Soc.*, 1919, **115**, 487.
Pyman, Reynolds, *J. Chem. Soc.*, 1908, **93**, 2079.

Tephrosin (*Hydroxydeguelin*)

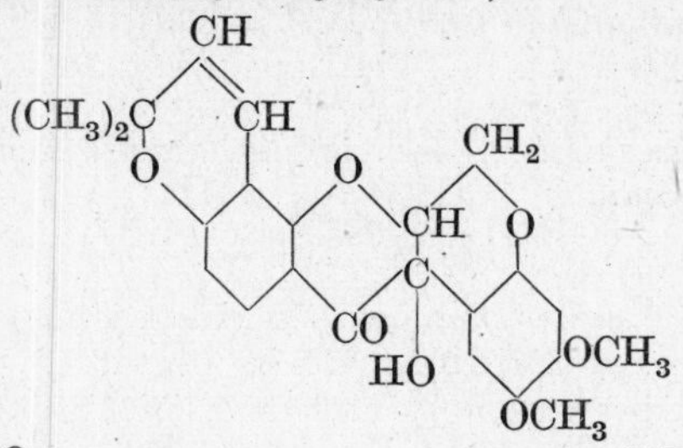

$C_{23}H_{22}O_7$ MW, 410

Constituent of derris root, cubé root (*Lonchocarpus nicou*) and leaves of *Cracca vogeli*. Prisms from MeOH–$CHCl_3$. M.p. 198°. Ox. ⟶ tephrosin-dicarboxylic acid.

Acetyl : cryst. from MeOH.Aq. M.p. 200°.

Clark, *J. Am. Chem. Soc.*, 1933, **55**, 759; 1932, **54**, 3000; 1931, **53**, 729.
Takei, Mayujima, Ono, *Chem. Abstracts*, 1933, **27**, 2954.
Clark, Claborn, *J. Am. Chem. Soc.*, 1932, **54**, 4454.
Butenandt, Hilgetag, *Ann.*, 1932, **495**, 172.

Teraconic Acid.

See Isopropylidenesuccinic Acid.

Teracrylic Acid (2 : 3-*Dimethyl-2-pentene-5-carboxylic acid*, 2-*isopropylidene-butyric acid*)

$$(CH_3)_2C{:}C(CH_3){\cdot}CH_2{\cdot}COOH$$

$C_7H_{12}O_2$ MW, 128

Liq. B.p. 218°. Spar. sol. H_2O.

Et ester : $C_9H_{16}O_2$. MW, 156. Liq. with fruity odour. B.p. 189–91°.

Fittig, Kraft, *Ann.*, 1881, **208**, 79.

Tereanilic Acid.

See 2 : 5-Diaminoterephthalic Acid.

Terebic Acid (2 : 2-*Dimethylparaconic acid*, 3 : 3-*dimethylbutyrolactone-2-carboxylic acid*)

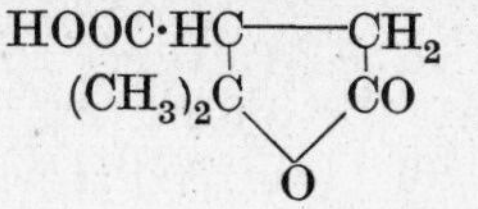

$C_7H_{10}O_4$ MW, 158

Cryst. from EtOH. M.p. 175°. Sol. boiling H_2O, warm EtOH. Spar. sol. cold H_2O. Heat of comb. C_v 778·4 Cal. $k = 2{\cdot}65 \times 10^{-4}$ at 25°.

Me ester : $C_8H_{12}O_4$. MW, 172. B.p. 148–9°/17 mm.

Et ester : $C_9H_{14}O_4$. MW, 186. B.p. 273–5°, 145–7°/15 mm.

Chloride : $C_7H_9O_3Cl$. MW, 176·5. B.p. 143°/12 mm.

Anilide : cryst. from EtOH. M.p. 176°.

Barbier, Locquin, *Bull. soc. chim.*, 1913, **13**, 231.
Simonsen, *J. Chem. Soc.*, 1907, **91**, 186.

Terephthalaldehyde (*Terephthaldialdehyde*, 1 : 4-*dialdehydobenzene*)

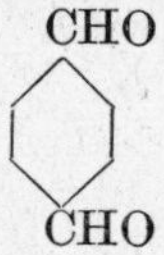

$C_8H_6O_2$ MW, 134

Needles from H_2O. M.p. 116°. B.p. 245–8°/771 mm. Sol. 5000 parts cold H_2O, 80 parts hot H_2O. Sol. Et_2O. Very sol. EtOH. Sol. alkalis, pptd. by acids. Sublimes. Difficultly volatile in steam. $K_2Cr_2O_7 + H_2SO_4$ ⟶ *p*-aldehydobenzoic acid. $Ac_2O + H_2SO_4$ ⟶ tetra-acetate.

Dioxime : terephthalaldoxime. $C_8H_8O_2N_2$. MW, 164. Cryst. M.p. 200°. Spar. sol. H_2O. Very sol. EtOH, Et_2O. *Di-Et ether* : cryst. M.p. 55°. *Diacetyl* : cryst. M.p. 155°.

Dihydrazone : yellowish-white cryst. from EtOH. M.p. 165° decomp.

Monophenylhydrazone : orange-yellow needles from Et_2O. M.p. 152–4°.

Di-phenylhydrazone : yellow scales from AcOH or acetoacetic ester. M.p. 278° decomp.

Di-p-nitrophenylhydrazone : cryst. from $PhNO_2$. Sinters at 272°, m.p. 281°.

Adams, Bullock, Wilson, *J. Am. Chem. Soc.*, 1923, **45**, 521.
Rosenmund, Zetzsche, *Ber.*, 1921, **54**, 2888.
Thiele, Günther, *Ann.*, 1906, **347**, 110.

Terephthalaldehydic Acid.

See *p*-Aldehydobenzoic Acid.

Terephthalamic Acid (*Terephthalic acid monoamide*)

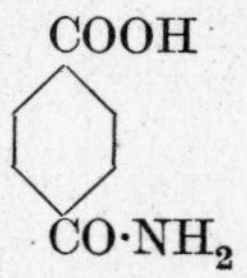

$C_8H_7O_3N$ MW, 165

Does not melt below 300°. Begins to sublime at 250°. Insol. hot H_2O and most org. solvents. Hyd. ⟶ terephthalic acid.

Me ester : $C_9H_9O_3N$. MW, 179. Cryst. from hot H_2O. M.p. 201°.

Nitrile: $C_8H_6ON_2$. MW, 146. Needles. M.p. 223°.

Kattwinkel, Wolffenstein, *Ber.*, 1904, **37**, 3222.

Terephthalic Acid (p-*Phthalic acid, benzene-1 : 4-dicarboxylic acid*)

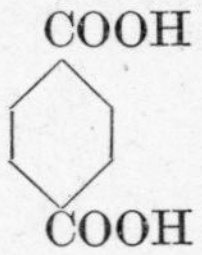

$C_8H_6O_4$ MW, 166

Needles. Sublimes without melting at about 300°. Sol. 67,000 parts cold H_2O. Insol. Et_2O, EtOH, AcOH, $CHCl_3$. Sol. hot EtOH. Heat of comb. C_p 770·9 Cal., C_v 771·2 Cal. Gives spar. sol. Ca, Sr and Ba salts. Red. ⟶ *cis*- and *trans*-hexahydroterephthalic acids.

Mono-Me ester: $C_9H_8O_4$. MW, 180. Needles from hot H_2O. M.p. about 230°. Sublimes.

Di-Me ester: $C_{10}H_{10}O_4$. MW, 194. Needles from Et_2O. M.p. 141–2°. Sol. 300 parts hot H_2O. Spar. sol. cold EtOH. Sublimes. Volatile in steam.

Mono-Et ester: $C_{10}H_{10}O_4$. MW, 194. Plates from C_6H_6. M.p. 171°.

Di-Et ester: $C_{12}H_{14}O_4$. MW, 222. Prisms from EtOH or pet. ether. M.p. 44°. B.p. 302°, 142°/2 mm. D_{45}^{45} 1·1098. Sol. Et_2O. Very sol. cold EtOH. Insol. H_2O.

Mono-propyl ester: $C_{11}H_{12}O_4$. MW, 208. M.p. 127–9°.

Dipropyl ester: $C_{14}H_{18}O_4$. MW, 250. Needles or plates from C_6H_6. M.p. 31°. B.p. 158°/4 mm. Very sol. hot EtOH, Et_2O.

Mono-isopropyl ester: needles from hot C_6H_6. M.p. 166°. Very sol. EtOH, Et_2O. Insol. H_2O.

Di-isopropyl ester: plates. M.p. 55–6°.

Mono-butyl ester: $C_{12}H_{14}O_4$. MW, 222. M.p. 122–4°.

Dibutyl ester: $C_{16}H_{22}O_4$. MW, 278. Needles. M.p. 16°. B.p. 180°/4 mm.

Mono-isobutyl ester: m.p. 151–4°.

Di-isobutyl ester: plates. M.p. 55°. B.p. 180°/6 mm.

Di-tert.-*butyl ester*: prisms from MeOH. M.p. 118°.

Di-l-*menthyl ester*: $C_{28}H_{42}O_4$. MW, 442. Needles from EtOH. M.p. 77–8°. $[\alpha]_D^{20}$ − 102·6° in $CHCl_3$.

Diphenyl ester: $C_{20}H_{14}O_4$. MW, 318. Needles from EtOH. M.p. 191°.

Monochloride: $C_8H_5O_3Cl$. MW, 184·5. Needles from C_6H_6. Does not melt below 300°.

Dichloride: $C_8H_4O_2Cl_2$. MW, 203. Needles or plates from ligroin. M.p. 83–4°.

Dibromide: $C_8H_4O_2Br_2$. MW, 292. Needles from pet. ether. M.p. 85°.

Mono-amide: *see* Terephthalamic Acid.

Diamide: $C_8H_8O_2N_2$. MW, 164. Plates from AcOH. Needles from H_2O. Does not melt below 250°.

Di-1-*naphthylamide*: needles from $PhNO_2$. Sinters at 325°, m.p. 334–5°.

Di-diphenylamide: needles from xylene. Sinters at 268°, m.p. 272–3° decomp.

Di-azide: plates from Me_2CO. M.p. 110°.

Di-hydrazide: needles from H_2O. Does not melt below 300°.

Mono-nitrile: *see* p-Cyanobenzoic Acid.

Di-nitrile: 1 : 4-dicyanobenzene. $C_8H_4N_2$. MW, 128. Needles from H_2O or MeOH. M.p. 222°. Very sol. hot AcOH. Spar. sol. EtOH, Et_2O. Insol. cold H_2O. Sublimes.

Dianilide: needles from acetoacetic ester or $PhNO_2$. M.p. 334–7°.

Carré, Libermann, *Compt. rend.*, 1934, **199**, 1422.
Smith, *J. Am. Chem. Soc.*, 1921, **43**, 1920.
Rosenmund, Zetzsche, *Ber.*, 1921, **54**, 2888.
Lyons, Reid, *J. Am. Chem. Soc.*, 1917, **39**, 1740.
Cohen, Pennington, *J. Chem. Soc.*, 1918, **113**, 63.

Terephthalophenone.

See p-Dibenzoylbenzene.

Terephthalyl Alcohol (p-*Xylylene glycol*, ω-*dihydroxy*-p-*xylene*)

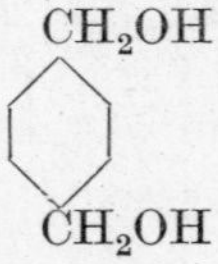

$C_8H_{10}O_2$ MW, 138

Needles. M.p. 115–16°. Sol. H_2O, EtOH, Et_2O.

Mono-Me ether: $C_9H_{12}O_2$. MW, 152. B.p. 152°/16 mm. D_4^{17} 1·076. n_D^{17} 1·529. *Acetyl*: b.p. 150°/16 mm. D_4^{20} 1·080. n_D^{20} 1·505. *Phenylurethane*: m.p. 62°.

Di-Me ether: $C_{10}H_{14}O_2$. MW, 166. Liq. B.p. 235°, 124°/18 mm. D_4^{16} 1·013. n_D^{16} 1·503.

Mono-Et ether: $C_{10}H_{14}O_2$. MW, 166. Liq. B.p. 250–2°, 154°/16 mm. D_4^{17} 1·047. n_D^{17} 1·520. Sol. EtOH, Et_2O. Insol. H_2O.

Di-Et ether: $C_{12}H_{18}O_2$. MW, 194. Liq. B.p. 251–2°/734 mm., 134°/15 mm. D_4^{18} 0·976. n_D^{18} 1·493.

Dibenzyl ether: $C_{22}H_{22}O_2$. MW, 318. M.p. 67°.

Quelet, *Bull. soc. chim.*, 1933, **53**, 222.

Teresantalic Acid

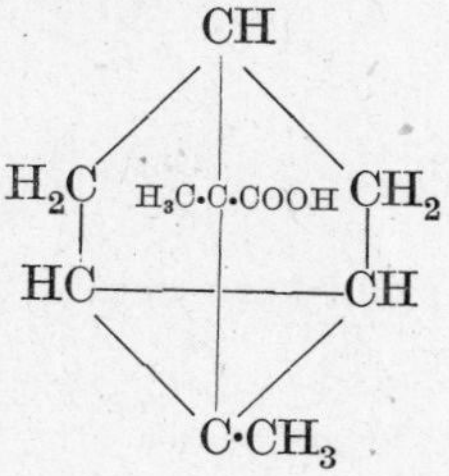

$C_{10}H_{14}O_2$ MW, 166

Occurs in sandalwood oil. Prisms from EtOH. M.p. 158°. B.p. 157–8°/20 mm. Sol. 1270 parts H_2O at 20°. $[\alpha]_D^{20}$ − 76·6° in C_6H_6. Volatile in steam. Stable to $KMnO_4$. Forms a hydrochloride. Dil. $H_2SO_4 \longrightarrow$ santene.

Ca salt: cryst. + $1\frac{1}{2}H_2O$ from H_2O. Decomp. at 100°.

Hydrochloride: cryst. from MeOH. M.p. 199°. Spar. sol. pet. ether.

Me ester: $C_{11}H_{16}O_2$. MW, 180. Oil. B.p. 88·5–89·5°/13 mm. D_4^{20} 1·0305. $[\alpha]_D^{20}$ − 60·79°. Na + EtOH $\longrightarrow$ teresantalol. *Hydrochloride*: two forms. (i) Leaflets from EtOH.Aq. M.p. 68°. B.p. 125–7°/10 mm. $[\alpha]_D^{20}$ + 9·22° in C_6H_6. (ii) Oil. *Hydrobromide*: oil. F.p. −10°. M.p. 20°.

Chloride: $C_{10}H_{13}OCl$. MW, 184·5. B.p. 100–4°/14 mm.

Anilide: b.p. 204–5°/11 mm.

Asahina, Ishidate, Momose, *Ber.*, 1935, **68**, 83.
Ruzicka, Liebl, *Helv. Chim. Acta*, 1926, **9**, 140.
Rupe, Tomi, *Ber.*, 1916, **49**, 2556.

Teresantalol

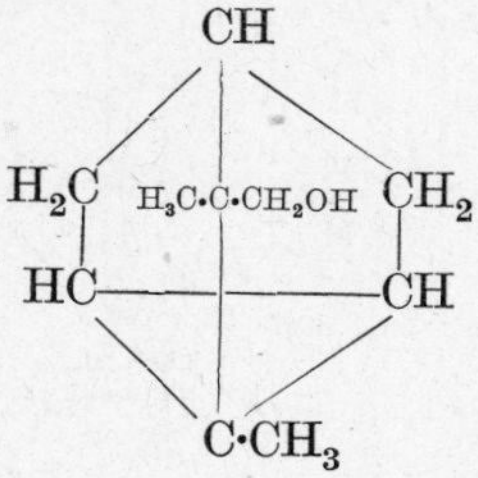

$C_{10}H_{16}O$ MW, 152

d-.

Constituent of Indian sandalwood oil. Prisms from pet. ether. M.p. 112–14°. B.p. 95–8°/9 mm. $[\alpha]_D$ + 11·58° in EtOH. Sublimes.

Acetyl: b.p. 102–3°/9–10 mm. D^{20} 1·019. n_D^{20} 1·470. $[\alpha]_D$ + 21°.

dl-.

Prisms from C_6H_6. M.p. 118°. B.p. 97–8°/10 mm. Stable to cold $KMnO_4$.

Asahina, Ishidate, *Ber.*, 1935, **68**, 952.
Semmler, Bartelt, *Ber.*, 1907, **40**, 3103.

Terpane.
See p-Menthane.

Terpenylic Acid (3 : 3-*Dimethylbutyrolactone-2-acetic acid*)

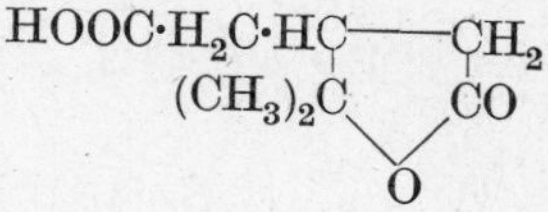

$C_8H_{12}O_4$ MW, 172

Plates or prisms + $1H_2O$ from H_2O. M.p. 57°, anhyd. 90°. Very sol. hot H_2O. Mod. sol. cold H_2O. Sublimes at 130–40°. Ox. $\longrightarrow$ terebic acid. HI (+ P) $\longrightarrow$ 2-isopropylglutaric acid.

Me ester: $C_9H_{14}O_4$. MW, 186. B.p. 145–7°/15 mm.

Et ester: $C_{10}H_{16}O_4$. MW, 200. M.p. 37·5°. B.p. 305°, 174–7°/15 mm.

Lawrence, *J. Chem. Soc.*, 1899, **75**, 530.
Wallach, *Ann.*, 1893, **277**, 118.
Fittig, Levy, *Ann.*, 1890, **256**, 109.

***m*-Terphenyl.**
1 : 3-Diphenylbenzene, *q.v.*

***p*-Terphenyl.**
1 : 4-Diphenylbenzene, *q.v.*

Terpin (p-*Menthandiol*-1 : 8)

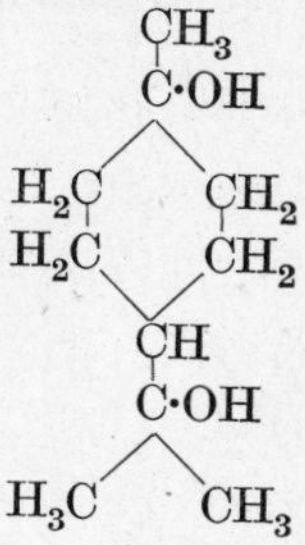

$C_{10}H_{20}O_2$ MW, 172

Cis:

Cryst. M.p. 105·5°. B.p. 258°. Absorbs moisture from the air. Heat of comb. C_v 1454·4 Cal. Dist. over Al_2O_3 at 200–80° $\longrightarrow$ dipentene. H (+ Ni) $\longrightarrow$ *p*-cymene. $(COOH)_2 \longrightarrow$ *d*-terpineol.

Diformyl: viscous oil. B.p. 176–7°/40 mm. D^{27} 1·067.

Diacetyl: b.p. 145°/14 mm.

Trans:
Prisms or plates from AcOEt. M.p. 156–8°. B.p. 263–5°. Very sol. EtOH. Spar. sol. H_2O, Et_2O, AcOEt.

Aschan, *Chem. Zentr.*, 1919, I, 284.
Wallach, *Ann.*, 1906, **350**, 154.

α-Terpinene ($\Delta^{1,3}$-p-*Menthadiene*)

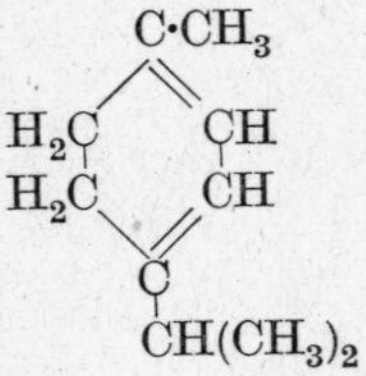

$C_{10}H_{16}$ MW, 136

Constituent of many essential oils. Oil with lemon odour. B.p. 173·5–174·8°/755 mm. D_4^{19} 0·8375. $n_D^{19\cdot7}$ 1·477. Resinifies on keeping. Heat of comb. C_v 1469·9 Cal.
Di-hydrochloride: terpinene dihydrochloride. Cryst. from MeOH. M.p. 53–4°. B.p. 108–9°/10 mm.
Di-hydrobromide: terpinene dihydrobromide. Plates from MeOH or AcOH. M.p. 58–9°.
Di-hydriodide: terpinene dihydriodide. Cryst. from MeOH. M.p. 76°.
Nitrosite: prisms. M.p. 155°. *Benzoate*: m.p. 77–8°.

Richter, Wolff, *Ber.*, 1930, **63**, 1714.
Wallach, *Ann.*, 1889, **252**, 133; 1887, **241**, 316; 1887, **239**, 35.

β-Terpinene ($\Delta^{3,1(7)}$-p-*Menthadiene*)

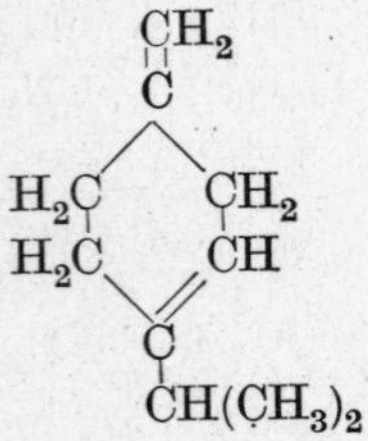

$C_{10}H_{16}$ MW, 136

Does not occur naturally. Oil. B.p. 173–4°. D^{22} 0·838. n_D^{22} 1·4754. Readily oxidised in air. HCl ⟶ terpinene dihydrochloride.
Tetrabromide: prisms from AcOEt. M.p. 154–5°.

Wallach, *Ann.*, 1908, **362**, 288.

γ-Terpinene ($\Delta^{1,4}$-p-*Menthadiene*)

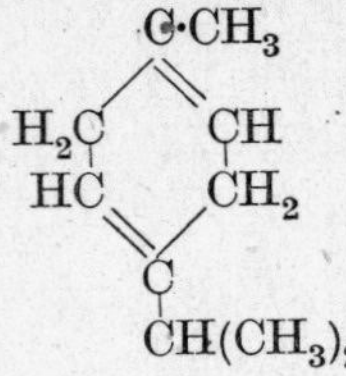

$C_{10}H_{16}$ MW, 136

Constituent of a few essential oils. B.p. 183°, 72·5°/18 mm. D_4^{20} 0·849. $n_D^{14\cdot5}$ 1·4765. Heat of comb. C_v 1468·9 Cal., C_p 1472 Cal. HCl ⟶ terpinene dihydrochloride.
Tetrabromide: plates from pet. ether. M.p. 128°.
Nitrosochloride: m.p. 111°.
Nitrolpiperidide: plates. M.p. 149°.
Nitrosate: needles from AcOH–MeOH. M.p. 116° decomp.

Richter, Wolff, *Ber.*, 1930, **63**, 1714.

Terpinene-terpin.
See *p*-Menthandiol-1 : 4.

(1)-Terpinenol (Δ^3-p-*Menthenol*-1, 4-*methyl*-1-*isopropylcyclohexenol*-4)

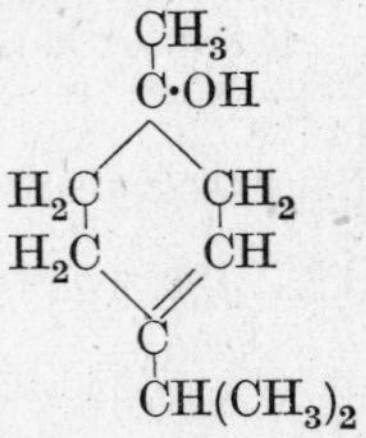

$C_{10}H_{18}O$ MW, 154

B.p. 208–10°. D^{18} 0·9265. n_D^{18} 1·4781. $KMnO_4$ ⟶ *p*-menthantriol-1 : 3 : 4.

Wallach, Meister, *Ann.*, 1908, **362**, 269.

(4)-Terpinenol (Δ^1-p-*Menthenol*-4, 1-*methyl*-4-*isopropylcyclohexenol*-4)

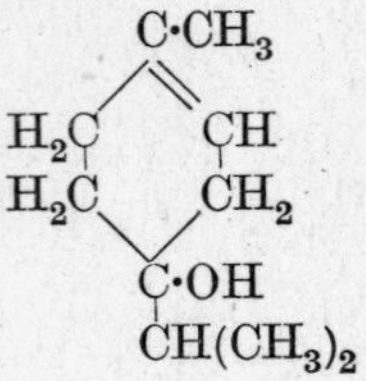

$C_{10}H_{18}O$ MW, 154

d-.
Occurs in many essential oils. B.p. 208–10°, 93–6°/1 mm. D^{20} 0·926. n_D^{19} 1·4785. $[\alpha]_D^{11}$ +24·5°. Dil. H_2SO_4 ⟶ *p*-menthandiol-1 : 4. $KMnO_4$ ⟶ *d*-menthantriol-1 : 2 : 4.

Formyl: b.p. 102–6°. D^{20} 0·975. n_D 1·4745.
Nitrosochloride: m.p. 111–12°.
Nitrolpiperidide: m.p. 172–4°.
Phenylurethane: m.p. 71–2°.
1-*Naphthylurethane*: m.p. 105·5–106·5°.

dl-.
Constituent of oil from leaf of *Liquidambar formosana*, Hance. B.p. 212–14°, 90°/11 mm. n_D 1·4803.
Nitrolpiperidide: Two forms. (i) Cryst. from EtOH. M.p. 155–6°. (ii) Cryst. from EtOH. M.p. 181–2°. More soluble.

Kafuku, Nonoe, Hata, *J. Chem. Soc. Japan*, 1934, **55**, 224.
Wallach, Meister, *Ann.*, 1908, **362**, 269.
Wallach, *Ber.*, 1907, **40**, 596.

α-Terpineol (Δ^1-p-*Menthenol*-8)

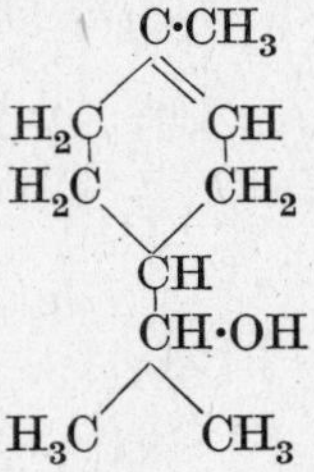

$C_{10}H_{18}O$ MW, 154

All forms occur in many essential oils.

d-.
M.p. 36·9°. B.p. 104°/15 mm. $D_4^{21\cdot5}$ 0·9475. n_D 1·4819. $[\alpha]_D^{20}$ + 100·5°.
Nitrosochloride: leaflets from MeOH. M.p. 107–8°.
Nitrolpiperidide: m.p. 151–2°.
Formate: b.p. 133–6°/40 mm. D_0 0·9989. $[\alpha]_D$ + 16·5°.
Acetate: b.p. 140°/40 mm. D_0^0 0·9828. $[\alpha]_D$ + 52·5°.
Hydrogen phthalate: $[\alpha]_D$ + 36·7°. *Morphine salt*: rhombic cryst. from MeOH. M.p. 142°.
Phenylurethane: needles from MeOH. M.p. 109·5°.

l-.
M.p. 37·0°. B.p. 104°/15 mm. D_4^{25} 0·9364. n_D^{25} 1·48054. $[\alpha]_D^{20}$ − 100·5°.
Nitrosochloride: needles from MeOH.Aq. M.p. 107–8°.
Nitrolpiperidide: m.p. 151–2°.
Formate: b.p. 135–8°/40 mm. D_0^0 0·9986. $[\alpha]_D$ − 69·4°.
Hydrogen phthalate: $[\alpha]_D$ − 36·7°. *Strychnine salt*: needles from EtOH. M.p. 207°.
Phenylurethane: m.p. 109·5°.

dl-.
M.p. 35°. B.p. 218·8–219·4°/752 mm., 99–100°/12 mm. D_{20}^{20} 0·935. n_D^{20} 1·4819. Non misc. with H_2O. Misc. with most org. solvents. Heat of comb. C_v 1475·1 Cal. $KMnO_4 \longrightarrow$ *p*-menthantriol-1 : 2 : 8 and terpenylic acid. H_2O at 250° $\longrightarrow$ dipentene. H·COOH $\longrightarrow$ terpinolene. H(+ Ni) $\longrightarrow$ *p*-cymene, H(+ Pd) $\longrightarrow$ *p*-menthanol-8.
Nitrosochloride: needles from AcOEt. Woolly needles from MeOH. M.p. 120–2°.
Nitrolpiperidide: m.p. 159–60°.
Me ether: $C_{11}H_{20}O$. MW, 168. B.p. 212°.
Acetate: b.p. 104–6°/11 mm. D_4^{20} 0·9659. $n_D^{19\cdot7}$ 1·4657.
Hydrogen phthalate: rods from AcOH. M.p. 117–18°. *Brucine salt*: rhombic cryst. from MeOH. M.p. 150°.
Phenylurethane: m.p. 113°.

Ransac, *Chem. Zentr.*, 1932, I, 63.
Fuller, Kenyon, *J. Chem. Soc.*, 1924, **125**, 2304.
Perkin, *J. Chem. Soc.*, 1904, **85**, 665.

β-Terpineol ($\Delta^{8(9)}$-p-*Menthenol*-1)

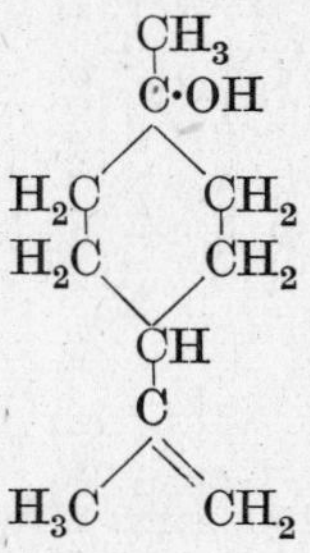

$C_{10}H_{18}O$ MW, 154

Does not occur naturally. Oil with odour of hyacinths. Solidifies on cooling to needles, m.p. 32–3°. B.p. 209–10°/752 mm., 90°/10 mm. D_{20}^{20} 0·919. n_D^{20} 1·4747. $KMnO_4 \longrightarrow$ *p*-menthantriol-1 : 8 : 9.
Dibromide: needles from EtOH–Et_2O. M.p. 114–15°.
Nitrosite: needles from Me_2CO.Aq. M.p. 78°.
Nitrosate: needles from EtOH.Aq. M.p. 125°.
Nitrosochloride: cryst. from EtOH.Aq. M.p. 103°.
Nitrolanilide: m.p. 145–6°.
Phenylurethane: m.p. 85°.

See first reference above and also
Stephen, Helle, *Ber.*, 1902, **35**, 2149.

γ-Terpineol ($\Delta^{4(8)}$-p-*Menthenol*-1)

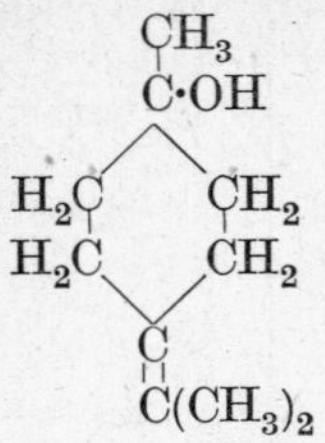

$C_{10}H_{18}O$ MW, 154

Thick prisms from Et_2O. M.p. 68–70°. Distils without decomp. $KMnO_4 \longrightarrow$ *p*-menthantriol-1 : 4 : 8. H·COOH $\longrightarrow$ terpinolene.

Dibromide : m.p. 114–15°.

Acetyl : b.p. 110–20°/16 mm. *Dibromide* : m.p. 103°. *Nitrosochloride* : blue leaflets from EtOH. M.p. 82°. *Nitrosobromide* : blue needles from EtOH. M.p. 81–2°.

Baeyer, *Ber.*, 1894, **27**, 443.

Terpin Hydrate

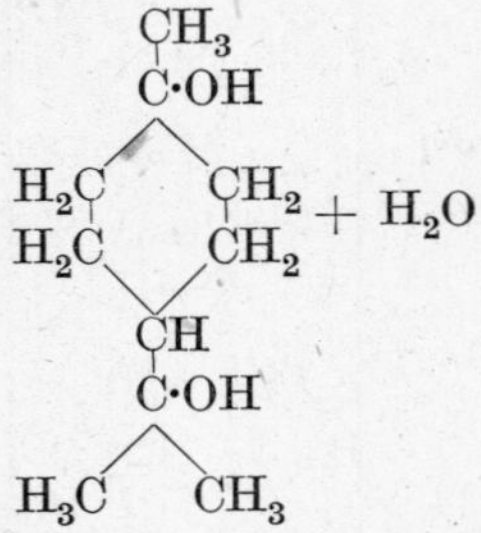

$C_{10}H_{20}O_2,H_2O$ MW, 190

Rhombic cryst. M.p. 123° decomp. $\longrightarrow$ *cis*-terpin. Eutectic containing 10% hydrate has m.p. 95°. Sol. 250 parts H_2O at 15°, 32 parts at 100°. Sol. 10 parts EtOH at 15°, 2 parts at 78°. Sol. 100 parts Et_2O, 200 parts $CHCl_3$ at 15°. Sol. 1 part of AcOH at b.p. Insol. pet. ether. $H_2SO_4 \longrightarrow$ orange col. Heat of comb. C_v 1449·1 Cal.

Claus, *Chem. Abstracts*, 1932, **26**, 127.
Aschan, *Chem. Zentr.*, 1919, I, 284.

Terpinolene ($\Delta^{1,4(8)}$-p-*Menthadiene*)

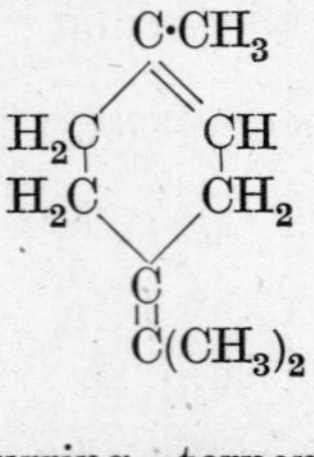

$C_{10}H_{16}$ MW, 136

Naturally occurring terpene hydrocarbon. B.p. 186°, 121°/111 mm., 76°/10 mm. Polymerises when dist. at atm. press. Very readily isomerises to terpinene. D_{15}^{15} 0·8633. n_D^{20} 1·4883. HCl $\longrightarrow$ dipentene dihydrochloride. $Ac_2O + H_2SO_4 \longrightarrow$ transient pink col.

Dibromide : prisms. M.p. 69–70°.

Tetrabromide : two forms. They show marked m.p. depression but give same terpinolene on debromination. (i) Rectangular plates from Me_2CO. M.p. 119°. (ii) Cryst. aggregates from EtOH, Me_2CO or AcOEt. M.p. 122°.

Henry, Paget, *J. Chem. Soc.*, 1931, **134**, 28.
Wallach, *Ann.*, 1909, **368**, 11.

Testosterone (*Androstenol*-17-*one*-3)

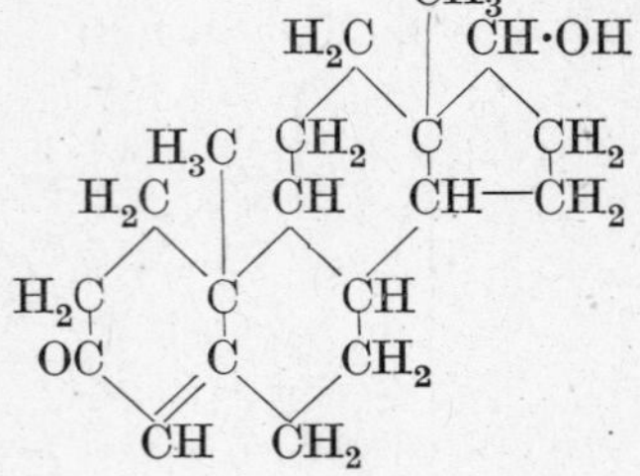

$C_{19}H_{28}O_2$ MW, 288

Hormone obtained from testes extract. Needles from Me_2CO. M.p. 154–154·5°. $[\alpha]_D$ + 109° in EtOH. Produces male characteristics in castrated animals.

Oxime : cryst. from EtOH.Aq. M.p. 222–3°.

Formyl : cryst. from hexane. M.p. 127–9°.

Acetyl : needles from Me_2CO.Aq. M.p. 140–1°. $[\alpha]_D^{20}$ + 87·8° in EtOH.

Propionyl : m.p. 121–3°.

Butyryl : needles from 70% MeOH. M.p. 111–13°.

Isobutyryl : needles from Me_2CO.Aq. M.p. 134–6°.

Palmityl : cryst. from MeOH. M.p. 72–4°.

Stearyl : cryst. from MeOH. M.p. 79–80°.

David, Dingemance, Freud, Laquer, *Z. physiol. Chem.*, 1935, **233**, 281.
Butenandt, Hanisch, *Ber.*, 1935, **68**, 1859.
Ruzicka, Wettstein, *Helv. Chim. Acta*, 1935, **18**, 1264; 1936, **19**, 1141.

Tetanthrene.

See Tetrahydrophenanthrene.

Tethracene.

See Tetrahydroanthracene.

Tethracenequinone.

See 1 : 2 : 3 : 4-Tetrahydroanthraquinone.

1 : 4 : 5 : 8-Tetra-aminoanthraquinone

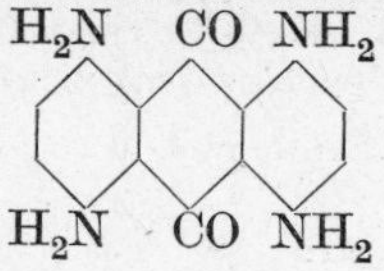

$C_{14}H_{12}O_2N_4$ MW, 268

Reddish-brown needles from EtOH. M.p. 332°. Sol. EtOH and $CHCl_3$ with greenish-blue col., in AcOEt with reddish-blue col., in Me_2CO with blue col. Spar. sol. H_2O with blue col.

1 : 4 : 5 : 8-N-*Tetra-Me* : $C_{18}H_{20}O_2N_4$. MW, 324. Cryst. Sol. $CHCl_3$, AcOEt with blue col. Sol. HCl with red col. turning violet on dilution.

Noelting, Wortmann, *Ber.*, 1906, **39**, 644.
Höchst, D.R.P., 156,803, (*Chem. Zentr.*, 1905, I, 313).

1 : 2 : 3 : 4-Tetra-aminobenzene

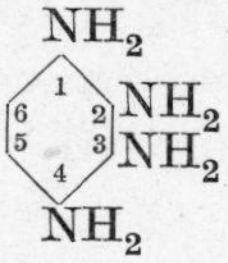

$C_6H_{10}N_4$ MW, 138

Free base oxidises very rapidly in air.

Nietzki, Geese, *Ber.*, 1899, **32**, 505.

1 : 2 : 3 : 5-Tetra-aminobenzene.

B,3HCl : needles + H_2O.
B,2H₂SO₄ : plates.
N-*Tetra-acetyl* : needles from AcOH. M.p. 245°.

Nietzki, Hagenbach, *Ber.*, 1897, **30**, 539.
Borsche, *Ber.*, 1923, **56**, 1939.

1 : 2 : 4 : 5-Tetra-aminobenzene.

Free base oxidises very readily in air.
B,4HCl : prisms. Sol. H_2O. Spar. sol. HCl.
B,H₂SO₄ : needles. Mod. sol. H_2O.
B₂,3H₂SO₄ : plates. Spar. sol. H_2O.
2 : 4-N-*Diphenyl* : $C_{18}H_{18}N_4$. MW, 290. Needles from C_6H_6. M.p. 207°.
1 : 2 : 4 : 5-N-*Tetraphenyl* : $C_{30}H_{26}N_4$. MW, 442. Needles. M.p. 173–4°.
1 : 2 : 4 : 5-N-*Tetra-acetyl* : needles from AcOH. M.p. 285°.

Nietzki, Hagenbach, *Ber.*, 1887, **20**, 334.
Nietzki, Müller, *Ber.*, 1889, **22**, 440.
Hewitt, Stevenson, *Ber.*, 1898, **31**, 1791.

2 : 4 : 2′ : 4′-Tetra-aminobenzophenone

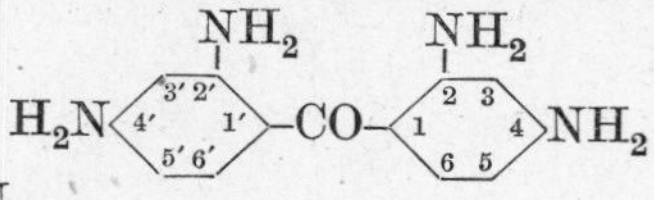

$C_{13}H_{14}ON_4$ MW, 242

Yellow prisms from EtOH. M.p. 202°. Evolves NH_3 above m.p. Sol. MeOH, Me_2CO, AcOEt. Spar. sol. $CHCl_3$, C_6H_6.

Gulland, Robinson, *J. Chem. Soc.*, 1925, 1499.

3 : 4 : 3′ : 4′-Tetra-aminobenzophenone.
Yellow needles from H_2O. M.p. 217°.

Montagne, *Ber.*, 1915, **48**, 1034.

2 : 4 : 2′ : 4′-Tetra-aminodiphenyl (2 : 2′-*Diaminobenzidine*)

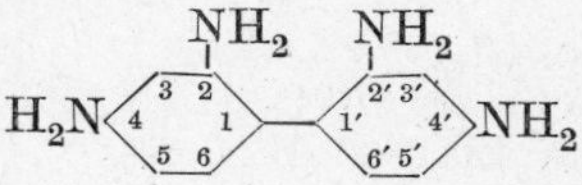

$C_{12}H_{14}N_4$ MW, 214

Leaflets from EtOH.Aq. M.p. 166°. 20% HCl or H_2SO_4 at 200° ⟶ 2 : 7-diaminocarbazole.

2 : 2′-N-*Tetra-Me* : $C_{16}H_{22}N_4$. MW, 270. Needles from EtOH. M.p. 165·5–166°. Sol. C_6H_6. Mod. sol. EtOH. Spar. sol. H_2O, ligroin.
4 : 4′-N-*Tetra-Me* : plates from C_6H_6–ligroin. M.p. 166°. Sol. EtOH, C_6H_6. Spar. sol. Et_2O, ligroin. Insol. H_2O.
2 : 4 : 2′ : 4′-N-*Tetra-acetyl* : needles from H_2O. M.p. 285°.

Täuber, *Ber.*, 1890, **23**, 797.
Elbs, Wohlfahrt, *J. prakt. Chem.*, 1902, **66**, 561.
Noelting, Fourneaux, *Ber.*, 1897, **30**, 2940.
Ullmann, Dieterle, *Ber.*, 1904, **37**, 33.

2 : 5 : 2′ : 5′-Tetra-aminodiphenyl.

Needles from toluene. M.p. 168°. Sol. H_2O, EtOH, $CHCl_3$. Spar. sol. Et_2O, C_6H_6. Insol. ligroin. HCl at 190° ⟶ 3 : 6-diaminocarbazole.

Täuber, *Ber.*, 1892, **25**, 130.

3 : 4 : 3′ : 4′-Tetra-aminodiphenyl (3 : 3′-*Diaminobenzidine*).

Plates. Rapidly blackens in air.
B,4HCl : needles + $2H_2O$. Sol. H_2O.
B,H₂SO₄ : needles. Sol. hot H_2O. Spar. sol. EtOH, Et_2O.
4 : 4′-N-*Tetra-Me* : plates from EtOH. M.p. 168°. Sol. EtOH. Insol. H_2O. $FeCl_3$ + HCl ⟶ violet col.

Brunner, Witt, *Ber.*, 1887, **20**, 1025.
Michler, Pattinson, *Ber.*, 1881, **14**, 2164; 1884, **17**, 118.

2 : 4 : 2′ : 4′-Tetra-aminodiphenylmethane

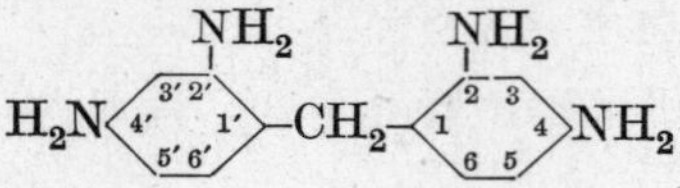

$C_{13}H_{16}N_4$ MW, 228

Cryst. from H_2O. M.p. 161°. Sol. EtOH. Mod. sol. H_2O. Spar. sol. C_6H_6. Insol. Et_2O.

4-N-*Di-Me*: $C_{15}H_{20}N_4$. MW, 256. Cryst. from toluene. M.p. 188–90°. Sol. EtOH, $CHCl_3$. Insol. H_2O.

4-N-*Me*-4′-N-*Di-Me*: $C_{16}H_{22}N_4$. MW, 270. Cryst. from toluene. M.p. 95°. Sol. EtOH, $CHCl_3$. Insol. H_2O.

4 : 4′-N-*Tetra-Me*: $C_{17}H_{24}N_4$. MW, 284. Needles from EtOH. M.p. 142°. Sol. $CHCl_3$, C_6H_6, hot EtOH. Mod. sol. Et_2O. Insol. H_2O.

4 : 4′-N-*Diacetyl*: needles from EtOH. M.p. 244°.

2 : 4 : 2′ : 4′-N-*Tetra-acetyl*: cryst. from H_2O. Mod. sol. EtOH. Spar. sol. H_2O.

2 : 4 : 2′ : 4′-N-*Tetrabenzoyl*: cryst. from EtOH. M.p. 275°.

Staedel, *Ann.*, 1883, **218**, 341.
Duval, *Compt. rend.*, 1906, **142**, 342.
Pinnow, *Ber.*, 1894, **27**, 3163.
Bayer, D.R.P., 133,709, (*Chem. Zentr.*, 1902, II, 615).

3 : 4 : 3′ : 4′-Tetra-aminodiphenylmethane.

Plates from H_2O or C_6H_6. M.p. 137–8°. Sol. hot H_2O. Spar. sol. EtOH, C_6H_6. Insol. Et_2O, Me_2CO. $FeCl_3$ + HCl ⟶ dark red col.

Meyer, Rohmer, *Ber.*, 1900, **33**, 257.

α : 4 : 4′ : 4″-Tetra-aminotriphenylmethane

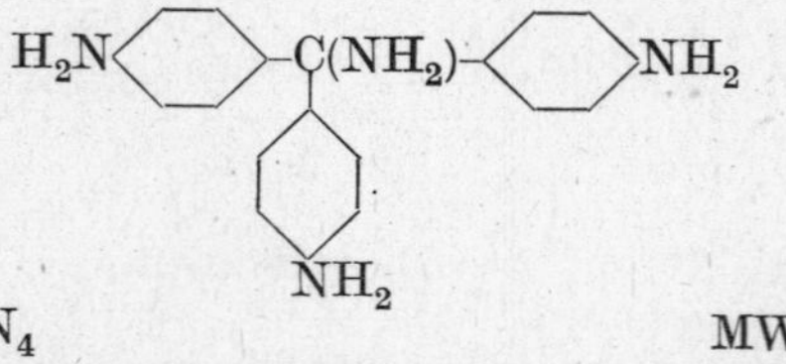

$C_{19}H_{20}N_4$ MW, 304

Yellow prisms. Sol. Py. Spar. sol. common org. solvents.

4 : 4′ : 4″-N-*Hexa-Me*: $C_{25}H_{32}N_4$. MW, 388. Leaflets from C_6H_6–ligroin. M.p. 190·5° decomp. Spar. sol. Et_2O, ligroin.

4 : 4′ : 4″-N-*Hexa-Et*: $C_{31}H_{44}N_4$. MW, 472. Needles from ligroin. M.p. 141·5–142·5°. Sol. Et_2O, C_6H_6. Mod. sol. ligroin.

Villiger, Kopetschni, *Ber.*, 1912, **45**, 2920.
Noelting, Saas, *Ber.*, 1913, **46**, 953.

2 : 3 : 4 : 6-Tetrabromoacetanilide.
See under 2 : 3 : 4 : 6-Tetrabromoaniline.

1 : 1 : 1 : 3-Tetrabromoacetone

$BrCH_2{\cdot}CO{\cdot}CBr_3$

$C_3H_2OBr_4$ MW, 374

Needles. M.p. 37–8°. B.p. 258° decomp., 139°/14 mm.

Tetrahydrate: prisms. M.p. 62°.

Mulder, *J. prakt. Chem.*, 1864, **91**, 475.
de Jong, *Rec. trav. chim.*, 1903, **22**, 286.
Dippy, Watson, Yates, *J. Chem. Soc.*, 1931, 2508.

1 : 1 : 3 : 3-Tetrabromoacetone

$Br_2CH{\cdot}CO{\cdot}CHBr_2$

$C_3H_2OBr_4$ MW, 374

Yellow oil. Decomp. on warming. Alkalis ⟶ bromoform.

Lederer, D.R.P., 98,009.

2 : 3 : 4 : 6-Tetrabromoaniline

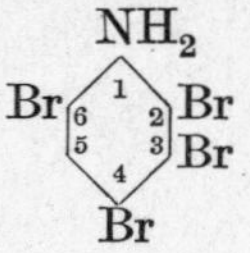

$C_6H_3NBr_4$ MW, 409

Cryst. from EtOH. M.p. 118°.

N-*Acetyl*: 2 : 3 : 4 : 6-tetrabromoacetanilide. Needles from C_6H_6. M.p. 228–9°.

N-*Diacetyl*: prisms from pet. ether. M.p. 164°.

$C_6H_3NBr_4,C_6H_3(NO_2)_3$-1 : 3 : 5: yellow needles. M.p. 107·5–108°.

N-*Thionyl*: yellow needles from C_6H_6. M.p. 78°.

Dains, Kenyon, *J. Am. Chem. Soc.*, 1931, **53**, 2363.
Sudborough, Beard, *J. Chem. Soc.*, 1910, **97**, 782.
Claus, Wallbaum, *J. prakt. Chem.*, 1897, **56**, 50.
Zincke, Kuchenbecker, *Ann.*, 1904, **330**, 57.

2 : 3 : 5 : 6-Tetrabromoaniline.

Needles from EtOH. M.p. 130°.

Claus, *J. prakt. Chem.*, 1895, **51**, 412.

2 : 3 : 9 : 10-Tetrabromoanthracene

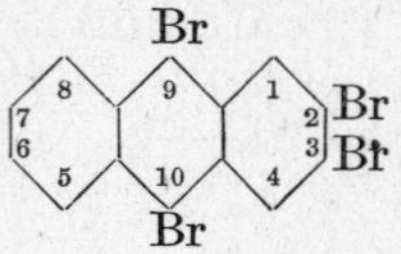

$C_{14}H_6Br_4$ MW, 494

Yellow needles from C_6H_6. M.p. 274° (265–6°). par. sol. EtOH, Et_2O, C_6H_6. Sublimes. x. ⟶ 2 : 3-dibromoanthraquinone.

Barnett, Cook, *J. Chem. Soc.*, 1935, 1489.
Meyer, Zahn, *Ann.*, 1913, **396**, 174.

2 : 6 : 9 : 10-Tetrabromoanthracene.

Cryst. from CCl_4 or toluene. M.p. 298–300°. Iod. sol. hot toluene. Spar. sol. EtOH, C_6H_6. x. ⟶ 2 : 6-dibromoanthraquinone.

Grandmougin, *Compt. rend.*, 1921, **173**, 1176.
Kaufler, Imhoff, *Ber.*, 1904, **37**, 4706.

Tetrabromoanthranilic Acid (3 : 4 : 5 : 6-*etrabromo-2-aminobenzoic acid*)

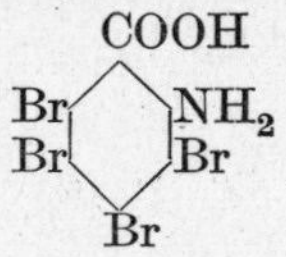

$_7H_3O_2NBr_4$ MW, 453

Needles from AcOH. M.p. 204–5°. Sol. tOH, AcOEt. Mod. sol. $CHCl_3$, AcOH, xylene.

Lesser, Weiss, *Ber.*, 1913, **46**, 3942.
Grandmougin, *Ber.*, 1914, **47**, 384.

1 : 2 : 3 : 4-Tetrabromoanthraquinone

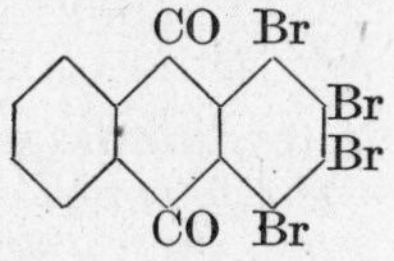

$_{14}H_4O_2Br_4$ MW, 524

Orange-red needles from ligroin. M.p. 200–2°.

Hofmann, *Monatsh.*, 1915, **36**, 820.

The following tetrabromoanthraquinones of nknown constitution have also been described :

(i) Yellow needles from $PhNO_2$ or xylene. I.p. 295°.

Bayer, D.R.P., 107,721, (*Chem. Zentr.*, 1900, I, 1176).

(ii) Yellow needles from CS_2. M.p. above 70°. Sublimes. NaOH fusion ⟶ alizarin.

Hammerschlag, *Ber.*, 1877, **10**, 1213.

(iii) Yellow leaflets from toluene, $CHCl_3$ or S_2. M.p. 295–300°.

Diehl, *Ber.*, 1878, **11**, 182.

1 : 2 : 3 : 5-Tetrabromobenzene

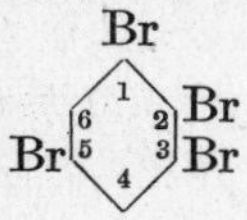

$_6H_2Br_4$ MW, 394

Needles from EtOH. M.p. 98·5°. B.p. 329°. Sol. Et_2O, C_6H_6, CS_2. Mod. sol. EtOH.

v. Richter, *Ber.*, 1875, **8**, 1426.
Zincke, Kuchenbecker, *Ann.*, 1904, **330**, 9, 54.

1 : 2 : 4 : 5-Tetrabromobenzene.

Cryst. from CS_2. M.p. 180–1°. D^{20} 3·027.

Scheufelen, *Ann.*, 1885, **231**, 187.
Jackson, Gallivan, *Am. Chem. J.*, 1896, **18**, 250.
MacKerrow, *Ber.*, 1891, **24**, 2940.
Zelinsky, *Ber.*, 1901, **34**, 2803.

2 : 3 : 4 : 5-Tetrabromobenzenesulphonic Acid

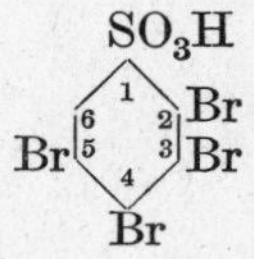

$C_6H_2O_3Br_4S$ MW, 474

Plates from H_2O. M.p. 168–9°. Sol. H_2O. Mod. sol. EtOH, Et_2O.

Chloride : $C_6HO_2ClBr_4S$. MW, 492·5. Plates from Et_2O. M.p. 120°.

Amide : $C_6H_3O_2NBr_4S$. MW, 473. Prisms from EtOH. Sinters and darkens at 240° (161°).

Spiegelberg, *Ann.*, 1879, **197**, 292.
Lenz, *Ann.*, 1876, **181**, 45.

2 : 3 : 4 : 6-Tetrabromobenzenesulphonic Acid.

Needles + $5H_2O$ from H_2O. Sol. EtOH, H_2O.

Chloride : leaflets from Et_2O. M.p. 96·5°.

Amide : needles from EtOH. M.p. about 245° decomp. Spar. sol. H_2O.

Bässmann, *Ann.*, 1878, **191**, 224.
Beckurts, *Ann.*, 1876, **181**, 216.
Knuth, *Ann.*, 1877, **186**, 299.

2 : 6 : 2′ : 6′-Tetrabromobenzidine

(2 : 6 : 2′ : 6′-*Tetrabromo*-4 : 4′-*diaminodiphenyl*)

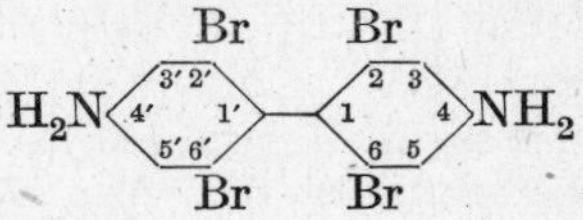

$C_{12}H_8N_2Br_4$ MW, 500

Cryst. from EtOH.Aq. M.p. 180°. Sol. EtOH, Et_2O, Me_2CO, $CHCl_3$, AcOEt. Spar. sol. ligroin.

4 : 4′-N-*Diacetyl* : prisms from EtOH. M.p. 269–70°.

Meyer, Meyer, Taeger, *Ber.*, 1920, **53**, 2045.

3 : 5 : 3′ : 5′-Tetrabromobenzidine
(3 : 5 : 3′ : 5′-*Tetrabromo*-4 : 4′-*diaminodiphenyl*).
Needles from xylene. M.p. 288°. Mod. sol. C_6H_6. Spar. sol. EtOH. Insol. H_2O, Et_2O, acids.

4 : 4′-N-*Diacetyl* : chars at about 340°.

4 : 4′-N-*Tetra-acetyl* : needles from C_6H_6. M.p. about 306°.

van Roosmalen, *Rec. trav. chim.*, 1934, **53**, 359.
Schlenk, *Ann.*, 1908, **363**, 335.
Mills, *J. Chem. Soc.*, 1894, **65**, 54.
Claus, Risler, *Ber.*, 1881, **14**, 86.

2 : 3 : 4 : 5-Tetrabromobenzoic Acid

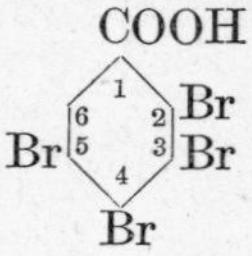

$C_7H_2O_2Br_4$ MW, 438

M.p. 234°. Very sol. EtOH, Me_2CO. Mod. sol. C_6H_6. Spar. sol. pet. ether.

Nitrile : C_7HNBr_4. MW, 419. Needles from EtOH. M.p. 124°.

Bunt, *Rec. trav. chim.*, 1929, **48**, 121.
Claus, Wallbaum, *J. prakt. Chem.*, 1897, **56**, 56.

2 : 3 : 4 : 6-Tetrabromobenzoic Acid.
Needles from C_6H_6. M.p. 179°. Sol. EtOH, Et_2O. Mod. sol. C_6H_6. Spar. sol. H_2O.

Me ester : $C_8H_4O_2Br_4$. MW, 452. Needles from EtOH. M.p. 77°.

Et ester : $C_9H_6O_2Br_4$. MW, 466. M.p. 31°.

Chloride : $C_7HOClBr_4$. MW, 456·5. Prisms from pet. ether. M.p. 58°. Sol. Et_2O, C_6H_6. Spar. sol. H_2O.

Nitrile : needles from EtOH. M.p. 123°. Volatile in steam.

Sudborough, *J. Chem. Soc.*, 1895, **67**, 597.
Claus, Wallbaum, *J. prakt. Chem.*, 1897, **56**, 52.
Sudborough, Karvé, *J. Indian Inst. Sci.*, 1919, **3**, 1.

2 : 3 : 5 : 6-Tetrabromobenzoic Acid.
Yellow plates from EtOH. M.p. 295°. Sol. C_6H_6. Spar. sol. EtOH.

Note.—In the literature this acid is described as of unknown constitution, but since it is different from the other two tetrabromobenzoic acids, it probably possesses the above structure.

Kunckell, Knigge, *Ber.*, 1906, **39**, 195.

Tetrabromo-*p*-benzoquinone.
See Bromanil.

1 : 1 : 2 : 2-Tetrabromobutane

$CH_3{\cdot}CH_2{\cdot}CBr_2{\cdot}CHBr_2$

$C_4H_6Br_4$ MW, 374

Cryst. Sublimes at 200°.

Bruylants, *Ber.*, 1875, **8**, 412.
Dupont, *Compt. rend.*, 1909, **148**, 1523.

1 : 1 : 2 : 3-Tetrabromobutane

$CH_3{\cdot}CHBr{\cdot}CHBr{\cdot}CHBr_2$

$C_4H_6Br_4$ MW, 374

B.p. 148–50°/25 mm.

Muskat, Grimsley, *J. Am. Chem. Soc.*, 1933, **55**, 2145.

1 : 1 : 3 : 3-Tetrabromobutane

$CH_3{\cdot}CBr_2{\cdot}CH_2{\cdot}CHBr_2$

$C_4H_6Br_4$ MW, 374

Fuming liq. D_4^{16} 2·7.

Mereshkowski, *Chem. Zentr.*, 1914, I, 2160.

1 : 2 : 2 : 3-Tetrabromobutane

$CH_3{\cdot}CHBr{\cdot}CBr_2{\cdot}CH_2Br$

$C_4H_6Br_4$ MW, 374

M.p. − 2°. B.p. 97·5°/7 mm. D_4^{20} 2·510. n^{20} 1·6070.

Hurd, Meinert, *J. Am. Chem. Soc.*, 1931, **53**, 293.

1 : 2 : 3 : 4-Tetrabromobutane (*Butadiene tetrabromide, erythrene tetrabromide*)

$BrCH_2{\cdot}CHBr{\cdot}CHBr{\cdot}CH_2Br$

$C_4H_6Br_4$ MW, 374

Exists in two isomeric forms.

(i) Needles from ligroin. M.p. 118–19°. B.p. 180–1°/60 mm. Spar. sol. ligroin. Volatile in steam.

(ii) Leaflets from pet. ether. M.p. 40–1°. Sol. EtOH, Et_2O, ligroin.

Perkin, Simonsen, *J. Chem. Soc.*, 1905, **87**, 857.
Ciamician, Magnaghi, *Ber.*, 1886, **19**, 570; 1887, **20**, 3064.
Jacobson, *J. Am. Chem. Soc.*, 1932, **54**, 1545.

2 : 2 : 3 : 3-Tetrabromobutane

$CH_3{\cdot}CBr_2{\cdot}CBr_2{\cdot}CH_3$

$C_4H_6Br_4$ MW, 374

Cryst. from ligroin. M.p. 243°. Sol. ligroin. Insol. EtOH. Dimorphous.

Faworski, *J. prakt. Chem.*, 1890, **42**, 144.
Wislicenus, Schmidt, *Ann.*, 1900, **313**, 225.

Tetrabromocatechol

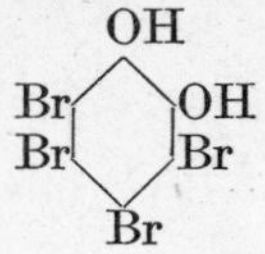

$C_6H_2O_2Br_4$ MW, 426

Needles from EtOH. M.p. 192–3°. $FeCl_3$ ⟶ dark blue col.

Mono-Me ether: tetrabromoguaiacol. $C_7H_4O_2Br_4$. MW, 440. Prisms from EtOH or $CHCl_3$. M.p. 162–3°. Sol. Et_2O, Me_2CO. Mod. sol. EtOH, $CHCl_3$. Spar. sol. AcOH. Insol. H_2O.

Di-Me ether: tetrabromoveratrol. $C_8H_6O_2Br_4$. MW, 454. Cryst. from CCl_4. M.p. 151–2° (118–20°).

Methylene ether: tetrabromomethylenedioxybenzene. $C_7H_2O_2Br_4$. MW, 438. Needles from EtOH. M.p. 208–9°.

Diacetyl: plates from C_6H_6. M.p. 215–16°.

Dibenzoyl: plates from C_6H_6–ligroin. M.p. 197–8°.

Frejka, Sefránek, *Chem. Zentr.*, 1936, I, 2338.
Jackson, Russe, *Am. Chem. J.*, 1906, **35**, 169, 178.
Zincke, *Ber.*, 1887, **20**, 1778.
Stenhouse, *Ann.*, 1875, **177**, 187.
Zetzsche, Sukiennik, *Helv. Chim. Acta*, 1927, **10**, 101.

ω : ω : 3 : 5-Tetrabromo-*o*-cresol (3 : 5-*Dibromo*-o-*hydroxybenzylidene bromide*)

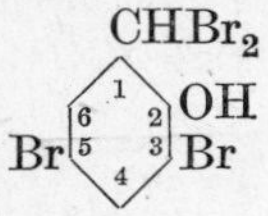

$C_7H_4OBr_4$ MW, 424

Needles from pet. ether. M.p. 99°.

Acetyl: needles from pet. ether. M.p. 113–14°.

Lindemann, Forth, *Ann.*, 1924, **435**, 226.

3 : 4 : 5 : 6-Tetrabromo-*o*-cresol.

Needles from $CHCl_3$ or AcOH. M.p. 208°. Sol. Et_2O. Mod. sol. $CHCl_3$, C_6H_6. Spar. sol. AcOH, ligroin.

Me ether: $C_8H_6OBr_4$. MW, 438. Needles from AcOH. M.p. 140·5°.

Acetyl: needles from EtOH.Aq. M.p. 154°.

Bonneaud, *Bull. soc. chim.*, 1910, **7**, 779.
Bodroux, *Compt. rend.*, 1898, **126**, 1283.
Zincke, Hedenström, *Ann.*, 1906, **350**, 276.
Anselmino, *Ber.*, 1902, **35**, 150.

ω : 2 : 4 : 6-Tetrabromo-*m*-cresol (2 : 4 : 6-*Tribromo*-m-*hydroxybenzyl bromide*)

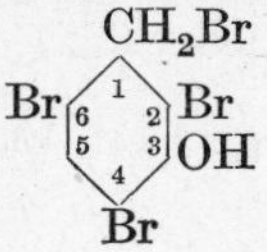

$C_7H_4OBr_4$ MW, 424

Needles from AcOH. M.p. 149°. Spar. sol. ligroin, pet. ether.

Acetyl: needles from AcOH. M.p. 104°.

Auwers, Richter, *Ber.*, 1899, **32**, 3382.

2 : 4 : 5 : 6-Tetrabromo-*m*-cresol.

Cryst. from AcOH. M.p. 194°.

Me ether: $C_8H_6OBr_4$. MW, 438. Needles from EtOH or AcOH. M.p. 145–6°.

Et ether: $C_9H_8OBr_4$. MW, 452. Needles from Et_2O. M.p. 108°.

Acetyl: needles from ligroin. M.p. 165–6°.

Benzoyl: plates from AcOH. M.p. 153–4°.

Bureš, Balada, *Chem. Abstracts*, 1928, **22**, 3643.
Bonneaud, *Bull. soc. chim.*, 1910, **7**, 780.
Anselmino, *Ber.*, 1902, **35**, 150.
Auwers, Burrows, *Ber.*, 1899, **32**, 3042.

ω : ω : 3 : 5-Tetrabromo-*p*-cresol (3 : 5-*Dibromo*-p-*hydroxybenzylidene bromide*)

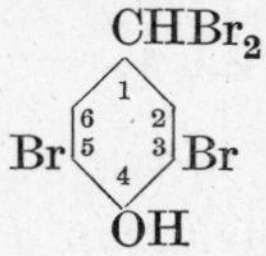

$C_7H_4OBr_4$ MW, 424

Needles from pet. ether. M.p. 98–101·5°. Sol. Et_2O, C_6H_6.

Me ether: $C_8H_6OBr_4$. MW, 438. Leaflets from ligroin. M.p. 60–4°.

Acetyl: leaflets from EtOH. M.p. 80°.

Lindemann, *Ann.*, 1923, **431**, 285.

ω : 2 : 3 : 5-Tetrabromo-*p*-cresol (2 : 3 : 5-*Tribromo*-p-*hydroxybenzyl bromide*).

Needles from ligroin. M.p. 122°. Sol. Et_2O, AcOH, C_6H_6. Mod. sol. ligroin.

Acetyl: needles from pet. ether. M.p. 116°.

Zincke, Wiederhold, *Ann.*, 1902, **320**, 210.
Auwers, Strecker, *Ann.*, 1904, **334**, 330.

2 : 3 : 5 : 6-Tetrabromo-*p*-cresol.

Needles from EtOH. M.p. 198–9°. Sol. Et_2O, C_6H_6, hot AcOH. Mod. sol. EtOH. Spar. sol. ligroin.

Acetyl : needles from AcOH. M.p. 156°.

Bonneaud, *Bull. soc. chim.*, 1910, **7**, 780.
Zincke, Wiederhold, *Ann.*, 1902, **320**, 207.
Zincke, Buff, *Ann.*, 1905, **341**, 327.

1 : 1 : 2 : 2-Tetrabromocyclobutane

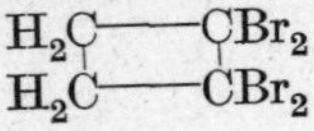

$C_4H_4Br_4$ MW, 372

Prisms from pet. ether. M.p. 126°. Sol. MeOH, EtOH, Et_2O, Me_2CO, $CHCl_3$, C_6H_6.

Willstätter, Bruce, *Ber.*, 1907, **40**, 3997.

1 : 2 : 3 : 4-Tetrabromocyclohexane

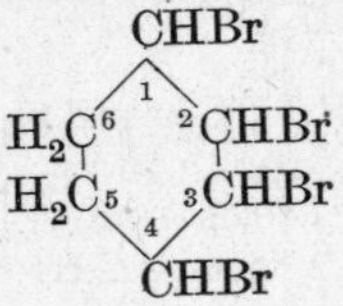

$C_6H_8Br_4$ MW, 400

Exists in two forms.
(i) Cryst. from Et_2O. M.p. 87–8°. NaOEt ⟶ bromobenzene.
(ii) Cryst. from MeOH. M.p. 155–6°.

Hofmann, Damm, *Chem. Zentr.*, 1926, I, 2343.
Harries, *Ber.*, 1912, **45**, 813.
Bodroux, Taboury, *Compt. rend.*, 1912, **154**, 1514.
Zelinsky, Gorsky, *Ber.*, 1908, **41**, 2483.

1 : 2 : 4 : 5-Tetrabromocyclohexane. Cryst. from $CHCl_3$. M.p. 184–5°.

Baeyer, *Ann.*, 1894, **278**, 96.
Zelinsky, Gorsky, *Ber.*, 1908, **41**, 2481.

2 : 4 : 6 : 8 - Tetrabromo-1 : 5 - diamino-anthraquinone

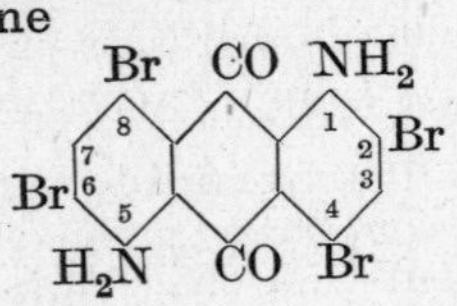

$C_{14}H_6O_2N_2Br_4$ MW, 554

Red needles from $PhNO_2$. M.p. about 340°.

Scholl *et al.*, *Ann.*, 1932, **494**, 221.

1 : 3 : 5 : 7 - Tetrabromo - 2 : 6 - diamino-anthraquinone

Yellowish-brown needles from $PhNO_2$. Does not melt below 360°.

Badische, D.R.P., 261,270, (*Chem. Zentr.*, 1913, II, 194).

2 : 6 : 2′ : 6′-Tetrabromodiphenyl

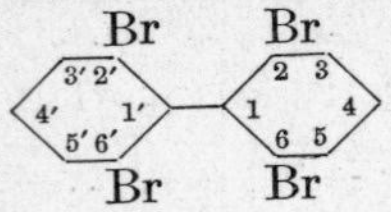

$C_{12}H_6Br_4$ MW, 470

Needles from EtOH. M.p. 215°. Mod. sol. common org. solvents.

Meyer, Meyer, Taeger, *Ber.*, 1920, **53**, 2050.

3 : 4 : 3′ : 4′-Tetrabromodiphenyl. Cryst. from AcOH. M.p. 169°.

Roosmalen, *Rec. trav. chim.*, 1934, **53**, 359.

3 : 5 : 3′ : 5′-Tetrabromodiphenyl. Cryst. from EtOH. M.p. 186°. Sol. Et_2O, C_6H_6. Mod. sol. EtOH.

See previous reference and also
Jacobson, *Ann.*, 1909, **367**, 347.

2 : 4 : 2′ : 4′-Tetrabromodiphenylamine

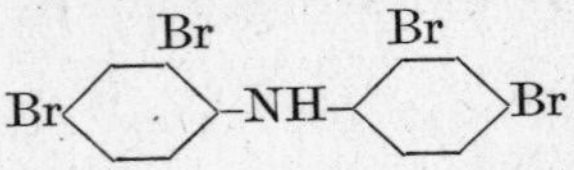

$C_{12}H_7NBr_4$ MW, 485

Needles or prisms. M.p. 182°. Sol. C_6H_6. Spar. sol. EtOH. Insol. H_2O.

N-*Me* : $C_{13}H_9NBr_4$. MW, 499 Prisms. M.p. 142°. Sol. C_6H_6. Mod. sol. EtOH.

Fries, *Ann.*, 1906, **346**, 213.
Hofmann, *Ann.*, 1864, **132**, 166.

***sym*.-Tetrabromoethane** (*Acetylene tetrabromide*)

$CHBr_2{\cdot}CHBr_2$

$C_2H_2Br_4$ MW, 346

Liq. B.p. 151°/54 mm., 125°/15 mm., 114°/2 mm. D_4^{20} 2·96725. n_D^{20} 1·637951. Zn + EtOH ⟶ *sym*.-dibromoethylene.

O'Meara, Clemmer, *Chem. Abstracts*, 1929, **23**, 1598.
Lespieau, *Compt. rend.*, 1919, **169**, 31.
Reboul, *Ann.*, 1862, **124**, 269.
Mouneyrat, *Bull. soc. chim.*, 1898, **19**, 498.

***unsym*.-Tetrabromoethane**

$BrCH_2{\cdot}CBr_3$

$C_2H_2Br_4$ MW, 346

Liq. B.p. 112·5°/18 mm. D_4^{20} 2·87482. n_D^{20} 1·627721.

Kaufmann, *Ber.*, 1922, **55**, 258.
Lennox, *Ann.*, 1862, **122**, 124.
Reboul, *Ann.*, 1862, **124**, 270.

Tetrabromoethylene (*Perbromoethylene*)

$Br_2C\colon CBr_2$

C_2Br_4 MW, 344

Needles from EtOH. M.p. 56·5°. B.p. 226–7°, 100°/15 mm. Sublimes. Volatile in steam.

Nekrassow, *Ber.*, 1927, **60**, 1758.
Biltz, *Ber.*, 1902, **35**, 1530.
Anschütz, *Ber.*, 1879, **12**, 2073.

Tetrabromoguaiacol.
See under Tetrabromocatechol.

1 : 2 : 2 : 3-Tetrabromohexane

$CH_3\cdot CH_2\cdot CH_2\cdot CHBr\cdot CBr_2\cdot CH_2Br$

$C_6H_{10}Br_4$ MW, 402

B.p. 130°/3 mm. D^{15} 2·1873. n_D^{15} 1·5850.

Bouis, *Ann. chim.*, 1928, **9**, 402.

1 : 2 : 3 : 4-Tetrabromohexane (1 : 3-*Hexadiene tetrabromide*)

$CH_3\cdot CH_2\cdot CHBr\cdot CHBr\cdot CHBr\cdot CH_2Br$

$C_6H_{10}Br_4$ MW, 402

Prisms. M.p. 91–2°.

Fournier, *Bull. soc. chim.*, 1896, **15**, 403.
Prévost, *Ann. chim.*, 1928, **10**, 176.

1 : 2 : 4 : 5-Tetrabromohexane

$CH_3\cdot CHBr\cdot CHBr\cdot CH_2\cdot CHBr\cdot CH_2Br$

$C_6H_{10}Br_4$ MW, 402

Exists in two forms.
(i) Plates from $CHCl_3$. M.p. 63–4°. Sol. Et_2O, $CHCl_3$, C_6H_6.
(ii) Liq. F.p. below −50°.

Griner, *Ann. chim. phys.*, 1892, **26**, 336.

1 : 2 : 5 : 6-Tetrabromohexane (*Diallyl tetrabromide*)

$BrCH_2\cdot CHBr\cdot CH_2\cdot CH_2\cdot CHBr\cdot CH_2Br$

$C_6H_{10}Br_4$ MW, 402

Exists in two stereoisomeric forms.
(i) Rhombic cryst. M.p. 64–5°. Sol. EtOH, Et_2O, AcOH, C_6H_6. Mod. sol. ligroin.
(ii) Cryst. M.p. 53–4°.

Griner, *Ann. chim. phys.*, 1892, **26**, 325.
Ciamician, Anderlini, *Ber.*, 1889, **22**, 2498.

2 : 3 : 4 : 5-Tetrabromohexane

$CH_3\cdot CHBr\cdot CHBr\cdot CHBr\cdot CHBr\cdot CH_3$

$C_6H_{10}Br_4$ MW, 402

Prisms from $CHCl_3$. M.p. 185° (182–3°).

Prévost, *Ann. chim.*, 1928, **10**, 113.

Note.—Two other tetrabromohexanes of unknown constitution have been described :
(i) Plates from AcOH. M.p. 162–3°.

Merling, *Ann.*, 1891, **264**, 346.

(ii) M.p. 163–5°.

Mouneyrat, *Ann. chim. phys.*, 1900, **20**, 569.

Tetrabromohydroquinone

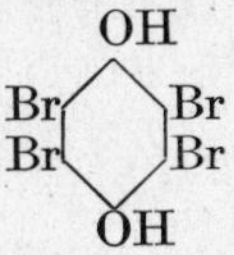

$C_6H_2O_2Br_4$ MW, 426

Prisms from EtOH–Et_2O. M.p. 244°. D^{21} 3·023. Sol. EtOH, Et_2O. Insol. H_2O. $FeCl_3$ in AcOH ⟶ bromanil.

Sarauw, *Ann.*, 1881, **209**, 125.
Bodroux, *Compt. rend.*, 1898, **126**, 1285.
Stenhouse, *Ann.*, 1854, **91**, 310.

Tetrabromoisophthalic Acid

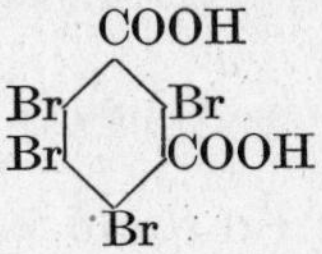

$C_8H_2O_4Br_4$ MW, 482

Needles from H_2O. M.p. 288–92°. Insol. C_6H_6.

Rupp, *Ber.*, 1896, **29**, 1631.

Tetrabromomethane.
See Carbon tetrabromide.

Tetrabromomethylenedioxybenzene.
See under Tetrabromocatechol.

1 : 2 : 6 : 8-Tetrabromonaphthalene

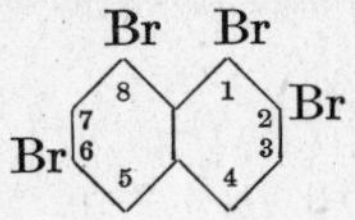

$C_{10}H_4Br_4$ MW, 444

Needles from C_6H_6. Does not melt below 315°.

Dhar, *J. Chem. Soc.*, 1920, **117**, 993.

1 : 3 : 5 : 8-Tetrabromonaphthalene.
Needles from C_6H_6. M.p. 310°.

See previous reference.

1 : 3 : 6 : 8-Tetrabromonaphthalene.
Needles from C_6H_6. Does not melt below 315°.

See previous reference.

1 : 4 : 6 : 7-Tetrabromonaphthalene. Needles from EtOH. M.p. 175°. Sublimes in plates. Sol. $CHCl_3$, C_6H_6. Very spar. sol. Et_2O.

Guareschi, *Gazz. chim. ital.*, 1886, **16**, 146.

1 : 3 : 4 : 6-Tetrabromo-2-naphthol

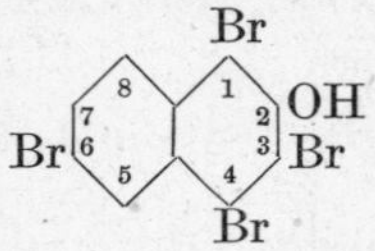

$C_{10}H_4OBr_4$ MW, 460

Needles from C_6H_6. M.p. 173–4°. Spar. sol. AcOH. Ox. ⟶ 4-bromophthalic acid.

Me ether: $C_{11}H_6OBr_4$. MW, 474. Needles from pet. ether. M.p. 149°.

Acetyl: needles from C_6H_6–AcOH. M.p. 192°.

Franzen, Stäuble, *J. prakt. Chem.*, 1922, **103**, 377.

Armstrong, Rossiter, *Chem. News*, 1891, **63**, 295.

1 : 3 : 5 : 6-Tetrabromo-2-naphthol. Needles from $CHCl_3$ or AcOH. M.p. 186°. Sol. C_6H_6. Spar. sol. EtOH, pet. ether.

Acetyl: needles from Me_2CO. M.p. 156°.

Fries, Schimmelschmidt, *Ann.*, 1930, **484**, 280.

1 : 3 : 6 : 7-Tetrabromo-2-naphthol. Needles from AcOH or C_6H_6. M.p. 174°. Sol. Et_2O, Me_2CO.

Acetyl: needles from EtOH or AcOH. M.p. 221°.

See previous reference.

2 : 3 : 4 : 5-Tetrabromonitrobenzene

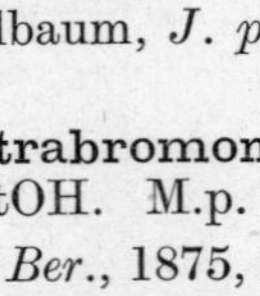

$C_6HO_2NBr_4$ MW, 439.

Needles from EtOH. M.p. 107°. Red. ⟶ 2 : 3 : 4 : 5-tetrabromoaniline.

Claus, Wallbaum, *J. prakt. Chem.*, 1897. **56**, 57.

2 : 3 : 4 : 6-Tetrabromonitrobenzene. Needles from EtOH. M.p. 96°.

v. Richter, *Ber.*, 1875, **8**, 1427.

2 : 3 : 5 : 6-Tetrabromonitrobenzene. Leaflets from EtOH. M.p. 168°.

Claus, *J. prakt. Chem.*, 1895, **51**, 412.

3 : 4 : 5 : 6-Tetrabromonitrobenzene-2-sulphonic Acid

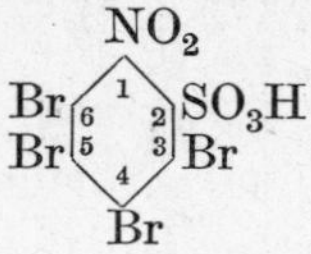

$C_6HO_5NBr_4S$ MW, 519

Needles + $1H_2O$ from H_2O. M.p. anhyd. 171–3°.

Chloride: $C_6O_4NClBr_4S$. MW, 537·5. Prisms from Et_2O. M.p. 172–3°.

Amide: $C_6H_2O_4N_2Br_4S$. MW, 518. Leaflets. Darkens at 260°, melting with decomp. at higher temp.

Spiegelberg, *Ann.*, 1878, **197**, 297.

2 : 4 : 5 : 6-Tetrabromonitrobenzene-3-sulphonic Acid. Needles. Easily sol. H_2O, EtOH. Conc. HCl in H_2SO_4 at 200° ⟶ 2 : 3 : 4 : 6-tetrabromonitrobenzene.

Chloride: plates from Et_2O. M.p. 147·5°.

Langfurth, *Ann.*, 1878, **191**, 202.

2 : 3 : 4 : 6-Tetrabromophenol

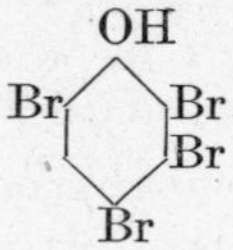

$C_6H_2OBr_4$ MW, 410

Needles from EtOH. M.p. 113° (120°). Very sol. EtOH. Sublimes.

Acetyl: leaflets from AcOH.Aq. M.p. 104–5°.

Hodgson, Walker, Nixon, *J. Chem. Soc.*, 1933, 1054.

Körner, *Ann.*, 1866, **137**, 210.

Tetrabromophthalic Acid

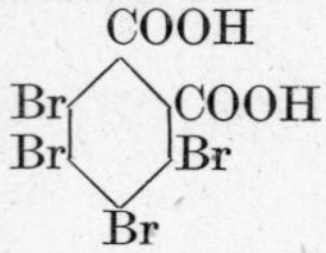

$C_8H_2O_4Br_4$ MW, 482

Needles from H_2O. M.p. 266° ⟶ anhydride.

Mono-Me ester: $C_9H_4O_4Br_4$. MW, 496. Cryst. from MeOH.Aq. M.p. 267°. Sol. EtOH, Et_2O, C_6H_6.

Anhydride: $C_8O_3Br_4$. MW, 464. Cryst. from AcOH–xylene. M.p. 279·5–280·5°.

Imide: $C_8HO_2NBr_4$. MW, 463. Yellow cryst. from AcOH. Does not melt below 380°. Spar. sol. C_6H_6, toluene, AcOH.

Anil: plates from AcOH. M.p. 279–80°.

o-*Nitroanil*: needles from AcOH. M.p. 98–298·5°.

m-*Nitroanil*: plates from xylene. M.p. 01·5–303°.

p-*Nitroanil*: needles from xylene. M.p. 31–331·5°.

o-*Tolil*: plates from C_6H_6 or AcOH. M.p. 91–3°.

m-*Tolil*: cryst. from C_6H_6. M.p. 273·5–74·5°.

p-*Tolil*: yellow needles from C_6H_6. M.p. 80–280·5°.

α-*Naphthylimide*: yellow needles from C_6H_6. I.p. 309–309·5°.

β-*Naphthylimide*: greenish-yellow plates. I.p. 305·5–308°.

Pratt, Young, *J. Am. Chem. Soc.*, 1918, **40**, 1416.
Hofmann, *Monatsh.*, 1915, **36**, 818.

1 : 1 : 1 : 2-Tetrabromopropane

$CH_3 \cdot CHBr \cdot CBr_3$

$C_3H_4Br_4$ MW, 360

B.p. 122°/15 mm. D_4^{20} 2·679. n_D^{20} 1·6187.

Bachman, *J. Am. Chem. Soc.*, 1935, **57**, 1090.

1 : 1 : 2 : 2-Tetrabromopropane (*Allylene tetrabromide*)

$CH_3 \cdot CBr_2 \cdot CHBr_2$

$C_3H_4Br_4$ MW, 360

Liq. B.p. 225–30° part. decomp., 105–7°/9 mm. D_4^{20} 2·687. n_D^{20} 1·6166.

Hurd, Meinert, Spence, *J. Am. Chem. Soc.*, 1930, **52**, 1142.
Oppenheim, *Ann.*, 1864, **132**, 124.

1 : 1 : 2 : 3-Tetrabromopropane

$BrCH_2 \cdot CHBr \cdot CHBr_2$

$C_3H_4Br_4$ MW, 360

B.p. 179–80°/80 mm., 138–40°/17 mm. D^0 2·76.

Mouneyrat, *Compt. rend.*, 1898, **127**, 276.
Lespieau, *Ann. chim. phys.*, 1897, **11**, 253.

1 : 1 : 3 : 3-Tetrabromopropane

$Br_2CH \cdot CH_2 \cdot CHBr_2$

$C_3H_4Br_4$ MW, 360

B.p. 154–6°/19 mm. D_4^0 2·7405, D_4^{21} 2·702. n_D^{21} 1·6225.

Demjanow, Dojarenko, *Ber.*, 1923, **56**, 2202.

1 : 2 : 2 : 3-Tetrabromopropane (*Allene tetrabromide*)

$BrCH_2 \cdot CBr_2 \cdot CH_2Br$

$C_3H_4Br_4$ MW, 360

Colourless liq. with odour resembling camphor. M.p. 10–11°. B.p. 215–30° decomp., 169–70°/80 mm., 115·5°/9 mm. D_4^{20} 2·703. n_D^{20} 1·6200. Zn dust in EtOH ⟶ allene.

Gustavson, Demjanow, *J. prakt. Chem.*, 1888, **38**, 204.
Hurd, Meinert, Spence, *J. Am. Chem. Soc.*, 1930, **52**, 1143.

2 : 3 : 5 : 6-Tetrabromopyridine

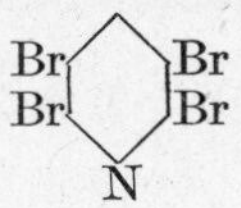

C_5HNBr_4 MW, 395

Needles from 50% AcOH. M.p. 103·5–104°.

Hertog, Wibaut, *Rec. trav. chim.*, 1932, **51**, 940.

2 : 3 : 4 : 5-Tetrabromopyrrole

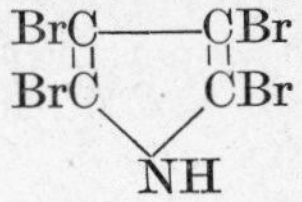

C_4HNBr_4 MW, 383

Needles from EtOH. Does not melt below 250°. Sol. EtOH. Spar. sol. H_2O. KI in EtOH ⟶ 2 : 3 : 4 : 5-tetraiodopyrrole.

N-*Me*: $C_5H_3NBr_4$. MW, 397. Needles from pet. ether. M.p. 154–5° ⟶ a blue liq.

N-*Et*: $C_6H_5NBr_4$. MW, 411. Needles from EtOH. M.p. 90° (83°). Spar. sol. EtOH. Insol. H_2O.

Plancher, Soncini, *Gazz. chim. ital.*, 1902, **32**, ii, 465.
Zanetti, *Ber.*, 1889, **22**, 2515.
de Varda, *Ber.*, 1888, **21**, 2871.

Tetrabromoquinone.
See Bromanil.

Tetrabromoresorcinol

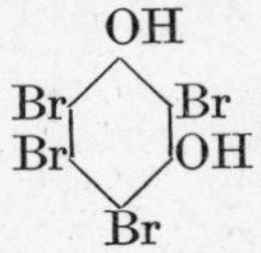

$C_6H_2O_2Br_4$ MW, 426

Needles from EtOH.Aq. M.p. 167° (163°). Sol. Et_2O, $CHCl_3$, hot EtOH. Spar. sol. H_2O.

Diacetyl: m.p. 114° (169°).

Claassen, *Ber.*, 1878, **11**, 1440.
Benedikt, *Monatsh.*, 1880, **1**, 366.

5 : 5 : 6 : 6-Tetrabromostearic Acid (*Taric acid tetrabromide*)

$CH_3\cdot[CH_2]_{10}\cdot CBr_2\cdot CBr_2\cdot[CH_2]_4\cdot COOH$

$C_{18}H_{32}O_2Br_4$ MW, 600

M.p. 125°.

Arnaud, *Compt. rend.*, 1902, **134**, 842; *Bull. soc. chim.*, 1892, **7**, 234.

8 : 8 : 9 : 9 - Tetrabromostearic Acid (*Stearolic acid tetrabromide*)

$CH_3\cdot[CH_2]_7\cdot CBr_2\cdot CBr_2\cdot[CH_2]_7\cdot COOH$

$C_{18}H_{32}O_2Br_4$ MW, 600

Cryst. from EtOH. M.p. 70°.

Overbeck, *Ann.*, 1866, **140**, 56.

8 : 9 : 11 : 12-Tetrabromostearic Acid (*Linoleic acid tetrabromide*)

$CH_3\cdot[CH_2]_4\cdot[CHBr]_2\cdot CH_2\cdot[CHBr]_2\cdot[CH_2]_7\cdot COOH$

$C_{18}H_{32}O_2Br_4$ MW, 600

Cryst. from Et_2O–pet. ether. M.p. 116–17° (112·3–114·3°). Sol. EtOH, Et_2O, $CHCl_3$, AcOH, C_6H_6. Insol. H_2O. Sn + HCl in EtOH ⟶ linoleic acid.

K salt.: cryst. from EtOH. M.p. 171° (154·7–158·8°).

Na salt: cryst. from EtOH. M.p. 194·2–201·1°.

Ca salt: cryst. from EtOH. M.p. 208·7–213·4°.

Sr salt: cryst. from EtOH. M.p. 200·4–206°.

Ba salt: cryst. from EtOH. M.p. 196·3–206·5.°

Me ester: $C_{19}H_{34}O_2Br_4$. MW, 614. M.p. 63° (50–6°).

Et ester: $C_{20}H_{36}O_2Br_4$. MW, 628. Needles. M.p. 63° (58–58·5°).

Propyl ester: $C_{21}H_{38}O_2Br_4$. MW, 642. Cryst. from MeOH. M.p. 45–50°.

Isopropyl ester: m.p. 50–2°.

Allyl ester: $C_{21}H_{36}O_2Br_4$. MW, 640. M.p. 72–80°.

Smit, *Rec. trav. chim.*, 1930, **49**, 539.
Santos, West, *Chem. Abstracts*, 1928, **22**, 761.
Oreta, West, *Chem. Abstracts*, 1927, **21**, 3889.
Hazura, *Monatsh.*, 1887, **8**, 149.
Rollet, *Z. physiol. Chem.*, 1909, **62**, 414.
Palmer, Wright, *Ind. Eng. Chem.*, 1914, **6**, 822.

Tetrabromoterephthalic Acid

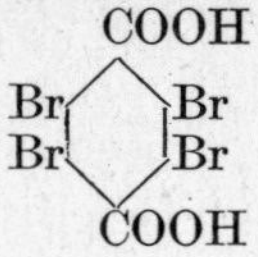

$C_8H_2O_4Br_4$ MW, 48

Needles from H_2O. M.p. about 300° decomp. Very spar. sol. EtOH, Et_2O, AcOH. Insol C_6H_6, cold H_2O.

Rupp, *Ber.*, 1896, **29**, 1626.

Tetrabromothiophene

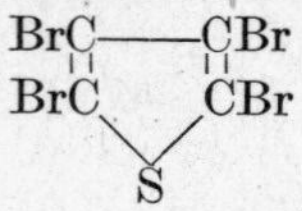

C_4Br_4S MW, 40

Needles from EtOH. M.p. 117–18°. B.p 326°, 170–3°/13 mm. Fuming HNO_3 ⟶ di bromomaleic acid.

Steinkopf, Jacob, Penz, *Ann.*, 1934 **512**, 149.

α : 2 : 4 : 6-Tetrabromotoluene.
See 2 : 4 : 6-Tribromobenzyl bromide.

2 : 3 : 4 : 5-Tetrabromotoluene

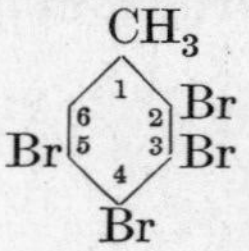

$C_7H_4Br_4$ MW, 40

Needles. M.p. 111–111·5°.

Nevile, Winther, *Ber.*, 1880, **13**, 976.

2 : 3 : 4 : 6-Tetrabromotoluene.
M. p. 105–8°.

Nevile, Winther, *Ber.*, 1880, **13**, 975.

2 : 3 : 5 : 6-Tetrabromotoluene.
Needles. M.p. 116–17°. Spar. sol. EtOH.

See previous reference.

2 : 4 : 5 : 6-Tetrabromo-*m*-toluidine

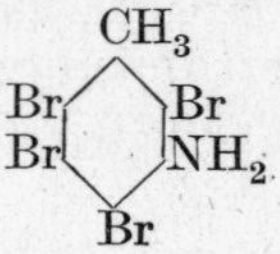

$C_7H_5NBr_4$ MW, 42

M.p. 223–4°. Mod. sol. EtOH.

See previous reference.

2 : 3 : 5 : 6-Tetrabromo-*p*-toluidine

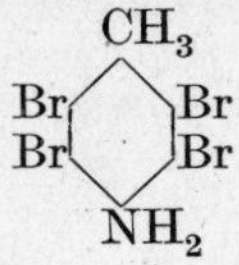

$C_7H_5NBr_4$ MW, 423

Needles. M.p. 226–7°.

Nevile, Winther, *Ber.*, 1881, **14**, 418.
Scheufelen, *Ann.*, 1885, **231**, 179.

Tetrabromoveratrol.
See under Tetrabromocatechol.

ω : ω : ω′ : ω′-Tetrabromo-*o*-xylene

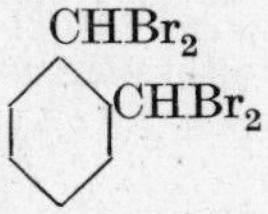

$C_8H_6Br_4$ MW, 422

Cryst. from EtOH. M.p. 116°. Sol. $CHCl_3$. Somewhat difficultly sol. EtOH. Insol. ligroin. K oxalate in EtOH.Aq. ⟶ *o*-phthalaldehyde.

Gabriel, Müller, *Ber.*, 1895, **28**, 1830.
Thiele, Günther, *Ann.*, 1906, **347**, 107.

3 : 4 : 5 : 6-Tetrabromo-*o*-xylene

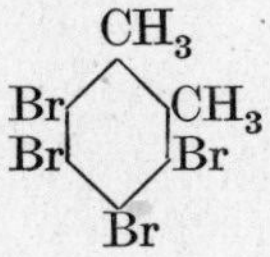

$C_8H_6Br_4$ MW, 422

Needles from C_6H_6. M.p. 262° (254–5°). B.p. 374–5°. Sol. hot C_6H_6. Very spar. sol. hot EtOH. Dil. HNO_3 + Br at 170° ⟶ tetrabromophthalic acid.

Blümlein, *Ber.*, 1884, **17**, 2492.
Klages, Sommer, *Ber.*, 1906, **39**, 2312.

ω : ω : ω′ : ω′-Tetrabromo-*m*-xylene

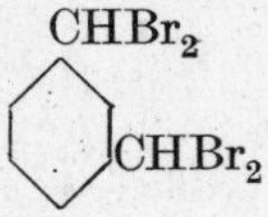

$C_8H_6Br_4$ MW, 422

Needles from EtOH. M.p. 107°. Sol. $CHCl_3$, AcOH, C_6H_6, ligroin. K oxalate in EtOH ⟶ isophthalaldehyde.

Thiele, Günther, *Ann.*, 1906, **347**, 109.

2 : 4 : 5 : 6-Tetrabromo-*m*-xylene

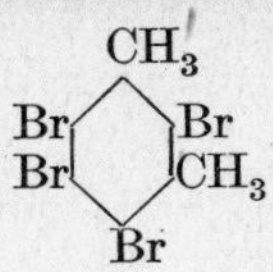

$C_8H_6Br_4$ MW, 422

M.p. 247° (241°). Sol. C_6H_6. Insol. EtOH.

Datta, Chatterjee, *J. Am. Chem. Soc.*, 1916, **38**, 2550.

ω : ω : ω′ : ω′-Tetrabromo-*p*-xylene

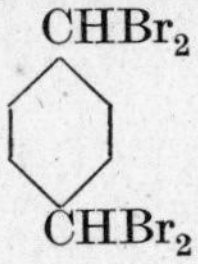

$C_8H_6Br_4$ MW, 422

Prisms from $CHCl_3$. M.p. 169°. Sol. C_6H_6. Spar. sol. EtOH. Hot. conc. H_2SO_4 ⟶ terephthalaldehyde + terephthalaldehydic acid.

Hönig, *Monatsh.*, 1888, **9**, 1150.
Thiele, Günther, *Ann.*, 1906, **347**, 110.

2 : 3 : 5 : 6-Tetrabromo-*p*-xylene

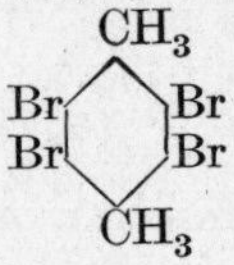

$C_8H_6Br_4$ MW, 422

Needles from toluene. M.p. 256–7° (253°). B.p. 355°. Very spar. sol. hot H_2O.

Zelinsky, Lepeschkin, *Chem. Zentr.*, 1913, II, 2126.
Jacobsen, *Ber.*, 1885, **18**, 359.

Tetrabutylammonium iodide.
See under Tributylamine.

Tetracarboxytetramethylmethane.
See Methane-tetracetic Acid.

Tetrachloroacetanilide.
See under Tetrachloroaniline.

1 : 1 : 1 : 3-Tetrachloroacetone

$CH_2Cl{\cdot}CO{\cdot}CCl_3$

$C_3H_2OCl_4$ MW, 196

Liq. with acrid odour which affects mucous membrane. B.p. 183°. D_4^{15} 1·624. n_D^{18} 1·497. Forms hydrate. NH_3 ⟶ $CHCl_3$ and chloroacetamide.

Hydrate: $C_3H_2OCl_4,4H_2O$. MW, 268. Prisms M.p. 46°.

Brochet, *Compt. rend.*, 1894, **119**, 1271.

1 : 1 : 3 : 3-Tetrachloroacetone

$CHCl_2 \cdot CO \cdot CHCl_2$

$C_3H_2OCl_4$ MW, 196

Liq. with strong acrid odour. B.p. 180–2°/718 mm. Forms cryst. hydrate. Forms bisulphite comp. Zn + $H_2SO_4 \longrightarrow$ acetone.

Hydrate: $C_3H_2OCl_4,4H_2O$. MW, 268. Plates. M.p. 48–9°.

Zincke, Kegel, *Ber.*, 1889, **22**, 1478.

2 : 3 : 4 : 5-Tetrachloroaniline

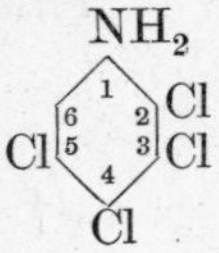

$C_6H_3NCl_4$ MW, 231

Needles from EtOH. M.p. 118–20°. Very sol. EtOH, Et_2O, AcOH, C_6H_6.

N-*Acetyl*: 2 : 3 : 4 : 5-tetrachloroacetanilide. $C_8H_5ONCl_4$. MW, 273. Cryst. M.p. 160–2°. Very sol. EtOH, Et_2O, AcOH.

Grandmougin, Seyder, *Ber.*, 1914, **47**, 2369.
Beilstein, Kurbatow, *Ann.*, 1879, **196**, 237.

2 : 3 : 5 : 6-Tetrachloroaniline.
Clusters of needles from ligroin. M.p. 90°. Very sol. EtOH, CS_2, ligroin.

N-*Acetyl*: 2 : 3 : 5 : 6-tetrachloroacetanilide. Needles. M.p. 181°. Very sol. EtOH. Spar. sol. AcOH.Aq. N-*Me*: m.p. 96–7°. N-*Et*: m.p. 73–4°.

Dyson, George, Hunter, *J. Chem. Soc.*, 1926, 3044.

Tetrachloroanisole.
See under Tetrachlorophenol.

1 : 2 : 3 : 4-Tetrachloroanthracene

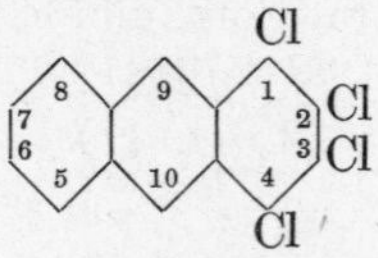

$C_{14}H_6Cl_4$ MW, 316

Needles from EtOH–$CHCl_3$. M.p. 148–9°. Very sol. $CHCl_3$, CS_2, C_6H_6. Mod. sol. hot AcOH. Spar. sol. EtOH, Et_2O. Ox. $\longrightarrow$ 1 : 2 : 3 : 4-tetrachloroanthraquinone.

Kircher, *Ann.*, 1887, **238**, 346.

1 : 3 : 9 : 10-Tetrachloroanthracene.
Yellow needles from AcOH. M.p. 164°. Sol. boiling AcOH. Spar. sol. EtOH. Ox. $\longrightarrow$ 1 : 3-dichloroanthraquinone.

Höchst, D.R.P., 282,818, (*Chem. Zentr.*, 1915, I, 772).
Meyer, Zahn, *Ann.*, 1913, **396**, 172.

1 : 4 : 5 : 8-Tetrachloroanthracene.
M.p. 285–6° (275°).

Note.—The positions occupied by the chlorine atoms are not definitely established.

Schilling, *Ber.*, 1913, **46**, 1068.

2 : 3 : 9 : 10-Tetrachloroanthracene.
Yellow needles from C_6H_6. M.p. 240–1°. Spar. sol. ord. org. solvents except hot C_6H_6. Ox. $\longrightarrow$ 2 : 3-dichloroanthraquinone.

Meyer, Zahn, *Ann.*, 1913, **396**, 177.

Tetrachloroanthranilic Acid

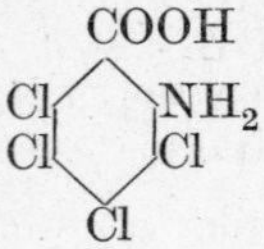

$C_7H_3O_2NCl_4$ MW, 275

Needles from H_2O or AcOH. M.p. 182°. Very sol. EtOH, Et_2O. Spar. sol. cold AcOH, C_6H_6. Insol. cold H_2O. Forms cryst. spar. sol. Ca, Ba salts. Heat above m.p. $\longrightarrow$ 2 : 3 : 4 : 5-tetrachloroaniline.

Me ester: $C_8H_5O_2NCl_4$. MW, 289. Needles from MeOH. M.p. 120–1°.

Badische, D.R.P., 220,839, (*Chem. Zentr.*, 1910, I, 1564).
Villiger, Blangey, *Ber.*, 1909, **42**, 3550.

1 : 2 : 3 : 4-Tetrachloroanthraquinone

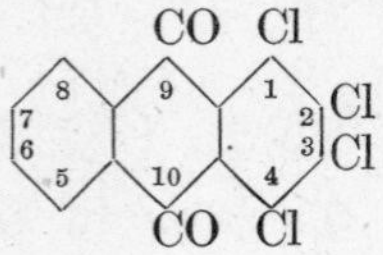

$C_{14}H_4O_2Cl_4$ MW, 346

Yellow needles. M.p. 191°. Very sol. C_6H_6, $CHCl_3$. Spar. sol. AcOH. Very spar. sol. EtOH, Et_2O. $HNO_3 \longrightarrow$ tetrachlorophthalic acid.

Kircher, *Ann.*, 1887, **238**, 345.

1 : 2 : 5 : 8-Tetrachloroanthraquinone.
Felted needles from AcOH. M.p. 282–3°.

Goldberg, *J. Chem. Soc.*, 1931, 1792.

1 : 2 : 6 : 7-Tetrachloroanthraquinone.
Golden-yellow needles from xylene. M.p. 242°. . cold conc. H_2SO_4.

Barnett, Goodway, Watson, *Ber.*, 1933, **66**, 1885.

1 : 4 : 5 : 8-Tetrachloroanthraquinone.
Yellow needles from AcOH or $PhNO_2$. M.p. 1–2°. Sol. H_2SO_4 ⟶ yellow col.

I.C.I., U.S.P., 1,969,044, (*Chem. Abstracts*, 1934, **28**, 6159); E.P., 364,141, (*Chem. Zentr.*, 1933, I, 2174).
Goldberg, *J. Chem. Soc.*, 1931, 1792.

2 : 3 : 6 : 7-Tetrachloroanthraquinone.
Pale yellow cryst. from *o*-dichlorobenzene. p. 348°. Insol. cold. conc. H_2SO_4.

Barnett, Goodway, Watson, *Ber.*, 1933, **66**, 1885.

1 : 2 : 3 : 4-Tetrachlorobenzene

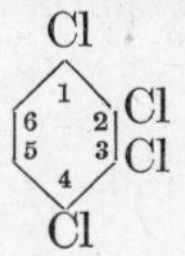

H_2Cl_4 MW, 216

Needles. M.p. 45–6°. B.p. 254°. Very sol. $_2$O, AcOH, CS_2, ligroin. Spar. sol. EtOH.

Cohen, Hartley, *J. Chem. Soc.*, 1905, **87**, 1365.

1 : 2 : 3 : 5-Tetrachlorobenzene.
Needles from EtOH. M.p. 51°. B.p. 246°. ry sol. CS_2, ligroin. Sol. C_6H_6. Spar. sol. d EtOH.

Willgerodt, Wilcke, *Ber.*, 1910, **43**, 2752.

1 : 2 : 4 : 5-Tetrachlorobenzene.
Needles from EtOH, Et_2O, C_6H_6, C_6H_6–OH or CS_2. M.p. 139·5–140·5°. B.p. 240°. . Et_2O, $CHCl_3$, CS_2, C_6H_6. Spar. sol. boiling OH. Insol. cold EtOH.

Qvist, *Chem. Zentr.*, 1934, II, 595.
Dow, U.S.P., 1,934,675, (*Chem. Zentr.*, 1934, I, 1390).
Pollak, Wienerberger, *Monatsh.*, 1914, **35**, 1472.

2 : 6 : 2′ : 6′-Tetrachlorobenzidine

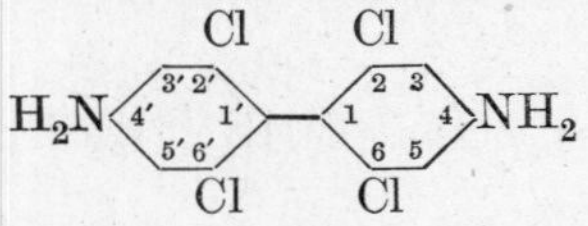

$H_8N_2Cl_4$ MW, 322

Cryst. M.p. 212°.
4 : 4′-N-*Diacetyl* : m.p. 312°.

Roosmalen, *Rec. trav. chim.*, 1934, **53**, 359.

3 : 5 : 3′ : 5′-Tetrachlorobenzidine.
Needles from EtOH–toluene. M.p. 226°. Very sol hot C_6H_6. Spar. sol. EtOH. Insol. Et_2O, ligroin.
4 : 4′-N-*Diacetyl* : m.p. 350°.
Tetra-acetyl : needles from AcOH. M.p. 265–6°.

See previous reference and also
Schlenk, *Ann.*, 1908, **363**, 334.

2 : 3 : 4 : 5-Tetrachlorobenzoic Acid

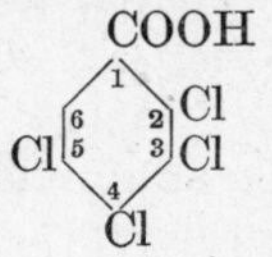

$C_7H_2O_2Cl_4$ MW, 260

Needles from EtOH. M.p. 186°. Sol. EtOH, Et_2O. Spar. sol. H_2O.
Et ester : $C_9H_6O_2Cl_4$. MW, 288. Needles from EtOH. M.p. 34·5°.
Nitrile : C_7HNCl_4. MW, 241. Needles. M.p. 84°.

Tust, *Ber.*, 1887, **20**, 2439.

2 : 3 : 4 : 6-Tetrachlorobenzoic Acid.
Nitrile : needles. M.p. 81°.

Claus, Wallbaum, *J. prakt. Chem.*, 1897, **56**, 48, 66.

2 : 3 : 5 : 6-Tetrachlorobenzoic Acid.
Nitrile : needles. M.p. 72°.

See previous reference.

2 : 4 : 2′ : 4′-Tetrachlorobenzophenone

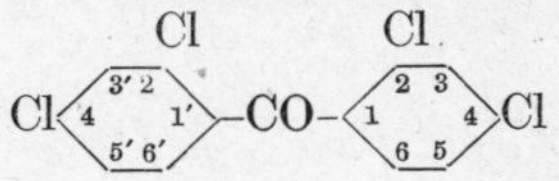

$C_{13}H_6OCl_4$ MW, 320

Cryst. M.p. 78°. Spar. sol. EtOH.Aq.

Cohen, *Rec. trav. chim.*, 1919, **38**, 116.

2 : 5 : 2′ : 4′-Tetrachlorobenzophenone.
Needles from EtOH. M.p. 176°.

Ganzmüller, *J. prakt. Chem.*, 1933, **138**, 312.

2 : 5 : 2′ : 5′-Tetrachlorobenzophenone.
Plates from EtOH. M.p. 128°. Very sol. hot EtOH, pet. ether. Spar. sol. cold EtOH.

Norris, Green, *Am. Chem. J.*, 1901, **26**, 498.

1 : 2 : 2 : 3-Tetrachlorobutane

$CH_3{\cdot}CHCl{\cdot}CCl_2{\cdot}CH_2Cl$

$C_4H_6Cl_4$ MW, 196

Liq. B.p. 85°/10 mm.

Garzarolli-Thurnlackh, *Ann.*, 1882, **213**, 372.

1 : 2 : 3 : 3-Tetrachlorobutane

$CH_3{\cdot}CCl_2{\cdot}CHCl{\cdot}CH_2Cl$

$C_4H_6Cl_4$ MW, 196

Liq. B.p. 90°/32 mm., 55–7°/10 mm. D_4^{20} 1·4204. n_D^{20} 1·4958.

du Pont, U.S.P., 1,964,720, (*Chem. Zentr.*, 1934, II, 3180).
Carothers, Berchet, *J. Am. Chem. Soc.*, 1933, **44**, 1631.

1 : 2 : 3 : 4-Tetrachlorobutane (*Butadiene tetrachloride, erythrene tetrachloride*)

$CH_2Cl{\cdot}CHCl{\cdot}CHCl{\cdot}CH_2Cl$

$C_4H_6Cl_4$ MW, 196

Prisms with camphor-like odour from EtOH. M.p. 73–4°. B.p. 130–40°/50 mm.

Backer, Strating, *Rec. trav. chim.*, 1935, **54**, 55.
Henninger, *Ann. chim. phys.*, 1886, **7**, 229.

Tetrachlorocatechol

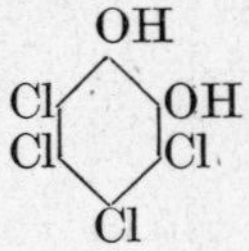

$C_6H_2O_2Cl_4$ MW, 248

Cryst. from EtOH.Aq. or C_6H_6: cryst. + $1H_2O$ from AcOH.Aq. M.p. 194–5°, anhyd. 110°. Cryst. + $3H_2O$ from AcOH.Aq., m.p. 94° Spar. sol. C_6H_6. Ox. ⟶ tetrachloro-*o*-benzoquinone.

Mono-Me ether: tetrachloroguaiacol. $C_7H_4O_2Cl_4$. MW, 262. Cryst. from hot H_2O. M.p. 185–6°.

Di-Me ether: tetrachloroveratrol. $C_8H_6O_2Cl_4$. MW, 276. Needles from AcOH. M.p. 190°.

Diacetyl: needles from AcOH. M.p. 190°.

Zincke, Küster, *Ber.*, 1888, **21**, 2729.

Tetrachloro-*o*-cresol

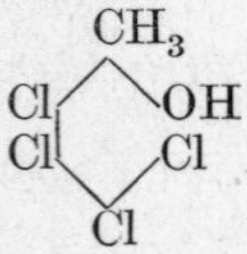

$C_7H_4OCl_4$ MW, 246

Needles from C_6H_6. M.p. 190°. Very s EtOH, Et_2O, AcOH, C_6H_6.

Me ether: $C_8H_6OCl_4$. MW, 260. Need from MeOH. M.p. 114°.

Acetyl: needles from AcOH. M.p. 136°.

Zincke, Pfaffendorf, *Ann.*, 1912, **394**,

Tetrachloro-*m*-cresol

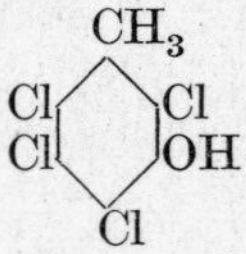

$C_7H_4OCl_4$ MW, 2

Needles from pet. ether. M.p. 189–9 Sol. ord. org. solvents.

Acetyl: needles from AcOH. M.p. 117°.

Crowther, McCombie, *J. Chem. Sc* 1913, **103**, 546.

Tetrachloro-*p*-cresol

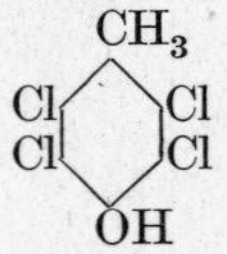

$C_7H_4OCl_4$ MW, 2

Needles from AcOH or C_6H_6–ligroin. M 190°. Very sol. EtOH, AcOH, $CHCl_3$, C_6 Spar. sol. ligroin.

Acetyl: needles from C_6H_6, plates fr AcOH.Aq. M.p. 112°.

Zincke, *Ann.*, 1903, **328**, 281.

2 : 4 : 6 : 8 - Tetrachloro - 1 : 5 - diamir anthraquinone

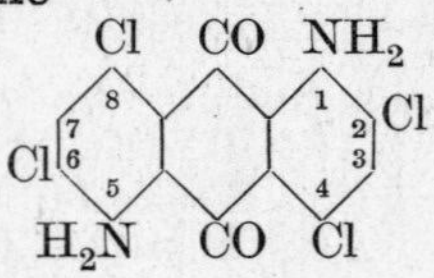

$C_{14}H_6O_2N_2Cl_4$ MW,

Brown needles from $PhNO_2$. Spar. sol. c $PhNO_2$. Insol. EtOH, cold AcOH. H_2SO_4 — olive col.

Badische, D.R.P., 158,951, (*Chem. Zen* 1905, I, 842).

2 : 4 : 5 : 7 - Tetrachloro - 1 : 8 - diamir anthraquinone.

Pale brown plates from $PhNO_2$. Sol. $PhNO_2$. Spar. sol. EtOH. H_2SO_4 ⟶ yel col.

See previous reference.

2 : 4 : 2′ : 4′-Tetrachlorodiphenyl

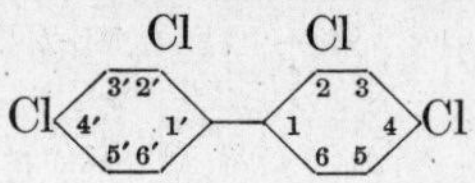

$C_{12}H_6Cl_4$ MW, 292

Cryst. from C_6H_6–ligroin. M.p. 83°. Very sol. warm EtOH, C_6H_6. Spar. sol. ligroin.

Ullmann, *Ann.*, 1904, **332**, 55.

2 : 5 : 2′ : 5′-Tetrachlorodiphenyl. Yellow cryst. from MeOH or pet. ether. M.p. 84–5°.

Meyer, Hofmann, *Monatsh.*, 1917, **38**, 145.

2 : 6 : 2′ : 6′-Tetrachlorodiphenyl. Plates. M.p. 199°.

Roosmalen, *Rec. trav. chim.*, 1934, **53**, 359.

3 : 4 : 3′ : 4′-Tetrachlorodiphenyl. Colourless needles from AcOH. M.p. 171°. B.p. 230°/50 mm. Very sol. EtOH, Et_2O.

See previous reference and also
Cain, *J. Chem. Soc.*, 1904, **85**, 7.

3 : 5 : 3′ : 5′-Tetrachlorodiphenyl. M.p. 162°.

Roosmalen, *Rec. trav. chim.*, 1934, **53**, 359.

2 : 4 : 2′ : 4′-Tetrachlorodiphenylamine

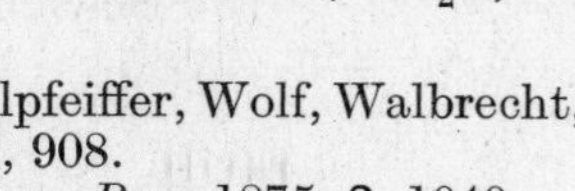

$C_{12}H_7NCl_4$ MW, 307

Prisms or needles. M.p. 141–2° (134°). Sol. EtOH, Et_2O, $CHCl_3$, CS_2, C_6H_6.

N-*Me*: $C_{13}H_9NCl_4$. MW, 321. Prisms. M.p. 96–7°. Sol. EtOH, Et_2O, $CHCl_3$, CS_2, C_6H_6.

Krollpfeiffer, Wolf, Walbrecht, *Ber.*, 1934, **67**, 908.
Gnehm, *Ber.*, 1875, **8**, 1040.

2 : 3 : 5 : 4′-Tetrachlorodiphenylamine. Cryst. from EtOH.Aq. M.p. 107–8°. Very sol. EtOH, Et_2O, ligroin.

Jacobson, *Ann.*, 1909, **367**, 339.

1 : 1 : 1 : 2-Tetrachloroethane

$CHCl·CCl_3$

$C_2H_2Cl_4$ MW, 168

Liq. B.p. 135·1°. D_0^{25} 1·5424.

I.G., D.R.P., 530,649, (*Chem. Zentr.*, 1931, II, 1920).
Prins, *Rec. trav. chim.*, 1926, **45**, 80.
Kokatnur, *J. Am. Chem. Soc.*, 1919, **41**, 123.

***sym.*-Tetrachloroethane** (1 : 1 : 2 : 2-*Tetrachloroethane, acetylene tetrachloride*)

$CHCl_2·CHCl_2$

$C_2H_2Cl_4$ MW, 168

Colourless liq. with odour similar to $CHCl_3$. F.p. − 43·8°. M.p. − 36°. B.p. 146·2°, 62°/45 mm., 55°/17 mm. D_4^{25} 1·5881, D^{15} 1·60255. n_D^{15} 1·49678. Volatile in steam. Sp. heat 0·286 cal./gm. at 20°. Solvent for P, S, fats, resins, cellulose acetate, rubber, etc. Non-inflammable. Alkalis ⟶ trichloroethylene. H_2O + Fe or Al ⟶ *sym.*-dichloroethylene. $AlCl_3$ at 110° ⟶ 1 : 1 : 1 : 2-tetrachloroethane. Narcotic and poisonous.

Ruhrchemie A.G., U.S.P., 2,016,658, (*Chem. Abstracts*, 1935, **29**, 8005).
Favorskiĭ, Margules, Davuidova, *Chem. Abstracts*, 1935, **29**, 7271.
Frydlender, *Chem. Abstracts*, 1935, **29**, 7935.
I.G., F.P., 739,183, (*Chem. Zentr.*, 1933, I, 2312).
Timmermans, *Bull. soc. chim. Belg.*, 1927, **36**, 502.

Tetrachloroethylene (*Perchloroethylene*)

$CCl_2{:}CCl_2$

C_2Cl_4 MW, 166.

Liq. F.p. − 22·35°. M.p. − 19°. B.p. 121·20°, 33·2°/30 mm. D^0 1·65582. n_D^{20} 1·50180. Heat of comb. C_p 162·5 Cal. Sp. heat at 20° 0·216 cal./gm. Cl ⟶ hexachloroethane. Vapour is poisonous. Extensively used as industrial solvent. Non-inflammable.

Frydlender, *Chem. Abstracts*, 1935, **29**, 7935.
Reilly, U.S.P., 1,947,491, (*Chem. Abstracts*, 1934, **28**, 2371).
Timmermans, Hennault-Roland, *J. chim. phys.*, 1930, **27**, 401.
Thusen, U.S.P., 1,590,265, (*Chem. Abstracts*, 1926, **20**, 3015).
Weisen, Wightman, *J. Phys. Chem.*, 1919, **23**, 415.

Tetrachloroguaiacol.
See under Tetrachlorocatechol.

Tetrachlorohydroquinone

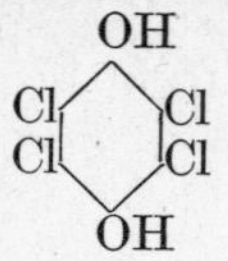

$C_6H_2O_2Cl_4$ MW, 248

Needles from AcOH. M.p. 232°. Sol. EtOH, Et_2O. Insol. H_2O, CCl_4, CS_2, C_6H_6. Sublimes.

Di-Me ether : $C_8H_6O_2Cl_4$. MW, 276. Needles. M.p. 164°. Sol. EtOH, AcOH. Mod. sol. Et_2O. Sublimes.

Me-Et ether : $C_9H_8O_2Cl_4$. MW, 290. Needles from EtOH. M.p. 101°. Sol. Et_2O, C_6H_6, ligroin. Mod. sol. EtOH, AcOH. Sublimes.

Di-Et ether : $C_{10}H_{10}O_2Cl_4$. MW, 304. Needles. M.p. 112°. Sol. EtOH, Et_2O. Sublimes.

Diacetyl : sublimes in needles. M.p. 245°.
Dipropionyl : cryst. M.p. 160°.
Dibutyryl : cryst. M.p. 137°.
Dibenzoyl : needles from CS_2. M.p. 232°.

Graebe, *Ann.*, 1868, **146**, 20.
Bouveault, *Compt. rend.*, 1899, **129**, 55.
Fiala, *Monatsh.*, 1885, **6**, 912.
Niemeyer, *Ann.*, 1885, **228**, 324.
Klinger, *Ann.*, 1911, **382**, 221.

Tetrachloroisophthalic Acid

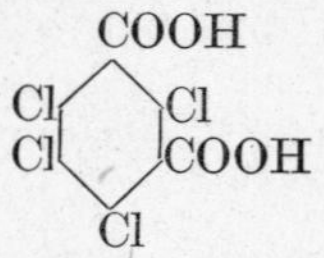

$C_8H_2O_4Cl_4$ MW, 304

Needles. M.p. 267–9°. Sol. EtOH. Very spar. sol. C_6H_6.

Rupp, *Ber.*, 1896, **29**, 1632.

Tetrachloromethane.

See Carbon tetrachloride.

1 : 2 : 3 : 4-Tetrachloronaphthalene

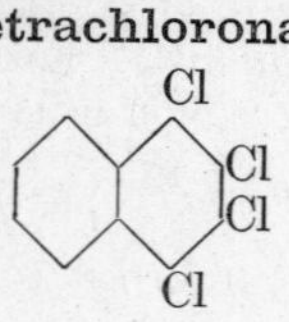

$C_{10}H_4Cl_4$ MW, 266

M.p. 198°.

v. Braun *et al.*, *Ber.*, 1923, **56**, 2337.

The following tetrachloronaphthalenes of unknown structure have also been described :

(i) Needles from Et_2O–ligroin. M.p. 130°.

Faust, Saame, *Ann.*, 1871, **160**, 72.
Widman, *Bull. soc. chim.*, 1877, **28**, 506.

(ii) Needles. M.p. 194°. Spar. sol. EtOH.

Atterberg, *Ber.*, 1876, **9**, 318.

(iii) Needles. M.p. 176°. Sol. C_6H_6. Mod. sol. EtOH, AcOH.

Atterberg, Widman, *Bull. soc. chim.*, 1877, **28**, 507.

(iv) Needles. M.p. 141°. Spar. sol. EtOH.

Atterberg, Widman, *Bull. soc. chim.*, 1877, **28**, 507.

(v) Needles. M.p. 180°. Spar. sol. EtOH.

Atterberg, Widman, *Bull. soc. chim.*, 1877, **28**, 514.

(vi) Needles. M.p. 159·5–160·5°.

Alén, *Bull. soc. chim.*, 1881, **36**, 435.

Tetrachlorophenetole.

See under Tetrachlorophenol.

2 : 3 : 4 : 5-Tetrachlorophenol

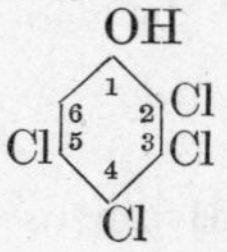

$C_6H_2OCl_4$ MW, 232

Needles from ligroin. M.p. 116–17°.
Benzoyl : m.p. 110°.

Holleman, *Rec. trav. chim.*, 1921, **40**, 318.
Tiessens, *Rec. trav. chim.*, 1931, **50**, 112.

2 : 3 : 4 : 6-Tetrachlorophenol.

Needles from ligroin. M.p. 70°. B.p. 150°/15 mm. Sol. EtOH, $CHCl_3$, CS_2, C_6H_6, ligroin. Mod. sol. pet. ether. Spar. sol. H_2O.

Me ether : 2 : 3 : 4 : 6-tetrachloroanisole. $C_7H_4OCl_4$. MW, 246. Needles from MeOH. M.p. 64–5°.

Et ether : 2 : 3 : 4 : 6-tetrachlorophenetole. $C_8H_6OCl_4$. MW, 260. Needles from EtOH. M.p. 55°.

Acetyl : cryst. from EtOH. M.p. 65–6°.
Benzoyl : m.p. 108°.

Lock, *Monatsh.*, 1936, **67**, 320.
Holleman, *Rec. trav. chim.*, 1921, **40**, 318
Tiessens, *Rec. trav. chim.*, 1931, **50**, 112.

2 : 3 : 5 : 6-Tetrachlorophenol.

Leaflets from ligroin. M.p. 115°.
Benzoyl : m.p. 136°.

See last two references above.

Tetrachlorophthalic Acid

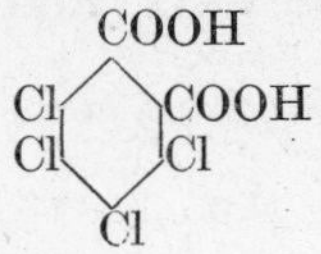

$C_8H_2O_4Cl_4$ MW, 304

Plates from H_2O. At 98° ⟶ anhydride. Very sol. Me_2CO. Sol. EtOH, Et_2O. Spar. sol. H_2O, $CHCl_3$, C_6H_6.

Mono-Me ester: $C_9H_4O_4Cl_4$. MW, 318. Needles. M.p. 142°.

Di-Me ester: $C_{10}H_6O_4Cl_4$. MW, 332. Prisms. M.p. 92°.

Mono-Et ester: $C_{10}H_6O_4Cl_4$. MW, 332. M.p. 94–5°.

Di-Et ester: $C_{12}H_{10}O_4Cl_4$. MW, 360. Cryst. M.p. 60·5°.

Dihexadecyl ester: plates from AcOEt. M.p. 49–50°.

Monobenzyl ester: m.p. 130–1°.

Dibenzyl ester: needles from MeOH. M.p. 92–3°.

Di-p-nitrobenzyl ester: needles from C_6H_6. M.p. 180–1°.

sym.-*Dichloride*: $C_8O_2Cl_6$. MW, 341. Prisms from pet. ether. M.p. 48°.

unsym.-*Dichloride*: needles from pet. ether. M.p. 137°.

Anhydride: $C_8O_3Cl_4$. MW, 286. Needles. M.p. 255°. Sublimes. Spar. sol. Et_2O.

Imide: $C_8HO_2NCl_4$. MW, 285. Plates from AcOH. M.p. 338–9°.

Anil: plates from AcOH. M.p. 268–9°.

o-*Nitroanil*: plates from C_6H_6. M.p. 272–3°.

m-*Nitroanil*: plates from AcOH–xylene. M.p. 300–301·5°.

p-*Nitroanil*: needles from C_6H_6. M.p. 292–7°.

o-*Tolil*: plates from AcOH. M.p. 232–236·5°.

m-*Tolil*: plates. M.p. 245·5–246·5°.

p-*Tolil*: exists in two forms. (i) Plates from AcOH. M.p. 207°. (ii) Yellow needles from AcOH. M.p. 214–15°.

β-*Naphthylimide*: m.p. 287°.

Salkind, Belikova, *Brit. Chem. Abstracts*, 1936, 331.
Kirpal, Kunze, *Ber.*, 1929, **62**, 2102.
Pratt, Perkins, *J. Am. Chem. Soc.*, 1918, **40**, 203.
Tingle, Bates, *J. Am. Chem. Soc.*, 1910, **32**, 1325.
Eckert, Steiner, *Monatsh.*, 1915, **36**, 272.
Graebe, *Ann.*, 1887, **238**, 332.
Meyer, Jugilewitsch, *Ber.*, 1897, **30**, 780.

1 : 1 : 1 : 2-Tetrachloropropane

$CH_3{\cdot}CHCl{\cdot}CCl_3$

$C_3H_4Cl_4$ MW, 182

Oil. M.p. − 65°. B.p. 152–3°. D^{20} 1·473. Insol. H_2O.

Henry, *Rec. trav. chim.*, 1905, **24**, 333.

1 : 1 : 2 : 2-Tetrachloropropane

$CH_3{\cdot}CCl_2{\cdot}CHCl_2$

$C_3H_4Cl_4$ MW, 182

Liq. B.p. 153°. D^{13} 1·47. Misc. with EtOH, Et_2O.

Borsche, Fittig, *Ann.*, 1865, **133**, 114.

1 : 1 : 2 : 3-Tetrachloropropane

$CH_2Cl{\cdot}CHCl{\cdot}CHCl_2$

$C_3H_4Cl_4$ MW, 182

Liq. B.p. 179–80°/756·6 mm. D^{15} 1·521.

Hartenstein, *J. prakt. Chem.*, 1873, **7**, 313.
Mouneyrat, *Bull. soc. chim.*, 1900, **21**, 621.

1 : 2 : 2 : 3-Tetrachloropropane

$CH_2Cl{\cdot}CCl_2{\cdot}CH_2Cl$

$C_3H_4Cl_4$ MW, 182

Liq. B.p. 164°. D^{17} 1·496.

Herzfelder, *Ber.*, 1893, **26**, 2436.

1 : 2 : 3 : 3-Tetrachloropropylene

$CHCl_2{\cdot}CCl{:}CHCl$

$C_3H_2Cl_4$ MW, 180

B.p. 165°. D_4^{34} 1·5274. n_D^{18} 1·5272.

Prins, *J. prakt. Chem.*, 1914, **89**, 421.

2 : 3 : 4 : 5-Tetrachloropyridine

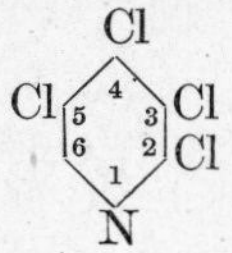

C_5HNCl_4 MW, 217

Needles from EtOH. M.p. 21–2°. B.p. 135–7°/24 mm. Volatile in steam.

Sell, Dootson, *J. Chem. Soc.*, 1899, **75**, 986; 1900, **77**, 3.

2 : 3 : 4 : 6-Tetrachloropyridine. Plates from 50% EtOH. M.p. 74–5°. B.p. 130–5°/16–20 mm. Insol. H_2O, acids.

Sell, Dootson, *J. Chem. Soc.*, 1898, **73**, 440; 1900, **77**, 1.

2 : 3 : 5 : 6-Tetrachloropyridine.
Cryst. from EtOH.Aq. M.p. 90–1°. B.p. 250–1°, 125–30°/16–20 mm. Sol. EtOH, Et_2O, pet. ether. Insol. H_2O, acids.

Sell, Dootson, *J. Chem. Soc.*, 1897, **71**, 1081; 1898, **73**, 439.

2 : 3 : 4 : 5-Tetrachloropyrrole

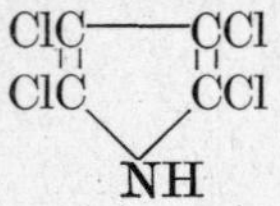

C_4HNCl_4 MW, 205

Plates from pet. ether. M.p. 110°. Sol. EtOH, Et_2O. Spar. sol. H_2O.
N-*Me*: $C_5H_3NCl_4$. MW, 219. Needles from pet. ether. M.p. 118–19°. Spar. sol. H_2O. Volatile in steam.
N-*Phenyl*: $C_{10}H_5NCl_4$. MW, 281. Cryst. from ligroin. M.p. 93°.

Anschütz, Beavis, *Ann.*, 1897, **295**, 30.
Mazzara, Borgo, *Gazz. chim. ital.*, 1904, **34**, i, 258.
Kalle, D.R.P., 38,423, (*Chem. Zentr.*, 1887, 423).
Ciamician, Silber, *Ber.*, 1885, **18**, 1763.

Tetrachlororesorcinol

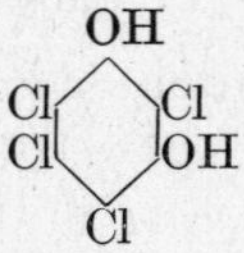

$C_6H_2O_2Cl_4$ MW, 248

Needles from H_2O. M.p. 141°. Sol. EtOH, Et_2O, AcOH, C_6H_6. Mod. sol. H_2O.
Di-Et ether: $C_{10}H_{10}O_2Cl_4$. MW, 304. Needles from EtOH. M.p. 73°. Sol. Et_2O, $CHCl_3$, AcOH, C_6H_6, ligroin. Spar. sol. EtOH.
Dipropyl ether: $C_{12}H_{14}O_2Cl_4$. MW, 332. Oil. Decomp. at 100°. Sol. EtOH, Et_2O, AcOH.
Diacetyl: needles. M.p. 145°.

Zincke, Fuchs, *Ber.*, 1892, **25**, 2689.
Jackson, Carlton, *Am. Chem. J.*, 1914, **31**, 379.

Tetrachloroterephthalic Acid

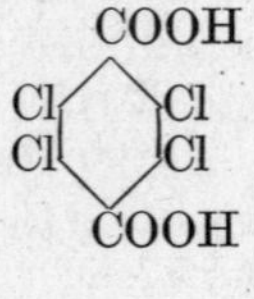

$C_8H_2O_4Cl_4$ MW, 304

Needles from AcOH. M.p. about 330° (279–81°). Sol. EtOH, Et_2O, AcOH. Insol. H_2O C_6H_6.

Qvist, Holmberg, *Chem. Zentr.*, 1932, II, 2816.
Rupp, *Ber.*, 1896, **29**, 1628.

Tetrachlorothiophene

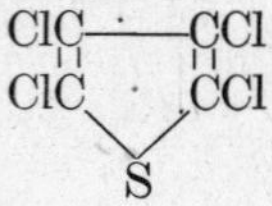

C_4Cl_4S MW, 222

Cryst. from EtOH.Aq. M.p. 36°. B.p. 240–5°.

Weitz, *Ber.*, 1884, **17**, 795.
Rosenberg, *Ber.*, 1886, **19**, 650.

2 : 3 : 4 : 5-Tetrachlorotoluene

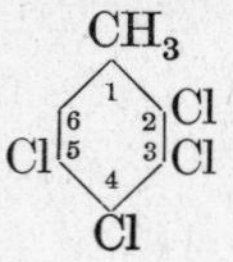

$C_7H_4Cl_4$ MW, 230

Needles from MeOH. M.p. 97–8°.

Cohen, Dakin, *J. Chem. Soc.*, 1904, **85**, 1285; 1906, **89**, 1454.

2 : 3 : 4 : 6-Tetrachlorotoluene.
Needles from EtOH. M.p. 91·5–92°.

Bureš, Trpisovska, *Chem. Zentr.*, 1936, I, 1209.
Cohen, Dakin, *J. Chem. Soc.*, 1904, **85**, 1280.

2 : 3 : 5 : 6-Tetrachlorotoluene.
Needles from MeOH. M.p. 93–4°. Sublimes.

Qvist, Holmberg, *Chem. Zentr.*, 1932, II, 2816.
Cohen, Dakin, *J. Chem. Soc.*, 1904, **85**, 1281.

Tetrachloroveratrol.
See under Tetrachlorocatechol.

ω : ω : ω′ : ω′-Tetrachloro-*o*-xylene

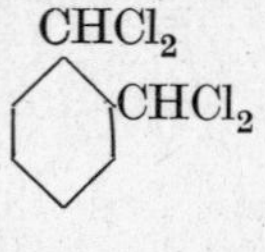

$C_8H_6Cl_4$ MW, 244.

Cryst. from Et_2O. M.p. 89°. B.p. 273–4°. D^0 1·601. Sol. EtOH, Et_2O, $CHCl_3$, C_6H_6. Insol. H_2O.

Hjelt, *Ber.*, 1885, **18**, 2879.
Colson, Gautier, *Ann. chim. phys.*, 1887, **11**, 25.

3 : 4 : 5 : 6-Tetrachloro-*o*-xylene

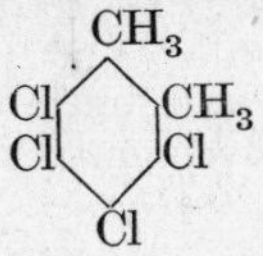

H_6Cl_4 MW, 244

Needles from Et_2O. M.p. 215°. Sublimes. . EtOH, Et_2O, C_6H_6. Non-volatile in steam.

Claus, Kautz, *Ber.*, 1885, **18**, 1369.
Datta, Chatterjee, *J. Am. Chem. Soc.*, 1917, **38**, 2549.

ω : ω : ω′ : ω′-Tetrachloro-*m*-xylene

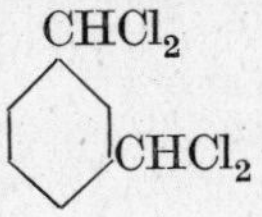

H_6Cl_4 MW, 244

B.p. 273°.

Colson, Gautier, *Bull. soc. chim.*, 1886, **45**, 509.

2 : 4 : 5 : 6-Tetrachloro-*m*-xylene

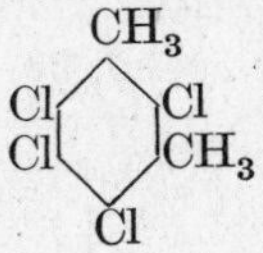

$_8H_6Cl_4$ MW, 244

Needles from EtOH–$CHCl_3$. M.p. 219° (212°). ol. Et_2O, $CHCl_3$, C_6H_6. Insol. EtOH.

Datta, Fernandes, *J. Am. Chem. Soc.*, 1917, **38**, 1810.
Bureš, Borgmann, *Chem. Zentr.*, 1928, I, 1171.

ω : ω : ω′ : ω′-Tetrachloro-*p*-xylene

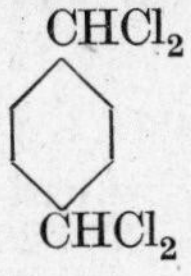

$_8H_6Cl_4$ MW, 244

Cryst. from Et_2O. M.p. 93°. D^0 1·606.

Colson, Gautier, *Ann. chim. phys.*, 1887, **11**, 24.

2 : 3 : 5 : 6-Tetrachloro-*p*-xylene

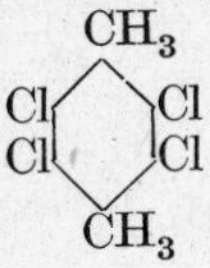

$C_8H_6Cl_4$ MW, 244

Needles from EtOH–Et_2O. M.p. 222° (218°). Sol. EtOH, Et_2O, C_6H_6.

Bureš, Rubeš, *Chem. Zentr.*, 1929, I, 507.
Datta, Fernandes, *J. Am. Chem. Soc.*, 1916, **38**, 1811.

Tetracosane

$CH_3{\cdot}[CH_2]_{22}{\cdot}CH_3$

$C_{24}H_{50}$ MW, 338

Isolated from paraffin from low-temperature coal tar. Cryst. from Et_2O. M.p. 54°. B.p. 237–40°/15 mm. (243–4°/15 mm.). n_D^{65} 1·43026, n_D^{80} 1·42448.

Levene, West, *J. Biol Chem.*, 1914, **18**, 478.
Gluud, *Ber.*, 1919, **52**, 1040.
Krafft, *Ber.*, 1882, **15**, 1718.

Tetracosanic Acid (n-*Tetracosanoic acid*. See also Lignoceric Acid)

$CH_3{\cdot}[CH_2]_{22}{\cdot}COOH$

$C_{24}H_{48}O_2$ MW, 368.

Plates from AcOH. M.p. 87·5–88° (85–6°).
Anhydride: $C_{48}H_{94}O_3$. MW, 718. M.p. 86·0–86·3°.
Me ester: $C_{25}H_{50}O_2$. MW, 382. M.p. 59·5–60°.
Et ester: $C_{26}H_{52}O_2$. MW, 396. M.p. 56–7°. B.p. 198–9°/0·24 mm.
Nitrile: $C_{24}H_{47}N$. MW, 349. M.p. 61·2° (55–6°).

Meyer, Brod, Soyka, *Monatsh.*, 1913, **34**, 1133.
Levene, West, Allen, van der Scheer, *J. Biol. Chem.*, 1915, **23**, 75.
Levene, Taylor, *J. Biol. Chem.*, 1924, **59**, 905.
Francis, Piper, Malkin, *Proc. Roy. Soc.*, 1930, **128** A, 214.
Bleyberg, Ulrich, *Ber.*, 1931, **64**, 2504.
Brigl, *Z. physiol. chem.*, 1915, **95**, 161.

Tetracosanol (1-*Hydroxytetracosane tetracosyl alcohol*. See also Lignoceryl Alcohol)

$CH_3{\cdot}[CH_2]_{22}{\cdot}CH_2OH$

$C_{24}H_{50}O$ MW, 354.

M.p. 76·5–77·5°. B.p. 210–210·5°/0·4 mm.
Acetyl: m.p. 57°.

Levene, Taylor, *J. Biol. Chem.*, 1924, **59**, 915.
Taylor, Levene, *J. Biol. Chem.*, 1928, **80**, 609.
Brigl, Fuchs, *Z. physiol. chem.*, 1922, **119**, 280.
Bleyberg, Ulrich, *Ber.*, 1931, **64**, 2504.

14-Tetracosenic Acid

$CH_3 \cdot [CH_2]_7 \cdot CH{:}CH \cdot [CH_2]_{13} \cdot COOH$

$C_{24}H_{46}O_2$ MW, 366

Cis:
See Nervonic Acid.
Trans:
Cryst. from EtOH. M.p. 61°.

Hale, Lycan, Adams, *J. Am. Chem. Soc.*, 1930, **52**, 4538.

Tetracosyl Alcohol.
See Tetracosanol.

Tetracosyl iodide (1-*Iodotetracosane*)

$CH_3 \cdot [CH_2]_{22} \cdot CH_2I$

$C_{24}H_{49}I$ MW, 464

M.p. 54·5–55·5°. B.p. 207–9°/0·35 mm.

Levene, Taylor, *J. Biol. Chem.*, 1924, **59**, 917.
Bleyberg, Ulrich, *Ber.*, 1931, **64**, 2504.

Tetradecahydroacridine.
See Perhydroacridine.

Tetradecahydroanthracene.
See Perhydroanthracene.

Tetradecane

$CH_3 \cdot [CH_2]_{12} \cdot CH_3$

$C_{14}H_{30}$ MW, 198

M.p. 5·5°. B.p. 252·5°, 158°/50 mm., 129·5°/15 mm., 98·5°/1 mm. D_4^{20} 0·7645.

Maman, *Chem. Zentr.*, 1936, I, 2332.
Krafft, *Ber.*, 1882, **15**, 1700.
Sorabji, *J. Chem. Soc.*, 1885, **47**, 41.

Tetradecane-1 : 14-dicarboxylic Acid.
See Thapsic Acid.

Tetradecanol-1.
See Tetradecyl Alcohol.

Tetradecanol-3.
See Ethylundecylcarbinol.

Tetradecanone-3.
See Ethyl undecyl Ketone.

Tetradecylacetylene (*Hexadecine*-1)

$CH_3 \cdot [CH_2]_{13} \cdot C{\vdots}CH$

$C_{16}H_{30}$ MW, 222

M.p. 15°. B.p. 155°/15 mm. D^{20} 0·7965.

Krafft, *Ber.*, 1896, **29**, 2236.

Tetradecyl Alcohol (*Tetradecanol*-1, *myristyl alcohol* 1-*hydroxytetradecane*)

$CH_3 \cdot [CH_2]_{12} \cdot CH_2OH$

$C_{14}H_{30}O$ MW, 214

Cryst. from EtOH.Aq. M.p. 39–39·5°. B.p. 170–3°/20 mm., 160°/10 mm. D_4^{38} 0·8236, D_4^{50} 0·8153.
Formyl: b.p. 166°/17 mm.
Acetyl: m.p. 14°. D_4^{25} 0·8581. n_D^{20} 1·4373.
Myristyl: plates from EtOH. M.p. 43°.
p-*Toluenesulphonyl*: m.p. 35°.
p-*Bromobenzenesulphonyl*: m.p. 51·5°.
p-*Methoxyphenylurethane*: m.p. 83°.
3 : 4-*Dimethoxyphenylurethane*: m.p. 79·5°.
Nitrate: liq. B.p. 175–80°/12 mm. slig decomp. Spar. sol. EtOH.

Ford, Marvel, *Organic Syntheses*, 193 X, 64.
Adkins, Folkers, *J. Am. Chem. So* 1931, **53**, 1096.
Ruhoff, Reid, *J. Am. Chem. Soc.*, 193 **55**, 3825.

Tetradecylaldehyde.
See Myristic Aldehyde.

Tetradecylamine (1-*Aminotetradecane*)

$CH_3 \cdot [CH_2]_{12} \cdot CH_2NH_2$

$C_{14}H_{31}N$ MW, 2

M.p. 37°. B.p. 162°/15 mm.
Acid succinate: needles. M.p. 123°.

Shukoff, Schestakoff, *J. prakt. Chem* 1903, **67**, 419.
Krafft, *Ber.*, 1890, **23**, 2361.

1-Tetradecylene

$CH_3 \cdot [CH_2]_{11} \cdot CH{:}CH_2$

$C_{14}H_{28}$ MW, 19

M.p. — 12°. B.p. 124·5–125°/15 mm. D 0·7745, D_4^{30} 0·7683. n_D^{22} 1·4392.

Klepper, *Chem. Abstracts*, 1929, **23**, 289
Krafft, *Ber.*, 1883, **16**, 3021.

Tetradecylic Acid.
See Myristic Acid.

Tetradecyl iodide (1-*Iodotetradecane*)

$CH_3 \cdot [CH_2]_{12} \cdot CH_2I$

$C_{14}H_{29}I$ MW, 32

B.p. 192–5°/17·5 mm., 128°/0·5 mm.

Levene, West, van der Scheer, *J. Bio Chem.*, 1915, **20**, 529.
Majima, Nakamura, *Ber.*, 1913, **46**, 409

Tetradecylmalonic Acid (*Pentadecane*-1 : 1 *dicarboxylic acid*)

$CH_3 \cdot [CH_2]_{13} \cdot CH{<}^{COOH}_{COOH}$

$C_{17}H_{32}O_4$ MW, 30

Cryst. from C_6H_6. M.p. 123–4° (117–18°) Very sol. boiling AcOH. Spar. sol. cold EtOH Insol. Et_2O.
Di-Et ester: $C_{21}H_{40}O_4$. MW, 356. Oil. B.p 190°/3 mm.

Monoamide : $C_{17}H_{33}O_3N$. MW, 299. Glistening cryst. Sol. boiling EtOH. Insol. H_2O, Et_2O. Heat $\longrightarrow$ palmitic amide.

Mononitrile : 1-cyanopalmitic acid. $C_{17}H_{31}O_2N$. MW, 281. Leaflets from AcOH. M.p. 75–6°.

> Chargaff, *Ber.*, 1932, **65**, 752.
> Hell, Jordanow, *Ber.*, 1891, **24**, 990.

Tetraethylammonium bromide

$$(C_2H_5)_4NBr$$

$C_8H_{20}NBr$ MW, 210

Cryst. from EtOH. Very sol. H_2O, EtOH, $CHCl_3$. D^{25} 1·3880.

B,Br_2 : orange-red needles from EtOH. M.p. 78° $\longrightarrow$ dark red liq.

Add. comp. with thiourea : $C_8H_{20}NBr +$ $2CH_4N_2S$. Prisms. M.p. 159–60°.

> Wagner, *Zeitschrift für Krystallographie und Mineralogie*, 1907, **43**, 190.
> Walden, *Chem. Zentr.*, 1912, I, 1958.

Tetraethylammonium chloride

$$(C_2H_5)_4NCl$$

$C_8H_{20}NCl$ MW, 165·5

Very hygroscopic. Very sol. H_2O, EtOH, $CHCl_3$, Me_2CO. D_4^{25} 1·1115.

$B,4H_2O$: prisms. M.p. 37·5°

> See last reference above and also
> Wagner, *Zeitschrift für Krystallographie und Mineralogie*, 1907, **43**, 189.

Tetraethylammonium hydroxide

$$(C_2H_5)_4N\cdot OH$$

$C_8H_{21}ON$ MW, 147

Known only in solution and in form of hydrates. Aq. sol. reacts alkaline and has bitter taste. Sucrose $+$ $CuSO_4 \longrightarrow$ blue sol. Hydrolyses fats.

$B,4H_2O$: needles. M.p. 49–50°. Very sol. H_2O.

$B,6H_2O$: m.p. 55°.

> Hofmann, *Ann.*, 1851, **78**, 263.
> Crichton, *J. Chem. Soc.*, 1907, **91**, 1794.

Tetraethylammonium iodide

$$(C_2H_5)_4NI$$

$C_8H_{20}NI$ MW, 257

Cryst. from warm H_2O. Does not melt below 200°. Sol. H_2O. Mod. sol. $CHCl_3$. Insol. Et_2O. D^4 1·559.

B,I_2 : prisms. M.p. 143°. Sol. Me_2CO, hot EtOH. Insol. Et_2O.

B,I_6 : cryst. M.p. 108°.

4 : 4′-Tetraethyldiaminotriphenyl-methane

Add. comp. with thiourea : $C_8H_{20}NI +$ $2CH_4N_2S$. M.p. 135°.

> Walden, *Chem. Zentr.*, 1914, I, 603.
> Wagner, *Zeitschrift für Krystallographie und Mineralogie*, 1907, **43**, 191.

4 : 4′-Tetraethyldiaminobenzhydrol

$$(C_2H_5)_2N\langle\rangle CH(OH)\langle\rangle N(C_2H_5)_2$$

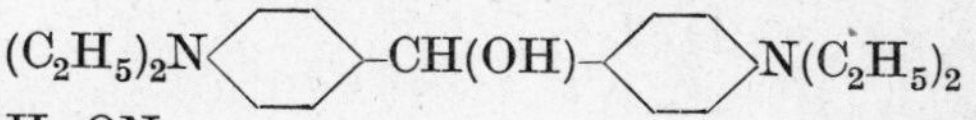

$C_{21}H_{30}ON_2$ MW, 326

Cryst. from pet. ether. M.p. 78°.

> Votoček, Köhler, *Ber.*, 1913, **46**, 1761.

4 : 4′-Tetraethyldiaminobenzophenone

$$(C_2H_5)_2N\langle\rangle CO\langle\rangle N(C_2H_5)_2$$

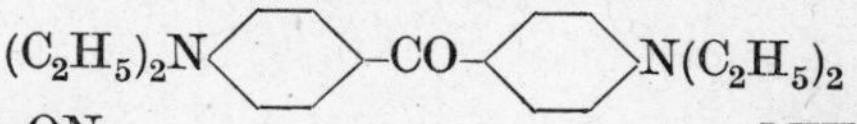

$C_{21}H_{28}ON_2$ MW, 324

Leaflets from EtOH. M.p. 95–6°. Intermediate for triphenylmethane dyes.

Anil : m.p. 124–5°.

> Votoček, Köhler, *Ber.*, 1913, **46**, 1761.

4 : 4′-Tetraethyldiaminodiphenyl disulphide (*Dithiodiethylaniline*, NN′-*tetra-ethyldithio-aniline*)

$$(C_2H_5)_2N\langle\rangle S\cdot S\langle\rangle N(C_2H_5)_2$$

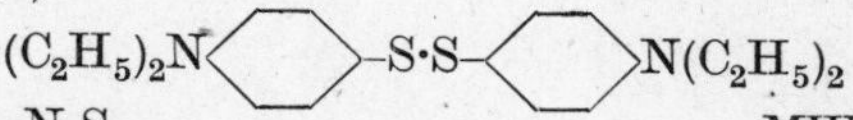

$C_{20}H_{28}N_2S_2$ MW, 360

Prisms from EtOH. M.p. 72°. Sol. CS_2. Spar. sol. EtOH, C_6H_6, ligroin, hot Et_2O.

> Holzmann, *Ber.*, 1887, **20**, 1637.

4 : 4′ - Tetraethyldiaminodiphenylmethane

$$(C_2H_5)_2N\langle\rangle CH_2\langle\rangle N(C_2H_5)_2$$

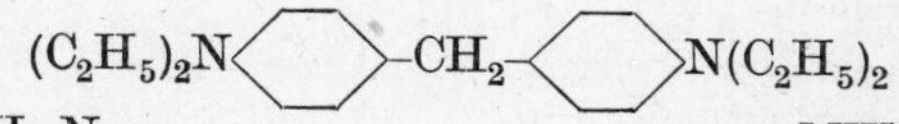

$C_{21}H_{30}N_2$ MW, 310

Cryst. from EtOH. M.p. 41°. B.p. 253°/10 mm.

Picrate : leaflets. M.p. 191°.

> Votoček, Köhler, *Ber.*, 1913, **46**, 1760.
> v. Braun, Kruber, *Ber.*, 1912, **45**, 2996.

4 : 4′ - Tetraethyldiaminotriphenylmethane

$$(C_2H_5)_2N\langle\rangle \underset{C_6H_5}{CH}\langle\rangle N(C_2H_5)_2$$

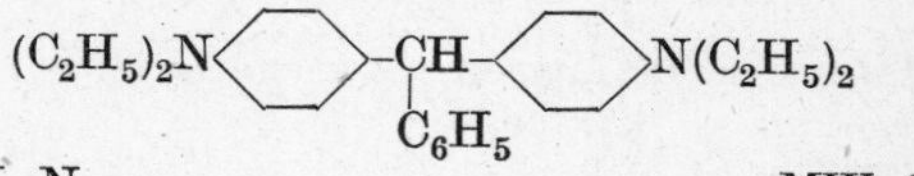

$C_{27}H_{34}N_2$ MW, 386

Needles from EtOH. M.p. 62°. Sol. EtOH, Et_2O, C_6H_6. Very spar. sol. H_2O.

Chloroplatinate: orange-red needles. M.p. 254–7°.

Doebner, *Ann.*, 1883, **217**, 265.
Decker, Becker, *Ann.*, 1913, **395**, 372.

N : N′-Tetraethyldithioaniline.
See Tetraethyldiaminodiphenyl disulphide.

Tetraethylene Glycol (*Diethyl ether di-β-hydroxyethyl] ether*)

$HO{\cdot}CH_2{\cdot}[CH_2{\cdot}O{\cdot}CH_2]_3{\cdot}CH_2OH$

$C_8H_{18}O_5$ MW, 194

B.p. 328°, 198°/14 mm., 157°/2 mm. D_4^{15} 1·1285. n_D^{15} 1·4609.

Cyclic carbonate: m.p. 42–4°. B.p. 128–30°/1 mm. D_4^{50} 1·1961. n_D^{50} 1·4569. Has slight odour of musk. Employed as perfume.

du Pont, F.P., 768,807, (*Chem. Abstracts*, 1935, **29**, 557).
Matignon, Moureu, Dodé, *Bull. soc. chim.*, 1934, **1**, 1308.
Hill, Carothers, *J. Am. Chem. Soc.*, 1933, **55**, 5034.

Tetraethylnaphthylenediamine.
See under Naphthylenediamine.

Tetraethylphenylenediamine.
See under Phenylenediamine.

Tetraethylsuccinic Acid

$(C_2H_5)_2C{\cdot}COOH$
$(C_2H_5)_2C{\cdot}COOH$

$C_{12}H_{22}O_4$ MW, 230

Cryst. from Et_2O–pet. ether. M.p. 149° ⟶ anhydride. Very sol. Et_2O. Sol. EtOH. Spar. sol. H_2O, pet. ether. $k = 4{\cdot}4 \times 10^{-4}$ at 25°.

Di-Et ester: $C_{16}H_{30}O_4$. MW, 286. B.p. 168–72°/25 mm. D_4^4 1·011.

Diamide: $C_{12}H_{24}O_2N_2$. MW, 228. Cryst. from pet. ether. M.p. 49–50°. B.p. 276–7°.

Dinitrile: $C_{12}H_{20}N_2$. MW, 192. Plates. M.p. 100–1°.

Anhydride: $C_{12}H_{20}O_3$. MW, 212. Prisms from pet. ether, with odour resembling camphor. M.p. 86°. B.p. 270°.

Verkade, Hartmann, *Rec. trav. chim.*, 1933, 52, 945.
Walker, Walker, *J. Chem. Soc.*, 1905, **87**, 964.

Tetraethylthiourea.
See under Thiourea.

Tetraethylthiuram disulphide

$(C_2H_5)_2N{\cdot}CS{\cdot}S{\cdot}S{\cdot}SC{\cdot}N(C_2H_5)_2$

$C_{10}H_{20}N_2S_4$ MW, 296

Cryst. M.p. 70°. Sol. warm EtOH. Spar. sol. Et_2O. Insol. H_2O. KOH fusion ⟶ diethylamine. Rubber vulcanisation accelerator.

Cummings, Simmons, *Ind. Eng. Chem.*, 1928, **20**, 1173.
Naugatuck, U.S.P., 1,782,111, (*Chem. Abstracts*, 1931, **25**, 303).
Roessler and Hasslacher, U.S.P., 1,796,977, (*Chem. Abstracts*, 1931, **25**, 2598).

Tetraethylurea.
See under Urea.

Tetrafluoromethane.
See Carbon tetrafluoride.

Tetrahydroacenaphthene (*Tetraphthene*)

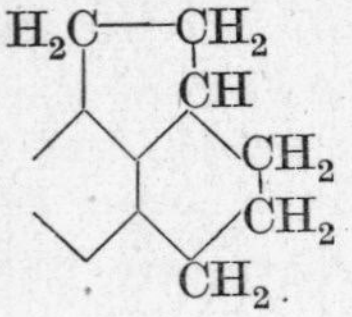

$C_{12}H_{14}$ MW, 158

M.p. 12°. B.p. 249·5°/719 mm., 115°/12 mm. Turns slightly yellow in air. D^{21} 1·0290. n_D 1·5777. Decolourises $KMnO_4$. Reacts very vigorously with $CrO_3 + H_2SO_4$.

Picrate: m.p. about 152–3°.

Padoa, Fabris, *Gazz. chim. ital.*, 1909, **39**, i, 331.
Bayer, D.R.P., 306,724, (*Chem. Zentr.*, 1918, II, 420).
v. Braun, Kirschbaum, *Ber.*, 1922, **55**, 1682.
Goswami, *Compt. rend.*, 1924, **179**, 1269.
Fleischer, Siefert, *Ann.*, 1921, **422**, 304.

Δ¹-Tetrahydroacetophenone.
See 1-Acetocyclohexene.

1 : 2 : 3 : 4-Tetrahydroacridine

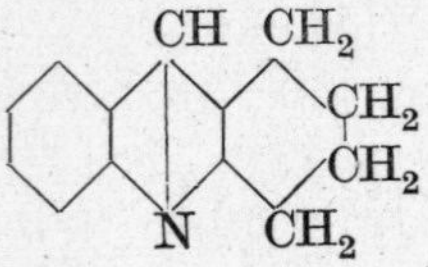

$C_{13}H_{13}N$ MW, 183

Cryst. from pet. ether. M.p. 54·5°.

B,HNO₃: pale yellow plates from EtOH. M.p. 160°.

B_2,H_2SO_4: needles from EtOH. M.p. 220°.

B_2,H_2PtCl_6: brownish-yellow needles from alc. HCl. M.p. 233–5°.

Picrate: yellow needles. M.p. 208° decomp.

Methiodide : needles from EtOH–Et_2O. M.p. 202–4°.

Perkin, Sedgwick, *J. Chem. Soc.*, 1924, **125**, 2446.
Borsche, *Ber.*, 1908, **41**, 2206.

1 : 2 : 3 : 4-Tetrahydroacridone

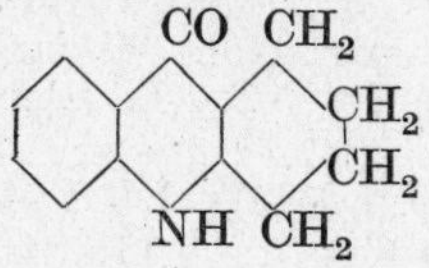

$C_{13}H_{13}ON$ MW, 199

Needles from EtOH or aniline. M.p. 358°. B.p. 360–70°/10 mm. Very sol. boiling aniline. Sol. EtOH with green fluor. Sublimation in air, or heat with H_2SO_4 ⟶ acridone.

Tiedtke, *Ber.*, 1909, **42**, 624.
Perkin, Sedgwick, *J. Chem. Soc.*, 1924, **125**, 2441.
v. Braun, Heymons, Manz, *Ber.*, 1931, **64**, 233.
Riedel, de Haen A.G., D.R.P., 532,397, (*Chem. Abstracts*, 1932, **26**, 151).

1 : 2 : 3 : 4-Tetrahydroanthracene (*Tethracene*)

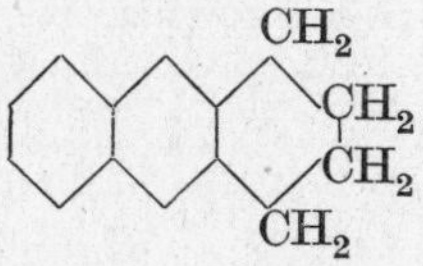

$C_{14}H_{14}$ MW, 182

Leaflets from EtOH. M.p. 103–5°. B.p. 170–3°/14 mm. CrO_3 in AcOH ⟶ 1 : 2 : 3 : 4-tetrahydroanthraquinone.

Picrate : reddish-yellow needles from EtOH. M.p. 116–17°.

Schroeter, *Ber.*, 1924, **57**, 2013; D.R.P., 463,830, (*Chem. Abstracts*, 1928, **22**, 4134).
Klepper, *Chem. Abstracts*, 1929, **23**, 3897.
Prokopetz, Khadzhinov, *Chem. Abstracts*, 1935, **29**, 7319.

1 : 2 : 3 : 4-Tetrahydroanthrahydroquinone (9 : 10-*Dihydroxy*-1 : 2 : 3 : 4-*tetrahydroanthracene*)

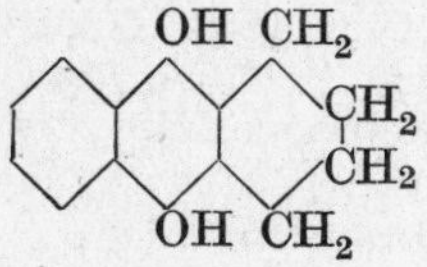

$C_{14}H_{14}O_2$ MW, 214

Greenish needles from AcOH. M.p. 208–16° decomp. Sol. alkalis with yellow col. Conc. H_2SO_4 ⟶ reddish-brown sol.

Diacetyl : cryst. from AcOH or EtOH. M.p. 204–6°.

Skita, *Ber.*, 1925, **58**, 2694.

1 : 2 : 3 : 4-Tetrahydroanthranol (9-*Hydroxy*-1 : 2 : 3 : 4-*tetrahydroanthracene*)

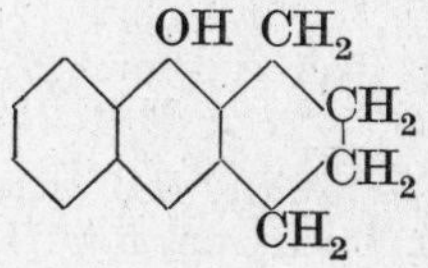

$C_{14}H_{14}O$ MW, 198

Pale yellow cryst. from ligroin. M.p. 108°. Sol. EtOH, Et_2O, AcOH. Very spar. sol. pet. ether. Sol. alkalis with strong yellowish-green fluor. No col. with $FeCl_3$.

Me ether : $C_{15}H_{16}O$. MW, 212. Reddish-yellow oil. B.p. 197°/14 mm., slight decomp.

Acetyl : needles from EtOH. M.p. 109°. Spar. sol. EtOH with violet fluor.

Benzoyl : m.p. 142°.

v. Braun, Bayer, *Ber.*, 1925, **58**, 2675.

1 : 2 : 3 : 4 - Tetrahydroanthraquinone (*Tethracenequinone*)

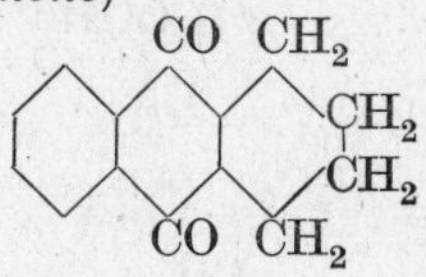

$C_{14}H_{12}O_2$ MW, 212

Golden-yellow needles from AcOH or AcOEt. M.p. 156–8°.

Schroeter, *Ber.*, 1924, **57**, 2014; D.R.P., 463,830, (*Chem. Abstracts*, 1928, **22**, 4134).
Skita, *Ber.*, 1925, **58**, 2694.

Δ²-Tetrahydroanthraquinone

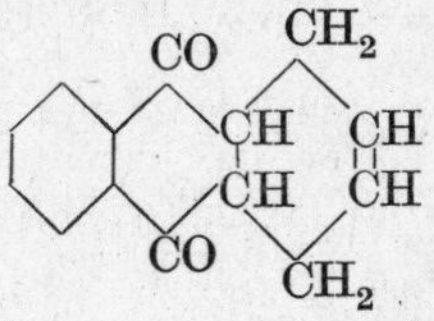

$C_{14}H_{12}O_2$ MW, 212

Cryst. from EtOH or ligroin. M.p. 102–3°. Sol. usual solvents on warming.

Diels, Alder, *Ann.*, 1928, **460**, 110.

Δ¹-Tetrahydrobenzaldehyde (*Cyclohexene-1-aldehyde*)

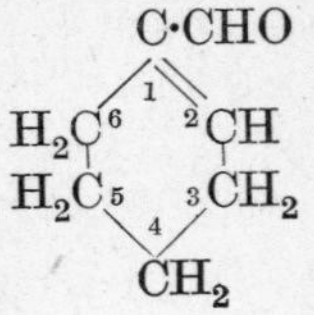

$C_7H_{10}O$ MW, 110

Oil.
Oxime: cryst. from ligroin. M.p. 97–9°.
Semicarbazone: cryst. M.p. 212–13°.

Borsche, Schmidt, *Ber.*, 1910, **43**, 3400.
v. Braun, Danziger, *Ber.*, 1913, **46**, 107.
Wallach, *Ann.*, 1908, **359**, 292.

Δ³-Tetrahydrobenzaldehyde (*Cyclohexene-3-aldehyde*).
Oil. B.p. 163·5–164·5°, 58°/17 mm., 51–2°/13 mm. D_4^{15} 0·9524. Polymerises very readily.
Semicarbazone: cryst. from C_6H_6–ligroin or MeOH.Aq. M.p. 153·5–154·5°.

Sobecki, *Ber.*, 1910, **43**, 1040.
Diels, Alder, *Ann.*, 1928, **460**, 121.

Tetrahydrobenzene.
See Cyclohexene.

Δ¹-Tetrahydrobenzoic Acid (*Cyclohexene-1-carboxylic acid*)

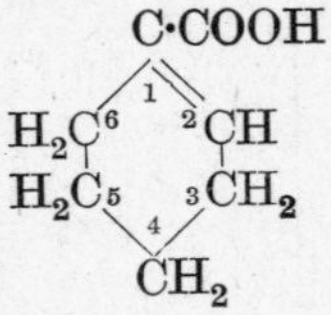

$C_7H_{10}O_2$ MW, 126

Plates. M.p. 38°. B.p. 238–40°/683 mm., 138°/14 mm., 133–4°/11 mm., 107°/3 mm. $D_4^{47\cdot2}$ 1·0717. n_{He}^{20} 1·49023.
Me ester: $C_8H_{12}O_2$. MW, 140. B.p. 193·5–194·5°. D_4^4 1·05607, D_{20}^{20} 1·04364.
Et ester: $C_9H_{14}O_2$. MW, 154. B.p. 206–8°, 143°/100 mm., 96°/16 mm., 84–6°/12 mm. D_4^{14} 1·0032. n_{He}^{20} 1·47167.
l-*Menthyl ester*: b.p. 178°/12 mm. $[\alpha]_D^{20}$ — 74·64° in EtOH.
Chloride: C_7H_9OCl. MW, 144·5. B.p. 86°/11 mm.
Nitrile: C_7H_9N. MW, 107. B.p. 81°/12 mm.
Amide: $C_7H_{11}ON$. MW, 125. Prisms from EtOH.Aq. M.p. 127–8°.

Darzens, Rost, *Compt. rend.*, 1911, **153**, 773.
Auwers, Krollpfeiffer, *Ber.*, 1915, **48**, 1396.
Ruzicka, Brugger, *Helv. Chim. Acta*, 1926, **9**, 402.
Boorman, Linstead, *J. Chem. Soc.*, 1935, 261.

Δ²-Tetrahydrobenzoic Acid (*Cyclohexene-3-carboxylic acid*).
Liq. B.p. 234–5°, 130°/18 mm. D_4^{20} 1·0820. n_D^{20} 1·4814. 1·34 parts sol. 100 parts H_2O at 20°. $k = 3{\cdot}05 \times 10^{-5}$ at 25°. Oxidises slowly in air to benzoic acid.
Me ester: b.p. 188–9°. D_{20}^{20} 1·0433.
l-*Menthyl ester*: b.p. 176°/12 mm. $[\alpha]_D^{20}$ — 59·44° in EtOH.
Amide: leaflets or prisms from EtOH. M.p. 144°.

See last reference above and also
Aschan, *Ann.*, 1892, **271**, 234.

Δ³-Tetrahydrobenzoic Acid (*Cyclohexene-4-carboxylic acid*).
M.p. about 13°. B.p. 237°/748 mm. Oxidises in air only very slowly.

Perkin, Tattersall, *J. Chem. Soc.*, 1907, **91**, 490.
Sobecki, *Ber.*, 1910, **43**, 1039.

Tetrahydro-*p*-benzoquinone (*Cyclohexandione*-1 : 4, 1 : 4-*diketocyclohexane*)

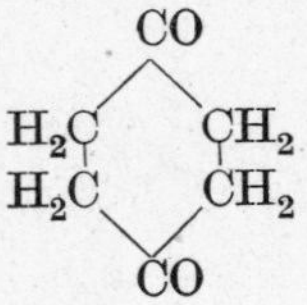

$C_6H_8O_2$ MW, 112

Needles from pet. ether, plates from H_2O. M.p. 78°. Sol. usual solvents. Warm $FeCl_3$ ⟶ *p*-benzoquinone.
Di-Me acetal: m.p. 80–1°.
Di-Et acetal: plates from EtOH. M.p. 89°.
Dioxime: cryst. from H_2O. M.p. 188°. Mod. sol. H_2O.
Monosemicarbazone: cryst. from EtOH. M.p. 221–2° decomp. Mod. sol. EtOH.
Di-thiosemicarbazone: cryst. M.p. 210–15°.

Meerwein, *Ann.*, 1913, **398**, 248.
Baeyer, *Ann.*, 1894, **278**, 91.
Stollé, *Ber.*, 1901, **34**, 1344.
Piloty, Steinbock, *Ber.*, 1902, **35**, 3109.

Tetrahydroberberine.
See Canadine.

Tetrahydrocarbazole

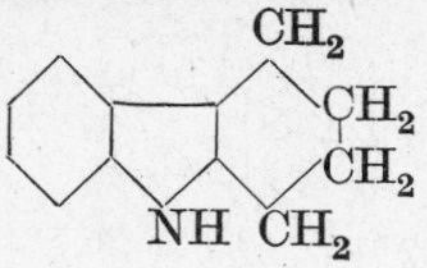

$C_{12}H_{13}N$ MW, 171

Leaflets from EtOH.Aq. M.p. 120° (116°). B.p. 325–30°. Turns brown in air. Very sol. EtOH, Et_2O, C_6H_6. Insol. H_2O. Volatile in superheated steam. KOH fusion ⟶ indole-2-carboxylic acid.

N-*Acetyl*: prisms from EtOH. M.p. 77°.
N-*Benzoyl*: m.p. 85°.
Picrate: dark red leaflets. M.p. 147°.

Bucherer, Brandt, *J. prakt. Chem.*, 1934, **140**, 129.
Perkin, Plant, *J. Chem. Soc.*, 1921, **119**, 1825.
Chem. Fabr. Weiler ter Meer, D.R.P., 374,098, (*Chem. Abstracts*, 1924, **18**, 2175).

Tetrahydrocarbazole-2-(or 4-)carboxylic Acid

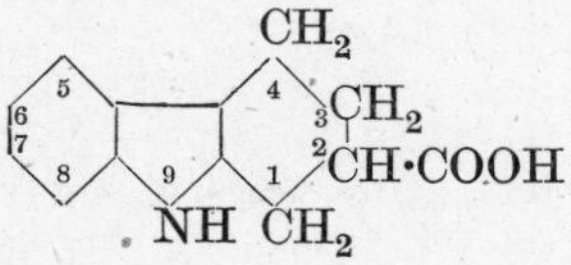

$C_{13}H_{13}O_2N$ MW, 215

Cryst. M.p. 230°.

Baeyer, Tutein, *Ber.*, 1889, **22**, 2185.

Tetrahydrocarbazole-3-carboxylic Acid.
Cryst. from C_6H_6. M.p. 195°. Sol. EtOH. Spar. sol. $CHCl_3$, C_6H_6, pet. ether.

Perkin, *J. Chem. Soc.*, 1904, **85**, 428.

Tetrahydrocarbazole-5-(or 7-)carboxylic Acid.
Prisms from AcOH. M.p. 287°.
Me ester: needles from MeOH. M.p. 155°.
Et ester: plates from EtOH.Aq. M.p. 146°.

See previous reference.

Tetrahydrocarbazole-6-carboxylic Acid.
Plates from EtOH.Aq. M.p. 282°.
Me ester: leaflets from AcOH.Aq. M.p. 158°.
Et ester: prisms from EtOH.Aq. M.p. 119°.

See previous reference.

Tetrahydrocarbazole-7-(or 5-)carboxylic Acid.
Prisms from AcOH. M.p. 210°.
Me ester: prisms from EtOH.Aq. M.p. 93°.

See previous reference.

Tetrahydrocarbazole-8-carboxylic Acid.
Prisms from C_6H_6. M.p. 203°.
Me ester: $C_{14}H_{15}O_2N$. MW, 229. Prisms from MeOH. M.p. 124°.
Et ester: $C_{15}H_{17}O_2N$. MW, 243. Needles from EtOH.Aq. M.p. 76°.

Collar, Plant, *J. Chem. Soc.*, 1926, 809.

Tetrahydrocarbazole-9-carboxylic Acid.
Not isolated as pure comp. owing to ease with which it loses CO_2.
Et ester: needles from EtOH. M.p. 65°.

Perkin, Plant, *J. Chem. Soc.*, 1923, **123**, 691.

Tetrahydrocarveol.
See Carvomenthol.
Tetrahydrocarvone.
See *p*-Menthanone-2.
Tetrahydrocinchoninic Acid.
See Tetrahydroquinoline-4-carboxylic Acid.
1 : 2 : 3 : 6-Tetrahydro-ψ-cumene.
See 1 : 4 : 5-Trimethylcyclohexene.
Tetrahydrocymene.
See Menthene.
Tetrahydroeucarvone.
See 2 : 6 : 6-Trimethylcycloheptanone.
Tetrahydroferulene.
See under Ferulene.
Tetrahydrofuran (*Tetramethylene oxide*)

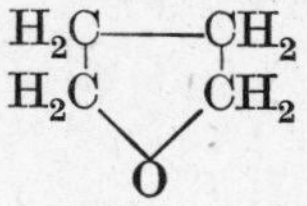

C_4H_8O MW, 72

Oil. F.p. – 65°. B.p. 64–5°. Sol. most org. solvents. Mod. sol. H_2O. D_4^{21} 0·888. n_D^{21} 1·40762. Bitter taste.

Starr, Hixon, *Organic Syntheses*, 1936, XVI, 77.
Bourguignon, *Chem. Zentr.*, 1908, I, 1630.

Tetrahydrofuran-carboxylic Acid.
See Tetrahydropyromucic Acid.
Tetrahydrofuran-2 : 5-dicarboxylic Acid

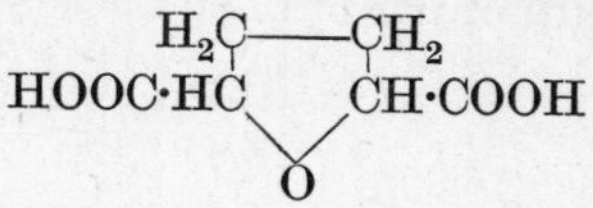

$C_6H_8O_5$ MW, 160

Cis:
Cryst. from AcOEt–pet. ether. M.p. 124–5°. Very sol. H_2O, EtOH, Me_2CO, AcOH. Mod. sol. Et_2O. Insol. $CHCl_3$, C_6H_6, pet. ether.

Dianilide : plates from EtOH. M.p. 208–9° decomp. Sol. Me_2CO, $CHCl_3$. Spar. sol. EtOH, hot C_6H_6. Insol. H_2O.

Anhydride : needles from $CHCl_3$–pet. ether. M.p. 128–9°. Sol. Et_2O, $CHCl_3$, AcOEt. Insol. pet. ether. Sublimes readily.

Trans :

Cryst. $+ H_2O$ from H_2O. M.p. 59–61°, anhyd. 94–5°. Very sol. H_2O, EtOH, Me_2CO, AcOH. Mod. sol. boiling Et_2O. Spar. sol. boiling C_6H_6, toluene, pet. ether.

Lean, *J. Chem. Soc.*, 1900, **77**, 110.
Le Sueur, Haas, *J. Chem. Soc.*, 1910, **97**, 181.

Tetrahydrofurfural (*Tetrahydro-2-furoic aldehyde*)

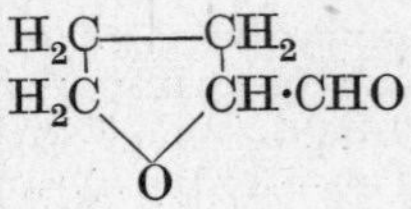

$C_5H_8O_2$ MW, 100

Mobile oil. B.p. 142–3°/779 mm., 45–7°/29 mm. D_4^{20} 1·0727. n_D^{20} 1·43658. Reduces hot Fehling's instantly, $NH_3.AgNO_3$ on standing. Decolourises alk. $KMnO_4$. Conc. HCl $\longrightarrow$ intense brick-red col.

Di-Et acetal : b.p. 194·5° (187–90°).

Di-[β-ethoxyethyl]-acetal : b.p. 131–6°/4–5 mm.

Diacetate : b.p. 134–6°/16 mm. (133°/29 mm.). D_4^{20} 1·1495. $n_D^{20\cdot3}$ 1·44052. Sol. usual org. solvents. Spar. sol. H_2O.

Phenylbenzylhydrazone : pale yellow needles from MeOH. M.p. 67°.

Scheibler, Sotscheck, Friese, *Ber.*, 1925, **58**, 1961; 1924, **57**, 1443.
Burdick, Adkins, *J. Am. Chem. Soc.*, 1934, **56**, 440.
Covert, Connor, Adkins, *J. Am. Chem. Soc.*, 1932, **54**, 1656.
Minné, Adkins, *J. Am. Chem. Soc.*, 1933, **55**, 304.

Tetrahydrofurfuryl Alcohol

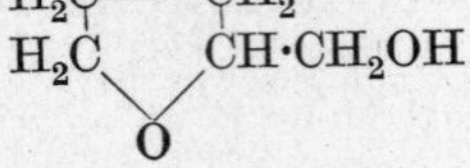

$C_5H_{10}O_2$ MW, 102

B.p. 177–8°/750 mm., 80–2°/20 mm. D_4^{25} 1·1326. n_D^{25} 1·4505. Absorbs moisture from the air. Solvent for fats, waxes, resins, etc.

Et ether : $C_7H_{14}O_2$. MW, 130. B.p. 152–4°/726 mm., 47–55°/11 mm.

Acetyl : b.p. 192–4°/740 mm., 88–90°/18 mm. D_4^{25} 1·0624. n_D^{25} 1·4350.

Iodoacetyl : b.p. 130°/5 mm.

Propionyl : b.p. 204–7°/756 mm., 85–7°/3 mm. D_4^{20} 1·044.

Butyryl : b.p. 225–7°/759 mm., 102–4°/4 mm. D_0^{20} 1·012.

Valeryl : b.p. 238–40°/756 mm., 97–9°/2 mm. D_0^{20} 0·999.

Pyruvyl : b.p. 110–30°/17 mm. *Semicarbazone* : leaflets. M.p. 184–6°.

Benzoyl : b.p. 300–2°/750 mm., 138–40°/2 mm. D_0^{20} 1·137.

Phenylurethane : cryst. from pet. ether. M.p. 61°.

Diphenylurethane : plates from MeOH. M.p. 81°.

Wienhaus, *Ber.*, 1920, **53**, 1656.
Zanetti, *J. Am. Chem. Soc.*, 1928, **50**, 1821.
du Pont, E.P., 337,296, (*Chem. Abstracts*, 1931, **25**, 1844).
Böhme, E.P., 388,703, (*Chem. Abstracts*, 1933, **27**, 4547).
Hewlett, *Chem. Abstracts*, 1933, **27**, 980.
Burdick, Adkins, *J. Am. Chem. Soc.*, 1934, **56**, 441.

Tetrahydrofuroic Acid.
See Tetrahydropyromucic Acid.

Tetrahydroiminazolone-2.
See Ethyleneurea.

4 : 5 : 6 : 7-Tetrahydroindazole

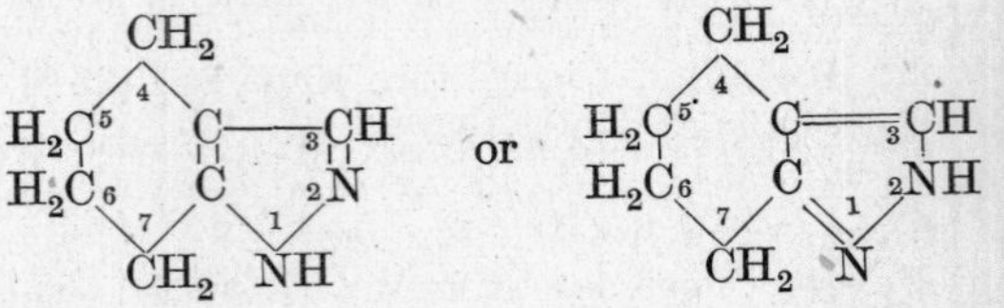

$C_7H_{10}N_2$ MW, 122

Cryst. M.p. 84°.

1-*Benzoyl* : prisms from pet. ether. M.p. 58·5–60°. B.p. 208°/13 mm. Sol. most org. solvents.

1-o-*Nitrobenzoyl* : cryst. from EtOH. M.p. 148–9°.

1-m-*Nitrobenzoyl* : needles from EtOH. M.p. 140–2°. Sol. $CHCl_3$, C_6H_6. Mod. sol. EtOH, Et_2O.

2-o-*Nitrobenzoyl* : cryst. from EtOH. M.p. 179–80°. Sol. Me_2CO, $CHCl_3$, C_6H_6. Less sol. EtOH, Et_2O.

2-m-*Nitrobenzoyl* : leaflets from EtOH. M.p. 118–118·5°.

Auwers, *Ann.*, 1927, **453**, 227.
Wallach, *Ann.*, 1903, **329**, 118.

4 : 5 : 6 : 7-Tetrahydroindazole-1-carboxylic Acid

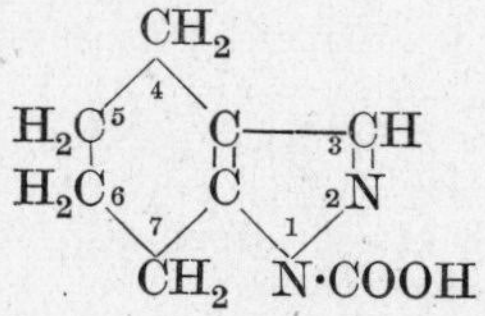

$C_8H_{10}O_2N_2$ MW, 166

Et ester : $C_{10}H_{14}O_2N_2$. MW, 194. B.p. 170°/18 mm. D_4^{20} 1·127. n_{He}^{20} 1·5147.

Chloride : $C_8H_9ON_2Cl$. MW, 184·5. Cryst. powder from C_6H_6. M.p. 162–5°.

Amide : cryst. from AcOH.Aq. M.p. 187°.

Auwers, *Ann.*, 1927, **453**, 230.

4 : 5 : 6 : 7-Tetrahydroindazole-2-carboxylic Acid.

Et ester : b.p. 170°/18 mm. D_4^{20} 1·138. n_{He}^{20} 1·5120.

Amide : cryst. M.p. 186–8°.

See previous reference and also
Wallach, *Ann.*, 1903, **329**, 117.

4 : 5 : 6 : 7-Tetrahydroindazole-3-carboxylic Acid.

Needles from AcOH. M.p. 254°. Mod. sol. AcOH. Spar. sol. EtOH. Very spar. sol. Et_2O, Me_2CO, C_6H_6.

Me ester : 1-o-*nitrobenzoyl*, needles from AcOH. M.p. 193–4°. Sol. hot EtOH, AcOH. Spar. sol. C_6H_6.

Et ester : cryst. from pet. ether. M.p. 106–7°. Sol. most org. solvents.

1-o-*Nitrobenzoyl* : m.p. 148–9°.

Auwers, *Ann.*, 1927, **453**, 232.
Auwers, Ernecke, Conrad, Ottens, *Ann.*, 1929, **469**, 68.

Δ¹-Tetrahydroisophthalic Acid (*Cyclohexene*-1 : 3-*dicarboxylic acid*)

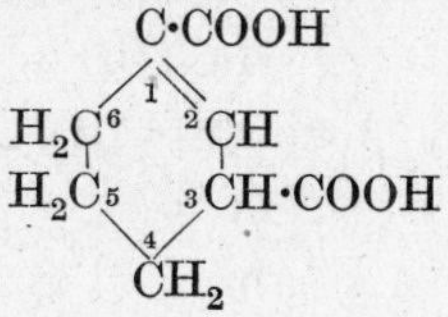

$C_8H_{10}O_4$ MW, 170

Cryst. from H_2O. M.p. 197–8° (168°). Very sol. H_2O, EtOH, AcOH. Spar. sol. $CHCl_3$, C_6H_6, pet. ether. $KMnO_4$ ⟶ succinic acid. Hot KOH or HCl ⟶ Δ³-tetrahydroisophthalic acid.

Mono-Me ester : $C_9H_{12}O_4$. MW, 184. Exists in two forms. (i) Prisms from hexane. M.p. 59°. (ii) Oil. B.p. 172–4°/1 mm.

Di-Me ester : $C_{10}H_{14}O_4$. MW, 198. B.p. 134–5°/7 mm.

Mono-Et ester : $C_{10}H_{14}O_4$. MW, 198. Exists in two forms. (i) Prisms from pet. ether. M.p. 44–5°. (ii) Cryst. from pet. ether. M.p. 40–1°. B.p. 169–73°/1 mm.

Di-Et ester : $C_{12}H_{18}O_4$. MW, 226. B.p. 150°/12 mm. D_4^{20} 1·0772. n_D 1·4722.

Amide : prisms from H_2O. M.p. 239°.

Anhydride : plates from C_6H_6–pet. ether. M.p. 78–80°. Sol. warm C_6H_6. Spar. sol. Et_2O.

Monoanilide : needles from AcOH.Aq. M.p. 190–2°.

Kon, Nandi, *J. Chem. Soc.*, 1933, 1631.
Farmer, Richardson, *J. Chem. Soc.*, 1926, 2174.
Perkin, Pickles, *J. Chem. Soc.*, 1905, **87**, 301.

Δ³-Tetrahydroisophthalic Acid (*Cyclohexene*-1 : 5-*dicarboxylic acid*).

Cryst. from H_2O. M.p. 243–4°. Sol. boiling formic acid. Spar. sol. boiling H_2O. $KMnO_4$ or HNO_3 ⟶ isophthalic acid.

Di-Me ester : b.p. 140–1°/7 mm.

Farmer, Richardson, *J. Chem. Soc.*, 1926, 2176.
Perkin, Pickles, *J. Chem. Soc.*, 1905, **87**, 306.

Δ⁴-Tetrahydroisophthalic Acid (*Cyclohexene*-3 : 5-*dicarboxylic acid*).

Cis :

Needles from H_2O. M.p. 165°. Very sol. hot H_2O. Hot KOH ⟶ Δ³-tetrahydroisophthalic acid.

Trans :

Cryst. M.p. 225–7°. Spar. sol. H_2O.

Perkin, Pickles, *J. Chem. Soc.*, 1905, **87**, 310.

1 : 2 : 3 : 4-Tetrahydroisoquinoline (Py-*Tetrahydroisoquinoline*)

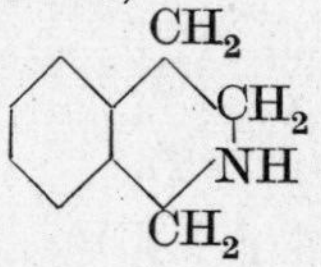

$C_9H_{11}N$ MW, 133

B.p. 232–3°. $D_4^{23\cdot1}$ 1·0642. $n_D^{23\cdot1}$ 1·5798. Spar. sol. H_2O. Heat of comb. C_v 1214 Cal. Reduces $NH_3.AgNO_3$.

B,HCl : plates. M.p. 195–7°.

B_2,H_2PtCl_6 : reddish-yellow plates. M.p. 231–2°.

Picrate : yellow needles from EtOH. M.p. 195°.

Picrolonate : m.p. 260° decomp.

N-*Me* : *see* Isokairoline.

N-*Et* : $C_{11}H_{15}N$. MW, 161. Pale yellow oil. B.p. 225–7°. *B,HI* : pale yellow needles from H_2O. M.p. 170°. *Picrate* : yellow needles from EtOH. M.p. 121°.

N-*Propyl* : $C_{12}H_{17}N$. MW, 175. B.p. 259–60°/743 mm.

N-*Isopropyl* : b.p. 256–8°/735 mm.

N-*Butyl* : $C_{13}H_{19}N$. MW, 189. B.p. 272–3°.

N-*Isoamyl* : $C_{14}H_{21}N$. MW, 203. B.p. 276–80°.

N-*Benzyl* : pale yellow oil. B.p. 194–7°/18 mm.

N-*Phenacyl* : yellow needles from EtOH. M.p. 100–1°.

N-*Acetyl* : cryst. from ligroin. M.p. 46°. B.p. 220–5°/70 mm. Sol. usual org. solvents.

N-*Benzoyl* : m.p. 129°. B.p. 245–50°/50 mm.

N-o-*Nitrobenzoyl* : needles from EtOH. M.p. 75–6°. Sol. EtOH, C_6H_6. Spar. sol. pet. ether.

Kondo, Ochiai, *Chem. Abstracts*, 1923, **17**, 3032.
Wedekind, Ney, *Ber.*, 1909, **42**, 2140 ; 1912, **45**, 1308.
Bamberger, Dieckmann, *Ber.*, 1893, **26**, 1213.
Pictet, Spengler, *Ber.*, 1911, **44**, 2034.
Pictet, D.R.P., 241,425, (*Chem. Zentr.*, 1912, I, 177).

5 : 6 : 7 : 8-Tetrahydroisoquinoline (Bz-*Tetrahydroisoquinoline*)

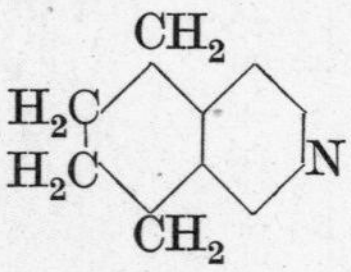

$C_9H_{11}N$ MW, 133

B.p. 218°. D_4^{10} 1·0504. n_D^{10} 1·57263.

Yamaguchi, *Chem. Abstracts*, 1927, **21**, 2696.

1 : 2 : 3 : 4 - Tetrahydroisoquinoline - 2 - carboxylic Acid

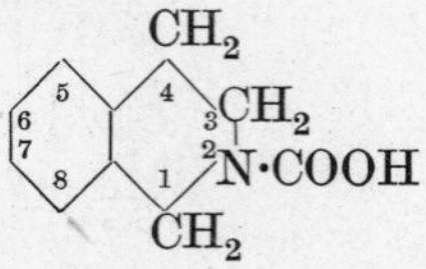

$C_{10}H_{11}O_2N$ MW, 177

Amide : $C_{10}H_{12}ON_2$. MW, 176. Leaflets from H_2O. M.p. 169°. Spar. sol. Et_2O.

Anilide : needles from EtOH. M.p. 144°. Spar. sol. EtOH, Et_2O. Insol. H_2O.

Bamberger, Dieckmann, *Ber.*, 1893, **26**, 1212.

1 : 2 : 3 : 4 - Tetrahydroisoquinoline - 3 - carboxylic Acid.

Cryst. from EtOH.Aq. M.p. 311° decomp. Mod. sol. warm H_2O. Spar. sol. $CHCl_3$. Insol. EtOH, Et_2O. Heat above m.p. ⟶ 1 : 2 : 3 : 4-tetrahydroisoquinoline.

Pictet, Spengler, *Ber.*, 1911, **44**, 2034.
Pictet, D.R.P., 241,425, (*Chem. Zentr.*, 1912, I, 177).

Tetrahydrolepidine.
See 4-Methyltetrahydroquinoline.

Tetrahydromesitylene.
See 1 : 3 : 5-Trimethylcyclohexene.

Tetrahydronaphthalene (*Tetralin*)

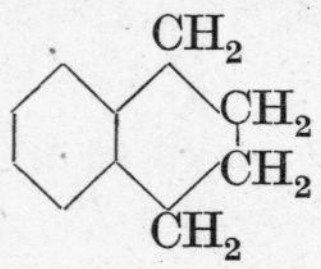

$C_{10}H_{12}$ MW, 132

M.p. — 35°. B.p. 207·3°, 90·8–91·2°/17 mm. D_4^{17} 0·9738. n_D^{17} 1·54529. Sp. heat 0·403 at 18°. Heat of vap. 79·32 cal. per gram. Heat of comb. C_p 1353 Cal. Crit. temp. 789°. Used extensively as solvent for org. substances. Non-toxic.

Graebe, Guye, *Ber.*, 1883, **16**, 3028.
Heaton, *Journal of Oil and Colour Chemists Association*, 1923, **6**, 93.
Inoue, *Chem. Abstracts*, 1924, **18**, 2697.
Gewerkschaft Mathias Stinnes, D.R.P., 610,829, (*Chem. Abstracts*, 1935, **29**, 5866).
I.C.I., E.P., 401,724, (*Chem. Abstracts*, 1934, **28**, 2723).

1 : 2 : 3 : 4-Tetrahydronaphthalene-1 : 2-dicarboxylic Acid

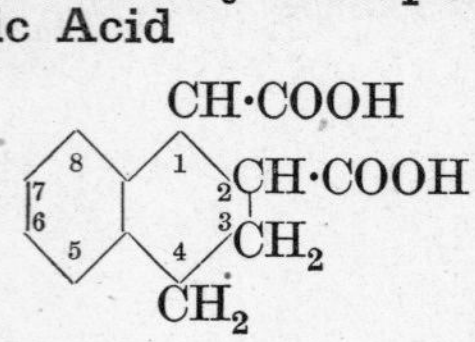

$C_{12}H_{12}O_4$ MW, 220

Needles. M.p. 193° (rapid heat.). Sol. Me_2CO. Mod. sol. EtOH, AcOH, hot H_2O. Spar. sol. C_6H_6.

Anhydride : $C_{12}H_{10}O_3$. MW, 202. Needles from MeOH. M.p. 66–7°. Sol. AcOH. Spar. sol. C_6H_6.

Auwers, Möller, *J. prakt. Chem.*, 1925, **109**, 142.

1 : 2 : 3 : 4-Tetrahydronaphthalene-1 : 8-dicarboxylic Acid (1 : 2 : 3 : 4-*Tetrahydronaphthalic acid*).

Prisms. M.p. 196°. Sol. EtOH. Spar. sol. warm H_2O. Almost insol. Et_2O. Above m.p. ⟶ anhydride.

Di-Me ester : $C_{14}H_{16}O_4$. MW, 248. Cryst. M.p. 74°.

Di-Et ester : $C_{16}H_{20}O_4$. MW, 276. M.p. 52°. B.p. 193°/17 mm.

Anhydride : cryst. from C_6H_6. M.p. 119°.

Cassares, Ranedo, *Chem. Abstracts*, 1923, **17**, 3030.

Willstätter, Jacquet, *Ber.*, 1918, **51**, 775.

1 : 2 : 3 : 4-Tetrahydronaphthalene-2 : 3-dicarboxylic Acid.

Plates. M.p. 199°. Very sol. EtOH, Me_2CO, $CHCl_3$. Sol. warm Et_2O. Spar. sol. cold H_2O. Above m.p. ⟶ anhydride.

Anhydride : prisms from Et_2O. M.p. 184°. Mod. sol. EtOH, $CHCl_3$. Spar. sol. Et_2O. Insol. cold H_2O.

Baeyer, Perkin, *Ber.*, 1884, **17**, 450.

Tetrahydronaphthalic Acid.

See Tetrahydronaphthalene-1 : 8-dicarboxylic Acid.

1 : 2 : 3 : 4-Tetrahydro-1-naphthoic Acid (ac-*Tetrahydro-α-naphthoic acid*)

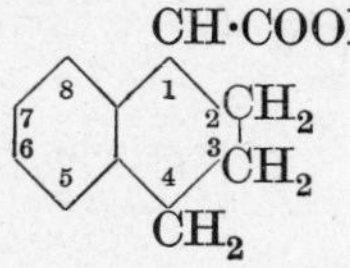

$C_{11}H_{12}O_2$ MW, 176

d-.

Cryst. from pet. ether. M.p. 49–50°. $[\alpha]_D$ + 14·01° in $CHCl_3$.

l-.

Plates from pet. ether. M.p. 52·5°. $[\alpha]_D$ − 52·34° in C_6H_6, − 15·95° in $CHCl_3$.

dl-.

Prisms from AcOEt. M.p. 85°. Very sol. most org. solvents. Mod. sol. hot H_2O. Sol. 1052 parts cold H_2O. $k = 4{\cdot}45 \times 10^{-5}$ at 25°.

Et ester : $C_{13}H_{16}O_2$. MW, 204. B.p. 279°/749 mm.

l-*Menthyl ester* : b.p. 207°/10 mm. $[\alpha]_D^{20}$ − 47·57° in EtOH.

Amide : $C_{11}H_{13}ON$. MW, 175. Needles from EtOH. M.p. 116°.

Pickard, Yates, *J. Chem. Soc.*, 1906, **89**, 1102.

Kay, Morton, *J. Chem. Soc.*, 1914, **105**, 1571.

5 : 6 : 7 : 8-Tetrahydro-1-naphthoic Acid (ar-*Tetrahydro-α-naphthoic acid*).

Prisms from H_2O. M.p. 128°. Very sol. EtOH. Sol. hot H_2O. Spar. sol. cold H_2O.

Et ester : b.p. 156–9°/12 mm.

Nitrile : $C_{11}H_{11}N$. MW, 157. B.p. 277–9°/721 mm.

Amide : needles from H_2O. M.p. 182°. Sol. boiling H_2O and most org. solvents.

Bamberger, Bordt, *Ber.*, 1889, **22**, 628.

I.G., F.P., 649,626, (*Chem. Abstracts*, 1929, **23**, 2986).

1 : 2 : 3 : 4-Tetrahydro-2-naphthoic Acid (ac-*Tetrahydro-β-naphthoic acid*)

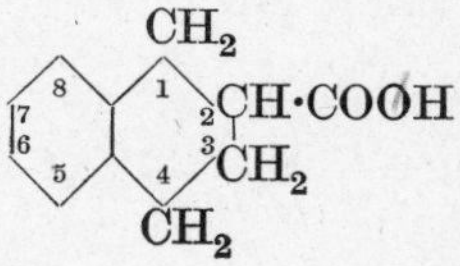

$C_{11}H_{12}O_2$ MW, 176

d-.

Prisms from AcOH.Aq. M.p. 99°. $[\alpha]_D$ + 40·35° in $CHCl_3$.

l-.

Prismatic needles from pet. ether. M.p. 99°. $[\alpha]_D$ − 51·82° in $CHCl_3$.

dl-.

Needles from hot EtOH.Aq. M.p. 96°. Sol. 1661 parts H_2O at 14°.

l-*Menthyl ester* : b.p. 218°/11 mm. $[\alpha]_D^{20}$ − 53·0° in C_6H_6.

Pickard, Yates, *J. Chem. Soc.*, 1906, **89**, 1103.

Baeyer, Besemfelder, *Ann.*, 1891, **266**, 198.

5 : 6 : 7 : 8-Tetrahydro-2-naphthoic Acid (ar-*Tetrahydro-β-naphthoic acid*).

Needles from EtOH. M.p. 154° (144°). B.p. 216°/14 mm. Insol. cold pet. ether.

Chloride : $C_{11}H_{11}OCl$. MW, 194·5. B.p. 162°/13 mm.

Amide : $C_{11}H_{13}ON$. MW, 175. Leaflets from EtOH–pet. ether. M.p. 137–8°.
Anilide : needles from EtOH. M.p. 147°.

v. Braun, Kirschbaum, Schumann, *Ber.*, 1920, **53**, 1161.
Coulson, *J. Chem. Soc.*, 1935, 80.

1 : 2 : 3 : 4-Tetrahydro-1-naphthol (*ac-Tetrahydro-α-naphthol*, 1-*hydroxy*-1 : 2 : 3 : 4-*tetrahydronaphthalene*, 1-*hydroxytetralin*)

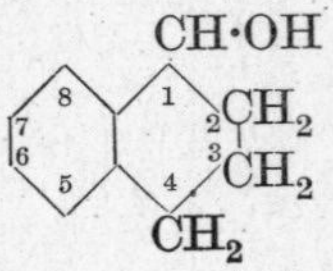

$C_{10}H_{12}O$ MW, 148

d-.
Pale yellow oil. B.p. 155–60°/25 mm. $[\alpha]_D$ + 28·2° in $CHCl_3$.

dl-.
Thick oil. B.p. 264°/716 mm., 176·5–178°/53 mm., 132–4°/12–13 mm. D^{17} 1·0896. n_D^{17} 1·5671. Sol. EtOH, Et_2O, $CHCl_3$, CS_2, C_6H_6. Spar. sol. H_2O.
Acetyl : b.p. 169°/34 mm., 105–10°/2 mm.
Phenylurethane : needles from ligroin. M.p. 121–2°.

Criegee, *Ann.*, 1930, **481**, 292.
Brochet, Cornubert, *Bull. soc. chim.*, 1922, **31**, 1280.
Strauss, Rohrbacher, *Ber.*, 1921, **54**, 57.
Bamberger, Lodter, *Ber.*, 1890, **23**, 197.

5 : 6 : 7 : 8-Tetrahydro-1-naphthol (*ar-Tetrahydro-α-naphthol*, 5-*hydroxy*-1 : 2 : 3 : 4-*tetrahydronaphthalene*, 5-*hydroxytetralin*, 1-*tetralol*).
Needles with strong phenolic odour. M.p. 68·5–69°. B.p. 264·5–265°. Very sol. most org. solvents. Less sol. hot H_2O.
Et ether : $C_{12}H_{16}O$. MW, 176. B.p. 259°/705 mm.
Acetyl : cryst. M.p. 73–5°.
Benzoyl : m.p. about 46°.

Jacobsen, Turnbull, *Ber.*, 1898, **31**, 897.
Brochet, Cornubert, *Bull. soc. chim.*, 1922, **31**, 1280.
I.G., F.P., 644,408, (*Chem. Abstracts*, 1930, **24**, 862); U.S.P., 1,858,627, (*Chem. Abstracts*, 1932, **26**, 3808).

1 : 2 : 3 : 4-Tetrahydro-2-naphthol (*ac-Tetrahydro-β-naphthol*, 2-*hydroxy*-1 : 2 : 3 : 4-*tetrahydronaphthalene*, 2-*hydroxytetralin*)

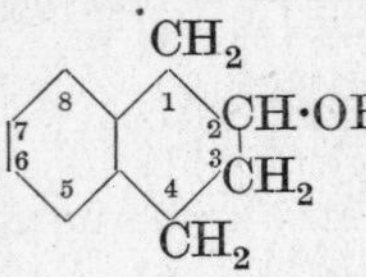

$C_{10}H_{12}O$ MW, 148

d-.
Needles from pet. ether. M.p. 50°. B.p. 141°/17 mm. $[\alpha]_D^{20}$ + 70·3° in $CHCl_3$.
Valeryl : b.p. 169°/11 mm. D_4^{16} 1·0317.
Pelargonyl : b.p. 195–7°/5 mm. D_4^{18} 0·9821.
Lauryl : cryst. M.p. 35–6°. B.p. 218°/3 mm. D_4^{17} 0·9677.
Phenylurethane : m.p. 119°.

l-.
Needles from pet. ether. M.p. 50°. B.p. 141°/17 mm. D_4^{61} 1·0589. $[\alpha]_D^{20}$ − 67·1° in $CHCl_3$.
Acetyl : b.p. 149°/18 mm. D_4^{14} 1·0926.
Propionyl : b.p. 158–9°/18 mm. D_4^{16} 1·0675.

dl-.
Viscous oil. B.p. 264°/716 mm., 172·6–173·5°/53 mm., 144·5–146·5°/20 mm. D^{17} 1·0715. n_D^{17} 1·5523. Sol. EtOH, Et_2O, $CHCl_3$, CS_2, C_6H_6. Spar. sol. H_2O. Turns brown in air.
Acetyl : b.p. 169°/34 mm.
Benzoyl : leaflets from EtOH. B.p. 254–5°/40 mm. Sol. hot EtOH, cold $CHCl_3$, C_6H_6.
Phenylurethane : needles. M.p. 99°.

Bamberger, Lodter, *Ber.*, 1890, **23**, 197.
Pickard, Kenyon, *J. Chem. Soc.*, 1912, **101**, 1431.
Brochet, Cornubert, *Bull. soc. chim.*, 1922, **31**, 1280.

5 : 6 : 7 : 8-Tetrahydro-2-naphthol (*ar-Tetrahydro-β-naphthol*, 6-*hydroxy*-1 : 2 : 3 : 4-*tetrahydronaphthalene*, 6-*hydroxytetralin*, 2-*tetralol*).
Needles from ligroin. M.p. 61·5–62·5° (58°). B.p. 275°/705 mm., 146°/13 mm. Very sol. EtOH, Et_2O, $CHCl_3$, C_6H_6, hot ligroin. Spar. sol. H_2O. No col. with $FeCl_3$.
Me ether : $C_{11}H_{14}O$. MW, 162. B.p. 129–31°/11 mm.
Et ether : $C_{12}H_{16}O$. MW, 176. Oil with pleasant odour. B.p. 132–3°/15 mm., 129°/11 mm. D^{20} 1·008.
Acetyl : viscous oil. B.p. 158°/14 mm.
Benzoyl : prisms. M.p. 96°. B.p. 220–2°/10 mm.
p-*Nitrobenzoyl* : m.p. 106·5°.

Cinnamoyl : m.p. 77·5°.
Diphenylurethane : m.p. 114°.

Schroeter, Schrauth, D.R.P., 299,603, (*Chem. Zentr.*, 1919, IV, 618).
Schroeter *et al.*, *Ann.*, 1922, **426**, 119.
Brochet, Cornubert, *Bull. soc. chim.*, 1922, **31**, 1280.
Thoms, Kross, *Arch. Pharm.*, 1927, **265**, 336.
I.G., F.P., 644,408, (*Chem. Abstracts*, 1930, **24**, 862).

1 : 2 : 3 : 4-Tetrahydro-1-naphthylamine (ac-*Tetrahydro-α-naphthylamine*)

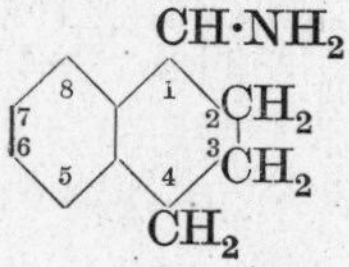

$C_{10}H_{13}N$ MW, 147

Oil with ammoniacal odour. B.p. 246·5°/714 mm. Sol. most org. solvents. Mod. sol. cold H_2O. Strong base.

B,HNO₂ : needles from H_2O. M.p. 138–9°.

B_2,H_2PtCl_6 : orange-yellow prisms + $2H_2O$. M.p. 140°, anhyd. 190°.

N-*Acetyl* : needles from EtOH.Aq. M.p. 148–9°. Sol. EtOH, AcOH. Spar. sol. cold H_2O.

N-2 : 4-*Dinitrophenyl* : golden-yellow leaflets from EtOH. M.p. 121°.

Bamberger, Bamman, *Ber.*, 1889, **22**, 964.
Green, Rowe, *J. Chem. Soc.*, 1918, **113**, 957.
Komatsu, Amatatsu, *Chem. Abstracts*, 1931, **25**, 500.

5 : 6 : 7 : 8-Tetrahydro-1-naphthylamine (ar-*Tetrahydro-α-naphthylamine*).

Oil. B.p. 275°, 233–5°/280 mm. D^{16} 1·0625. $n_D^{23·1}$ 1·58964. Weak base. Reduces warm alc. Ag sols.

N-*Me* : $C_{11}H_{15}N$. MW, 161. Pale yellow liq. B.p. 150–2°/12 mm. *Picrate* : reddish-yellow cryst. powder. M.p. 174°.

N-*Di-Me* : $C_{12}H_{17}N$. MW, 175. B.p. 261–2°/721 mm., 131–131·5°/16 mm. Reduces Ag salts. *Methiodide* : prisms from H_2O. M.p. 164·5°. Sol. EtOH. Spar. sol. H_2O.

N-*Et* : $C_{12}H_{17}N$. MW, 175. B.p. 286–7°/717 mm. Sol. most org. solvents. Spar. sol. H_2O.

N-2 : 4-*Dinitrophenyl* : red leaflets from EtOH. M.p. 134°.

N-*Acetyl* : needles. M.p. 158°. Sol. EtOH, Et_2O, $CHCl_3$, C_6H_6.

Bamberger, Althausse, *Ber.*, 1888, **21**, 1789.
Bamberger, Helwig, *Ber.*, 1889, **22**, 1315.
Bayer, D.R.P., 305,347, (*Chem. Zentr.*, 1918, I, 977).
Cassella, D.R.P., 479,401, (*Chem. Abstracts*, 1929, **23**, 4710).
I.G., D.R.P., 581,831, (*Chem. Abstracts*, 1934, **28**, 1059) ; Swiss P., 127,524. (*Chem. Abstracts*, 1929, 23, 1143).

1 : 2 : 3 : 4 - Tetrahydro - 2 - naphthyl - amine (ac-*Tetrahydro-β-naphthylamine*)

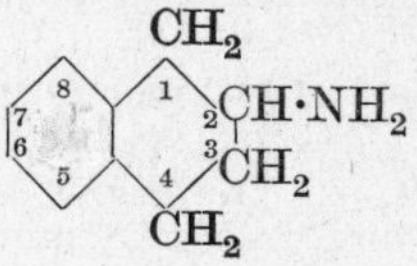

$C_{10}H_{13}N$ MW, 147

d-.

B,HCl : needles. M.p. 243–5°. $[\alpha]_D^{12}$ + 71·9° in H_2O.

N-*Acetyl* : needles from C_6H_6. M.p. 104–6°. $[\alpha]_D^{16·5}$ + 36·9° in C_6H_6.

N-*Benzoyl* : needles from Me_2CO. M.p. 155–7°. $[\alpha]_D^{19}$ + 58° in Me_2CO.

l-.

B,HCl : cryst. from Me_2CO. M.p. 243–5°. $[\alpha]_D^{16}$ − 69·7° in H_2O.

dl-.

B.p. 249°/710 mm. decomp., 140–140·5°/20 mm., 118·5°/8 mm. $D_4^{22·2}$ 1·0295. $n_D^{22·2}$ 1·56039. Sol. most org. solvents. Spar. sol. cold H_2O. Turns brown in air. Absorbs CO_2.

B,HCl : plates from H_2O. M.p. 237°.

N-*Me* : $C_{11}H_{15}N$. MW, 161. B.p. 118–119·8°/9 mm. D_4^{20} 1·024. Sol. most org. solvents. Spar. sol. H_2O. N-*Acetyl* : yellowish syrup. B.p. 190–210°/17 mm. Sol. most org. solvents. Spar. sol. H_2O.

N-*Di-Me* : $C_{12}H_{17}N$. MW, 175. Oil with strong violet fluor. B.p. 132·3–133·3°/11 mm. Sol. most org. solvents. Spar. sol. H_2O. *B,HCl* : leaflets. M.p. 214–15° decomp. *Methiodide* : cryst. from EtOH. M.p. 228°.

N-*Et* : $C_{12}H_{17}N$. MW, 175. B.p. 267°/724 mm., 153°/23 mm. Volatile in steam. *B,HCl* : needles. M.p. 223·5°. *Picrate* : orange-red needles from H_2O. M.p. 183·5°. N-*Acetyl* : b.p. 328°/718 mm. Sol. most org. solvents. Insol. H_2O.

N-*Formyl* : needles from C_6H_6. M.p. 61°.

Sol. EtOH, Et_2O, $CHCl_3$, C_6H_6. Insol. cold H_2O, ligroin.

N-*Acetyl* : needles from C_6H_6. M.p. 107·5°. Sol. $CHCl_3$, C_6H_6. Mod. sol. hot H_2O, EtOH. Spar. sol. Et_2O. Insol. ligroin.

N-*Benzoyl* : needles from C_6H_6. M.p. 150–1°. Sol. hot C_6H_6. Spar. sol. hot H_2O.

Bamberger, Müller, *Ber.*, 1889, **22**, 1301.
Waser, *Ber.*, 1916, **49**, 1203.
Waser, Möllering, *Organic Syntheses*, Collective Vol., I, 486.
I.G., D.R.P., 581,831, (*Chem. Abstracts*, 1934, **28**, 1059).

5 : 6 : 7 : 8-Tetrahydro-2-naphthylamine (ar-*Tetrahydro*-β-*naphthylamine*).

Needles from ligroin. M.p. 38°. B.p. 275–7°/713 mm. Sol. most org. solvents.

N-*Me* : b.p. 267·5°/210 mm. Sol. most org. solvents. Spar. sol. H_2O.

N-*Di-Me* : b.p. 287°/718 mm., 168°/23 mm. Reduces Ag salts.

N-*Et* : b.p. 291–3°. Sol. most org. solvents. Spar. sol. H_2O. Reduces hot $NH_3.AgNO_3$. *B,HCl* : needles. M.p. 173·5°.

N-*Di-Et* : b.p. 298°/709 mm., 167°/16 mm. Sol. most org. solvents. Spar. sol. H_2O.

N-*Acetyl* : needles. M.p. 107°. Sol. EtOH.

N-*Benzoyl* : m.p. 167°.

Picrate : m.p. 204°.

Bamberger, Müller, *Ber.*, 1889, **22**, 1304.
Bamberger, Kitschelt, *Ber.*, 1890, **23**, 882.
Cassella, D.R.P., 479,401, (*Chem. Abstracts*, 1929, **23**, 4710).
I.G., D.R.P., 581,831, (*Chem. Abstracts*, 1934, **28**, 1059).

Δ^3-Tetrahydronicotinic Acid.
See Guvacine.

Tetrahydropalmatine

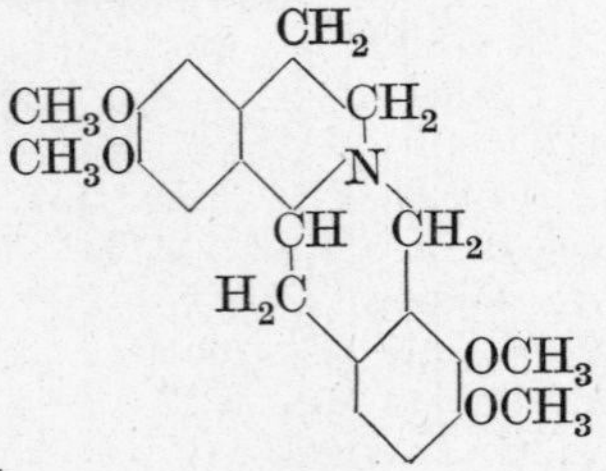

$C_{21}H_{25}O_4N$ MW, 355

d-.

Alkaloid from buds of *Corydalis cava*. M.p. 143°. $[\alpha]_D^{20}$ + 291° in EtOH. Turns yellow in air.

B,HCl : m.p. 266°.

l-.

M.p. 141–2°. $[\alpha]_D^{14}$ − 290·8° in EtOH.

dl-.

B,HCl : needles from H_2O. M.p. 215°.

B,HI : orange-yellow needles. M.p. 241° decomp.

B,HAuCl₄ : plates from EtOH.Aq. M.p. 201°.

B_2,H_2PtCl_6 : orange cryst. powder. M.p. 228°. decomp.

Methiodide : exists in two forms. (i) Cryst. from MeOH. M.p. 230°. (ii) M.p. 266° decomp.

Späth, Mosettig, Tröthandl, *Ber.*, 1923, **56**, 875.
Späth, Mosettig, *Ber.*, 1926, **59**, 1496.
Späth, Leithe, *Ber.*, 1930, **63**, 3007.
Haworth, Koepfli, Perkin, *J. Chem. Soc.*, 1927, 553.

1 : 2 : 3 : 4 - Tetrahydrophenanthrene (*Tetanthrene*)

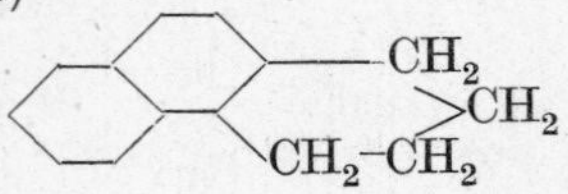

$C_{14}H_{14}$ MW, 182

Cryst. from MeOH. M.p. 33–4°. B.p. 173°/11 mm. D_4^{40} 1·0601. Sol. EtOH, Et_2O, $CHCl_3$, AcOH, C_6H_6, ligroin. Sol. 15 parts MeOH.

Picrate : reddish-yellow needles from EtOH. M.p. 111°.

Schroeter, Müller, Huang, *Ber.*, 1929, **62**, 652.

Tetrahydrophenol.
See Cyclohexenol.

Δ^1-Tetrahydrophthalic Acid (*Cyclohexene-1 : 2-dicarboxylic acid*)

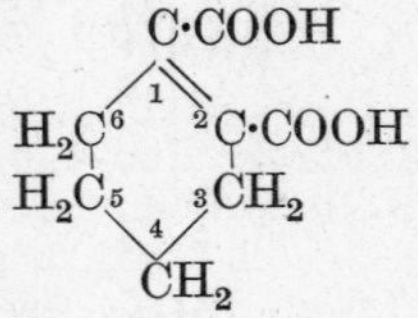

$C_8H_{10}O_4$ MW, 170

Plates from H_2O. Heat ⟶ anhydride before melting. Boil with alkalis ⟶ Δ^2-tetrahydrophthalic acid. Alk. $KMnO_4$ ⟶ adipic acid.

Di-Et ester : $C_{12}H_{18}O_4$. MW, 226. B.p. 160°/14 mm., 147°/10 mm. $D_4^{19\cdot2}$ 1·0803. $n_{He}^{19\cdot2}$ 1·47466.

Monoamide : $C_8H_{11}O_3N$. MW, 169. Needles from EtOH. Decomp. at 170° ⟶ Δ^1-tetrahydrophthalimide.

Anhydride : $C_8H_8O_3$. MW, 152. Plates from Et_2O. M.p. 74°. Sol. Et_2O.

Imide : $C_8H_9O_2N$. MW, 151. Cryst. from

EtOH, Et_2O, or ligroin. M.p. 169–70°. Sol. Me_2CO, $CHCl_3$.

Anil: leaflets or needles from AcOH. M.p. 137°. Sol. EtOH, AcOH, Me_2CO.

Monoanilide: cryst. M.p. 155° (rapid heat.). Sol. EtOH, Me_2CO. Spar. sol. C_6H_6. $FeCl_3 \longrightarrow$ pale green col.

Kon, Nandi, *J. Chem. Soc.*, 1933, 1633.
Hückel, Lampert, *Ber.*, 1934, **67**, 1812.
Baeyer, *Ann.*, 1890, **258**, 203.
Küster, *Z. physiol. Chem.*, 1908, **55**, 520.

Δ^2-Tetrahydrophthalic Acid (*Cyclohexene-1 : 6-dicarboxylic acid*).

Prisms. M.p. 215° (rapid heat.). Sol. 114 parts H_2O at 10°. k (first) $= 7{\cdot}4 \times 10^{-5}$ at 25°; (second) $= 3{\cdot}2 \times 10^{-7}$ at 100°. Above 220° $\longrightarrow$ anhydride.

Di-Et ester: b.p. 155°/12 mm. D_4^{20} 1·0760. n_D 1·4700.

Dichloride: $C_8H_8O_2Cl_2$. MW, 207. Yellow oil. B.p. 129°/14 mm.

Anhydride: prisms from Et_2O. M.p. 78–9°.

Imide: m.p. 172–3°. Sol. EtOH, Et_2O, $CHCl_3$, Me_2CO. Insol. cold H_2O.

See first reference above and also
Küster, *Z. physiol. Chem.*, 1908, **55**, 520.
Baeyer, *Ann.*, 1890, **258**, 199.
Kaufmann, Voss, *Ber.*, 1923, **56**, 2513.

Δ^3-Tetrahydrophthalic Acid (*Cyclohexene-3 : 4-dicarboxylic acid*).

Free acid not isolated. $k = 5{\cdot}81 \times 10^{-4}$ at 25°.

Anhydride: leaflets. M.p. 70°. Sol. EtOH. Spar. sol. H_2O.

p-*Methoxyanil*: leaflets. M.p. 88°.

Abati, de Bernardinis, *Gazz. chim. ital.*, 1906, **36**, ii, 824.

Δ^4-Tetrahydrophthalic Acid (*Cyclohexene-4 : 5-dicarboxylic acid*).

Cis:

Prisms from H_2O. M.p. 174° (166°). Sol. 108 parts H_2O at 6°.

Anhydride: cryst. from ligroin. M.p. 103–4° (58–9°). Sol. usual org. solvents. Spar. sol. ligroin, pet. ether.

Trans:

d-.

Powder. M.p. 165°. $[\alpha]_D^{25} + 115{\cdot}2°$.

Anhydride: leaflets. M.p. 128°. Sol. EtOH, C_6H_6. $[\alpha]_D^{25} + 6{\cdot}6°$ in EtOH.

l-.

Powder. M.p. 167°. Mod. sol. EtOH. $[\alpha]_D^{25} - 97{\cdot}4°$.

dl-.

Leaflets from H_2O. M.p. 215–18°. Sol. 690 parts H_2O at 6°.

Di-Me ester: $C_{10}H_{14}O_4$. MW, 198. M.p. 39–40°.

Anhydride: cryst. from C_6H_6–ligroin. M.p. 130° (141°).

Diels, Alder, *Ber.*, 1929, **62**, 2087; *Ann.*, 1928, **460**, 113.
Abati, de Horatio, *Gazz. chim. ital.*, 1909, **39**, i, 558.
Baeyer, *Ann.*, 1892, **269**, 203.
I.G., U.S.P., 1,944,731, (*Chem. Abstracts*, 1934, **28**, 2016).

1 : 4 : 5 : 6-Tetrahydro-α-picoline.

6-Methyl-1 : 2 : 3 : 4-tetrahydropyridine, *q.v.*

Tetrahydropyran (*Pentamethylene oxide, pyran tetrahydride*)

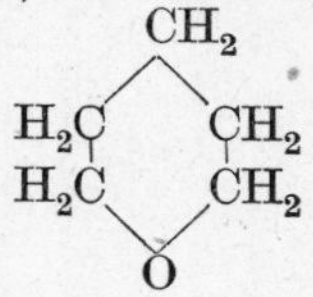

$C_5H_{10}O$ MW, 86

Liq. with characteristic odour. B.p. 88°/760 mm. $D_0^{18\cdot5}$ 0·883, D_4^{15} 0·8855. $n_D^{18\cdot5}$ 1·4195. Volatile in steam.

Clarke, *J. Chem. Soc.*, 1912, **101**, 1802.
Paul, *Bull. soc. chim.*, 1933, **53**, 1493.
Allen, Hibbert, *J. Am. Chem. Soc.*, 1934, **56**, 1398.

Tetrahydropyran-4-carboxylic Acid

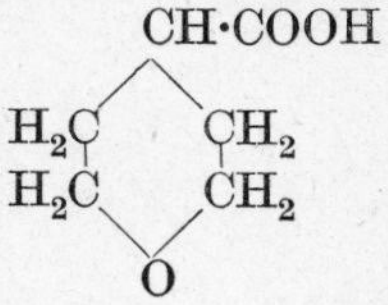

$C_6H_{10}O_3$ MW, 130

Cryst. from Et_2O. M.p. 87°. Sol. H_2O. Spar. sol. pet. ether.

Me ester: $C_7H_{12}O_3$. MW, 144. Liq. with pleasant odour. B.p. 80·5–81°/16 mm.

Et ester: $C_8H_{14}O_3$. MW, 158. B.p. 82·5°/12 mm.

Chloride: $C_6H_9O_2Cl$. MW, 148·5. B.p. 85–6°/16 mm.

Amide: $C_6H_{11}O_2N$. MW, 129. Plates from EtOH. M.p. 179°.

Nitrile: C_6H_9ON. MW, 111. B.p. 82–3°/10 mm. Very sol. H_2O.

Anilide: plates from EtOH. M.p. 163°. Almost insol. Et_2O.

Gibson, Johnson, *J. Chem. Soc.*, 1930, 2527.
v. Braun, Kohler, *Ber.*, 1917, **50**, 1658.

Tetrahydropyran-4 : 4-dicarboxylic Acid

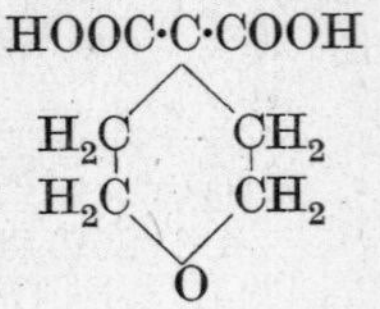

$C_7H_{10}O_5$ MW, 174

Leaflets from Et_2O–pet. ether. M.p. 172–3°. Sol. Et_2O. Spar. sol. pet. ether. Above m.p. ⟶ tetrahydropyran-4-carboxylic acid.
Di-Et ester: $C_{11}H_{18}O_5$. MW, 230. B.p. 152–5°/21 mm., 134–5°/12 mm.
Mononitrile: $C_7H_9O_3N$. MW, 155. Prisms from H_2O. M.p. 160–2°. Very sol. hot H_2O. *Et ester*: $C_9H_{13}O_3N$. MW, 183. B.p. 125°/16 mm. *Amide*: $C_7H_{10}O_2N_2$. MW, 154. Plates from EtOH. M.p. 158°.

See previous references.

Tetrahydropyrethrolone.
See 4-Methyl-3-*n*-amylcyclopentanolone-2.

Tetrahydropyrethrone.
See 3-Methyl-2-*n*-amylcyclopentanone.

1 : 2 : 3 : 4-Tetrahydropyridine (Δ^2-*Piperideine*)

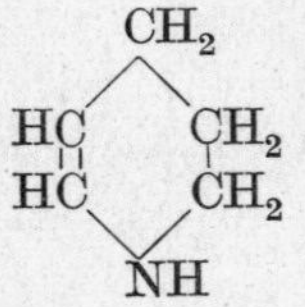

C_5H_9N MW, 83

Decomp. on boiling with formation of a dimer.
B,HCl: m.p. 230°.
B,HBr: m.p. 178°.
Acetyl: b.p. 219·5–220·5°. $D_4^{16\cdot5}$ 1·0531. Sol. usual org. solvents.
Dimer: cryst. M.p. 61°. Sol. EtOH, Et_2O, $CHCl_3$, AcOH, C_6H_6. Heat of comb. C_v 1532·7 Cal. Reduces Ag salts.

Lellmann, Schwaderer, *Ber.*, 1889, **22**, 1320.
Wolffenstein, *Ber.*, 1892, **25**, 2782.
Paal, Hubaleck, *Ber.*, 1901, **34**, 2761.

Δ^3 - Tetrahydropyridine - 3 - carboxylic Acid.
See Guvacine.

Tetrahydropyromucic Acid (*Tetrahydrofuran-2-carboxylic acid, tetrahydro-β-furoic acid*)

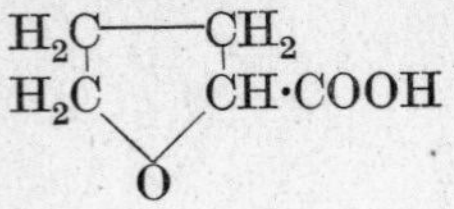

$C_5H_8O_3$ MW, 116

Cryst. M.p. 21°. B.p. 145°/25 mm., 131°/14 mm. D_{20}^{20} 1·1933. n_D^{19} 1·4585. $k = 1\cdot4 \times 10^{-4}$ at 25°.
Et ester: $C_7H_{12}O_3$. MW, 144. Liq. with pleasant fruity odour. B.p. 82°/11 mm. D_{20}^{20} 1·0792. n_D^{18} 1·4445. Sol. EtOH, Et_2O. Insol. H_2O.
Amide: $C_5H_9O_2N$. MW, 115. Leaflets from Et_2O. M.p. 80°. B.p. 135–40°/20 mm. Sol. H_2O, $CHCl_3$. Spar. sol. Et_2O.
Nitrile: C_5H_7ON. MW, 97. B.p. 80–2°/23 mm. n_D^{25} 1·4351.

Wienhaus, Sorge, *Ber.*, 1913, **46**, 1929.
Kaufmann, Adams, *J. Am. Chem. Soc.*, 1923, **45**, 3041.
Williams, *Ber.*, 1927, **60**, 2512.

Tetrahydro-α-pyrone.
See δ-Valerolactone.

Tetrahydro-γ-pyrone

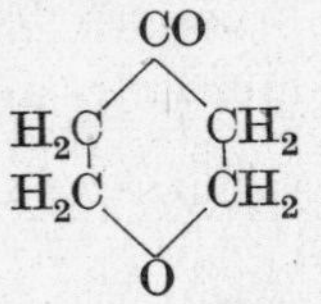

$C_5H_8O_2$ MW, 100

B.p. 163–6°/742 mm., 67–9°/18 mm. Misc. with H_2O. $D^{24\cdot5}$ 1·0795. $n_D^{24\cdot5}$ 1·4529.
Oxime: cryst. from EtOH. M.p. 87–8°.
Phenylsemicarbazone: needles from EtOH.Aq. M.p. 169°.

Borsche, *Ber.*, 1915, **48**, 683.
Borsche, Thiele, *Ber.*, 1923, **56**, 2012.
Cornubert, Robinet, *Bull. soc. chim.*, 1933, **53**, 565.

Tetrahydropyrrole.
See Pyrrolidine.

1 : 2 : 3 : 4-Tetrahydroquinaldine (2-*Methyl*-1 : 2 : 3 : 4-*tetrahydroquinoline*)

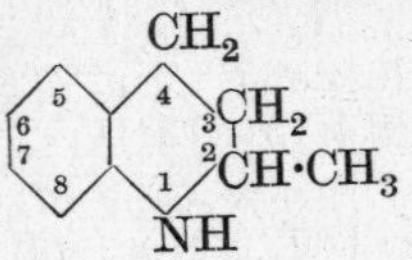

$C_{10}H_{13}N$ MW, 147

d-.
Oil. $[\alpha]_D^{20} + 58{\cdot}1°$.
B,HCl: plates + H_2O from EtOH. M.p.)6·5–197·5°. $[\alpha]_D^{21\cdot4} + 66{\cdot}1°$ in H_2O.
N-*Et*: $C_{12}H_{17}N$. MW, 175. B.p. 256°. D_4^{20} 9942. $[\alpha]_D^{20} + 12{\cdot}1°$.
N-*Benzoyl*: cryst. $[\alpha]_D^{18} - 247°$ in C_6H_6.

l-.
B.p. 158–9°/59 mm. $D_4^{14\cdot5}$ 1·0207. n_D^{24} 1·5705. isc. with usual org. solvents.
B,HCl: plates + H_2O from EtOH. M.p.)6·5–197·5°. $[\alpha]_D^{19} - 60{\cdot}4°$ in H_2O.
N-*Benzoyl*: cryst. from EtOH. M.p. 117·5–18°. Sol. C_6H_6. Mod. sol. EtOH. $[\alpha]_D^{25} + 324°$ C_6H_6.
N-o-*Nitrobenzoyl*: yellow needles from EtOH. .p. 110°. Sol. EtOH, Me_2CO, AcOH, C_6H_6. $]_D^{20} + 17{\cdot}1°$ in EtOH.
N-m-*Nitrobenzoyl*: needles from EtOH. M.p. 7°. $[\alpha]_D^{20} + 241{\cdot}6°$ in EtOH.
N-p-*Nitrobenzoyl*: yellowish cryst. from C_6H_6–et. ether. M.p. 110°. $[\alpha]_D^{20} + 369{\cdot}6°$ in EtOH.
N-p-*Toluenesulphonyl*: cryst. from EtOH. .p. 109°. $[\alpha]_D^{20} - 137°$ in EtOH.
Picrate: yellow plates or needles from EtOH. .p. 148–50°. $[\alpha]_D^{20} - 33{\cdot}0°$ in EtOH.

dl-.
B.p. 246–8°/709 mm., 115–16°/12 mm. D_4^{18} 0208. n_D^{22} 1·5727. Sol. EtOH, Et_2O, C_6H_6. par. sol. H_2O. Heat of comb. C_v 1380·6 Cal.
B,HCl: m.p. 190° (128–30°).
N-*Me*: $C_{11}H_{15}N$. MW, 161. B.p. 247–8°, 14°/28 mm. n_D^{19} 1·5678. Turns brown in air. *Iethiodide*: needles from EtOH. M.p. 205°.
N-*Et*: b.p. 256°.
N-*Benzoyl*: cryst. from AcOEt. M.p. 119·2° .16°). Sol. most org. solvents.
N-m-*Nitrobenzoyl*: pale yellow leaflets. M.p. 14°.
Picrate: prisms from EtOH. M.p. 153–4°.

Pope, Peachey, *J. Chem. Soc.*, 1899, **75**, 1082.
Pope, Winmill, *J. Chem. Soc.*, 1912, **101**, 2311.
v. Braun, Gmelin, Schultheiss, *Ber.*, 1923, **56**, 1344.
Tröger, Ungar, *J. prakt. Chem.*, 1926, **112**, 251.

5:6:7:8-Tetrahydroquinaldine (2-*Iethyl-5:6:7:8-tetrahydroquinoline*).
B.p. 225°/762 mm., 101–4°/12 mm. D_4^{16} ·0000. n_D^{23} 1·5310.
B,HCl: m.p. 164°.
B_2,H_2PtCl_6: m.p. 198°.

Methiodide: m.p. 118°. Hygroscopic.
Picrate: lemon-yellow cryst. M.p. 157° (154°).

See last two references above and also Basu, *Ann.*, 1934, **512**, 131.

Tetrahydroquinaldinic Acid.
See Tetrahydroquinoline-2-carboxylic Acid.

1:2:3:4-Tetrahydroquinazoline

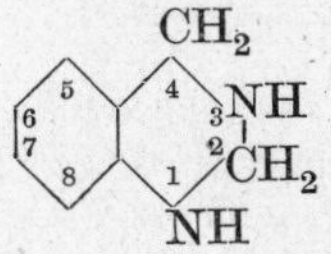

$C_8H_{10}N_2$ MW, 134

Leaflets from C_6H_6–ligroin, m.p. 78–9°: cryst. + H_2O from H_2O, m.p. 49–51°.
B,HCl: needles from EtOH. M.p. 193–5°.
B_2,H_2PtCl_6: orange-yellow needles. Does not melt below 270°.
3-N-*Allyl*: oil. B.p. 270–2°.
3-N-*Phenyl*: needles from EtOH. M.p. 119°.
3-N-o-*Tolyl*: cryst. from Et_2O. M.p. 140°.
3-N-p-*Tolyl*: needles from EtOH. M.p. 127°.

Busch, Dietz, *J. prakt. Chem.*, 1896, **53**, 418.
Busch, *J. prakt. Chem.*, 1895, **51**, 129.
Gabriel, *Ber.*, 1903, **36**, 811.

1:2:3:4-Tetrahydroquinoline (*Py-Tetrahydroquinoline*)

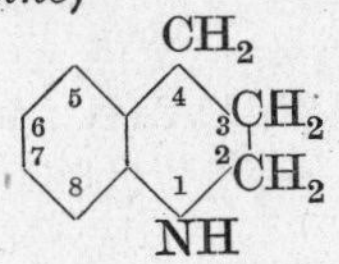

$C_9H_{11}N$ MW, 133

B.p. 249–50°/755 mm. $D_4^{23\cdot9}$ 1·0546. Heat of comb. C_v 1226·6 Cal. $n_D^{23\cdot9}$ 1·5933.
B,HCl: prisms from EtOH. M.p. 180–1°.
B,HBr: m.p. 167°.
B,HI: needles from MeOH. M.p. 170°.
N-*Allyl*: b.p. 264–6°/755 mm. *B,HI*: m.p. 141°.
N-*Benzyl*: needles from EtOH. M.p. 36–7°. B.p. 218–22°/38 mm.
N-o-*Nitrobenzyl*: m.p. 111°.
N-m-*Nitrobenzyl*: red prisms from EtOH. M.p. 99°.
N-p-*Nitrobenzyl*: light red cryst. from EtOH. M.p. 102°.
N-*Acetyl*: b.p. 295°.
N-*Benzoyl*: plates from EtOH. M.p. 76°.
N-*Me*: *see* Kairoline.

N-*Et* : *see* Kairoline A.

Hoffmann, Koenigs, *Ber.*, 1883, **16**, 728.
Wedekind, *Ber.*, 1902, **35**, 185.
Lellmann, Pekrun, *Ann.*, 1890, **259**, 50.
Skita, Meyer, *Ber.*, 1912, **45**, 3594.

5 : 6 : 7 : 8-Tetrahydroquinoline (Bz-*Tetrahydroquinoline*).

B.p. 222°. D_4^{22} 1·025. No col. with $FeCl_3$.
B_2,H_2PtCl_6 : yellow cryst. Decomp. at 210°.
Picrate : m.p. 157°.

v. Braun, Lemke, *Ann.*, 1930, **478**, 190.

1 : 2 : 3 : 4-Tetrahydroquinoline-2-carboxylic Acid (1 : 2 : 3 : 4-*Tetrahydroquinaldinic acid*)

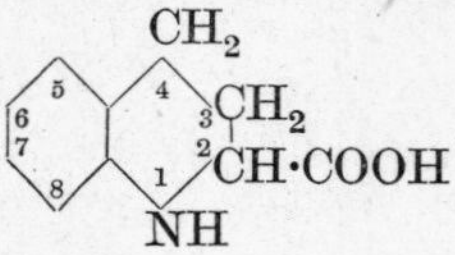

$C_{10}H_{11}O_2N$ MW, 177

Brownish-yellow cryst. from C_6H_6. M.p. 112–13°.
B,HCl : cryst. + $2H_2O$ from HCl.Aq. M.p. 115–20°, anhyd. 200° decomp.
Me ester : $C_{11}H_{13}O_2N$. MW, 191. B.p. 180°/15 mm. *B,HCl* : cryst. from MeOH–Et_2O. M.p. 191°.
N-*Nitroso* : needles from EtOH, AcOEt or C_6H_6. Decomp. at 132°.
N-*Acetyl* : prisms. M.p. 175–6°.
N-*Benzoyl* : m.p. 187–8°.

Wieland, Hettche, Hoshino, *Ber.*, 1928, **61**, 2377.

1 : 2 : 3 : 4-Tetrahydroquinoline-4-carboxylic Acid (1 : 2 : 3 : 4-*Tetrahydrocinchoninic acid*).

Free acid not isolated.
B,HCl : prisms + H_2O from H_2O. $FeCl_3$ ⟶ brownish-green col. ⟶ green on standing.
Me ester : cryst. from pet. ether. M.p. 88°.
N-*Nitroso* : reddish-yellow cryst. powder. M.p. 69–70°.
N-*Me* : kairoline-4-carboxylic acid. $C_{11}H_{13}O_2N$. MW, 191. Prisms + $2H_2O$ from EtOH. M.p. 169–70° decomp. Very sol. EtOH. Spar. sol. Et_2O, $CHCl_3$, C_6H_6. Bitter taste. *Anhydride* : oil. B.p. 279°/744 mm. Sol. EtOH, Et_2O. Insol. H_2O.
N-*Acetyl* : cryst. from H_2O. M.p. 164·5°. Spar. sol. cold H_2O, EtOH. Insol. Et_2O.
N-*Nitroso* : yellowish needles from H_2O. M.p. 137°. Sol. EtOH, hot H_2O. Less sol. Et_2O.

Weidel, *Monatsh.*, 1882, **3**, 61.
Weidel, Hazura, *Monatsh.*, 1884, **5**, 643.
v. Braun, Lemke, *Ann.*, 1930, **478**, 194.

5 : 6 : 7 : 8-Tetrahydroquinoline-4-carboxylic Acid (5 : 6 : 7 : 8-*Tetrahydrocinchonini acid*).

Cryst. from H_2O. M.p. 242° decomp. So H_2O. Spar. sol. EtOH. Long heating ⟶ 5 : 6 : 7 : 8-tetrahydroquinoline.

v. Braun, Lemke, *Ann.*, 1930, **478**, 190.

1 : 2 : 3 : 4-Tetrahydroquinoline-5-carboxylic Acid.

Needles or leaflets from EtOH.Aq. M.p 146–7°.
N-*Me* : kairoline-5-carboxylic acid. Needle from EtOH.Aq. M.p. 164°. Sol. EtOH. Les sol. Et_2O. Spar. sol. H_2O.
N-*Nitroso* : yellow prisms from EtOH.A M.p. 186° decomp.

Fischer, Körner, *Ber.*, 1884, **17**, 765.
Lellmann, Alt, *Ann.*, 1887, **237**, 315.

1 : 2 : 3 : 4-Tetrahydroquinoline-6-carboxylic Acid.

Needles. Decomp. about 170°. Sol. EtOH Et_2O. C_6H_6. Spar. sol. cold H_2O.
N-*Me* : kairoline-6-carboxylic acid. Cryst from C_6H_6. M.p. about 224° decomp. Sol EtOH. Less sol. Et_2O, C_6H_6. Spar. sol. col H_2O.
N-*Et* : leaflets from C_6H_6. M.p. about 200 decomp.
N-*Acetyl* : needles from H_2O. M.p. 187°. Sol EtOH, $CHCl_3$, C_6H_6. Less sol. hot H_2O. Insol Et_2O, ligroin.
N-*Nitroso* : yellowish prisms from C_6H_6 Decomp. about 181°.

Fischer, Endres, *Ber.*, 1902, **35**, 2613.
Kunckell, Vollhase, *Ber.*, 1909, **42**, 3198.

1 : 2 : 3 : 4-Tetrahydroquinoline-7-carboxylic Acid.

Leaflets from EtOH.Aq. M.p. 189°. Sol MeOH, EtOH, $CHCl_3$. Less sol. Et_2O, C_6H_6 Spar. sol. H_2O.
N-*Me* : kairoline-7-carboxylic acid. Cryst from C_6H_6. M.p. 185°.
N-*Et* : prisms from C_6H_6. M.p. 163–4°.
N-*Nitroso* : yellowish prisms from C_6H_6 Decomp. at 191°.

Fischer, Endres, *Ber.*, 1902, **35**, 2612.

1 : 2 : 3 : 4-Tetrahydroquinoline-8-carboxylic Acid.

Needles from ligroin or EtOH.Aq. M.p 163°. Sol. EtOH, Et_2O, $CHCl_3$, C_6H_6, CS_2 Very spar. sol. hot H_2O. Neutral or alkalin sols. show blue fluor. Sublimes.

N-*Me* : kairoline-8-carboxylic acid. Needles from C_6H_6. M.p. 218–19°.
N-*Et* : leaflets from EtOH.Aq. M.p. 196–7°.
N-*Nitroso* : plates from C_6H_6. Decomp. about 124°.

Fischer, Endres, *Ber.*, 1902, **35**, 2611.
Tafel, *Ber.*, 1894, **27**, 825.

1 : 2 : 3 : 4-Tetrahydroquinoxaline (*Ethylene-o-phenylenediamine*)

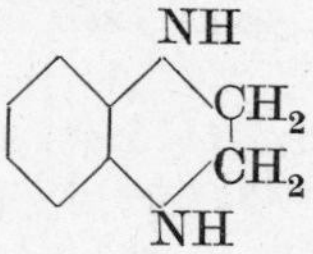

$C_8H_{10}N_2$ MW, 134

Leaflets from H_2O, Et_2O or pet. ether. M.p. 96·5–97°. B.p. 288·5–289·5°. Very sol. Et_2O. Sol. EtOH, $CHCl_3$, C_6H_6, hot H_2O. Spar. sol. boiling pet. ether. Alk. $K_3Fe(CN)_6$ ⟶ quinoxaline. $FeCl_3$ ⟶ violet col. with conc. sols., blue with dilute.
N-*Me* : $C_9H_{12}N_2$. MW, 148. Pale yellow oil. Sol. EtOH, Et_2O, C_6H_6, $CHCl_3$, pet. ether. Spar. sol. boiling H_2O. $FeCl_3$ ⟶ blue col.
N : N′-*Diacetyl* : cryst. from Et_2O. M.p. 144°. B.p. 350° decomp. Sol. H_2O. Mod. sol. EtOH, $CHCl_3$, C_6H_6. Spar. sol. Et_2O.
N : N′-*Dibenzenesulphonyl* : cryst. from AcOH. M.p. 180°.
N : N′-*Dinitroso* : pale yellow microneedles from $CHCl_3$–ligroin. M.p. 168° decomp.

I.G., D.R.P., 495,101, (*Chem. Abstracts*, 1930, **24**, 3251).
Hinsberg, Strupler, *Ann.*, 1895, **287**, 225.
Ris, *Ber.*, 1888, **21**, 378.
Merz, Ris, *Ber.*, 1887, **20**, 1191, 1196.

Tetrahydrosantonin.
See Santonan.
Tetrahydrosantoninic Acid.
See Santonanic Acid.
4 : 5 : 6 : 7-Tetrahydroskatole (3-*Methyl*-4 : 5 : 6 : 7-*tetrahydroindole*)

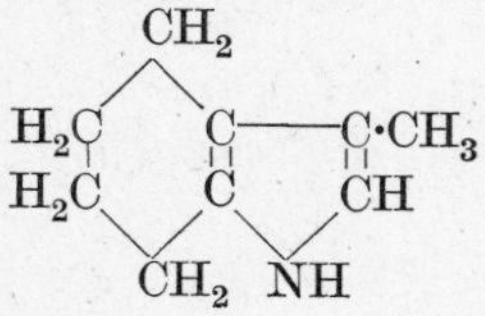

$C_9H_{13}N$ MW, 135

B.p. 105°/12 mm. D_4^{14} 0·9698.

v. Braun, Bayer, Blessing, *Ber.*, 1924, **57**, 400.

Δ¹-Tetrahydroterephthalic Acid (*Cyclohexene*-1 : 4-*dicarboxylic acid*)

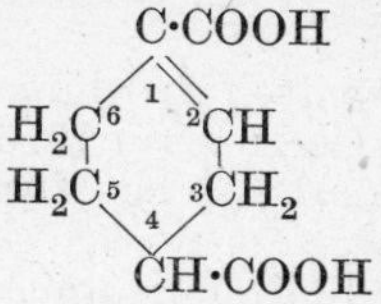

$C_8H_{10}O_4$ MW, 170

Prisms from H_2O. Does not melt below 300°. Sol. 4066 parts cold H_2O. Sublimes. k (first) = $5·0 \times 10^{-5}$ at 25°; (second) = $2·8 \times 10^{-6}$ at 100°. Heat of comb. C_v 882·8 Cal. Alk. $KMnO_4$ ⟶ oxalic acid.
Di-Me ester : $C_{10}H_{14}O_4$. MW, 198. Needles from H_2O. M.p. 39° (37°). B.p. 153·3–154·5°/20 mm., 147°/9 mm. Very sol. most solvents. Heat of comb. C_v 1226 Cal.
Di-l-menthyl ester : needles from EtOH. M.p. 125°. $[\alpha]_D^{20}$ − 69·4° in $CHCl_3$.
Diphenyl ester : plates from AcOEt or Me_2CO. M.p. 145°. Sol. EtOH, Et_2O, $CHCl_3$, ligroin.

Rupe, *Ann.*, 1910, **373**, 123.
Baeyer, *Ann.*, 1888, **245**, 159.

Δ²-Tetrahydroterephthalic Acid (*Cyclohexene*-3 : 6-*dicarboxylic acid*).

Cis :
Plates from H_2O. M.p. 150·5°. Sol. 37 parts cold H_2O.
Trans :
Rhombohedra from H_2O. M.p. 220°. Sol. 588 parts cold H_2O. Very sol. hot H_2O.
Di-Me ester : plates or prisms from ligroin. M.p. 3°.
Diphenyl ester : plates from C_6H_6–ligroin. M.p. 107°.
Dibenzyl ester : cryst. from EtOH. M.p. 48°.

See first reference above and also
Baeyer, *Ann.*, 1889, **251**, 279, 306.
Baeyer, Herb, *Ann.*, 1890, **258**, 39.

Tetrahydrothiazine.
See 1 : 4-Thiazan.
Tetrahydrothiophene (*Tetramethylene sulphide*)

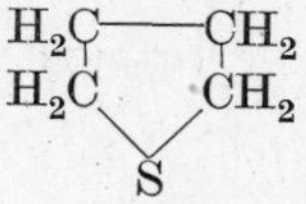

C_4H_8S MW, 88

Mobile liq. with penetrating odour. B.p. 118–19°. D_4^{18} 0·9607. n_D^{18} 1·4871. Volatile in steam. Misc. with most solvents except H_2O. $KMnO_4$ ⟶ sulphone, m.p. 20–1° (8–10°), b.p.

285–8°/743 mm., 153–4°/18 mm., 149·5–150°/15 mm. Forms add. comp. with one mol. $HgCl_2$, needles, m.p. 124·5–125·5°.

Grischkewitsch-Trochimowski, *J. Russ. Phys.-Chem. Soc.*, 1916, **48**, 901.
Bost, Conn, *Chem. Abstracts*, 1933, **27**, 5323.
Backer, Bolt, *Rec. trav. chim.*, 1935, **54**, 539.

Tetrahydrothiophene-2-carboxylic Acid

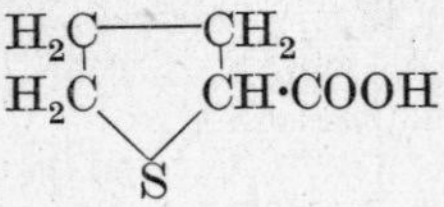

$C_5H_8O_2S$ MW, 132

Plates from H_2O. M.p. 51°. Very sol. H_2O, EtOH. Spar. sol. Et_2O. Heat of comb. C_v 753·3 Cal. $k = 1·15 \times 10^{-4}$ at 25°. Volatile in steam. Reduces boiling $NH_3.AgNO_3$.
Me ester: $C_6H_{10}O_2S$. MW, 146. B.p. 206°.

Ernst, *Ber.*, 1887, **20**, 518.

Tetrahydrothiophene-2 : 5-dicarboxylic Acid

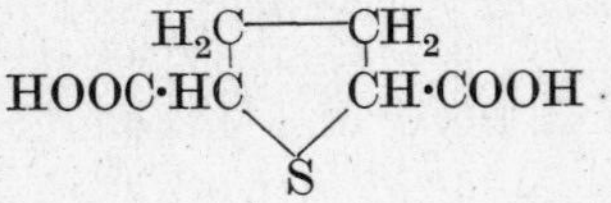

$C_6H_8O_4S$ MW, 176

Plates. M.p. 162°. Sol. H_2O. Less sol. Et_2O. Reduces warm $NH_3.AgNO_3$.

Ernst, *Ber.*, 1886, **19**, 3275.

Tetrahydrothiopyran.
See Pentamethylene sulphide.
Tetrahydrothiotolene.
See Methyltetrahydrothiophene.
Tetrahydrotoluene.
See Methylcyclohexene.
Δ^1-Tetrahydro-*o*-toluic Acid (2-*Methylcyclohexene*-1-*carboxylic acid*)

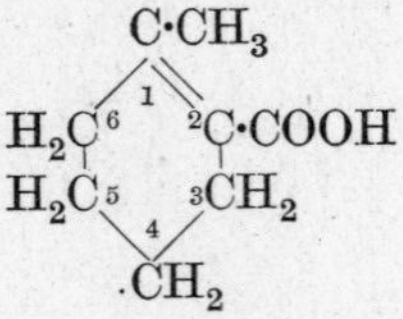

$C_8H_{12}O_2$ MW, 140

Needles from H_2O. M.p. 87° (79–80°). Sol. EtOH, Me_2CO, pet. ether. Spar. sol. H_2O. Ox. ⟶ 3-acetobutyric acid.
Et ester: $C_{10}H_{16}O_2$. MW, 168. B.p. 148°/100 mm.

Kay, Perkin, *J. Chem. Soc.*, 1905, **87**, 1068.
Mazza, di Mase, *Gazz. chim. ital.*, 1927, **57**, 300.

Δ^2-Tetrahydro-*o*-toluic Acid (6-*Methylcyclohexene*-1-*carboxylic acid*).
Cryst. from pet. ether. M.p. 80°.

Mazza, Cremona, *Gazz. chim. ital.*, 1927, **57**, 318.

Δ^3-Tetrahydro-*o*-toluic Acid (4-*Methylcyclohexene*-3-*carboxylic acid*).
Cis:
B.p. 145–6°/20 mm. Ox. ⟶ *trans*-form.
Et ester: b.p. 143–4°/100 mm.
Trans:
M.p. 60–2°. B.p. 162–3°/50 mm.
Et ester: b.p. 144–6°/100 mm.

Perkin, *J. Chem. Soc.*, 1911, **99**, 744.

Δ^4-Tetrahydro-*o*-toluic Acid (5-*Methylcyclohexene*-4-*carboxylic acid*).
Thick syrup. B.p. 180–1°/100 mm., 143°/20 mm., 135°/12 mm. Ox. ⟶ methylbutane-1 : 2 : 4-tricarboxylic acid.
Et ester: b.p. 140°/100 mm.

Perkin, *J. Chem. Soc.*, 1911, **99**, 754.

Δ^5-Tetrahydro-*o*-toluic Acid (3-*Methylcyclohexene*-4-*carboxylic acid*).
B.p. 139°/20 mm., 114–30°/9 mm.
Et ester: b.p. 204–8°, 138–9°/100 mm.

Perkin, *J. Chem. Soc.*, 1911, **99**, 735.
Skita, Ardan, Krauss, *Ber.*, 1908, **41**, 2944.

Δ^6-Tetrahydro-*o*-toluic Acid (2-*Methylcyclohexene*-3-*carboxylic acid*).
B.p. 140–2°/20 mm.

Perkin, *J. Chem. Soc.*, 1911, **99**, 738.

Δ^1-Tetrahydro-*m*-toluic Acid (1-*Methylcyclohexene*-3-*carboxylic acid*)

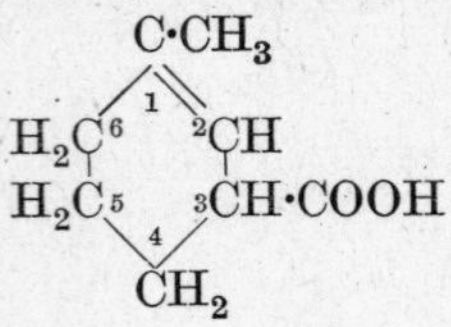

$C_8H_{12}O_2$ MW, 140

l-.
$[\alpha]_D$ — 49·7° in AcOEt.
Me ester: $C_9H_{14}O_2$. MW, 154. B.p. 144–7°/100 mm.

dl-.

B.p. 140–2°/20 mm., 123°/7 mm. Ox. ⟶ adipic acid + 4-aceto-*n*-valeric acid.

Et ester: $C_{10}H_{16}O_2$. MW, 168. B.p. 128°/60 mm.

Perkin, Tattersall, *J. Chem. Soc.*, 1907, **91**, 496.
Haworth, Perkin, *J. Chem. Soc.*, 1913, **103**, 2237.
Boorman, Linstead, *J. Chem. Soc.*, 1935, 264.

Δ^2-Tetrahydro-*m*-toluic Acid (*3-Methylcyclohexene-1-carboxylic acid*).

M.p. 26°. B.p. 150°/11 mm., 130°/7 mm. Spar. sol. H_2O. Ox. ⟶ 1-methyladipic acid.

See last reference above and also
Perkin, Tattersall, *J. Chem. Soc.*, 1905, **87**, 1095.

Δ^3-Tetrahydro-*m*-toluic Acid (*5-Methylcyclohexene-1-carboxylic acid*).

d-.

M.p. 62–4°. $[\alpha]_D$ + 40·1° in AcOEt. Volatile in steam.

Et ester: b.p. 150–1°/100 mm. $[\alpha]_D$ + 32·5° in AcOEt.

l-.

$[\alpha]_D$ − 35·8° in AcOEt.

dl-.

Plates from formic acid. M.p. 60°. B.p. 155–60°/25 mm. Very sol. most solvents. Ox. ⟶ 2-methyladipic acid.

Et ester: b.p. 146–8°/100 mm., 105°/11 mm. D_4^{18} 0·9762. n_{He}^{20} 1·4695.

Auwers, *Ann.*, 1923, **432**, 98.
Perkin, Tattersall, *J. Chem. Soc.*, 1905, **87**, 1093.
Luff, Perkin, *J. Chem. Soc.*, 1910, **97**, 2151.

Δ^4-Tetrahydro-*m*-toluic Acid (*5-Methylcyclohexene-3-carboxylic acid*).

B.p. 143–6°/20 mm.

Et ester: b.p. 142–4°/100 mm.

Perkin, *J. Chem. Soc.*, 1910, **97**, 2146.

Δ^5-Tetrahydro-*m*-toluic Acid (*6-Methylcyclohexene-4-carboxylic acid*).

d-.

B.p. 142–5°/20 mm. $[\alpha]_D^{16}$ + 33° in AcOEt.

Et ester: b.p. 140–1°/100 mm. $[\alpha]_D^{16}$ + 30·5° in AcOEt.

l-.

B.p. 142°/20 mm. $[\alpha]_D^{15}$ — 30·9° in AcOEt.

Et ester: b.p. 140–2°/100 mm. $[\alpha]_D^{15}$ — 27·4° in AcOEt.

dl-.

B.p. 177–80°/100 mm., 145°/20 mm.

Et ester: b.p. 141–3°/100 mm.

Perkin, *J. Chem. Soc.*, 1910, **97**, 2139.

Δ^6-Tetrahydro-*m*-toluic Acid (*2-Methylcyclohexene-4-carboxylic acid*).

d-.

B.p. 138–40°/18 mm. $[\alpha]_D$ + 108° in AcOEt.

l-.

$[\alpha]_D$ − 98·6° in AcOEt.

dl-.

B.p. 184–6°/100 mm.

Et ester: b.p. 146°/100 mm.

Fisher, Perkin, *J. Chem. Soc.*, 1908, **93**, 1886.
Haworth, Perkin, *J. Chem. Soc.*, 1913, **103**, 2233.

Δ^1-Tetrahydro-*p*-toluic Acid (*1-Methylcyclohexene-4-carboxylic acid*)

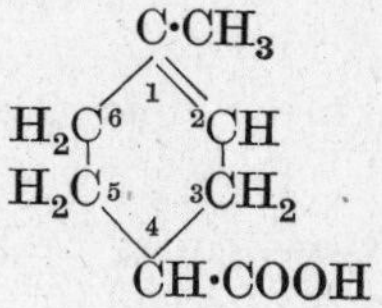

$C_8H_{12}O_2$ MW, 140

d-.

M.p. about 99°. $[\alpha]_D$ + 55°.

Et ester: $C_{10}H_{16}O_2$. MW, 168. B.p. 145–7°/100 mm. $[\alpha]_D$ + 50°.

l-.

Cryst. from pet. ether. M.p. about 99°. $[\alpha]_D$ − 58°.

Et ester: b.p. 145–7°/100 mm. $[\alpha]_D$ − 52°.

dl-.

Needles from H_2O. M.p. 99°. B.p. 140–5°/15 mm. Sol. AcOH. Spar. sol. H_2O. Conc. H_2SO_4 ⟶ *p*-toluic acid.

Et ester: b.p. 155–7°/100 mm., 105–8°/12 mm.

Chloride: $C_8H_{11}OCl$. MW, 158·5. B.p. 110–14°/40 mm., 90°/19 mm.

Amide: $C_8H_{13}ON$. MW, 139. Needles or leaflets from H_2O. M.p. 182°.

Lehmann, Paasche, *Ber.*, 1935, **68**, 1069.
Meldrum, Perkin, *J. Chem. Soc.*, 1908, **93**, 1424.

Δ³-Tetrahydro-*p*-toluic Acid (4-*Methylcyclohexene*-1-*carboxylic acid*).

d-.
Prisms from H_2O. M.p. 136–7° (133°). $[\alpha]_D$ + 100·1° in AcOEt.
Et ester: b.p. 154°/100 mm. $[\alpha]_D$ + 86·5°. D_{20}^{20} 0·9757. n_D^{20} 1·4688.

l-.
Prisms from AcOEt. M.p. 133–4°. Sol. AcOH, AcOEt, pet. ether. Spar. sol. cold EtOH. $[\alpha]_D^{17}$ − 100·8° in AcOEt.
Et ester: b.p. 154°/100 mm. $[\alpha]_D^{18}$ − 83·5°.

dl-.
Prismatic needles from AcOH.Aq. M.p. 132–4°. Very sol. EtOH, Et_2O, AcOH, $CHCl_3$, C_6H_6. Less sol. cold CS_2, ligroin.
Et ester: b.p. 152–3°/100 mm. D_{15}^{15} 0·9792. n_α^{15} 1·4659.
Amide: leaflets from EtOH.Aq. M.p. 148°. Sol. EtOH. Spar. sol. H_2O.

Einhorn, Willstätter, *Ann.*, 1894, **280**, 163.
Perkin, Pickles, *J. Chem. Soc.*, 1905, **87**, 645.
Kay, Perkin, *J. Chem. Soc.*, 1906, **89**, 844.
Chou, Perkin, *J. Chem. Soc.*, 1911, **99**, 534.

Δ¹-Tetrahydro-*o*-toluic Aldehyde (2-*Methylcyclohexene*-1-*aldehyde*)

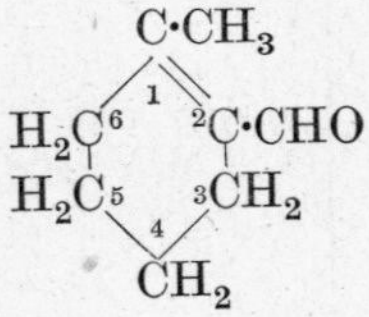

$C_8H_{12}O$ MW, 124

Needles. M.p. 98–101°. B.p. 75–6°/12 mm.
Semicarbazone: cryst. from MeOH. M.p. 208–12°. Insol. H_2O.
p-*Nitrophenylhydrazone*: cryst. from AcOH. M.p. 160–3°.

Bernhauer, Neubauer, *Biochem. Z.*, 1932, **251**, 173.

Δ⁴-Tetrahydro-*o*-toluic Aldehyde (5-*Methylcyclohexene*-4-*aldehyde*).
Liq. B.p. 83°/38 mm., 75°/22 mm.
Semicarbazone: m.p. 168°.

Diels, Alder, *Ann.*, 1929, **470**, 85.
I.G., U.S.P., 1,944,731, (*Chem. Abstracts*, 1934, **28**, 2016).

Δ²-Tetrahydro-*m*-toluic Aldehyde (3-*Methylcyclohexene*-1-*aldehyde*)

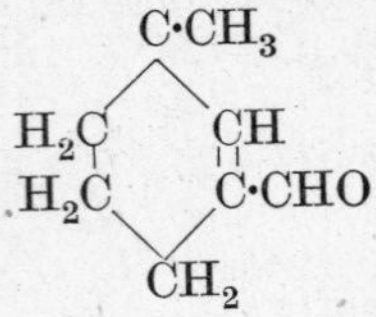

$C_8H_{12}O$ MW, 124

Semicarbazone: m.p. 206–7°. Spar. sol. most solvents.

Wallach, *Ann.*, 1906, **347**, 344.

Δ¹-Tetrahydro-*p*-toluic Aldehyde (1-*Methylcyclohexene*-4-*aldehyde*)

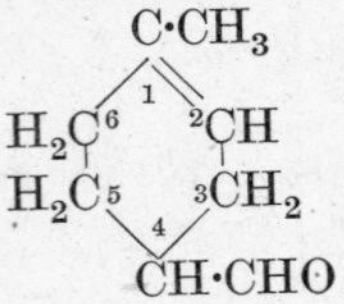

$C_8H_{12}O$ MW, 124

B.p. 63–4°/10 mm.
Semicarbazone: m.p. 146°.

Diels, Alder, *Ann.*, 1929, **470**, 87.
See also Lehmann, Paasche, *Ber.*, 1935, **68**, 1068.

Δ³-Tetrahydro-*p*-toluic Aldehyde (4-*Methylcyclohexene*-1-*aldehyde*).
Semicarbazone: m.p. 192–4°.

Wallach, Evans, *Ann.*, 1906, **347**, 346.

Tetrahydrotoluquinoline.
See 6-, 7-, and 8-Methyltetrahydroquinolines.
Tetrahydrotolylacetic Acid.
See Methylcyclohexenylacetic Acid.
Tetrahydrotubanol.
See 2-Isoamylresorcinol.
2 : 3 : 4 : 5-Tetrahydroxyacetophenone

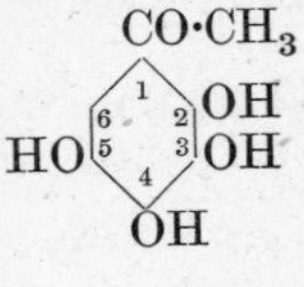

$C_8H_8O_5$ MW, 184

3 : 4-*Di-Me ether*: $C_{10}H_{12}O_5$. MW, 212. Yellow needles from Et_2O. M.p. 119–21°. Sol. EtOH, $CHCl_3$, C_6H_6. Conc. H_2SO_4 ⟶ yellow sol.

Bargellini, *Gazz. chim. ital.*, 1916, **46**, i, 253.

2 : 3 : 4 : 6-Tetrahydroxyacetophenone.
Pale yellow needles from EtOH or AcOH.Aq. M.p. 204–5°.
3 : 4-*Di-Me ether* : needles from EtOH.Aq. M.p. 166–8° (162–3°). Conc. H_2SO_4 ⟶ orange-yellow sol.
2 : 3 : 4-*Tri-Me ether* : $C_{11}H_{14}O_5$. MW, 226. Needles from EtOH. M.p. 164–5°.
3 : 4 : 6-*Tri-Me ether* : cubes from EtOH. M.p. 112–13° (125–6°). *Acetyl* : m.p. 106°. *Benzoyl* : m.p. 120–2°.
Tetra-Me ether : $C_{12}H_{16}O_5$. MW, 240. Needles from EtOH.Aq. M.p. 53–4° (43–5°). B.p. 310°. *Oxime* : m.p. 103–5°. *Semicarbazone* : m.p. 128–30°.
Phenylhydrazone : red prismatic needles. M.p. 248–51° decomp.

Bargellini, Bini, *Gazz. chim. ital.*, 1911, **41**, ii, 18.
Bargellini, Zoras, *Gazz. chim. ital.*, 1934, **64**, 192.
Bargellini, *Gazz. chim. ital.*, 1919, **49**, ii, 47.
Nierenstein, *J. Chem. Soc.*, 1917, **111**, 6.

Tetrahydroxyacetophenone.
See also Trihydroxyphenacyl Alcohol.
Tetrahydroxyadipic Acid.
See Mucic Acid, Allomucic Acid, *and* Saccharic Acid.
Tetrahydroxy-1-aminocaproic Acid.
See Glucosaminic Acid.
1 : 2 : 5 : 10-Tetrahydroxyanthracene (1 : 5 : 6-*Trihydroxyanthrone*, 1 : 5 : 6-*trihydroxyanthranol*)

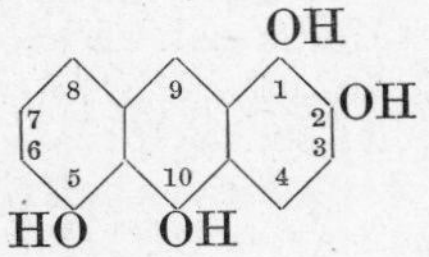

$C_{14}H_{10}O_4$ MW, 242

Cryst. from EtOH.Aq. M.p. 258°.
Mono-Me ether : $C_{15}H_{12}O_4$. MW, 256. Cryst. from EtOH. M.p. 140°.

Graebe, Thode, *Ann.*, 1906, **349**, 218.

1 : 2 : 6 : 10-Tetrahydroxyanthracene (2 : 5 : 6-*Trihydroxyanthrone*, 2 : 5 : 6-*trihydroxyanthranol*).
Yellow cryst. M.p. 258°. NaOH ⟶ reddish-yellow sol. Conc. H_2SO_4 ⟶ brownish-yellow sol.
Tri-Me ether : $C_{17}H_{16}O_4$. MW, 284. Needles from C_6H_6. M.p. 169–70°. Sol. hot C_6H_6. Mod. sol. hot EtOH, AcOH.
Tetra-acetyl : m.p. 250–60°.

Bayer, D.R.P., 117,923, (*Chem. Zentr.*, 1901, I, 600).
Graebe, Thode, *Ann.*, 1906, **349**, 214.
Bistrzycki, Yssel de Schepper, *Ber.*, 1898, **31**, 2799.

1 : 2 : 7 : 10-Tetrahydroxyanthracene (3 : 4 : 6-*Trihydroxyanthrone*, 3 : 4 : 6-*trihydroxyanthranol*).
Yellow needles.
1 : 2 : 7-*Tri-Me ether* : needles from EtOH. M.p. 149°. *Acetyl* : needles. M.p. 127°.
Tetra-acetyl : needles from EtOH. M.p. 167°.

MacMaster, Perkin, *J. Chem. Soc.*, 1927, 1309.
Graebe, Bernhard, *Ann.*, 1906, **349**, 227.
Liebermann, *Ber.*, 1888, **21**, 443.

1 : 2 : 9 : 10-Tetrahydroxyanthracene (1 : 2 : 10-*Trihydroxyanthrone*, 1 : 2 : 10-*trihydroxyanthranol*, 1 : 2-*dihydroxyanthrahydroquinone*, *leuco-alizarin*).
Brown leaflets from AcOH. M.p. 150°. Very sol. EtOH with yellow col. Conc. H_2SO_4 ⟶ brown col. ⟶ red on standing. NaOH ⟶ red sol.

Grandmougin, *J. prakt. Chem.*, 1907, **76**, 141.

1 : 3 : 9 : 10-Tetrahydroxyanthracene (*Dihydropurpuroxanthin*, *leuco-purpuroxanthin*, 1 : 3 : 10-*trihydroxyanthrone*, 1 : 3 : 10-*trihydroxyanthranol*, 1 : 3-*dihydroxyanthrahydroquinone*).
Pale yellow needles. Sol. Et_2O. NaOH ⟶ brown sol. Oxidises in air to purpuroxanthin.

Rosenstiehl, *Ann. chim. phys.*, 1879, **18**, 230.

1 : 4 : 9 : 10-Tetrahydroxyanthracene (*Dihydroquinizarin*, *leuco-quinizarin*, 1 : 4 : 10-*trihydroxyanthrone*, 1 : 4 : 10-*trihydroxyanthranol*, 1 : 4-*dihydroxyanthrahydroquinone*).
Yellow needles. M.p. 156° (131–6°). Alkalis ⟶ red sols. Sol. EtOH, AcOH with yellow col. and weak blue fluor. Conc. H_2SO_4 ⟶ yellow sol.
Tetra-acetyl : pale yellow cryst. from AcOH. M.p. 240–2°.

M.L.B., D.R.P., 207,668, (*Chem. Zentr.*, 1909, I, 1287).
Zahn, Ochwat, *Ann.*, 1928, **462**, 72.
Meyer, Sander, *Ann.*, 1920, **420**, 123.

2 : 3 : 6 : 7-Tetrahydroxyanthracene.
Tetra-Me ether: $C_{18}H_{18}O_4$. MW, 298. Cryst. from EtOH. M.p. 173°. Most sols. show blue fluor.

Robinson, *J. Chem. Soc.*, 1915, **107**, 272.

2 : 3 : 9 : 10-Tetrahydroxyanthracene (*Dihydrohystazarin*, 2 : 3 : 9-*trihydroxyanthrone*, 2 : 3 : 9-*trihydroxyanthranol*, *leuco-hystazarin*).
Tetra-acetyl: needles from EtOH. M.p. 217–19°.

Schöller, *Ber.*, 1889, **22**, 684.

2 : 6 : 9 : 10-Tetrahydroxyanthracene (*Dihydroanthraflavic acid*, 2 : 6 : 10-*trihydroxyanthrone*, 2 : 6 : 10-*trihydroxyanthranol*, *leuco-anthraflavic acid*).
Tetra-acetyl: needles. M.p. 274°.

Liebermann, *Ber.*, 1888, **21**, 1173.

2 : 7 : 9 : 10-Tetrahydroxyanthracene (*Dihydroisoanthraflavic acid*, 2 : 7 : 10-*trihydroxyanthrone*, 2 : 7 : 10-*trihydroxyanthranol*, *leuco-isoanthraflavic acid*).
Tetra-acetyl: needles. M.p. 235–40°.

Liebermann, *Ber.*, 1888, **21**, 1173.

1 : 2 : 3 : 4-Tetrahydroxyanthraquinone

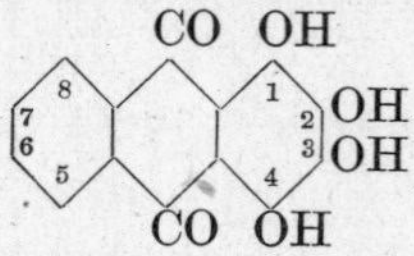

$C_{14}H_8O_6$ MW, 272

Green needles. Conc. H_2SO_4 ⟶ red sol. KOH ⟶ red sol.
Tetra-acetyl: yellow needles. M.p. 205°. Sol. boiling KOH with violet-red col.

Slama, *Chem. Zentr.*, 1899, II, 966.
Bayer, D.R.P., 125,579, (*Chem. Zentr.*, 1901, II, 1188).

1 : 2 : 3 : 5-Tetrahydroxyanthraquinone (*α-Hydroxyanthragallol*).
Yellow needles from EtOH. Does not melt below 350°. Sol. EtOH, Me_2CO, AcOH. Spar. sol. Et_2O, $CHCl_3$, C_6H_6. Insol. H_2O. Conc. H_2SO_4 ⟶ violet sol.
Tetra-acetyl: needles from AcOH. M.p. 207–9°.

Liebermann, Kostanecki, *Ann.*, 1888, **244**, 360; 1887, **240**, 270.

1 : 2 : 3 : 7-Tetrahydroxyanthraquinone (*β-Hydroxyanthragallol*).
Red needles from EtOH. M.p. 380°. Sol. EtOH, Me_2CO, AcOH. Spar. sol. H_2O, Et_2O. Insol. $CHCl_3$, C_6H_6. Conc. H_2SO_4 ⟶ brownish-yellow sol. Sublimes slowly with decomp.
Tetra-acetyl: yellow plates from AcOH. M.p. 189°. Sol. EtOH, $CHCl_3$, AcOH.

Liebermann, Kostanecki, Noah, *Ann.* 1888, **244**, 360; 1887, **240**, 271.

1 : 2 : 4 : 6-Tetrahydroxyanthraquinone (*Hydroxyflavopurpurin*).
Cryst. Sol. EtOH, Py. Less sol. AcOH. Conc. H_2SO_4 ⟶ bluish-red sol.
Tetra-acetyl: m.p. 202°.

Dimroth, Fick, *Ann.*, 1916, **411**, 324.
Bayer, D.R.P., 67,061.

1 : 2 : 4 : 7-Tetrahydroxyanthraquinone (*Hydroxyanthrapurpurin*).
Cryst. from EtOH, Py, or AcOH. Sol. EtOH, AcOH. NaOH ⟶ bluish-red sol. Conc. H_2SO_4 ⟶ cherry-red sol.
2 : 7-*Diacetyl*: orange needles from AcOH. M.p. 224–5°. Sol. AcOEt.
Tetra-acetyl: m.p. 214·5°.

Dimroth, Friedemann, Kammerer, *Ber.*, 1920, **53**, 483.
Dimroth, Fick, *Ann.*, 1916, **411**, 328.
Bayer, D.R.P., 67,061.

1 : 2 : 5 : 6-Tetrahydroxyanthraquinone. *See* Rufiopin.

1 : 2 : 5 : 8-Tetrahydroxyanthraquinone. *See* Quinalizarin.

1 : 2 : 6 : 7-Tetrahydroxyanthraquinone.
Orange needles from $PhNO_2$. Does not melt below 330°. Mod. sol. $PhNO_2$. Spar. sol. EtOH, C_6H_6. Conc. H_2SO_4 ⟶ violet sol. NaOH ⟶ violet sol.
1 : 2 : 6-*Tri-Me ether*: $C_{17}H_{14}O_6$. MW, 314. Yellow needles from AcOH. M.p. 269–70°.
Tetra-Me ether: $C_{18}H_{16}O_6$. MW, 328. Yellow needles from AcOH. M.p. 244–5° (239°).
Tetra-acetyl: cryst. from AcOH. M.p. 239–41°.

Bistrzycki, Krauer, *Helv. Chim. Acta*, 1923, **6**, 768.
Jacobson, Adams, *J. Am. Chem. Soc.*, 1925, **47**, 2017.

1 : 2 : 7 : 8-Tetrahydroxyanthraquinone.
Red prisms from AcOH. M.p. 315° (292°) decomp. Sol. Py. Spar. sol. EtOH, AcOH, $PhNO_2$, toluene. NaOH ⟶ blue sol. Conc. H_2SO_4 ⟶ violet-red sol. Sublimes.
Diacetyl deriv.: m.p. 242°.

Tetra-acetyl: yellow needles. M.p. 238–40° decomp.

Bayer, D.R.P., 103,988, (*Chem. Zentr.*, 1899, II, 922).
Heller, *Z. angew. Chem.*, 1929, **42**, 170.

1 : 3 : 5 : 7-Tetrahydroxyanthraquinone. *See* Anthrachrysazin.

1 : 4 : 5 : 8-Tetrahydroxyanthraquinone. Brown needles from C_6H_6–ligroin. Does not melt below 300° (246°). Insol. H_2O. NaOH ⟶ blue sol. Conc. H_2SO_4 ⟶ greenish-blue sol. with red. fluor.

Tetra-Me ether: orange leaflets from AcOH. M.p. 317°. Sol. boiling AcOH, xylene, $PhNO_2$. Spar. sol. EtOH, C_6H_6, hot H_2O. Conc. H_2SO_4 ⟶ greenish-blue sol.

Tetra-acetyl: pale yellow needles from AcOH. Decomp. above 258°. Conc. H_2SO_4 ⟶ blue col.

Fischer, Ziegler, *J. prakt. Chem.*, 1912, **86**, 300.
Frey, *Ber.*, 1912, **45**, 1361.
Bayer, D.R.P., 143,804, (*Chem. Zentr.*, 1903, II, 475).
S.C.I., Bâle, D.R.P., 533,340, (*Chem. Abstracts*, 1932, **26**, 480).
Marshall, *J. Chem. Soc.*, 1937, 255.

2 : 3 : 6 : 7-Tetrahydroxyanthraquinone. Orange-yellow. Turns brown at 360°. Sol. alkalis with greenish-yellow col.

Tetra-Me ether: yellow needles from AcOH or $PhNO_2$. M.p. 346° (344°). Conc. H_2SO_4 ⟶ green sol. Sublimes.

2 : 6-*Di-Me*-3 : 7-*di-Et ether*: $C_{20}H_{20}O_6$. MW, 356. Yellow needles from AcOH. M.p. 288°. Conc. H_2SO_4 ⟶ green sol.

2 : 3 : 6-*Tri-Me-7-Et ether*: $C_{19}H_{18}O_6$. MW, 342. Yellow needles from AcOH. M.p. 290°. Conc. H_2SO_4 ⟶ green sol.

Tetra-acetyl: yellow cryst. from AcOH. M.p. 300° decomp.

Vanzetti, Dreyfus, *Gazz. chim. ital.*, 1934, **64**, 392.
Vanzetti, Oliverio, *Gazz. chim. ital.*, 1930, **60**, 620.
Haworth, Mavin, *J. Chem. Soc.*, 1931, 1365.

1 : 2 : 3 : 4-Tetrahydroxybenzene. *See* Apionol.

1 : 2 : 3 : 5-Tetrahydroxybenzene

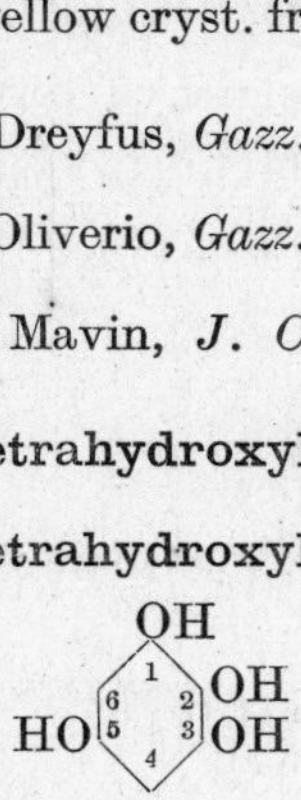

$C_6H_6O_4$ MW, 142

Needles from H_2O. M.p. 165°. Sol. H_2O, EtOH, AcOEt. Insol. $CHCl_3$, C_6H_6. Decomp. easily in air. $FeCl_3$ ⟶ red col.

2-*Me ether*: *see* Iretol.

1 : 3-*Di-Me ether*: $C_8H_{10}O_4$. MW, 170. Needles. M.p. 159°. Sol. EtOH, Et_2O. Sol. alkalis with green col. Decomp. in moist air.

2-*Et ether*: $C_{10}H_{14}O_4$. MW, 198. Yellowish needles from ligroin. M.p. 119°. Sol. most org. solvents. $FeCl_3$ ⟶ green col. *Diacetyl*: needles from boiling H_2O. M.p. 128°. Sol. EtOH. Spar. sol. H_2O.

1 : 2 : 3-*Tri-Me ether*: *see* Antiarol.

Tetra-Me ether: *see under* Antiarol.

2-*Et ether*: $C_8H_{10}O_4$. MW, 170. Needles. M.p. 220°. *Triacetyl*: cryst. from C_6H_6–ligroin. M.p. 74°. B.p. 232°/17 mm.

1 : 2 : 3-*Tri-Et ether*: $C_{12}H_{18}O_4$. MW, 226. Needles from H_2O. M.p. 105°. Sol. EtOH, Et_2O.

Oettinger, *Monatsh.*, 1895, **16**, 256.
Will, *Ber.*, 1888, **21**, 610.
Kohner, *Monatsh.*, 1899, **20**, 938.
Nierenstein, *J. Chem. Soc.*, 1917, **111**, 5.

1 : 2 : 4 : 5-Tetrahydroxybenzene. Leaflets from AcOH. M.p. 215–20°. Very sol. H_2O, EtOH, Et_2O. Less sol. AcOH. Aq. sol. turns brown in air.

2-*Me ether*: *triacetyl*, cryst. from MeOH or AcOH. M.p. 142°.

1 : 4-*Di-Me ether*: needles. M.p. 170° (166°). Sol. EtOH, warm $CHCl_3$.

Tetra-Me ether: $C_{10}H_{14}O_4$. MW, 198. Needles from H_2O. M.p. 103°. Sol. EtOH, C_6H_6. Spar. sol. cold H_2O.

1 : 4-*Di-Et ether*: $C_{10}H_{14}O_4$. MW, 198. Needles from hot H_2O. M.p. 138°. *Diacetyl*: leaflets. M.p. 148°.

Tetra-Et ether: $C_{14}H_{22}O_4$. MW, 254. Leaflets from EtOH.Aq. M.p. 143°. Sublimes. Volatile in steam.

1 : 4-*Dipropyl ether*: $C_{12}H_{18}O_4$. MW, 226. Needles from ligroin. M.p. 95°. Very sol. most solvents. Conc. H_2SO_4 ⟶ greenish sol.

Tetra-acetyl: leaflets from AcOH. M.p. 226–7° (217°).

Jackson, Beggs, *J. Am. Chem. Soc.*, 1914, **36**, 1216.
Nietzki, Schmidt, *Ber.*, 1888, **21**, 2377.
Schüler, *Arch. Pharm.*, 1907, **245**, 281.
Nietzki, Rechberg, *Ber.*, 1890, **23**, 1214.
Erdtmann, *Chem. Abstracts*, 1934, **28**, 1337.

2 : 3 : 4 : 5-Tetrahydroxybenzoic Acid

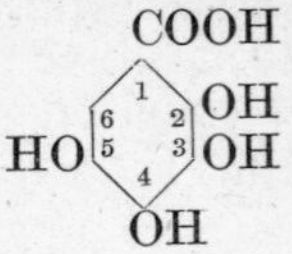

$C_7H_6O_6$ MW, 186

2 : 5-*Di-Me ether* : $C_9H_{10}O_6$. MW, 214. Cryst. from AcOEt. M.p. 147 8°. Sol. H_2O, EtOH, Et_2O, AcOEt. Insol. ligroin. $FeCl_3 \longrightarrow$ blue col. *Di-Et ether* : $C_{13}H_{18}O_6$. MW, 270. Pale yellow cryst. from pet. ether. M.p. 83°. B.p. 95°/0·2 mm.

3 : 5-*Di-Me ether* : pale yellow cryst. M.p. 165° decomp. Sol. EtOH, C_6H_6. $FeCl_3 \longrightarrow$ brown col. *Diacetyl* : cryst. Decomp. at 112° (162°). Sol. EtOH. Insol. H_2O.

3 : 4 : 5-*Tri-Me ether* : $C_{10}H_{12}O_6$. MW, 228. Cryst. M.p. 191° decomp. Sol. EtOH, Et_2O, C_6H_6. Spar. sol. H_2O, ligroin. *Me ester* : $C_{11}H_{14}O_6$. MW, 242. Cryst. M.p. 85°. Sol. EtOH, Et_2O. Insol. H_2O.

Tetra-Me ether : $C_{11}H_{14}O_6$. MW, 242. Needles from EtOH.Aq. M.p. 87·5°. Sol. EtOH, boiling H_2O, Me_2CO, AcOEt, C_6H_6.

Bartolotti, *Gazz. chim. ital.*, 1892, **22**, i, 562.
Hamburg, *Monatsh.*, 1898, **19**, 603.
Wesseley, Demmer, *Ber.*, 1928, **61**, 1281.
Bogert, Plant, *J. Am. Chem. Soc.*, 1915, **37**, 2733.

2 : 3 : 4 : 6-Tetrahydroxybenzoic Acid.

Needles from H_2O. M.p. 308–10° decomp.

Tetra-Me ether : needles from EtOH. M.p. 184–6° (149–50°). *Me ester* : $C_{12}H_{16}O_6$. MW, 256. Needles from C_6H_6. M.p. 134–6°. *Chloride* : $C_{11}H_{13}O_5Cl$. MW, 260·5. Needles from pet. ether. M.p. 104°. *Nitrile* : $C_{11}H_{13}O_4N$. MW, 223. Needles from EtOH. M.p. 114°.

Tetra-acetyl : needles from MeOH. M.p. 274–6°.

Tetrabenzoyl : prismatic needles from EtOH. M.p. 248–9°.

Nierenstein, *J. Chem. Soc.*, 1917, **111**, 5.
Bargellini, Madesani, *Gazz. chim. ital.*, 1931, **61**, 684.

2 : 3 : 4 : 5-Tetrahydroxybenzophenone

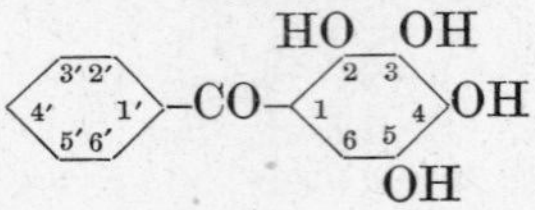

$C_{13}H_{10}O_5$ MW, 246

3 : 4-*Di-Me ether* : $C_{15}H_{14}O_5$. MW, 274. Yellow prisms from H_2O. M.p. 140–2°. Sol. EtOH, AcOH, C_6H_6. Conc. $H_2SO_4 \longrightarrow$ yellow sol.

Bargellini, *Gazz. chim. ital.*, 1916, **46**, i, 254.

2 : 3 : 4 : 6-Tetrahydroxybenzophenone.

Tri-Me ether : $C_{16}H_{16}O_5$. MW, 288. Needles from ligroin. M.p. 87–9°. Sol. EtOH, $CHCl_3$, Me_2CO, C_6H_6. Insol. H_2O. Alc. $FeCl_3 \longrightarrow$ reddish-brown col. Conc. $H_2SO_4 \longrightarrow$ yellow sol. $\longrightarrow$ green $\longrightarrow$ dark violet on warming. *Acetyl* : needles from EtOH.Aq. M.p. 130–2°. Sol. EtOH, Me_2CO, $CHCl_3$, C_6H_6.

Tetra-Me ether : $C_{17}H_{18}O_5$. MW, 302. Needles from ligroin. M.p. 125–6°. Sol. EtOH, Me_2CO, C_6H_6. Insol. H_2O. Conc. $H_2SO_4 \longrightarrow$ yellow sol. $\longrightarrow$ dark violet on warming.

Bargellini, *Gazz. chim. ital.*, 1915, **45**, i, 89.

2 : 3 : 4 : 2′-Tetrahydroxybenzophenone.

Yellow plates + H_2O from H_2O. M.p. 100°, anhyd. 149°. Sol. EtOH, AcOH, Et_2O. Spar. sol. C_6H_6, ligroin. Sublimes.

Tetra-acetyl : cryst. from EtOH or AcOH. M.p. 118°.

Badische, D.R.P., 49,149.
Graebe, Eichengrun, *Ann.*, 1892, **269**, 307.
Atkinson, Heilbron, *J. Chem. Soc.*, 1926, 2690.

2 : 3 : 4 : 3′-Tetrahydroxybenzophenone.

Yellow needles. M.p. 133°.

See first reference above.

2 : 3 : 4 : 4′-Tetrahydroxybenzophenone.

Yellowish needles. M.p. above 200°.

Badische, D.R.P., 49,149.

2 : 4 : 5 : 4′-Tetrahydroxybenzophenone.

4 : 5 : 4′-*Tri-Me ether* : yellow needles from EtOH.Aq. M.p. 127–8°. Sol. EtOH, Me_2CO, $CHCl_3$, C_6H_6. Alc. $FeCl_3 \longrightarrow$ yellowish-green col.

Tetra-Me ether : yellow cryst. powder. M.p. 122–4°. Sol. Me_2CO, $CHCl_3$, C_6H_6. Conc. $H_2SO_4 \longrightarrow$ orange-yellow sol. *Phenylhydrazone* : m.p. 173–4°.

Bargellini, Martegiani, *Atti accad. Lincei*, 1911, **20**, II, 188.

2 : 4 : 6 : 2′-Tetrahydroxybenzophenone.

Golden-yellow leaflets from EtOH. Blackens on heating. Very spar. sol. EtOH. Insol.

H_2O, most org. solvents. Has paralytic action on heart in large doses.

Karrer, *Helv. Chim. Acta*, 1921, **4**, 992.

2 : 4 : 6 : 3′-Tetrahydroxybenzophenone. Pale yellow leaflets from H_2O. Decomp. at 246°. Sol. EtOH, hot H_2O. Spar. sol. Et_2O. Alc. $FeCl_3$ ⟶ purple col. Alkalis ⟶ orange sols. Conc. H_2SO_4 ⟶ yellow sol.

Nishikawa, Robinson, *J. Chem. Soc.*, 1922, **121**, 842.

2 : 4 : 6 : 4′-Tetrahydroxybenzophenone. Pale brown prisms from H_2O. M.p. 210°. Alc. $FeCl_3$ ⟶ brown col. Alkalis ⟶ yellow sols.

Tetra-Me ether: prisms from EtOH. M.p. 146°.

4′-*Carboethoxyl*: yellow needles from EtOH.Aq. M.p. 172°.

Nishikawa, Robinson, *J. Chem. Soc.*, 1922, **121**, 843.
Kostanecki, Tambor, *Ber.*, 1906, **39**, 4024.

2 : 3 : 2′ : 3′-Tetrahydroxybenzophenone. *Tetra-Me ether*: cryst. M.p. 145°.

Staudinger, Schlenker, Goldstein, *Helv. Chim. Acta*, 1921, **4**, 341.

2 : 4 : 2′ : 4′-Tetrahydroxybenzophenone. Yellow needles + $1\frac{1}{2}H_2O$ from H_2O. M.p. 193–5°. Sol. MeOH, EtOH, Et_2O, Me_2CO, AcOH. Mod. sol. hot H_2O, $CHCl_3$, C_6H_6. $FeCl_3$ ⟶ dark brown col.

Tetra-Me ether: yellowish leaflets from EtOH.Aq. M.p. 130°. Conc. H_2SO_4 ⟶ yellow sol.

Tambor, *Ber.*, 1910, **43**, 1889.
Meyer, Conzetti, *Ber.*, 1897, **30**, 971.
Shoesmith, Haldane, *J. Chem. Soc.*, 1924, **125**, 113.

2 : 4 : 2′ : 6′-Tetrahydroxybenzophenone. Cryst. + H_2O from H_2O. M.p. about 200°. Sol. hot H_2O.

Graebe, *Ann.*, 1889, **254**, 302.

2 : 4 : 3′ : 4′-Tetrahydroxybenzophenone. Needles + $2H_2O$ from H_2O. M.p. anhyd. 202°. Sol. EtOH, Et_2O, Me_2CO, AcOH. Less sol. H_2O. Spar. sol. C_6H_6. Insol. ligroin. Aq. sol. shows green fluor.

3′-*Me ether*: $C_{14}H_{12}O_5$. MW, 260. Yellowish needles from H_2O. M.p. 210°. Sol. EtOH, Et_2O. Spar. sol. H_2O. $FeCl_3$ ⟶ intense reddish-brown col.

Tetra-Me ether: prisms from EtOH. M.p. 126° (107°). Conc. H_2SO_4 ⟶ yellow sol.

M.L.B., D.R.P., 72,446.
Hoesch, v. Zarzecki, *Ber.*, 1917, **50**, 465.
Komarowski, Kostanecki, *Ber.*, 1894, **27**, 2000.
Mitter, Paul, *J. Indian Chem. Soc.*, 1931, **8**, 274.

2 : 4 : 3′ : 5′-Tetrahydroxybenzophenone. *Tetra-Me ether*: needles from C_6H_6–pet. ether. M.p. 73–4°. Sol. EtOH, Et_2O, $CHCl_3$, hot C_6H_6. Spar. sol. AcOH. Insol. pet. ether. Conc. H_2SO_4 ⟶ yellow sol.

Mauthner, *J. prakt. Chem.*, 1913, **87**, 407.

2 : 5 : 2′ : 5′-Tetrahydroxybenzophenone. *Tetra-Me ether*: yellowish cryst. from EtOH. M.p. 109°. Sol. $CHCl_3$, C_6H_6. Less sol. EtOH, Et_2O, AcOH. *Oxime*: cryst. M.p. 134·5°. *Phenylhydrazone*: m.p. 170°.

Kauffmann, Grombach, *Ann.*, 1906, **344**, 74.
Kauffmann, Fritz, *Ber.*, 1908, **41**, 4425.
Staudinger, Schlenker, Goldstein, *Helv. Chim. Acta*, 1921, **4**, 341.

2 : 5 : 2′ : 6′-Tetrahydroxybenzophenone. Yellow needles from H_2O. M.p. 200–2° decomp.

Tetra-Et ether: $C_{21}H_{26}O_5$. MW, 358. Leaflets or needles from EtOH. M.p. 93–5°. Spar. sol. EtOH.

Tetra-acetyl: leaflets from EtOH. M.p. 118–19°.

Baeyer, *Ann.*, 1870, **155**, 259.
Herzig, *Monatsh.*, 1892, **13**, 412.

2 : 5 : 3′ : 4′-Tetrahydroxybenzophenone. *Tetra-Me ether*: prisms from EtOH.Aq. M.p. 101–2°. Conc. H_2SO_4 ⟶ orange sol.

König, Kostanecki, *Ber.*, 1906, **39**, 4030.

2 : 6 : 2′ : 6′-Tetrahydroxybenzophenone. *Tetra-Me ether*: plates from C_6H_6. M.p. 204°. Very sol. $CHCl_3$. Mod. sol. EtOH, AcOH. Spar. sol. Et_2O, C_6H_6.

Baeyer, *Ann.*, 1910, **372**, 130.

3 : 4 : 3′ : 4′-Tetrahydroxybenzophenone. Cryst. from H_2O. M.p. 227–8°.

Tetra-Me ether: prisms from EtOH. M.p. 145°. Sol. EtOH, C_6H_6. Spar. sol. pet. ether. *Oxime*: cryst. from EtOH. M.p. 145°.

M.L.B., D.R.P., 72,446.
Kostanecki, Tambor, *Ber.*, 1906, **39**, 4027.
Perkin, Weizmann, *J. Chem. Soc.*, 1906, **89**, 1661.

2 : 4 : 3′ : 5′-Tetrahydroxybenzophenone.

Tetra-Me ether: needles from C_6H_6. M.p. 114–15°. Sol. EtOH, Et_2O, $CHCl_3$, hot C_6H_6. Spar. sol. AcOH. Insol. ligroin. Conc. H_2SO_4 ⟶ yellow sol.

Mauthner, *J. prakt. Chem.*, 1913, **87**, 407.

Tetrahydroxy-*p*-benzoquinone

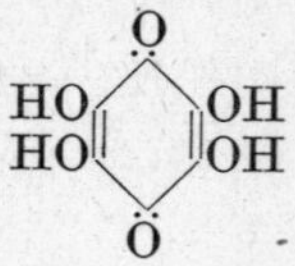

$C_6H_4O_6$ MW, 172

Bluish-black cryst. Very sol. EtOH, hot H_2O. Spar. sol. Et_2O, cold H_2O. Strong dibasic acid.

Di-Na salt: bluish-black cryst. with metallic green lustre.

Diphenyl ether: $C_{18}H_{12}O_6$. MW, 324. Reddish-brown plates from EtOH. M.p. 276°. Sol. AcOH. Spar. sol. EtOH, hot $CHCl_3$. Insol. Et_2O, C_6H_6, CS_2, ligroin. *Di-Me ether*: $C_{20}H_{16}O_6$. MW, 352. Golden-yellow needles from C_6H_6–EtOH. M.p. 171°. Sol. $CHCl_3$. Mod. sol. EtOH, C_6H_6, AcOH. Spar. sol. Et_2O, CS_2. Insol. ligroin. *Di-Et ether*: $C_{22}H_{20}O_6$. MW, 380. Orange-yellow needles from EtOH. M.p. 128°. Sol. EtOH, $CHCl_3$. Spar. sol. Et_2O, AcOH.

Tetraphenyl ether: $C_{30}H_{20}O_6$. MW, 476. Red prisms from C_6H_6. M.p. 229–30°. Spar. sol. CS_2, boiling AcOH. Very spar. sol. warm Me_2CO. Insol. EtOH, Et_2O, ligroin.

Diacetyl: yellow leaflets. M.p. 205°. Mod. sol. EtOH, Et_2O. Spar. sol. H_2O.

Jackson, Grindley, *Am. Chem. J.*, 1895, **17**, 647.

M.L.B., D.R.P., 368,741, (*Chem. Abstracts*, 1924, **18**, 991).

Maquenne, *Ann. chim. phys.*, 1887, **12**, 112.

1 : 2 : 3 : 4-Tetrahydroxybutane.

See Erythritol.

2 : 4 : 2′ : 4′-Tetrahydroxychalkone (2 : 4-*Dihydroxyphenyl* 2 : 4-*dihydroxystyryl ketone*)

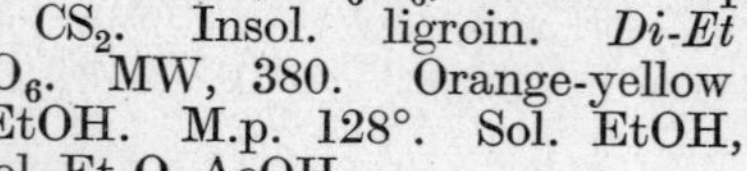

$C_{15}H_{12}O_5$ MW, 272

2 : 4 : 4′-*Tri-Me ether*: $C_{18}H_{18}O_5$. MW, 314. Yellow needles from EtOH. M.p. 157°. Conc. H_2SO_4 ⟶ red sol. *Acetyl*: Pale yellow cryst. from EtOH. M.p. 110–12°.

4 : 2′ : 4′-*Tri-Me ether*: greenish-yellow needles from Me_2CO. M.p. 156°.

Tetra-Me ether: $C_{19}H_{20}O_5$. MW, 328. Yellowish needles from EtOH. M.p. 128°. Sol. Me_2CO, $CHCl_3$, CS_2, C_6H_6. Spar. sol. Et_2O, ligroin.

Bhalla, Rây, *J. Chem. Soc.*, 1933, 290.

Kostanecki, Lampe, Triulzi, *Ber.*, 1906, **39**, 92.

Kauffmann, Kieser, *Ber.*, 1913, **46**, 3797.

2 : 4 : 2′ : 5′-Tetrahydroxychalkone (2 : 5-*Dihydroxyphenyl* 2 : 4-*dihydroxystyryl ketone*).

2 : 4 : 5′-*Tri-Me ether*: orange-yellow needles from EtOH. M.p. 118°. Conc. H_2SO_4 ⟶ red col. *Acetyl*: yellowish needles from EtOH. M.p. 87°.

Tetra-Me ether: cryst. from EtOH.Aq. M.p. 112°.

Kauffmann, Kieser, *Ber.*, 1913, **46**, 3798.

Bonifazi, Kostanecki, Tambor, *Ber.*, 1906, **39**, 88.

3 : 4 : 2′ : 4′-Tetrahydroxychalkone.

See Butein.

3 : 4 : 2′ : 5′-Tetrahydroxychalkone (2 : 5-*Dihydroxyphenyl* 3 : 4-*dihydroxystyryl ketone*).

3 : 5′-*Di-Me ether*: $C_{17}H_{16}O_5$. MW, 300. Orange-red leaflets from EtOH. M.p. 122–3°. Conc. H_2SO_4 ⟶ yellowish-red sol.

Milobedzka, Kostanecki, Lampe, *Ber.*, 1910, **43**, 2164.

3 : 4 : 3′ : 4′-Tetrahydroxychalkone (3 : 4-*Dihydroxyphenyl* 3 : 4-*dihydroxystyryl ketone*).

Tetra-Me ether: yellow prisms from EtOH. M.p. 116° (110°). Conc. H_2SO_4 + AcOH ⟶ dark red sol.

Kauffmann, Kieser, *Ber.*, 1913, **46**, 3798.

Perkin, Rây, Robinson, *J. Chem. Soc.*, 1926, 951.

3 : 5 : 3′ : 4′-Tetrahydroxychalkone (3 : 4-*Dihydroxyphenyl* 3 : 5-*dihydroxystyryl ketone*).

Tetra-Me ether: yellow needles from EtOH.Aq. M.p. 103–4°. Sol. EtOH, C_6H_6, warm ligroin. Insol. pet. ether. Conc. H_2SO_4 ⟶ blood-red sol.

Mauthner, *J. prakt. Chem.*, 1920, **100**, 182.

2 : 2′ : 3′ : 4′-Tetrahydroxychalkone (2:3:4-*Trihydroxyphenyl* 2-*hydroxystyryl ketone*).

Yellow needles from 75% MeOH. M.p. 224–5° decomp. Very sol. EtOH, Me_2CO. Spar. sol. boiling xylene. Insol. H_2O, $CHCl_3$.

C_6H_6. Conc. H_2SO_4 ⟶ deep brown sol. Alkalis ⟶ deep brown sols.

2 : 3′ : 4′-*Tri-Me ether*: pale yellow needles from EtOH. M.p. 105°. Conc. H_2SO_4 ⟶ orange-red sol. *Acetyl*: needles from EtOH. M.p. 88°.

Ellison, *J. Chem. Soc.*, 1927, 1723.
Cohen, Kostanecki, *Ber.*, 1904, **37**, 2628.

2 : 2′ : 4′ : 5′ - Tetrahydroxychalkone (2:4:5-*Trihydroxyphenyl 2-hydroxystyryl ketone*).

2′ : 4′ : 5′-*Tri-Me ether*: green needles from EtOH. M.p. 159–60° decomp. Conc. H_2SO_4 ⟶ orange sol. *Acetyl*: golden needles from EtOH.Aq. M.p. 121°.

Reigrodski, Tambor, *Ber.*, 1910, **43**, 1967.

2 : 2′ : 4′ : 6′ - Tetrahydroxychalkone (2:4:6-*Trihydroxyphenyl 2-hydroxystyryl ketone*).

2 : 4′ : 6′-*Tri-Me ether*: yellow cryst. from boiling MeOH. M.p. 106–8°. Conc. H_2SO_4 ⟶ orange-red col.

Bargellini, Peratoner, *Gazz. chim. ital.*, 1919, **49**, ii, 67.

3 : 2′ : 3′ : 4′ - Tetrahydroxychalkone (2:3:4-*Trihydroxyphenyl 3-hydroxystyryl ketone*).

Yellow needles from 80% MeOH. M.p. 219–20°. Conc. H_2SO_4 ⟶ deep orange sol. Alkalis ⟶ deep brown sols.

3 : 3′ : 4′-*Tri-Me ether*: yellow needles from EtOH. M.p. 127–8°. Conc. H_2SO_4 ⟶ orange-yellow sol. *Acetyl*: yellowish needles from EtOH. M.p. 80–1°.

Ellison, *J. Chem. Soc.*, 1927, 1723.
Kostanecki, Schleifenbaum, *Ber.*, 1904, **37**, 2631.

4 : 2′ : 3′ : 4′ - Tetrahydroxychalkone (2:3:4-*Trihydroxyphenyl 4-hydroxystyryl ketone*).

3′ : 4′-*Di-Me ether*: yellow needles from EtOH.Aq. M.p. 106°.

4 : 3′ : 4′-*Tri-Me ether*: yellow plates. M.p. 131–2°. Conc. H_2SO_4 ⟶ orange-yellow sol. *Acetyl*: yellowish prisms from EtOH.Aq. M.p. 89–90°.

Tetra-Me ether: pale yellow needles from EtOH. M.p. 94°.

Russell, *J. Chem. Soc.*, 1934, 220.
Kuroda, Matsukuma, *Chem. Zentr.*, 1932, I, 2169.
Kostanecki, Schreiber, *Ber.*, 1905, **38**, 2749.

4 : 2′ : 4′ : 5′ - Tetrahydroxychalkone (2:4:5-*Trihydroxyphenyl 4-hydroxystyryl ketone*).

4 : 4′ : 5′-*Tri-Me ether*: red needles from EtOH.Aq. M.p. 130°. Sol. EtOH, C_6H_6. Conc. H_2SO_4 ⟶ orange-yellow sol.

Tetra-Me ether: yellow needles from EtOH. M.p. 123–4°. Conc. H_2SO_4 ⟶ intense red sol.

Kuroda, Matsukuma, *Chem. Zentr.*, 1932, I, 2169.
Bargellini, Aureli, *Atti accad. Lincei*, 1911, **20**, II, 123.
Bargellini, Aurutin, *Gazz. chim. ital.*, 1910, **40**, ii, 346.

4 : 2′ : 4′ : 6′ - Tetrahydroxychalkone (2:4:6-*Trihydroxyphenyl 4-hydroxystyryl ketone*).

4′ : 6′-*Di-Me ether*: orange-red needles from C_6H_6. M.p. 188°. Conc. H_2SO_4 ⟶ dark yellow sol. *Diacetyl*: pale yellow needles from MeOH. M.p. 147°.

4 : 4′ : 6′-*Tri-Me ether*: yellow needles from EtOH. M.p. 113°. Conc. H_2SO_4 ⟶ orange sol. *Acetyl*: yellowish leaflets from EtOH. M.p. 120°.

2′ : 4′ : 6′-*Tri-Me ether*: golden-yellow cryst. from MeOH. M.p. 195–6°. Conc. H_2SO_4 ⟶ orange-red sol. *Acetyl*: yellow cryst. from MeOH. M.p. 108°.

Tetra-Me ether: pale yellow cryst. from EtOH.Aq. M.p. 119–21°. Conc. H_2SO_4 ⟶ orange-red sol.

4-*Carbomethoxyl*: yellow cryst. from MeOH.Aq. M.p. 166°.

Mosimann, Tambor, *Ber.*, 1916, **49**, 1701.
Kuroda, Matsukuma, *Chem. Zentr.*, 1932, I, 2169.
Bargellini, *Gazz. chim. ital.*, 1914, **44**, ii, 424.
Kostanecki, Tambor, *Ber.*, 1904, **37**, 792.

2′ : 3′ : 4′ : 6′ - Tetrahydroxychalkone (2 : 3 : 4 : 6-*Tetrahydroxyphenyl styryl ketone*).

Tetra-Me ether: yellowish needles from EtOH.Aq. M.p. 74–5°. Sol. C_6H_6. Conc. H_2SO_4 ⟶ orange-red sol.

Bargellini, Bini, *Gazz. chim. ital.*, 1911, **41**, ii, 18.

1 : 3 : 4 : 5 - Tetrahydroxycyclohexane-1-carboxylic Acid.

See Quinic Acid.

2 : 6 : 2′ : 6′ - Tetrahydroxy - 1 : 1′ - dinaphthyl

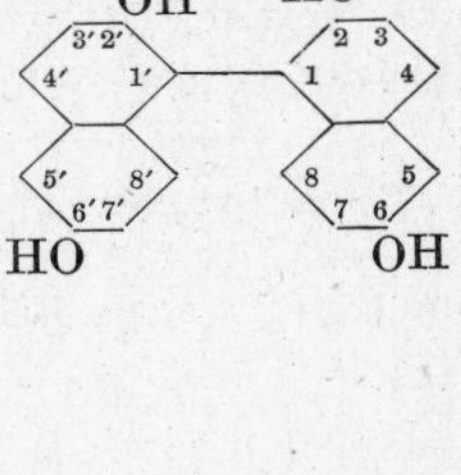

$C_{20}H_{14}O_4$ MW, 318

M.p. 318–20°. Autoxidises readily, especially in alk. sol.

Ioffe, Kusnetzow, *Chem. Zentr.*, 1936, I, 2935.

3 : 4 : 3′ : 4′-Tetrahydroxy-1 : 1′-dinaphthyl.

Needles from 30% AcOH. M.p. 205–10° decomp. (176–8°). Sol. AcOH. Spar. sol. Et_2O, C_6H_6, CS_2. Insol. H_2O.

Tetra-Me ether: $C_{24}H_{22}O_4$. MW, 374. Leaflets from EtOH. M.p. 145–7°. B.p. 200–20°/0·67 mm. Sol. most org. solvents. Spar. sol. EtOH, pet. ether. Conc. $H_2SO_4 \longrightarrow$ bluish-violet col.

Tetra-acetyl: needles from AcOH. M.p. 165–6° decomp. Sol. usual solvents.

Korn, *Ber.*, 1884, **17**, 3025.
Strauss, Bernoully, Mautner, *Ann.*, 1925, **444**, 190.

1 : 4 : 1′ : 4′-Tetrahydroxy-2 : 2′-dinaphthyl

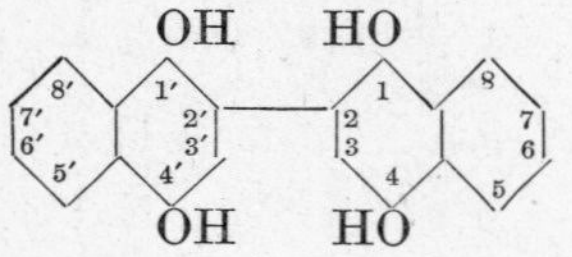

$C_{20}H_{14}O_4$ MW, 318

Needles from AcOH. Blackens at 205°. Spar. sol. cold EtOH. Insol. H_2O. Alc. sol. turns violet in air.

Tetra-acetyl: needles from AcOH. M.p. 226–7°.

Meldola, Hughes, *J. Chem. Soc.*, 1890, **57**, 632.
See also Liebermann, Schlossberg, *Ber.*, 1899, **32**, 546.

2 : 4 : 2′ : 4′-Tetrahydroxydiphenyl

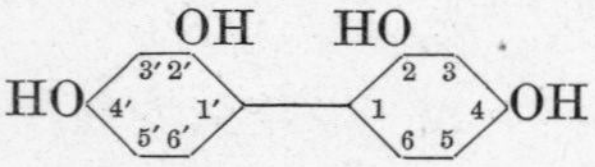

$C_{12}H_{10}O_4$ MW, 218

Needles from boiling H_2O. M.p. 226–7°. Sol. EtOH, Et_2O, Me_2CO, AcOEt.

Tetra-Me ether: $C_{16}H_{18}O_4$. MW, 274. Cryst. from MeOH. M.p. 93°.

Tetra-acetyl: needles from Et_2O. M.p. 120°. Sol. EtOH, Et_2O, Me_2CO, $CHCl_3$, AcOH, C_6H_6.

Meyer, Desamari, *Ber.*, 1909, **42**, 2823.
Bayer, D.R.P., 90,341.

2 : 4 : 2′ : 5′-Tetrahydroxydiphenyl (*Resorcylhydroquinone*).

Needles from C_6H_6. M.p. 131° under CO_2. Very sol. H_2O, EtOH, Et_2O. Mod. sol. C_6H_6 ligroin. Spar. sol. CS_2. Alkalis $\longrightarrow$ olive-green sols.

Tetra-acetyl: needles from ligroin. M.p. 120° under CO_2. Sol. $CHCl_3$, AcOEt, C_6H_6. Mod. sol. EtOH, Et_2O, ligroin, hot H_2O. Insol. cold NaOH.

Pummerer, Huppmann, *Ber.*, 1927, **60**, 1446.

2 : 4 : 3′ : 4′-Tetrahydroxydiphenyl.

See Sappanin.

2 : 5 : 2′ : 5′-Tetrahydroxydiphenyl (*Dihydroquinone*).

Colourless prisms. M.p. 237° decomp. Sol. EtOH, Et_2O, Me_2CO, hot H_2O. Spar. sol. $CHCl_3$, C_6H_6. $FeCl_3 \longrightarrow$ red col.

Tetra-Me ether: $C_{16}H_{18}O_4$. MW, 274. M.p. 104°. Sol. AcOH, C_6H_6, hot EtOH. Spar. sol. Et_2O.

Barth, Schreider, *Monatsh.*, 1884, **5**, 590.
Ullmann, Loewenthal, *Ann.*, 1904, **332**, 69.

3 : 4 : 3′ : 4′-Tetrahydroxydiphenyl (*Dicatechol*).

Cryst. from H_2O. M.p. 229–30°.

Tetra-Me ether: diveratrol. Needles from MeOH.Aq. M.p. 133°. Conc. $H_2SO_4 \longrightarrow$ golden-yellow sol. $\longrightarrow$ olive-green col. on warming.

Seer, Karl, *Monatsh.*, 1913, **34**, 647.
Späth, Gibian, *Monatsh.*, 1930, **55**, 347.

3 : 5 : 3′ : 5′-Tetrahydroxydiphenyl (*Diresorcinol*).

Needles + $2H_2O$ from hot H_2O. M.p. anhyd. 310°. Mod. sol. hot H_2O. Prac. insol. AcOH. Zn dust dist. $\longrightarrow$ diphenyl. $FeCl_3 \longrightarrow$ light blue col.

Tetra-Me ether: white cryst. M.p. 108°.

Tetra-Et ether: $C_{20}H_{26}O_4$. MW, 330. Leaflets. M.p. 110°. Sol. Et_2O.

Tetra-acetyl: m.p. 157–9°.

Benedikt, Julius, *Monatsh.*, 1884, **5**, 177.
v. Friedrichs, *Chem. Zentr.*, 1916, I, 975.

2 : 6 : 2′ : 6′-Tetrahydroxydiphenyl.

Tetra-Me ether: cryst. from Me_2CO.Aq. M.p. 175–6°.

v. Arendonk, Cupery, Adams, *J. Am. Chem. Soc.*, 1933, **55**, 4227.

2 : 5 : 2′ : 5′-Tetrahydroxydiphenyl sulphide

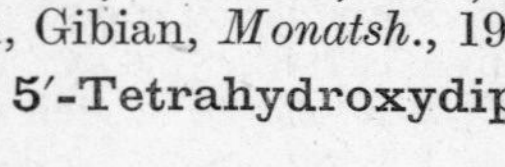

$C_{12}H_{10}O_4S$ MW, 250

Cryst. M.p. 227–9°.

Tetra-Me ether: $C_{16}H_{18}O_4S$. MW, 306. Amorph. M.p. 97–100°. Sol. Me_2CO, hot EtOH.

Badische, D.R.P., 175,070, (*Chem. Zentr.*, 1906, I, 1466).

Smiles, Le Rossignol, *J. Chem. Soc.*, 1908, **93**, 760.

5 : 6 : 7 : 4′-Tetrahydroxyflavanone. *See* Isocarthamidin.

5 : 7 : 8 : 4′-Tetrahydroxyflavanone. *See* Carthamidin.

7 : 3′ : 4′ : 5′-Tetrahydroxyflavanone

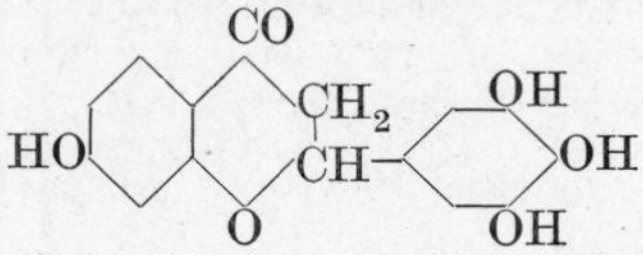

$C_{15}H_{12}O_6$ MW, 288

Tetra-Me ether: $C_{19}H_{20}O_6$. MW, 344. Needles from EtOH. M.p. 148–9°. Conc. H_2SO_4 ⟶ yellow sol.

Dean, Nierenstein, *J. Am. Chem. Soc.*, 1925, **47**, 1681.

3 : 5 : 7 : 2′-Tetrahydroxyflavone. *See* Datiscetin.

3 : 5 : 7 : 4′-Tetrahydroxyflavone. *See* Kæmpferol.

3 : 7 : 8 : 2′-Tetrahydroxyflavone (7 : 8 : 2′-*Trihydroxyflavonol*)

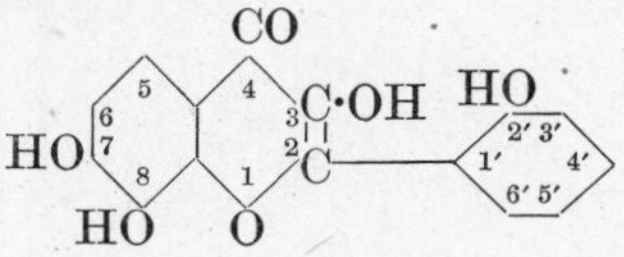

$C_{15}H_{10}O_6$ MW, 286

Pale yellow needles. M.p. 298° decomp. NaOH ⟶ reddish-yellow sol.

7 : 8 : 2′-*Tri-Me ether*: $C_{18}H_{16}O_6$. MW, 328. Cryst. from EtOH. M.p. 212–14°. NaOH ⟶ yellow sol. Conc. H_2SO_4 ⟶ greenish-yellow sol. *Acetyl*: needles from EtOH.Aq. M.p. 138–9°.

Cohen, Kostanecki, *Ber.*, 1904, **37**, 2630.

3 : 7 : 8 : 3′-Tetrahydroxyflavone (7 : 8 : 3′-*Trihydroxyflavonol*).

Pale yellow needles from EtOH.Aq. M.p. 260°. Conc. H_2SO_4 ⟶ greenish-yellow sol. Alkalis ⟶ brownish-yellow sols.

7 : 8 : 3′-*Tri-Me ether*: pale yellow needles. M.p. 188–9°. Spar. sol. EtOH. Conc. H_2SO_4 ⟶ pale yellow sol. *Acetyl*: needles from EtOH.Aq. M.p. 165°.

Tetra-acetyl: needles from EtOH.Aq. M.p. 166–7°.

Kostanecki, Schleifenbaum, *Ber.*, 1904, **37**, 2633.

3 : 7 : 8 : 4′-Tetrahydroxyflavone (7 : 8 : 4′-*Trihydroxyflavonol*).

Pale yellow needles + H_2O from EtOH. M.p. anhyd. 319° decomp. Dil. NaOH ⟶ orange-red sol. Conc. H_2SO_4 ⟶ yellow sol. with weak green fluor.

7 : 8 : 4′-*Tri-Me ether*: pale yellow needles from EtOH. M.p. 198°. Conc. H_2SO_4 ⟶ pale yellow sol. *Acetyl*: needles from EtOH.Aq. M.p. 157°.

Tetra-acetyl: needles from EtOH.Aq. M.p. 175°.

Kostanecki, Schreiber, *Ber.*, 1905, **38**, 2751.

5 : 6 : 7 : 4′-Tetrahydroxyflavone. *See* Scutellarein.

5 : 7 : 8 : 4′-Tetrahydroxyflavone.

Yellow needles from AcOH.Aq. M.p. 247–8°. Alkalis ⟶ reddish-brown sols. $FeCl_3$ ⟶ greenish-brown col.

5 : 8 : 4′-*Tri-Me ether*: yellow cryst. from EtOH. M.p. 279–80° (258°). *Acetyl*: m.p. 194·5°.

Tetra-Me ether: needles. M.p. 207–8°.

Tetra-acetyl: needles from EtOH. M.p. 252–3°.

Furukawa, Tamaki, *Chem. Abstracts*, 1932, **26**, 142.

Hattori, *Acta Phytochimica*, 1931, **5**, 219.

Wesselý, *Monatsh.*, 1930, **56**, 97.

3 : 6 : 2′ : 4′-Tetrahydroxyflavone (6 : 2′ : 4′-*Trihydroxyflavonol*).

Pale yellow needles + H_2O from EtOH.Aq. M.p. anhyd. 285°. Dil. NaOH ⟶ greenish-yellow sol. with greenish fluor. Conc. H_2SO_4 ⟶ pale yellow sol. with weak green fluor.

6 : 2′ : 4′-*Tri-Me ether*: pale yellow cryst. from EtOH or C_6H_6. M.p. 193°. Conc. H_2SO_4 ⟶ greenish-yellow sol. with light green fluor. *Acetyl*: prismatic needles from EtOH.Aq. M.p. 162°.

Tetra-acetyl: needles from EtOH.Aq. M.p. 163°.

Bonifazi, Kostanecki, Tambor, *Ber.*, 1906, **39**, 90.

3 : 6 : 3′ : 4′-Tetrahydroxyflavone (6 : 3′ : 4′-*Trihydroxyflavonol*).

Yellow needles from EtOH. M.p. 335° decomp. Alc. sol. shows greenish fluor. NaOH

⟶ reddish-yellow sol. Conc. H_2SO_4 ⟶ orange sol. with greenish fluor.

6 : 3′ : 4′-*Tri-Me ether*: yellowish needles from EtOH. M.p. 189–90°. Conc. H_2SO_4 ⟶ yellow sol. with greenish fluor. *Acetyl*: needles from EtOH.Aq. M.p. 140–1°.

Tetra-acetyl: needles from EtOH or AcOH–EtOH. M.p. 197–8°. Spar. sol. EtOH.

Kostanecki, Kugler, *Ber.*, 1904, **37**, 781.
Auwers, Pohl, *Ann.*, 1914, **405**, 287.

3 : 7 : 2′ : 4′-Tetrahydroxyflavone.

See Resomorin.

3 : 7 : 3′ : 4′-Tetrahydroxyflavone.

See Fisetin.

5 : 7 : 2′ : 4′-Tetrahydroxyflavone.

Needles from EtOH or AcOH. M.p. 332–5° (277°) decomp. Conc. H_2SO_4 ⟶ pale yellow sol. with violet-blue fluor.

2′ : 4′-*Di-Me ether*: pale yellow needles from AcOH.Aq. + HCl. M.p. 258–9°. Mod. sol. boiling EtOH. Spar. sol. Et_2O. Insol. H_2O. Alc. $FeCl_3$ ⟶ weak greenish-brown col. Alkalis ⟶ bright yellow sols. Conc. H_2SO_4 ⟶ pale yellow sol. with blue fluor.

Robinson, Venkataraman, *J. Chem. Soc.*, 1929, 65.

5 : 7 : 3′ : 4′-Tetrahydroxyflavone.

See Luteolin.

7 : 8 : 3′ : 4′-Tetrahydroxyflavone.

Yellow needles from EtOH.Aq. M.p. 309–10° decomp. Conc. H_2SO_4 ⟶ pale yellow col. with no fluor. NaOH ⟶ orange-red sol. Alc. $FeCl_3$ ⟶ dark green col.

Tetra-Me ether: yellow needles from EtOH. M.p. 198–9°.

Tetra-acetyl: needles from EtOH. M.p. 218°.

Badhwar, Kang, Venkataraman, *J. Chem. Soc.*, 1932, 1109.

6 : 3′ : 4′ : 5′-Tetrahydroxyflavone.

Yellow needles from EtOH.Aq. M.p. 347°. Conc. H_2SO_4 ⟶ bright yellow sol. with no fluor. NaOH ⟶ bright red sol. Alc. $FeCl_3$ ⟶ intense green col.

3′ : 4′ : 5′-*Tri-Me ether*: pale orange plates from EtOH.Aq. M.p. 232–3°. No col. with $FeCl_3$. Conc. H_2SO_4 ⟶ bright yellow sol. with weak green fluor. *Acetyl*: needles from EtOH. M.p. 185°.

Tetra-acetyl: needles from EtOH–AcOH. M.p. 258–9°.

Chadha, Venkataraman, *J. Chem. Soc.*, 1933, 1075.

7 : 2′ : 4′ : 6′-Tetrahydroxyflavone.

Yellow plates from EtOH. M.p. 240°. Spar. sol. $CHCl_3$. Conc. H_2SO_4 ⟶ yellow sol. with greenish fluor.

Cullinane, Algar, Ryan, *Chem. Abstracts*, 1929, **23**, 4472.

7 : 3′ : 4′ : 5′-Tetrahydroxyflavone.

Needles + H_2O from EtOH.Aq. M.p. 340° decomp. Mod. sol. hot EtOH. NaOH ⟶ orange-red sol. Conc. H_2SO_4 ⟶ yellow sol. with weak greenish-yellow fluor.

Tetra-Me ether: needles. M.p. 191–2°. Mod. sol. boiling EtOH with violet fluor. Conc. H_2SO_4 ⟶ yellowish sol. with weak green fluor.

Tetra-acetyl: leaflets from EtOH. M.p. 215°.

Kostanecki, Plattner, *Ber.*, 1902, **35**, 2546.

1 : 3 : 4 : 5-Tetrahydroxyhexahydrobenzoic Acid.

See Quinic Acid.

Tetrahydroxyisovaleraldehyde.

See Apiose.

Tetrahydroxyisovaleric Acid.

See Apionic Acid.

Tetrahydro-xylene.

See Dimethylcyclohexene.

Tetrahydroxymethane.

See Orthocarbonic Acid.

3 : 5 : 7 : 8-Tetrahydroxy-1-methyl-anthraquinone

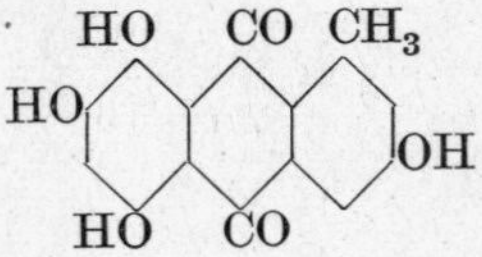

$C_{15}H_{10}O_6$ MW, 286

Light red needles from EtOH or Py. Sol. EtOH, AcOH, Py. Spar. sol. C_6H_6.

Tetra-acetyl: m.p. 185–6°.

Dimroth, Fick, *Ann.*, 1916, **411**, 325.

1 : 3 : 5 : 8-Tetrahydroxy-2-methyl-anthraquinone

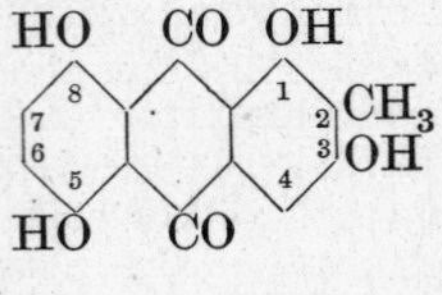

$C_{15}H_{10}O_6$ MW, 286

Yellowish-red plates from 50% AcOH. M.p. 276–7°.

Tetra-acetyl : yellow plates from AcOH. M.p. 223°.

Charlesworth, Robinson, *J. Chem. Soc.*, 1934, 1531.

1 : 4 : 5 : 8 - Tetrahydroxy - 2 - methyl - anthraquinone (*Cynodontin*).

Found in *Helminthosporium cynodontis*, M., and *Helminthosporium euchalœnœ*, Z. Cryst. from Py. M.p. 260°. Sol. most org. solvents. NaOH ⟶ deep bluish-violet sol. Conc. H_2SO_4 ⟶ blue sol. with red fluor.

Tetra-acetyl : m.p. 224–5°.

Raistrick, Robinson, Todd, *Biochem. J.*, 1933, 27, 1170.
I.C.I., E.P., 420,362; F.P., 770,972, (*Chem. Abstracts*, 1935, **29**, 816).

Tetrahydroxymethyl-methane.
See Pentaerythritol.

1 : 2 : 3 : 4 - Tetrahydroxynaphthalene (*Leucoisonaphthazarin*)

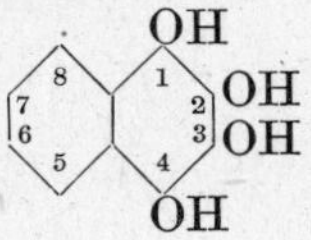

$C_{10}H_8O_4$ MW, 192

Cryst. from C_6H_6, leaflets from Et_2O–pet. ether. M.p. 225°. Sol. H_2O, most org. solvents. Spar. sol. C_6H_6, pet. ether. Easily decomp.

Tetra-acetyl : needles from AcOH. M.p. 220°. Mod. sol. EtOH, C_6H_6.

Zincke, Ossenbeck, *Ann.*, 1899, **307**, 16.
Leeds, *J. Am. Chem. Soc.*, 1880, **2**, 285.

1 : 2 : 4 : 6-Tetrahydroxynaphthalene.
Tetra-acetyl : leaflets from AcOH. M.p. 181–2°.

Dimroth, Kerkovius, *Ann.*, 1913, **399**, 39.

1 : 2 : 4 : 7-Tetrahydroxynaphthalene.
Tetra-acetyl : cryst. from ligroin. M.p. 140–1°.

See previous reference.

1 : 4 : 5 : 8 - Tetrahydroxynaphthalene (*Leuconaphthazarin*).

Yellow plates or prisms from HCl. M.p. 153–4°. Mod. sol. EtOH, C_6H_6. Spar. sol. H_2O, pet. ether. Turns red in air.

Tetra-Me ether : $C_{14}H_{16}O_4$. MW, 248. Cryst. from AcOH. M.p. about 170°. Sol. AcOH, toluene, xylene.

1 : 4-*Diacetyl* : plates from AcOEt. M.p. 241–3°. Very sol. Me_2CO. Sol. EtOH. Insol. $CHCl_3$, xylene.

Tetra-acetyl : leaflets from AcOH. M.p. 277–9° decomp. Sol. hot AcOH. Spar. sol. other solvents.

Zincke, Schmidt, *Ann.*, 1895, **286**, 37.
Badische, D.R.P., 129,074, (*Chem. Zentr.*, 1902, I, 691).
Perkin, Weizmann, *J. Chem. Soc.*, 1906, **89**, 1658.
Wheeler, Edwards, *J. Am. Chem. Soc.*, 1916, **38**, 387; 1917, **39**, 2465.

2 : 3 : 4 : 6-Tetrahydroxyphenacyl Alcohol.
See Gossypitol.

1 : 4 : 5 : 6-Tetrahydroxyphenanthrene

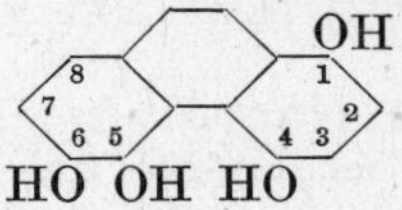

$C_{14}H_{10}O_4$ MW, 242

Tetra-Me ether : $C_{18}H_{18}O_4$. MW, 298. Light brown needles from MeOH. M.p. 118–20°.
Picrate : dark chocolate needles from EtOH. M.p. 158°.

Gulland, Virden, *J. Chem. Soc.*, 1928, 1486.

2 : 3 : 5 : 6-Tetrahydroxyphenanthrene.
2 : 6-*Di-Me ether* : sinomenol. $C_{16}H_{14}O_4$. MW, 270. M.p. 176°. *Diacetyl* : m.p. 206°.
Tetra-Me ether : cryst. from EtOH. M.p. 124–5°. *Picrate* : m.p. 123–5°.

Kondo, Ochiai, *Chem. Abstracts*, 1928, 22, 4532.
Goto, *Chem. Abstracts*, 1927, 21, 1654.

Tetrahydroxyphenyl styryl Ketone.
See 2′ : 3′ : 4′ : 6′-Tetrahydroxychalkone.

8 : 9 : 11 : 12-Tetrahydroxystearic Acid.
See Sativic Acid.

Tetrahydroxysuccinic Acid.
See Diketosuccinic Acid.

Tetrahydroxytetramethylmethane.
See Pentaerythritol.

2 : 3 : 4 : 5 - Tetrahydroxytoluene (5-*Methylapionol*)

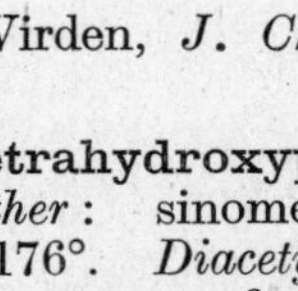

$C_7H_8O_4$ MW, 156

Cryst. from toluene. M.p. 170–1°. Sol. H_2O, EtOH. Spar. sol. C_6H_6, toluene. NaOH ⟶ intense green col. ⟶ blue on shaking in air.

4-*Me ether* : $C_8H_{10}O_4$. MW, 170. *Triacetyl* : m.p. 91–2°.
Tetra-Me ether : $C_{11}H_{16}O_4$. MW, 212. M.p. 51–2°.
Tetra-acetyl : cryst. from MeOH. M.p. 132–3°. Sol. most org. solvents.

Thiele, Winter, *Ann.*, 1900, **311**, 352.
Erdtman, *Chem. Abstracts*, 1934, **28**, 1337.

2 : 3 : 4 : 6-Tetrahydroxytoluene.
4-*Me ether* : cryst. Oxidises at 134°. Sol. H_2O, AcOEt. Mod. sol. EtOH, Et_2O. Insol. C_6H_6, ligroin. *Triacetyl* : cryst. from AcOEt. M.p. 174°.

Konya, *Monatsh.*, 1900, **21**, 430.

2 : 3 : 5 : 6-Tetrahydroxytoluene.
Tetra-acetyl : needles from EtOH. M.p. 198°.

Fichter, *Ann.*, 1908, **361**, 401.

1 : 2 : 8 : 9-Tetrahydroxyxanthone

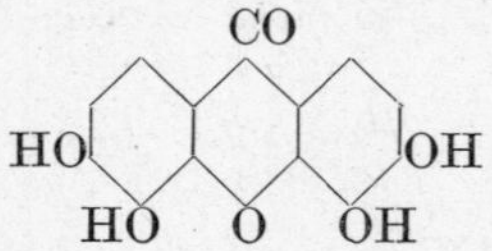

$C_{13}H_8O_6$ MW, 260

Light brown cryst. powder. Sol. EtOH, Me_2CO. Spar. sol. hot H_2O. Insol. $CHCl_3$, C_6H_6. NaOH $\longrightarrow$ yellowish-brown sol.
Tetra-acetyl : cryst. from C_6H_6. M.p. 237°.

Buchka, *Ann.*, 1881, **209**, 270.

2 : 4 : 5 : 6-Tetrahydroxy-*m*-xylene

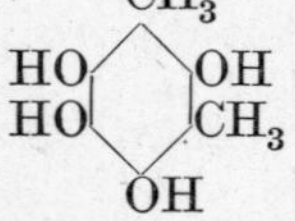

$C_8H_{10}O_4$ MW, 170

Needles from Et_2O–ligroin. M.p. 189° (rapid heat.). Sol. H_2O, EtOH, Et_2O. Insol. ligroin. Conc. H_2SO_4 $\longrightarrow$ green col. $\longrightarrow$ bluish-violet on dilution.
4-*Me ether* : prisms from C_6H_6. M.p. 125°. *Triacetyl* : cryst. from EtOH. M.p. 76°. Sol. EtOH, Et_2O, C_6H_6, ligroin.
Tetra-acetyl : needles from boiling EtOH. M.p. 154°. Sol. Et_2O. Insol. cold H_2O, EtOH.

Brunnmayr, *Monatsh.*, 1900, **21**, 10.
Bosse, *ibid.*, 1028.

2 : 3 : 5 : 6-Tetrahydroxy-*p*-xylene

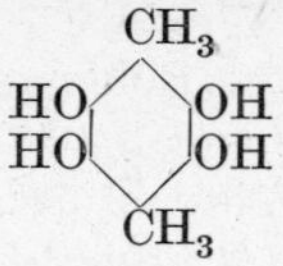

$C_8H_{10}O_4$ MW, 170

2 : 5-*Diacetyl* : needles from AcOH. M.p. 223°.
Tetra-acetyl : needles from EtOH. M.p. 242°.

Fichter, *Ann.*, 1908, **361**, 378.

***sym*.-Tetraiodoacetone**

$I_2CH{\cdot}CO{\cdot}CHI_2$

$C_3H_2OI_4$ MW, 562

Yellow needles. M.p. 142°. Very sol. Me_2CO.

Angeli, Levi, *Gazz. chim. ital.*, 1893, **23**, ii, 97.
Lederer, D.R.P., 95,440.

1 : 2 : 3 : 4-Tetraiodobenzene

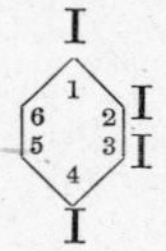

$C_6H_2I_4$ MW, 582

Prisms from CS_2 or Et_2O–AcOH. M.p. 136° (114°). Sublimes. Sol. EtOH, Et_2O, $CHCl_3$.

Willgerodt, Arnold, *Ber.*, 1901, **34**, 3353.
Körner, Belasio, *Atti accad. Lincei*, 1908, **17**, I, 688.

1 : 2 : 3 : 5-Tetraiodobenzene.
Cryst. from AcOH or Et_2O. M.p. 148°. Sublimes. Sol. boiling AcOH. Spar. sol. EtOH, Et_2O, $CHCl_3$.

Willgerodt, Arnold, *Ber.*, 1901, **34**, 3350.

1 : 2 : 4 : 5-Tetraiodobenzene.
Needles from Et_2O, prisms from C_6H_6. M.p. 254° (165°). Sol. AcOH, CS_2. Very spar. sol. EtOH, Et_2O. Sublimes in vacuo.

Willgerodt, Arnold, *Ber.*, 1901, **34**, 3352.
Körner, Belasio, *Atti accad. Lincei*, 1908, **17**, I, 687.

Tetraiodobenzoquinone.
See Iodanil.

Tetraiodoethylene (*Periodoethylene*)

$I_2C{:}CI_2$

C_2I_4 MW, 532

Lemon-yellow leaflets from AcOH. M.p. 192° (187°). D^{20} 2·983. Very sol. CS_2.

Spar. sol. abs. EtOH. Forms add. comps. with amines. Dissociates in sunlight $\longrightarrow I_2 + C_2I_2$.

Datta, Prosad, *J. Am. Chem. Soc.*, 1917, **39**, 451.
Biltz, Küppers, *Ber.*, 1904, **37**, 4415.

Tetraiodoisophthalic Acid

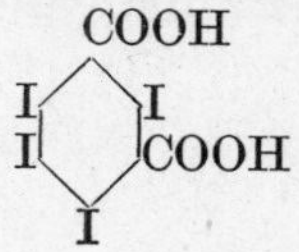

$C_8H_2O_4I_4$ MW, 670

Prisms from AcOH. M.p. 308–12° decomp. Sol. MeOH. Very spar. sol. Et_2O, AcOH.

Rupp, *Ber.*, 1896, **29**, 1632.

Tetraiodomethane.
See Carbon tetraiodide.

Tetraiodophthalic Acid

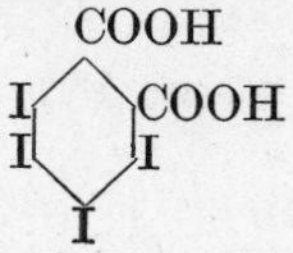

$C_8H_2O_4I_4$ MW, 670

Needles from $PhNO_2$. M.p. 324–7°. Very spar. sol. EtOH, Et_2O, AcOH.

Mono-Me ester: $C_9H_4O_4I_4$. MW, 684. Yellow cryst. from AcOH. M.p. 298° decomp.

Anhydride: $C_8O_3I_4$. MW, 652. Yellow needles from $PhNO_2$. M.p. 325° (320–5°).

Rupp, *Ber.*, 1896, **29**, 1634.
Pratt, Shup, *J. Am. Chem. Soc.*, 1918, **40**, 254.

Tetraiodopyrrole.
See Iodol.

Tetraiodoterephthalic Acid

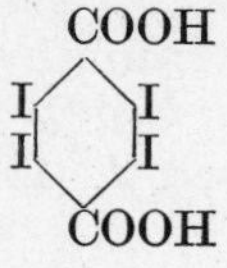

$C_8H_2O_4I_4$ MW, 670

Prisms from AcOH. M.p. 315–20° decomp. Sol. EtOH. Spar. sol. Et_2O, AcOH, C_6H_6.

Di-Me ester: $C_{10}H_6O_4I_4$. MW, 698. Cryst. from xylene. M.p. 310–12°. Very spar. sol. H_2O.

Di-Et ester: $C_{12}H_{10}O_4I_4$. MW, 726. Cryst. from xylene. M.p. 262·5°.

Dipropyl ester: $C_{14}H_{14}O_4I_4$. MW, 754. M.p. 239°.

Dichloride: $C_8O_2Cl_2I_4$. MW, 707. Cryst. from $CHCl_3$. M.p. 279°. Very stable towards NaOH.

Lütjens, *Ber.*, 1896, **29**, 2836.
Rupp, *ibid.*, 1629.

2 : 3 : 4 : 5-Tetraiodotoluene

$C_7H_4I_4$ MW, 596

Yellow needles from C_6H_6. M.p. 284–5°. Mod. sol. C_6H_6. Spar. sol. EtOH.

Wheeler, *Am. Chem. J.*, 1910, **44**, 506.

2 : 3 : 4 : 6-Tetraiodotoluene.
Needles from C_6H_6. M.p. 170°. Spar. sol. EtOH.

Wheeler, *Am. Chem. J.*, 1910, **44**, 133.

2 : 3 : 5 : 6-Tetraiodotoluene.
Needles from C_6H_6. M.p. 125°. Sol. C_6H_6. Spar. sol. EtOH.

Wheeler, *Am. Chem. J.*, 1910, **44**, 499.

1 : 3 : 4 : 6-Tetraketo-1 : 6-diphenylhexane.
See Diphenacyl Diketone.

Tetralin.
See Tetrahydronaphthalene.

Tetralol.
See Tetrahydronaphthol.

Tetralone.
See Ketotetrahydronaphthalene.

2 : 3 : 4 : 6-Tetramethylacetanilide.
See under Isoduridine.

Tetramethylacetone.
Di-isopropyl Ketone, *q.v.*

Tetramethylalloxantin.
See Amalic Acid.

Tetramethylammonium bromide

$(CH_3)_4NBr$

$C_4H_{12}NBr$ MW, 154

Volatile cryst. Sublimes with decomp. above 230°. Sol. H_2O. Spar. sol. abs. EtOH. Insol. Et_2O, $CHCl_3$.

Duvillier, Buisine, *Ann. chim. phys.*, 1881, **23**, 327.
Schmidt, *Ann.*, 1892, **267**, 265.

Tetramethylammonium chloride

$(CH_3)_4NCl$

$C_4H_{12}NCl$ MW, 109·5

Volatile cryst. Decomp. above 230° to trimethylamine + CH_3Cl. Sol. H_2O, EtOH. Insol. $CHCl_3$.

Vincent, Chappuis, *Bull. soc. chim.*, 1886, **45**, 502.

Tetramethylammonium hydroxide

$(CH_3)_4N{\cdot}OH$

$C_4H_{13}ON$ MW, 91

Pentahydrate (+ $5H_2O$): hygroscopic needles. M.p. 63°. Decomp. on dist. to trimethylamine and CH_3OH. Very sol. H_2O. Absorbs CO_2 rapidly. Gentle warming at 40–50° ⟶ *trihydrate* (+ $3H_2O$), m.p. 60°. Careful warming *in vacuo* ⟶ *monohydrate* (+ $1H_2O$), decomp. at 130° to trimethylamine and CH_3OH. Very powerful alkali, comparable with NaOH. The salts form a large number of add. comps. with metal and other halides.

Walker, Johnston, *J. Chem. Soc.*, 1905, **87**, 958.
Schmidt, *Ann.*, 1892, **267**, 267.
Hofmann, *Ann.*, 1851, **79**, 18.

Tetramethylammonium iodide

$(CH_3)_4NI$

$C_4H_{12}NI$ MW, 201

Prisms. Decomp. above 230°. Spar. sol. cold H_2O, abs. EtOH. Insol. Et_2O, $CHCl_3$. Triboluminescent.

Chablay, *Ann. chim.*, 1914, **1**, 477.
Hofmann, *Ann.*, 1851, **79**, 16.

1 : 3 : 5 : 7-Tetramethylanthracene

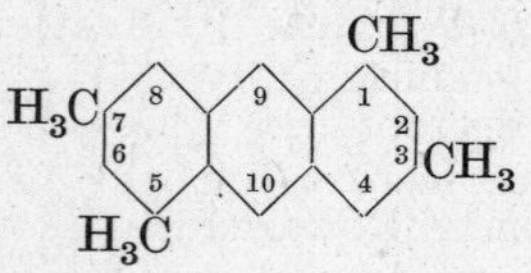

$C_{18}H_{18}$ MW, 234

Yellowish leaflets from EtOH. M.p. 163–4°. *Picrate*: m.p. 189–90°.

Seer, *Monatsh.*, 1912, **33**, 42.

1 : 3 : 6 : 8-Tetramethylanthracene. Pale yellow plates with green fluor. from AcOH. M.p. 281–3° (280°). Sol. hot EtOH, hot Et_2O. Mod. sol. $CHCl_3$. CrO_3 in AcOH ⟶ 1 : 3 : 6 : 8-tetramethylanthraquinone.

Seer, *Monatsh.*, 1912, **33**, 36.
Anschütz, *Ann.*, 1886, **235**, 174.
Dewar, Jones, *J. Chem. Soc.*, 1904, **85**, 217.

2 : 3 : 6 : 7-Tetramethylanthracene. Pale yellow plates from CS_2. M.p. 301°. Sublimes. Sol. AcOH, CS_2, C_6H_6. Spar. sol. EtOH.

Morgan, Coulson, *J. Chem. Soc.*, 1931, 2331.

1 : 3 : 5 : 7-Tetramethylanthraquinone

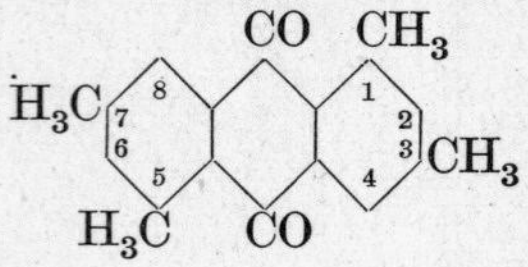

$C_{18}H_{16}O_2$ MW, 264

Yellow needles from EtOH. M.p. 235°. Sol. AcOH, C_6H_6. Very spar. sol. EtOH. Sol. conc. H_2SO_4 with deep red col. Sublimes. HNO_3 (D 1·1) at 190–210° ⟶ anthraquinone-1 : 3 : 5 : 7-tetracarboxylic acid. Dist. with Zn dust ⟶ 1 : 3 : 5 : 7-tetramethylanthracene.

Seer, *Monatsh.*, 1912, **33**, 39.

1 : 3 : 6 : 8-Tetramethylanthraquinone. M.p. 228–30° (172–3°).

Seer, *Monatsh.*, 1912, **33**, 36.
Dewar, Jones, *J. Chem. Soc.*, 1904, **85**, 218.
Börnstein, Schliewiensky, Szczesny-Heyl, *Ber.*, 1926, **59**, 2815.

2 : 3 : 5 : 8-Tetramethylanthraquinone. Yellow needles. M.p. 178°.

Fieser, Fieser, *J. Am. Chem. Soc.*, 1935, **57**, 1679.

2 : 3 : 6 : 7-Tetramethylanthraquinone. Yellow needles or plates from AcOH. M.p. 330°. Sublimes. Sol. conc. H_2SO_4 with deep red col.

Morgan, Coulson, *J. Chem. Soc.*, 1931, 2329.

2 : 3 : 6 : 8-Tetramethylanthraquinone. Yellow needles. M.p. 196°.

Fieser, Fieser, *J. Am. Chem. Soc.*, 1935, **57**, 1679.

2 : 4 : 5 : 4′-Tetramethylazobenzene (5-p-*Tolueneazo-ψ-cumene*)

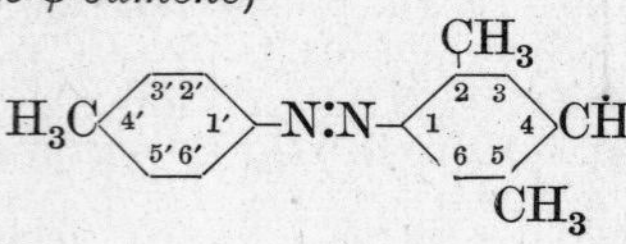

$C_{16}H_{18}N_2$ MW, 238

Yellow needles. M.p. 58°.

Michaelis, Petow, *Ber.*, 1898, **31**, 994.

2:3:2′:3′-Tetramethylazobenzene (3:3′-*Azo-o-xylene*).

Orange needles. M.p. 110–11°. Sol. EtOH, Et_2O, C_6H_6.

Noelting, Stricker, *Ber.*, 1888, **21**, 3139.

2:4:2′:4′-Tetramethylazobenzene (4:4′-*Azo-m-xylene*).

Red needles from EtOH. M.p. 129° (126°). Sol. EtOH, Et_2O.

Noelting, Stricker, *Ber.*, 1888, **21**, 3141.
Vorländer, Meyer, *Ann.*, 1902, **320**, 128.

2:4:3′:5′-Tetramethylazobenzene (4:5′-*Azo-m-xylene*).

Red plates or needles from EtOH. M.p. 46–7°. Sol. common org. solvents.

Zincke, Jaenke, *Ber.*, 1888, **21**, 543.

2:5:2′:5′-Tetramethylazobenzene (2:2′-*Azo-p-xylene*).

Yellow needles. M.p. 119°.

Noelting, Stricker, *Ber.*, 1888, **21**, 3143.

3:4:3′:4′-Tetramethylazobenzene (4:4′-*Azo-o-xylene*).

Red needles. M.p. 140–1°.

Noelting, Stricker, *Ber.*, 1888, **21**, 3140.

3:5:3′:5′-Tetramethylazobenzene (5:5′-*Azo-m-xylene*).

Orange needles. M.p. 136–7°. Sol. EtOH, Et_2O.

Noelting, Stricker, *Ber.*, 1888, **21**, 3142.

2 : 3 : 4 : 5-Tetramethylbenzaldehyde

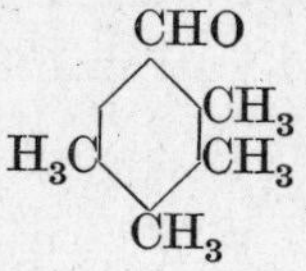

$C_{11}H_{14}O$ MW, 162

Cryst. M.p. 39°. Very sol. most org. solvents. Oxidises in air. $KMnO_4 \longrightarrow$ 2 : 3 : 4 : 5-tetramethylbenzoic acid.

Semicarbazone : needles from EtOH. M.p. 229–30°.

Auwers, Köckritz, *Ann.*, 1907, **352**, 316.

1 : 2 : 3 : 4-Tetramethylbenzene. *See* Prehnitene.

1 : 2 : 3 : 5-Tetramethylbenzene. *See* Isodurene.

1 : 2 : 4 : 5-Tetramethylbenzene. *See* Durene.

***N* : *N′*-Tetramethylbenzidine** (4 : 4′-*Tetramethyldiaminodiphenyl*)

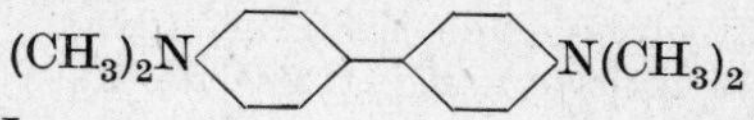

$C_{16}H_{20}N_2$ MW, 240

Needles from C_6H_6–pet. ether. M.p. 198° (193°). B.p. above 360°. Very sol. $CHCl_3$. Sol. hot AcOEt, hot C_6H_6. Spar. sol. Et_2O, boiling ligroin. Very spar. sol. MeOH, EtOH. Non-volatile in steam.

Monomethochloride : m.p. 228°. Sol. H_2O, EtOH.

Monomethiodide : needles from H_2O. M.p. 263°.

König, Seifert, *Ber.*, 1934, **67**, 2119.
Willstätter, Kalb, *Ber.*, 1904, **37**, 3765.
Ullmann, Dieterle, *ibid.*, 29.

2 : 3 : 4 : 5-Tetramethylbenzoic Acid (*Prehnitine-carboxylic acid*)

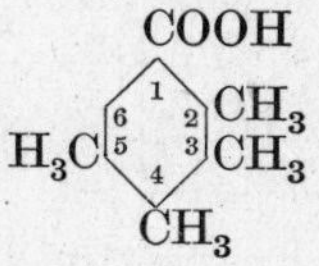

$C_{11}H_{14}O_2$ MW, 178

Needles from EtOH or ligroin. M.p. 168–9° (165°). Volatile in steam.

Me ester : $C_{12}H_{16}O_2$. MW, 192. Needles from $CHCl_3$. M.p. 36°. Sol. EtOH, Et_2O, $CHCl_3$, ligroin.

Amide : $C_{11}H_{15}ON$. MW, 177. Needles from EtOH. M.p. 222°. Spar. sol. Et_2O.

v. Meyer, Molz, *Ber.*, 1897, **30**, 1279.
Smith, Harris, *J. Am. Chem. Soc.*, 1935, **57**, 1292.

2 : 3 : 4 : 6-Tetramethylbenzoic Acid (*Isodurene-carboxylic acid*).

Prisms from ligroin. M.p. 164–5°.

Amide : needles from H_2O. M.p. 141–2°.

Nitrile : $C_{11}H_{13}N$. MW, 159. Cryst. from EtOH. M.p. 68–9°. Stable to HCl at 200°. HCl at 250° $\longrightarrow$ isodurene.

Gattermann, *Ber.*, 1899, **32**, 1118.

2 : 3 : 5 : 6 - Tetramethylbenzoic Acid (*Durene-carboxylic acid*).

Prisms from H_2O or ligroin. M.p. 179° (176·5°). Sol. EtOH, boiling H_2O. Volatile in steam. Sublimes. HCl at 200–20° $\longrightarrow$ durene.

Me ester : leaflets from EtOH. M.p. 59°.

Amide : cryst. from H_2O. M.p. 178°.

Nitrile: needles from EtOH. M.p. 76–7°. Conc. HCl at 210–20° ⟶ durene.

Jacobsen, *Ber.*, 1889, **22**, 1223.
Gattermann, *Ber.*, 1899, **32**, 1119.
Meyer, Wöhler, *Ber.*, 1896, **29**, 2572.

2 : 3 : 4 : 6 - Tetramethylbenzophenone (*Benzoylisodurene*)

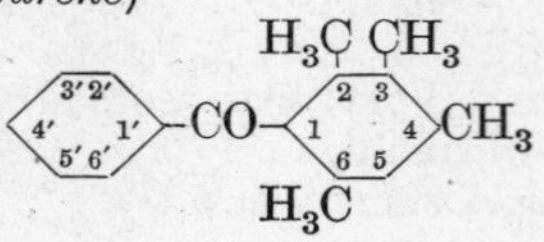

$C_{17}H_{18}O$ MW, 238

Cryst. M.p. 62–3°. B.p. about 300°.

Essner, Gossin, *Bull. soc. chim.*, 1884, **42**, 171.

2 : 3 : 5 : 6 - Tetramethylbenzophenone (*Benzoyldurene*).

M.p. 119°. B.p. 343–343·5°/725 mm. Very sol. hot EtOH. KOH fusion ⟶ durene + benzoic acid.

Friedel, Crafts, Ador, *Ann. chim. phys.*, 1884, **1**, 511.

2 : 4 : 5 : 4′-Tetramethylbenzophenone.
Viscous oil. B.p. 220°/22 mm.
Oxime: cryst. from EtOH. M.p. 151°.

Morgan, Coulson, *J. Chem. Soc.*, 1929, 2554.

2 : 4 : 2′ : 4′-Tetramethylbenzophenone.
B.p. 190°/10 mm., 188°/7 mm. D^{15} 1·043. n_D^{12} 1·5876. Does not react with hydroxylamine or phenylhydrazine. Zn dust in alc. alk. sol. ⟶ 2 : 4-dimethylbenzoic acid.

Böeseken, *Rec. trav. chim.*, 1907, **26**, 285.
Cohen, *Rec. trav. chim.*, 1919, **38**, 119.

2 : 5 : 2′ : 5′-Tetramethylbenzophenone.
Viscous liq. B.p. 325–7°. Prolonged boiling ⟶ 1 : 4 : 6-trimethylanthracene.

Elbs, *J. prakt. Chem.*, 1887, **35**, 481.

3 : 4 : 3′ : 4′-Tetramethylbenzophenone.
Cryst. from EtOH. M.p. 140°. Sol. $CHCl_3$, C_6H_6. Spar. sol. Et_2O.
Oxime: cryst. from EtOH. M.p. 147°.
Phenylhydrazone: yellow micro-cryst. M.p. 130°.

Bistrzycki, Reintke, *Ber.*, 1905, **38**, 844.

2 : 3 : 5 : 6-Tetramethylbenzoquinone.
See Duroquinone.

2 : 2 : 3 : 3-Tetramethylbutane (*Hexamethylethane, di*-tert.-*butyl*)

$(CH_3)_3C{\cdot}C(CH_3)_3$

C_8H_{18} MW, 114

Cryst. from Et_2O. M.p. 104° (100·7–101·4°). B.p. 106–7°. Volatile.

Flood, Calingaert, *J. Am. Chem. Soc.*, 1934, **56**, 1211.
Whitmore, Stehman, Herndon, *J. Am. Chem. Soc.*, 1933, **55**, 3807.

2 : 3 : 2′ : 3′-Tetramethylcarbanilide (2 : 3 : 2′ : 3′-*Tetramethyldiphenylurea*)

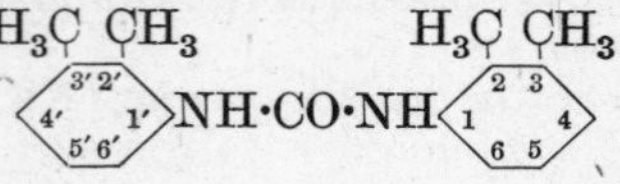

$C_{17}H_{20}ON_2$ MW, 268

Cryst. from EtOH. M.p. 242°.

Mazourewitch, *Bull. soc. chim.*, 1924, **35**, 1185.

2 : 4 : 2′ : 4′-Tetramethylcarbanilide (2 : 4 : 2′ : 4′-*Tetramethyldiphenylurea*).
Needles from AcOH. M.p. 263–5°.

Thomson, Wilson, *J. Chem. Soc.*, 1933, 1263.

2 : 5 : 2′ : 5′-Tetramethylcarbanilide (2 : 5 : 2′ : 5′-*Tetramethyldiphenylurea*).
Needles from AcOH. M.p. 285° (sealed tube).

See previous reference.

3 : 4 : 3′ : 4′-Tetramethylcarbanilide (3 : 4 : 3′ : 4′-*Tetramethyldiphenylurea*).
M.p. 236°.

Mailhe, *Compt. rend.*, 1923, **176**, 903.

1 : 2 : 3 : 4-Tetramethylcyclohexane (*Hexahydroprehnitene*)

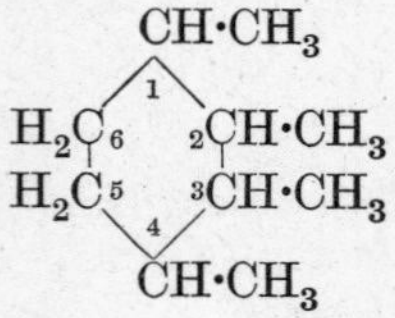

$C_{10}H_{20}$ MW, 140

B.p. 84°/5 mm. D_4^{20} 0·8219. n_D^{20} 1·4531.

Mitchell, Marvel, *J. Am. Chem. Soc.*, 1933, **55**, 4278.

1 : 2 : 3 : 5-Tetramethylcyclohexane (*Hexahydroisodurene*).

Cis:

B.p. 168–70°/762 mm. D_4^{20} 0·8166. n_{He}^{20} 1·44847.

Trans :

B.p. 162–4°/765 mm. D_4^{20} 0·8140. n_{He}^{20} 1·44657.

Eisenlohr, *Chem. Abstracts*, 1926, **20**, 171.

1 : 2 : 4 : 5-Tetramethylcyclohexane (*Hexahydrodurene*).

The following compounds have been described :

(i) B.p. 172–4°/730 mm. D_4^{20} 0·7759. n_D^{20} 1·4205.

Pictet, Ramseyer, Kaiser, *Ann. chim.*, 1918, **10**, 297.

(ii) B.p. 169–170·5°/711 mm. D_4^{20} 0·811. n_D^{20} 1·4451.

Willstätter, Hatt, *Ber.*, 1912, **45**, 1473.

(iii) B.p. 160·5–161·5°. $D_4^{13·1}$ 0·7910. $n_D^{13·1}$ 1·437.

Auwers, *Ann.*, 1920, **420**, 108.

(iv)

Cis :

B.p. 171°/755 mm. D_4^{20} 0·8122. n_{He}^{20} 1·44647.

Trans :

B.p. 166–8°. D_4^{20} 1·8100. n_{He}^{20} 1·44446.

Eisenlohr, *Chem. Abstracts*, 1926, **20**, 171.

1 : 2 : 2 : 3-Tetramethylcyclopentane-1-carboxylic Acid.

See Campholic Acid.

1 : 2 : 3 : 3-Tetramethylcyclopentene.

See Campholene.

3 : 3′-Tetramethyldiaminobenzhydrol

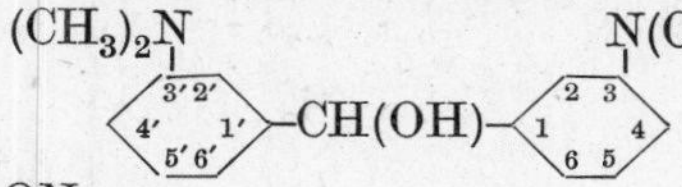

$C_{17}H_{22}ON_2$ MW, 270

Prisms from Et_2O. M.p. 72–3°. Sols. in acids are colourless.

Baeyer, *Ann.*, 1907, **354**, 194.

3 : 4′-Tetramethyldiaminobenzhydrol.

Needles from EtOH. M.p. 100–1°. Sol. hot AcOH with yellowish-green col.

Baeyer, *Ann.*, 1907, **354**, 191.

4 : 4′-Tetramethyldiaminobenzhydrol (*Michler's Hydrol*).

Green leaflets from C_6H_6. M.p. 98° (102–3°). Sol. Et_2O, AcOH, C_6H_6, hot EtOH. Insol. H_2O. 1 mol. Br in cold ⟶ *p*-dimethylaminobenzaldehyde + *p*-bromodimethylaniline. Gives blue col. with H·CHO, CH_3·CHO, chloral, Me_2CO, C_6H_5·CHO, and acetophenone. Intermediate for basic dyes.

Me ether : $C_{18}H_{24}ON_2$. MW, 284. Cryst. from ligroin. M.p. 71–2°. Sol. EtOH, Et_2O, C_6H_6. Spar. sol. ligroin.

Benzyl ether : plates from ligroin. M.p. 102–3°.

Dimethiodide : leaflets from EtOH. M.p. 195°.

B,$C_6H_3(NO_2)_3$-1 : 3 : 5 : black needles. M.p. 75·5°.

Bogert, Ruderman, *J. Am. Chem. Soc.*, 1922, **44**, 2616.
Cohen, *Rec. trav. chim.*, 1919, **38**, 121.
Badische, D.R.P., 27,032.
Bielecki, Koleniew, *Chem. Zentr.*, 1908, II, 877.
Möhlau, Heinze, *Ber.*, 1902, **35**, 360.
National Aniline & Chemical Co., U.S.P., 1,942,820, (*Chem. Zentr.*, 1934, I, 2826).

2 : 2′-Tetramethyldiaminobenzophenone

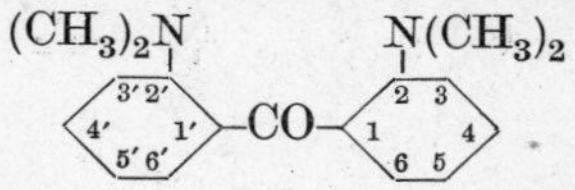

$C_{17}H_{20}ON_2$ MW, 268

Yellow prisms or needles from EtOH. M.p. 122° (117–18°). Sol. EtOH, Et_2O, C_6H_6. Spar. sol. H_2O. Volatile in steam. Does not form oxime or phenylhydrazone.

Picrate : yellow leaflets from EtOH. Decomp. at 160–2°.

Baeyer, *Ber.*, 1905, **38**, 2764.
Bertram, *J. prakt. Chem.*, 1902, **65**, 340.

3 : 3′-Tetramethyldiaminobenzophenone.

Yellow prisms from EtOH.Aq. M.p. 59–60°. Sol. most org. solvents. Sols. in acids are colourless.

Baeyer, *Ann.*, 1907, **354**, 193.

3 : 4′-Tetramethyldiaminobenzophenone.

Brownish-yellow cryst. from EtOH or Et_2O. M.p. 77–78·5°.

Hydrochloride : needles from EtOH. M.p. 278–80° decomp. Decomp. by H_2O.

Baeyer, *Ann.*, 1907, **354**, 190.

4 : 4′-Tetramethyldiaminobenzophenone (*Michler's Ketone*).

Leaflets from EtOH. M.p. 179° (172–172·5°). B.p. above 360° decomp. Sol. warm C_6H_6. Mod. sol. EtOH. Very spar. sol. Et_2O. Insol. H_2O. NaHg in EtOH ⟶ 4 : 4′-tetramethyldiaminobenzhydrol. Intermediate for basic dyes.

Oxime : cryst. from EtOH. M.p. 233°.

Phenylhydrazone : needles from C_6H_6–EtOH. M.p. 174–5°.
Di-Me acetal : pale yellow needles from MeOH. M.p. 130°.
Di-Et acetal : m.p. 118°.
Dimethobromide : yellowish plates + $2H_2O$ from EtOH.Aq. M.p. anhyd. 168°.
Dimethiodide : yellowish leaflets from EtOH. M.p. 105°. At 150° decomp. into its components.
Hydrazone : yellow needles from EtOH. M.p. 150°.
Azine : brownish-red prisms from xylene. M.p. 253°.
Picrate : purple-red prisms. M.p. 156–7°.

Michler, Moro, *Ber.*, 1879, **12**, 1168.
Michler, *Ber.*, 1876, **9**, 716.
Fehrmann, *Ber.*, 1887, **20**, 2845.

2 : 2′-Tetramethyldiaminodiphenyl

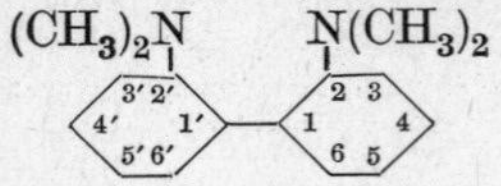

$C_{16}H_{20}N_2$ MW, 240

Plates from pet. ether. M.p. 72–3°.
Hydriodide : m.p. 256–7°.
Methiodide : prisms from H_2O. M.p. 190–2°.

Shaw, Turner, *J. Chem. Soc.*, 1933, 139.

3 : 3′-Tetramethyldiaminodiphenyl.
Needles from EtOH. M.p. 126–8°.

Dutt, *J. Chem. Soc.*, 1926, 1181.

4 : 4′-Tetramethyldiaminodiphenyl.
See N : *N′*-Tetramethylbenzidine.

Tetramethyldiaminodiphenyl disulphide
(*Dithiodimethylaniline, tetramethyldithioaniline*)

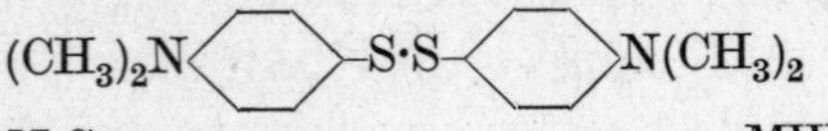

$C_{16}H_{20}N_2S_2$ MW, 304

Yellow needles from EtOH. M.p. 118°. Sol. CS_2. Spar. sol. EtOH, Et_2O, ligroin, hot C_6H_6. Insol. H_2O.

Söderbäck, *Ann.*, 1919, **419**, 276.
Merz, Weith, *Ber.*, 1886, **19**, 1571.

Tetramethyldiaminodiphenyl Ether.
See under N-Dimethyl-*p*-aminophenol.

3 : 3′ - Tetramethyldiaminodiphenyl - methane

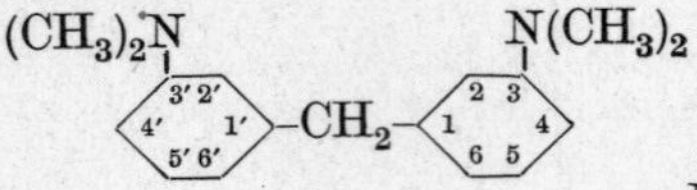

$C_{17}H_{22}N_2$ MW, 254

Yellowish oil with green fluor.
Dimethiodide : needles from H_2O. M.p. 165°.

Scholl, *Monatsh.*, 1918, **39**, 236.

4 : 4′ - Tetramethyldiaminodiphenyl - methane (*Methane Base*).

Leaflets or plates from EtOH or ligroin. M.p. 91°. B.p. 390°. Non-volatile in steam. Sol. Et_2O, C_6H_6, hot EtOH. Sol. acids. Ox. ⟶ Michler's Hydrol ⟶ Michler's Ketone.
B,$C_6H_4(NO_2)_2$-1 : 3 : red cryst. M.p. 76°.
B,$C_6H_3(NO_2)_3$-1 : 3 : 5 : violet needles. M.p. 114°.
Monopicrate : yellow leaflets. M.p. 185°.
Dipicrate : m.p. 178°.
Dimethiodide : yellow leaflets. Becomes green at 193° and melts at 214° decomp.
N : N′-*Dioxide* : needles + $2H_2O$ from EtOH–Et_2O. M.p. 147°, anhyd. 156°. Very sol. H_2O, EtOH. Reacts alkaline in solution. *B,2HCl* : m.p. 165·5–166° decomp. . *Dipicrate* : yellow needles from EtOH. M.p. 150·5–151° decomp.

Cohn, *Chem.-Ztg.*, 1900, **24**, 564.
Fischl, *Monatsh.*, 1914, **35**, 531.
Votoček, Krauz, *Ber.*, 1909, **42**, 1604.
Nathansohn, Müller, *Ber.*, 1889, **22**, 1882.
Höchst, D.R.P., 107,718, (*Chem. Zentr.*, 1900, I, 1110).

3 : 4′ - Tetramethyldiaminotriphenyl - methane

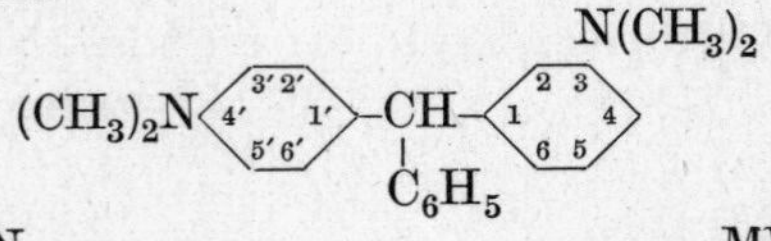

$C_{23}H_{26}N_2$ MW, 330

Cryst. from EtOH. M.p. 83–4°. Mod. sol. Et_2O, hot EtOH.

Baeyer, *Ann.*, 1907, **354**, 197.

4 : 4′ - Tetramethyldiaminotriphenyl - methane (*Leuco-Malachite Green*).

Cryst. in three forms. (i) Needles from C_6H_6. M.p. 102°. (ii) Plates from EtOH. M.p. 93–4°. (iii) Cryst. of lower indefinite m.p. Distils undecomp. in small quantities. Sol. Et_2O, C_6H_6, toluene. Mod. sol. EtOH. Spar. sol. ligroin. Insol. H_2O.
B,$C_6H_3(NO_2)_3$-1 : 3 : 5 : m.p. 88·5–89°.
Dimethiodide : plates or needles from H_2O. M.p. 231° (218–22°) decomp. into components.
N : N′-*Dioxide* : needles + 2 or $4H_2O$ from $CHCl_3$. M.p. 131·5–132·5°, anhyd. 188–9°.

Very sol. H_2O, EtOH. Very spar. sol. Et_2O, ligroin. Reacts alkaline.

Nencki, *Monatsh.*, 1888, **9**, 1148.
Fischer, *Ann.*, 1881, **206**, 122, 136.
Fischer, Fischer, Lehmann, *Ber.*, 1879, **12**, 798.

2 : 4 : 2′ : 4′-Tetramethyldiphenyl

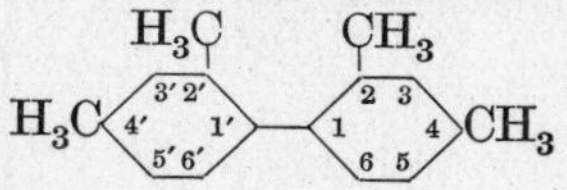

$C_{16}H_{18}$ MW, 210

Cryst. from EtOH. M.p. 41°. B.p. 288°/722 mm. Sol. Et_2O, C_6H_6, warm EtOH.

Scholl, Liese, Michelson, Grunewald, *Ber.*, 1910, **43**, 513.

2 : 5 : 2′ : 5′-Tetramethyldiphenyl.
Cryst. from EtOH. M.p. 50°. B.p. 284°/732 mm. Sol. Et_2O, C_6H_6.

Ullmann, Meyer, *Ann.*, 1904, **332**, 47.

3 : 4 : 3′ : 4′-Tetramethyldiphenyl.
Yellowish needles from EtOH. M.p. 76–7°. Sol. $CHCl_3$, Me_2CO, AcOEt, C_6H_6. Volatile in steam.

Crossley, Hampshire, *J. Chem. Soc.*, 1911, **99**, 726.

2 : 4 : 2′ : 4′-Tetramethyldiphenylamine

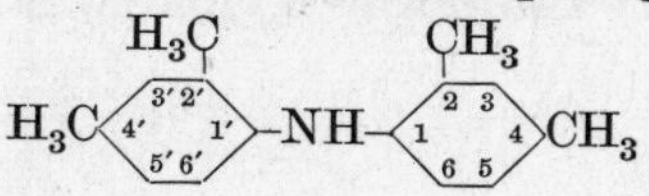

$C_{16}H_{19}N$ MW, 225

Cryst. M.p. 58–58·5°. B.p. 305–10°.
B,HCl : m.p. 166° decomp.

Müller, *Ber.*, 1887, **20**, 1042.
Bamberger, Brun, *Helv. Chim. Acta*, 1924, **7**, 118.

3 : 4 : 3′ : 4′-Tetramethyldiphenylamine.
Viscous oil. B.p. 340–5° decomp. (330–45°). Volatile in steam.

Müller, *Ber.*, 1887, **20**, 1041.

Tetramethyldiphenylurea.
See Tetramethylcarbanilide.

4 : 8 : 12 : 16-Tetramethyleicosane.
See Bixane.

Tetramethylene.
See Cyclobutane.

Tetramethylene bromide.
See 1 : 4-Dibromobutane.

Tetramethylene chloride.
See 1 : 4-Dichlorobutane.

Tetramethylenediamine.
See Putrescine.

Tetramethylene Glycol (1 : 4-*Dihydroxybutane, butandiol*-1 : 4)

$$OH{\cdot}CH_2{\cdot}CH_2{\cdot}CH_2{\cdot}CH_2OH$$

$C_4H_{10}O_2$ MW, 90

Viscous liq. Solidifies in freezing mixture to colourless needles, m.p. 16°. B.p. 230°, 120°/10 mm. Sol. H_2O, EtOH. Spar. sol. Et_2O. D^{20} 1·020. Dil. $HNO_3 \longrightarrow$ succinic acid. Bitter taste. Ppd. from aq. sol. by K_2CO_3.

Di-Me ether : $C_6H_{14}O_2$. MW, 118. B.p. 133°. D^{15} 0·8664. n_D^{15} 1·4031.

Me-Et ether : $C_7H_{16}O_2$. MW, 132. B.p. 145–6°/757 mm. D_4^{18} 0·8484. n_D^{18} 1·4012. Sol. EtOH, Et_2O.

Di-Et ether : $C_8H_{18}O_2$. MW, 146. B.p. 155–7°/730 mm., 59–60°/18 mm. D_4^{20} 0·8455. n_D^{20} 1·40610.

Dipropyl ether : $C_{10}H_{22}O_2$. MW, 174. B.p. 94–5°/20 mm. D_4^{20} 0·8409. n_D^{20} 1·41368.

Di-isopropyl ether : b.p. 77–8°/18 mm. D_4^{20} 0·8310. n_D^{20} 1·40954.

Diacetyl : m.p. 12°. B.p. 230°, 124°/20 mm. D^{15} 1·0479. n_D^{15} 1·4251.

Carbonate : m.p. 59°.

Succinate : *monomer*, m.p. 42°. B.p. 95–6°/2 mm. D_4^{60} 1·1732. n_D^{20} 1·4567. *Dimer*: m.p. 121°.

Azelate : *monomer*, m.p. 9°. B.p. 123–4°/2 mm.

Sebacate : *monomer*, m.p. 6°. B.p. 136–8°/2 mm.

Dibenzoyl : prisms or needles from pet. ether. M.p. 57·5° (53°).

Di-phenylurethane : cryst. from $CHCl_3$. M.p. 183–183·5°.

Di-1-naphthylurethane : needles from butyl alcohol. M.p. 198°.

Wojcik, Adkins, *J. Am. Chem. Soc.*, 1934, **56**, 2423.
Tallman, *ibid.*, 128.
Müller, Clostermeyer, *Monatsh.*, 1928, **49**, 28.
Bennett, Heathcoat, *J. Chem. Soc.*, 1929, 271.
Böeseken, *Rec. trav. chim.*, 1915, **34**, 100.

Tetramethyleneimine.
See Pyrrolidine.

Tetramethylene iodide.
See 1 : 4-Di-iodobutane.

Tetramethylene oxide.
See Tetrahydrofuran.

Tetramethylene sulphide.
See Tetrahydrothiophene.

Tetramethylene sulphone.
See under Tetrahydrothiophene.

Tetramethylethane.
See Dimethylbutane.

Tetramethylethylene.
See 2 : 3-Dimethylbutylene-2.

Tetramethylethylene glycol.
See Pinacol.

2 : 6 : 11 : 15-Tetramethylhexadecane.
See Crocetane.

Tetramethylhydracrylic Acid.
See 2-Hydroxy-1 : 1-dimethylisovaleric Acid.

2 : 3 : 2′ : 3′-Tetramethylhydrazobenzene (3 : 3′-*Hydrazo*-o-*xylene*)

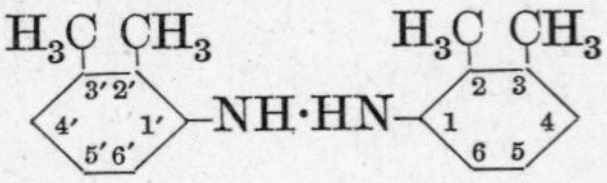

$C_{16}H_{20}N_2$ MW, 240

Colourless needles from EtOH. M.p. 149–50° (139–40°). Sol. most org. solvents. Oxidises easily in air.

Bamberger, *Ber.*, 1926, **59**, 428.

2 : 4 : 2′ : 4′-Tetramethylhydrazobenzene (4 : 4′-*Hydrazo*-m-*xylene*).
Needles from EtOH. M.p. 125–6° (120–2°).

See previous reference.

2 : 5 : 2′ : 5′-Tetramethylhydrazobenzene (2 : 2′-*Hydrazo*-p-*xylene*).
Needles from EtOH. M.p. 145°.

Nölting, Stricker, *Ber.*, 1888, **21**, 3143.

3 : 4 : 3′ : 4′-Tetramethylhydrazobenzene (4 : 4′-*Hydrazo*-o-*xylene*).
Needles from EtOH. M.p. 113–14° (106–7°).

Bamberger, *Ber.*, 1926, **59**, 428.

3 : 5 : 3′ : 5′-Tetramethylhydrazobenzene (5 : 5′-*Hydrazo*-m-*xylene*).
Needles from EtOH. M.p. 124–5°. Oxidises readily in air.

Nölting, Stricker, *Ber.*, 1888, **21**, 3142.

Tetramethylhydroquinone.
See Durohydroquinone.

Tetramethylhydurilic Acid.
See Deoxyamalic Acid.

Tetramethylmethane (2-*Methylisobutane, neopentane,* 2 : 2-*dimethylpropane*)

$C(CH_3)_4$

C_5H_{12} MW, 72

F.p. — 19·5°. B.p. 9·4°/760 mm. D_0^0 0·613. n_D^0 1·3513.

Whitmore, Fleming, *J. Am. Chem. Soc.*, 1933, **55**, 3803.

Tetramethylmethane - tetracarboxylic Acid.
See Methane-tetracetic Acid.

1 : 2 : 4 : 8-Tetramethylnaphthalene

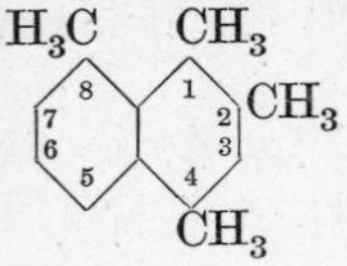

$C_{14}H_{16}$ MW, 184

Oil. B.p. 150°/10 mm.
Picrate: red needles. M.p. 145·5°.

Ruzicka, Ehmann, Mörgeli, *Helv. Chim. Acta*, 1933, **16**, 324.

1 : 2 : 5 : 6-Tetramethylnaphthalene.
Cryst. from EtOH. M.p. 118°. B.p. 150–60°/10 mm.
Picrate: red needles. M.p. 156–7° (154–154·5°).
Styphnate: cryst. from C_6H_6. M.p. 166° (162°).
$C_{14}H_{16},C_6H_3(NO_2)_3$-1 : 3 : 5 : orange-red needles from MeOH. M.p. 180–180·5° (178·5–179°).

Brunner, Hofer, Stein, *Monatsh.*, 1933, **63**, 96.
Ruzicka, Ehmann, Mörgeli, *Helv. Chim. Acta*, 1933, **16**, 320.

1 : 2 : 5 : 7-Tetramethylnaphthalene.
B.p. 155–8°/12 mm.
Picrate: orange-yellow needles from MeOH. M.p. 144–5°.
Styphnate: orange-yellow needles from MeOH. M.p. 144–5°.
$C_{14}H_{16},C_6H_3(NO_2)_3$-1 : 3 : 5 : pale yellow needles from EtOH. M.p. 167–8°.

Hosking, Brandt, *Ber.*, 1935, **68**, 289.
Ruzicka, Ehmann, Mörgeli, *Helv. Chim. Acta*, 1933, **16**, 323.

1 : 2 : 5 : 8-Tetramethylnaphthalene.
Oil. B.p. 150°/9 mm.
Picrate: red cryst. M.p. 137–8°.
$C_{14}H_{16},C_6H_3(NO_2)_3$-1 : 3 : 5 : orange - yellow needles. M.p. 158–9°.

Ruzicka, Ehmann, Mörgeli, *Helv. Chim. Acta*, 1933, **16**, 322.

1 : 2 : 6 : 8-Tetramethylnaphthalene.
Oil. B.p. 166–8°/15 mm.
Picrate: orange-red needles. M.p. 133·5–134°.
Styphnate: orange needles. M.p. 135–6°.

Ruzicka, Ehmann, Mörgeli, *Helv. Chim. Acta*, 1933, **16**, 321.

2 : 2 : 4 : 4-Tetramethylpentanol-3.
See Di-*tert*.-butylcarbinol.

2 : 2 : 4 : 4-Tetramethylpentanone-3.
See Pivalone.

2 : 3 : 4 : 5-Tetramethylphenol.
See Prehnitenol.

Tetramethylphenylenediamine.
See under Phenylenediamine.

1 : 2 : 4 : 5-Tetramethylpiperazine

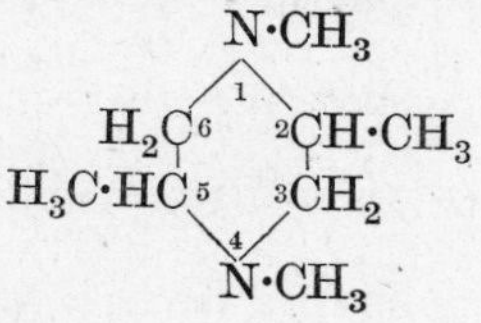

$C_8H_{18}N_2$ MW, 142

Syrup.
B,2HI : m.p. 257° decomp.
B,HI : cryst. M.p. 178° decomp.
Dimethiodide : cryst. from MeOH. M.p. 250°.
Dihydroxymethylate : cryst. from Et_2O–pet. ether. M.p. 224°.

Abderhalden, Haas, *Z. physiol. Chem.*, 1925, **149**, 94.

1 : 2 : 4 : 6-Tetramethylpiperazine.
Colourless liq. B.p. 163–4°. Misc. with H_2O and most org. solvents in all proportions.
B_2,H_2PtCl_6 : orange needles + $2H_2O$ from H_2O. Darkens at 270°. Decomp. at 275°.
Monomethiodide : needles from Et_2O–EtOH. M.p. 227°.
d-*Camphor*-β-*sulphonate* : needles or prisms from EtOH–Me_2CO. M.p. 223°. $[\alpha]_{5461}$ + 21·6° in H_2O.
d-α-*Bromocamphor*-β-*sulphonate* : cryst. from Me_2CO. M.p. 175°. $[\alpha]_{5461}$ + 97·4° in H_2O.
d - α - *Bromocamphor* - π - *sulphonate* : needles from Me_2CO. M.p. 249°. $[\alpha]_{5461}$ + 88·1° in H_2O.
Picrate : yellow cryst. Decomp. at 280°.

Pope, Read, *J. Chem. Soc.*, 1914, **105**, 224.

2 : 2 : 5 : 5-Tetramethylpiperazine.
Dinitroso deriv. : cryst. from AcOH. M.p. 208–10°.

Conant, Aston, *J. Am. Chem. Soc.*, 1928, **50**, 2788.

2 : 3 : 5 : 6-Tetramethylpiperazine.
Five optically inactive stereoisomeric forms are possible.

I.
Colourless needles. M.p. 45°. B.p. 177–8°. Readily sol. H_2O, $CHCl_3$.
Dihydrate : needles from Me_2CO. M.p. 84–5°. Very sol. H_2O $\longrightarrow$ alk. sol.
B,2HCl : prisms from EtOH.Aq. Does not melt below 300°.
Dinitroso deriv. : needles from EtOH. M.p. 157°.
Dibenzoyl : plates from EtOH. M.p. 247–8°.
Di-p-*toluenesulphonyl* : cryst. from Py. M.p. 308–9°.

II.
Liq. B.p. 183°. Very sol. H_2O.
B,2HCl : prisms from EtOH. Does not melt below 300°.
Dinitroso deriv. : yellow prisms from EtOH. M.p. 101–2°.
Dibenzoyl : prisms from Me_2CO–pet. ether. M.p. 175–6°.
Mono-p-*toluenesulphonyl* : needles from EtOH. M.p. 81–2°.
Di-p-*toluenesulphonyl* : plates from Py.Aq. M.p. 222°.
d-*Camphor*-10-*sulphonate* : m.p. 89–90°. $[\alpha]^{15}_{5461}$ + 35·7° in $CHCl_3$.

III.
Colourless cryst. M.p. 67–8°. B.p. 195–6°.
B,2HCl : plates + $1H_2O$ from EtOH.Aq. Does not melt below 300°.
Dinitroso deriv. : yellow prisms from EtOH. M.p. 173–4°.
Monobenzoyl : prisms from pet. ether. M.p. 85°.
Dibenzoyl : prisms from EtOH. M.p. 163–4°.
Mono-p-*toluenesulphonyl* : plates from EtOH.Aq., or pet. ether. M.p. 138–9°.
N-*Me* : $C_9H_{20}N_2$. MW, 156. M.p. 4–5°. B.p. 201–2°. Very hygroscopic. *Monohydrate* : prisms from Me_2CO. M.p. 73–4°. *B,HI* : prisms from EtOH or H_2O. M.p. 161–2°. *B,2HCl* : needles from EtOH.Aq.–Me_2CO. M.p. about 300°. *B,2HI* : prisms from EtOH. M.p. 240° decomp. *Nitroso deriv.* : m.p. 24–5°. B.p. 155–7°/15 mm.
N : N-*Di-Me* : $C_{10}H_{22}N_2$. MW, 170. B.p. 211–12°. *Monomethiodide* : needles from MeOH–Me_2CO. M.p. 272–4°.

IV.
Hydrated needles from H_2O. M.p. 53–5°.
B,2HCl : prisms from H_2O. Does not melt below 300°.
Dinitroso deriv. : yellow prisms from Me_2CO. M.p. 189–90°.

V.
B,2HCl : prisms from EtOH.Aq.

Dinitroso deriv. : yellow prisms from EtOH or Me_2CO. M.p. 116–17°.

Dibenzoyl : needles from Me_2CO or pet. ether. M.p. 146–7°.

Stoehr, Brandes, *J. prakt. Chem.*, 1897, **55**, 74.
Kipping, *J. Chem. Soc.*, 1937, 368; 1932, 1336; 1931, 1160; 1929, 2889.

1 : 2 : 5 : 5-Tetramethylpiperidine

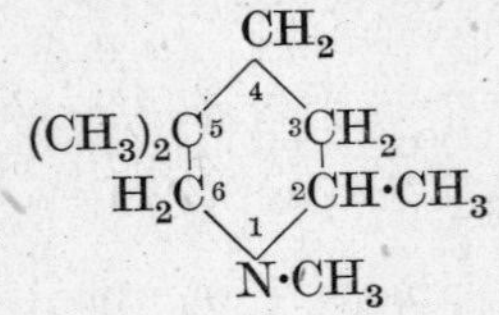

$C_9H_{19}N$ MW, 141

Liq. B.p. 147–8°.

B,HCl : m.p. about 221° decomp.

Mannich, Lesse, *Arch. Pharm.*, 1933, **271**, 92, (*Chem. Abstracts*, 1934, **28**, 477).

2 : 2 : 6 : 6-Tetramethylpiperidine.

Liq. B.p. 155·5–156·5°. Volatile in steam. $D_4^{16\cdot2}$ 0·8367.

Hydrate : needles. M.p. 28°.

B_2,H_2SO_4 : cryst. M.p. 270°.

B,H_2SO_4 : prisms from H_2O. M.p. 174°.

B,HNO_2 : cryst. from $CHCl_3$. Decomp. at 270°.

$B,HAuCl_4$: yellow needles from H_2O. M.p. 165°.

B_2,H_2PtCl_6 : orange-red prisms from H_2O. M.p. 262°.

N-*Benzoyl* : plates from EtOH. M.p. 41–2°.

Franchimont, Friedmann, *Rec. trav. chim.*, 1905, **24**, 404.

2 : 2 : 6 : 6-Tetramethyl-γ-piperidone.

See Triacetonamine.

1 : 3 : 4 : 5-Tetramethylpyrazole

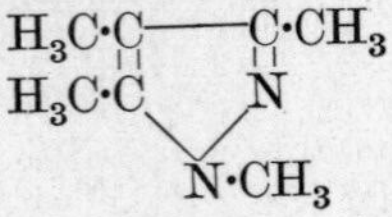

$C_7H_{12}N_2$ MW, 124

Liq. with unpleasant odour. Cryst. on cooling. B.p. 190–3°. Misc. in all proportions with H_2O, Et_2O, EtOH.

Picrate : m.p. 176–8°.

Rojahn, Kühling, *Arch. Pharm.*, 1926, **264**, 337, (*Chem. Abstracts*, 1926, **20**, 2856).
Knorr, Oettinger, *Ann.*, 1894, **279**, 246.

2 : 3 : 4 : 5-Tetramethylpyridine

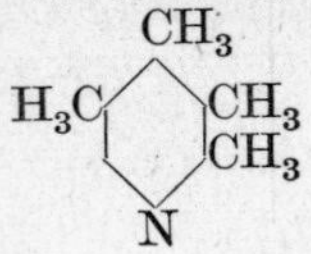

$C_9H_{13}N$ MW, 135

Liq. B.p. 232–4°. Mod. misc. with H_2O. $KMnO_4$ ⟶ pyridine-2 : 3 : 4 : 5-tetracarboxylic acid.

$B,HAuCl_4$: yellow needles from H_2O. M.p. 216–18°.

$B,(HgCl_2)_2,HCl$: needles from H_2O. M.p. 159°.

B_2,H_2PtCl_6 : needles from H_2O. M.p. 209–10° decomp.

Picrate : needles from H_2O. M.p. 170–2°.

Ahrens, *Ber.*, 1895, **28**, 796.

2 : 3 : 4 : 5-Tetramethylpyrrole

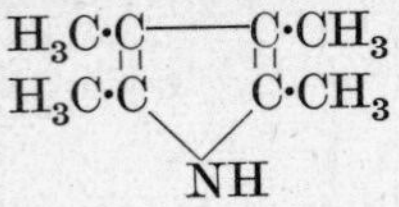

$C_8H_{13}N$ MW, 123

Leaflets from EtOH.Aq. or pet. ether. M.p. 111°. B.p. 130°/7 mm. Misc. with most org solvents. Volatile in steam with part. decomp.

Picrate : yellow cryst. from C_6H_6, EtOH, or Et_2O. M.p. 130°.

Styphnate : reddish-brown needles. M.p. 159°.

Signaigo, Adkins, *J. Am. Chem. Soc.*, 1936, **58**, 714.
Nenitzescu, Solomonica, *Ber.*, 1931, **64**, 1928.
Fischer, Zerweck, *Ber.*, 1923, **56**, 525.
Fischer, Bartholomäus, *Z. physiol. Chem.*, 1913, **87**, 269; 1913, **83**, 65.

2 : 2 : 5 : 5-Tetramethylpyrrolidine

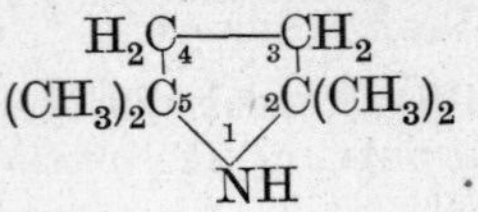

$C_8H_{17}N$ MW, 127

Pale rose-coloured oil. B.p. 108°. With pine splint ⟶ red col. Isatin + H_2SO_4 ⟶ greenish-blue col.

Benzoyl : cryst. M.p. 67·5–68°. Sol. cold pet. ether.

Pace, *Chem. Abstracts*, 1928, **22**, 3890.
Konowalow, Wojnitsch - Sjanoshenski, *Chem. Zentr.*, 1905, II, 830.

2 : 3 : 4 : 5-Tetramethylpyrrolidine.

N-*Et*: $C_{10}H_{21}N$. MW, 255. B.p. 163–5°. D^{15} 0·8064. n_D^{25} 1·4343.

Signaigo, Adkins, *J. Am. Chem. Soc.*, 1936, **58**, 715.

2 : 4 : 5 : 7-Tetramethylquinoline

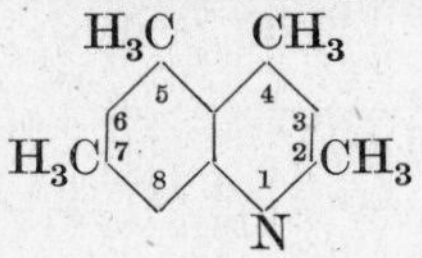

$C_{13}H_{15}N$ MW, 185

Cryst. from pet. ether. M.p. 59°.

Mikeska, Adams, *J. Am. Chem. Soc.*, 1920, **42**, 2394.

2 : 4 : 5 : 8-Tetramethylquinoline.

Pale yellow cryst. M.p. 48°. B.p. 168–72°/12 mm. Acid sol. ⟶ bluish-violet fluorescence.

B,HCl: sinters at 243°. M.p. 254°.

Picrate: needles from EtOH. M.p. 161°.

Braun, Gmelin, Petzold, *Ber.*, 1924, **57**, 389.

2 : 4 : 6 : 8-Tetramethylquinoline.

Plates from Et_2O or pet. ether. M.p. 86°. B.p. 284–5°. Very sol. Et_2O.

B,H_2SO_4: needles from EtOH–Et_2O. M.p. 243° decomp.

Mikeska, Adams, *J. Am. Chem. Soc.*, 1920, **42**, 2394.

2 : 5 : 6 : 8-Tetramethylquinoline.

Oil. F.p. 20° to cryst. mass. B.p. 297–300°. Very sol. EtOH, Et_2O. Insol. H_2O.

Doebner, Miller, *Ber.*, 1884, **17**, 1710.

Tetramethylsuccinic Acid (2 : 3-*Dimethylbutane*-2 : 3-*dicarboxylic acid*)

$$\begin{array}{l}(CH_3)_2C\cdot COOH \\ (CH_3)_2C\cdot COOH\end{array}$$

$C_8H_{14}O_4$ MW, 174

Cryst. M.p. 200°. Sol. 201 parts H_2O at 13·5°. Very sol. EtOH, C_6H_6. Spar. sol. Et_2O, $CHCl_3$, CS_2. Insol. ligroin. $k = 3{\cdot}14 \times 10^{-4}$ at 25°. Heat above m.p. ⟶ anhydride.

Mono-Me ester: $C_9H_{16}O_4$. MW, 188. Prisms from pet. ether. M.p. 68°. $k = 1{\cdot}22 \times 10^{-5}$ at 25°.

Di-Me ester: $C_{10}H_{18}O_4$. MW, 202. Prisms from ligroin. M.p. 31°. Very sol. most org. solvents.

Mono-Et ester: $C_{10}H_{18}O_4$. MW, 202. Viscous oil. Dist. ⟶ anhydride + C_2H_5OH.

Di-Et ester: $C_{12}H_{22}O_4$. MW, 230. B.p. 219°/13 mm. D_4^{20} 0·995. n_{He}^{20} 1·436.

Imide: $C_8H_{13}O_2N$. MW, 155. Needles from C_6H_6–ligroin. M.p. 187°. Spar. sol. ligroin. Sublimes.

p-*Tolylimide*: needles from EtOH.Aq. M.p. 90°.

2-*Naphthylimide*: needles from EtOH.Aq. M.p. 152°.

Anhydride: $C_8H_{12}O_3$. MW, 156. Needles from ligroin. M.p. 147°. B.p. 230·5°. Spar. sol. H_2O, ligroin. Sublimes.

Di-nitrile: $C_8H_{12}N_2$. MW, 136. Plates or prisms from EtOH.Aq. M.p. 169°.

Mono-anilide: cryst. from Et_2O–pet. ether. M.p. 91·5–92°.

Anil: needles from EtOH.Aq. M.p. 88°.

Mono-p-toluidide: cryst. M.p. 116–17°.

p-*Tolil*: cryst. M.p. 91·5°.

Auwers, Ungemach, *Ber.*, 1935, **68**, 351.
Auwers, Ottens, *Ber.*, 1924, **57**, 440.
Auwers, Meyer, *Ber.*, 1890, **23**, 297.

1 : 1 : 2 : 6 - Tetramethyl - 1 : 2 : 3 : 4 - tetrahydronaphthalene.

See Irene.

1 : 1 : 2 : 6-Tetramethyltetralin.

See Irene.

Tetramethylthiourea.

See under Thiourea.

Tetramethylthiuram disulphide

$$(CH_3)_2N\cdot CS\cdot S\cdot S\cdot CS\cdot N(CH_3)_2$$

$C_6H_{12}N_2S_4$ MW, 240

White cryst. from $CHCl_3$–EtOH. M.p. 146°. Very sol. $CHCl_3$. Spar. sol. EtOH, Et_2O. KCN ⟶ tetramethylthiuram sulphide. Used as accelerator in vulcanisation of rubber.

Cummings, Simmons, *Ind. Eng. Chem.*, 1928, **20**, 1173, (*Brit. Chem. Abstracts*, 1929, B, 28).
Romani, *Chem. Abstracts*, 1922, **16**, 854.
v. Braun, Stechele, *Ber.*, 1903, **36**, 2280.
v. Braun, *Ber.*, 1902, **35**, 820.

Tetramethylthiuram sulphide

$$(CH_3)_2N\cdot CS\cdot S\cdot CS\cdot N(CH_3)_2$$

$C_6H_{12}N_2S_3$ MW, 208

Yellow cryst. from EtOH. M.p. 104°. Very sol. EtOH, $CHCl_3$. Spar. sol. cold Et_2O. Stable to dil. acids. Alkalis ⟶ dimethylamine.

See previous references.

Tetramethylurea.

See under Urea.

Tetramethyluric Acid

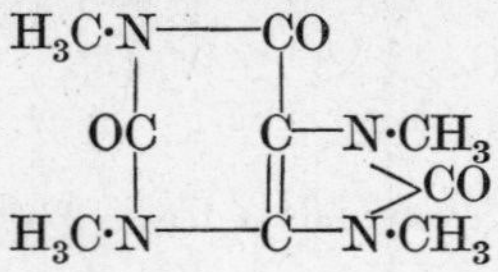

$C_9H_{12}N_4O_3$ MW, 224

Needles from H_2O. M.p. 228°. Dist. without decomp. Very sol. hot H_2O, boiling $CHCl_3$. Mod. sol. EtOH. Spar. sol. Et_2O, cold H_2O. Decomp. by warm alkalis. Gives murexide reaction. Bitter taste.

Fischer, *Ber.*, 1899, **32**, 2732, 2742; 1884, **17**, 1784.

Tetra*peri*naphthylenecyclo-octadiene.
See Fluorocyclene.

Tetrandrine
Constitution represented by

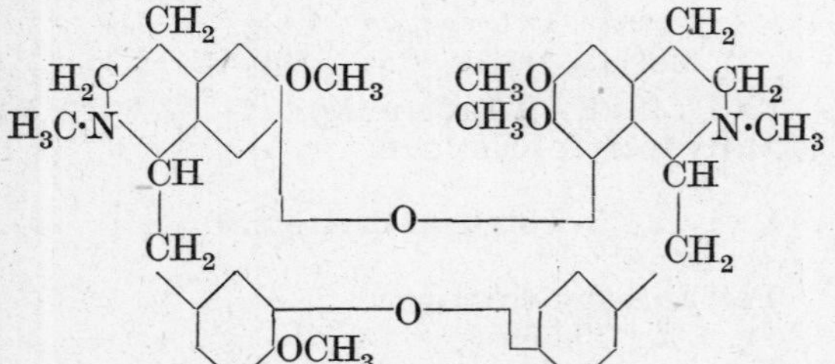

or

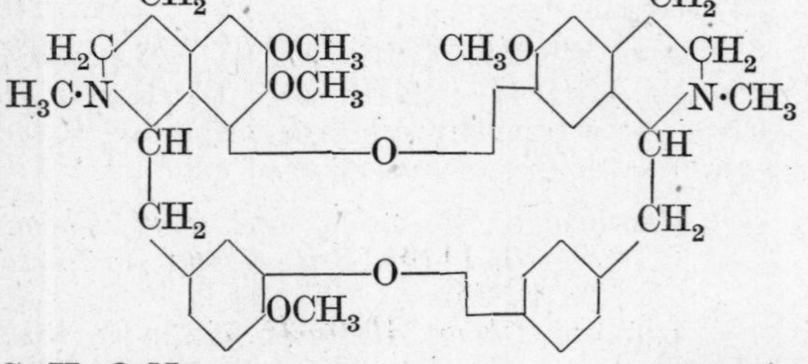

$C_{38}H_{42}O_6N_2$ MW, 622

dl-.
Colourless prisms from MeOH. M.p. 252°.

l-.
See Phaeanthine.

d-.
Alkaloid extracted from roots of *Stephania tetrandra*, S. Moore. Constituent of the Chinese drug, Han-Fang-Chi. Colourless needles. M.p. 217–18°. Sol. Et_2O, Me_2CO, $CHCl_3$. Mod. sol. EtOH. Insol. H_2O, pet. ether. $[\alpha]_D^{26} + 252{\cdot}4°$ in $CHCl_3$. Poisonous. Affects central nervous system, respiratory and skeletal muscles. Ha action on paramecia similar to that of quinine.

B,2HCl: prisms from EtOH. Softens a 263°. Decomp. at 266°. $[\alpha]_D^{27} + 224{\cdot}2°$ in H_2C

B,2HBr: needles from EtOH. Decomp. a 270°. $[\alpha]_D^{27} + 200{\cdot}7°$ in H_2O.

B,2HNO₃: prisms from EtOH.Aq. Soften at 205°. Decomp. at 208°. $[\alpha]_D^{26} + 211{\cdot}2°$ i H_2O.

B,(COOH)₂: needles. Softens at 147·5–148·5° Decomp. at 165–70°.

B,2CH₃I: needles + $2H_2O$ from Me_2CO.Aq M.p. 269° decomp.

Picrate: decomp. at 235–42°.

Kondo, Keimatsu, *Ber.*, 1935, **68**, 1505.
Chen, Chen, *J. Biol. Chem.*, 1935, **109** 681.

1 : 3 : 7 : 9-Tetranitroacridone

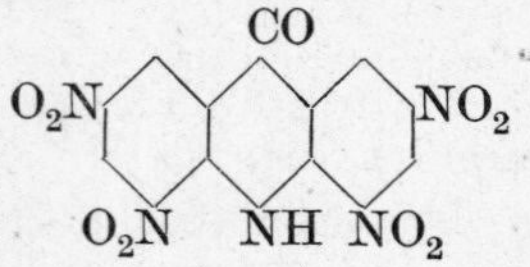

$C_{13}H_5O_9N_5$ MW, 37

Yellow cryst. Does not melt below 350° Sol. hot alkalis. Spar. sol. org. solvents Sublimes. KOH ⟶ cherry-red sol. from which K salt crystallises in red plates.

Lehmstedt, *Ber.*, 1931, **64**, 2383.
Edinger, Arnold, *J. prakt. Chem.*, 1901 **64**, 488.

2 : 4 : 5 : 7-Tetranitro-aloe-emodin.
See Aloetic Acid.

2 : 3 : 4 : 6-Tetranitroaniline

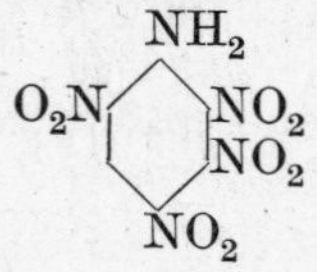

$C_6H_3O_8N_5$ MW, 27

Yellow cryst. from AcOH. M.p. 220°. Slightl hygroscopic. Sol. AcOH, $PhNO_2$. Spar. sol $CHCl_3$, C_6H_6, ligroin. Insol. cold H_2O. Sol. parts boiling Me_2CO, 3 parts *o*-nitrotoluene a 140°, 3 parts nitroxylene at 150°, and 24 part boiling xylene. Slowly decomp. with steam a 100°. Warm moist Me_2CO, boiling with H_2O or with AcONa in Me_2CO.Aq. ⟶ 2 : 4 : 6 trinitro-3-aminophenol. Boiling EtOH ⟶ 2 : 4 : 6-trinitro-3-aminophenetole. Explosive.

N-*Acetyl*: 2 : 3 : 4 : 6-tetranitroacetanilide M.p. about 170° decomp.

N-*Me*: m.p. 127°.

N-*Di-Me* : m.p. 153°.

Forster, Coulson, *J. Chem. Soc.*, 1922, **121**, 1992.
Duin, *Rec. trav. chim.*, 1917, **37**, 115.

Tetranitroanisole.
See under Tetranitrophenol.

1 : 3 : 5 : 7-Tetranitroanthraflavic Acid
1 : 3 : 5 : 7-*Tetranitro*-2 : 6-*dihydroxyanthraquinone*)

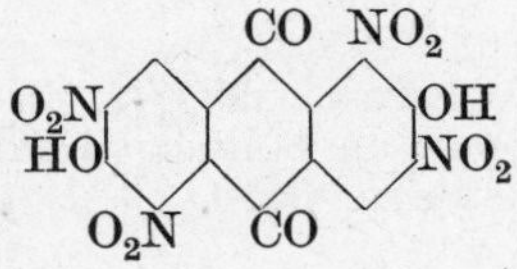

$C_{14}H_4O_{12}N_4$ MW, 420

Yellow needles. Explodes at 307·6° without melting. Very sol. hot H_2O ⟶ red sol. Sol. EtOH, Et_2O ⟶ red sols. Gives salt with NH_3. Boiling conc. HNO_3 ⟶ 2 : 4 : 6-trinitro-*m*-hydroxybenzoic acid.

Wolffenstein, Paar, *Ber.*, 1913, **46**, 596.
Schunck, Roemer, *Ber.*, 1878, **11**, 1178.
Schardinger, *Ber.*, 1875, **8**, 1487.

2:4:6:8-Tetranitroanthrarufin (2:4:6:8-*Tetranitro*-1 : 5-*dihydroxyanthraquinone*)

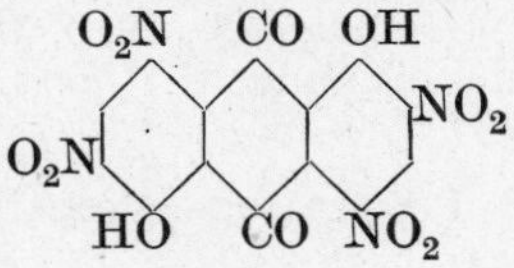

$C_{14}H_4O_{12}N_4$ MW, 420

Yellow plates from conc. HNO_3. Gives cryst. Na, K and Mg hydrated salts. Red. ⟶ 2 : 4 : 6 : 8-tetra-aminoanthrarufin. Boiling conc. HNO_3 ⟶ 2 : 4 : 6-trinitro-*m*-hydroxybenzoic acid.

Wolffenstein, Paar, *Ber.*, 1913, **46**, 592.
Liebermann, *Ber.*, 1879, **12**, 188.

1 : 2 : 3 : 5-Tetranitrobenzene

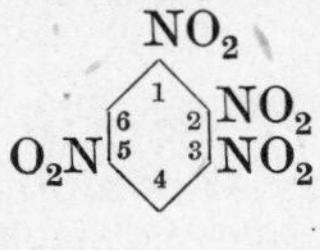

$C_6H_2O_8N_4$ MW, 258

Yellow cryst. from $CHCl_3$. M.p. 126°. Mod. sol. warm $CHCl_3$, C_6H_6. Spar. sol. Et_2O, CS_2. Aq. alkalis ⟶ picric acid.

Hollemann, *Rec. trav. chim.*, 1930, **49**, 117.
Borsche, *Ber.*, 1923, **56**, 1942.

1 : 2 : 4 : 5-Tetranitrobenzene.
Pale yellow needles from EtOH.Aq. M.p. 188°.

Borsche, Feske, *Ber.*, 1926, **59**, 820.

1 : 3 : 6 : 8-Tetranitrocarbazole

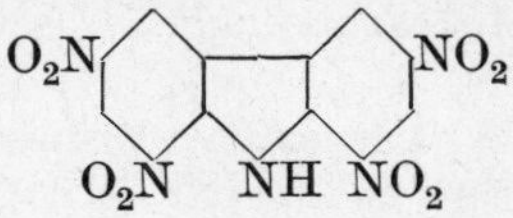

$C_{12}H_5O_8N_5$ MW, 347

Pale yellow plates + $PhNO_2$ from $PhNO_2$, golden-yellow needles from AcOH. Darkens at 200°, m.p. 289°.

N-*Me* : $C_{13}H_7O_8N_5$. MW, 361. Yellow needles from Me_2CO. M.p. 277°. Insol. common org. solvents.

N-*Et* : $C_{14}H_9O_8N_5$. MW, 375. Cryst. from Me_2CO. M.p. 216°.

N-*Phenyl* : $C_{18}H_9O_8N_5$. MW, 423. Cryst. M.p. 244° (255°). Sol. Me_2CO, C_6H_6. Insol. H_2O, EtOH, Et_2O, $CHCl_3$, CCl_4, CS_2.

van Alphen, *Rec. trav. chim.*, 1932, **51**, 183.
Raudnitz, *Ber.*, 1927, **60**, 741.
Borsche, Scholten, *Ber.*, 1917, **50**, 608.

2 : 4 : 5 : 7-Tetranitrochrysazin.
See Chrysamminic Acid.

2 : 4 : 5 : 6-Tetranitro-*m*-cresol

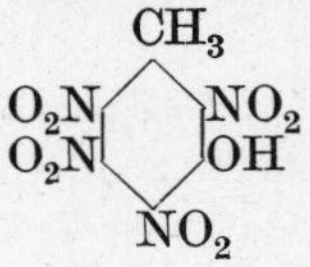

$C_7H_4O_9N_4$ MW, 288

Cryst. from $CHCl_3$. M.p. 175°. Very sol. H_2O, EtOH ⟶ yellow sols. Boiling H_2O ⟶ 2 : 4 : 6-trinitro-3 : 5-dihydroxytoluene. Bitter taste. Explosive.

Blanksma, *Rec. trav. chim.*, 1908, **27**, 34.

Tetranitrodihydroxyanthraquinone.
See Tetranitroanthrarufin *and* Tetranitroanthraflavic Acid.

2 : 4 : 2′ : 4′-Tetranitrodiphenyl

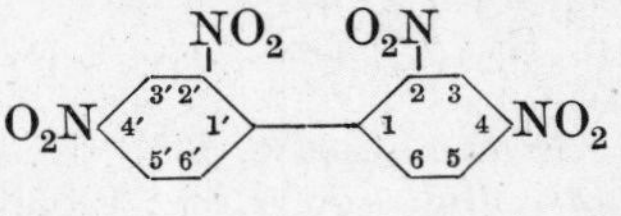

$C_{12}H_6O_8N_4$ MW, 334

Yellow prisms from C_6H_6. M.p. 165–6°. Very sol. AcOH, C_6H_6. Spar. sol. EtOH, Et_2O.

Swann Research Inc., U.S.P., 1,870,627, (*Chem. Zentr.*, 1932, II, 2729).
Ullmann, Bielecki, *Ber.*, 1901, **34**, 2177.

2 : 6 : 2′ : 6′-Tetranitrodiphenyl.
Yellowish needles from AcOH. M.p. 217–18°.

Borsche, Rantscheff, *Ann.*, 1911, **379**, 176.

3 : 4 : 2′ : 4′-Tetranitrodiphenyl.
Pale yellow cubes from MeOH. M.p. 173°.

Blakey, Scarborough, *J. Chem. Soc.*, 1927, 3006.

3 : 4 : 3′ : 4′-Tetranitrodiphenyl.
Yellow prisms. M.p. 186°. Very sol. AcOH, C_6H_6. Insol. ligroin.

Ullmann, Bielecki, *Ber.*, 1901, **34**, 2179.

2 : 4 : 6 : 2′-Tetranitrodiphenylamine

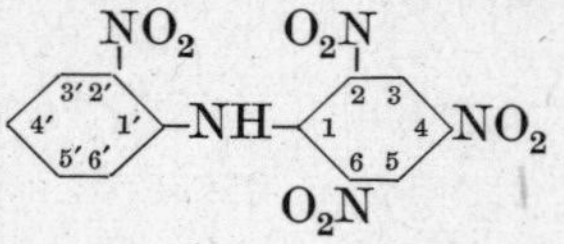

$C_{12}H_7O_8N_5$ MW, 349

Yellow prismatic needles from AcOH. M.p. 234°. Sol. 600 parts toluene at 20°, 770 parts AcOH at 20°. Sol. hot dil. $Na_2CO_3 \longrightarrow$ orange-red sol.

Juillard, *Bull. soc. chim.*, 1905, **33**, 1187.

2 : 4 : 6 : 3′-Tetranitrodiphenylamine.
Orange-yellow cryst. from AcOH. M.p. 213°. Spar. sol. boiling EtOH. Insol. Et_2O.

Duin, Lennep, *Rec. trav. chim.*, 1919, **38**, 368.
Austen, *Ber.*, 1874, **7**, 1248.

2 : 4 : 6 : 4′-Tetranitrodiphenylamine.
Yellow plates or prisms from toluene. M.p. 223°. Sol. 330 parts toluene at 20°, 200 parts AcOH at 20°. Sol. hot dil. $Na_2CO_3 \longrightarrow$ red sol. Insol. cold EtOH.

Duin, Lennep, *Rec. trav. chim.*, 1919, **38**, 359.

2 : 4 : 2′ : 4′-Tetranitrodiphenylamine.
Reddish-brown plates from EtOH, yellow needles and prisms from AcOH. M.p. 199°. Sol. 44 parts Me_2CO at 17°. Sol. NaOH $\longrightarrow$ scarlet sol. Spar. sol. cold EtOH, AcOH, toluene.

Ryan, Ryan, *Chem. Abstracts*, 1919, **13**, 957.
Carter, *Chem. Zentr.*, 1913, II, 859.
Juillard, *Bull. soc. chim.*, 1905, **33**, 1186.

2 : 4 : 2′ : 4′-Tetranitrodiphenylmethane

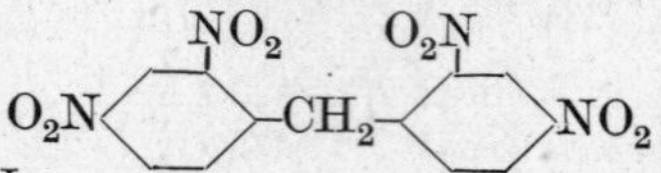

$C_{13}H_8O_8N_4$ MW, 348

Yellow prisms from AcOH. M.p. 173°.

Matsumura, *J. Am. Chem. Soc.*, 192[illegible] **51**, 817.

1 : 1 : 2 : 2-Tetranitroethane (sym.-*Tetra nitroethane*)

$$(O_2N)_2HC{\cdot}CH(NO_2)_2$$

$C_2H_2O_8N_4$ MW, 21[illegible]

Di-K salt: $C_2O_8N_4K_2$. MW, 286. Yellow prisms with metallic reflex from MeOH.Aq Explodes at 268° (275°) or by percussion. Spar sol. cold H_2O. Insol. MeOH, EtOH, AcOH Aq. sol. decomp. on boiling. Cold dil. H_2SO_4 $\longrightarrow$ dinitromethane. $HNO_3 + H_2SO_4 \longrightarrow$ hexa-nitroethane.

Hunter, *J. Chem. Soc.*, 1924, **125**, 1483.
Will, *Ber.*, 1914, **47**, 963.

Tetranitromethane

$$C(NO_2)_4$$

CO_8N_4 MW, 196

F.p. 13° (12·5°). B.p. 125·7°, 21–3°/22 mm. (34–5°/20 mm.). Misc. with EtOH, Et_2O. Insol. H_2O. $D_4^{21\cdot2}$ 1·6377. $n_a^{21\cdot2}$ 1·43416. Heat of comb. C_v 89·6 Cal. Gives yellow col. with cyclopropane derivs. and unsaturated comps.

McKie, *J. Soc. Chem. Ind.*, 1925, **44**, 430T.
Berger, *Compt. rend.*, 1910, **151**, 814.
Hammick, Young, *J. Chem. Soc.*, 1936, 1464.

***N*:2 : 4 : 6-Tetranitro-*N*-methylaniline.**
See Tetryl.

1 : 2 : 5 : 8-Tetranitronaphthalene

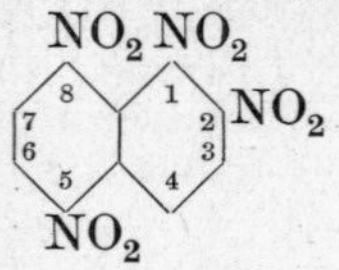

$C_{10}H_4O_8N_4$ MW, 308

Needles from ethyl benzoate, prisms from conc. HNO_3. Decomp. at 270–310°. Spar. sol. EtOH, Me_2CO, AcOH, $CHCl_3$. Ox. $\longrightarrow$ 3 : 6-dinitrophthalic acid. Red. $\longrightarrow$ naphthazarin.

Will, *Ber.*, 1895, **28**, 369.

1 : 2 : 6 : 8-Tetranitronaphthalene.
White powder. Does not melt below 300°.

Dhar, *J. Chem. Soc.*, 1920, **117**, 1004.

1 : 3 : 5 : 8-Tetranitronaphthalene.
Pale yellow tetrahedra from Me_2CO. M.p. 194–5°. Very sol. Me_2CO, conc. HNO_3. Spar. sol. EtOH, AcOH, $CHCl_3$. Sol. alkalis $\longrightarrow$ red sols. Ox. $\longrightarrow$ 3 : 6-dinitrophthalic acid.

1-*Naphthylamine add. comp.*: black needles from C_6H_6. Decomp. at 162°.

2-*Naphthylamine add. comp.*: bronze-green needles. M.p. 163–4°.

Will, *Ber.*, 1895, **28**, 369.
See also previous reference.

1 : 3 : 6 : 8-Tetranitronaphthalene.

Yellow needles from EtOH or C_6H_6. M.p. 207°. Explodes on strong heating. Dil. HNO_3 $\longrightarrow$ 3 : 5-dinitrophthalic acid.

Naphthalene add. comp.: yellow needles from C_6H_6. M.p. 191–2°.

1-*Naphthylamine add. comp.*: purple needles from C_6H_6. M.p. 204–5°.

2-*Naphthylamine add. comp.*: brown plates from C_6H_6. M.p. 211–12°.

See previous references.

2 : 4 : 5 : 7-Tetranitro-1-naphthol

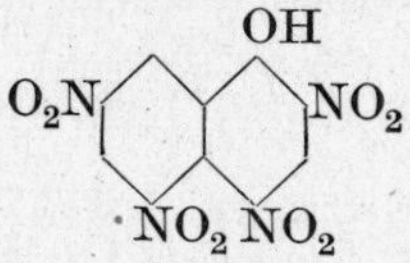

$C_{10}H_4O_9N_4$ MW, 324

Yellow plates or needles from AcOH. M.p. 180°. Sol. 220 parts C_6H_6 at 18°. Spar. sol. cold AcOH. Gives cryst. Na, K, Ag, Ca and Ba salts.

Merz, Weith, *Ber.*, 1882, **15**, 2714.

2 : 4 : 5 : 7-Tetranitro-1-naphthylamine

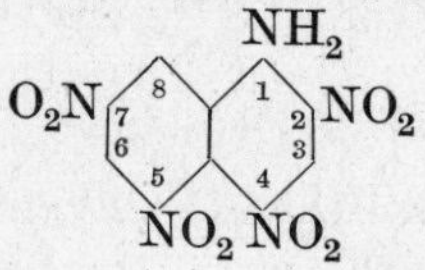

$C_{10}H_5O_8N_5$ MW, 323

Pale yellow needles from EtOH or C_6H_6. M.p. 194°. Spar. sol. warm EtOH, C_6H_6.

N-*Phenyl*: $C_{16}H_9O_8N_5$. MW, 399. Orange-yellow needles + C_6H_6 from C_6H_6, dark red needles from EtOH. M.p. 162·5°. Sol. C_6H_6. Spar. sol. warm EtOH, Et_2O. Boiling NaOH.Aq. $\longrightarrow$ 2 : 4 : 5 : 7-tetranitro-1-naphthol.

Merz, Weith, *Ber.*, 1882, **15**, 2717.

2 : 4 : 5 : 8-Tetranitro-1-naphthylamine.

Yellow needles from EtOH. M.p. 202°.

N-*Phenyl*: orange needles + C_6H_6 from C_6H_6, dark red needles from EtOH. M.p. 253°. Spar. sol. warm EtOH, C_6H_6.

See previous reference.

Tetranitrophenetole.

See under Tetranitrophenol.

2 : 3 : 4 : 6-Tetranitrophenol

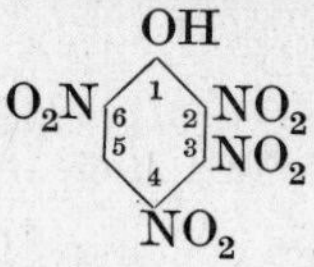

$C_6H_2O_9N_4$ MW, 274

Pale yellow cryst. from $CHCl_3$. M.p. 140°.

Me ether: 2 : 3 : 4 : 6 - tetranitroanisole. $C_7H_4O_9N_4$. MW, 288. Leaflets. M.p. 94°. Spar. sol. H_2O, EtOH, Et_2O.

Blanksma, *Rec. trav. chim.*, 1902, **21**, 256.
Claessen, D.R.P., 289,446, (*Chem. Zentr.*, 1916, I, 240).

2 : 3 : 5 : 6-Tetranitrophenol.

Me ether: 2 : 3 : 5 : 6-tetranitroanisole. Exists in two forms. (i) Cryst. from EtOH. M.p. 154°. (ii) Pale yellow needles from C_6H_6. M.p. 112°.

Et ether: 2 : 3 : 5 : 6-tetranitrophenetole. $C_8H_6O_9N_4$. MW, 302. Yellow cryst. from EtOH. M.p. 115°.

Blanksma, *Rec. trav. chim.*, 1904, **23**, 114; 1905, **24**, 42.
Devergnes, *Chem. Abstracts*, 1929, **23**, 4207.

Tetranitroresorcinol

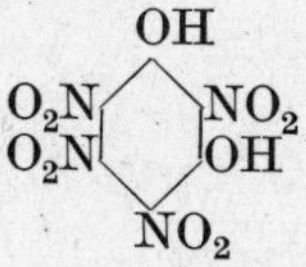

$C_6H_2O_{10}N_4$ MW, 290

Cryst. from $CHCl_3$ or CCl_4. M.p. 152°. Bitter taste. Explosive.

Mono-Me ether: $C_7H_4O_{10}N_4$. MW, 304. Cryst. from $CHCl_3$ or CCl_4. M.p. 115°. Bitter taste. Explosive.

Mono-Et ether: $C_8H_6O_{10}N_4$. MW, 318. Cryst. from $CHCl_3$ or CCl_4. M.p. 110°. Bitter taste. Explosive.

Blanksma, *Rec. trav. chim.*, 1908, **27**, 35.

2 : 4 : 6 : 2′-Tetranitrostilbene

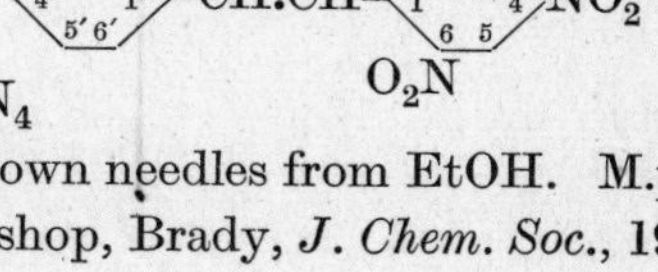

$C_{14}H_8O_8N_4$ MW, 360

Pale brown needles from EtOH. M.p. 181°.

Bishop, Brady, *J. Chem. Soc.*, 1922, 2367.

2 : 4 : 6 : 3′-Tetranitrostilbene.
Lemon-yellow leaflets from $Me_2CO–C_6H_6$.
M.p. 159°.

See previous reference.

2 : 4 : 6 : 4′-Tetranitrostilbene.
Yellow needles. M.p. 196°. Sol. AcOH. Spar.
sol. EtOH, C_6H_6.

Ullmann, Gschwind, *Ber.*, 1908, **41**, 2297.

2 : 4 : 2′ : 4′-Tetranitrostilbene.
Yellow needles from AcOH or $PhNO_2$. M.p.
266–7° decomp. Insol. Et_2O.

Escales, *Ber.*, 1904, **37**, 3599.
Green, Baddiley, *J. Chem. Soc.*, 1908, **93**,
1725.

2 : 6 : 2′ : 6′-Tetranitrostilbene.
Yellow needles from $PhNO_2$. M.p. 250°. Sol.
Me_2CO. Insol. EtOH, Et_2O, ligroin.

Reich, Wetter, Widmer, *Ber.*, 1912, **45**,
3059.

2 : 3 : 4 : 6-Tetranitrotoluene

$$\begin{array}{c} CH_3 \\ O_2N \diagup\!\!\!\!\diagdown NO_2 \\ | \quad NO_2 \\ NO_2 \end{array}$$

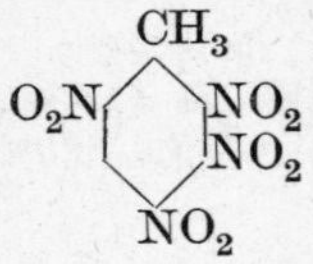

$C_7H_4O_8N_4$ MW, 272
Cryst. from $CHCl_3$ or conc. HNO_3. M.p.
136·5°.

Holleman, *Rec. trav. chim.*, 1930, **49**, 501.

Tetraphenyldiarsine.
See Phenylcacodyl.
***sym.*-Tetraphenylethane**
$$(C_6H_5)_2CH·CH(C_6H_5)_2$$
$C_{26}H_{22}$ MW, 334
Prisms from $CHCl_3$. M.p. 211°. B.p. 358–
62°, 260°/16 mm.

Montagne, *Rec. trav. chim.*, 1906, **25**, 407.
Morris, Thomas, Brown, *Ber.*, 1910, **43**,
2959.

***unsym.*-Tetraphenylethane**   (*α-Benzyl-
tritan, triphenylbenzylmethane*)
$$C_6H_5·CH_2·C(C_6H_5)_3$$
$C_{26}H_{22}$ MW, 334
Plates from AcOEt. M.p. 144°. B.p. 277–80°/
21 mm. Mod. sol. C_6H_6. Spar. sol. EtOH, Et_2O.

Gomberg, Cone, *Ber.*, 1906, **39**, 1463.

1 : 1 : 2 : 2 - Tetraphenylethyl   Alcohol
(*Hydroxy*-sym.-*tetraphenylethane*,   *α-benzhydryl-
benzhydrol*)

$$(C_6H_5)_2CH·C\!\!<\!\!\begin{array}{c}C_6H_5\\OH\\C_6H_5\end{array}$$

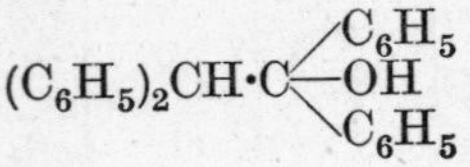

$C_{26}H_{22}O$ MW, 350
Needles from C_6H_6. M.p. 326°. Mod. sol.
EtOH, Et_2O, C_6H_6, ligroin.
Benzoyl : prisms from AcOEt. M.p. 155°.
Phenylurethane : cryst. from C_6H_6–pet. ether.
M.p. 163–5°.

Richard, *Compt. rend.*, 1934, **198**, 1242.
Bergmann, Wagenberg, *Ber.*, 1930, **63**,
2591.

1 : 2 : 2 : 2 - Tetraphenylethyl   Alcohol
(*ω-Triphenylmethylbenzyl alcohol*,   *hydroxy*-un-
sym.-*tetraphenylethane*)

$$(C_6H_5)_3C·CH\!\!<\!\!\begin{array}{c}C_6H_5\\OH\end{array}$$

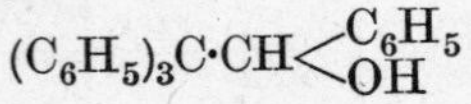

$C_{26}H_{22}O$ MW, 350
Plates from EtOH. M.p. 151°.
Acetyl : cryst. from EtOH. M.p. 131°.

Schlenk, Ochs, *Ber.*, 1916, **49**, 611.

Tetraphenylethylene
$$(C_6H_5)_2C\!:\!C(C_6H_5)_2$$
$C_{26}H_{20}$ MW, 332
Plates from EtOH–C_6H_6. M.p. 223–4° (220–
1°). B.p. 415–25°. Sol. C_6H_6. Spar. sol.
EtOH, Et_2O.

Mackenzie, *J. Chem. Soc.*, 1922, **121**, 1697.

Tetraphenylethylene Glycol.
See Benzpinacol.
Tetraphenylethylene oxide.
See Benzpinacolin.
Tetraphenylfuran.
See Lepidene.
1 : 1 : 3 : 3-Tetraphenylguanidine

$$(C_6H_5)_2N·\overset{4}{\underset{2}{C}}·N(C_6H_5)_2 \quad \text{with } \overset{4}{N}H$$

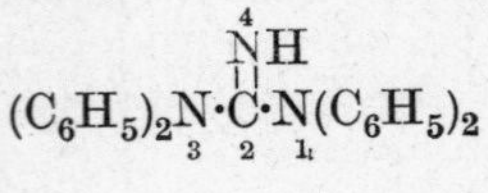

$C_{25}H_{21}N_3$ MW, 363
Cryst. from ligroin. M.p. 130–1°. Sol. EtOH,
Et_2O, C_6H_6. Insol. H_2O.
4-N-*Benzoyl* : cryst. from EtOH. M.p. 142–4°.

Weith, *Ber.*, 1874, **7**, 843.
Johnson, Chemoff, *J. Am. Chem. Soc.*,
1912, **34**, 170.

1 : 1 : 3 : 4-Tetraphenylguanidine

$$C_6H_5\cdot NH\cdot \overset{N\cdot C_6H_5}{\overset{||}{C}}\cdot N(C_6H_5)_2$$

$C_{25}H_{21}N_3$ MW, 363

Cryst. from EtOH. M.p. 137–40°.
Chloroplatinate : m.p. 240–2°.

Steindorff, *Ber.*, 1904, **37**, 964.

Tetraphenylhydrazine

$$(C_6H_5)_2N\cdot N(C_6H_5)_2$$

$C_{24}H_{20}N_2$ MW, 336

Prisms from $CHCl_3$–EtOH. M.p. 147° decomp. Sol. Me_2CO, $CHCl_3$, C_6H_6. Spar. sol. EtOH.

Chattaway, Ingle, *J. Chem. Soc.*, 1895, **67**, 1091.
Wieland, Gambarjan, *Ber.*, 1906, **39**, 1500.

1 : 1 : 2 : 3-Tetraphenylisopropyl Alcohol
(2-*Hydroxy*-1 : 1 : 2 : 3-*tetraphenylpropane*)

$$C_6H_5\cdot CH_2\cdot \overset{C_6H_5}{\overset{|}{C}}(OH)\cdot CH(C_6H_5)_2$$

$C_{27}H_{24}O$ MW, 364

Needles from ligroin. M.p. 135–6°. Sol. EtOH, C_6H_6. Mod. sol. ligroin.
Acetyl : needles from benzine. M.p. 151–3°.

Bergmann, Weiss, *Ber.*, 1931, **64**, 1489.
Orékhoff, *Bull. soc. chim.*, 1919, **25**, 186.

Tetraphenylmethane

$$C(C_6H_5)_4$$

$C_{25}H_{20}$ MW, 320

Cryst. from C_6H_6. M.p. 282°. B.p. 431°. Insol. Et_2O, AcOH, ligroin. Sublimes in needles. Sol. H_2SO_4 with red col.

Gomberg, Kamm, *J. Am. Chem. Soc.*, 1917, **39**, 2009.
Gomberg, Cone, *Ber.*, 1906, **39**, 1463.

Tetraphenylphenylenediamine.
See under Phenylenediamine.
Tetraphenylphosphonium halides.
See under Triphenylphosphine.
1 : 1 : 1 : 3-Tetraphenylpropane

$$C_6H_5\cdot CH_2\cdot CH_2\cdot C(C_6H_5)_3$$

$C_{27}H_{24}$ MW, 348

Prisms from EtOH. M.p. 126°.

Wieland, Kloss, *Ann.*, 1929, **470**, 214.

1 : 1 : 2 : 3-Tetraphenylpropane

$$C_6H_5\cdot CH_2\cdot \overset{C_6H_5}{\overset{|}{C}H}\cdot CH(C_6H_5)_2$$

$C_{27}H_{24}$ MW, 348

Needles from EtOH. M.p. 87–9°.

Bergmann, Weiss, *Ber.*, 1931, **64**, 1491.

1 : 1 : 3 : 3-Tetraphenylpropane

$$(C_6H_5)_2CH\cdot CH_2\cdot CH(C_6H_5)_2$$

$C_{27}H_{24}$ MW, 348

Needles from EtOH. M.p. 139°. Sol. Et_2O, $CHCl_3$, C_6H_6.

Wittig, Obermann, *Ber.*, 1934, **67**, 2056.
Vorländer, Siebert, *Ber.*, 1906, **39**, 1028.

1 : 1 : 2 : 3-Tetraphenylpropyl Alcohol
(1-*Hydroxy*-1 : 1 : 2 : 3-*tetraphenylpropane*)

$$C_6H_5\cdot CH_2\cdot \overset{C_6H_5}{\overset{|}{C}H}\cdot C(OH)(C_6H_5)_2$$

$C_{27}H_{24}O$ MW, 364

Needles from EtOH. M.p. 165°.

Sernagiotto, *Chem. Abstracts*, 1920, **14**, 1672.

1 : 1 : 3 : 3-Tetraphenylpropyl Alcohol
(1-*Hydroxy*-1 : 1 : 3 : 3-*tetraphenylpropane*)

$$(C_6H_5)_2CH\cdot CH_2\cdot C(OH)(C_6H_5)_2$$

$C_{27}H_{24}O$ MW, 364

Needles. M.p. 95–6°. Sol. EtOH, Et_2O. Spar. sol. ligroin.

Kohler, *Ann. Chem. J.*, 1904, **31**, 651.

1 : 2 : 2 : 3-Tetraphenylpropyl Alcohol
(1-*Hydroxy*-1 : 2 : 2 : 3-*tetraphenylpropane*)

$$C_6H_5\cdot CH_2\cdot \underset{C_6H_5}{\underset{|}{\overset{C_6H_5}{\overset{|}{C}}}}\cdot CH(OH)\cdot C_6H_5$$

$C_{27}H_{24}O$ MW, 364

Cryst. from pet. ether. M.p. 141–2°.

Schlenk *et al.*, *Ann.*, 1928, **463**, 261.

1 : 2 : 3 : 3-Tetraphenylpropyl Alcohol
(1-*Hydroxy*-1 : 2 : 3 : 3-*tetraphenylpropane*)

$$(C_6H_5)_2CH\cdot \overset{C_6H_5}{\overset{|}{C}H}\cdot CH(OH)\cdot C_6H_5$$

$C_{27}H_{24}O$ MW, 364

Cryst. from Et_2O. M.p. 132°. Sol. EtOH, AcOH. Mod. sol. Et_2O.

Japp, Klingemann, *J. Chem. Soc.*, 1890, **57**, 669.

1 : 1 : 2 : 3-Tetraphenylpropylene (1 : 1 : 2-*Triphenyl-2-benzylethylene*)

$$C_6H_5 \cdot CH_2 \cdot C(C_6H_5){:}C(C_6H_5)_2$$

$C_{27}H_{22}$ MW, 346

Needles from methyl ethyl ketone. M.p. 142°. Sol. $CHCl_3$, C_6H_6, CCl_4. Spar. sol. Et_2O. Prac. insol. cold EtOH, AcOH.

Bergmann, Weiss, *Ber.*, 1931, **64**, 1489.
Meisenheimer, Schlichenmaier, *Ann.*, 1927, **456**, 151.

1 : 1 : 3 : 3-Tetraphenylpropylene

$$(C_6H_5)_2CH \cdot CH{:}C(C_6H_5)_2.$$

$C_{27}H_{22}$ MW, 346

Cryst. from EtOH. M.p. 127–8°. Sol. Me_2CO, $CHCl_3$, C_6H_6. Spar. sol. pet. ether. Sol. conc. H_2SO_4 with yellow col.

Wittig, Obermann, *Ber.*, 1934, **67**, 2054.
Vorländer, Siebert, *Ber.*, 1906, **39**, 1032.

1 : 2 : 3 : 3-Tetraphenylpropylene

$$(C_6H_5)_2CH \cdot C(C_6H_5){:}CH \cdot C_6H_5$$

$C_{27}H_{22}$ MW, 346

Needles from EtOH. M.p. 131°.

Bergmann, Weiss, *Ber.*, 1931, **64**, 1489.

Tetraphenylpyrazine.
See Amaron.

2 : 3 : 4 : 6-Tetraphenylpyridine

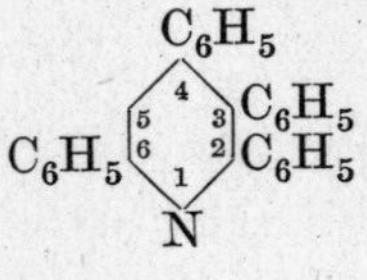

$C_{29}H_{21}N$ MW, 383

Needles from EtOH. M.p. 182°. Sol. EtOH, Et_2O, AcOH, C_6H_6. Insol. ligroin.

Picrate: yellow needles from Et_2O. M.p. 192°.

Dilthey, Böttler, *Ber.*, 1919, **52**, 2048.
Dilthey, Nüsslein, Meyer, Kaffer, *J. prakt. Chem.*, 1922, **104**, 33.

2 : 3 : 5 : 6-Tetraphenylpyridine.
Prisms from EtOH–C_6H_6. M.p. 233·5°. Sol. $CHCl_3$, CS_2. Mod. sol. EtOH, Me_2CO, C_6H_6. Spar. sol. Et_2O, AcOH, ligroin. Sol. conc. H_2SO_4 with blue fluor.

Carpenter, *Ann.*, 1898, **302**, 233.

1 : 2 : 3 : 5-Tetraphenylpyrrole

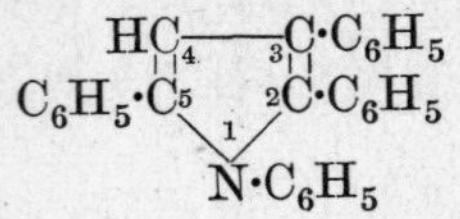

$C_{28}H_{21}N$ MW, 371

Needles from AcOH. M.p. 197°. Sol. Et_2O, C_6H_6. Mod. sol. EtOH, AcOH.

Smith, *J. Chem. Soc.*, 1890, **57**, 646.

2 : 3 : 4 : 5-Tetraphenylpyrrole.
Needles from AcOH. M.p. 214–15°. Prac. insol. EtOH. Sol. conc. H_2SO_4 with yellow col.

N-*Me*: $C_{29}H_{23}N$. MW, 385. Plates from Et_2O. M.p. 214°. Sol. EtOH, Et_2O, $CHCl_3$, C_6H_6.

N-*Et*: $C_{30}H_{25}N$. MW, 399. Needles from $CHCl_3$. M.p. 221°.

N-*Acetyl*: needles from AcOH or C_6H_6. M.p. 226°. Prac. insol. EtOH.

Robinson, Robinson, *J. Chem. Soc.*, 1918, **113**, 644.
Fehrlin, *Ber.*, 1889, **22**, 555.

Tetraphenylthiophene (*Thionessal*)

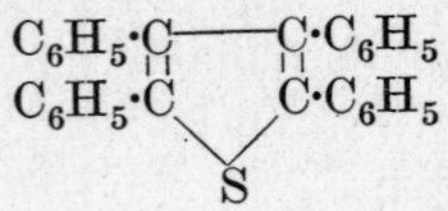

$C_{28}H_{20}S$ MW, 388

Needles from EtOH. M.p. 184–5°. B.p. about 400°. Mod. sol. Et_2O, CS_2, C_6H_6. Spar. sol. ligroin. Very spar. sol. EtOH.

Bergman, *J. Chem. Soc.*, 1936, 505.
Dilthey *et al.*, *Ber.*, 1935, **68**, 1159.

Tetraphenylthiourea.
See under Thiourea.

Tetraphenylurea.
See under Urea.

Tetraphthene.
See Tetrahydroacenaphthene

1 : 2 : 4 : 5-Tetrazine

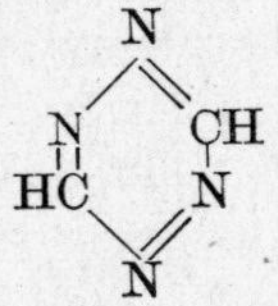

$C_2H_2N_4$ MW, 82

Crimson cryst. M.p. 99°. Sol. H_2O, EtOH, Et_2O, liq. NH_3. Sol. H_2SO_4 with red col. Sublimes. Volatile at room temp.

Wood, Bergstrom, *J. Am. Chem. Soc.*, 1933, **55**, 3649.
Curtius, Darapsky, Müller, *Ber.*, 1907, **40**, 84.

1 : 2 : 3 : 4-Tetrazole (*Pyrro-αββ'-triazole*)

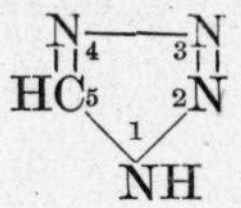

CH_2N_4 MW, 70

Plates from EtOH. M.p. 156°. Sol. H_2O, EtOH, Me_2CO, AcOH. Spar. sol. Et_2O, C_6H_6. Sublimes. Salts are explosive.
N-*Me*: *see* 1-Methyl-1 : 2 : 3 : 4-tetrazole.
N-*Phenyl*: *see* 1-Phenyl-1 : 2 : 3 : 4-tetrazole.

Freund, Paradies, *Ber.*, 1901, **34**, 3110.
Pechmann, Wedekind, *Ber.*, 1895, **28**, 1693.

Tetrolaldehyde (*Allylene-*1*-aldehyde, methylacetylene-aldehyde*)

$CH_3 \cdot C{:}C \cdot CHO$

C_4H_4O MW, 68

F.p. − 26°. B.p. 106·5–107°, 27–8°/34 mm. D_0^0 0·944, D_0^{17} 0·9265. n_D^{17} 1·4467. Readily oxidises in air.
Oxime: needles. M.p. 108–9°.
Semicarbazone: m.p. 158°.
Hydrazone: liq. B.p. 170° decomp., 63–5°/5 mm. $D_0^{18.5}$ 0·9768. $n_D^{18.5}$ 1·530. Misc. with H_2O, EtOH, Et_2O.
p-*Nitrophenylhydrazone*: yellow needles from EtOH.Aq. M.p. 157–8°.
Azine: yellow needles from EtOH. M.p. 123–4°.
Di-Me acetal: b.p. 144·5°. D^{15} 0·954.
Di-Me acetal: b.p. 169–70°, 62–5°/15 mm. D_0^{16} 0·9012. n_D^{16} 1·4269.

Claisen, *Ber.*, 1911, **44**, 1166.
Viguier, *Compt. rend.*, 1911, **152**, 1491.

Tetrolic Acid (*Methylacetylene-carboxylic acid, methylpropiolic acid, allylene-*1*-carboxylic acid*)

$CH_3 \cdot C{:}C \cdot COOH$

$C_4H_4O_2$ MW, 72

Plates from Et_2O or CS_2. M.p. 77–8°. B.p. 203°, 99–100°/18 mm. $k = 2{\cdot}46 \times 10^{-3}$ at 25°. Sol. H_2O, EtOH, Et_2O, $CHCl_3$, CS_2. Volatile in steam. At 211° ⟶ allylene.

Et ester: $C_5H_8O_2$. MW, 100. Oil. B.p. 163–4°. $D_4^{24.1}$ 0·9621. $n_{He}^{24.1}$ 1·43495.
Chloride: C_3H_3OCl. MW, 90·5. Liq. Fumes in air. Very unstable.
Amide: C_3H_5ON. MW, 71. Cryst. from EtOH. M.p. 147–8°. Mod. sol. H_2O, EtOH. Spar. sol. Et_2O. Volatile in steam.

Feist, *Ann.*, 1906, **345**, 104.
Auwers, *Ber.*, 1935, **68**, 1637.
Bourguel, Yvon, *Bull. soc. chim.*, 1929, **45**, 1067.

Tetronal.
See Ethylsulphonal.

Tetronic Acid (*Dihydroxycrotonic lactone,* 3*-hydroxyacetoacetic lactone,* 2*-ketobutyrolactone,* 2 : 4*-diketotetrahydrofuran*)

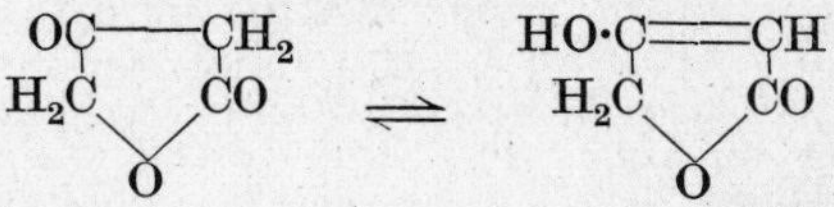

$C_4H_4O_3$ MW, 100

Plates from EtOH–ligroin. Sinters at 135°. M.p. 141°. Very sol. H_2O, warm EtOH. Spar. sol. Et_2O, $CHCl_3$, ligroin, C_6H_6. Strong monobasic acid. Decomposes bicarbonates. $FeCl_3$ ⟶ dark red col. Heat conc. aq. sol. ⟶ anhydrotetronic acid.
Anhydride: anhydrotetronic acid. $C_8H_6O_2$. MW, 182. Needles + $1H_2O$ from hot H_2O. M.p. 263° decomp. Sol. EtOH. Spar. sol. cold H_2O, Et_2O, $CHCl_3$, C_6H_6. Decomposes bicarbonates. $FeCl_3$ ⟶ red. col.
Oxime: plates from hot EtOH. Decomp. at 146°. Very sol. H_2O. Sol. EtOH, Et_2O. No col. with $FeCl_3$.
Benzoyl: plates or prisms from $CHCl_3$–ligroin. M.p. 120°.
Phenylhydrazone: prisms from EtOH.Aq. M.p. 128°.

Wolff, Schwabe, *Ann.*, 1896, **291**, 234.

Tetrophane (3 : 4-*Dihydro-*1 : 2*-naphthacridine-*14*-carboxylic acid*)

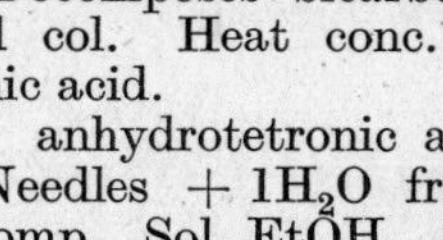

$C_{18}H_{13}O_2N$ MW, 275

Yellow needles. M.p. 252° decomp. to 3 : 4-dihydro-1 : 2-naphthacridine. Very sol. tetralin.

Mod. sol. AcOH. Spar. sol. EtOH. Insol. Et_2O, C_6H_6.

Et ester: $C_{20}H_{17}O_2N$. MW, 303. Needles. M.p. 80°.

Amide: $C_{18}H_{14}ON_2$. MW, 274. Colourless powder from EtOH–pet. ether. M.p. 220–2°.

v. Braun, Wolff, *Ber.*, 1922, **55**, 3679.

Tetryl (N-*Nitro*-N-*methyl*-2 : 4 : 6-*trinitro-aniline, methylpicrylnitramine*)

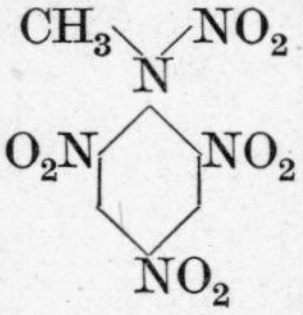

$C_7H_5O_8N_5$ MW, 287

Yellow prisms from EtOH. M.p. 131–2°. D^{19} 1·57. Sol. Me_2CO, Py. Mod. sol. AcOEt, C_6H_6. Spar. sol. MeOH, EtOH. Explodes on heating to about 180–90°. NaOH ⟶ picric acid. Used as explosive chiefly in admixture with other explosives such as trinitrotoluene (T.N.T.).

van Duin, *Rec. trav. chim.*, 1918, **37**, 112.
Tanner, *Chem. Met. Eng.*, 1923, **29**, 404.

Thalline (6-*Methoxy*-1 : 2 : 3 : 4-*tetrahydro-quinoline*)

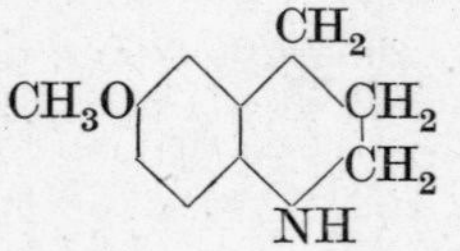

$C_{10}H_{13}ON$ MW, 163

Rhombic cryst. from H_2O, prisms from EtOH or pet. ether, m.p. 42–3°. B.p. 283°/735 mm. Very sol. EtOH, Et_2O, C_6H_6. Spar. sol. H_2O, pet. ether. Difficultly volatile in steam. HCl, H_2SO_4 and AcOH salts have antipyretic action. Ox. agents ⟶ emerald green col. $FeCl_3$ on boiling ⟶ brownish-green or rose col.

B_2,HI: prisms from EtOH. M.p. 155–6°.

N-*Me*: $C_{11}H_{15}ON$. MW, 177. Oil. B.p. 227–228·5°, 150–1°/10 mm. Dil. HCl sol. + $FeCl_3$ ⟶ dark red col. Cl water ⟶ reddish-yellow col. *Methiodide*: needles + $1H_2O$ from H_2O, prisms from EtOH. M.p. 223–4° decomp. *Picrate*: yellow plates. M.p. 164°.

N-*Et*: $C_{12}H_{17}ON$. MW, 191. Yellow oil. B.p. 287–287·5° slight decomp. Misc. with EtOH, Et_2O. Very sol. min. acids. Insol. H_2O. *Ethiodide*: needles. M.p. 131–3°.

N-*Allyl*: $C_{13}H_{17}ON$. MW, 203. Yellow oil. B.p. 176°/12 mm.

N-*Acetyl*: prisms from Et_2O–pet. ether. M.p. 46–7°.

Picrate: yellow needles. M.p. 162°.

Skraup, *Monatsh.*, 1885, **6**, 767.

Thalloperazine

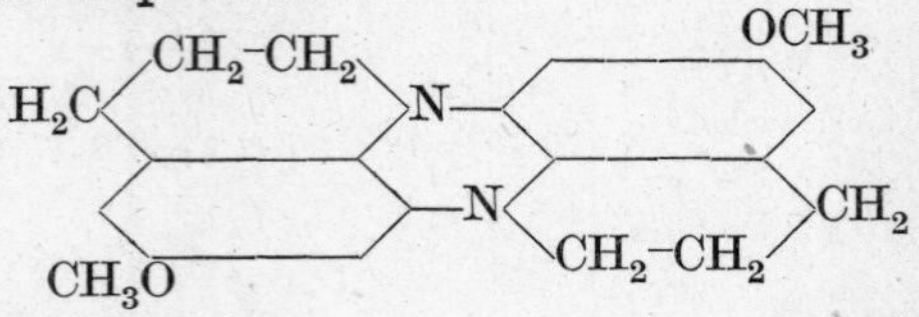

$C_{20}H_{22}O_2N_2$ MW, 322

Yellow cryst. from AcOEt. M.p. 160°. Sol. C_6H_6. Mod. sol. Et_2O. Spar. sol. AcOEt, cold EtOH. H_2SO_4 ⟶ red sol. with reddish-green fluorescence; with H_2O, violet ⟶ pink.

Wieland, Haas, *Ber.*, 1920, **53**, 1342.

Thamnol (2 : 3 : 5-*Trihydroxy*-p-*toluic aldehyde*)

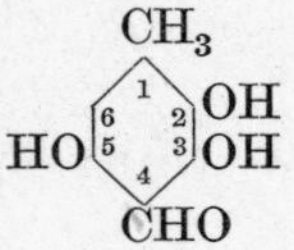

$C_8H_8O_4$ MW, 168

Yellow prisms from C_6H_6. M.p. 186°. Sol. EtOH, Et_2O, AcOEt, Py. Spar. sol. cold C_6H_6. Sol. H_2O ⟶ acid sol. Sol. alkalis ⟶ intense yellow col. Alc. $FeCl_3$ ⟶ green col.

3 : 5-*Di-Me ether*: $C_{10}H_{12}O_4$. MW, 196. Yellow prisms from C_6H_6. M.p. 104°.

Triacetyl: needles from EtOH. M.p. 133°.

Anil: brownish leaflets. M.p. 128–9°.

Phenylhydrazone: brownish-red spears from EtOH. M.p. 194° decomp.

p-*Nitrophenylhydrazone*: brownish-violet needles from EtOH.Aq. M.p. about 320° decomp.

Koller, Hamburg, *Monatsh.*, 1935, **65**, 378.
Asahina, Fuzikawa, *Ber.*, 1932, **65**, 58.
Asahina, Ihara, *Ber.*, 1929, **62**, 1204.

Thamnolic Acid

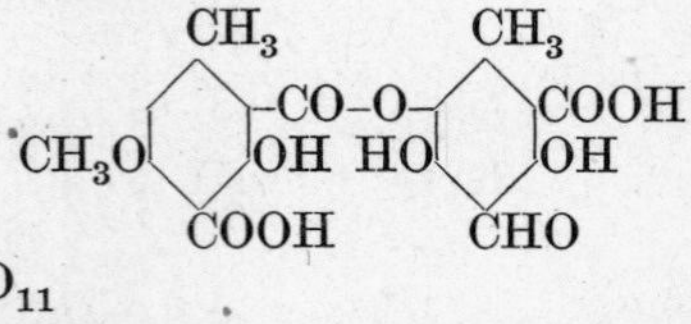

$C_{19}H_{16}O_{11}$ MW, 420

Constituent of many lichens. Colourless prisms from Me_2CO. M.p. 223°. Sol. alkalis and alk. carbonates ⟶ yellow sols. Alc. $FeCl_3$ ⟶

brownish-red col. Loses CO_2 on heating to 120–30° with Me_2CO.

Anil: orange-yellow cryst. from EtOH. M.p. 206–8°.

Phenylhydrazone: yellow prisms from EtOH. M.p. 173–4°.

p-*Nitrophenylhydrazone*: orange-yellow cryst. from EtOH. M.p. 238–9°.

Asahina, Hiraiwa, *Ber.*, 1936, **69**, 330.
Asahina, Ihara, *Ber.*, 1929, **62**, 1196.

Thapsic Acid (*Thapsiaic acid, 1 : 14-tetradecane-dicarboxylic acid*)

HOOC·$[CH_2]_{14}$·COOH

$C_{16}H_{30}O_4$ MW, 286

Occurs as ester in roots of *Thapsia garganica*, Linn., and in wax of *Juniperus sabina*. Plates from EtOH or AcOEt. M.p. 126°. Sol. EtOH. Spar. sol. Et_2O. Insol. H_2O, CS_2, C_6H_6. Distils undecomp. Ac_2O ⟶ anhydride.

Di-Me ester: $C_{18}H_{34}O_4$. MW, 314. M.p. 51–2°. B.p. 150–60°/0·3 mm.

Di-Et ester: $C_{20}H_{38}O_4$. MW, 342. Cryst. M.p. 39°. B.p. 160–5°/0·3 mm. Very sol. Et_2O, EtOH. Spar. sol. pet. ether.

Anhydride: $C_{16}H_{28}O_3$. MW, 268. Cryst. powder from C_6H_6. M.p. 71°. Boiling H_2O ⟶ thapsic acid.

Dianilide: cryst. from MeOH. M.p. 163°.

Schmid, Kemeny, *Monatsh.*, 1935, **66**, 3.
Bougault, *Compt. rend.*, 1910, **150**, 875.
Canzoneri, *Gazz. chim. ital.*, 1883, **13**, 516.

Thapsin (*Calycopterin*)

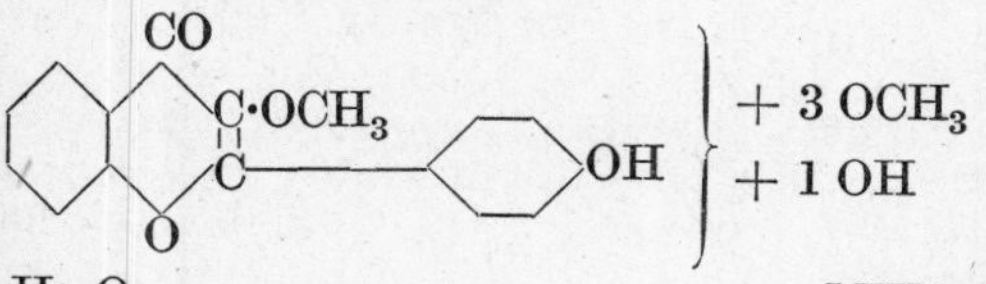

$C_{19}H_{18}O_8$ MW, 374

Occurs in Spanish fox-glove (*Digitalis thapsi*, Linn.), and leaves of *Calycopteris floribunda*, Lamk. Yellow prisms from AcOH, needles from Et_2O. M.p. 225–6°. Very sol. $CHCl_3$, Me_2CO. Sol. EtOH. Spar. sol. Et_2O. Insol. H_2O, pet. ether. Alkalis ⟶ yellow sols. $FeCl_3$ ⟶ green col. HI ⟶ calycopteretin. KOH fusion ⟶ *p*-hydroxybenzoic acid.

Di-Me ether: $C_{21}H_{22}O_8$. MW, 402. Yellow prisms or rhombohedra from EtOH. M.p. 130°.

Di-Et ether: $C_{23}H_{26}O_8$. MW, 430. Yellow cryst. from EtOH. M.p. 130°.

Diacetyl: colourless plates or needles from EtOH. M.p. 129°.

Dibenzoyl: m.p. 165°.

Karrer, Venkataraman, *Nature*, 1935, **135**, 878.
Ratnagiriswaran, Sehra, Venkataraman, *Biochem. J.*, 1934, **28**, 1964.
Karrer, *Helv. Chim. Acta*, 1934, **17**, 1560.

Thebaine (*Methyl ether of enol of codeinone*)

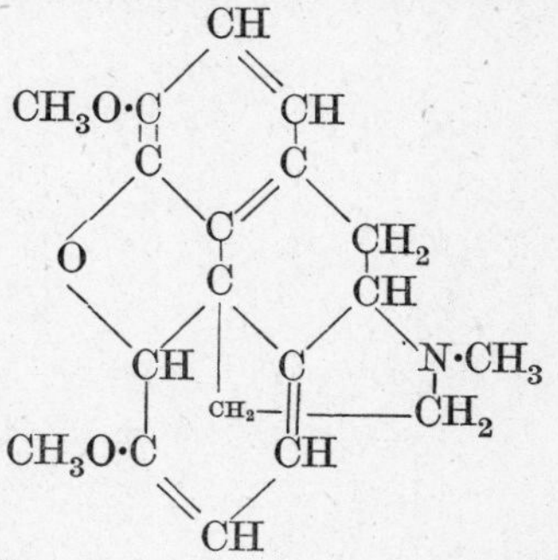

$C_{19}H_{21}O_3N$ MW, 311

Plates from EtOH.Aq., prisms from EtOH. M.p. 193°. Very sol. EtOH, $CHCl_3$. Sol. 140 parts Et_2O at 10°, 18 parts cold C_6H_6. Sol. H_2SO_4 ⟶ red col. Tasteless. $[\alpha]_D$ − 218·6° in EtOH. Decomp. by dil. min. acids. Dil. HCl ⟶ thebenin. Very poisonous.

Picrate: m.p. 217°.

v. Braun, Cahn, *Ann.*, 1926, **451**, 55.
Schöpf, Winterholder, *Ann.*, 1927, **452**, 232.

Thebainol

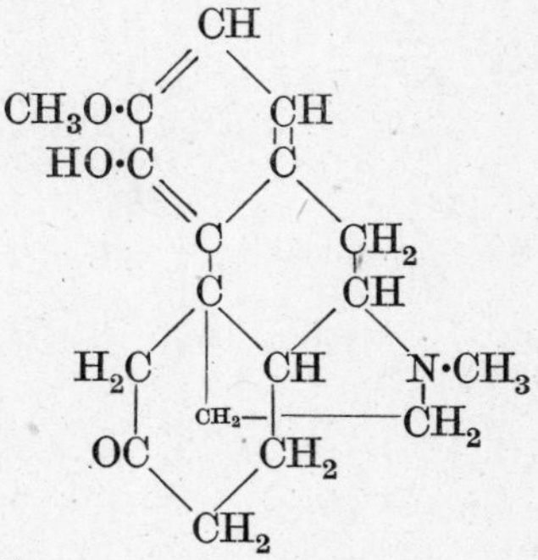

$C_{18}H_{23}O_3N$ MW, 301

Cryst. + MeOH from MeOH, m.p. 50–4°; colourless prisms from Et_2O, m.p. 135–6°. $[\alpha]_D^{25}$ + 67·05° in EtOH. Sol. dil. alkalis. Forms cryst. Na salt. Forms benzylidene and piperonylidene derivs.

Oxime: cryst. from EtOH. M.p. 217–18°. $[\alpha]_D^{18}$ + 104·2° in AcOH.Aq.

Semicarbazone : needles from EtOH–AcOEt. M.p. 217–18°.

Perchlorate : cryst. from EtOH. M.p. 245°.

Methiodide : prisms from EtOH. M.p. 243° decomp.

Gulland, *J. Chem. Soc.*, 1928, 706.
Schöpf, Borkowsky, *Ann.*, 1927, **458**, 170.
Gulland, Robinson, *J. Chem. Soc.*, 1923, **123**, 998.
Pschorr, *Ber.*, 1905, **38**, 3167.

Thebainone

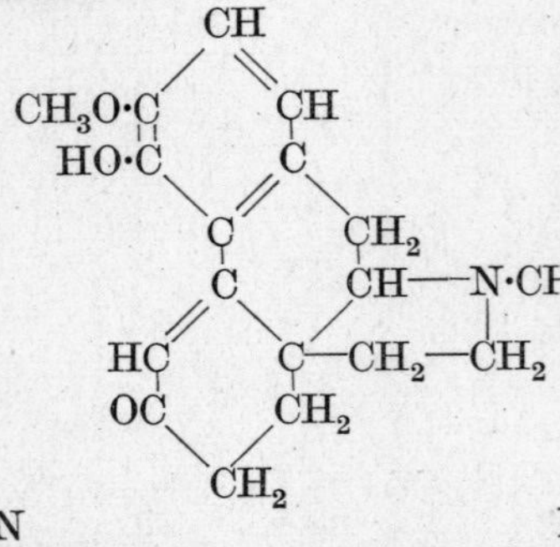

$C_{18}H_{21}O_3N$ MW, 299

Colourless needles $+ \frac{1}{2}H_2O$ from EtOH.Aq. M.p. 151–2°. Loses H_2O at 100° in vacuo. Very sol. Me_2CO, $CHCl_3$, C_6H_6. Spar. sol. Et_2O. Sol. 250 parts cold H_2O, 120 parts hot. Sol. 4 parts EtOH, 5 parts AcOEt. Yellow aq. sol. reacts alkaline. Sol. alkalis ⟶ yellow col. Sol. conc. HCl, H_2SO_4. Forms benzylidine and piperonylidene derivs.

B,HI : needles from H_2O. M.p. 258–9°.

Me ether : $C_{19}H_{23}O_3N$. MW, 313. Prisms from MeOH. M.p. 156°. *Methiodide* : plates from EtOH. M.p. 256°.

Oxime : prisms $+ \frac{1}{2}H_2O$ from EtOH.Aq. M.p. 200–1° (185–6°). *B,HCl* : needles from H_2O. M.p. 290–1°.

Semicarbazone : needles from AcOEt. M.p. 227°.

Methiodide : needles from EtOH.Aq. M.p. 255–6° (223°).

Acetyl : prisms from Et_2O–pet. ether. M.p. 100–1°. *Methiodide* : prisms from EtOH. M.p. 223–5°. *Semicarbazone* : needles from EtOH. M.p. 249°. *Phenylhydrazone* : prisms from EtOH. M.p. 225–6°.

Picrate : prisms from EtOH. M.p. 250–3°.

Schöpf, Hirsch, *Ann.*, 1931, **489**, 240.
Gulland, *J. Chem. Soc.*, 1928, 702.
Schöpf, Borkowsky, *Ann.*, 1927, **458**, 148.
Gulland, Robinson, *J. Chem. Soc.*, 1923, 998.
Pschorr, *Ber.*, 1905, **38**, 3163.

Thebaol (4-*Hydroxy*-3 : 6-*dimethoxyphenanthrene*)

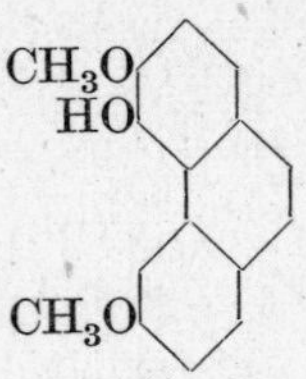

$C_{16}H_{14}O_3$ MW, 254

Plates and columns from AcOH. M.p. 94°. Very sol. EtOH, Et_2O, $CHCl_3$, Me_2CO, C_6H_6. Spar. sol. AcOH, ligroin. Zn dust dist. ⟶ phenanthrene.

Me ether : methylthebaol. $C_{17}H_{16}O_3$. MW, 268. Thick oil. *Picrate* : reddish-brown needles from EtOH. M.p. 110–12°.

Acetyl : plates from EtOH. M.p. 118–22°. *Picrate* : red needles. M.p. 139°.

Benzoyl : needles from AcOH. M.p. 160–1°.

Pschorr, *Ber.*, 1912, **45**, 2218.
Freund, Göbel, *Ber.*, 1897, **30**, 1371, 1389.

Thebenine (1 : 5-*Dihydroxy*-6-*methoxy*-4-[β-*methylaminoethyl*]-*phenanthrene*)

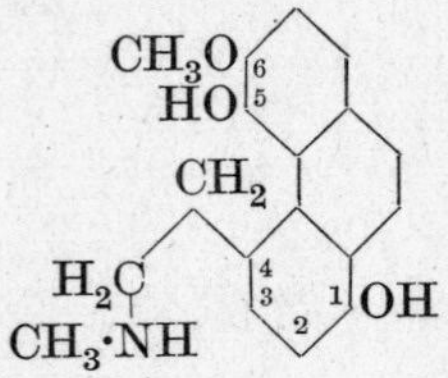

$C_{18}H_{19}O_3N$ MW, 297

Amorph. Spar. sol. boiling EtOH. Sol. aq. KOH. Insol. Et_2O, C_6H_6. Sol. conc. H_2SO_4 ⟶ blue col. Readily oxidises especially in presence of alkalis. Zn dust dist. ⟶ pyrene.

B,HCl : plates $+ 3H_2O$. Sinters at 231°. M.p. 235°.

B_2,H_2SO_4 : yellow plates $+ 1H_2O$. Sinters at 205°. M.p. 209–10°.

Oxalate : prisms. M.p. 275–6°.

1-*Me ether* : methebenine. $C_{19}H_{21}O_3N$. MW, 311. Cryst. or amorph. from EtOH. Sinters at 155°. M.p. 165–7°. Pptd. from alk. sol. with CO_2. Hot dil. HCl ⟶ thebenine. *B,HCl* : needles from EtOH. M.p. 250°. *B,HI* : plates from EtOH.Aq. Sinters at 190°. M.p. 195–8°. *Sulphate* : needles. M.p. 238·5°. N : 5-*Diacetyl* : plates from EtOH. M.p. 179°. N : 5-*Dibenzoyl* : needles from EtOH. M.p. 159°.

N-*Me* : *methiodide* : thebeninmethin methiodide. Cryst. from EtOH. M.p. 206–8°.

N : 1-*Di-Me* : $C_{20}H_{23}O_3N$. MW, 325. *Meth-*

iodide: methebeninmethin methiodide. Columns from EtOH.Aq. M.p. 215°.

1 : 5-*Di-Me ether* : *methiodide* : aggregates of needles from EtOH. M.p. 247°. *Methosulphate* : needles from EtOH or Et_2O. Sinters at 268°. M.p. 277°.

1-*Et ether* : ethebenine. $C_{20}H_{23}O_3N$. MW, 325. Yellow, amorph. *B,HCl* : microplates from EtOH.Aq. M.p. 248°. *B,HI* : plates + $1H_2O$ from H_2O. Sinters at 200°. M.p. 206–7°. N : 5-*Diacetyl* : cryst. from EtOH. M.p. 163°.

N-*Me* : 1-*Et* : $C_{21}H_{25}O_3N$. MW, 339. *Methiodide* : ethebeninmethin methiodide. Plates from EtOH.Aq. Sinters at 210°. M.p. 215°.

1-*Propyl ether* : prothebenine. $C_{21}H_{25}O_3N$. MW, 339. Needles from EtOH. Sinters at 167°. M.p. 172–3°. *B,HCl* : plates from EtOH. Sinters at 215°. M.p. 221–2°. *B,HI* : plates. M.p. 212–13°.

N : 1 : 5-*Triacetyl* : hydrated needles from EtOH.Aq. M.p. 72–80°. Anhyd. cryst. from abs. EtOH. M.p. 160–1°.

Gulland, Virden, *J. Chem. Soc.*, 1928, 921.
Pschorr, *Ann.*, 1910, **373**, 69.
Freund, Holthof, *Ber.*, 1899, **32**, 179, 181.
Freund, Michaels, *Ber.*, 1897, **30**, 1375.

Thebenol

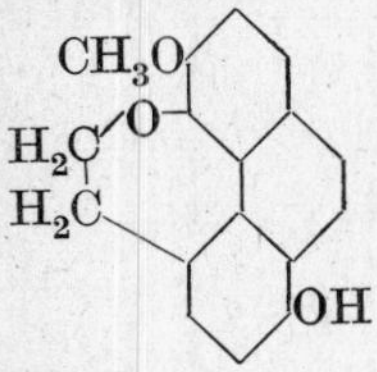

or

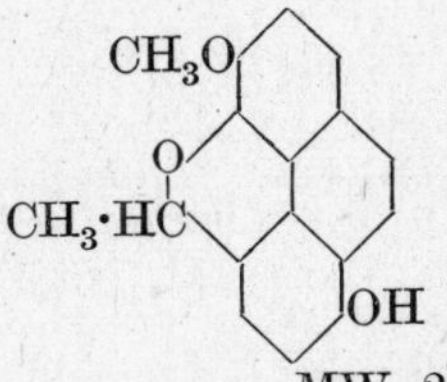

$C_{17}H_{14}O_3$ MW, 266

Rhombohedra from hot AcOH. M.p. 186–8°. Very sol. EtOH, Et_2O. Sol. C_6H_6, KOH.Aq. Insol. H_2O, ligroin, Na_2CO_3, NH_4OH. Alc. sol. reduces $AgNO_3$. Zn dust dist., or heat with HI(+ P) $\longrightarrow$ pyrene. KOH fusion $\longrightarrow$ northebenol.

Na salt : cryst. ppt. M.p. about 210–12°.

Me ether : methebenol. $C_{18}H_{16}O_3$. MW, 280. Plates from AcOH. M.p. 133–4°. Very sol. $CHCl_3$. *Picrate* : m.p. 106°.

Et ether : $C_{19}H_{18}O_3$. MW, 294. Plates from AcOH. M.p. 104°. Spar. sol. EtOH, ligroin.

Propyl ether : $C_{20}H_{20}O_3$. MW, 308. Plates from AcOH. M.p. 103–5°.

Gulland, Virden, *J. Chem. Soc.*, 1928, 921.
Sieglitz, Koch, *Ber.*, 1925, **58**, 78.
Pschorr, *Ann.*, 1910, **373**, 61.
Freund, Holthof, *Ber.*, 1899, **32**, 184.
Freund, Michaels, *Ber.*, 1897, **30**, 1380.

Theelin.
See Œstrone.

Theelol.
See Œstriol.

Theïne.
See Caffeïne.

Thelephoric Acid

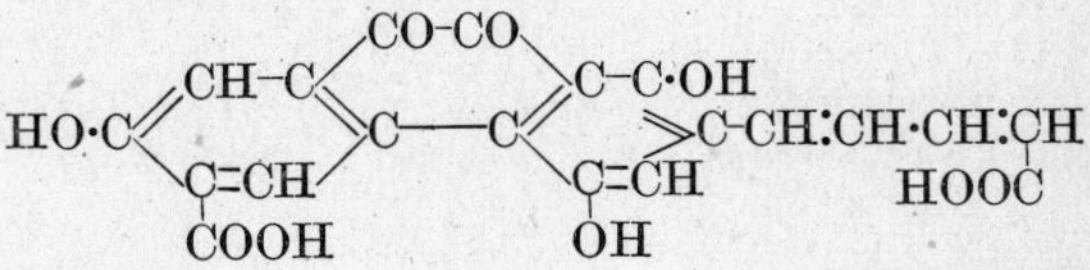

$C_{20}H_{12}O_9$ MW, 396

Isolated from *Thelephora palmata*. Black powder with metallic reflex. Almost insol. in all org. solvents except Py.

Triacetyl : orange-yellow needles from $PhNO_2$. Decomp. at 330°.

Kögl, Erxleben, Jänecke, *Ann.*, 1930, **482**, 110.

Theobromine (3 : 7-*Dimethylxanthine*, 3 : 7-*dimethyl*-2 : 6-*dihydroxypurine*)

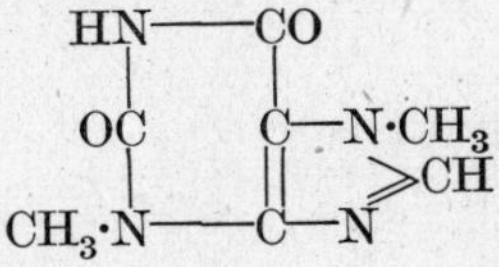

$C_7H_8O_2N_4$ MW, 180

Important alkaloid constituent of cacao beans, kola nuts, etc. Rhombic microcryst. Sublimes at 290°. Insol. ligroin, cold Et_2O, cold $CHCl_3$, C_6H_6. Sol. 1600 parts H_2O at 17°, 3125 parts Et_2O at b.p. $k = 11{\cdot}1 \times 10^{-11}$ at 25° ($4{\cdot}6 \times 10^{-14}$ at 40°). $CrO_3 \longrightarrow$ methylparabanic acid + methylamine. Methylation $\longrightarrow$ caffeïne. Faintly basic. Salts decomp. by H_2O. Forms more stable salts with bases. Alkaloid and salts have diuretic action.

Perchlorate : cryst. + $1H_2O$. Decomp. at 271–3°.

Hg salt : darkens at 295–305°. M.p. 310°.

B,HgNO₃ : prisms. Does not melt below 300°.

N-*Me* : *see* Caffeïne.

N-*Et* : $C_9H_{12}O_2N_4$. MW, 208. Needles from H_2O. M.p. 164–5°. Sublimes. *B,HAuCl₄* : needles. M.p. 226°.

N-*Propyl* : $C_{10}H_{14}O_2N_4$. MW, 222. Needles from H_2O. M.p. 136°. *B,HAuCl₄* : needles. M.p. 95°.

N-*Butyl* : $C_{11}H_{16}O_2N_4$. MW, 236. Needles from H_2O. M.p. 119°.

N-*Isobutyl* : m.p. 129–30°. *B,HAuCl₄* : needles. M.p. 97°.

Methochloride: colourless columns. M.p. 320–40° decomp. Very sol. H_2O.

Methochloroaurate: yellow woolly needles. M.p. 265° decomp.

Biltz, Max, *Ann.*, 1921, **423**, 320.
Dubosc, *Chem. Zentr.*, 1932, IV, 956.

Theocin.
See Theophylline.

Theophylline (*Theocin*, 1 : 3-*dimethylxanthine*, 1 : 3-*dimethyl*-2 : 6-*dihydroxypurine*)

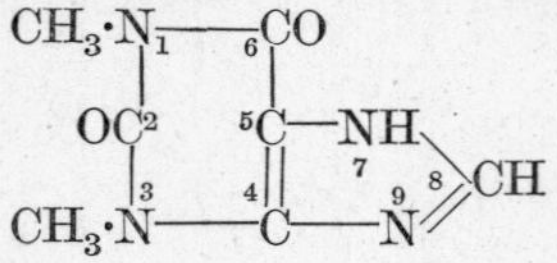

$C_7H_8O_2N_4$ MW, 180

Alkaloid constituent of tea leaves. Needles or plates + $1H_2O$ from hot H_2O. M.p. 264°. Very sol. warm H_2O. Spar. sol. cold EtOH. $k = 16{\cdot}2 \times 10^{-10}$ at 25° ($5{\cdot}46 \times 10^{-14}$ at 40°). Methylation ⟶ caffeïne. Alkaloid and metallic salts have diuretic action. Comps. with Na acetate and Na salicylate are important diuretics.

7-N-*Me*: *see* Caffeïne.

7-N-*Propyl*: $C_{10}H_{14}O_2N_4$. MW, 222. *B,HAuCl*$_4$: yellow needles + $2H_2O$. M.p. 214°.

7-N-*Isopropyl*: *B,HAuCl*$_4$: yellow needles from EtOH.Aq. M.p. 183°. *B,H*$_2$*PtCl*$_6$: orange-yellow cryst. + $2H_2O$. M.p. 201°.

7-N-*Acetyl*: needles from $CHCl_3$. M.p. 158°.

7-N-*Benzoyl*: needles from EtOH. M.p. 202°.

Yoshitomi, *Chem. Abstracts*, 1925, **19**, 2303.
Biltz, Strufe, *Ann.*, 1914, **404**, 137, 170.
Schwabe, *Arch. pharm.*, 1907, **245**, 312.
Fischer, *Ber.*, 1897, **30**, 553.

Thermopsine

$C_{15}H_{20}ON_2$ MW, 244

Alkaloid isolated from *Thermopsis lanceolata*. Pale yellow cryst. from Me_2CO. M.p. 206–206·5° (203–5°). Sol. H_2O, Et_2O, EtOH, $CHCl_3$. Spar. sol. Me_2CO, pet. ether. $[\alpha]_D^{20}$ − 159·6° in EtOH.

B,HCl: m.p. 247–8° decomp.

B,HI: needles from EtOH. M.p. 294–6°. (306–8° decomp.).

Chloroaurate: m.p. 183–4° decomp.

Chloroplatinate: orange-red prisms. Decomp. at 245–7° (254–6°).

Methiodide: prisms from MeOH. M.p. 241–2° decomp.

Picrate: yellow prisms from EtOH–Me_2CO. M.p. 229–31° decomp. (208–9°).

Picrolonate: m.p. 173–5° decomp.

Orechoff, *Chem. Zentr.*, 1935, II, 2215.
Orechoff, Gurewitsch, *Ber.*, 1935, **68**, 820.
Orechoff, Norkina, Gurewitsch, *Ber.*, 1933, **66**, 627.

Thevetin

$C_{42}H_{66}O_{18}$ MW, 858

Glucoside from leaves of *Thevetia nereïfolia*, Juss., etc. Needles from EtOH or isopropyl alcohol. Softens at 193–4°. M.p. 210°. Sol. EtOH, C_3H_7OH, Py. Spar. sol. H_2O, Et_2O, Me_2CO, $CHCl_3$, C_6H_6. Gives positive Legal test. $[\alpha]_D^{28}$ − 62·5°. Hyd. ⟶ thevetigenin + glucose + digitalose (?).

Tschesche, *Ber.*, 1936, **69**, 2368.
Elderfield, *J. Biol. Chem.*, 1936, **115**, 247.
Chen, Chen, *J. Biol. Chem.*, 1934, **105**, 231.

Thialdine (*Thioacetaldehyde-ammonia*, 2 : 4 : 6-*trimethyl*-5 : 6-*dihydro*-1 : 3 : 5-*dithiazine*)

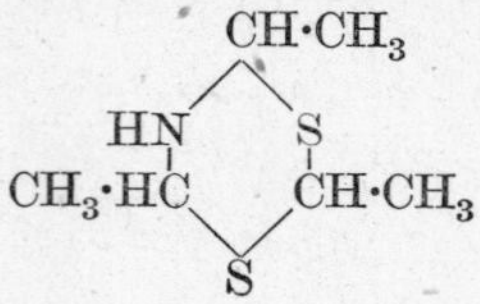

$C_6H_{13}NS_2$ MW, 163

Cryst. M.p. 43°. Very sol. Et_2O. Sol. EtOH. Spar. sol. H_2O. Volatile in steam. Forms cryst. salts with acids.

B,HCNS: needles. M.p. 132° decomp.

N-*Me*: $C_7H_{15}NS_2$. MW, 177. Needles from EtOH. M.p. 79°. Very sol. Et_2O. Spar. sol. cold EtOH. Insol. cold H_2O. *B,HCNS*: columns from EtOH. M.p. 120°.

Marckwald, *Ber.*, 1886, **19**, 2381.

Thianthrene.
See Diphenylene disulphide.

Thiasine.
See Ergothioneine.

1 : 4-Thiazan (*Tetrahydrothiazine*, *thiomorpholine*)

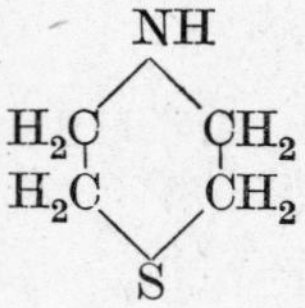

C_4H_9NS MW, 103

Colourless liq. B.p. 169°. Misc. with H_2O and most org. solvents.

B,HCl: needles from C_6H_6. Softens at 145°. M.p. 160–5°.

Chloroplatinate: does not melt below 250°.

N-*Me*: $C_5H_{11}NS$. MW, 117. B.p. 163–4°. Misc. with H_2O. D_4^{20} 0·9924. n_a^{20} 1·50176. *B,HCl*: m.p. 239°. *Picrate*: yellow needles from EtOH. M.p. 226° decomp.

N-*Et*: $C_6H_{13}NS$. MW, 131. B.p. 184°. Misc. with H_2O. D_4^{20} 0·98854. n_a^{20} 1·50180. *B,HCl*: m.p. 188°. *Chloroplatinate*: decomp. at 222°. *Picrate*: yellow needles from Me_2CO–EtOH. M.p. 185–6°.

N-*Phenyl*: $C_{10}H_{13}NS$. MW, 179. Cryst. from toluene. M.p. 108–11°.

Ethiodide: cryst. from EtOH. M.p. 260°.

Picrate: orange needles from EtOH. M.p. 198° decomp.

Picrolonate: orange prisms from EtOH. M.p. 242° decomp.

Lawson, Reid, *J. Am. Chem. Soc.*, 1925, **47**, 2830.
Helfrich, Reid, *J. Am. Chem. Soc.*, 1920, **42**, 1226.
Davies, *J. Chem. Soc.*, 1920, **117**, 306.
Clarke, *J. Chem. Soc.*, 1912, **101**, 1586.

Thiazole

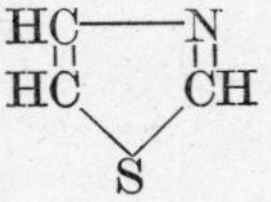

C_3H_3NS MW, 85

Liq. B.p. 116·8°. D^{17} 1·1998.

B,HgCl₂: cryst. ppt. Softens at 200°. M.p. 225° decomp.

B,HgCl₂,HCl: needles. M.p. 103–4°.

B₂,H₂PtCl₆: prisms + $2H_2O$. Decomp. at 250°.

B,HAuCl₄: yellow prisms from EtOH. M.p. 258° decomp.

Picrate: needles. Sinters at 150°. M.p. 159–60° decomp.

Gabriel, Bachstez, *Ber.*, 1914, **47**, 3169.
Popp, *Ann.*, 1889, **250**, 275.

4 : 5-Thiazoline (4 : 5-*Dihydrothiazole*)

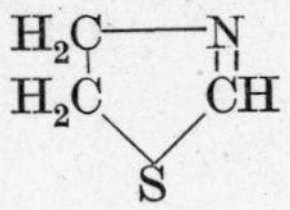

C_3H_5NS MW, 87

B.p. 137·5–138°/747 mm.

Picrate: yellow plates. M.p. 150–1°.

Gabriel, *Ber.*, 1916, **49**, 1111.

Thienone.

See Dithienyl Ketone.

2-Thienylacetic Acid (*Thiophene-2-acetic acid*)

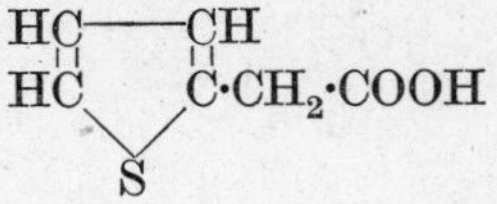

$C_6H_6O_2S$ MW, 142

Cryst. M.p. 76°. Sol. hot H_2O, EtOH, Et_2O.

Ernst, *Ber.*, 1886, **19**, 3281.

2-Thienylglycollic Acid

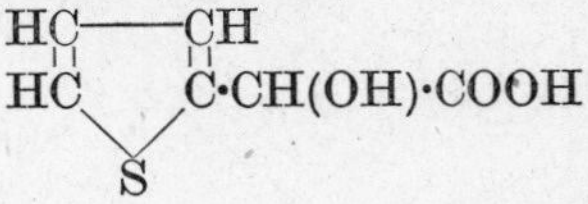

$C_6H_6O_3S$ MW, 158

Needles from C_6H_6. M.p. 115°. Very sol. H_2O, EtOH, Et_2O. Red. ⟶ thienylacetic acid. $MnO_2 + H_2O$ ⟶ thiophene-2-aldehyde.

See previous reference.

2-Thienylglyoxylic Acid

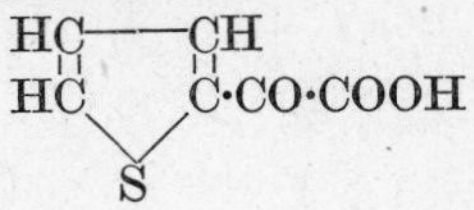

$C_6H_4O_3S$ MW, 156

Cryst. + $1H_2O$. M.p. 58–9°, anhyd. 91·5°. Very sol. H_2O. Very strong acid. Heat ⟶ thiophene-2-aldehyde. Ox. ⟶ thiophene-2-carboxylic acid. AcOH sol. + AcOH–H_2SO_4 ⟶ brown ⟶ green ⟶ violet ⟶ blue col.

Me ester: $C_7H_6O_3S$. MW, 170. M.p. 28·5°. *Oxime*: needles from EtOH.Aq. Softens at 97°. M.p. 104–5°.

Et ester: $C_8H_8O_3S$. MW, 184. Oil with fragrant odour. B.p. 264–5° slight decomp. *Oxime*: needles. M.p. 122–3°.

Amide: $C_6H_5O_2NS$. MW, 155. Needles. M.p. 88°. Very sol. EtOH, Et_2O. Insol. H_2O.

Oxime: needles. M.p. 145–6° decomp. *Acetyl*: prisms. M.p. 85–7° decomp.

Phenylhydrazone: yellow needles from Et_2O. M.p. 164–5° decomp.

Bradley, *Ber.*, 1886, **19**, 2116.
Peter, *Ber.*, 1885, **18**, 537.

Thioacetic Acid

$$CH_3{\cdot}CO{\cdot}SH \rightleftharpoons CH_3{\cdot}CS{\cdot}OH$$

C_2H_4OS MW, 76

B.p. 93°. D^{10} 1·075. Very sol. EtOH. Sol. H_2O. $k = 4{\cdot}69 \times 10^{-4}$ at 25°.

Bi salt: prisms. M.p. 85°.

S-*Me ester*: C_3H_6OS. MW, 90. B.p. 95–6°.

O-*Me ester*: pale yellow liq. B.p. 88–91°. D_4^{28} 0·9002. n_D^{28} 1·4212. Insol. H_2O.
S-*Et ester*: C_4H_8OS. MW, 104. B.p. 116–17°. D_4^{28} 0·9755. n_D^{28} 1·4503.
O-*Et ester*: b.p. 105–7°. D_4^{17} 0·8980.
S-*Propyl ester*: $C_5H_{10}OS$. MW, 118. B.p. 135–7°.
O-*Propyl ester*: b.p. 125–30°. D_4^{28} 0·8952. n_D^{28} 1·4283.
S-*Isopropyl ester*: b.p. 124–7°.
O-*Isopropyl ester*: b.p. 119–22°. D_4^{22} 0·8901.
O-*Butyl ester*: $C_6H_{12}OS$. MW, 132. B.p. 146–9°. D_4^{29} 0·8883. n_D^{22} 1·4501, n_D^{28} 1·4196.
O-*Isobutyl ester*: b.p. 135–40°. D_4^{26} 0·8875. n_D^{26} 1·4316.
S-*Phenyl ester*: C_8H_8OS. MW, 152. B.p. 228–30°. D^{23} 1·117. n_D^{22} 1·5706.
O-*Phenyl ester*: b.p. 90–4°/38 mm. D_4^{20} 0·9914.
O-*Benzyl ester*: $C_9H_{10}OS$. MW, 166. B.p. 115–20°/27–9 mm. D_4^{25} 1·0296. n_D^{26} 1·5492.
Anhydride: *see* Diacetyl sulphide.
Amide: thioacetamide. C_2H_5NS. MW, 75. Prisms from Et_2O. M.p. 107·5–108·5° (115°). Sol. H_2O, EtOH. Spar. sol. Et_2O.
Hydrazide: m.p. 59°.
Anilide: thioacetanilide. Needles from H_2O. M.p. 75–6°.
o-*Toluidide*: needles from ligroin. M.p. 91–2°.
m-*Toluidide*: needles. M.p. 42–3°.
p-*Toluidide*: prisms from EtOH.Aq. M.p. 129·5–130·5°.
o-*Anisidide*: yellow plates. M.p. 52–3°.
p-*Anisidide*: needles. M.p. 114°.

Baker, Reid, *J. Am. Chem. Soc.*, 1929, **51**, 1568.
Sakurada, *Brit. Chem. Abstracts*, 1927, 133.
Clarke, Hartman, *J. Am. Chem. Soc.*, 1924, **46**, 1732.
Delépine, *Compt. rend.*, 1911, **153**, 281.
Schoff, *Ber.*, 1895, **28**, 1205.

Thioacridol.
See Thioacridone.

Thioacridone (9-*Mercaptoacridine, thioacridol*)

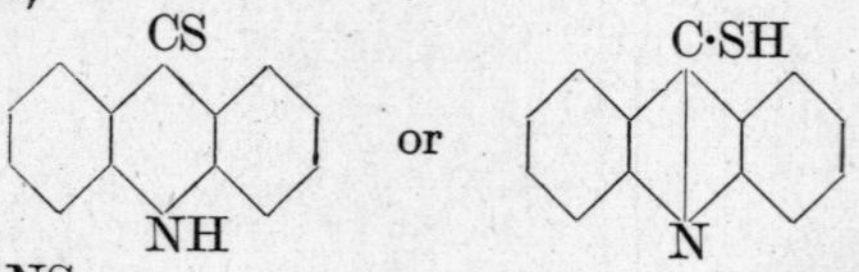

$C_{13}H_9NS$ MW, 211

Brownish-yellow needles + $1H_2O$ from 2% NaOH. M.p. 275°. Loses H_2O at 120° over H_2SO_4. Sol. Me_2CO. Spar. sol. other org. solvents. Sol. conc. acids, alkalis and NH_4OH. Insol. alkali carbonates. Salts are unstable and decomp. by H_2O.
S-*Me*: $C_{14}H_{11}NS$. MW, 225. Greenish-yellow needles from EtOH. M.p. 113–14°. *Hydrochloride*: yellow needles. M.p. 198°. *Sulphate*: m.p. 156–7°. *Nitrate*: m.p. 117–18°. *Picrate*: needles from EtOH–$CHCl_3$. M.p. 205°.
S-*Et*: $C_{15}H_{13}NS$. MW, 239. Yellow needles from pet. ether. M.p. 65°. *Picrate*: yellow needles from $CHCl_3$–EtOH. M.p. 182–3°.
N-*Phenyl*: $C_{19}H_{13}NS$. MW, 287. Red cryst. from AcOH. M.p. 227–8°. Sol. Me_2CO, $CHCl_3$, C_6H_6. Mod. sol. EtOH, AcOH.
S-2 : 4-*Dinitrophenyl*: yellow needles from xylene. M.p. 290° decomp. *Picrate*: yellow needles. M.p. 226° decomp.
S-2 : 4 : 6-*Trinitrophenyl*: thioacridol picryl ether. Red needles from $CHCl_3$. M.p. 233° decomp.
S-*Benzyl*: needles from EtOH.Aq. M.p. 109°. *Hydrochloride*: yellow leaflets. Decomp. at 140–1°. *Sulphate*: m.p. 179–80° decomp. *Nitrate*: yellow leaflets. M.p. 106–7° decomp. *Picrate*: yellowish-brown needles from EtOH. M.p. 189–90°.
S-o-*Nitrobenzyl*: yellow leaflets. M.p. 129–30°. *Picrate*: yellow cryst. M.p. 190–1°.
S-p-*Nitrobenzyl*: yellow cryst. from Me_2CO. M.p. 152°. *Picrate*: m.p. 204°.
S-*Benzoyl*: yellow leaflets from EtOH–$CHCl_3$. M.p. 209°. *Picrate*: greenish-yellow needles from EtOH–$CHCl_3$. M.p. 190°.

Edinger, *J. prakt. Chem.*, 1903, **68**, 88.
Edinger, Arnold, *J. prakt. Chem.*, 1901, **64**, 196, 487.
Kalle, D.R.P., 120,586, (*Chem. Zentr.*, 1901, I, 1254).
Schönberg, Schütz, Nickel, *Ber.*, 1928, **61**, 1383.

Thioaniline.
See 4 : 4′-Diaminodiphenyl sulphide.

Thioanisaldehyde (p-*Methylmercaptobenzaldehyde*)

C_8H_8OS MW, 152

Yellowish plates from ligroin. M.p. 78°. B.p. 273°. Sol. common org. solvents.
Phenylhydrazone: m.p. 138° (136°).

Friedländer, Lenk, *Ber.*, 1912, **45**, 2089.
Mitra, *Chem. Abstracts*, 1933, **27**, 3923.

Thioanisidine.
See under Aminothiophenol.
Thioanisole (*Methyl phenyl sulphide*)

$$C_6H_5 \cdot SCH_3$$

C_7H_8S MW, 124

B.p. 187–8°, 58–60°/6 mm. D_4^{25} 1·0533. n_D^{25} ·5832.

Knapp, *Monatsh.*, 1930, **56**, 68 (*Footnote*).
Suter, Hansen, *J. Am. Chem. Soc.*, 1932, **54**, 4101.
Brand, Kranz, *J. prakt. Chem.*, 1927, **115**, 143.

Thioanisole-ω-carboxylic Acid.
See Phenylthioglycollic Acid.
Thioanthrol.
See Mercaptoanthracene.
Thioargyrium.
See under Dithiosalicylic Acid.
Thioaspirin.
See under Thiosalicylic Acid.
Thiobarbituric Acid (*Malonylthiourea*)

$$\begin{array}{ccc} HN & \!\!\!\!\!\!\!--- & CO \\ SC & & CH_2 \\ HN & \!\!\!\!\!\!\!--- & CO \end{array}$$

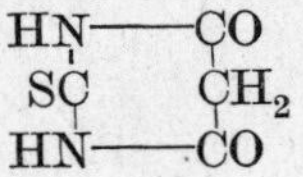

$C_4H_4O_2N_2S$ MW, 144

Plates from H_2O. M.p. 235° decomp. (rapid heat.).

Michael, *J. prakt. Chem.*, 1894, **49**, 38.
Harwood, *Chem. Abstracts*, 1933, **27**, 1676.

Thiobenzamide.
See under Thiobenzoic Acid.
Thiobenzanilide.
See under Thiobenzoic Acid.
Thiobenzhydrol (*Benzhydryl mercaptan, x-mercaptodiphenylmethane*)

$$C_6H_5 \cdot CH(SH) \cdot C_6H_5$$

$C_{13}H_{12}S$ MW, 200

Yellow oil. B.p. 128–30°/1·2 mm.

Staudinger, Siegwart, *Ber.*, 1916, **49**, 1920.

Thiobenzilic Acid (*α-Mercaptodiphenylacetic acid*)

$$(C_6H_5)_2C(SH) \cdot COOH$$

$C_{14}H_{12}O_2S$ MW, 244

Plates from AcOH. M.p. 147·5–149°. Sol. EtOH, Et_2O, Me_2CO, AcOH, C_6H_6, boiling MeOH. Very spar. sol. boiling H_2O.

Bettschart, Bistrzycki, *Helv. Chim. Acta*, 1919, **2**, 127.

Thiobenzoic Acid

$$C_6H_5 \cdot CO \cdot SH \text{ or } C_6H_5 \cdot CS \cdot OH$$

C_7H_6OS MW, 138

Yellow oil. Solidifies in ice and then melts about 24°. Very sol. EtOH, Et_2O, CS_2. Insol. H_2O. Volatile in steam. Decomp. on dist.
NH_4 *salt* : cryst. M.p. 118°. Sol. H_2O.
O-*Me ester* : C_8H_8OS. MW, 152. Yellow liq. B.p. 110–12°/10 mm. Insol. H_2O. Fumes in air.
S-*Me ester* : b.p. 231–2°, 134°/25 mm. D_{25}^{25} 1·1381.
S-*Et ester* : $C_9H_{10}OS$. MW, 166. B.p. 252–3°, 146°/31 mm. D_{25}^{25} 1·0977.
S-*Propyl ester* : $C_{10}H_{12}OS$. MW, 180. B.p. 251–5°, 144°/13 mm. D_{25}^{25} 1·0724.
S-*Butyl ester* : $C_{11}H_{14}OS$. MW, 194. B.p. 160°/23 mm. D_{25}^{25} 1·0514.
S-sec.-n-*Butyl ester* : b.p. 151°/23 mm. D_{25}^{25} 1·0488.
S-*Isobutyl ester* : b.p. 150°/20 mm. D_{25}^{25} 1·0457.
S-tert.-*Butyl ester* : b.p. 110°/28 mm. D_{25}^{25} 1·0468.
S-*Phenyl ester* : $C_{13}H_{10}OS$. MW, 214. Needles from EtOH or C_6H_6. M.p. 56°. $n_D^{56·5}$ 1·6231. Sol. EtOH, Et_2O, $CHCl_3$, CS_2. KOH ⟶ thiophenol + benzoic acid.
S-p-*Tolyl ester* : cryst. from EtOH. M.p. 75°.
S-*Benzyl ester* : cryst. from EtOH. M.p. 39·5°.
Amide : thiobenzamide. C_7H_7NS. MW, 137. Needles. M.p. 115–16°. N-*Benzoyl* : red cryst. M.p. 117°.
Methylamide : C_8H_9NS. MW, 151. Yellow needles from EtOH. M.p. 79°.
Anilide : thiobenzanilide. Yellow plates or prisms. M.p. 101·5–102° (96°).
N-*Me-anilide* : m.p. 63° (59°). B.p. 331–2°.
o-*Toluidide* : m.p. 85–6°.
p-*Toluidide* : yellow needles from EtOH.Aq. M.p. 128·5–129·5°.
Piperidide : yellow plates from MeOH.Aq. M.p. 63–4°. B.p. 205°/12 mm.
Anhydride : *see* Dibenzoyl sulphide.

Engelhardt, Latschinow, Malyschew, *Z. Chem.*, 1868, 354.
Kym, *Ber.*, 1899, **32**, 3533 (*Note*).
Hantzsch, Scharf, *Ber.*, 1913, **46**, 3584.
Gabriel, Heymann, *Ber.*, 1890, **23**, 158.

Thiobenzophenone (*Diphenyl thioether*)

$$C_6H_5 \cdot CS \cdot C_6H_5$$

$C_{13}H_{10}S$ MW, 198

Blue needles from pet. ether. M.p. 53–4°. B.p. 174°/14 mm. Very sol. $CHCl_3$, C_6H_6.

Spar. sol. pet. ether, cold EtOH. Standing in air ⟶ benzophenone.

Staudinger, Freudenberger, *Organic Syntheses*, 1931, XI, 94.

Thiobenzyl Alcohol.
See Benzyl Mercaptan.

Thiobiuret

$$\underset{5}{H_2N}\cdot\underset{4}{CO}\cdot\underset{3}{NH}\cdot\underset{2}{CS}\cdot\underset{1}{NH_2}$$

$C_2H_5ON_3S$ MW, 119

Needles + $1H_2O$ from H_2O. M.p. anhyd. 186°. Sol. EtOH, AcOH. Mod. sol. H_2O. Insol. CS_2, ligroin, C_6H_6. Sol. alkalis.
5-*Phenyl*: cryst. from EtOH. M.p. 186°.
1 : 5-*Diphenyl*: m.p. 161°.

Wunderlich, *Ber.*, 1886, **19**, 452.
Hecht, *Ber.*, 1892, **25**, 749.

Thiobutyric Acid

$CH_3\cdot CH_2\cdot CH_2\cdot CO\cdot SH$ or $CH_3\cdot CH_2\cdot CH_2\cdot CS\cdot OH$

C_4H_8OS MW, 104

B.p. 130°. Sol. EtOH. Spar. sol. H_2O.
S-*Phenyl ester*: $C_{10}H_{12}OS$. MW, 180. Yellow liq. B.p. 210–12°/20 mm. Volatile in steam.
Anilide: needles from AcOH.Aq. M.p. 32–3°.

Ulrich, *Ann.*, 1859, **109**, 280.

Thiocarbamic Acid

$H_2N\cdot CO\cdot SH$ or $H_2N\cdot CS\cdot OH$

CH_3ONS MW, 77

Known only in form of its salts and esters.
NH_4 *salt*: colourless cryst. Very sol. H_2O. Spar. sol. EtOH. Insol. Et_2O. Dry salt rapidly turns yellow in air ⟶ $(NH_4)_2S$.
S-*Me ester*: C_2H_5ONS. MW, 91. Prisms from Et_2O. M.p. 107–8° (95–8°). N-*Acetyl*: needles from C_6H_6. M.p. 145·5–146°.
O-*Me ester*: m.p. 43°. N-*Acetyl*: cryst. from pet. ether. M.p. 79–80°.
Et ester: *see* Thiourethane.
O-*Propyl ester*: C_4H_9ONS. MW, 119. Cryst. M.p. 35°.
S-*Isopropyl ester*: plates. M.p. 125°.
S-*Isobutyl ester*: $C_5H_{11}ONS$. MW, 133. Plates from H_2O. M.p. 102–3°. Volatile in steam.
O-*Isobutyl ester*: plates from H_2O. M.p. 51–3° (36°).
S-*Phenyl ester*: C_7H_7ONS. MW, 153. Plates from C_6H_6 or H_2O. M.p. 96–8°.
O-*Phenyl ester*: needles from EtOH. M.p. 132–132·5°.
S-*Benzyl ester*: C_8H_9ONS. MW, 167. Plates from C_6H_6. M.p. 125°.
Amide: *see* Thiourea.

Wheeler, Barnes, *Am. Chem. J.*, 1899, **22**, 146.
Kretzschmar, *J. prakt. Chem.*, 1873, **7**, 474.
Salomon, *J. prakt. Chem.*, 1873, **8**, 115.

Thiocarbamide.
See Thiourea.

Thiocarbanilide (sym.-*Diphenylthiourea*)

$C_6H_5\cdot NH\cdot CS\cdot NH\cdot C_6H_5$

$C_{13}H_{12}N_2S$ MW, 22

Leaflets from EtOH. M.p. 154–5° (150·5°). Sol. EtOH, Et_2O. Mod. sol. H_2O. Insol. CS_2. Sol. alkalis, re-ppd. by acids. Triboluminescent. Very bitter taste.
B,HgCl₂: m.p. 85°.
B_2,HgI_2: m.p. 183°.
B,HgI_2: yellow prisms. M.p. 139°.
$B_2,AuCl_3$: prisms. M.p. 194°.
$B_2,CuBr_2$: prisms. M.p. 187°.
$B_2,CdBr_2$: m.p. 140°.
$B_2,ZnCl_2$: prisms. M.p. 172°.
$B_2,SnCl_4$: prisms. M.p. 260°.

Fry, *J. Am. Chem. Soc.*, 1913, **35**, 1541.
Drozdov, *Chem. Abstracts*, 1932, **26**, 5293.
Mistry, Guha, *Chem. Abstracts*, 1931, **25**, 1504.
Silesia Verein, D.R.P., 559,814, (*Chem. Zentr.*, 1933, I, 2463).
Rubber Service Labs., U.S.P., 1,688,707 (*Chem. Abstracts*, 1929, **23**, 156).

Thiocarbazide (*Thiocarbohydrazide, dihydrazide of thiocarbonic acid*)

$$\underset{5}{H_2N}\cdot\underset{4}{NH}\cdot\underset{3}{CS}\cdot\underset{2}{NH}\cdot\underset{1}{NH_2}$$

CH_6N_4S MW, 106

Cryst. from H_2O. Decomp. at 170°.
1 : 5-*Diacetyl*: hygroscopic cryst. M.p. 204–5°.
1-*Phenyl*: $C_7H_{10}N_4S$. MW, 182. Tables from EtOH. M.p. 149–50°. Sol. EtOH, AcOH, Py, alkalis. Spar. sol. Me_2CO, $CHCl_3$, C_6H_6, HCl. *B,HCl*: plates. M.p. 181°.
1-*Me*-1-*Phenyl*: $C_8H_{12}N_4S$. MW, 196. Prisms from EtOH. M.p. 228–9° decomp.

Guha, Roy-Choudhury, *J. Indian Chem. Soc.*, 1928, **5**, 149.
Guha, De, *J. Chem. Soc.*, 1924, 1215.

Thiocarbonic Acid

$HO\cdot CO\cdot SH$ or $HO\cdot CS\cdot OH$

CH_2O_2S MW, 78

Does not exist in free state.
O : S-*Di-Me ester*: $C_3H_6O_2S$. MW, 106. Oil

with ethereal odour. B.p. 120–1°. $D_4^{21\cdot5}$ 1·1203. n_D^{23} 1·4524.

O-*Di-Me ester* : b.p. 119–20°. D_4^2 1·1028. n_D^{24} 1·4596.

O-S-*Di-Et ester* : $C_5H_{10}O_2S$. MW, 134. B.p. 156°. D^{18} 1·0285.

O-*Di-Et ester* : b.p. 158–9°. $D_4^{17\cdot5}$ 1·0267. $n_D^{17\cdot5}$ 1·4601.

O : S-*Diphenyl ester* : $C_{13}H_{10}O_2S$. MW, 230. Needles from EtOH. M.p. 56°.

O-*Diphenyl ester* : plates from EtOH. M.p. 106°. Sol. most ord. org. solvents. Insol. H_2O.

Anhydride : *see* Carbonyl sulphide.
Amide : *see* Thiocarbamic Acid.
Chloride : *see* Thiocarbonyl chloride.
Hydrazide : *see* Thiocarbazide.
Nitrile : *see* Thiocyanic acid.
Anil : *see* Phenyl isothiocyanate.

Delépine, *Ann. chim.*, 1912, **25**, 547; *Compt. rend.*, 1910, **150**, 878; *Bull. soc. chim.*, 1910, **7**, 409, 727.

Thiocarbonyl chloride (*Thiophosgene*)

$CSCl_2$

CCl_2S MW, 115

Red liq. with acrid odour. B.p 73–6°. Fumes in air. D^{15} 1·5085. n_D^{20} 1·5442. When pure is not decomp. by light. Slowly decomp. by cold H_2O, rapidly with hot EtOH or NaOEt ⟶ esters.

Dyson, *Organic Syntheses*, 1926, VI, 86.

Thiocarbonyl tetrachloride.
See Perchloromethyl Mercaptan.

Thiocarbostyril (2-*Mercaptoquinoline*, 2-*quinolyl mercaptan*)

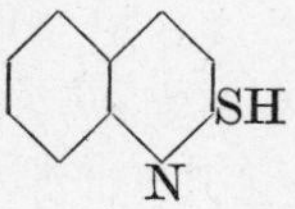

C_9H_7NS MW, 161

Yellow plates from EtOH.Aq. M.p. 175°. Very sol. hot EtOH, Et_2O, $CHCl_3$, CS_2, C_6H_6. Insol. cold H_2O. Sol. acids, alkalis.

S-*Me* : $C_{10}H_9NS$. MW, 175. *Methiodide* : yellow cryst. from EtOH. M.p. 189°.

N-*Me* : greenish-yellow needles or prisms from EtOH. M.p. 118°. Spar. sol. hot H_2O.

S-*Et* : $C_{11}H_{11}NS$. MW, 189. Liq. Decomp. on dist. *B,HI* : yellow cryst. from EtOH–Et_2O. M.p. 154°. B_2,H_2PtCl_6 : cryst. + H_2O. M.p. 190°. decomp.

Fischer, *Ber.*, 1899, **32**, 1305.

Thiocarvacrol (2-*Mercapto*-p-*cymene*, 2-*methyl-5-isopropylthiophenol*)

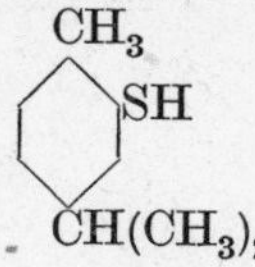

$C_{10}H_{14}S$ MW, 166

Colourless liq. with aromatic odour. B.p. 235–6°. $D^{17\cdot5}$ 0·9975. Misc. with EtOH. Insol. H_2O.

Hg salt : needles. M.p. 109°.

S-*Me* : $C_{11}H_{16}S$. MW, 180. Liq. with unpleasant odour. B.p. 244°.

Kekulé, Fleischer, *Ber.*, 1873, **6**, 1088.

Thiocatechol (2-*Hydroxythiophenol*, o-*hydroxyphenyl mercaptan*)

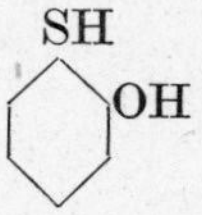

C_6H_6OS MW, 126

Oil with strong odour. M.p. 5–6°. B.p. 216–17°/750·7 mm. D_0^0 1·2373. Sol. Et_2O. Spar. sol. H_2O. Readily oxidises in alk. sol. to disulphide.

O-*Me ether* : *o*-methoxythiophenol, *o*-mercaptoanisole, thioguiacol. C_7H_8OS. MW, 140. Liq. B.p. 218–19°.

O-*Et ether* : *o*-mercaptophenetole. $C_8H_{10}OS$. MW, 154. Liq. B.p. 226–7°.

Di-Me ether : *o*-methoxythioanisole. $C_8H_{10}OS$. MW, 154. Liq. B.p. 237°.

Di-Et ether: *o*-ethoxythiophenetole. $C_{10}H_{14}OS$. MW, 182. Liq. B.p. 248–50°.

Friedländer, Mauthner, *Chem. Zentr.*, 1904, II, 1176.
Gattermann, *Ber.*, 1899, **32**, 1147.
Haitinger, *Monatsh.*, 1883, **4**, 170.

Thiochroman (*Dihydrobenzthiopyran*)

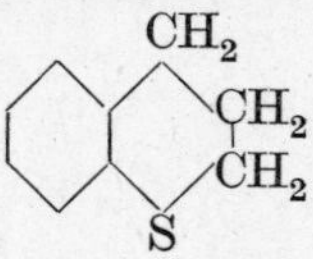

$C_9H_{10}S$ MW, 150

Yellow liq. B.p. 128–30°/15 mm. Volatile in steam. $KMnO_4$ ⟶ thiochroman-S-dioxide.

S-*Dioxide* : $C_9H_{10}O_2S$. MW, 182. Cryst. from hot H_2O. M.p. 88·5°. Sol. H_2O. Very sol. Et_2O.

v. Braun, *Ber.*, 1910, **43**, 3225.

Thiochromanone

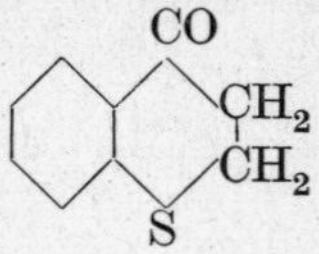

C_9H_8OS MW, 164

Colourless leaflets with mint-like odour from pet. ether. M.p. 29–30°. B.p. 154°/12 mm. $H_2SO_4 \longrightarrow$ red col.

Oxime: plates from EtOH–petrol. M.p. 98–100°.

Semicarbazone: needles from EtOH. M.p. 219–20°.

Krollpfeiffer, Schultze, *Ber.*, 1923, **56**, 1822.

Thiochrome

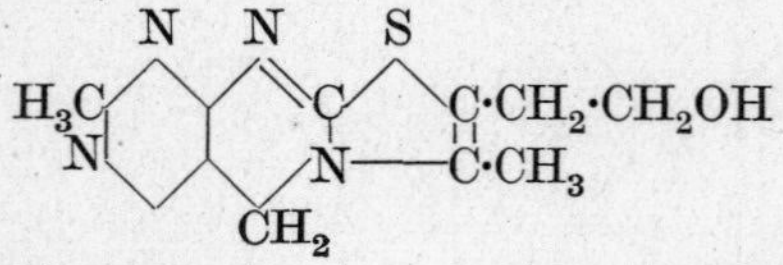

$C_{12}H_{14}ON_4S$ MW, 262

The colouring matter of yeast. Yellow prisms from $CHCl_3$. M.p. 227–8°. Sol. MeOH. Mod. sol. H_2O. Spar. sol. EtOH, Et_2O, Me_2CO, $CHCl_3$. Gives blue fluor. in neutral or alk. sol. Sublimes in high vacuum. Has no physiological activity.

Todd, Bergel, *J. Chem. Soc.*, 1936, 1560.
Todd, Bergel, Fraenkel-Conrat, Jacob, *J. Chem. Soc.*, 1936, 1601.
Kuhn, Vetter, *Ber.*, 1935, **68**, 2375.
Barger, Bergel, Todd, *ibid.*, 2257.
Kuhn, Wagner-Jauregg, Klaveren, Vetter, *Z. physiol. Chem.*, 1935, **234**, 196.

Thiochromone (1 : 4-*Benzthiopyrone*)

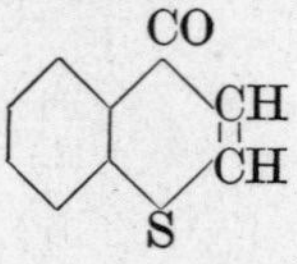

C_9H_6OS MW, 162

Colourless needles from ligroin. M.p. 78°.

Arndt *et al.*, *Ber.*, 1925, **58**, 1620.

Thiocoumarandione.
See Thionaphthenequinone.

1 - Thiocoumarin (o - *Mercaptocinnami lactam*)

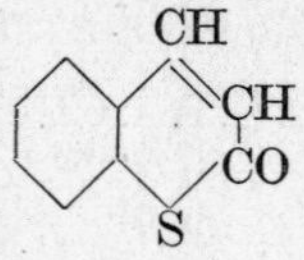

C_9H_6OS MW, 16

Needles from ligroin. M.p. 80–80·5°. Spar sol. H_2O. Volatile in steam.

Phenylhydrazone: yellow plates from EtOH M.p. 140°.

Simonis, Elias, *Ber.*, 1916, **49**, 765.

Thiocoumarone.
See Thionaphthene.

***o*-Thiocresol** (o-*Mercaptotoluene*)

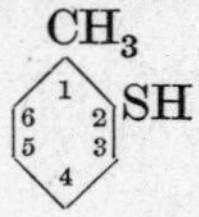

C_7H_8S MW, 124

Plates. M.p. 15°. B.p. 194·3°, 124·7°/100 mm., 106°/50 mm. Sol. EtOH. Insol. H_2O. Volatile in steam. Ox. $\longrightarrow$ di-*o*-tolyl disulphide. $H_2SO_4 \longrightarrow$ blue col.

S-*Et*: $C_9H_{12}S$. MW, 152. Liq. B.p. 120°.
S-*Phenyl*: *see* Phenyl *o*-tolyl sulphide.
S-o-*Tolyl*: *see* Di-*o*-tolyl sulphide.

Hübner, Post, *Ann.*, 1873, **169**, 30.

***m*-Thiocresol** (m-*Mercaptotoluene*).

Liq. B.p. 195·4°, 126°/100 mm., 107·5°/50 mm. Sol. EtOH. Insol. H_2O. Volatile in steam. D_4^0 1·06251. Ox. $\longrightarrow$ di-*m*-tolyl disulphide.

S-*Phenyl*: *see* Phenyl *m*-tolyl sulphide.
S-m-*Tolyl*: *see* Di-*m*-tolyl sulphide.

Hübner, Post, *Ann.*, 1873, **169**, 51.

***p*-Thiocresol** (p-*Mercaptotoluene*).

Plates from EtOH.Aq. or Et_2O. M.p. 43–4°. B.p. 195°, 124·9°/100 mm., 71·4°/10·6 mm. Sol. EtOH, Et_2O. $H_2SO_4 \longrightarrow$ blue col. Ox. $\longrightarrow$ di-*p*-tolyl disulphide. Conc. $H_2SO_4 \longrightarrow$ 2 : 6-dimethylthianthrene. Produces eczema on skin.

S-*Me*: *see* Methyl *p*-tolyl sulphide.
S-*Et*: $C_9H_{12}S$. MW, 152. B.p. 220–1°, 105°/15 mm. $D^{17·5}$ 1·0016.
S-*Isopropyl*: $C_{10}H_{14}S$. MW, 166. Oil. B.p. 228°, 110°/14 mm.
S-*Phenyl*: *see* Phenyl *p*-tolyl sulphide.
S-p-*Tolyl*: *see* Di-*p*-tolyl sulphide.

Fischer, *Ber.*, 1915, **48**, 96, 100.
Bourgeois, *Rec. trav. chim.*, 1899, **18**, 437.

Thiocresol-carboxylic Acid.
See Mercaptotoluic Acid.

Thio-*p*-cresotinic Acid.
See 4-Mercapto-*m*-toluic Acid.

Thiocyanic Acid

HS·C⋮N

CHNS MW, 59

Gas. Forms colourless cryst. on cooling which rapidly melt at 5° to yellow liq. Sol. H_2O, EtOH, Et_2O in all proportions. Dil. aq. sols. are stable.

Me ester : *see* Methyl thiocyanate.

Et ester : *see* Ethyl thiocyanate.

Propyl ester : C_4H_7NS. MW, 101. Liq. with unpleasant odour. B.p. 163°.

Isopropyl ester : *see* Isopropyl thiocyanate.

Butyl ester : C_5H_9NS. MW, 115. B.p. 184·5–185·5°/743 mm. D_4^{25} 0·9563.

Isobutyl ester : *see* Isobutyl thiocyanate.

Amyl ester : $C_6H_{11}NS$. MW, 129. B.p. 90–1°/16 mm. D_4^{25} 0·9412. n_D^{25} 1·462.

Isoamyl ester : yellow oil. B.p. 197°.

Allyl ester : *see* Allyl thiocyanate.

Phenyl ester : C_7H_5NS. MW, 135. Liq. B.p. 231°. $D^{17·5}$ 1·155.

Benzyl ester : *see* Benzyl thiocyanate.

Allen, *J. Am. Chem. Soc.*, 1935, **57**, 198.
Shriner, *Organic Syntheses*, 1931, XI, 92.
Dienske, *Rec. trav. chim.*, 1927, **46**, 154.
Kaufmann, Oehring, *Ber.*, 1926, **59**, 187.

Thiodiethylamine.
See 2 : 2′-Diaminodiethyl sulphide.

Thiodiglycol (*Dihydroxydiethyl sulphide*)

HO·CH$_2$·CH$_2$·S·CH$_2$·CH$_2$OH

$C_4H_{10}O_2S$ MW, 122

Syrup. B.p. 164–6°/20 mm. Misc. in all proportions with H_2O. Combines with $CaCl_2$.

Diphenyl ether : $C_{16}H_{18}O_2S$. MW, 274. Needles from EtOH. M.p. 42°.

Di-1-*naphthyl ether* : $C_{24}H_{22}O_2S$. MW, 374. Light brown cryst. M.p. 94·5°. Spar. sol. EtOH.

Di-2-*naphthyl ether* : cryst. M.p. 129°. Spar. sol. EtOH.

Dibenzoyl : cryst. from EtOH. M.p. 65°.

Di-p-*nitrobenzoyl* : powder. M.p. 107·7°.

Di-p-*aminobenzoyl* : powder. M.p. 184·5°.

Nenitzescu, Scărlătescu, *Ber.*, 1935, **68**, 588.
Faber, Miller, *Organic Syntheses*, 1932, XII, 68.
Helfrich, Reid, *J. Am. Chem. Soc.*, 1920, **42**, 1208.

Thiodiglycollic Acid (*Dimethyl sulphide dicarboxylic acid, dicarboxydimethyl sulphide*)

HOOC·CH$_2$·S·CH$_2$·COOH

$C_4H_6O_4S$ MW, 150

Cryst. from AcOEt–C_6H_6. M.p. 129°. Sol. 2·37 parts H_2O at 18°. Very sol. EtOH. $k = 6–7·5 \times 10^{-4}$ at 25°. Ox. ⟶ dimethyl sulphone dicarboxylic acid. Red. ⟶ acetic acid. H_2O_2 ⟶ thionyldiglycollic acid.

Di-Me ester : $C_6H_{10}O_4S$. MW, 178. B.p. 135°/11 mm.

Di-Et ester : $C_8H_{14}O_4S$. MW, 206. B.p. 267–8°.

Monoamide : $C_4H_7O_3NS$. MW, 149. Prisms. M.p. 125°. Spar. sol. cold H_2O. Sol. hot H_2O. Heat ⟶ imide. o-*Toluidide* : needles from EtOH.Aq. M.p. 150–1°. m-*Toluidide* : cryst. from EtOH.Aq. M.p. 97–8°. p-*Toluidide* : plates from EtOH.Aq. M.p. 148–9°.

Anhydride : $C_4H_4O_3S$. MW, 132. Needles from $CHCl_3$. M.p. 102°. B.p. 158°/10 mm. Very sol. hot $CHCl_3$. Spar. sol. hot Et_2O.

Nitrile : $C_4H_4N_2S$. MW, 112. Plates from MeOH. M.p. 45·5–46·5°.

Monoanilide : cryst. from H_2O. M.p. 103°.

Dianilide : needles from EtOH. M.p. 168°.

Beckurts, Frerichs, *J. prakt. Chem.*, 1906, **74**, 50.
Lovén, *Ber.*, 1894, **27**, 3059.

Thiodiphenylamine (*Phenthiazine*)

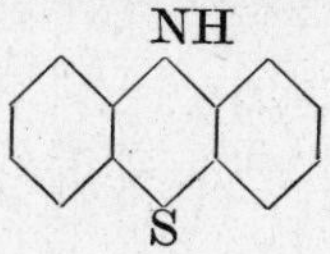

$C_{12}H_9NS$ MW, 199

Yellow plates from EtOH. M.p. 182°. B.p 371°, 290°/40 mm. Sol. Et_2O, C_6H_6. Spar. sol. cold EtOH, ligroin. Sublimes. Alc. $FeCl_3$ ⟶ green col. Heat with Zn ⟶ diphenylamine. Boil sol. with Cu ⟶ carbazole.

N-*Me* : $C_{13}H_{11}NS$. MW, 213. Exists in two forms. (α-) Long prisms from EtOH. M.p. 99·3°. B.p. 360–5°. Sol. C_6H_6. Mod. sol. Et_2O. Spar. sol. cold EtOH, AcOH. H_2SO_4 ⟶ reddish-brown sol. (β-) Yellow needles from EtOH–C_6H_6. M.p. 78–9°. Sol. warm C_6H_6. Spar. sol. hot EtOH. Insol. H_2O.

N-*Et* : $C_{14}H_{13}NS$. MW, 227. Prisms from EtOH. M.p. 102°.

N-*Phenyl* : $C_{18}H_{13}NS$. MW, 275. Cryst. from EtOH. M.p. 89–90°.

N-*Benzyl* : $C_{19}H_{15}NS$. MW, 289. Cryst. from EtOH. M.p. 130°.

N-*Acetyl*: prisms from EtOH. M.p. 197–197·5°.

Kehrmann, Dardel, *Ber.*, 1922, **55**, 2349.
Knoevenagel, *J. prakt. Chem.*, 1914, **89**, 11.
Holzmann, *Ber.*, 1888, **21**, 2065.
Bernsthen, *Ann.*, 1885, **230**, 88.

Thioethanolamine.
See 2-Mercaptoethylamine.

Thioethyl Alcohol.
See Ethyl Mercaptan.

Thioethylamine.
See 2 : 2′-Diaminodiethyl sulphide.

Thioflavanone

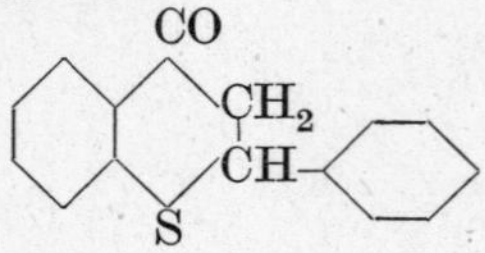

$C_{15}H_{12}OS$ MW, 240

Colourless needles from EtOH or pet. ether–CS_2. M.p. 55–6°. Sol. Et_2O, C_6H_6. Sol. $H_2SO_4 \longrightarrow$ red col. Insol. alkalis.

Arndt, *Ber.*, 1923, **56**, 1274.

Thioflavone

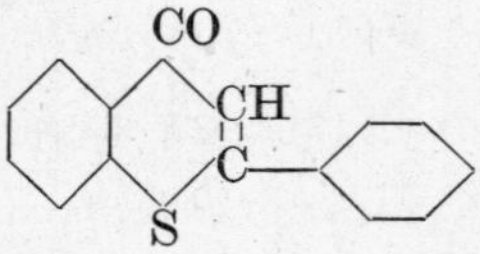

$C_{15}H_{10}OS$ MW, 238

Needles from EtOH. M.p. 129–30° (125°). Alc. I $\longrightarrow$ blue col. $H_2SO_4 \longrightarrow$ yellow col. Forms salts readily hyd. by H_2O.

Arndt *et al.*, *Ber.*, 1925, **58**, 1620.
Ruhemann, *Ber.*, 1913, **46**, 2197.

Thioformic Acid

H·CO·SH

CH_2OS MW, 62

Unstable liq.

Amide: thioformamide. CH_3NS. MW, 61. Prisms from AcOEt or EtO–pet. ether. M.p. 28–9°. Very sol. EtOH, Me_2CO, AcOEt. Sol. Et_2O. Insol. CS_2, ligroin, C_6H_6, cold $CHCl_3$. Gradually decomp.

Ethylamide: C_3H_7NS. MW, 89. B.p. 125°/14 mm.

Diethylamide: $C_5H_{11}NS$. MW, 117. Oil. Cryst. on cooling. M.p. below 0°. B.p. 116–17°/14 mm. Spar. misc. with hot H_2O.

Anilide: thioformanilide. Needles from H_2O, plates from EtOH.Aq. M.p. 137·5° decomp.

o-*Toluidide*: needles from EtOH. M.p. 100–1°.

p-*Toluidide*: cryst. from EtOH. M.p. 173·5°.

Willstätter, Wirth, *Ber.*, 1909, **42**, 1911.

Thioglucose.
See Glucothiose.

Thioglycollic Acid (*Mercaptoacetic acid*)

$HS\cdot CH_2\cdot COOH$

$C_2H_4O_2S$ MW, 92

F.p. − 16·5°. B.p. 123°/29 mm., 107–8°/16 mm. D^{20} 1·3253. Oxidises in air. $NH_3 + FeCl_3 \longrightarrow$ dark red $\longrightarrow$ violet col.

Et ester: $C_4H_8O_2S$. MW, 120. B.p. 156–8°, 55°/17 mm. D^{15} 1·0964. *Ag salt*: yellow needles from Me_2CO. M.p. 75–7°. *Hg salt*: needles from Et_2O. M.p. 56·5°. *Bi salt*: yellow cryst. from EtOH. M.p. 82·9°.

Amide: C_2H_5ONS. MW, 91. Needles. M.p. 52°. Very sol. H_2O. Spar. sol. EtOH. Oxidises in air.

Anilide: needles from H_2O or EtOH. M.p. 110·5–111°.

o-*Toluidide*: needles from EtOH.Aq. M.p. 84–5°.

m-*Toluidide*: needles from EtOH.Aq. M.p. 152–3°.

p-*Toluidide*: needles from EtOH. M.p. 125–6°.

S-*Et*: $C_4H_8O_2S$. MW, 120. Oil. F.p. − 8·7°. B.p. 117–18°/11 mm. D^{20}_{20} 1·1518. *Et ester*: $C_6H_{12}O_2S$. MW, 148. B.p. 187–9°. D^4 1·0469. *Amide*: C_4H_9ONS. MW, 119. M.p. 44°.

S-*Propyl*: $C_5H_{10}O_2S$. MW, 134. Oil. *Amide*: m.p. 53°.

S-*Butyl*: $C_6H_{12}O_2S$. MW, 148. Yellow oil. B.p. 140–4°/10–15 mm. Insol. H_2O.

S-*Phenyl*: $C_8H_8O_2S$. MW, 168. Cryst. M.p. 60°. *Amide*: m.p. 103–4°.

S-*Benzyl*: $C_9H_{10}O_2S$. MW, 182. Cryst. M.p. 61–3°.

S-*Acetyl*: yellow oil. B.p. 158–9°/17 mm. *Chloride*: b.p. 93–5°/20 mm.

Holmberg, *J. prakt. Chem.*, 1934, **141**, 93.
Larsson, *Chem. Zentr.*, 1928, II, 234.

Thioguaiacol.
See under Thiocatechol.

Thiohydantoic Acid (*Thioureidoacetic acid, thiocarbaminylglycine*, N-*carboxymethylthiourea*)

$\underset{4}{H_2N}\cdot \underset{3}{CS}\cdot \underset{2}{NH}\cdot \underset{1}{CH_2}\cdot COOH$

$C_3H_6O_2N_2S$ MW, 134

Needles or prisms from EtOH. M.p. 170–1° decomp. Very sol. hot H_2O, EtOH. HgO ⟶ hydantoic acid.

Et ester: $C_5H_{10}O_2N_2S$. MW, 162. Cryst. from H_2O. M.p. about 65°. Very sol. H_2O, EtOH, C_6H_6. Insol. Et_2O, pet. ether. 4-N-*Acetyl*: prisms. M.p. 104–5°. 4-N-*Benzoyl*: needles from EtOH. M.p. 128–9°.

4-N-*Acetyl*: needles. M.p. 205° decomp.

4-N-*Benzoyl*: needles from EtOH, plates from H_2O. M.p. 202°.

Wheeler, Nicolet, Johnson, *Am. Chem. J.*, 1911, **46**, 456.
Komatsu, *Chem. Zentr.*, 1911, II, 537.

2-Thiohydantoin (*4-Keto-2-thiotetrahydro-iminazole*)

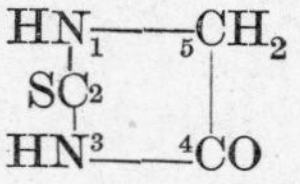

$C_3H_4ON_2S$ MW, 116

Yellow prisms from H_2O. M.p. 228° decomp. Very sol. hot EtOH, Et_2O, alkalis. Spar. sol. H_2O. Gives cryst. K salt. Hot aq. $Ba(OH)_2$ ⟶ thiohydantoic acid.

3-N-*Me*: $C_4H_6ON_2S$. MW, 130. Needles from $CHCl_3$–ligroin. M.p. 161°. Very sol. hot H_2O, EtOH, Et_2O. Spar. sol. $CHCl_3$. Insol. ligroin.

1 : 3-N-*Di-Me*: $C_5H_8ON_2S$. MW, 144. Cryst. from C_6H_6–pet. ether. M.p. 94·5°. Very sol. hot H_2O. Sol. EtOH, Et_2O, $CHCl_3$, C_6H_6.

3-N-*Allyl*: $C_6H_8ON_2S$. MW, 156. Cryst. from ligroin. M.p. 108°. Sol. hot H_2O, EtOH, AcOH. Spar. sol. $CHCl_3$, ligroin, C_6H_6.

3-N-*Phenyl*: $C_9H_8ON_2S$. MW, 192. Yellow plates from EtOH. M.p. 240–2° decomp.

1 : 3-N-*Diphenyl*: $C_{15}H_{12}ON_2S$. MW, 268. Yellow prisms from AcOH, needles from EtOH. M.p. 212°. Sol. hot AcOH. Spar. sol. Et_2O, EtOH, ligroin, C_6H_6.

3-N-*Benzyl*: $C_{10}H_{10}ON_2S$. MW, 206. Cryst. from EtOH. M.p. 128°.

3-N-o-*Tolyl*: yellow plates from EtOH. M.p. 149–50°.

3-N-p-*Tolyl*: yellow cryst. from EtOH. M.p. 228°.

1-N-*Acetyl*: plates from EtOH. M.p. 175–6°.

1-N *Benzoyl*: prisms from EtOH. M.p. 165°.

Johnson, Hill, Bailey, *J. Am. Chem. Soc.*, 1915, **37**, 2406.
Johnson, *Am. Chem. J.*, 1913, **49**, 68.
Marckwald, Neumark, Stelzner, *Ber.*, 1891, **24**, 3285.

4-Thiohydantoin

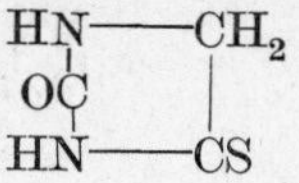

$C_3H_4ON_2S$ MW, 116

Needles from hot H_2O. Decomp. above 200°. Sol. NaOH ⟶ red sol.

Johnson, Chernoff, *J. Am. Chem. Soc.*, 1912, **34**, 1208.

Thiohydracrylic Acid (*2-Mercaptopropionic acid*)

$$HS{\cdot}CH_2{\cdot}CH_2{\cdot}COOH$$

$C_3H_6O_2S$ MW, 106

Cryst. M.p. 16·8°. B.p. 110·5–111·5°. $D^{20\cdot8}$ 1·218. Sol. H_2O, EtOH, Et_2O. Ox. ⟶ dithiohydracrylic acid. $FeCl_3$ ⟶ blue col.

Biilmann, *Ann.*, 1906, **348**, 126.
Lovén, *J. prakt. Chem.*, 1884, **29**, 376.

Thiohydroquinone (p-*Mercaptophenol*, p-*hydroxythiophenol*)

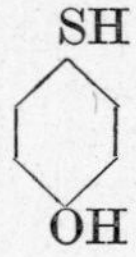

C_6H_6OS MW, 126

Cryst. with strong odour. M.p. 29–30°. B.p. 166–8°/45 mm., 133–7°/11 mm. Sol. H_2O.

O-*Me ether*: *p*-mercaptoanisole, *p*-methoxythiophenol. C_7H_8OS. MW, 140. B.p. 227°, 89–90°/5 mm. D_4^{25} 1·1313. n_D^{25} 1·5801. Volatile in steam.

S-*Me*: *p*-hydroxythioanisole. Plates from pet. ether. M.p. 84–5°. *Me ether*: *p*-methoxythioanisole. $C_8H_{10}OS$. MW, 154. M.p. 25–6°. B.p. 99–100°/4 mm. D_4^{25} 1·1069. n_D^{25} 1·5764. *Et ether*: *p*-ethoxythioanisole. $C_9H_{12}OS$. MW, 168. M.p. 19–20°. B.p. 98–100°/5 mm. D_4^{25} 1·0693. n_D^{25} 1·5618. *Acetyl*: needles from pet. ether. M.p. 43–4°.

O-*Et ether*: *p*-mercaptophenetole. $C_8H_{10}OS$. MW, 154. B.p. 232–5°. Volatile in steam.

S-*Et*: *p*-hydroxythiophenetole. Cryst. from pet. ether. M.p. 39–41°. *Me ether*: *p*-methoxythiophenetole. $C_9H_{12}OS$. MW, 168. B.p. 103°/5 mm. D_4^{25} 1·0674. n_D^{25} 1·5600. *Et ether*: *p*-ethoxythiophenetole. $C_{10}H_{14}OS$. MW, 182. B.p. 110–12°/6 mm.

S-*Propyl*: propyl *p*-hydroxyphenyl sulphide. $C_9H_{12}OS$. MW, 168. Cryst. from pet. ether. M.p. 33–33·5°. *Me ether*: propyl *p*-methoxyphenyl sulphide. $C_{10}H_{14}OS$. MW, 182. B.p. 110–11°/5 mm. D_4^{25} 1·0424. n_D^{25} 1·5545.

S-*Butyl*: butyl *p*-hydroxyphenyl sulphide. $C_{10}H_{14}OS$. MW, 182. Cryst. from pet. ether. M.p. 49–50°. *Me ether*: butyl *p*-methoxyphenyl sulphide. $C_{11}H_{16}OS$. MW, 196. B.p. 120°/5 mm. D_4^{25} 1·0303. n_D^{25} 1·5445.

S-n-*Amyl*: *n*-amyl *p*-hydroxyphenyl sulphide. $C_{11}H_{16}OS$. MW, 196. Cryst. from pet. ether. M.p. 55–6°. *Me ether*: *n*-amyl *p*-methoxyphenyl sulphide. $C_{12}H_{18}OS$. MW, 210. B.p. 127°/5 mm. D_4^{25} 1·0149. n_D^{25} 1·5380.

S-n-*Hexyl*: *n*-hexyl *p*-hydroxyphenyl sulphide. $C_{12}H_{18}OS$. MW, 210. Cryst. from pet. ether. M.p. 58–9°. *Me ether*: *n*-hexyl *p*-methoxyphenyl sulphide. $C_{13}H_{20}OS$. MW, 224. B.p. 142°/5 mm. D_4^{25} 0·9975. n_D^{25} 1·5315.

S-*Phenyl*: *p*-hydroxydiphenyl sulphide. $C_{12}H_{10}OS$. MW, 202. Prisms from pet. ether. M.p. 50–1°. Sol. EtOH, Et_2O, AcOH, C_6H_6. Spar. sol. H_2O. *Me ether*: *p*-methoxydiphenyl sulphide. $C_{13}H_{12}OS$. MW, 216. Plates from EtOH.Aq. M.p. 88°. p-*Nitrobenzoyl*: yellow prisms from EtOH. M.p. 74–5°.

S-p-*Tolyl*: *p*-tolyl *p*-hydroxyphenyl sulphide. $C_{13}H_{12}OS$. MW, 216. Plates from pet. ether. M.p. 67–8°. Spar. sol. H_2O. *Me ether*: *p*-tolyl *p*-methoxyphenyl sulphide. $C_{14}H_{14}OS$. MW, 230. Plates from EtOH. M.p. 45–6°. B.p. 181–2°/4 mm.

Miller, Read, *J. Am. Chem. Soc.*, 1933, **55**, 1224.
Suter, Hansen, *J. Am. Chem. Soc.*, 1932, **54**, 4101.
Zincke, Ebel, *Ber.*, 1914, **47**, 1104.
Gattermann, *Ber.*, 1899, **32**, 1148.
Leuckart, *J. prakt. Chem.*, 1890, **41**, 192.

Thioindigo

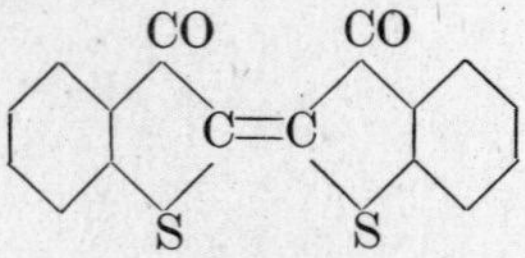

$C_{16}H_8O_2S_2$ MW, 296

Brownish-red needles with bronze reflex from xylene, red cryst. from C_6H_6. Does not melt below 280°. Very sol. hot $PhNO_2$. Spar. sol. hot EtOH, $CHCl_3$, CS_2. Sublimes. Red sol. in xylene shows reddish-yellow fluorescence. Sol. H_2SO_4 ⟶ bluish-green or blue col. Fairly stable to ox. agents. HNO_3 ⟶ thioindigo-S-oxide. Red. ⟶ Thioindigo White.

S-*Oxide*: $C_{16}H_8O_3S_2$. MW, 312. Scarlet cryst. from $CHCCl_3$ or xylene. M.p. about 325° decomp. Sol. $CHCl_3$, $PhNO_2$, Py. Spar. sol. EtOH, Me_2CO, C_6H_6. H_2SO_4 ⟶ violet sol.

Jezierski, *Chem. Abstracts*, 1935, **29**, 2161.
Kalle, D.R.P., 194,254, (*Chem. Zentr.*, 1908, I, 1116).
Friedländer, *Ann.*, 1907, **351**, 411.

Thioindigo White (*Leucothioindigo*)

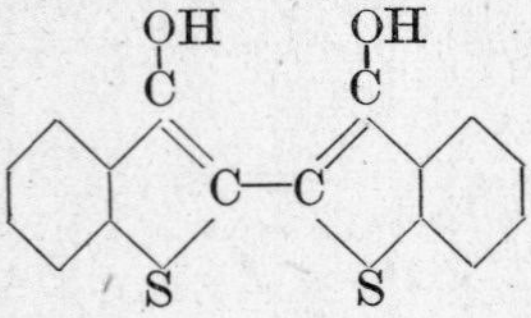

$C_{16}H_{10}O_2S_2$ MW, 298

White ppt. Turns red in air. Sol. most org. solvents. Very sol. dil. NaOH ⟶ sol. which reddens in air. Insol. H_2O.

Diacetyl: colourless needles from Ac_2O or xylene. M.p. 248° decomp. (240°).

Monobenzoyl: needles from xylene. M.p. 225° decomp.

Dibenzoyl: cryst. from xylene. M.p. 227°.

Posner, Wallis, *Ber.*, 1924, **57**, 1673.
Tschilikin, *Chem. Zentr.*, 1916, I, 942.
Béchamp, *Compt. rend.*, 1909, **148**, 1678.

Thioindoxyl (3-*Hydroxythionaphthene*)

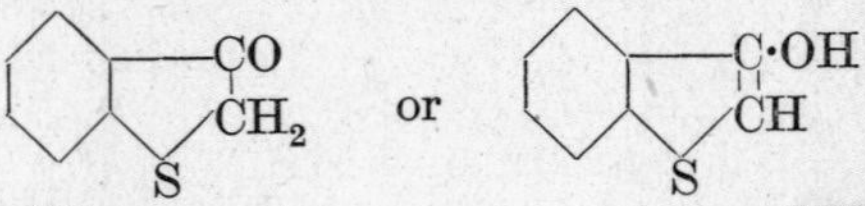

C_8H_6OS MW, 150

Needles from H_2O. M.p. 71°. Very sol. most org. solvents. Spar. sol. cold H_2O. Sol. alkalis in which it is readily oxidised. Turns red in air.

Me ether: C_9H_8OS. MW, 164. Oil. B.p. 260–1°. *Picrate*: brownish-red needles from EtOH. M.p. 112°.

Et ether: $C_{10}H_{10}OS$. MW, 178. Oil. B.p. 154°/19 mm. $D_4^{17\cdot6}$ 1·1591.

Acetyl: yellow oil. B.p. 165°/18 mm.

Semicarbazone: needles from EtOH. M.p. 224–5°.

p-*Nitrophenylhydrazone*: exists in two forms.
(i) Reddish-brown powder. M.p. 185–90°.
(ii) Reddish-brown powder. M.p. 251–61°.

McClelland, D'Silva, *J. Chem. Soc.*, 1931, 2974.
Auwers, Thies, *Ber.*, 1920, **53**, 2291.
Friedländer, *Ann.*, 1907, **351**, 408.
Auwers, *Ann.*, 1912, **393**, 379.

Thioindoxylic Acid (*3-Hydroxythionaphthene-2-carboxylic acid, thioindoxyl-2-carboxylic acid*)

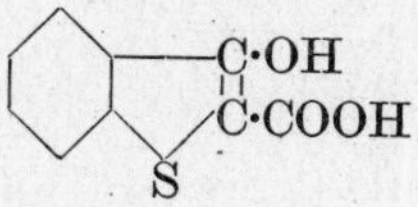

$C_9H_6O_3S$ MW, 194

Free acid is very unstable and loses CO_2 readily. Very sol. EtOH, AcOH. Sol. H_2O.

Me ether: $C_{10}H_8O_3S$. MW, 208. Prisms from MeOH. M.p. 173°. Sol. MeOH, EtOH. Spar. sol. C_6H_6, ligroin.

Et ether: $C_{11}H_{10}O_3S$. MW, 222. Prisms from MeOH. M.p. 158°. Very sol. EtOH. Sol. C_6H_6. Spar. sol. ligroin.

Me ester: $C_{10}H_8O_3S$. MW, 208. Cryst. from EtOH.Aq. M.p. 107–8° (104°).

Et ester: $C_{11}H_{10}O_3S$. MW, 222. Cryst. from ligroin. M.p. 73–4°.

Methylamide: red needles from MeOH. M.p. 122–3°.

Ethylamide: needles from EtOH.Aq. M.p. 135°.

Benzylamide: needles from EtOH. M.p. 134°.

Anilide: needles from EtOH. M.p. 231°.

Acetyl: needles from EtOH. M.p. 180°.

Auwers, *Ann.*, 1912, **393**, 372.
Friedländer, *Ann.*, 1907, **351**, 405.

Thioisoamyl Alcohol.
See Isoamyl Mercaptan.

Thioisobutyl Alcohol.
See Isobutyl Mercaptan.

Thioisopropyl Alcohol.
See Isopropyl Mercaptan.

Thiolactic Acid (*1-Mercaptopropionic acid*)

$CH_3{\cdot}CH(SH){\cdot}COOH$

$C_3H_6O_2S$ MW, 106

d-.

B.p. 95–100°/16 mm. $[\alpha]_D^{20} + 38{\cdot}32°$.

l-.

Oil. $D^{19{\cdot}2}$ 1·193. $[\alpha]_D^{15} - 45{\cdot}47°$.

dl-.

Oil. B.p. 98·5–99°/14 mm. Sol. H_2O, EtOH, Et_2O. $FeCl_3 \longrightarrow$ indigo-blue col.

Et ester: $C_5H_{10}O_2S$. MW, 134. Liq. Spar. sol. H_2O.

S-*Benzyl*: prisms. M.p. 73–4°.

Lovén, *J. prakt. Chem.*, 1884, **29**, 368; 1908, **78**, 65.
Biilmann, *Ann.*, 1906, **348**, 124.
Levene, Mikeska, *J. Biol. Chem.*, 1924, **60**, 1.
Larsson, *Chem. Abstracts*, 1928, **22**, 4470.

Thiomalic Acid (*Mercaptosuccinic acid*)

$$\begin{array}{l} HS{\cdot}CH{\cdot}COOH\ \alpha \\ \quad CH_2{\cdot}COOH\ \beta \end{array}$$

$C_4H_6O_4S$ MW, 150

d-.

M.p. 152–3° (138°). $[\alpha]_D^{17} + 64{\cdot}4°$ in EtOH.

β-*Monoamide*: $C_4H_7O_3NS$. MW, 149. M.p. 125°. $[\alpha]_D^{18} + 82{\cdot}5°$ in Me_2CO.

l-.

M.p. 152–3° $[\alpha]_D^{17} - 64{\cdot}8°$ in EtOH.

β-*Monoamide*: m.p. 125°. $[\alpha]_D^{18} - 82{\cdot}9°$ in Me_2CO.

dl-.

Cryst. M.p. 149–50°. Sol. H_2O, EtOH, Me_2CO. Mod. sol. Et_2O. Very spar. sol. C_6H_6. $k = 5{\cdot}23 \times 10^{-4}$ at 25°. $FeCl_3 \longrightarrow$ blue col.

Di-Et ester: $C_8H_{14}O_4S$. MW, 206. Oil. B.p. about 246° part. decomp.

β-*Monoamide*: cryst. from EtOH. M.p. 103°.

S-*Benzyl*: needles from EtOH.Aq. M.p. 181°.

Holmberg, Lenander, *Chem. Zentr.*, 1918, I, 1146.
Biilmann, *Ann.*, 1905, **339**, 371.
Levene, Mikeska, *J. Biol. Chem.*, 1924, **60**, 685.
Holmberg, *Chem. Zentr.*, 1916, I, 968.

Thiomorpholine.
See 1 : 4-Thiazan.

Thionaphthene (*2 : 3-Benzthiophene, thiocoumarone*)

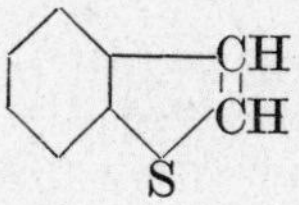

C_8H_6S MW, 134

Present in lignite tar. Leaflets with odour resembling naphthalene. M.p. 32°. B.p. 221–2°. Sol. common org. solvents. Volatile in steam. Sol. conc. H_2SO_4 with cherry-red col. disappearing on heating. $H_2O_2 \longrightarrow$ S-oxide.

Picrate: yellow needles from EtOH. M.p. 149°.

S-*Oxide*: $C_8H_6O_2S$. MW, 166. M.p. 142°.

Gattermann, Lockhart, *Ber.*, 1893, **26**, 2808.
Bezdrik, Friedländer, Koeniger, *Ber.*, 1908, **41**, 231, 236.
Chmelewsky, Friedländer, *Ber.*, 1913, **46**, 1907.
Weissgerber, Kruber, *Ber.*, 1920, **53**, 1551.

Thionaphthene-2-carboxylic Acid

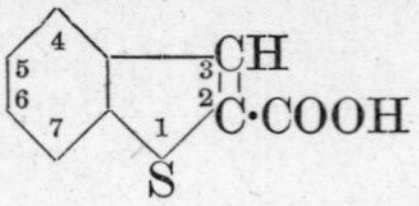

$C_9H_6O_2S$ MW, 178

Needles from H_2O. Mp. 236° (114°). Very sol. Et_2O. Spar. sol. C_6H_6, cold H_2O. Hot alkalis ⟶ thionaphthene.

Me ester: $C_{10}H_8O_2S$. MW, 192. Prisms from EtOH. M.p. 72–3°. B.p. 176–80°/13 mm.

Et ester: $C_{11}H_{10}O_2S$. MW, 206. Cryst. from EtOH. M.p. 36–7°.

Chloride: C_9H_5OClS. MW, 196·5. Leaflets from ligroin. M.p. 88–9°. B.p. 173–5°/19 mm.

Amide: C_9H_7ONS. MW, 177. Needles from H_2O. M.p. 177°.

Hydrazide: leaflets from EtOH. M.p. 184–5°.

Azide: needles from EtOH. M.p. 108° decomp.

Ges. für Teerverwertung, D.R.P., 341,837, (*Chem. Zentr.*, 1921, IV, 1225).
Weissgerber, Kruber, *Ber.*, 1920, **53**, 1561.
Friedländer, Lenk, *Ber.*, 1912, **45**, 2087.

Thionaphthene-3-carboxylic Acid. Cryst. from EtOH.Aq. M.p. 174–5°. Sol. common org. solvents. Prac. insol. H_2O. Volatile in steam.

Me ester: oil. B.p. 285–7°/750 mm., 165–6°/17 mm.

Et ester: oil. B.p. 304–6°/750 mm., 172–3°/17 mm.

Chloride: m.p. about 50°. B.p. 296–8°/758 mm.

Amide: needles from EtOH. M.p. 197–8°.

Anilide: needles from C_6H_6. M.p. 172–3°.

Komppa, Weekman, *J. prakt. Chem.*, 1933, **138**, 116.
Komppa, *J. prakt. Chem.*, 1929, **122**, 331.

Thionaphthenequinone (2:3-*Diketodihydrothionaphthene*, 2 : 3-*diketothiocoumaran*, *thiocoumarandione*)

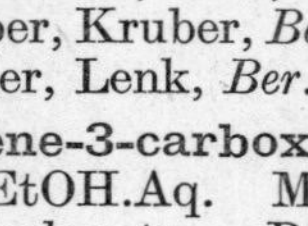

$C_8H_4O_2S$ MW, 164

Yellow prisms from EtOH. M.p. 121°. B.p. about 247°. Sol. EtOH, Me_2CO, AcOH, C_6H_6. Spar. sol. cold ligroin. Mod. volatile in steam. Sol. dil. NaOH with orange-yellow col. ⟶ 2-mercaptobenzoylformic acid.

2-*Oxime*: yellowish-red cryst. from EtOH. M.p. 170–1°. O-*Me ether*: reddish-yellow needles from EtOH. M.p. 125°. *Acetyl*: yellow needles from xylene. M.p. 174° (168°). *Benzoyl* yellow plates from C_6H_6. M.p. 170°. *Benzenesulphonyl*: yellow needles from xylene. M.p. 231°. *Phenylhydrazone*: yellow needles from EtOH. M.p. 172°.

3-*Oxime*: yellow needles from EtOH.Aq. M.p. 186°.

3-*Phenylhydrazone*: 3-benzeneazo-2-hydroxythionaphthene. Orange-red cryst. from EtOH M.p. 165–6°.

Di-phenylhydrazone: orange-red needles from C_6H_6. M.p. 199–200°.

3-p-*Nitrophenylhydrazone*: red cryst. from xylene. M.p. 271–2°.

2-*Anil*: yellowish-red needles from EtOH M.p. 151–2°.

2-p-*Tolil*: brownish-red needles from EtOH M.p. 159°.

Kalle, D.R.P., 241,623, (*Chem. Zentr.* 1912, I, 174).
Bezdrik, Friedländer, Koeniger, *Ber.* 1908, **41**, 235.

1-Thionaphthol (1-*Naphthyl mercaptan* 1-*mercaptonaphthalene*, α-*thionaphthol*)

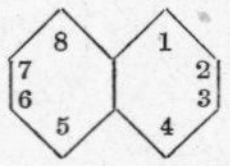

$C_{10}H_8S$ MW, 16

B.p. 208·5°/200 mm., 187·2°/50 mm., 161°/2 mm., 144·8°/10·3 mm. D_4^{23} 1·1549. Sol. EtOH Et_2O. Spar. sol. aq. alkalis. Volatile in steam.

Me ether: *see* Methyl 1-naphthyl sulphide.

Et ether: ethyl 1-naphthyl sulphide. $C_{12}H_{12}S$ MW, 188. B.p. 175–6°/25 mm., 167–167·5° 15 mm. D_4^0 1·1198, D_4^{50} 1·0797.

Phenyl ether: *see* Phenyl 1-naphthyl sulphide

o-*Tolyl ether*: *o*-tolyl 1-naphthyl sulphide $C_{17}H_{14}S$. MW, 250. Oil. B.p. 227·5°/11 mm D_4^{15} 1·1504.

m-*Tolyl ether*: *m*-tolyl 1-naphthyl sulphide Oil. B.p. 229°/11 mm. D_4^{15} 1·1445.

p-*Tolyl ether*: *p*-tolyl 1-naphthyl sulphide Cryst. from EtOH. M.p. 40·5°. B.p. 232·5°/1 mm.

Naphthyl ether: *see* Dinaphthyl sulphide.

Benzyl ether: benzyl 1-naphthyl sulphide Leaflets from EtOH. M.p. 78–80°.

Acetyl: pale yellow liq. B.p. 200–3°/25 mm. 188°/15 mm. D_4^{50} 1·1519.

Bourgeois, *Rec. trav. chim.*, 1899, **18**, 441 *Ber.*, 1895, **28**, 2328.
Fichter, Tamm, *Ber.*, 1910, **43**, 3033.
Leuckart, *J. prakt. Chem.*, 1890, **41**, 216

2-Thionaphthol (2-*Naphthyl mercaptan*, 2-*mercaptonaphthalene*, β-*thionaphthol*).

Cryst. from EtOH. M.p. 81°. B.p. 286°, 210·5°/100 mm., 189°/50 mm., 162·7°/20 mm., 153·5°/15 mm., 146·3°/10·3 mm. Very sol. EtOH, Et_2O, pet. ether. Spar. sol. H_2O. Spar. volatile in steam.

Me ether: *see* Methyl 2-naphthyl sulphide.

Et ether: ethyl 2-naphthyl sulphide. M.p. 16°. B.p. 170·5°/15 mm.

Phenyl ether: *see* Phenyl 2-naphthyl sulphide.

o-*Tolyl ether*: *o*-tolyl 2-naphthyl sulphide. Oil. B.p. 229·5°/11 mm. D_4^{15} 1·1420.

m-*Tolyl ether*: *m*-tolyl 2-naphthyl sulphide. Needles from EtOH.Aq. M.p. 60°. B.p. 235°/11 mm.

p-*Tolyl ether*: *p*-tolyl 2-naphthyl sulphide. Leaflets from EtOH.Aq. M.p. 68°. B.p. 237°/11 mm.

Naphthyl ether: *see* Dinaphthyl sulphide.

Acetyl: m.p. 53·5°. B.p. 191°/15 mm.

Zincke, Eismayer, *Ber.*, 1918, **51**, 755.
Leuckart, *J. prakt. Chem.*, 1890, **41**, 219.
Fichter, Tamm, *Ber.*, 1910, **43**, 3034.

Thioneine.

See Ergothioneine.

Thionessal.

See Tetraphenylthiophene.

Thionylaniline

$C_6H_5N{:}SO$

C_6H_5ONS MW, 139

Yellow liq. with acrid aromatic odour. B.p. 200°. D^{15} 1·2360. Sol. EtOH. Decomp. by H_2O, dil. acids, alkalis, ⟶ aniline + SO_2. Cl in pet. ether ⟶ 2 : 4 : 6-trichloroaniline hydrochloride.

Michaelis, *Ber.*, 1891, **24**, 746.

Thionyl-*o*-toluidine

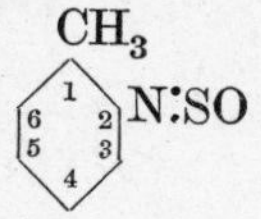

C_7H_7ONS MW, 153

Liq. B.p. 184°/100 mm.

Michaelis, *Ann.*, 1893, **274**, 226.

Thionyl-*m*-toluidine.

Yellow oil. B.p. 220°. Volatile in steam.

See previous reference.

Thionyl-*p*-toluidine.

Yellow cryst. M.p. 9°. B.p. 224°. D^{15} 1·1685.

See previous reference.

Thio-oxalic Acid

HO·CS·COOH or HOOC·CO·SH

$C_2H_2O_3S$ MW, 106

Free acid does not exist.

Di-Me ester: $C_4H_6O_3S$. MW, 134. B.p. 50–3°/21 mm.

Di-Et ester: $C_6H_{10}O_3S$. MW, 162. B.p. 217°. D^0 1·1446. Hyd. ⟶ oxalic acid.

S-p-*Tolyl ester*: $C_9H_8O_3S$. MW, 196. Plates or needles from pet. ether. M.p. 100° decomp. Very sol. Et_2O, EtOH. Spar. sol. pet. ether. Sol. H_2O with decomp. *Anilide*: needles from EtOH. M.p. 137°.

Amide: *see* Thio-oxamic Acid.

Diamide: *see under* Thio-oxamic Acid.

Nitrile: C_2HONS. MW, 87. *Anilide*: orange-yellow needles. M.p. 82°. o-*Toluidide*: m.p. 64°.

Anilide: yellow needles from H_2O, yellow plates from EtOH.Aq. M.p. 101–2°. *Amide*: oxanilic acid thioamide. Yellow prisms from EtOH. M.p. 176°.

Dianilide: thio-oxanilide. Yellow needles from AcOH or EtOH. M.p. 144–5°.

Di-o-toluidide: yellow needles and plates from EtOH. M.p. 126°.

Di-m-toluidide: yellow needles and plates from EtOH. M.p. 88–9°.

Di-p-toluidide: yellow needles from EtOH. M.p. 153–4°.

Reissert, *Ber.*, 1904, **37**, 3720.
Morley, Saint, *J. Chem. Soc.*, 1883, **43**, 400.

Thio-oxamic Acid

$H_2N{\cdot}CS{\cdot}COOH$

$C_2H_3O_2NS$ MW, 105

Exists only as salts and esters.

Me ester: $C_3H_5O_2NS$. MW, 119. Yellow needles. M.p. 86°. Very sol. EtOH, Et_2O. Sol. H_2O.

Et ester: $C_4H_7O_2NS$. MW, 133. Yellow prisms. M.p. 63°. Very sol. hot H_2O, EtOH, Et_2O.

Isobutyl ester: $C_6H_{11}O_2NS$. MW, 161. Yellow needles or prisms from EtOH. M.p. 58°. Sol. EtOH, Et_2O. Spar. sol. H_2O.

Amide: thio-oxamide. $C_2H_4ON_2S$. MW, 104. Yellow needles from EtOH. Spar. sol. cold H_2O, cold EtOH.

Nitrile: cyanthioformamide. $C_2H_2N_2S$. Yellow needles. M.p. 87–90° decomp. Sol. H_2O. Very unstable.

Anilide: thio-oxanilic acid amide. Yellow needles from EtOH. M.p. 169–70°.

Weddige, *J. prakt. Chem.*, 1874, **10**, 200; **9**, 133.

Thiophene

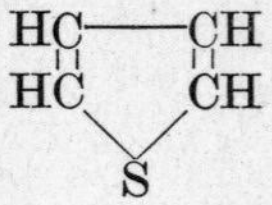

C_4H_4S MW, 84

F.p. − 37·1°. M.p. 29·8°. B.p. 84°. D_4^{20} 1·0617. n_D^{20} 1·5246. Heat of comb. C_p 670·9 Cal., C_v 669·5 Cal., (vapour) C_p 610·6 Cal. Red hot tube ⟶ 2 : 2′-dithienyl + 3 : 3′-dithienyl. Sol. H_2SO_4 ⟶ red ⟶ deep brown col. H_2SO_4 + nitrite ⟶ blue col. Isatin + H_2SO_4 ⟶ indophenin. Thalline in pet. ether + HNO_3 ⟶ intense violet col. ⟶ red ⟶ yellow: disappears with H_2O.

Jurjew, *Ber.*, 1936, **69**, 440, 1002.
Phillips, *Organic Syntheses*, 1932, XII, 72.
I.G., E.P., 305,603.

Thiophene-acetic Acid.
See Thienylacetic Acid.

Thiophene-carboxylic Acid.
See Thiophenic Acid.

Thiophene-2 : 4-dicarboxylic Acid (*Thiophene-α : β′-dicarboxylic acid*)

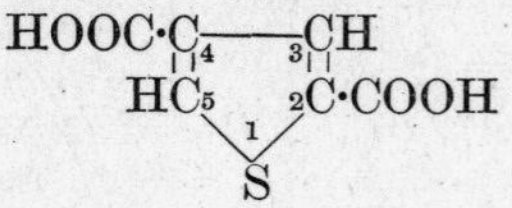

$C_6H_4O_4S$ MW, 172

Decomp. at 280° with part. sublimation. Very sol. hot H_2O, spar. sol. cold.

Di-Me ester: $C_8H_8O_4S$. MW, 200. Plates from EtOH.Aq. M.p. 120–1°.

Di-Et ester: $C_{10}H_{12}O_4S$. MW, 228. M.p. 35–6°.

Zelinsky, *Ber.*, 1887, **20**, 2021.

Thiophene-2 : 5-dicarboxylic Acid (*Thiophene-α : α′-dicarboxylic acid*).

Cryst. powder. Does not melt below 350°. Sol. Et_2O. Spar. sol. H_2O. Sublimes.

Di-Me ester: needles from Et_2O, prisms from EtOH. M.p. 151° (145°).

Di-Et ester: needles from EtOH. M.p. 51·5°. Sol. EtOH.

Dinitrile: $C_6H_2N_2S$. MW, 134. Cryst. from Et_2O. M.p. 92–92·5°.

Hinsberg, *Ber.*, 1912, **45**, 2414.
Jaekel, *Ber.*, 1886, **19**, 190.

Thiophene-tetracarboxylic Acid

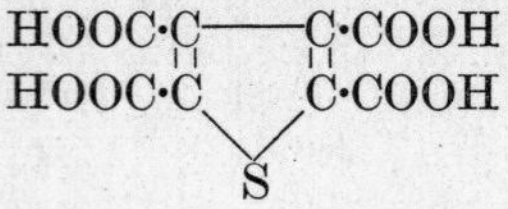

$C_8H_4O_8S$ MW, 26

Tetra-Me ester: $C_{12}H_{12}O_8S$. MW, 316 Prisms from EtOH. M.p. 126–8°. Very so hot EtOH, AcOEt. Spar. sol. hot H_2O.

Michael, *Ber.*, 1895, **28**, 1635.

Thiophenetole (*Ethyl phenyl sulphide*)

$C_6H_5{\cdot}S{\cdot}CH_2{\cdot}CH_3$

$C_8H_{10}S$ MW, 13

Liq. with unpleasant odour. B.p. 204°. D 1·024. $n_D^{22\cdot5}$ 1·5662. $KMnO_4$ ⟶ ethyl pheny sulphone.

Otto, *Ber.*, 1880, **13**, 1275.

α-Thiophenic Acid (*Thiophene-2-carboxyli acid*)

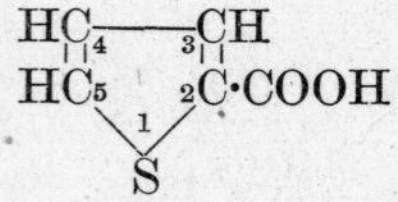

$C_5H_4O_2S$ MW, 12

Needles from H_2O. M.p. 126–7°. Very sol hot H_2O, EtOH, Et_2O. Sol. $CHCl_3$. Spar. sol pet. ether. Sol. 140 parts H_2O at 25°. Ha irritating odour. $k = 3{\cdot}2 \times 10^{-4}$ at 25°. Hea of comb. C_v 645·4 Cal., C_p 646·3 Cal. Red ⟶ tetrahydrothiophene-2-carboxylic acid Dist. Ca salt ⟶ 2 : 2′-dithienyl ketone Isatin + H_2SO_4 ⟶ blue sol.

Et ester: $C_7H_8O_2S$. MW, 156. B.p. 218° 115°/25 mm., 96°/18 mm. $D_4^{16\cdot3}$ 1·1623.

Chloride: C_5H_3OClS. MW, 146·5. B.p 190°.

Amide: C_5H_7ONS. MW, 127. Cryst. powde from EtOH. M.p. 180° (174°). Spar. sol Et_2O.

Anhydride: $C_{10}H_6O_3S_2$. MW, 238. Cryst M.p. 62°. B.p. 218–20°/15 mm.

Nitrile: 2-cyanthiophene. C_5H_3NS. MW 109. Oil. B.p. 192°. Volatile in steam.

Hydrazide: needles from H_2O. M.p. 136°.

Azide: yellow plates. M.p. 37°.

Anilide: plates. M.p. 140°.

Steinkopf, Ohse, *Ann.*, 1924, **437**, 18.
Voerman, *Rec. trav. chim.*, 1907, **26**, 296.
Nahnsen, *Ber.*, 1884, **17**, 2195.

β-Thiophenic Acid (*Thiophene-3-carboxylic acid*).

Needles from H_2O. M.p. 138·4°. Sol. 230 parts H_2O at 25°. Sublimes. Volatile in steam. $k = 7{\cdot}8 \times 10^{-5}$ at 25°. Gives indophenin reaction.

Amide: needles from Et_2O. M.p. 177·5–178°. Spar. sol. Et_2O.

Voerman, *Rec. trav. chim.*, 1907, **26**, 297.

Thiophenin.
See 2-Aminothiophene.

Thiophenol (*Phenyl mercaptan, mercaptobenzene*)

$C_6H_5{\cdot}SH$

C_6H_6S MW, 110

Liq. with penetrating odour. B.p. 169·5°, 103·6°/100 mm., 86·2°/50 mm., 77°/30 mm. D_4^{25} 1·0728, D_4^{50} 1·0491, D_4^{75} 1·0254. $n_D^{23\cdot2}$ 1·5861. Forms metallic salts. Oxidises in air, especially in alcoholic ammonia solution, to diphenyl disulphide.

Me ether: *see* Thioanisole.
Et ether: *see* Thiophenetole.
Phenyl ether: *see* Diphenyl sulphide.
Acetyl: *see* S-Phenyl ester under Thioacetic Acid.
Benzoyl: *see* S-Phenyl ester under Thiobenzoic Acid.

Adams, Marvel, *Organic Syntheses*, Collective Vol. I, 490.
Winter, *Am. Chem. J.*, 1904, **31**, 572.

Thiophosgene.
See Thiocarbonyl chloride.

Thiopropionic Acid

$CH_3{\cdot}CH_2{\cdot}CO{\cdot}SH$ or $CH_3{\cdot}CH_2{\cdot}CS{\cdot}OH$

C_3H_6OS MW, 90

Liq. with pungent sulphur-like odour.

S-*Me ester*: C_4H_8OS. MW, 104. B.p. 119–20°.

O-*Et ester*: $C_5H_{10}OS$. MW, 118. B.p. 130–2°. D_4^{19} 0·9451. n_D^{19} 1·46281. Insol. H_2O.

Amide: C_3H_7NS. MW, 89. Leaflets from C_6H_6. M.p. 41–3°. Very sol. C_6H_6. Spar. sol. H_2O, EtOH, Et_2O.

Anilide: needles from AcOH.Aq. M.p. 67–67·5°.

Delépine, *Bull. soc. chim.*, 1911, **9**, 907.
Weigert, *Ber.*, 1903, **36**, 1009.
Hubacher, *Ann.*, 1890, **259**, 229.

Thiopropyl Alcohol.
See Propyl Mercaptan.

Thio-γ-pyrone

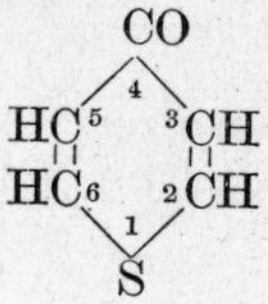

C_5H_4OS MW, 112

Prisms from CCl_4. M.p. 110°. Mod. sol. H_2O, EtOH, Et_2O. Spar. sol. ligroin. Sol. conc. H_2SO_4.

HCl salt: m.p. 135° (not sharp).

Add. comp. with $HgCl_2$: needles from H_2O. M.p. 189°.

Arndt, Bekir, *Ber.*, 1930, **63**, 2395.

Thioresorcinol (m-*Hydroxythiophenol*, m-*mercaptophenol*)

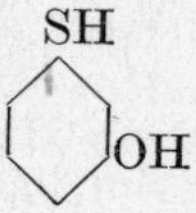

C_6H_6OS MW, 126

Cryst. with penetrating odour. M.p. 16–17°. B.p. 168°/35 mm. Sol. common org. solvents except pet. ether. Spar. sol. H_2O. Volatile in steam.

O-*Me ether*: *m*-mercaptoanisole, *m*-methoxythiophenol. C_7H_8OS. MW, 140. Liq. B.p. 224–5°, 112–14°/20 mm., 96–100°/9–10 mm.

S-*Me ether*: *m*-hydroxythioanisole, methyl *m*-hydroxyphenyl sulphide. Cryst. M.p. 15°. B.p. 224° slight decomp., 148–51°/14 mm. Sol. common org. solvents except pet. ether. Volatile in steam.

S-*Et ether*: *m*-hydroxythiophenetole, ethyl *m*-hydroxyphenyl sulphide. $C_8H_{10}OS$. MW, 154. B.p. 238–9°, 104–5°/9–10 mm.

Watson, Dutt, *J. Chem. Soc.*, 1922, **121**, 2415.
Zincke, Ebel, *Ber.*, 1914, **47**, 927.
Szathmáry, *Ber.*, 1910, **43**, 2487.
Mauthner, *Ber.*, 1906, **39**, 3596.

Thiosalicylic Acid (o-*Mercaptobenzoic acid*)

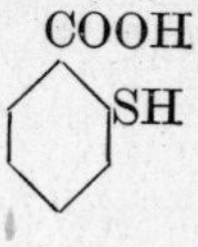

$C_7H_6O_2S$ MW, 154

Leaflets or needles from EtOH or AcOH. M.p. 164–5°. Sol. EtOH, AcOH. Spar. sol. hot H_2O. Oxidises in air $\longrightarrow$ diphenyl disulphide 2 : 2′-dicarboxylic acid. $FeCl_3$ in alc. sol. $\longrightarrow$ blue col. Alk. $KMnO_4 \longrightarrow$ 2-sulphobenzoic acid.

Me ether: *see* S-Methylthiosalicylic Acid.

Et ether: S-Ethylthiosalicylic acid. $C_9H_{10}O_2S$. MW, 182. Yellowish cryst. M.p. 134–5°. Sol. EtOH, AcOH. Very spar. sol. H_2O. *Et ester*: $C_{11}H_{14}O_2S$. MW, 210. Cryst. M.p. 27–8°. B.p. 152–3°/10 mm.

Phenyl ether: *see* Diphenyl sulphide 2-carboxylic Acid.

Nitrophenyl ether: *see* Nitrodiphenyl sulphide 2-carboxylic Acid.

p-*Tolyl ether*: cryst. from MeOH. M.p. 215–16°.

2-*Naphthyl ether*: leaflets from EtOH. M.p. 200–1°.

Benzyl ether: needles. M.p. 189°.

Acetyl: thioaspirin. Needles from C_6H_6. M.p. 125°.

Me ester: $C_8H_8O_2S$. MW, 168. Oil. B.p. 262–3°/728 mm. Volatile in steam.

Phenyl ester: thiosalol. $C_{13}H_{10}O_2S$. MW, 230. Cryst. from MeOH. M.p. 91°. Sol. EtOH, Et_2O. Spar. sol. ligroin.

Allen, Mackay, *Organic Syntheses*, 1932, XII, 76.
Mayer, *Ber.*, 1909, **42**, 1134.

Thiosalol.

See under Thiosalicylic Acid.

Thiosemicarbazide

$H_2N{\cdot}CS{\cdot}NH{\cdot}NH_2$

CH_5N_3S MW, 91

Needles from H_2O. M.p. 181–3°.

Hydrochloride: m.p. 186–90°.

Derivatives are given elsewhere under their own names.

Freund, Schander, *Ber.*, 1896, **29**, 2501.

Thiosinamine.

See Allylthiourea.

Thiothymol (3-*Mercapto*-p-*cymene*, 3-*methyl*-6-*isopropylthiophenol*, *thymyl mercaptan*)

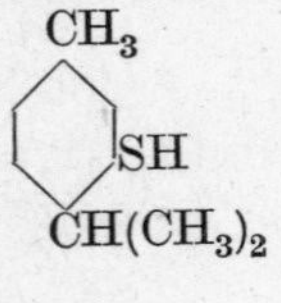

$C_{10}H_{14}S$ MW, 166

B.p. 230–1°.

$Hg(C_{10}H_{13}S)_2$: greenish cryst. from EtOH. M.p. 78°.

Fittica, *Ann.*, 1874, **172**, 305, 325.

Thiotolene.

See Methylthiophene.

Thio-α-toluic Acid.

See Phenylthioacetic Acid.

Thio-*o*-toluic Acid (o-*Methylthiobenzoic acid*)

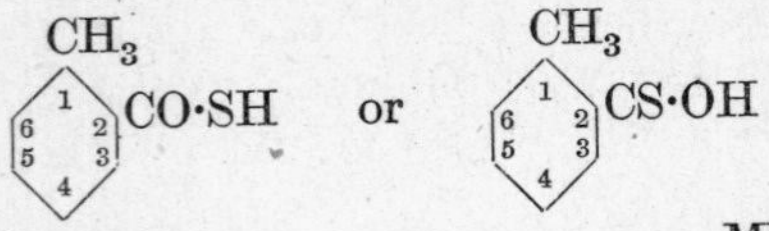

C_8H_8OS MW, 152

Yellow oil. B.p. 133°/35 mm. D_{25}^{25} 1·1451. Sol. EtOH, Et_2O. Insol. H_2O.

S-*Et ester*: $C_{10}H_{12}OS$. MW, 180. Yellow oil. B.p. 133°/15 mm. D_{25}^{25} 1·0513. Sol. EtOH, Et_2O. Insol. H_2O.

Amide: *o*-methylthiobenzamide. C_8H_9NS. MW, 151. M.p. 88°.

Phenylhydrazide: m.p. 116–18°.

Sachs, Reid, *J. Am. Chem. Soc.*, 1916, **38**, 2748.

Thio-*p*-toluic Acid (p-*Methylthiobenzoic acid*).

Greenish prisms from pet. ether. M.p. 43·5–44°. B.p. 131°/15 mm. Very volatile in steam.

S-*Et ester*: b.p. 150°/18 mm. D_{25}^{25} 1·0708. Sol. EtOH, Et_2O. Insol. H_2O.

O-*Et ester*: b.p. 140–5°/70 mm. D_4^{20} 0·9992.

S-p-*Nitrobenzyl ester*: yellow cryst. from EtOH. M.p. 97°.

Amide: *p*-methylthiobenzamide. Cryst. M.p. 168°. N-*Benzoyl*: red prisms from EtOH. M.p. 135–6°.

Anilide: yellow needles from EtOH. M.p. 140–1°.

p-*Toluidide*: yellow cryst. from Me_2CO. M.p. 165–6°.

See previous reference.

Thiourea (*Thiocarbamide, thiocarbonic acid diamide*)

$H_2N{\cdot}CS{\cdot}NH_2 \rightleftharpoons HN{:}C(SH){\cdot}NH_2$
Isothiourea

CH_4N_2S MW, 76

Rhombohedra or needles from EtOH. M.p 180°. Sol. H_2O, EtOH. Spar. sol. Et_2O. Reacts neutral. Forms add. comps. with metallic salts and oxides. Prolonged heating at 170° $\longrightarrow$ NH_4CNS. $Ag_2O \longrightarrow$ dicyandiamide.

Hydrochloride: m.p. 136–7°.

B_4,NH_4Cl: cryst. from EtOH. M.p. 154°.

B_4,NH_4Br: needles from EtOH. M.p. 180°.

B_4,NH_4I: cryst. from EtOH. M.p. 186°.

S-*Me*: *see* S-Methylisothiourea.

N : S-*Diacetyl*: yellow prisms from AcOH.Aq M.p. 153°.

Tri-Me: prisms from C_6H_6–ligroin. M.p 87–8°. Sol. H_2O, EtOH, $CHCl_3$.

N-*Tetra-Me*: m.p. 78°. B.p. 245°.
N-*Tetra-Et*: b.p. 264–6°, 130°/12 mm. D_4^{18} 0·9662. n_D^{26} 1·5225.
Triphenyl: needles from EtOH. M.p. 152°. Spar. sol. cold EtOH.
N-*Tetraphenyl*: needles from EtOH. M.p. 194·5–195·5°. Sol. C_6H_6. Mod. sol. Et_2O. Spar. sol. EtOH. Insol. H_2O.
Other thiourea derivatives are given separately elsewhere.

Kirchoff, Akonjans, *Chem. Zentr.*, 1935, I, 2165.
Giua, *Chem. Abstracts*, 1925, **19**, 1561.
I.G., F.P., 655,457, (*Chem. Zentr.*, 1929, II, 487).
Ciba, U.S.P., 2,006,762, (*Chem. Abstracts*, 1935, **29**, 5463).
Werner, *J. Chem. Soc.*, 1912, **101**, 2185.
Schenck, *Z. physiol. Chem.*, 1912, **77**, 370.
Delépine, *Bull soc. chim.*, 1902, **27**, 814.
I.G., D.R.P., 526,799, (*Chem. Abstracts*, 1931, **25**, 4892).
Gebhardt, *Ber.*, 1884, **17**, 2092.

Thiourethane

$H_2N{\cdot}CS{\cdot}OC_2H_5$ or $H_2N{\cdot}CO{\cdot}SC_2H_5$

C_3H_7ONS MW, 105

O-*Ester*: Xanthogenamide.
Pyramids. M.p. 40–1° (16°). Decomp. on dist. D_4^{20} 1·069. n_D^{20} 1·520.
N-*Di-Me*: $C_5H_{11}ONS$. MW, 133. M.p. 15°. D_4^{20} 1·028. n_D^{20} 1·5075.
N-*Di-Et*: $C_7H_{15}ONS$. MW, 161. B.p. 114°/20 mm.
N-*Acetyl*: prisms from H_2O. M.p. 101°.
N-*Isovaleryl*: prisms from Me_2CO. M.p. 56°.
N-*Carbomethoxyl*: needles. M.p. 83°.
S-*Ester*:
Plates. M.p. 102° (109°). Sol. EtOH, Et_2O, hot H_2O. Insol. cold H_2O.
N-*Acetyl*: prisms from C_6H_6. M.p. 98°.

Battegay, Hégazi, *Helv. Chim. Acta*, 1933, **16**, 1005.
Homberg, *Chem. Abstracts*, 1930, **24**, 2111.
Wheeler, Barnes, *Am. Chem. J.*, 1899, 22, 148.

Thioxan (1 : 4-*Oxthian*)

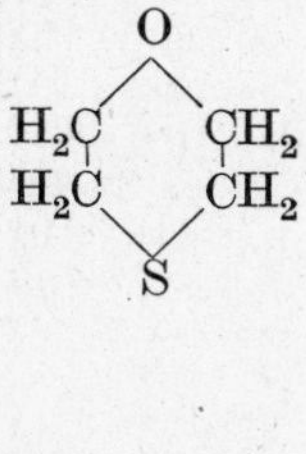

C_4H_8OS MW, 104

M.p. − 17°. B.p. 147°, 109·8°/233 mm., 86·5°/97 mm., 69·9°/47 mm. D_4^{20} 1·1178. n_D^{20} 1·5081. Spar. sol. H_2O.
Ethiodide: yellow cryst. from EtOH. M.p. 85°.
Dibromide: m.p. 75–80° decomp.
Di-iodide: cryst. from Et_2O. M.p. 66–7°.
Mercurichloride: needles from EtOH. M.p. 171°.

Johnson, *J. Chem. Soc.*, 1933, 1530.
Fromm, Ungar, *Ber.*, 1923, **56**, 2288.
Clarke, *J. Chem. Soc.*, 1912, **101**, 1806.

Thioxanthene (*Diphenylmethane sulphide, dibenzthiopyran*)

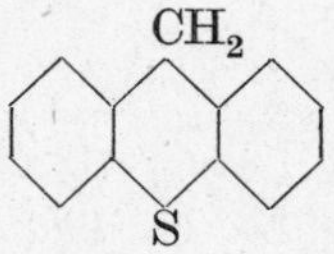

$C_{13}H_{10}S$ MW, 198

Cryst. from EtOH–$CHCl_3$. M.p. 128°. B.p. 340°/730 mm. Sol. $CHCl_3$. Spar. sol. Et_2O, cold EtOH. Sublimes. $CrO_3 \longrightarrow$ benzophenone sulphone.
S-*Oxide*: diphenylmethane sulphoxide. Plates from pet. ether. M.p. 109–10°.
S-*Dioxide*: *see* Diphenylmethane sulphone.

Graebe, Schultefs, *Ann.*, 1891, **263**, 12.

Thioxanthone (9-*Ketothioxanthene*)

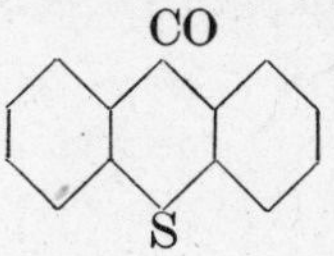

$C_{13}H_8OS$ MW, 212

Yellow needles from $CHCl_3$. M.p. 209° (207°). Sublimes. Sol. AcOH, $CHCl_3$, CS_2, C_6H_6. Insol. H_2O. Red. $\longrightarrow$ thioxanthene. $CrO_3 \longrightarrow$ benzophenone sulphone.
S-*Dioxide*: *see* Benzophenone sulphone.
Hydrazone: yellow leaflets from EtOH–C_6H_6. M.p. 115°.

Gomberg, Britton, *J. Am. Chem. Soc.*, 1921, **43**, 1945.
Graebe, Schultefs, *Ann.*, 1891, **263**, 8.

Thioxene.
See Dimethylthiophene.

***m*-4-Thioxylenol** (4-*Mercapto*-m-*xylene*, 2 : 4-*dimethylphenyl mercaptan*)

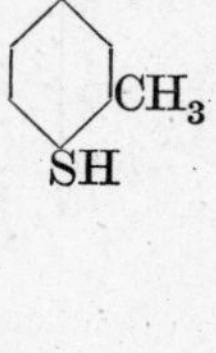

$C_8H_{10}S$ MW, 138

B.p. 207–8° (214°).

S-*Phenyl* : 2 : 4-dimethyldiphenyl sulphide. B.p. 172·5°/11 mm. D_4^{15} 1·0817.

S-p-*Tolyl* : 2 : 4 : 4′-trimethyldiphenyl sulphide. B.p. 188°/11 mm. D_4^{15} 1·0614.

Gattermann, *Ber.*, 1899, **32**, 1147.

p-2-Thioxylenol (2-*Mercapto*-p-*xylene*, 2 : 5-*dimethylphenyl mercaptan*)

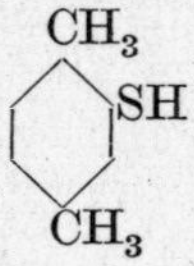

$C_8H_{10}S$ MW, 138

B.p. 211–12° (205°).

S-*Phenyl* : 2 : 5-dimethyldiphenyl sulphide. B.p. 171°/11 mm. D_4^{15} 1·0795.

S-p-*Tolyl* : 2 : 5 : 4′-trimethyldiphenyl sulphide. B.p. 185°/11 mm. D_4^{15} 1·0606.

S-*Benzyl* : m.p. 35°. B.p. 200°/15 mm.

See previous reference.

Thiuram disulphide

$H_2N{\cdot}CS{\cdot}S{\cdot}S{\cdot}CS{\cdot}NH_2$

$C_2H_4N_2S_4$ MW, 184

Plates from Me_2CO–$CHCl_3$. M.p. 153° decomp. Sol. Me_2CO, hot EtOH. Insol. H_2O, Et_2O, $CHCl_3$. Heat ⟶ CS_2 + NH_4CNS.

Freund, Bachrach, *Ann.*, 1895, **285**, 201.

Threonic Acid (*Trihydroxybutyric acid*)

$HO{\cdot}CH_2{-}C(OH)(H){-}C(H)(OH){-}COOH$

$C_4H_8O_5$ MW, 136

d-.

Syrup. $[\alpha]_D$ about − 30° in H_2O.

Phenylhydrazide : laminæ from EtOH. M.p. 157–8°. $[\alpha]_D^{20}$ − 29° to − 31°.

Brucine salt : plates. M.p. 214°. $[\alpha]_D^{20}$ −32·4° in H_2O.

Quinine salt : needles from EtOH. M.p. 168°. $[\alpha]_D^{20}$ − 116·99° in H_2O.

Strychnine salt : plates from dil. EtOH. M.p. 115–21°. $[\alpha]_D^{20}$ − 28·5° in H_2O.

l-.

Syrup. $[\alpha]_D^{19}$ + 9·54°.

Phenylhydrazide : m.p. 157°. $[\alpha]_D^{20}$ about + 29°.

Me ester : $C_5H_{10}O_5$. MW, 150. *Tri-Me ether* : b.p. 120°/13 mm. n_D^{15} 1·4275. $[\alpha]_{5780}^{18}$ + 49° in MeOH, + 31° in H_2O. D^{15} 1·090.

Amide : $C_4H_9O_4N$. MW, 135. M.p. 88–90°. $[\alpha]_D^{20}$ + 58° in H_2O. *Tri-Me ether* : m.p. 78°. $[\alpha]_{5780}^{20}$ + 44° in H_2O, + 68° in MeOH.

Quinine salt : m.p. 163–5°

dl-.

M.p. 98–9°.

Phenylhydrazide : m.p. 167·5°.

Jensen, Upson, *J. Am. Chem. Soc.*, 1925, **47**, 3023.
Nef, *Ann.*, 1914, **403**, 265.
Nef, Hedenburg, Glattfeld, *J. Am. Chem. Soc.*, 1917, **39**, 1642.
Braun, *J. Am. Chem. Soc.*, 1932, **54**, 1137.
Haworth, Hirst, Smith, *J. Chem. Soc.* 1934, 1558.
Glattfeld, Hoen, *J. Am. Chem. Soc.*, 1935, **57**, 1407.
Reichstein, Grüssner, Bosshard, *Helv. Chim. Acta*, 1935, **18**, 605.
Herbert *et al.*, *J. Chem. Soc.*, 1933, 1284.

Threose (*Trihydroxybutyraldehyde*)

$HO{\cdot}CH_2{-}C(OH)(H){-}C(H)(OH){-}CHO$

$C_4H_8O_4$ MW, 120

d-.

M.p. 126–32°. Very hygroscopic. $[\alpha]_D^{22}$ +29·09° ⟶ 19·59° in H_2O. NaHg ⟶ *d*-erythritol.

Phenylosazone : m.p. 164–5°.

Phenylbenzylhydrazone : needles from C_6H_6. M.p. 194·5°.

Acetone deriv. : m.p. 84°. $[\alpha]_D^{22}$ − 15·27° in Me_2CO.

Diacetamide deriv. : prisms. M.p. 166°. $[\alpha]_D$ − 10·9° in H_2O.

Diacetyl : m.p. 140–2°. $[\alpha]_D^{23}$ + 83·52° ⟶ 34·31° in $CHCl_3$. Reduces Fehling's.

Triacetyl : m.p. 113–14°. $[\alpha]_D^{20}$ + 35·5° in $CHCl_3$.

l-.

Obtained only in solution. $[\alpha]_D^{2}$ − 24·6° in H_2O. Reduces Fehling's in the cold.

Phenylosazone : cryst. from C_6H_6. M.p. 165–6°.

Diacetamide deriv. : cryst. from 95% EtOH. M.p. 165–6°.

Maquenne, *Ann. chim. phys.*, 1901, **24**, 404.
Ruff, *Ber.*, 1901, **34**, 1370.
Deulofeu, *J. Chem. Soc.*, 1929, 2458; *J. Am. Chem. Soc.*, 1936, **58**, 855.
Steiger, Reichstein, *Helv. Chim. Acta*, 1936, **19**, 1016.
Mendive, *Chem. Abstracts*, 1932, **26**, 2433.
Freudenberg, *Ber.*, 1932, **65**, 168.
Hockett, *J. Am. Chem. Soc.*, 1934, **56**, 994.

Thujaketone (*Tanacet-ketone*, 2-*isopropyl*-1-*hexenone*-5)

$$(CH_3)_2CH\cdot \overset{CH_2}{\overset{\|}{C}}\cdot CH_2\cdot CH_2\cdot CO\cdot CH_3$$

$C_9H_{16}O$ MW, 140

B.p. 184–6°. D^{20} 0·854. n_D 1·441.
Oxime: b.p. 118–20°/15 mm.
Semicarbazone: m.p. 143°.

Tiemann, Semmler, *Ber.*, 1897, **30**, 439.
Wallach, *Ann.*, 1893, **272**, 116.

Thujane (*Sabinane*)

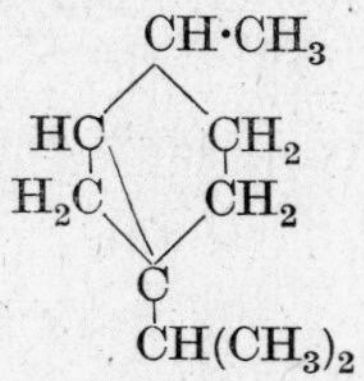

$C_{10}H_{18}$ MW, 138

d-.
Mobile oil with faint odour. B.p. 157°/758 mm. D_4^{20} 0·8139. n_D^{20} 1·43759. $[\alpha]_D$ + 62·03°.

Tschugaev, Fomin, *Compt. rend.*, 1910, **151**, 1058.
Henderson, Robertson, *J. Chem. Soc.*, 1923, **123**, 1715.
Zelinsky, Turowa-Pollak, *Ber.*, 1929, **62**, 2868.

Thujol.
See Thujyl Alcohol.

Thujone

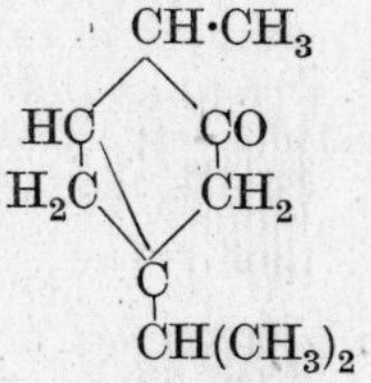

$C_{10}H_{16}O$ MW, 152

Two stereoisomers are known.

α-.
Constituent of many essential oils. Oil with fresh odour. B.p. 199–201°, 103–4°/40 mm. D^{20} 0·9152. n_D^{20} 1·4530. $[\alpha]_D^{20}$ − 11·58°. Heat ⟶ carvacrol + carvotanacetone. Boiling alc. H_2SO_4 ⟶ β-thujone ⟶ isothujone.
Oxime: liq. $[\alpha]_D^{19}$ − 29·25° in Et_2O.
Semicarbazone: (i) Prisms from MeOH. M.p. 186–8°. $[\alpha]_D$ + 64·4° in EtOH. (ii) Amorphous. M.p. 100–10°. $[\alpha]_D^{20}$ + 53·71°.

2 : 4-*Dinitrophenylhydrazone*: orange-yellow plates from EtOH. M.p. 116–17°.
m-*Nitrobenzoylhydrazone*: m.p. 156–156·3°.

β-. Tanacetone.
Constituent of many essential oils. Oil with odour resembling menthol. B.p. 201–2°. $D_4^{15\cdot1}$ 0·9193. $n_D^{13\cdot6}$ 1·4540. $[\alpha]_D^{20}$ + 77·33°. Heat of comb. C_v 1429·9 Cal. Alc. KOH ⟶ α-thujone. Heat ⟶ carvotanacetone. Boiling dil. H_2SO_4 ⟶ isothujone. Na + EtOH ⟶ thujyl alcohol. Forms cryst. bisulphite comp.
Oxime: tanacetone oxime. Prisms. M.p. 54–5°. B.p. 135–6°/20 mm. $[\alpha]_D^{11}$ + 105·1° in MeOH. *Benzoyl*: cryst. from MeOH. M.p. 52–3°.
Hydrazone: b.p. 149°/35 mm. D_0^{22} 0·9504. n_D^{22} 1·4952. $[\alpha]_D$ + 123·75°.
Semicarbazone: (i) Hexagonal cryst. M.p. 174–5°. $[\alpha]_D^{15}$ + 218·04° in MeOH. (ii) Rhombic cryst. M.p. 170–2°.

Challenger, *Industrial Chemist*, 1928, **4**, 315.
Paolini, *Chem. Abstracts*, 1926, **20**, 1072.
Östling, Roth, *Ber.*, 1913, **46**, 313.
Rose, Livingstone, *J. Am. Chem. Soc.*, 1912, **34**, 201.

Thujyl Alcohol (β-*Thujyl alcohol*, *tanacetyl alcohol*, *thujol*)

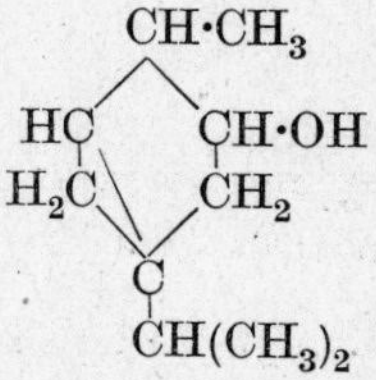

$C_{10}H_{18}O$ MW, 154

Eight active and four racemic isomers are possible. Occurs free and combined as ester in several essential oils. Characteristic constants for the commercial product (mixture of isomers) are :—b.p. 208–10° (220°), 92·5°/13 mm. D^{25} 0·9266. n_D^{25} 1·4621. Heat of comb. C_v 1477·1 Cal.
Me ether: $C_{11}H_{20}O$. MW, 168. D_4^{20} 0·8771. n_D 1·44541.

Two dextro- and one lævorotatory modifications are described in the literature.

d-. β-Thujyl alcohol.
B.p. 206°. D_4^{20} 0·9187. n_D^{16} 1·4625. $[\alpha]_D^{20}$ + 116·93°. CrO_3 ⟶ β-thujone.
Hydrogen phthalate: needles from pet. ether. M.p. 120°. $[\alpha]_D$ + 91·3° in EtOH. *Ag salt*: m.p. 85–6°. *Strychnine salt*: needles from EtOH.Aq. M.p. 177–8°. $[\alpha]_D$ + 36·8°.

d-. δ-Thujyl alcohol.
B.p. 206°. n_D 1·4759. $[\alpha]_D$ +50·01°.
Hydrogen phthalate: cryst. from pet. ether. M.p. 95–6°. $[\alpha]_D$ + 2·3° in EtOH.

l-.
M.p. 28°. $[\alpha]_D^{20}$ − 9·12° in toluene.

Tschugajew, Fomin, *Ber.*, 1912, **45**, 1295.
Paolini, Lomonaco, *Atti accad. Lincei*, 1914, **23**, (II), 128.
Rose, Livingstone, *J. Am. Chem. Soc.*, 1912, **34**, 202.

Thujylamine

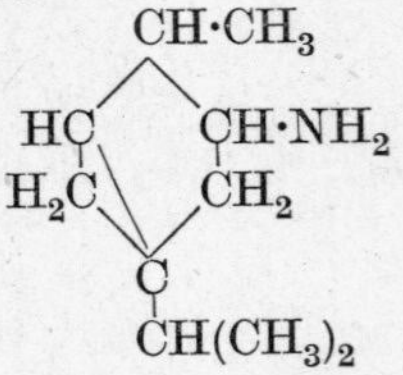

$C_{10}H_{19}N$ MW, 153

As with thujyl alcohol, eight active and four racemic modifications are possible. Three thujylamines are described but the constitution of one only is substantiated.

α-.
B.p. 198–9°.

β-. From β-thujone.
B.p. 198–205°, 75–90°/14 mm. D^{17} 0·876. n_D 1·46782. $[\alpha]_D$ + 22·34°. Dist. hydrochloride ⟶ isothujene.
B,HCl: m.p. 210–14°. $[\alpha]_D^{16}$ + 32·67° in EtOH.

β-. From β-thujone-oxime. Tanacetylamine.
B.p. 195°, 80·5°/14 mm. D_4^{20} 0·8712. n_D^{20} 1·4608. $[\alpha]_D$ + 101·00°. Dist. hydrochloride ⟶ isothujene.
B,HCl: m.p. 260–1°.
Nitrate: cryst. from H_2O. M.p. 167–8°. $[\alpha]_D$ + 82·03°.
Carbonate: m.p. 106–7°.
N-*Di-Me*: $C_{12}H_{23}N$. MW, 181. B.p. 213·5–214°. D_4^{20} 0·8606. $[\alpha]_D$ + 141·76°.

Kondakow, Skworzow, *J. prakt. Chem.*, 1904, **69**, 178.
Tschugajew, *Ber.*, 1901, **34**, 2278.
Wallach, *Ann.*, 1893, **272**, 109.

Thymacetin.
See under 6-Aminothymol.

Thymine (*5-Methyluracil*)

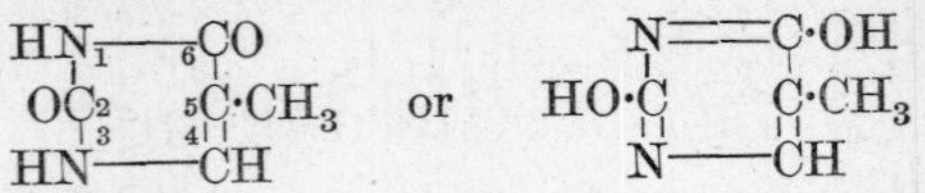

$C_5H_6O_2N_2$ MW, 126

Plates from H_2O. M.p. 326° (318–20°). Sol. 250 parts H_2O at 25°. Spar. sol. EtOH, Et_2O. Sublimes. Heat of comb. C_v 566·4 Cal.
1-N-*Me*: 1 : 5-dimethyluracil. $C_6H_8O_2N_2$. MW, 140. Prisms from H_2O. M.p. 202–5° decomp. Very sol. hot EtOH, Me_2CO.
3-N-*Me*: 3 : 5-dimethyluracil. Needles or prisms from H_2O. M.p. 280–2°.
1 : 3-N-*Di-Me*: 1 : 3 : 5-trimethyluracil. $C_7H_{10}O_2N_2$. MW, 154. Needles from EtOH. M.p. 153°. Very sol. H_2O, $CHCl_3$. Spar. sol. Et_2O, pet. ether.

Bergmann, Currie, *J. Am. Chem. Soc.*, 1933, **55**, 1734.
Johnson, Clapp, *J. Biol. Chem.*, 1908, **5**, 56.

Thyminose.
See 2-Ribodesose.

Thymohydroquinone (*2 : 5-Dihydroxy-p-cymene, thymoquinol, hydrothymoquinone*)

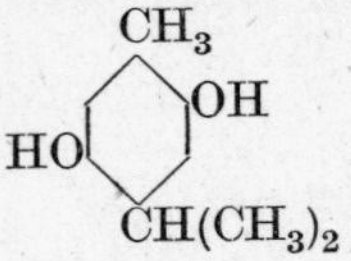

$C_{10}H_{14}O_2$ MW, 166

Occurs free and combined as ether in several essential oils. Prisms. M.p. 143° (139·5°). B.p. 290°. Very sol. EtOH, Et_2O. Sol. hot H_2O. Insol. C_6H_6. Sublimes. Heat of comb. C_p 1308·6 Cal., C_v 1308·1 Cal. Ox. ⟶ thymoquinone.
Di-Me ether: $C_{12}H_{18}O_2$. MW, 194. B.p. 248–50°, 118°/12 mm. D^{22} 0·998. n_D^{22} 1·51339.
Diacetyl: m.p. 73–5°.
Dibenzoyl: pale yellow needles from EtOH. M.p. 141–2°.
Phenylurethane: leaflets from EtOH. M.p. 232–3°.
α-*Naphthylurethane*: cryst. from EtOH. M.p. 147–8°.

Sherk, *Chem. Zentr.*, 1921, III, 218.
Sabatier, Mailhe, *Compt. rend.*, 1908, **146**, 458.

Thymohydroxycuminic Acid.
See 3-Hydroxycuminic Acid.

Thymol (3-*Hydroxy*-p-*cymene*, 3-*hydroxy*-4-*isopropyltoluene*, 3-*methyl*-6-*isopropylphenol*, 4-*isopropyl*-m-*cresol*)

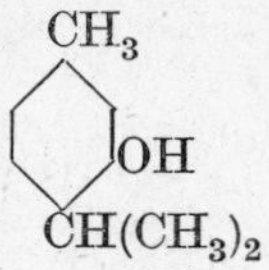

$C_{10}H_{14}O$ MW, 150

Constituent of numerous essential oils. Plates with odour of thyme from AcOEt, AcOH or Me_2CO. M.p. 51·5°. B.p. 233·5°. Sol. 1176 parts H_2O at 19·4°. Very sol. EtOH, Et_2O, AcOH, $CHCl_3$, C_6H_6. Heat of comb. C_p 1353·75 Cal. Crit. temp. 425·1°. Red. ⟶ menthol + menthone. Ox. ⟶ thymohydroquinone or di-thymol. $KNO_2 + H_2SO_4$ ⟶ green ⟶ blue col. Possesses antiseptic properties.

Me ether: $C_{11}H_{16}O$. MW, 164. Occurs naturally. Liq. with ethereal odour. B.p. 211–12°/745 mm., 94–6°/15 mm. D_4^{14} 0·9388.

Et ether: $C_{12}H_{18}O$. MW, 178. B.p. 224–8°. D_0^0 0·9334.

Propyl ether: $C_{13}H_{20}O$. MW, 192. B.p. 243°. D_0^0 0·9276.

Butyl ether: $C_{14}H_{22}O$. MW, 206. B.p. 258·3°. D_0^0 0·9230.

d-*Amyl ether*: $C_{15}H_{24}O$. MW, 220. B.p. 250–60°. D^{18} 0·934. n_D^{17} 1·5056. $[\alpha]_D^{18}$ + 4·17°.

Isoamyl ether: b.p. 242–3°/746·5 mm. n_D^{14} 1·4923.

Phenyl ether: $C_{16}H_{18}O$. MW, 226. B.p. 297°/766 mm., 176°/25 mm. D^{15} 1·0113.

Benzyl ether: $C_{17}H_{20}O$. MW, 240. B.p. 221–3°/35 mm. D_{18}^{18} 1·0063. n_D^{20} 1·5511.

p-*Nitrobenzyl ether*: $C_{17}H_{19}O_3N$. MW, 285. Cryst. from EtOH.Aq. M.p. 85·5°.

Formyl: b.p. 81°/2 mm. D^0 1·015. n_D^{20} 1·49606.

Acetyl: b.p. 242–3°. D^0 1·009.

Oxalate: needles from EtOH. M.p. 61°.

Benzoyl: plates. M.p. 33°.

3 : 5-*Dinitrobenzoyl*: needles. M.p. 103·2°.

Phenylurethane: cryst. from EtOH.Aq. M.p. 106·5–107°.

α-*Naphthylurethane*: m.p. 160°.

Rheinische Kampher-Fabrik., E.P., 308,681 (*Chem. Zentr.*, 1931, II, 1492).
Austerweil, Lemay, *Bull. soc. chim.*, 1927, **41**, 454.
Frisch, D.R.P., 615,470, (*Chem. Zentr.*, 1936, **107**, I, 883; *Chem. Abstracts*, 1935, **29**, 6252).
Hund, U.S.P., 1,967,440.

Thymomenthone.

See under Menthone.

Thymoquinol.

See Thymohydroquinone.

Thymoquinone (1-*Methyl*-4-*isopropylcyclohexadiene*-3 : 6-*dione*, 2-*methyl*-5-*isopropyl*-1 : 4-*benzoquinone*)

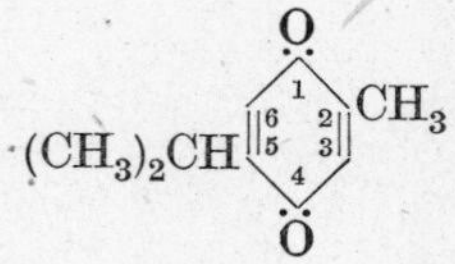

$C_{10}H_{12}O_2$ MW, 164

Occurs in oil from wood of *Callitris quadrivalvis*, Vent., and *Monarda fistulosa*. Bright yellow tablets with penetrating odour. M.p. 45·5°. B.p. 232°. Very sol. EtOH, Et_2O. Sol. $CHCl_3$, C_6H_6. Spar. sol. H_2O. Volatile in steam. Heat of comb. C_p 1274·6 Cal., C_v 1273·4 Cal. In light ⟶ dithymoquinone. EtOH + light ⟶ thymohydroquinone. Red. ⟶ thymohydroquinone.

Thymohydroquinone add. comp.: dark violet needles. M.p. 64°.

1-*Oxime*: *see* 6-Nitrosothymol.

4-*Oxime*: *see* 5-Nitrosocarvacrol.

1 : 4-*Dioxime*: $C_{10}H_{14}O_2N_2$. MW, 194. Prisms from EtOH. Darkens at 200°. Decomp. at 235°. *Diacetyl*: plates or needles from ligroin. M.p. 110°. *Dibenzoyl*: needles from C_6H_6. M.p. 199–200°.

1-*Semicarbazone*: yellow needles from EtOH. M.p. 201–2° decomp.

1 : 4-*Disemicarbazone*: cryst. from AcOH. M.p. 237°.

1-*Phenylsemicarbazone*: dark yellow needles from AcOH. M.p. 204–5°.

1 : 4-*Diphenylsemicarbazone*: dark yellow cryst. powder. Decomp. at 242°.

1-*Phenylhydrazone*: reddish-yellow needles from EtOH. M.p. 93°.

1-o-*Nitrophenylhydrazone*: red needles from MeOH. M.p. 145°.

1-[2 : 4-*Dinitrophenyl*]-*hydrazone*: dark red needles from EtOH. M.p. 179–80°.

Tseng, Hu, Chu, *J. Chinese Chem. Soc.*, 1934, **2**, 151.
Kremers, Hixon, Wakeman, *Organic Syntheses*, 1926, VI, 92.
Liebermann, Iljinski, *Ber.*, 1885, **18**, 3194, 3220.

o-Thymotinic Acid (3-*Hydroxy*-4-*isopropyl*-o-*toluic acid*, 3-*hydroxy*-1-*methyl*-4-*isopropyl*-

benzene-2-carboxylic acid, 6-methyl-3-isopropyl-salicylic acid)

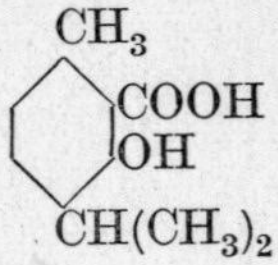

$C_{11}H_{14}O_3$ MW, 194

Needles from H_2O, C_6H_6 or ligroin. M.p. 127°. Sol. 10,000 parts H_2O at 20°. Sol. EtOH, Et_2O, AcOH, $CHCl_3$, C_6H_6. Volatile in steam. $FeCl_3$ $\longrightarrow$ dark blue col. Strong bactericide.

Me ester: $C_{12}H_{16}O_3$. MW, 208. Yellow oil. B.p. 142°/18·5 mm.

Et ester: $C_{13}H_{18}O_3$. MW, 222. Yellow oil. B.p. 153°/18·5 mm.

Acetonyl ester: $C_{14}H_{18}O_4$. MW, 250. Needles from EtOH. M.p. 75°. Very sol. hot EtOH, Et_2O, Me_2CO, C_6H_6. Has local anæsthetic action.

Spallino, Provenzal, *Gazz. chim. ital.*, 1909, **39**, 326.

p-Thymotinic Acid (*5-Hydroxy-4-isopropyl-*o*-toluic acid, 5-hydroxy-1-methyl-4-isopropyl-benzene-2-carboxylic acid*)

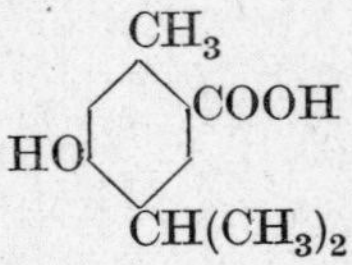

$C_{11}H_{14}O_3$ MW, 194

Plates from EtOH.Aq. M.p. 157°. Very sol. EtOH, Et_2O, $CHCl_3$, C_6H_6. Spar. sol. hot H_2O. No col. with $FeCl_3$.

Me ether: 2-methyl-5-isopropylanisic acid. $C_{12}H_{16}O_3$. MW, 208. Needles from EtOH. M.p. 138–9°. Very sol. EtOH, Et_2O, $CHCl_3$, C_6H_6. Spar. sol. cold H_2O. *Cu salt*: blue cryst. from EtOH–ligroin. Decomp. at 190°. *Et ester*: $C_{14}H_{20}O_3$. MW, 236. Liq. with unpleasant odour. B.p. 163–4°/13 mm. D_4^{25} 1·032. *Amide*: $C_{12}H_{17}O_2N$. MW, 207. Needles from EtOH. M.p. 158–9°. Sol. EtOH, AcOH. Spar. sol. Et_2O, ligroin. *Nitrile*: $C_{12}H_{15}ON$. MW, 189. Cryst. from ligroin. M.p. 69–70°. B.p. 158–60°/16 mm. Very sol. EtOH, Et_2O, $CHCl_3$. Sol. ligroin.

Et ether: $C_{13}H_{18}O_3$. MW, 222. Prisms from EtOH. M.p. 159°. Spar. sol. H_2O. *Amide*: $C_{13}H_{19}O_2N$. MW, 221. Needles from EtOH. M.p. 127°.

Me ester: $C_{12}H_{16}O_3$. MW, 208. Cryst. from Et_2O or C_6H_6. M.p. 97–8°.

Nitrile: $C_{11}H_{13}ON$. MW, 175. Cryst. from C_6H_6. M.p. 115–16°.

Houben, Fischer, *Ber.*, 1931, **64**, 245.
Grignard, Bellet, Courtot, *Ann. chim.*, 1915, **4**, 50.
Gattermann, *Ann.*, 1888, **244**, 69.
Kobek, *Ber.*, 1883, **16**, 2102.

p-Thymotinic Aldehyde (*5-Hydroxy-4-iso-propyl-*o*-toluic aldehyde, 6-aldehydothymol, 4-hydroxy-2-methyl-5-isopropylbenzaldehyde*)

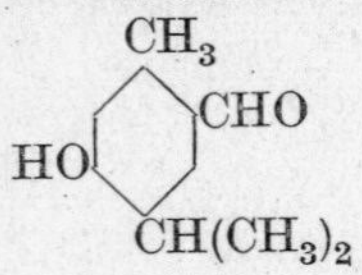

$C_{11}H_{14}O_2$ MW, 178

Needles from hot H_2O. M.p. 133°. Very sol. EtOH, Et_2O, $CHCl_3$, C_6H_6. Spar. sol. hot H_2O. Forms cryst. bisulphite comp. No col. with $FeCl_3$.

Me ether: 2-methyl-5-isopropylanisaldehyde. $C_{12}H_{16}O_2$. MW, 192. B.p. 278°. Very sol. EtOH, Et_2O, C_6H_6. *Anil*: plates from ligroin. M.p. 80°.

Anil: pale yellow needles. M.p. 142°.

Gattermann, Berchelmann, *Ber.*, 1898, **31**, 1767.
Kobek, *Ber.*, 1883, **16**, 2097.

Thymylamine (*5-Methyl-2-isopropylaniline, 3-amino-*p*-cymene*)

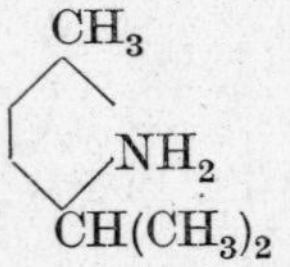

$C_{10}H_{15}N$ MW, 149

Oil with unpleasant odour. B.p. 230°. Volatile in steam. Misc. with EtOH, Et_2O. Spar. sol. H_2O.

Acetyl: needles from EtOH. M.p. 112°.

Lloyd, *Ber.*, 1887, **20**, 1259.

Thyroxine

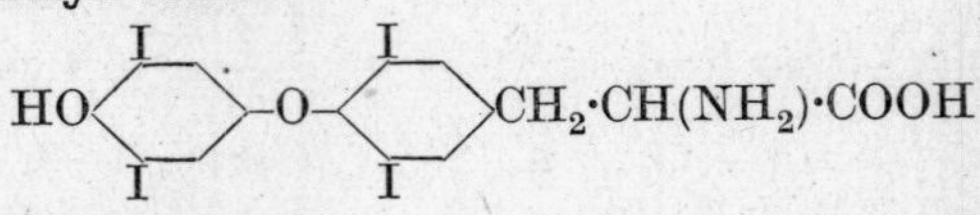

$C_{15}H_{11}O_4NI_4$ MW, 777

dl-.

Isolated from thyroid gland. Needles by addition of AcOH to alk. EtOH.Aq. sol. Darkens at 220°. M.p. 231–3° (250°) decomp. Very spar. sol. H_2O. Insol. org. solvents. Sol. NH_3, and alc. alkalis. Increases rate of basal metabolism.

Me ester: $C_{16}H_{13}O_4NI_4$. MW, 791. Prisms from EtOH.Aq. M.p. 156°. Spar. sol. H_2O, org. solvents except EtOH. *B,HCl*: needles from EtOH–HCl. M.p. 221·5°. N-*Acetyl*: plates from anisole. M.p. 208–9° decomp. N-*Chloroacetyl*: prisms from C_6H_6. M.p. 159–60°.

Et ester: $C_{17}H_{15}O_4NI_4$. MW, 805. N-*Diacetyl*: needles. M.p. 216–17° (230°).

N-*Acetyl*: cryst. from AcOH.Aq. M.p. 210–15° decomp.

N-*Chloroacetyl*: cryst. from AcOH.Aq. M.p. 201–2° decomp.

l-.

M.p. 235°. $[\alpha]_{5461}$ — 4·45° in EtOH–NaOH.

d-.

$[\alpha]^{21}_{5461}$ + 2·97° in EtOH–NaOH.

Harington, Slater, *Biochem. J.*, 1930, **24**, 456.
Thyroxine, Kendall, (Chem. Catalog. Co., New York, 1929).
Ashley, Harington, *Biochem. J.*, 1929, **23**, 1178; 1928, **22**, 1436.
Harington, *Biochem. J.*, 1928, **22**, 1429; 1926, **20**, 293.
Harington, Barger, *Biochem. J.*, 1927, **21**, 169.

Tiglic Acid (cis-1 : 2-*Dimethylacrylic acid*, 1-*methylcrotonic acid*, 1-*ethylidenepropionic acid*)

$$\begin{array}{l} CH_3\cdot CH \\ \quad\ \ \| \\ CH_3\cdot C\cdot COOH \end{array}$$

$C_5H_8O_2$ MW, 100

Occurs as glyceride in croton oil, as ester in Roman cumin oil. Tablets and columns from H_2O. M.p. 64°. B.p. 198·5°. D_4^{76} 0·9641. n_α^{76} 1·43297. Sol. hot H_2O. Heat of comb. 626·6 Cal. $k = 0.957 \times 10^{-5}$ at 25°. HI (+ P) $\longrightarrow$ 1-methylbutyric acid.

Me ester: $C_6H_{10}O_2$. MW, 114. B.p. 139·4–139·6°/766 mm. D_4^{20} 0·94980. n_D^{20} 1·43700.

Et ester: $C_7H_{12}O_2$. MW, 128. B.p. 156°/752 mm., 80·5–81·5°/45 mm., 55·5°/11 mm. $D_4^{19.5}$ 0·9247. $n_{He}^{19.5}$ 1·43554.

Isoamyl ester: $C_{10}H_{18}O_2$. MW, 170. Occurs in Roman cumin oil. B.p. 204–5°.

d-*Citronellyl ester*: $C_{15}H_{26}O_2$. MW, 238. Liq. with pleasant odour. B.p. 144–5°/7 mm. D_{15}^{15} 0·9090.

Geranyl ester: $C_{15}H_{24}O_2$. MW, 236. Liq. with pleasant odour. B.p. 149–51°/7 mm. D_{15}^{15} 0·9279.

p-*Bromophenacyl ester*: cryst. from EtOH. M.p. 67·9°.

Chloride: C_5H_7OCl. MW, 118·5. B.p. 45°/12 mm.

Anilide: cryst. from pet. ether. M.p. 77°.

2-*Naphthylamide*: cryst. M.p. 96°.

Michael, Ross, *J. Am. Chem. Soc.*, 1933, **55**, 3692.
Auwers, Wissebach, *Ber.*, 1923, **56**, 715.
Auwers, *Ann.*, 1923, **432**, 70.
Blaise, *Bull. soc. chim.*, 1903, **29**, 330.

Tiglic Aldehyde (1 : 2-*Dimethylacrolein*)

$$\begin{array}{c} \quad\quad CH_3 \\ CH_3\cdot CH{:}C\cdot CHO \end{array}$$

C_5H_8O MW, 84

Liq. with penetrating odour. B.p. 116·5–117·5°/738 mm., 63·2–65·0°/119 mm. D_4^{20} 0·8710. n_D^{20} 1·4475. Sol. 40–50 parts H_2O. Misc. with EtOH, Et_2O. Oxidises in air. Forms cryst. bisulphite comp.

Oxime: cryst. from Et_2O. M.p. 43°. B.p. 66–7°/10 mm.

Semicarbazone: needles from EtOH. M.p. 219° (234°).

Phenylhydrazone: needles from petrol. M.p. 92–4°. B.p. 163–8°/17 mm., 155–60°/9 mm. Sol. EtOH, Et_2O, $CHCl_3$, C_6H_6. Mod. sol. petrol, pet. ether.

p-*Nitrophenylhydrazone*: cryst. from EtOH.Aq. M.p. 181°.

2 : 4-*Dinitrophenylhydrazone*: red cryst. from AcOEt–Me_2CO. M.p. 206–7° (222°).

Pummerer, Reindel, *Ber.*, 1933, **66**, 335.
Shepard, Johnson, *J. Am. Chem. Soc.*, 1932, **54**, 4390.
Auwers, Krender, *Ber.*, 1925, **58**, 1978.
Grignard, Ablemann, *Bull. soc. chim.*, 1910, **7**, 643.

Tigliceric Acid (1 : 2-*Dimethylglyceric acid*)

$$\begin{array}{c} \quad\quad\quad CH_3 \\ CH_3\cdot CH(OH)\cdot C(OH)\cdot COOH \end{array}$$

$C_5H_{10}O_4$ MW, 134

Stereoisomeric with angliceric acid. Prisms from Et_2O. M.p. 88°. Very sol. H_2O, EtOH, Me_2CO. Spar. sol. cold Et_2O. Insol. $CHCl_3$, C_6H_6, ligroin. Most salts sol. H_2O.

Fittig, Penschuck, *Ann.*, 1894, **283**, 109.

Tigogenin

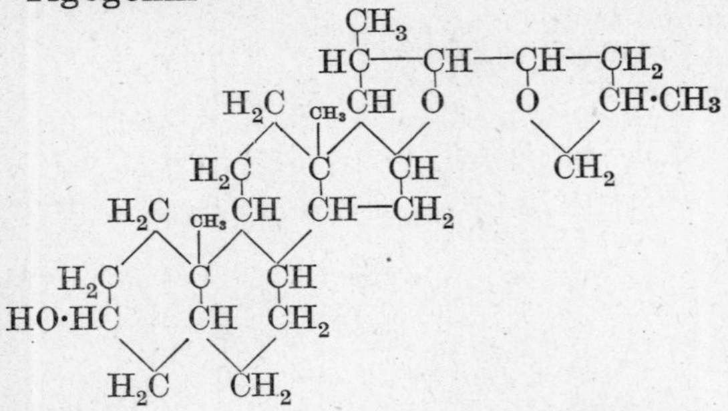

$C_{27}H_{44}O_3$ MW, 416

Occurs in *Digitalis purpurea*, *D. lanata*, *Chlorugalum pomeridianum*. Cryst. + $1H_2O$ from EtOH. M.p. 205–6°. Sol. Et_2O, Me_2CO, pet. ether. $[\alpha]_D^{18}$ − 67·2° in $CHCl_3$.

Acetyl: plates from MeOH. M.p. 202°. $[\alpha]_D^{18}$ − 74·4° in $CHCl_3$.

Benzoyl: cryst. from MeOH–$CHCl_3$. M.p. 230–3°. $[\alpha]_{5461}^{22\cdot5}$ − 68° in $CHCl_3$.

o-*Bromobenzoyl*: cryst. from EtOH–$CHCl_3$. M.p. 210–12°. $[\alpha]_{5461}^{27}$ − 56° in $CHCl_3$.

Jacobs, Fleck, *J. Biol. Chem.*, 1930, **88**, 545.
Liang, Noller, *J. Am. Chem. Soc.*, 1935, **57**, 526.
Tschesche, Hagedorn, *Ber.*, 1935, **68**, 1416, 2247.

Tigonin

$C_{56}H_{92}O_{27}$ MW, 1196

Glucoside present in leaves of *Digitalis lanata*. Amorph. from EtOH. Sinters at 220°. M.p. 260°. Absorbs $2H_2O$ in moist air. Forms add. comp. with cholesterol. Hyd. ⟶ tigogenin + galactose + glucose + xylose.

Cholesterol add. comp.: needles from MeOH. Decomp. above 200°.

Tschesche, *Ber.*, 1936, **69**, 1665.

Tin diethyl

$Sn(C_2H_5)_2$

$C_4H_{10}Sn$ MW, 177

Yellow oil. Decomp. on dist. ⟶ Sn + tin tetra-ethyl. Sol. EtOH, Et_2O, ligroin, C_6H_6. Insol. H_2O. Oxidises in air ⟶ diethyl tin oxide. Cl ⟶ Et_2SnCl_2. Reduces $AgNO_3$.

Pfeiffer, *Ber.*, 1911, **44**, 1270.

Tin tetra-*n*-amyl

$Sn(CH_2{\cdot}CH_2{\cdot}CH_2{\cdot}CH_2{\cdot}CH_3)_4$

$C_{20}H_{44}Sn$ MW, 403

Colourless stable liq. B.p. 181°/10 mm. D_4^{20} 1·0206. n_D^{20} 1·4720. Heat of comb. 3384 Cal.

Jones, Evans, Gulwell, Griffiths, *J. Chem. Soc.*, 1935, 41.

Tin tetra-*active*-amyl

$Sn(CH_2{\cdot}CH(CH_3){\cdot}CH_2{\cdot}CH_3)_4$

$C_{20}H_{44}Sn$ MW, 403

Colourless stable liq. B.p. 174°/10 mm. D_4^{20} 1·0222. n_D^{20} 1·4730.

See previous reference.

Tin tetrabenzyl

$Sn(CH_2{\cdot}C_6H_5)_4$

$C_{28}H_{28}Sn$ MW, 483

Prisms from pet. ether. M.p. 42–3°. Very sol. most org. solvents. Spar. sol. pet. ether. Oxidises in air ⟶ benzaldehyde.

Smith, Kipping, *J. Chem. Soc.*, 1912, **101**, 2559.

Tin tetra-*n*-butyl

$Sn(CH_2{\cdot}CH_2{\cdot}CH_2{\cdot}CH_3)_4$

$C_{16}H_{36}Sn$ MW, 347

Colourless stable liq. B.p. 145°/10 mm. D_4^{20} 1·0572. n_D^{20} 1·4730. Heat of comb. 2773 Cal.

Jones, Evans, Gulwell, Griffiths, *J. Chem. Soc.*, 1935, 41.

Tin tetracyclohexyl

$Sn\left[-CH{<}\begin{matrix}CH_2-CH_2\\CH_2-CH_2\end{matrix}{>}CH_2\right]_4$

$C_{24}H_{44}Sn$ MW, 451

Plates from C_6H_6. M.p. 263–4°. Very sol. hot C_6H_6. Spar. sol. hot EtOH, warm Et_2O. Insol. H_2O.

Krause, Pohland, *Ber.*, 1924, **57**, 535.

Tin tetraethyl

$Sn(C_2H_5)_4$

$C_8H_{20}Sn$ MW, 235

Colourless stable liq. F.p. − 112°. B.p. 175°, 73°/10 mm. $D_4^{19\cdot7}$ 1·1988. $n_D^{19\cdot7}$ 1·4724. Sol. Et_2O. Insol. H_2O. Heat of comb. 1521 Cal.

Emmert, Eller, *Ber.*, 1911, **44**, 2331.
Pfeiffer, Schnurmann, *Ber.*, 1904, **37**, 320.

Tin tetraisoamyl

$Sn(CH_2{\cdot}CH_2{\cdot}CH(CH_3)_2)_4$

$C_{20}H_{44}Sn$ MW, 403

Liq. B.p. 188°/24 mm. $D_4^{19\cdot6}$ 1·0353. n_D^{16} 1·4724.

Krause, *Ber.*, 1918, **51**, 1456.

Tin tetraisobutyl

$Sn(CH_2 \cdot CH(CH_3)_2)_4$

$C_{16}H_{36}Sn$ MW, 347

Needles. M.p. — 13°. B.p. 143°/16·5 mm. D_4^{23} 1·0540. n_D^{23} 1·4742.

Grüttner, Krause, *Ber.*, 1917, **50**, 1806.

Tin tetramethyl

$Sn(CH_3)_4$

$C_4H_{12}Sn$ MW, 179

Liq. with ethereal odour. B.p. 78°. $D_4^{25\cdot5}$ 1·29136. n_D 1·52009. Insol. H_2O. Reduces alc. $AgNO_3$.

Kraus, Callis, U.S.P., 1,639,947, (*Chem. Abstracts*, 1927, **21**, 3180).
Cahours, *Ann.*, 1860, **114**, 372.

Tin tetraphenyl

$Sn(C_6H_5)_4$

$C_{24}H_{20}Sn$ MW, 427

Prisms from $CHCl_3$ or dipropylamine, needles from Py. M.p. 225·7°. Very sol. at the boil in $CHCl_3$, AcOH, CS_2, Py, C_6H_6. Spar. sol. EtOH, Et_2O. Insol. pet. ether.

Chambers, Scherer, *J. Am. Chem. Soc.*, 1926, **48**, 1054.
Emmert, Eller, *Ber.*, 1911, **44**, 2331.
Pope, Peachey, *Chem. News*, 1904, **89**, 20.

Tin tetrapropyl

$Sn(CH_2 \cdot CH_2 \cdot CH_3)_4$

$C_{12}H_{28}Sn$ MW, 291

Colourless stable liq. B.p. 228°, 112°/10 mm. Heat of comb. 2163 Cal.

Pfeiffer, *Z. anorg. Chem.*, 1910, **68**, 121.

Tin tetra-*o*-tolyl

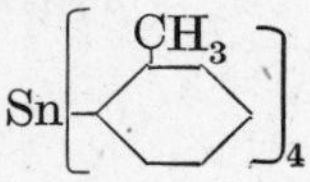

$C_{28}H_{28}Sn$ MW, 483

Cryst. from C_6H_6. M.p. 214–15°. Very sol. C_6H_6. Sol. Et_2O. Insol. EtOH.

Krause, Becker, *Ber.*, 1920, **53**, 185.
Krause, Schmitz, *Ber.*, 1919, **52**, 2158.

Tin tetra-*p*-tolyl

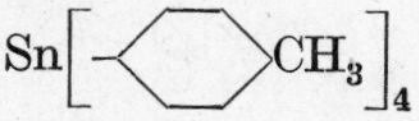

$C_{28}H_{28}Sn$ MW, 483

Needles from Py. M.p. 230°. Very sol. hot AcOEt, $CHCl_3$, CS_2, C_6H_6, hot Py. Spar. sol. Et_2O, EtOH, hot AcOH.

Pfeiffer, *Z. anorg. Chem.*, 1910, **68**, 122.

T.N.T.

See 2 : 4 : 6-Trinitrotoluene.

Tobias Acid.

See 2-Naphthylamine-1-sulphonic Acid.

α-Tocopherol (*Anti-sterility vitamin, vitamin E*)

$C_{29}H_{50}O_2$ (?) MW, 430 (?)

α-Tocopherol is a constituent of wheat-germ oil. Concentrates with high activity can be obtained from hempseed oil, cotton-seed oil, crude olive oil, green leafy vegetables, many seeds and muscle tissues. Viscous oil. Sol. most solvents. Shows absorption maxima at 292 mμ and 298 mμ. Thermostable. Resistant to light, acids, alkalis and mild oxidation.

Allophanate: cryst. from MeOH. M.p. 158–60°.

p-*Nitrophenylurethane*: cryst. from MeOH. M.p. 129–31°.

Evans, Emerson, Emerson, *J. Biol. Chem.*, 1936, **113**, 319.

***p*-Tolamidine** (p-*Tolenylamidine*)

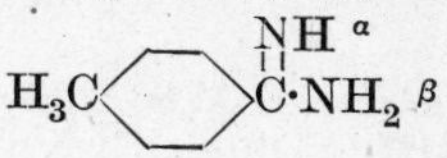

$C_8H_{10}N_2$ MW, 134

Plates from C_6H_6. M.p. 101–2°.

B,HCl: prisms + $\frac{1}{2}H_2O$ from H_2O. M.p. 213°.

B_2,H_2SO_4: prisms + $2H_2O$. Does not melt below 240°.

B,H_2SO_4: plates from EtOH–Et_2O. M.p. 240–1°.

B,HNO_2: needles. M.p. 133°.

B,HNO_3: prisms from EtOH, m.p. 154°; cryst. + H_2O from H_2O, m.p. 95°.

B_2,H_2PtCl_6: yellow needles. M.p. 225°.

α : β-N-*Di-Me*: $C_{10}H_{14}N_2$. MW, 162. *B,HCl*: needles from H_2O. M.p. 200°. *B_2,H_2PtCl_6*: cryst. + $2H_2O$. M.p. 95°.

β-N-*Et*: $C_{10}H_{14}N_2$. MW, 162. *B,HCl*: needles. M.p. 212°. *B_2,H_2PtCl_6*: needles + $4H_2O$. M.p. 65°.

β-N-*Phenyl*: $C_{14}H_{14}N_2$. MW, 210. Cryst. from C_6H_6. M.p. 149°. Very sol. EtOH. Spar. sol. C_6H_6, hot ligroin.

β-N-*Acetyl*: plates from EtOH–AcOEt. M.p. 108°.

β-N-p-*Toluyl*: needles from EtOH. M.p. 145°.

Bernton, *Chem. Zentr.*, 1919, III, 329.
Glock, *Ber.*, 1888, **21**, 2653.

Tolamine.

See Chloramine-T.

Tolane (sym.-*Diphenylacetylene*)

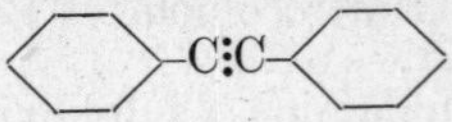

$C_{14}H_{10}$ MW, 178

Plates or columns from EtOH. M.p. 62·5°. Dist. without decomp. Very sol. Et_2O, hot EtOH. Spar. sol. cold EtOH. Heat of comb. C_p 1738·2 Cal., C_v 1736·7 Cal. Latent heat of fusion 28·7 cal./gm. Ox. ⟶ benzoic acid. Conc. H_2SO_4 at 60° ⟶ deoxybenzoin. Red. ⟶ isostilbene + stilbene + dibenzyl.

$C_{14}H_{10}$,$C_6H_3(NO_2)_3$-1 : 3 : 5 : yellow plates. M.p. 96°.

Picrate : yellow plates. M.p. 111°.

Weissberger, *J. Chem. Soc.*, 1935, 855.
Fittig, *Ann.*, 1873, **168**, 74.

Tolane dibromide (α : β-*Dibromostilbene*, 1 : 2-*dibromo*-1 : 2-*diphenylethylene*)

$C_6H_5·CBr⁚CBr·C_6H_5$

$C_{14}H_{10}Br_2$ MW, 338

Exists in two forms, probably stereoisomeric.

α-.

Plates or needles. M.p. 205–6°. Spar. sol. Et_2O, hot EtOH. Difficultly volatile in steam. Heat with H_2O at 170–80° ⟶ β-form. Hot alc. KOH ⟶ tolane.

β-.

Needles. M.p. 64°. Very sol. Et_2O, EtOH. Difficultly volatile in steam. Heat with H_2O at 170–80° ⟶ α-form. Hot alc. KOH ⟶ tolane.

Staudinger, *Ber.*, 1916, **49**, 1972.
Limpricht, Schwanert, *Ber.*, 1871, **4**, 379.

Tolane dichloride (α : β-*Dichlorostilbene*, 1 : 2-*dichloro*-1 : 2-*diphenylethylene*)

$C_6H_5·CCl⁚CCl·C_6H_5$

$C_{14}H_{10}Cl_2$ MW, 249

Exists in two forms, probably stereoisomeric.

α-.

Plates from EtOH. M.p. 140–2° (153°). B.p. 183°/18 mm. Sol. 130 parts EtOH at 24°. Very sol. Et_2O. Heat. ⟶ β-form. HI(+ P) ⟶ dibenzyl. NaHg or alc. KOH ⟶ tolane.

β-.

Needles. M.p. 63°. B.p. 178°/18 mm. Sol. 10 parts EtOH at 24°. Very sol. Et_2O. Heat. ⟶ α-form.

Staudinger, *Ber.*, 1916, **49**, 1971.
Loeb, *Ber.*, 1903, **36**, 3060.
See also last reference above.

Tolidine.
See Diaminodimethyldiphenyl.

***m*-Tolil** (*Di*-m-*tolyl diketone*, 3 : 3′-*dimethylbenzil*)

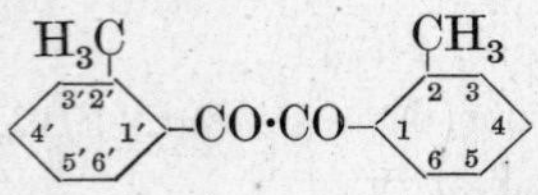

$C_{16}H_{14}O_2$ MW, 238

Yellowish-white needles from EtOH. M.p. 103°.

Ekecrantz, Ahlquist, *Chem. Zentr.*, 1908, II, 1689.

***p*-Tolil** (*Di*-p-*tolyl diketone*, 4 : 4′-*dimethylbenzil*).

Yellow plates from EtOH. M.p. 104–5°. Sol. Et_2O, AcOH, C_6H_6. Alc. sol. + KOH ⟶ violet col.

Dioxime : *syn*- : α-*p*-tolildioxime. Plates or needles. M.p. 217°. Spar. sol. EtOH, Et_2O, AcOH. *Diacetyl* : prisms. M.p. 133–4°. *Anti*- : β-*p*-tolildioxime. Needles. M.p. 225°. Very sol. EtOH. *Diacetyl* : m.p. 144°. *Amphi*- : γ-*p*-tolildioxime. Needles + $1CHCl_3$ from $CHCl_3$. Sinters about 200°. M.p. 229–32°. Long heat. at 200° ⟶ β-dioxime.

Monohydrazone : needles from EtOH. M.p. 139–40°.

Dihydrazone : needles from EtOH. M.p. 137°.

Vorländer, *Ber.*, 1911, **44**, 2461.
Tschugajew, Spiro, *Ber.*, 1908, **41**, 2221.

***p*-Tolilic Acid** (4 : 4′-*Dimethylbenzilic acid*, *di*-p-*tolylglycollic acid*, α-*hydroxy-di*-p-*tolylacetic acid*)

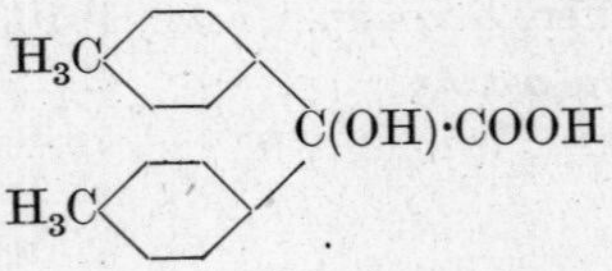

$C_{16}H_{16}O_3$ MW, 256

Colourless needles from H_2O. M.p. 135°. Sol. most org. solvents. Spar. sol. ligroin. Insol. cold H_2O. H_2SO_4 ⟶ purple col.

Me ester : $C_{17}H_{18}O_3$. MW, 270. Needles from EtOH. M.p. 82°. Very sol. EtOH, Et_2O, $CHCl_3$.

Anhydride : $C_{32}H_{30}O_5$. MW, 494. Prisms from EtOH. M.p. 164°.

Acetyl : cryst. from pet. ether. M.p. 92°.

Gattermann, *Ann.*, 1906, **347**, 364.
Gisiger, *Ber.*, 1906, **39**, 3589.

Toliminazole.
See Methylbenziminazole.

o-Toluamide

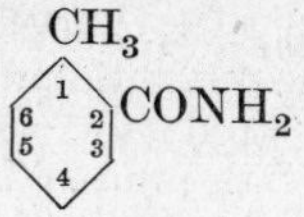

C_8H_9ON MW, 135

Plates from H_2O, needles from EtOH. M.p. 147° (138°). Sol. hot H_2O, EtOH. Spar. sol: Et_2O, C_6H_6. NaHg in slightly acid sol. ⟶ *o*-tolylcarbinol. NaHg in slightly alk. sol. ⟶ dihydro-*o*-toluamide. EtOH + H_2SO_4 ⟶ ethyl *o*-toluate.

N-*Me*: $C_9H_{11}ON$. MW, 149. Needles from H_2O. M.p. 75°.

N-*Di-Me*: $C_{10}H_{13}ON$. MW, 163. Liq. B.p. 147°/18 mm. D^{25} 1·033.

N-*Benzoyl*: needles from EtOH.Aq. M.p. 158–9°.

Noller, *Organic Syntheses*, 1933, XIII, 94.

m-Toluamide.

Needles from Et_2O. M.p. 97° (93°). Spar. sol. Et_2O, C_6H_6.

N-*Me*: m.p. 44·5–45°. Sol. H_2O, EtOH, Et_2O.

N-*Di-Me*: b.p. 148°/12 mm. D^{15} 1·043.

Remsen, Reid, *Am. Chem. J.*, 1899, **21**, 289.

p-Toluamide.

Needles or plates from H_2O, needles from C_6H_6. M.p. 155° (165°). Very sol. hot H_2O, EtOH, Et_2O. Spar. sol. cold H_2O, $CHCl_3$, C_6H_6.

N-*Me*: plates from H_2O. M.p. 145–145·5°.

N-*Di-Me*: cryst. from EtOH. M.p. 41°. B.p. 156°/10 mm. Sol. H_2O, EtOH.

N-*Et*: $C_{10}H_{13}ON$. MW, 163. Needles from H_2O. M.p. 90°.

N-*Acetyl*: prisms from EtOH.Aq. M.p. 147°.

N-*Benzoyl*: needles from EtOH.Aq. M.p. 119°.

McMaster, Langreck, *J. Am. Chem. Soc.*, 1917, **39**, 106.

Tolubenzyl cyanide.

See under Tolylacetic Acid.

Toluene (*Methylbenzene*)

$C_6H_5 \cdot CH_3$

C_7H_8 MW, 92

Constituent of many mineral oils. Important constituent of coal tar oil. Liq. F.p. — 95·0°. B.p. 110·6°, 102·6°/600 mm., 79·7°/288 mm., 14·5°/14·56 mm. Vap. press. at 0° 6·5 mm., at 20° 22 mm., at 50° 93·5 mm., at 60° 141·5 mm., at 70° 203 mm., at 80° 292·5 mm., at 100° 558 mm. Very slightly sol. H_2O. D_4^0 0·8845, D_4^{20} 0·866. n_D^{20} 1·49613. Heat of comb. C_p 937·4 Cal., C_v 938·5 Cal., C_p (vapour) 955·68 Cal. Crit. temp. 320·8°. Crit. press. 41·6 atm. Specific heat 0·404 cal./gm. at 25°. Latent heat of fusion 0·0016 Cal. Latent heat of vap. 0·00094 Cal. at 110·2°. Forms constant b.p. mixture with acetic acid, b.p. 104–104·2°.

Picrate: pale yellow cryst. M.p. 88·2°.

Perkin, *J. Chem. Soc.*, 1896, **69**, 1191.

Tolueneazoanisole.

See under Hydroxymethylazobenzene.

Tolueneazobenzoic Acid.

See Methylazobenzene-carboxylic Acid.

Tolueneazocresol.

See Hydroxydimethylazobenzene.

5-p-Tolueneazo-ψ-cumene.

See 2 : 4 : 5 : 4′-Tetramethylazobenzene.

2-o-Tolueneazo-1-naphthol (1 : 2-*Naphthoquinone*-2-o-*tolylhydrazone*)

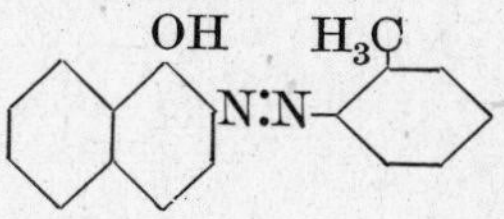

$C_{17}H_{14}ON_2$ MW, 262

Red leaflets. M.p. 156°. Sol. most org. solvents.

Me ether: $C_{18}H_{16}ON_2$. MW, 276. Orange-yellow needles from EtOH. M.p. 84–5°. Sol. Et_2O, C_6H_6, $CHCl_3$. Less sol. ligroin. Conc. H_2SO_4 ⟶ red sol.

Et ether: $C_{19}H_{18}ON_2$. MW, 290. Yellow needles from EtOH. M.p. 51°. Sol. EtOH, Et_2O, C_6H_6, $CHCl_3$. Less sol. pet. ether. Conc. H_2SO_4 ⟶ ruby-red sol.

Zincke, Rathgen, *Ber.*, 1886, **19**, 2492.
Charrier, Ferreri, *Gazz. chim. ital.*, 1914, **44**, ii, 234.

2-m-Tolueneazo-1-naphthol (1:2-*Naphthoquinone*-2-m-*tolylhydrazone*).

Red needles from EtOH. M.p. 117–18°. Very sol. C_6H_6, $CHCl_3$. Sol. Et_2O. Spar. sol. pet. ether. Insol. cold EtOH. Conc. H_2SO_4 ⟶ red sol.

Me ether: yellow leaflets from EtOH. M.p. 49–50°. Sol. most org. solvents. Conc. H_2SO_4 ⟶ red sol.

Et ether: orange-red prisms from EtOH. M.p. 22°. Very sol. Et_2O, C_6H_6, $CHCl_3$. Sol. EtOH. Conc. H_2SO_4 ⟶ ruby-red sol.

Charrier, Ferreri, *Gazz. chim. ital.*, 1914, **44**, ii, 235.

2-*p*-Tolueneazo-1-naphthol (1 : 2-*Naphthoquinone*-2-p-*tolylhydrazone*).

Red needles from EtOH. M.p. 145°. Sol. EtOH, C_6H_6, AcOH. Spar. sol. pet. ether. Insol. alkalis. Conc. H_2SO_4 ⟶ red sol.

Me ether: orange-red needles from EtOH. M.p. 77–8°. Sol. Et_2O, boiling EtOH, C_6H_6, $CHCl_3$. Spar. sol. pet. ether. Conc. H_2SO_4 ⟶ ruby-red sol.

Et ether: orange-yellow needles from EtOH. M.p. 51°. Sol. most org. solvents. Conc. H_2SO_4 ⟶ ruby-red sol.

See previous reference and also
Charrier, Casale, *Gazz. chim. ital.*, 1914, **44**, i, 611.

4-*o*-Tolueneazo-1-naphthol (1 : 4-*Naphthoquinone*-o-*tolylhydrazone*)

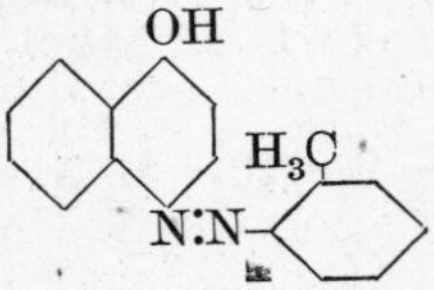

$C_{17}H_{14}ON_2$ MW, 262

Red needles from 66% EtOH. M.p. 144–6°. Sol. EtOH, C_6H_6, AcOH. Less sol. pet. ether.

Me ether: $C_{18}H_{16}ON_2$. MW, 276. Reddish-brown needles. M.p. 93°. Sol. usual org. solvents.

Et ether: $C_{19}H_{18}ON_2$. MW, 290. Red plates from EtOH. M.p. 94°.

Zincke, Rathgen, *Ber.*, 1886, **19**, 2488.

4-*p*-Tolueneazo-1-naphthol (1 : 4-*Naphthoquinone*-p-*tolylhydrazone*).

Dark red cryst. from $PhNO_2$. M.p. 209–10°. Sol. Me_2CO, $PhNO_2$, aniline. Spar. sol. EtOH, C_6H_6, AcOH.

Me ether: cryst. M.p. 103–4°.

Et ether: red needles from EtOH. M.p. 126–7°.

Acetyl: yellowish needles from pet. ether. M.p. 101–2°.

See previous reference and also
Witt, Schmidt, *Ber.*, 1892, **25**, 1019.

1-*o*-Tolueneazo-2-naphthol (1 : 2-*Naphthoquinone*-1-o-*tolylhydrazone*)

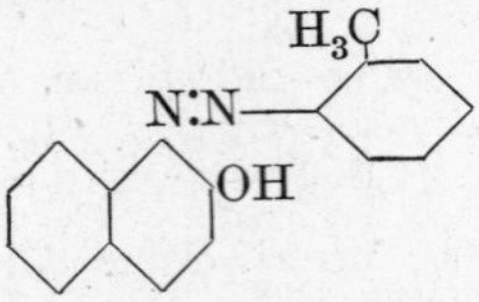

$C_{17}H_{14}ON_2$ MW, 262

Red needles from AcOH. M.p. 131° (130°).

Me ether: $C_{18}H_{16}ON_2$. MW, 276. Red plates from EtOH. M.p. 58°. Sol. most org. solvents. Conc. H_2SO_4 ⟶ red sol. *B,2HNO₃*: green needles. M.p. 71° decomp. Sol. EtOH, Et_2O. Mod. sol. $CHCl_3$. Spar. sol. C_6H_6, ligroin.

Et ether: $C_{19}H_{18}ON_2$. MW, 290. Red needles from EtOH. M.p. 36°. Sol. most org. solvents. *$B,2HNO_3$*: green leaflets. M.p. 62–3°. Mod. sol. EtOH, $CHCl_3$. Spar. sol. C_6H_6, ligroin.

Norman, *J. Chem. Soc.*, 1912, **101**, 1920.
Charrier, Ferreri, *Gazz. chim. ital.*, 1912, **42**, ii, 124; 1913, **43**, i, 549.

1-*m*-Tolueneazo-2-naphthol (1 : 2-*Naphthoquinone*-1-m-*tolylhydrazone*).

Red needles from C_6H_6. M.p. 141° (137°). Sol. most org. solvents. Conc. H_2SO_4 ⟶ violet sol.

Me ether: red plates from EtOH. M.p. 81°. Sol. EtOH, Et_2O, C_6H_6, $CHCl_3$. Spar. sol. pet. ether. Conc. acids ⟶ red sols. *$B,2HNO_3$*: green leaflets. M.p. 72°. Sol. EtOH, $CHCl_3$. Less sol. Et_2O, C_6H_6. Spar. sol. pet. ether.

Et ether: red leaflets from ligroin. M.p. 84°. Sol. most org. solvents. *$B,2HNO_3$*: green leaflets. M.p. 84° decomp. Sol. EtOH, $CHCl_3$. Insol. C_6H_6.

See previous references.

1-*p*-Tolueneazo-2-naphthol (1 : 2-*Naphthoquinone*-1-p-*tolylhydrazone*).

Red needles or plates from AcOH. M.p. 134–5°. Sol. EtOH, Me_2CO, C_6H_6, AcOH.

Me ether: red plates from EtOH. M.p. 68°. Sol. most org. solvents. Conc. H_2SO_4 ⟶ ruby-red sol. *$B,2HNO_3$*: red needles. M.p. 77° decomp. Sol. warm $CHCl_3$. Spar. sol. Et_2O. Insol. C_6H_6.

Et ether: red needles from EtOH. M.p. 51°. Very sol. Et_2O, C_6H_6, $CHCl_3$. Less sol. EtOH, pet. ether. *$B,2HNO_3$*: red leaflets. M.p. 94° decomp. Mod. sol. EtOH, $CHCl_3$. Less sol. Et_2O, C_6H_6. Insol. ligroin.

See previous references.

Tolueneazophenetole.
See under Hydroxy-methylazobenzene.

Tolueneazophenol.
See Hydroxy-methylazobenzene.

Tolueneazotoluidine.
See Aminodimethylazobenzene.

Tolueneazoxylenol.
See 2-Hydroxy-3 : 5 : 4′-trimethylazobenzene

Toluene-dicarboxylic Acid.
See Methylphthalic Acid, Methylisophthalic Acid, *and* Methylterephthalic Acid.

Toluene-2 : 4-disulphonic Acid

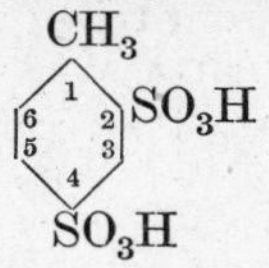

$C_7H_8O_6S_2$ MW, 252

Thick oil. Ox. of K salt ⟶ 2 : 4-disulphobenzoic acid. Fuse K salt with H·COONa ⟶ 4-methylisophthalic acid.

Difluoride: $C_7H_6O_4F_2S_2$. MW, 256. Plates from petrol. M.p. 87–8°. Sol. Me_2CO, AcOEt, $PhNO_2$. Mod. sol. EtOH, Et_2O, CS_2. Spar. sol. pet. ether.

Dichloride: $C_7H_6O_4Cl_2S_2$. MW, 289. Prisms from Et_2O. M.p. 56°. Very sol. Et_2O, C_6H_6.

Dibromide: $C_7H_6O_4Br_2S_2$. MW, 378. Cryst. from Et_2O. M.p. 78°.

Diamide: $C_7H_{10}O_4N_2S_2$. MW, 250. Prisms from EtOH or H_2O. M.p. 190–1°. Sol. warm H_2O. Very sol. EtOH, NH_4OH.

Dianilide: prisms from EtOH.Aq., needles from C_6H_6, plates from Me_2CO. M.p. 189°.

Di-o-toluidide: cryst. M.p. 170–1°.

Di-m-toluidide: cryst. M.p. 138°.

Steinkopf, *J. prakt. Chem.*, 1927, **117**, 38.
Wynne, Bruce, *J. Chem. Soc.*, 1898, **73**, 757.
Gnehm, Forrer, *Ber.*, 1877, **10**, 542.

Toluene-2 : 5-disulphonic Acid.

Dichloride: prisms or plates from C_6H_6 or C_6H_6–pet. ether. M.p. 98°. Very sol. AcOEt, $CHCl_3$, CS_2, C_6H_6. Spar. sol. pet. ether.

Diamide: prisms. M.p. 224°. Spar. sol. H_2O.

Dianilide: needles from C_6H_6 or EtOH.Aq. M.p. 178°.

See second reference above.

Toluene-2 : 6-disulphonic Acid.

Dichloride: prisms from pet. ether or C_6H_6. M.p. 88°. Very sol. Et_2O, $CHCl_3$, C_6H_6. Spar. sol. pet. ether.

Diamide: needles. Does not melt below 260°. Mod. sol. EtOH. Spar. sol. H_2O.

Dianilide: prisms from EtOH.Aq. or C_6H_6. M.p. 162°.

Wynne, Bruce, *J. Chem. Soc.*, 1898, **73**, 771.

Toluene-3 : 4-disulphonic Acid.

Forms cryst. spar. sol. Ba salt.

Dichloride: scales from C_6H_6–pet. ether, m.p. 111°; cryst. + $\frac{1}{2}C_6H_6$ from C_6H_6, m.p. 70–80°.

Diamide: m.p. 235–9° (slight decomp.). Very sol. H_2O, EtOH.

Dianilide: plates from Me_2CO, prisms from EtOH. M.p. 190°.

Wynne, Bruce, *J. Chem. Soc.*, 1898, **73**, 751.
Klason, *Ber.*, 1887, **20**, 356.

Toluene-3 : 5-disulphonic Acid.

Needles. Very sol. H_2O, EtOH.

Dichloride: prisms from Et_2O. M.p. 95°. Very sol. Et_2O. Spar. sol. pet. ether.

Diamide: prisms from H_2O. M.p. 216°. Sol. hot H_2O, EtOH. Spar. sol. cold H_2O.

Dianilide: scales from C_6H_6 or EtOH.Aq. M.p. 153°.

Wynne, Bruce, *J. Chem. Soc.*, 1898, **73**, 734, 738.
Richter, *Ann.*, 1885, **230**, 326.

Toluene-*o*-sulphinic Acid

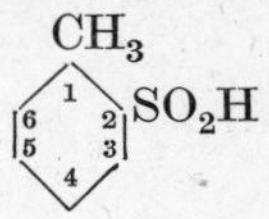

$C_7H_8O_2S$ MW, 156

Needles. M.p. 80°. Very sol. most org. solvents. Easily decomp. Salts very sol. H_2O.

Höchst, D.R.P., 224,019, (*Chem. Zentr.*, 1910, II, 513).
Gattermann, *Ber.*, 1899, **32**, 1140.

Toluene-*m*-sulphinic Acid.

Unstable oil with strong bleaching properties.

Troeger, Hille, *J. prakt. Chem.*, 1905, **71**, 207.

Toluene-*p*-sulphinic Acid.

d-.

Et ester: $C_9H_{12}O_2S$. MW, 184. B.p. 60–1°/high vacuum. n_D^{25} 1·5309. $[\alpha]_{5461}^{25}$ + 0·92°.

l-.

Et ester: b.p. 63°/high vacuum. n_D^{25} 1·5309. $[\alpha]_{5461}^{25}$ − 6·72°.

Butyl ester: b.p. 84°/less than 0·1 mm. D_4^{25} 1·066. n_D^{25} 1·5195.

Anilide: plates from EtOH.Aq. M.p. 134°. B.p. 75–6°/less than 0·1 mm. $[\alpha]_{5461}^{17}$ − 1·1° in $CHCl_3$.

dl-.

Dark plates or needles from H_2O. M.p. 85°. Very sol. EtOH, Et_2O. Spar. sol. cold H_2O, hot C_6H_6. Hygroscopic. Very readily oxidised to toluene-*p*-sulphonic acid. Zn + H_2SO_4 ⟶ *p*-thiocresol. Alc. MeI ⟶ methyl *p*-tolyl sulphone. Forms spar. sol. Ag salt.

NH_4 salt: needles from EtOH. M.p. 175° decomp.

Et ester: b.p. 99–104°/0·1 mm. n_D^{25} 1·5309. D_4^{25} 1·114.

Butyl ester: b.p. 90–95°/0·1 mm. D_4^{25} 1·066. n_D^{25} 1·5195.

Anhydride: $C_{14}H_{14}O_3S_2$. MW, 294. M.p. 75°. Decomp. on standing.

Chloride: C_7H_7OClS. MW, 174·5. Needles. M.p. 54–8°.

Amide: C_7H_9ONS. MW, 155. Needles. M.p. 120°.

Anilide: m.p. 138°.

Whitmore, Hamilton, *Organic Syntheses*, Collective Vol. I, 479.

Phillips, *J. Chem. Soc.*, 1925, 2552.

v. Braun, Kaiser, *Ber.*, 1923, **56**, 549.

Toluene-*o*-sulphonamide

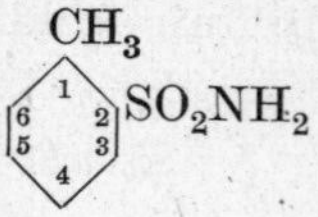

$C_7H_9O_2NS$ MW, 171

Octahedra from EtOH, prisms from H_2O. M.p. 156·3°. Sol. 958 parts H_2O at 9°, 28 parts EtOH at 5°. Electrolytic oxidation of alk. metal salts ⟶ saccharin.

N-*Me*: $C_8H_{11}O_2NS$. MW, 185. Plates from C_6H_6–ligroin. M.p. 74–5°. Very sol. EtOH, Me_2CO, $CHCl_3$. Spar. sol. ligroin, hot H_2O. Insol. cold C_6H_6.

N-*Chloro deriv.*: $C_7H_8O_2NClS$. MW, 205·5. *Na salt*: prisms + $2H_2O$. Explodes (anhyd.) at 170–5°. *K salt*: prisms + H_2O. Explodes (anhyd.) about 145°.

N-*Dichloro deriv.*: $C_7H_7O_2NCl_2S$. MW, 240. Plates from $CHCl_3$–pet. ether. M.p. 33°.

N-*Bromo deriv.*: $C_7H_8O_2NBrS$. MW, 250. *Na salt*: yellow plates + $1H_2O$. Explodes (anhyd.) about 135–40°. *K salt*: yellow plates. Decomp. (anhyd.) at 130–5°.

N-*Dibromo deriv.*: $C_7H_7O_2NBr_2S$. MW, 329. Orange plates from $CHCl_3$–pet. ether. M.p. 80°. Very sol. $CHCl_3$. Spar. sol. pet. ether.

N-*Benzoyl*: *N-o*-toluenesulphonylbenzamide. Plates or prisms from Et_2O. M.p. 110–12°.

Ullmann, *Encyclopedia of Tech. Chem.*, (Edition 2. Berlin–Vienna 1928), II, 251.

Chattaway, *J. Chem. Soc.*, 1905, **87**, 152.

Toluene-*m*-sulphonamide.

Plates or cryst. aggregates from H_2O, prisms from EtOH. M.p. 108°. Sol. 130 parts H_2O at 25°. Sol. EtOH.

Griffin, *Am. Chem. J.*, 1897, **19**, 174.

Toluene-*p*-sulphonamide.

Plates + $2H_2O$ from H_2O. M.p. 105°, anhyd. 137·5°. Sol. 515 parts H_2O at 9°, 13·5 parts EtOH at 5°.

N-*Me*: $C_8H_{11}O_2NS$. MW, 185. Plates from EtOH.Aq. M.p. 78–9°.

N-*Di-Me*: $C_9H_{13}O_2NS$. MW, 199. Needles from petrol. M.p. 86–7°. Sol. AcOEt, C_6H_6. Mod. sol. Et_2O, EtOH. Spar. sol. H_2O.

N-*Et*: $C_9H_{13}O_2NS$. MW, 199. Cryst. from ligroin, plates from EtOH.Aq. M.p. 64°.

N-*Di-Et*: $C_{11}H_{17}O_2NS$. MW, 227. Cryst. from ligroin. M.p. 60°. Spar. sol. H_2O, ligroin.

N-*Propyl*: $C_{10}H_{15}O_2NS$. MW, 213. Cryst. from ligroin. M.p. 52°.

N-*Butyl*: $C_{11}H_{17}O_2NS$. MW, 227. M.p. 43°.

N-*Hexyl*: $C_{13}H_{21}O_2NS$. MW, 255. M.p. 62°.

N-*Heptyl*: $C_{14}H_{23}O_2NS$. MW, 269. M.p. 27°.

N-*Benzyl*: $C_{14}H_{15}O_2NS$. MW, 261. Prisms from EtOH. M.p. 115–16°.

N-*Dibenzyl*: $C_{21}H_{21}O_2NS$. MW, 351. Needles from MeOH. M.p. 80·8°

N-*Chloro*: *Na salt*: *see* Chloramine-T. *K salt*: plates + H_2O. Explodes (anhyd.) about 160–5°.

N-*Dichloro*: *see* Dichloramine-T.

N-*Bromo*: $C_7H_8O_2NBrS$. MW, 250. *Na salt*: yellow prisms + $3H_2O$. Decomp. (anhyd.) at 145–50°. *K salt*: yellow plates + $2H_2O$. Decomp. (anhyd.) at 145–50°.

N-*Dibromo*: $C_7H_7O_2NBr_2S$. MW, 329. Orange plates from $CHCl_3$. M.p. 104°.

N-*Acetyl*: needles. M.p. 139°.

N-*Benzoyl*: prisms or needles from EtOH. M.p. 147–50°.

Steinkopf, *J. prakt. Chem.*, 1927, **117**, 25.

Chattaway, *J. Chem. Soc.*, 1905, **87**, 152.

Wolkow, *Z. Chem.*, 1870, **323**, 578.

Toluene-α-sulphonamide (*Benzylsulphonamide*)

$C_6H_5{\cdot}CH_2{\cdot}SO_2NH_2$

$C_7H_9O_2NS$ MW, 171

Prisms or needles from hot H_2O, needles from EtOH. M.p. 105°. Very sol. hot H_2O, EtOH.

N-*Me*: $C_8H_{11}O_2NS$. MW, 185. Needles. M.p. 109–10°. Sol. hot H_2O, EtOH, Et_2O.

N-*Di-Me*: $C_9H_{13}O_2NS$. MW, 199. Plates from $CHCl_3$–ligroin. M.p. 101°.

N-*Et*: $C_9H_{13}O_2NS$. MW, 199. Leaflets from Et_2O–ligroin. M.p. 65–6°.

N-*Di-Et* : $C_{11}H_{17}O_2NS$. MW, 227. Leaflets from Et_2O–ligroin. M.p. 29°.

Ingold, Ingold, Shaw, *J. Chem. Soc.*, 1927, 818.
Curtius, Haas, *J. prakt. Chem.*, 1921, **102**, 102, 104, 106.
Johnson, Ambler, *J. Am. Chem. Soc.*, 1914, **36**, 381.

Toluenesulphonbromide.
See under Toluenesulphonic Acid.
Toluenesulphonchloride.
See under Toluenesulphonic Acid.
Toluenesulphonfluoride.
See under Toluenesulphonic Acid.
Toluene-*o*-sulphonic Acid

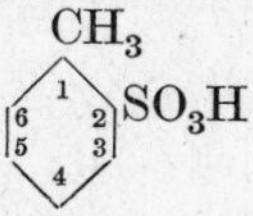

$C_7H_8O_3S$ MW, 172

Hygroscopic plates + $2H_2O$. Heat. at 140–50° ⟶ toluene-*p*-sulphonic acid. Ox. ⟶ *p*-sullphobenzoic acid. KOH fusion ⟶ *o*-cresol + salicylic acid. Gives spar. sol. Ag, Pb salts.

-*Menthyl ester* : $C_{17}H_{26}O_3S$. MW, 310. Prisms. M.p. 78°.

Phenyl ester : $C_{13}H_{12}O_3S$. MW, 248. M.p. 52°.

o-*Nitrophenyl ester* : $C_{13}H_{11}O_5NS$. MW, 293. Plates from EtOH. M.p. 131–4°.

o-*Tolyl ester* : $C_{14}H_{14}O_3S$. MW, 262. Cryst. from EtOH. M.p. 50–1°.

m-*Tolyl ester* : cryst. from EtOH. M.p. 60°.

p-*Tolyl ester* : cryst. from EtOH. M.p. 70–1°.

Fluoride : toluene-*o*-sulphonfluoride. $C_7H_7O_2FS$. MW, 174. Oil. B.p. 223–5°, 146·2°/83 mm., 133·9°/56·5 mm. n_D^{20} 1·5007.

Chloride : toluene-*o*-sulphonchloride. $C_7H_7O_2ClS$. MW, 190·5. Cryst. from $CHCl_3$. M.p. 67·5°. B.p. 126°/10 mm.

Bromide : toluene-*o*-sulphonbromide. $C_7H_7O_2BrS$. MW, 235. Cryst. M.p. 13°. B.p. 137·5–138°/10 mm.

Amide : *see* Toluene-*o*-sulphonamide.

Anilide : plates from EtOH.Aq. M.p. 136°.

o-*Toluidide* : m.p. 134°.

Terlinck, *Chem. Abstracts*, 1927, **21**, 1978.
Steinkopf, *J. prakt. Chem.*, 1927, **117**, 38.
Holleman, Caland, *Ber.*, 1911, **44**, 2505.
Ullmann, Lehner, *Ber.*, 1905, **38**, 732.

Toluene-*m*-sulphonic Acid.

Free acid is an oil.

Chloride : toluene-*m*-sulphonchloride. F.p. 11·7°. Decomp. by boiling H_2O.

Amide : *see* Toluene-*m*-sulphonamide.

Anilide : prisms from EtOH. M.p. 96°.

o-*Toluidide* : prisms and plates. M.p. 108°.

m-*Toluidide* : m.p. 103°.

p-*Toluidide* : prisms. M.p. 106°.

Holleman, Caland, *Ber.*, 1911, **44**, 2504, 2515.
Griffin, *Am. Chem. J.*, 1897, **19**, 173, 189.

Toluene-*p*-sulphonic Acid.

Hygroscopic plates + $1H_2O$ from H_2O. M.p. 92° (104–5°). Ox. ⟶ *p*-sulphobenzoic acid. KOH fusion ⟶ *p*-cresol + *p*-hydroxybenzoic acid.

Me ester : $C_8H_{10}O_3S$. MW, 186. Cryst. from Et_2O–ligroin. M.p. 28°. Very sol. EtOH, Et_2O, C_6H_6. Insol. H_2O.

Et ester : $C_9H_{12}O_3S$. MW, 200. Cryst. from AcOEt. M.p. 33–4°. B.p. 173°/15 mm. D_4^{48} 1·166.

Propyl ester : $C_{10}H_{14}O_3S$. MW, 214. B.p. 154–6°/3 mm. D_4^{20} 1·144. n_D^{20} 1·4998.

Butyl ester : $C_{11}H_{16}O_3S$. MW, 228. B.p. 163–5°/3 mm. D_4^{20} 1·120. n_D^{20} 1·5050.

sec.-n-*Butyl ester* : decomp. on heating. D_4^{20} 1·140. n_D^{20} 1·5100.

Isobutyl ester : b.p. 163–5°/3 mm. D_4^{20} 1·125. n_D^{20} 1·5050.

n-*Amyl ester* : $C_{12}H_{18}O_3S$. MW, 242. B.p. 169–70°/3 mm. D_4^{20} 1·140. n_D^{20} 1·5100.

Phenyl ester : $C_{13}H_{12}O_3S$. MW, 248. Needles from EtOH. M.p. 95–6°. Very sol. EtOH, Et_2O, C_6H_6. Insol. H_2O.

Benzyl ester : $C_{14}H_{14}O_3S$. MW, 262. Cryst. M.p. 58°.

l-*Menthyl ester* : $C_{17}H_{26}O_3S$. MW, 310. Needles. M.p. 97°. $[\alpha]_D^{20}$ − 66·8° in $CHCl_3$. Spar. sol. cold EtOH.

1-*Naphthyl ester* : $C_{17}H_{14}O_3S$. MW, 298. Needles from EtOH. M.p. 83–4°.

2-*Naphthyl ester* : plates from EtOH or C_6H_6–ligroin. M.p. 125°.

Anhydride : $C_{14}H_{14}O_5S_2$. MW, 326. Cryst. from Et_2O. M.p. 122–5°.

Fluoride : toluene-*p*-sulphonfluoride. $C_7H_7O_2FS$. MW, 174. Needles from pet. ether. M.p. 43–4°. B.p. 112·5°/16 mm.

Chloride : toluene-*p*-sulphonchloride. $C_7H_7O_2ClS$. MW, 190·5. Cryst. from Et_2O or pet. ether. M.p. 71°. B.p. 145–6°/15 mm.

Bromide : toluene-*p*-sulphonbromide. $C_7H_7O_2BrS$. MW, 235. Columns. M.p. 96°.

Iodide : toluene-*p*-sulphoniodide. $C_7H_7O_2IS$. MW, 282. Yellow powder. M.p. 84–5° decomp.

Amide : *see* Toluene-*p*-sulphonamide.

Hydrazide : plates or needles from H_2O. M.p. 112°.

Phenylhydrazide: needles from EtOH. M.p. 155° decomp.
Azide: plates. M.p. 22°.
Anilide: needles from Et_2O–EtOH. M.p. 103°.
m-*Nitroanilide*: needles from EtOH.Aq. M.p. 139°.
p-*Nitroanilide*: yellow prisms from EtOH, needles from C_6H_6. M.p. 191°.
o-*Toluidide*: prisms from EtOH, needles from AcOH.Aq. M.p. 110°.
m-*Toluidide*: m.p. 114°.
p-*Toluidide*: needles from AcOH. M.p. 118–19°.
1-*Naphthylamide*: prisms from EtOH. M.p. 157°.
2-*Naphthylamide*: needles, plates or prisms from EtOH. M.p. 133°.
A,CH_3NH_2: hygroscopic cryst. M.p. 125°.
A,$(CH_3)_2NH$: prisms. M.p. 78°.
A,$(CH_3)_3N$: rosettes. M.p. 92°.
A,$C_2H_5NH_2$: m.p. 111°.
A,$(C_2H_5)_2NH$: clusters of cryst. M.p. 88°.
A,$(C_2H_5)_3N$: m.p. 65°.

Curtius, Kraemer, *J. prakt. Chem.*, 1930, **125**, 323.
Steinkopf, *J. prakt. Chem.*, 1927, **117**, 22.
Gilman, Beaber, *J. Am. Chem. Soc.*, 1925, **47**, 522.
Holleman, Caland, *Ber.*, 1911, **44**, 2505.

Toluene-α-sulphonic Acid (*Benzylsulphonic acid*)

$C_6H_5 \cdot CH_2 \cdot SO_3H$

$C_7H_8O_3S$ MW, 172

Hygroscopic cryst. Forms spar. sol. Ba salt.
Fluoride: $C_7H_7O_2FS$. MW, 174. Needles from petrol. M.p. 90–1°.
Chloride: $C_7H_7O_2ClS$. MW, 190·5. Prisms from Et_2O, needles from C_6H_6. M.p. 93°. Very sol. Et_2O, warm C_6H_6.
Amide: *see* Toluene-α-sulphonamide.
Hydrazide: plates from EtOH. M.p. 131–2° decomp.
Phenylhydrazide: m.p. 173° decomp.
Azide: needles from EtOH. M.p. 54°.
Anilide: needles from EtOH. M.p. 102°.
p-*Nitroanilide*: cryst. from EtOH.Aq. M.p. 155°.
o-*Toluidide*: m.p. 83°.
m-*Toluidide*: m.p. 75°.
p-*Toluidide*: prisms from EtOH. M.p. 113°.
1-*Naphthylamide*: yellow needles from EtOH. M.p. 166°.
2-*Naphthylamide*: needles. M.p. 148·5°.

Medwedew, Alexejewa, *Ber.*, 1932, **65**, 131.
Clutterbuck, Cohen, *J. Chem. Soc.*, 1923, **123**, 2507.
Johnson, Ambler, *J. Am. Chem. Soc.*, 1914, **36**, 381.
Fromm, Palma, *Ber.*, 1906, **39**, 3312.

Toluenesulphoniodide.
See under Toluene-*p*-sulphonic Acid.
Toluene-tricarboxylic Acid.
See Methyltrimellitic Acid *and* Methyltrimesic Acid.
Toluene-2 : 4 : 6-trisulphonic Acid

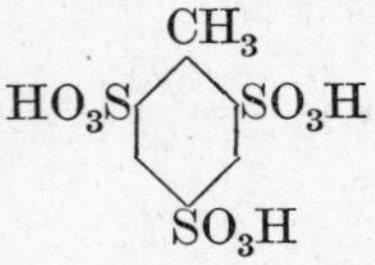

$C_7H_8O_9S_3$ MW, 332

Needles + $6H_2O$ (after drying in vacuo). Retains $3H_2O$ at 100°. M.p. 145°. The trihydrate is hygroscopic. Very sol. H_2O.
Trichloride: $C_7H_5O_6Cl_3S_3$. MW, 387·5. Plates from $CHCl_3$. M.p. 153°. Spar. sol. boiling Et_2O.
Triamide: $C_7H_{11}O_6N_3S_3$. MW, 329. Cryst. Does not melt below 300°. Sol. warm NH_3. Insol. H_2O.

Claesson, *Ber.*, 1881, **14**, 307.

Toluhydroquinone (*Toluquinol, homohydroquinone, homoquinol, 2-methylhydroquinone, 2 : 5-dihydroxytoluene, hydrotoluquinone*)

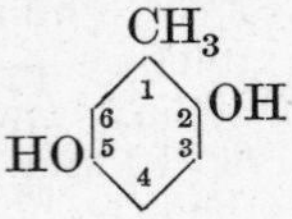

$C_7H_8O_2$ MW, 124

Plates from C_6H_6. M.p. 124–5°. B.p. 163°/11 mm. Very sol. H_2O, EtOH, Et_2O. Spar. sol. C_6H_6, ligroin. Sol. alkalis, alk. carbonates. Sublimes. Heat of comb. C_v 836·3 Cal. Reduces $NH_3.AgNO_3$ and Fehling's. $CrO_3 \longrightarrow$ *p*-toluquinone. $CaCl_2 \longrightarrow$ bluish-green $\longrightarrow$ brown col. $FeCl_3 \longrightarrow$ brownish-red or yellow col.
2-*Me ether*: $C_8H_{10}O_2$. MW, 138. Needles from C_6H_6–petrol. M.p. 46–46·5°. Very sol. cold EtOH, Et_2O, Me_2CO, $CHCl_3$, C_6H_6. Spar. sol. pet. ether, cold H_2O.
5-*Me ether*: needles from hot H_2O. M.p. 70·5–71·5°. B.p. 240–5°. Very sol. cold Et_2O, EtOH, $CHCl_3$. Spar. sol. pet. ether, cold H_2O.

Di-Me ether : $C_9H_{12}O_2$. MW, 152. Cryst. M.p. 15°. B.p. 214–18°. Volatile in steam.

5-*Et ether* : $C_9H_{12}O_2$. MW, 152. Prisms or needles from EtOH.Aq. M.p. 55–55·5°. Very sol. hot ligroin and most org. solvents. Spar. sol. hot H_2O. Volatile in steam.

Di-Et ether : $C_{11}H_{16}O_2$. MW, 180. Needles from cold ligroin. M.p. 24–5°. B.p. 247–9°.

Acetyl deriv. : needles from pet. ether. M.p. 92°.

Diacetyl : needles or prisms from H_2O, AcOH or ligroin. M.p. 49°.

Dibenzoyl : cryst. M.p. 119–20°.

Schmid, *Monatsh.*, 1911, **32**, 437.
Bamberger, *Ann.*, 1912, **390**, 175.
Henderson, Boyd, *J. Chem. Soc.*, 1910, **97**, 1667.

α-Toluic Acid.
See Phenylacetic Acid.

o-Toluic Acid (2-*Methylbenzoic acid*)

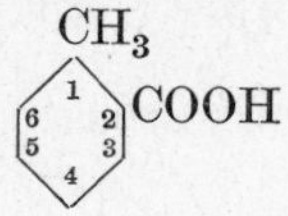

$C_8H_8O_2$ MW, 136

Prisms from H_2O. M.p. 107–8° (102°). B.p. 258·5–259°. Very sol. EtOH. Sol. hot H_2O. Volatile in steam. Heat of comb. C_v 929·8 Cal., C_p 929·4 Cal. $k = 1{\cdot}35 \times 10^{-4}$ at 25°. Ox. ⟶ phthalic acid. Na + amyl alcohol ⟶ *trans.*-hexahydro-*o*-toluic acid.

Na salt : plates + $2H_2O$. M.p. 227–8°.

K salt : m.p. 188–9°.

Me ester : $C_9H_{10}O_2$. MW, 150. Cryst. below − 50°. B.p. 213°, 97°/15 mm. D^{15} 1·073.

Et ester : $C_{10}H_{12}O_2$. MW, 164. B.p. 227°, 102–102·5°/13 mm. $D_4^{21\cdot5}$ 1·0325. $n_D^{21\cdot6}$ 1·507.

d-*Amyl ester* : $C_{13}H_{18}O_2$. MW, 206. B.p. 265–8°. D_4^{20} 0·985. $n_D^{19\cdot6}$ 1·4984. $[\alpha]_D^{20}$ + 5·94°.

l-*Menthyl ester* : $C_{18}H_{26}O_2$. MW, 274. B.p. 191°/15 mm. D_4^{20} 0·9982. $[\alpha]_D^{20}$ − 84·35°.

Phenyl ester : $C_{14}H_{12}O_2$. MW, 212. Yellow oil. B.p. 306°/754 mm.

Benzyl ester : $C_{15}H_{14}O_2$. MW, 226. Oil. B.p. 315°. D^{17} 1·12.

p-*Nitrobenzyl ester* : $C_{15}H_{13}O_4N$. MW, 271. Cryst. from EtOH.Aq. M.p. 90·7°.

p-*Bromphenacyl ester* : $C_{16}H_{13}O_3Br$. MW, 333. M.p. 56·9°.

Anhydride : $C_{16}H_{14}O_3$. MW, 254. Cryst. from Et_2O or C_6H_6. M.p. 39°. B.p. 220–1°/11 mm.

Chloride : C_8H_7OCl. MW, 154·5. B.p. 206–8°, 110–11°/29 mm., 99–100°/14 mm.

Bromide : C_8H_7OBr. MW, 199. B.p. 133–6°/37 mm.

Amide : *see o*-Toluamide.

Nitrile : *see o*-Tolunitrile.

Imide : cryst. from EtOH. M.p. 147–8°.

Hydrazide : needles from EtOH.Aq. or Et_2O. M.p. 124°.

Anilide : m.p. 125°.

p-*Toluidide* : m.p. 144°.

Clarke, Taylor, *Organic Syntheses*, 1931, XI, 96.

m-Toluic Acid (3-*Methylbenzoic acid*).

Prisms from H_2O. M.p. 111–13°. B.p. 263°. Sol. 1170 parts H_2O at 15°, 60 parts at 100°. Very sol. EtOH, Et_2O. Sublimes. Volatile in steam. Heat of comb. C_v 928·5 Cal., C_p 929·1 Cal. $k = 5{\cdot}6 \times 10^{-5}$ at 25°. Ox. ⟶ isophthalic acid. Red. ⟶ hexahydro-*m*-toluic acid.

Na salt : m.p. about 310°.

Me ester : oil. B.p. 215°. D^{15} 1·066.

Et ester : b.p. 227°, 133°/38 mm., 103–5°/10 mm. D_{20}^{20} 1·0301. $n_D^{21\cdot6}$ 1·505.

Propyl ester : $C_{11}H_{14}O_2$. MW, 178. B.p. 240°.

d-*Amyl ester* : b.p. 266–8°/725 mm. D^{20} 0·976. n_D 1·4929. $[\alpha]_D^{20}$ + 6·59°.

l-*Menthyl ester* : b.p. 228–9°/36 mm., 197°/15 mm. D_4^{20} 0·9931. $[\alpha]_D^{20}$ − 87·59°.

p-*Nitrobenzyl ester* : cryst. from EtOH.Aq. M.p. 86·6°.

p-*Bromphenacyl ester* : m.p. 108°.

Anhydride : cryst. from pet. ether. M.p. 71°. B.p. 230°/17 mm. Sol. most org. solvents.

Chloride : m.p. − 23°. B.p. 219–20°/773 mm., 136–8°/31 mm., 109°/15 mm. D_4^{20} 1·173.

Bromide : b.p. 136–7°/52 mm.

Amide : *see m*-Toluamide.

Nitrile : *see m*-Tolunitrile.

Hydrazide : plates from EtOH.Aq. M.p. 97°.

Adams, Ulich, *J. Am. Chem. Soc.*, 1920, **42**, 608.
Reuter, *Ber.*, 1884, **17**, 2028.

p-Toluic Acid (4-*Methylbenzoic acid*).

Cryst. from hot H_2O. M.p. 181°. B.p. 274–5°. Very sol. EtOH, MeOH, Et_2O. Spar. sol. H_2O. Volatile in steam. Sublimes. Heat of comb. C_p 927·4 Cal., C_v 926·8 Cal. $k = 4{\cdot}3 \times 10^{-5}$ at 25°. Dist. with CaO ⟶ toluene. Ox. ⟶ terephthalic acid. Na + amyl alcohol ⟶ hexahydro-*p*-toluic acid.

Me ester : cryst. with intense unpleasant odour from MeOH.Aq. or pet. ether. M.p. 33·2°. B.p. 217°.

Et ester : b.p. 228°, 122°/22 mm., 110°/12 mm. D_{25}^{25} 1·024. $n_D^{18\cdot2}$ 1·5089.

d-*Amyl ester* : b.p. 271–2°. D_4^{20} 0·982. $n_D^{19\cdot1}$ 1·4975. $[\alpha]_D^{20}$ + 6·67°.

Isoamyl ester: $C_{13}H_{18}O_2$. MW, 206. B.p. 271°.

l-*Menthyl ester*: cryst. M.p. 40–1°. B.p. 196–8°/11 mm. $[\alpha]_D^{20}$ − 89·93°.

Phenyl ester: plates from EtOH. M.p. 83°.

p-*Nitrobenzyl ester*: cryst. from EtOH.Aq. M.p. 104·5°.

p-*Bromphenacyl ester*: m.p. 153°.

Anhydride: plates from MeOH, needles from EtOH. M.p. 95°. Stable to boiling H_2O.

Chloride: m.p. − 2 to − 1·5°. B.p. 214–16°, 102°/15 mm.

Bromide: b.p. 145–9°/42 mm.

Amide: *see* *p*-Toluamide.

Nitrile: *see* *p*-Tolunitrile.

Imide: needles from C_6H_6. M.p. 155°.

Hydrazide: plates from EtOH.Aq. M.p. 117°.

Anilide: needles or plates from EtOH. M.p. 147–8°.

o-*Nitroanilide*: yellow prisms from EtOH. M.p. 110°.

p-*Toluidide*: needles from EtOH. M.p. 165° (158–9°).

Herb, *Ann.*, 1890, **258**, 10.
Gattermann, Schmidt, *Ann.*, 1888, **244**, 51.

α-Toluic Aldehyde.

See Phenylacetaldehyde.

o-Toluic Aldehyde (2-*Methylbenzaldehyde*)

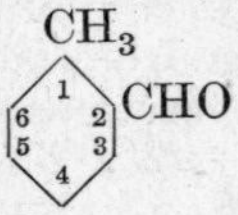

C_8H_8O MW, 120

B.p. 197°, 94°/10 mm. D_4^{19} 1·0386. n_D^{19} 1·549. KCN + EtOH ⟶ *o*-toluoin. Ox. in air ⟶ *o*-toluic acid. Red. ⟶ *o*-tolylcarbinol. Sol. H_2SO_4 ⟶ greenish-orange sol.

Oxime: needles from pet. ether. M.p. 49°. Very sol. hot H_2O, EtOH, Et_2O, CS_2, C_6H_6. Spar. sol. pet. ether. N-*Acetyl*: cryst. from Et_2O. M.p. 55–6°.

Semicarbazone: needles from amyl alcohol. M.p. 212° (196°).

Hydrazone: m.p. 97°.

Phenylhydrazone: m.p. 105–6°.

p-*Nitrophenylhydrazone*: red needles from EtOH. M.p. 222°.

2 : 4-*Dinitrophenylhydrazone*: orange-red plates from AcOH. M.p. 193–4°.

Rupe, Bernstein, *Helv. Chim. Acta*, 1930, **13**, 460.
Stephen, *J. Chem. Soc.*, 1925, 1874.
Gattermann, *Ann.*, 1912, **393**, 218.
Gattermann, Maffezoli, *Ber.*, 1903, **36**, 4152.

***m*-Toluic Aldehyde** (3-*Methylbenzaldehyde*).

B.p. 199°, 93–4°/17 mm. $D_4^{21\cdot4}$ 1·0189. $n_D^{21\cdot4}$ 1·541. Oxidises in air to *m*-toluic acid. HNO_3 ⟶ isophthalic acid.

Semicarbazone: needles from EtOH, plates from amyl alcohol. M.p. 223–4° (206°).

Phenylhydrazone: prisms from ligroin or EtOH.Aq. M.p. 90°.

Rupe, Bernstein, *Helv. Chim. Acta*, 1930, **13**, 462.
Sommelet, *Compt. rend.*, 1913, **157**, 853.

***p*-Toluic Aldehyde** (4-*Methylbenzaldehyde*).

Liq. with peppermint odour. B.p. 204–5°, 106°/10 mm. $D_4^{16\cdot7}$ 1·0194. $n_D^{16\cdot6}$ 1·547. KCN + EtOH ⟶ 4 : 4′-dimethylbenzoin. Oxidises in air to *p*-toluic acid. Forms cryst. bisulphite comp. Sol. H_2SO_4 ⟶ orange-brown sol.

Polymer: $(C_8H_8O)_x$. Cryst. from C_6H_6. M.p. 215°. Insol. cold EtOH, Et_2O, AcOH.

Di-Et acetal: $C_{12}H_{18}O_2$. MW, 194. B.p. 116–19°/12 mm. D^{22} 1·006. n^{22} 1·47603.

NH_3 add. comp.: cryst. M.p. 43–4°.

Oxime: *syn*-. M.p. 108–10°. Steam dist. of alk. sol. ⟶ *anti*-. N-*Acetyl*: m.p. 85°. *Anti*-: m.p. 79–80°.

Semicarbazone: needles from EtOH, plates from amyl alcohol. M.p. 234° (215°).

Hydrazone: cryst. mass. M.p. 56°. B.p. 148°/12 mm.

Phenylhydrazone: plates from EtOH. M.p. 121° (108°).

o-*Nitrophenylhydrazone*: red needles from EtOH.Aq. M.p. 183°.

m-*Nitrophenylhydrazone*: m.p. 155°.

p-*Nitrophenylhydrazone*: dark red needles with green fluor. from EtOH. M.p. 200·5°.

2 : 4-*Dinitrophenylhydrazone*: orange-yellow cryst. from $PhNO_2$. M.p. 232·5–234·5°.

p-*Bromphenylhydrazone*: m.p. 162° decomp.

I.C.I., E.P., 397,124, (*Chem. Abstracts* 1934, **28**, 778).
Coleman, Craig, *Organic Syntheses*, 1932 XII, 80.
Hinkel, Ayling, Morgan, *J. Chem. Soc.* 1932, 2793.
Gattermann, Koch, *Ber.*, 1897, **30**, 1623.

***o*-Toluidine** (2-*Aminotoluene*, o-*tolylamine*)

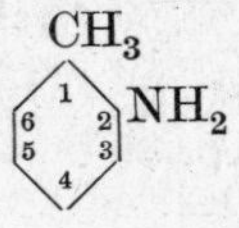

C_7H_9N MW, 10

Liq. Cryst. on cooling to two forms. α-. M.p about − 21°. β- (stable form). M.p. abou

— 15·5°. B.p. 200·6°/754·6 mm., 121°/80 mm. D_{20}^{20} 1·0053. n_D^{20} 1·5688. Sol. EtOH, Et_2O. Spar. sol. H_2O. Specific heat 0·49 cal./gm. at 15–64°. Heat of comb. C_v 963·8 Cal., C_p 969·93 Cal. $k = 3·5 \times 10^{-10}$ at 25°. Volatile in steam. $MnO_2 + H_2SO_4 \longrightarrow$ toluquinone. $KMnO_4 \longrightarrow$ 2 : 2′-dimethylazobenzene. Dil. H_2SO_4 sol. + CrO_3 in dil. $H_2SO_4 \longrightarrow$ blue col. $\longrightarrow$ reddish-violet col. on dilution. Forms Ca and Na derivs.

$C_7H_9N,C_6H_3(NO_2)_3$-1 : 3 : 5 : light red needles. M.p. 125–7°.

B,HCl: cryst. M.p. 215°. B.p. 242·2°.

B,H_3PO_3: needles. M.p. 174°.

$B,HClO_3$: plates from EtOH. Explodes at 88°.

B_2,H_2PtBr_6: yellowish-red needles. M.p. 225–6° decomp.

$B,CH_2(COOH)_2$: prisms. Decomp. at 108°.

$B,ClCH_2 \cdot COOH$: m.p. 95°.

$B_2,(COOH)_2$: m.p. 167°.

$B,(COOH)_2$: plates. M.p. 171°.

$B,(CH_2 \cdot COOH)_2$: prisms. Decomp. at 60°.

$B_2,ZnCl_2$: cryst. from EtOH. M.p. 227°.

$B_2,ZnBr_2$: cryst. from EtOH. M.p. 218°.

N-*Me*: *see N*-Methyl-*o*-toluidine.

N-*Di-Me*: *see* Dimethyl-*o*-toluidine.

N-*Et*: *see N*-Ethyl-*o*-toluidine.

N-*Di-Et*: *see* Diethyl-*o*-toluidine.

N-*Propyl*: *see N*-Propyl-*o*-toluidine.

N-*Butyl*: $C_{11}H_{17}N$. MW, 163. Oil with pleasant odour. B.p. 258–60°/771 mm.

N-*Isobutyl*: *see N*-Isobutyl-*o*-toluidine.

N-*Isoamyl*: *see N*-Isoamyl-*o*-toluidine.

N-*Allyl*: $C_{10}H_{13}N$. MW, 147. B.p. 225–30°.

N-β-*Hydroxyethyl*: *see N*-β-Hydroxyethyl-*o*-toluidine.

N-*Phenyl*: *see* 2-Methyldiphenylamine.

N-*Diphenyl*: *see* Diphenyl-*o*-toluidine.

N-*Tolyl*: *see* Ditolylamine.

N-*Benzyl*: *see N*-Benzyl-*o*-toluidine.

N-*Dibenzyl*: $C_{21}H_{21}N$. MW, 287. Cryst. M.p. 42°. B.p. 223°/10 mm. D_4^{65} 1·02347. n_D^{65} 1·58324.

N-*Picryl*: $C_{13}H_{10}O_6N_4$. MW, 318. Orange-red prisms from EtOH–Me_2CO. M.p. 164°.

N-*Formyl*: *see* Formo-*o*-toluidide.

N-*Acetyl*: *see* Acet-*o*-toluidide.

N-*Diacetyl*: *N-o*-tolyldiacetamide. Cryst. M.p. 18°. B.p. 200·5–201°/100 mm., 144–5°/11 mm.

N-*Benzoyl*: benz-*o*-toluidide. Needles from AcOEt–Me_2CO. M.p. 145–6°.

N-*Dibenzoyl*: *N-o*-tolyldibenzamide. Prisms from EtOH. M.p. 111–12°.

N-p-*Toluenesulphonyl*: m.p. 185·5–186·2°.

N-1-*Naphthalenesulphonyl*: m.p. 237°.

Picrate: cryst. from EtOH. M.p. 212–15° decomp.

Tanner, Lasselle, *J. Am. Chem. Soc.*, 1926, **48**, 2163.

Courtot, Petitcolas, *Bull. soc. chim.*, 1926, **39**, 452.

Blanksma, *Rec. trav. chim.*, 1909, **28**, 109.

***m*-Toluidine** (3-*Aminotoluene*, m-*tolylamine*).

Liq. Cryst. on strong cooling. M.p. — 43·6°. B.p. 203·2°. D_{25}^{25} 0·990. n_D^{20} 1·56859. Sol. EtOH, Et_2O. Very spar. sol. H_2O. Heat of comb. C_v 964·6 Cal., C_p 965·6 Cal. $k = 5·5 \times 10^{-10}$ at 25°. Volatile in steam. Ox. $\longrightarrow$ toluquinone. Sol. in dil. $H_2SO_4 + CrO_3$ in dil. $H_2SO_4 \longrightarrow$ yellowish-brown col. Sol. in dil. H_2SO_4 + $HNO_3 \longrightarrow$ dark red col.

$C_7H_9N,C_6H_3(NO_2)_3$-1 : 3 : 5 : light red needles. M.p. 93°.

B,HCl: plates from H_2O. M.p. 228°. B.p. 249·8°.

$B,HClO_4$: m.p. 200° decomp.

B_2,H_2PtBr_6: red scales. M.p. 266° decomp.

$B,CH_2(COOH)_2$: prisms. Decomp. at 93°.

$B,(CH_2 \cdot COOH)_2$: columns. Decomp. at 121°.

N-*Me*: *see N*-Methyl-*m*-toluidine.

N-*Di-Me*: *see* Dimethyl-*m*-toluidine.

N-*Et*: *see N*-Ethyl-*m*-toluidine.

N-*Di-Et*: *see* Diethyl-*m*-toluidine.

N-*Phenyl*: *see* 3-Methyldiphenylamine.

N-*Diphenyl*: *see* Diphenyl-*m*-toluidine.

N-*Tolyl*: *see* Ditolylamine.

N-*Benzyl*: *see N*-Benzyl-*m*-toluidine.

N-*Dibenzyl*: $C_{21}H_{21}N$. MW, 287. Cryst. M.p. 78°. B.p. 229°/10 mm.

N-*Picryl*: two forms. α-. Yellow prisms from EtOH–HCl. M.p. 130°. β-. Orange-red needles from alc. NH_3. M.p. 129·5°.

N-*Formyl*: *see* Formo-*m*-toluidide.

N-*Acetyl*: *see* Acet-*m*-toluidide.

N-*Benzoyl*: benz-*m*-toluidide. Prisms from EtOH.Aq. M.p. 125°.

N-*Dibenzoyl*: *N-m*-tolyldibenzamide. Needles from EtOH. M.p. 140–1°.

N-p-*Toluenesulphonyl*: m.p. 171–172·5°.

N-1-*Naphthalenesulphonyl*: m.p. 195–6°.

Buchka, Schachtebeck, *Ber.*, 1889, **22**, 840.

Blanksma, *Rec. trav. chim.*, 1906, **25**, 370.

Ehrlich, *Ber.*, 1882, **15**, 2011.

***p*-Toluidine** (4-*Aminotoluene*, p-*tolylamine*).

Cryst. + $1H_2O$ from H_2O or EtOH.Aq. M.p. 42°, anhyd. 44·5–45°. Anhyd. in moist air $\longrightarrow$ monohydrate. B.p. 200·3°, 133·7°/100 mm.,

100·2°/25 mm., 82·2°/10 mm. Sol. 285 parts H_2O at 11·5°. Very sol. EtOH.Aq., MeOH, Et_2O, Me_2CO, CS_2. Volatile in steam. D^{50}_{50} 0·973. $n_D^{59·1}$ 1·55324. Heat of comb. C_v 957·9 Cal., C_p 958·8 Cal., C_p (liq.) 973·5 Cal. $k = 1·48 \times 10^{-9}$ at 25°. Alk. $KMnO_4 \longrightarrow$ 4 : 4′-dimethylazobenzene. Acid $KMnO_4 \longrightarrow$ *p*-nitrosotoluene. Reduces alc. $NH_3.AgNO_3$ in the cold. Dil. H_2SO_4 sol. + $HNO_3 \longrightarrow$ blue $\longrightarrow$ violet $\longrightarrow$ red $\longrightarrow$ brown col. Slightly acid sol. + $FeCl_3 \longrightarrow$ pale yellow $\longrightarrow$ red col. Forms metallic derivs. with Ca and Na.

B,HCl : needles from AcOH–Et_2O. M.p. 243°. B.p. 257·5°.

B_2,H_2PtBr_6 : yellowish-red cryst. M.p. 268–9°.

$B,ClCH_2{\cdot}COOH$: needles. M.p. 101–2°.

$B,Cl_2CH{\cdot}COOH$: needles. M.p. 140–1°.

$B,Cl_3C{\cdot}COOH$: cryst. M.p. 137°.

$B_2,(COOH)_2$: m.p. 183–4°.

$B,(COOH)_2$: m.p. 178°.

$B,CH_2(COOH)_2$: m.p. 114°.

$B,(CH_2{\cdot}COOH)_2$: m.p. 123–4°.

$B,C_6H_5{\cdot}COOH$: m.p. 52·5°.

$B_2,AgNO_3$: plates. M.p. 101° decomp.

N-*Me* : *see* *N*-Methyl-*p*-toluidine.

N-*Di-Me* : *see* Dimethyl-*p*-toluidine.

N-*Et* : *see* *N*-Ethyl-*p*-toluidine.

N-*Di-Et* : *see* Diethyl-*p*-toluidine.

N-*Propyl* : *see* *N*-Propyl-*p*-toluidine.

N-*Isopropyl* : *see* *N*-Isopropyl-*p*-toluidine.

N-*Butyl* : $C_{11}H_{17}N$. MW, 163. Oil. B.p. 264–5°/766 mm. Volatile in steam. *B,HCl* : needles or prisms from EtOH. M.p. 150–1°.

N-*Dibutyl* : $C_{15}H_{25}N$. MW, 219. Oil. B.p. 282–4°/764 mm. *Picrate* : yellow cryst. from Et_2O–pet. ether. M.p. 131–2°.

N-*Isobutyl* : *see* *N*-Isobutyl-*p*-toluidine.

N-*Allyl* : $C_{10}H_{13}N$. MW, 147. Oil. B.p. 232–4°. *B,HCl* : m.p. 131–2°.

N-β-*Hydroxyethyl* : *see* *N*-β-Hydroxyethyl-*p*-toluidine.

N-*Phenyl* : *see* 4-Methyldiphenylamine.

N-*Tolyl* : *see* Ditolylamine.

N-*Benzyl* : *see* *N*-Benzyl-*p*-toluidine.

N-*Dibenzyl* : $C_{21}H_{21}N$. MW, 287. Cryst. M.p. 56°. B.p. 233°/11 mm. D^{65}_4 1·03721. n_D^{65} 1·60109.

N-*Picryl* : two forms. α-. Yellow needles from Me_2CO, $CHCl_3$, CCl_4 or C_6H_6. M.p. 164°. β-. Dark red needles from Py. M.p. 164°.

N-*Bornyl* : $C_{17}H_{25}N$. MW, 243. Needles. M.p. 33°. B.p. 162°/3 mm. Very sol. EtOH, Et_2O, C_6H_6. *B,HCl* : cryst. powder. M.p. 214° decomp.

N-*Formyl* : *see* Formo-*p*-toluidide.

N-*Acetyl* : *see* Acet-*p*-toluidide.

N-*Diacetyl* : *N*-*p*-tolyldiacetamide. Cryst. M.p. 48°. B.p. 160–1°/15 mm.

N-*Benzoyl* : benz-*p*-toluidide. Needles from EtOH. M.p. 158°. B.p. 232°. N-*Nitroso* : needles from Me_2CO.Aq. M.p. 75° decomp.

N-*Dibenzoyl* : *N*-*p*-tolyldibenzamide. Prisms from EtOH. M.p. 142–4°.

N-p-*Toluenesulphonyl* : m.p. 193–194·5°.

N-1-*Naphthalenesulphonyl* : m.p. 181°.

Picrate : m.p. 180–1° decomp.

Blanksma, *Rec. trav. chim.*, 1909, **28**, 109; 1906, **25**, 370.

Popov, *Chem. Abstracts*, 1934, **28**, 1671.

Kock, *Ber.*, 1887, **20**, 1568.

Graebe, *Ber.*, 1901, **34**, 1778.

***o*-Toluidine-3 : 5-disulphonic Acid**

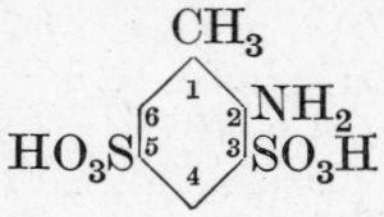

$C_7H_9O_6NS_2$ MW, 267

Needles + $1\frac{1}{2}H_2O$ from H_2O. Decomp. at 240°. Very sol. H_2O, EtOH. Insol. C_6H_6.

Dichloride : $C_7H_7O_4NCl_2S_2$. MW, 304. Cryst. from C_6H_6–pet. ether. M.p. 153°.

Dianilide : cryst. from EtOH.Aq. M.p. 188°.

Pollak, Pollak, Riesz, *Monatsh.*, 1931, **58**, 128.

Nevile, Winther, *Ber.*, 1882, **15**, 2992.

***o*-Toluidine-4 : 5-disulphonic Acid.**

Needles. Spar. sol. Forms spar. sol. Ba salt.

Wynne, Bruce, *J. Chem. Soc.*, 1898, **73**, 745.

***p*-Toluidine-2 : 5-disulphonic Acid**

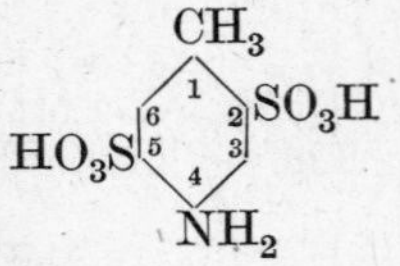

$C_7H_9O_6NS_2$ MW, 267

Needles + $2\frac{1}{2}H_2O$. Decomp. at 290°. Very sol. H_2O. Spar. sol. EtOH. Forms spar. sol. Ba salt.

Dichloride : $C_7H_7O_4NCl_2S_2$. MW, 304. Yellow prisms from $CHCl_3$. M.p. 156°. Sol. Et_2O, $CHCl_3$, C_6H_6. Spar. sol. ligroin. N-*Acetyl* : cryst. from pet. ether. M.p. 125°. N-*Chloracetyl* : cryst. from pet. ether. M.p. 118–19°.

Diamide : $C_7H_{11}O_4N_3S_2$. MW, 265. Needles from H_2O. M.p. 257°. Sol. H_2O, EtOH, Me_2CO.

Dianilide: plates from EtOH.Aq. M.p. 196–7°.

Pollak, Pollak, Riesz, *Monatsh.*, 1931, **58**, 126.
Riesz, Pollak, Wittels, *Ann.*, 1931, **487**, 267.
Lustig, Katscher, *Monatsh.*, 1927, **48**, 93.

p-Toluidine-2 : 6-disulphonic Acid.

Prisms + H_2O. Very sol. H_2O. Spar. sol. EtOH. Ppd. by EtOH from H_2O.

Kornatzki, *Ann.*, 1883, **221**, 198.

p-Toluidine-3 : 5-disulphonic Acid.

Needles + $2H_2O$, aggregates of cryst. + $1H_2O$. Anhyd. at 120°. Decomp. at 200°. Very sol. H_2O. Mod. sol. EtOH. Decomp. with H_2O at 140° ⟶ *p*-toluidine-3-sulphonic acid.

Wynne, Bruce, *J. Chem. Soc.*, 1898, **73**, 734.
Richter, *Ann.*, 1885, **230**, 315.

o-Toluidine-3-sulphonic Acid

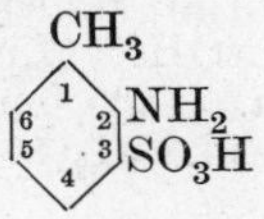

$C_7H_9O_3NS$ MW, 187

Needles. Very sol. hot H_2O. Warm with aq. $FeCl_3$ ⟶ reddish-yellow col.

Pechmann, *Ann.*, 1874, **173**, 215.

o-Toluidine-4-sulphonic Acid.

Needles or prisms + $1H_2O$. Anhyd. over H_2SO_4. Sol. 104 parts H_2O at 11°. Insol. EtOH. $k = 2{\cdot}5 \times 10^{-4}$ at 25°. $FeCl_3$ ⟶ dark violet col. NaOH fusion ⟶ anthranilic acid.

Fluoride: $C_7H_8O_2NFS$. MW, 189. Needles from EtOH.Aq. M.p. 96–7°. Very sol. Me_2CO. Sol. Et_2O, AcOEt, C_6H_6. Mod. sol. EtOH, CS_2, pet. ether. Spar. sol. H_2O. N-*Acetyl*: needles from EtOH. M.p. 188·5–189·5°.

Chloride: $C_7H_8O_2NClS$. MW, 205·5. N-*Acetyl*: prisms from C_6H_6. M.p. 144°. N-*Benzoyl*: needles from C_6H_6. M.p. 196°.

Amide: $C_7H_{10}O_2N_2S$. MW, 186. Columns. M.p. 176°. Very sol. hot H_2O. Spar. sol. EtOH. Insol. Et_2O, C_6H_6. *B,HCl*: needles. M.p. 240°.

N-*Me*: $C_8H_{11}O_3NS$. MW, 201. Plates from hot H_2O. Sol. 60 parts H_2O at 15°.

N-*Di-Et*: $C_{11}H_{17}O_3NS$. MW, 243. Plates + $1H_2O$ from H_2O. Spar. sol. cold H_2O, EtOH.

N-*Benzoyl*: plates. M.p. 203°.

I.G., D.R.P., 573,193, (*Chem. Zentr.*, 1933, II, 445).
Steinkopf, *J. prakt. Chem.*, 1927, **117**, 26.
Wynne, Bruce, *J. Chem. Soc.*, 1898, **73**, 745.

o-Toluidine-5-sulphonic Acid.

Plates or columns from $1H_2O + H_2O$. Anhyd. at 120° over H_2SO_4. Sol. 32 parts H_2O at 19°. $k = 7{\cdot}53 \times 10^{-4}$ at 25°. Characteristic col. with PbO_2 in aq. sol.

N-*Me*: needles from H_2O. Sol. H_2O.

N-*Di-Me*: $C_9H_{13}O_3NS$. MW, 215. Prisms from H_2O. Very sol. hot H_2O. Insol. EtOH.

Schultz, Lucas, *J. Am. Chem. Soc.*, 1927, **49**, 299.
Nevile, Winther, *Ber.*, 1880, **13**, 1941.

o-Toluidine-6-sulphonic Acid.

Needles. Sol. 293 parts H_2O at 22°.

Pagel, *Ann.*, 1875, **176**, 305.

m-Toluidine-4-sulphonic Acid

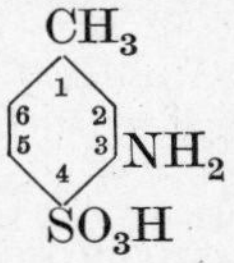

$C_7H_9O_3NS$ MW, 187

Needles + H_2O. Sol. 715 parts H_2O at 16°.

Hayduck, *Ann.*, 1874, **174**, 350.

m-Toluidine-6-sulphonic Acid.

Plates. Chars above 275°. Spar. sol. H_2O. $k = 3{\cdot}57 \times 10^{-4}$ at 25°.

NH_4 salt: m.p. 190°.

Quilico, *Gazz. chim. ital.*, 1926, **56**, 626.
Seyewetz, Bloch, *Bull. soc. chim.*, 1907, **1**, 327.

p-Toluidine-2-sulphonic Acid

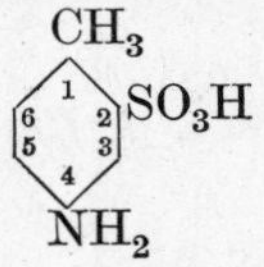

$C_7H_9O_3NS$ MW, 187

Prisms + $1H_2O$. Decomp. at high temps. Sol. 220 parts H_2O at 20°. Insol. EtOH. $k = 4{\cdot}08 \times 10^{-5}$ at 25°. $FeCl_3$ ⟶ red col. Reduces $NH_3.AgNO_3$ on warming.

Fluoride: $C_7H_8O_2NFS$. MW, 189. Yellow cryst. from EtOH. M.p. 62°. Sol. Et_2O, AcOEt, C_6H_6. Insol. H_2O. N-*Acetyl*: needles from C_6H_6. M.p. 120–1°.

Chloride : $C_7H_8O_2NClS$. MW, 205·5. N-*Acetyl* : prisms from Me_2CO.Aq. M.p. 124°. N-*Chloracetyl* : plates from petrol. M.p. 87°.

Amide : $C_7H_{10}O_2N_2S$. MW, 186. Needles or plates. M.p. 164°. Sol. hot H_2O, EtOH. N-*Acetyl* : cryst. from H_2O. M.p. 242°. N-*Chloracetyl* : needles from H_2O. M.p. 231°.

N-*Me* : $C_8H_{11}O_3NS$. MW, 201. Plates. Sol. H_2O. Insol. org. solvents. Decomp. on boiling aq. sol.

N-*Et* : $C_9H_{13}O_3NS$. MW, 215. Yellow prisms + $1H_2O$ from H_2O. Spar. sol. H_2O. Very spar. sol. EtOH.

N-*Di-Et* : $C_{11}H_{17}O_3NS$. MW, 243. Prisms + $1H_2O$ from H_2O. Does not melt. Spar. sol. H_2O. Insol. Et_2O.

N-*Isopropyl* : $C_{10}H_{15}O_3NS$. MW, 229. Prisms from H_2O. Does not melt below 300°. Spar. sol. EtOH.

N-*Acetyl* : needles + $2H_2O$ from dil. HCl. *Anilide* : leaflets from EtOH. M.p. 230°.

Anilide : m.p. 146–7°.

Pollak, Pollak, Riesz, *Monatsh.*, 1931, **58**, 125.
Steinkopf, *J. prakt. Chem.*, 1927, **117**, 37.
Johnson, Smiles, *J. Chem. Soc.*, 1923, **123**, 2385.

***p*-Toluidine-3-sulphonic Acid.**

Needles + $\frac{1}{2}H_2O$. Sol. 214 parts H_2O. $k = 8{\cdot}5 \times 10^{-4}$ at 25°. Aq. sol. + $PbO_2 \longrightarrow$ red col. Decomp. with H_2O at 130°. Gives Ag salt, spar. sol. H_2O at 100°.

N-*Me* : $C_8H_{11}O_3NS$. MW, 201. Prisms from H_2O. Decomp. on heating.

N-*Di-Et* : prisms + $1H_2O$ from H_2O. M.p. 243°. Sol. H_2O. Insol. Et_2O, C_6H_6. *K salt* : plates + $1\frac{1}{2}H_2O$. M.p. 297°.

N-*Di-isopropyl* : $C_{13}H_{21}O_3NS$. MW, 271. Cryst. + $2H_2O$ from H_2O. M.p. 222–3°.

Leitch, E.P., 257,979, (*Chem. Zentr.*, 1927, I, 1745).
Witt, Uerményi, *Ber.*, 1913, **46**, 301.
Wynne, Bruce, *J. Chem. Soc.*, 1898, **73**, 738.

Toluidinoacetic Acid.
See Tolylglycine.
Toluidinobenzoic Acid.
See Methyldiphenylamine-carboxylic Acid.
2-Toluidinoethyl Alcohol.
See *N*-β-Hydroxyethyltoluidine.
Toluidinophenol.
See Hydroxy-methyldiphenylamine.
Tolunitranilic Acid.
See 5-Nitro-3 : 6-dihydroxytoluquinone.

***o*-Tolunitrile** (o-*Cyanotoluene*)

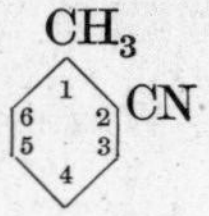

C_8H_7N MW, 117

Liq. M.p. − 13 to − 14°. B.p. 205·2°, 90°/15 mm., 82·3°/11 mm. D^{25}_{25} 0·9912. n^{25}_D 1·52720. Heat of comb. C_v 1030 Cal., C_p 1030·7 Cal. Red. $\longrightarrow$ *o*-xylylamine. Hyd. $\longrightarrow$ *o*-toluic acid.

Clarke, Read, *Organic Syntheses*, Collective Vol. I, 500.

***m*-Tolunitrile** (m-*Cyanotoluene*).

Liq. M.p. − 23·5 to − 23°. B.p. 210–12°, 84·5°/10 mm. D^{20} 1·0316. Red. $\longrightarrow$ *m*-xylylamine. $H_2O_2 \longrightarrow$ *m*-toluamide.

Bayer, D.R.Ps., 259,363, 259,364, (*Chem. Zentr.*, 1913, I, 1741).
Buchka, Schachtebeck, *Ber.*, 1889, **22**, 841.

***p*-Tolunitrile** (p-*Cyanotoluene*).

Needles from EtOH. M.p. 29°. B.p. 217·6°, 90·5–91°/11 mm. D^{30}_{30} 0·9805. $KMnO_4 \longrightarrow$ terephthalamic acid. $H_2O_2 \longrightarrow$ *p*-toluamide.

Clarke, Read, *Organic Syntheses*, Collective Vol. I, 500.

Toluoin.
See Dimethylbenzoin.
Toluylenediamine.
See Tolylenediamine.
Toluquinaldine.
See 2 : 6-, 2 : 7-, and 2 : 8-Dimethylquinoline.
Toluquinhydrone.
See under Toluquinone.
Toluquinol.
See Toluhydroquinone.
Toluquinoline.
See 6-, 7-, *and* 8-Methylquinoline.

***o*-Toluquinone** (3-*Methyl*-o-*benzoquinone*)

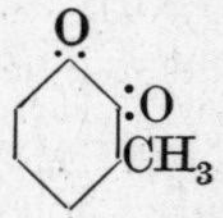

$C_7H_6O_2$ MW, 122

Dark red prisms and needles from Et_2O or pet. ether. Sol. $Et_2O \longrightarrow$ green sol. Warm, or standing in $Et_2O \longrightarrow$ dimer.

Dimer : $C_{14}H_{12}O_4$. MW, 244. Yellow prisms and plates from $CHCl_3$–pet. ether. M.p. 194–5°.

Very sol. $CHCl_3$. Insol. Et_2O, pet. ether. Gives no quinone reactions.

Dioxime: yellowish-brown needles from H_2O. M.p. about 140° decomp. Sol. EtOH, AcOH. Mod. sol. H_2O, C_6H_6.

Willstätter, Müller, *Ber.*, 1911, **44**, 2178.

Toluquinone (p-*Toluquinone, methylquinone, 2-methyl*-p-*benzoquinone*)

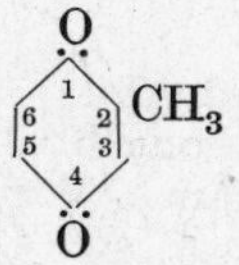

$C_7H_6O_2$ MW, 122

Yellow plates or needles. M.p. 69°. Sol. EtOH, Et_2O. Spar. sol. cold H_2O. Volatile in steam. Sublimes. Heat of comb. C_v 805·0 Cal., C_p 805·3 Cal. Mod. conc. $H_2SO_4 \longrightarrow$ polymer. Red. $\longrightarrow$ toluhydroquinone. Triphenylmagnesium chloride $\longrightarrow$ toluquinhydrone. Aq. sol. + alkali $\longrightarrow$ brownish-red col.

Polymer: powder. Does not melt below 300°. Very sol. EtOH, Et_2O. Sol. AcOH. Spar. sol. H_2O. Insol. C_6H_6.

Toluhydroquinone comp.: toluquinhydrone. $C_{14}H_{14}O_4$. MW, 246. Black needles. M.p. 96–7°.

1-*Oxime*: *see* 6-Nitroso-*m*-cresol.

4-*Oxime*: *see* 5-Nitroso-*o*-cresol.

1-*Oxime*-4-*imide*: *see* 6-Nitroso-*m*-toluidine.

4-*Oxime*-1-*imide*: *see* 5-Nitroso-*o*-toluidine.

Dioxime: needles. Decomp. at 234°. Sol. EtOH, Et_2O, hot H_2O. Spar. sol. $CHCl_3$, C_6H_6. Insol. ligroin. N-*Diacetyl*: needles from EtOH.Aq. M.p. 120°. N-*Benzoyl*: yellow cryst. from EtOH. M.p. 180° decomp.

1-*Chloroimide*: C_7H_6ONCl. MW, 155·5. Yellow columns from EtOH. M.p. 75°.

4-*Chloroimide*: yellow needles. M.p. 87–8°.

Dichloroimide: $C_7H_6N_2Cl_2$. MW, 189. Yellow needles. M.p. 74°. Spar. sol. H_2O. Sol. EtOH.

1-*Imide*-4-*semicarbazone*: monohydrated reddish-brown needles from Me_2CO–C_6H_6. M.p. 85–6° decomp.

4-*Semicarbazone*: yellow needles from EtOH. M.p. 178–9°.

1 : 4-*Disemicarbazone*: orange-red. M.p. 240° decomp.

4-*Phenylsemicarbazone*: dark red cryst. from EtOH. M.p. 198–9° decomp.

1 : 4-*Diphenylsemicarbazone*: red. cryst. powder. Decomp. at 246°.

Di-2 : 4-*dinitrophenylhydrazone*: greyish-black needles from $PhNO_2$. M.p. 269°.

4-*Benzoylphenylhydrazone*: yellow plates from C_6H_6. M.p. 151°.

Clark, *Am. Chem. J.*, 1892, **14**, 565.
Borsche, Müller, Bodenstein, *Ann.*, 1929, **472**, 214.

Toluquinoxaline.

See 6-Methylquinoxaline.

2-*p*-Toluylbenzoic Acid (4′-*Methylbenzophenone-2-carboxylic acid*)

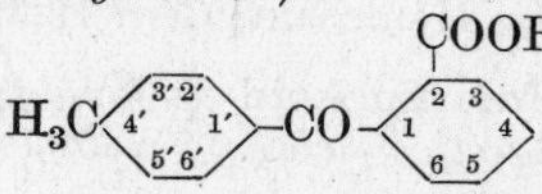

$C_{15}H_{12}O_3$ MW, 240

Prisms + $1H_2O$ from EtOH–toluene. M.p. 146° (139–40°). Sol. EtOH, Et_2O, Me_2CO, C_6H_6, boiling toluene. Spar. sol. H_2O. Ox. $\longrightarrow$ benzophenone-2 : 4′-dicarboxylic acid.

Me ester: $C_{16}H_{14}O_3$. MW, 254. Plates from MeOH. M.p. 61° (53°). Sol. EtOH, C_6H_6. Pale yellow sol. in conc. H_2SO_4.

Et ester: $C_{17}H_{16}O_3$. MW, 268. Plates. M.p. 68–9°.

Amide: $C_{15}H_{13}O_2N$. MW, 239. Needles from H_2O. M.p. 175–6°. Sol. MeOH, Et_2O, AcOH. Spar. sol. C_6H_6, ligroin.

Friedel, Crafts, *Bull. soc. chim.*, 1881, **35** 505.
Heller, Schülke, *Ber.*, 1908, **41**, 3632.
Fieser, *Organic Syntheses*, Collective Vol. I, 503.
Limpricht, *Ann.*, 1898, **299**, 306.

4-*p*-Toluylbenzoic Acid (4′-*Methylbenzophenone-4-carboxylic acid*).

Needles from MeOH. M.p. 228°. Sol. EtOH, Me_2CO. Spar. sol. H_2O, $CHCl_3$, C_6H_6.

Me ester: needles from MeOH. M.p. 126°.

Chloride: $C_{15}H_{11}O_2Cl$. MW, 258·5. Cryst. from pet. ether. M.p. 110°.

Amide: prisms from EtOH. M.p. 196°.

Limpricht, Claus, *Ann.*, 1900, **312**, 92.

***m*-Toluylformic Acid** (m-*Tolylglyoxylic acid*, α-*keto*-m-*tolylacetic acid, 3-methylbenzoylformic acid*)

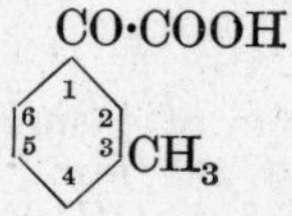

$C_9H_8O_3$ MW, 164

Colourless needles from C_6H_6–pet. ether. M.p. 78–82°. B.p. 148–50°/15–16 mm. Sol. EtOH, Et_2O, C_6H_6. Insol. H_2O. Decomp. on dist. under atm. press. $\longrightarrow$ *m*-toluic acid + *m*-toluic aldehyde. H_2SO_4 + thiophene on C_6H_6 sol. ⟶ red ⟶ bluish-violet col.

Me ester: $C_{10}H_{10}O_3$. MW, 178. B.p. 246–50°/763 mm. slight decomp., 137–8°/11–12 mm.

Et ester: $C_{11}H_{12}O_3$. MW, 192. Oil with pleasant odour. B.p. 250–5° part. decomp., 141–2°/11–12 mm.

Phenylhydrazone: yellow needles from AcOH.Aq. M.p. 158°.

Posner, Heumann, *Ber.*, 1923, **56**, 1624.

***p*-Toluylformic Acid** (p-*Tolylglyoxylic acid*, α-*keto*-p-*tolylacetic acid*, 4-*methylbenzoylformic acid*).

Needles from ligroin. M.p. 97°. B.p. 164°/10 mm. Sol. most org. solvents. Spar. sol. hot H_2O. Dist. at ord. press. ⟶ *p*-toluic acid + *p*-toluic aldehyde. Hot H_2SO_4 ⟶ *p*-toluic acid. Ox. ⟶ *p*-toluic acid + terephthalic acid. Red. ⟶ *p*-tolylglycollic acid + *p*-tolylacetic acid.

Et ester: $C_{11}H_{12}O_3$. MW, 192. Liq. B.p. 260–70°, 154–6°/18 mm. *Phenylhydrazone*: cryst. from ligroin–pet. ether. M.p. 94°.

Amide: $C_9H_9O_2N$. MW, 163. Prisms from EtOH. M.p. 160°.

Nitrile: C_9H_7ON. MW, 145. Prisms. M.p. 92°. Insol. H_2O. *Oxime*: leaflets from H_2O. M.p. 117°.

Phenylhydrazone: yellow needles from C_6H_6–ligroin. M.p. 145–6°.

Avogadro, *Gazz. chim. ital.*, 1923, **53**, 698.
Auwers, *Ber.*, 1911, **44**, 600.
Bouveault, *Bull. soc. chim.*, 1897, **17**, 363, 367.

Toluylic Acid.

See Phenylacetic Acid.

Toluylphenol.

See 2′, *and* 4′-Hydroxy-4-methylbenzophenone.

***o*-Tolylacetaldehyde**

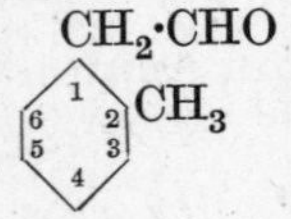

$C_9H_{10}O$ MW, 134

Liq. with odour of jasmine. B.p. 219–21°/742 mm., 142–3°/90 mm., 92°/10 mm. D_4^{10} 1·0241. Misc. with EtOH, Et_2O, $CHCl_3$. Spar. misc. with H_2O, C_6H_6, ligroin.

Oxime: needles. M.p. 102–3°. Sol. Et_2O, EtOH, $CHCl_3$. Spar. sol. H_2O, C_6H_6, ligroin.

Spath, *Monatsh.*, 1915, **36**, 8.

***m*-Tolylacetaldehyde.**

Pleasant-smelling, pale yellow oil. B.p. 99–100°/18 mm. Reduces $NH_3.AgNO_3$. Hot alkalis ⟶ resin.

Benzoylhydrazone: needles from EtOH.Aq. M.p. 129–30°.

m-*Nitrobenzoylhydrazone*: yellow needles from EtOH.Aq. M.p. 115–16°.

Curtius, Marangolo, *J. prakt. Chem.*, 1916, **94**, 337.

***p*-Tolylacetaldehyde.**

Needles. M.p. about 40°. B.p. 221–2°, 96°/10 mm., 80–2°/3 mm. Very sol. Et_2O. Sol. EtOH, $CHCl_3$. Spar. sol. C_6H_6. Insol. H_2O. Slowly oxidises in air to *p*-tolylacetic acid. Readily decomp. by acids. Electrolytic red. ⟶ β-*p*-tolylethyl alcohol. Forms bisulphite comp.

Oxime: prisms from Et_2O. M.p. 126–126·5°. Very sol. Et_2O, $CHCl_3$. Sol. C_6H_6, ligroin. Insol. H_2O.

Semicarbazone: cryst. from EtOH. M.p. about 208°.

Knorr, Weissenborn, Laage, U.S.P., 1,899,340, (*Chem. Zentr.*, 1932, II, 2747); D.R.P., 591,452, (*Chem. Zentr.*, 1932, II, 2748).
Spath, *Ber.*, 1914, **47**, 767.
Auwers, *Ber.*, 1906, **39**, 3761.

Tolyl acetate.

See under Cresol.

***o*-Tolylacetic Acid** (2-*Methylphenylacetic acid*)

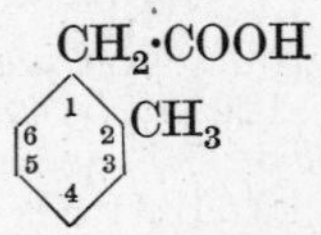

$C_9H_{10}O_2$ MW, 150

Needles from H_2O. M.p. 88–9°. Very sol. hot H_2O. Ox. ⟶ phthalic acid. Electrolytic red. ⟶ β-*o*-tolylethyl alcohol.

Amide: $C_9H_{11}ON$. MW, 149. Plates from H_2O. M.p. 161°. Very sol. hot EtOH. Spar. sol. cold H_2O, Et_2O. Sublimes.

Nitrile: *o*-tolubenzyl cyanide, *o*-xylyl cyanide. C_9H_9N. MW, 131. Liq. B.p. 244°. D^{22} 1·0156.

Schorigin, *Ber.*, 1910, **43**, 1941.
Radziszewski, Wispek, *Ber.*, 1885, **18**, 1281.

***m*-Tolylacetic Acid** (3-*Methylphenylacetic acid*).

Needles. M.p. 61°. Very sol. hot H_2O. Electrolytic red. ⟶ β-*m*-tolylethyl alcohol.

Me ester: $C_{10}H_{12}O_2$. MW, 164. B.p. 228–9°. $D^{17.5}$ 1·044.

Et ester: $C_{11}H_{14}O_2$. MW, 178. B.p. 237–8°. $D^{17.5}$ 1·018.

Amide: needles from H_2O. M.p. 141°. Sol. hot EtOH. Spar. sol. cold H_2O, Et_2O. Sublimes in plates.

Nitrile: *m*-tolubenzyl cyanide, *m*-xylyl cyanide. B.p. 240–1°. D^{22} 1·0022.

Radziszewski, Wispek, *Ber.*, 1885, **18**, 1282.
Seńkowski, *Monatsh.*, 1888, **9**, 855.

p-Tolylacetic Acid (*4-Methylphenylacetic acid*).

Needles or plates from H_2O. M.p. 94°. B.p. 265–7°. Sol. hot H_2O, EtOH, Et_2O, $CHCl_3$, C_6H_6. Sublimes. Electrolytic red. ⟶ β-*p*-tolylethyl alcohol.

Et ester: liq. with unpleasant odour. B.p. 240°.

Amide: plates from H_2O. M.p. 185°. Sol. hot EtOH. Spar. sol. cold H_2O, Et_2O. Sublimes.

Nitrile: *p*-tolubenzyl cyanide, *p*-xylyl cyanide. F.p. 18°. M.p. 18°. B.p. 242–3°. D^{22} 0·9922.

Schorigin, *Ber.*, 1910, **43**, 1941.
Radziszewski, Wispek, *Ber.*, 1885, **18**, 1281.

o-Tolylacetone (*β-Keto-α-*o*-tolylpropane, 2-acetonyltoluene, methyl* o*-tolubenzyl ketone, methyl* o*-xylyl ketone*)

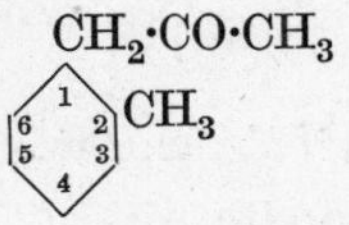

$C_{10}H_{12}O$ MW, 148

Liq. B.p. 227°, 122°/23 mm.

Oxime: m.p. 75°.

Semicarbazone: m.p. 181°.

Ruzicka, Ehmann, Weisz, *Helv. Chim. Acta*, 1932, **15**, 159.
Tiffeneau, *Ann. chim. phys.*, 1907, **10**, 195.

m-Tolylacetone (*β-Keto-α-*m*-tolylpropane, 3-acetonyltoluene, methyl* m*-tolubenzyl ketone, methyl* m*-xylyl ketone*).

Liq. B.p. 228–9°. D^0 1·019.

Semicarbazone: m.p. 139°.

See last reference above.

p-Tolylacetone (*β-Keto-α-*p*-tolylpropane, 4-acetonyltoluene, methyl* p*-tolubenzyl ketone, methyl* p*-xylyl ketone*).

Liq. B.p. 232–3°, 109–10°/12 mm. Forms bisulphite comp.

Oxime: prisms from pet. ether. M.p. 90–1°.

Semicarbazone: m.p. 158°.

Ruzicka, Ehmann, Rierink, *Helv. Chim. Acta*, 1932, **15**, 160.
Tiffeneau, *Ann. chim. phys.*, 1907, **10**, 195.

ω-p-Tolylacetophenone.
See 4-Methyldeoxybenzoin.

p-Tolylacetylene

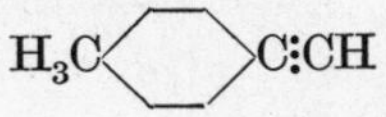

C_9H_8 MW, 116

Prisms. M.p. 23°. B.p. 168°, 65–7°/18 mm. D^{25} 0·9159. n_D^{25} 1·5447. Gives explosive Cu and Ag derivs.

Otto, *J. Am. Chem. Soc.*, 1934, **56**, 1393.
Vaughn, *ibid.*, 2064.
Gattermann, *Ann.*, 1906, **347**, 359.

2-p-Tolylacrolein.
See p-Methylcinnamaldehyde.

2-Tolylacrylic Acid.
See o-, m-, and p-Methylcinnamic Acid.

Tolylaminophenol.
See Hydroxy-methyldiphenylamine.

Tolylanisidine.
See under Hydroxy-methyldiphenylamine.

N-Tolylanthranilic Acid.
See Methyldiphenylamine-carboxylic Acid.

p-Tolyl azide (p-*Azidotoluene*)

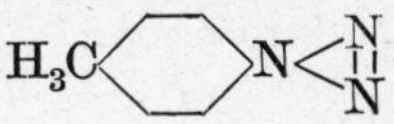

$C_7H_7N_3$ MW, 133

Yellow oil. B.p. 80°/10 mm. Decomp. at 180°. D_4^{23} 1·0527. Volatile in steam.

Lindemann, Thiele, *Ber.*, 1928, **61**, 1529.
Ponzio, *Gazz. chim. ital.*, 1916, **46**, 57.
Dimroth, Pfister, *Ber.*, 1910, **43**, 2760.

Tolylazoimide.
See Methylbenztriazole.

Tolylbenzoic Acid.
See Methyldiphenyl-carboxylic Acid.

Tolylbenzylamine.
See N-Benzyltoluidine.

p-Tolylbenzylcarbinol (*β-Phenyl-α-*p*-tolylethyl alcohol, α-hydroxy-4-methyldiphenylethane*)

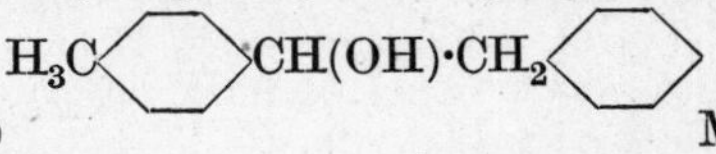

$C_{15}H_{16}O$ MW, 212

Needles. M.p. 107–8° (66°). Dist. without decomp. above 360°. Sol. EtOH, Et_2O, $CHCl_3$, C_6H_6.

Tiffeneau, Lévy, *Bull. soc. chim.*, 1931, **49**, 1738.
Mann, *Ber.*, 1881, **14**, 1646.

Tolyl benzyl Ketone.
See 2′-, 3′, *and* 4′-Methyldeoxybenzoin.

Tolylbutane.
See Butyltoluene.

Tolylbutenone.
See Methyl methylstyryl Ketone.

***o*-Tolylcarbamic Acid** (o-*Methylcarbanilic acid*)

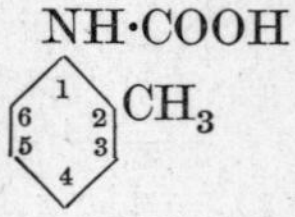

$C_8H_9O_2N$ MW, 151

β-*Chloroethyl ester* : $C_{10}H_{12}O_2NCl$. MW, 213·5. Needles from C_6H_6. M.p. 45°. B.p. 209–10°/37 mm.

γ-*Chloropropyl ester* : $C_{11}H_{14}O_2NCl$. MW, 227·5. Needles from ligroin. M.p. 49° (46–46·5°). B.p. 182·5°/4·5 mm. (170–5°/5 mm.).

Butyl ester : $C_{12}H_{17}O_2N$. MW, 207. Prisms. M.p. 45·5°.

Chattaway, Saerens, *J. Chem. Soc.*, 1920, **117**, 711.
Adams, Segur, *J. Am. Chem. Soc.*, 1923, **45**, 787.
Adams, Pierce, *ibid.*, 793.

***p*-Tolylcarbamic Acid** (p-*Methylcarbanilic acid*).

Et ester : *p*-tolylurethane. $C_{10}H_{13}O_2N$. MW, 179. B.p. 243–7°, 128–32°/12 mm.

Butyl ester : prisms. M.p. 63°.

β-*Chloroethyl ester* : cryst. from C_6H_6. M.p. 61°.

γ-*Chloropropyl ester* : straw-coloured oil. B.p. 188°/4·5 mm. D_{20}^{20} 1·186. n_D^{18} 1·494.

See previous references.

***o*-Tolylcarbinol** (2-*Methylbenzyl alcohol*)

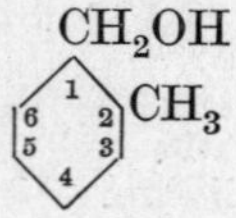

$C_8H_{10}O$ MW, 122

Needles. M.p. 36°. B.p. 219°, 135°/30 mm. D^{40} 1·023. Sol. 100 parts cold H_2O, 60 parts at the boil. Very sol. EtOH, Et_2O, $CHCl_3$. Ox. ⟶ *o*-toluic aldehyde.

Me ether : $C_9H_{12}O$. MW, 136. Oil with unpleasant odour. B.p. 187–8°.

Et ether : $C_{10}H_{14}O$. MW, 150. Sweet-smelling oil. B.p. 208–10°.

Isoamyl ether : $C_{13}H_{20}O$. MW, 192. Oil with aromatic odour. B.p. 125°/15 mm.

Acetyl : liq. B.p. 228–30°/753 mm.

Urethane : m.p. 79°.

Colson, *Ann. chim.*, 1885, **6**, 115.

***m*-Tolylcarbinol** (3-*Methylbenzyl alcohol*).

Oil. B.p. 217°. D^{17} 0·9157. Sol. 20 parts cold H_2O. Misc. with EtOH, Et_2O. Ox. ⟶ *m*-toluic aldehyde + *m*-toluic acid.

Et ether : b.p. 202°/740 mm. D^{17} 0·9302.

Acetyl : oil. B.p. 226°.

Colson, *Ann. chim.*, 1885, **6**, 117.
Radziszewski, Wispek, *Ber.*, 1882, **15**, 1747.

***p*-Tolylcarbinol** (4-*Methylbenzyl alcohol*).

Needles. M.p. 60°. B.p. 217°. Sol. EtOH, Et_2O. Spar. sol. cold H_2O, mod. sol. hot.

Et ether : b.p. 203°/740 mm. D^{17} 0·9304.

Acetyl : oil. B.p. 220°.

Oddo, *Gazz. chim. ital.*, 1911, **41**, 285.
Cannizzaro, *Ann.*, 1862, **124**, 255.

2-*p*-Tolylcinchoninic Acid.
See 2-*p*-Tolylquinoline-4-carboxylic Acid.

2:3-Tolylenediamine (2:3-*Diaminotoluene*, 3-*methyl*-o-*phenylenediamine*)

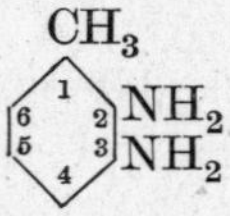

$C_7H_{10}N_2$ MW, 122

Cryst. M.p. 63–4°. B.p. 255°. Sol. most. org. solvents. Boiling H·COOH ⟶ 4-methylbenziminazole.

Gabriel, Thieme, *Ber.*, 1919, **52**, 1081.

2:4-Tolylenediamine (2:4-*Diaminotoluene*, 4-*methyl*-m-*phenylenediamine*, unsym.-m-*toluylenediamine*).

Needles from H_2O, prisms from EtOH. M.p. 99°. B.p. 292°, 148–50°/8 mm. Very sol. boiling H_2O, EtOH, Et_2O. Aq. sol. darkens in air. Reduces warm $NH_3.AgNO_3$. Ox. ⟶ 2-amino-4-nitrotoluene + 2 : 4-dinitrotoluene. Sol. in dil. HCl on warming with dil. $KClO_3$ ⟶ light violet col.

2-N-*Me* : $C_8H_{12}N_2$. MW, 136. Oil. B.p. 273°. 2-N-*Benzoyl* : needles. M.p. 167°.

2-N-*Di-Me* : *see* 2-*N*-Dimethyl-2 : 4-tolylenediamine.

4-N-*Di-Me* : *see* 4-*N*-Dimethyl-2 : 4-tolylenediamine.

N-*Tetra-Me* : $C_{11}H_{18}N_2$. MW, 178. Brownish-yellow oil. B.p. 255–6°/757 mm., 148–50°/24–6 mm. D^{24} 0·9661. *Picrate* : prisms from AcOEt. M.p. 162–3°.

2-N-*Et*: $C_9H_{14}N_2$. MW, 150. Liq. B.p. 274–5°.

4-N-*Et*: liq. B.p. 289–91°.

2-N-*Di-Et*: $C_{11}H_{18}N_2$. MW, 178. Yellow oil. B.p. 259°. Volatile in steam. *B,2HCl*: cryst. + H_2O. M.p. 213–15°.

4-N-*Butyl*: $C_{11}H_{18}N_2$. MW, 178. Needles from Et_2O. M.p. 53°. Spar. sol. H_2O, ligroin.

4-N-*Phenyl*: *see* 3-Amino-4-methyldiphenylamine.

4-N-*Et*-4-*Phenyl*: $C_{15}H_{18}N_2$. MW, 226. Cryst. from ligroin. M.p. 59–60°.

4-N-p-*Tolyl*: *see* 3-Amino-4 : 4′-dimethyldiphenylamine.

2-N-*Benzyl*: $C_{14}H_{16}N_2$. MW, 212. Needles. M.p. 81°. Very sol. EtOH, Et_2O. Insol. cold H_2O.

4-N-*Formyl*: cryst. from H_2O. M.p. 113–14°.

2 : 4-N-*Diformyl*: needles from H_2O. M.p. 176–7°.

2-N-*Acetyl*: needles. M.p. 140°.

4-N-*Acetyl*: prisms or needles. M.p. 161·5°.

2 : 4-N-*Diacetyl*: needles. M.p. 224°.

4-N-*Benzoyl*: prisms. M.p. 142°.

2 : 4-N-*Dibenzoyl*: plates from AcOH. M.p. 224°.

2-N-*Benzenesulphonyl*: plates from EtOH. M.p. 138°.

4-N-*Benzenesulphonyl*: m.p. 138°.

2 : 4-N-*Dibenzenesulphonyl*: needles. M.p. 191°.

4-N-p-*Toluenesulphonyl*: cryst. powder. M.p. 160°.

2 : 4-N-*Di*-p-*toluenesulphonyl*: needles. M.p. 192–3°.

Mahood, Schaffner, *Organic Syntheses*, 1931, XI, 32.
Gnehm, Blumer, *Ann.*, 1899, **304**, 106.

2 : 5-Tolylenediamine (2:5-*Diaminotoluene*, 2-*methyl*-p-*phenylenediamine*, p-*toluylenediamine*).

Plates from C_6H_6. M.p. 64°. B.p. 273–4°. Sol. H_2O, EtOH, Et_2O, hot C_6H_6. Spar. sol. cold C_6H_6. $MnO_2 + H_2SO_4 \longrightarrow$ toluquinone.

2-N-*Me*: $C_8H_{12}N_2$. MW, 136. Thick oil. B.p. 276–276·5°. Rapidly oxidises in air. 2-p-*Toluenesulphonyl*: plates from EtOH.Aq. M.p. 118–19°.

2-N-*Di-Me*: *see* 2-*N*-Dimethyl-2 : 5-tolylenediamine.

5-N-*Di-Me*: *see* 5-*N*-Dimethyl-2 : 5-tolylenediamine.

2 : 5-N-*Tetra-Me*: $C_{11}H_{18}N_2$. MW, 178. Oil. B.p. 260°. $FeCl_3 \longrightarrow$ blue col. *Monomethiodide*: needles from H_2O. M.p. 160°.

2-N-*Et*: $C_9H_{14}N_2$. MW, 150. Thick oil. B.p. 272° (in hydrogen). *B,2HCl*: m.p. 124° decomp. 5-N-*Benzoyl*: needles from C_6H_6–ligroin. M.p. 174°.

2-N-*Di-Et*: $C_{11}H_{18}N_2$. MW, 178. M.p. 24°. B.p. 266–7°.

5-N-o-*Tolyl*: *see* 4-Amino-3 : 2′-dimethyldiphenylamine.

2 : 5-N-*Di*-p-*tolyl*: $C_{21}H_{22}N_2$. MW, 302. Plates from AcOH. M.p. 112–13°.

2 : 5-N-*Diacetyl*: prisms from EtOH.Aq. M.p. 220°.

2-N-*Benzenesulphonyl*: needles from H_2O. M.p. 147°.

2-N-p-*Toluenesulphonyl*: prisms from EtOH.Aq. M.p. 150°.

Nietzki, *Ber.*, 1877, **10**, 1157.

2 : 6-Tolylenediamine (2:6-*Diaminotoluene*, 2-*methyl*-m-*phenylenediamine*).

Prisms from H_2O. M.p. 105°. $FeCl_3 \longrightarrow$ deep brown col.

N-*Diacetyl*: m.p. 202–3°.

Ullmann, *Ber.*, 1884, **17**, 1959.

3 : 4-Tolylenediamine (3:4-*Diaminotoluene*, 4-*methyl*-o-*phenylenediamine*, unsym.-o-*toluylenediamine*).

Plates from ligroin. M.p. 89–90°. B.p. 265°. Mod. sol. cold H_2O. Sublimes. Base and salts rapidly oxidise in aq. sol. in air. Boiling H·COOH $\longrightarrow$ 5-methylbenziminazole.

4-N-*Me*: $C_8H_{12}N_2$. MW, 136. Plates from Et_2O. M.p. 43–4°. B.p. 260°/752 mm. *B,HCl*: plates from EtOH. M.p. 175–80°. *B,2HCl*: prisms from EtOH. M.p. 175–85° decomp. $(B,COOH)_2$: needles. M.p. 124°. *Picrate*: yellow cryst. M.p. 164°. 3 : 4-N-*Diacetyl*: plates from H_2O. M.p. 183–4°. 4-N-p-*Toluenesulphonyl*: needles. M.p. 133°.

3 : 4-N-*Di-Me*: $C_9H_{14}N_2$. MW, 150. Oil. B.p. 259–60°/740 mm. $FeCl_3 \longrightarrow$ red col. *B,2HCl*: needles. M.p. 125°.

4-N-*Di-Me*: *see* 4-*N*-Dimethyl-3 : 4-tolylenediamine.

3 : 4-N-*Tetra-Me*: $C_{11}H_{18}N_2$. MW, 178. Liq. B.p. 224·5–225·5°/717 mm.

3-N-*Et*: $C_9H_{14}N_2$. MW, 150. Needles from pet. ether. M.p. 59°. Becomes violet in air. $FeCl_3 \longrightarrow$ red col.

4-N-*Et*: plates from CS_2.Aq. M.p. 55°. Very sol. most org. solvents. Not very stable. *B,HCl*: cryst. from EtOH. M.p. 176°. $B_2,(COOH)_2$: needles. M.p. 151°. 3-N-*Acetyl*: cryst. from EtOH. M.p. 177°.

3 : 4-N-*Di-Et* : *see sym.*-Diethyl-3 : 4-tolylenediamine.

4-N-*Butyl* : $C_{11}H_{18}N_2$. MW, 178. Very readily oxidises. 4-N-*Acetyl* : needles from Et_2O–pet. ether. M.p. 102°. 3 : 4-N-*Diacetyl* : cryst. from EtOH.Aq. M.p. 130°.

3-N-*Phenyl* : *see* 6-Amino-3-methyldiphenylamine.

4-N-*Phenyl* : *see* 2-Amino-4-methyldiphenylamine.

3-N-p-*Tolyl* : *see* 6-Amino-3 : 4′-dimethyldiphenylamine.

4-N-p-*Tolyl* : *see* 2-Amino-4 : 4′-dimethyldiphenylamine.

3-N-*Acetyl* : cryst. from $CHCl_3$–pet. ether. M.p. about 95°.

4-N-*Acetyl* : needles. M.p. 131–2°.

3 : 4-N-*Diacetyl* : needles from H_2O. M.p. 210°.

3-N-*Benzoyl* : needles from C_6H_6. M.p. 158°.

4-N-*Benzoyl* : needles from EtOH or C_6H_6. M.p. 193–4°.

3 : 4-N-*Dibenzoyl* : needles from AcOH. M.p. 263–4°.

3-N-*Benzenesulphonyl* : needles from C_6H_6. M.p. 134–5°.

4-N-*Benzenesulphonyl* : needles from EtOH.Aq. M.p. 146–7°.

3 : 4-N-*Dibenzenesulphonyl* : plates from EtOH. M.p. 178–9°.

4-N-p-*Toluenesulphonyl* : needles. M.p. 140°.

Reilly, Hickinbottom, *J. Chem. Soc.*, 1919, **115**, 177.
Fischer, *Ber.*, 1893, **26**, 194.
Bamberger, Wulz, *Ber.*, 1891, **24**, 2082.
Noelting, Stoecklin, *ibid.*, 565.

3 : 5-Tolylenediamine (3 : 5-*Diaminotoluene, 5-methyl*-m-*phenylenediamine*, sym.-m-*toluylenediamine*).

Oil. B.p. 283–5°. Very sol. H_2O.

B,2HCl : needles. M.p. 255–60° decomp.

3 : 5-N-*Diphenyl* : $C_{19}H_{18}N_2$. MW, 274. Cryst. from AcOH. M.p. 105°. Sol. cold EtOH, Et_2O, CS_2, C_6H_6. 3 : 5-N-*Diacetyl* : needles. M.p. 160°. 3 : 5-N-*Dibenzoyl* : needles from C_6H_6–ligroin. M.p. 190–1°.

3 : 5-N-*Diacetyl* : prisms from EtOH. M.p. 235–6°.

Davis, *J. Chem. Soc.*, 1902, **81**, 873.

1-Tolylethyl Alcohol.
See Methyltolylcarbinol.

Tolylethylene.
See Methylstyrene.

***o*-Tolylglycine** (o-*Toluidinoacetic acid*)

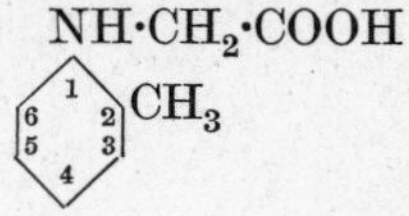

$C_9H_{11}O_2N$ MW, 165

Needles from EtOH. M.p. 149–50° (160°). Very sol. EtOH, Et_2O. Insol. cold H_2O. $k = 5{\cdot}9 \times 10^{-5}$ at 25°. Reduces silver salts.

Et ester : $C_{11}H_{15}O_2N$. MW, 193. Cryst. M.p. 26°. B.p. 280°. D^{20} 1·058.

Amide : $C_9H_{12}ON_2$. MW, 164. Needles from H_2O. M.p. 140°. Sol. EtOH, hot H_2O.

N-*Et* : $C_{11}H_{15}O_2N$. MW, 193. Cryst. from C_6H_6. M.p. 63–4°.

N-*Formyl* : cryst. from H_2O. M.p. 113–15°.

N-*Acetyl* : plates from EtOH.Aq. M.p. 210–12°. $k = 2{\cdot}19 \times 10^{-4}$ at 25°.

N-*Chloroacetyl* : plates from C_6H_6. M.p. 116–17°.

N-*Bromoacetyl* : plates from H_2O. M.p. 124°.

Staats, *Ber.*, 1880, **13**, 137.
Ehrlich, *Ber.*, 1883, **16**, 204.
Steppes, *J. prakt. Chem.*, 1900, **62**, 491.

***m*-Tolylglycine** (m-*Toluidinoacetic acid*).

Et ester : plates from EtOH. M.p. 68°. Sol. EtOH, Et_2O, AcOH. Very spar. sol. hot H_2O.

Ehrlich, *Ber.*, 1882, **15**, 2011.
Gault, *Bull. soc. chim.*, 1908, **3**, 372.

***p*-Tolylglycine** (p-*Toluidinoacetic acid*).

Plates from Et_2O–pet. ether. M.p. 132° (120–1°). Insol. pet. ether, cold H_2O. Unstable in air. $k = 1{\cdot}5 \times 10^{-5}$ at 25°. Reduces Tollen's reagent.

Et ester : m.p. 52–3° (48–9°). B.p. 279° slight decomp. Very sol. Et_2O. Mod. sol. cold EtOH. Very spar. sol. hot H_2O.

Amide : cryst. from H_2O. M.p. 168° (162–3°). Sol. EtOH, C_6H_6, hot H_2O. Insol. cold H_2O.

Nitrile : $C_9H_{10}N_2$. MW, 146. Cryst. M.p. 62°. Very sol. common org. solvents except ligroin. N-*Me* : m.p. 57°. B.p. 156–7°/9 mm.

Anilide : needles from H_2O. M.p. 82–3°.

N-*Acetyl* : plates from H_2O. M.p. 175–6°.

Steppes, *J. prakt. Chem.*, 1900, **62**, 487.
Bischoff, Hausdörfer, *Ber.*, 1892, **25**, 2282.
v. Miller, Plöchl, Sieber, *Ber.*, 1898, **31**, 2715.
M.L.B., D.R.P., 175,797, (*Chem. Zentr.*, 1906, II, 1700).

Tolylglycollic Acid.
See Methylmandelic Acid.

p-Tolylglyoxal (p-*Toluylformaldehyde*)

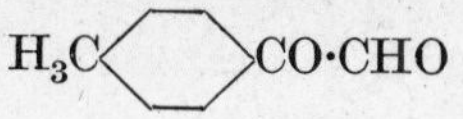

$C_9H_8O_2$ MW, 148

Needles + $1H_2O$. M.p. anhyd. 111–12° (101°). Sol. EtOH, Et_2O, $CHCl_3$, C_6H_6. Spar. sol. H_2O, ligroin.

Aldoxime: needles from C_6H_6. M.p. 100°.
Acetyl: plates from MeOH. M.p. 67–8°.
Phenylhydrazone: plates from EtOH. M.p. 165°.
Dioxime: *see* p-Tolylglyoxime.
Phenylosazone: yellow needles from EtOH. M.p. 145°.

Müller, v. Pechmann, *Ber.*, 1889, **22**, 2560.
Neuberg, Ostendorf, *Biochem. Z.*, 1935, **279**, 459.

p-Tolylglyoxime

$C_9H_{10}O_2N_2$ MW, 178

α-*Form*:
M.p. 170–1°. Above m.p. ⟶ β-form.
Diacetyl: m.p. 115°.
Monobenzyl: m.p. 147–8°.

β-*Form*:
M.p. 192–3°. Forms Ni salt.
Diacetyl: m.p. 73–4°.
Dibenzoyl: m.p. 170°.

Avogadro, *Gazz. chim. ital.*, 1923, **53**, 698.

Tolylglyoxylic Acid.
See Toluylformic Acid.

o-Tolylguanidine (*Guanyl*-o-*toluidine*)

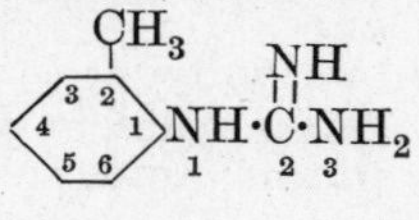

$C_8H_{11}N_3$ MW, 149

B,HCl: cryst. from $Me_2CO–Et_2O$. M.p. 133–5°. Sol. H_2O, Me_2CO. Insol. Et_2O.
Nitrate: cryst. from H_2O. M.p. 133°. Very bitter taste.
Picrate: m.p. 223–4°.
3-*Phenyl*: *see* Phenyl-o-tolylguanidine.

Braun, *J. Am. Chem. Soc.*, 1933, **55**, 1281.
M.L.B., D.R.P., 172,979, (*Chem. Zentr.*, 1906, II, 984).

m-Tolylguanidine (*Guanyl*-m-*toluidine*).
Sulphate: cryst. from $EtOH–Et_2O$. M.p. 215–17°. Sol. H_2O. Insol. Et_2O.

Braun, *J. Am. Chem. Soc.*, 1933, **55**, 1282.

p-Tolylguanidine (*Guanyl*-p-*toluidine*).
B,HCl: cryst. from $EtOH–Et_2O$. M.p. 136–7°. Sol. H_2O, EtOH. Insol. Et_2O.
B,HNO$_3$: m.p. 146–7°. Very bitter taste.
3-*Phenyl*: *see* Phenyl-p-tolylguanidine.

See previous reference and also
Kämpf, *Ber.*, 1904, **37**, 1683.

o-Tolylhydrazine (o-*Hydrazinotoluene*)

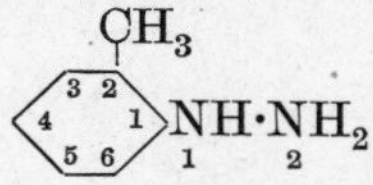

$C_7H_{10}N_2$ MW, 122

Needles. M.p. 59° (56°). Sol. EtOH, Et_2O, $CHCl_3$. Spar. sol. cold ligroin.
B,HNO$_3$: m.p. 98–100° (sinters about 75°).
2-N-*Phenyl*: *see* 2-Methylhydrazobenzene.
2-N-*Formyl*: plates from H_2O. M.p. 120°.
2-N-*Acetyl*: leaflets from H_2O. M.p. 104°.
2-N-*Propionyl*: plates from H_2O. M.p. 83–4°.
2-N-*Isobutyryl*: leaflets from C_6H_6–pet. ether. M.p. 93°.
2-N-*Benzoyl*: needles. M.p. 180°.

Fischer, Bösler, *Ann.*, 1882, **212**, 338.
Gallinek, v. Richter, *Ber.*, 1885, **18**, 3175.

m-Tolylhydrazine (m-*Hydrazinotoluene*).
Oil. B.p. 240–4°.
B,HNO$_3$: needles. M.p. 145–7°.
2-N-*Phenyl*: *see* 3-Methylhydrazobenzene.
2-N-*Propionyl*: m.p. 131°.

Buchka, Schachtebeck, *Ber.*, 1889, **22**, 841.

p-Tolylhydrazine (p-*Hydrazinotoluene*).
Leaflets from Et_2O. M.p. 65–6° (61°). B.p. 240–4° slight decomp. Sol. EtOH, Et_2O, C_6H_6. Spar. sol. H_2O.
B,HNO$_3$: leaflets. M.p. 152–3°.
2-N-*Phenyl*: *see* 4-Methylhydrazobenzene.
2-N-*Formyl*: prisms or needles from EtOH. M.p. 166·5°.
2-N-*Acetyl*: cryst. M.p. 130° (127°).
2-N-*Propionyl*: needles from H_2O. M.p. 170°.
2-N-*Isobutyryl*: leaflets. M.p. 147–8°.
1-N-*Benzoyl*: leaflets from C_6H_6. M.p. 68–70°. 2-N-*Acetyl*: needles from C_6H_6. M.p. 135°.
2-N-*Benzoyl*: leaflets from C_6H_6. M.p. 146°.
1 : 2-N-*Dibenzoyl*: leaflets from EtOH. M.p. 188°.

McPherson, Stratton, *J. Am. Chem. Soc.*, 1915, **37**, 908.
Bamberger, *Ber.*, 1898, **31**, 582.
Fischer, *Ber.*, 1876, **9**, 890.

Tolyl α-hydroxybenzyl Ketone.
See Methylbenzoin.

***N*-*o*-Tolylhydroxylamine** (o-*Hydroxylaminotoluene*)

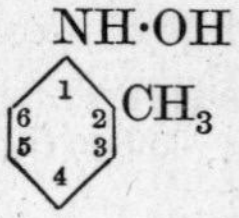

C_7H_9ON MW, 123

Needles from Et_2O–C_6H_6. M.p. 44°. Sol. EtOH, Et_2O, C_6H_6. Spar. sol. ligroin.

Bamberger, Rising, *Ann.*, 1901, **316**, 278.
Bretschneider, *J. prakt. Chem.*, 1897, **55**, 293.

***N*-*m*-Tolylhydroxylamine** (m-*Hydroxylaminotoluene*).
Leaflets from C_6H_6–pet. ether. M.p. 68·5°. Sol. EtOH, Et_2O, $CHCl_3$, hot C_6H_6. Mod. sol. hot H_2O. Spar. sol. ligroin.

Bamberger, Rising, *Ann.*, 1901, **316**, 283.

***N*-*p*-Tolylhydroxylamine** (p-*Hydroxylaminotoluene*).
Leaflets from C_6H_6. M.p. 94°. Sol. EtOH, Et_2O, $CHCl_3$, hot C_6H_6. Insol. cold ligroin. At 115–20° ⟶ *p*-azoxytoluene.

Willstätter, Kubli, *Ber.*, 1908, **41**, 1937.
Bamberger, Rising, *Ann.*, 1901, **316**, 280.

Tolylisobutylamine.
See N-Isobutyl-toluidine.

***o*-Tolyl isocyanate** (o-*Tolylcarbonimide*)

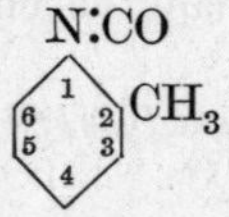

C_8H_7ON MW, 133

Liq. B.p. 185–6°.

Gattermann, Cantzler, *Ber.*, 1892, **25**, 1086.
Haager, Doht, *Monatsh.*, 1906, **27**, 271.

***m*-Tolyl isocyanate** (m-*Tolylcarbonimide*).
B.p. 195–8° (183°). *m*-Toluidine ⟶ di-*m*-tolylurea.

Haager, Doht, *Monatsh.*, 1906, **27**, 273.
Gattermann, Cantzler, *Ber.*, 1892, **25**, 1089.

***p*-Tolyl isocyanate** (p-*Tolylcarbonimide*).
Liq. B.p. 187°/751 mm.

See first reference above and also
Kühn, Henschel, *Ber.*, 1888, **21**, 505 (*Note*).

Tolylnaphthylamine.
See under Naphthylamine.

Tolyl naphthyl sulphide.
See under Thionaphthol.

***o*-Tolylnitromethane** (ω-*Nitro*-o-*xylene*)

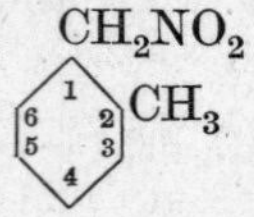

$C_8H_9O_2N$ MW, 151

M.p. 12–14°. B.p. 145–6°/23 mm., slight decomp., 138–9°/20 mm. D_0^{18} 1·1423. n_D^{18} 1·5439. Turns red on standing.

Konowalow, *Chem. Zentr.*, 1905, II, 817.
Wislicenus, Wren, *Ber.*, 1905, **38**, 503.

***m*-Tolylnitromethane** (ω-*Nitro*-m-*xylene*).
Yellowish liq. B.p. 140°/35 mm. decomp., 128–32°/19 mm. D_0^0 1·1370.

Konowaloff, *Chem. Zentr.*, 1899, I, 1238.
Heilmann, *Ber.*, 1890, **23**, 3165.
Wislicenus, Wren, *Ber.*, 1905, **38**, 505.

***p*-Tolylnitromethane** (ω-*Nitro*-p-*xylene*).
M.p. 11–12°. B.p. 150–1°/35 mm. slight decomp. D_0^{20} 1·1234. n_D^{20} 1·53106.

Konowaloff, *Chem. Zentr.*, 1899, I, 1238.
Wislicenus, Wren, *Ber.*, 1905, **38**, 506.

Tolylphenetidine.
See under Hydroxy-methyldiphenylamine.

4-*p*-Tolylphenol.
See 4′-Hydroxy-4-methyldiphenyl.

Tolylphenylenediamine.
See 4′-Amino-2-methyldiphenylamine, 2′-Amino-4-methyldiphenylamine, *and* 4′-Amino-4-methyldiphenylamine.

2-Tolylpropionaldehyde.
See o-, and p-Methylhydrocinnamaldehyde.

1-*p*-Tolylpropionic Acid.
See p-Methylhydratropic Acid.

2-Tolylpropionic Acid.
See o-, m-, and p-Methylhydrocinnamic Acid.

1-Tolyl-2-pyridylethylene.
See Methylstyrylpyridine.

2-*m*-Tolylquinoline (ψ-*Flavoline*)

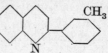

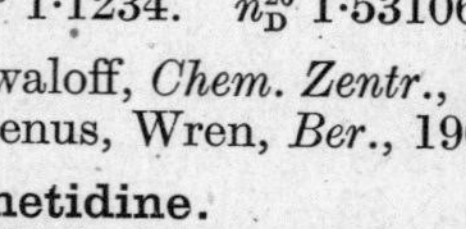

$C_{16}H_{13}N$ MW, 219

Needles from C_6H_6–ligroin. M.p. 77°.

Weidel, Bamberger, *Monatsh.*, 1888, **9**, 109.

2-*p*-Tolylquinoline.

Pale yellow plates from EtOH.Aq. M.p. 83°. B.p. 240°/15 mm.

Picrate: m.p. 194°.

Methiodide: decomp. at 192°.

Methosulphate: needles from EtOH–Et_2O. M.p. 158–9°.

Methopicrate: m.p. 157–8°.

Le Fèvre, Le Fèvre, Pearson, *J. Chem. Soc.*, 1934, 41.
v. Braun, Brauns, *Ber.*, 1927, **60**, 1255.

2-*p*-Tolylquinoline-4-carboxylic Acid (4'-*Methylcinchophene*, 4'-*methylatophan*, 2-p-*tolylcinchonic acid*)

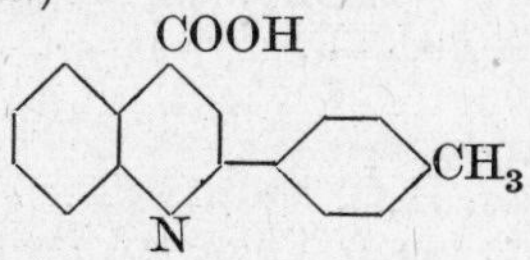

$C_{17}H_{13}O_2N$ MW, 263

Cryst. from EtOH. M.p. 211°. Loses CO_2 at 250°.

Me ester: $C_{18}H_{15}O_2N$. MW, 277. Cryst. M.p. 101°.

Et ester: $C_{19}H_{17}O_2N$. MW, 291. Yellow needles from 70% EtOH. M.p. 54°. Sol. most org. solvents.

Propyl ester: $C_{20}H_{19}O_2N$. MW, 305. Yellow cryst. from EtO_2. M.p. 32°. Sol. usual solvents.

2-*Chloroethyl ester*: $C_{19}H_{16}O_2NCl$. MW, 325·5. Needles from 70% MeOH. M.p. 79°.

Chloride: $C_{17}H_{12}ONCl$. MW, 281·5. *B,HCl*: cryst. M.p. 188°.

Amide: $C_{17}H_{14}ON_2$. MW, 262. Needles from EtOH. M.p. 208°. Sol. cold Me_2CO. Less sol. C_6H_6, toluene.

Hydrazide: cryst. from chlorobenzene. M.p. 232–3°. Sol. propyl alcohol, amyl alcohol, chlorobenzene. Less sol. MeOH, EtOH, isopropyl alcohol, C_6H_6, toluene, xylene. Insol. Et_2O. *Picrate*: prisms from EtOH. Does not melt below 300°.

v. Braun, Brauns, *Ber.*, 1927, **60**, 1255.
John, Ottawa, *J. prakt. Chem.*, 1931, **131**, 314.
Du Puis, Lindwall, *J. Am. Chem. Soc.*, 1934, **56**, 471.

1-*o*-Tolylsemicarbazide

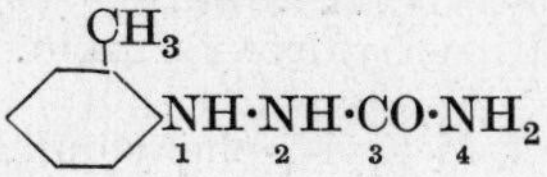

$C_8H_{11}ON_3$ MW, 165

Needles. M.p. 159–60°. Mod. sol. H_2O. Insol. Et_2O, C_6H_6.

4-N-*Me*: m.p. 158–9°.

4-N-*Et*: needles from EtOH. M.p. 130–1°.

4-N-*Phenyl*: needles from EtOH. M.p. 142°.

Pinner, *Ber.*, 1888, **21**, 1221.

1-*m*-Tolylsemicarbazide.

Leaflets from H_2O or EtOH.Aq. M.p. 183–4°. Insol. Et_2O. Employed as antipyretic under name of Marietin.

4-N-*Phenyl*: needles from EtOH. M.p. 159°.

Bayer, D.R.P., 157,572, (*Chem. Zentr.*, 1905, I, 196).

1-*p*-Tolylsemicarbazide.

Leaflets or needles. M.p. 190–1° (187–8°). Sol. hot H_2O, hot EtOH.

4-N-*Phenyl*: needles from AcOEt. M.p. 171°.

Bamberger, *Ber.*, 1902, **35**, 1428.
Pinner, *Ber.*, 1888, **21**, 1222.

2-*m*-Tolylsemicarbazide

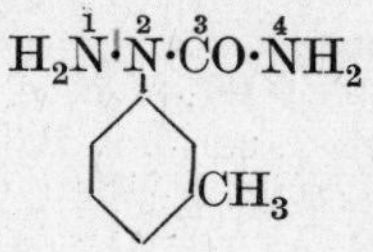

$C_8H_{11}ON_3$ MW, 165

Needles. M.p. 88°. At 140° ⟶ 1-*m*-tolylsemicarbazide.

4-N-*Me*: m.p. 119–20°.

4-N-*Phenyl*: needles from EtOH–Et_2O. M.p. 112°.

Bayer, D.R.P., 163,035, (*Chem. Zentr.*, 1905, II, 1298).

4-*o*-Tolylsemicarbazide

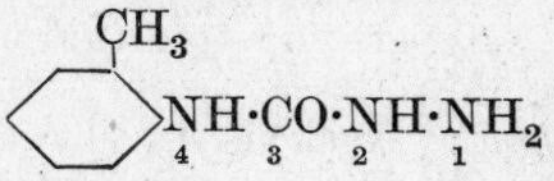

$C_8H_{11}ON_3$ MW, 165

Cryst. from H_2O or EtOH.Aq. M.p. 142–3° decomp.

B,HCl: cryst. from dil. HCl. M.p. 184–6° decomp.

Lei, Sah, Shih, *J. Chinese Chem. Soc.*, 1935, **3**, 246.
Borsche, *Ber.*, 1905, **38**, 835.

4-*p*-Tolylsemicarbazide.

Needles from EtOH. M.p. 259–60°. Spar. sol. hot H_2O.

B,HCl: needles from dil. HCl. M.p. 242°.

Sah, Lei, *J. Chinese Chem. Soc.*, 1934, **2**, 167.

Tolyl styryl Ketone.
See 2-, 3-, *and* 4-Methylchalkone.

o-Tolylthiourea

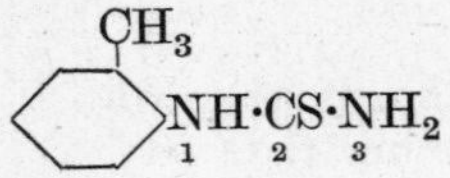

$C_8H_{10}N_2S$ MW, 166

Cryst. from H_2O. M.p. 162° (158°). Sol. EtOH, boiling H_2O. Spar. sol. Et_2O.
1-N-*Me* : *see unsym.*-Methyl-*o*-tolylthiourea.
3-N-*Me* : *see sym.*-Methyl-*o*-tolylthiourea.
3-N-*Et* : *sym.*-ethyl-*o*-tolylthiourea. Prisms from EtOH. M.p. 83–4°.
3-N-*Phenyl* : *see N*-Phenyl-*N'*-*o*-tolylthiourea.

Dyson, Hunter, *J. Soc. Chem. Ind.*, 1926, **45**, 81T.
Heller, Bauer, *J. prakt. Chem.*, 1902, **65**, 371.
Staats, *Ber.*, 1880, **13**, 136.

m-Tolylthiourea.
Prisms from EtOH. M.p. 110–11°. Sol. EtOH, Et_2O. Mod. sol. hot H_2O.
3-N-*Phenyl* : *see N*-Phenyl-*N'*-*m*-tolylthiourea.
3-N-*Propionyl* : prisms from EtOH. M.p. 86–7°.

See first reference above and also
Heller, Bauer, *J. prakt. Chem.*, 1902, **65**, 366, 377.

p-Tolylthiourea.
Plates from EtOH. M.p. 188° (182°). Mod. sol. hot EtOH. Spar. sol. cold H_2O.
3-N-*Me* : *see sym.*-Methyl-*p*-tolylthiourea.
3-N-*Et* : *sym.*-ethyl-*p*-tolylthiourea. Prisms from EtOH. M.p. 95–6°.
3-N-*Isoamyl* : *sym.*-isoamyl-*p*-tolylthiourea. Needles from EtOH. M.p. 217° decomp.
3-N-*Phenyl* : *see N*-Phenyl-*N'*-*p*-tolylthiourea.

I.G., F.P., 762,310, (*Chem. Zentr.*, 1934, II, 1992).
Staats, *Ber.*, 1880, **13**, 136.
Clermont, Wehrlin, *Bull. soc. chim.*, 1876, **26**, 126.

o-Tolylurea

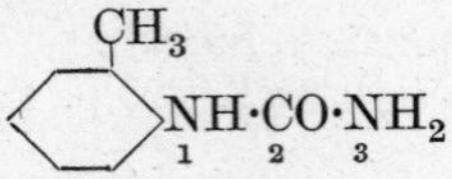

$C_8H_{10}ON_2$ MW, 150

Leaflets from EtOH. M.p. 190–1° (182°). Sol. $EtOH_2$ Et_2O. Insol. cold H_2O.
3-N-*Phenyl* : *see N*-Phenyl-*N'*-*o*-tolylurea.
3-N-o-*Nitrophenyl* : cryst. from EtOH. M.p. 189°.
3-N-*Acetyl* : needles from EtOH. M.p. 168–9°.
3-N-*Isobutyryl* : needles from EtOH. M.p. 134–5°.
3-N-*Palmityl* : needles from EtOH. M.p. 98°.
3-N-*Stearyl* : m.p. 94–5°.
3-N-*Benzoyl* : needles from AcOH. M.p. 210°.

Lei, Sah, Shih, *J. Chinese Chem. Soc.*, 1935, **3**, 246.
v. Braun, *Ber.*, 1908, **41**, 2152.
Walther, Wlodkowski, *J. prakt. Chem.*, 1899, **59**, 273.

m-Tolylurea.
Leaflets from H_2O. M.p. 142°.
3-N-*Phenyl* : *see N*-Phenyl-*N'*-*m*-tolylurea.
1-N-*Nitroso* : yellow needles from Et_2O–pet. ether. M.p. 80°.

Walther, Wlodkowski, *J. prakt. Chem.*, 1899, **59**, 275.
Pierron, *Bull. soc. chim.*, 1906, **35**, 1200.

p-Tolylurea.
Needles from H_2O. M.p. 182–3° (172°). Sol. EtOH.
1-N-*Me* : *see unsym.*-Methyl-*p*-tolylurea.
3-N-*Phenyl* : *see N*-Phenyl-*N'*-*p*-tolylurea.
3-N-*Acetyl* : needles from EtOH. M.p. 199–200°.
3-N-*Isobutyryl* : needles from EtOH. M.p. 138–9°.
3-N-*Palmityl* : m.p. 89–90°.
3-N-*Benzoyl* : needles from EtOH. M.p. 222–3°.
1-N-*Nitroso* : yellow cryst. from Et_2O–pet. ether. M.p. 83°.

Walther, Wlodkowski, *J. prakt. Chem.*, 1899, **59**, 275.
Sah, *Science Reports National Tsing-Hua University*, 1934, **2**, 227.
Thate, *Rec. trav. chim.*, 1929, **48**, 116.

p-Tolylurethane.
See under p-Tolylcarbamic Acid.

p-Tolyl p-xylyl Ketone.
See 4 : 4'-Dimethyldeoxybenzoin.

Tolysin.
See under 6-Methyl-2-phenylquinoline-4-carboxylic Acid.

Torulin.
See Vitamin B_1.

Toxicarol

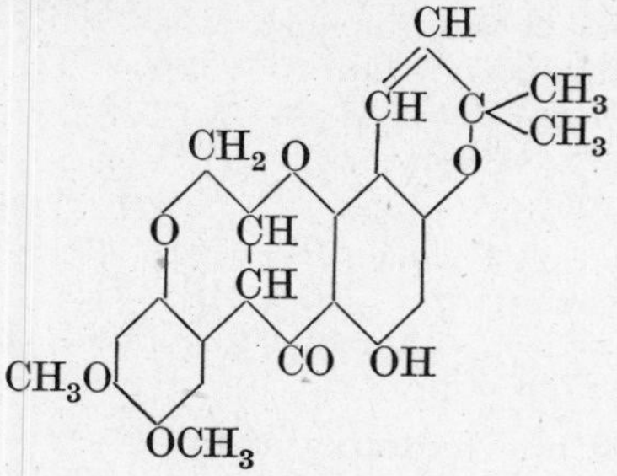

or

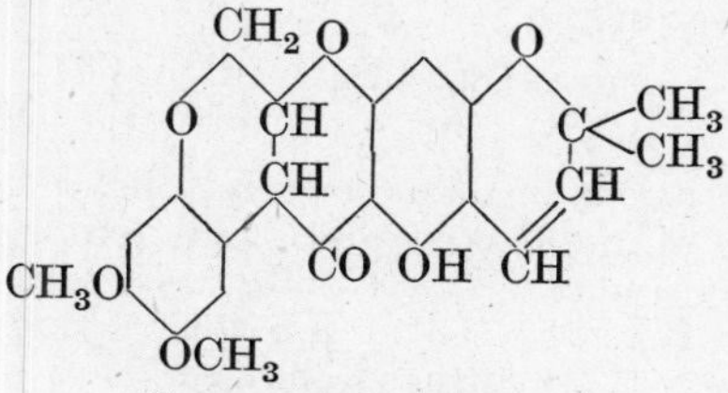

Suggested structures

$C_{23}H_{22}O_7$ MW, 410

Obtained from derris root. Greenish-yellow plates from EtOH. M.p. 218–20°. Properties closely related to those of rotenone.

Monoacetyl deriv.: cryst. from Me_2CO–pet. ether. M.p. 182·5°.

Benzoyl deriv.: needles from C_6H_6–$CHCl_3$. M.p. 202°.

Heyes, Robertson, *J. Chem. Soc.*, 1935, 681.
Butenandt, Hilgetag, *Ann.*, 1933, **506**, 169.
Clark, *J. Am. Chem. Soc.*, 1930, **52**, 2461.

Trehalose (*Mycose*)

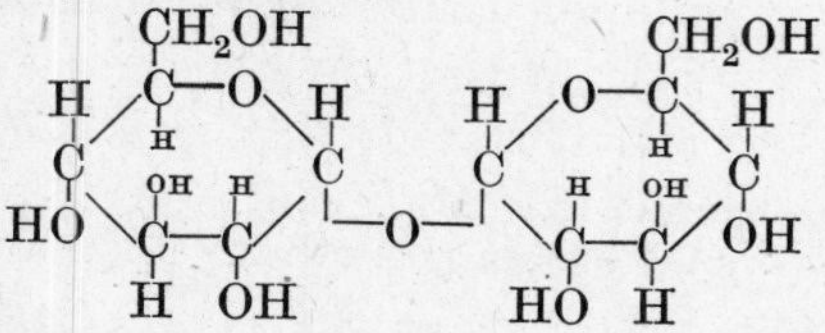

$C_{12}H_{22}O_{11}$ MW, 342

Occurs in fungi, moulds, ergot, algæ, yeast, etc. Prisms + $2H_2O$ from EtOH. M.p. hydrate 97°, anhyd. 210° (203°). Sweet taste. $[\alpha]_D^{20}$ hydrate + 178·3° in H_2O, $[\alpha]_D^{20}$ anhyd. + 197·0° in H_2O. Sol. H_2O. Spar. sol. EtOH. Insol. Et_2O. Does not reduce Fehling's. Non-fermentable. Does not form an osazone. Hyd. by dil. acids ⟶ glucose. HNO_3 ⟶ oxalic acid.

Hexa-acetyl: m.p. 93–6°. $[\alpha]_D^{19}$ + 158·3° in $CHCl_3$.

Octa-acetyl: cryst. from EtOH. M.p. 97–8° (97°, 96–8°, 80°, 70–5°, 100–2° after drying in vacuo). $[\alpha]_D^{20}$ + 162·3° in $CHCl_3$.

Octa-nitrate: laminæ from EtOH. M.p. 124°. Decomp. at 136°. $[\alpha]_D^{18}$ + 173·8° in AcOH.

Octa-Me ether: yellow liq. B.p. 170°/0·03 mm. $[\alpha]_D^{20}$ + 199·8° in C_6H_6.

Schlubach, Maurer, *Ber.*, 1925, **58**, 1183.
Berthelot, *Ann. chim. phys.*, 1859, **55**, 272, 291.
v. Lippmann, *Ber.*, 1912, **45**, 3431.
Will, Lenze, *Ber.*, 1898, **31**, 85.
Pangborn, Anderson, *J. Biol. Chem.*, 1933, **101**, 105.
Bredereck, *Ber.*, 1930, **63**, 959.
Harding, *Sugar*, 1923, **25**, 476, (*Chem. Abstracts*, 1924, **18**, 78).

Triacetin (*Triacetylglycerol, glycerol triacetate*)

$CH_2{\cdot}O{\cdot}CO{\cdot}CH_3$
$CH{\cdot}O{\cdot}CO{\cdot}CH_3$
$CH_2{\cdot}O{\cdot}CO{\cdot}CH_3$

$C_9H_{14}O_6$ MW, 218

Colourless liq. B.p. 258–60°, 172°/40 mm. Sol. EtOH, Et_2O, C_6H_6, $CHCl_3$. Sol. H_2O to 70% at 15°. Prac. insol. CS_2, ligroin. D_4^{25} 1·1562.

Perkin, Simonsen, *J. Chem. Soc.*, 1905, **87**, 858.
Böttinger, *Ann.*, 1891, **263**, 359.

1 : 3 : 5-Triacetobenzene (1 : 3 : 5-*Triacetylbenzene*)

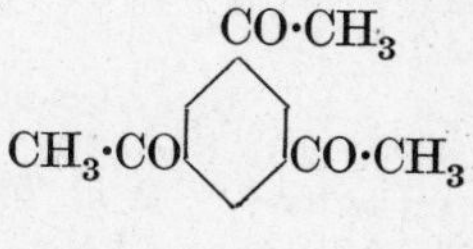

$C_{12}H_{12}O_3$ MW, 204

Needles from EtOH or AcOH. M.p. 163°. Sol. AcOH. Spar. sol. H_2O, EtOH, Et_2O. HNO_3 ⟶ trimesic acid.

Viguier, *Compt. rend.*, 1911, **153**, 1232.
Claisen, Stylos, *Ber.*, 1888, **21**, 1145.

Triacetonalkamine (4-*Hydroxy*-2 : 2 : 6 : 6-*tetramethylpiperidine*)

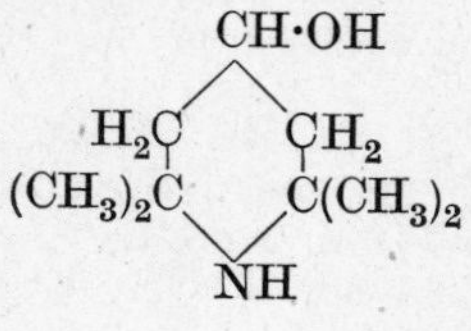

$C_9H_{19}ON$ MW, 157

Plates from Et_2O, hydrated cryst. from H_2O. M.p. 129°. Very sol. H_2O. Spar. sol. Et_2O. Sublimes.

N-*Me*: $C_{10}H_{21}ON$. MW, 171. Hydrated plates from H_2O. M.p. anhyd. 74°. B.p. 125°/12 mm. Very sol. warm H_2O.

O : N-*Di-Me*: $C_{11}H_{23}ON$. MW, 185. Oil. B.p. 217–21°. Spar. sol. H_2O.

O-*Benzoyl*: needles from EtOH.Aq. M.p. 97–8°. *B,HCl*: m.p. 240°.

O : N-*Dibenzoyl*: cryst. $+1H_2O$ from EtOH.Aq. M.p. 200°.

N-*Nitroso*: pale yellow needles from C_6H_6–pet. ether. M.p. 93°.

Orthner, *Ann.*, 1927, **456**, 252.
Harries, *Ann.*, 1918, **417**, 121.
Clarke, Francis, *Ber.*, 1912, **45**, 2060.

Triacetonamine (4-*Keto*-2 : 2 : 6 : 6-*tetramethylpiperidine*, 2 : 2 : 6 : 6-*tetramethyl-γ-piperidone*)

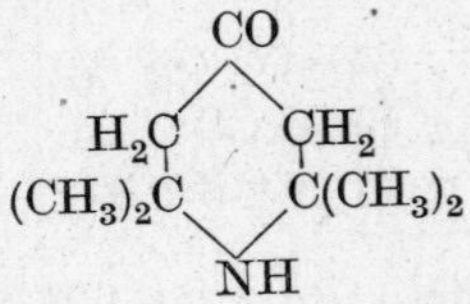

$C_9H_{17}ON$ MW, 155

Plates + $1H_2O$ from Et_2O, m.p. 58°. Anhyd. needles from dry Et_2O, m.p. 34·9°. B.p. 205°. Sol. H_2O, EtOH, Et_2O. Red. ⟶ triacetonalkamine. Forms unstable Na deriv.

B_2,H_2CrO_4: yellow prisms. Decomp. at 105°.

Oxime: prisms from EtOH. M.p. 153°.

Semicarbazone: cryst. from EtOH. M.p. 219–20°.

N-*Me*: 1 : 2 : 2 : 6 : 6-pentamethyl-γ-piperidone. $C_{10}H_{19}ON$. MW, 169. Yellow liq. with unpleasant odour. B.p. 200° decomp., 122°/23 mm. *B,HI*: m.p. 172°.

N-*Et*: $C_{11}H_{21}ON$. MW, 183. Liq. *B_2,H_2PtCl_6*: orange prisms from H_2O. M.p. 157–8° decomp.

N-*Allyl*: $C_{12}H_{21}ON$. MW, 195. Liq. *B_2,H_2PtCl_6*: orange-yellow plates or prisms. M.p. 148°.

N-*Benzyl*: $C_{16}H_{23}ON$. MW, 245. *B,HCl*: plates or prisms from EtOH–Et_2O. M.p. 137–8°. *B_2,H_2PtCl_6*: orange-red cryst. M.p. 147–8° decomp.

N-*Bromo*: $C_9H_{16}ONBr$. MW, 234. Cryst. from pet. ether. M.p. 44°. Spar. sol. H_2O.

N-*Nitroso*: needles from H_2O or EtOH.Aq. M.p. 72–3°. Very sol. EtOH, Et_2O. Volatile in steam. Sublimes.

N-*OH*: triacetone-hydroxylamine. $C_9H_{17}O_2N$. MW, 171. Cryst. from pet. ether. M.p. 50–1°. Sol. dil. alkalis and acids. Reduces $NH_3.AgNO_3$. *B,HI*: m.p. 180°. *Oxime*: cryst. from pet. ether. M.p. 126–7°.

Francis, *J. Chem. Soc.*, 1927, 2897.
Clarke, Francis, *Ber.*, 1912, **45**, 2064.
Harries, *Ann.*, 1918, **417**, 171.
Harries, Lehmann, *Ber.*, 1897, **30**, 232, 2736.

Triacetone-hydroxylamine.
See under Triacetonamine.

Triacontane

$$CH_3{\cdot}[CH_2]_{28}{\cdot}CH_3$$

$C_{30}H_{62}$ MW, 422

Constituent of many mineral oils, of the wax coating of apple skins and of numerous flowers, *Arnica montana*, *Linaria vulgaris*, etc. Plates from C_6H_6. M.p. 66°. B.p. 235°/1 mm. Very sol. hot C_6H_6. Spar. sol. hot EtOH.

Landa, *Chem. Abstracts*, 1929, **23**, 4667.
Gascard, *Ann. chim.*, 1921, **15**, 332.

Triacontane-1-carboxylic Acid.
See Melissic Acid.

***n*-Triacontanic Acid**

$$CH_3{\cdot}[CH_2]_{28}{\cdot}COOH$$

$C_{30}H_{60}O_2$ MW, 452

Colourless plates from Me_2CO. M.p. 93·5–94°. Spar. sol. Et_2O, Me_2CO.

Me ester: $C_{31}H_{62}O_2$. MW, 466. Colourless plates from pet. ether. M.p. 71·5°.

Et ester: $C_{32}H_{64}O_2$. MW, 480. Colourless plates from EtOH. M.p. 70·5°.

Robinson, *J. Chem. Soc.*, 1934, 1544.

***n*-Triacontanol** (1-*Hydroxytriacontane*)

$$CH_3{\cdot}[CH_2]_{28}{\cdot}CH_2OH$$

$C_{30}H_{62}O$ MW, 438

Plates from C_6H_6. M.p. 86·5°.

Acetyl: plates from pet. ether. M.p. 69°.

Robinson, *J. Chem. Soc.*, 1934, 1545.

Triallylamine

$$(CH_2{:}CH{\cdot}CH_2)_3N$$

$C_9H_{15}N$ MW, 137

Liq. with unpleasant odour. B.p. 155–6°. D^{14} 0·8094.

Grosheintz, *Bull. soc. chim.*, 1879, **31**, 391.

Triallyl phosphate.
See under Phosphoric Acid.

Triallyltricyanamide (*Sinamin, allylcyanamide*)

$C_{12}H_{18}N_6$ MW, 246

Cryst. + $\frac{1}{2}H_2O$ from H_2O. M.p. 100° with loss of H_2O. Strongly alkaline.

Will, *Ann.*, 1844, **52**, 15.

1 : 2 : 3-Triaminoanthraquinone

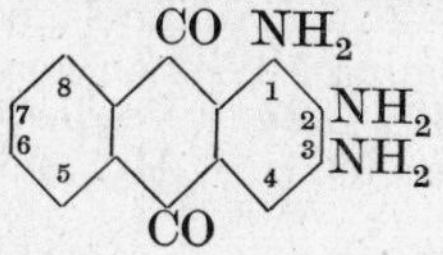

$C_{14}H_{11}O_2N_3$ MW, 253

Black needles from $PhNO_2$. M.p. 325° decomp. Sol. conc. H_2SO_4 ⟶ red sol.

Scholl, Eberle, Tritsch, *Monatsh.*, 1911, 32, 1044.

Scholl, Schneider, Eberle, *Ber.*, 1904, **37**, 4438.

1 : 2 : 4-Triaminoanthraquinone.

Bluish-red powder. Does not melt below 300°.

1 : 2 : 4-N-*Triphenyl* : 1 : 2 : 4-trianilino-anthraquinone. $C_{32}H_{23}O_2N_3$. MW, 481. Black needles from $PhNO_2$ or Py. Spar. sol. EtOH. Conc. H_2SO_4 ⟶ yellow sol. ⟶ red on warming.

Terres, *Monatsh.*, 1921, **41**, 608.

Bayer, D.R.P., 151,511, (*Chem. Zentr.*, 1904, I, 1507).

1 : 2 : 3-Triaminobenzene

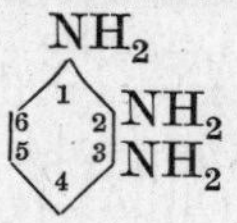

$C_6H_9N_3$ MW, 123

Cryst. M.p. up to 103°. B.p. 336°. Sol. H_2O, EtOH, Et_2O. Reacts strongly alkaline. $FeCl_3$ ⟶ violet ⟶ brown ppt. Sol. in conc. H_2SO_4 + trace HNO_3 ⟶ dark blue col. Reduces $NH_3.AgNO_3$. Boiling AcOH ⟶ 4-acetylamino-2-methylbenziminazole.

2-N-*Phenyl* : *see* 2 : 6-Diaminodiphenylamine.

Salkowski, *Ann.*, 1872, **163**, 23.

1 : 2 : 4-Triaminobenzene.

Plates from $CHCl_3$. M.p. below 100°. B.p. about 340°. Sol. H_2O, EtOH. Mod. sol. $CHCl_3$. Spar. sol. Et_2O. Turns brown in air. $FeCl_3$ ⟶ red col.

1-N-*Di-Me* : 2 : 4-diamino-*N*-dimethylaniline. $C_8H_{13}N_3$. MW, 151. Needles from ligroin. M.p. 44°. B.p. 218–19°/90 mm., 178°/22 mm. Sol. H_2O. Turns dark blue in air. Aq. sol. + ox. agents ⟶ red sol. *B,2HCl* : cryst. M.p. 225°. *B,2HBr* : m.p. 207° decomp. *B,2HI* : plates + $\frac{1}{2}$EtOH from EtOH. M.p. 190° decomp. 2 : 4-N-*Diacetyl* : cryst. + $1\frac{1}{2}H_2O$ from H_2O, m.p. 82°; cryst. from C_6H_6 or AcOEt, m.p. 153°.

2 : 4-N-*Tetra-Me* : $C_{10}H_{17}N_3$. MW, 179. Liq. B.p. 209·4°/112 mm., 180·5°/45 mm. D_4^{22} 1·0203. Has caustic action. *B,2HCl* : cryst. powder. M.p. 164°. *B,2HBr* : m.p. 179°. *B,2HI* : prisms. M.p. 175° decomp. *Picrate* : m.p. 169° decomp. 1-N-*Acetyl* : plates from ligroin. M.p. 85°. 1-N-*Benzenesulphonyl* : prisms from ligrion. M.p. 84°.

1 : 2 : 4-N-*Hexa-Me* : $C_{12}H_{21}N_3$. MW, 207. Liq. B.p. 210°/136 mm., 184°/40 mm. *Trimethiodide* : needles + 2MeOH from MeOH. M.p. 164·5° decomp.

1-N-*Phenyl* : *see* 2 : 4-Diaminodiphenylamine.

2 : 4-N-*Diphenyl* : 4-amino-3-anilinodiphenylamine. $C_{18}H_{17}N_3$. MW, 275. Needles from C_6H_6–ligroin. M.p. 107°. Spar. sol. H_2O, ligroin. Sol. Et_2O, C_6H_6.

1-N-*Acetyl* : 2 : 4-diaminoacetanilide. Prisms. M.p. 158–9°.

1 : 4-N-*Diacetyl* : cryst. M.p. 231–2°.

1 : 2 : 4-N-*Tribenzoyl* : needles from AcOH. M.p. 260°.

Hinsberg, *Ber.*, 1886, **19**, 1253.

Wurster, Sendtner, *Ber.*, 1879, **12**, 1806.

1 : 3 : 5-Triaminobenzene.

Free base not isolated.

1 : 3 : 5-N-*Triphenyl* : 1 : 3 : 5-trianilinobenzene. $C_{24}H_{21}N_3$. MW, 351. Needles from EtOH. M.p. 193°. Sol. Et_2O. Spar. sol. cold EtOH, C_6H_6. Conc. H_2SO_4 ⟶ violet-red col. on warming. *B,HCl* : yellow powder. M.p. below 100°. B_2,H_2PtCl_6 : yellow ppt. M.p. 251° decomp. 1 : 3 : 5-N-*Trinitroso* : brown needles from EtOH. M.p. 264–5°. 1 : 3 : 5-N-*Triacetyl* : needles from EtOH. M.p. 172–3°.

1 : 3 : 5-N-*Tri-p-tolyl* : $C_{27}H_{27}N_3$. MW, 393. Needles from EtOH. M.p. 186–7°. Spar. sol. cold EtOH. Conc. H_2SO_4 ⟶ bluish-green on warming. 1 : 3 : 5-N-*Trinitroso* : needles from EtOH. M.p. 233–4°. 1 : 3 : 5-N-*Triacetyl* : needles from EtOH. M.p. 192–3°. 1 : 3 : 5-N-*Tribenzoyl* : prisms from EtOH. M.p. 281–2°.

1 : 3 : 5-N-*Triacetyl* : plates from EtOH. M.p. 208°.

1 : 3 : 5-N-*Tribenzoyl* : needles from EtOH–C_6H_6. Does not melt below 350°.

Minunni, *Gazz. chim. ital.*, 1890, **20**, 322.

Hepp, *Ann.*, 1882, **215**, 348.

2 : 3 : 5-Triaminobenzoic Acid

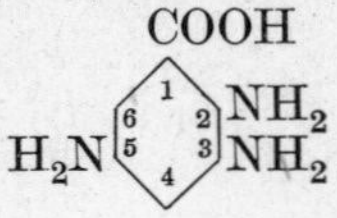

$C_7H_9O_2N_3$ MW, 167

Cryst. from H_2O. Chars on heating evolving NH_3. Very sol. hot H_2O. Spar. sol. hot EtOH. Insol. Et_2O. Aq. sol. rapidly becomes red. $FeCl_3 \longrightarrow$ brown ppt.

2-N-*Phenyl* : 3 : 5-diamino-2-anilinobenzoic acid, 4 : 6-diaminodiphenylamine-2-carboxylic acid. $C_{13}H_{13}O_2N_3$. MW, 243. Cryst. M.p. 237–8° decomp. Very sol. EtOH, AcOH. Spar. sol. Et_2O, C_6H_6, hot H_2O.

Cohn, Schifferes, *Chem. Zentr.*, 1902, I, 1293.
Griess, *Ber.*, 1882, **15**, 2199.

2 : 4 : 6-Triaminobenzoic Acid.

$HNO_3 \longrightarrow$ intense yellow sol., violet on neutralisation. Hydrochloride + boiling $H_2O \longrightarrow$ phloroglucinol.

Hydrochloride : prisms from H_2O.

Cassella, D.R.P., 102,358, (*Chem. Zentr.*, 1899, I, 1263).

3 : 4 : 5-Triaminobenzoic Acid.

Needles + $\frac{1}{2}H_2O$ from hot H_2O. Loses H_2O at 100°. Sol. hot H_2O. Spar. sol. cold H_2O. Insol. hot EtOH. Reacts acid. Dist. $\longrightarrow$ 1 : 2 : 3-triaminobenzene. Sol. in conc. H_2SO_4 + trace $HNO_3 \longrightarrow$ bluish-green $\longrightarrow$ dark blue col.

Salkowski, *Ann.*, 1872, **163**, 12.

2 : 4 : 4′ - Triaminodiphenyl (2 - *Amino-benzidine*)

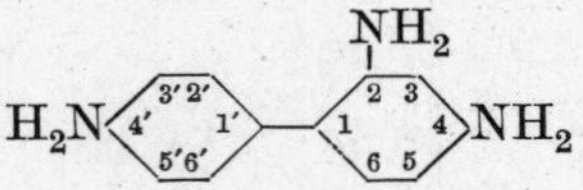

$C_{12}H_{13}N_3$ MW, 199

Needles. M.p. 134°.

4 : 4′-N-*Di*-p-*toluenesulphonyl* : m.p. 198°.

Tauber, *Ber.*, 1890, **23**, 798.

2 : 5 : 4′-Triaminodiphenyl.

5-N-*Di-Me* : $C_{14}H_{17}N_3$. MW, 227. Cryst. M.p. 87–9°. Sol. EtOH, dil. min. acids. Spar. sol. H_2O, ligroin. $FeCl_3 \longrightarrow$ violet $\longrightarrow$ blue col. *Picrate* : yellow prisms. M.p. 127°. 2 : 4′-N-*Diacetyl* : needles from EtOH.Aq. M.p. 233°.

Jacobson, Kunz, *Ann.*, 1898, **303**, 354.

1 : 2 : 4-Triaminonaphthalene

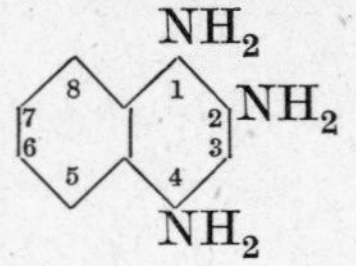

$C_{10}H_{11}N_3$ MW, 173

1-N-*Phenyl* : 2 : 4-diamino-1-anilinonaphthalene, 2 : 4-diamino-1-*N*-phenylnaphthylamine. $C_{16}H_{15}N_3$. MW, 249. Needles from C_6H_6. M.p. 190°. Sol. AcOH, C_6H_6. Very spar. sol. ligroin, Et_2O.

1 : 2 : 4 - N - *Triphenyl* : 1 : 2 : 4 - trianilino - naphthalene. $C_{28}H_{23}N_3$. MW, 401. Needles from EtOH or C_6H_6–ligroin. M.p. 148°.

1 - N - p - *Tolyl* : 2 : 4 - diamino - 1 - *N* - *p* - tolyl-naphthylamine. $C_{17}H_{17}N_3$. MW, 263. Needles from C_6H_6. M.p. 176–7°. Very readily oxidised. Resinifies in air.

1 : 2 : 4-N-*Tri*-p-*tolyl* : $C_{31}H_{29}N_3$. MW, 443. Needles from EtOH. M.p. 159–60°.

1-N-*Acetyl* : 2 : 4-diamino-1-acetnaphthalide. Brown needles. M.p. 189°.

1 : 2 : 4-N-*Triacetyl* : white cryst. M.p. 301°.

1-N-*Benzenesulphonyl* : needles from toluene–pet. ether. M.p. 195–7°.

Panizzon-Favre, *Gazz. chim. ital.*, 1924, **54**, 826.
Ullmann, Bruck, *Ber.*, 1908, **41**, 3937.
Fischer, Hepp, *Ann.*, 1890, **256**, 250.

1 : 2 : 5-Triaminonaphthalene.

B,HCl : cryst. Turns brown in H_2O.

1 : 2 : 5-N-*Tribenzoyl* : yellow powder. M.p. 268°.

Finzi, *Chem. Abstracts*, 1925, **19**, 2661.

1 : 2 : 6-Triaminonaphthalene.

2-N-*Me* : $C_{11}H_{13}N_3$. MW, 187. 2-N-p-*Toluenesulphonyl* : prisms from C_6H_6–pet. ether. Decomp. at 185°.

1 : 2 : 6-N-*Triacetyl* : needles from AcOH. M.p. 280° decomp.

1 : 2 : 6-N-*Tribenzoyl* : needles from AcOH. M.p. 277°.

2-N-p-*Toluenesulphonyl* : needles from toluene. M.p. 190°.

Loewe, *Ber.*, 1890, **23**, 2544.

1 : 3 : 6-Triaminonaphthalene.

Sol. H_2O. Acid. sol. + nitrite $\longrightarrow$ deep brown col.

Sulphate : needles. Spar. sol. H_2O.

Kalle, D.R.P., 89,061.

1 : 3 : 7-Triaminonaphthalene.
Sol. H_2O, EtOH. Aq. sol. + HNO_3 ⟶ deep brown col. Salt sols + $FeCl_3$ ⟶ violet col.
Sulphate : cryst. Spar. sol. hot H_2O.

Kalle, D.R.P., 90,905.

1 : 3 : 8-Triaminonaphthalene.
B,3HI : needles.

Aguiar, Lautemann, *Bull. soc. chim.*, 1865, **3**, 263.

1 : 2 : 3-Triaminopropane

$H_2N{\cdot}CH_2{\cdot}CH(NH_2){\cdot}CH_2{\cdot}NH_2$

$C_3H_{11}N_3$ MW, 89

Viscous oil. B.p. 190°, 92–3°/9 mm. Sol. H_2O.
B,3HCl,H$_2$O : plates. M.p. 250°.
B,3HCl,AuCl$_3$: yellow prisms. M.p. 210–12°.
B,3HCl,PtCl$_4$: yellow needles. M.p. 220° decomp.
B,2HCl,HI : cryst. from H_2O. M.p. 303–4° decomp.
B,3HBr : m.p. 307–10°.
Triacetyl : cryst. from EtOH. M.p. 200–2°.
Tribenzoyl : m.p. 217–18°.
Picrate : yellow needles. Does not melt below 270°.

Pope, Mann, *Compt. rend.*, 1924, **178**, 2085.
Brackebusch, *Ber.*, 1873, **6**, 1290.

4 : 4′ : 4″-Triaminotriphenylcarbinol
(*Pararosaniline base*)

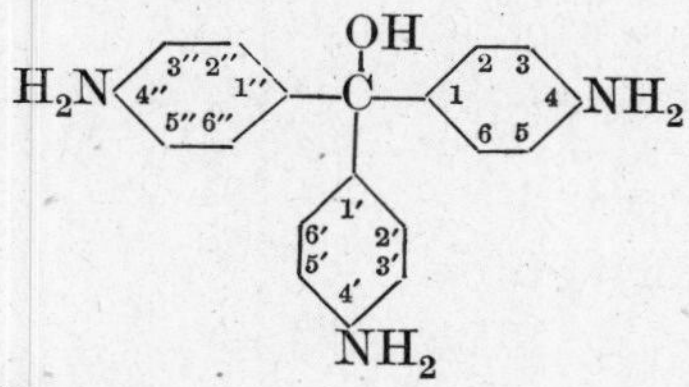

$C_{19}H_{19}ON_3$ MW, 305

Colourless plates. M.p. about 205°. Turns red in air. Very spar sol. H_2O. Sol. EtOH. Insol. Et_2O. Heat of comb. C_v 2481·0 Cal., C_p 2483·5 Cal. Red. ⟶ paraleucaniline. H_2O at 270° ⟶ 4 : 4′-dihydroxybenzophenone. KCN ⟶ triaminotriphenylacetonitrile.
Me ether : $C_{20}H_{21}ON_3$. MW, 319. Plates + $1Et_2O$ from Et_2O, m.p. 105° ; plates + $1C_6H_6$ from C_6H_6, m.p. 135°.
4 : 4′ : 4″-N-*Triacetyl* : needles from Me_2CO–Et_2O. M.p. 192°.

Wieland, Scheuing, *Ber.*, 1921, **54**, 2527.
M.L.B., D.R.P., 300,467, (*Chem. Zentr.*, 1917, II, 579).
Zimmermann, Müller, *Ber.*, 1885, **18**, 997.
Fischer, *Ber.*, 1882, **15**, 678 ; 1880, **13**, 2205.
Fischer, *Ann.*, 1878, **194**, 274.

2 : 4′ : 4″-Triaminotriphenylmethane

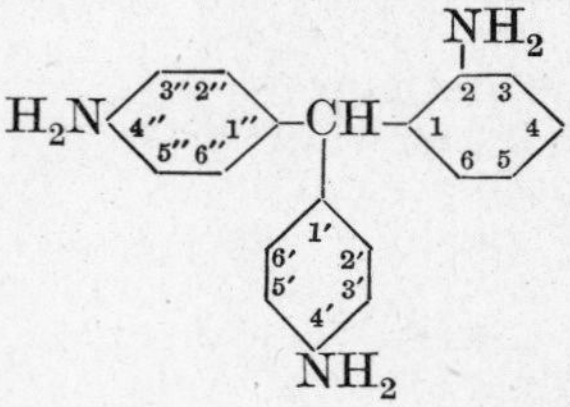

$C_{19}H_{19}N_3$ MW, 289

Cryst. from EtOH. M.p. 165°.

Renouf, *Ber.*, 1883, **16**, 1305.

3 : 4′ : 4″-Triaminotriphenylmethane.
Needles + $1C_6H_6$ from C_6H_6, m.p. 145° ; cryst. from Et_2O–petrol, m.p. 150°. Sol. EtOH.

Fischer, Ziegler, *Ber.*, 1880, **13**, 672.

4 : 4′ : 4″-Triaminotriphenylmethane
(*Paraleucaniline*).
Plates from H_2O, EtOH or C_6H_6. M.p. 202·5° (208°). Ox. ⟶ pararosaniline base. Diazotise + EtOH ⟶ triphenylmethane.
4 : 4′ : 4″-N-*Triacetyl* : reddish plates from EtOH. M.p. 201°.
B,C$_6$H$_3$(NO$_2$)$_3$-1 : 3 : 5 : black prisms. M.p. 140°.

Fischer *et al.*, *J. prakt. Chem.*, 1909, **79**, 563 ; *Ann.*, 1878, **194**, 268.

Triaminotriazine.
See Melamine.
3 : 4 : 5-Triamino-1 : 2 : 4-triazole.
See Guanazine.
Tri-*n*-amylamine

$(CH_3{\cdot}CH_2{\cdot}CH_2{\cdot}CH_2{\cdot}CH_2)_3N$

$C_{15}H_{33}N$ MW, 227

Liq. B.p. 240–5°, 130°/14 mm.

Marvel, Scott, Amstutz, *J. Am. Chem. Soc.*, 1929, **51**, 3640.
Mailhe, *Compt. rend.*, 1918, **166**, 997.

Tri-*active*-amylamine

$$(CH_3{\cdot}CH_2{\cdot}\underset{}{\overset{CH_3}{\overset{|}{C}}}H{\cdot}CH_2)_3N$$

$C_{15}H_{33}N$ MW, 227

Liq. B.p. 230–7°. D^{13} 0·7964.

Plimpton, *J. Chem. Soc.*, 1881, **39**, 335.

Triamyl phosphate.
See under Phosphoric Acid.

Trianilinoanthraquinone.
See under Triaminoanthraquinone.

Trianilinobenzene.
See under Triaminobenzene.

Trianilinomethane.
See under Orthoformic Acid.

Trianilinonaphthalene.
See under Triaminonaphthalene.

Triazo-.
See Azido-, *and* individual azides.

1 : 2 : 3-Triazole (*Osotriazole*)

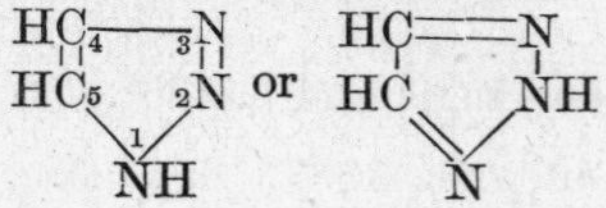

$C_2H_3N_3$ MW, 69

M.p. 23°. B.p. 203°/739 mm. Sol. ord. org. solvents. Insol. ligroin. Hygroscopic.

1-N-*Phenyl*: *see* 1-Phenyl-1 : 2 : 3-triazole.

1-N-*Benzyl*: $C_9H_9N_3$. MW, 159. Cryst. M.p. 61°. B.p. 180–3°/16 mm.

1-N-*Benzoyl*: needles from $CHCl_3$ or Et_2O. M.p. 100–2°.

Pechmann, Baver, *Ber.*, 1909, **42**, 673.
Zincke, *Ann.*, 1900, **311**, 317.
Dimroth, *Ber.*, 1902, **35**, 1044.

1 : 2 : 4-Triazole (*Pyrrodiazole*)

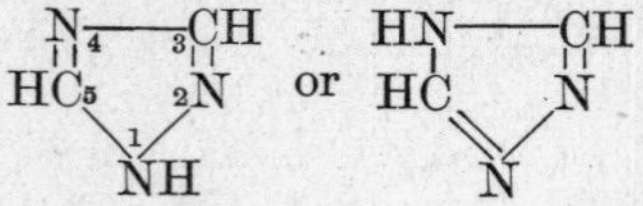

$C_2H_3N_3$ MW, 69

Needles from Et_2O or C_6H_6. M.p. 120–1°. B.p. 260°. Sol. H_2O, EtOH. Forms comps. with metals and metallic salts.

B,HCl: plates. M.p. 169°.

Oxalate: cryst. from H_2O. Decomp. at 251°.

B_2,H_2PtCl_6: needles. M.p. 73–5°.

1-*Phenyl*: *see* 1-Phenyl-1 : 2 : 4-triazole.

3-*Phenyl*: *see* 3-Phenyl-1 : 2 : 4-triazole.

Pellizzari, *Gazz. chim. ital.*, 1911, **41**, 20; *Atti accad. Lincei*, 1902, **11**, 20.
Paolini, Baj, *Gazz. chim. ital.*, 1931, **61**, 557.
Bladin, *Ber.*, 1892, **25**, 745.

Tribenzamide

$$C_6H_5{\cdot}CO{\cdot}N(CO{\cdot}C_6H_5)_2$$

$C_{21}H_{15}O_3N$ MW, 329

Needles from EtOH. M.p. 207–8° (202°). Sublimes. Heat. of comb. 2425·5 Cal. Hyd. by KOH.

Titherley, *J. Chem. Soc.*, 1904, **85**, 1187.
Wheeler, Walden, Metcalf, *J. Am. Chem. Soc.*, 1898, **20**, 73.

1 : 3 : 5-Tribenzoylbenzene

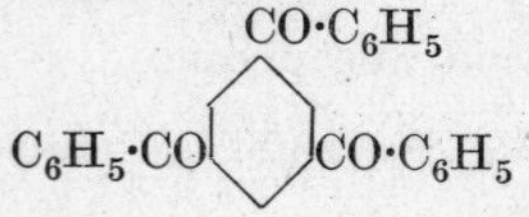

$C_{27}H_{18}O_3$ MW, 390

Needles from EtOH. M.p. 118–19°.

Trioxime: m.p. 198°.

Monophenylhydrazone: m.p. 84°.

Claisen, *Ann.*, 1894, **281**, 307.

Tribenzoylmethane

$$C_6H_5{\cdot}CO{\cdot}CH{<}\begin{matrix}CO{\cdot}C_6H_5\\CO{\cdot}C_6H_5\end{matrix}$$

or

$$C_6H_5{\cdot}C(OH){:}C{<}\begin{matrix}CO{\cdot}C_6H_5\\CO{\cdot}C_6H_5\end{matrix}$$

$C_{22}H_{16}O_3$ MW, 328

α- or Enol form:

Cryst. M.p. (in Jena glass) 155°, (in soft glass) 240–5°. More sol. than keto-form. $FeCl_3 \longrightarrow$ red col. EtOH or $CH_3COCl \longrightarrow$ keto-form.

β- or Keto form:

Needles from EtOH or Me_2CO. M.p. 223–6° (231°), in Jena glass 245–50°. $FeCl_3 \longrightarrow$ brownish-red col. Conc. $H_2SO_4 \longrightarrow$ yellow col. NaOEt $\longrightarrow$ enol-form.

Dieckmann, *Ber.*, 1916, **49**, 2209.
Abell, *J. Chem. Soc.*, 1912, **101**, 998.
Claisen, *Ann.*, 1896, **291**, 92.

Tribenzylamine

$$(C_6H_5{\cdot}CH_2)_3N$$

$C_{21}H_{21}N$ MW, 287

Plates or prisms from Et_2O. M.p. 92°. B.p. 230°/13 mm. Sol. hot EtOH, Et_2O. Spar. sol. H_2O. Hot HCl $\longrightarrow$ dibenzylamine + benzyl chloride.

B,HCl: prisms from EtOH. M.p. 227–8°.

B,HBr: prisms. M.p. 208°.

B,HI: prisms from AcOH. M.p. 185–8° (178°).

B,HNO_3: cryst. from EtOH. M.p. 120°.

B_2,H_2SO_4: prisms from EtOH. M.p. 106–7°.

B,Benzenesulphonic acid: needles from H_2O. M.p. 200°.

B,p-Toluenesulphonic acid: m.p. 205·2–207·7°.

Methochloride: needles from H_2O, plates from EtOH. M.p. 202°.

Methiodide: needles from H_2O, plates from EtOH. M.p. 184°.

Ethiodide: needles from H_2O. M.p. 190°.

Scheibler, Beiser, Cobler, Schmidt, *Ber.*, 1934, **67**, 1509.

Mason, *J. Chem. Soc.*, 1893, **63**, 1314.

Tribenzyl phosphate.

See under Phosphoric Acid.

Tribromoacetaldehyde.

See Bromal.

Tribromoacetanilide.

See under Tribromoaniline.

Tribromoacetic Acid

$CBr_3{\cdot}COOH$

$C_2HO_2Br_3$ MW, 297

White cryst. M.p. 131°. B.p. 245° decomp. Sol. H_2O, EtOH, Et_2O. Boiling H_2O or EtOH $\longrightarrow$ bromoform.

Et ester: $C_4H_5O_2Br_3$. MW, 325. B.p. 225°, 148°/73 mm. D_{20}^{20} 2·230. n_D^{13} 1·54377.

Bromide: C_2OBr_4, MW, 360. B.p. 210–15°, 88–90°/12 mm.

Amide: $C_2H_2ONBr_3$. MW, 296. M.p. 121–2°. Sol. Et_2O, hot EtOH. Sublimes.

Nitrile: C_2NBr_3. MW, 278. Oil. B.p. 170°. Sol. EtOH, Et_2O, C_6H_6.

Schäffer, *Ber.*, 1871, **4**, 370.

1 : 1 : 1-Tribromoacetone

$CH_3{\cdot}CO{\cdot}CBr_3$

$C_3H_3OBr_3$ MW, 295

B.p. 255° decomp. $NH_3 \longrightarrow$ bromoform.

Étard, *Compt. rend.*, 1892, **114**, 754.

ω-Tribromoacetophenone

$C_6H_5{\cdot}CO{\cdot}CBr_3$

$C_8H_5OBr_3$ MW, 357

B.p. 174°/14 mm.

Myddleton, Barrett, Seager, *J. Am. Chem. Soc.*, 1930, **52**, 4409.

2 : 4 : 6-Tribromoacetophenone

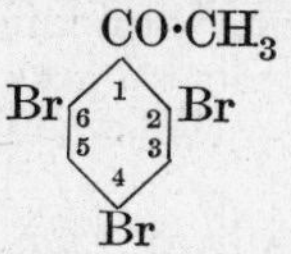

$C_8H_5OBr_3$ MW, 357

Needles from EtOH.Aq. M.p. 93·5°. Sol. EtOH, Et_2O, C_6H_6.

Fuchs, *Monatsh.*, 1915, **36**, 136.

3 : 4 : 5-Tribromoacetophenone.

Cryst. from EtOH. M.p. 134–5°. Sol. EtOH, C_6H_6. Mod. sol. Et_2O, pet. ether, hot H_2O.

Phenylhydrazone: yellow cryst. from pet. ether. M.p. 129–34° decomp.

Semicarbazone: cryst. from AcOH. M.p. 265° decomp.

Azine: m.p. 300°.

Bruining, *Rec. trav. chim.*, 1922, **41**, 655.

Tribromoacet-toluidide.

See under Tribromotoluidine.

Tribromo-*o*-aminobenzoic Acid.

See Tribromoanthranilic Acid.

2 : 4 : 6-Tribromo-*m*-aminobenzoic Acid

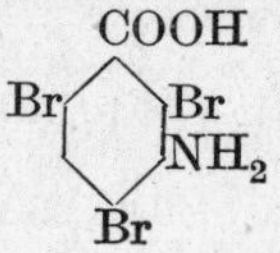

$C_7H_4O_2NBr_3$ MW, 374

Needles from H_2O. M.p. 170·5°. Sol. EtOH. Spar. sol. H_2O. Decomp. on dist. $\longrightarrow$ 2 : 4 : 6-tribromoaniline.

Me ester: $C_8H_6O_2NBr_3$. MW, 388. M.p. 96–7°.

Et ester: $C_9H_8O_2NBr_3$. MW, 402. M.p. 61–2°.

Nitrile: $C_7H_3N_2Br_3$. MW, 355. Needles from EtOH. M.p. 177–8°. Sol. EtOH, $CHCl_3$, Me_2CO.

Sudborough, Karvé, *Chem. Abstracts*, 1920, **14**, 3652.

Sudborough, Lloyd, *J. Chem. Soc.*, 1899, **75**, 589.

2 : 4 : 6-Tribromo-*m*-aminophenol

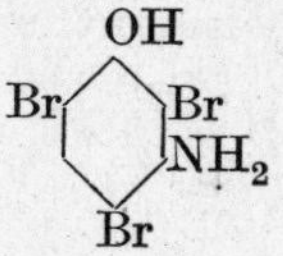

$C_6H_4ONBr_3$ MW, 346

Needles from pet. ether. M.p. 119°. Sol. EtOH, Et_2O, $CHCl_3$, C_6H_6. Spar. sol. pet. ether. $FeCl_3 \longrightarrow$ green col.

O : N : N-*Triacetyl*: m.p. 136°.

p-Toluenesulphonate: prisms from EtOH. M.p. 146–7°.

Bamberger, *Ber.*, 1915, **48**, 1355.

2 : 4 : 6-Tribromoaniline

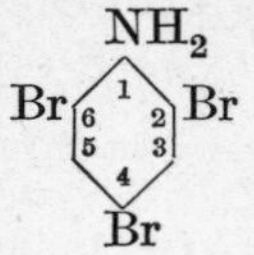

$C_6H_4NBr_3$ MW, 330

Needles from C_6H_6 or EtOH. M.p. 122° (120°). Sol. Et_2O, hot EtOH. Insol. H_2O. Sn + HCl ⟶ 2 : 4-dibromoaniline. Hot conc. HCl ⟶ 2 : 4 : 6-trichloroaniline.

B,HBr : needles. M.p. 195–6°.

N-*Me* : 2 : 4 : 6 - tribromomethylaniline. $C_7H_6NBr_3$. MW, 344. Needles from MeOH. M.p. 39°. N-*Acetyl* : m.p. 101°.

N-*Di-Me* : 2 : 4 : 6-tribromodimethylaniline. $C_8H_8NBr_3$. MW, 358. Oil. B.p. 301°/750 mm.

N-*Et*: 2:4:6-tribromoethylaniline. $C_8H_8NBr_3$. MW, 358. Needles from AcOH. M.p. 45°.

N-*Formyl* : 2 : 4 : 6 - tribromoformanilide. Needles from EtOH. M.p. 221·5°.

N-*Acetyl* : 2 : 4 : 6 - tribromoacetanilide. Needles from EtOH. M.p. 232°.

N-*Diacetyl* : needles from EtOH. M.p. 127–8°.

N-*Propionyl* : prisms from EtOH. M.p. 203°.

N-*Benzoyl* : 2 : 4 : 6 - tribromobenzanilide. Needles from EtOH. M.p. 204°.

Silberstein, *J. prakt. Chem.*, 1883, **27**, 101.
Asinger, *J. prakt. Chem.*, 1935, **142**, 299.

3 : 4 : 5-Tribromoaniline.

Cryst. from EtOH. M.p. 123°.

N-*Acetyl* : 3 : 4 : 5 - tribromoacetanilide. Needles from Et_2O. M.p. 255–6°.

N-*Benzoyl* : 3 : 4 : 5 - tribromobenzanilide. Cryst. from EtOH. M.p. 210°.

Asinger, *J. prakt. Chem.*, 1935, **142**, 300.

Tribromoanisole.

See under Tribromophenol.

2 : 9 : 10-Tribromoanthracene

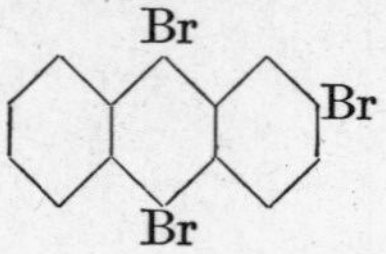

$C_{14}H_7Br_3$ MW, 415

Cryst. from amyl alcohol. M.p. 171°. Very sol. C_6H_6. Spar. sol. EtOH. CrO_3 ⟶ 2-bromoanthraquinone.

Barnett, Cook, *J. Chem. Soc.*, 1925, 1490.
Grandmougin, *Compt. rend.*, 1921, **173**, 1176.

3 : 4 : 5-Tribromoanthranilic Acid (3 : 4 : 5-*Tribromo-o-aminobenzoic acid*)

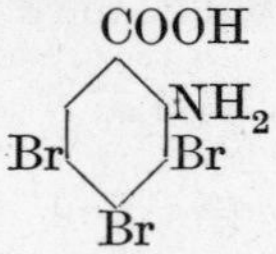

$C_7H_4O_2NBr_3$ MW, 374

Cryst. from EtOH.Aq. Decomp. at 240°.

I.G., D.R.P., 528,115, (*Chem. Zentr.*, 1931, II, 1927).
See also Lesser, Weiss, *Ber.*, 1913, **46**, 3941.

2 : 3 : 5-Tribromobenzaldehyde

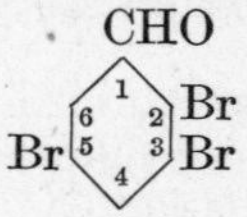

$C_7H_3OBr_3$ MW, 343

Cryst. from pet. ether. M.p. 114°. Sol. EtOH. Insol. H_2O.

Blanksma, *Chem. Zentr.*, 1912, II, 1964.

2 : 4 : 6-Tribromobenzaldehyde.

Cryst. from EtOH. M.p. 99°. Sol. EtOH, Et_2O, C_6H_6.

Oxime : needles from EtOH.Aq. M.p. 175°.

See previous reference.

3 : 4 : 5-Tribromobenzaldehyde.

Cryst. from EtOH.Aq. M.p. 109°. Sol. EtOH, C_6H_6. Insol. H_2O.

Oxime : needles from EtOH.Aq. M.p. 172°.
Phenylhydrazone : yellow plates. M.p. 158°.
Semicarbazone : needles from Py. M.p. 314°.
Diacetate : cryst. from EtOH. M.p. 100°.
Azine : yellow needles + $2H_2O$. M.p. 315°.

Janse, *Rec. trav. chim.*, 1921, **40**, 285.

1 : 2 : 3-Tribromobenzene

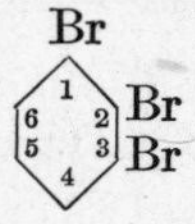

$C_6H_3Br_3$ MW, 315

Plates from EtOH. M.p. 87·8°.

Körner, *Gazz. chim. ital.*, 1874, **4**, 408.
Jackson, Gallivan, *Am. Chem. J.*, 1898, **20**, 179.

1 : 2 : 4-Tribromobenzene.

Needles with aromatic odour from EtOH. M.p. 44–5°. B.p. 275°. Sol. EtOH, Et_2O. Spar. sol. C_6H_6.

Jackson, Gallivan, *Am. Chem. J.*, 1896, **18**, 241.

1 : 3 : 5-Tribromobenzene.
Needles or prisms from EtOH. M.p. 120°. B.p. 271°. Spar. sol. hot EtOH. Insol. H_2O. NaOMe at 130° ⟶ 3 : 5-dibromophenol.

Coleman, Talbot, *Organic Syntheses*, 1933, XIII, 96.

2 : 3 : 4-Tribromobenzoic Acid

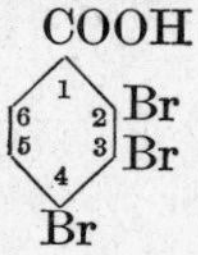

$C_7H_3O_2Br_3$ MW, 359

Needles from C_6H_6. M.p. 197–8°.

Cohen, Dutt, *J. Chem. Soc.*, 1914, **105**, 511.

2 : 3 : 5-Tribromobenzoic Acid.
Needles from EtOH. M.p. 193–4°. Sol. Et_2O, Me_2CO, hot EtOH. Spar. sol. C_6H_6, pet. ether.
Ba salt : cryst. + $5H_2O$. Very sol. H_2O.
Me ester : $C_8H_5O_2Br_3$. MW, 373. Needles from EtOH.Aq. M.p. 77°.

Cohen, Dutt, *J. Chem. Soc.*, 1914, **105**, 512.
Blanksma, *Chem. Zentr.*, 1912, II, 1965.

2 : 4 : 5-Tribromobenzoic Acid.
Needles from C_6H_6. M.p. 195–6°.

Cohen, Dutt, *J. Chem. Soc.*, 1914, **105**, 515.

2 : 4 : 6-Tribromobenzoic Acid.
Prisms from H_2O. M.p. 194°.
Me ester : needles from EtOH.Aq. M.p. 69°.
Et ester : $C_9H_7O_2Br_3$. MW, 387. M.p. 80°.
Chloride : $C_7H_2OBr_3Cl$. MW, 377·5. Plates from pet. ether. M.p. 48°.
Amide : $C_7H_4ONBr_3$. MW, 358. Prisms. M.p. 195°.
Dimethylamide : $C_9H_8ONBr_3$. MW, 386. Prisms from C_6H_6–pet. ether. M.p. 85–6°.
Nitrile : $C_7H_2NBr_3$. MW, 340. Needles from EtOH. M.p. 128°.
Anilide : needles from EtOH. M.p. 237°.

Asinger, *J. prakt. Chem.*, 1935, **142**, 296.
Buning, *Rec. trav. chim.*, 1921, **40**, 327.
Cohen, Dutt, *J. Chem. Soc.*, 1914, **105**, 516.

3 : 4 : 5-Tribromobenzoic Acid.
Needles from C_6H_6 or EtOH.Aq. M.p. 240°.
Me ester : needles from EtOH. M.p. 154°.
Et ester : needles. M.p. 126°.
Chloride : needles from pet. ether. M.p. 83°.
Amide : needles from EtOH.Aq. M.p. 200°.
Anilide : needles from EtOH. M.p. 220°.

Asinger, *J. prakt. Chem.*, 1935, **142**, 298.
See also last reference above.

2 : 4 : 6-Tribromobenzophenone

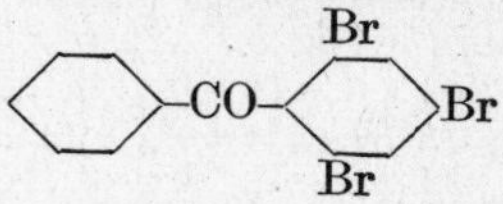

$C_{13}H_7OBr_3$ MW, 419

Cryst. from C_6H_6–pet. ether. M.p. 147°.

Montagne, *Rec. trav. chim.*, 1908, **27**, 353.

2 : 3 : 5-Tribromo-*p*-benzoquinone (*Tribromoquinone*)

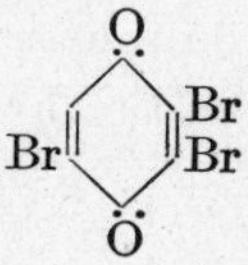

$C_6HO_2Br_3$ MW, 345

Yellow plates from EtOH. M.p. 147°. Sol. EtOH, Et_2O, $CHCl_3$, C_6H_6. Sublimes. NaOH ⟶ green col.

Sarauw, *Ann.*, 1881, **209**, 120.

2:4:6-Tribromobenzyl bromide (*α:2:4:6-Tetrabromotoluene*)

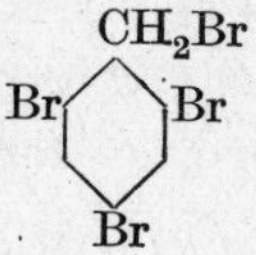

$C_7H_4Br_4$ MW, 408

Needles from EtOH or AcOH. M.p. 75°. B.p. 202°/18 mm.

Asinger, *J. prakt. Chem.*, 1935, **142**, 296.

Tribromobenzyl cyanide.
See under Tribromophenylacetic Acid.

1 : 1 : 2-Tribromobutane

$CH_3{\cdot}CH_2{\cdot}CHBr{\cdot}CHBr_2$

$C_4H_7Br_3$ MW, 295

Yellow oil with camphor-like odour. B.p. 216·2°, 98°/14 mm. D_4^{15} 2·1913. Darkens on heating at atm. press.

Kaufmann, Schweitzer, *Ber.*, 1922, **55**, 264.

1 : 2 : 2-Tribromobutane

$CH_3{\cdot}CH_2{\cdot}CBr_2{\cdot}CH_2Br$

$C_4H_7Br_3$ MW, 295

B.p. 213·8°, 112–15°/40 mm., 90·1°/14 mm. D_4^{15} 2·1761.

Lépingle, *Bull. soc. chim.*, 1926, **39**, 741.

1 : 2 : 3-Tribromobutane

$CH_3 \cdot CHBr \cdot CHBr \cdot CH_2Br$

$C_4H_7Br_3$ MW, 295

B.p. 110–13°/19 mm., 100–1°/14 mm., 94–6°/6 mm. D_4^{16} 2·190. n_D^{15} 1·5691.

Slobodin, *Chem. Abstracts*, 1935, **29**, 4732.
Delaby, *Compt. rend.*, 1923, **176**, 589.

1 : 2 : 4-Tribromobutane

$BrCH_2 \cdot CH_2 \cdot CHBr \cdot CH_2Br$

$C_4H_7Br_3$ MW, 295

B.p. 115–17°/10 mm. D_0^{18} 2·234. n_D^{18} 1·574.

Pariselle, *Ann. chim. phys.*, 1911, **24**, 323.

2 : 2 : 3-Tribromobutane

$CH_3 \cdot CHBr \cdot CBr_2 \cdot CH_3$

$C_4H_7Br_3$ MW, 295

B.p. 206·5°, 83–4°/11·5 mm. D_4^{15} 2·1806.

Lépingle, *Bull. soc. chim.*, 1926, **39**, 741.

1 : 3 : 4-Tribromo-*sec.*-*n*-butyl Alcohol (*Erythritol tribromohydrin*, 1 : 3 : 4-*tribromo*-2-*hydroxybutane*)

$BrCH_2 \cdot CHBr \cdot CH(OH) \cdot CH_2Br$

$C_4H_7OBr_3$ MW, 311

B.p. 148–50°/14 mm.

Pariselle, *Ann. chim. phys.*, 1911, **24**, 405.

1 : 1 : 1-Tribromo-*tert.*-butyl Alcohol (*Brometone*)

$(CH_3)_2C(OH) \cdot CBr_3$

$C_4H_7OBr_3$ MW, 311

Cryst. with camphor-like odour from EtOH.Aq. M.p. 167–76°.
Acetyl: cryst. from EtOH. M.p. 43–4°.
Propionyl: cryst. from EtOH. M.p. 27°.
Butyryl: b.p. 144–5°/13 mm.

Aldrich, *J. Am. Chem. Soc.*, 1911, **33**, 387.

3 : 4 : 5-Tribromocatechol

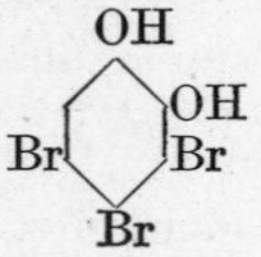

$C_6H_3O_2Br_3$ MW, 347

Cryst. + $1H_2O$. M.p. 144°. Sol. EtOH, Et_2O, Me_2CO. Spar. sol. $CHCl_3$, pet. ether. Insol. H_2O.
Di-Me ether: 3 : 4 : 5-tribromoveratrol. $C_8H_7O_2Br_3$. MW, 375. Needles. M.p. 86–7°. Sol. $CHCl_3$, C_6H_6. Spar. sol. cold EtOH.
Diacetyl: cryst. M.p. 120°.

Frejka, Šefránek, *Chem. Zentr.*, 1936, I 2338.
Chem. Fabrik, von Heyden, D.R.P. 207,544, (*Chem. Zentr.*, 1909, I, 1283) 215,337, (*Chem. Zentr.*, 1909, II, 1710)

3 : 4 : 5-Tribromo-*o*-cresol

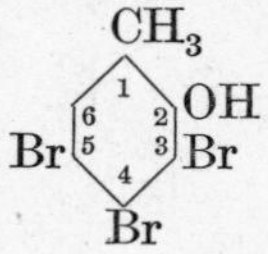

$C_7H_5OBr_3$ MW, 345

Needles from petrol. M.p. 89°. Sol. EtOH Et_2O, AcOH, C_6H_6. Spar. sol. petrol.
Acetyl: plates from AcOH. M.p. 106–7°.

Kohn, Aron, *Monatsh.*, 1929, **53**, 49.
Janney, *Ann.*, 1913, **398**, 367.

3 : 5 : 6-Tribromo-*o*-cresol. Needles from petrol. M.p. 91°. Sol. Et_2O AcOH, C_6H_6. Spar. sol. petrol. $NaNO_2$ in AcOH ⟶ 3 : 4-dibromo-6-nitro-*o*-cresol.
Me ether: $C_8H_7OBr_3$. MW, 359. Needles from EtOH. M.p. 71°. B.p. 308–11°/745 mm.
Acetyl: cryst. from AcOH. M.p. 76–7°.
Benzoyl: prisms from C_6H_6. M.p. 133°.

Kohn, Aron, *Monatsh.*, 1929, **53**, 54.

4 : 5 : 6-Tribromo-*o*-cresol. Needles from pet. ether. M.p. 106°.
Me ether: cryst. from EtOH. M.p. 105° B.p. 320°.

Kohn Soltész, *Monatsh.*, 1925, **46**, 250.

2 : 4 : 6-Tribromo-*m*-cresol

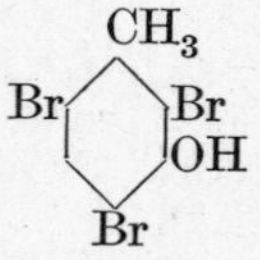

$C_7H_5OBr_3$ MW, 345

Needles from EtOH or pet. ether. M.p. 81·5–82°. Cryst. + 1AcOH from AcOH. Ox. ⟶ 3 : 5-dibromotoluquinone.
Et ether: $C_9H_9OBr_3$. MW, **373**. Needles from EtOH. M.p. 36°.
Acetyl: needles from EtOH. M.p. 68°.
Benzoyl: needles from EtOH. M.p. 84–5°.
Benzenesulphonyl: plates from EtOH. M.p. 117–117·5°.

p-*Toluenesulphonyl* : plates from EtOH. M.p. 113–14°.

Huston, Peterson, *J. Am. Chem. Soc.*, 1933, **55**, 3882.
Jost, Richter, *Ber.*, 1923, **56**, 122.
van Erp, *Rec. trav. chim.*, 1911, **30**, 302.
Claus, Hirsch, *J. prakt. Chem.*, 1889, **39**, 59.

2 : 3 : 5-Tribromo-*p*-cresol

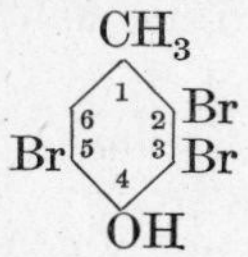

$C_7H_5OBr_3$ MW, 345

Needles from petrol. M.p. 102°. Sol. EtOH, Et_2O, AcOH, C_6H_6, hot Na_2CO_3.Aq. Spar. sol. petrol.
Acetyl : needles from ligroin. M.p. 77°.

Zincke, Wiederhold, *Ann.*, 1902, **320**, 205.

2 : 3 : 6-Tribromo-*p*-cresol.
Benzoyl : plates from Me_2CO. M.p. 120°.
p-*Nitrobenzoyl* : plates from $Me_2CO–CHCl_3$. Softens at 156°, m.p. 159–60°.

Jadhav, Rangwala, *Chem. Zentr.*, 1935, I, 2976.

3 : 5 : 6-Tribromo-ψ-cumene (3 : 5 : 6-*Tribromo*-1 : 2 : 4-*trimethylbenzene*)

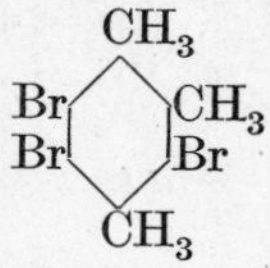

$C_9H_9Br_3$ MW, 357

Cryst. M.p. 229–30°. Sol. boiling toluene, hot AcOH. Spar. sol. hot EtOH.

Fittig, Laubinger, *Ann.*, 1869, **151**, 267.

3 : 4 : 5-Tribromo-*o*-dinitrobenzene

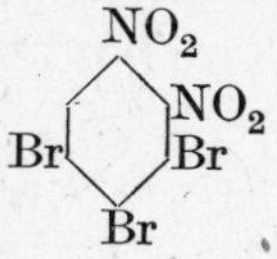

$C_6HO_4N_2Br_3$ MW, 405

Plates or prisms. M.p. 162–4°. Sol. AcOH, $CHCl_3$, C_6H_6, EtOH, Et_2O, hot ligroin. Insol. H_2O. Boiling dil. NaOH ⟶ 4 : 5 : 6-tribromo-*o*-nitrophenol.

Körner, Contardi, *Atti accad. Lincei*, 1906, **15**, 586.

2 : 4 : 5-Tribromo-*m*-dinitrobenzene

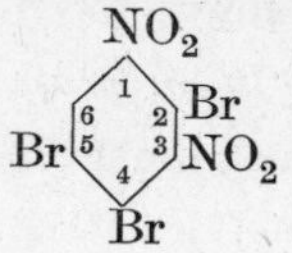

$C_6HO_4N_2Br_3$ MW, 405

Yellow scales. M.p. 135·5°. Sol. hot EtOH, Et_2O, CS_2. Spar. sol. cold EtOH. Red. ⟶ 5-bromo-*m*-phenylenediamine.

Jackson, Gallivan, *Ber.*, 1895, **28**, 190.

2 : 4 : 6-Tribromo-*m*-dinitrobenzene.
Colourless prisms or needles from EtOH. M.p. 192°. Very sol. Et_2O, C_6H_6, CS_2. Sol. hot EtOH. Spar. sol. cold EtOH. Insol. H_2O. Red. ⟶ 2 : 4 : 6 - tribromo - *m* - phenylenediamine. Zn + HCl ⟶ *m*-phenylenediamine.

Jackson, Koch, *Am. Chem. J.*, 1899, **21**, 519.

4 : 5 : 6-Tribromo-*m*-dinitrobenzene.
Cryst. from EtOH. M.p. 150–1°. Sol. Me_2CO, AcOH, $CHCl_3$, C_6H_6. Spar. sol. EtOH, ligroin. Alc. NH_3 at 100° ⟶ 5 : 6-dibromo-2 : 4-dinitroaniline.

van de Bunt, *Rec. trav. chim.*, 1929, **48**, 128.
Jackson, Earle, *Am. Chem. J.*, 1901, **26**, 51.

2 : 3 : 4-Tribromodiphenyl

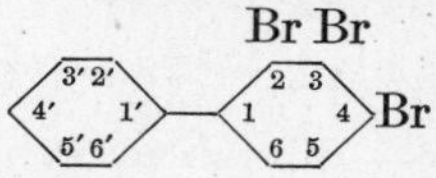

$C_{12}H_7Br_3$ MW, 391

Needles. M.p. 225–7°.

Bellavita, *Chem. Zentr.*, 1936, I, 2342.

2 : 4 : 5-Tribromodiphenyl.
Prisms. M.p. 68°.

Bellavita, *Chem. Zentr.*, 1936, I, 2341.

2 : 4 : 6-Tribromodiphenyl.
Needles from MeOH. M.p. 64°.

Blakey, Scarborough, *J. Chem. Soc.*, 1927, 3008.

2 : 5 : 4′-Tribromodiphenyl.
Yellow needles from EtOH. M.p. 76°.

Bellavita, *Gazz. chim. ital.*, 1935, **65**, 643.

2 : 3′ : 4′-Tribromodiphenyl.
Needles from EtOH. M.p. 91°.

Bellavita, *Gazz. chim. ital.*, 1935, **65**, 644.

4 : 5 : 4′-Tribromodiphenyl.
Prisms. M.p. 102°.

Bellavita, *Chem. Zentr.*, 1936, I, 2342.

1 : 1 : 2-Tribromoethane

$CH_2Br{\cdot}CHBr_2$

$C_2H_3Br_3$ MW, 267

M.p. — 26°. B.p. 187–8°/721 mm., 83°/18 mm. D_4^{20} 2·57896. n_D^{20} 1·58902. Alc. KOH ⟶ 1 : 1-dibromoethylene + bromoacetylene + acetylene.

Wurtz, *Ann.*, 1857, **104**, 243.

2 : 2 : 2-Tribromoethyl Alcohol (*Tribromoethanol, Avertin*)

$CBr_3{\cdot}CH_2OH$

$C_2H_3OBr_3$ MW, 283

Needles or prisms. M.p. 80°. B.p. 92–3°/10 mm. Sol. EtOH, Et_2O, C_6H_6, warm pet. ether. Spar. sol. H_2O. Used in anæsthesia.
Chloroformyl: b.p. 103°/10 mm.
Urethane: prisms from EtOH. M.p. 86–7°. Very sol. H_2O. Sol. EtOH, Et_2O.

I.G., D.R.P., 565,157, (*Chem. Zentr.*, 1933, I, 1514); E.P., 370,490, (*Chem. Zentr.*, 1932, II, 3303).
Willstätter, Duisberg, *Ber.*, 1923, **56**, 2284.

Tribromoethylene

$CHBr{:}CBr_2$

C_2HBr_3 MW, 265

B.p. 162·5°, 75°/15 mm. $D^{20·5}$ 2·708. n_D^{25} 1·62475. O ⟶ dibromoacetyl bromide. In air ⟶ pentabromoethane. Zn + EtOH ⟶ acetylene + bromoacetylene.
Hg comp.: prisms from $CHCl_3$. M.p. 141°.

Dehn, *J. Am. Chem. Soc.*, 1912, **34**, 286.

Tribromohydrin.
See 1 : 2 : 3-Tribromopropane.

2 : 4 : 6-Tribromo-*m*-hydroxybenzoic Acid

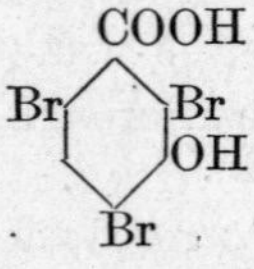

$C_7H_3O_3Br_3$ MW, 375

Needles + ½H_2O from H_2O. Anhyd. at 100°. M.p. 146–7°. Sol. EtOH, Et_2O, AcOH. Mod. sol. $CHCl_3$. Insol. C_6H_6. Boiling HI ⟶ *m*-hydroxybenzoic acid.
Me ether: 2 : 4 : 6-tribromo-*m*-methoxybenzoic acid. $C_8H_5O_3Br_3$. MW, 389. Cryst. from AcOH.Aq. M.p. 154°.
Me ester: $C_8H_5O_3Br_3$. MW, 389. Plates and needles from ligroin. M.p. 119–21°. Sol. most org. solvents.
Amide: $C_7H_4O_2NBr_3$. MW, 374. M.p. 221°.
Nitrile: $C_7H_2ONBr_3$. MW, 356. Yellow needles from ligroin. M.p. 168°. Spar. sol. ligroin. *Acetyl*: yellowish-white plates from EtOH.Aq. M.p. 156–8°.
Acetyl: cryst. from MeOH or $CHCl_3$–pet. ether. M.p. 192–3°.

Bull, Ross, Fuson, *J. Am. Chem. Soc.*, 1935, **57**, 764.
Luck, Hosaews, *Monatsh.*, 1933, **62**, 186.
Leulier, Pinet, *Bull. soc. chim.*, 1927, **41**, 1362.
Werner, *Bull. soc. chim.*, 1886, **46**, 276.

Tribromohydroxybenzyl bromide.
See Tetrabromocresol.

1 : 1 : 2-Tribromoisobutane

$(CH_3)_2CBr{\cdot}CHBr_2$

$C_4H_7Br_3$ MW, 295

B.p. 205–6° decomp., 121–4°/57 mm., 110–14°/15 mm. D_4^{21} 2·0169.

Norton, Williams, *Am. Chem. J.*, 1887, **9**, 89.

1 : 2 : 3-Tribromoisobutane

BrH_2C, CH_3 > $CBr{\cdot}CH_2Br$

$C_4H_7Br_3$ MW, 295

B.p. 173–83°/235 mm., 108–9°/18 mm. D_4^{14} 2·2106. n_D^{14} 1·57012.

Mereshkowski, *Chem. Zentr.*, 1914, I, 2160.
Norton, Williams, *Am. Chem. J.*, 1887, **9**, 88.

Tribromomethane.
See Bromoform.

1 : 2 : 4-Tribromonaphthalene

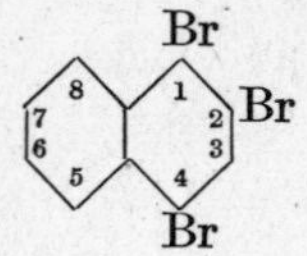

$C_{10}H_5Br_3$ MW, 365

Needles. M.p. 113–14°. Very sol. Et_2O, $CHCl_3$, CS_2, C_6H_6. Mod. sol. EtOH, Me_2CO. Ox. ⟶ phthalic acid.

Prager, *Ber.*, 1885, **18**, 2164.

1 : 2 : 6-Tribromonaphthalene.
Needles from EtOH. M.p. 118°. Very sol. EtOH, Et_2O, ligroin. Slowly volatile in steam. Sublimes.

Claus, Philipson, *J. prakt. Chem.*, 1891, **43**, 53.

1 : 3 : 6-Tribromonaphthalene.
Needles from EtOH, plates from H_2O. M.p. 98° (86·5°). Sol. most. org. solvents. Sublimes.

Franzen, Stäuble, *J. prakt. Chem.*, 1920, **101**, 58.
Claus, Jäck, *J. prakt. Chem.*, 1898, **57**, 17.

1 : 4 : 5-Tribromonaphthalene.
Needles. M.p. 86°. Very sol. EtOH.

Salkind, Belikoff, *Ber.*, 1931, **64**, 958.
John, *Bull. soc. chim.*, 1877, **28**, 515.

1 : 4 : 6-Tribromonaphthalene.
Needles from EtOH. M.p. 86–7°. Very sol. EtOH, Et_2O.

Salkind, Belikoff, *Ber.*, 1931, **64**, 959.
Glaser, *Ann.*, 1865, **135**, 43.

3 : 4 : 6-Tribromo-1 : 2-naphthoquinone

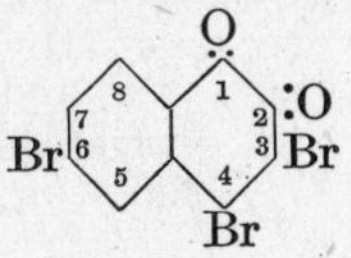

$C_{10}H_3O_2Br_3$ MW, 395

Red needles from C_6H_6. M.p. 193°.
Quinoxaline with o-*phenylenediamine* : yellow needles from AcOH. M.p. 250°.

Fries, Schimmelschmidt, *Ann.*, 1930, **484**, 274.

3 : 5 : 6-Tribromo-1 : 2-naphthoquinone.
Red needles from C_6H_6–petrol. M.p. 184°. Mod. sol. EtOH, AcOH, petrol.
Quinoxaline with o-*phenylenediamine* : yellow needles from toluene. M.p. 271°.

Fries, Schimmelschmidt, *Ann.*, 1930, **484**, 282.

1 : 3 : 6-Tribromo-2-naphthylamine

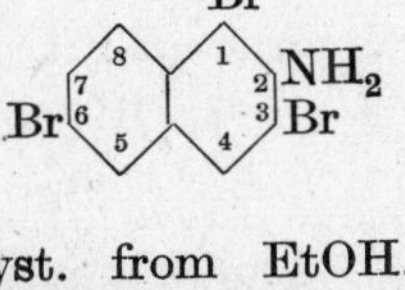

$C_{10}H_6NBr_3$ MW, 380

Pale red cryst. from EtOH. M.p. 143°. Very sol. Et_2O, $CHCl_3$. Spar. sol. EtOH, pet. ether. Ox. ⟶ 4-bromophthalic acid.
N-*Acetyl* : 1 : 3 : 6-tribromo-2-acetnaphthalide. Needles from EtOH. M.p. 250–1°.
N-*Diacetyl* : plates from EtOH. M.p. 159°.
N-p-*Toluenesulphonyl* : needles from AcOH. M.p. 184°.

Bell, *J. Chem. Soc.*, 1932, 2734.
Franzen, Stäuble, *J. prakt. Chem.*, 1920, **101**, 61.

3 : 4 : 5-Tribromo-*o*-nitroaniline

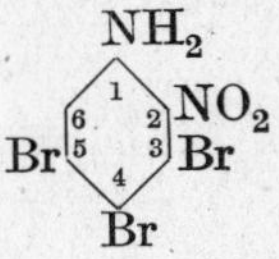

$C_6H_3O_2N_2Br_3$ MW, 375

Yellow needles. M.p. 134°. Sol. EtOH. Spar. sol. hot H_2O.
N-*Acetyl* : 3 : 4 : 5-tribromo-2-nitroacetanilide. Needles from EtOH or C_6H_6, prisms from AcOEt. M.p. 229–30°.

Körner, Contardi, *Atti accad. Lincei*, 1906, **15**, 581.

4 : 5 : 6-Tribromo-*o*-nitroaniline.
Yellow needles. M.p. 166°. Very sol. Me_2CO, $CHCl_3$, C_6H_6. Sol. MeOH, Et_2O, AcOH. Spar. sol. EtOH. Insol. H_2O, ligroin.
N-*Me* : $C_7H_5O_2N_2Br_3$. MW, 389. M.p. 128°.
N-*Et* : $C_8H_7O_2N_2Br_3$. MW, 403. M.p. 130°.
N-*Phenyl* : 4 : 5 : 6-tribromo-2-nitrodiphenylamine. $C_{12}H_7O_2N_2Br_3$. MW, 451. Light red prisms or yellow needles. M.p. 138–9°. Sol. Et_2O, $CHCl_3$, C_6H_6. Spar. sol. EtOH, AcOH. Insol. H_2O, ligroin.
N-*Acetyl* : needles. M.p. 221°.

Jackson, Fiske, *Am. Chem. J.*, 1903, **30**, 74.
Blanksma, *Rec. trav. chim.*, 1902, **21**, 414.

2 : 4 : 6-Tribromo-*m*-nitroaniline

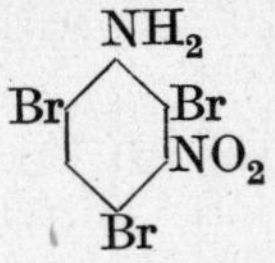

$C_6H_3O_2N_2Br_3$ MW, 375

Yellow needles from EtOH. M.p. 120·5°. Very sol. EtOH.
N-*Acetyl* : 2 : 4 : 6-tribromo-3-nitroacetanilide. Cryst. from EtOH or AcOH, needles from C_6H_6. M.p. 208–9° (216–17°).
N-*Diacetyl* : cryst. from EtOH. M.p. 168–9° (175–6°).

N-*Chloro* : $C_8H_4O_3N_2ClBr_3$. MW, 409·5. Prisms from $CHCl_3$–pet. ether. M.p. 159°.

Jackson, Jones, *Am. Chem. J.*, 1913, **49**, 48.

2 : 3 : 6-Tribromo-*p*-nitroaniline

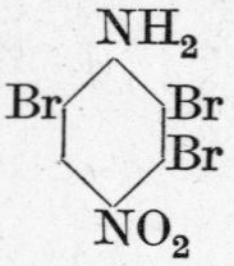

$C_6H_3O_2N_2Br_3$ MW, 375

Yellow needles. M.p. 159°. Spar. sol. cold EtOH. Insol. H_2O. Slowly volatile in steam.

Orton, *J. Chem. Soc.*, 1902, **81**, 499.

Tribromonitroanisole.
See under Tribromonitrophenol.

2 : 3 : 4-Tribromonitrobenzene

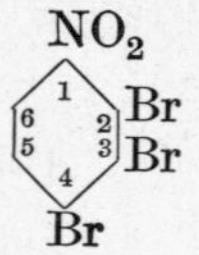

$C_6H_2O_2NBr_3$ MW, 360

Cryst. from EtOH. M.p. 85·4°. Very sol. Et_2O, AcOEt, C_6H_6. Mod. sol. EtOH. Slowly volatile in steam. Sublimes with difficulty.

Körner, Contardi, *Atti accad. Lincei*, 1906, **15**, 583.

2 : 3 : 5-Tribromonitrobenzene.
Needles. M.p. 81° (119·5°). Volatile in steam. Red. ⟶ 2 : 3 : 5-tribromoaniline.

Claus, Wallbaum, *J. prakt. Chem.*, 1897, **56**, 58.

2 : 3 : 6-Tribromonitrobenzene.
Colourless plates or prisms from EtOH–Et_2O. Sublimes at 185° without melting. Very spar. sol. EtOH.

Körner, *Jahresber. Fortschr. Chem.*, 1875, 314.

2 : 4 : 5-Tribromonitrobenzene.
Needles from EtOH. M.p. 93·5°. Sol. Et_2O, hot EtOH, CS_2. Dist. without decomp. Volatile in steam. Sublimes. Red. ⟶ 2 : 4 : 5-tribromoaniline.

Körner, *Jahresber. Fortschr. Chem.*, 1875, 313.

2 : 4 : 6-Tribromonitrobenzene.
Colourless prisms from $CHCl_3$. M.p. 124·5°. B.p. about 177°/11 mm. Sol. Et_2O, boiling AcOH, $CHCl_3$. Spar. sol. boiling EtOH. Red. ⟶ 2 : 4 : 6-tribromoaniline.

Orton, *J. Chem. Soc.*, 1903, **83**, 806.
Hantzsch, Blagden, *Ber.*, 1900, **33**, 2553.

3 : 4 : 5-Tribromonitrobenzene.
Colourless cryst. from EtOH–Et_2O. M.p. 112°. Volatile in steam. Sublimes. Red. ⟶ 3 : 4 : 5-tribromoaniline. NaOH ⟶ 2 : 6-dibromo-*p*-nitrophenol.

Asinger, *J. prakt. Chem.*, 1935, **142**, 299.
Körner, Contardi, *Atti accad. Lincei*, 1906, **15**, 585.

Tribromonitrodiphenylamine.
See under Tribromonitroaniline.

Tribromonitromethane.
See Bromopicrin.

Tribromonitrophenetole.
See under Tribromonitrophenol.

3 : 4 : 6-Tribromo-*o*-nitrophenol

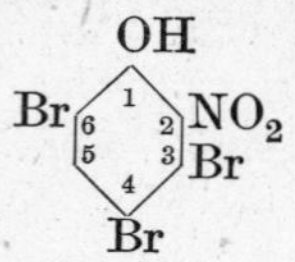

$C_6H_2O_3NBr_3$ MW, 376

Pale yellow plates from H·COOH.Aq. M.p. 127°.

Me ether : 3 : 4 : 6-tribromo-*o*-nitroanisole. $C_7H_4O_3NBr_3$. MW, 390. Colourless prisms from H·COOH.Aq. M.p. 72°.

Hodgson, Walker, Smith, *J. Chem. Soc.*, 1933, 1055.

4 : 5 : 6-Tribromo-*o*-nitrophenol.
Yellow prisms from C_6H_6 or MeOH. M.p. 123°. Very sol. Me_2CO, hot C_6H_6, $CHCl_3$. Sol. EtOH, Et_2O, AcOH. Insol. cold C_6H_6.

Me ether : 4 : 5 : 6-tribromo-*o*-nitroanisole. Needles from EtOH or H·COOH. M.p. 109°. Very sol. Et_2O, $CHCl_3$, C_6H_6. Spar. sol. EtOH, AcOH, ligroin. Insol. H_2O.

Et ether : 4 : 5 : 6-tribromo-*o*-nitrophenetole. $C_8H_6O_3NBr_3$. MW, 404. Cryst. M.p. 74°. Rapidly turns brown in air.

See previous reference and also
Jackson, Fiske, *Am. Chem. J.*, 1903, **30**, 71.

2 : 4 : 6-Tribromo-*m*-nitrophenol

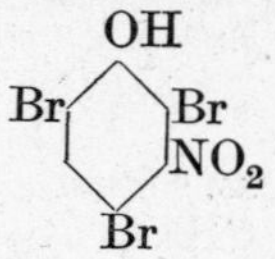

$C_6H_2O_3NBr_3$ MW, 376

Cryst. from ligroin. M.p. 89–90°. Sol. EtOH, Et_2O, $CHCl_3$, C_6H_6. Spar. sol. warm H_2O. Decomposes cold aq. carbonates. Forms spar. sol. Ag and Ba salts. Red. ⟶ *m*-aminophenol.

Me ether: 2 : 4 : 6-tribromo-*m*-nitroanisole. $C_7H_4O_3NBr_3$. MW, 390. Plates from EtOH. M.p. 82°.

Et ether: 2 : 4 : 6-tribromo-*m*-nitrophenetole. $C_8H_6O_3NBr_3$. MW, 404. Prisms from Et_2O. M.p. 79°. Very sol. Et_2O.

Propionyl: scales from EtOH.Aq. M.p. 70–1°.

p-*Toluenesulphonyl*: needles from EtOH. M.p. 146–7°.

Henley, Turner, *J. Chem. Soc.*, 1930, 935.
Bamberger, *Ber.*, 1915, **48**, 1344.

2 : 3 : 6-Tribromo-*p*-nitrophenol

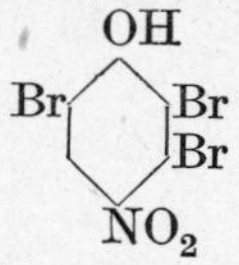

$C_6H_2O_3NBr_3$ MW, 376

Pale yellow needles from hot H_2O. M.p. 151° decomp.

Hodgson, Smith, *J. Chem. Soc.*, 1932, 505.

3 : 4 : 5-Tribromo-*o*-nitrotoluene

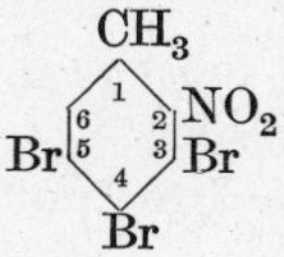

$C_7H_4O_2NBr_3$ MW, 374

Cryst. from EtOH. M.p. 104–5°.

Cohen, Dutt, *J. Chem. Soc.*, 1914, **105**, 515.

3 : 5 : 6-Tribromo-*o*-nitrotoluene.
Cryst. from EtOH. M.p. 88·5–90° (93°). Sol. hot EtOH, C_6H_6. Spar. sol. pet. ether.

Cohen, Dutt, *J. Chem. Soc.*, 1914, **105**, 512.

2 : 4 : 6-Tribromo-*m*-nitrotoluene

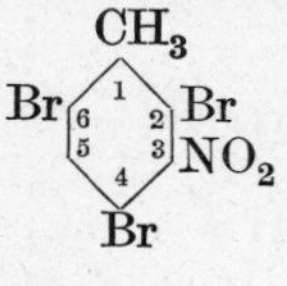

$C_7H_4O_2NBr_3$ MW, 374

Cryst. M.p. 74–75·5°.

Cohen, Dutt, *J. Chem. Soc.*, 1914, **105**, 515.

2 : 5 : 6-Tribromo-*m*-nitrotoluene.
Yellow needles from EtOH. M.p. 91–2°.

Cohen, Dutt, *J. Chem. Soc.*, 1914, **105**, 514.

2 : 3 : 5-Tribromo-*p*-nitrotoluene

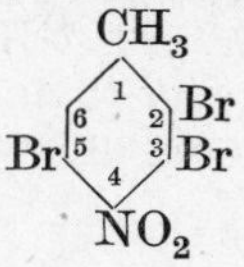

$C_7H_4O_2NBr_3$ MW, 374

Cryst. from EtOH. M.p. 67–8°.

Cohen, Dutt, *J. Chem. Soc.*, 1914, **105**, 512.

2 : 3 : 6-Tribromo-*p*-nitrotoluene.
Cryst. from AcOH. M.p. 106·5–107°.

Cohen, Dutt, *J. Chem. Soc.*, 1914, **105**, 514.

Tribromophenetole.
See under Tribromophenol.

2 : 3 : 4-Tribromophenol

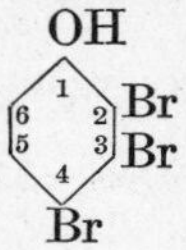

$C_6H_3OBr_3$ MW, 331

Prisms from H·COOH.Aq. M.p. 95°.

Me ether: 2 : 3 : 4-tribromoanisole. $C_7H_5OBr_3$. MW, 345. M.p. 106°.

Hodgson, Walker, Nixon, *J. Chem. Soc.*, 1933, 1054.

2 : 3 : 5-Tribromophenol.
Needles or plates from H_2O or ligroin. M.p. 94–5°. Very sol. EtOH, Et_2O, Me_2CO, hot ligroin, alkalis. Spar. sol. H_2O. Volatile in steam. $FeCl_3$ ⟶ brownish-violet col.

Me ether: 2 : 3 : 5-tribromoanisole. M.p. 82°. B.p. 305–12°.

Bamberger, Kraus, *Ber.*, 1906, **39**, 4251.
Kohn, Karlin, *Monatsh.*, 1927, **48**, 599.

2 : 4 : 5-Tribromophenol.
Needles from dichloroethane–pet. ether. M.p. 87°.

Me ether: 2 : 4 : 5-tribromoanisole. Needles. M.p. 105°. B.p. 306–9°/775 mm.

Benzoyl: m.p. 99°.

o-*Bromo*-p-*toluenesulphonyl*: plates from EtOH. M.p. 107–8°.

Hodgson, Walker, Nixon, *J. Chem. Soc.*, 1933, 1054.
Turner, Henley, *J. Chem. Soc.*, 1930, 933.

2 : 4 : 6-Tribromophenol (*Bromol*).

Needles from EtOH, prisms from C_6H_6, cryst. + 1AcOH from AcOH. M.p. 94°. Sol. 14,000 parts H_2O at 15°. Very sol. EtOH. Sublimes. $NaNO_2$ in AcOH ⟶ 4 : 6-dibromo-*o*-nitrophenol. Forms spar. sol. NH_4 salt. Stronger antiseptic than phenol or thymol.

Me ether: 2 : 4 : 6-tribromoanisole. $C_7H_5OBr_3$. MW, 345. Needles from EtOH. M.p. 88°. Sol. 100 parts H_2O at 15°.

Et ether: 2 : 4 : 6-tribromophenetole. $C_8H_7OBr_3$. MW, 359. Prisms from EtOH. M.p. 72–3°.

Propyl ether: $C_9H_9OBr_3$. MW, 373. Needles from EtOH. M.p. 33–4°.

Allyl ether: $C_9H_7OBr_3$. MW, 371. Needles. M.p. 77°.

p-*Nitrobenzyl ether*: $C_{13}H_8O_3NBr_3$. MW, 466. M.p. 163·5°.

Acetyl: colourless plates or needles from EtOH. M.p. 87°.

Propionyl: needles. M.p. 65°.

Benzoyl: m.p. 81°.

p-*Bromobenzenesulphonyl*: cryst. from EtOH. M.p. 139–40°.

p-*Toluenesulphonyl*: cryst. from EtOH. M.p. 113°.

van Erp, *Rec. trav. chim.*, 1911, **30**, 280.
Orton, Coates, Burdett, *J. Chem. Soc.*, 1907, **91**, 47.
Körner, *Ann.*, 1866, **137**, 203.

2 : 4 : 6-Tribromophenylacetic Acid

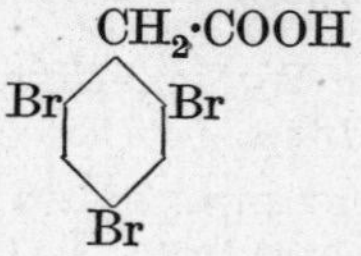

$C_8H_5O_2Br_3$ MW, 373

M.p. 157–8°.

Amide: $C_8H_6ONBr_3$. MW, 372. M.p. 162–3°.

Nitrile: 2 : 4 : 6-tribromobenzyl cyanide. $C_8H_4NBr_3$. MW, 354. M.p. 138–9°. Sol. EtOH. Insol. H_2O.

Henraut, *Chem. Zentr.*, 1924, II, 1342.

3 : 4 : 5-Tribromo-*o*-phenylenediamine

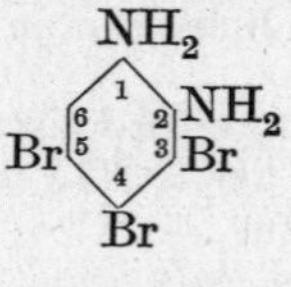

$C_6H_5N_2Br_3$ MW, 345

Cryst. from EtOH. M.p. 91°. Very sol. Et_2O, Me_2CO. Sol. EtOH, AcOH, C_6H_6. Insol. H_2O, ligroin. Turns brown in air.

Jackson, *Am. Chem. J.* 1903, **30**, 78.

2 : 4 : 6-Tribromo-*m*-phenylenediamine

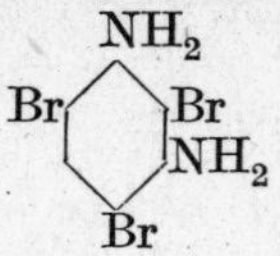

$C_6H_5N_2Br_3$ MW, 345

Needles from EtOH. M.p. 158°. Very sol. Et_2O, $CHCl_3$, C_6H_6. Spar. sol. ligroin. Zn + HCl ⟶ *m*-phenylenediamine.

1 : 3-N-*Diacetyl*: plates from AcOH. Does not melt below 330°.

Jackson, Calvert, *Am. Chem. J.*, 1896, **18**, 470.

2 : 4 : 6-Tribromophenylhydrazine

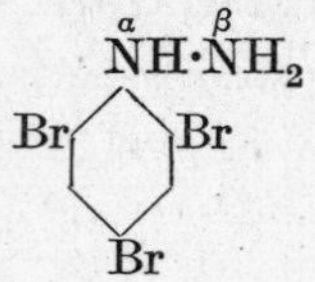

$C_6H_5N_2Br_3$ MW, 345

Needles from pet. ether. M.p. 146°. Sol. boiling AcOH. Spar. sol. boiling EtOH.

β-N-*Acetyl*: prisms from MeOH. M.p. 188°.

α : β-N-*Diacetyl*: needles from EtOH. M.p. 144–5°.

β-N-*Benzoyl*: yellow needles from EtOH. M.p. 172°.

Chattaway, Vonderwahl, *J. Chem. Soc.*, 1915, **107**, 1507.

Tribromophloroglucinol

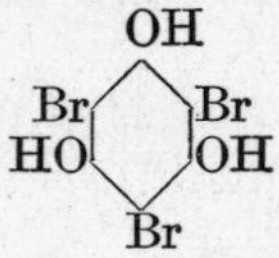

$C_6H_3O_3Br_3$ MW, 363

Cryst. + $3H_2O$ from H_2O. M.p. anhyd. 152–3° (149–50°). Sn + HCl ⟶ phloroglucinol.

Me ether: $C_7H_5O_3Br_3$. MW, 377. Needles from C_6H_6. M.p. 123°. Very sol. H_2O, EtOH, $CHCl_3$. *Diacetyl*: needles from EtOH. M.p. 112–14°.

Tri-Me ether: $C_9H_9O_3Br_3$. MW, 405. Needles from EtOH. M.p. 145°.

Di-Et ether: $C_{10}H_{11}O_3Br_3$. MW, 419. Needles from AcOH.Aq. M.p. 63–5°.

Tri-Et ether: $C_{12}H_{15}O_3Br_3$. MW, 447. Needles from AcOH. M.p. 102–4°.

Monoacetyl: needles from C_6H_6–pet. ether. M.p. 169°.

Triacetyl : needles from EtOH. M.p. 181–3°.

Herzig, Kaserer, *Monatsh.*, 1902, **23**, 577.
Perkin, Simonsen, *J. Chem. Soc.*, 1905, **87**, 863.

1 : 1 : 2-Tribromopropane

$CH_3{\cdot}CHBr{\cdot}CHBr_2$

$C_3H_5Br_3$ MW, 281

B.p. 200–1°, 100–3°/20 mm., 83°/6 mm. D_4^{20} 2·356. n_D^{20} 1·573983.

Mereshkowsky, *Ann.*, 1923, **431**, 239.
Bachman, *J. Am. Chem. Soc.*, 1935, **57**, 1090.

1 : 2 : 2-Tribromopropane

$CH_3{\cdot}CBr_2{\cdot}CH_2Br$

$C_3H_5Br_3$ MW, 281

B.p. 190–1°, 80·6°/20 mm. D^{12} 2·23. n_D^{20} 1·566963.

Mereshkowsky, *Ann.*, 1923, **431**, 241.

1 : 2 : 3-Tribromopropane (*Glycerol tribromohydrin, tribromohydrin*)

$BrCH_2{\cdot}CHBr{\cdot}CH_2Br$

$C_3H_5Br_3$ MW, 281

M.p. 16–17°. B.p. 219–21°, 115–20°/30 mm., 100–3°/18 mm. $D_{15}^{18.5}$ 2·3955. n_D^{18} 1·584. Zn dust + EtOH ⟶ propylene + allyl bromide. Alc. KOH ⟶ ethyl propargyl ether. Ag acetate ⟶ triacetin.

Johnson, McEwen, *Organic Syntheses*, Collective Vol. I, 507.

1 : 1 : 2-Tribromopropionic Acid

$CH_2Br{\cdot}CBr_2{\cdot}COOH$

$C_3H_3O_2Br_3$ MW, 311

Cryst. from CS_2. M.p. 95° (92°). Very sol. EtOH, Et_2O, CS_2, C_6H_6. Spar. sol. cold H_2O. Baryta ⟶ 1 : 2-dibromoacrylic acid.

Et ester : $C_5H_7O_2Br_3$. MW, 339. Liq. with aromatic odour. B.p. 140–2°/30 mm. D^{23} 2·084. n_D^{23} 1·532.

Michael, Norton, *Am. Chem. J.*, 1880, **2**, 18.
Berlande, *Bull. soc. chim.*, 1925, **37**, 1390.

1 : 2 : 2-Tribromopropionic Acid

$CHBr_2{\cdot}CHBr{\cdot}COOH$

$C_3H_3O_2Br_3$ MW, 311

Leaflets. M.p. 118°. Very sol. EtOH, Et_2O. Sol. $CHCl_3$, CS_2, C_6H_6, ligroin, hot H_2O. Baryta ⟶ 1 : 2-dibromoacrylic acid.

Hill, Andrews, *Am. Chem. J.*, 1882, **4**, 180.

2 : 3 : 5-Tribromopyridine

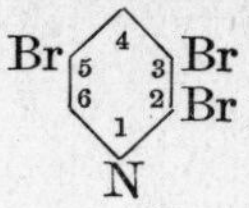

$C_5H_2NBr_3$ MW, 316

Needles from EtOH.Aq. M.p. 46°. Sol. EtOH, Et_2O, C_6H_6. Volatile in steam. Feebly basic.

B_2,$HgCl_2$: cryst. from EtOH.Aq. M.p. 181–2°.

Fischer, Chur, *J. prakt. Chem.*, 1916, **93**, 372.
Hertog, Wibaut, *Rec. trav. chim.*, 1932, **51**, 940.

2 : 3 : 6-Tribromopyridine. M.p. 82°.

See last reference above.

2 : 4 : 6-Tribromopyridine. Leaflets from EtOH. M.p. 107°.

Hertog, Wibaut, *Rec. trav. chim.*, 1932, **51**, 946.

3 : 4 : 5-Tribromopyridine. Cryst. from EtOH. M.p. 106–7°.

Hertog, Wibaut, *Rec. trav. chim.*, 1932, **51**, 950.

Tribromopyrogallol

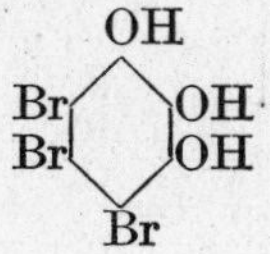

$C_6H_3O_3Br_3$ MW, 363

Reddish or brownish needles or leaflets + $1H_2O$ from EtOH.Aq. M.p. 168–70°. Very sol. EtOH. Sol. hot H_2O.

Tri-Me ether : $C_9H_9O_3Br_3$. MW, 405. Cryst. M.p. 81·5°.

Tri-Et ether : $C_{12}H_{15}O_3Br_3$. MW, 447. M.p. 38–9°.

Moore, Thomas, *J. Am. Chem. Soc.*, 1917, **39**, 987.

2 : 4 : 6-Tribromoresorcinol

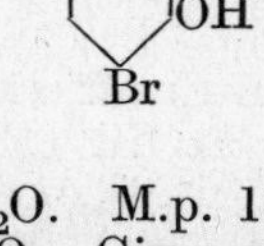

$C_6H_3O_2Br_3$ MW, 347

Needles from H_2O. M.p. 112°. Sol. EtOH. Spar. sol. cold H_2O. Gives reactions of quinones.

Me ether : $C_7H_5O_2Br_3$. MW, 361. Needles. M.p. 104° (99°). Sol. EtOH, Et_2O, C_6H_6, ligroin.

Di-Me ether : $C_8H_7O_2Br_3$. MW, 375. Cryst. from EtOH.Aq. M.p. 68–9°. Sol. EtOH, Et_2O, C_6H_6, ligroin. Insol. H_2O.

Me-Et ether : $C_9H_9O_2Br_3$. MW, 389. Needles from EtOH.Aq. M.p. 75°.

Di-Et ether : $C_{10}H_{11}O_2Br_3$. MW, 403. M.p. 68–9°.

Monoacetyl : cryst. from CS_2. M.p. 114°.

Diacetyl : needles. M.p. 108°.

Monobenzoyl : prisms from $CHCl_3$–pet. ether. M.p. 120°.

Benedikt, *Monatsh.*, 1883, **4**, 227.
Raiford, Heyl, *Am. Chem. J.*, 1910, **44**, 215.

Tribromosuccinic Acid

$CBr_2·COOH$
$CHBr·COOH$

$C_4H_3O_4Br_3$ MW, 355

Plates from Et_2O–C_6H_6. M.p. 136°. Very sol. H_2O, EtOH, Et_2O. Mod. sol. C_6H_6. Very spar. sol. CS_2, ligroin. Hot $H_2O \longrightarrow$ 2 : 2-dibromoacrylic acid.

Lossen, Bergau, *Ann.*, 1906, **348**, 265.

2 : 3 : 4-Tribromotoluene

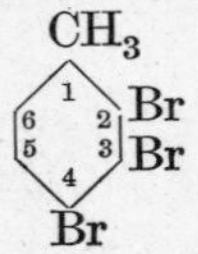

$C_7H_5Br_3$ MW, 329

Cryst. from AcOH. M.p. 45–6°. D^{20} 2·456.

Cohen, Dutt, *J. Chem. Soc.*, 1914, **105**, 510.

2 : 3 : 5-Tribromotoluene.

Cryst. from Et_2O–toluene. M.p. 53–4°. D^{17} 2·467.

Cohen, Dutt, *J. Chem. Soc.*, 1914, **105**, 511, 520.

2 : 3 : 6-Tribromotoluene.

Leaflets from ligroin or $CHCl_3$. M.p. 58–9° (60·5°). D^{17} 2·471.

Cohen, Dutt, *J. Chem. Soc.*, 1914, **105**, 513, 519.

2 : 4 : 5-Tribromotoluene.

Needles from EtOH. M.p. 112–13°. D^{17} 2·472.

Cohen, Dutt, *J. Chem. Soc.*, 1914, **105**, 515, 520.

2 : 4 : 6-Tribromotoluene.

Needles from Et_2O–AcOEt. M.p. 70° (65–6°). D^{17} 2·479. Very spar. sol. EtOH.

Cohen, Dutt, *J. Chem. Soc.*, 1914, **105**, 515.

3 : 4 : 5-Tribromotoluene.

Needles from Et_2O–EtOH. M.p. 91° (88–9°). D^{17} 2·429.

Asinger, *J. prakt. Chem.*, 1935, **142**, 297.

2 : 4 : 6-Tribromo-*m*-toluic Acid

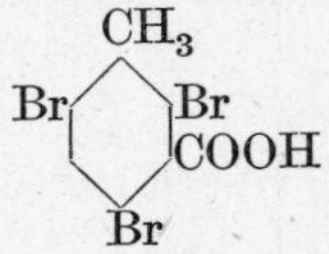

$C_8H_5O_2Br_3$ MW, 373

Needles from 50% MeOH. M.p. 187–188·5° after sintering at 160°.

Amide : $C_8H_6ONBr_3$. MW, 372. Cryst. from 50% EtOH. M.p. 199–200°.

Nitrile : $C_8H_4NBr_3$. MW, 354. Cryst. from pet. ether or cyclohexane. M.p. 122–3°.

Weissberger, Bach, Strasser, *J. Chem. Soc.*, 1935, 70.

3 : 5 : 6-Tribromo-*o*-toluidine

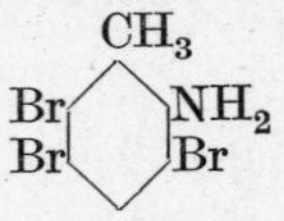

$C_7H_6NBr_3$ MW, 344

M.p. 87°. Sol. Et_2O, C_6H_6, hot EtOH. Mod. sol. pet. ether.

N-*Acetyl* : 3 : 5 : 6-tribromoacet-*o*-toluidide. M.p. 218°.

Blanksma, *Chem. Zentr.*, 1914, I, 971.

2 : 4 : 6-Tribromo-*m*-toluidine

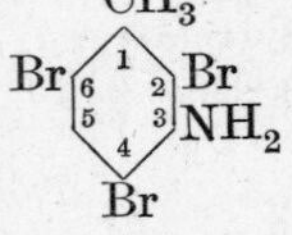

$C_7H_6NBr_3$ MW, 344

Needles from EtOH. M.p. 101°. Spar. sol. EtOH.

N-*Acetyl* : 2 : 4 : 6-tribromoacet-*m*-toluidide. Cryst. from EtOH. M.p. 205° (155°).

N-*Diacetyl* : m.p. 103°.

Cohen, Dutt, *J. Chem. Soc.*, 1914, **105**, 515.
Fuchs, *Monatsh.*, 1915, **36**, 132.
Bureš, Balada, *Chem. Zentr.*, 1927, II, 1345.

2 : 5 : 6-Tribromo-*m*-toluidine.
M.p. 93–4°.
N-*Acetyl* : 2 : 5 : 6-tribromoacet-*m*-toluidide. M.p. 179–81°.

Nevile, Winther, *Ber.*, 1880, **13**, 974.

4 : 5 : 6-Tribromo-*m*-toluidine.
M.p. 96–96·8°.
N-*Acetyl* : 4 : 5 : 6-tribromoacet-*m*-toluidide. Needles from EtOH. M.p. 171–3°.

Cohen, Dutt, *J. Chem. Soc.*, 1914, **105**, 510.

2 : 3 : 5-Tribromo-*p*-toluidine

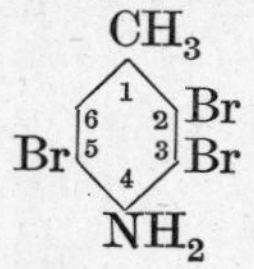

$C_7H_6NBr_3$ MW, 344

Needles from EtOH. M.p. 82·5–83°.

Nevile, Winther, *Ber.*, 1881, **14**, 418.

2 : 3 : 6-Tribromo-*p*-toluidine.
Needles from EtOH. M.p. 118°. Volatile in steam.

Cohen, Dutt, *J. Chem. Soc.*, 1914, **105**, 514.

3 : 5 : 6-Tribromotoluquinone (3 : 5 : 6-*Tribromo-2-methylbenzoquinone*)

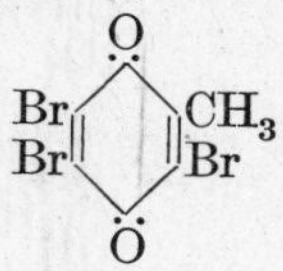

$C_7H_3O_2Br_3$ MW, 359

Yellow plates from EtOH. M.p. 235–6°. Sol. Et_2O, C_6H_6. Very spar. sol. cold EtOH. Insol. H_2O.

Fichter, Rinderspacher, *Helv. Chim. Acta*, 1927, **10**, 41.
Zincke, Klostermann, *Ber.*, 1907, **40**, 679.

Tribromoveratrol.
See under Tribromocatechol.

3 : 4 : 5-Tribromo-*o*-xylene

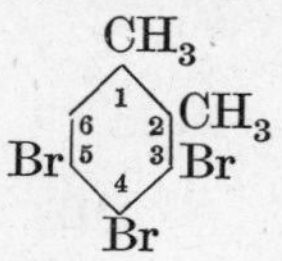

$C_8H_7Br_3$ MW, 343

Needles from Me_2CO. M.p. 105°.

Jaeger, Blanksma, *Rec. trav. chim.*, 1906, **25**, 354.

3 : 4 : 6-Tribromo-*o*-xylene.
Needles. M.p. 86°. Sol. Et_2O, C_6H_6. Spar. sol. cold EtOH, cold Me_2CO.

See previous reference.

2 : 4 : 5-Tribromo-*m*-xylene

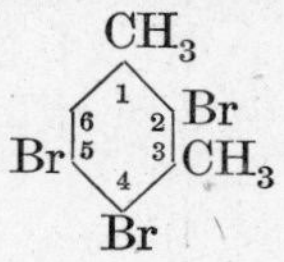

$C_8H_7Br_3$ MW, 343

Cryst. from EtOH. M.p. 87°.

Jaeger, Blanksma, *Rec. trav. chim.*, 1906, **25**, 361.

2 : 4 : 6-Tribromo-*m*-xylene.
Prisms from Et_2O–C_6H_6. M.p. 85°.

Jaeger, Blanksma, *Rec. trav. chim.*, 1906, **25**, 357.

4 : 5 : 6-Tribromo-*m*-xylene.
Cryst. M.p. 105°.

See previous reference.

2 : 3 : 5-Tribromo-*p*-xylene

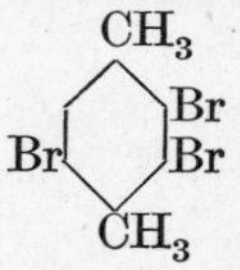

$C_8H_7Br_3$ MW, 343

M.p. 89°. Sol. Et_2O. Spar. sol. Me_2CO, cold EtOH.

Jaeger, Blanksma, *Rec. trav. chim.*, 1906, **25**, 362.

Tributylamine

$(CH_3{\cdot}CH_2{\cdot}CH_2{\cdot}CH_2)_3N$

$C_{12}H_{27}N$ MW, 185

B.p. 216·5°. D_{20}^{20} 0·7782.
B,HFeCl$_4$: yellow needles. M.p. 171°.
Butyl iodide : tetrabutylammonium iodide. M.p. 144–5°. Sol. H_2O, EtOH.
Picrate : m.p. 105·6°.
Butyl picrate : tetrabutylammonium picrate. M.p. 90·3°.
Benzyl chloride : tributylbenzylammonium chloride. M.p. 185°.

I.G., F.P., 685,345, (*Chem. Abstracts*, 1930, **24**, 5765).
Skita, Keil, *Monatsh.*, 1929, **53** and **54**, 759.
Lieben, Rossi, *Ann.*, 1871, **158**, 172.

Tributylbenzylammonium chloride.
See under Tributylamine.

Tributyl phosphate.
See under Phosphoric Acid.

Tributyrin (*Glycerol tri-n-butyrate*)

$CH_2 \cdot O \cdot CO \cdot CH_2 \cdot CH_2 \cdot CH_3$
$CH \cdot O \cdot CO \cdot CH_2 \cdot CH_2 \cdot CH_3$
$CH_2 \cdot O \cdot CO \cdot CH_2 \cdot CH_2 \cdot CH_3$

$C_{15}H_{26}O_6$ MW, 302

Colourless liq. with bitter taste. B.p. 305–10° (287–8°), 190°/15 mm. n_D^{20} 1·43587. D^{21} 1·027.

Weatherby, McIlvaine, Matlin, *J. Am. Chem. Soc.*, 1925, **47**, 2249.

Tricaprin.
See under n-Capric Acid.

Tricaproin.
See under n-Caproic Acid.

Tricaprylin.
See under n-Caprylic Acid.

Tricarballylic Acid (*Propane*-1 : 2 : 3-*tricarboxylic acid*)

$CH_2 \cdot COOH$ α
$CH \cdot COOH$ β
$CH_2 \cdot COOH$

$C_6H_8O_6$ MW, 176

Prisms from H_2O or Et_2O. M.p. 166°. Sol. H_2O, EtOH. Mod. sol. Et_2O. $k = 2{\cdot}2 \times 10^{-4}$ at 25°.

α-Me ester: $C_7H_{10}O_6$. MW, 190. Oil. $k = 7{\cdot}5 \times 10^{-5}$ at 25°.

β-Me ester: oil. $k = 9{\cdot}35 \times 10^{-5}$ at 25°.

Tri-Me ester: $C_9H_{14}O_6$. MW, 218. B.p. 205–8°/48 mm., 150°/13 mm. D_4^{20} 1·18221. n_D 1·4398.

Tri-Et ester: $C_{12}H_{20}O_6$. MW, 260. Oil. B.p. 295–305°, 180–5°/20 mm. Spar. sol. H_2O.

Triallyl ester: $C_{15}H_{20}O_6$. MW, 296. B.p. 215°/24 mm. $D_4^{18{\cdot}4}$ 1·0953. $n_D^{15{\cdot}9}$ 1·46747.

Trichloride: $C_6H_5O_3Cl_3$. MW, 231·5. Liq. B.p. 140°/14 mm.

Triamide: $C_6H_{11}O_3N_3$. MW, 173. Prisms from H_2O. M.p. 205–7° decomp. Sol. H_2O. Insol. EtOH, Et_2O, $CHCl_3$.

Trinitrile: 1 : 2 : 3-tricyanopropane. $C_6H_5N_3$. MW, 119. Needles from Et_2O. M.p. 47°. Sol. hot H_2O. Spar. sol. Et_2O, cold EtOH.

Trihydrazide: cryst. from EtOH.Aq. M.p. 195–6°. *B,3HCl*: m.p. 148° decomp.

Trianilide: needles from $PhNO_2$. M.p. 252°.

αβ-*Anhydride*: $C_6H_6O_5$. MW, 158. Needles from AcOH–$CHCl_3$. M.p. 131–2°. B.p. 215–25°/45 mm. Sol. H_2O, EtOH, AcOH. Spar. sol. Et_2O, $CHCl_3$.

αβ-*Imide*: $C_6H_7O_4N$. MW, 157. Prisms from C_6H_6. M.p. 127–8°. Sol. H_2O, EtOH. Spar. sol. Et_2O, C_6H_6. *Amide*: cryst. from EtOH.Aq. M.p. 173°.

αβ-*Anil*: $C_{12}H_{11}O_4N$. MW, 233. Plates from H_2O. M.p. 137°. *Me ester*: $C_{13}H_{13}O_4N$. MW, 247. Needles from Et_2O–EtOH. M.p. 106°. *Et ester*: $C_{14}H_{15}O_4N$. MW, 261. Needles. M.p. 90°. *Anilide*: needles from EtOH.Aq. M.p. 168°.

Clarke, Murray, *Organic Syntheses*, Collective Vol. I, 508.
Bertram, *Ber.*, 1905, **38**, 1620.
Bone, Sprankling, *J. Chem. Soc.*, 1902, **81**, 34.
Emery, *Ber.*, 1891, 24, 597; 1889, **22**, 2920.

Tricetin (5 : 7 : 3′ : 4′ : 5′ - *Pentahydroxy - flavone*)

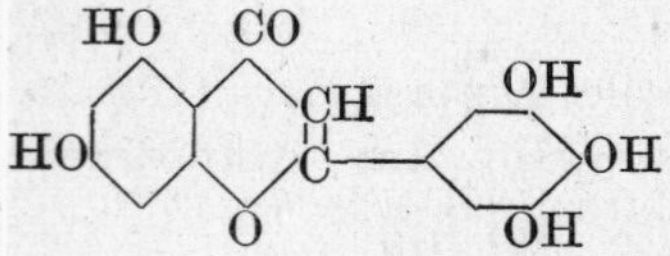

$C_{15}H_{10}O_7$ MW, 302

Needles + H_2O from EtOH.Aq. Decomp. above 330°. Conc. H_2SO_4 ⟶ yellow sol. NaOH ⟶ orange-red sol. Alc. $FeCl_3$ ⟶ reddish-brown col. ⟶ olive-green.

3′ : 5′-*Di-Me ether*: *see* Tricin.

3′ : 4′ : 5′-*Tri-Me ether*: $C_{18}H_{16}O_7$. MW, 344. Yellow needles from AcOH. M.p. 269–70°. Conc. H_2SO_4 and NaOH give yellow sols. Alc. $FeCl_3$ ⟶ reddish-brown to olive-green col. *Diacetyl*: needles from EtOH. M.p. 160–2°.

Penta-Me ether: $C_{20}H_{20}O_7$. MW, 372. Needles from MeOH. M.p. 192–3°.

Tetra-acetyl: needles. M.p. 260–1°.

Penta-acetyl: needles from EtOH–AcOH. M.p. 244° (241–2°).

Anderson, *Chem. Zentr.*, 1932, II, 3899; 1933, II, 2012.

Trichloroacetaldehyde.
See Chloral.

Trichloroacetanilide.
See under Trichloroaniline.

Trichloroacetic Acid

$CCl_3 \cdot COOH$

$C_2HO_2Cl_3$ MW, 163·5

Deliquescent cryst. M.p. 58°. B.p. 196·5°, 141–2°/25 mm. D_{70}^{70} 1·6237. Sol. H_2O. $k = 1{\cdot}2$ approx. Hot H_2O or dil. alkalis ⟶ chloroform + CO_2. Conc. alkalis ⟶ formic acid.

Me ester: $C_3H_3O_2Cl_3$. MW, 177·5. B.p. 152°, 52–4°/12 mm.

Et ester: $C_4H_5O_2Cl_3$. MW, 191·5. B.p. 167·1°/754·8 mm., 60–1°/12 mm. D^{1}_{15} 1·3886. n_D^{20} 1·45068.

Propyl ester: $C_5H_7O_2Cl_3$. MW, 205·5. B.p. 187°.

Isobutyl ester: $C_6H_9O_2Cl_3$. MW, 219·5. B.p. 187–9°.

active-*Amyl ester*: $C_7H_{11}O_2Cl_3$. MW, 233·5. B.p. 210–12°/721 mm. D_4^{22} 1·233. $n_D^{21·4}$ 1·4517. $[\alpha]_D^{22}$ + 3·54°.

Allyl ester: $C_5H_5O_2Cl_3$. MW, 203·5. B.p. 183–4°/766 mm.

Vinyl ester: $C_4H_3O_2Cl_3$. MW, 189·5. B.p. 149°.

Phenyl ester: $C_8H_5O_2Cl_3$. MW, 239·5. B.p. 254–5° decomp.

2-*Naphthyl ester*: m.p. 86–7°.

Benzyl ester: viscous oil. B.p. 178·5°/50 mm. D_4^4 1·3887. $n_D^{18·8}$ 1·5288.

Anhydride: $C_4O_3Cl_6$. MW, 309. B.p. 222–4° decomp., 140°/110 mm. D^{20} 1·6908.

Chloride: C_2OCl_4. MW, 182. B.p. 118° D_4^0 1·6564.

Bromide: C_2OCl_3Br. MW, 226·5. B.p. 143°. D_{15}^{15} 1·900.

Iodide: C_2OCl_3I. MW, 273·5. B.p. about 180°.

Amide: $C_2H_2ONCl_3$. MW, 162·5. Cryst. from H_2O. M.p. 141°. B.p. 238–9°/746 mm. Sol. EtOH, Et_2O. Spar. sol. H_2O. Sublimes in plates.

Methylamide: cryst. from Et_2O. M.p. 105–6°.

Dimethylamide: b.p. 230–3° slight decomp. D^{15} 1·441.

Ethylamide: cryst. M.p. 74°. B.p. 229–30° slight decomp.

Diethylamide: prisms with odour of peppermint. M.p. 27°.

Nitrile: C_2NCl_3. MW, 144·5. B.p. 83–4°. $D^{12·2}$ 1·439.

Imide: di-trichloroacetamide. $C_4HO_2NCl_6$. MW, 308. Cryst. from pet. ether. M.p. 86°.

Anilide: cryst. from EtOH.Aq. M.p. 95–7°.

o-*Nitroanilide*: yellow needles from EtOH. M.p. 70–2°.

p-*Nitroanilide*: needles from EtOH. M.p. 146–7°.

Anschütz, Haslam, *Ann.*, 1889, **253**, 124.
Judson, *Ber.*, 1870, **3**, 782.
Clermont, *Ann. chim. phys.*, 1885, **6**, 135.

Trichloro-acetoisopropyl Alcohol.
See Chloralacetone.

1 : 1 : 1-Trichloroacetone

$CH_3·CO·CCl_3$

$C_3H_3OCl_3$ MW, 161·5

Liq. with odour of camphor. B.p. 149°/764 mm. (134°), 57°/48 mm.

Semicarbazone: needles. M.p. 140° decomp.

Blaise, *Compt. rend.*, 1912, **155**, 1253.
Schlotterbeck, *Ber.*, 1909, **42**, 2561.

1 : 1 : 3-Trichloroacetone

$CH_2Cl·CO·CHCl_2$

$C_3H_3OCl_3$ MW, 161·5

B.p. 172°.

Cloëz, *Ann. chim. phys.*, 1886, **9**, 176.

Trichloro-acet-toluidide.
See under Trichlorotoluidine.

Trichloroacrylic Acid

$CCl_2{:}CCl·COOH$

$C_3HO_2Cl_3$ MW, 175·5

Prisms from CS_2. M.p. 76°. Sol. EtOH, Et_2O, $CHCl_3$, hot H_2O. Spar. sol. cold H_2O. k = about 5·4 × 10^{-2} at 25°.

Et ester: $C_5H_5O_2Cl_3$. MW, 203·5. Liq. with odour of peppermint. B.p. 192–4°, 112–14°/50 mm. D_4^{20} 1·3740. n_D^{20} 1·4839.

Anhydride: $C_6O_3Cl_6$. MW, 333. Cryst. M.p. 39–40°. Insol. H_2O.

Chloride: C_3OCl_4. MW, 194. B.p. 158°. $n_D^{18·5}$ 1·52709.

Amide: $C_3H_2ONCl_3$. MW, 174·5. Needles. M.p. 96–7°. Sol. EtOH, Et_2O, hot H_2O. Spar. sol. cold H_2O.

Nitrile: C_3NCl_3. MW, 156·5. Cryst. M.p. 20°. $n_D^{20·5}$ 1·5100.

Prins, D.R.P., 261,689, (*Chem. Zentr.*, 1913, II, 394).
Fritsch, *Ann.*, 1897, **297**, 315.
Mabery, *Am. Chem. J.*, 1887, **9**, 3.

2 : 4 : 6-Trichloro-*m*-aminophenol

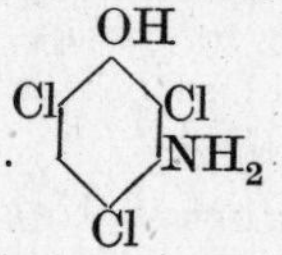

$C_6H_4ONCl_3$ MW, 212·5

Leaflets from ligroin. M.p. 95–6°. Sol. EtOH, Et_2O, $CHCl_3$, C_6H_6. Spar. sol. H_2O. Aq. sol. ⟶ violet-red col. with $FeCl_3$.

N-*Acetyl*: needles from toluene. M.p. 185–186·5°. $FeCl_3$ ⟶ violet col.

Jacobs, Heidelberger, Rolf, *J. Am. Chem. Soc.*, 1919, **41**, 463.
Daccomo, *Ber.*, 1885, **18**, 1166.

2 : 3 : 6-Trichloro-*p*-aminophenol

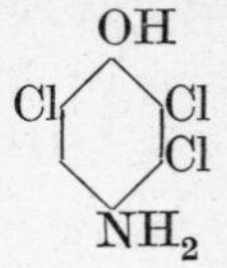

$C_6H_4ONCl_3$ MW, 212·5

Needles from EtOH. M.p. 159° ⟶ a brown liq. Sol. EtOH, Et_2O, hot H_2O.

N-2 : 4-*Dinitrophenyl* : orange-red cryst. M.p. 211°. *Acetyl* : yellow prisms. M.p. 153°.

Kohn, Fink, *Monatsh.*, 1930, **56**, 138.
Schmitt, Andresen, *J. prakt. Chem.*, 1881, **24**, 426.

2 : 3 : 4-Trichloroaniline

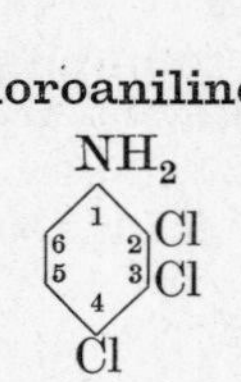

$C_6H_4NCl_3$ MW, 196·5

Needles from ligroin. M.p. 67·5°. B.p. 292°/774 mm. Sol. EtOH.

N - *Acetyl* : 2 : 3 : 4 - trichloroacetanilide. Needles. M.p. 123°.

Zincke, Kuchenbecker, *Ann.*, 1904, **330**, 56.
Beilstein, Kurbatow, *Ann.*, 1879, **196**, 233.

2 : 3 : 5-Trichloroaniline.

Needles from pet. ether. M.p. 73°.

Hodgson, Kershaw, *J. Chem. Soc.*, 1929, 2921.

2 : 3 : 6-Trichloroaniline.

Cryst. from EtOH. M.p. 63–4°.

N-*Acetyl* : 2 : 3 : 6-trichloroacetanilide. Cryst. from EtOH.Aq. M.p. 172–3° (134·5°).

Hüffer, *Rec. trav. chim.*, 1921, **40**, 457.
Chattaway, Orton, Hurtley, *J. Chem. Soc.*, 1900, **77**, 802.

2 : 4 : 5-Trichloroaniline.

Needles from ligroin. M.p. 96·5°. B.p. about 270°. Sol. EtOH, CS_2. Spar. sol. ligroin. Volatile in steam.

N-*Acetyl* : 2 : 4 : 5-trichloroacetanilide. Needles from C_6H_6. M.p. 190°.

Dyson, George, Hunter, *J. Chem. Soc.*, 1926, 3044.
Beilstein, Kurbatow, *Ann.*, 1879, **196**, 233.

2 : 4 : 6-Trichloroaniline.

Needles from ligroin. M.p. 78·5°. B.p. 262°/746 mm. Sol. EtOH, Et_2O, CS_2, ligroin.

N - *Me* : 2 : 4 : 6 - trichloromethylaniline $C_7H_6NCl_3$. MW, 210·5. Needles. M.p. 32°. B.p. 260°. N-*Acetyl* : m.p. 89–90°. N-*Benzoyl* : m.p. 96–7°.

N-*Di-Me* : 2 : 4 : 6-trichlorodimethylaniline $C_8H_8NCl_3$. MW, 224·5. B.p. 247°/745 mm.

N-*Et* : 2 : 4 : 6-trichloroethylaniline. $C_8H_8NCl_3$. MW, 224·5. B.p. 148–53°/25 mm. N-*Acetyl* : m.p. 50–1°. N-*Benzoyl* : m.p. 127–8°.

N - *Formyl* : 2 : 4 : 6 - trichloroformanilide. Needles from EtOH. M.p. 180°.

N - *Acetyl* : 2 : 4 : 6 - trichloroacetanilide. Needles. M.p. 207–8° (204°).

N-*Diacetyl* : prisms from EtOH. M.p. 81–2°.
N-*Propionyl* : prisms from EtOH. M.p. 161°.
N-*Benzoyl* : needles from EtOH. M.p. 174°.
Picrate : crimson prisms from EtOH. M.p. 82·5°.

Chattaway, Irving, *J. Chem. Soc.*, 1933, 142.
Beilstein, Kurbatow, *Ann.*, 1879, **196**, 230.

3 : 4 : 5-Trichloroaniline.

Needles from EtOH.Aq. M.p. 100° (89°).

N-*Acetyl* : 3 : 4 : 5-trichloroacetanilide. M.p. 207–8°.

Dyson, George, Hunter, *J. Chem. Soc.*, 1926, 3043.
Holleman, *Rec. trav. chim.*, 1918, **37**, 196.

Trichloroanisole.

See under Trichlorophenol.

1 : 2 : 3-Trichloroanthraquinone

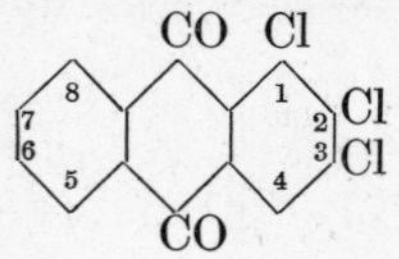

$C_{14}H_5O_2Cl_3$ MW, 311·5

Yellow needles from AcOH. M.p. 194–5°.

Goldberg, *J. Chem. Soc.*, 1931, 1789.

1 : 2 : 4-Trichloroanthraquinone.

Yellow cryst. from $CHCl_3$. M.p. 185·5°. Sol. $CHCl_3$, C_6H_6. Mod. sol. Et_2O, AcOH. Spar. sol. EtOH.

Graebe, Rostowzew, *Ber.*, 1901, **34**, 2113.
Goldberg, *J. Chem. Soc.*, 1931, 1771.

1 : 2 : 5-Trichloroanthraquinone.

Yellow needles from AcOH. M.p. 235–6°.

Goldberg, *J. Chem. Soc.*, 1931, 1792.
Cf. Schilling, *Ber.*, 1913, **46**, 1068.

1 : 2 : 6-Trichloroanthraquinone.
Yellow needles from AcOH. M.p. 222–3°.

Goldberg, *J. Chem. Soc.*, 1931, 1784.

1 : 2 : 7-Trichloroanthraquinone.
Needles from AcOH. M.p. 225–6° (259–60°).

Goldberg, *J. Chem. Soc.*, 1931, 1786.
Keimatsu, Hirano, Tanabe, *Chem. Abstracts*, 1929, **23**, 4214.

1 : 3 : 6-Trichloroanthraquinone.
Yellow needles from AcOH. M.p. 212–13°.

Goldberg, *J. Chem. Soc.*, 1931, 1790.

1 : 3 : 7-Trichloroanthraquinone.
Lemon-yellow needles from AcOH. M.p. 216–17°.

See previous reference.

1 : 4 : 5-Trichloroanthraquinone.
Yellow needles from AcOH. M.p. 258° (253–4°).

Badische, D.R.P., 214,714, (*Chem. Zentr.*, 1909, II, 1603).
Goldberg, *J. Chem. Soc.*, 1931, 1791.
Cf. Schilling, *Ber.*, 1913, **46**, 1068.

1 : 4 : 6-Trichloroanthraquinone.
Yellow needles from AcOH. M.p. 238°.

Goldberg, *J. Chem. Soc.*, 1931, 1784.
Jaroschy, *Monatsh.*, 1913, **34**, 3.

2 : 3 : 5-Trichloroanthraquinone.
Yellow needles from AcOH. M.p. 227–8°.

Goldberg, *J. Chem. Soc.*, 1932, 80.

2 : 3 : 6-Trichloroanthraquinone.
Yellow needles from AcOH. M.p. 245°.

Goldberg, *J. Chem. Soc.*, 1932, 81.

2 : 3 : 4-Trichlorobenzaldehyde

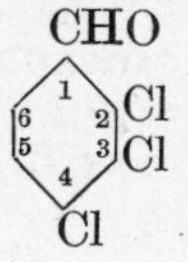

$C_7H_3OCl_3$ MW, 209·5

Needles from EtOH. M.p. 90°.

Seelig, *Ann.*, 1887, **237**, 149.

2 : 3 : 5-Trichlorobenzaldehyde.
Needles from EtOH. M.p. 56°. Sol. most org. solvents. Volatile in steam. $KMnO_4$ ⟶ 2 : 3 : 5-trichlorobenzoic acid.

Hodgson, Beard, *J. Chem. Soc.*, 1927, 2382.

2 : 3 : 6-Trichlorobenzaldehyde.
Needles from ligroin. M.p. 86–7°.

Geigy, D.R.P., 199,943, (*Chem. Zentr.*, 1908, II, 363).

2 : 4 : 5-Trichlorobenzaldehyde.
Needles. M.p. 112–13°. Sol. EtOH, Et_2O, $CHCl_3$, CS_2, C_6H_6. Volatile in steam. Oxidises in air.

Seelig, *Ann.*, 1887, **237**, 148.
Beilstein, Kuhlberg, *Ann.*, 1869, **152**, 238.

2 : 4 : 6-Trichlorobenzaldehyde.
Needles from ligroin. M.p. 58–9°.

Geigy, D.R.P., 199,943, (*Chem. Zentr.*, 1908, II, 363).

3 : 4 : 5-Trichlorobenzaldehyde.
Needles from EtOH.Aq. M.p. 90–1°. $KMnO_4$ ⟶ 3 : 4 : 5-trichlorobenzoic acid.
Phenylhydrazone : yellow cryst. M.p. 147°.
p-*Nitrophenylhydrazone* : orange needles from $PhNO_2$. M.p. 342°.
Semicarbazone : cryst. from EtOH. M.p. 252–4°.

van der Bunt, *Rec. trav. chim.*, 1929, **48**, 131.

1 : 2 : 3-Trichlorobenzene

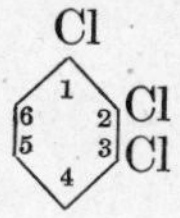

$C_6H_3Cl_3$ MW, 181·5

Plates from EtOH. M.p. 53–4°. B.p. 218–19°. Mod. sol. EtOH. Volatile in steam.

Holleman, *Rec. trav. chim.*, 1918, **37**, 196.
Beilstein, Kurbatow, *Ann.*, 1878, **192**, 234.

1 : 2 : 4-Trichlorobenzene.
M.p. 17°. B.p. 210°. D^{26} 1·4460.

van de Lande, *Rec. trav. chim.*, 1932, **51**, 98.
Cohen, Hartley, *J. Chem. Soc.*, 1905, **87**, 1363.

1 : 3 : 5-Trichlorobenzene.
Needles. M.p. 63·5°. B.p. 208·5°/763·8 mm.

Holleman, *Rec. trav. chim.*, 1918, **37**, 198.
Jackson, Lamai, *Am. Chem. J.*, 1896, **18**, 667.

2 : 3 : 4-Trichlorobenzoic Acid

$C_7H_3O_2Cl_3$ MW, 225·5

Needles from H_2O. M.p. 186–7°.

Cohen, Dakin, *J. Chem. Soc.*, 1902, **81**, 1328.

2 : 3 : 5-Trichlorobenzoic Acid.

Needles from H_2O. M.p. 163°. Sol. common org. solvents. Spar. sol. H_2O. Non-volatile in steam.

Chloride: $C_7H_2OCl_4$. MW, 244. Cryst. from AcOEt. M.p. 36°.

Amide: $C_7H_4ONCl_3$. MW, 224·5. Needles from AcOH.Aq. M.p. 204–5°.

Nitrile: $C_7H_2NCl_3$. MW, 206·5. Needles from EtOH.Aq. M.p. 87°. Volatile in steam.

Hodgson, Beard, *J. Chem. Soc.*, 1927, 2382.
Cohen, Dakin, *J. Chem. Soc.*, 1902, **81**, 1331.
Matthews, *J. Chem. Soc.*, 1901, **79**, 46.

2 : 4 : 5-Trichlorobenzoic Acid.

Needles from H_2O. M.p. 162–4°. Sol. EtOH. Prac. insol. cold H_2O. Sublimes in needles.

Et ester: $C_9H_7O_2Cl_3$. MW, 253·5. Needles from EtOH. M.p. 65°. Mod. sol. EtOH.

Chloride: m.p. 41°. B.p. 272° slight decomp. Sol. Et_2O, CS_2, C_6H_6.

Amide: needles from C_6H_6. M.p. 167·5°. Sol. EtOH. Spar. sol. hot H_2O. Very spar. sol. Et_2O, CS_2.

Cohen, Dakin, *J. Chem. Soc.*, 1902, **81**, 1335.
Beilstein, Kuhlberg, *Ann.*, 1869, **152**, 234.

2 : 4 : 6-Trichlorobenzoic Acid.

Cryst. from H_2O. M.p. 164°. Sol. EtOH, Et_2O, $CHCl_3$.

Chloride: oil. B.p. 275°.

Amide: cryst. M.p. 181°. Mod. sol. hot H_2O.

Nitrile: needles. M.p. 77·5°. Sol. EtOH, Et_2O. Spar. sol. hot H_2O.

Cohen, Dakin, *J. Chem. Soc.*, 1902, **81**, 1336.
Sudborough, *J. Chem. Soc.*, 1895, **67**, 602.

3 : 4 : 5-Trichlorobenzoic Acid.

Needles from EtOH.Aq. M.p. 210°. Sol. EtOH, Et_2O, C_6H_6. Spar. sol. CS_2. Prac. insol. H_2O. Sublimes in needles. Spar. volatile in steam.

Et ester: needles. M.p. 86°.

Chloride: prisms. M.p. 36°. Sol. Et_2O, CS_2, C_6H_6.

Amide: needles from C_6H_6. M.p. 176°. Sol. EtOH, Et_2O. Insol. H_2O.

van der Bunt, *Rec. trav. chim.*, 1929, **48**, 132.
Salkowski, *Ann.*, 1872, **163**, 28.

2 : 4 : 6-Trichlorobenzophenone

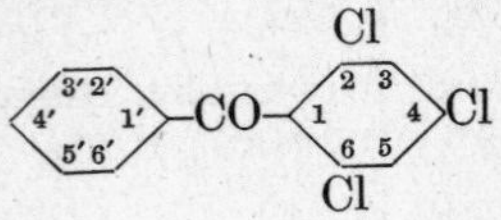

$C_{13}H_7OCl_3$ MW, 285·5

Cryst. from pet. ether. M.p. 130·5°. B.p. 356°/763 mm.

Montagne, *Rec. trav. chim.*, 1907, **26**, 274

2 : 5 : 2′-Trichlorobenzophenone.

Needles from EtOH. M.p. 145–7°.

Ganzmüller, *J. prakt. Chem.*, 1933, **138**, 311.

Trichloro-*p*-benzoquinone

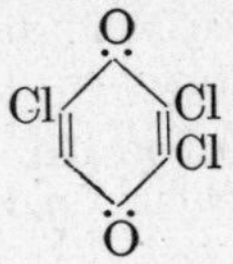

$C_6HO_2Cl_3$ MW, 211·

Yellow plates from EtOH. M.p. 169–70° Sol. Et_2O, hot EtOH. Insol. cold H_2O. Sublimes.

Erdélyi, *Ber.*, 1930, **63**, 1200.
v. Knapp, Schultz, *Ann.*, 1881, **210**, 174

Trichlorobromomethane (*Trichloromethyl bromide*)

CCl_3Br

CCl_3Br MW, 198·

M.p. – 21°. B.p. 104·3°. D_4^0 2·0549 Photochem. reaction with Cl ⟶ carbon tetrachloride. Sensitive to light.

Wonters, *Bull. sci. acad. roy. Belg.*, 193· **20**, 782.
Löw, *Z. Chem.*, 1869, 624.

1 : 2 : 3-Trichlorobutane

$CH_3·CHCl·CHCl·CH_2Cl$

$C_4H_7Cl_3$ MW, 161·

B.p. 165–8°/725 mm., 79–80°/32 mm., 62–3°/ 3 mm. D^0 1·3241. Sol. EtOH, Et_2O, $CHCl_3$. ısol. H_2O.

de Montmollin, Matile, *Helv. Chim. Acta*, 1924, **7**, 106.
Charon, *Ann. chim. phys.*, 1899, **17**, 230.
Note.—Losanitsch, *Chem. Zentr.*, 1913, II, 754, described a trichlorobutane of unknown constitution, b.p. 90°/16 mm.

2 : 2 : 3-Trichloro-*n*-butyl Alcohol

$CH_3·CHCl·CCl_2·CH_2OH$

$_4H_7OCl_3$ MW, 177·5

Prisms. M.p. 61·5–62°. B.p. 199–200°, 120°/ 5 mm. Sol. EtOH, Et_2O. Spar. sol. H_2O. educes warm Fehling's. $HNO_3 \longrightarrow$ 1 : 1 : 2- ichlorobutyric acid.

Phosphate: needles from EtOH. M.p. 85·3°.

Mering, *Z. physiol. Chem.*, 1882, **6**, 493.
Garzarolli-Thurnlakh, Popper, *Ann.*, 1884, **223**, 166.

Trichloro-*tert*.-butyl Alcohol.

See Acetone-chloroform.

1 : 1 : 2-Trichlorobutyraldehyde.

See Butylchloral.

1 : 1 : 3-Trichlorobutyraldehyde

$CH_2Cl·CH_2·CCl_2·CHO$

$_4H_5OCl_3$ MW, 175·5

Liq. Spar. sol. H_2O. Forms no hydrate. xidises slowly in air. $HNO_3 \longrightarrow$ 1 : 1 : 3-tri- ılorobutyric acid. Forms bisulphite comp.

Natterer, *Monatsh.*, 1883, **4**, 551.

1 : 1 : 2-Trichlorobutyric Acid

$CH_3·CHCl·CCl_2·COOH$

$_4H_5O_2Cl_3$ MW, 191·5

Plates or needles from pet. ether. M.p. 60°. .p. 236–8°. k = about 0·18 at 18°.

Et ester: $C_6H_9O_2Cl_3$. MW, 219·5. B.p. 212°,)1·5°/17 mm. D^{20}_{20} 1·3138.

Chloride: $C_4H_4OCl_4$. MW, 210. B.p. 162–6°.

Amide: $C_4H_6ONCl_3$. MW, 190·5. Plates om EtOH. M.p. 96°. Spar. sol. H_2O.

Krämer, Pinner, *Ber.*, 1870, **3**, 389.
Valentin, *Ber.*, 1895, **28**, 2661.

1 : 1 : 3-Trichlorobutyric Acid

$CH_2Cl·CH_2·CCl_2·COOH$

$_4H_5O_2Cl_3$ MW, 191·5

Cryst. M.p. 73–5°. Sol. 20 parts H_2O.

Natterer, *Monatsh.*, 1883, **4**, 551.

1 : 2 : 2-Trichlorobutyric Acid

$CH_3·CCl_2·CHCl·COOH$

$_4H_5O_2Cl_3$ MW, 191·5

Plates from ligroin. M.p. 51·5–52°. Sol. EtOH, Et_2O, $CHCl_3$, CS_2, C_6H_6. Spar. sol. H_2O.

Szenic, Taggesell, *Ber.*, 1895, **28**, 2665.

3 : 3 : 3-Trichlorobutyric Acid

$CCl_3·CH_2·CH_2·COOH$

$C_4H_5O_2Cl_3$ MW, 191·5

M.p. 57°.

Anhydride: $C_8H_8O_3Cl_6$. MW, 365. B.p. 138–40°/20 mm. D^{20}_4 0·970.

Baroni, *Gazz. chim. ital.*, 1933, **63**, 23.

3 : 4 : 5-Trichlorocatechol

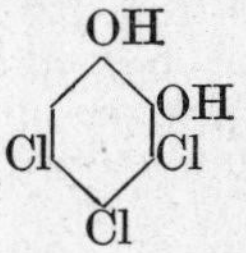

$C_6H_3O_2Cl_3$ MW, 213·5

Two hydrates are known:

(i) + $1H_2O$. Prisms from AcOH. M.p. 115° (104–5°). Sol. EtOH, Et_2O, AcOH. Insol. cold H_2O. $FeCl_3 \longrightarrow$ green col.

(ii) + $\frac{1}{2}H_2O$. Prisms from C_6H_6. M.p. 134–5°.

1(or 2)-*Me ether*: trichloroguaiacol. $C_7H_5O_2Cl_3$. MW, 227·5. Needles from pet. ether. M.p. 107–8°. Volatile in steam. *Benzoyl*: cryst. from ligroin. M.p. 128–9°.

2(or 1)-*Me ether*: needles. M.p. 114–15°. Sol. EtOH, Et_2O. Insol. H_2O. Volatile in steam. $FeCl_3 \longrightarrow$ green col.

Di-Me ether: 3 : 4 : 5-trichloroveratrol. $C_8H_7O_2Cl_3$. MW, 241·5. Needles. M.p. 68–9°. Sol. C_6H_6, hot EtOH. Insol. H_2O.

Cousin, *Ann. chim. phys.*, 1903, **29**, 60, 90.
Jackson, Boswell, *Am. Chem. J.*, 1906, **35**, 526.
Peratoner, Ortoleva, *Gazz. chim. ital.*, 1898, **28**, 230.

3 : 4 : 5-Trichloro-*o*-cresol

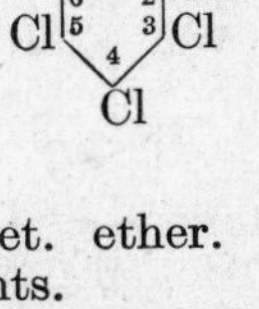

$C_7H_5OCl_3$ MW, 211·5

Needles from pet. ether. M.p. 77°. Sol. common org. solvents.

Acetyl: needles from MeOH.Aq. M.p. 45°.

Zincke, Preiss, *Ann.*, 1918, **417**, 204.

3 : 5 : 6-Trichloro-*o*-cresol.
Needles from AcOH. M.p. 62°. Sol. common org. solvents except pet. ether.
Benzoyl : needles from EtOH. M.p. 110°.

Zincke, Preiss, *Ann.*, 1918, **417**, 205.

2 : 4 : 6-Trichloro-*m*-cresol

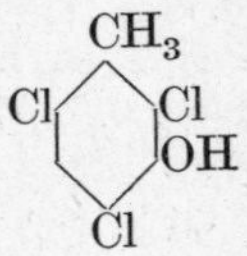

$C_7H_5OCl_3$ MW, 211·5

Needles or plates from H_2O. M.p. 47°. B.p. 265°, 142–4°/14 mm. Sol. common org. solvents. Spar. sol. H_2O. Volatile in steam. Complex with cuprammonium sulphate employed as a fungicide.
Me ether : $C_8H_7OCl_3$. MW, 225·5. Needles from AcOH.Aq. M.p. 54–5° (46°).
Et ether : $C_9H_9OCl_3$. MW, 239·5. M.p. 35·5°.
Phenyl ether : $C_{13}H_9OCl_3$. MW, 287·5. M.p. 103°.
Acetyl : cryst. from Et_2O. M.p. 35° (32°). B.p. 273–4°.
Benzoyl : plates. M.p. 53°.
Benzenesulphonyl : plates. M.p. 121°.
p-*Toluenesulphonyl* : plates. M.p. 92–3°.

Huston, Chen, *J. Am. Chem. Soc.*, 1933, **56**, 4218.
Crowther, McCombie, *J. Chem. Soc.*, 1913, **103**, 542.
Raiford, *Am. Chem. J.*, 1911, **46**, 423.

2 : 3 : 5-Trichloro-*p*-cresol

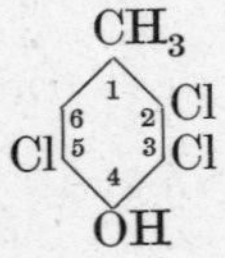

$C_7H_5OCl_3$ MW, 211·5

Needles from AcOH or pet. ether. M.p. 66–7°.
Acetyl : needles from AcOH.Aq. M.p. 37–8°.
Benzoyl : plates from EtOH.Aq. M.p. 89°.

Zincke, *Ann.*, 1903, **328**, 279.

2 : 3 : 6-Trichloro-*p*-cresol.
Cryst. from AcOH. M.p. 85–6°.

Datta, Mitter, *J. Am. Chem. Soc.*, 1919, **41**, 2034.

3 : 4 : 5-Trichloro-*o*-dinitrobenzene

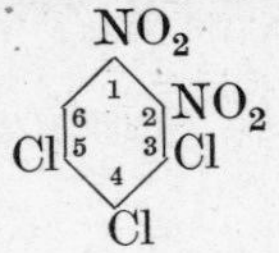

$C_6HO_4N_2Cl_3$ MW, 271·5

Yellow cryst. from EtOH. M.p. 105–6°.

Hüffer, *Rec. trav. chim.*, 1921, **40**, 451.

3 : 4 : 6-Trichloro-*o*-dinitrobenzene.
Yellow prisms. M.p. 70–1°.

Hüffer, *Rec. trav. chim.*, 1921, **40**, 453.

2 : 4 : 5-Trichloro-*m*-dinitrobenzene

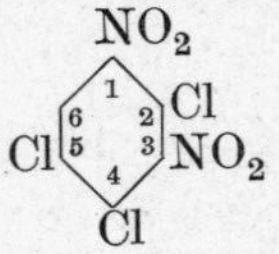

$C_6HO_4N_2Cl_3$ MW, 271·5

Pale yellow prisms from EtOH. M.p. 103·5°. B.p. 335°. D^{25} 1·850. Sol. Et_2O, CS_2, C_6H_6, hot EtOH.

Qvist, Salo, *Chem. Zentr.*, 1936, I, 540.
Hüffer, *Rec. trav. chim.*, 1921, **40**, 452.

2 : 4 : 6-Trichloro-*m*-dinitrobenzene.
Prisms from EtOH. M.p. 129·5°. Sol. Me_2CO, $CHCl_3$, CS_2, C_6H_6.

Jackson, Wing, *Am. Chem. J.*, 1887, **9**, 353.
Hüffer, *Rec. trav. chim.*, 1921, **40**, 451.

4 : 5 : 6-Trichloro-*m*-dinitrobenzene.
Greenish-yellow needles from EtOH. M.p. 94°.

Hüffer, *Rec. trav. chim.*, 1921, **40**, 452.

2 : 3 : 5-Trichloro-*p*-dinitrobenzene

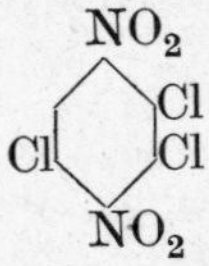

$C_6HO_4N_2Cl_3$ MW, 271·5

Yellow needles from EtOH. M.p. 102·5°.

Hüffer, *Rec. trav. chim.*, 1921, **40**, 457.

2 : 3 : 5-Trichlorodiphenyl

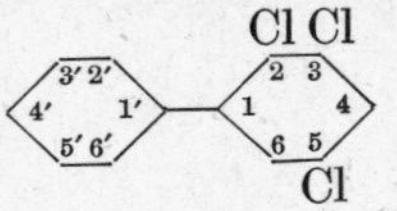

$C_{12}H_7Cl_3$ MW, 257·5

Needles from EtOH.Aq. M.p. 41°.

Hinkel, Hey, *J. Chem. Soc.*, 1928, 2790.

2 : 5 : 4′-Trichlorodiphenyl.
M.p. 67°.

Bellavita, *Gazz. chim. ital.*, 1935, **65**, 632.

3 : 4 : 2′-Trichlorodiphenyl.
M.p. 65–6° (54°).

See previous reference and also
Mascarelli, Gatti, Longo, *Gazz. chim. ital.*, 1933, **63**, 654.

3 : 5 : 2′-Trichlorodiphenyl.
Pale yellow needles from EtOH. M.p. 58°.

Hinkel, Hey, *J. Chem. Soc.*, 1928, 2791.

3 : 5 : 4′-Trichlorodiphenyl.
Needles from EtOH. M.p. 88°.

See previous reference.

1 : 1 : 1-Trichloroethane (*Methylchloroform*)

$CH_3{\cdot}CCl_3$

$C_2H_3Cl_3$ MW, 133·5

B.p. 74·9°/758 mm. D^{25}_{25} 1·31144. n^{21} 1·419861.

Städel, *Ann.*, 1879, **195**, 184.
I.G., D.R.P., 523,436, (*Chem. Zentr.*, 1931, I, 3607).

1 : 1 : 2-Trichloroethane

$CH_2Cl{\cdot}CHCl_2$

$C_2H_3Cl_3$ MW, 133·5

F.p. − 35·5°. B.p. 113·7°. D^{20}_4 1·4416.

Prins, *Rec. trav. chim.*, 1926, **45**, 80.

2 : 2 : 2-Trichloroethyl Alcohol

$CCl_3{\cdot}CH_2OH$

$C_2H_3OCl_3$ MW, 149·5

Plates. M.p. 19°. B.p. 151°, 94–7°/125 mm. Very hygroscopic. Misc. in all proportions with EtOH, Et_2O. Spar. sol. H_2O. Sol. aq. KOH. Reduces warm Fehling's. Fuming $HNO_3 \longrightarrow$ trichloroacetic acid. $PCl_5 \longrightarrow$ 2 : 2 : 2-trichloroethyl phosphite. $PCl_5 \longrightarrow$ 2 : 2 : 2-trichloroethyl phosphate.

p-*Nitrobenzoyl* : prisms from EtOH. M.p. 71°.

p-*Aminobenzoyl* : needles from pet. ether. M.p. 87°.

Urethane : needles. M.p. 64–5°.

1-*Naphthylurethane* : cryst. from ligroin. M.p. 120°.

Phosphite : oil. B.p. 263°.

Phosphate : cryst. M.p. 73–4°. Sol. Et_2O. Spar. sol. ligroin.

Chalmers, *Organic Syntheses*, 1935, XV, 80.
Dean, Wolf, *J. Am. Chem. Soc.*, 1936, **58**, 332.

Trichloroethylene

$CHCl{:}CCl_2$

C_2HCl_3 MW, 131·5

F.p. − 86·4°. M.p. − 73°. B.p. 88–90°, 25°/73 mm. D^{15} 1·4397. n_D^{2} (1·47820. Non-inflammable and employed as a germicide and industrial solvent especially for fats, oils, etc. Resembles chloroform in odour.

Igi, *J. Chem. Ind. Japan*, 1920, **23**, 1217.
Clayton Aniline Co., D.R.P., 222,622, (*Chem. Zentr.*, 1910, II, 121).
Sastry, *Chem. Zentr.*, 1916, II, 306.

Trichloroguaiacol.
See under Trichlorocatechol.

Trichlorohydrin.
See 1 : 2 : 3-Trichloropropane.

Trichlorohydroquinone

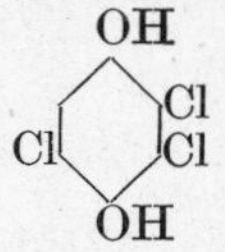

$C_6H_3O_2Cl_3$ MW, 213·5

Prisms from H_2O. M.p. 136°. Sol. EtOH, Et_2O. Sol. 160 parts H_2O at 16°. Sublimes in plates.

Di-Et ether : 2 : 3 : 5-trichloro-1 : 4-diethoxybenzene. $C_{10}H_{11}O_2Cl_3$. MW, 269·5. Needles from EtOH. M.p. 68·5°.

Diacetyl : sublimes in needles. M.p. 153°.

Conant, Fieser, *J. Am. Chem. Soc.*, 1923, **45**, 2206.
Graebe, *Ann.*, 1868, **146**, 27.
Levy, Schultz, *Ann.*, 1881, **210**, 153.

2 : 2 : 2-Trichloro-1-hydroxy-acetylpropylamine.
See Chloralacetamide.

2 : 2 : 2-Trichloro-1-hydroxyethylacetamide.
See Chloralacetamide.

2 : 2 : 2-Trichloro-1-hydroxyethylformamide.
See Chloralamide.

3 : 3 : 3-Trichloro-2-hydroxypropyl phenyl Ketone.
See Chloralacetophenone.

2 : 2 : 3-Trichloro-1-hydroxyvaleric Acid

$CH_3{\cdot}CHCl{\cdot}CCl_2{\cdot}CH(OH){\cdot}COOH$

$C_5H_7O_3Cl_3$ MW, 221·5

Tablets. M.p. 140°. Sol. EtOH, Et_2O. Spar. sol. C_6H_6. Prac. insol. H_2O.

Et ester : $C_7H_{11}O_3Cl_3$. MW, 249·5. Prisms. M.p. 40°. B.p. 255° decomp.

Amide: $C_5H_8O_2NCl_3$. MW, 220·5. Cryst. from C_6H_6 or pet. ether. M.p. 119°. Sol. EtOH, Et_2O. Spar. sol. H_2O, C_6H_6.

Nitrile: butylchloral cyanhydrin. $C_5H_6ONCl_3$. MW, 202·5. Plates from aq. HCl. M.p. 101–2°. B.p. 230° decomp. Sol. EtOH, Et_2O. Spar. sol. H_2O, C_6H_6. *Acetyl*: yellow oil. B.p. 240–52° decomp.

Acetyl: needles + $1H_2O$. M.p. 84°. Anhyd. comp. is a syrup.

Pinner, Klein, *Ber.*, 1878, **11**, 1488.
Pinner, Bischoff, *Ann.*, 1875, **179**, 99.

1 : 1 : 1-Trichloroisopropyl Alcohol (*Isopral*)

$CH_3{\cdot}CH(OH){\cdot}CCl_3$

$C_3H_5OCl_3$ MW, 163·5

M.p. 50–1°. B.p. 161·8°/773 mm. Sol. ord. org. solvents. Spar. sol. H_2O. Resembles camphor in odour.

Bayer, D.R.P., 151,545, (*Chem. Zentr.*, 1904, I, 1586).
Garzarolli-Thurnlackh, *Ann.*, 1881, **210**, 77.
Serantes, *Anales de la asociacion quimica Argentina*, 1924, **12**, 199 (*Bibl.*).

2 : 2 : 2-Trichlorolactic Acid

$CCl_3{\cdot}CH(OH){\cdot}COOH$

$C_3H_3O_3Cl_3$ MW, 193·5

Prisms. M.p. anhyd. 124°. B.p. 140–70°/45 mm. Sol. H_2O, EtOH, Et_2O, $CHCl_3$. $k = 4{\cdot}65 \times 10^{-3}$ at 25°.

Me ester: $C_4H_5O_3Cl_3$. MW, 207·5. Liq. B.p. 98–100°/12 mm.

Et ester: $C_5H_7O_3Cl_3$. MW, 221·5. Plates. M.p. 66–7°. B.p. 233–7°. Insol. H_2O. Sol. alkalis. *Et ether*: $C_7H_{11}O_3Cl_3$. MW, 249·5. Liq. B.p. 128–30°/12 mm. D_4^{20} 1·34115. *Acetyl*: b.p. 121–121·5°/16 mm. D^{20} 1·367. *Urethane*: needles from Et_2O–pet. ether. M.p. 57·5°.

Propyl ester: $C_6H_9O_3Cl_3$. MW, 235·5. B.p. 248–50°, 115–17°/12 mm. D_4^{20} 1·51628.

Isobutyl ester: $C_7H_{11}O_3Cl_3$. MW, 249·5. B.p. 236–8°, 111–12°/12 mm. D_4^{20} 1·53216.

Amide: $C_3H_4O_2NCl_3$. MW, 192·5. Needles. M.p. 96°. Sol. EtOH, Et_2O. Spar. sol. cold H_2O. O-*Acetyl*: needles. M.p. 94–5°.

Nitrile: chloral cyanhydrin. $C_3H_2ONCl_3$. MW, 174·5. Tablets from CS_2 or H_2O. M.p. 61°. B.p. 215–20° slight decomp. Sol. H_2O, EtOH, Et_2O. *Acetyl*: cryst. M.p. 31°. B.p. 208°. *Urethane*: tablets from EtOH.Aq. M.p. 115–16°.

Anilide: prisms from $CHCl_3$. M.p. 164–5° decomp.

Acetyl: cryst. from C_6H_6. M.p. 65°.

Kölln, *Ann.*, 1918, **416**, 232.
Anschütz, Haslam, *Ann.*, 1889, **253**, 129.
Pinner, *Ber.*, 1884, **17**, 1997.

Trichloromethane.
See Chloroform.

Trichloromethyl bromide.
See Trichlorobromomethane.

Trichloromethyl chloroformate (*Diphosgene, perchloromethyl chloroformate, superpalite*)

$ClCO{\cdot}OCCl_3$

$C_2O_2Cl_4$ MW, 198

Oily liq. B.p. 128°, 49°/50 mm. D^{14} 1·6525. n_D^{22} 1·4566. Decomp. on strong heating to $COCl_2$. Very toxic and asphyxiating. Used during Great War as a poison gas under the name of Green Cross.

Grignard, Rivat, Urbain, *Compt. rend.*, 1919, **169**, 1075, 1143.
Kling, Florentin, Lassieur, Schmutz, *Compt. rend.*, 1919, **169**, 1166.

Trichloromethyl sulphochloride.
See Perchloromethyl Mercaptan.

1 : 2 : 3-Trichloronaphthalene

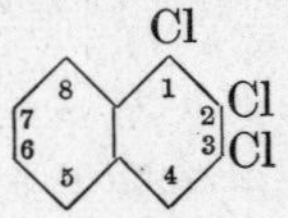

$C_{10}H_5Cl_3$ MW, 231·5

Prisms from Et_2O–EtOH. M.p. 81°.

Faust, Saame, *Ann.*, 1871, **160**, 71.
Armstrong, Wynne, *Chem. News*, 1890, **61**, 272.

1 : 2 : 4-Trichloronaphthalene.
Needles. M.p. 92°.

Cleve, *Ber.*, 1890, **23**, 954.
Armstrong, Wynne, *Chem. News*, 1890, **61**, 273.

1 : 2 : 5-Trichloronaphthalene.
Needles from EtOH. M.p. 78–78·5°. Sol. EtOH, $CHCl_3$, AcOH, C_6H_6.

Armstrong, Wynne, *Chem. News*, 1889, **59**, 188; 1890, **62**, 164.

1 : 2 : 6-Trichloronaphthalene.
Needles from EtOH. M.p. 92·5°. Sol. $CHCl_3$.

Armstrong, Wynne, *Chem News*, 1889, **59**, 189; 1890, **61**, 274.

1 : 2 : 7-Trichloronaphthalene.
Needles from EtOH. M.p. 88°.

Armstrong, Wynne, *Chem. News*, 1889, **59**, 189; 1895, **71**, 254.

1 : 2 : 8-Trichloronaphthalene.
Needles from EtOH. M.p. 83°.

Armstrong, Wynne, *Chem. News*, 1895, **71**, 253.

1 : 3 : 5-Trichloronaphthalene.
Yellow needles from EtOH. M.p. 103° (94°). Sol. common org. solvents.

Friedländer, Karamessinis, Schenk, *Ber.*, 1922, **55**, 49.
Armstrong, Wynne, *Chem. News*, 1890, **61**, 273; 1896, **73**, 55.

1 : 3 : 6-Trichloronaphthalene.
Needles. M.p. 80·5°.

Armstrong, Wynne, *Chem. News*, 1890, **62**, 164; 1895, **71**, 254.

1 : 3 : 7-Trichloronaphthalene.
Needles from EtOH. M.p. 113°. Mod. sol. EtOH.

Armstrong, Wynne, *Chem. News*, 1890, **61**, 93, 275; 1897, **76**, 69.

1 : 3 : 8-Trichloronaphthalene.
Needles from EtOH. M.p. 89·5°.

Armstrong, Wynne, *Chem. News*, 1890, **61**, 94.

1 : 4 : 5-Trichloronaphthalene.
Needles. M.p. 131°. Sol. AcOH, warm EtOH.

Armstrong, Wynne, *Chem. News*, 1890, **61**, 273.
I.G., F.P., 683,792, (*Chem. Zentr.*, 1930, II, 1446).

1 : 4 : 6-Trichloronaphthalene.
Needles from EtOH. M.p. 65°. Spar. sol. boiling EtOH.

Armstrong, Wynne, *Chem. News*, 1890, **61**, 94, 275; 1890, **62**, 162.

1 : 6 : 7-Trichloronaphthalene.
Needles. M.p. 109·5°.

Armstrong, Wynne, *Chem. News*, 1890, **61**, 275; 1895, **71**, 253.

2 : 3 : 6-Trichloronaphthalene.
Cryst. from MeOH–EtOH. M.p. 145° (90·5–91°).

Franzen, Stäuble, *J. prakt. Chem.*, 1922, **103**, 377.
Armstrong, Wynne, *Chem. News*, 1890, **61**, 275; 1890, **62**, 163.

2 : 3 : 4-Trichloro-1-naphthol

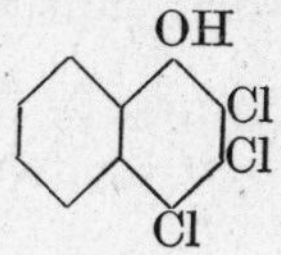

$C_{10}H_5OCl_3$ MW, 247·5

Needles from ligroin. M.p. 168° (159–60°). Sol. Et_2O. Mod. sol. AcOH, warm EtOH.
Acetyl: needles. M.p. 123–4°.

Franzen, Stäuble, *J. prakt. Chem.*, 1922, **103**, 385.
Zincke, *Ber.*, 1888, **21**, 1036.

1 : 3 : 4-Trichloro-2-naphthol

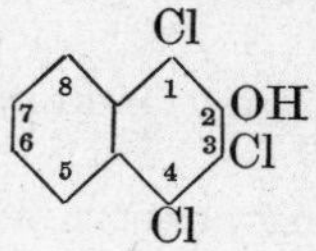

$C_{10}H_5OCl_3$ MW, 247·5

Needles. M.p. 162°.
Acetyl: needles from AcOH. M.p. 133·5–134°.

Zincke, *Ber.*, 1888, **21**, 3390, 3554.

1 : 4 : 5-Trichloro-2-naphthol.
Needles from AcOH. M.p. 157–8°.
Acetyl: m.p. 129°.

Armstrong, Rossiter, *Chem. News*, 1891, **63**, 136.

2 : 3 : 4-Trichloronitrobenzene

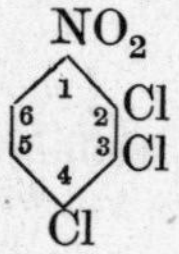

$C_6H_2O_2NCl_3$ MW, 226·5

Needles. M.p. 55·5°. Sol. CS_2. Spar. sol. EtOH.

Tiessens, *Rec. trav. chim.*, 1931, **50**, 112.
Holleman, van Haeften, *Rec. trav. chim.*, 1921, **40**, 69.

2 : 3 : 5-Trichloronitrobenzene.
Yellow needles from 80% EtOH. M.p. 45°.

Hodgson, Kershaw, *J. Chem. Soc.*, 1929, 2920.
Holleman, van Haeften, *Rec. trav. chim.*, 1921, **40**, 72.

2 : 3 : 6-Trichloronitrobenzene.
Needles from EtOH. M.p. 88–9°. Sol. EtOH. Spar. sol. ligroin.

Beilstein, Kurbatow, *Ann.*, 1878, **192**, 232.
Holleman, van Haeften, *Rec. trav. chim.*, 1921, **40**, 69.

2 : 4 : 5-Trichloronitrobenzene.
Prisms from EtOH or CS_2. M.p. 57°. B.p. 288°. D^{22} 1·790. Sol. Et_2O, C_6H_6, CS_2. Spar. sol. EtOH.

Holleman, van Haeften, *Rec. trav. chim.*, 1921, **40**, 71.
Cohen, Bennett, *J. Chem. Soc.*, 1905, **87**, 321.

2 : 4 : 6-Trichloronitrobenzene.
Needles from EtOH. M.p. 69°. Spar. sol. EtOH.

Holleman, van Haeften, *Rec. trav. chim.*, 1921, **40**, 74.

3 : 4 : 5-Trichloronitrobenzene.
Pale yellow cryst. M.p. 72·5°. Spar. volatile in steam.

Holleman, *Rec. trav. chim.*, 1921, **40**, 69.

Trichloronitromethane.
See Chloropicrin.

Trichlorophenetole.
See under Trichlorophenol.

2 : 3 : 4-Trichlorophenol

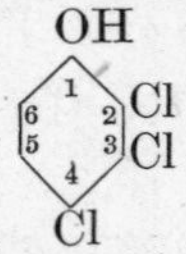

$C_6H_3OCl_3$ MW, 197·5

Needles from ligroin. M.p. 83·5°. $k = 2{\cdot}22 \times 10^{-8}$ at 25°.
Me ether : 2 : 3 : 4-trichloroanisole. $C_7H_5OCl_3$. MW, 211·5. Prisms from EtOH. M.p. 69·5°.
Benzoyl : needles from EtOH. M.p. 141°.

Holleman, *Rec. trav. chim.*, 1920, **39**, 743.
Tiessens, *Rec. trav. chim.*, 1931, **50**, 112.
Hodgson, Kershaw, *J. Chem. Soc.*, 1930, 1421.

2 : 3 : 5-Trichlorophenol.
Cryst. M.p. 62°. Very hygroscopic. $k = 4{\cdot}33 \times 10^{-8}$ at 25°.
Me ether : 2 : 3 : 5-trichloroanisole. Needles from EtOH. M.p. 84°.
Benzoyl : needles from ligroin. M.p. 103°.

Tiessens, *Rec. trav. chim.*, 1931, **50**, 114.
Hodgson, Kershaw, *J. Chem. Soc.*, 1929, 2921.

2 : 3 : 6-Trichlorophenol.
Needles from pet. ether. M.p. 58°. $k = 7{\cdot}37 \times 10^{-7}$ at 25°.
Benzoyl : cryst. from EtOH. M.p. 90°.

Holleman, *Rec. trav. chim.*, 1920, **39**, 742.
Tiessens, *Rec. trav. chim.*, 1931, **50**, 113.

2 : 4 : 5-Trichlorophenol.
Needles from pet. ether. M.p. 68°. B.p. 244–8°/746 mm. $k = 3{\cdot}76 \times 10^{-8}$ at 25°.
Me ether : 2 : 4 : 5-trichloroanisole. Needles from EtOH. M.p. 77·5°. B.p. 252–5°/742 mm.
Benzoyl : needles from EtOH. M.p. 92–3°.

Holleman, *Rec. trav. chim.*, 1920, **39**, 737.
Kohn, Fink, *Monatsh.*, 1931, **58**, 83.
Tiessens, *Rec. trav. chim.*, 1931, **50**, 114.

2 : 4 : 6-Trichlorophenol.
Needles from AcOH. M.p. 69·5°. B.p. 246°. D_4^{75} 1·4901. $k = 3{\cdot}76 \times 10^{-8}$ at 25°. Sol. EtOH, Et_2O. Volatile in steam.
Me ether : 2 : 4 : 6-trichloroanisole. Needles from EtOH. M.p. 61–2°. B.p. 240°/738 mm. Sublimes.
Et ether : 2 : 4 : 6-trichlorophenetole. $C_8H_7OCl_3$. MW, 225·5. Prisms. M.p. 43–4°. B.p. 246°.
Acetyl : b.p. 261–2°.
Propionyl : b.p. 262·5–264·5°.
Butyryl : b.p. 272–5°.
Benzoyl : needles from EtOH. M.p. 75·5°.
p-*Nitrobenzoyl* : m.p. 105–6°.

Kohn, Fink, *Monatsh.*, 1931, **58**, 88.
Tiessens, *Rec. trav. chim.*, 1931, **50**, 115.
Datta, Mitter, *J. Am. Chem. Soc.*, 1919, **41**, 2032.

3 : 4 : 5-Trichlorophenol.
Needles from ligroin. M.p. 101° (91°). B.p. 271–7°/746 mm. $k = 1{\cdot}77 \times 10^{-8}$ at 25°.
Me ether : 3 : 4 : 5-trichloroanisole. M.p. 63°. B.p. 256–61°.
Benzoyl : needles from EtOH. M.p. 120°.

Holleman, *Rec. trav. chim.*, 1920, **39**, 740.
Tiessens, *Rec. trav. chim.*, 1931, **50**, 113.
Kohn, Kramer, *Monatsh.*, 1928, **49**, 161.

Trichlorophloroglucinol

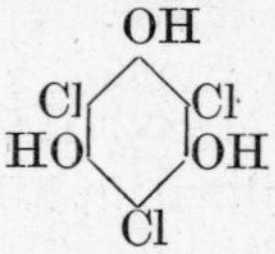

$C_6H_3O_3Cl_3$ MW, 229·5

Cryst. from EtOH. M.p. 136°. Sol. EtOH. Prac. insol. H_2O, cold C_6H_6.
Di-Me ether : $C_8H_7O_3Cl_3$. MW, 257·5. Cryst. from C_6H_6. M.p. 93–5°. *Acetyl* : m.p. 58–9°.

Tri-Me ether: $C_9H_9O_3Cl_3$. MW, 271·5. Needles from EtOH. M.p. 130–1°. Volatile in steam.
Triacetyl: plates from AcOH.Aq. M.p. 167–8°.

Zincke, Kegel, *Ber.*, 1889, **22**, 1476.

3 : 4 : 5-Trichlorophthalic Acid

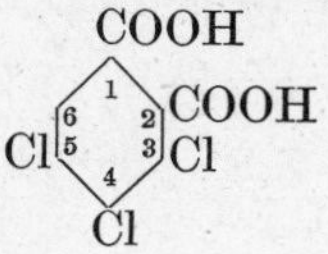

$C_8H_3O_4Cl_3$ MW, 269·5

Yellow cryst. Heat ⟶ anhydride.
Anhydride: $C_8HO_3Cl_3$. MW, 251·5. M.p. 157°. Sublimes in needles.

Claus, Kautz, *Ber.*, 1885, **18**, 1370.

3 : 4 : 6-Trichlorophthalic Acid.
Cryst. from H_2O. Above 130° ⟶ anhydride.
Anhydride: m.p. 148°. Sublimes in needles. Hot H_2O ⟶ acid.
Imide: $C_8H_2O_2NCl_3$. MW, 250·5. Needles from EtOH. M.p. 236°. Sol. EtOH, Et_2O. Mod. sol. hot H_2O.

Graebe, Rostowzew, *Ber.*, 1901, **34**, 2107.

1 : 1 : 1-Trichloropropane

$CH_3{\cdot}CH_2{\cdot}CCl_3$

$C_3H_5Cl_3$ MW, 147·5

B.p. 145–50°. Heat with $Ag_2O + H_2O$ ⟶ propionic acid.

v. Arkel, *Rec. trav. chim.*, 1932, **51**, 1101.
Spring, Lecrenier, *Bull. soc. chim.*, 1887, **48**, 625.

1 : 1 : 2-Trichloropropane (*α-Chloropropylidene chloride*)

$CH_3{\cdot}CHCl{\cdot}CHCl_2$

$C_3H_5Cl_3$ MW, 147·5

Oil. B.p. 140° (132°). D^{25} 1·372.

Klebanski, Wolkenstein, *Chem. Zentr.*, 1935, II, 3298.
Herzfelder, *Ber.*, 1893, **26**, 1258.

1 : 1 : 3-Trichloropropane (*β-Chloropropylidene chloride*)

$CH_2Cl{\cdot}CH_2{\cdot}CHCl_2$

$C_3H_5Cl_3$ MW, 147·5

B.p. 146–8°. D^{15} 1·362.

Kirrman, Pacaud, Dosque, *Bull. soc. chim.*, 1934, **1**, 864.
Romburgh, *Bull. soc. chim.*, 1882, **37**, 100.

1 : 2 : 2-Trichloropropane (*Chloroisopropylidene chloride*)

$CH_3{\cdot}CCl_2{\cdot}CH_2Cl$

$C_3H_5Cl_3$ MW, 147·5

B.p. 123°. D^{25} 1·318.

Herzfelder, *Ber.*, 1893, **26**, 1259.

1 : 2 : 3-Trichloropropane (*Trichlorohydrin, glycerol trichlorohydrin*)

$CH_2Cl{\cdot}CHCl{\cdot}CH_2Cl$

$C_3H_5Cl_3$ MW, 147·5

B.p. 158°. D^{15} 1·417.

Carré, Mauclère, *Compt. rend.*, 1931, **192**, 1568.
Fittig, Pfeffer, *Ann.*, 1865, **135**, 359.

1 : 1 : 2-Trichloropropionic Acid

$CH_2Cl{\cdot}CCl_2{\cdot}COOH$

$C_3H_3O_2Cl_3$ MW, 177·5

Prisms from CS_2. M.p. 50–2°. Sol. H_2O, EtOH, C_6H_6.
Et ester: $C_5H_7O_2Cl_3$. MW, 205·5. B.p. 121°/55 mm. D^{25} 1·36. n^{25} 1·458.

Berlande, *Bull. soc. chim.*, 1925, **37**, 1385.

2 : 3 : 4-Trichloropyridine

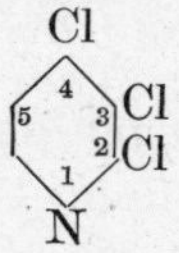

$C_5H_2NCl_3$ MW, 182·5

Needles. M.p. 45–7°. Sublimes in vacuo.

Graf, *J. prakt. Chem.*, 1933, **138**, 235.

2 : 3 : 5-Trichloropyridine.
Needles from 50% EtOH. M.p. 50°. Sol. Et_2O, Me_2CO, $CHCl_3$, C_6H_6. Mod. sol. EtOH, pet. ether. Insol. H_2O, dil. acids.

Räth, *Ann.*, 1931, **486**, 78.
Fischer, Chur, *J. prakt. Chem.*, 1916, **93**, 371.

2 : 4 : 6-Trichloropyridine.
M.p. 33°.

Graf, *J. prakt. Chem.*, 1932, **133**, 44.

3 : 4 : 5-Trichloropyridine.
Needles from EtOH.Aq. M.p. 76–7°. Sol. Et_2O, $CHCl_3$, C_6H_6, pet. ether. Mod. sol. EtOH. Spar. sol. H_2O. Sol. conc. min. acids.
B_2,$HgCl_2$: needles. M.p. 168–70°.

Dohrn, Diedrich, *Ann.*, 1932, **494**, 298.
Sell, *J. Chem. Soc.*, 1905, **87**, 800.

Trichloropyrogallol

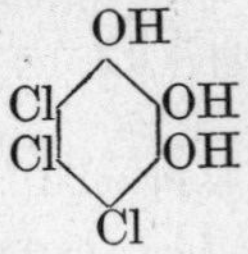

$C_6H_3O_3Cl_3$ MW, 229·5

Needles + $3H_2O$. M.p. anhyd. 185° (177°). Sol. EtOH, Et_2O, hot H_2O. Spar. $CHCl_3$, CCl_4, CS_2, C_6H_6.

Tri-Me ether: $C_9H_9O_3Cl_3$. MW, 271·5. Cryst. from EtOH. M.p. 54°. Spar. volatile in steam.

Triacetyl: needles from AcOH.Aq. M.p. 122°.

Hantzsch, Schniter, *Ber.*, 1887, **20**, 2036.
Webster, *J. Chem. Soc.*, 1884, **45**, 205.

2 : 4 : 6-Trichlororesorcinol

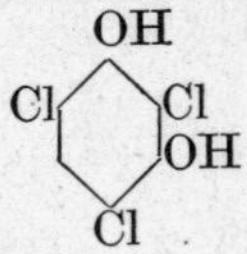

$C_6H_3O_2Cl_3$ MW, 213·5

Cryst. from H_2O. M.p. 83°. Sol. EtOH, Et_2O. Spar. sol. H_2O.

Diacetyl: prisms from EtOH. M.p. 116°.

Likhosherstov, *Chem. Abstracts*, 1934, **28**, 1675.
Zincke, Rabinowitsch, *Ber.*, 1890, **23**, 3767.

ω-Trichlorotoluene.
See Benzotrichloride.

2 : 3 : 4-Trichlorotoluene

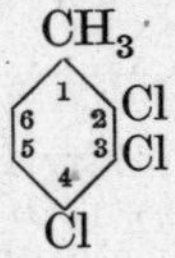

$C_7H_5Cl_3$ MW, 195·5

Needles from EtOH. M.p. 41°. B.p. 231–2°/716 mm. Sol. common org. solvents. Dil. $HNO_3 \longrightarrow$ 2 : 3 : 4-trichlorobenzoic acid.

Seelig, *Ann.*, 1887, **237**, 132, 156.

2 : 3 : 5-Trichlorotoluene.

Needles from EtOH. M.p. 45–6°. B.p. 229–31°/757 mm. Dil. $HNO_3 \longrightarrow$ 2 : 3 : 5-trichlorobenzoic acid.

Cohen, Dakin, *J. Chem. Soc.*, 1902, **81**, 1343.

2 : 3 : 6-Trichlorotoluene.

Needles from EtOH. M.p. 45–6°. Dil. $HNO_3 \longrightarrow$ 2 : 3 : 6-trichlorobenzoic acid.

See previous reference.

2 : 4 : 5-Trichlorotoluene.

Needles from EtOH. M.p. 82°. B.p. 229–30°/716 mm., 152°/25 mm. Dil. $HNO_3 \longrightarrow$ 2 : 4 : 5-trichlorobenzoic acid. Sublimes in needles.

Fichter, Glanztein, *Ber.*, 1916, **49**, 2481.
Feldman, Kopeliowitsch, *Chem. Zentr.*, 1936, I, 2550.
Qvist, Holmberg, *Chem. Zentr.*, 1932, II, 2816.
B.D.C., E.P., 169,025, (*Chem. Zentr.*, 1922, IV, 376).

2 : 4 : 6-Trichlorotoluene.

Needles from EtOH. M.p. 38° (33–4°). Volatile in steam. Dil. $HNO_3 \longrightarrow$ 2 : 4 : 6-trichlorobenzoic acid.

Bureš, Trpišovska, *Chem. Zentr.*, 1936, I, 1209.
Cohen, Dakin, *J. Chem. Soc.*, 1902, **81**, 1335.

3 : 4 : 5-Trichlorotoluene.

M.p. 44·5–45·5°. B.p. 245·5–247°. Volatile in steam. Dil. $HNO_3 \longrightarrow$ 3 : 4 : 5-trichlorobenzoic acid.

Cohen, Dakin, *J. Chem. Soc.*, 1902, **81**, 1337.

ω-Trichloro-*o*-toluic Acid (*Benzotrichloride-o-carboxylic acid*)

$C_8H_5O_2Cl_3$ MW, 239·5

Needles from C_6H_6. M.p. 141–4°.

Me ester: $C_9H_7O_2Cl_3$. MW, 253·5. B.p. 125°/1 mm.

Et ester: $C_{10}H_9O_2Cl_3$. MW, 267·5. Mobile liq. Decomp. on dist.

Chloride: $C_8H_4OCl_4$. MW, 258. Cryst. from pet. ether. M.p. 87°. B.p. 145–55°/20 mm.

Nitrile: *o*-cyanobenzotrichloride. $C_8H_4NCl_3$. MW, 220·5. Cryst. from EtOH. M.p. 94–5°. B.p. 280°. Conc. HCl in sealed tube $\longrightarrow$ phthalic acid.

Anilide: cryst. from C_6H_6. M.p. 165–70°.

Davies, Perkin, *J. Chem. Soc.*, 1922, **121**, 2213.
Ott, *Ber.*, 1922, **55**, 2123.

ω-Trichloro-*m*-toluic Acid (*Benzotrichloride-m-carboxylic acid*).

Plates. M.p. 142°. Sol. $CHCl_3$, C_6H_6. Spar. sol. formic acid.

Me ester: needles from Me_2CO–MeOH. M.p. 55°.
Chloride: oil. B.p. 287°/754 mm.

See first reference above.

ω-Trichloro-*p*-toluic Acid (*Benzotrichloride*-p-*carboxylic acid*).
Plates. M.p. 196–7°. Sol. EtOH, Et_2O, $CHCl_3$, C_6H_6. Spar. sol. formic acid.
Me ester: plates. M.p. 55°.
Et ester: plates. M.p. 57°.
Chloride: oil. B.p. 296°/756 mm.
Amide: $C_8H_6ONCl_3$. MW, 238·5. Needles from C_6H_6. M.p. 180°.

Davies, Perkin, *J. Chem. Soc.*, 1922, **121**, 2214.
Böeseken, Gelissen, *Rec. trav. chim.*, 1924, **43**, 869.

3 : 4 : 6-Trichloro-*o*-toluidine

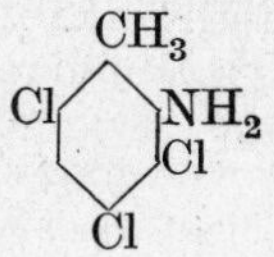

$C_7H_6NCl_3$ MW, 210·5

Needles from EtOH. M.p. 89°. Volatile in steam.
N-*Acetyl*: 3 : 4 : 6-trichloroaceto-*o*-toluidide. Needles from EtOH.Aq. M.p. 199°.
N-*Benzoyl*: plates from EtOH. M.p. 230°.

Levy, Stephen, *J. Chem. Soc.*, 1931, 78.

2 : 4 : 5-Trichloro-*m*-toluidine

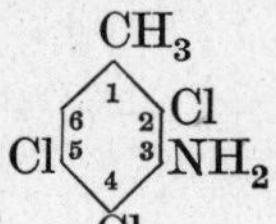

$C_7H_6NCl_3$ MW, 210·5

Needles from EtOH. M.p. 94–5°.
N-*Acetyl*: 2 : 4 : 5-trichloroacet-*m*-toluidide. Needles from EtOH. M.p. 190–1°.
N-*Benzoyl*: needles. M.p. 213°. Spar. sol. hot EtOH.

Seelig, *Ann.*, 1887, **237**, 141.
Schultz, *Ann.*, 1877, **187**, 278.

2 : 4 : 6-Trichloro-*m*-toluidine.
Needles from EtOH. M.p. 85° (77–8°).
N-*Acetyl*: 2 : 4 : 6-trichloroacet-*m*-toluidide. Needles from EtOH. M.p. 192° (181°).
N-*Diacetyl*: m.p. 81–2°.

N-*Benzoyl*: leaflets. M.p. 218°.

Bureš, Trpišovska, *Chem. Zentr.*, 1936, I, 1209.
Cohen, Dakin, *J. Chem. Soc.*, 1902, **81**, 1335.

2 : 5 : 6-Trichloro-*m*-toluidine.
Cryst. from MeOH.Aq. M.p. 66–7°.

Cohen, Dakin, *J. Chem. Soc.*, 1904, **85**, 1281.

3 : 4 : 5-Trichloroveratrol.
See under 3 : 4 : 5-Trichlorocatechol.

3 : 4 : 5-Trichloro-*o*-xylene

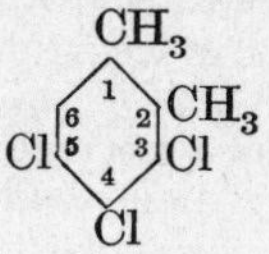

$C_8H_7Cl_3$ MW, 209·5

Needles from EtOH. M.p. 96°. B.p. 261°. Sol. Et_2O, $CHCl_3$, C_6H_6, pet. ether, hot EtOH. Volatile in steam.

Hinkel, *J. Chem. Soc.*, 1920, **117**, 1301.
Cf. Claus, Kautz, *Ber.*, 1885, **18**, 1369.

3 : 5 : 6-Trichloro-*o*-xylene.
Cryst. from EtOH. M.p. 47·5°. B.p. 230–40°. Sol. Et_2O, $CHCl_3$, AcOEt, C_6H_6, pet. ether. Mod. sol. MeOH, EtOH.

Hinkel, *J. Chem. Soc.*, 1920, **117**, 1300.

2 : 4 : 5-Trichloro-*m*-xylene

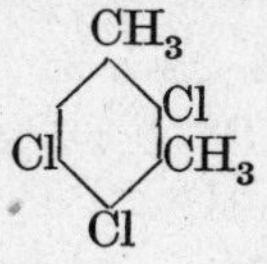

$C_8H_7Cl_3$ MW, 209·5

M.p. 95–6°. B.p. 225–60°.

I.G., F.P., 650,732, (*Chem. Abstracts*, 1929, **23**, 3233).
General Aniline Works Inc., U.S.P., 1,796,108, (*Chem. Zentr.*, 1931, I, 3610).
Cf. Bureš, Borgmann, *Chem. Zentr.*, 1928, I, 1171.

2 : 3 : 5-Trichloro-*p*-xylene

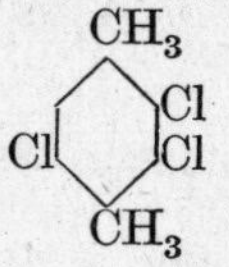

$C_8H_7Cl_3$ MW, 209·5

Needles. M.p. 96°. Sol. EtOH, Et_2O, C_6H_6, pet. ether. Insol. H_2O.

Bureš, Rubeš, *Chem. Zentr.*, 1929, I, 507.

Tricin (*Tricetin* 3′ : 5′-*dimethyl ether*, 5 : 7 : 4′-*trihydroxy*-3′ : 5′-*dimethoxyflavone*)

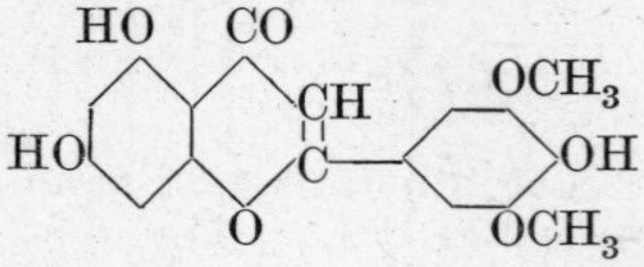

$C_{17}H_{14}O_7$ MW, 330

Colouring matter of leaves of Khapli wheat. Yellow needles from AcOH.Aq. M.p. 291–2°. Conc. H_2SO_4 ⟶ yellow sol. Alc. $FeCl_3$ ⟶ reddish-brown col.

4′-Benzyl ether: $C_{24}H_{20}O_7$. MW, 420. Pale orange prismatic needles from Me_2CO.Aq. M.p. 234°. Conc. H_2SO_4 ⟶ pale yellow col. Alc. $FeCl_3$ ⟶ greenish-brown col.

Diacetyl deriv.: pale yellow needles. M.p. 211–13°.

Triacetyl: needles from EtOH–AcOH. M.p. 251–4°.

Tri-Me ether: 5 : 7 : 3′ : 4′ : 5′-pentamethoxy-flavone. $C_{20}H_{20}O_7$. MW, 372. Needles from MeOH. M.p. 192–3°.

Anderson, *Chem. Zentr.*, 1932, II, 3899; 1933, II, 2012.

Gulati, Venkataraman, *J. Chem. Soc.*, 1933, 1644.

Tricosane

$CH_3{\cdot}[CH_2]_{21}{\cdot}CH_3$

$C_{23}H_{48}$ MW, 324

Present in Pennsylvania petroleum. Leaflets from EtOH. M.p. 48°. B.p. 234°/15 mm.

Read, Andrews, *J. Soc. Chem. Ind.*, 1920, **39**, 290T.

Tricosanic Acid

$CH_3{\cdot}[CH_2]_{20}{\cdot}CH_2{\cdot}COOH$

$C_{23}H_{46}O_2$ MW, 354

Cryst. from C_6H_6. M.p. 78–9° (80–1°).

Me ester: $C_{24}H_{48}O_2$. MW, 368. Cryst. from Me_2CO. M.p. 55–6°.

Et ester: $C_{25}H_{50}O_2$. MW, 382. Cryst. from Me_2CO. M.p. 52–3°. B.p. 198–9°/0·27 mm.

Nitrile: $C_{23}H_{45}N$. MW, 335. Cryst. from Me_2CO. M.p. 53·5–54·5°.

Ashton, Robinson, Smith, *J. Chem. Soc.*, 1936, 285.

Levene, Taylor, *J. Biol. Chem.*, 1924, **59**, 905.

Tricosanol-1.

See Tricosyl Alcohol.

Tricosanol-12 (*Diundecylcarbinol*)

$CH_3{\cdot}[CH_2]_{10}{\cdot}CH(OH){\cdot}[CH_2]_{10}{\cdot}CH_3$

$C_{23}H_{48}O$ MW, 340

Cryst. M.p. 75·5°. Sol. AcOH, pet. ether.

Grün, Ulbrich, Krezil, *Z. angew. Chem.*, 1926, **39**, 424.

Tricosyl Alcohol (*Tricosanol*-1)

$CH_3{\cdot}[CH_2]_{21}{\cdot}CH_2OH$

$C_{23}H_{48}O$ MW, 340

Cryst. from Me_2CO. M.p. 73·5–74·5°. B.p. 191–3°/0·7 mm.

Levene, Taylor, *J. Biol. Chem.*, 1924, **59**, 915.

Tricyanomethane.

See Cyanoform.

1 : 2 : 3-Tricyanopropane.

See under Tricarballylic Acid.

Tricyanotrimethylamine.

See under Triglycolamidic Acid.

Tricyclal

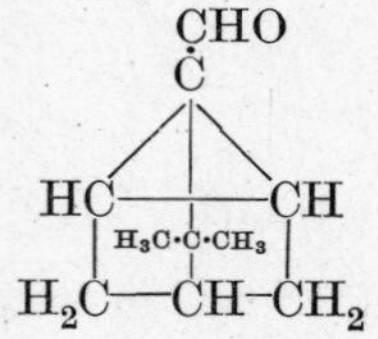

$C_{10}H_{14}O$ MW, 150

M.p. 85–90°. B.p. 113–15°/31 mm.

Semicarbazone: needles from EtOH.Aq. M.p. 219–20° decomp.

Azine: prisms from EtOH. M.p. 171–2°.

Lipp, *Ber.*, 1920, **53**, 778.

Tricyclene (1 : 2 : 2-*Trimethyl*-3 : 6-*methylenebicyclo*-[0, 1, 3]-*hexane, cyclene*)

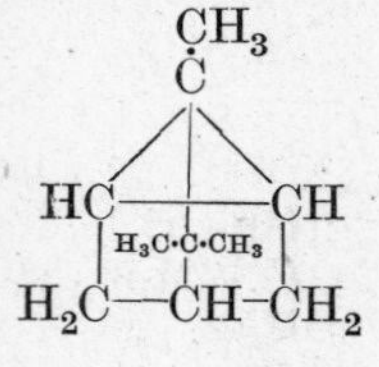

$C_{10}H_{16}$ MW, 136

Cryst. from EtOH. M.p. 64–5° (67–8°). B.p. 152–3°. D^{80} 0·8268. n_a^{80} 1·4296.

Nametkin, Zabrodin, *Ann.*, 1925, **441**, 185.

Lipp, *Ber.*, 1920, **53**, 779.

Komppa, *Ber.*, 1929, **62**, 1369.

Chem. Fabrik a. Actien, D.R.P., 353,933, (*Chem. Zentr.*, 1922, IV, 499).

Tricyclenic Acid (*Dehydrocamphenilic acid*)

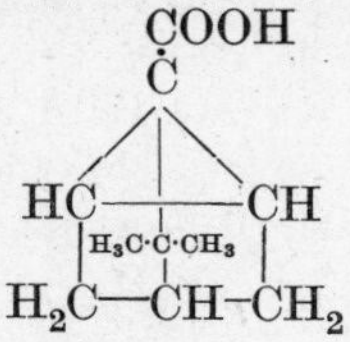

$C_{10}H_{14}O_2$ MW, 166

Plates from EtOH or C_6H_6. M.p. 148–9°. B.p. 262–4°, 145°/12 mm. Sol. EtOH, C_6H_6, pet. ether. Insol. H_2O.

Me ester: $C_{11}H_{16}O_2$. MW, 180. M.p. 45·5° (38°). B.p. 99°/14 mm. $D_4^{42\cdot6}$ 1·0255. $n_D^{42\cdot6}$ 1·46953.

Et ester: $C_{12}H_{18}O_2$. MW, 194. B.p. 100–1°/10 mm. D^{20} 1·0143. n_D^{20} 1·47299.

Chloride: $C_{10}H_{13}OCl$. MW, 184·5. M.p. 37·5–38·5°. B.p. 116–17°/15 mm.

Amide: $C_{10}H_{15}ON$. MW, 165. Leaflets from C_6H_6. M.p. 117–18°.

Nitrile: $C_{10}H_{13}N$. MW, 147. M.p. 65–70°. B.p. 100–2°/12 mm.

Lipp, *Ber.*, 1920, **53**, 774.
Komppa, *Ber.*, 1929, **62**, 1366.

Tridecanal.
See Tridecyl Aldehyde.

Tridecane

$CH_3{\cdot}[CH_2]_{11}{\cdot}CH_3$

$C_{13}H_{28}$ MW, 184

M.p. – 6·2°. B.p. 234°, 130°/30 mm., 114°/15 mm. D_4^{20} 0·7571.

Krafft, *Ber.*, 1882, **15**, 1699.

Tridecanol-1.
See Tridecyl Alcohol.

Tridecanol-2.
See Methylundecylcarbinol.

Tridecanol-3.
See Ethyl-*n*-decylcarbinol.

Tridecanone-2.
See Methyl undecyl Ketone.

Tridecanone-3.
See Ethyl *n*-decyl Ketone.

2-Tridecylacrylic Acid.
See Gaidic Acid.

Tridecyl Alcohol (*Tridecanol*-1)

$CH_3{\cdot}[CH_2]_{11}{\cdot}CH_2OH$

$C_{13}H_{28}O$ MW, 200

M.p. 30·5°. B.p. 155–6°/15 mm., 117°/0·5 mm.

Propionyl: tridecyl propionate. M.p. – 0·4°. B.p. 195°/30 mm. D_4^{25} 0·8574. n_D^{20} 1·4363.

4′-Iodoxenylurethane: m.p. 144–144·5°.

Levene, West, Scheer, *J. Biol. Chem.*, 1915, **20**, 528.

Tridecyl Aldehyde (*Tridecanal*)

$CH_3{\cdot}[CH_2]_{11}{\cdot}CHO$

$C_{13}H_{26}O$ MW, 198

M.p. 14°. B.p. 156°/23 mm.

Oxime: needles from EtOH.Aq. M.p. 80·5°.

Semicarbazone: plates from EtOH. M.p. 106°.

Le Sueur, *J. Chem. Soc.*, 1905, **87**, 1903.

Tridecylamine (1-*Aminotridecane*)

$CH_3{\cdot}[CH_2]_{11}{\cdot}CH_2NH_2$

$C_{13}H_{29}N$ MW, 199

M.p. 27°. B.p. 265°. Sol. EtOH, Et_2O.

Lutz, *Ber.*, 1886, **19**, 1436.
Blau, *Monatsh.*, 1905, **26**, 101.

1-Tridecylenic Acid (2-n-*Decylacrylic acid*, 1-*dodecylene*-1-*carboxylic acid*)

$CH_3{\cdot}[CH_2]_9{\cdot}CH{:}CH{\cdot}COOH$

$C_{13}H_{24}O_2$ MW, 212

B.p. 167–71°/2 mm. D^{30} 0·8995. n_D^{20} 1·46121.

Chloride: $C_{13}H_{23}OCl$. MW, 230·5. B.p. 131°/3 mm. D^{20} 0·9380.

Amide: $C_{13}H_{25}ON$. MW, 211. M.p. 116°.

Zaar, *Chem. Abstracts*, 1930, **24**, 2108.

10-Tridecylenic Acid (*Isotridecylenic acid*, 2-*dodecylene*-12-*carboxylic acid*)

$CH_3{\cdot}CH{:}CH{\cdot}[CH_2]_9{\cdot}COOH$

$C_{13}H_{24}O_2$ MW, 212

Plates from pet. ether. M.p. 28–9°. B.p. 183–5°/13·5 mm., 161–2°/4 mm.

Chuit, Boelsing, Hausser, Malet, *Helv. Chim. Acta*, 1927, **10**, 122.

11-Tridecylenic Acid (1-*Dodecylene*-12-*carboxylic acid*)

$CH_2{:}CH{\cdot}[CH_2]_{10}{\cdot}COOH$

$C_{13}H_{24}O_2$ MW, 212

Plates from EtOH.Aq. M.p. 38–9°. B.p. 192°/20 mm., 185°/15 mm., 162°/3 mm. Sol. EtOH, Et_2O, C_6H_6, pet. ether.

Me ester: $C_{14}H_{26}O_2$. MW, 226. B.p. 143°/8 mm., 133°/3 mm. D_{20}^{20} 0·8819. n_D^{20} 1·4438.

Et ester: $C_{15}H_{28}O_2$. MW, 240. B.p. 150°/8 mm. D^{15} 0·880.

Chuit, Boelsing, Hausser, Malet, *Helv. Chim. Acta*, 1927, **10**, 118.
Tomecko, Adams, *J. Am. Chem. Soc.*, 1927, **49**, 529.

Tridecylic Acid (*Tridecoic acid, dodecane-1-carboxylic acid*)

$CH_3{\cdot}[CH_2]_{11}{\cdot}COOH$

$C_{13}H_{26}O_2$ MW, 214

Cryst. from Me_2CO. M.p. 44·5–45·5°. B.p. 199–200°/24 mm.

Zn salt: needles from isoamyl alcohol. M.p. 128°.

Et ester: $C_{15}H_{30}O_2$. MW, 242. B.p. 197–8°/60 mm., 178–80°/20 mm., 163–5°/5 mm.

Propyl ester: $C_{16}H_{32}O_2$. MW, 256. B.p. 194°/30 mm. D_4^{25} 0·8555. n_D^{20} 1·4357.

Amide: $C_{13}H_{27}ON$. MW, 213. M.p. 100°.

Nitrile: $C_{13}H_{25}N$. MW, 195. B.p. 275°.

Ruhoff, *Organic Syntheses*, 1936, XVI, 35.
Levene, West, Allen, Scheer, *J. Biol. Chem.*, 1915, **23**, 73.

Triethanolamine.
See 2 : 2′ : 2′′-Trihydroxytriethylamine.

ω : 2 : 4-Triethoxyacetophenone.
See under Fisetol.

3 : 4 : 5-Triethoxybenzoic Acid.
See under Gallic Acid.

Triethylamine

$(CH_3{\cdot}CH_2)_3N$

$C_6H_{15}N$ MW, 101

M.p. — 114·75°. B.p. 89·4°. D_4^0 0·7495, D_4^{25} 0·7255. n_D^{20} 1·4003. Readily oxidised by $KMnO_4$.

B,HCl: cryst. from EtOH. M.p. 253–4°.

B,HBr: cryst. from $CHCl_3$ or EtOH. M.p. 248°.

B,HI: m.p. 181°. Sol. $CHCl_3$, EtOH.

B,HNO₃: m.p. 99–100°.

B,HBr,HgBr₂: m.p. 124–5°.

B₂,3CHI₃: yellow cryst. from EtOH. M.p. 81–3°.

B,H₂S: needles. M.p. 55–7° (closed tube).

Acetate: b.p. 162° decomp.

Picrate: needles from EtOH. M.p. 172–3°.

Skita, Keil, *Monatsh.*, 1929, **53** and **54**, 757.
I.G., E.P., 283,163, (*Chem. Zentr.*, 1929, I, 1509); F.P., 685,345, (*Chem. Zentr.*, 1931, I, 1824).
Hofmann, *Ann.*, 1850, **73**, 91.
Rakshit, *J. Am. Chem. Soc.*, 1913, **35**, 1782.

Triethylarsine (*Arsenic triethyl*)

$(C_2H_5)_3As$

$C_6H_{15}As$ MW, 162

B.p. 140°/736 mm. D_4^{20} 1·150. n_D^{20} 1·467. Sol. EtOH, Et_2O. Insol. H_2O. Fumes in air and inflames when heated.

Cahours, *Ann.*, 1862, **122**, 202.
Hofmann, *Ann.*, 1857, **103**, 357.

1 : 2 : 4-Triethylbenzene

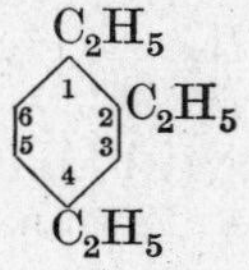

$C_{12}H_{18}$ MW, 162

B.p. 217–18°/755 mm. 99°/15 mm. D_4^{17} 0·8819. n_D^{17} 1·4983.

Klages, *J. prakt. Chem.*, 1902, **65**, 398.

1 : 3 : 5-Triethylbenzene.

B.p. 218°, 95°/14 mm. D_4^{20} 0·8633. n_D^{17} 1·4951. $CrO_3 \longrightarrow$ trimesic acid.

Gattermann, Fritz, Beck, *Ber.*, 1899, **32**, 1122.

2 : 4 : 6-Triethylbenzoic Acid

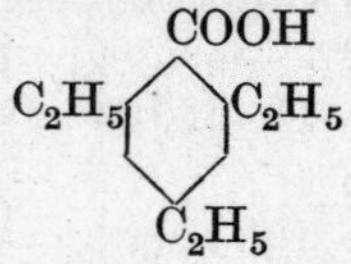

$C_{13}H_{18}O_2$ MW, 206

Plates from ligroin. M.p. 113°.

Amide: $C_{13}H_{19}ON$. MW, 205. Needles from ligroin. M.p. 155–6°.

Gattermann, Fritz, Beck, *Ber.*, 1899, **32**, 1123.

Triethyl borate (*Ethyl borate*)

$B(O{\cdot}CH_2{\cdot}CH_3)_3$

$C_6H_{15}O_3B$ MW, 146

Liq. B.p. 118·6°. D^{26} 0·864. n_D 1·3808. Rapidly hyd. by H_2O.

Khotinskii, Pupko, *Chem. Zentr.*, 1929, II, 2763.

Triethylcarbinol (3-*Ethylpentanol*-3)

$(C_2H_5)_3C{\cdot}OH$

$C_7H_{16}O$ MW, 116

Liq. with penetrating camphor-like odour. B.p. 140–2°. $D_4^{22\cdot4}$ 0·8407. $n_D^{22\cdot3}$ 1·4266.

Allophanate: m.p. 182–3°.

Moyer, Marvel, *Organic Syntheses*, 1931, XI, 98.
Böeseken, Wildschut, *Rec. trav. chim.*, 1932, **51**, 168.
Edgar, Calingaert, Marker, *J. Am. Chem. Soc.*, 1929, **51**, 1486.

Triethyl citrate

$CH_2{\cdot}CO{\cdot}OC_2H_5$
$C(OH){\cdot}CO{\cdot}OC_2H_5$
$CH_2{\cdot}CO{\cdot}OC_2H_5$

$C_{12}H_{20}O_7$ MW, 276

Oil. B.p. 294°, 230°/100 mm., 212°/30–5 mm. D_4^{20} 1·1369. n_D^{20} 1·44554.

Et ether: $C_{14}H_{24}O_7$. MW, 304. Oil. B.p. 237–8°/150 mm. D_4^{20} 1·1022. n_D^{20} 1·4484.

Acetyl: 2-acetoxytricarballylic triethyl ester. B.p. 197°/15 mm. Sol. EtOH, Et_2O.

Conen, *Ber.*, 1879, **12**, 1653.

Triethylene Glycol (*Ethylene glycol di-β-hydroxyethyl ether, di-β-hydroxyethoxyethane*)

$HO{\cdot}CH_2{\cdot}CH_2{\cdot}O{\cdot}CH_2{\cdot}CH_2{\cdot}O{\cdot}CH_2{\cdot}CH_2OH$

$C_6H_{14}O_4$ MW, 150

Liq. B.p. 285°, 165°/14 mm., 134°/2 mm. D_4^{15} 1·1274. n_D^{15} 1·4578. Misc. with H_2O, EtOH. Spar. sol. Et_2O.

Matignon, Moureau, Dodé, *Bull. soc. chim.*, 1934, **1**, 1311.

Triethylmethane.
See 3-Ethylpentane.

Triethyl phosphate.
See under Phosphoric Acid.

Triethylphosphine (*Phosphorus triethyl*)

$(C_2H_5)_3P$

$C_6H_{15}P$ MW, 118

Colourless liq. with odour of hyacinths. B.p. 127°. D_4^{15} 0·800. n_D^{15} 1·458. Misc. with EtOH, Et_2O. Insol. H_2O.

Add. comp. with CS_2: red cryst. from Et_2O or EtOH. M.p. 121–2° decomp.

B_2,CuI: plates from ligroin. M.p. 39°.

B,AuCl: needles or prisms. M.p. 80°.

B_2,$PdCl_2$: yellow prisms from Et_2O.

Slotta, Tschesche, *Ber.*, 1927, **60**, 298.

Triethylstibine (*Antimony triethyl*)

$(C_2H_5)_3Sb$

$C_6H_{15}Sb$ MW, 207

Liq. B.p. 158·5°/730 mm. D^{16} 1·3244. Sol. EtOH, Et_2O. Insol. H_2O. Spontaneously inflammable.

Paneth, Loleit, *J. Chem. Soc.*, 1935, 371.
Dyke, Davies, Jones, *J. Chem. Soc.*, 1930, 465.

Triethylurea.
See under Urea.

Trifluoromethane.
See Fluoroform.

Triformin (*Glycerol triformate*)

$CH_2{\cdot}O{\cdot}CHO$
$CH{\cdot}O{\cdot}CHO$
$CH_2{\cdot}O{\cdot}CHO$

$C_6H_8O_6$ MW, 176

M.p. 18°. B.p. 266°/762 mm. D^{18} 1·320. n_D^{18} 1·4412. Insol. cold H_2O. Hyd. by hot H_2O.

Romburgh, *Z. physik. Chem.*, 1910, **70**, 459.

Triformoxime (N-*Trihydroxytrimethylenetriamine, trimolecular formaldoxime*)

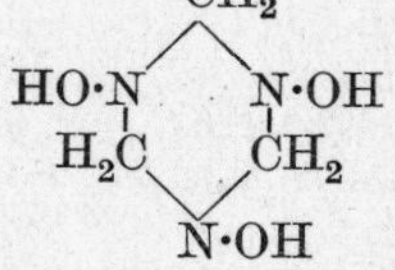

$C_3H_9O_3N_3$ MW, 135

Amorphous. Insol. H_2O, EtOH, Et_2O. Sol. dil. acids, conc. aq. NaOH. Forms coloured salts with Fe, Ni, Mn. H_2O at 130° $\longrightarrow$ formaldoxime.

Scholl, *Ber.*, 1891, **24**, 575.

Trigenic Acid.
See Trigonic Acid.

Trigenolline.
See Trigonelline.

Triglycolamidic Acid (*Trimethylamine-1 : 1′ : 1″-tricarboxylic acid*)

$N(CH_2{\cdot}COOH)_3$

$C_6H_9O_6N$ MW, 191

Prisms from H_2O. Decomp. at 242°. Spar. sol. H_2O.

Tri-Me ester: $C_9H_{15}O_6N$. MW, 233. B.p. 167°/13 mm. D_4^{17} 1·2130. n^{20} 1·4500.

Tri-Et ester: $C_{12}H_{21}O_6N$. MW, 275. Viscous oil. B.p. 193°/18 mm.

Triamide: $C_6H_{12}O_3N_4$. MW, 188. Plates from Alc. NH_3. Decomp. at 205–6°.

Trinitrile: tricyanotrimethylamine. $C_6H_6N_4$. MW, 134. Needles from EtOH. M.p. 125–6°.

Curtius, *J. prakt. Chem.*, 1917, **96**, 232.
Dubsky, Wensink, *Ber.*, 1916, **49**, 1041.

Triglycylglycine (*Glycyl-diglycyl-glycine*)

$NH_2{\cdot}CH_2{\cdot}CO{\cdot}[NH{\cdot}CH_2{\cdot}CO]_2{\cdot}NH{\cdot}CH_2{\cdot}COOH$

$C_8H_{14}O_5N_4$ MW, 246

Colourless powder. Darkens at 220–70° with evolution of NH_3. Very spar. sol. cold H_2O. Sol hot H_2O.

Me ester: $C_9H_{16}O_5N_4$. MW, 260. Needles or

prisms from MeOH. Darkens at 240°. *Hydrochloride*: plates. M.p. 198–200°.

Et ester: *see* Biuret Base.

Benzoyl: m.p. 235°.

Fischer, *Ber.*, 1904, **37**, 2501.

Trigonelline (N-*Methylnicotinic ac ic betaine, trigenolline, coffearin, gynesin*)

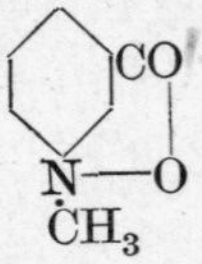

$C_7H_7O_2N$ MW, 137

Constituent of fruit and seeds of species of *Strophanthus*, *Cannabis sativa*, coffee, etc. Prisms $+ 1H_2O$ from EtOH.Aq. M.p. anhyd. 218° decomp. Very sol. H_2O. Sol. EtOH. Insol. Et_2O, $CHCl_3$. $FeCl_3 \longrightarrow$ red col.

B,HCl: needles or prisms from EtOH. M.p. 245–50° decomp.

B,HI: m.p. 220° decomp.

Schulze, *Z. physiol. Chem.*, 1909, **60**, 155.

Trigonic Acid (*Trigenic acid, ethylidene biuret*)

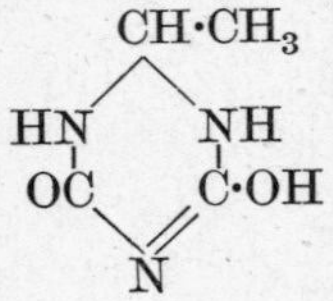

$C_4H_7O_2N_3$ MW, 129

Prisms or needles from H_2O. Insol. EtOH. N-*Diacetyl*: m.p. 171–2°.

Ostrogovich, Ostrogovich, *Chem. Zentr.*, 1936, II, 476.

Liebig, Wöhler, *Ann.*, 1846, **59**, 296.

2 : 3 : 4-Trihydroxyacetophenone.

See Gallacetophenone.

2 : 3 : 5-Trihydroxyacetophenone

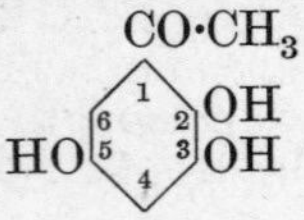

$C_8H_8O_4$ MW, 168

Yellow needles from AcOH. M.p. 206–7°. Sol. EtOH, hot AcOH. Spar. sol. hot C_6H_6.

2 : 3 : 5-*Tri-Me ether*: 2 : 3 : 5-trimethoxyacetophenone. $C_{11}H_{14}O_4$. MW, 210. Cryst. from ligroin. M.p. 102–3°.

p-*Nitrophenylhydrazone*: cryst. from EtOH.Aq. M.p. 241–2° decomp.

Triacetyl: needles from ligroin. M.p. 106–7°.

Mauthner, *J. prakt. Chem.*, 1933, **136**, 214.

2 : 4 : 5-Trihydroxyacetophenone.

Red needles from H_2O. M.p. 200–2° decomp. Sol. H_2O, hot EtOH, Me_2CO. Insol. C_6H_6, petrol. $FeCl_3 \longrightarrow$ green col. Conc. $H_2SO_4 \longrightarrow$ yellowish-green col. Ac_2O + AcONa $\longrightarrow$ 6 : 7-diacetoxy-4-methylcoumarin.

4-*Me ether*: $C_9H_{10}O_4$. MW, 182. Yellow plates from H_2O. M.p. 165–6°. *Diacetyl*: needles from H_2O. M.p. 118–19°.

5-*Me ether*: yellow needles from H_2O. M.p. 166°. $FeCl_3 \longrightarrow$ red col. *Diacetyl*: needles from H_2O. M.p. 127–8°.

4 : 5-*Di-Me ether*: $C_{10}H_{12}O_4$. MW, 196. Yellow needles from H_2O. Cryst. from toluene. M.p. 114–15°. *Oxime*: cryst. from EtOH.Aq. M.p. 162°. *Acetyl*: needles from EtOH.Aq. M.p. 147°.

2 : 4 : 5-*Tri-Me ether*: cryst. from H_2O, EtOH.Aq., or toluene. M.p. 102°. *Semicarbazone*: cryst. from EtOH.Aq. M.p. 206°.

Diacetyl deriv.: prisms from C_6H_6. M.p. 165–6°.

2 : 4 : 5-*Triacetyl*: cryst. from CCl_4. M.p. 110–11°. *Oxime*: cryst. from EtOH.Aq. M.p. 126–7°. *Semicarbazone*: plates from EtOH. M.p. 186–8°.

Smith, Haller, *J. Am. Chem. Soc.*, 1934, **56**, 237.

Mauthner, *Chem. Abstracts*, 1934, **28**, 3392.

2 : 4 : 6-Trihydroxyacetophenone.

See Phloracetophenone.

3 : 4 : 5-Trihydroxyacetophenone (5-*Acetopyrogallol*).

Needles from H_2O. M.p. 187–8°. Sol. EtOH, Et_2O, AcOH, Me_2CO. Spar. sol. C_6H_6. Insol. pet. ether, ligroin. Aq. $FeCl_3 \longrightarrow$ green col. Alc. $FeCl_3 \longrightarrow$ blue col.

3 : 4 : 5-*Tri-Me ether*: needles from ligroin. M.p. 72° (78°). *Oxime*: needles from H_2O. Prisms from EtOH. M.p. 102–3°. *Semicarbazone*: cryst. from H_2O. M.p. 178–9°.

3 : 4 : 5-*Triacetyl*: needles from ligroin. M.p. 111–12°.

Semicarbazone: needles from EtOH. M.p. 216–17°.

p-*Nitrophenylhydrazone*: red cryst. from AcOH.Aq. Decomp. at 260°.

Mauthner, *J. prakt. Chem.*, 1927, **115**, 137.

Bogert, Isham, *J. Am. Chem. Soc.*, 1914, **36**, 523.

2 : 4 : 6-Trihydroxyanisole.

See Iretol.

Trihydroxyanthranol.

See Tetrahydroxyanthracene.

1 : 2 : 3-Trihydroxyanthraquinone.
See Anthragallol.

1 : 2 : 4-Trihydroxyanthraquinone.
See Purpurin.

1 : 2 : 5-Trihydroxyanthraquinone (*Hydroxyanthrarufin*)

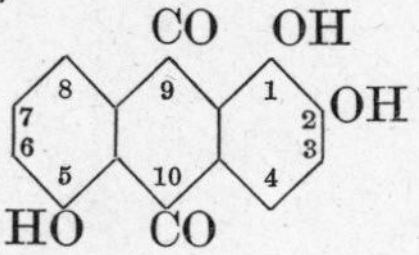

$C_{14}H_8O_5$ MW, 256

Red needles from AcOH. M.p. 273–4°. Conc. $H_2SO_4 \longrightarrow$ violet col.

2-*Me ether*: $C_{15}H_{10}O_5$. MW, 270. Yellow cryst. from EtOH. M.p. 229°.

1 : 2-*Di-Me ether*: $C_{16}H_{12}O_5$. MW, 284. Orange needles from EtOH. M.p. 230·5–231·5°.

1 : 2 : 5-*Tri-Me ether*: $C_{17}H_{14}O_5$. MW, 298. Yellow plates from EtOH. M.p. 203–4°.

1 : 2 : 5-*Triacetyl*: yellow needles from EtOH. M.p. 228–9°.

Puntambecker, Adams, *J. Am. Chem. Soc.*, 1927, **49**, 488.

1 : 2 : 6-Trihydroxyanthraquinone.
See Flavopurpurin.

1 : 2 : 7-Trihydroxyanthraquinone.
See Anthrapurpurin.

1 : 2 : 8-Trihydroxyanthraquinone (*Hydroxychrysazin*).

Red needles from AcOH. M.p. 239–40°. Sublimes. Conc. $H_2SO_4 \longrightarrow$ reddish-violet col.

2-*Me ether*: $C_{15}H_{10}O_5$. MW, 270. Orange needles from $CHCl_3$–MeOH. M.p. 220°.

2 : 8-*Di-Me ether*: $C_{16}H_{12}O_5$. MW, 284. Brownish-yellow cryst. from $CHCl_3$–MeOH. M.p. 193°.

1 : 2 : 8-*Tri-Me ether*: $C_{17}H_{14}O_5$. MW, 298. Yellow needles from MeOH. M.p. 157°.

1 : 2 : 8-*Triacetyl*: yellow needles. M.p. 224°.

Höchst, D.R.P., 196,980, (*Chem. Zentr.*, 1908, I, 1505).
Graebe, Thode, *Ann.*, 1906, **349**, 221.

1 : 3 : 8-Trihydroxyanthraquinone.

Yellow prisms. M.p. 275°. Insol. most org. solvents except Py. Sublimes in vacuo at 200°. Conc. $H_2SO_4 \longrightarrow$ yellow col. Red sols. in alkalis.

Eder, Hauser, *Helv. Chim. Acta*, 1925, **8**, 134.

1 : 4 : 5-Trihydroxyanthraquinone.

Red needles from $PhNO_2$ or Py.

4-*Acetyl*: yellow needles from AcOH. M.p. 165°.

British Celanese, E.P., 346,355, (*Chem. Abstracts*, 1932, **26**, 1948).

1 : 4 : 6-Trihydroxyanthraquinone.

Reddish-brown powder. Does not melt below 300°. Spar. sol. hot H_2O. Sol. alkalis $\longrightarrow$ violet col. $Pb(OAc)_4 \longrightarrow$ 1 : 4 : 9 : 10-diquinone.

6-*Acetyl*: cryst. from AcOH.

Crossley, *J. Am. Chem. Soc.*, 1918, **40**, 404.

1 : 3 : 4 - Trihydroxyanthraquinone - 2 - carboxylic Acid.
See Purpurin-3-carboxylic Acid.

Trihydroxyanthrone.
See Tetrahydroxyanthracene.

2 : 3 : 4-Trihydroxybenzaldehyde

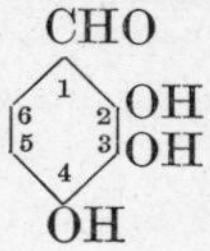

$C_7H_6O_4$ MW, 154

Needles from H_2O. M.p. 161–2°.

3 : 4-*Di-Me ether*: $C_9H_{10}O_4$. MW, 182. Needles from H_2O, prisms from petrol. M.p. 74°. *Phenylhydrazone*: yellow prisms from MeOH. M.p. 156°.

2 : 3 : 4-*Tri-Me ether*: 2 : 3 : 4-trimethoxybenzaldehyde. $C_{10}H_{12}O_4$. MW, 196. Prisms from petrol. M.p. 37° (30°). *Phenylhydrazone*: yellow prisms from MeOH. M.p. 155–6°.

2 : 3 : 4-*Tri-Et ether*: 2 : 3 : 4-triethoxybenzaldehyde. $C_{13}H_{18}O_4$. MW, 238. Cryst. M.p. 70°.

Oxime: needles from H_2O. M.p. 204° decomp.

Baker, Smith, *J. Chem. Soc.*, 1931, 2544.
Schaaf, Labouchère, *Helv. Chim. Acta*, 1924, **7**, 357.
Barger, Ewins, *J. Chem. Soc.*, 1910, **97**, 2258.
Gattermann, Berchelmann, *Ber.*, 1898, 31, 1768.

2 : 3 : 5-Trihydroxybenzaldehyde.

2 : 3-*Di-Me ether*: cryst. from H_2O. M.p. 152°.

2 : 3 : 5-*Tri-Me ether*: 2 : 3 : 5-trimethoxybenzaldehyde. Cryst. from EtOH.Aq. M.p. 71°.

Smith, Laforge, *J. Am. Chem. Soc.*, 1931, **53**, 3074.

2 : 4 : 5-Trihydroxybenzaldehyde.

Cryst. from H_2O. M.p 223°. $FeCl_3 \longrightarrow$ green col.

4-*Me ether*: 2 : 5-dihydroxyanisaldehyde. $C_8H_8O_4$. MW, 168. Prisms from EtOH or AcOH. M.p. 209°. Spar. sol. hot EtOH, AcOH, Me_2CO. $FeCl_3 \longrightarrow$ bluish-green col.

4 : 5-*Di-Me ether*: 6-hydroxyveratric aldehyde. $C_9H_{10}O_4$. MW, 182. Needles from H_2O. Plates from EtOH.Aq. M.p. 105°. $FeCl_3 \longrightarrow$ green col.

2 : 4 : 5-*Tri-Me ether*: *see* Asarylaldehyde.

4-*Me*-5-*Et ether*: $C_{10}H_{12}O_4$. MW, 196. Prisms from MeOH. M.p. 112–13°. Sol. EtOH, Me_2CO. Spar. sol. H_2O. $FeCl_3 \longrightarrow$ green col.

5-*Me*-4-*Et ether*: prisms from MeOH. M.p. 91°. *Phenylhydrazone*: m.p. 157–8°.

2 : 4-*Di-Me*-5-*Et ether*: $C_{11}H_{14}O_4$. MW, 210. Needles from MeOH. M.p. 110°.

2 : 4 : 5-*Tri-Et ether*: 2 : 4 : 5-triethoxybenzaldehyde. $C_{13}H_{18}O_4$. MW, 238. Cryst. from EtOH. M.p. 95°.

4-*Benzoyl*: plates from EtOH.Aq. M.p. 184°.

2 : 4 : 5-*Triacetyl*: prisms from EtOH. M.p. 115°.

Head, Robertson, *J. Chem. Soc.*, 1930, 2436.

Gattermann, Köbner, *Ber.*, 1899, **32**, 282.

2 : 4 : 6-Trihydroxybenzaldehyde (*Phloroglucinaldehyde*).

Needles + $2H_2O$ from H_2O. Darkens on heating. $FeCl_3 \longrightarrow$ red col.

2-*Me ether*: needles from EtOH. M.p. 200–2°. 4 : 6-*Diacetyl*: plates from ligroin. M.p. 107°.

4-*Me ether*: 2-*benzoyl*, plates from EtOH. M.p. 109°.

4 : 6-*Di-Me ether*: needles or plates from MeOH. M.p. 70–1°. 2-*Benzoyl*: needles from AcOEt. M.p. 148°.

2 : 4 : 6-*Tri-Me ether*: 2 : 4 : 6-trimethoxybenzaldehyde. Needles from EtOH. M.p. 118°. *Oxime*: needles from MeOH. M.p. 201–3°.

Oxime: cryst. + $1H_2O$ from H_2O. Decomp. at 195°.

Diacetyl deriv.: needles from EtOH.Aq. M.p. 102–3°.

Triacetyl: prisms from EtOH. M.p. 156–7° (151°).

2-*Benzoyl*: prisms from $CHCl_3$. M.p. 198–200°.

Malkin, Nierenstein, *J. Am. Chem. Soc.*, 1931, **53**, 241.

Robinson *et al.*, *J. Chem. Soc.*, 1930, 804; 1928, 1457; 1927, 1712; 1925, 1184.

Gattermann, Köbner, *Ber.*, 1899, 32, 280.

3 : 4 : 5-Trihydroxybenzaldehyde.

See Gallaldehyde.

1 : 2 : 3-Trihydroxybenzene.

See Pyrogallol.

1 : 2 : 4-Trihydroxybenzene (*Hydroxyhydroquinone, hydroxyquinol*)

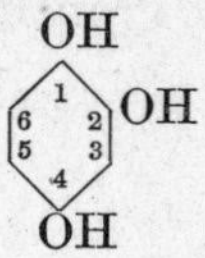

$C_6H_6O_3$ MW, 126

Plates from Et_2O. M.p. 140·5°. Sol. H_2O, EtOH, Et_2O. Insol. $CHCl_3$, CS_2, C_6H_6. Oxidises in air. Conc. $H_2SO_4 \longrightarrow$ green col. $\longrightarrow$ red on warming. $FeCl_3 + NaOH \longrightarrow$ red col. $Ag_2O \longrightarrow$ 2-hydroxy-*p*-benzoquinone.

Picrate: orange-red needles. M.p. 96°.

1-*Me ether*: $C_7H_8O_3$. MW, 140. Prisms from C_6H_6. M.p. 66–7°. 2 : 4-*Diacetyl*: prisms from MeOH. M.p. 62–4°.

2-*Me ether*: plates from H_2O. Prisms from C_6H_6. M.p. 84°. 1 : 4-*Diacetyl*: needles from MeOH. M.p. 93–4°.

1 : 2 : 4-*Tri-Me ether*: $C_9H_{12}O_3$. MW, 168. Liq. B.p. 247°.

1 : 2-*Methylene ether*: *see* Sesamol.

2-*Et ether*: $C_8H_{10}O_3$. MW, 154. Prisms from EtOH. M.p. 112·5°.

1 : 2-*Di-Et ether*: $C_{10}H_{14}O_3$. MW, 182. Cryst. from C_6H_6 or EtOH. M.p. 65–7°.

1 : 2 : 4-*Tri-Et ether*: $C_{12}H_{18}O_3$. MW, 210. Needles from EtOH.Aq. M.p. 34°.

1 : 2 : 4-*Triacetyl*: cryst. from EtOH. M.p. 96–7°.

Healey, Robinson, *J. Chem. Soc.*, 1934, 1626.

Vliet, *Organic Syntheses*, Collective Vol. I, 310.

1 : 3 : 5-Trihydroxybenzene.

See Phloroglucinol.

2 : 3 : 4-Trihydroxybenzil

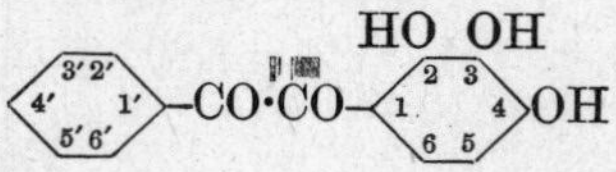

$C_{14}H_{10}O_5$ MW, 258

Needles from H_2O. M.p. 143°. Sol. H_2O, EtOH, Et_2O, C_6H_6.

Oxime: yellow cryst. M.p. 144°.

Dioxime: cryst. from EtOH. M.p. 168°.

Noelting, Kadiera, *Ber.*, 1906, **39**, 2059.

2 : 4 : 6-Trihydroxybenzil.

Colourless needles from EtOH.Aq. Darkens at 260°, m.p. 287°. $FeCl_3 \longrightarrow$ purple col. Reduces Fehling's.

Triacetyl : m.p. 248°.

Marsh, Stephen, *J. Chem. Soc.*, 1925, 1636.

2 : 4 : 2′-Trihydroxybenzil.

2′-*Me ether* : $C_{15}H_{12}O_5$. MW, 272. Darkens at 210°, m.p. 223°. 2 : 4-*Diacetyl* : m.p. 144°.

See previous reference.

2 : 4 : 4′-Trihydroxybenzil.

4′-*Me ether* : darkens at 225°, m.p. 234°. 2 : 4-*Diacetyl* : m.p. 178·5°.

See previous reference.

2 : 3 : 4-Trihydroxybenzoic Acid (*Pyrogallol-4-carboxylic acid*)

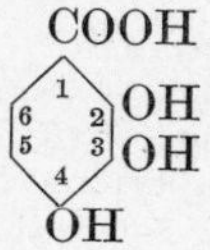

$C_7H_6O_5$ MW, 170

Needles + H_2O from H_2O. Decomp. at 207–8° (215–20°). Sol. EtOH. Spar. sol. Et_2O. Sublimes in CO_2. $FeCl_3$ ⟶ violet col. Hot H_2O ⟶ pyrogallol.

Me ester : $C_8H_8O_5$. MW, 184. Needles + $2\frac{1}{2}H_2O$ from H_2O. M.p. 151–2°. 4-*Me-ether* : $C_9H_{10}O_5$. MW, 198. Needles from EtOH.Aq. M.p. 101–4°. 4-*Me ether*-2 : 3-*diacetyl* : plates from MeOH. M.p. 108°. 3 : 4-*Di-Me ether* : $C_{10}H_{12}O_5$. MW, 212. Needles or prisms from EtOH. M.p. 75–8°. 3 : 4-*Di-Me ether-2-acetyl* : cryst. from EtOH. M.p. 62–4°. 2 : 3-*Di-Me ether-4-benzoyl* : cryst. from EtOH.Aq. M.p. 79–80°.

Et ester : $C_9H_{10}O_5$. MW, 198. Cryst. + $1H_2O$ from H_2O. M.p. anhyd. 102°.

Hydrazide : grey cryst. M.p. above 180° decomp.

4-*Me ether* : $C_8H_8O_5$. MW, 184. Needles from H_2O. M.p. 207–8°. $FeCl_3$ ⟶ blue col.

2 : 3-*Di-Me ether* : $C_9H_{10}O_5$. MW, 198. Plates from H_2O. M.p. 154–5°. Insol. ligroin. Sol. MeOH, AcOEt, Me_2CO. $FeCl_3$ ⟶ brownish-yellow col.

3 : 4-*Di-Me ether* : needles from H_2O. M.p. 169–72°.

2 : 3 : 4-*Tri-Me ether* : $C_{10}H_{12}O_5$. MW, 212. Cryst. from H_2O or petrol. M.p. 99°. *Me ester* : $C_{11}H_{14}O_5$. MW, 226. Oil. B.p. 281°. *Chloride* : $C_{10}H_{11}O_4Cl$. MW, 230·5. Cryst. from petrol. M.p. 42°. B.p. 175°/11 mm. *Amide* : $C_{10}H_{13}O_4N$. MW, 211. M.p. 130–1°.

2 : 3 : 4-*Tri-Et ether* : $C_{13}H_{18}O_5$. MW, 254. Cryst. from EtOH. M.p. 105°.

2 : 3-*Diacetyl* : needles + $1H_2O$ from MeOH.Aq. M.p. anhyd. 157°.

2 : 3 : 4-*Triacetyl* : prisms from xylene. M.p. 164°.

4-*Benzoyl* : plates from MeOH.Aq. M.p. 210–11°.

2 : 3-*Diacetyl-4-benzoyl* : needles from petrol-$CHCl_3$. M.p. 161–2°.

Hemmelmayr, *Monatsh.*, 1917, **38**, 81, 88.
Pacsu, *Ber.*, 1923, **56**, 418.
Kostanecki, *Ber.*, 1885, **18**, 3205.

2 : 3 : 5-Trihydroxybenzoic Acid.

2 : 3-*Di-Me ether* : cryst. M.p. 186–8°.

2 : 3 : 5-*Tri-Me ether* : plates from H_2O. M.p. 105° (141–3°).

Smith, Laforge, *J. Am. Chem. Soc.*, 1931, **53**, 3074.
Faltis, Kloiber, *Monatsh.*, 1929, **53** and **54**, 633.

2 : 3 : 6-Trihydroxybenzoic Acid.

2 : 3-*Di-Me ether* : needles from H_2O. M.p. 82°.

2 : 3 : 6-*Tri-Me ether* : cryst. from H_2O. M.p. 145–6°.

Smith, Laforge, *J. Am. Chem. Soc.*, 1931, **53**, 3075.

2 : 4 : 5-Trihydroxybenzoic Acid (*Hydroxyhydroquinone-carboxylic acid*).

Needles + $\frac{1}{2}H_2O$ from H_2O. M.p. 217–18° decomp. $FeCl_3$ ⟶ blue to red col. Loses CO_2 with H_2O at 100°.

4 : 5-*Di-Me ether* : $C_9H_{10}O_5$. MW, 198. Brown needles from H_2O. M.p. 202° decomp. *Me ester* : $C_{10}H_{12}O_5$. MW, 212. Needles from H_2O. M.p. 95°.

2 : 4 : 5-*Tri-Me ether* : *see* Asarylic Acid.

2 : 4-*Di-Me-5-Et ether* : $C_{11}H_{14}O_5$. MW, 226. Needles from H_2O, prisms from C_6H_6. M.p. 137°.

2 : 5-*Di-Me-4-Et ether* : prisms from H_2O. M.p. 130°.

2 : 4 : 5-*Tri-Et ether* : $C_{13}H_{18}O_5$. MW, 254. Needles from EtOH.Aq. M.p. 134°.

2 : 4 : 5-*Triacetyl* : plates or needles from C_6H_6. M.p. 162–3°.

Head, Robertson, *J. Chem. Soc.*, 1930, 2439.

2 : 4 : 6-Trihydroxybenzoic Acid (*Phloroglucinol-carboxylic acid*).

Cryst. + $1H_2O$. Decomp. on heating. $FeCl_3$ ⟶ blue col. Absorbs O in alk. sol.

Me ester : $C_8H_8O_5$. MW, 184. Cryst. from EtOH.Aq. M.p. 174–6°. 4-*Me-2-Et ether* :

$C_{11}H_{14}O_5$. MW, 226. Needles from EtOH. M.p. 97–9°. 2 : 4 : 6-*Tri-acetyl* : needles from MeOH. M.p. 77–9°.

Et ester : $C_9H_{10}O_5$. MW, 198. Prisms or needles + $1H_2O$ from H_2O, prisms from ligroin. M.p. 129°. $FeCl_3$ ⟶ violet col. 2 : 6-*Di-Et ether* : $C_{13}H_{18}O_5$. MW, 256. Prisms from MeOH. M.p. 180–1°.

4-*Me ether* : $C_8H_8O_5$. MW, 184. Grey needles from Et_2O–C_6H_6. M.p. 141° decomp. *Me ester* : $C_9H_{10}O_5$. MW, 198. Needles from MeOH. M.p. 114–16°.

2 : 6-*Di-Me ether* : $C_9H_{10}O_5$. MW, 198. Plates. M.p. 175° decomp. *Me ester* : $C_{10}H_{12}O_5$. MW, 212. Plates from MeOH.Aq. M.p. 189° decomp.

4 : 6-*Di-Me ether* : needles from Et_2O–C_6H_6. M.p. 152–4° decomp. *Me ester* : needles from MeOH. M.p. 107–9°.

2 : 4 : 6-*Tri-Me ether* : $C_{10}H_{12}O_5$. MW, 212. Needles from EtOH.Aq. M.p. 142–4° decomp. *Me ester* : $C_{11}H_{14}O_5$. MW, 226. Cryst. from MeOH. M.p. 67–70°. *Et ester* : $C_{12}H_{16}O_5$. MW, 240. Needles from ligroin. M.p. 77–8°.

4-*Me*-2 : 6-*Di-Et ether* : $C_{12}H_{16}O_5$. MW, 240. Plates from MeOH. M.p. 168°.

4-*Acetyl* : needles from MeOH. M.p. 177–8°.

Skraup, *Monatsh.*, 1889, **10**, 724.
Sonn, Winzer, *Ber.*, 1928, **61**, 2303.

3 : 4 : 5-Trihydroxybenzoic Acid.
See Gallic Acid.

2 : 3 : 4-Trihydroxybenzophenone.
See Gallobenzophenone.

2 : 4 : 5-Trihydroxybenzophenone

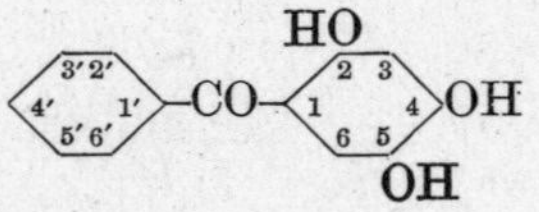

$C_{13}H_{10}O_4$ MW, 230

5-*Me ether* : $C_{14}H_{12}O_4$. MW, 244. Yellow needles from EtOH. M.p. 183–5°.

4 : 5-*Di-Me ether* : $C_{15}H_{14}O_4$. MW, 258. Greenish-yellow cryst. from EtOH.Aq. M.p. 106–7°. 2-*Acetyl* : yellow needles from EtOH.Aq. M.p. 108–10°.

2 : 4 : 5-*Tri-Me ether* : $C_{16}H_{16}O_4$. MW, 272. Yellow needles from H_2O. M.p. 97°. *Phenylhydrazone* : leaflets. M.p. 178–9°.

Bargellini, Martegiani, *Atti accad. Lincei*, 1911, **20**, 184.

2 : 4 : 6-Trihydroxybenzophenone.
See Phlorbenzophenone.

2 : 3 : 4′-Trihydroxybenzophenone.

Yellow needles from MeOH.Aq. M.p. 169°. $FeCl_3$ ⟶ brownish-green col.

Tri-Me ether : $C_{16}H_{16}O_4$. MW, 272. Cryst. from MeOH.Aq. M.p. 86°.

Baker, Smith, *J. Chem. Soc.*, 1936, 348.

2 : 4 : 4′-Trihydroxybenzophenone.

Yellow needles from H_2O. M.p. 200°. $FeCl_3$ ⟶ purple col.

4′-*Me ether* : $C_{14}H_{12}O_4$. MW, 244. Needles from H_2O. M.p. 165°. 2 : 4-*Diacetyl* : needles from EtOH.Aq. M.p. 128–30°.

Tri-Me ether : needles from EtOH. M.p. 73–4°.

Triacetyl : needles from H_2O. M.p. 96–8°.

Komarowski, Kostanecki, *Ber.*, 1894, **27**, 1999.

2 : 6 : 2′-Trihydroxybenzophenone.

Yellow cryst. from EtOH.Aq. M.p. 133–4°. Sol. hot H_2O. NaOH ⟶ yellow col.

Michael, *Am. Chem. J.*, 1883, **5**, 89.

3 : 4 : 5-Trihydroxybenzophenone.

Yellow plates + $1H_2O$, colourless anhyd. cryst. from $CHCl_3$. M.p. anhyd. 177–8°. Very sol. hot H_2O. Sol. EtOH, Et_2O, Me_2CO. Spar. sol. C_6H_6, petrol.

Fischer, *Ber.*, 1909, **42**, 1018.

3 : 4 : 3′-Trihydroxybenzophenone.

Tri-Me ether : $C_{16}H_{16}O_4$. MW, 272. Needles from MeOH. M.p. 83–4°. *Oxime* : prisms from EtOH. M.p. 128°.

Lea, Robinson, *J. Chem. Soc.*, 1926, 2355.

3 : 4 : 4′-Trihydroxybenzophenone.

Tri-Me ether : needles from EtOH. M.p. 98–9°.

Kostanecki, Tambor, *Ber.*, 1906, **39**, 4026.

3 : 5 : 4′-Trihydroxybenzophenone.

Tri-Me ether : needles from C_6H_6. M.p. 97–8°.

Mauthner, *J. prakt. Chem.*, 1913, **87**, 406.

2 : 4 : 6-Trihydroxybenzyl Alcohol

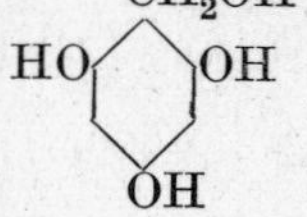

$C_7H_8O_4$ MW, 156

2 : 4 : 6-*Tri-Me ether* : $C_{10}H_{14}O_4$. MW, 198. Cryst. from pet. ether. M.p. 63°.

Freudenberg, Harder, *Ann.*, 1927, **451**, 222.

3 : 4 : 5-Trihydroxybenzyl Alcohol.
See Gallyl Alcohol.

3 : 4 : 5-Trihydroxybenzylamine.
See Gallylamine.

1 : 2 : 3-Trihydroxybutane.
See 1-Methylglycerol.

1 : 2 : 4-Trihydroxybutane (1 : 2 : 4-*Butantriol*)

$$HO{\cdot}CH_2{\cdot}CH_2{\cdot}CH(OH){\cdot}CH_2OH$$

$C_4H_{10}O_3$ MW, 106

Hygroscopic syrup with sweet, burning taste. B.p. 179°/13 mm. D^{20} 1·18. n_D^{20} 1·47.

4-Me ether : $C_5H_{12}O_3$. MW, 120. B.p. 121°/12 mm. D^0 1·11. n_D^{20} 1·448. *Di-phenylurethane* : m.p. 111–12°.

1-Et ether : $C_6H_{14}O_3$. MW, 134. Slightly yellow oil. B.p. 210°.

4-Et ether : b.p. 130°/14 mm. D ' 1·08. n_D^{15} 1·45. *Di-phenylurethane* : m.p. 98–9°. *Tri-phenylurethane* : needles from C_6H_6. M.p. 149–52°.

1 : 4-*Diacetyl* : b.p. 161–3°/18 mm. D_0^{16} 1·15. n_D^{16} 1·446.

Triacetyl : b.p. 150°/11 mm. D_0^{19} 1·13. n_D^{19} 1·436.

Pariselle, *Ann. chim.*, 1911, **24**, 346.
Wagner, *Ber.*, 1894, **27**, 2437.

1 : 3 : 3-Trihydroxybutane (1 : 3 : 3-*Butantriol*)

$$HO{\cdot}CH_2{\cdot}CH_2{\cdot}\overset{OH}{\underset{OH}{C}}{\cdot}CH_3$$

$C_4H_{10}O_3$ MW, 106

Tri-Me-ether : $C_7H_{16}O_3$. MW, 148. B.p. 63°/20 mm. D_4^{20} 0·9398. n_D^{20} 1·4112.

Tri-Et ether : $C_{10}H_{22}O_3$. MW, 192. B.p. 75°/9 mm. D_4^{2} '0·8940. n_D^{20} 1·4148.

Tributyl ether : $C_{16}H_{34}O_2$. MW, 276. B.p. 120°/3 mm. D_4^{20} 0·8745. n_D^{20} 1·4310.

Dykstra, *J. Am. Chem. Soc.*, 1935, **57**, 2257.

1 : 2 : 3-Trihydroxybutyraldehyde.
See Erythrose *and* Threose.

1 : 2 : 3-Trihydroxybutyric Acid.
See Threonic Acid.

2 : 3 : 4-Trihydroxybutyrophenone (4-*Butyrylpyrogallol*)

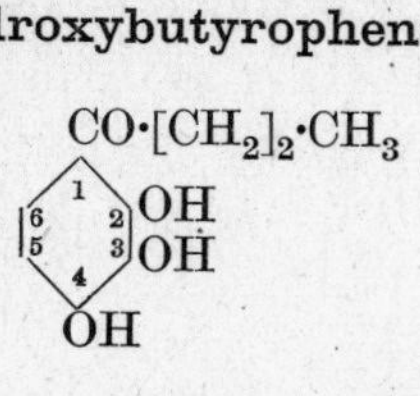

$C_{10}H_{12}O_4$ MW, 196

Yellow needles. M.p. anhyd. 100°.

Badische, D.R.Ps., 49,149, 50,451.

2 : 4 : 6-Trihydroxybutyrophenone.
See Phlorbutyrophenone.

3 : 4 : 5-Trihydroxybutyrophenone (5-*Butyrylpyrogallol*).

Tri-Me ether : $C_{13}H_{18}O_4$. MW, 238. Needles from MeOH. M.p. 51–52·5°. Sol. common org. solvents. p-*Nitrophenylhydrazone* : m.p. 160°.

Bogert, Isham, *J. Am. Chem. Soc.*, 1914, **36**, 526.

2 : 3 : 4-Trihydroxycaproic Acid (*Digitoxic acid*)

$$CH_3{\cdot}CH(OH){\cdot}CH(OH){\cdot}CH(OH){\cdot}CH_2{\cdot}COOH$$

$C_6H_{12}O_5$ MW, 164

Colourless syrup. $HNO_3 \longrightarrow$ 1 : 2-dihydroxyglutaric acid.

Quinine salt : needles or columns. M.p. 164°. Very sol. MeOH.Aq. Spar. sol. cold H_2O.

Brucine salt : columns from EtOH–Et_2O. M.p. 124°. Very sol. H_2O. Mod. sol. EtOH.

Phenylhydrazide : cryst. from EtOH. M.p. 159°.

Zemplén, *Ber.*, 1923, **56**, 688.
Kiliani, *Arch. pharm.*, 1913, **251**, 579.

2 : 3 : 4-Trihydroxycaproic Aldehyde.
See Digitoxose.

2 : 3 : 4-Trihydroxycinnamic Acid (*Daphnetic acid*)

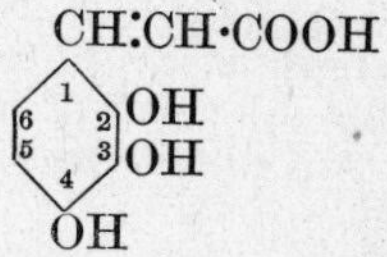

$C_9H_8O_5$ MW, 196

Tri-Me ether : $C_{12}H_{14}O_5$. MW, 238. Needles from EtOH. M.p. 172°.

4-Me-2 : 3-Di-Et-ether : $C_{14}H_{18}O_5$. MW, 266. Cryst. from pet. ether. M.p. 157–8°.

Tri-Et ether : $C_{15}H_{20}O_5$. MW, 280. Cryst. M.p. 193°. Very sol. hot EtOH, Et_2O, C_6H_6. Insol. H_2O, CS_2. Ox. $\longrightarrow$ 2 : 3 : 4-trimethoxybenzaldehyde and 2 : 3 : 4-trimethoxybenzoic acid.

Will, Jung, *Ber.*, 1884, **17**, 1086.

2 : 4 : 5-Trihydroxycinnamic Acid (*Aesculetic acid*).

Me ester : $C_{10}H_{10}O_5$. MW, 210. Cryst. M.p. 109°.

5-Me ether : $C_{10}H_{10}O_5$. MW, 210. Pale yellow needles + $1H_2O$ from H_2O. M.p. 178–80° decomp. Spar. sol. Et_2O. Boiling dil. acids eliminates CO_2.

Tri-Me ether : $C_{12}H_{14}O_5$. MW, 238. Needles from EtOH.Aq. M.p. 169°. Sol. EtOH, Et_2O, C_6H_6. Spar. sol. cold H_2O. *Me ester* : $C_{13}H_{16}O_5$.

MW, 252. Prisms from EtOH.Aq. M.p. 109°. Sol. EtOH, Et_2O, $CHCl_3$, C_6H_6. Insol. H_2O.

Tri-Et ether: $C_{15}H_{20}O_5$. MW, 280. Two forms. (i) Cryst. from EtOH. M.p. 102–3°. Conc. HCl ⟶ (ii). Ox. ⟶ triethoxybenzaldehyde and triethoxybenzoic acid. *Et ester*: $C_{17}H_{24}O_5$. MW, 308. Pale yellow prisms. M.p. 51°. (ii) Cryst. from EtOH.Aq. M.p. 144°. Dist. with slight decomp. Sol. EtOH, Et_2O, C_6H_6. Very spar. sol. H_2O. *Et ester*: plates from EtOH. M.p. 75°.

Will, *Ber.*, 1883, **16**, 2109.
Tiemann, Will, *Ber.*, 1882, **15**, 2082.

2 : 4 : 6-Trihydroxycinnamic Acid.

Tri-Me ether: $C_{12}H_{14}O_5$. MW, 238. Yellowish-white needles. M.p. 218° decomp. Very sol. MeOH. Spar. sol. H_2O, Et_2O. *Me ester*: $C_{13}H_{16}O_5$. MW, 252. Needles. M.p. 134–5°.

Herzig, Wenzel, Gehringer, *Monatsh.*, 1903, **24**, 868.

3 : 4 : 5-Trihydroxycinnamic Acid.

Needles + $1H_2O$ from H_2O. Anhyd. at 120°. M.p. 207–8° decomp. Very sol. EtOH, Me_2CO, hot H_2O. Spar. sol. cold H_2O, Et_2O, AcOH. Insol. $CHCl_3$, C_6H_6, CS_2, pet. ether. Sol. conc. H_2SO_4 ⟶ yellow sol. Reduces cold $NH_3.AgNO_3$, and Fehling's on warming. KCN sol. ⟶ red ⟶ violet ⟶ yellowish-green col.

3 : 5-*Di-Me ether*: *see* Sinapic Acid.

Tri-Me ether: *see under* Sinapic Acid.

Triacetyl: needles from $CHCl_3$–petrol. M.p. 168°.

Rosenmund, Boehm, *Ann.*, 1924, **437**, 144.

1 : 2 : 3-Trihydroxycyclohexane.

See Pyrogallitol.

1 : 2 : 4-Trihydroxycyclohexane

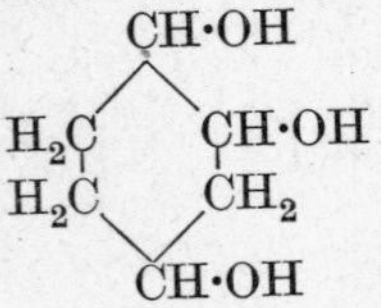

$C_6H_{12}O_3$ MW, 132

Cryst. from EtOH–Et_2O. M.p. 122°.

Zelinsky, Titowa, *Ber.*, 1931, **64**, 140.

1 : 3 : 5-Trihydroxycyclohexane.

See Phloroglucitol.

Trihydroxydiacetylbenzene.

See Gallodiacetophenone.

5 : 7 : 4′ - Trihydroxy - 3 : 5′ - dimethoxy - flavonol.

See Syringetin.

1 : 1 : 1-Trihydroxyethane.

See Orthoacetic Acid.

5 : 7 : 2′-Trihydroxyflavanone

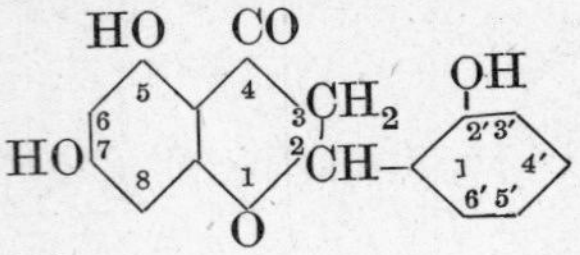

$C_{15}H_{12}O_5$ MW, 272

Needles from AcOH.Aq. M.p. 185–7°. $FeCl_3$ ⟶ red col.

2′-*Me ether*: *see* Citronetin.

5(7)-*Me ether*: $C_{16}H_{14}O_5$. MW, 286. Cryst. from EtOH. M.p. 192°. $FeCl_3$ ⟶ reddish-brown col.

Tri-Me ether: $C_{18}H_{18}O_5$. MW, 314. Needles from EtOH. M.p. 124–5°. Sol. conc. H_2SO_4 ⟶ yellowish-brown col.

Shinoda, Sato, *Chem. Zentr.*, 1931, II, 2326.

5 : 7 : 3′-Trihydroxyflavanone.

Plates from AcOH. M.p. 240–1°. $FeCl_3$ ⟶ violet-brown col.

3′-*Me ether*: $C_{16}H_{14}O_5$. MW, 286. Plates. M.p. 179–80°. *Oxime*: plates from EtOH.Aq. M.p. 194–5°. 5(7)-*Me ether*: $C_{17}H_{16}O_5$. MW, 300. Plates from EtOH. M.p. 96°. *Diacetyl*: cryst. from EtOH. M.p. 106–7°.

5(7)-*Me ether*: needles from EtOH. M.p. 182°.

Acetyl: cryst. from C_6H_6–pet. ether. M.p. 43–5°.

See previous reference.

5 : 7 : 4′-Trihydroxyflavanone.

See Naringenin.

7 : 3′ : 4′-Trihydroxyflavanone.

See Butin.

5 : 6 : 7-Trihydroxyflavone.

See Baicalein.

5 : 7 : 8-Trihydroxyflavone.

See Norwogonin.

5 : 7 : 4′-Trihydroxyflavone.

See Apigenin.

6 : 7 : 4′-Trihydroxyflavone

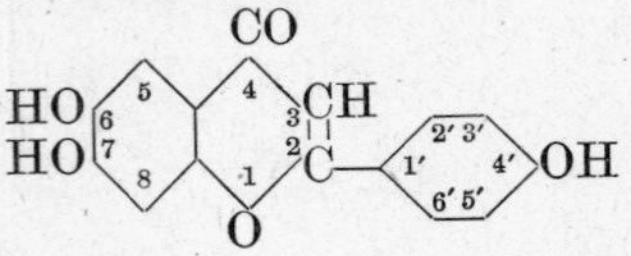

$C_{15}H_{10}O_5$ MW, 270

Yellow needles + $1H_2O$ from AcOH.Aq. Anhyd. at 110°. Decomp. at 300°. Sol. EtOH, NaOH.Aq. Alc. $FeCl_3$ ⟶ green col.

Conc. $H_2SO_4 \longrightarrow$ yellow sol. with green fluor.

Di-Me ether : $C_{17}H_{14}O_5$. MW, 298. Cryst. + H_2O. M.p. 158–62° decomp. [Sol. EtOH, AcOH. Spar. sol. C_6H_6. Alc. $FeCl_3 \longrightarrow$ red col. *Acetyl* : cryst. from EtOH. M.p. 164–6°.

Tri-Me ether : $C_{18}H_{16}O_5$. MW, 312. Needles from EtOH. M.p. 184–6°. Sol. AcOH, C_6H_6. Fluor. sol. in EtOH. Sol. conc. $H_2SO_4 \longrightarrow$ yellow sol. with green fluor.

Triacetyl : needles from AcOH. M.p. 234–6°.

Bargellini, Grippa, *Gazz. chim. ital.*, 1927, **57**, 605.

7 : 8 : 4′-Trihydroxyflavone.

Yellow needles from EtOH.Aq. Sinters at 279°, m.p. 299–300° decomp. Conc. $H_2SO_4 \longrightarrow$ yellow sol. Alc. $FeCl_3 \longrightarrow$ green col. NaOH.Aq. $\longrightarrow$ orange sol.

Tri-Me ether : yellow needles from EtOH. M.p. 189–90°.

Triacetyl : white needles. M.p. 183°.

Badhwar, Kang, Venkataraman, *J. Chem. Soc.*, 1932, 1109.

7 : 3′ : 4′-Trihydroxyflavone.

3′ : 4′-Di-Me ether : $C_{17}H_{14}O_5$. MW, 298. Plates from AcOH.Aq. M.p. 255°. Sol. EtOH with violet fluor. No col. with $FeCl_3$.

Baker, *J. Chem. Soc.*, 1933, 1387.

3′ : 4′ : 5′-Trihydroxyflavone.

Pale yellow needles from EtOH.Aq. Does not melt below 280°. Conc. $H_2SO_4 \longrightarrow$ yellow sol. NaOH $\longrightarrow$ red sol. $FeCl_3 \longrightarrow$ green ppt.

Tri-Me ether : $C_{18}H_{16}O_5$. MW, 312. Needles from EtOH.Aq. M.p. 174–5°.

Triacetyl : prisms from EtOH. M.p. 195–6°.

Hattori, *Chem. Zentr.*, 1932, II, 710.

Trihydroxyflavonol.
See Tetrahydroxyflavone.

Trihydroxyglutaric Acid

I. Arabo-trihydroxyglutaric Acid.

$$
\begin{array}{c}
\text{COOH} \\
\text{HO–C–H} \\
\text{HO–C–H} \\
\text{H–C–OH} \\
\text{COOH}
\end{array}
$$

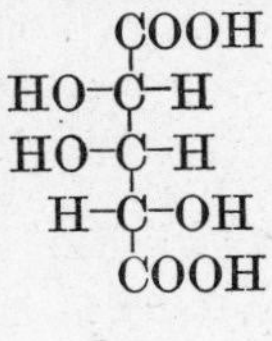

$C_5H_8O_7$ MW, 180

d-.

Plates from H_2O, cryst. from Me_2CO. M.p. 128°. Very sol. H_2O. Sol. EtOH, hot Me_2CO. $[\alpha]_D^{20} + 22.2°$ in H_2O.

Di-Me ester : $C_7H_{12}O_7$. MW, 208. *Tri-Me*

ether : $C_{10}H_{18}O_7$. MW, 250. B.p. about 143°/15 mm., 100°/0·1 mm. n_D^{21} 1·4353. $[\alpha]_D^{20} -$ 47·5° in MeOH, $[\alpha]_D^{20} - 42.5°$ in H_2O.

Diamide : $C_5H_{10}O_5N_2$. MW, 178. *Tri-Me ether* : $C_8H_{16}O_5N_2$. MW, 220. M.p. 232–3° decomp. $[\alpha]_D^{20} - 49°$ in H_2O.

l-.

Plates from EtOH. M.p. 127°. $[\alpha]_D^{18} - 23.3°$ in H_2O. $k = 1.32 \times 10^{-3}$ at 25°. *Ag salt* : m.p. 173°. *Quinine salt* : needles + $5H_2O$ from H_2O. M.p. 180°. $[\alpha]_D - 112.5°$. *Brucine salt* : needles from EtOH.Aq. M.p. 175–6°. $[\alpha]_D - 41.67°$.

Di-Me ester : *tri-Me ether*, syrup. B.p. 143°/18 mm., 74–6°/·005 mm. Sol. H_2O and most org. solvents. n_D^{20} 1·4350. $[\alpha]_D + 47.3°$ in MeOH, $[\alpha]_D + 45°$ in H_2O.

Diamide : *tri-Me ether*, prisms from MeOH. M.p. 232–3°. $[\alpha]_D + 50.0°$ in H_2O.

dl-.

Cryst. from Me_2CO. M.p. 154·5° decomp. Very sol. H_2O, EtOH. Sol. Me_2CO. $k = 6.9 \times 10^{-4}$ at 25°.

Hirst, Smith, *J. Chem. Soc.*, 1928, 3153.
Votoček, *Ber.*, 1910, **43**, 472.
Nef, *Ann.*, 1914, **403**, 252.
Ruff, *Ber.*, 1899, **32**, 558.
Haworth, Hirst, Jones, *J. Chem. Soc.*, 1927, 2428.

II. Xylo-trihydroxyglutaric Acid.

$$
\begin{array}{c}
\text{COOH} \\
\text{H–C–OH} \\
\text{HO–C–H} \\
\text{H–C–OH} \\
\text{COOH}
\end{array}
$$

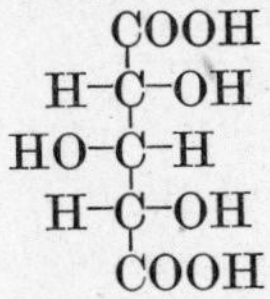

Cryst. from AcOEt. M.p. 152° decomp. Very sol. H_2O, hot EtOH. Spar. sol. hot Me_2CO. Insol. Et_2O, $CHCl_3$. Optically inactive. Heat of comb. C_v 389·5 Cal. $k = 6.6 \times 10^{-4}$ at 25°. Evap. aq. sol. $\longrightarrow$ lactone. HI(+ P) $\longrightarrow$ glutaric acid. Reduces $NH_3.AgNO_3$ but not Fehling's.

Di-phenylhydrazide : plates. Sinters at 175°, decomp. at 210°.

Di-Me ester : 1 : 2-*Di-Me ether*. $C_9H_{16}O_7$. MW, 236. Oil. B.p. 132°/12 mm. 97–9°/ 0·003 mm. Hyd. $\longrightarrow$ lactone of 1 : 2-dimethoxyglutaric acid.

Diamide : *tri-Me ether*, m.p. 195–8° (194–5°).

Schmidt, Zeiser, *Ber.*, 1934, **67**, 2124.
Fischer, Herborn, *Ber.*, 1896, **29**, 1965.
Haworth, Jones, *J. Chem. Soc.*, 1927, 2349.
Hirst, *J. Chem. Soc.*, 1926, 350.

Trihydroxyheptane.
See Heptantriol.

Trihydroxyhexane.
See Hexantriol.

2 : 4 : 6-Trihydroxyisobutyrophenone.
See Phlorisobutyrophenone.

5 : 7 : 4′-Trihydroxyisoflavone.
See Genistein.

2 : 4 : 6-Trihydroxyisophthalic Acid (*Phloroglucinol-dicarboxylic acid*)

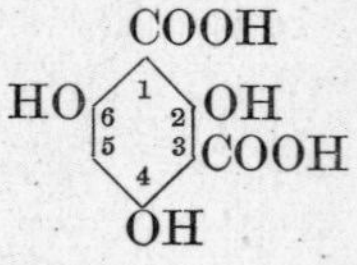

$C_8H_6O_7$ MW, 214

Free acid unknown.

Di-Me ester: $C_{10}H_{10}O_7$. MW, 242. Needles or prisms from MeOH. M.p. 145–6°.

Di-Et ester: $C_{12}H_{14}O_7$. MW, 270. Needles from EtOH. M.p. 104° (107–8°). *Triacetyl*: prisms from EtOH. M.p. 96–8°.

Tri-Me ether: $C_{11}H_{12}O_7$. MW, 256. Prisms from H_2O. Sinters at 260°. *Di-Me ester*: $C_{13}H_{16}O_7$. MW, 284. Plates from Et_2O. M.p. 120–1°. Sol. $CHCl_3$, Me_2CO, AcOEt, AcOH, C_6H_6. Mod. sol. MeOH, Et_2O. Spar. sol. ligroin. *Di-Et ester*: $C_{15}H_{20}O_7$. MW, 312. Plates from EtOH. M.p. 90–1°. Sol. EtOH, Et_2O. Spar. sol. pet. ether.

Leuchs, *Ann.*, 1928, **460**, 1.
Leuchs, Dzieng, *Ann.*, 1924, **440**, 151.
Leuchs, Simion, *Ber.*, 1911, **44**, 1878.

4 : 5 : 6-Trihydroxyisophthalic Acid (*Gallocarboxylic acid, pyrogallol*-4 : 6-*dicarboxylic acid*).

Needles + $3H_2O$ from H_2O. M.p. 283° decomp. Hot $Ac_2O \longrightarrow$ pyrogallol triacetate.

Tri-Me ether: prisms from MeOH. M.p. 191°. *Di-Me ester*: plates from MeOH. M.p. 35–6°.

Feist, Awe, *Ber.*, 1926, **59**, 175.

2 : 4 : 6-Trihydroxymesitylene (2 : 4 : 6-*Trimethylphloroglucinol*)

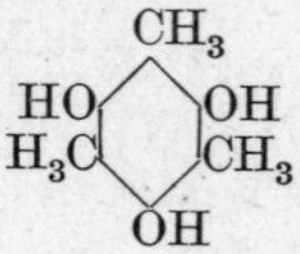

$C_9H_{12}O_3$ MW, 168

Needles from AcOH. M.p. 184°. Sol. MeOH, EtOH, AcOEt, hot H_2O. Spar. sol. C_6H_6, hot pet. ether. Reduces $NH_3.AgNO_3$. $FeCl_3 \longrightarrow$ reddish-violet col.

Mono-Me ether: $C_{10}H_{14}O_3$. MW, 182. Needles from H_2O or C_6H_6. M.p. 121°. B.p. 196–8°/20 mm. *Diacetyl*: cryst. from MeOH.Aq. M.p. 66–8°.

Mono-Et ether: $C_{11}H_{16}O_3$. MW, 196. Cryst. from $CHCl_3$. M.p. 130°.

Triacetyl: prisms from C_6H_6. M.p. 165–7°.

Weidel, Wenzel, *Monatsh.*, 1898, **19**, 257.

Trihydroxymethane.
See Orthoformic Acid.

5 : 7 : 3′-Trihydroxy-4′-methoxyflavanone.
See Hesperetin.

5 : 7 : 4′-Trihydroxy-3′-methoxyflavanone.
See Homoeriodictyol.

3 : 5 : 7-Trihydroxy-4′-methoxyflavone.
See Kaempferide.

5 : 7 : 3′-Trihydroxy-4′-methoxyflavone.
See Diosmetin.

5 : 7 : 4′-Trihydroxy-3′-methoxyflavone.
See Chrysoeriol.

2 : 5 : 8-Trihydroxy-1-methylanthraquinone

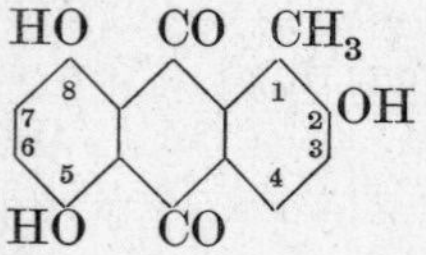

$C_{15}H_{10}O_5$ MW, 270

Dark red needles from $CHCl_3$. M.p. 270°. Sol. alkalis and conc. H_2SO_4 with bluish-red col.

2-*Me ether*: $C_{16}H_{12}O_5$. MW, 284. Dark red needles from AcOH. M.p. 249–249·5°. Sol. conc. H_2SO_4 with bluish-violet col., in alkalis with bluish-red col.

Gardner, Adams, *J. Am. Chem. Soc.*, 1923, **45**, 2455.
Graves, Adams, *ibid.*, 2439.

3 : 5 : 8-Trihydroxy-1-methylanthraquinone.

Red needles from EtOH. M.p. 260°.

Triacetyl: yellow needles from C_6H_6. M.p. 179°.

Dimroth, Fick, *Ann.*, 1916, **411**, 330.

3 : 7 : 8-Trihydroxy-1-methylanthraquinone.
See 8-Methylflavopurpurin.

4 : 5 : 8-Trihydroxy-1-methylanthraquinone.

Red needles from AcOH. M.p. 276–8°. Mod. sol. cold EtOH. Sublimes. Sol. alkalis with violet-red col., in conc. H_2SO_4 with blue to bluish-violet col. Alc. $FeCl_3 \longrightarrow$ greenish-brown col.

5 : 8-*Di-Me ether* : $C_{17}H_{14}O_5$. MW, 298. Red needles from Me_2CO. M.p. 224°. Sol. alkalis with red col., in conc. H_2SO_4 with blue to bluish-red col.

Tri-Me ether : $C_{18}H_{16}O_5$. MW, 312. Yellow needles from EtOH. M.p. 249–250·5°.

Triacetyl : m.p. 197°.

Keimatsu, Hirano, Yoshimi, *Chem. Zentr.*, 1930, II, 2384.
Gardner, Adams, *J. Am. Chem. Soc.*, 1923, **45**, 2455.
Graves, Adams, *ibid.*, 2439.

4 : 7 : 8 - Trihydroxy - 1 - methylanthra - quinone.

Red needles from AcOH. M.p. 301° (decomp. at 290°).

7 : 8-*Di-Me ether* : yellow needles from AcOEt. M.p. 168–9°. *Acetyl* : yellow needles from EtOH. M.p. 173–4°.

Triacetyl : yellow needles from EtOH. M.p. 204–5°.

Jacobson, Adams, *J. Am. Chem. Soc.*, 1925, **47**, 2011.

5 : 6 : 7 - Trihydroxy - 1 - methylanthra - quinone.

See 5-Methylanthragallol.

6 : 7 : 8 - Trihydroxy - 1 - methylanthra - quinone.

See 8-Methylanthragallol.

1 : 5 : 6 - Trihydroxy - 2 - methylanthra - quinone.

See Morindone.

1 : 5 : 8 - Trihydroxy - 2 - methylanthra - quinone

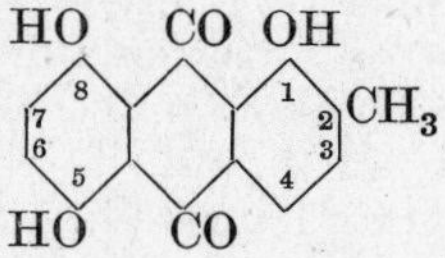

$C_{15}H_{10}O_5$ MW, 270

Red needles from AcOH. M.p. 253–4°. Very sol. Et_2O, C_6H_6, toluene. Mod. sol. EtOH. Sublimes at 250–60°. Sol alkalis with red col., in conc. H_2SO_4 with bluish-red col. Alc. $FeCl_3 \longrightarrow$ red col.

5 : 8-*Di-Me ether* : $C_{17}H_{14}O_5$. MW, 298. Red needles from AcOH. M.p. 165°. Sol. alkalis with red col., in conc. H_2SO_4 with blue to bluish-red col.

Tri-Me ether : $C_{18}H_{16}O_5$. MW, 312. Red needles from EtOH. M.p. 206·5–207°.

Triacetyl : yellow needles. M.p. 215°.

Keimatsu, Hirano, *Chem. Zentr.*, 1930, II, 1551.
Graves, Adams, *J. Am. Chem. Soc.*, 1923, **45**, 2439.

1 : 7 : 8 - Trihydroxy - 2 - methylanthra - quinone.

Brownish-yellow needles from AcOH.Aq. M.p. 287–8°. Sol. NaOH with red col., in conc. H_2SO_4 with bluish-red col.

Tri-Me ether : yellow needles from AcOEt. M.p. 209–10°. Sol. conc. H_2SO_4 with reddish-purple col.

Jacobson, Adams, *J. Am. Chem. Soc.*, 1925, **47**, 288.
Simonsen, *J. Chem. Soc.*, 1924, **125**, 726.

3 : 5 : 6 - Trihydroxy - 2 - methylanthra - quinone.

Orange-red needles from $PhNO_2$. Does not melt below 330°.

5 : 6-*Di-Me ether* : $C_{17}H_{14}O_5$. MW, 298. Yellow needles from AcOH. M.p. about 310°.

Triacetyl : yellow needles from EtOH. M.p. 232–3°.

Jacobson, Adams, *J. Am. Chem. Soc.*, 1925, 47, 2011.

3 : 5 : 8 - Trihydroxy - 2 - methylanthra - quinone.

See Rhababerone.

3 : 7 : 8 - Trihydroxy - 2 - methylanthra - quinone.

See 7-Methylflavopurpurin.

4 : 5 : 6 - Trihydroxy - 2 - methylanthra - quinone.

Tri-Me ether : needles from AcOH.Aq. M.p. 164–5°. Sol. conc. H_2SO_4 with reddish-purple col.

Simonsen, *J. Chem. Soc.*, 1924, **125**, 724.

4 : 5 : 7 - Trihydroxy - 2 - methylanthra - quinone.

See Frangula-emodin.

4 : 5 : 8 - Trihydroxy - 2 - methylanthra - quinone.

See Helminthosporin.

5 : 6 : 7 - Trihydroxy - 2 - methylanthra - quinone.

See 6-Methylanthragallol.

6 : 7 : 8 - Trihydroxy - 2 - methylanthra - quinone.

See 7-Methylanthragallol.

5 : 7 : 4′-Trihydroxy-2-methylisoflavone.

See 2-Methylgenistein.

1 : 4 : 5-Trihydroxy-2-methylxanthone.
See Ravenelin.

1 : 2 : 3-Trihydroxynaphthalene (*Naphthopyrogallol*)

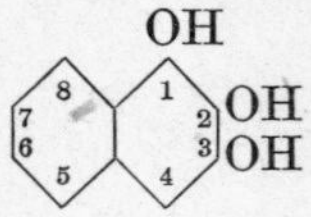

$C_{10}H_8O_3$ MW, 176

Prisms. Decomp. above 250°. Sol. H_2O, EtOH, Me_2CO.

Triacetyl: prisms from AcOH. M.p. 250–5°.

Zincke, Noack, *Ann.*, 1897, **295**, 17.

1 : 2 : 4-Trihydroxynaphthalene.
Needles from C_6H_6. M.p. 154°. Sol. H_2O, EtOH, Et_2O, $CHCl_3$. Spar. sol. C_6H_6.

Triacetyl: plates from EtOH.Aq. M.p. 134·5°.

Bayer, D.R.P., 101,607, (*Chem. Zentr.*, 1899, I, 1094).
Thiele, Winter, *Ann.*, 1911, **311**, 345.

1 : 3 : 6-Trihydroxynaphthalene.
Cryst. from H_2O. M.p. 95°. Sol. H_2O, EtOH, Et_2O, Me_2CO. Spar. sol. $CHCl_3$, C_6H_6, pet. ether. $FeCl_3$ ⟶ yellowish-brown col.

Triacetyl: needles from EtOH.Aq. M.p. 112–13°.

Meyer, Hartmann, *Ber.*, 1905, **38**, 3950.

1 : 4 : 5-Trihydroxynaphthalene.
See α-Hydrojuglone.

1 : 4 : 6-Trihydroxynaphthalene.
Needles from Et_2O–pet. ether. M.p. 138–40°. Very unstable in moist air.

Triacetyl: needles from EtOH. M.p. 94–5°.

Fischer, Bauer, *J. prakt. Chem.*, 1916, **94**, 8.

1 : 6 : 7-Trihydroxynaphthalene.
Yellow needles from xylene. M.p. 177°. Sol. EtOH, Et_2O. Spar. sol. C_6H_6. $FeCl_3$ ⟶ blue col.

Tri-Me ether: $C_{13}H_{14}O_3$. MW, 218. Prisms from ligroin. M.p. 127–8°.

Triacetyl: greenish cryst. from EtOH.Aq. M.p. 143–4°.

Friedländer, Silberstern, *Monatsh.*, 1902, **23**, 530.

5 : 6 : 8-Trihydroxy-1 : 4-naphthoquinone.
See Naphthopurpurin.

Trihydroxypentane.
See Pentantriol.

2 : 4 : 6 - Trihydroxyphenacyl Alcohol
(2 : 4 : 6 : α-*Tetrahydroxyacetophenone*)

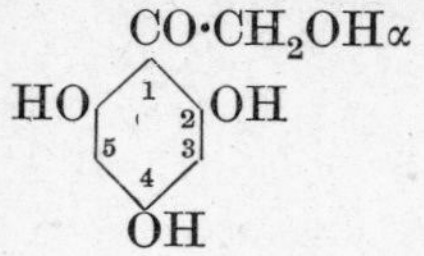

$C_8H_8O_5$ MW, 184

α-*Me ether*: $C_9H_{10}O_5$. MW, 198. Needles from hot H_2O. M.p. 192°. $FeCl_3$ ⟶ violet col.

4 : 6 : α-*Tri-Me ether*: $C_{11}H_{14}O_5$. MW, 226. Needles from EtOH. M.p. 102–4°. *Oxime*: needles from MeOH.Aq. M.p. 147–9°.

Tetra-Me ether: $C_{12}H_{16}O_5$. MW, 240. Cryst. from MeOH. M.p. 50°. No col. with $FeCl_3$.

4 : 6 : α-*Tri-Et ether*: $C_{14}H_{20}O_5$. MW, 268. Needles from EtOH. M.p. 96–7°.

Herzig, Hoffmann, *Ber.*, 1909, **42**, 156.
Perkin, *J. Chem. Soc.*, 1911, **99**, 1724.
Slater, Stephen, *J. Chem. Soc.*, 1920, **117**, 316.

3 : 4 : 5 - Trihydroxyphenacyl Alcohol
(3 : 4 : 5 : α-*Tetrahydroxyacetophenone*).

α-*Me ether*: *triacetyl*, cryst. from EtOH. M.p. 132–3°.

3 : 5-*Di-Me ether*: $C_{10}H_{12}O_5$. MW, 212. Needles + H_2O from boiling H_2O. M.p. 93–5°, anhyd. 132°. Reduces cold Fehling's. Alc. $FeCl_3$ ⟶ weak olive-green col. *Diacetyl*: prismatic needles from MeOH. M.p. 123°. 4-*Benzoyl*: prismatic needles from 50% EtOH. M.p. 173–5°. *Dibenzoyl*: micro-needles from C_6H_6–pet. ether. M.p. 128°.

3 : 4 : 5-*Tri-Me ether*: α-*acetyl*, m.p. 88°.

Tetra-Me ether: needles from C_6H_6–pet. ether. M.p. 54°. B.p. 212°/15 mm. *Semicarbazone*: needles from EtOH.Aq. M.p. 158°.

3 : 4 : 5-*Triacetyl*: needles from C_6H_6. M.p. 87–8°. Sol. Et_2O, Me_2CO, AcOEt, C_6HCl_3, hot EtOH, C_6H_6. Spar. sol. H_2O. Insol. pet. ether. No col. with $FeCl_3$. Reduces cold Fehling's.

Tetra-acetyl: cryst. from EtOH. M.p. 124–5°.

3 : 4 : 5-*Tribenzoyl*: α-*formyl*, prismatic needles from formic acid. M.p. 116–17°. α-*Acetyl*: pale yellow plates from EtOH. M.p. 138–40°. α-p-*Toluenesulphonyl*: needles. M.p. 148°.

Pratt, Robinson, *J. Chem. Soc.*, 1925, 173.
Levy, Posternack, Robinson, *J. Chem. Soc.*, 1931, 2705.
Reynolds, Robinson, *J. Chem. Soc.*, 1934, 1040.

1 : 2 : 4-Trihydroxyphenanthraquinone

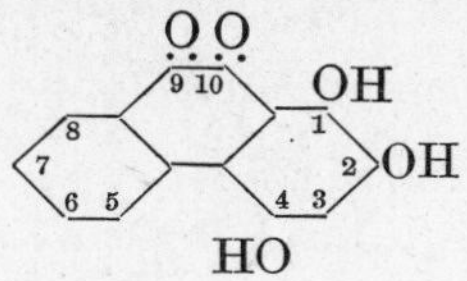

$C_{14}H_8O_5$ MW, 256

Very readily oxidised in air. Very sol. EtOH. Spar. sol. most other org. solvents. Does not crystallise, and decomposes on heating. Sol. alkalis with green col. ⟶ pale red in air. Sol. conc. H_2SO_4 with green col., in Py with cornflower-blue col.

Triacetyl: orange plates from toluene. M.p. 227–8° decomp.

Fieser, *J. Am. Chem. Soc.*, 1929, **51**, 1939.

1 : 3 : 4-Trihydroxyphenanthraquinone. Dark red cryst. from EtOH. Very unstable to air. Spar. sol. H_2O. Sol. alkalis with green col. ⟶ pink in air. Sol. conc. H_2SO_4 with red col., in Py with red col. ⟶ green on dilution with H_2O.

Triacetyl: yellow needles from AcOH. Decomp. at 240°.

Fieser, *J. Am. Chem. Soc.*, 1929, **51**, 1940.

2 : 3 : 4-Trihydroxyphenanthraquinone. Brownish-red powder. M.p. 185° decomp.

Monosemicarbazone: brownish-red powder from EtOH. Decomp. at 270°.

Phenazine: $C_{20}H_{12}O_3N_2$. Brown microcryst. from EtOH. M.p. 255° decomp.

Schmidt, Schairer, *Ber.*, 1923, **56**, 1337.

1 : 3 : 4-Trihydroxyphenanthrene

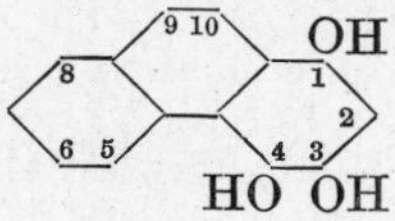

$C_{14}H_{10}O_3$ MW, 226

Triacetyl: needles from C_6H_6–pet. ether. M.p. 138°.

Fieser, *J. Am. Chem. Soc.*, 1929, **51**, 1940.

1 : 5 : 6-Trihydroxyphenanthrene.

1 : 5-*Di-Me ether*: $C_{16}H_{14}O_3$. MW, 254. Reddish-brown plates from EtOH.Aq. M.p. 164–5°. *Acetyl*: prisms from AcOH. M.p. 96–7°.

5 : 6-*Di-Me ether*: prisms from EtOH. M.p. 182–3°. 1-*Et ether*: $C_{18}H_{18}O_3$. MW, 282. Plates from MeOH. M.p. 100°.

Tri-Me ether: $C_{17}H_{16}O_3$. MW, 268. Plates from MeOH. M.p. 138°.

Pschorr, *Ber.*, 1912, **45**, 2220; 1900, **33**, 181.

3 : 4 : 5-Trihydroxyphenanthrene. Plates from H_2O. M.p. 148°. Sol. EtOH, Et_2O, $CHCl_3$.

Tri-Me ether: cryst. from MeOH. M.p. 90°. *Picrate*: red plates from MeOH. M.p. 166°.

Pschorr, *Ann.*, 1912, **391**, 53.

3 : 4 : 6-Trihydroxyphenanthrene.

3 : 6-*Di-Me ether*: *see* Thebaol.

Tri-Me ether: oil. *Picrate*: red needles from EtOH. M.p. 109–10° (110–12°).

Pschorr, Seydel, Stöhrer, *Ber.*, 1902, **35**, 4406.

Vongerichten, *Ber.*, 1902, **35**, 4411.

Trihydroxyphenyl hydroxystyryl Ketone.

See Tetrahydroxychalkone.

3 : 4 : 5-Trihydroxyphthalic Acid (*Pyrogallol*-4 : 5-*dicarboxylic acid*)

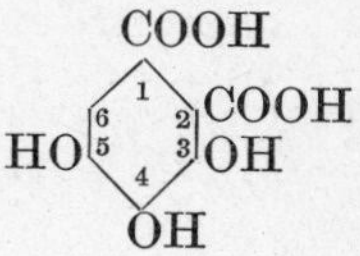

$C_8H_6O_7$ MW, 214

3 : 5-*Di-Me ether*: $C_{10}H_{10}O_7$. MW, 242. Cryst. from H_2O. M.p. 225–7°. *Anhydride*: $C_{10}H_8O_6$. MW, 224. Needles from toluene. M.p. 177–9°.

Tri-Me ether: $C_{11}H_{12}O_7$. MW, 256. Plates from H_2O. M.p. 176–7° decomp. $FeCl_3$ ⟶ yellow col. 1-*Me ester*: $C_{12}H_{14}O_7$. MW, 270. Needles from MeOH. M.p. 138–41°. *Di-Me ester*: $C_{13}H_{16}O_7$. MW, 284. Cryst. M.p. 64–5°. *Anhydride*: $C_{11}H_{10}O_6$. MW, 238. Needles from C_6H_6. M.p. 147°.

Alimchandani, Meldrum, *J. Chem. Soc.*, 1920, **117**, 964.

Feist, Dschu, *Chem. Zentr.*, 1927, II, 58.

3 : 4 : 6-Trihydroxyphthalic Acid.

Tri-Me ether: prisms + $1H_2O$ from H_2O. M.p. 216–17° (185°).

Faltis, Kloiber, Gutlohn, Attia, *Monatsh.*, 1929, **53** and **54**, 632.

Trihydroxypropane.

See Glycerol *and* Orthopropionic Acid.

2 : 3 : 4-Trihydroxypropiophenone (4-*Propionylpyrogallol*)

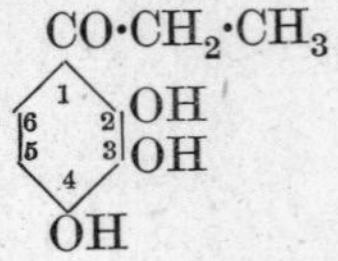

$C_9H_{10}O_4$ MW, 182

Yellow needles. M.p. 127°.

Badische, D.R.P., 42,149.

2 : 4 : 5-Trihydroxypropiophenone.

4 : 5-*Di-Me ether*: $C_{11}H_{14}O_4$. MW, 210. Needles from EtOH.Aq. M.p. 124–6°. $FeCl_3$ ⟶ green col. *Acetyl*: needles from EtOH.Aq. M.p. 117–18°. *Benzoyl*: needles. M.p. 110–11°.

Tri-Me ether: $C_{12}H_{16}O_4$. MW, 224. Needles from H_2O. M.p. 106–8°. *Oxime*: plates from EtOH.Aq. M.p. 106–8°. *Semicarbazone*: (i) plates from EtOH.Aq. M.p. 182. (ii) Prisms from H_2O. M.p. 166–7°.

Bargellini, Martegiani, *Gazz. chim. ital.*, 1911, **41**, 449.

2 : 4 : 6-Trihydroxypropiophenone.

See Phloropropiophenone.

3 : 4 : 5-Trihydroxypropiophenone.

Tri-Me ether: needles from ligroin. M.p. 51–2°. Sol. EtOH, AcOH, warm ligroin. p-*Nitrophenylhydrazone*: red needles from EtOH. M.p. 182–3°.

Mauthner, *J. prakt. Chem.*, 1926, **112**, 269.

2 : 3 : 5-Trihydroxyterephthalic Acid

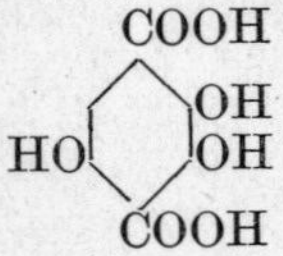

$C_8H_6O_7$ MW, 214

Orange-yellow prisms from AcOH. M.p. 247° decomp. Sol. common org. solvents.

Di-Et ester: $C_{12}H_{14}O_7$. MW, 270. Yellow needles from Me_2CO. M.p. 116°. *Triacetyl*: cryst. from Me_2CO.Aq. M.p. 100°.

Liebermann, Lisser, *Ann.*, 1934, **513**, 184.

2 : 3 : 4-Trihydroxytoluene (4-*Methylpyrogallol*)

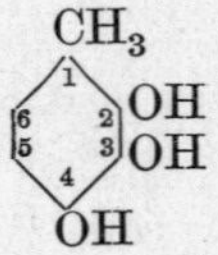

$C_7H_8O_3$ MW, 140

Needles. M.p. 140–1°.

Majima, Okazaki, *Ber.*, 1916, **49**, 1492.

2 : 3 : 5-Trihydroxytoluene.

3-*Me ether*: $C_8H_{10}O_3$. MW, 154. Needles. M.p. 128–9°. Sol. EtOH, Et_2O, AcOH. Spar. sol. ligroin. Reduces Fehling's.

2 : 3-*Di-Me ether*: $C_9H_{12}O_3$. MW, 168. Plates from C_6H_6. M.p. 140–1°.

Henrich, Nachtigall, *Ber.*, 1903, **36**, 894.

2 : 3 : 6-Trihydroxytoluene.

2-*Me ether*: needles from ligroin. M.p. 117–18°.

Majima, Okazaki, *Ber.*, 1916, **49**, 1490.

2 : 4 : 5-Trihydroxytoluene.

Prisms from C_6H_6. M.p. 131–2°. Sol. H_2O. Aq. sol. oxidises readily.

4-*Me ether*: $C_8H_{10}O_3$. MW, 154. Needles from H_2O. M.p. 124°. Sol. common org. solvents, hot H_2O.

4-*Et ether*: $C_9H_{12}O_3$. MW, 168. Tablets from C_6H_6. M.p. 131°. Sublimes.

Tri-Me ether: $C_{10}H_{16}O_3$. MW, 182. Plates from MeOH.Aq. M.p. 55°. Sol. Et_2O, EtOH, pet. ether.

Triacetyl: cryst. from EtOH. M.p. 114–15°.

Thiele, Winter, *Ann.*, 1900, **311**, 349.
Luff, Perkin, Robinson, *J. Chem. Soc.*, 1910, **97**, 1137.
Bayer, D.R.P., 101,607, (*Chem. Zentr.*, 1899, I, 1094).

2 : 4 : 6 - Trihydroxytoluene (2-*Methylphloroglucinol*).

Needles from AcOEt. M.p. 214–16°. Sol. H_2O, EtOH, Et_2O, AcOEt, hot AcOH. Insol. C_6H_6, pet. ether. Sublimes.

2-*Me ether*: $C_8H_{10}O_3$. MW, 154. Prisms + $1H_2O$ from H_2O. M.p. 91°, anhyd. 117–19°. Sol. EtOH, Et_2O, hot H_2O, hot C_6H_6.

4-*Me ether*: needles from xylene. M.p. 124°. B.p. 195–8°/20 mm. Sol. EtOH, AcOEt. Spar. sol. H_2O, ligroin.

2 : 4-*Di-Me ether*: $C_9H_{12}O_3$. MW, 168. Needles from xylene–ligroin. M.p. 60–1°. B.p. 178–80°/20 mm. Sol. EtOH, Et_2O, C_6H_6. Spar. sol. H_2O, ligroin. 6-*Et ether*: $C_{11}H_{16}O_3$. MW, 196. Cryst. from 75% EtOH. M.p. 38°. B.p. 149–51°/16 mm.

2 : 4 : 6-*Tri-Me ether*: $C_{10}H_{14}O_3$. MW, 182. Cryst. M.p. 10–13°. B.p. 140–2°/18 mm.

4-*Et ether*: $C_9H_{12}O_3$. MW, 168. Needles from C_6H_6. M.p. 136–7°. B.p. 195–200°/13 mm. Sol. EtOH, Et_2O. *Diacetyl*: plates from EtOH. M.p. 91°.

Triacetyl : needles from ligroin. M.p. 76° (52°).

Herzig, Wenzel, *Monatsh.*, 1916, **37**, 573.
Boehm, *Ann.*, 1901, **318**, 286.
Herzig, Theuer, *Monatsh.*, 1900, **21**, 855.

3 : 4 : 5-Trihydroxytoluene (5-*Methylpyrogallol*).

Needles from C_6H_6. M.p. 120°. Sublimes in needles.

3 : 5-*Di-Me ether* : cryst. from EtOH. M.p. 36°. B.p. 265°, 145–6°/12 mm. Sol. H_2O, Et_2O.

3 : 4-*Di-Me ether* : *see* Iridol.

Tri-Me ether : *see under* Iridol.

Triacetyl : cryst. M.p. 99°.

Rosauer, *Monatsh.*, 1898, **19**, 565.
Hofmann, *Ber.*, 1879, **12**, 1376.

ω-Trihydroxytoluene.

See Orthobenzoic Acid.

3 : 4 : 5-Trihydroxy-*o*-toluic Acid

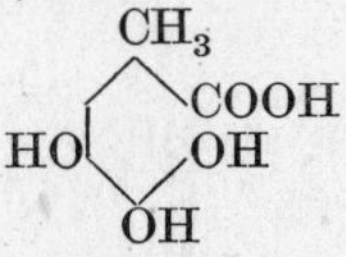

$C_8H_8O_5$ MW, 184

Me ester : $C_9H_{10}O_5$. MW, 198. Cryst. M.p. 155°.

Koller, Hamburg, *Monatsh.*, 1935, **65**, 373.

2 : 4 : 6-Trihydroxy-*m*-toluic Acid (4-*Methylphloroglucinol-2-carboxylic acid*)

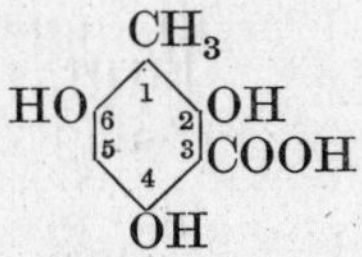

$C_8H_8O_5$ MW, 184

M.p. 177°.

4-*Me ether* : $C_9H_{10}O_5$. MW, 198. Cryst. from Et_2O–C_6H_6. M.p. 147° decomp. Sol. EtOH. Insol. H_2O, ligroin. *Me ester* : $C_{10}H_{12}O_5$. MW, 212. Cryst. from EtOH. M.p. 132–3°. Spar. sol. EtOH. *Diacetyl* : cryst. from EtOH. M.p. 75–7°.

Me ester : cryst. from MeOH. M.p. 144–5°.

Triacetyl : cryst. from C_6H_6. M.p. 163–4°.

Schreier, Wenzel, *Monatsh.*, 1904, **25**, 312.
Herzig, Wenzel, Graetz, *Monatsh.*, 1902, **23**, 100.

2 : 4 : 6-Trihydroxy-*m*-toluic Aldehyde

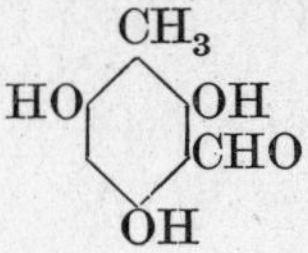

$C_8H_8O_4$ MW, 168

Cryst. + $\frac{1}{2}H_2O$ from H_2O. Decomp. at 130°. Sol. EtOH, AcOH, AcOEt. Spar. sol. H_2O, Et_2O. Insol. $CHCl_3$, C_6H_6, ligroin.

Oxime : yellow cryst. Decomp. at 140°.

Herzig, Wenzel, Kerényi, *Monatsh.*, 1903, **24**, 876.

2 : 3 : 5-Trihydroxy-*p*-toluic Aldehyde.

See Thamnol.

2 : 2′ : 2″-Trihydroxytriethylamine (*Triethanolamine*)

$N(CH_2{\cdot}CH_2OH)_3$

$C_6H_{15}O_3N$ MW, 149

Oil. B.p. 277–9°/150 mm. D^{20} 1·1242. n_D^{20} 1·4852. Darkens in air. Non-volatile in steam. Completely miscible with H_2O, EtOH. Sol. $CHCl_3$. Spar. sol. Et_2O, C_6H_6, ligroin.

B,HCl: cryst. from EtOH. M.p. 177°. Spar. sol. H_2O, EtOH.

B,HAuCl$_4$: plates + H_2O. M.p. anhyd. 77–8°.

B$_2$,*H*$_2$*PtCl*$_6$: cryst. from EtOH. M.p. 118–19°.

Triacetyl : oil. B.p. 206–7°/27 mm. Very sol. EtOH, Et_2O. Insol. H_2O.

N-*Oxide* : cryst. from EtOH. M.p. 104–105·5°. Very sol. H_2O, EtOH. Spar. sol. $CHCl_3$, Me_2CO. Insol. AcOEt, ligroin. Reduces hot $NH_3.AgNO_3$ but not Fehling's. Sweet taste. *Picrate* : deliquescent cryst. from EtOH–Et_2O. M.p. 73–4°.

I.G., F.P., 650,574, (*Chem. Abstracts*, 1929, **23**, 3232).
Jones, Burns, *J. Am. Chem. Soc.*, 1925, **47**, 2966.
Wurtz, *Ann.*, 1862, **121**, 227.

5 : 7 : 5′-Trihydroxy-6 : 3′ : 4′-trimethoxyisoflavone.

See Irigenin.

4 : 6 : 3′-Trihydroxy-5 : 2 : 5′-trimethyl-2-hydroxymethyl-diphenyl Ether.

See Hyposalazinol.

4 : 4′ : 4″-Trihydroxytriphenylmethane.

See Leucaurine.

3 : 6 : 7-Trihydroxytropane.

See Teloidine.

2 : 3 : 6-Trihydroxyxanthone

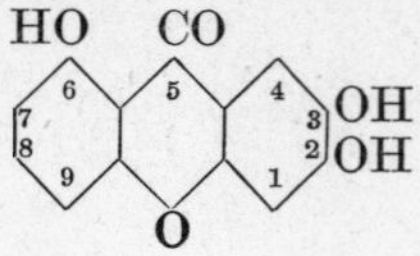

$C_{13}H_8O_5$ MW, 244

Pale yellow needles + $2H_2O$ from EtOH.Aq. M.p. 328–30° decomp. Sol. EtOH. Spar. sol. H_2O. Insol. Me_2CO, Py. Sol. alkalis with yellow col.

6-*Me ether*: $C_{14}H_{10}O_5$. MW, 258. Needles from EtOH. Decomp. at 249–51°. *Diacetyl*: needles from EtOH. M.p. 231–2° decomp.

2 : 3-*Di-Me ether*: $C_{15}H_{12}O_5$. MW, 272. Yellow needles from EtOH. M.p. 228–31° decomp. *Acetyl*: needles from EtOH. M.p. 224–5° decomp.

Tri-Me ether: $C_{16}H_{14}O_5$. MW, 286. Yellow needles from EtOH. M.p. 194–5°.

Triacetyl: yellow needles from EtOH. M.p. 226–7°.

Nierenstein, *Ber.*, 1913, **46**, 650.
Dean, Nierenstein, *J. Chem. Soc.*, 1920, 802.

2 : 4 : 7-Trihydroxyxanthone.
See Gentisein.

Tri-indole.
See under Indole.

Tri-iodoacetanilide.
See under Tri-iodoaniline.

Tri-iodoacetic Acid

$CI_3{\cdot}COOH$

$C_2HO_2I_3$ MW, 438

Yellow leaflets. M.p. 150° decomp. Warm AcOH ⟶ CO_2 + iodoform.

Angeli, *Ber.*, 1893, **26**, 596.

2 : 3 : 5-Tri-iodoaniline

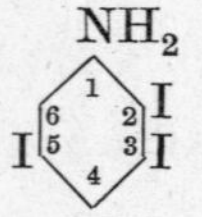

$C_6H_4NI_3$ MW, 471

Needles. M.p. 116°. Mod. sol. EtOH, AcOH, C_6H_6. Spar. sol. Et_2O, ligroin.

Acetyl: 2 : 3 : 5-tri-iodoacetanilide. Needles. M.p. 227°. Sublimes slowly above 200°. Spar. sol. usual solvents.

Brenans, *Bull. soc. chim.*, 1904, **31**, 131.

2 : 3 : 6-Tri-iodoaniline.
Needles from EtOH or EtOH–Et_2O. M.p. 116·8°.

Körner, Belasio, *Atti accad. Lincei*, 1908, **17**, I, 689.

2 : 4 : 5-Tri-iodoaniline.
Needles from EtOH–Et_2O. M.p. 117·8°.

Acetyl: 2 : 4 : 5-tri-iodoacetanilide. Needles. M.p. 241·5°. Spar. sol. EtOH, Et_2O.

See previous reference.

2 : 4 : 6-Tri-iodoaniline.
Needles from EtOH. M.p. 185·5° (184°). Sol. AcOH, CS_2. Mod. sol. hot EtOH.

Wheeler, Johns, *Am. Chem. J.*, 1910, **43**, 405.
Michael, Norton, *Ber.*, 1878, **11**, 111.
Jackson, Whitmore, *J. Am. Chem. Soc.*, 1915, **37**, 1528.

3 : 4 : 5-Tri-iodoaniline.
Needles from EtOH–Me_2CO. M.p. 174·5° decomp. Very sol. $CHCl_3$, Me_2CO, pet. ether. Sol. C_6H_6. Mod. sol. EtOH, Et_2O.

Kalb, Schweizer, Zellner, Berthold, *Ber.*, 1926, **59**, 1867.

Tri-iodoanisole.
See under Tri-iodophenol.

1 : 2 : 3-Tri-iodobenzene

$C_6H_3I_3$ MW, 456

Needles from EtOH, prisms from C_6H_6. M.p. 116°. Very sol. EtOH, Et_2O, $CHCl_3$.

Körner, Belasio, *Atti accad. Lincei*, 1908, **17**, I, 687.
See also Kalb, Schweizer, Zellner, Berthold, *Ber.*, 1926, **59**, 1862.

1 : 2 : 4-Tri-iodobenzene.
Needles from EtOH. M.p. 91·5° (77°). Sol. EtOH, $CHCl_3$.

Körner, Belasio, *Atti accad. Lincei*, 1908, **17**, I, 683.
Brenans, *Bull. soc. chim.*, 1914, **15**, 383.

1 : 3 : 5-Tri-iodobenzene.
Needles from AcOH. M.p. 184·2° (180°). Sol. boiling AcOH. Spar. sol. EtOH, Et_2O, $CHCl_3$, C_6H_6. Insol. H_2O. Volatile in steam.

Jackson, Behr, *Am. Chem. J.*, 1901, **26**, 58.
Körner, Contardi, *Atti accad. Lincei*, 1913, **22**, I, 832.

2 : 3 : 5-Tri-iodobenzoic Acid

$C_7H_3O_2I_3$ MW, 500

Prisms from EtOH. M.p. 224–6°. Sol. Et_2O, hot EtOH. Spar. sol. boiling C_6H_6. Insol. H_2O.

Wheeler, Johns, *Am. Chem. J.*, 1910, **43**, 407.

2 : 4 : 5-Tri-iodobenzoic Acid.

Needles from EtOH. M.p. 248°. Mod. sol. hot EtOH, Et_2O. Insol. hot H_2O, C_6H_6.

Wheeler, Johns, *Am. Chem. J.*, 1910, **44**, 451.

3 : 4 : 5-Tri-iodobenzoic Acid.

Prisms from EtOH. M.p. 288°. Sol. EtOH. Insol. H_2O.

Wheeler, Liddle, *Am. Chem. J.*, 1909, **42**, 458.

1 : 1 : 1-Tri-iodoethane (*Methyliodoform*)

$CH_3{\cdot}CI_3$

$C_2H_3I_3$ MW, 408

Yellow cryst. from EtOH. M.p. 95° decomp. Very sol. Et_2O, C_6H_6, CS_2. Spar. sol. EtOH, ligroin.

Boissieu, *Bull. soc. chim.*, 1888, **49**, 16.
Emschwiller, *Compt. rend.*, 1933, **196**, 1028.

Tri-iodomethane.

See Iodoform.

Tri-iodophenetole.

See under Tri-iodophenol.

2 : 3 : 5-Tri-iodophenol

$C_6H_3OI_3$ MW, 472

Prismatic needles from C_6H_6–ligroin. M.p. 114°. Sol. usual org. solvents.

Et ether : 2 : 3 : 5-tri-iodophenetole. $C_8H_7OI_3$. MW, 500. Needles. M.p. 121°.

Acetyl : needles. M.p. 123°. Sol. EtOH, AcOH.

Brenans, *Bull. soc. chim.*, 1904, **31**, 132; 1914, **15**, 383.

2 : 4 : 6-Tri-iodophenol.

Needles from EtOH.Aq. M.p. 158–9°. Sol. 50 parts 95% EtOH. Mod. sol. Et_2O, Me_2CO. Spar. volatile in steam. Warm conc. $HNO_3 \longrightarrow$ picric acid.

Me ether : 2 : 4 : 6-tri-iodoanisole. $C_7H_5OI_3$. MW, 486. Leaflets from C_6H_6, needles from Et_2O. M.p. 98–9°.

Et ether : 2 : 4 : 6-tri-iodophenetole. Prismatic needles from Et_2O. M.p. 83°.

Propyl ether : $C_9H_9OI_3$. MW, 514. Needles. M.p. 81°.

Allyl ether : $C_9H_7OI_3$. MW, 512. Needles from C_6H_6. M.p. 113–14°. Spar. sol. Et_2O.

Acetyl : needles or prisms from C_6H_6. M.p. 156°.

p-*Nitrobenzoyl* : m.p. 181°.

Brenans, *Bull. soc. chim.*, 1901, **25**, 630, 820.
Marsh, *J. Chem. Soc.*, 1927, 3164.
Brenans, Girod, *Compt. rend.*, 1928, **186**, 1851.

2 : 4 : 6-Tri-iodoresorcinol

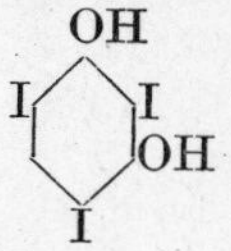

$C_6H_3O_2I_3$ MW, 488

Needles from CS_2. M.p. 145°. Sol. EtOH, Et_2O, CS_2. Spar. sol. hot H_2O.

Diacetyl : needles. M.p. 170°. Sol. EtOH, Et_2O.

Claassen, *Ber.*, 1878, **11**, 1442.
Michael, Norton, *Ber.*, 1876, **9**, 1752.

2 : 3 : 4-Tri-iodotoluene

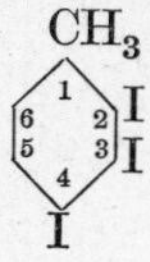

$C_7H_5I_3$ MW, 470

Light brown needles from EtOH. M.p. 92°. Sol. C_6H_6. Mod. sol. EtOH.

Wheeler, *Am. Chem. J.*, 1910, **44**, 506.

2 : 3 : 5-Tri-iodotoluene.

Orange plates from EtOH. M.p. 72–3°. Spar. volatile in steam.

See previous reference.

2 : 3 : 6-Tri-iodotoluene.

Needles from EtOH. M.p. 80·5°. Spar. sol. EtOH. Spar. volatile in steam.

Wheeler, *Am. Chem. J.*, 1910, **44**, 135.

2 : 4 : 5-Tri-iodotoluene.
Brownish needles from EtOH. M.p. 118–20°. Spar. volatile in steam.

Wheeler, *Am. Chem. J.*, 1910, **44**, 140, 500.
Cf. Neumann, *Ann.*, 1887, **241**, 56.

2 : 4 : 6-Tri-iodotoluene.
Needles from C_6H_6. M.p. 105°. Spar. sol. EtOH.

Wheeler, *Am. Chem. J.*, 1910, **44**, 501.
Cf. Neumann, *Ann.*, 1887, **241**, 56.

3 : 4 : 5-Tri-iodotoluene.
Needles from EtOH. M.p. 122–3°.

Wheeler, Liddle, *Am. Chem. J.*, 1909, **42**, 450.

Tri-isoamylamine

$[(CH_3)_2CH{\cdot}CH_2{\cdot}CH_2]_3N$

$C_{15}H_{33}N$ MW, 227

Liq. B.p. 237° (257°, 265–70°). D^{13} 0·7882, D_4^{20} 0·7859. Heat of comb. C_v 2452·1 Cal.

B,HCl : cryst. Sol. EtOH, Et_2O. Spar. sol. H_2O.

Isoamyliodide : tetra-isoamylammonium iodide. Prisms. M.p. 83°. D_4^{95} 1·0914. Spar. sol. H_2O.

Wallach, *Ann.*, 1905, **343**, 68.
Plimpton, *J. Chem. Soc.*, 1881, **39**, 332.
Hofmann, *Ann.*, 1851, **79**, 22.
Matter, D.R.P., 301,450, (*Chem. Zentr.*, 1918, I, 53).

Tri-isobutylamine

$[(CH_3)_2CH{\cdot}CH_2]_3N$

$C_{12}H_{27}N$ MW, 185

F.p. −24°. B.p. 184–6°. $D_4^{17\cdot3}$ 0·7711. $n_D^{17\cdot3}$ 1·42519. Non-misc. with H_2O. Heat of comb. C_v 1969 Cal.

Methochloroplatinate : m.p. 174°.
Ethochloroplatinate : m.p. 170°.
Propylchloroplatinate : m.p. 168°.
Butylchloroplatinate : m.p. 162°.

Ladenburg, *Ber.*, 1879, **12**, 949.
Malbot, *Ann. chim. phys.*, 1888, **13**, 493.

Tri-isobutyl phosphate.
See under Phosphoric Acid.

Tri-isobutyrin (*Glycerol tri-isobutyrate*)

$CH_2{\cdot}O{\cdot}CO{\cdot}CH(CH_3)_2$
$CH{\cdot}O{\cdot}CO{\cdot}CH(CH_3)_2$
$CH_2{\cdot}O{\cdot}CO{\cdot}CH(CH_3)_2$

$C_{15}H_{26}O_6$ MW, 302

Liq. B.p. 282–4°, 173–6°/24 mm.

Guth, *Zeitschrift für Biologie*, 1903, **44**, 97.

1 : 2 : 4-Tri-isopropylbenzene

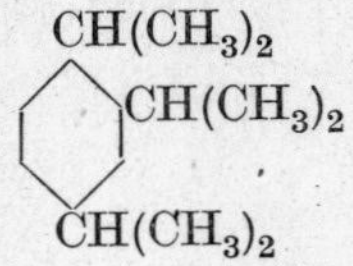

$C_{15}H_{24}$ MW, 204

Liq. B.p. 244°, 237°/736 mm., 113–14°/14 mm. D_{25}^{25} 0·8599. n_D^{25} 1·4896.

Slanina, Sowa, Nieuwland, *J. Am. Chem. Soc.*, 1935, **57**, 1549.
Kirrmann, Graves, *Bull. soc. chim.*, 1934, **1**, 1494.

Tri-isopropyl phosphate.
See under Phosphoric Acid.

Tri-isovalerin (*Isovalerin, glycerol tri-isovalerate*)

$CH_2{\cdot}O{\cdot}CO{\cdot}CH_2{\cdot}CH(CH_3)_2$
$CH{\cdot}O{\cdot}CO{\cdot}CH_2{\cdot}CH(CH_3)_2$
$CH_2{\cdot}O{\cdot}CO{\cdot}CH_2{\cdot}CH(CH_3)_2$

$C_{18}H_{32}O_6$ MW, 344

B.p. 330–5°/763 mm., 209·5–210·5°/27 mm. D^{20} 0·9984. n_D^{20} 1·43535.

Newman, Trikojus, Harker, *Chem. Abstracts*, 1926, **20**, 2658.

2 : 4 : 6 - Triketo - 1 : 1 - dimethylcyclohexane.
See Filicinic Acid.

2 : 4 : 6-Triketo-*n*-heptane.
See Diacetylacetone.

Triketohexane.
See Hexantrione.

Triketopentane.
See Pentantrione.

1 : 3 : 5-Triketopimelic Acid (*Acetonedioxalic acid, xanthochelidonic acid*)

$HOOC{\cdot}CO{\cdot}CH_2{\cdot}CO{\cdot}CH_2{\cdot}CO{\cdot}COOH$

$C_7H_6O_7$ MW, 202

Amorph. Very unstable. Sol. H_2O, EtOH. Less sol. Et_2O. On standing ⟶ chelidonic acid. Forms stable salts.

Mono K salt : cryst. ppt. Mod. sol. cold H_2O.

Di-Et ester : $C_{11}H_{14}O_7$. MW, 258. Exists in mono- and di-enol forms. (i) *Mono-enol form* : prisms from EtOH. M.p. 104°. Sol. 60 parts Et_2O. Mod. sol. hot EtOH, C_6H_6. Warm ⟶ dienol form. (ii) *Dienol form* : yellow cryst. powder. M.p. 98°. Sol. 40 parts Et_2O. In solution is partially converted into monoenol form.

Lerch, *Monatsh.*, 1884, **5**, 375.
Claisen, *Ber.*, 1891, **24**, 116; D.R.P., 57,648.
Willstätter, Pummerer, *Ber.*, 1904, **37**, 3734.

2 : 3 : 4-Triketotetrahydroquinoline.
See Quinisatin.

Trilaurin (*Glycerol trilaurate, laurin*)

$CH_2{\cdot}O{\cdot}CO{\cdot}[CH_2]_{10}{\cdot}CH_3$
$CH{\cdot}O{\cdot}CO{\cdot}[CH_2]_{10}{\cdot}CH_3$
$CH_2{\cdot}O{\cdot}CO{\cdot}[CH_2]_{10}{\cdot}CH_3$

$C_{39}H_{74}O_6$ MW, 638

Found in laurel leaves, mahuba seeds and in fats of many other seeds. Needles from EtOH. M.p. 49° (45·6°). D_4^{60} 0·8944. n_D^{60} 1·44039. Sol. Et_2O, $CHCl_3$, C_6H_6, pet. ether. Spar. sol. cold EtOH. Heat of comb. C_v 4707 Cal.

Bömer, Engel, *Chem. Abstracts*, 1929, **23**, 4676.
André, *Compt. rend.*, 1927, **184**, 227.
Averil, Roche, King, *J. Am. Chem. Soc.*, 1929, **51**, 870.

Trimellitic Acid (*Benzene* 1 : 2 : 4-*tricarboxylic Acid*)

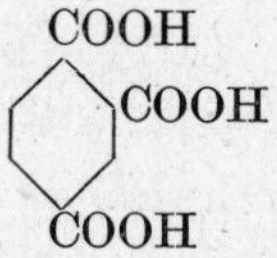

$C_9H_6O_6$ MW, 210

Cryst. from AcOH or EtOH.Aq. M.p. 238° (229–30°). Sol. EtOH. Spar. sol. Me_2CO. Insol. $CHCl_3$, CCl_4, C_6H_6, CS_2. Sol. 20 parts boiling AcOH. k (first) = $3{\cdot}2 \times 10^{-3}$ at 25°: (second) = $1{\cdot}1 \times 10^{-4}$ at 25°.

1-*Me ester*: $C_{10}H_8O_6$. MW, 224. Exists in two forms; m.p. 177°, and m.p. 203·5–205·5°. Sol. H_2O, Et_2O, MeOH, hot AcOH (part. decomp.). Spar. sol. $CHCl_3$, CCl_4, CS_2. Very spar. sol. C_6H_6, pet. ether. k (first) = $1{\cdot}8 \times 10^{-3}$ at 25°: (second) = $7{\cdot}8 \times 10^{-5}$ at 25°.

2-*Me ester*: powder. M.p. 208°. Sol. hot H_2O. Mod. sol. Et_2O. Insol. $CHCl_3$, CCl_4, CS_2. k (first) = $2{\cdot}6 \times 10^{-3}$ at 25°: (second) = $9{\cdot}9 \times 10^{-5}$ at 25°.

4-*Me ester*: leaflets from H_2O. M.p. 145–7°. Sol. Et_2O. Mod. sol. H_2O. Insol. pet. ether. k (first) = $2{\cdot}89 \times 10^{-3}$ at 25°: (second) = $1{\cdot}1 \times 10^{-5}$ at 25°.

1 : 2-*Di-Me ester*: $C_{11}H_{10}O_6$. MW, 238. Needles from CS_2, C_6H_6 or Et_2O–pet. ether. M.p. 115·5–117°, solidifies and then remelts at 121°. B.p. above 200°/12 mm. $k = 3{\cdot}4 \times 10^{-4}$ at 25°.

Tri-Me ester: $C_{12}H_{12}O_6$. MW, 252. Thick oil. F.p. — 13°. B.p. 194°/12 mm.

Tri-Et ester: $C_{15}H_{18}O_6$. MW, 294. B.p. 238°/28 mm.

1-*Amide*: $C_9H_7O_5N$. MW, 209. Yellowish cryst. from MeOH–C_6H_6. M.p. 185–6°. Sol. EtOH. Mod. sol. H_2O. Spar. sol. Et_2O, C_6H_6. k (first) = $4{\cdot}4 \times 10^{-4}$ at 25°.

2-*Amide*: cryst. from MeOH–C_6H_6. M.p. 199–200°. Sol. EtOH. Mod. sol. H_2O. Spar. sol. Et_2O, C_6H_6. k (first) = $7{\cdot}6 \times 10^{-4}$ at 25°.

4-*Amide*: cryst. from Et_2O–C_6H_6. M.p. 166°. Sol. H_2O, EtOH. Insol. $CHCl_3$, CCl_4, C_6H_6.

2-*Nitrile*: $C_9H_5O_4N$. MW, 191. Yellow amorph. mass. Sol. H_2O, EtOH, Et_2O.

Anhydride: anhydrotrimellitic acid. Needles. M.p. 162·5–163·5° (157°). B.p. 240–5°/14 mm. Sol. hot H_2O. *Me ester*: cryst. M.p. 94–9°.

Schultze, *Ann.*, 1908, **359**, 143.
Wegscheider, Perndanner, Auspitzer, *Monatsh.*, 1910, **31**, 1267.
Morgan, Coulson, *J. Chem. Soc.*, 1929, 2554.

Trimercaptobenzene.
See Trithiophloroglucinol.

Trimesic Acid (*Benzene*-1 : 3 : 5-*tricarboxylic acid*)

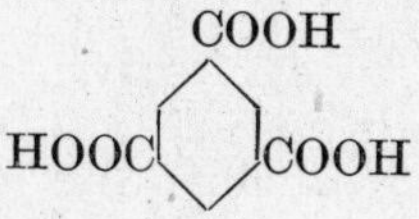

$C_9H_6O_6$ MW, 210

Needles or prisms from H_2O. M.p. about 380°. Very sol. EtOH. Sol. Et_2O. Sol. 40 parts H_2O at 23°. Heat of comb. C_v 768·5 Cal.

Mono-Me ester: $C_{10}H_8O_6$. MW, 224. Cryst. + H_2O from H_2O. M.p. anhyd. 205–8°. Sol. EtOH, Et_2O.

Tri-Me ester: $C_{12}H_{12}O_6$. MW, 252. Needles. M.p. 144°.

Tri-Et ester: $C_{15}H_{18}O_6$. MW, 294. Prisms or needles from EtOH. M.p. 133·5–134·5°. Very sol. Et_2O, MeOH, AcOEt, $CHCl_3$, CS_2. Sol. hot EtOH, AcOH, C_6H_6. Insol. H_2O.

Tri-isoamyl ester: $C_{24}H_{36}O_6$. MW, 420. Cryst. M.p. 28–9°. B.p. 278–80°/15 mm.

Trihydrazide: micro-plates from H_2O. Decomp. above 300°. Spar. sol. EtOH.

Wolff, Heip, *Ann.*, 1899, **305**, 153.
Wislicenus, v. Wrangell, *Ann.*, 1911, **381**, 372.
Ullmann, Uzbachian, *Ber.*, 1903, **36**, 1799.
v. Schaak, U.S.P., 1,706,639, (*Chem. Abstracts*, 1929, 23, 2187).

3 : 4 : 5-Trimethoxy-1-allylbenzene.
See Elemicin.

3 : 4 : 5-Trimethoxycinnamic Acid.
See under Sinapic Acid.

6 : 7 : 8-Trimethoxycoumarin.
See under Fraxetin.

7 : 3′ : 5′-Trimethoxydelphinidin chloride.
See Hirsutidin chloride.

3 : 4 : 5-Trimethoxyphenylacetic Acid.
See under Iridic Acid.

3 : 4 : 5-Trimethoxyphenyl-ethylamine.
See Mescaline.

2 : 4 : 5-Trimethoxy-1-propenylbenzene.
See Asarone.

3 : 4 : 5-Trimethoxy-1-propenylbenzene.
See under Elemicin.

Trimethylacetaldehyde.
See Pivalic Aldehyde.

Trimethylacetic Acid.
See Pivalic Acid.

1 : 1 : 1-Trimethylacetone.
See Pinacolin.

2 : 4 : 5-Trimethylacetophenone (*5-Aceto-ψ-cumene*)

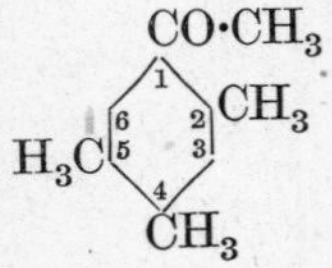

$C_{11}H_{14}O$ MW, 162

F.p. 11°. B.p. 246–7°, 137–8°/20 mm. $D_4^{14\cdot7}$ 1·0039. $n_D^{14\cdot9}$ 1·541. Sol. EtOH, Et_2O, CS_2, AcOH, C_6H_6.

Oxime: cryst. from ligroin. M.p. 85–6°.

Semicarbazone: plates from EtOH. M.p. 204°.

Auwers, Köckritz, *Ann.*, 1907, **352**, 313.
Klages, Allendorff, *Ber.*, 1898, **31**, 1005.

2 : 4 : 6-Trimethylacetophenone (*Acetomesitylene*).

B.p. 240·5°/735 mm., 90°/3 mm. D^{20} 0·9754. n_D^{20} 1·5175.

Noller, Adams, *J. Am. Chem. Soc.*, 1924, **46**, 1893.
Meyer, Molz, *Ber.*, 1897, **30**, 1271.

ω-Trimethylacetophenone.
See tert.-Butyl phenyl Ketone.

Trimethylacrylic Acid (*3-Methyl-2-butylene-2-carboxylic acid*, *1-isopropylidene-propionic acid*)

$$(CH_3)_2C{:}\overset{\overset{\displaystyle CH_3}{|}}{C}{\cdot}COOH$$

$C_6H_{10}O_2$ MW, 114

Long needles from H_2O. M.p. 70–1°. Sol. 20 parts H_2O at 19°. Sol. hot EtOH, Et_2O, $CHCl_3$, C_6H_6, ligroin. Spar. sol. hot H_2O. $k = 3{\cdot}9 \times 10^{-5}$ at 25°.

Et ester: $C_8H_{14}O_2$. MW, 142. B.p. 154–6° (153–7°/750 mm.). $D_4^{19\cdot3}$ 0·9072. $n_D^{19\cdot3}$ 1·430.

Nitrile: C_6H_9N. MW, 95. B.p. 155–7°. D^{18} 0·8447. Insol. H_2O.

Perkin, *J. Chem. Soc.*, 1896, **69**, 1479.
Henry, *Chem. Zentr.*, 1899, I, 195.
Merling, Welde, *Ann.*, 1909, **366**, 140.

1 : 1 : 4-Trimethyladipic Acid (*2-Methylhexane-2 : 5-dicarboxylic acid*)

$$\begin{array}{l}(CH_3)_2C{\cdot}COOH\\ \qquad\quad |\\ \qquad\ \ CH_2\\ \qquad\quad |\\ \qquad\ \ CH_2\\ \qquad\quad |\\ CH_3{\cdot}CH{\cdot}COOH\end{array}$$

$C_9H_{16}O_4$ MW, 188

Prisms from H_2O or dil. formic acid. M.p. 117° (114–15°). Mod. sol. dil. formic acid. Spar. sol. H_2O.

Auwers, Hessenland, *Ber.*, 1908, **41**, 1815.
Wallach, Kempe, *Ann.*, 1903, **329**, 91.

1 : 3 : 3-Trimethylallyl Alcohol (*1 : 3-Dimethylcrotonyl alcohol*, *1 : 3-dimethyl-2-butenol-1*)

$$(CH_3)_2C{:}CH{\cdot}\overset{\overset{\displaystyle CH_3}{|}}{CH}{\cdot}OH$$

$C_6H_{12}O$ MW, 100

d-.

B.p. 129°/760 mm., 43°/17 mm. D_4^{20} 0·8436. n_D^{17} 1·4297. $[\alpha]_{5461}^{22} + 11{\cdot}04°$.

Acid phthalate: needles from pet. ether. M.p. 44°. $[\alpha]_{5461} + 16{\cdot}7°$ in $CHCl_3$, $+ 22{\cdot}2°$ in C_6H_6. *Brucine salt*: needles from Me_2CO. M.p. 144°. $[\alpha]_{5461} - 23{\cdot}0°$ in $CHCl_3$.

Aceytl: b.p. 51°/15 mm. n_D^{20} 1·4202. $[\alpha]_{5461}^{22} - 4{\cdot}72°$.

Benzoyl: b.p. 139°/17 mm. n_D^{20} 1·5047. $[\alpha]_{5461}^{20} + 35{\cdot}71°$.

l-.

B.p. 129°/760 mm., 43°/18 mm. n_D^{17} 1·4298. $[\alpha]_{5461}^{20} - 2{\cdot}60°$.

Acid phthalate: needles from pet. ether. M.p. 44°. $[\alpha]_{5461} - 14{\cdot}2°$ in CS_2. *Strychnine salt*: needles from $CHCl_3$ + 4 vols. Me_2CO. $[\alpha]_{5461}$ − 24·89°.

dl-.

B.p. 131–3° (125–35°).

Acid phthalate: prisms from Et_2O–pet. ether. M.p. 81·5°.

Acetyl: b.p. 50°/15 mm. n_D^{20} 1·4201.

Benzoyl: b.p. 138°/19 mm. n_D^{20} 1·5045.

Duveen, Kenyon, *J. Chem. Soc.*, 1936, 1451.

Trimethylamine

$(CH_3)_3N$

C_3H_9N MW, 59

Liq. with fishy odour. M.p. − 117·2°. B.p. 3·2–3·8°/746·6 mm. D_4^0 0·6709, D_4^{-79} 0·7537. Heat of comb. C_v 592·1 Cal. $k = 7·4 \times 10^{-5}$ at 25°. Crit. temp. 160·5°. Crit. press. 41 atm. Misc. with H_2O, EtOH. Heat with ethylene chlorohydrin ⟶ choline chloride.

B,11H₂O: m.p. 5·34°.

B,HCl: needles from EtOH. M.p. 277–8° decomp. Sublimes at 200°. Sol. EtOH. Mod. sol. $CHCl_3$. Insol. Et_2O.

B,HBr: prisms from EtOH. M.p. 243–5°.

B,HI: prisms from 95% EtOH. M.p. 263°. Sol. H_2O. Spar. sol. EtOH. Insol. Et_2O, $CHCl_3$.

B,HAuCl₄: yellow prisms from EtOH. M.p. 287° (237°).

Picrate: pale yellow prisms. M.p. 216°.

Oxide: *see* Trimethylamine oxide.

Adams, Brown, *Organic Syntheses*, Collective Vol. I, 514.
Schmitz, D.R.P., 270,260, (*Chem. Zentr.*, 1914, I, 830).
Koeppen, *Ber.*, 1905, **38**, 883.
Schmidt, *Ann.*, 1892, **267**, 267.
Dreyfus, E.P., 398,502, (*Chem. Abstracts*, 1934, **28**, 1357).

Trimethylamine oxide (*Trimethyloxamine*)

$(CH_3)_3NO$

C_3H_9ON MW, 75

Widely distributed in fish and animal tissues. Needles + $2H_2O$ from H_2O. M.p. 255–7° (208°), anhyd. 96°. Sol. H_2O, MeOH. Less sol. EtOH. Heat at 180° ⟶ formaldehyde + trimethylamine. Reacts strongly alkaline. Does not reduce Fehling's.

B,HCl: needles from EtOH. M.p. 218°. Sol. H_2O, hot MeOH.

B,HI: prisms from EtOH. M.p. 130° decomp. Sol. H_2O, EtOH. Insol. Et_2O.

B,HAuCl₄: yellow cryst. M.p. 200°.

B₂,H₂PtCl₆: m.p. 228–9° decomp.

Picrate: yellow needles. M.p. 196–8°.

Hoppe-Seyler, Schmidt, *Zeitschrift für Biologie*, 1928, **87**, 59.
Meisenheimer, *Ann.*, 1913, **397**, 287.
Dunstan, Goulding, *J. Chem. Soc.*, 1899, **75**, 792, 1005.

Trimethylamine-tricarboxylic Acid.
See Triglycolamidic Acid.

Trimethyl-ω-aminoethylcyclopentene.
See Camphylamine.

2 : 4 : 6-Trimethylanisole.
See under Mesitol.

1 : 2 : 4-Trimethylanthracene

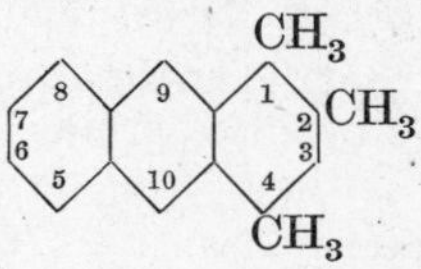

$C_{17}H_{16}$ MW, 220

Cryst. M.p. 243°.

Gresly, *Ann.*, 1886, **234**, 239.
Wende, *Ber.*, 1887, **20**, 868.
I.G., E.P., 253,911, (*Chem. Abstracts*, 1927, **21**, 2478).

1 : 3 : 6-Trimethylanthracene.

Cryst. M.p. 222°. Sol. Me_2CO, CS_2, C_6H_6. Mod. sol. Et_2O, AcOH. Spar. sol. EtOH, ligroin.

Elbs, *J. prakt. Chem.*, 1890, **41**, 142.

1 : 3 : 10-Trimethylanthracene.

Yellow cryst. from pet. ether. M.p. 100°.

Barnett, Hewett, *Ber.*, 1931, **64**, 1577.

1 : 4 : 9-Trimethylanthracene.

Pale yellow cryst. from MeOH. M.p. 81°. Sols. show strong fluor.

Barnett, Low, *Ber.*, 1931, **64**, 53.

2 : 3 : 6-Trimethylanthracene.

Found in low-temperature coal tar. Pale yellow flakes with bluish fluor. from boiling AcOH. M.p. 255°.

Morgan, Coulson, *J. Chem. Soc.*, 1929, 2555; *J. Soc. Chem. Ind.*, 1934, **53**, 71T.

2 : 3 : 9-Trimethylanthracene.

Pale yellow cryst. from AcOEt. M.p. 125°. Sols. show strong fluor.

Barnett, Morrison, *Ber.*, 1931, **64**, 538.

1 : 2 : 4-Trimethylanthraquinone

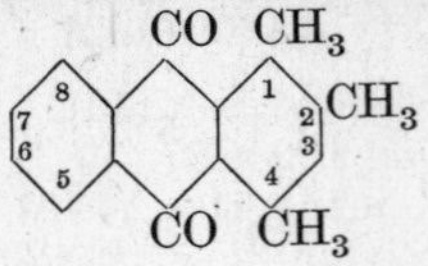

$C_{17}H_{14}O_2$ MW, 250

Yellow needles from xylene–EtOH. M.p. 162–3°. Sol. Et_2O, C_6H_6. Spar. sol. EtOH.

Gresly, *Ann.*, 1886, **234**, 241.
Elbs, *J. prakt. Chem.*, 1890, **41**, 123.

1 : 3 : 6-Trimethylanthraquinone. Pale yellow needles from AcOH. M.p. 192°.

Mayer, Stark, *Ber.*, 1931, **64**, 2010.
Elbs, *J. prakt. Chem.*, 1890, **41**, 143.

1 : 3 : 7-Trimethylanthraquinone. Pale yellow needles from AcOH. M.p. 128–9°.

Mayer, Stark, *Ber.*, 1931, **64**, 2010.

1 : 4 : 5-Trimethylanthraquinone. Yellow needles from AcOH. M.p. 146–7°.

See previous reference.

1 : 4 : 6-Trimethylanthraquinone. Yellow needles from AcOH. M.p. 143°.

See previous reference.
Cf. Elbs, *J. prakt. Chem.*, 1890, **41**, 142.

2 : 3 : 6-Trimethylanthraquinone. Very pale yellow needles from boiling AcOH. M.p. 240°.

Morgan, Coulson, *J. Chem. Soc.*, 1929, 2555.
Fieser, Seligman, *J. Am. Chem. Soc.*, 1934, **56**, 2695.

Trimethylarsine (*Arsenic trimethyl*)

$As(CH_3)_3$

C_3H_9As MW, 120

Colourless liq. B.p. about 70°, (48–51°). Absorbs O from the air to give the oxide. Combines direct with S and halogens. Very poisonous.

B,HgCl₂: needles from hot H_2O. M.p. 224–6°.

B,2HgCl₂: plates from hot aq. $HgCl_2$. M.p. 264–5° decomp.

Hibbert, *Ber.*, 1906, **39**, 161.
Gryszkiewicz-Trochimowski, Zambrzycki, *Chem. Abstracts*, 1927, **21**, 3612.
Challenger, Higginbottom, Ellis, *J. Chem. Soc.*, 1933, 95.
Challenger, Higginbottom, *Biochem. J.*, 1935, **29**, 1757.

2 : 4 : 5-Trimethylbenzaldehyde (*5-Aldehydo-ψ-cumene*)

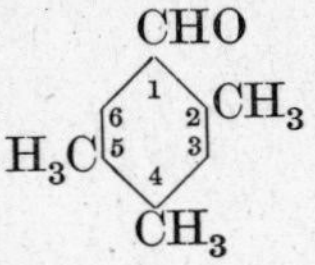

$C_{10}H_{12}O$ MW, 148

Plates from EtOH. M.p. 43·5° (42°). B.p. 243°, 121°/10 mm. Turns yellow in air.

Oxime: needles from ligroin. M.p. 102°.

Semicarbazone: prisms from EtOH. M.p. 243–4°.

Hydrazone: cryst. M.p. 70°. B.p. 165–6°.

Picrate: yellow cryst. powder. M.p. 170–1°.

Phenylhydrazone: leaflets from AcOH. M.p. 127°.

Gattermann, *Ann.*, 1906, **347**, 375.
Auwers, Köckritz, *Ann.*, 1907, **352**, 310.

2 : 4 : 6-Trimethylbenzaldehyde (*β-Isoduryl aldehyde, mesityl aldehyde, aldehydomesitylene*).

B.p. 237–40°, 192°/50 mm. Fuming HNO_3 + AcOH ⟶ 3-nitro-deriv., m.p. 61°.

Di-Me acetal: b.p. 242–3°/741 mm.

Oxime: *syn*-, needles. M.p. 180–1°. Less sol. than *anti*-form in ord. org. solvents. *Anti*-. Prisms from Et_2O. M.p. 124°. Heat with dil. HCl ⟶ *syn*.-form ⟶ 2 : 4 : 6-trimethylbenzonitrile. *Acetate*: m.p. 68°.

Phenylhydrazone: cryst. from EtOH.Aq. Decomp. in air.

Hinkel, Ayling, Morgan, *J. Chem. Soc.*, 1932, 2797; 1931, 1170.
Wenzel, *Monatsh.*, 1914, **35**, 968.
Fischer, Giebe, *Ber.*, 1898, **31**, 548.
Hantzsch, Lucas, *Ber.*, 1895, **28**, 747.

3 : 4 : 5-Trimethylbenzaldehyde (*5-Aldehydohemimellitene*).

Needles from dil. EtOH. M.p. 52°.

Krömer, *Ber.*, 1891, **24**, 2413.

1 : 2 : 3-Trimethylbenzene. *See* Hemimellitene.

1 : 2 : 4-Trimethylbenzene. *See* ψ-Cumene.

1 : 3 : 5-Trimethylbenzene. *See* Mesitylene.

2 : 3 : 4-Trimethylbenzoic Acid. *See* Prehnitylic Acid.

2 : 3 : 5-Trimethylbenzoic Acid. *See* γ-Isodurylic Acid.

2 : 3 : 6-Trimethylbenzoic Acid

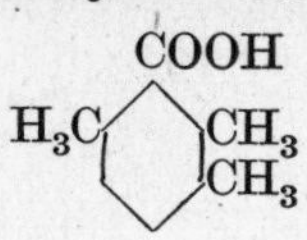

$C_{10}H_{12}O_2$ MW, 164

Needles from H_2O or pet. ether. M.p. 84° (rapid heat.), 105–6° (after solidification).

Lapworth, Wechsler, *J. Chem. Soc.*, 1907, **91**, 994.

2 : 4 : 5-Trimethylbenzoic Acid.
See Durylic Acid.

2 : 4 : 6-Trimethylbenzoic Acid.
See β-Isodurylic Acid.

3 : 4 : 5-Trimethylbenzoic Acid.
See α-Isodurylic Acid.

2 : 4 : 5 - Trimethylbenzophenone (5-*Benzoyl-ψ-cumene*)

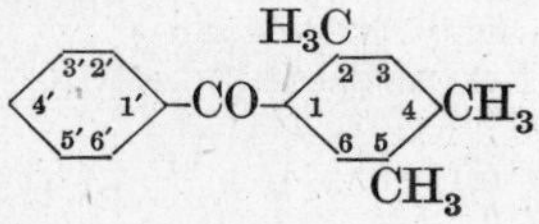

$C_{16}H_{16}O$ MW, 224

B.p. 328°/760 mm., 211°/23 mm. D_4^{18} 1·0332.

Klages, Allendorff, *Ber.*, 1898, **31**, 1001.
Elbs, *J. prakt. Chem.*, 1887, **35**, 491.

2 : 4 : 6-Trimethylbenzophenone (*Benzoylmesitylene*).

Prisms from EtOH–Et_2O. M.p. 35·5°. B.p. 318–20° (326·5–327°/777 mm.), 189°/17 mm. Sol. Me_2CO, $CHCl_3$, AcOH, pet. ether.

Louise, *Ann. chim. phys.*, 1885, **6**, 202.
Elbs, *J. prakt. Chem.*, 1887, **35**, 486.

2 : 4 : 4′-Trimethylbenzophenone (4-p-*Toluyl*-m-*xylene*).

Pale yellow viscous oil. B.p. 340°, 169°/4 mm. Does not react with phenylhydrazine or semicarbazide. Reacts only very slowly with hydroxylamine. Hot conc. $H_2SO_4 \longrightarrow$ *p*-toluic acid + *m*-xylene.

Oxime : cryst. from EtOH. M.p. 132°.

Morgan, Coulson, *J. Chem. Soc.*, 1929, 2209.

2 : 5 : 4′-Trimethylbenzophenone (2-p-*Toluyl*-p-*xylene*).

Rhombic plates from EtOH. M.p. 54°. B.p. 337°/760 mm., 202°/23 mm. Unreactive towards usual ketonic reagents.

See previous reference.

2:3:5-Trimethyl-*p*-benzoquinone (2:3:5-*Trimethylquinone, ψ-cumoquinone*)

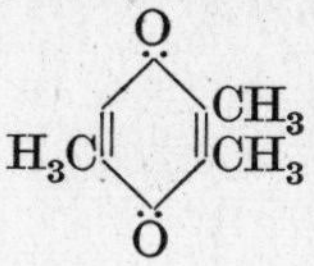

$C_9H_{10}O_2$ MW, 150

Yellow needles from Et_2O. M.p. 32° (11°). Volatile in steam.

1-*Oxime* : golden-yellow needles from EtOH. M.p. 184°. Possesses strong quinone odour.

4-*Oxime* : yellow needles. M.p. 134°. Odourless.

Noelting, Baumann, *Ber.*, 1885, **18**, 1152.
Nietzki, Schneider, *Ber.*, 1894, **27**, 1430.

2 : 4 : 5-Trimethylbenzoylformic Acid (2 : 4 : 5-*Trimethylphenylglyoxylic acid*)

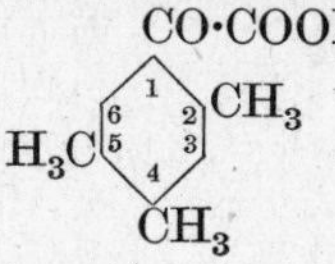

$C_{11}H_{12}O_3$ MW, 192

Needles. M.p. 76° (61–2°). Sol. EtOH, Et_2O, $CHCl_3$, hot H_2O.

Et ester : $C_{13}H_{16}O_3$. MW, 220. B.p. 175–6°/10 mm.

Claus, *J. prakt. Chem.*, 1890, **41**, 509.
Bouveault, *Bull. soc. chim.*, 1897, **17**, 363, 369.

2 : 4 : 6-Trimethylbenzoylformic Acid (2 : 4 : 6-*Trimethylphenylglyoxylic acid*).

Pale yellow cryst. from CS_2. M.p. 117–18° (114–17°). Sol. EtOH, Et_2O, $CHCl_3$, C_6H_6. Spar. sol. CS_2, ligroin. $k = 5{\cdot}27 \times 10^{-2}$ at 25°. Decomp. on dist.

Me ester : $C_{12}H_{14}O_3$. MW, 206. B.p. 253–5° (273–5°), 170°/100 mm.

Et ester : b.p. 265–7°, 164–5°/10 mm. Turns brown on standing.

Hydrazone : needles + H_2O. M.p. 200° decomp. Sol. EtOH. Mod. sol. boiling H_2O. Insol. Et_2O, $CHCl_3$, C_6H_6.

Bouveault, *Bull. soc. chim.*, 1897, **17**, 371.
Claus, *J. prakt. Chem.*, 1890, **41**, 504.
Wenzel, *Monatsh.*, 1914, **35**, 948.

2 : 3 : 4-Trimethylbenzyl Alcohol

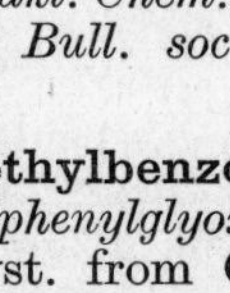

$C_{10}H_{14}O$ MW, 150

Needles from pentane. M.p. 49–50°. B.p. 110–30°/0·5 mm. Sol. usual org. solvents.

Reichstein, Cohen, Ruth, Meldahl, *Helv. Chim. Acta*, 1936, **19**, 416.

2 : 4 : 5-Trimethylbenzyl Alcohol.
Needles from EtOH. M.p. 168°.

Krömer, *Ber.*, 1891, **24**, 2411.

2 : 4 : 6-Trimethylbenzyl Alcohol (*Mesitylcarbinol*).
Needles. M.p. 88–9°. B.p. 140–1°/15 mm. Sol. usual org. solvents.

Carré, *Bull. soc. chim.*, 1910, **7**, 842.

2 : 4 : 5-Trimethylbenzylamine (*ω-Amino-1 : 2 : 4 : 5-tetramethylbenzene*)

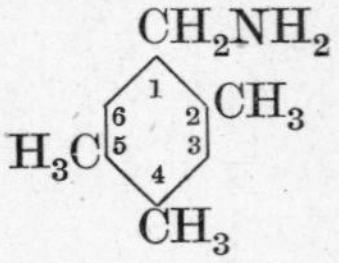

$C_{10}H_{15}N$ MW, 149

Two compounds of this structure have been described in the literature.
(i) Needles from EtOH.Aq. M.p. 64·5°. Sol. EtOH, $CHCl_3$. Insol. cold H_2O.
B,HCl : prisms or needles. M.p. 240–2° decomp.

Krömer, *Ber.*, 1891, **24**, 2409.

(ii) Leaflets from MeOH.Aq. M.p. 52°. Sol. usual solvents. Spar. sol. cold H_2O.
B,HCl : plates. M.p. 275–6°. Sol. hot H_2O.
Acetyl : needles. M.p. 143·5°. Mod. sol. EtOH, C_6H_6. Spar. sol. H_2O.

Willstätter, Kubli, *Ber.*, 1909, **42**, 4156.

3 : 4 : 5-Trimethylbenzylamine (*ω-Amino-1 : 2 : 3 : 5-tetramethylbenzene*).
Leaflets from boiling H_2O. M.p. 123°.
B,HCl : needles from EtOH. M.p. 270°.
$B,HAuCl_4$: red prisms. M.p. 162–5° decomp.
B_2,H_2PtCl_6 : rhombohedra. M.p. 219–20° decomp.
Picrate : yellow needles from EtOH.Aq. M.p. 239–40° decomp.

Krömer, *Ber.*, 1891, **24**, 2411.

1 : 8 : 8-Trimethylbicyclo-[1, 2, 3]-octanone-2.
See Homocamphor.
1 : 8 : 8-Trimethylbicyclo-[1, 2, 3]-octanone-3.
See Homoepicamphor.

Trimethyl borate (*Methyl borate*)

$B(OCH_3)_3$

$C_3H_9O_3B$ MW, 104

B.p. 55–6° (65°). D^0 0·940, D^{20} 0·915. Burns with green flame. Hyd. by H_2O.

Schiff, *Ann.*, *Suppl.*, 1867, **5**, 183.
Gasselin, *Ann. chim. phys.*, 1894, **3**, 22.
Cohn, *Pharmazeutische Zentralhalle*, 1911, **52**, 480.

1 : 1 : 4-Trimethylbutadiene-1 : 3.
See 2-Methyl-2 : 4-hexadiene.
1 : 2 : 4-Trimethylbutadiene-1 : 3.
See 3-Methyl-2 : 4-hexadiene.
1 : 5 : 5 - Trimethyl - 6 - α - butenylcyclohexene.
See Ionane.
Trimethyl-*n*-butylmethane.
See 2 : 2-Dimethyl-*n*-hexane.
1 : 3 : 6-Trimethylcarbazole

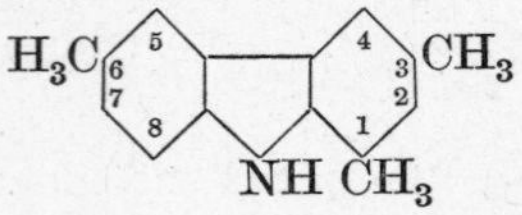

$C_{15}H_{15}N$ MW, 209

Cryst. from pet. ether. M.p. 126°. Sol. EtOH, AcOH, C_6H_6.
N-*Nitroso* : yellow needles from pet. ether. M.p. 139°.

Fries, Böker, Wallbaum, *Ann.*, 1934, **509**, 94.

1 : 3 : 7-Trimethylcarbazole.
Leaflets from EtOH. M.p. 119°.
Picrate : deep red cryst. M.p. 177°.

Borsche, *Ann.*, 1908, **359**, 77.

2 : 4 : 6-Trimethylcarbazole.
Prisms from pet. ether. M.p. 198°.

Fries, Böker, Wallbaum, *Ann.*, 1934, **509**, 98.

Trimethylcarbinol.
See tert.-Butyl Alcohol.
1 : 2 : 2 - Trimethyl - 3 - carboxycyclopentylacetic Acid.
See Homoepicamphoric Acid.
1 : 2 : 2 - Trimethyl - 3 - carboxymethyl - cyclopentane-1-carboxylic Acid.
See Homocamphoric Acid.

2 : 4 : 5-Trimethylcinnamic Acid

$$CH{:}CH{\cdot}COOH$$

H_3C ... CH_3 (ring, positions 1 2 3 4 5 6)

CH_3

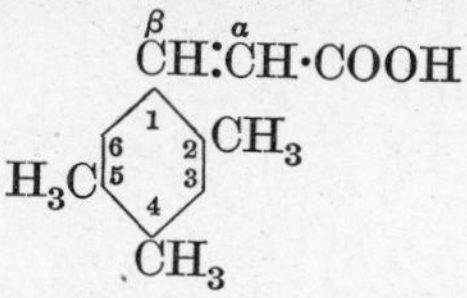

$C_{12}H_{14}O_2$ MW, 190

Plates from EtOH.Aq. M.p. 154–5°.

> Smith, Tawney, *J. Am. Chem. Soc.*, 1934, **56**, 2169.
> Smith, Denyes, *J. Am. Chem. Soc.*, 1936, **58**, 306.

2 : 4 : 6-Trimethylcinnamic Acid.

Needles from EtOH.Aq. or AcOH.Aq. M.p. 176°. Sol. EtOH, Et_2O, AcOH, C_6H_6, toluene. Spar. sol. $CHCl_3$, CCl_4, CS_2.

Et ester : $C_{14}H_{18}O_2$. MW, 218. Cryst. from EtOH.Aq. or pet. ether. M.p. 40°. B.p. 170°/16 mm. Very sol. EtOH, Et_2O, AcOH, AcOEt, $CHCl_3$, C_6H_6, ligroin, pet. ether.

> Böck, Lock, Schmidt, *Monatsh.*, 1934, **64**, 413.

2 : 4 : β-Trimethylcinnamic Acid.

Et ester : $C_{14}H_{18}O_2$. MW, 218. B.p. 160–70°/20 mm.

> Heilbron, Wilkinson, *J. Chem. Soc.*, 1930, 2540.
> Mazurewitsch, *Chem. Zentr.*, 1914, I, 1999.

2 : 5 : β-Trimethylcinnamic Acid.

Cis :
Oil.

Et ester : b.p. 150–4°/20 mm., 148–50°/12 mm.

Trans :
Needles from pet. ether. M.p. 68°. Sol. most solvents.

> Auwers, Risse, *Ann.*, 1933, **502**, 294.
> Ruzicka, Ehmann, Hefti, Altana, *Helv. Chim. Acta*, 1932, **15**, 157.

2 : α : β-Trimethylcinnamic Acid.

Et ester : pale yellow oil. B.p. 128–32°/11 mm.

> Ruzicka, Ehmann, Hartnagel, Hausschild, *Helv. Chim. Acta*, 1932, **15**, 150.

4 : α : β-Trimethylcinnamic Acid.

Leaflets from EtOH.Aq. M.p. 163°.
Et ester : b.p. 149–149·5°/10 mm. (141–141·5°/11 mm.). $D_4^{18·7}$ 1·0024. $n_D^{18·4}$ 1·519.

> Auwers, *Ann.*, 1917, **413**, 278.
> Rupe, Steiger, Fiedler, *Ber.*, 1914, **47**, 73.

Trimethyl citrate

$$CH_2{\cdot}CO{\cdot}OCH_3$$
$$C(OH){\cdot}CO{\cdot}OCH_3$$
$$CH_2{\cdot}CO{\cdot}OCH_3$$

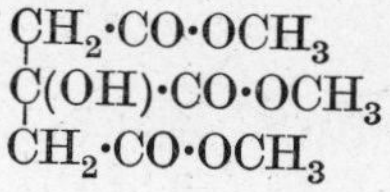

$C_9H_{14}O_7$ MW, 234

M.p. 78–9°. B.p. 283–7° decomp. ⟶ aconitic acid trimethyl ester.

2-Acetyl : 2-acetoxytricarballylic trimethyl ester. B.p. 280–2° decomp., 171°/15 mm.

Me ether : $C_{10}H_{16}O_7$. MW, 248. B.p. 159–60°/12 mm. Sol. EtOH, Et_2O.

> Hunäus, *Ber.*, 1876, **9**, 1750.
> Anschütz, *Ann.*, 1903, **327**, 229.
> Saint-Evre, *Ann.*, 1847, **60**, 325.

Trimethylcycloheptadienone.

See Eucarvone.

1 : 1 : 2-Trimethylcycloheptane

$$H_3C{\diagdown}C{\diagup}CH_3$$

H_2C^7 ... $^2CH{\cdot}CH_3$
H_2C^6 ... $^3CH_2$
H_2C^5 —— $^4CH_2$

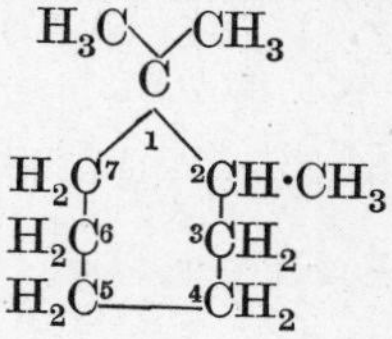

$C_{10}H_{20}$ MW, 140

Liq. B.p. 104–5°/100 mm. D_4^{20} 0·8243. n_D^2 1·4527.

> Ruzicka, Seidel, *Helv. Chim. Acta*, 1936, **19**, 430.

1 : 1 : 4-Trimethylcycloheptane (*Eucarvane*).

Liq. B.p. 162–3°/720 mm. D_4^{20} 0·8011. n_D^{20} 1·4420.

> See previous reference.

2 : 6 : 6-Trimethylcycloheptanol

$$CH{\cdot}OH$$

H_2C ... $CH{\cdot}CH_3$
$(CH_3)_2C$ ... CH_2
H_2C —— CH_2

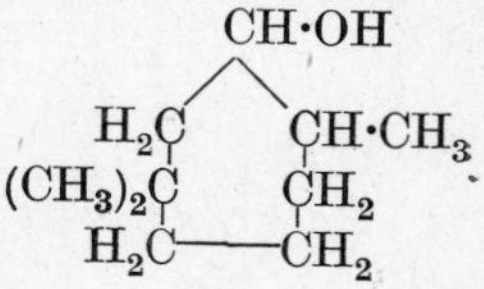

$C_{10}H_{20}O$ MW, 156

Liq. B.p. 216°. D^{24} 0·9096. n_D 1·4639.
Phenylurethane : m.p. 76°.

> Wallach, *Ann.*, 1914, **403**, 90.
> Wallach, Köhler, *Ann.*, 1905, **339**, 96, 106.

2 : 2 : 3-Trimethylcycloheptanone

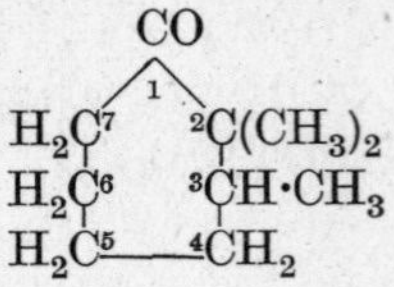

$C_{10}H_{18}O$ MW, 154

B.p. 80–3°/12 mm.
Semicarbazone : m.p. 169–70°.

Naef, D.R.P., 580,713, (*Chem. Abstracts*, 1934, **28**, 1716).
Ruzicka, Seidel, *Helv. Chim. Acta*, 1936, **19**, 430.

2 : 6 : 6-Trimethylcycloheptanone (*Tetrahydroeucarvone*).

Liq. with peppermint odour. B.p. 208–9°, 85·5°/12 mm. D^{18} 0·9095. n_D^{18} 1·4568.
Semicarbazone : exists in two forms. (i) Cryst. M.p. 191–2°. Spar. sol. AcOEt. (ii) Needles. M.p. 161–3°. Sol. AcOEt.

Wallach, *Ann.*, 1911, **381**, 67 ; 1914, **403**, 89.
Wallach, Köhler, *Ann.*, 1905, **339**, 107.

1 : 4 : 4-Trimethylcycloheptene (*Eucarvene*)

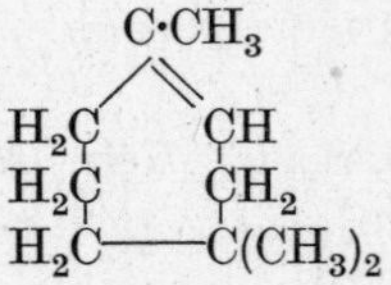

$C_{10}H_{18}$ MW, 138

Liq. B.p. 161–5°/720 mm. D_4^{20} 0·8185. n_D^{20} 1·4561.

Ruzicka, Seidel, *Helv. Chim. Acta*, 1936, **19**, 431.

1 : 1 : 3-Trimethylcyclohexane

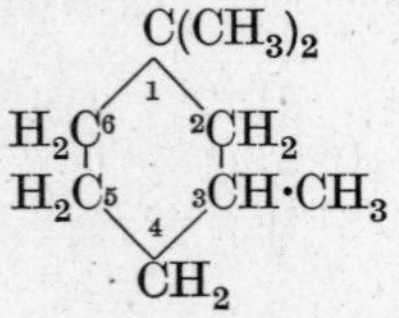

C_9H_{18} MW, 126

B.p. 137–8°. D_4^{25} 0·7868. n_D^{20} 1·4362. Heat of comb. C_v 1406 Cal.

Auwers, *Ann.*, 1920, **420**, 109.
Knoevenagel, *Ann.*, 1897, **297**, 202.

1 : 2 : 3-Trimethylcyclohexane (*Hexahydrohemimellitene*).

Cis :
B.p. 144–6°/755 mm. D_4^{20} 0·7930. n_{He}^{20} 1·43682.
Trans :
B.p. 142–143·5°/762 mm. D_4^{20} 0·7914. n_{He}^{20} 1·43582.

Eisenlohr, *Fortschritte der Chemie, Physik, und Physikalischen Chemie*, 1925, **18**, 552.

1 : 2 : 4-Trimethylcyclohexane (*Hexahydro-ψ-cumene*).

Found in petroleum from Maki, Echigo Province.
Cis :
B.p. 146° (142°). D_4^{20} 0·786. n_D^{20} 1·43209.
Trans :
B.p. 140–1°, 138·5–139·5°/755 mm. D_4^{20} 0·7813. n_{He}^{20} 1·43121.

Iimori, Kikuchi, *Chem. Abstracts*, 1928, **22**, 496.
Eisenlohr, *Fortschritte der Chemie, Physik, und Physikalischen Chemie*, 1925, **18**, 553.

1 : 3 : 5-Trimethylcyclohexane (*Hexahydromesitylene*).

Cis :
B.p. 140·0–140·5°/752 mm. D_4^{20} 0·7773. n_H^{20} 1·43010.
Trans :
B.p. 138·5–139·0°/754 mm. D_4^{20} 0·7720. n_H^{20} 1·42740.

Adams, Marshall, *J. Am. Chem. Soc.*, 1928, **50**, 1970.
Eisenlohr, *Fortschritte der Chemie, Physik, und Physikalischen Chemie*, 1925, **18**, 554.

1 : 2 : 2-Trimethylcyclohexanol

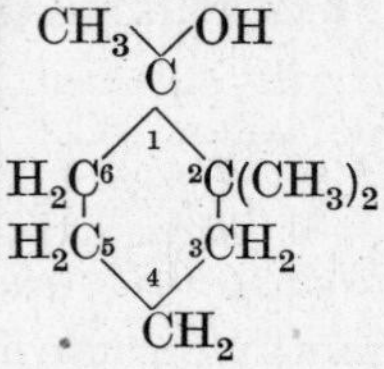

$C_9H_{18}O$ MW, 142

Oil. B.p. 81·4–81·8°/20 mm., 75·8°/16 mm. $D_4^{18\cdot4}$ 0·9274. $n_D^{18\cdot4}$ 1·469.
Hydrate, $\frac{1}{2}H_2O$: cryst. M.p. 41°.

Auwers, Lange, *Ann.*, 1913, **401**, 322.

1 : 2 : 6-Trimethylcyclohexanol.
B.p. 78°/23 mm. D_4^{15} 0·9126. n_D^{15} 1·4598.

Zelinsky, Dvorjantchik, *Bull. soc. chim.*, 1904, 32, 746.

1 : 3 : 3-Trimethylcyclohexanol.
Prisms. M.p. 74° (72·5°). Sol. most org. solvents.

Crossley, Gilling, *J. Chem. Soc.*, 1910, **97**, 2220.

1 : 3 : 5-Trimethylcyclohexanol.
B.p. 181°, 82–3°/19 mm. $D_4^{16\cdot8}$ 0·8876. $n_D^{16\cdot3}$ 1·454.

Wallach, *Ann.*, 1913, **396**, 284.

1 : 4 : 4-Trimethylcyclohexanol.
Needles. M.p. 58°. B.p. 79–80°/15 mm., 75°/11 mm.

Auwers, Lange, *Ann.*, 1913, **401**, 317.

2 : 2 : 3-Trimethylcyclohexanol.
B.p. 85–7°/15 mm.

Ruzicka, *Helv. Chim. Acta*, 1919, **2**, 159.

2 : 2 : 5-Trimethylcyclohexanol.
See Pulenol.

2 : 2 : 6-Trimethylcyclohexanol.
Cryst. from EtOH or pet. ether. M.p. 51°. B.p. 186–7°/753 mm., 87°/28 mm. D_4^{20} 0·9128. n_D^{20} 1·4600.

Haller, *Compt. rend.*, 1913, **157**, 181.
Masson, *Compt. rend.*, 1912, **154**, 518.

2 : 3 : 3-Trimethylcyclohexanol.
Needles. M.p. 28°. B.p. 197°. Very sol. org. solvents.

Crossley, Renouf, *J. Chem. Soc.*, 1911, **99**, 1108; 1915, **107**, 607.

2 : 3 : 6-Trimethylcyclohexanol.
B.p. 193–5°/747 mm. D_4^{17} 0·9119.

Zelinsky, Reformatski, *Ber.*, 1895, **28**, 2945.

2 : 4 : 4-Trimethylcyclohexanol.
Viscous oil. B.p. 192–3°.

Wallach, Scheunert, *Ann.*, 1902, **324**, 106.

2 : 4 : 5-Trimethylcyclohexanol.

Cis :
B.p. 191–3°, 84°/17 mm.
Phenylurethane : cryst. from EtOH. M.p. 83·5°.

Trans :
B.p. 196°, 112°/35 mm.
Phenylurethane : cryst. from EtOH. M.p. 95°.

Acid phthalate : cryst. from Et_2O–ligroin. M.p. 81–83·5°.

Skita, *Ber.*, 1920, **53**, 1800.

3 : 3 : 5-Trimethylcyclohexanol (*Dihydroisophorol*).

Cis :
B.p. 201–3°/750 mm., 92°/12 mm. D_4^{16} 0·9006. n_D^{16} 1·4550.
Acetyl : b.p. about 209–10°.

Trans :
Cryst. M.p. 52° (37°). B.p. 196·5°/770 mm., 95°/15 mm.
Acetyl : b.p. 209–10°.

Skita, Meyer, *Ber.*, 1912, **45**, 3593.
Knoevenagel, Fischer, *Ann.*, 1897, **297**, 128, 194.

2 : 2 : 5-Trimethylcyclohexanone.
See Pulenone.

2 : 2 : 6-Trimethylcyclohexanone

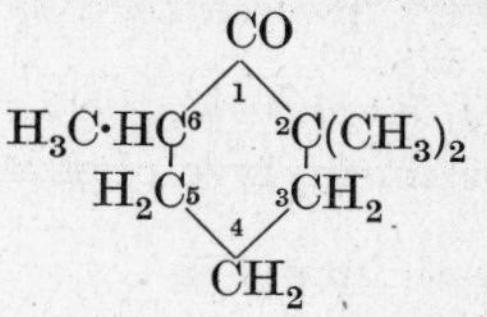

$C_9H_{16}O$ MW, 140

B.p. 178–9°, 66–7°/10 mm. D_4^{18} 0·9043. n_D^{18} 1·4493.
Oxime : cryst. from EtOH. M.p. 106° (104·5–105°). B.p. 126–7°/17 mm.
Semicarbazone : m.p. 220–1°.

Masson, *Compt. rend.*, 1912, **154**, 517.
Haller, Cornubert, *Bull. soc. chim.*, 1927, **41**, 377.
Cornubert, *ibid.*, 894.

2 : 3 : 3-Trimethylcyclohexanone.
Liq. B.p. 190·5–191°/750 mm. D_{15}^{15} 0·9213.
Oxime : needles from pet. ether or EtOH.Aq. M.p. 95°. Sol. most org. solvents.
Semicarbazone : cryst. from EtOH. M.p. 206° decomp. Spar. sol. AcOEt, $CHCl_3$, Me_2CO, C_6H_6.

Crossley, Renouf, *J. Chem. Soc.*, 1911, **99**, 1110.

2 : 3 : 6-Trimethylcyclohexanone.
B.p. 190–1°, 79–80°/20 mm. D_4^{18} 0·9129, D^{21} 0·9058. n_D^{21} 1·4464. Non-misc. with H_2O. Does not form bisulphite comp.

Cornubert, Humeau, *Bull. soc. chim.*, 1931, **49**, 1483.
Zelinsky, Reformatski, *Ber.*, 1895, **28**, 2944.

2 : 4 : 4-Trimethylcyclohexanone.
Present in acetone oil. B.p. 191°, 61°/11 mm. D_4^{20} 0·902. n_D^{20} 1·4493.
Oxime: cryst. from Et_2O. M.p. 108–9°.
Semicarbazone: m.p. 164–5° (162°).

Auwers, *Ann.*, 1920, **420**, 111.
Pringsheim, Bondi, *Ber.*, 1925, **58**, 1414.
Wallach, Scheunert, *Ann.*, 1902, **324**, 107.

2 : 4 : 5-Trimethylcyclohexanone.
Cis:
B.p. 193°. D_4^{20} 0·897. n_D^{20} 1·4479.
Oxime: cryst. from MeOH. M.p. 105°.
Semicarbazone: needles from MeOH. M.p. 204° (175·5–176°).

Skita, *Ber.*, 1920, **53**, 1800.
Auwers, *Ann.*, 1920, **420**, 103.

2 : 4 : 6-Trimethylcyclohexanone.
B.p. 184–5°/748 mm. D_4^{20} 0·8992. n_D^{20} 1·4458.
Semicarbazone: m.p. 228°.

Cornubert, Maurel, *Bull. soc. chim.*, 1931, **49**, 1528.
Haller, *Compt. rend.*, 1913, **157**, 740.

2 : 5 : 5-Trimethylcyclohexanone.
B.p. 185°.
Semicarbazone: m.p. 170°.

Blanc, *Bull. soc. chim.*, 1908, **3**, 786.

3 : 3 : 4-Trimethylcyclohexanone.
B.p. 184–8°, 70–5°/11 mm.
Oxime: cryst. from H_2O. M.p. 100°.
Semicarbazone: m.p. 177°.

v. Braun, Keller, Weissbach, *Ann.*, 1931, **490**, 188.

3 : 3 : 5 - Trimethylcyclohexanone (*Dihydroisophorone*).
Present in acetone oil. Yellow oil. B.p. 188·5–189·5°, 53·5–54°/11 mm. D^{19} 0·8919. n_D^{15} 1·4454.
Oxime: cryst. from EtOH. M.p. 58°.
Semicarbazone: cryst. from MeOH. M.p. 204° (202°).
2 : 4-*Dinitrophenylhydrazone*: m.p. 145–7°.

Pringsheim, Bondi, *Ber.*, 1925, **58**, 1414.
Knoevenagel, *Ann.*, 1897, **297**, 198.
Skita, *Ber.*, 1909, **42**, 1630.

1 : 2 : 3-Trimethylcyclohexene

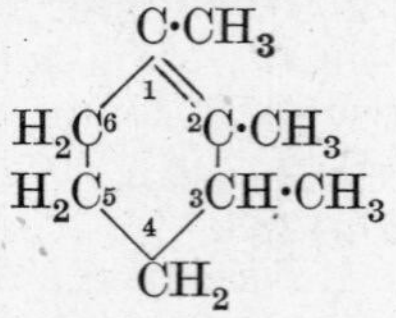

C_9H_{16} MW, 124

B.p. 149·6–150°/749 mm. $D_4^{11·75}$ 0·8347. $n_D^{11·75}$ 1·463.

Auwers, Krollpfeiffer, *Ber.*, 1915, **48**, 1231.

1 : 3 : 5-Trimethylcyclohexene (*Tetrahydromesitylene*).
B.p. 142·5–143·5°. $D_4^{14·3}$ 0·8025. $n_D^{13·5}$ 1·449.
Nitrosochloride: m.p. 134°.

Wallach, *Ann.*, 1913, **396**, 284.
Auwers, Hinterseber, Treppmann, *Ann.*, 1915, **410**, 270.

1 : 4 : 4-Trimethylcyclohexene.
See Pulenene.

1 : 4 : 5-Trimethylcyclohexene (1 : 2 : 3 : 6-*Tetrahydro-ψ-cumene*).
B.p. 144–6°. D_4^{20} 0·805. n_D^{20} 1·4482.

Auwers, *Ann.*, 1920, **420**, 105.

1 : 5 : 5-Trimethylcyclohexene (*α-Cyclogeraniolene*).
B.p. 139–41°/759 mm. D_4^{23} 0·7981. $n_D^{21·5}$ 1·44612.
Nitrosate: cryst. M.p. 102–4°.
Nitrosochloride: bluish cryst. from MeOH.Aq. M.p. 100–20°.

Wallach, Scheunert, *Ann.*, 1902, **324**, 101.
Crossley, Gilling, *J. Chem. Soc.*, 1910, **97**, 2221.

1 : 6 : 6-Trimethylcyclohexene.
Liq. B.p. 146·2–147·2°/767 mm. (144–6°). $D_4^{20·3}$ 0·8217. $n_D^{20·4}$ 1·456.
Nitrosochloride: needles from AcOEt. M.p. 133–4°. Insol. MeOH, Me_2CO.

Auwers, Lange, *Ann.*, 1915, **409**, 174.
Godchot, Bedos, *Compt. rend.*, 1925, **181**, 921.

1 : 1 : 3 - Trimethylcyclohexene - carboxylic Acid.
See Cyclogeranic Acid.

1 : 2 : 2-Trimethylcyclohexene-3-carboxylic Acid-1.
See Camphorenic Acid.

1 : 3 : 5-Trimethylcyclohexenol-3

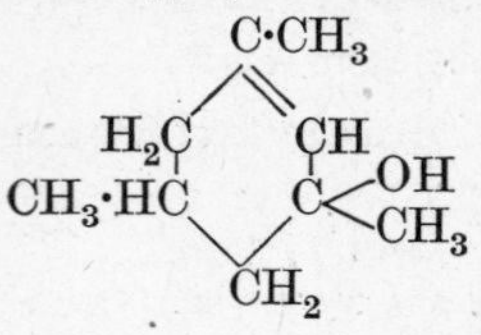

$C_9H_{16}O$ MW, 140

Cryst. M.p. 46°. B.p. 87–90°/17 mm. $D_4^{20·2}$ 0·9132. $n_D^{19·3}$ 1·4735. Heat of comb. C_v 1350–9 Cal.

Auwers, Peters, *Ber.*, 1910, **43**, 3087.

3 : 3 : 6-Trimethylcyclohexenol-4.
See βγ-Pulenenol.

1 : 3 : 3-Trimethylcyclohexenol-6

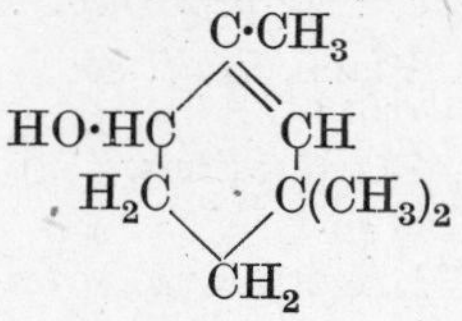

$C_9H_{16}O$ MW, 140

Oil. B.p. 193°/760 mm. D_4^{13} 0·9310. Misc. with usual org. solvents. Insol. H_2O. Volatile in steam.
Acetyl : b.p. 206–7°.

Bougault, *Compt. rend.*, 1910, **150**, 534.

1 : 4 : 4-Trimethylcyclohexenone-3.
See αβ-Pulenenone.

1 : 5 : 5-Trimethylcyclohexenone-3.
See Isophorone.

1 : 6 : 6-Trimethylcyclohexenone-3 (*Isocamphorphorone*)

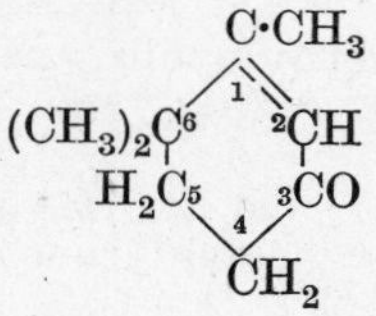

$C_9H_{14}O$ MW, 138

Liq. B.p. 217°/760 mm., 97–9°/13 mm. D^{20} 0·9424. n_D 1·48458.
Semicarbazone : needles from AcOEt. M.p. 211°.

Tiemann, *Ber.*, 1897, **30**, 249.

2 : 6 : 6-Trimethylcyclohexenone-3.
B.p. 194–6° (192°). D_4^{20} 0·930. n_D^{20} 1·4779.
Oxime : prisms from Et_2O–ligroin. M.p. 128–9°. B.p. 131–2°/15 mm.
Semicarbazone : cryst. from MeOH.Aq. M.p. 158–9°. Mod. sol. Et_2O.

Bougault, *Compt. rend.*, 1910, **150**, 534.
Auwers, *Ann.*, 1920, **420**, 110.
Wallach, Scheunert, *Ann.*, 1902, **324**, 103.

4 : 4 : 5-Trimethylcyclohexenone-3.
B.p. 85–90°/14 mm.
Semicarbazone : cryst. from EtOH. M.p. 185–7°.

Ruzicka, *Helv. Chim. Acta*, 1919, **2**, 159.

2 : 3 : 3-Trimethylcyclohexenone-4

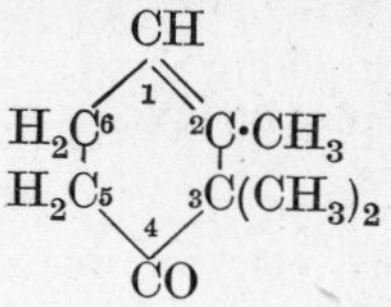

$C_9H_{14}O$ MW, 138

B.p. 85–90°/12 mm.
Semicarbazone : cryst. from MeOH. M.p. 168–71°.

Ruzicka, *Helv. Chim. Acta*, 1919, **2**, 158.

3 : 3 : 6-Trimethylcyclohexenone-4.
See βγ-Pulenenone.

1 : 1 : 2-Trimethylcyclopentane (*Camphoceane, dihydroisolaurolene*)

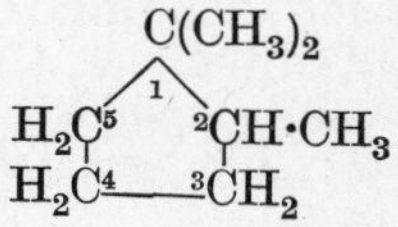

C_8H_{16} MW, 112

Liq. with camphoraceous odour. B.p. 113–113·5°/750 mm. D_4^{18} 0·7728, D_0^{20} 0·7661. n_D^{18} 1·4238, n_D^{20} 1·4199. Heat of comb. C_v 1252·8 Cal. Dil. $HNO_3 \longrightarrow$ 1 : 1-dimethylglutaric acid.

Zelinsky, Lepeschkin, *Ann.*, 1901, **319**, 315.
Crossley, Renouf, *J. Chem. Soc.*, 1906, **89**, 43.
Kishner, *Chem. Zentr.*, 1911, I, 543.

1 : 1 : 3-Trimethylcyclopentane.
B.p. 115–16°/760 mm. D_4^{20} 0·7703. n_D^{20} 1·4223.

Zelinsky, Uspensky, *Ber.*, 1913, **46**, 1470.
Dey, Linstead, *J. Chem. Soc.*, 1935, 1064.

1 : 2 : 3-Trimethylcyclopentane (*Dihydrolaurolene, laurolan*).
B.p. 114–15°. D_4^4 0·7718, D_4^{19} 0·7688. n_D^{19} 1·4230. $HNO_3 \longrightarrow$ oxalic acid.

Zelinsky, Lepeschkin, *Chem. Zentr.*, 1902, I, 33.
Crossley, Renouf, *J. Chem. Soc.*, 1906, **89**, 27, 40.

1 : 2 : 4-Trimethylcyclopentane.
B.p. 112·5–113°. D_4^{20} 0·7565. n_D^{20} 1·4156. Heat of comb. C_v 1255·7 Cal.

Zelinsky, *Bull. soc. chim.*, 1904, **32**, 747.

1 : 2 : 3-Trimethylcyclopentane-1-carboxylic Acid.
See Laurolanic Acid.

2 : 2 : 3-Trimethylcyclopentane-1-carboxylic Acid.
See Norisocampholic Acid.

1 : 1 : 2-Trimethylcyclopentane-5-carboxylic Acid.
See Lauronic Acid.

1 : 2 : 2-Trimethylcyclopentane-1 : 3-dicarboxylic Acid.
See Camphoric Acid.

1 : 2 : 2-Trimethylcyclopentanol

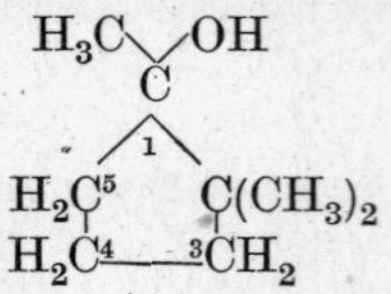

$C_8H_{16}O$ MW, 128

Liq. B.p. 156°/755 mm., 80–1°/49 mm., 60°/15 mm. D_0^{20} 0·9102. n_D^{20} 1·4513. Dist. with cryst. oxalic acid ⟶ isolaurolene.

Hydrate, $\frac{1}{2}H_2O$: needles from Et_2O. M.p. 59–60°.

Kishner, *Chem. Zentr.*, 1911, I, 543.

1 : 2 : 4-Trimethylcyclopentanol.

d-.

B.p. 157–8°/747 mm. D_4^{21} 0·8850. n_D^{21} 1·4424. $[\alpha]_D$ + 15°.

Zelinsky, *Bull. soc. chim.*, 1904, **32**, 747.

1 : 2 : 5-Trimethylcyclopentanol.
B.p. 56–60°/8 mm. D_4^{15} 0·9121. $n_D^{16\cdot7}$ 1·4554. Heat with anhyd. oxalic acid or P_2O_5 ⟶ laurolene.

Noyes, Kyriakides, *J. Am. Chem. Soc.*, 1910, **32**, 1065.

2 : 3 : 4-Trimethylcyclopentanol.
Liq. with menthol odour. B.p. 68–70°/12 mm. Insol. H_2O.

Willstätter, Clarke, *Ber.*, 1914, **47**, 309.

2 : 2 : 3-Trimethylcyclopentanone

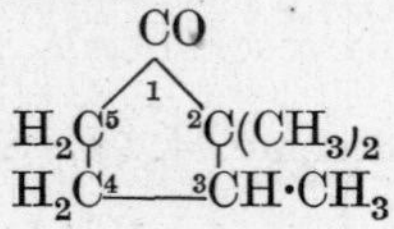

$C_8H_{14}O$ MW, 126

Exists in active and inactive forms.

Active form:
Liq. B.p. 164–5°.
Oxime: leaflets from pet. ether. M.p. 107–8°. Sol. EtOH, pet. ether.
Semicarbazone: m.p. 188°. Spar. sol. cold EtOH.

Inactive form:
B.p. 164°.
Oxime: plates. M.p. 105°.
Semicarbazone: m.p. 210–12°.

Blaise, Blanc, *Bull. soc. chim.*, 1902, **27**, 76.
Blanc, Desfontaines, *Compt. rend.*, 1903, **136**, 1143.

2 : 2 : 5-Trimethylcyclopentanone.
Exists in active and inactive forms.

Active form:
B.p. 152–3°.
Oxime: cryst. from MeOH.Aq. M.p. 60–2°. Very sol. org. solvents.
Semicarbazone: m.p. 150–1°. Very sol. MeOH, Et_2O.

Inactive form:
B.p. 152°. D_4^{20} 0·8781. n_D^{20} 1·4306.
Oxime: prisms from pet. ether. M.p. 62°.

Blanc, *Bull. soc. chim.*, 1908, **3**, 290, 782.
Haller, Cornubert, *Compt. rend.*, 1914, **158**, 300.
Wallach, Kempe, *Ann.*, 1903, **329**, 94.

2 : 3 : 3-Trimethylcyclopentanone.
Liq. B.p. 167–9°/760 mm. D_4^{20} 0·8956. Insol. H_2O.
Oxime: needles from EtOH.Aq. M.p. 105·5°.
Semicarbazone: plates from EtOH. M.p. 221·5–222° decomp.

van Kregten, *Rec. trav. chim.*, 1916, **36**, 77.
Noyes, *Ber.*, 1899, **32**, 2291.

2 : 3 : 5-Trimethylcyclopentanone.

d-.

B.p. 158–9°/770 mm. D_4^{19} 0·8778. n_D^{19} 1·4316. $[\alpha]_D^{19}$ + 103° 41′.

Haller, Cornubert, *Compt. rend.*, 1914, **158**, 1619.

3 : 3 : 4-Trimethylcyclopentanone.
Liq. B.p. 172–4°. n_D^{20} 1·4390.
Oxime: liq. B.p. 116–20°/14 mm.
Semicarbazone: cryst. from MeOH. M.p. 162–3°.

v. Braun, *Ann.*, 1931, **490**, 132.
See also v. Braun, Mannes, Reuter, *Ber.*, 1933, **66**, 1499.

3 : 3 : 5-Trimethylcyclopentanone.
B.p. 160–1°. D_4^{18} 0·8785. n_D^{18} 1·433.
Semicarbazone: cryst. from EtOH. M.p. 171–3°.

Dey, Linstead, *J. Chem. Soc.*, 1935, 1063.
Wallach, *Ann.*, 1918, **414**, 331.

1 : 2 : 3-Trimethylcyclopentene.
See Laurolene.

1 : 5 : 5-Trimethylcyclopentene.
See Isolaurolene.

1 : 1 : 2-Trimethylcyclopentene-2-carboxylic Acid-3.
See β-Campholytic Acid.

1 : 1 : 2-Trimethylcyclopentene-2-carboxylic Acid-5.
See α-Campholytic Acid.

1 : 2 : 3-Trimethylcyclopentene-3-carboxylic Acid.
See Laurolenic Acid.

2 : 2 : 3-Trimethylcyclopentylacetic Acid.
See Isocampholic Acid.

1 : 1 : 2-Trimethylcyclopropane

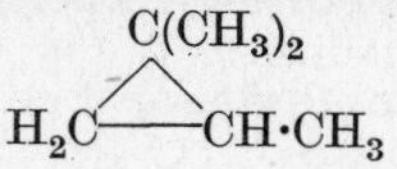

C_6H_{12} MW, 84

B.p. 56–7°/750 mm. (52·8°/756 mm.). $D_4^{15\cdot3}$ 0·6888, $D_4^{19\cdot5}$ 0·6822. $n_D^{14\cdot5}$ 1·3896, $n_D^{19\cdot5}$ 1·3848. Polymerises on shaking with conc. H_2SO_4.

Kishner, *Chem. Zentr.*, 1912, I, 2025.
Zelinsky, Zelikow, *Ber.*, 1901, **34**, 2859.

1 : 2 : 3-Trimethylcyclopropane.
B.p. 65–7°/755 mm. D_4^{18} 0·6946. n_D^{18} 1·3945.

Zelinsky, Zelikow, *Ber.*, 1901, **34**, 2863.

1 : 3 : 5-Trimethyldiphenylmethane.
See Phenylmesitylmethane.

Trimethyldiphenyl sulphide.
See under Thioxylenol.

2 : 6 : 10-Trimethyldodecane.
See Farnesane.

Trimethylene.
See Cyclopropane.

Trimethylene-aniline.
See under Trimethyleneimine.

Trimethylene bromide.
See 1 : 3-Dibromopropane.

Trimethylene bromohydrin.
See 3-Bromopropyl Alcohol.

Trimethylene chloride.
See 1 : 3-Dichloropropane.

Trimethylene chlorobromide.
See 1-Chloro-3-bromopropane.

Trimethylene chlorohydrin.
See 3-Chloropropyl Alcohol.

Trimethylene cyanide.
See under Glutaric Acid.

Trimethylenediamine (1 : 3-*Diaminopropane*)

$H_2N{\cdot}CH_2{\cdot}CH_2{\cdot}CH_2{\cdot}NH_2$

$C_3H_{10}N_2$ MW, 74

Liq. with ammoniacal odour. B.p. 135–6°/738 mm. D_4^{25} 0·884. Misc. with EtOH, Et_2O, $CHCl_3$, C_6H_6. $k = 3{\cdot}5 \times 10^{-4}$ at 25°.

B,2HCl: cryst. M.p. 243°. Sol. H_2O. Spar. sol. EtOH. Insol. Et_2O.

B,H_2PtCl_6: m.p. 240° decomp.

1 : 3-N-*Tetra-Me*: $C_7H_{18}N_2$. MW, 130. Oil. B.p. 144°/760 mm. $D_4^{18\cdot7}$ 0·7837. $n_\alpha^{18\cdot7}$ 1·4215. Misc. with H_2O, EtOH, Et_2O. *B,H_2PtCl_6*: cryst. from 50% EtOH. Decomp. at 246–7°. *Picrate*: cryst. M.p. 205°.

1-N-*Di-Et*: $C_7H_{18}N_2$. MW, 130. B.p. 75°/20 mm.

1 : 3-N-*Tetra-Et*: $C_{11}H_{26}N_2$. MW, 186. B.p. 205–9°. *$B,2HCl,HgCl_2$*: prisms from H_2O. M.p. 124–5°.

1 : 3-N-*Diacetyl*: prisms from EtOH. M.p. 101°. Sol. H_2O, EtOH, $CHCl_3$. Spar. sol. C_6H_6. Insol. Et_2O, ligroin. Weak base.

1 : 3-N-*Dibenzoyl*: cryst. powder from C_6H_6. M.p. 147–8°. Sol. EtOH, $CHCl_3$. Mod. sol. cold C_6H_6.

1 : 3-N-*Dicarbomethoxyl*: plates from Et_2O. M.p. 74–5°. Sol. H_2O, EtOH, $CHCl_3$. Spar. sol. Et_2O. Insol. C_6H_6, ligroin.

1 : 3-N-*Dicarbethoxyl*: prisms from Et_2O. M.p. 42°. B.p. 210°/30 mm. Sol. EtOH, Et_2O, $CHCl_3$. Spar. sol. ligroin. Insol. H_2O.

Dipicrate: yellow leaflets.

Clarke, *J. Chem. Soc.*, 1913, **103**, 1699.
Fischer, Koch, *Ber.*, 1884, **17**, 1799.
Putochin, *Ber.*, 1926, **59**, 625.
Ing, Manske, *J. Chem. Soc.*, 1926, 2351.

Trimethylene Glycol (1 : 3-*Dihydroxypropane, propandiol*-1 : 3)

$HO{\cdot}CH_2{\cdot}CH_2{\cdot}CH_2{\cdot}OH$

$C_3H_8O_2$ MW, 76

Pale yellow liq. B.p. 210–11°, 109–10°/12 mm. D_4^{20} 1·0597. n_D^{20} 1·43983. Misc. with H_2O, EtOH. $H_2O_2 \longrightarrow$ propionaldehyde.

$B,2HNO_3$: viscous liq. D^{15} 1·408. Sol. MeOH, Et_2O, Me_2CO, $CHCl_3$, C_6H_6. Sol. 5 parts EtOH, 410 parts H_2O. Spar. sol. CS_2.

Me ether: $C_4H_{10}O_2$. MW, 90. B.p. 153·15–153·2°/768 mm. D_4^{20} 0·9434. n_D^{20} 1·41259. *Phenyl ether*: b.p. 230–1°. *Formyl*: b.p. 146–7°/767 mm. D_4^{15} 1·0057. *Acetyl*: b.p. 162–163·5°/762 mm. D_4^{15} 0·9803.

Et ether: $C_5H_{12}O_2$. MW, 104. B.p. 162·1–162·2°. D_4^{20} 0·91691. n_D^{20} 1·41666. Misc. with H_2O. *Phenyl ether*: b.p. 328–30°. *Formyl*: b.p. 157·5–159°/742 mm. D_4^{15} 0·9731. *Acetyl*: b.p. 174·5–175·5°. D_4^{15} 0·9567.

Di-Et ether: $C_7H_{16}O_2$. MW, 132. B.p. 140–1°. D_{25}^{25} 0·835. Insol. H_2O.

Propyl ether: $C_6H_{14}O_2$. MW, 118. B.p. 170–2°. D_4^{15} 0·9076. *Formyl*: b.p. 174·5–176°.

Methylene ether: *see* 1 : 3-Dioxan.

Phenyl ether: $C_9H_{12}O_2$. MW, 152. B.p. 249–50°/764 mm.

Diphenyl ether: 1 : 3-diphenoxypropane. $C_{15}H_{16}O_2$. MW, 228. Leaflets from EtOH. M.p. 61°. B.p. 338–40°. Sol. EtOH, Et_2O. Insol. H_2O.

Di-o-tolyl ether: b.p. 341–3°, 225°/28 mm.

Di-m-tolyl ether: plates from EtOH. M.p. 91°.

Di-p-tolyl ether: needles from EtOH. M.p. 94°.

Di-1-naphthyl ether: needles from EtOH. M.p. 103–4°.

Di-2-naphthyl ether: plates from AcOH. M.p. 148–9°.

Formyl: b.p. 195–7°/757 mm. D_4^{15} 1·1405.

Acetyl: b.p. 202·5–204°.

Diacetyl: b.p. 209–10°. D^{19} 1·070. Sol. 8–10 parts H_2O.

Dibenzoyl: prisms or needles from pet. ether. M.p. 57·5° (53°).

Di-p-toluenesulphonyl: m.p. 93–4°.

Diphenylurethane: m.p. 137–137·5°.

Di-1-naphthylurethane: m.p. 164°.

Gattermann, *Ann.*, 1907, **357**, 379.
Henry, *Chem. Zentr.*, 1899, I, 968; 1907, I, 1314.
Blechta, *Chem. Abstracts*, 1922, **16**, 2991.
Rayner, *J. Soc. Chem. Ind.*, 1926, **45**, 265T, 287T.
Werkmann, Gillen, *Journal of Bacteriology*, 1932, **23**, 167.
Palomaa, *Chem. Zentr.*, 1913, II, 1959.

Trimethyleneimine (*Azetidine*)

$$H_2C{<}\begin{matrix}CH_2\\CH_2\end{matrix}{>}NH$$

C_3H_7N MW, 57

Liq. with ammoniacal odour. B.p. 63°/748 mm. $D^{20\cdot4}$ 0·8436. Misc. with H_2O, EtOH.

B,HAuCl₄: golden-yellow cryst. M.p. 192°. Spar. sol. cold H_2O.

B_2,H_2PtCl_6: orange-yellow needles. M.p. 203° decomp.

Picrate: yellow needles. M.p. 166–7°.

N-*Phenyl*: trimethylene-aniline. Oil. B.p. 242–5°, 130–2°/16 mm.

Howard, Marckwald, *Ber.*, 1899, **32**, 2032.
Scholtz, *ibid.*, 2255.

Trimethylene iodide.
See 1 : 3-Di-iodopropane.

Trimethylene iodohydrin.
See 3-Iodopropyl Alcohol.

Trimethylene methylene dioxide.
See 1 : 3-Dioxan.

Trimethylene oxide

$$H_2C{<}\begin{matrix}CH_2\\CH_2\end{matrix}{>}O$$

C_3H_6O MW, 58

Liq. with pleasant aromatic odour. B.p. 47·8°. D_4^{25} 0·8930. n^{25} 1·3897. Misc. with H_2O.

Allen, Hibbert, *J. Am. Chem. Soc.*, 1934, **56**, 1399.
Derick, Bissell, *J. Am. Chem. Soc.*, 1916, **38**, 2478.

2 : 6-Trimethylenepiperidine.
See Granatanine.

2 : 5-Trimethylenepyrrolidine.
See Nortropane.

Trimethylene sulphide

$$H_2C{<}\begin{matrix}CH_2\\CH_2\end{matrix}{>}S$$

C_3H_6S MW, 74

Mobile liq. with disagreeable odour. B.p. 93·8–94·2°/752 mm. D_4^{23} 1·0284. n_D^{23} 1·5059.

Dimethiodide: needles. M.p. 98·5–99·5°.

B,HgCl₂: cryst. Decomp. at 93–5°. Spar. sol. H_2O, EtOH, Et_2O.

Bost, Conn, *Oil and Gas Journal*, 1933, **32**, No. 3, 17.
Grischkewitsch-Trochimowski, *Chem. Zentr.*, 1923, III, 773.

Trimethylene sulphone

$$H_2C{<}\begin{matrix}CH_2\\CH_2\end{matrix}{>}SO_2$$

$C_3H_6O_2S$ MW, 106

Needles from H_2O, MeOH–Et_2O, or Et_2O–pet. ether. M.p. 75·5–76°. Sol. H_2O, EtOH. Spar. sol. Et_2O.

See second reference above.

Trimethylene-trinitroamine.
See Hexogen.

Trimethylethylene.
See 2-Methylbutylene-2.

Trimethylethylene chlorohydrin.
See 3-Chloro-*tert.*-amyl Alcohol.

1 : 1 : 2 - Trimethyl - 2 - ethylhydracrylic Acid.
See 2-Hydroxy-1 : 1 : 2-trimethyl-*n*-valeric Acid.

2 : 3 : 5-Trimethyl-4-ethylpyrrole.
See Phyllopyrrole

2 : 3 : 4-Trimethylfuran

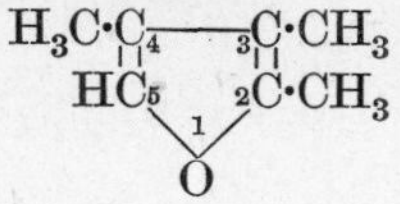

$C_7H_{10}O$ MW, 110

Liq. B.p. 54–5°/57 mm.

> Reichstein, Zschokke, Syz, *Helv. Chim. Acta*, 1932, **15**, 1116.

2 : 3 : 5-Trimethylfuran (2 : 4 : 5-*Trimethylfuran*).

B.p. 114°/720 mm., 51·5°/62 mm.

> Reichstein, Zschokke, Syz, *Helv. Chim. Acta*, 1932, **15**, 1115.

Trimethylfuran-carboxylic Acid.

See Trimethyl-β-furoic Acid *and* Trimethyl-pyromucic Acid.

3 : 4 : 5-Trimethylfurfural

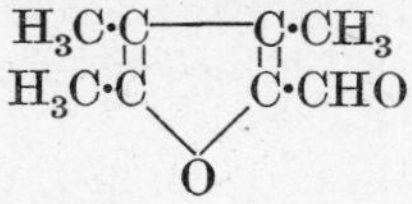

$C_8H_{10}O_2$ MW, 138

Cryst. M.p. 31–2°. B.p. 68°/0·3 mm.

> Reichstein, Zschokke, Syz, *Helv. Chim. Acta*, 1932, **15**, 1117.

2 : 4 : 5-Trimethyl–β–furoic Acid (2 : 4 : 5-*Trimethylfuran*-3-*carboxylic acid*)

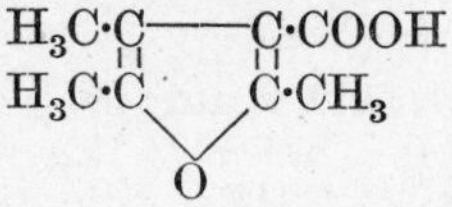

$C_8H_{10}O_3$ MW, 154

Cryst. from pet. ether. M.p. 131–2°. Sol. most org. solvents except pet. ether. Spar. sol. H_2O.

Et ester : $C_{10}H_{14}O_3$. MW, 182. B.p. 100–5°/12 mm.

> Reichstein, Zschokke, Syz, *Helv. Chim. Acta*, 1932, **15**, 1114.

Trimethylglucose.

See under Glucose.

1 : 1 : 2-Trimethylglutaric Acid (1 : 1 : 2-*Trimethylpropane*-1 : 3-*dicarboxylic acid*, 2 : 3-*dimethylbutane*-1 : 3-*dicarboxylic acid*)

$$(CH_3)_2C \cdot COOH$$
$$CH_3 \cdot CH$$
$$CH_2 \cdot COOH$$

$C_8H_{14}O_4$ MW, 174

Cryst. M.p. 112°. Sol. H_2O, most org. solvents.

Anhydride : prisms from pet. ether. M.p. 39°.

Monoanilide : plates from EtOH.Aq. M.p. 155°. Sol. most org. solvents.

> Perkin, Thorpe, *J. Chem. Soc.*, 1897, **71**, 1187.

1 : 1 : 3-Trimethylglutaric Acid (2-*Methylpentane*-2 : 4-*dicarboxylic acid*)

$$(CH_3)_2C \cdot COOH$$
$$CH_2$$
$$CH_3 \cdot CH \cdot COOH$$

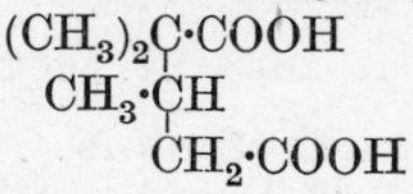

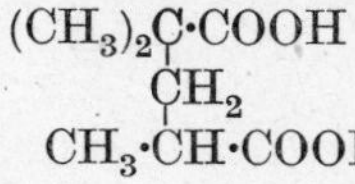

$C_8H_{14}O_4$ MW, 174

Leaflets from H_2O. M.p. 97° (95°). Sol. usual org. solvents. Less sol. H_2O. $k = 3·48 \times 10^{-5}$ at 25°. Sublimes.

Di-Et ester : $C_{12}H_{22}O_4$. MW, 230. B.p. 230–1°. D^0 1·012.

Anhydride : needles from ligroin. M.p. 95–6°. B.p. 262°.

Imide : cryst. M.p. 139°. Sublimes.

Monoanilide : needles. M.p. 165°. Sol. EtOH. Spar. sol. Et_2O. Insol. C_6H_6, ligroin.

> Auwers, Meyer, *Ber.*, 1889, **22**, 2013.
> Auwers, *Ann.*, 1896, **292**, 224 ; *Ber.*, 1898, **31**, 2113.

1 : 2 : 2-Trimethylglutaric Acid (2 : 2-*Dimethylbutane*-1 : 3-*dicarboxylic acid*)

$$CH_3 \cdot CH \cdot COOH$$
$$(CH_3)_2C$$
$$CH_2 \cdot COOH$$

$C_8H_{14}O_4$ MW, 174

Cryst. from C_6H_6. M.p. 88–9°. Very sol. warm H_2O. Spar. sol. C_6H_6. $k = 1·43 \times 10^{-4}$.

Di-Et ester : b.p. 247–9°.

Anhydride : prisms from AcOEt–pet. ether. M.p. 87–8° (82°).

Imide : needles from H_2O. M.p. 126°. Sol. hot H_2O.

Monoanilide : needles from MeOH.Aq. M.p. 150–1°.

> Perkin, Thorpe, *J. Chem. Soc.*, 1899, **75**, 65.
> Crossley, Renouf, *J. Chem. Soc.*, 1911, **99**, 1108.
> Ray, *J. Am. Chem. Soc.*, 1929, **51**, 930.

1 : 2 : 3-Trimethylglutaric Acid (3-*Methylpentane*-2 : 4-*dicarboxylic acid*)

$$CH_3 \cdot CH \cdot COOH$$
$$CH_3 \cdot CH$$
$$CH_3 \cdot CH \cdot COOH$$

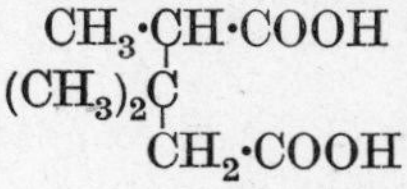

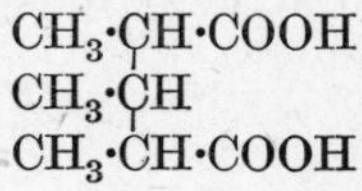

$C_8H_{14}O_4$ MW, 174

Cryst. from C_6H_6. M.p. 134°.

Ray, *J. Am. Chem. Soc.*, 1928, **50**, 558; 1931, **53**, 1174.
See also Michael, Ross, *J. Am. Chem. Soc.*, 1931, **53**, 1175.

1 : 2 : 5-Trimethylglyoxaline (1 : 2 : 5-*Trimethyliminazole*)

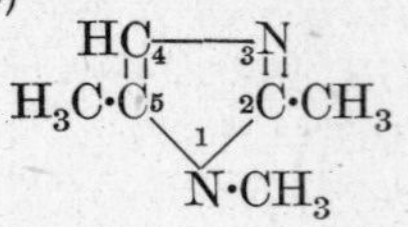

$C_6H_{10}N_2$ MW, 110

Brown mobile oil.
B,HAuCl$_4$: orange-yellow plates from dil. HCl. M.p. 186–7°.
Picrate : pale yellow needles from H_2O. M.p. 208–9°.

Grindley, Pyman, *J. Chem. Soc.*, 1927, 3134.

1 : 4 : 5-Trimethylglyoxaline (1 : 4 : 5-*Trimethyliminazole*).

Cryst. M.p. 46°. B.p. 117°/20 mm. Sol. H_2O, EtOH, Et_2O.
B,HCl : cryst. + H_2O. M.p. 80°, anhyd. 199°. Sol. H_2O, EtOH. Insol. Et_2O.
B,HNO$_3$: cryst. + H_2O. M.p. 46°. Sol. H_2O, EtOH. Insol. Et_2O.
B,HAuCl$_4$: yellow cryst. M.p. 202°.
B$_2$,H$_2$PtCl$_6$: yellow cryst. from H_2O. M.p. 224–5°.
Picrate : yellow cryst. from H_2O. M.p. 218°.
Methiodide : needles from EtOH–Et_2O. M.p. 158°. Sol. H_2O, EtOH. Insol. Et_2O.

Jowett, *J. Chem. Soc.*, 1905, **87**, 405.

2 : 4 : 5-Trimethylglyoxaline (2 : 4 : 5-*Trimethyliminazole*).

Needles from Et_2O–ligroin. M.p. 132·5–133° (130–1°). Sol. H_2O, most org. solvents. Aq. sol. reacts strongly alkaline. Bitter taste.
B,HCl : needles from EtOH. M.p. 316°.
Picrate : prisms from H_2O. M.p. 163°.

v. Pechmann, *Ber.*, 1888, **21**, 1415.
Fargher, Pyman, *J. Chem. Soc.*, 1919, **115**, 232.

2 : 4 : 6-Trimethylheptanol-4.
See Methyldi-isobutylcarbinol.

2 : 4 : 4-Trimethylhexanol-3.
See Isopropyl-*tert.*-amylcarbinol.

Trimethylhydracrylic Acid.
See Hydroxydimethylbutyric Acid.

Trimethyl - hydroxyethyl - ammonium hydroxide.
See Choline.

Trimethyl - hydroxyisopropyl - ammonium hydroxide.
See α-Methylcholine.

Trimethyl - hydroxymethyl - ammonium hydroxide.
See Formocholine.

Trimethyl - hydroxypropyl - ammonium hydroxide.
See β-Methylcholine.

Trimethyliminazole.
See Trimethylglyoxaline.

1 : 2 : 3-Trimethylindole

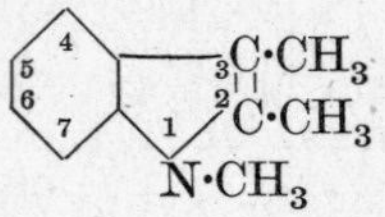

$C_{11}H_{13}N$ MW, 159

Leaflets. M.p. 18°. B.p. 283–4°/750 mm. Very sol. EtOH, Et_2O, C_6H_6. Mod. sol. hot H_2O. Sol. conc. HCl.
Picrate : dark red needles from C_6H_6. M.p. 150°.

Degen, *Ann.*, 1886, **236**, 160.
Ciamician, Piccinini, *Ber.*, 1896, **29**, 2470.

1 : 2 : 5-Trimethylindole.

Leaflets from EtOH.Aq. M.p. 56–7°. Very sol. ligroin. Volatile in steam.

Bayer, D.R.P., 128,660, (*Chem. Zentr.*, 1902, I, 610); 137,117, (*Chem. Zentr.*, 1903, I, 109).

2 : 3 : 5-Trimethylindole.

Leaflets from EtOH. M.p. 121·5°. B.p. 297°. Sol. EtOH, $CHCl_3$, ligroin. Spar. sol. H_2O. Sol. conc. HCl. Volatile in steam. $FeCl_3$ in AcOH $\longrightarrow$ green $\longrightarrow$ blue col.
Picrate : brownish-red needles from EtOH. M.p. 189° (177–80°).
N-*Nitroso* : golden-yellow needles from EtOH. M.p. 73°. Very sol. EtOH, AcOH. Spar. sol. H_2O.

Wolff, *Ber.*, 1888, **21**, 3361.
Grgin, *Monatsh.*, 1906, **27**, 739.

2 : 3 : 7-Trimethylindole.

Leaflets from EtOH. M.p. 79°. B.p. 282–3°.
Picrate : purplish-red needles from C_6H_6–ligroin. M.p. 152°.

Wolff, *Ber.*, 1888, **21**, 3362.

2 : 4 : 7-Trimethylindole.

Liq. B.p. 158–9°/13 mm.

v. Braun, Bayer, Blessing, *Ber.*, 1924, **57**, 402.

2 : 4 : 6-Trimethylisophthalic Acid (2 : 4 : 6-*Trimethylbenzene*-1 : 3-*dicarboxylic acid, mesitylene*-2 : 6-*dicarboxylic acid*)

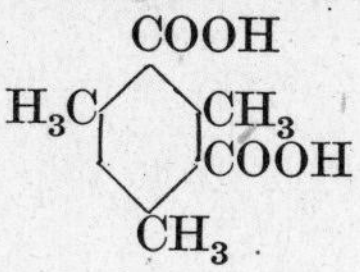

$C_{11}H_{12}O_4$ MW, 208

Cryst. from AcOEt. M.p. 289° (283°). Sol. usual org. solvents.

Dinitrile: $C_{11}H_{10}N_2$. MW, 170. Prisms from EtOH.Aq. M.p. 142°.

Johnson, Fuson, *J. Am. Chem. Soc.*, 1934, **56**, 1418.
Küster, Stallberg, *Ann.*, 1894, **278**, 219.

1 : 3 : 9-Trimethylisoxanthine.
See Isocaffeine.

Trimethylketol (*Dimethylacetylcarbinol*, 2-*methyl-2-butanolone*-3, 3-*keto*-tert.-*amyl alcohol*)

$(CH_3)_2C(OH)\cdot CO\cdot CH_3$

$C_5H_{10}O_2$ MW, 102

Liq. with sweet odour. B.p. 141–2°, 50°/18 mm. D_4^{21} 0·9632.

Me ether: *oxime*, prisms from ligroin. M.p. 92–3°. B.p. 190°/742 mm. Sol. H_2O, EtOH. Less sol. ligroin. Volatile in steam.

Oxime: leaflets from ligroin. M.p. 85–6° (96–100°).

Semicarbazone: cryst. from $CHCl_3$–pet. ether. M.p. 165°.

Phenylhydrazone: plates from EtOH. M.p. 83–5°.

Faworsky, *J. prakt. Chem.*, 1913, **88**, 662.
Diels, Johlin, *Ber.*, 1911, **44**, 405.
Schmidt, Austin, *Ber.*, 1902, **35**, 3724.

Trimethyl-lactic Acid.
See Hydroxydimethylbutyric Acid.

Trimethylmalic Acid (*Hydroxytrimethylsuccinic acid*)

$CH_3\cdot C(OH)\cdot COOH$
$(CH_3)_2C\cdot COOH$

$C_7H_{12}O_5$ MW, 176

Plates from H_2O, prisms from AcOEt. M.p. 159–60° (153–5°). M.p. depends on rate of heating. Very sol. H_2O, EtOH, Et_2O, Me_2CO. Sol. AcOEt. Insol. C_6H_6, ligroin. $k = 9{\cdot}4 \times 10^{-4}$ at 25°.

Di-Et ester: $C_{11}H_{20}O_5$. MW, 232. B.p. 122–3°/9 mm. D_{18}^{18} 1·066.

Anhydride: *acetyl*, needles from boiling ligroin. M.p. 67–8°. Sol. usual solvents except H_2O, ligroin.

β-*Lactone*: needles from C_6H_6–pet. ether. M.p. 120° (118–20°).

Auwers, v. Campenhausen, *Ber.*, 1896, **29**, 1544.
Bergroth, Komppa, *Ber.*, 1896, **29**, 1620.
Komppa, *Chem. Zentr.*, 1898, II, 1168; *Ber.*, 1902, **35**, 534.

2 : 4 : 5-Trimethylmandelic Acid (2 : 4 : 5-*Trimethylphenylglycollic acid*)

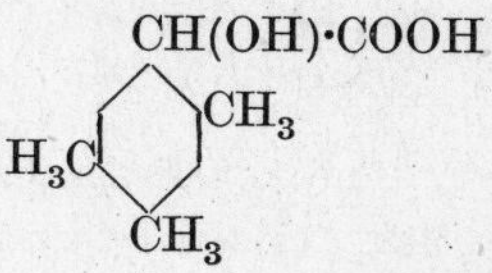

$C_{11}H_{14}O_3$ MW, 194

Cryst. from C_6H_6. M.p. 137·5–138·5° (133–5°).

Gattermann, *Ann.*, 1906, **347**, 376.
Fisher, Walling, *J. Am. Chem. Soc.*, 1935, **57**, 1564.
Smith, MacMullen, *J. Am. Chem. Soc.*, 1936, **58**, 633.

2 : 4 : 6-Trimethylmandelic Acid.
See Mesitylglycollic Acid.

Trimethylmethane.
See Isobutane.

Trimethylmethane-tricarboxylic Acid.
See Methane-triacetic Acid.

1 : 2 : 3-Trimethylnaphthalene

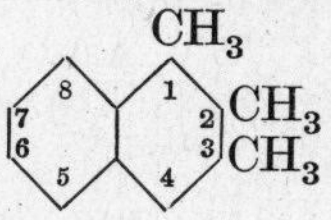

$C_{13}H_{14}$ MW, 170

B.p. 125–30°/12 mm.

Picrate: light orange-yellow needles from EtOH. M.p. 142·5°.

Styphnate: yellow. M.p. 143·5°.

Ruzicka, Ehmann, Keller, Schütze, *Helv. Chim. Acta*, 1932, **15**, 143.

1 : 2 : 4-Trimethylnaphthalene.
Leaflets from EtOH. M.p. 50°. B.p. 146°/12 mm.

Picrate: orange needles from MeOH. M.p. 147·5°.

Styphnate: orange-yellow needles. M.p. 123·5°.

Ruzicka, Ehmann, Tombe, Ramondt, *Helv. Chim. Acta*, 1932, **15**, 145.

1 : 2 : 5-Trimethylnaphthalene.
M.p. 31–2°. B.p. 147–8°/11 mm. D_4^{22} 1·0103. n_D^{22} 1·6093.
Picrate : cryst. from EtOH. M.p. 137–8°.
Styphnate : cryst. from EtOH. M.p. 131°.

Ruzicka, Hosking, *Helv. Chim. Acta*, 1930, **13**, 1411.
Heilbron, Wilkinson, *J. Chem. Soc.*, 1930, 2546.

1 : 2 : 6-Trimethylnaphthalene.
B.p. 146°/10 mm.
Picrate : orange needles. M.p. 121–2° (120–1°).
Styphnate : yellow needles. M.p. 148°.

Ruzicka, Ehmann, Cuenat, Biasotti, *Helv. Chim. Acta*, 1932, **15**, 146.

1 : 2 : 7-Trimethylnaphthalene.
See Sapotalin.

1 : 2 : 8-Trimethylnaphthalene.
B.p. 152–5°/14 mm.
Picrate : reddish-orange needles from EtOH. M.p. 139–40° (133°).
Styphnate : golden-yellow needles from EtOH. M.p. 144·5°.

Ruzicka, Ehmann, Hartnagel, Hausschild, *Helv. Chim. Acta*, 1932, **15**, 149.
Ruzicka, Hofmann, Frei, *Helv. Chim. Acta*, 1936, **19**, 391.

1 : 3 : 5-Trimethylnaphthalene.
Prisms from MeOH. M.p. 47° (43°). B.p. 139·5°/10 mm.
Picrate : orange-yellow needles from MeOH. M.p. 141–2° (140°).
Styphnate : golden-yellow needles. M.p. 138° (136·5°).

Heilbron, Wilkinson, *J. Chem. Soc.*, 1930, 2540.
Ruzicka, Ehmann, Weber, *Helv. Chim. Acta*, 1932, **15**, 153.

1 : 3 : 6-Trimethylnaphthalene.
B.p. 140–4°/10 mm.
Picrate : light orange needles. M.p. 115°.
Styphnate : yellow needles. M.p. 148°.

Ruzicka, Ehmann, Arni, Bernasconi, *Helv. Chim. Acta*, 1932, **15**, 154.

1 : 3 : 7-Trimethylnaphthalene.
B.p. 131–3°/9 mm. D_4^{21} 0·9801. n_D^{15} 1·5972.
Picrate : orange-yellow needles from MeOH. M.p. 142°.
Styphnate : golden-orange cryst. from MeOH. M.p. 151·5°.

Ruzicka, Ehmann, Pieth, Thomann, *Helv. Chim. Acta*, 1932, **15**, 155.

1 : 3 : 8-Trimethylnaphthalene.
Plates from MeOH. M.p. 48°.
Picrate : orange-red needles from EtOH. M.p. 125°.
Styphnate : golden needles from EtOH. M.p. 140·5°.

Heilbron, Wilkinson, *J. Chem. Soc.*, 1930, 2542.

1 : 4 : 5-Trimethylnaphthalene.
Leaflets from MeOH. M.p. 63°. B.p. 145°/12 mm.
Picrate : deep reddish-orange needles. M.p. 144–5°.
Styphnate : reddish-brown needles. M.p. 129–30°.

Ruzicka, Ehmann, Hefti, Altuna, *Helv. Chim. Acta*, 1932, **15**, 156.

1 : 4 : 6-Trimethylnaphthalene.
B.p. 140–2°/15 mm.
Picrate : orange-red needles. M.p. 133°.
Styphnate : golden-yellow cryst. M.p. 114°.

Ruzicka, Ehmann, Addink, *Helv. Chim. Acta*, 1932, **15**, 158.

1 : 6 : 7-Trimethylnaphthalene (*2 : 3 : 5-Trimethylnaphthalene*).
Cryst. from MeOH. M.p. 28°. B.p. 138°/12 mm.
Picrate : golden-orange needles from MeOH. M.p. 125° (122·5°).
Styphnate : golden-yellow needles. M.p. 148–9° (146°).

Wilkinson, *J. Chem. Soc.*, 1931, 1333.
Ruzicka, Ehmann, Weisz, *Helv. Chim. Acta*, 1932, **15**, 159.
Barnett, Sanders, *J. Chem. Soc.*, 1933, 437.
Ruzicka, *Helv. Chim. Acta*, 1936, **19**, 423.

2 : 3 : 6-Trimethylnaphthalene.
M.p. 92–3°. B.p. 263–4°, 146–8°/14 mm.
Picrate : orange-yellow needles from MeOH. M.p. 130°.
Styphnate : yellow needles from MeOH. M.p. 165°.

Ruzicka, Ehmann, Rierink, *Helv. Chim. Acta*, 1932, **15**, 160.
Collie, *J. Chem. Soc.*, 1893, **63**, 336.

2 : 5 : 8-Trimethylnonanol-5.
See Methyldi-isoamylcarbinol.

2 : 2 : 3-Trimethylpentane

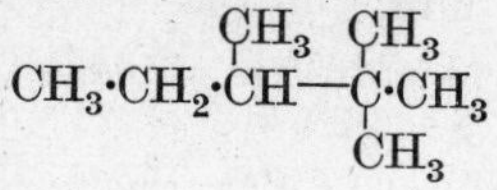

C_8H_{18} MW, 114

B.p. 110·2°. D_4^{20} 0·7173. n_D^{20} 1·4030.

Laughlin, Whitmore, *J. Am. Chem. Soc.*, 1933, **55**, 2608.

2 : 2 : 4-Trimethylpentane

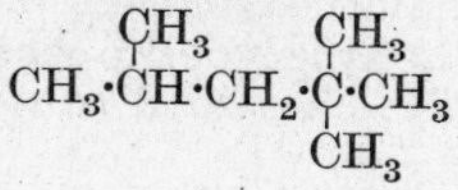

C_8H_{18} MW, 114

F.p. −107·41°. B.p. 99·3°. D_4^{20} 0·6918. n_D^{20} 1·3916.

Petrov, Andreev, Chapluigin, *Chem. Abstracts*, 1933, **27**, 266.
Edgar, Calingaert, *J. Am. Chem. Soc.*, 1929, **51**, 1546.

2 : 3 : 3-Trimethylpentane

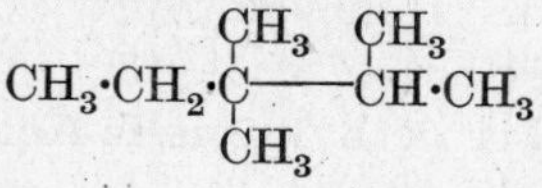

C_8H_{18} MW, 114

B.p. 113·6°/760 mm. D_4^{20} 0·7258. n_D^{20} 1·4074.

Laughlin, Whitmore, *J. Am. Chem. Soc.*, 1933, **55**, 2608.

2 : 3 : 4-Trimethylpentane

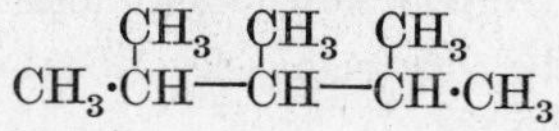

C_8H_{18} MW, 114

B.p. 112·8°/760 mm., 111·5°/732 mm. D_4^{20} 0·7197. n_D^{20} 1·4045.

See previous reference.

Trimethylpentanol.
See Methylethyl-*tert.*-butylcarbinol *and* Isopropyl-*tert.*-butylcarbinol.

2 : 2 : 4-Trimethylpentanone-3.
See Isopropyl-*tert.*-butyl Ketone.

2 : 3 : 3-Trimethyl-1-pentene

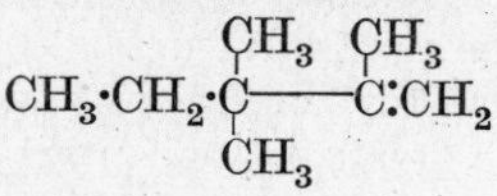

C_8H_{16} MW, 112

B.p. 108·2°/760 mm. D_4^{20} 0·7363. n_D^{20} 1·4178.

Laughlin, Whitmore, *J. Am. Chem. Soc.*, 1933, **55**, 2608.

2 : 4 : 4-Trimethyl-1-pentene

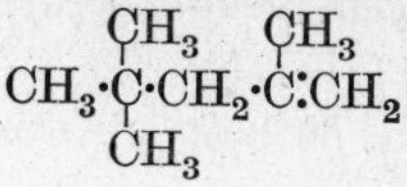

C_8H_{16} MW, 112

One constituent of "di-isobutylene" (or "isodibutylene"). F.p. −93·6°. B.p. 101·2°/760 mm., 100·1°/737 mm. D_4^{20} 0·7151. n_D^{20} 1·4082.

Tongberg, Pickens, Fenske, Whitmore, *J. Am. Chem. Soc.*, 1932, **54**, 3706.
Whitmore, Church, *ibid.*, 3710 (*Bibl.*).
See also Petrow, Anzus, Ardrejew, *Bull. soc. chim.*, 1933, **53**, 327 (*Bibl.*).

2 : 3 : 4-Trimethyl-2-pentene

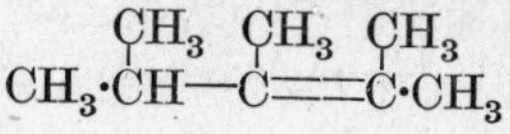

C_8H_{16} MW, 112

B.p. 114·3°/739 mm. n_D^{20} 1·4263.

Whitmore, Laughlin, *J. Am. Chem. Soc.*, 1932, **54**, 4392.

2 : 4 : 4-Trimethyl-2-pentene

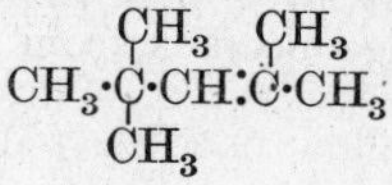

C_8H_{16} MW, 112

One constituent of "di-isobutylene" (or "isodibutylene"). F.p. − 106·5°. B.p. 104·5°/760 mm., 103·4°/737 mm. D_4^{20} 0·7211. n_D^{20} 1·4158.

Tongberg, Pickens, Fenske, Whitmore, *J. Am. Chem. Soc.*, 1932, **54**, 3706.
Whitmore, Church, *ibid.*, 3710 (*Bibl.*).
See also Petrow, Anzus, Ardrejew, *Bull. soc. chim.*, 1933, **53**, 327.

3 : 4 : 4-Trimethyl-2-pentene

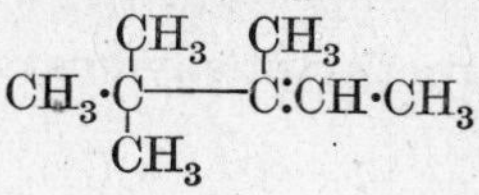

C_8H_{16} MW, 112

B.p. 111·9°/760 mm. D_4^{20} 0·7395. n_D^{20} 1·4232.

Laughlin, Whitmore, *J. Am. Chem. Soc.*, 1933, **55**, 2608.

1 : 2 : 7-Trimethylphenanthrene

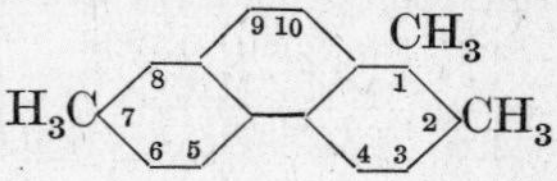

$C_{17}H_{16}$ MW, 220

Plates from EtOH. M.p. 120–1°.
Picrate: orange needles. M.p. 148–9°.
Styphnate: orange needles. M.p. 169–70°.

Haworth, Bolam, *J. Chem. Soc.*, 1932, 2250.

1 : 2 : 8-Trimethylphenanthrene.
Plates from EtOH. M.p. 144–5°. B.p. 210–20°/15 mm.
Picrate: orange-red needles from EtOH. M.p. 163°.

Haworth, Mavin, *J. Chem. Soc.*, 1932, 2723.
Ruzicka, Hosking, *Helv. Chim. Acta*, 1931, **14**, 203.

1 : 3 : 7-Trimethylphenanthrene.
Prisms from MeOH. M.p. 68–9°.
Picrate: pale orange needles from EtOH. M.p. 163–4°.
Styphnate: yellow needles. M.p. 160–1°.

Haworth, Bolam, *J. Chem. Soc.*, 1932, 2250.

1 : 4 : 7-Trimethylphenanthrene.
Prisms from EtOH. M.p. 72–3°.
Picrate: orange needles from MeOH. M.p. 141–2°.
Styphnate: yellow needles. M.p. 129–30°.

Haworth, Letsky, Mavin, *J. Chem. Soc.*, 1932, 1789.

1 : 6 : 7-Trimethylphenanthrene.
Plates from EtOH. M.p. 123–4°.
Picrate: orange needles. M.p. 165–6°.
Styphnate: yellow needles. M.p. 111–12°.

Haworth, Bolam, *J. Chem. Soc.*, 1932, 2251.

Trimethylphenol.
See Hemimellitenol, Hydroxy-ψ-cumene, *and* Mesitol.

2 : 4 : 5-Trimethylphenylacetic Acid (5-*ψ-Cumylacetic acid*)

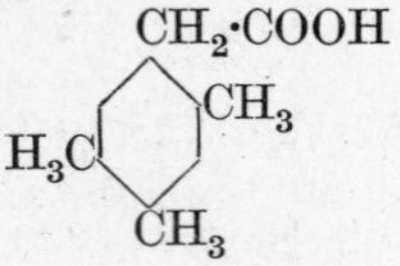

$C_{11}H_{14}O_2$ MW, 178

Needles from H_2O. M.p. 128–9° (118°). Sol. usual org. solvents. Sublimes.
Amide: $C_{11}H_{15}ON$. MW, 177. Leaflets from H_2O. M.p. 174°. Sol. EtOH, Et_2O, $CHCl_3$. Sublimes.
Nitrile: $C_{11}H_{13}N$. MW, 159. M.p. 9–10°. B.p. 133–7°/4 mm.

Smith, MacMullen, *J. Am. Chem. Soc.*, 1936, **58**, 632.
Willgerodt, *J. prakt. Chem.*, 1909, **80**, 185.
Willgerodt, Scholz, *J. prakt. Chem.*, 1910, **81**, 388.

2 : 4 : 6-Trimethylphenylacetic Acid.
See Mesitylacetic Acid.

Trimethylphenylenediamine.
See under Phenylenediamine.

Trimethylphenylglycollic Acid.
See Mesitylglycollic Acid *and* Trimethylmandelic Acid.

2 : 4 : 6-Trimethylphloroglucinol.
See 2 : 4 : 6-Trihydroxymesitylene.

Trimethyl phosphate.
See under Phosphoric Acid.

Trimethylphosphine

$(CH_3)_3P$

C_3H_9P MW, 76

B.p. 40–2°. Insol. H_2O.

Cahours, Hofmann, *Ann.*, 1857, **104**, 29.
Dreschel, *J. prakt. Chem.*, 1874, **10**, 180.

1 : 2 : 5-Trimethylpimelic Acid (3-*Methylheptane*-2 : 6-*dicarboxylic acid*)

$$HOOC\cdot\overset{CH_3}{\overset{|}{C}H}\cdot CH_2\cdot CH_2\cdot\overset{CH_3}{\overset{|}{C}H}-\overset{CH_3}{\overset{|}{C}H}\cdot COOH$$

$C_{10}H_{18}O_4$ MW, 202

Oil. B.p. 213–15°/15 mm. Dist. with KOH ⟶ 2 : 3 : 6-trimethylcyclohexanone.

Zelinsky, Reformatsky, *Ber.*, 1895, **28**, 2944.

1 : 2 : 6-Trimethylpiperidine

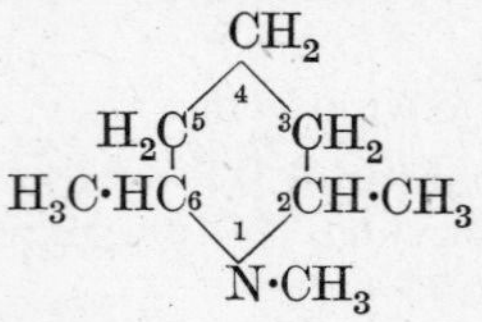

$C_8H_{17}N$ MW, 127

Cis:
Mobile liq. B.p. 50–5°/12 mm.
B,HAuCl₄: m.p. 174–5°.
Methiodide: m.p. 275°.

Mannich, *Arch. Pharm.*, 1934, **272**, 356.

2 : 2 : 4-Trimethylpiperidine.
B.p. 148°. D^{15} 0·832. Sol. EtOH, Et_2O. Mod. sol. H_2O. Turns yellow in air. $FeCl_3$ ⟶ red ppt.

$B,HAuCl_4$: prisms. M.p. 135°.
B_2,H_2PtCl_6 : red cryst. M.p. 215–16° decomp.
Methiodide : prisms from H_2O or EtOH. M.p. 266° decomp.

Issoglio, *Chem. Zentr.*, 1908, II, 1444.

2 : 2 : 6-Trimethylpiperidine.
B.p. 138–9°.
B,HCl : m.p. 236–7°.
$B,HAuCl_4$: rhombohedra from *N*/HCl. M.p. 127–9°.
Picrate : rhombohedra from H_2O. M.p. 195–6°.

Gough, King, *J. Chem. Soc.*, 1928, 2444.

2 : 4 : 6-Trimethylpiperidine.
B.p. 165–6° (151–3°). D^4 0·8430. Misc. with EtOH, Et_2O. Spar. sol. H_2O.
B,HBr : exists in two forms. (i) Needles from H_2O. M.p. 204–9°. Sol. C_6H_6. (ii) M.p. above 270°. Spar. sol. C_6H_6.

Koenigs, Bernhart, Ibele, *Ber.*, 1907, **40**, 3199, 3206.
Skita, Brunner, *Ber.*, 1916, **49**, 1601.

2 : 2 : 6-Trimethyl-γ-piperidone.
See Vinyldiacetonamine.

Trimethylpropionic Acid.
See 1 : 2-Dimethylbutyric Acid *and tert.*-Butylacetic Acid.

1 : 3 : 4-Trimethylpyrazole

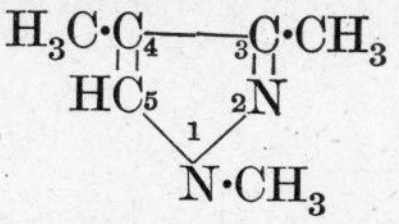

$C_6H_{10}N_2$ MW, 110

Oil. B.p. 160°. $D_4^{17·7}$ 0·9567. $n_{He}^{17·7}$ 1·48663.
Picrate : dark yellow leaflets from H_2O. M.p. 163·5–164·5°. Very spar. sol. Et_2O.

Auwers, Cauer, *J. prakt. Chem.*, 1930, **126**, 202.

1 : 3 : 5-Trimethylpyrazole.
Needles with iodoform odour. M.p. 37°. B.p. 170°/755 mm. $D_4^{57·8}$ 0·9130. $n_{He}^{57·8}$ 1·45893.
$B,HAuCl_4$: needles + H_2O from H_2O. M.p. 91–4°.
B_2,H_2PtCl_6 : cryst. M.p. 187–91°. Very sol. H_2O.
Picrate : m.p. 147° (144–5°).

Rojahn, Kühling, *Arch. Pharm.*, 1926, **264**, 337.
Knorr, *Ann.*, 1894, **279**, 232.

1 : 4 : 5-Trimethylpyrazole.
Oil. B.p. 176–7°. $D_4^{17·8}$ 0·9685. $n_{He}^{17·8}$ 1·48485.
Picrate : pale yellow needles from EtOH. M.p. 175–6°. Mod. sol. H_2O, EtOH, C_6H_6. Spar. sol. Et_2O.

Auwers, Cauer, *J. prakt. Chem.*, 1930, **126**, 202.

3 : 4 : 5-Trimethylpyrazole.
Leaflets from H_2O. M.p. 138–9°. B.p. 232–3°/753 mm. Sol. EtOH, Et_2O, $CHCl_3$, C_6H_6. Volatile in steam.
B,HCl : needles. Decomp. at 265°.
B_2,H_2PtCl_6 : yellow cryst. + $2H_2O$. Decomp. about 200°.
Picrate : yellow needles from H_2O or EtOH. M.p. 239–41°.
1-N-o-*Nitrobenzoyl* : cryst. from EtOH. M.p. 128–9°. Sol. Et_2O, Me_2CO, AcOH, C_6H_6. Spar. sol. EtOH, pet. ether.

Auwers, Cauer, Wolter, *J. prakt. Chem.*, 1930, **126**, 175.
v. Rothenburg, *J. prakt. Chem.*, 1895, **52**, 51.
Knorr, Oettinger, *Ann.*, 1894, **279**, 244.
Posner, *Ber.*, 1901, **34**, 3981.

1 : 2 : 3-Trimethylpyrazolone-5

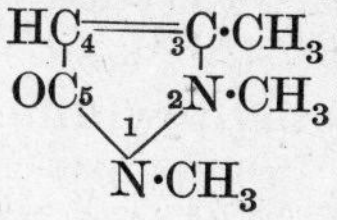

$C_6H_{10}ON_2$ MW, 126

B.p. 306–9°/751 mm.
B_2,H_2PtCl_6 : prisms from EtOH.Aq. Decomp. at 197–8°.
Picrate : needles from H_2O. M.p. 211–12° decomp. Spar. sol. H_2O.

Knorr, *Ber.*, 1906, **39**, 3267.

1 : 3 : 4-Trimethylpyrazolone-5.
Needles from C_6H_6. M.p. 133–4°. B.p. 154°/19 mm. Sol. EtOH, H_2O. Spar. sol. Et_2O, C_6H_6, pet. ether.
Picrate : greenish-yellow needles from EtOH. M.p. 148°.

Auwers, Bähr, *J. prakt. Chem.*, 1927, **116**, 82.

3 : 4 : 4-Trimethylpyrazolone-5.
Two compounds of this structure are described in the literature.
(i) Prisms from EtOH. M.p. 109·5°. Sol. H_2O, Et_2O, Me_2CO, $CHCl_3$, AcOH. Less sol. EtOH. Almost insol. pet. ether. No col. with $FeCl_3$.

Backer, *Rec. trav. chim.*, 1926, **45**, 86.

(ii) Cryst. from EtOH or H_2O. M.p. 269° (262–3°).
Acetyl : cryst. powder. M.p. 168°.

v. Rothenburg, *J. prakt. Chem.*, 1895, **52**, 43.
De, Dutt, *J. Indian Chem. Soc.*, 1930, **7**, 478.

2 : 3 : 4-Trimethylpyridine (αβγ-*Collidine*)

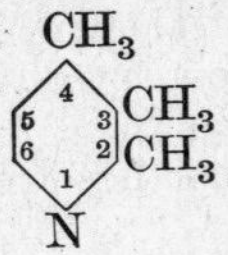

$C_8H_{11}N$ MW, 121

Found in low temperature coal tar. B.p. 192–3°. D^{15} 0·9127 (0·9566). Sol. H_2O, EtOH, Et_2O. $KMnO_4 \longrightarrow$ carbocinchomeronic acid. Easily decomp.
B_2,H_2PtCl_6 : yellow prisms from H_2O. M.p. 259°.
$B,HAuCl_4$: yellow needles from H_2O. M.p. about 182–3°.
Picrate : yellow needles. M.p. 163–4°.

Guareschi, *Chem. Zentr.*, 1900, I, 1161.
Oparina, *Ber.*, 1931, **64**, 563, 574.

2 : 3 : 5-Trimethylpyridine (αββ'-*Collidine*).
Found in low temperature coal tar. B.p. 182–3°/739 mm. Spar. sol. H_2O. Volatile in steam.
$B,HAuCl_4$: needles from H_2O. M.p. 146–7°.
B_2,H_2PtCl_6 : yellow needles from dil. HCl. M.p. 227–8°.
Picrate : yellow needles. M.p. 183° (179°).

Komatsu, Mohri, *J. Chem. Soc. Japan*, 1931, **52**, 722.
Oparina, *Ber.*, 1931, **64**, 563.

2 : 3 : 6-Trimethylpyridine (αβα'-*Collidine*).
Found in low temperature coal tar. B.p. 176–8°/759 mm., 173–4°/734 mm.
$B,HAuCl_4$: needles. M.p. 106°.
B_2,H_2PtCl_6 : cryst. + H_2O. M.p. 250–2° decomp.
Picrate : yellow needles. M.p. 146°.

Oparina, *Ber.*, 1931, **64**, 573.
Eckert, Loria, *Monatsh.*, 1917, **38**, 228, 240.
Basu, Banerjee, *J. Indian Chem. Soc.*, 1935, **12**, 665.

2 : 4 : 5-Trimethylpyridine (αγβ'-*Collidine*).
B.p. 165–8°. Spar. sol. H_2O. $KMnO_4 \longrightarrow$ berberonic acid.
B_2,H_2PtCl_6,H_2O : red cryst. Decomp. at 205°.
$B,HAuCl_4$: plates or needles from dil. HCl. M.p. 129–31°.
Picrate : orange needles. M.p. 128–31°.

Ahrens, *Ber.*, 1896, **29**, 2998.

2 : 4 : 6-Trimethylpyridine (γ-*Collidine*, αγα'-*collidine*).
Found in low temperature coal tar. B.p. 171–2° (175–8°). D^{20} 0·917. $k = 2{\cdot}05 \times 10^{-7}$ at 25°.
B,HI : prisms. Decomp. at 250°.
B_2,H_2SO_4 : needles or prisms. M.p. 205°.
$B,HAuCl_4$: needles + H_2O. M.p. 53°, anhyd. 112–13°.
B_2,H_2PtCl_6 : yellow cryst. from H_2O. M.p. 223–4° decomp.
$B,HCl,2HgCl_2$: needles from H_2O. M.p. 158–60°.
Picrate : yellow needles from H_2O. M.p. 155–6°.
Methoperchlorate : prisms from H_2O. M.p. 206–7°.

Hantzsch, *Ann.*, 1882, **215**, 32.
Dürkopf, *Ber.*, 1888, **21**, 2713.

3 : 4 : 5-Trimethylpyromucic Acid (3 : 4 : 5-*Trimethylfuran-2-carboxylic acid*, 3 : 4 : 5-*trimethyl-α-furoic acid*)

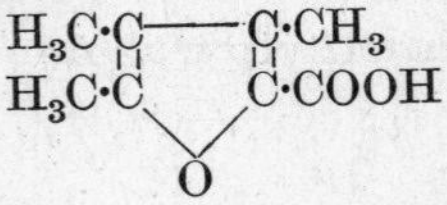

$C_8H_{10}O_3$ MW, 154

Cryst. from pet. ether. M.p. 185° decomp.

Reichstein, Zschokke, Syz, *Helv. Chim. Acta*, 1932, **15**, 1117.

1 : 2 : 5-Trimethylpyrrole

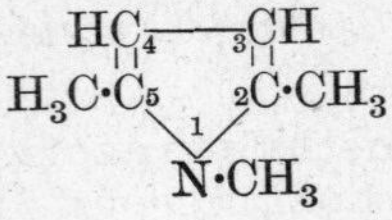

$C_7H_{11}N$ MW, 109

B.p. 169°/746 mm. (162–4°), 55–6°/9 mm. Sol. EtOH, Et_2O, $CHCl_3$, C_6H_6. Spar. sol. H_2O. Volatile in steam. Hot aq. $FeCl_3 \longrightarrow$ deep cherry-red col.

Lukeš, *Chem. Abstracts*, 1932, **26**, 4328.
Lukeš, Přeučil, *Chem. Zentr.*, 1936, I, 2082.
Knorr, *Ann.*, 1886, **236**, 304.

2 : 3 : 4-Trimethylpyrrole.
Prisms. M.p. 39°. B.p. 71–72·5°/10 mm. Volatile in steam.

Picrate : yellow leaflets from EtOH. M.p. 148° (140°).

Piloty, Hirsch, *Ann.*, 1913, **395**, 66.
Fischer, Walach, *Ann.*, 1926, **450**, 114; 1926, **447**, 47.

2 : 3 : 5-Trimethylpyrrole.
B.p. 180°/768 mm., 79–80°/15 mm.
B_2,Hg($HgCl_2$)$_4$: m.p. 120–5° decomp. Sol. AcOH. Spar. sol. H_2O. Insol. most org. solvents.

Korschun, *Ber.*, 1905, **38**, 1129.
Nenitzescu, Solomonica, *Ber.*, 1931, **64**, 1928.
Fischer, Müller, *Z. physiol. Chem.*, 1925, **148**, 155.
Piloty, Hirsch, *Ann.*, 1913, **395**, 68.

1 : 2 : 2-Trimethylpyrrolidine

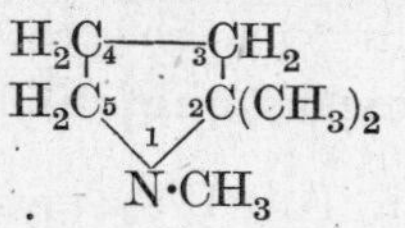

$C_7H_{15}N$ MW, 113

Liq. B.p. 130–5°.

Lukeš, *Chem. Abstracts*, 1931, **25**, 102.

1 : 2 : 4-Trimethylpyrrolidine.
B.p. 111–13°. D^{15} 0·790.
B,$HAuCl_4$: golden-yellow ppt. M.p. 98–9°.
B_2,H_2PtCl_6 : orange-yellow prisms. M.p. 179–80°. Sol. H_2O.

Jacobi, Merling, *Ann.*, 1894, **278**, 9.

1 : 2 : 5-Trimethylpyrrolidine.
B.p. 115–16°/750 mm. $D_4^{9\cdot2}$ 0·8149. $n_a^{9\cdot2}$ 1·4335. Spar. sol. H_2O.
B,$HAuCl_4$: golden-yellow cryst. M.p. about 178°.
B_2,H_2PtCl_6 : orange-yellow leaflets from EtOH. Decomp. at 190–210°.
Picrate : cryst. from EtOH. M.p. about 163°. Spar. sol. H_2O.
Picrolonate : needles. M.p. about 193°. Sol. H_2O.
Methiodide : cryst. from EtOH. M.p. 310°.

Knorr, Rabe, *Ber.*, 1901, **34**, 3500.
Tafel, Neugebauer, *Ber.*, 1890, **23**, 1548.
Merling, *Ann.*, 1891, **264**, 334.

2 : 3 : 5-Trimethylpyrrolidine.
B.p. 126–8°. D^{15} 0·816. Misc. with H_2O.
B_2,H_2PtCl_6 : orange-red prisms. M.p. 205–6° decomp.

Jacobi, Merling, *Ann.*, 1894, **278**, 13.

Trimethylpyruvic Acid (tert.-*Butylglyoxylic acid*, 1-*keto*-2 : 2-*dimethylpropionic acid*, 1-*keto*-tert.-*butylacetic acid*)

$(CH_3)_3C{\cdot}CO{\cdot}COOH$

$C_6H_{10}O_3$ MW, 130

Needles from Et_2O. M.p. 90–1° (82°). B.p. 189°/747 mm., 80°/15 mm. Sol. Et_2O. Less sol. $CHCl_3$, CS_2, C_6H_6. Spar. sol. H_2O. Ox. $\longrightarrow$ pivalic acid. Volatile in steam.
Me ester : $C_7H_{12}O_3$. MW, 144. B.p. 160–2°, 69–70°/20 mm. D_4^0 0·994. *Oxime* : cryst. from Et_2O–pet. ether. M.p. 66°. *Semicarbazone* : cryst. from EtOH.Aq. M.p. 125°.
Et ester : $C_8H_{14}O_3$. MW, 158. B.p. 76–7°/20 mm., 68°/15 mm. D^0 0·9716. *Oxime* : cryst. M.p. 22–3°. B.p. 131–3°/20 mm. *Semicarbazone* : cryst. from EtOH.Aq. M.p. 115°.
Oxime : leaflets + H_2O from EtOH. M.p. 85–6°, anhyd. 121°.
Semicarbazone : cryst. from H_2O. M.p. 195° (181°).
Phenylhydrazone : yellowish needles from EtOH.Aq. M.p. 157–8° decomp.

Richard, *Ann. chim. phys.*, 1910, **21**, 360.
Glückermann, *Monatsh.*, 1889, **10**, 771.

2 : 3 : 4-Trimethylquinoline (3 : 4-*Dimethylquinaldine*)

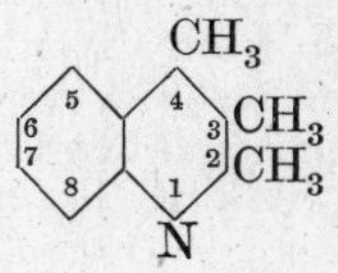

$C_{12}H_{13}N$ MW, 171

Cryst. M.p. 92° (65°). B.p. 285°, 156–8°/12 mm.
B,HCl : m.p. 274°. Spar. sol. EtOH.
B_2,H_2PtCl_6 : reddish-yellow. M.p. 215°.
Methiodide : yellow. M.p. 260°. Spar. sol. EtOH.
Picrate : cryst. from EtOH. M.p. 216°.

v. Braun, Gmelin, Petzold, *Ber.*, 1924, **57**, 387.
Combes, *Compt. rend.*, 1888, **106**, 143.

2 : 3 : 6-Trimethylquinoline (3 : 6-*Dimethylquinaldine*).
Cryst. from ligroin. M.p. 86–7°. B.p. 285°. Sol. Et_2O. Mod. sol. EtOH. Spar. sol. C_6H_6, ligroin. Insol. H_2O.
Picrate : yellow leaflets from EtOH. M.p. 212° decomp.

v. Miller, *Ber.*, 1890, **23**, 2268.

2 : 3 : 8-Trimethylquinoline (3 : 8-*Dimethylquinaldine*).

Found in Californian petroleum. Plates from 50% EtOH. M.p. 55–6°. B.p. 280°/747 mm., part. decomp. Sol. most org. solvents. Spar. sol. H_2O. Volatile in steam.

B,HCl : needles from H_2O or EtOH. Darkens at 230°, decomp. at 260°.

B,HNO₃ : needles from 95% EtOH. M.p. 160·5° decomp.

B,H₂SO₄ : prisms from 95% EtOH. Decomp. at about 275°.

Picrate : yellow cryst. from AcOH. Decomp. at 242–5°.

Poth *et al.*, *J. Am. Chem. Soc.*, 1930, **52**, 1245.

2 : 4 : 6-Trimethylquinoline (4 : 6-*Dimethylquinaldine*).

Needles + H_2O from H_2O + trace EtOH. M.p. 39·4°, anhyd. 65·5°. B.p. 281–2°, 146–8°/13·5 mm. Sol. EtOH, Et_2O, $CHCl_3$, Me_2CO, C_6H_6, pet. ether. Spar. sol. H_2O. Bitter taste. Sweet odour. Spar. volatile in steam.

B,HCl : needles from H_2O. M.p. 268–72°.

B,HBr : needles from EtOH.Aq. M.p. about 265–70°.

B_2,H_2SO_4 : needles from EtOH. M.p. 221–2°.

$B,HAuCl_4$: yellow needles. M.p. 140° decomp.

Tartrate : cryst. from EtOH. M.p. 172°.

Picrate : greenish-yellow needles from Me_2CO. M.p. 200–1°. Spar. sol. hot EtOH.

Picrolonate : yellow needles from C_6H_6–EtOH. M.p. about 245°.

Methiodide : pale yellow needles from EtOH. M.p. 245–7° (225–6°).

Ethochloride : needles from EtOH–Et_2O. Decomp. at 247°. Very sol. H_2O, EtOH.

Ethobromide : leaflets from EtOH. Decomp. at 246°. Very sol. H_2O.

Pfitzinger, *J. prakt. Chem.*, 1888, **38**, 41.
Knoll, D.R.Ps., 363,582–3, (*Chem. Abstracts*, 1924, **18**, 991).
Bähr, *Ber.*, 1922, **55**, 1925.
Fischer, Scheibe, Müller, Merkel, *J. prakt. Chem.*, 1920, **100**, 97.

2 : 4 : 7-Trimethylquinoline (4 : 7-*Dimethylquinaldine*).

Liq. B.p. 280–1°. D^{20} 1·0337. n_D^{24} 1·59732. Forms hydrate with $1H_2O$, m.p. 48°.

B,HCl : cryst. + $2H_2O$. Sublimes at 310°.

B,HBr : cryst. + H_2O. Decomp. at 351°.

B,HI : decomp. at 320°.

$B,HAuCl_4$: m.p. 152°.

B_2,H_2PtCl_6 : decomp. at 272°.

B_2,H_2SO_4 : cryst. + H_2O. M.p. 233°.

Picrate : decomp. at 232°.

Methiodide : sublimes at 322°.

Yamaguchi, *J. Pharm. Soc. Japan*, 1924, **503**, 23.

2 : 4 : 8-Trimethylquinoline (4 : 8-*Dimethylquinaldine*).

Found in petroleum. Cryst. M.p. 42°. B.p. 269–70° (280°/746 mm.). n_D^{50} 1·5855.

B,HCl : cryst. + $2H_2O$. M.p. 238°.

B,HBr : cryst. + $2H_2O$. M.p. anhyd. 251°.

B,HI : cryst. + H_2O. M.p. 224°.

$B,HAuCl_4$: m.p. 191°.

B,H_2SO_4 : cryst. + H_2O. M.p. 263°.

Picrate : m.p. 193°.

Methiodide : decomp. at 229°.

Perrin, Bailey, *J. Am. Chem. Soc.*, 1933, **55**, 4136.
See also previous reference.

2 : 6 : 8-Trimethylquinoline (6 : 8-*Dimethylquinaldine*).

Leaflets from EtOH.Aq., prisms from pet. ether. M.p. 46°. B.p. 266–7°/780 mm., 260°/719 mm. Very sol. EtOH, Et_2O, pet. ether. Insol. H_2O. Volatile in steam.

B,HCl : prisms. M.p. 207°.

B,HBr : prisms. M.p. 172–3°.

B,HI : yellow prisms. M.p. 223–4°.

B_2,H_2PtCl_6 : brown cryst. M.p. 206–7°.

Picrate : yellow prisms. M.p. 187–9°.

d-*Camphorsulphonate* : m.p. 231–2°.

Panajotow, *Ber.*, 1887, **20**, 32.
v. Miller, Plöchl, *Ber.*, 1896, **29**, 1472.
Jones, Evans, *J. Chem. Soc.*, 1911, **99**, 335.

5 : 6 : 8-Trimethylquinoline.

Prisms. M.p. 42–3°. B.p. 285–7°. Sol. usual solvents.

B,HNO₃ : needles. Spar. sol. H_2O.

B,H₂SO₄ : prisms from EtOH.

Berend, *Ber.*, 1885, **18**, 376.
Wikander, *Ber.*, 1900, **33**, 646.

2 : 4 : 6-Trimethylresorcinol.

See Mesorcinol.

3 : 4 : 6-Trimethylsalicylaldehyde (6-*Hydroxy*-2 : 4 : 5-*trimethylbenzaldehyde*)

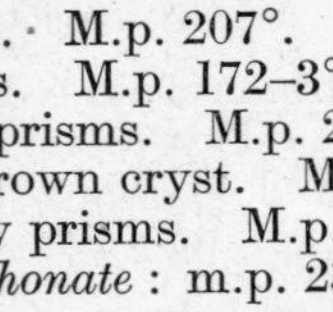

$C_{10}H_{12}O_2$ MW, 164

Plates from EtOH. M.p. 78–9°.

Gattermann, *Ann.*, 1906, **347**, 379.

3 : 5 : 6 - Trimethylsalicylaldehyde (6-*Hydroxy*-2 : 3 : 5-*trimethylbenzaldehyde*).

Yellow needles from EtOH. M.p. 105–6°. Sol. Et_2O, $CHCl_3$, AcOH. Spar. sol. cold EtOH. Insol. H_2O. Sublimes. $FeCl_3 \longrightarrow$ blue col.

Auwers, *Ber.*, 1884, **17**, 2976.

4 : 5 : 6 - Trimethylsalicylaldehyde (6-*Hydroxy*-2 : 3 : 4-*trimethylbenzaldehyde*).

Pale yellow needles or prisms from MeOH. M.p. 77–8°. Sol. Me_2CO, $CHCl_3$, C_6H_6. Alc. $FeCl_3 \longrightarrow$ intense green col.

Semicarbazone: cryst. from AcOH. Does not melt below 280°.

Auwers, Ziegler, *Ann.*, 1921, **425**, 276.

Trimethylsalicylic Acid.

See 6-Hydroxydurylic Acid *and* 6-Hydroxy-γ-isodurylic Acid.

3 : 5 : 6-Trimethylsaligenin (6-*Hydroxy*-2 : 3 : 5-*trimethylbenzyl alcohol*)

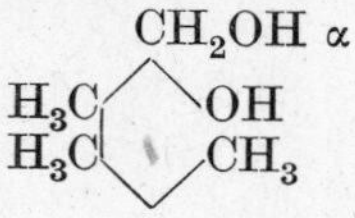

$C_{10}H_{14}O_2$ MW, 166

Needles from pet. ether. M.p. 91–2°. $FeCl_3$ in EtOH.Aq. $\longrightarrow$ blue col. $FeCl_3$ in EtOH $\longrightarrow$ bluish-green col.

α-*Me ether*: $C_{11}H_{16}O_2$. MW, 180. Needles from MeOH.Aq. M.p. 44–5°. Sol. usual org. solvents.

α-*Acetyl*: needles from AcOH.Aq. M.p. 57–8°. Sol. EtOH, C_6H_6, AcOH, pet. ether.

Diacetyl: needles from MeOH.Aq. M.p. 50–51·5°. Sol. usual org. solvents.

Manasse, *Ber.*, 1902, **35**, 3844.
Zincke, v. Hohorst, *Ann.*, 1907, **353**, 362.

Trimethylstibine (*Antimony trimethyl*)

$(CH_3)_3Sb$

C_3H_9Sb MW, 165

B.p. 82° (80·6°). Sol. EtOH, Et_2O, CS_2. Insol. H_2O. D^{15} 1·523. n_D^{15} 1·42. Oxidises in air and takes fire. Combines with O, S, and halogens to give oxide, sulphide, and halide respectively. Pptes Ag and Hg from their sols.

Hibbert, *Ber.*, 1906, **39**, 160.
Paneth, Loleit, *J. Chem. Soc.*, 1935, 371.

Trimethylsuccinic Acid (2-*Methylbutane*-2 : 3-*dicarboxylic acid*)

$(CH_3)_2C{\cdot}COOH$ α
$CH_3{\cdot}CH{\cdot}COOH$ β

$C_7H_{12}O_4$ MW, 160

d-.

Cryst. from H_2O. M.p. 140°. $[\alpha]_D + 4{\cdot}83°$ in H_2O.

Quinine salt: m.p. 197–8°. Spar. sol. H_2O.

dl-.

Prisms from H_2O. M.p. 152° (148–9°). Sol. 10 parts H_2O at 15°. Sol. EtOH, Et_2O, Me_2CO, $CHCl_3$, AcOEt. Spar. sol. C_6H_6. Insol. ligroin, CS_2. $k = 3{\cdot}22 \times 10^{-4}$ at 25°. Heat of comb. C_v 5183 Cal. Spar. volatile in steam.

β-*Et ester*: $C_9H_{16}O_4$. MW, 188. Liq. B.p. 158°/14 mm.

Di-Et ester: $C_{11}H_{20}O_4$. MW, 216. B.p. 226°, 111°/14 mm. D_4^{20} 0·993. n_{He}^{20} 1·427.

β-*Nitrile*: $C_7H_{11}O_2N$. MW, 141. Needles. M.p. 126°. Very sol. EtOH, $CHCl_3$. Spar. sol. cold H_2O. Insol. ligroin.

Anhydride: cryst. M.p. 38·5° (33°). B.p. 227°/746 mm., 106–7°/15 mm. Sol. usual solvents except cold H_2O, ligroin. Heat of comb. C_v 5884·2 Cal.

Monoanilide: needles from EtOH.Aq. M.p. 134–5°. Sol. EtOH, $CHCl_3$. Insol. ligroin.

Mono-p-toluidide: plates from EtOH. M.p. 126°. Sol. EtOH, Et_2O, $CHCl_3$, AcOH. Mod. sol. hot C_6H_6. Spar. sol. hot H_2O. Insol. ligroin.

Mono-2-naphthalide: prisms from EtOH.Aq. M.p. 153°.

Bone, Perkin, *J. Chem. Soc.*, 1895, **67**, 427.
Auwers, Oswald, *Ann.*, 1895, **285**, 260, 283, 298.
Paolini, *Gazz. chim. ital.*, 1900, **30**, ii, 508.
Bone, Sprankling, *J. Chem. Soc.*, 1899, **75**, 858.
v. Braun, Keller, Weissbach, *Ann.*, 1931, **490**, 186.

Trimethylsulphonium bromide

$(CH_3)_3SBr$

C_3H_9BrS MW, 157

Cryst. from H_2O. Decomp. at 172°. Reacts neutral in aq. sol.

Steinkopf, Müller, *Ber.*, 1923, **56**, 1929.

Trimethylsulphonium chloride

$(CH_3)_3SCl$

C_3H_9ClS MW, 112·5

Cryst. Decomp. at 100°. Very sol. EtOH. Very hygroscopic.

Blättler, *Monatsh.*, 1919, **40**, 420.

Trimethylsulphonium iodide

$(CH_3)_3SI$

C_3H_9IS MW, 204

Cryst. from EtOH. Decomp. at 203–7°.

Steinkopf, Müller, *Ber.*, 1923, **56**, 1928.

Trimethyltetrahydrobenzaldehyde.
See Cyclocitral.

1 : 1 : 6 - Trimethyl - 1 : 2 : 3 : 4 - tetrahydronaphthalene.
See Ionene.

1 : 2 : 2 - Trimethyl - 1 : 2 : 3 : 4 - tetrahydroquinoline

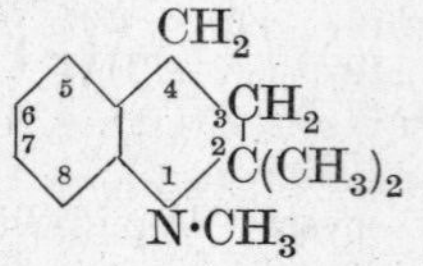

$C_{12}H_{17}N$ MW, 175

B.p. 269–70°/745 mm. n_D^{19} 1·5823. Volatile in steam.

Picrate: m.p. 178°.

Freund, Richard, *Ber.*, 1909, **42**, 1112.

1 : 2 : 4 - Trimethyl - 1 : 2 : 3 : 4 - tetrahydroquinoline.

B.p. about 250°/759 mm.

Picrate: yellow prisms. M.p. 126–7°.

Methiodide: cryst. from EtOH. M.p. 215°.

Ciamician, Piccinini, *Ber.*, 1896, **29**, 2468.
Fischer, Meyer, *Ber.*, 1890, **23**, 2633.

1 : 2 : 8 - Trimethyl - 1 : 2 : 3 : 4 - tetrahydroquinoline.

Liq. B.p. 242–5°.

Doebner, v. Miller, *Ber.*, 1883, **16**, 2470.

1 : 6 : 8 - Trimethyl - 1 : 2 : 3 : 4 - tetrahydroquinoline.

B,HI: prisms from MeOH–Et_2O. M.p. 164–5°.

Ewins, *J. Chem. Soc.*, 1913, **103**, 104.

2 : 2 : 4 - Trimethyl - 1 : 2 : 3 : 4 - tetrahydroquinoline.

Needles. M.p. 41°. B.p. 119–22°/10 mm. $D^{65\cdot4}$ 0·9531. $n_{He}^{65\cdot4}$ 1·53592.

Reddelien, Thurm, *Ber.*, 1932, **65**, 1520.

2 : 4 : 6 - Trimethyl - 1 : 2 : 3 : 4 - tetrahydroquinoline.

B.p. 265–6°/758 mm. (261·5°/762·5 mm.). D_4^{31} 0·97548. n_D^{31} 1·544354.

Yamaguchi, *Chem. Abstracts*, 1927, **21**, 2696.

2 : 4 : 7 - Trimethyl - 1 : 2 : 3 : 4 - tetrahydroquinoline.

B.p. 269–70°. D_4^{20} 0·9857. n_D^{20} 1·55591.

See previous reference.

2 : 4 : 8 - Trimethyl - 1 : 2 : 3 : 4 - tetrahydroquinoline.

B.p. 260–1°. D_4^{40} 0·98639. n_D^{20} 1·55598.

Yamaguchi, *Chem. Abstracts*, 1927, **21**, 2696.

2 : 6 : 8 - Trimethyl - 1 : 2 : 3 : 4 - tetrahydroquinoline.

Plates. M.p. 50–51°. B.p. 260–1°/780 mm., 142–3°/14 mm.

B,HCl: prisms from H_2O. M.p. 208–9°.

B,HBr: prisms. M.p. 222–3°.

B_2,H_2PtCl_6: brown prisms. M.p. 210°.

Picrate: yellow prisms from EtOH. M.p. 179°.

N-*Acetyl*: needles from EtOH. M.p. 108–9°.

N-*Benzoyl*: prisms from EtOH. M.p. 143°.

N-*Nitroso*: yellowish needles from EtOH. M.p. 68–9°.

Jones, Evans, *J. Chem. Soc.*, 1911, **99**, 335.

5 : 6 : 8 - Trimethyl - 1 : 2 : 3 : 4 - tetrahydroquinoline.

Oil. B.p. 287–90°.

B,HCl: needles. M.p. about 238° decomp. Mod. sol. H_2O.

Wikander, *Ber.*, 1900, **33**, 648.

2 : 3 : 4 - Trimethyl - 5 : 6 : 7 : 8 - tetrahydroquinoline

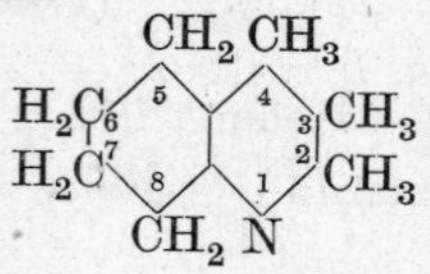

$C_{12}H_{17}N$ MW, 175

B.p. 145–7°/13 mm. In moist air ⟶ dihydrate, m.p. 32°.

B,HCl: m.p. 174°. Hygroscopic.

Methiodide: m.p. 125–6°.

Picrate: m.p. 147°. Spar. sol. EtOH.

v. Braun, Gmelin, Petzold, *Ber.*, 1924, **57**, 387.

2 : 4 : 6 - Trimethyl - 5 : 6 : 7 : 8 - tetrahydroquinoline.

B.p. 256–7°. D_4^{14} 0·9845. n_D^{14} 1·53007.

Yamaguchi, *Chem. Abstracts*, 1927, **21**, 2696.

2 : 4 : 7 - Trimethyl - 5 : 6 : 7 : 8 - tetrahydroquinoline.
Cryst. M.p. 20–1°. B.p. 259–60°. $D_4^{26.5}$ 0·97559. $n_D^{26.5}$ 1·52111.

See previous reference.

2 : 4 : 8 - Trimethyl - 5 : 6 : 7 : 8 - tetrahydroquinoline.
B.p. 251–2°. D_4^{14} 0·99196. n_D^{14} 1·53575.

Yamaguchi, *Chem. Abstracts*, 1927, **21**, 2696.

2 : 6 : 7 - Trimethyl - 5 : 6 : 7 : 8 - tetrahydroquinoline.
B.p. 239–40°/752 mm. n^{31} 1·5212.
B_2,H_2PtCl_6 : m.p. 187°.
Picrate : cryst. from EtOH.Aq. M.p. 105°.

Basu, *Ann.*, 1934, **514**, 295.

1 : 1 : 4-Trimethyltetramethylene Glycol.
See 2-Methylhexandiol-2 : 5.

2 : 3 : 4-Trimethylthiophene

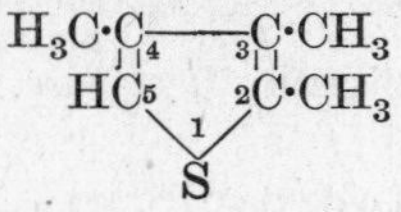

$C_7H_{10}S$ MW, 126

Liq. B.p. 160–3°.

v. Meyer, *Die Thiophengruppe*, 60.
Zelinsky, *Ber.*, 1887, **20**, 2025.

2 : 3 : 5-Trimethylthiophene.
B.p. 163–5°/746 mm. D_4^{20} 0·9753. n_D^{20} 1·5131.

Youtz, Perkins, *J. Am. Chem. Soc.*, 1929, **51**, 3514.

Trimethylthiourea.
See under Thiourea.
ω-Trimethyltoluene.
See tert.-Butylbenzene.
1 : 1 : 2-Trimethyltricarballylic Acid.
See Camphoronic Acid.
2 : 4 : 6-Trimethyl-1 : 3 : 5-trioxan.
See Paraldehyde.
1 : 3 : 5-Trimethyluracil.
See under Thymine.
Trimethylurea.
See under Urea.
1 : 3 : 7-Trimethyluric Acid

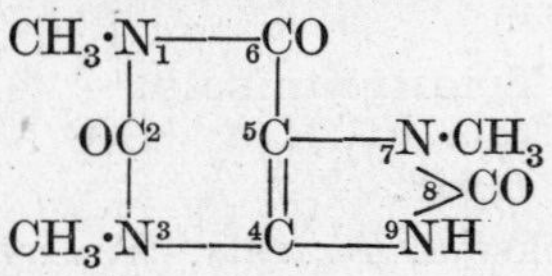

$C_8H_{10}O_3N_4$ MW, 210

Needles from H_2O. M.p. 345° (335°) decomp. $k = 2{\cdot}9 \times 10^{-5}$ at 25°. Spar. sol. cold H_2O, EtOH, Et_2O.

Biltz, Pardon, *J. prakt. Chem.*, 1934, **140**, 220.
Biltz, Heyn, *Ann.*, 1917, **413**, 179.

1 : 3 : 9-Trimethyluric Acid.
Plates. Decomp. at 347° (340°). Sol. NH_3. Spar. sol. EtOH, $CHCl_3$. Insol. H_2O. Sol. 30 parts boiling H_2O. $k = 1{\cdot}3 \times 10^{-6}$ at 25°. Reduces $NH_3.AgNO_3$ on boiling.

Biltz, Strufe, *Ann.*, 1921, **423**, 242.
Biltz, Pardon, *Ann.*, 1935, **515**, 241; *Ber.*, 1930, **63**, 2878.

1 : 7 : 9-Trimethyluric Acid.
Needles from EtOH or H_2O. M.p. 345° (338°). Mod. sol. hot H_2O. Spar. sol. hot EtOH, $CHCl_3$. $k = 1{\cdot}00 \times 10^{-4}$ at 25°. Sublimes.

Biltz, Krzikalla, *Ann.*, 1921, **423**, 180.

3 : 7 : 9-Trimethyluric Acid.
Needles. M.p. 373–5°. $k = 1{\cdot}7 \times 10^{-6}$ at 25°.

Biltz, Damm, *Ann.*, 1917, **413**, 186.
Biltz, Pardon, *Ber.*, 1930, **63**, 2876.

Trimyristin (*Glycerol trimyristate*)

$CH_2{\cdot}O{\cdot}CO{\cdot}[CH_2]_{12}{\cdot}CH_3$
$CH{\cdot}O{\cdot}CO{\cdot}[CH_2]_{12}{\cdot}CH_3$
$CH_2{\cdot}O{\cdot}CO{\cdot}[CH_2]_{12}{\cdot}CH_3$

$C_{45}H_{86}O_6$ MW, 722

Found in nutmegs. Exists in polymorphous forms. (i) Unstable. M.p. 32·1°. (ii) Unstable. M.p. 41·8°. (iii) Stable. Plates from Et_2O. M.p. 56·5°.

Sol. Et_2O, $CHCl_3$, C_6H_6, pet. ether. Spar. sol. EtOH, CS_2, ligroin. D_4^{60} 0·8848. n_D^{60} 1·44285. Heat of comb. C_p 6650 Cal.

Beal, *Organic Syntheses*, Collective Vol. I, 524.
Bömer, Engel, *Chem. Abstracts*, 1929, **23**, 4676.

2 : 4 : 6-Trinitroacetanilide.
See under Picramide.
Trinitroaminoanisole.
See under Trinitroaminophenol.
Trinitroaminophenetole.
See under Trinitroaminophenol.

2 : 4 : 6-Trinitro-*m*-aminophenol

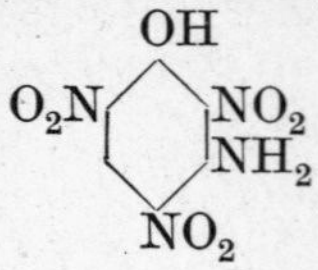

$C_6H_4O_7N_4$ MW, 244

Cryst. from C_6H_6. M.p. 178–9°.

Me ether: 2 : 4 : 6-trinitro-*m*-aminoanisole, 2 : 4 : 6-trinitro-*m*-anisidine. $C_7H_6O_7N_4$. MW, 258. Cryst. from MeOH. M.p. 131°.

Et ether: 2 : 4 : 6-trinitro-*m*-aminophenetole, 2 : 4 : 6-trinitro-*m*-anisidine. $C_8H_8O_7N_4$. MW, 272. Cryst. from AcOH. M.p. 107°.

N-*Me*: $C_7H_6O_7N_4$. MW, 258. Yellow cryst. M.p. 158°.

v. Duin, v. Lennep, *Rec. trav. chim.*, 1920, **39**, 149.
Flürscheim, D.R.P., 243,079, (*Chem. Zentr.*, 1912, I, 620).

2 : 3 : 5-Trinitro-*p*-aminophenol

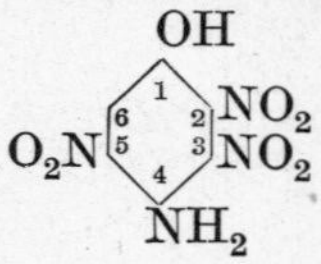

$C_6H_4O_7N_4$ MW, 244

Me ether: 2 : 3 : 5-trinitro-*p*-aminoanisole, 2 : 3 : 5-trinitro-*p*-anisidine. Reddish-brown needles from H_2O. M.p. 127–8°. Sol. Me_2CO, $PhNO_2$. Mod. sol. Et_2O, C_6H_6. N-*Acetyl*: needles from AcOH.Aq. or Me_2CO.Aq. M.p. 242°. Spar. sol. boiling H_2O. Insol. Et_2O, C_6H_6. N-*Benzoyl*: m.p. 220–30°. N-p-*Toluenesulphonyl*: needles from Me_2CO. M.p. 217°.

Et ether: 2 : 3 : 5-trinitro-*p*-aminophenetole, 2 : 3 : 5-trinitro-*p*-phenetidine. Red needles with green metallic reflex from MeOH. M.p. 126–7°. Sol. Me_2CO, hot EtOH, AcOH, $PhNO_2$. N-*Acetyl*: needles. M.p. about 245°. Sol. Me_2CO, AcOH. Spar. sol. hot EtOH, C_6H_6.

N-*Acetyl*: brownish cryst. from AcOH. M.p. 191–2°. Very sol. EtOH, AcOH.

Reverdin, Meldola, *J. prakt. Chem.*, 1913, **88**, 787.
Reverdin, Fürstenberg, *ibid.*, 323.
Reverdin, *Ber.*, 1911, **44**, 2364.

2 : 3 : 6-Trinitro-*p*-aminophenol.

Red needles from AcOH. Decomp. about 145°.

Me ether: 2 : 3 : 6-trinitro-*p*-aminoanisole, 2 : 3 : 6-trinitro-*p*-anisidine. Dark red cryst. from EtOH. M.p. 138–9°. N-*Acetyl*: needles from EtOH. M.p. 194°. N-*Benzoyl*: needl from AcOH.Aq. M.p. 205°.

N-*Acetyl*: yellow needles from AcOH. M.p 178–9° decomp. Sol. hot EtOH. Spar. so hot H_2O.

N-*Propionyl*: yellowish-brown needles fro AcOH. M.p. 178–9°.

Meldola, Reverdin, *J. Chem. Soc.*, 191 **103**, 1484.
Meldola, Hay, *J. Chem. Soc.*, 1909, **9** 1380.
Meldola, Kuntzen, *J. Chem. Soc.*, 191 **97**, 455.

2 : 3 : 4-Trinitroaniline

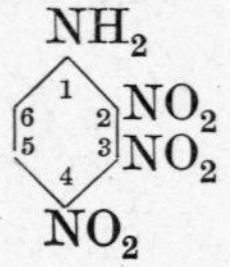

$C_6H_4O_6N_4$ MW, 22

N-*Di-Me*: $C_8H_8O_6N_4$. MW, 256. Orang rhombohedra from Me_2CO or C_6H_6. M.p. 154 D^{17} 1·551.

v. Romburgh, *Rec. trav. chim.*, 1887, 253.

2 : 4 : 5-Trinitroaniline.

Pale yellow needles from AcOH.

N-*Di-Me*: red cryst. from Me_2CO–C_6H M.p. 196°. D^{17} 1·585.

Witt, Witte, *Ber.*, 1908, **41**, 3095.
See also previous reference.

2 : 4 : 6-Trinitroaniline.

See Picramide.

Trinitroanisidine.

See under Trinitroaminophenol.

2 : 3 : 4-Trinitroanisole

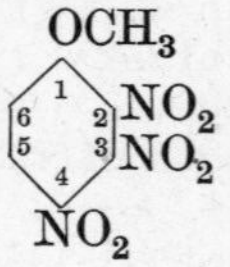

$C_7H_5O_7N_3$ MW, 24

Yellow leaflets from EtOH. M.p. 155°. So Me_2CO. Spar. sol. EtOH, C_6H_6. Very spa sol. ligroin.

Vermeulen, *Chem. Zentr.*, 1912, I, 724.
Meldola, Eyre, *J. Chem. Soc.*, 1902, **8** 993.

2 : 3 : 5-Trinitroanisole.

Leaflets from EtOH or HNO_3. M.p. 106·8 (104°). D^{15} 1·618.

Blanksma, *Rec. trav. chim.*, 1904, **23**, 11

2 : 4 : 5-Trinitroanisole.
Cryst. from EtOH. M.p. 106–7°. Spar. sol. ligroin.

Vermeulen, *Rec. trav. chim.*, 1912, **31**, 102.

2 : 4 : 6-Trinitroanisole.
See under Picric Acid.

3 : 4 : 5-Trinitroanisole.
Cryst. M.p. 119–20°.

Vermeulen, *Rec. trav. chim.*, 1912, **31**, 103.

2 : 4 : 6-Trinitrobenzaldehyde

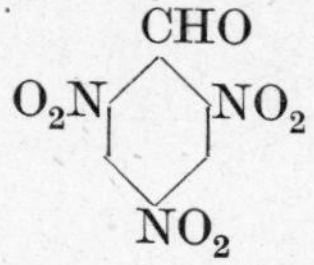

$C_7H_3O_7N_3$ MW, 241

Plates from C_6H_6. M.p. 119°. Conc. NH_3.Aq. in EtOH ⟶ 1 : 3 : 5-trinitrobenzene.

Oxime: cryst. from EtOH. M.p. 158°. Sol. EtOH, Me_2CO.

Semicarbazone: pale yellow leaflets from AcOH. M.p. 214° decomp.

Phenylhydrazone: reddish-brown needles. M.p. 202°. Sol. hot Me_2CO. Spar. sol. EtOH, Et_2O, C_6H_6.

p-*Nitrophenylhydrazone*: light red needles from hot Me_2CO. M.p. 247°. Mod. sol. AcOEt, $PhNO_2$. Spar. sol. EtOH, $CHCl_3$, AcOH.

Sachs, Everding, *Ber.*, 1902, **35**, 1236; D.R.P., 121,745, (*Chem. Zentr.*, 1901, II, 69).
Secareanu, *Bull. soc. chim.*, 1932, **51**, 591; *Ber.*, 1931, **64**, 837.

2 : 4 : 6-Trinitrobenzanilide.
See under Picramide.

1 : 2 : 3-Trinitrobenzene

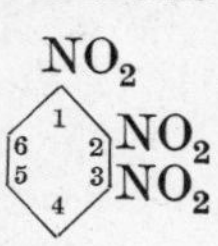

$C_6H_3O_6N_3$ MW, 213

Yellowish needles or prisms from MeOH. M.p. 127·5° (121°). Sol. 10 parts boiling EtOH.

Borsche, *Ber.*, 1923, **56**, 1500.
Körner, Contardi, *Atti accad. Lincei*, 1914, **23**, II, 464.

1 : 2 : 4-Trinitrobenzene.
Pale yellow prisms from MeOH.Aq. M.p. 61–2° (57·5°). Very sol. C_6H_6. Sol. EtOH, MeOH, Et_2O, $CHCl_3$. Heat of comb. C_p 678·5 Cal.

Körner, Contardi, *Atti accad. Lincei*, 1914, **23**, I, 634.
Borsche, *Ber.*, 1923, **56**, 1498.

1 : 3 : 5-Trinitrobenzene.
Exists in dimorphous forms. Cryst. from EtOH or HNO_3. M.ps. 122·48° and 61°. Sol. MeOH, $CHCl_3$, C_6H_6. Spar. sol. EtOH, Et_2O, CS_2. Sol. 2500 parts cold H_2O. Heat of comb. C_p 663·8 Cal.

Heinemann, E.P., 102,216, (*Chem. Abstracts*, 1917, **11**, 889).
Radcliffe, Pollitt, *J. Soc. Chem. Ind.*, 1921, **40**, 45, 90T.
Drummond, *J. Soc. Chem. Ind.*, 1922, **41**, 338T.
Desvergnes, *Chimie et industrie*, 1931, **25**, 3, 291 (*Bibl.*).
Secareanu, *Bull. soc. chim.*, 1932, **51**, 591.
Clarke, Hartman, *Organic Syntheses*, Collective Vol. I, 526.

2 : 3 : 4-Trinitrobenzoic Acid

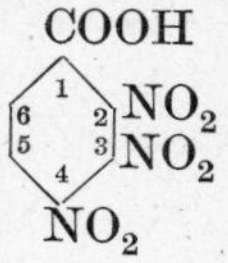

$C_7H_3O_8N_3$ MW, 257

Prisms from H_2O or C_6H_6. M.p. 202–3°. Sol. EtOH, Me_2CO. Mod. sol. H_2O, C_6H_6. Insol. pet. ether. Explodes when heated in quantities greater than 1 gm.

Et ester: $C_9H_7O_8N_3$. MW, 285. Needles. M.p. 79–80°. Sol. Me_2CO, $CHCl_3$, C_6H_6, Et_2O. Spar. sol. pet. ether.

Giua, *Gazz. chim. ital.*, 1915, **45**, i, 348.

2 : 3 : 5-Trinitrobenzoic Acid.
Leaflets + $2H_2O$. from H_2O. M.p. 82°, anhyd. 171°.

Körner, Contardi, *Atti accad. Lincei*, 1915, **24**, I, 893.

2 : 3 : 6-Trinitrobenzoic Acid.
Fine white needles + $2H_2O$ from H_2O. M.p. 55°, anhyd. 160° decomp. Above 160° or by boiling with H_2O ⟶ 1 : 2 : 4-trinitrobenzene.

Körner, Contardi, *Atti accad. Lincei*, 1916, **25**, II, 348.

2 : 4 : 5-Trinitrobenzoic Acid.
Plates from H_2O. M.p. 194·5° decomp. Sol. EtOH, Et_2O. Mod. sol. C_6H_6. Spar. sol. pet. ether.

Me ester: $C_8H_5O_8N_3$. MW, 271. Cryst. from MeOH. M.p. 102°. Sol. usual org. solvents.

Et ester: $C_9H_7O_8N_3$. MW, 285. Leaflets from EtOH.Aq. M.p. 84°. Sol. Me_2CO, Et_2O, $CHCl_3$, C_6H_6. Spar. sol. pet. ether.

Giua, *Gazz. chim. ital.*, 1915, **45**, i, 350.

2 : 4 : 6-Trinitrobenzoic Acid.

Rhombohedra from H_2O. M.p. 228·7° (210°). Above m.p. or with conc. NH_3.Aq. in EtOH ⟶ 1 : 3 : 5-trinitrobenzene.

Me ester: orange-yellow plates from EtOH.Aq. M.p. 160–1°.

Et ester: orange-yellow plates. M.p. 156–7°.

Propyl ester: $C_{10}H_9O_8N_3$. MW, 299. Plates. M.p. 145–6°.

Isopropyl ester: yellow plates. M.p. 154–5°.

Butyl ester: $C_{11}H_{11}O_8N_3$. MW, 313. Plates. M.p. 125–6°.

Isobutyl ester: m.p. 127–8°.

n-*Amyl ester*: $C_{12}H_{13}O_8N_3$. MW, 327. M.p. 124–5°.

Isoamyl ester: m.p. 134–5°.

Phenyl ester: $C_{13}H_7O_8N_3$. MW, 333. Cryst. from EtOH. M.p. 170·5–171·5°.

Chloride: $C_7H_2O_7N_3Cl$. MW, 275·5. Plates from C_6H_6. M.p. 163° (158°). Spar. sol. Et_2O.

Amide: $C_7H_4O_7N_4$. MW, 256. Cryst. from Me_2CO–C_6H_6–pet. ether. M.p. 264°.

Methylamide: $C_8H_6O_7N_4$. MW, 270. M.p. 285°.

Dimethylamide: $C_9H_8O_7N_4$. MW, 284. M.p. 144°.

Anhydride: $C_{14}H_4O_{15}N_6$. MW, 496. Needles. M.p. 270°.

Clarke, Hartman, *Organic Syntheses*, Collective Vol. I, 528.
Chang, Kao, *J. Chinese Chem. Soc.*, 1935, **3**, 256.
Krauz, Turek, *Chimie et industrie*, 1926, Special No., 526.
Lüttgen, D.R.P., 226,225, (*Chem. Zentr.*, 1910, II, 1174).

3 : 4 : 5-Trinitrobenzoic Acid.

Greenish-yellow needles + Et_2O from Et_2O. M.p. 168° decomp.

Körner, Contardi, *Atti accad. Lincei*, 1914, **23**, II, 467.

2:4:6-Trinitro-3-*n*-butyltoluene (2 : 4 : 6-*Trinitro-3-methyl*-n-*butylbenzene*)

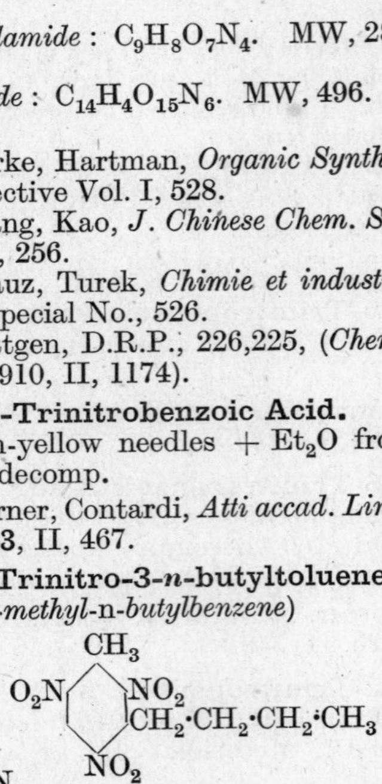

$C_{11}H_{13}O_6N_3$ MW, 283

Fine needles from EtOH. M.p. 78·5°. Odourless. Turns pink, then yellowish-brown in light.

de Capeller, *Helv. Chim. Acta*, 1928, **11**, 168.

2 : 4 : 6 - Trinitro - 3 - *tert*. - butyltoluene (2 : 4 : 6-*Trinitro-3-methyl*-tert.-*butylbenzene*)

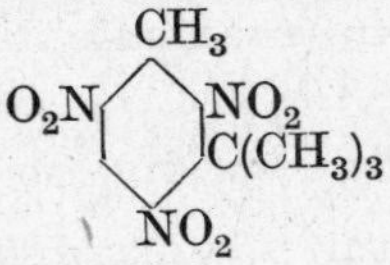

$C_{11}H_{13}O_6N_3$ MW, 283

Yellowish needles from EtOH. M.p. 96–7°. Sol. EtOH, Et_2O, $CHCl_3$, C_6H_6, pet. ether. Insol. H_2O. Strong odour of musk. Non-poisonous.

Baur, *Compt. rend.*, 1890, **111**, 239.

2 : 4 : 6-Trinitro-5-*tert*.-butyl-*m*-xylene (*Xylene musk*)

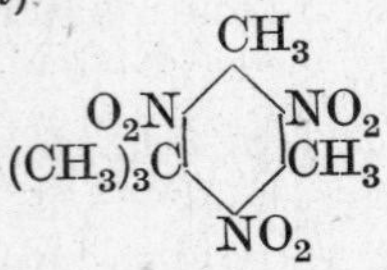

$C_{12}H_{15}O_6N_3$ MW, 297

Needles from EtOH. M.p. 110°. Possesses strong musk-like odour.

Baur, *Ber.*, 1891, **24**, 2841.
Fabr. de Thann et Mulhouse, D.R.P., 77,299.

3 : 4 : 5-Trinitrocatechol

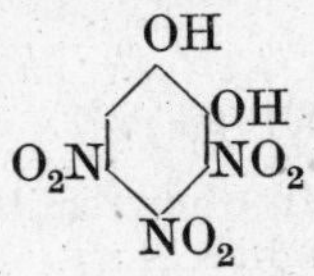

$C_6H_3O_8N_3$ MW, 245

Di-Me ether: *see* 3 : 4 : 5-Trinitroveratrol.

Di-Et ether: $C_{10}H_{11}O_8N_3$. MW, 301. Needles. M.p. 122°.

Blanksma, *Rec. trav. chim.*, 1905, **24**, 42.

3 : 4 : 5-Trinitro-*o*-cresol

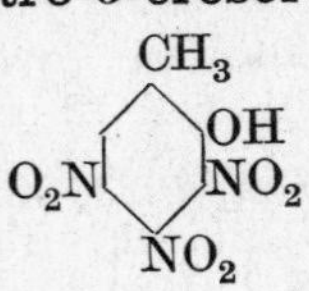

$C_7H_5O_7N_3$ MW, 243

Orange-yellow prisms from Me_2CO. M.p. 102°. Very sol. $CHCl_3$. Sol. EtOH, Et_2O, Me_2CO, AcOEt. Spar. sol. cold H_2O.

Me ether: $C_8H_7O_7N_3$. MW, 257. Needles from EtOH.Aq. M.p. 111–12°. Sol. hot EtOH.Aq., AcOH.

Sommer, *J. prakt. Chem.*, 1903, **67**, 554.
Nölting, Collin, *Ber.*, 1884, **17**, 270.

2 : 4 : 6-Trinitro-*m*-cresol

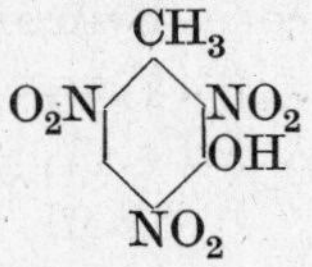

$C_7H_5O_7N_3$ MW, 243

Yellow needles from EtOH. M.p. 109–10°. Sol. 123 parts boiling and 446 parts cold H_2O. Sol. EtOH, Et_2O, Me_2CO, C_6H_6.

Me ether: $C_8H_7O_7N_3$. MW, 257. Prisms from EtOH. M.p. 94°.

Et ether: $C_9H_9O_7N_3$. MW, 271. Leaflets from EtOH. M.p. 75°. Sol. Et_2O, Me_2CO, $CHCl_3$, C_6H_6. Turns yellow in air.

Acetyl: pale yellow plates from C_6H_6. M.p. 135°.

Datta, Varma, *J. Am. Chem. Soc.*, 1919, **41**, 2041.
Giua, *Gazz. chim. ital.*, 1919, **49**, ii, 164.
Beilstein, Kellner, *Ann.*, 1863, **128**, 165.

Trinitro-ψ-cumene (3 : 5 : 6-*Trinitro*-1 : 2 : 4-*trimethylbenzene*)

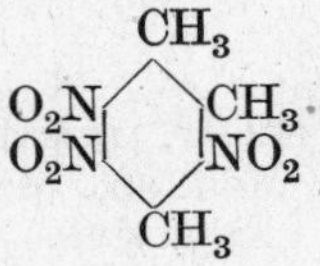

$C_9H_9O_6N_3$ MW, 255

Prisms. M.p. 185°. Very sol. boiling C_6H_6, toluene. Spar. sol. EtOH.

Schultz, *Ber.*, 1909, **42**, 3608.
Fittig, Laubinger, *Ann.*, 1869, **151**, 261.

2 : 4 : 6-Trinitrodiphenyl

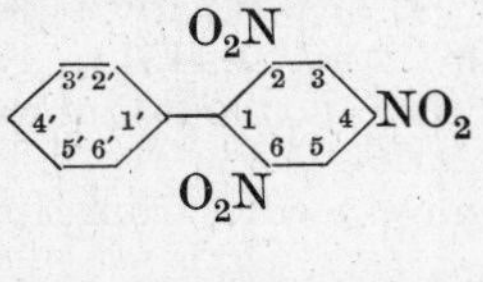

$C_{12}H_7O_6N_3$ MW, 289

Pale yellowish needles from EtOH. M.p. 130°.

Gull, Turner, *J. Chem. Soc.*, 1929, 498.

2 : 4 : 2′-Trinitrodiphenyl.

Pale yellow prisms from AcOH. M.p. 150–1°.

See previous reference.

2 : 4 : 4′-Trinitrodiphenyl.

Pale yellow cubes from AcOH or HNO_3. M.p. 176°.

See previous reference.

2 : 4 : 6-Trinitrodiphenylamine (*Picrylaniline*, N-*phenylpicramide*)

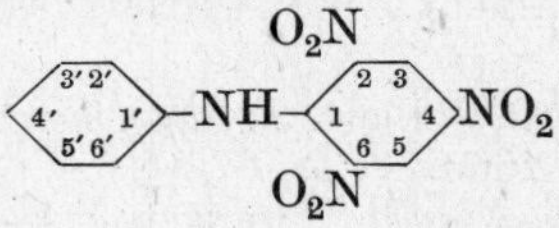

$C_{12}H_8O_6N_4$ MW, 304

Yellow needles from EtOH. M.p. 179° (177°). Sol. warm AcOH, C_6H_6. Insol. ligroin.

Giua, Cherchi, *Gazz. chim. ital.*, 1919, **49**, ii, 157.
Ullmann, Nádai, *Ber.*, 1908, **41**, 1876.
Le Fèvre, *J. Chem. Soc.*, 1931, 813.

2 : 4 : 2′-Trinitrodiphenylamine.

Yellow prisms from EtOH or AcOH. M.p. 183–4°.

Juillard, *Bull. soc. chim.*, 1905, **33**, 1185.

2 : 4 : 3′-Trinitrodiphenylamine.

Pale brown plates or yellow needles from AcOH. M.p. 194–5° (190°). Mod. sol. hot AcOH. Spar. sol. hot EtOH. Conc. H_2SO_4 ⟶ pale yellow sol.

v. der Kam, *Rec. trav. chim.*, 1926, **45**, 732.
Kym, Ringer, *Ber.*, 1915, **48**, 1681.

2 : 4 : 4′-Trinitrodiphenylamine.

Yellow needles from EtOH or AcOH. M.p. 189° (181°). Sol. Me_2CO. Spar. sol. AcOH, toluene.

See first reference above and also
Juillard, *Bull. soc. chim.*, 1905, **33**, 1182.
Wieland, Lecher, *Ann.*, 1912, **392**, 167.

2 : 4 : 5-Trinitrodiphenyl Ether

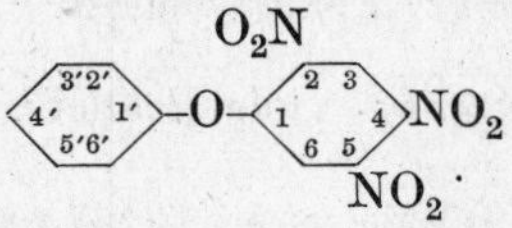

$C_{12}H_7O_7N_3$ MW, 305

Cryst. from EtOH. M.p. 106°. Sol. EtOH.

Westf.-Anhalt. Sprengstoff A.-G., D.R.P., 281,053, (*Chem. Zentr.*, 1915, I, 74).

2 : 4 : 6-Trinitrodiphenyl Ether (*Picric acid phenyl ether, phenyl picrate*).

Yellowish prisms from EtOH–C_6H_6. M.p. 153°. Sol. C_6H_6. Mod. sol. EtOH, $CHCl_3$, AcOH. Spar. sol. Et_2O. Insol. H_2O, ligroin.

Jackson, Earle, *Am. Chem. J.*, 1903, **29**, 213.

2 : 4 : 2′-Trinitrodiphenyl Ether.
Yellow needles from EtOH–AcOH. M.p. 137·5°.

Raiford, Colbert, *J. Am. Chem. Soc.*, 1926, **48**, 2660.

2 : 4 : 3′-Trinitrodiphenyl Ether.
Yellow tablets from EtOH–AcOH. M.p. 136°.

Raiford, Colbert, *J. Am. Chem. Soc.*, 1926, **48**, 2660.
Westf.-Anhalt. Sprengstoff A.-G., D.R.P., 281,053, (*Chem. Zentr.*, 1915, I, 74).

2 : 4 : 4′-Trinitrodiphenyl Ether.
Yellow tablets from EtOH–AcOH. M.p. 116° (100°).

See first reference above.

1 : 1 : 1-Trinitroethane

$CH_3 \cdot C(NO_2)_3$

$C_2H_3O_6N_3$ MW, 167

Cryst. M.p. 56°. Sol. usual org. solvents. Spar. sol. H_2O. Heat of comb. C_v 1777 Cal. Very volatile.

Hantzsch, Rinckenberger, *Ber.*, 1899, **32**, 637.

2 : 4 : 7-Trinitrofluorenone

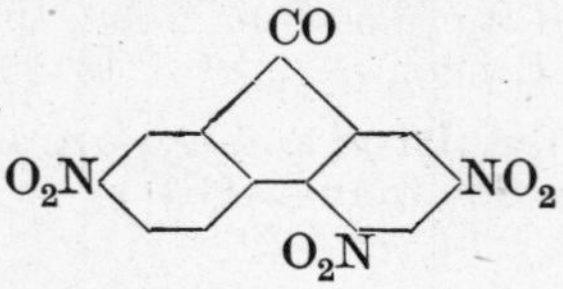

$C_{13}H_5O_7N_3$ MW, 315

Pale yellow needles from AcOH or C_6H_6. M.p. 176°. Very sol. Me_2CO, $CHCl_3$, C_6H_6.
Oxime: needles from EtOH. M.p. 260° decomp.
Semicarbazone: pale yellow. M.p. 299° decomp.
Phenylhydrazone: violet leaflets. M.p. 276° decomp.

Bell, *J. Chem. Soc.*, 1928, 1990.
Schmidt, Bauer, *Ber.*, 1905, **38**, 3760.

3 : 4 : 6-Trinitroguaiacol

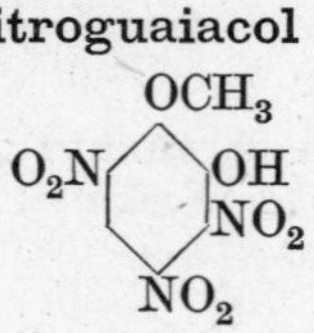

$C_7H_5O_8N_3$ MW, 259

Yellow prisms from $CHCl_3$. M.p. 129° decomp.
Me ether: *see* 3 : 4 : 6-Trinitroveratrol.

Pollecoff, Robinson, *J. Chem. Soc.*, 1918, **113**, 653.

1 : 3 : 5 - Trinitrohexahydro - 1 : 3 : 5-triazine.
See Hexogen.

2 : 4 : 6-Trinitro-*m*-hydroxybenzoic Acid

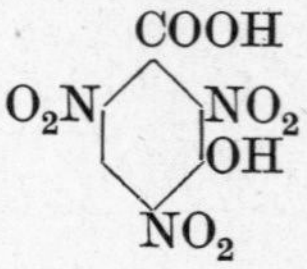

$C_7H_3O_9N_3$ MW, 273

Plates and prisms + H_2O from H_2O. M.p. about 105°. Sublimes. Blackens at 200°. Sol. H_2O, EtOH, Et_2O. Bitter taste.
Nitrile: $C_7H_2O_7N_4$. MW, 254. Yellowish needles or leaflets from dil. HNO_3. M.p. 131–2°.

Schardinger, *Ber.*, 1875, **8**, 1487.
Borsche, Gahrtz, *Ber.*, 1906, **39**, 3365.
Beilstein, Geitner, *Ann.*, 1866, **139**, 11.

Trinitromesitylene

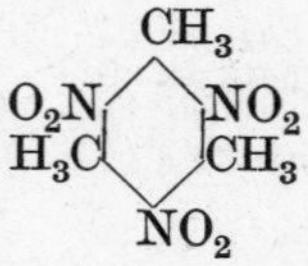

$C_9H_9O_6N_3$ MW, 255

Needles from EtOH, prisms from Me_2CO. M.p. 235° (232°). Mod. sol. Me_2CO. Spar. sol. hot EtOH, Et_2O. Explosive.

Fittig, *Ann.*, 1867, **141**, 134.
Blanksma, *Rec. trav. chim.*, 1902, **21**, 336.

Trinitromethane (*Nitroform*)

$CH(NO_2)_3$

CHO_6N_3 MW, 151

Colourless cryst. M.p. 15°. B.p. 45–7°/22 mm. $D_4^{24\cdot3}$ 1·5967. $n_{He}^{24\cdot3}$ 1·44511. Sol. H_2O with intense yellow col. Explodes on rapid heating. Forms metallic salts.
NH_4 salt: yellow needles from H_2O. Decomp. about 200°.
K salt: yellow cryst. from H_2O. Explodes at 97–9°. Sol. H_2O. Spar. sol. EtOH. Insol. Et_2O.

Chattaway, Harrison, *J. Chem. Soc.*, 1916, **109**, 171.
Hantzsch, Rinckenberger, *Ber.*, 1899, **32**, 631.

1 : 2 : 4-Trinitronaphthalene

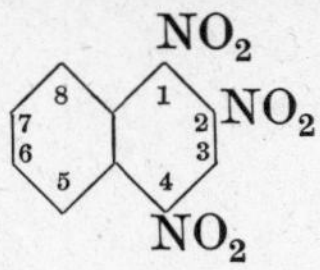

$C_{10}H_5O_6N_3$ MW, 263

Yellow needles from AcOH. M.p. 258°.

Contardi, Mor, *Chem. Abstracts*, 1925, **19**, 827.

1 : 2 : 5-Trinitronaphthalene.

Needles from EtOH. M.p. 112–13°.

Will, *Ber.*, 1895, **28**, 377.

1 : 3 : 5-Trinitronaphthalene.

Rhombohedra from $CHCl_3$. M.p. 122°. Sol. EtOH, AcOH. Mod. sol. $CHCl_3$.

de Aguiar, *Ber.*, 1872, **5**, 897.

1 : 3 : 8-Trinitronaphthalene.

Cryst. from EtOH, $CHCl_3$, or AcOH. M.p. 218°. Spar. sol. Et_2O, $CHCl_3$.

Friedländer, *Ber.*, 1899, **32**, 3531.
Kalle, D.R.P., 117,368, (*Chem. Zentr.*, 1901, I, 347).
Rindl, *J. Chem. Soc.*, 1913, **103**, 1914.

1 : 4 : 5-Trinitronaphthalene.

Pale yellow leaflets from HNO_3. M.p. 154°. Sol. 95 parts C_6H_6, 156 parts $CHCl_3$, 260 parts Et_2O, 894 parts 90% EtOH, 4017 parts CS_2, 20,193 parts ligroin, at 18·5°.

de Aguiar, *Ber.*, 1872, **5**, 904.

2 : 4 : 5-Trinitro-1-naphthol (*Naphthopicric acid*)

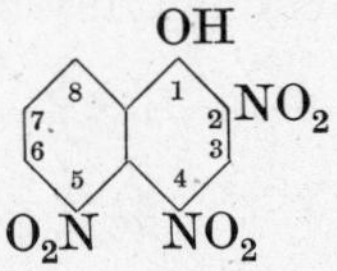

$C_{10}H_5O_7N_3$ MW, 279

Yellow leaflets or prisms from AcOH. M.p. 189·5°. Sol. 364 parts cold AcOH. Spar. sol. EtOH, Et_2O, AcOEt, C_6H_6, xylene, hot H_2O.

Me ether: $C_{11}H_7O_7N_3$. MW, 293. Yellow leaflets from AcOH. M.p. 150·5–151·5° (128°). Spar. sol. EtOH, $CHCl_3$, C_6H_6.

Et ether: $C_{12}H_9O_7N_3$. MW, 307. Yellow needles from EtOH. M.p. 149–50°. Very sol. AcOH. Spar. sol. Et_2O, $CHCl_3$, C_6H_6.

Diehl, Merz, *Ber.*, 1878, **11**, 1662.
Kehrmann, Steiner, *Ber.*, 1900, **33**, 3281.
Staedel, *Ann.*, 1883, **217**, 170.
Rindl, *J. Chem. Soc.*, 1913, **103**, 1913.

2 : 4 : 7-Trinitro-1-naphthol.

Yellow prisms from C_6H_6 or AcOH. M.p. 145°.

Kehrmann, Haberkant, *Ber.*, 1898, **21**, 2420.
Kehrmann, Steiner, *Ber.*, 1900, **33**, 3285.

2 : 4 : 8-Trinitro-1-naphthol.

Yellow prisms. M.p. 175°. Spar. sol. cold H_2O.

Graebe, *Ber.*, 1899, **32**, 2879.
Rindl, *J. Chem. Soc.*, 1913, **103**, 1916.

1 : 5 : 8-Trinitro-2-naphthol

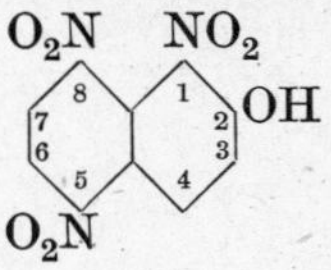

$C_{10}H_5O_7N_3$ MW, 279

Me ether: $C_{11}H_7O_7N_3$. MW, 293. Yellow needles from AcOH. M.p. 191°.

Will, *Ber.*, 1895, **28**, 372.

1 : 6 : 8-Trinitro-2-naphthol.

Me ether: needles from AcOH. M.p. 213°. Insol. EtOH, Et_2O, $CHCl_3$, C_6H_6.

Et ether: $C_{12}H_9O_7N_3$. MW, 307. Pale yellow needles from AcOH. M.p. 186°. Spar. sol. EtOH, $CHCl_3$, C_6H_6.

Staedel, *Ann.*, 1883, **217**, 171.

2 : 4 : 5-Trinitro-1-naphthylamine

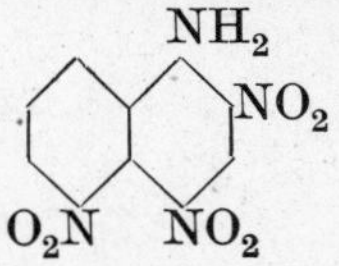

$C_{10}H_6O_6N_4$ MW, 278

Yellow needles from Me_2CO. M.p. 315–17° (decomp. at 310°). Mod. sol. Me_2CO, Ac_2O. Spar. sol. most other solvents.

N-*Me*: $C_{11}H_8O_6N_4$. MW, 292. Light brown leaflets from AcOEt. M.p. 206°. Sol. Me_2CO warm AcOH. Mod. sol. AcOEt, $CHCl_3$. Spar. sol. EtOH, Et_2O, CS_2, C_6H_6, pet. ether.

N-*Di-Me*: $C_{12}H_{10}O_6N_4$. MW, 306. Orange leaflets from AcOH. M.p. 194·5–195·5°.

N-*Et*: $C_{12}H_{10}O_6N_4$. MW, 306. Yellowish-brown needles from EtOH. M.p. 160°. Sol. Me_2CO. Mod. sol. AcOH, $CHCl_3$, C_6H_6, warm EtOH. Spar. sol. Et_2O, CS_2, pet. ether.

N-*Propyl*: $C_{13}H_{12}O_6N_4$. MW, 320. Yellow needles from AcOH. M.p. 139°.

N-*Butyl*: $C_{14}H_{14}O_6N_4$. MW, 334. Yellow needles from AcOH. M.p. 121°.

N-*Amyl* : $C_{15}H_{16}O_6N_4$. MW, 348. Yellow needles. M.p. 144–5°.

N-*Phenyl* : $C_{16}H_{10}O_6N_4$. MW, 354. Plates from AcOH. M.p. 218·5°. Mod. sol. AcOH, C_6H_6. Insol. EtOH, Et_2O, pet. ether.

N-*Acetyl* : cryst. from AcOH. Decomp. at 275°. Sol. Ac_2O. Mod. sol. AcOH.

Talen, *Rec. trav. chim.*, 1928, **47**, 355.
Groeneveld, *Rec. trav. chim.*, 1931, **50**, 692.
Rindl, *J. Chem. Soc.*, 1913, **103**, 1915.

1 : 6 : 8-Trinitro-2-naphthylamine

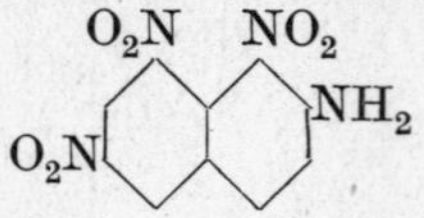

$C_{10}H_6O_6N_4$ MW, 278

M.p. 300° decomp. Sol. Me_2CO, AcOH, C_6H_6. Spar. sol. EtOH, Et_2O, $CHCl_3$. Insol. CS_2, pet. ether.

N-*Me* : m.p. 257° decomp.
N-*Di-Me* : pale yellow needles. M.p. 226°.
N-*Et* : orange needles. M.p. 216°.
N-*Propyl* : m.p. 186°. *Acetyl* : m.p. 179–80°.
N-*Isopropyl* : m.p. 209°.
N-*Butyl* : yellow needles. M.p. 156°.
N-*Isobutyl* : m.p. 179°.
N-*Amyl* : m.p. 181°.
N-*Isoamyl* : yellow needles. M.p. 164°.
N-*Acetyl* : pale yellow cryst. from AcOH. M.p. 239–40°. Sol. AcOH, Me_2CO. Mod. sol. EtOH, AcOEt, pet. ether.

v. der Kam, *Rec. trav. chim.*, 1926, **45**, 727.
Staedel, *Ann.*, 1883, **217**, 174.

Trinitrophenetidine.
See under Trinitroaminophenol.

2 : 3 : 4-Trinitrophenetole

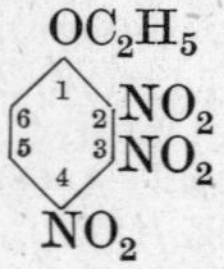

$C_8H_7O_7N_3$ MW, 257

Cryst. from EtOH. M.p. 117°.

Blanksma, *Rec. trav. chim.*, 1908, **27**, 51.

2 : 3 : 5-Trinitrophenetole.
Pale yellow cryst. M.p. 80°.

Blanksma, *Rec. trav. chim.*, 1905, **24**, 41.

2 : 4 : 6-Trinitrophenetole.
See under Picric Acid.

2 : 3 : 6-Trinitrophenol

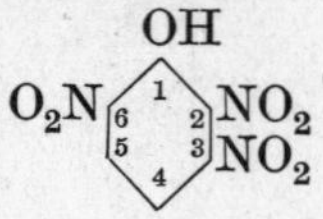

$C_6H_3O_7N_3$ MW, 229

Yellow needles from H_2O. M.p. 119°. Sol. EtOH, AcOH, C_6H_6.

Henriques, *Ann.*, 1882, **215**, 325.
See also Reverdin, Meldola, *J. prakt. Chem.*, 1913, **88**, 796.

2 : 4 : 5-Trinitrophenol.
Needles from H_2O or EtOH.Aq. M.p. 96°. Very sol. EtOH, Et_2O, C_6H_6. Spar. sol. cold H_2O. Very bitter taste.

Me ether : *see* 2 : 4 : 5-Trinitroanisole.
Phenyl ether : *see* 2 : 4 : 5-Trinitrodiphenyl Ether.

Henriques, *Ann.*, 1882, **215**, 329.

2 : 4 : 6-Trinitrophenol.
See Picric Acid.

2 : 4 : 6-Trinitrophenylacetic Acid

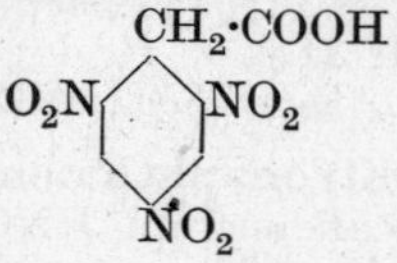

$C_8H_5O_8N_3$ MW, 271

Needles from C_6H_6. M.p. 161°. Heat with H_2O or EtOH $\longrightarrow$ 2 : 4 : 6-trinitrotoluene.

Jackson, Phinney, *Am. Chem. J.*, 1899, **21**, 430.

2 : 4 : 6-Trinitrophenylhydrazine (*Picrylhydrazine*)

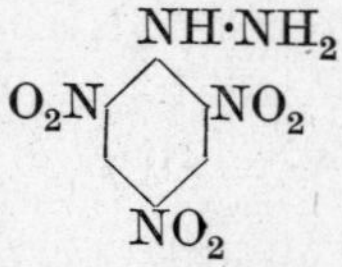

$C_6H_5O_6N_5$ MW, 243

Red plates from EtOH. M.p. 186° (175°). Sol. AcOH. Mod. sol. EtOH. Spar. sol. H_2O, Et_2O, $CHCl_3$, C_6H_6. Reduces Fehling's and $NH_3.AgNO_3$.

Acetyl : m.p. 223° (214° decomp.).

Giua, Cherchi, *Gazz. chim. ital.*, 1919, **49**, ii, 152.
Curtius, Dedichen, *J. prakt. Chem.*, 1894, **50**, 271.

2 : 4 : 6-Trinitrophenylnitramine.
See Picrylnitramine.

Trinitrophloroglucinol

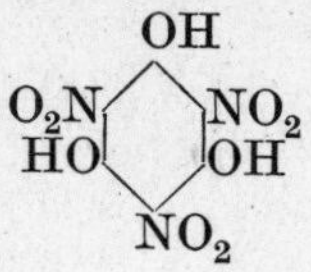

$C_6H_3O_9N_3$ MW, 261

Yellow needles $+ H_2O$ from H_2O. M.p. anhyd. 147° decomp. Sol. hot H_2O, EtOH, Et_2O. Explodes above m.p. Sublimes.

Tri-Et ether: $C_{12}H_{15}O_9N_3$. MW, 345. Plates from EtOH. M.p. 119–20°. Very sol. Me_2CO, $CHCl_3$, C_6H_6. Sol. hot EtOH, AcOH. Mod. sol. CS_2. Spar. sol. ligroin.

Triphenyl ether: $C_{24}H_{15}O_9N_3$. MW, 489. Needles from C_6H_6–EtOH. M.p. 175°. Very sol. Me_2CO, $CHCl_3$. Sol. AcOH, C_6H_6. Spar. sol. EtOH, Et_2O, CS_2, ligroin.

Tribenzyl ether: $C_{27}H_{21}O_9N_3$. MW, 531. Needles from EtOH–C_6H_6. M.p. 171°.

Freudenberg, Fikentscher, Wenner, *Ann.*, 1925, **442**, 322.
Jackson, Warren, *Am. Chem. J.*, 1893, **15**, 611.
Jackson, Smith, *Am. Chem. J.*, 1904, **32**, 173.
Blanksma, *Rec. trav. chim.*, 1908, **27**, 35.

2 : 4 : 6-Trinitroresorcinol.
See Styphnic Acid.

2 : 4 : 2′-Trinitrostilbene

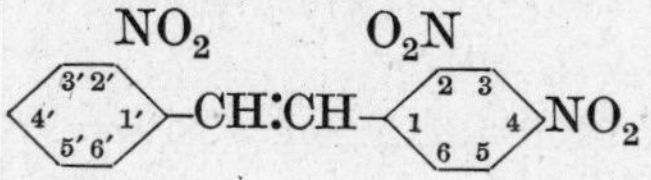

$C_{14}H_9O_6N_3$ MW, 315

Greenish-yellow cryst. from AcOH. M.p. 194–5°.

Thiele, Escales, *Ber.*, 1901, **34**, 2847.

2 : 4 : 3′-Trinitrostilbene.
Yellow needles from AcOH. M.p. 183–4°. Spar. sol. boiling EtOH.

See previous reference.

2 : 4 : 4′-Trinitrostilbene.
Dark orange needles from AcOH. M.p. 240° (234–5°). Sol. about 70 parts boiling AcOH.

Nisbet, *J. Chem. Soc.*, 1927, 2082.
Thiele, Escales, *Ber.*, 1901, **34**, 2846.
Bayer, D.R.P., 124,681, (*Chem. Zentr.*, 1901, II, 1029).

2 : 3 : 4-Trinitrotoluene

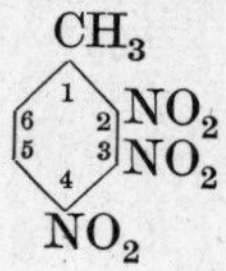

$C_7H_5O_6N_3$ MW, 227

Prisms from Me_2CO. M.p. 112°. Sol. Et_2O, Me_2CO, C_6H_6. Mod. sol. boiling EtOH. Explodes at 290–310°.

Gornall, Robinson, *J. Chem. Soc.*, 1926, 1981.
Will, *Ber.*, 1914, **47**, 710.

2 : 3 : 5-Trinitrotoluene.
Yellowish prisms from EtOH–Et_2O. M.p. 97·5°.

Körner, Contardi, *Atti accad. Lincei*, 1915, **24**, I, 891.

2 : 3 : 6-Trinitrotoluene.
Needles from EtOH. M.p. 111°. Sol. 9 parts boiling EtOH.

Körner, Contardi, *Atti accad. Lincei*, 1916, **25**, II, 345.
Brady, Taylor, *J. Chem. Soc.*, 1920, **117**, 876.

2 : 4 : 5-Trinitrotoluene.
Yellowish plates from Me_2CO. M.p. 104°. Sol. Et_2O, Me_2CO, C_6H_6. Mod. sol. hot EtOH, AcOH. Explodes at 290–310°.

Hepp, *Ann.*, 1882, **215**, 366.
Will, *Ber.*, 1914, **47**, 710.

2 : 4 : 6-Trinitrotoluene.
Rhombohedra from EtOH. M.p. 80·8°. Very sol. C_6H_6. Mod. sol. Et_2O. Sol. 700 parts boiling H_2O. This compound is the explosive known as T.N.T., but the commercial product usually contains small quantities of other nitrotoluenes according to the method of manufacture.

Copisarow, *Chem. News*, 1916, **113**, 37; 1915, **112**, 247.
Jackson, Phinney, *Am. Chem. J.*, 1899, **21**, 431.

3 : 4 : 5-Trinitrotoluene.
Greenish-yellow prisms or plates from EtOH. M.p. 137·5°. Sol. 100 parts 95% EtOH at 15°.

Körner, Contardi, *Atti accad. Lincei*, 1914, **23**, II, 466.

2 : 3 : 5-Trinitro-*p*-toluic Acid

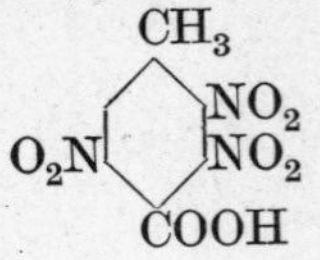

$C_8H_5O_8N_3$ MW, 271

White plates. M.p. 230–1°.

Me ester: $C_9H_7O_8N_3$. MW, 285. Needles from MeOH. M.p. 114–15°.

Et ester: $C_{10}H_9O_8N_3$. MW, 299. Prisms from EtOH. M.p. 87–8°.

Giua, *Gazz. chim. ital.*, 1922, **52**, i, 183.

2 : 4 : 6-Trinitro-*m*-toluidine

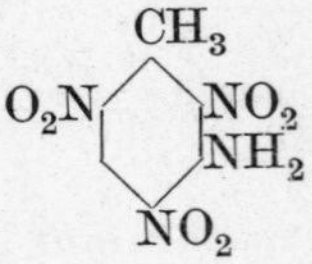

$C_7H_6O_6N_4$ MW, 242

Yellow prismatic leaflets from EtOH. M.p. 138° (136°). Sol. EtOH, Et_2O.

N-*Me*: $C_8H_8O_6N_4$. MW, 256. Yellow cryst. M.p. 138°.

N-*Et*: $C_9H_{10}O_6N_4$. MW, 270. Yellow cryst. M.p. 98°.

Blanksma, *Rec. trav. chim.*, 1902, **21**, 332.
Reverdin, Dresel, Delétra, *Ber.*, 1904, **37**, 2095.

Trinitrotrimethylenetriamine.

See Hexogen.

4 : 4′ : 4″-Trinitrotriphenylcarbinol

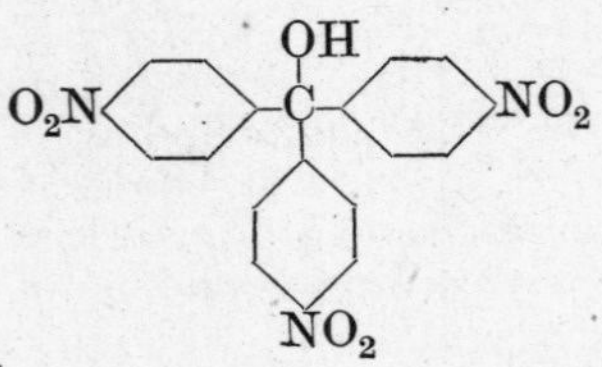

$C_{19}H_{13}O_7N_3$ MW, 395

Exists in two modifications.

(i) Prisms from AcOH or C_6H_6. M.p. 189°.

(ii) Rhombohedra from C_6H_6 or MeOH. M.p. 167°.

Sol. AcOH, C_6H_6. Spar. sol. hot EtOH, Et_2O, CS_2. Heat of comb. C_v 2218 Cal.

Fischer, Schmidt, *Chem. Zentr.*, 1904, **I**, 460.
Fischer, Fischer, *Ber.*, 1904, **37**, 3355.

4 : 4′ : 4″-Trinitrotriphenylmethane

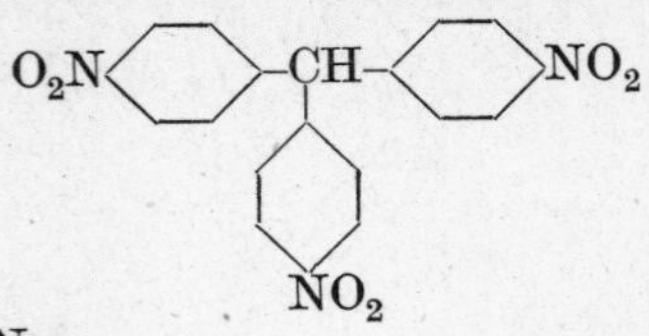

$C_{19}H_{13}O_6N_3$ MW, 379

Cryst. from C_6H_6. M.p. 212·5°. Spar. sol. AcOH, C_6H_6. Sol. alc. KOH with intense violet-blue col. Heat of comb. C_v 2272·8 Cal.

Montagne, *Rec. trav. chim.*, 1905, **24**, 125.
Hantzsch, Hein, *Ber.*, 1919, **52**, 495.

3 : 4 : 5-Trinitroveratrol

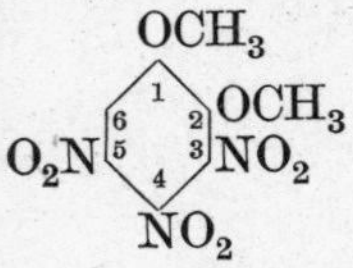

$C_8H_7O_8N_3$ MW, 273

Prisms from EtOH. M.p. 145°. Sol. hot EtOH, Et_2O. Insol. H_2O.

Vermeulen, *Rec. trav. chim.*, 1929, **48**, 969.
Klemenc, *Monatsh.*, 1912, **33**, 389.
Blanksma, *Rec. trav. chim.*, 1904, **23**, 114.

3 : 4 : 6-Trinitroveratrol.

Pale yellow needles from EtOH. M.p. 174°. Sol. Me_2CO, AcOEt. Spar. sol. EtOH, AcOH, $CHCl_3$. Decomp. slowly by cold NaOH and boiling Na_2CO_3.Aq.

Pollecoff, Robinson, *J. Chem. Soc.*, 1918, **113**, 655.

3 : 4 : 5-Trinitro-*o*-xylene

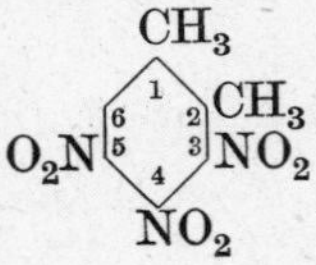

$C_8H_7O_6N_3$ MW, 241

Needles from EtOH. M.p. 115°. Sol. Me_2CO, AcOEt, $CHCl_3$, C_6H_6. Mod. sol. EtOH.

Crossley, Renouf, *J. Chem. Soc.*, 1909, **95**, 211.

3 : 4 : 6-Trinitro-*o*-xylene.

Yellowish needles from EtOH. M.p. 72°. Sol. most org. solvents except EtOH, pet. ether. Turns yellow in air.

See previous reference.

2 : 4 : 5-Trinitro-*m*-xylene

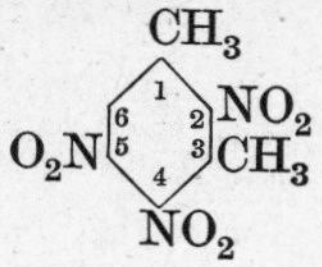

$C_8H_7O_6N_3$ MW, 241

Yellow cryst. from EtOH. M.p. 90°. D^{14} 1·553. Sol. 50 parts EtOH at 25°. Sol. HNO_3.

Blanksma, *Rec. trav. chim.*, 1909, **28**, 95; 1906, **25**, 167.

2 : 4 : 6-Trinitro-*m*-xylene.
Pale yellow prisms or leaflets from C_6H_6–EtOH. M.p. 182°. D^{19} 1·604. Sol. 2500 parts EtOH at 20°. Spar. sol. warm HNO_3.

Blanksma, *Rec. trav. chim.*, 1906, **25**, 178.
Beilstein, Luhmann, *Ann.*, 1867, **144**, 274.

4 : 5 : 6-Trinitro-*m*-xylene.
Prisms from EtOH. M.p. 125°. D^{19} 1·494. Sol. 80 parts EtOH at 20°. Sol. warm HNO_3.

Blanksma, *Rec. trav. chim.*, 1906, **25**, 168.

2 : 3 : 5-Trinitro-*p*-xylene

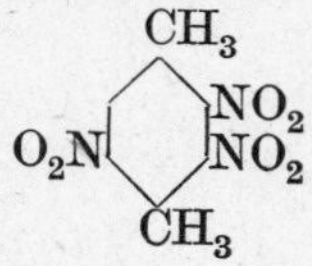

$C_8H_7O_6N_3$ MW, 241

Needles from EtOH or leaflets from EtOH–C_6H_6. M.p. 139–40° (137°). D^{19} 1·59. Turns yellow in air.

Fittig, Ahrens, Mattheides, *Ann.*, 1868, **147**, 23.
Giua, *Gazz. chim. ital.*, 1919, **49**, ii, 149 (*Note*).

2 : 4 : 6-Trinitro-*m*-5-xylenol (*Xylopicric acid*)

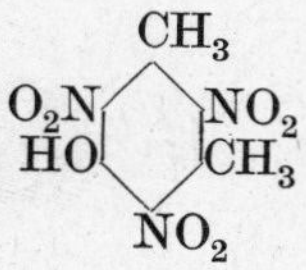

$C_8H_7O_7N_3$ MW, 257

Needles from dil. HNO_3. M.p. 108° (104°). Spar. sol. H_2O with yellow col.

Me ether: $C_9H_9O_7N_3$. MW, 271. Needles from EtOH. M.p. 127°. Sol. AcOH, hot EtOH. Insol. H_2O.

Blanksma, *Rec. trav. chim.*, 1902, **21**, 329.
Knecht, Hibbert, *Ber.*, 1904, **37**, 3477.

2 : 4 : 6-Trinitro-*m*-5-xylidine

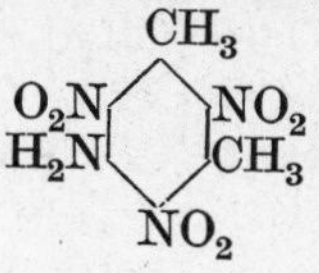

$C_8H_8O_6N_4$ MW, 256

Yellow cryst. M.p. 206°.

N-*Me*: $C_9H_{10}O_6N_4$. MW, 270. Yellow cryst. M.p. 165°.

N-*Et*: $C_{10}H_{12}O_6N_4$. MW, 284. M.p. 122°.

Blanksma, *Rec. trav. chim.*, 1906, **25**, 374; 1902, **21**, 331.

Triolein (*Olein, glycerol trioleate*)

$CH_2·O·CO·[CH_2]_7·CH{:}CH·[CH_2]_7·CH_3$
$CH·O·CO·[CH_2]_7·CH{:}CH·[CH_2]_7·CH_3$
$CH_2·O·CO·[CH_2]_7·CH{:}CH·[CH_2]_7·CH_3$

$C_{57}H_{104}O_6$ MW, 884

Found in olive oil, butter fat, and other vegetable oils. F.p. – 4°. B.p. 235–40°/18 mm. D_4^{50} 0·8992. n_D^{60} 1·4561. Very sol. Et_2O. Spar. sol. EtOH. Tasteless. Odourless.

Amberger, Bromig, *Biochem. Z.*, 1922, **130**, 252.
Bellucci, *Gazz. chim. ital.*, 1912, **42**, ii, 291.
Bournot, *Biochem. Z.*, 1914, **65**, 156.

Trional.
See Methylsulphonal.

Triorsellinic Acid.
See Gyrophoric Acid.

1 : 3 : 5-Trioxan.
See Trioxymethylene.

Trioxymethylene (*Metaformaldehyde*, 1:3:5-*trioxan*)

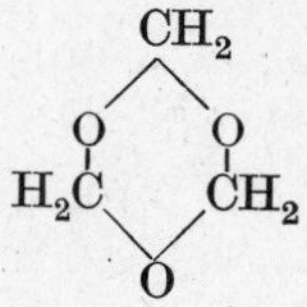

$C_3H_6O_3$ MW, 90

Cryst. from Et_2O. M.p. 64° (61°). B.p. 114·5°/759 mm. Sol. EtOH, Et_2O, $CHCl_3$, CCl_4, CS_2, C_6H_6. Spar. sol. pet. ether. Sol. 5 parts H_2O at 25°. Sublimes at 46° undecomp. in presence of traces of moisture.

Diacetyl: b.p. 113–15°/2 mm. Misc. with Et_2O.

Staudinger, Lüthy, *Helv. Chim. Acta*, 1925, **8**, 51, 65.
Hammick, Boeree, *J. Chem. Soc.*, 1922, **121**, 2738.

Tripalmitin (*Palmitin, glycerol tripalmitate*)

$CH_2{\cdot}O{\cdot}CO{\cdot}[CH_2]_{14}{\cdot}CH_3$
$CH{\cdot}O{\cdot}CO{\cdot}[CH_2]_{14}{\cdot}CH_3$
$CH_2{\cdot}O{\cdot}CO{\cdot}[CH_2]_{14}{\cdot}CH_3$

$C_{51}H_{98}O_6$ MW, 806

Needles from Et_2O. M.p. 65·5°. D_4^{70} 0·8752. n_D^{80} 1·43807. Very sol. Et_2O. Spar. sol. EtOH.

Bellucci, *Gazz. chim. ital.*, 1912, **42**, ii, 290.
Stephenson, *Biochem. J.*, 1913, **7**, 432.
Averill, Roche, King, *J. Am. Chem. Soc.*, 1929, **51**, 870.

Tri-*peri*naphthylenebenzene.
See Decacyclene.

Tripetroselin.
See under Petroselic Acid.

Triphenylacetic Acid (*Triphenylmethane-α-carboxylic acid*)

$(C_6H_5)_3C{\cdot}COOH$

$C_{20}H_{16}O_2$ MW, 288

Prisms from EtOH. M.p. 267°. Mod. sol. MeOH, EtOH, AcOH, ligroin. Spar. sol. $CHCl_3$, CS_2, C_6H_6. Very weak acid. Above m.p. part. decomp. $\longrightarrow$ CO_2 + triphenylmethane. Warm conc. $H_2SO_4 \longrightarrow CO$ + triphenylcarbinol.

Me ester: $C_{21}H_{18}O_2$. MW, 302. Needles from C_6H_6. M.p. 186°. Sol. Me_2CO, C_6H_6. Spar. sol. MeOH, Et_2O, ligroin.

Et ester: $C_{22}H_{20}O_2$. MW, 316. M.p. 120–1°.

Propyl ester: $C_{23}H_{22}O_2$. MW, 330. M.p. 98–9°.

Isopropyl ester: m.p. 84°.

Butyl ester: $C_{24}H_{24}O_2$. MW, 344. M.p. 99–99·6°.

sec.-n-*Butyl ester*: m.p. 101–2°.

Isobutyl ester: m.p. 88–9°.

n-*Amyl ester*: $C_{25}H_{26}O_2$. MW, 358. M.p. 76°.

Isoamyl ester: needles. M.p. 78·5–79·5°.

Phenyl ester: $C_{26}H_{20}O_2$. MW, 364. Needles from C_6H_6. M.p. 124·5–125°.

Benzyl ester: m.p. 99·5°.

Chloride: $C_{20}H_{15}OCl$. MW, 306·5. Prisms from C_6H_6 or ligroin. M.p. 128–9° decomp.

Amide: $C_{20}H_{17}ON$. MW, 287. Prisms from toluene. M.p. 246–7° (238°). Very spar. sol. EtOH, Et_2O.

Nitrile: α-cyanotriphenylmethane. $C_{20}H_{15}N$. MW, 269. Plates from Me_2CO.Aq. M.p. 127–8°.

Anhydride: $C_{40}H_{30}O_3$. MW, 558. Cryst. from C_6H_6. M.p. 163°.

Anilide: cryst. from AcOH. M.p. 173·5–174·5° (167–8°). N-*Benzoyl*: needles from C_6H_6. M.p. 185–6°.

Norris, Cresswell, *J. Am. Chem. Soc.*, 1934, **56**, 423.
Schlenk, Marcus, *Ber.*, 1914, **47**, 1666.
Elbs, Tölle, *J. prakt. Chem.*, 1885, **32**, 624.
Bistrzycki, Mauron, *Ber.*, 1907, **40**, 4062.
Schmidlin, Hodgson, *Ber.*, 1908, **41**, 441.
Fischer, Fischer, *Ann.*, 1878, **194**, 260.

Triphenylacrylic Acid.
See α : β-Diphenylcinnamic Acid.

Triphenylamine

$(C_6H_5)_3N$

$C_{18}H_{15}N$ MW, 245

Cryst. from AcOEt. M.p. 127°. B.p. 365°. Sol. Et_2O, C_6H_6. Spar. sol. cold EtOH. Does not combine with picric acid or alkyl iodides.

Hydrochloride: m.p. 214°.

Hager, *Organic Syntheses*, Collective Vol. I, 529.
Piccard, Kharasch, *J. Am. Chem. Soc.*, 1918, **40**, 1077.

Triphenylamine-2-carboxylic Acid (*Diphenylanthranilic acid*)

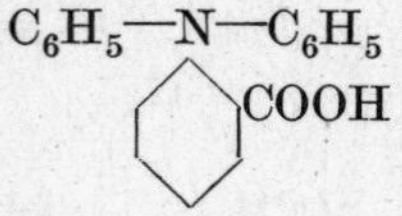

$C_{19}H_{15}O_2N$ MW, 289

Yellow feathery cryst. from AcOH. M.p. 208°. Heat above m.p. $\longrightarrow$ triphenylamine. Sol. conc. H_2SO_4 with blue col.

Goldberg, Nimerovsky, *Ber.*, 1907, **40**, 2449.

Triphenylarsine (*Arsenic triphenyl*)

$(C_6H_5)_3As$

$C_{18}H_{15}As$ MW, 306

Needles from EtOH.Aq. M.p. 60·5°. B.p. above 360° in CO_2. Very sol. Et_2O, C_6H_6. Spar. sol. cold EtOH. Insol. H_2O.

B_2,H_2PtCl_6: yellow leaflets from $CHCl_3$. M.p. 285°.

Hydroxymethylate: cryst. from EtOH.Aq. M.p. 125–6°.

Methochloride: needles. M.p. 121°. Very sol. H_2O, EtOH.

Methiodide: yellow leaflets from EtOH. M.p. 176°.

Ethiodide: needles from EtOH–Et_2O. M.p. 158°.

Pope, Turner, *J. Chem. Soc.*, 1920, **117**, 1447.
Hilpert, Herrmann, *Ber.*, 1913, **46**, 2223.
Philips, *Ber.*, 1886, **19**, 1031.
Michaelis, *Ann.*, 1902, **321**, 160.

1 : 2 : 3-Triphenylbenzene

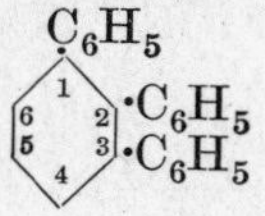

$C_{24}H_{18}$ MW, 306

M.p. 150–5°.

Knoevenagel, Vieth, *Ann.*, 1894, **281**, 72.

1 : 3 : 5-Triphenylbenzene.
Needles from AcOH. M.p. 172°. Distils undecomp. Sol. C_6H_6. Mod. sol. EtOH, Et_2O. CrO_3 in AcOH ⟶ benzoic acid. Causes malignant growths in mice.

Odell, Hines, *J. Am. Chem. Soc.*, 1913, **35**, 82.
Reddelien, *Ber.*, 1913, **46**, 2716.
Knoll, D.R.P., 250,236, (*Chem. Zentr.*, 1912, II, 1084).

Triphenylbenzoylmethane.
See Benzpinacolin.

Triphenyl borate.
See under Phenol.

Triphenylcarbinol (*α-Hydroxytriphenylmethane, tritanol*)

$$(C_6H_5)_3C{\cdot}OH$$

$C_{19}H_{16}O$ MW, 260

Plates from EtOH. M.p. 164–5°. B.p. 380°. Sol. EtOH, Et_2O, C_6H_6. Heat of comb. C_p 2342·0 Cal., C_v 2340·0 Cal. H (+ Ni) at 400°, HI in AcOH, or hot H·COOH ⟶ triphenylmethane.

Me ether: $C_{20}H_{18}O$. MW, 274. Plates from MeOH. M.p. 83–4°.
Et ether: $C_{21}H_{20}O$. MW, 288. Cryst. from EtOH. M.p. 84–5°.
Propyl ether: $C_{22}H_{22}O$. MW, 302. Cryst. from EtOH–Et_2O. M.p. 56°.
Isopropyl ether: m.p. 113°.
Phenyl ether: $C_{25}H_{20}O$. MW, 336. Leaflets or prisms from Et_2O–pet. ether. M.p. 103°.
Benzyl ether: plates from EtOH. M.p. 106–7°.
Acetyl: triphenylmethyl acetate. Cryst. from AcOEt–ligroin. M.p. 87–8°.

Morton, Stevens, *J. Am. Chem. Soc.*, 1931, **53**, 4030.
Stadnikow, *Ber.*, 1924, **57**, 6.

Triphenylcarbinol-3-carboxylic Acid (*α-Hydroxytriphenylmethane-3-carboxylic acid*)

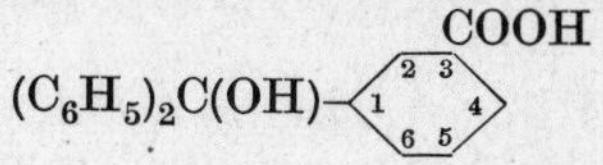

$C_{20}H_{16}O_3$ MW, 304

Cryst. from EtOH. M.p. 166–7°. Sol. conc. H_2SO_4 with yellow col.

Bistrzycki, Gyr, *Ber.*, 1904, **37**, 3698.

Triphenylcarbinol-4-carboxylic Acid (*α-Hydroxytriphenylmethane-4-carboxylic acid*).
Needles from AcOH. M.p. 203·5° (200°). Sol. EtOH, Et_2O, C_6H_6. Insol. H_2O.
Me ester: $C_{21}H_{17}O_3$. MW, 318. Cryst. from MeOH. M.p. 119°.

Staudinger, Clar, *Ber.*, 1911, **44**, 1631.
Bistrzycki, Gyr, *Ber.*, 1904, **37**, 657.

Triphenyldihydroglyoxaline.
See Amarin.

Triphenylene (*9 : 10 - Benzphenanthrene, 1 : 2 : 3 : 4-dibenznaphthalene*)

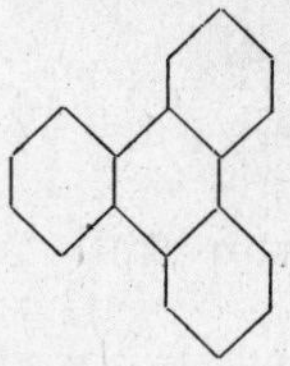

$C_{18}H_{12}$ MW, 228

Occurs to a small extent in coal-tar. Needles from EtOH. M.p. 198°. Sublimes. Sol. $CHCl_3$, C_6H_6. Mod. sol. EtOH, AcOH. Sols exhibit weak blue fluor. HNO_3 at 150° ⟶ mellitic acid.

Mannich, *Ber.*, 1907, **40**, 160.
Schmidt, Schultz, *Ann.*, 1880, **203**, 135.

1 : 1 : 1-Triphenylethane.
See α-Methyltriphenylmethane.

1 : 1 : 2-Triphenylethane

$$C_6H_5{\cdot}CH_2{\cdot}CH(C_6H_5)_2$$

$C_{20}H_{18}$ MW, 258

Leaflets from EtOH. M.p. 54·5°. B.p. 348–9°, 216–17°/14 mm. Forms a K salt.

Böeseken, Bastet, *Rec. trav. chim.*, 1913, **32**, 199.
Klages, Heilmann, *Ber.*, 1904, **37**, 1455.

Triphenylethyl Alcohol.
See Hydroxytriphenylethane.

1 : 1 : 2-Triphenylethylene (*α-Phenylstilbene*)

$C_6H_5 \cdot CH{:}C(C_6H_5)_2$

$C_{20}H_{16}$ MW, 256

Leaflets from EtOH or AcOH. M.p. 72–3°. B.p. 220–1°/14 mm. Heat of comb. C_v 2510·3 Cal.

Stadnikow, *Ber.*, 1914, **47**, 2140.
Staudinger, Kon, *Ann.*, 1911, **384**, 89.

2 : 4 : 5-Triphenylglyoxaline.
See Lophine.

α-Triphenylguanidine

$C_6H_5 \cdot NH \cdot C(:N \cdot C_6H_5) \cdot NH \cdot C_6H_5$

$C_{19}H_{17}N_3$ MW, 287

Prisms from EtOH. M.p. 144–144·5°. D^{16} 1·163. Dist. in $CO_2 \longrightarrow$ carbanilide. Conc. KOH $\longrightarrow CO_2 +$ aniline. Rubber vulcanisation accelerator (T.P.G.).

B,HCl: prisms + $1H_2O$. M.p. 241–2°.

Picrate: yellow cryst. from EtOH. M.p. 180°.

Connolly, Dyson, *J. Chem. Soc.*, 1935, 680.
Hofmann, *Ber.*, 1869, 2, 458.
Alway, Vail, *Am. Chem. J.*, 1902, **28**, 162.

β-Triphenylguanidine

$C_6H_5 \cdot NH \cdot C(:NH) \cdot N(C_6H_5)_2$

$C_{19}H_{17}N_3$ MW, 287

Plates. M.p. 131°. Sol. EtOH, Et_2O. Spar. sol. C_6H_6.

v. Braun, *Ber.*, 1900, **33**, 2725.
Weith, Schröder, *Ber.*, 1875, **8**, 295.

Triphenylhexahydrotriazine.
See Anhydroformaldehydeaniline.

Triphenylmethane (*Tritan*)

$(C_6H_5)_2CH \cdot C_6H_5$

$C_{19}H_{16}$ MW, 244

Cryst. from EtOH in two forms. (i) Labile, m.p. 81°. (ii) Stable, m.p. 94°. B.p. 190–215°/10 mm. D_4^{99} 1·01405. Sol. Et_2O, $CHCl_3$, hot EtOH. Spar. sol. AcOH. Very spar. sol. ligroin. Heat of comb. C_p 2387·3 Cal., C_v 2385·1 Cal. $CrO_3 \longrightarrow$ triphenylcarbinol + benzophenone. $PCl_5 \longrightarrow$ triphenylchloromethane.

Norris, *Organic Syntheses*, Collective Vol. I, 532.
Schmidlin, Garcia-Banùs, *Ber.*, 1912, **45**, 3189.

Triphenylmethane-α-carboxylic Acid.
See Triphenylacetic Acid.

Triphenylmethane-2-carboxylic Acid (*2-Benzhydrylbenzoic acid*)

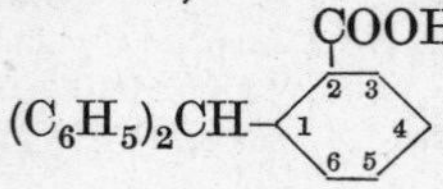

$C_{20}H_{16}O_2$ MW, 288

Needles from EtOH. M.p. 162°. Sublimes. Sol. EtOH, Et_2O, AcOH, C_6H_6. Spar. sol. ligroin. Insol. H_2O.

Me ester: $C_{21}H_{18}O_2$. MW, 302. Prisms from MeOH. M.p. 98°.

Nitrile: 2-cyanotriphenylmethane. $C_{20}H_{15}N$. MW, 269. Needles from EtOH. M.p. 89°. B.p. 270–85°/20–30 mm. Sol. EtOH, Et_2O, $CHCl_3$, AcOH, C_6H_6. Insol. ligroin.

Drory, *Ber.*, 1891, **24**, 2573.
Gresly, *Ann.*, 1886, **234**, 242.

Triphenylmethane-4-carboxylic Acid (*4-Benzhydrylbenzoic acid*).

Needles from AcOH.Aq. M.p. 165°. Sol. EtOH, Et_2O, C_6H_6. Prac. insol. H_2O.

Chloride: $C_{20}H_{15}OCl$. MW, 306·5. Cryst. from pet. ether. M.p. 89–90°.

Nitrile: 4-cyanotriphenylmethane. Prisms from MeOH. M.p. 100°. Sol. EtOH, Et_2O, AcOH, C_6H_6.

Anilide: cryst. from AcOH. M.p. 196°.

Staudinger, Clar, *Ber.*, 1911, **44**, 1628.
Moses, *Ber.*, 1900, **33**, 2630.

Triphenylmethyl.
See Hexaphenylethane.

ω-Triphenylmethyl-benzyl Alcohol.
See 1 : 2 : 2 : 2-Tetraphenylethyl Alcohol.

Triphenylmethyl bromide (*α-Bromotriphenylmethane, trityl bromide, triphenylbromomethane*)

$(C_6H_5)_3CBr$

$C_{19}H_{15}Br$ MW, 323

Pale yellow cryst. from CS_2. M.p. 152°. B.p. 230°/15 mm. Boiling AcOH $\longrightarrow$ triphenylcarbinol. NH_3 in C_6H_6 sol. $\longrightarrow$ triphenylmethylamine.

Allen, Kölliker, *Ann.*, 1885, **227**, 110.
Wieland, *Ber.*, 1909, 42, 3024 (*Footnote*).

Triphenylmethyl chloride (*α-Chlorotriphenylmethane, triphenylchloromethane, trityl chloride*)

$(C_6H_5)_3CCl$

$C_{19}H_{15}Cl$ MW, 278·5

Cryst. from C_6H_6 or pet. ether. M.p. 112–13°. Sol. Et_2O, $CHCl_3$, CS_2, C_6H_6. Heat of comb. C_v 2346·5 Cal., C_p 2348·5 Cal. Above 250° ⟶ triphenylmethane + a little 9-phenylfluorene. Employed for characterisation of alcohols as triphenylmethyl ethers.

Gomberg, *Ber.*, 1900, **33**, 3147.
Norris, Sanders, *Am. Chem. J.*, 1901, **25**, 60.

Triphenylmethyl iodide (*α-Iodotriphenylmethane, trityl iodide*)

$(C_6H_5)_3CI$

$C_{19}H_{15}I$ MW, 370

Yellowish cryst. which rapidly turn dark brown. M.p. 132°.

$C_{19}H_{15}I,5I$: prisms. M.p. 90°.

Gomberg, *Ber.*, 1900, **33**, 3158; 1902, **35**, 1835.

2 : 4 : 5-Triphenyloxazole (*Benzilam, azobenzil*)

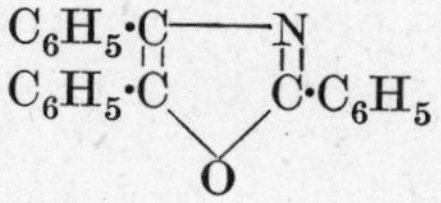

$C_{21}H_{15}ON$ MW, 297

Prisms. M.p. 115·5–116·5°. Sol. C_6H_6 with feeble blue fluor. CrO_3 ⟶ benzoic acid.

Schönberg, *Ber.*, 1921, **54**, 242.
McKenzie, Barrow, *J. Chem. Soc.*, 1913, **103**, 1334.

Triphenyl phosphate

$(C_6H_5O)_3PO$

$C_{18}H_{15}O_4P$ MW, 326

Prisms from EtOH. M.p. 49°. B.p. 245°/11 mm. Sol. Et_2O, $CHCl_3$, C_6H_6. Mod. sol. EtOH. Insol. H_2O.

Heim, *Ber.*, 1883, **16**, 1765.
A.G.F.A., D.R.P., 246,871, (*Chem. Zentr.*, 1912, I, 1875).

Triphenylphosphine

$(C_6H_5)_3P$

$C_{18}H_{15}P$ MW, 262

Plates or prisms from Et_2O. M.p. 80°. Dist. undecomp. above 360° in indifferent atmosphere. n_D^{69} 1·52475. Very sol. Et_2O. Sol. $CHCl_3$, AcOH, C_6H_6. Mod. sol. EtOH. Insol. H_2O. Heat of comb. C_p 2480·7 Cal., C_v 2483·95 Cal. Triboluminescent.

B,HI : needles. M.p. 215° decomp.

Methiodide : leaflets. M.p. 182–3°.

Ethiodide : leaflets from EtOH.Aq. M.p. 164–5°.

B,C_6H_5Br : tetraphenylphosphonium bromide. M.p. 286–8°.

B,C_6H_5Cl : tetraphenylphosphonium chloride. M.p. 265°.

B,C_6H_5I : tetraphenylphosphonium iodide. M.p. 333°.

Dodonow, Medox, *Ber.*, 1928, **61**, 907.
Michaelis, v. Soden, *Ann.*, 1885, **229**, 298.

Triphenyl phosphite.

See under Phenol.

1 : 1 : 2-Triphenylpropionic Acid (*Diphenylbenzylacetic acid, 1 : 1-diphenylhydrocinnamic acid*)

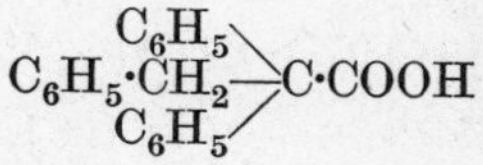

$C_{21}H_{18}O_2$ MW, 302

Needles from EtOH.Aq. M.p. 162° (132°). Sol. Et_2O, hot EtOH.Aq. Very spar. sol. H_2O.

Me ester : $C_{22}H_{20}O_2$. MW, 316. M.p. 127°.

Benzyl ester : prisms from EtOH. M.p. 85°. B.p. 270°/2 mm.

Chloride : $C_{21}H_{17}OCl$. MW, 320·5. M.p. 90–1°.

Amide : $C_{21}H_{19}ON$. MW, 301. Needles from EtOH. M.p. 111°.

Nitrile : $C_{21}H_{17}N$. MW, 283. Plates or needles. M.p. 126°.

Ramart, *Bull. soc. chim.*, 1924, **35**, 196.
Neure, *Ann.*, 1889, **250**, 143, 147.

1 : 2 : 2-Triphenylpropionic Acid (*Phenylbenzhydrylacetic acid*)

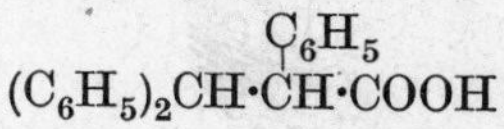

$C_{21}H_{18}O_2$ MW, 302

Needles from EtOH or pet. ether. M.p. 222–3° (211°). Sol. EtOH, Et_2O. Spar. sol. ligroin. Insol. H_2O.

Me ester : plates from EtOH. M.p. 159°.

Et ester : $C_{23}H_{22}O_2$. MW, 330. Leaflets from EtOH. M.p. 122–3°.

Propyl ester : $C_{24}H_{24}O_2$. MW, 344. M.p. 109°.

Isopropyl ester : m.p. 138°.

Phenyl ester : $C_{27}H_{22}O_2$. MW, 378. M.p. 124°.

Benzyl ester : m.p. 117°.

Chloride : cryst. from pet. ether. M.p. 94°.

Amide : needles from EtOH.Aq. M.p. 213°.

Nitrile : plates from MeOH. M.p. 102°.

Kohler, Heritage, *Am. Chem. J.*, 1905, **33**, 156.
Banús, Salas, *Chem. Zentr.*, 1935, II, 3770.
Banús, Boqué, *ibid.*

2 : 2 : 2-Triphenylpropionic Acid (2 : 2-*Diphenylhydrocinnamic acid*)

$(C_6H_5)_3C{\cdot}CH_2{\cdot}COOH$

$C_{21}H_{18}O_2$ MW, 302

Prisms from EtOH. M.p. 177°. Very sol. Et_2O. Sol. EtOH.
Et ester : prisms. M.p. 125° (81°).
Chloride : m.p. 128–9° (132°).
Amide : m.p. 198°.
Nitrile : cryst. from EtOH. M.p. 140°.

Fosse, *Bull. soc. chim.*, 1931, **49**, 159.
Henderson, *J. Chem. Soc.*, 1887, **51**, 226.

1 : 3 : 4-Triphenylpyrazole (1 : 3 : 4-*Triphenyl*-1 : 2-*diazole*)

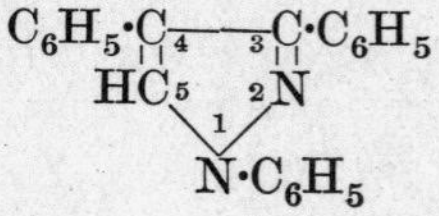

$C_{21}H_{16}N_2$ MW, 296

Needles from EtOH. M.p. 207° (185°). Very sol. C_6H_6. Spar. sol. EtOH, ligroin, cold AcOH. Insol. dil. acids. Sol. conc. H_2SO_4 with yellow col.

Rupe, Gisiger, *Helv. Chim. Acta*, 1925, **8**, 351.

1 : 3 : 5-Triphenylpyrazole.
Needles or plates from Et_2O. M.p. 140–140·5° (137–8°). Sol. $CHCl_3$, AcOH, C_6H_6. Spar. sol. EtOH, Et_2O. Insol. H_2O.
Methiodide : needles from H_2O. M.p. 176° ⟶ components.

Knorr, Laubmann, *Ber.*, 1888, **21**, 1206.
Wislicenus, *Ann.*, 1899, **308**, 253.

1 : 4 : 5-Triphenylpyrazole.
Needles from EtOH or AcOH. M.p. 212° (206°). B.p. about 400° undecomp. Sol. $CHCl_3$, hot AcOH, hot C_6H_6. Spar. sol. Et_2O, hot EtOH.

Japp, Tingle, *J. Chem. Soc.*, 1897, **71**, 1143.
Wislicenus, Ruthing, *Ann.*, 1911, **379**, 257.

2 : 3 : 6-Triphenylpyridine

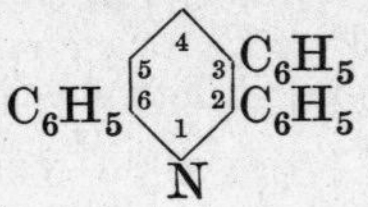

$C_{23}H_{17}N$ MW, 307

Needles from EtOH. M.p. 115°.
Picrate : yellow prisms from EtOH. M.p. 163°.

Allen, Barker, *J. Am. Chem. Soc.*, 1932, **54**, 742.

2 : 4 : 6-Triphenylpyridine (*Acetophenine*).
Colourless prisms from EtOH. M.p. 137·5° (135°). Very spar. sol. cold EtOH. Sol. conc. H_2SO_4 with blue fluor.
Picrate : yellow needles from EtOH. M.p. 192·5°.

Reddelien, *Ber.*, 1920, **53**, 334.

Triphenylstibine (*Antimony triphenyl*)

$(C_6H_5)_3Sb$

$C_{18}H_{15}Sb$ MW, 351

Prisms from pet. ether. M.p. 53° (50°). B.p. above 220°/1 mm. D_4^{50} 1·4075, D_4^{100} 1·3597. Very sol. Et_2O, $CHCl_3$, AcOH, C_6H_6, pet. ether. Spar. sol. EtOH.

Hiers, *Organic Syntheses*, Collective Vol. I, 535.

Triphenylthiourea.
See under Thiourea.
Triphenylurea.
See under Urea.
Tripropin.
See under Propionic Acid.
Tripropylamine

$(CH_3{\cdot}CH_2{\cdot}CH_2)_3N$

$C_9H_{21}N$ MW, 143

Liq. B.p. 156·5°. D_4^{20} 0·753. $n_D^{19·4}$ 1·41756. $k = 4·43\ (5·5) \times 10^{-4}$ at 25°.
B,HCl : hygroscopic needles. M.p. 90°.
B,HBr : needles. M.p. 180°.
$B,HAuBr_4$: m.p. 149°.
$B,HBr,HgBr_2$: needles. M.p. 104°.
Methiodide : methyltripropylammonium iodide. Leaflets from EtOH–Et_2O. M.p. 207–8°.
Ethiodide : ethyltripropylammonium iodide. Prisms from EtOH. M.p. 238° decomp.
B,I_2 : cryst. from EtOH. M.p. 65–6°.

Skita, Keil, *Monatsh.*, 1929, **53** and **54**, 758.

Tripropyl phosphate.
See under Phosphoric Acid.
Trisalicylin.
See under Salicylic Acid.
Tristearin (*Glycerol tristearate, stearin*)

$CH_2O{\cdot}CO{\cdot}[CH_2]_{16}{\cdot}CH_3$
$CHO{\cdot}CO{\cdot}[CH_2]_{16}{\cdot}CH_3$
$CH_2O{\cdot}CO{\cdot}[CH_2]_{16}{\cdot}CH_3$

$C_{57}H_{110}O_6$ MW, 890

Present in many natural fats. Cryst. from Et_2O. M.p. 72° (70·8°). D_4^{90} 0·8559. n_D^{80} 1·4385. Sol. $CHCl_3$, C_6H_6, hot EtOH. Mod. sol. boiling Et_2O, boiling pet. ether. Insol. cold EtOH.

Bellucci, *Gazz. chim. ital.*, 1912, **42**, ii, 291.

Tritan.
See Triphenylmethane.
Tritanol.
See Triphenylcarbinol.
Trithiophloroglucinol (1 : 3 : 5-*Trimercaptobenzene*)

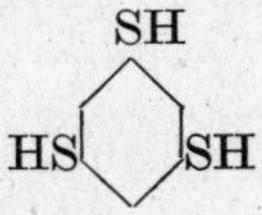

$C_6H_6S_3$ MW, 174

Needles. M.p. 57–60°. Sol. Et_2O, CS_2.
Tri-Me ether : $C_9H_{12}S_3$. MW, 216. Needles from EtOH. M.p. 66–8°.
Triacetyl : needles from EtOH. M.p. 73–4°.

Pollak, Carniol, *Ber.*, 1909, **42**, 3252.

Tri-*p*-tolylcarbinol (α-*Hydroxy*-4 : 4′ : 4″-*trimethyltriphenylmethane*)

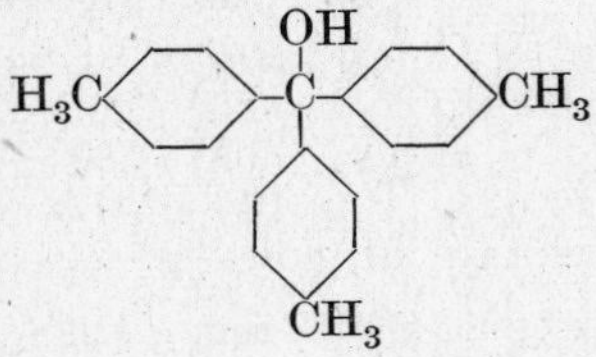

$C_{22}H_{22}O$ MW, 302

Prisms from Et_2O–ligroin. M.p. 96°. Sol. EtOH, Et_2O, C_6H_6. Spar. sol. pet. ether. H_2SO_4 ⟶ greenish-red col.
Et ether : $C_{24}H_{26}O$. MW, 330. Needles from pet. ether. M.p. 111°.

Gomberg, *Ber.*, 1904, **37**, 1629.
Mothwurf, *ibid.*, 3153.
Tousley, Gomberg, *J. Am. Chem. Soc.*, 1904, **26**, 1516.

Tri-*p*-tolylmethane

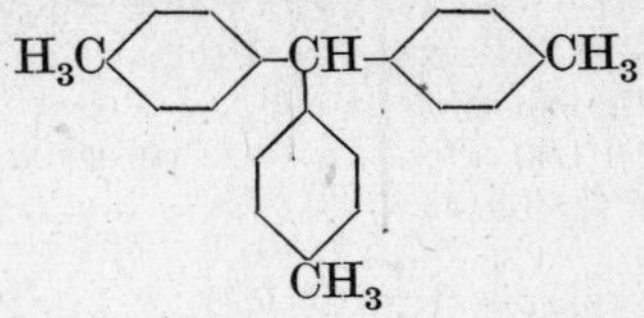

$C_{22}H_{22}$ MW, 286

Prisms. M.p. 63°. B.p. 225–30°/15 mm. Spar. sol. EtOH, AcOH.

Tousley, Gomberg, *J. Am. Chem. Soc.*, 1904, **26**, 1520.
Mothwurf, *Ber.*, 1904, **37**, 3155.

Tri-*p*-tolylmethyl chloride (α-*Chlorotri*-p-*tolylmethane*)

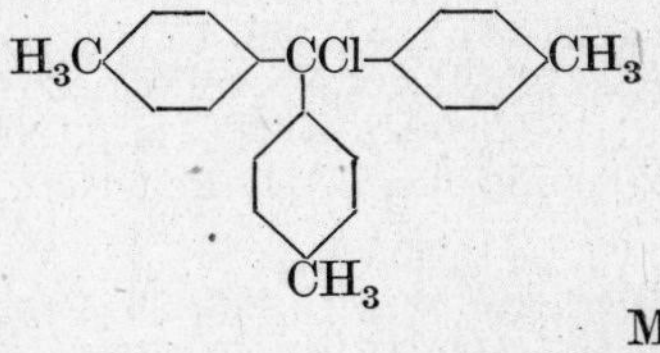

$C_{22}H_{21}Cl$ MW, 320·5

Cryst. from AcOEt. M.p. 184–5° (173°). Sol. C_6H_6, CS_2, pet. ether. H_2SO_4 ⟶ tri-*p*-tolylcarbinol.

Mothwurf, *Ber.*, 1904, **37**, 3156.
Gomberg, *ibid.*, 1627.

Tritopine.
See Laudanidine.
Tröger's Base (1 : 2′-*Methylene*-3-p-*tolyl*-6-*methyl*-1 : 2 : 3 : 4-*tetrahydroquinazoline*)

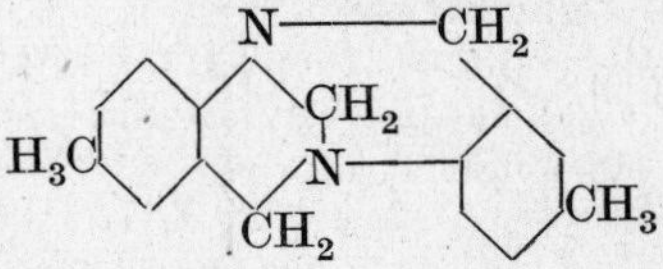

$C_{17}H_{18}N_2$ MW, 250

Needles from EtOH.Aq. M.p. 135–6°.
Hydrochloride : m.p. 213°.
Picrate : cryst. from EtOH. M.p. 188–9°.

Wagner, *J. Am. Chem. Soc.*, 1935, **57**, 1296.
Spielman, *ibid.*, 583.

Tropacocaine (ψ-*Tropyl ester of benzoic acid, benzoyl-ψ-tropeïn*)

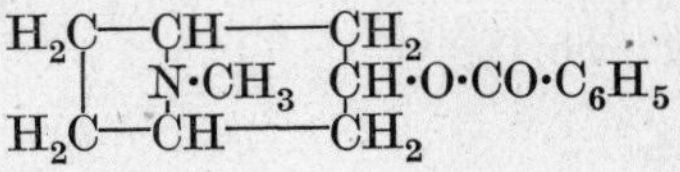

$C_{15}H_{19}O_2N$ MW, 245

Constituent of Java coca leaves. Plates. M.p. 49°. Sol. EtOH, Et_2O, $CHCl_3$, ligroin,

C_6H_6. Hot conc. HCl $\longrightarrow$ ψ-tropine + benzoic acid. $H_2O_2 \longrightarrow$ N-oxide. Resorcinol + conc. $H_2SO_4 \longrightarrow$ yellow $\longrightarrow$ violet $\longrightarrow$ red col. 2-Naphthol + conc. $H_2SO_4 \longrightarrow$ grey $\longrightarrow$ dark blue col. Produces paralysis of central nervous system. Poisonous. Exhibits local anæsthetic properties.

B,HCl : plates from EtOH. M.p. 283°.

$B,HAuCl_4$: yellow needles from H_2O. M.p. 208°.

B_2,H_2PtCl_6 : yellow needles. M.p. 276–8°.

d-*Camphor-β-sulphonic acid salt* : prisms from EtOH–AcOEt. M.p. 176–7°. $[\alpha]_D + 11\cdot1°$ in H_2O.

α-*Bromo*-[d-*camphor*]-π-*sulphonic acid salt* : prisms from EtOH, m.p. 190°; needles + $3H_2O$ from H_2O, m.p. 73°. $[\alpha]_D + 47\cdot3°$ in H_2O.

$B,C_6H_5 \cdot COOH$: m.p. 60–1°.

N-*Oxide* : $C_{15}H_{19}O_3N$. MW, 261. Cryst. M.p. 152–3°. *Hydrochloride* : m.p. 200°.

Picrate : needles. Darkens at 215–20°, m.p. 240–2°.

> Willstätter, *Ber.*, 1896, **29**, 943.
> Hesse, *Ann.*, 1892, **271**, 208.

Tropane (*Dihydrotropidine*)

$$\begin{array}{ccc} H_2C\!\!-\!\!CH\!\!-\!\!\!-\!\!CH_2 \\ |\quad N\cdot CH_3\quad CH_2 \\ H_2C\!\!-\!\!CH\!\!-\!\!\!-\!\!CH_2 \end{array}$$

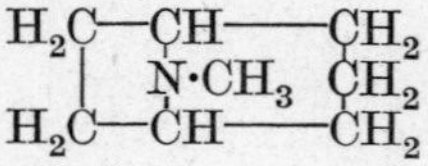

$C_8H_{15}N$ MW, 125

Liq. B.p. 167°. D_4^{20} 0·931. Misc. with cold H_2O. Spar. misc. with hot H_2O. $H_2O_2 \longrightarrow$ tropane-N-oxide. Dist. of hydrochloride in current of HCl $\longrightarrow$ nortropane.

$B,HAuCl_4$: plates from EtOH. M.p. 245–6°.

B_2,H_2PtCl_6 : orange-yellow plates from H_2O. Decomp. at 229–30°.

N-*Oxide* : $C_8H_{15}ON$. MW, 141. Hygroscopic cryst. B_2,H_2PtCl_6 : orange-yellow needles. M.p. 228° decomp.

Methiodide : cryst. from H_2O. Does not melt below 300°.

Picrate : needles. M.p. 281° decomp.

> Hess, *Ber.*, 1918, **51**, 1007.

Tropanol.
See Tropine.
ψ-Tropanol.
See ψ-Tropine.
Tropanone.
See Tropinone.
Tropeïn.
See under Tropine.
Tropene.
See Tropidine.

Tropic Acid (1-*Phenylhydracrylic acid*, β-*hydroxyhydratropic acid*, 2-*hydroxy*-1-*phenylpropionic acid*, α-*hydroxymethylphenylacetic acid*)

$$\begin{array}{c} C_6H_5 \\ | \\ HO\cdot CH_2 \cdot CH \cdot COOH \end{array}$$

$C_9H_{10}O_3$ MW, 166

d-.

Needles, scales or prisms from H_2O, needles from C_6H_6. M.p. 129–30°. $[\alpha]_D^{16} + 72\cdot2°$ in EtOH, $[\alpha]_D + 81\cdot6°$ in H_2O.

Quinine salt : needles or plates from EtOH. M.p. 191·5–192·5°. Spar. sol. H_2O. $[\alpha]_D - 104°$ in EtOH.

l-.

Needles from H_2O, plates from AcOEt. M.p. 129–30°. Spar. sol. cold C_6H_6. Sol. AcOEt, methyl ethyl ketone. $[\alpha]_D^{13} - 72\cdot5°$ in EtOH, $[\alpha]_D - 81\cdot2°$ in H_2O.

Quinine salt : plates or needles from EtOH. M.p. 185–6°. More sol. EtOH than *d*-salt. $[\alpha]_D - 140\cdot7°$ in EtOH.

Tropine ester : *see* Hyoscyamine.

Scopine ester : *see* Hyoscine.

dl-.

Needles or plates from H_2O, cryst. from C_6H_6. M.p. 118°. Sol. 49 parts H_2O at 14·5°. Very sol. hot H_2O. Sol. EtOH, Et_2O. Spar. sol. C_6H_6. Insol. CS_2. $k = 7\cdot50 \times 10^{-5}$ at 25°. Resolved into active components through quinine salt. Heat at 160° $\longrightarrow$ tropide. Ox. $\longrightarrow C_6H_5 \cdot CHO + C_6H_5 \cdot COOH$. Boiling aq. $Ba(OH)_2$ or aq. KOH $\longrightarrow$ atropic acid. Conc. HCl at 140° $\longrightarrow$ α-isatropic acid.

Me ester : $C_{10}H_{12}O_3$. MW, 180. Needles. M.p. 36·5–37·5°. B.p. 159–62°/19 mm.

Tropine ester : *see* Atropine.

Amide : $C_9H_{11}O_2N$. MW, 165. Plates and needles from H_2O. M.p. 169·5°. Sol. hot H_2O. Spar. sol. cold H_2O.

Me ether : $C_{10}H_{12}O_3$. MW, 180. Cryst. from petrol. M.p. 62°. B.p. 134–6°/0·3 mm.

Acetyl : plates. M.p. 88–90°.

> Chambon, *Compt. rend.*, 1928, **186**, 1630.
> King, Palmer, *J. Chem. Soc.*, 1922, **121**, 2577.
> McKenzie, Wood, *J. Chem. Soc.*, 1919, **115**, 838.
> Wislicenus, Bilhuber, *Ber.*, 1918, **51**, 1237.

Tropidine (2-*Tropene*)

$$\begin{array}{ccc} H_2C\!\!-\!\!CH\!\!-\!\!\!-\!\!CH \\ |\quad N\cdot CH_3\quad CH \\ H_2C\!\!-\!\!CH\!\!-\!\!\!-\!\!CH_2 \end{array}$$

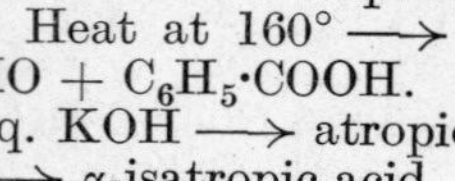

$C_8H_{13}N$ MW, 123

Liq. B.p. 163°. Sol. EtOH. Et_2O. Spar. misc. with hot H_2O. Mod. misc. with cold H_2O. D_4^{20} 0·953. n_α^{19} 1·4884. Volatile in steam. $H_2O_2 \longrightarrow$ *N*-oxide. Red. $\longrightarrow$ tropane. Stable to hot H_2SO_4 and alkalis.

B,HAuCl₄: m.p. 212°.

B_2,H_2PtCl_6: orange-red cryst. Decomp. at 217°.

N-*Oxide*: $C_8H_{13}ON$. MW, 139. Hygroscopic cryst. *B_2,H_2PtCl_6*: orange-yellow plates from H_2O. M.p. about 220° decomp.

Methiodide: cryst. from H_2O or EtOH. M.p. about 300°.

Picrate: yellow needles from H_2O. M.p. about 285° decomp.

Willstätter, *Ber.*, 1901, **34**, 142.

Tropigenin.
See Nortropine.

Tropilene (*Cycloheptenone*-3)

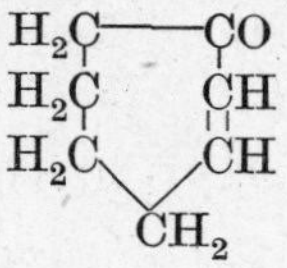

$C_7H_{10}O$ MW, 110

Liq. B.p. 186–8°. Insol. H_2O. D^0 1·0091. Reduces $NH_3.AgNO_3$ and Fehling's. Ox. $\longrightarrow$ adipic and oxalic acids. Zn + AcOH $\longrightarrow$ methylcyclohexanone. Catalytic red. $\longrightarrow$ suberone.

Oxime: cryst. from ligroin. M.p. 80–8°.

Kötz, Blendermann, Mähnert, Rosenbusch, *Ann.*, 1913, **400**, 80.

Tropilidene ($\Delta^{1:3:5}$-*Cycloheptatriene*)

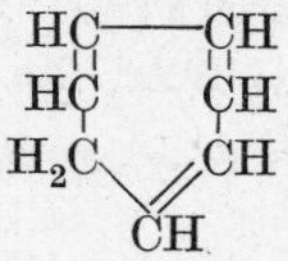

C_7H_8 MW, 92

Liq. B.p. 117°/749 mm. $D_4^{18\cdot5}$ 0·8875. $n_\alpha^{17\cdot5}$ 1·51751. Resinifies on standing in air. Alc. sol. + conc. $H_2SO_4 \longrightarrow$ dark brownish-red col.

Willstätter, *Ann.*, 1901, **317**, 204, 269.

Tropine (3-*Tropanol*)

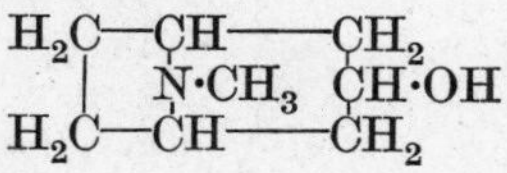

$C_8H_{15}ON$ MW, 141

Hygroscopic plates from Et_2O. M.p. 63°. B.p. 229°. Very sol. H_2O, EtOH. Difficultly volatile in steam. $k = 2\cdot74 \times 10^{-4}$ at 25°. NaOEt $\longrightarrow$ ψ-tropine. $H_2O_2 \longrightarrow$ *N*-oxide. $CrO_3 \longrightarrow$ tropinone. $KMnO_4$ in alk. sol. $\longrightarrow$ nortropine. Acid $KMnO_4 \longrightarrow$ tropinone. H_2SO_4 + AcOH $\longrightarrow$ tropidine. Soda-lime dist. $\longrightarrow$ tropilidine. HI + $PH_4I \longrightarrow$ tropane.

B,HAuCl₄: yellow plates. M.p. 210–12° decomp.

B_2,H_2PtCl_6: yellowish-red plates from H_2O. M.p. 197–8° decomp.

d-*Camphor*-β-*sulphonic acid salt*: plates from EtOH–AcOEt or $CHCl_3$. M.p. 236°. $[\alpha]_D$ + 32·1° in $CHCl_3$.

Picrate: yellow needles from H_2O. Decomp. at about 275°.

Me ether: $C_9H_{17}ON$. MW, 155. Cryst. powder. Does not melt below 300°. Very sol. H_2O, hot EtOH. Spar. sol. Et_2O.

Acetyl: acetyltropeïn. Liq. B.p. 235–7°.

Benzoyl: benzoyltropeïn. Plates + $2H_2O$, m.p. 56°: anhyd. cryst. from Et_2O, m.p. 41–2°. B.p. 175–80°. *B,HCl*: prisms from EtOH. M.p. 275°.

N-*Oxide*: $C_8H_{15}O_2N$. MW, 157. M.p. 238°.

Mandelic ester: *see* Homatropine.

l-*Tropic ester*: *see* Hyoscyamine.

dl-*Tropic ester*: *see* Atropine.

Phenylcarbamic ester: *see* Uretropine.

Willstätter, *Ber.*, 1902, **35**, 1870.

ψ-Tropine (ψ-3-*Tropanol*)

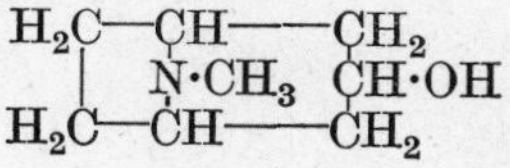

$C_8H_{15}ON$ MW, 141

Stereoisomer of tropine. Prisms from C_6H_6–pet. ether or ligroin. M.p. 108–9°. B.p. 240–1°. Very sol. H_2O, EtOH, $CHCl_3$, C_6H_6. Sol. Et_2O. Ox. $\longrightarrow$ tropinone. Dil. alk. $KMnO_4 \longrightarrow$ nor-ψ-tropine. $H_2O_2 \longrightarrow$ *N*-oxide. AcOH + $H_2SO_4 \longrightarrow$ tropidine.

B,HCl: needles from EtOH. Sinters at 250°. M.p. 280–2° decomp.

B,HAuCl₄: yellow plates or needles from H_2O. M.p. 225° decomp.

B_2,H_2PtCl_6: orange-red plates + $4H_2O$ from H_2O. M.p. anhyd. 206°.

d-*Camphor*-β-*sulphonic acid salt*: prisms from EtOH–AcOEt. M.p. 224–6°. $[\alpha]_D$ + 26·3° in EtOH.

Picrate: needles or prisms from H_2O. Darkens at 245°, m.p. 258–9° decomp.

Benzoyl: *see* Tropacocaine.

N-*Oxide*: $C_8H_{15}O_2N$. MW, 157. M.p. 229°.

Hydrochloride: m.p. 286°. *Picrate*: m.p. 257° decomp.

Willstätter, *Ber.*, 1901, **34**, 3165.

Tropinic Acid (N-*Methylpyrrolidine*-5-*carboxylic acid*-2-*acetic acid*)

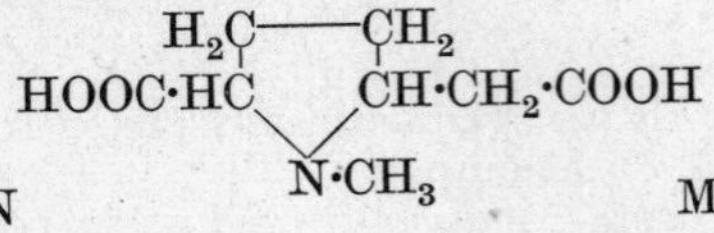

$C_8H_{13}O_4N$ MW, 187

d-.

Cryst. from H_2O or EtOH.Aq. M.p. (rapid heat.) 253° decomp., (slow heat.) 247–8°. Sol. cold H_2O. Spar. sol. EtOH. Insol. Et_2O, C_6H_6. $[\alpha]_D$ + 14·8° in H_2O. Decolourises $KMnO_4$ sol. in cold.

Di-Me ester: $C_{10}H_{17}O_4N$. MW, 215. Oil. *Picrate*: needles. M.p. 120–1°. *Methiodide*: plates and needles from MeOH. M.p. 176–7° decomp.

l-.

Cryst. from H_2O. M.p. 243°. $[\alpha]_D^{20}$ − 14·8° in H_2O.

dl-.

Needles from EtOH.Aq. M.p. about 248° decomp. Sol. H_2O. Spar. sol. EtOH. Insol. Et_2O, C_6H_6. Resolved through cinchonine salt. Loses CO_2 on heating above m.p. Decolourises $KMnO_4$ sol. in cold. $CrO_3 + H_2SO_4 \longrightarrow$ *N*-methylsuccinimide. HI(+ P) $\longrightarrow$ *N*-methylpyrrolidine.

B_2,H_2PtCl_6: orange-yellow cryst. Decomp. at 100–10°.

Di-Me ester: $C_{10}H_{17}O_4N$. MW, 215. Oil. B.p. 268–72° (part. decomp.). *Picrate*: orange-yellow prisms from EtOH. M.p. 121°. *Methiodide*: prisms + $\frac{1}{2}H_2O$ from H_2O or EtOH.Aq., anhyd. plates from EtOH–Et_2O. M.p. 171–2° decomp.

Di-Et ester: $C_{12}H_{21}O_4N$. MW, 243. Oil. B.p. 160°/18·5 mm.

Willstätter, *Ber.*, 1898, **31**, 1547.
Liebermann, *Ber.*, 1891, **24**, 2587.

Tropinone (3-*Tropanone*)

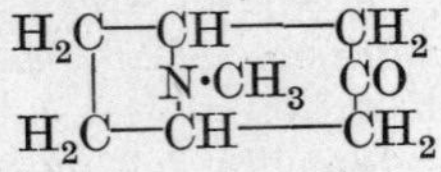

$C_8H_{13}ON$ MW, 139

Needles from pet. ether. M.p. 42°. B.p. 224–5°, 125°/40 mm., 113°/25 mm. Very sol. most org. solvents. Reacts alkaline. Reduces warm $AgNO_3$. $H_2O_2 \longrightarrow$ *N*-oxide.

B,HCl: prisms from EtOH. M.p. about 188–9° decomp.

$B,HAuCl_4$: yellow prisms from dil. HCl. M.p. about 163° decomp.

B_2,H_2PtCl_6: orange-red prisms. M.p. 191–2° decomp.

d-*Camphor*-β-*sulphonic acid salt*: cryst. from AcOEt. M.p. 216° decomp.

Picrate: yellow needles from H_2O. M.p. 220° decomp.

N-*Oxide*: $C_8H_{13}O_2N$. MW, 155. M.p. 98°.

Oxime: prisms from ligroin. M.p. 115–16°. Very sol. H_2O, EtOH, warm Me_2CO, AcOEt, $CHCl_3$, C_6H_6. *B,HCl*: prisms from EtOH. M.p. 242° decomp. *Methiodide*: prisms from EtOH.Aq. M.p. 236° decomp.

Semicarbazone: plates from EtOH. M.p. 212–13°.

Methiodide: cryst. from H_2O. M.p. 273–5°.

Dibenzylidene deriv.: yellow prisms. M.p. 152°.

Schöpf, Lehmann, *Ann.*, 1935, **518**, 1.
Willstätter, Bommer, *Ann.*, 1926, **422**, 30.
Robinson, *J. Chem. Soc.*, 1917, **111**, 766.
Willstätter, *Ber.*, 1896, **29**, 396, 947; 1898, **31**, 1540; 1900, **33**, 1169.

Tropylamine (3-*Aminotropane*)

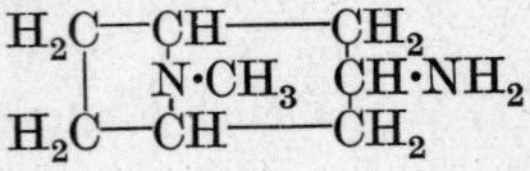

$C_8H_{16}N_2$ MW, 140

Liq. B.p. 211°, 91–2°/12 mm. Hot Na amylate $\longrightarrow$ ψ-tropylamine.

$B,2HAuCl_4$: prisms and plates. M.p. 220–1° decomp.

B,H_2PtCl_6: red plates from H_2O. M.p. 257° decomp.

Picrate: plates. M.p. 235° decomp.

Willstätter, Müller, *Ber.*, 1898, **31**, 1211.

ψ-Tropylamine (ψ-3-*Aminotropane*)

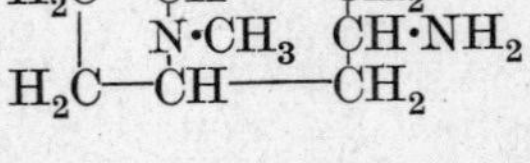

$C_8H_{16}N_2$ MW, 140

Stereoisomer of tropylamine. Liq. B.p. 213°, 107°/26 mm., 98–100°/17·5 mm. Sol. H_2O with heat evolution. Sol. EtOH, Et_2O. Strong base. Absorbs CO_2 from the air. Stable to hot Na amylate.

$B,2HAuCl_4$: plates, needles or prisms, with or without H_2O from H_2O. M.p. 223–4° decomp.

B,H_2PtCl_6: orange-yellow plates + $2H_2O$. M.p. 257° decomp.

Picrate: yellow cryst. M.p. 236–8° decomp.

Willstätter, Müller, *Ber.*, 1898, **31**, 1208.

Truxane (*Bisindene*)

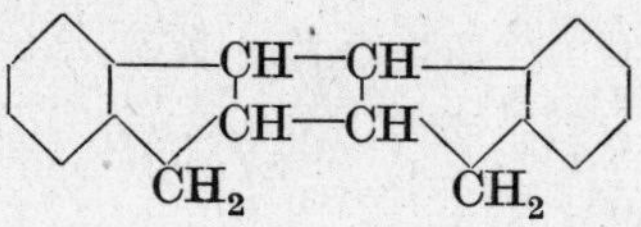

$C_{18}H_{16}$ MW, 232

Plates. M.p. 116°. Dist. ⟶ indene. Dist. undecomp. at low pressures.

Stobbe, Zschoch, *Ber.*, 1927, **60**, 462.

Truxillamic Acid.
See under Truxillic Acid.
Truxillanilic Acid.
See under Truxillic Acid.
α-Truxillic Acid (2 : 4-*Diphenylcyclobutone*-1 : 3-*dicarboxylic acid*)

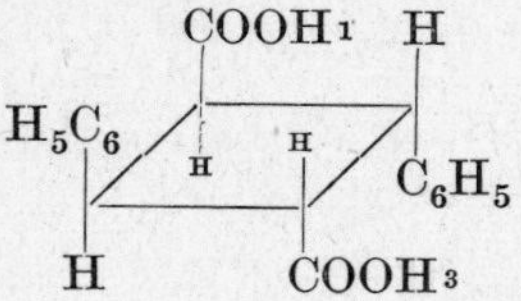

$C_{18}H_{16}O_4$ MW, 296

Needles from EtOH.Aq, cryst. + 2MeOH from MeOH. M.p. 285°. Very sol. hot EtOH. Sol. hot AcOH. Spar. sol. Et_2O, Me_2CO, CS_2, C_6H_6, hot H_2O. Sublimes in high vacuum. $k = 4{\cdot}97 \times 10^{-5}$ at 25°. Heat of comb. C_v 2084·8 Cal., C_p 2086 Cal. KOH fusion ⟶ ε-truxillic acid. Dist. ⟶ cinnamic acid. Ac_2O at 210° ⟶ γ-truxillic anhydride. Fuming H_2SO_4 ⟶ truxone. Forms very insol. Ag salt.

Mono-Me ester: $C_{19}H_{18}O_4$. MW, 310. Needles. M.p. 195°. Sol. C_6H_6, cold Na_2CO_3.

Di-Me ester: $C_{20}H_{20}O_4$. MW, 324. Plates or needles from MeOH. M.p. 174°. B.p. about 330°. Spar. sol. cold MeOH, AcOH.

Mono-Et ester: $C_{20}H_{20}O_4$. MW, 324. Cryst. from EtOH. M.p. 171°.

Di-Et ester: $C_{22}H_{24}O_4$. MW, 352. Needles. M.p. 146°. Spar. sol. EtOH.

Dichloride: $C_{18}H_{14}O_2Cl_2$. MW, 333. Prisms + $\frac{1}{2}C_6H_6$ from C_6H_6–ligroin. M.p. 125°. $AlCl_3$ ⟶ truxone.

1-*Amide*: α-truxillamic acid. $C_{18}H_{17}O_3N$. Needles from AcOH. M.p. 261°. Sol. EtOH, AcOH, Me_2CO. Insol. Et_2O, C_6H_6, ligroin.

3-*Anilide*: α-truxillanilic acid. $C_{24}H_{21}O_3N$. MW, 371. *d*-. Needles from EtOH.Aq. M.p. 205°. $[\alpha]_D^{20}$ + 21·8° in Me_2CO. *l*-. Needles from EtOH.Aq. M.p. 205°. $[\alpha]_D^{19}$ − 23·0° in Me_2CO. *dl*-. Needles from EtOH.Aq. M.p. 235°. Sol. EtOH, Me_2CO, AcOEt. Insol. Et_2O, C_6H_6, ligroin.

Stoermer, Stroh, *Ber.*, 1935, **68**, 2108.
Stoermer, Wegner, Carl, *Ber.*, 1923, **56**, 1683, 1690.
Stoermer, Foerster, *Ber.*, 1919, **52**, 1256.
Kohler, *Am. Chem. J.*, 1907, **28**, 238.

γ-Truxillic Acid (2 : 4-*Diphenylcyclobutane*-1 : 3-*dicarboxylic acid*)

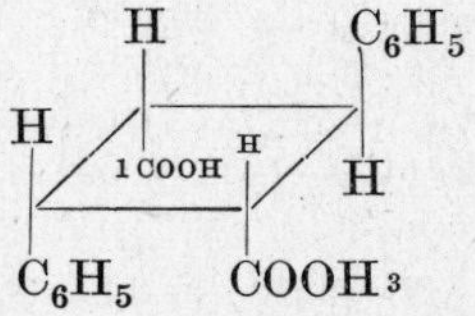

$C_{18}H_{16}O_4$ MW, 296

dl-.

Needles from EtOH.Aq. cryst. from AcOH. M.p. 228°. Very sol. Et_2O. Spar. sol. hot H_2O. $k = 1{\cdot}08 \times 10^{-4}$ at 25°. Heat. at 280° or HCl at 175° ⟶ α-truxillic acid. Dist. ⟶ cinnamic acid. KOH fusion ⟶ α- and ε-truxillic acids.

Mono-Me ester: $C_{19}H_{18}O_4$. MW, 310. Needles from EtOH.Aq. M.p. 183·5–184·0°. Sol. EtOH, Me_2CO, hot C_6H_6. Mod. sol. Et_2O, AcOH, C_6H_6. Insol. H_2O, ligroin, pet. ether.

Di-Me ester: $C_{20}H_{20}O_4$. MW, 324. Needles from MeOH.Aq. M.p. 126°. Sol. cold MeOH, AcOH.

Mono-Et ester: $C_{20}H_{20}O_4$. MW, 324. Needles from EtOH.Aq. M.p. 173–174·5°. Very sol. EtOH, Et_2O, AcOH, C_6H_6.

Di-Et ester: $C_{22}H_{24}O_4$. MW, 352. Needles from EtOH.Aq. M.p. 98°. Sol. EtOH, Et_2O, AcOH, C_6H_6. Spar. sol. pet. ether.

Anhydride: $C_{18}H_{14}O_3$. MW, 278. Needles from $CHCl_3$–EtOH. M.p. 191° (180–3°).

Dichloride: $C_{18}H_{14}O_2Cl_2$. MW, 333. Needles from C_6H_6–ligroin. M.p. 140°. $AlCl_3$ ⟶ truxone.

3-*Amide*: γ-truxillamic acid. $C_{18}H_{17}O_3N$. MW, 295. Prisms from AcOH.Aq. M.p. 240°. Insol. Et_2O, C_6H_6, pet. ether.

Imide: $C_{18}H_{15}O_2N$. MW, 277. Cryst. from AcOH or EtOH. M.p. 208°. Sol. C_6H_6. Spar. sol. Et_2O. Insol. pet. ether.

Et-imide: $C_{20}H_{19}O_2N$. MW, 305. Cryst. from EtOH.Aq. M.p. 142°.

Phenyl-imide: $C_{24}H_{19}O_2N$. MW, 353. Cryst. from AcOH.Aq. M.p. 194°.

3-*Anilide*: γ-truxillanilic acid. $C_{24}H_{21}O_3N$. MW, 371. Needles from EtOH.Aq. M.p. 228°. Sol. EtOH, Me_2CO. Insol. Et_2O, C_6H_6, ligroin.

Mono-p-toluidide: needles from EtOH.Aq. M.p. 268°.
Di-p-toluidide: needles from EtOH or AcOH. M.p. 289°.
Di-phenylhydrazide: m.p. 305°.

d-.
Mono-Me ester: cryst. from AcOH. M.p. 145·5–147°. $[\alpha]_D^{18}$ + 6·48° in Me_2CO.
Mono-Et ester: cryst. from AcOH. M.p. 142·5–143°. $[\alpha]_D^{19}$ + 19·14° in Me_2CO.
3-*Amide*: cryst. from EtOH. M.p. 258–9°.
3-*Anilide*: needles from Et_2O–ligroin. M.p. 228°. Sol. Et_2O, $CHCl_3$. Insol. C_6H_6, ligroin. $[\alpha]_D^{21}$ + 48·7° in Me_2CO.

l-.
Mono-Me ester: needles from EtOH.Aq. M.p. 145·5–147°.
Mono-Et ester: cryst. from EtOH.Aq. M.p. 142·5–143°. $[\alpha]_D^{19}$ − 16·48° in Me_2CO.
3-*Amide*: leaflets from AcOH.Aq. M.p. 258–9°. $[\alpha]_D^{20}$ − 11·05° in AcOH.
3-*Anilide*: needles from Et_2O–ligroin. M.p. 228°. $[\alpha]_D^{23}$ − 49·54° in Me_2CO.

Stoermer, Cruse, *Ber.*, 1935, **68**, 2120.
Schenk, *Ber.*, 1930, **63**, 2706.
Stoermer, Fretwurst, *Ber.*, 1925, **58**, 2718.
Stoermer, Wegner, Carl, *Ber.*, 1923, **56**, 1683.
Stoermer, Emmel, *Ber.*, 1920, **53**, 497.
Lie, *Ber.*, 1889, **22**, 126.

ε-Truxillic Acid (2 : 4-*Diphenylcyclobutane*-1 : 3-*dicarboxylic acid*)

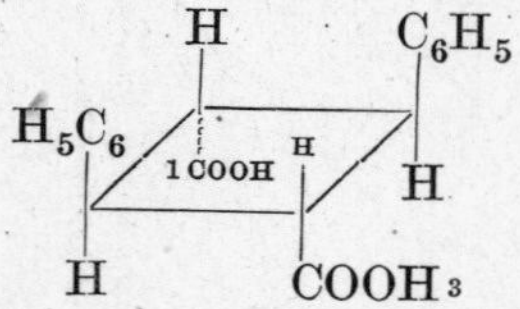

$C_{18}H_{16}O_4$ MW, 296

Needles from EtOH.Aq. or Et_2O. M.p. 192°. Sol. EtOH, Et_2O, $CHCl_3$. Insol. ligroin. Ba and Ca salts more sol. in cold than in hot H_2O.
Di-NH_4 salt: cryst. Decomp. at 186°.
Mono-Me ester: $C_{19}H_{18}O_4$. MW, 310. Prisms from MeOH. M.p. 131°.
Di-Me ester: $C_{20}H_{20}O_4$. MW, 324. Prisms from EtOH.Aq. M.p. 64°.
Di-Et ester: $C_{22}H_{24}O_4$. MW, 352. Prisms from EtOH. M.p. 34°.
Dichloride: $C_{18}H_{14}O_2Cl_2$. MW, 333. Prisms from ligroin. M.p. 106–7°.
Imide: $C_{18}H_{15}O_2N$. MW, 277. Needles from EtOH.Aq. M.p. 198°. Sol. Et_2O, EtOH, Me_2CO, AcOH. Insol. C_6H_6, ligroin. *K salt*: cryst. M.p. 224°.
Et-imide: $C_{20}H_{19}O_2N$. MW, 305. Needles from EtOH. M.p. 144°.
Phenylimide: $C_{24}H_{19}O_2N$. MW, 353. Needles from AcOH. M.p. 252°.
3-*Amide*: ε-truxillamic acid. $C_{18}H_{17}O_3N$. MW, 295. Needles from EtOH. M.p. 213°. Sol. EtOH, AcOH, hot H_2O. Insol. C_6H_6, ligroin.
3-*Anilide*: ε-truxillanilic acid. $C_{24}H_{21}O_3N$. MW, 371. Needles from EtOH. M.p. 239°.

Stoermer, Cruse, *Ber.*, 1935, **68**, 2121.
Stoermer, Neumaerker, Schmidt, *Ber.*, 1925, **58**, 2707, 2715.
Stoermer, Emmel, *Ber.*, 1920, **53**, 497.

η-Truxillic Acid (peri-*Truxillic acid*, 2 : 4-*diphenylcyclobutane*-1 : 3-*dicarboxylic acid*)

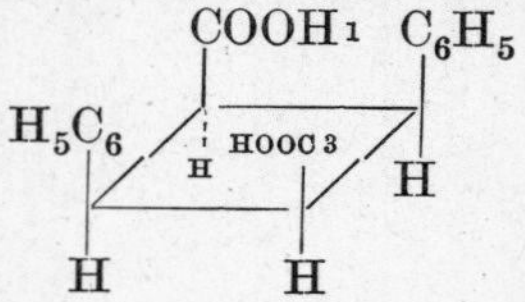

$C_{18}H_{16}O_4$ MW, 296

Cryst. from AcOH–C_6H_6. M.p. 266° (287°) decomp. Sol. EtOH. Insol. Et_2O, C_6H_6. KOH fusion ⟶ ε-truxillic acid.
Mono-Me ester: $C_{19}H_{18}O_4$. MW, 310. Cryst. from MeOH. M.p. 192°.
Di-Me ester: $C_{20}H_{20}O_4$. MW, 324. Cryst. from MeOH. M.p. 104–5°.
Anhydride: $C_{18}H_{14}O_3$. MW, 278. Prisms from AcOH. M.p. 285°.
1-*Amide*: η-truxillamic acid. $C_{18}H_{17}O_3N$. MW, 295. Prisms from AcOH–C_6H_6. M.p. 256·5°. Spar. sol. AcOH. Insol. EtOH.
Imide: $C_{18}H_{15}O_2N$. MW, 277. Cryst. M.p. 237°.
1-*Anilide*: η-truxillanilic acid. $C_{24}H_{21}O_3N$. MW, 371. Cryst. from EtOH. M.p. 247°.

Stoermer, Möller, *Ber.*, 1935, **68**, 2131, 2132.
Stoermer, Bachér, *Ber.*, 1924, **57**, 15.

***epi*-Truxillic Acid** (2 : 4-*Diphenylcyclobutane*-1 : 3-*dicarboxylic acid*)

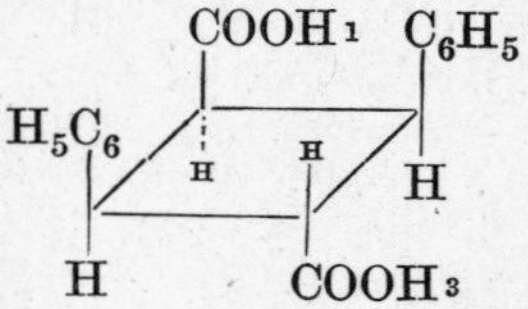

$C_{18}H_{16}O_4$ MW, 296

Cryst. from EtOH.Aq. or C_6H_6–AcOH. M.p. 285–7°. Very spar. sol. Et_2O, C_6H_6. Heat at m.p. ⟶ ε-truxillic acid. Ac_2O ⟶ ε-acid. KOH fusion ⟶ ε-acid.

1-*Mono-Me ester*: $C_{19}H_{18}O_4$. MW, 310. Cryst. from MeOH. M.p. 204·5°.

3-*Mono-Me ester*: prisms from MeOH. M.p. 141°.

Di-Me ester: $C_{20}H_{20}O_4$. MW, 324. Cryst. M.p. 111–12°.

3-*Amide*: *epi*-truxillamic acid. $C_{18}H_{17}O_3N$. MW, 295. Cryst. M.p. 263°.

Stoermer, Möller, *Ber.*, 1935, **68**, 2132.
Stoermer, Bachér, *Ber.*, 1924, **57**, 15.

Truxinamic Acid.
See under Truxinic Acid.

Truxinanilic Acid.
See under Truxinic Acid.

β-Truxinic Acid (3 : 4-*Diphenylcyclobutane*-1 : 2-*dicarboxylic acid, isotruxillic acid*)

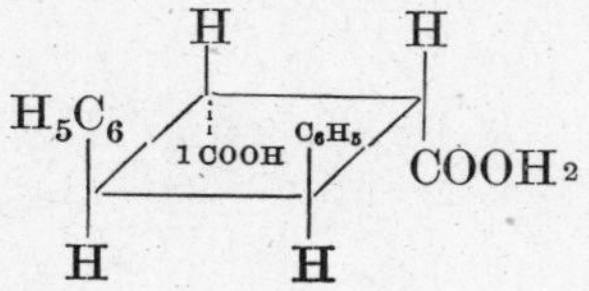

$C_{18}H_{16}O_4$ MW, 296

Cryst. from AcOH. M.p. 209–209·5°. Mod. sol. hot H_2O. KOH fusion ⟶ δ-truxinic acid. Dist. ⟶ cinnamic acid + stilbene. Ox. ⟶ benzil + benzoic acid. Readily forms anhydride. Forms cryst. insol. Ca and Ba salts.

Di-NH_4 salt: cryst. M.p. 187°. Sol. hot EtOH.

Mono-Me ester: $C_{19}H_{18}O_4$. MW, 310. Cryst. from C_6H_6. M.p. 164°.

Di-Me ester: $C_{20}H_{20}O_4$. MW, 324. Plates from Et_2O. M.p. 76°. Very sol. EtOH, Et_2O. Heat. of comb. C_p. 2422·9 Cal., C_v 2421·1 Cal.

Mono-Et ester: $C_{20}H_{20}O_4$. MW, 324. Cryst. from C_6H_6. M.p. 133°. Sol. EtOH, Et_2O. Spar. sol. C_6H_6. Insol. ligroin.

Di-Et ester: $C_{22}H_{24}O_4$. MW, 352. Cryst. M.p. 49–50°.

Mono-d-*menthyl ester*: $C_{28}H_{34}O_4$. MW, 434. Cryst. from EtOH. M.p. 208°. Sol. Me_2CO, Et_2O, warm C_6H_6. Spar. sol. hot ligroin. $[\alpha]_D^{20}$ − 20·9° in Me_2CO.

Mono-l-*menthyl ester*: needles from EtOH. M.p. 149°. Very sol. Et_2O, EtOH, Me_2CO, C_6H_6. Sol. hot ligroin. $[\alpha]_D^{20}$ − 37·3° in Me_2CO.

Anhydride: $C_{18}H_{14}O_3$. MW, 278. Prisms from C_6H_6. M.p. 116°.

Dichloride: $C_{18}H_{14}O_2Cl_2$. MW, 333. Plates from C_6H_6–pet. ether. M.p. 96°. Very sol. Et_2O, $CHCl_3$, C_6H_6. Spar. sol. pet. ether.

2-*Amide*: β-truxinamic acid. $C_{18}H_{17}O_3N$. MW, 295. Cryst. from EtOH.Aq. M.p. 194°. Sol. EtOH, Me_2CO. Insol. Et_2O, C_6H_6, ligroin.

Imide: $C_{18}H_{15}O_2N$. MW, 277. Prisms from EtOH. M.p. 224–5°. Sol. AcOH.

Phenylimide: $C_{24}H_{19}O_2N$. MW, 353. Cryst. M.p. 184°.

2-*Anilide*: β-truxinanilic acid. $C_{24}H_{21}O_3N$. MW, 371. *dl*-. Cryst. from Me_2CO.Aq. M.p. 210°. d-*Menthyl ester*: m.p. 171°. $[\alpha]_D^{20}$ − 63° in Me_2CO.

Stoermer, Lachmann, *Ber.*, 1926, **59**, 642.
Stoermer, Laage, *Ber.*, 1921, **54**, 96.
Stobbe, *Ber.*, 1919, **52**, 666.

δ-Truxinic Acid (3 : 4-*Diphenylbutane*-1 : 2-*dicarboxylic acid*)

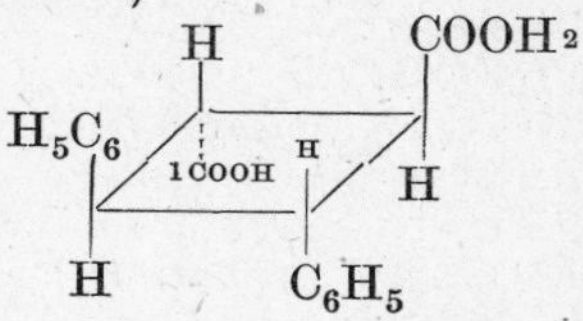

$C_{18}H_{16}O_4$ MW, 296

dl-.

Cryst. from C_6H_6–AcOH, needles from hot H_2O, plates + $1C_6H_6$ from C_6H_6. M.p. 175°. Very sol. EtOH, Et_2O, $CHCl_3$. Spar. sol. boil. H_2O, C_6H_6.

NH_4 salt: prisms. M.p. 206–8° decomp.

Di-Me ester: $C_{20}H_{20}O_4$. MW, 324. Needles from MeOH.Aq. M.p. 77°. Sol. EtOH, C_6H_6, ligroin.

Dichloride: $C_{18}H_{14}O_2Cl_2$. MW, 333. Cryst. from C_6H_6–ligroin. M.p. 78°. Unstable in air. Sol. Et_2O, $CHCl_3$, CS_2, C_6H_6. Spar. sol. ligroin.

2-*Amide*: δ-truxinamic acid. $C_{18}H_{17}O_3N$. MW, 295. M.p. 189°.

2-*Anilide*: δ-truxinanilic acid. $C_{24}H_{21}O_3N$. MW, 371. M.p. 225°.

d-.

Cryst. M.p. 157–8°. $[\alpha]_D^{20}$ + 8·06° in Me_2CO.

Quinine salt: needles from EtOH.Aq. M.p. 135° decomp.

l-.

Needles. M.p. 158–9°. $[\alpha]_D^{20}$ − 8·3° in Me_2CO.

Cinchonine salt: cryst. from EtOH.Aq. M.p. 192°.

Di-Me ester: cryst. from MeOH. M.p. 45°. $[\alpha]_D^{20}$ − 11·1° in Me_2CO.

2-*Amide*: m.p. 206°.

Stoermer, Bachér, *Ber.*, 1922, **55**, 1860.
Stoermer, Klockmann, *Ber.*, 1925, **58**, 1164.

ζ-Truxinic Acid (3 : 4-*Diphenylbutane*-1 : 2-*dicarboxylic acid*)

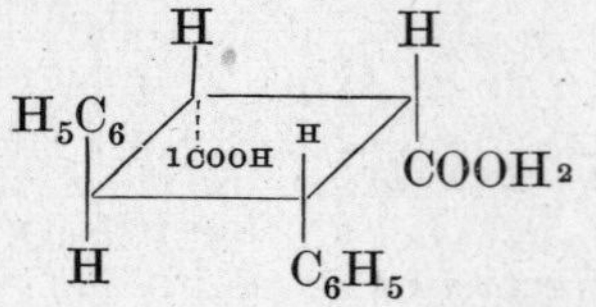

$C_{18}H_{16}O_4$ MW, 296

dl-.

Needles from Me_2CO.Aq. M.p. 239°. Sol. EtOH, Et_2O, Me_2CO. Spar. sol. AcOH, $CHCl_3$, CS_2, C_6H_6. Insol. H_2O, pet. ether. KOH fusion or hot HCl ⟶ δ-truxinic acid. Forms spar. sol. Ca and Ba salts.

NH_4 salt: needles. Decomp. at 160°.

1-*Mono-Me ester*: $C_{19}H_{18}O_4$. MW, 310. Cryst. from MeOH. M.p. 198°. Sol. EtOH, Et_2O, AcOH, C_6H_6. *Chloride*: cryst. from C_6H_6–ligroin. M.p. 104–5°.

2-*Mono-Me ester*: cryst. from MeOH. M.p. 201°. Sol. EtOH, Et_2O, AcOH, C_6H_6. *Chloride*: cryst. from C_6H_6–ligroin. M.p. 120°.

Di-Me ester: $C_{20}H_{20}O_4$. MW, 324. Cryst. from EtOH. M.p. 116°.

Mono-Et ester: $C_{20}H_{20}O_4$. MW, 324. Cryst. from EtOH. M.p. 190°. Sol. EtOH, Et_2O, AcOH, C_6H_6.

Di-Et ester: $C_{22}H_{24}O_4$. MW, 352. Needles. M.p. 80°. Sol. EtOH, Et_2O, Me_2CO, $CHCl_3$, C_6H_6.

Anhydride: $C_{18}H_{14}O_3$. MW, 278. Cryst. from C_6H_6. M.p. 150°. Sol. EtOH, Me_2CO, $CHCl_3$, C_6H_6. Spar. sol. Et_2O, pet. ether. Stable to H_2O.

Dichloride: $C_{18}H_{14}O_2Cl_2$. MW, 333. Prisms from C_6H_6–pet. ether. M.p. 150°. Sol. EtOH, Et_2O, $CHCl_3$, C_6H_6. Spar. sol. ligroin, pet. ether.

1-*Amide*: ζ-truxinamic acid. $C_{18}H_{17}O_3N$. MW, 295. Needles from MeOH. M.p. 222°. Sol. AcOH.

2-*Amide*: needles from Me_2CO. M.p. 204°.

Imide: $C_{18}H_{15}O_2N$. MW, 277. Needles from EtOH. M.p. 168–168·5°. Sol. hot Na_2CO_3.

Phenylimide: $C_{24}H_{19}O_2N$. MW, 353. Needles from EtOH. M.p. 180°.

1-*Anilide*: ζ-truxinanilic acid. $C_{24}H_{21}O_3N$. MW, 371. Cryst. from epichlorohydrin. M.p. 237°.

2-*Anilide*: needles from EtOH.Aq. M.p. 214°.

d-.

Cryst. from Me_2CO. M.p. 222°. $[\alpha]_D^{20}$ + 65·42 in EtOH.

Di-Me ester: cryst. from MeOH. M.p. 106°. $[\alpha]_D$ + 89·88° in Me_2CO.

l-.

Cryst. from Me_2CO. M.p. 222°. $[\alpha]_D^{20}$ − 78·37° in EtOH.

Cinchonine salt: needles from EtOH. M.p. 192°.

Anhydride: cryst. M.p. 162°. $[\alpha]_D$ − 145·84° in Me_2CO.

Dichloride: cryst. M.p. 160°. $[\alpha]_D$ − 98·6° in C_6H_6.

Stoermer, Klockmann, *Ber.*, 1925, **58**, 1164.
Stoermer, Scholtz, *Ber.*, 1921, **54**, 85.

α-Truxone

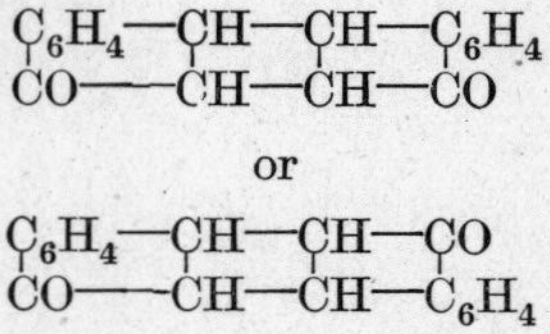

$C_{18}H_{12}O_2$ MW, 260

Plates from AcOH, powder from C_6H_6, needles from dil. HNO_3. M.p. 294°. Spar. sol. most org. solvents. Sublimes. Very stable to oxidising agents.

Dioxime: needles. Does not melt below 300°. Spar. sol. most org. solvents. *Di-Me ether*: cryst. from EtOH. M.p. 214°. *Diacetyl*: needles. M.p. 261°.

Anil: needles. M.p. 270° decomp.

Phenylhydrazone: yellow needles. M.p. 270°.

Stobbe, Zschoch, *Ber.*, 1927, **60**, 470.
Stoermer, Foerster, *Ber.*, 1919, **52**, 1255.

Trypaflavine.

See under 2 : 8-Diaminoacridine.

Tryparsamide

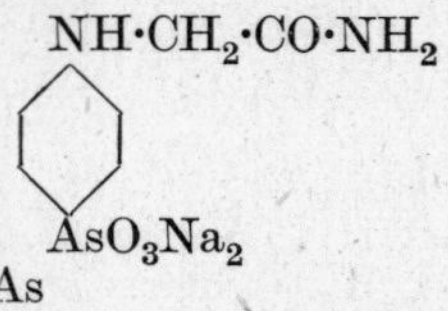

$C_8H_9O_4N_2Na_2As$ MW, 318

Cryst. + $3H_2O$. Employed in treatment of trypanosome and spirochæte infections. Low toxicity.

Jacobs, Heidelberger, *Organic Syntheses*, Collective Vol. I, 475.

Tryptamine.

3-[-ω-Aminoethyl]-indole, *q.v.*

Tryptophane (1-*Amino*-2-[3-*indolyl*]-*propionic acid*, 2-[3-*indolyl*]-α-*alanine*)

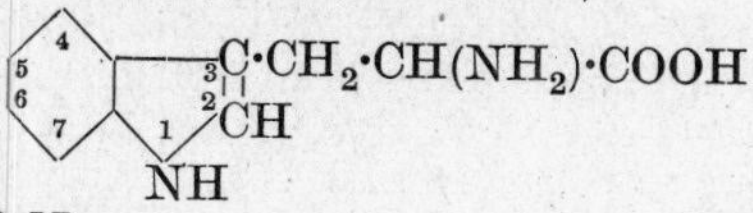

$C_{11}H_{12}O_2N_2$ MW, 204

l-.

Constituent of many plants. Enzymatic hyd. product of most plant and animal proteins. Plates from EtOH.Aq. M.p. 278° (252°, 289°). Sol. boiling H_2O, hot EtOH. Spar. sol. cold H_2O, EtOH. Insol. $CHCl_3$. Aq. sol. shows acid reaction. $[\alpha]_D^{20}$ − 33·4° in EtOH, $[\alpha]_D^{20}$ + 6·1° in *N*/NaOH. Heat with Py or 25% HCl at 170° ⟶ *dl*-. $FeCl_3$ ⟶ indole-3-aldehyde. Br water ⟶ reddish-violet col. KOH fusion ⟶ skatole + oxalic acid + glyoxylic acid.

B,HCl: needles from MeOH. M.p. 257° decomp.

Picrate: red needles and plates. M.p. 195–6° slight decomp.

Picrolonate: orange-red needles from H_2O. M.p. 203–4° decomp.

Me ester: $C_{12}H_{14}O_2N_2$. MW, 218. Plates from Et_2O. M.p. 89·5°. Very sol. MeOH. Sol. Et_2O, AcOEt. Spar. sol. pet. ether. *B,HCl*: microneedles from MeOH or AcOEt. M.p. 214° decomp.

Chloride: $C_{11}H_{11}ON_2Cl$. MW, 222·5. *B,HCl*: darkens at 172°, sinters at 208°, m.p. 228° decomp.

Amide: $C_{11}H_{13}ON_3$. MW, 203. M.p. 167–70°. $[\alpha]_D^{20}$ − 7·9° in EtOH.

Et-amide: $C_{13}H_{17}ON_3$. MW, 231. M.p. 67–9°. $[\alpha]_D^{20}$ − 14·4° in EtOH.

Di-Et amide. $C_{15}H_{21}ON_3$. MW, 259. M.p. 183–5°. $[\alpha]_D^{20}$ − 24·7° in EtOH.

Anilide: m.p. 83–5°. $[\alpha]_D^{20}$ − 9·5° in EtOH.

Et-anilide: m.p. 97–9°. $[\alpha]_D^{20}$ − 4·2° in EtOH.

N-*Chloroacetyl*: plates from H_2O. M.p. 159°.

N-*Benzenesulphonyl*: cryst. from EtOH.Aq. M.p. 185° decomp.

dl-.

Plates from EtOH.Aq. M.p. 275–82°.

α-N-*Me*: $C_{12}H_{14}O_2N_2$. MW, 218. Needles from EtOH.Aq. Darkens at 280°, m.p. 297° decomp. *Picrate*: plates from MeOH–pet. ether. M.p. 186° decomp.

α-N-*Di-Me*: $C_{13}H_{16}O_2N_2$. MW, 232. Needles from Et_2O–pet. ether. M.p. 49–50°. *Methiodide*: needles from MeOH. M.p. 210–11°. *Picrate*: prisms from MeOH. M.p. 170–1°.

N-3 : 5-*Dinitrobenzoyl*: m.p. 240°.

N-*Benzenesulphonyl*: m.p. 185° decomp.

N-p-*Toluenesulphonyl*: needles from Me_2CO. M.p. 176°.

Boyd, Robson, *Biochem. J.*, 1935, **29**, 2256.
Gordon, Jackson, *J. Biol. Chem.*, 1935, **110**, 151.
Hoshino, Shimodaira, *Ann.*, 1935, **520**, 25.
Bauguess, Berg, *J. Biol. Chem.*, 1934, **106**, 618.
Cox, King, *Organic Syntheses*, 1930, X, 100.

Tryptophol (2-[3-*Indolyl*]-*ethyl alcohol*, 3-ω-*hydroxyethylindole*)

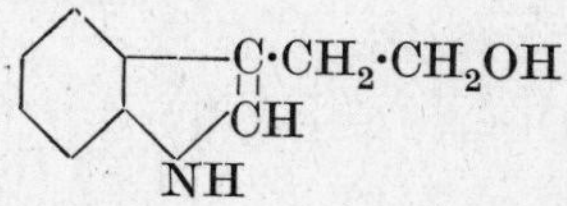

$C_{10}H_{11}ON$ MW, 161

Prisms from C_6H_6–pet. ether, plates from Et_2O–pet. ether. M.p. 59°. Sol. MeOH, EtOH, Et_2O, Me_2CO, $CHCl_3$, AcOH, AcOEt. Spar. sol. cold H_2O, ligroin, pet. ether. Heat or boil. with alkalis ⟶ indole. Sol. warm conc. H_2SO_4 ⟶ red col.

N-*Benzoyl*: yellow prisms and plates from ligroin. M.p. 76°.

Picrate: red needles from H_2O. M.p. 100–1°.

Phenylurethane: m.p. 130–1°.

Jackson, *J. Biol. Chem.*, 1930, **88**, 659.
Ehrlich, *Ber.*, 1912, **45**, 884.

Tsugalactone.

See Tsugaresinol.

Tsugaresinol (*Tsugalactone*, *conidendrin*, *sulphite liquors lactone*)

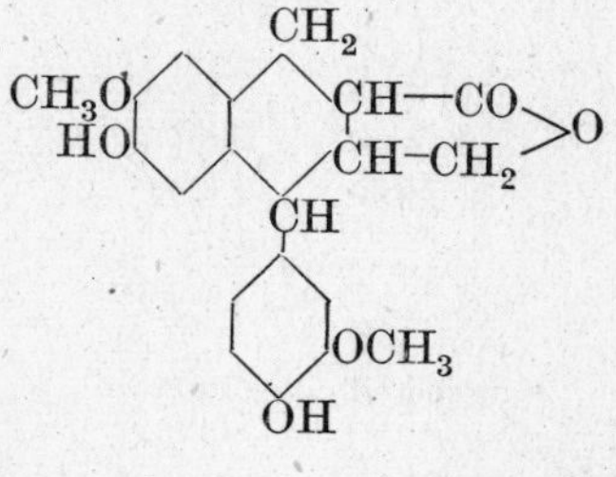

$C_{20}H_{20}O_6$ MW, 356

Constituent of spruce resin and of the wood of *Tsuga Sieboldii*. Found in sulphite waste liquors from wood pulp manufacture. Cryst. from EtOH. M.p. 254–5°. Sol. EtOH, Et_2O, C_6H_6. Insol. pet. ether. $[\alpha]_D^{20}$ − 54·5° in Me_2CO. Alc. $FeCl_3$ ⟶ green col. Conc.

H_2SO_4 + $NaNO_2$ ⟶ brown ⟶ red ⟶ blue col.

Di-Me ether: $C_{22}H_{24}O_6$. MW, 384. M.p. 178·5–179°. $[\alpha]_D^{18}$ − 99·4° in Me_2CO.

Di-Et ether: $C_{24}H_{28}O_6$. MW, 412. Needles from EtOH. M.p. 178–9°.

Diacetyl: cryst. from EtOH–Me_2CO. M.p. 204–5° (222°). $[\alpha]_D^{18}$ − 68·4° in Me_2CO.

Di-p-nitrobenzoyl: prisms from $CHCl_3$–Et_2O. M.p. 257–8°.

Emde, Schartner, *Helv. Chim. Acta*, 1935, **18**, 344.
Haworth, Sheldrick, *J. Chem. Soc.*, 1935, 636.
Kawamura, *Chem. Zentr.*, 1932, II, 60.
Holmberg, *Ber.*, 1921, **54**, 2406.

Tubaic Acid

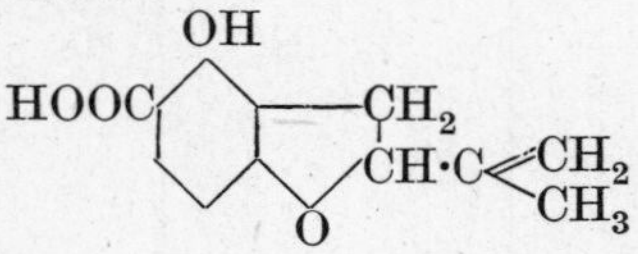

$C_{12}H_{12}O_4$ MW, 220

Needles from Et_2O–pet. ether. M.p. 129°. $[\alpha]_D^{20}$ − 73·0° in $CHCl_3$. Loses CO_2 at 185–200°. $FeCl_3$ ⟶ red col.

Me ester: $C_{13}H_{14}O_4$. MW, 234. Needles from MeOH.Aq. M.p. 52°. $[\alpha]_D^{19}$ − 72·8° in $CHCl_3$. $FeCl_3$ ⟶ red col.

Me ether: $C_{13}H_{14}O_4$. MW, 234. Cryst. from EtOH.Aq. M.p. 78°. *Me ester*: $C_{14}H_{16}O_4$. MW, 248. Oil. B.p. 175°/4·5 mm.

Acetyl: m.p. 133°.

Haller, La Forge, *J. Am. Chem. Soc.*, 1932, **54**, 1988; 1930, **52**, 3211.
Takei, Koide, *Ber.*, 1929, **62**, 3032.

Tuduranine

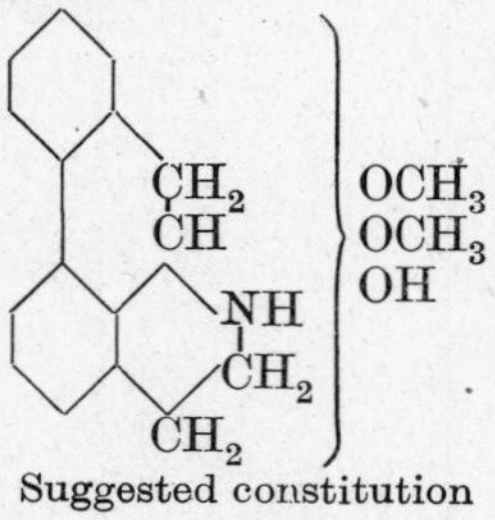

Suggested constitution

$C_{18}H_{19}O_3N$ MW, 297

Alkaloid from *Sinomenium acutum*. Poorly cryst. M.p. 105–25°. Sol. most org. solvents. Sol. alkalis. $FeCl_3$ ⟶ faint col. H·CHO + H_2SO_4 ⟶ fuchsin-red col.

B,HCl: prisms from H_2O. M.p. 286° decomp. $[\alpha]_D^{14·5}$ − 148° in MeOH.Aq.

Me ether: $C_{19}H_{21}O_3N$. MW, 311. N-*Acetyl*: prisms from EtOH. M.p. 189°. $[\alpha]_D^{18}$ − 400·17° in $CHCl_3$.

N-*Me*: $C_{19}H_{21}O_3N$. MW, 311. *Methiodide*: cryst. from EtOH. M.p. 224°.

N-*Et*-O-*Et*: $C_{22}H_{27}O_3N$. MW, 353. *Ethiodide*: M.p. 238°. $[\alpha]_D^{15}$ − 112·47° in $CHCl_3$.

N-*Di-Et*-O-*Et*: $C_{24}H_{31}O_3N$. MW, 381. *Ethiodide*: m.p. 163–4°.

N-*Acetyl*: prisms from MeOH. M.p. 277°. $[\alpha]_D^{18}$ − 395·24° in MeOH–$CHCl_3$.

O : N-*Diacetyl*: prisms from MeOH or EtOH. M.p. 170°. $[\alpha]_D^{14}$ − 321·7° in MeOH.

Goto, *Ann.*, 1935, **521**, 175.

Turanose

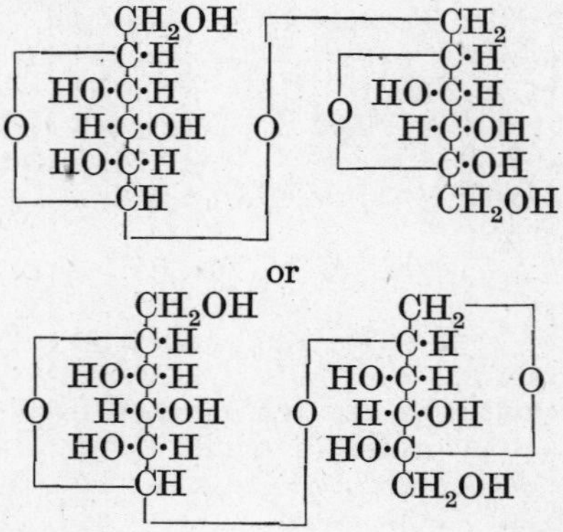

$C_{12}H_{22}O_{11}$ MW, 342

Amorphous powder, or prisms + ½MeOH from MeOH. M.p. 65–70° (60–5°), MeOH free 157°. Sol. H_2O, MeOH. Less sol. EtOH. Sweet taste. $[\alpha]_D^{20}$ + 65–8° in H_2O, ($[\alpha]_D^{22}$ + 22·0° ⟶ + 75·3° in H_2O). Reduces Fehling's. Hyd. by dil. acids or by yeast ⟶ glucose + fructose.

Phenylosazone: yellow needles from dil. EtOH. M.p. 215–20° decomp. Sol. hot H_2O.

Hepta-Me ether: yellow syrup. B.p. 185–90°/0·2 mm., 162–3°/0·06 mm. $[\alpha]_D^{19}$ + 106·0° ⟶ 104·8° in EtOH. n_D 1·4652. *Me glucoside*: yellow syrup. B.p. 159–62°/0·15 mm. $[\alpha]_D^{19}$ + 106·7° in H_2O, + 109·7° in EtOH.

Hepta-acetyl: (i) needles from Et_2O. M.p. 140–1°. $[\alpha]_D^{20}$ + 37° in $CHCl_3$. (ii) Prisms. M.p. 147°. $[\alpha]_D^{20}$ + 38·7° ⟶ 41·7° in $CHCl_3$.

Fischer, *Ber.*, 1894, **27**, 2488.
Zemplén, Braun, *Ber.*, 1926, **59**, 2230.
Zemplén, *ibid.*, 2539.
Leitch, *J. Chem. Soc.*, 1927, 588.
Aagaard, *Chem. Abstracts*, 1930, **24**, 1089.
Pacsu, *J. Am. Chem. Soc.*, 1931, **53**, 3099; 1933, **55**, 2451.
Hudson, Pacsu, *J. Am. Chem. Soc.*, 1930, **52**, 2519.

Turicine

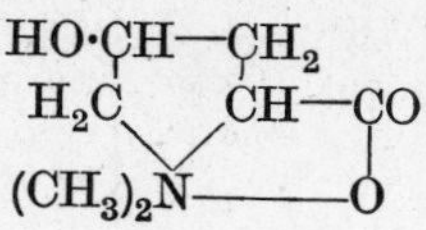

$C_7H_{13}O_3N$ MW, 159

Constituent of *Betonica wiesen* and *Stachys silvatica.* Stereoisomeric with betonicine. Needles or prisms + $1H_2O$ from EtOH.Aq. M.p. anhyd. 260° decomp. Very sol. H_2O. $[\alpha]_D$ + 41·5° (anhyd.) in H_2O. Pptd. from aq. sol. by phosphotungstic acid.

B,HCl : needles or plates from EtOH. Decomp. at 224°. $[\alpha]_D$ + 25·7° in H_2O.

B,HAuCl₄ : yellow prisms. Decomp. at 230–2°.

B₂,H₂PtCl₆,H₂O : m.p. 223° decomp.

Goodson, Clewer, *J. Chem. Soc.*, 1919, **115**, 931.
Küng, Trier, *Z. physiol. Chem.*, 1913, **85**, 209.

Turmerone (*Tumerone*)

$C_{15}H_{22}O$ MW, 218

Occurs in essential oil from *Curcuma longa.* Oil. B.p. 125–6°/10 mm.

Rupe, Clar, Pfau, Plattner, *Helv. Chim. Acta*, 1934, **17**, 372.

***ar*-Turmerone**

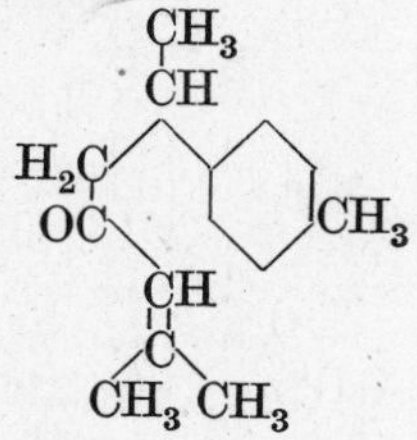

$C_{15}H_{20}O$ MW, 216

Occurs in essential oil from *Curcuma longa.* Pale yellow oil. B.p. 159–60°/10 mm. D^{20} 0·9571. n_D^{20} 1·5219. $[\alpha]_D^{20}$ + 82·21°.

Oxime : oil. B.p. 179–80°/10 mm.

Semicarbazone : needles from C_6H_6. M.p. 108–9°.

2 : 4-*Dinitrophenylhydrazone* : orange-yellow needles. M.p. 133–4°.

Rupe, Gassmann, *Helv. Chim. Acta*, 1936, **19**, 569.
See also previous reference.

Tyramine (*Tyrosamine*, 2-p-*hydroxyphenylethylamine*, p-β-*aminoethylphenol*)

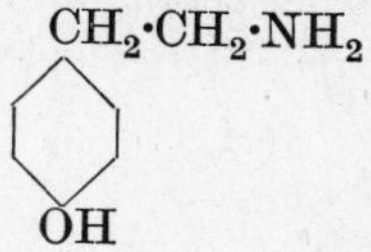

$C_8H_{11}ON$ MW, 137

Chief pressor base found in some extracts of ergot, putrified animal tissues, mature cheese, mistletoes. Cryst. from EtOH or anisole, plates or needles from C_6H_6. M.p. 164–164·5°. B.p. 205–7°/25 mm., 195°/13 mm., 165–7°/2 mm. Spar. sol. xylene. Sol. 95 parts H_2O at 15°. Sol. 8 parts boiling EtOH. Aq. sol. reacts alkaline. KOH fusion ⟶ *p*-hydroxybenzoic acid. Hydrochloride + KNO_3 in neutral sol. ⟶ tyrosol.

B,HCl : cryst. from EtOH–Et_2O. M.p. 269°.

Oxalate : m.p. 203–4°.

Picrate : prisms. M.p. 206°.

Me ether : $C_9H_{13}ON$. MW, 151. Oil with fish-like odour. B.p. 138–40°/20 mm., 132–4°/14 mm. Very spar. sol. H_2O. Absorbs CO_2 from the air. *B,HCl* : plates from EtOH. M.p. 271–2°. N-*Benzenesulphonyl* : cryst. from EtOH or C_6H_6–pet. ether. M.p. 79–80°.

N-*Me* : $C_9H_{13}ON$. MW, 151. Prisms from EtOH, plates from C_6H_6. M.p. 130°. B.p. 183–5°/9 mm. Spar. sol. H_2O. *B,HCl* : plates or needles from EtOH–Et_2O. M.p. 148·5°. *B,(COOH)₂* : needles from EtOH. M.p. 250° decomp. *B₂,H₂PtCl₆* : yellow needles. M.p. 205°. *Picrate* : m.p. 149°. *Picrolonate* : m.p. 234–5°. N-*Acetyl* : needles from H_2O, plates from EtOH or AcOEt. M.p. 142°. N-*Benzenesulphonyl* : plates from EtOH–Et_2O. M.p. 133·5°. *Dibenzoyl* : prisms from pet. ether. M.p. 99°.

N-*Di-Me* : *see* Hordenine.

N-*Et* : $C_{10}H_{15}ON$. MW, 165. Needles from EtOH. M.p. 157–8°. B.p. 185–7°/9 mm. *B,HCl* : pale red needles from EtOH–Et_2O. M.p. 184–5°. *B,(COOH)₂* : plates from EtOH. M.p. 245° decomp. *Picrolonate* : m.p. 216° decomp.

N-*Chloroacetyl* : cryst. M.p. 109°.

N-*Benzoyl* : plates from EtOH. M.p. 162°.

O : N-*Dibenzoyl* : needles from EtOH.Aq. M.p. 172°.

Buck, *J. Am. Chem. Soc.*, 1933, **55**, 3389.
Waser, *Helv. Chim. Acta*, 1925, **8**, 766.
Barger, *J. Chem. Soc.*, 1909, **95**, 1127, 1722.

o-Tyrosine (2-o-*Hydroxyphenyl-α-alanine*, 1-*amino-2-o-hydroxyphenyl-propionic acid*, 2-*hydroxy-α-aminohydrocinnamic acid*)

$CH_2 \cdot CH(NH_2) \cdot COOH$

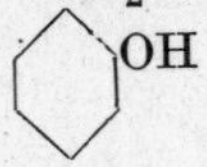

$C_9H_{11}O_3N$ MW, 181

Needles from H_2O, plates from EtOH.Aq. M.p. 249–50°. Sol. 500 parts H_2O at 17°. Sol. warm AcOH. Insol. Et_2O. $FeCl_3$ ⟶ red ⟶ violet col.

B,HCl: prisms. Decomp. at 180°.

Me ester: $C_{10}H_{13}O_3N$. MW, 195. *B,HCl*: m.p. 179°.

Anhydride: *diacetyl*, needles from EtOH. M.p. 225°.

Me ether: $C_{10}H_{13}O_3N$. MW, 195. Needles from H_2O. M.p. 206° decomp.

N-*Benzoyl*: cryst. from H_2O. M.p. 176°.

Dibenzoyl: cryst. from C_6H_6. M.p. 172°.

Dickinson, Marshall, *J. Chem. Soc.*, 1929, 1497.

Ueda, *Chem. Zentr.*, 1928, I, 2618.

Johnson, Scott, *J. Am. Chem. Soc.*, 1915, **37**, 1853.

m-Tyrosine (2-m-*Hydroxyphenyl-α-alanine*, 1-*amino-2-m-hydroxyphenyl-propionic acid*, 3-*hydroxy-α-aminohydrocinnamic acid*)

$CH_2 \cdot CH(NH_2) \cdot COOH$

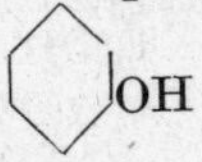

$C_9H_{11}O_3N$ MW, 181

Needles or plates from H_2O, plates from EtOH.Aq. M.p. 275° (280°). Sol. 120 parts H_2O at 17°, 22 parts at 100°. Sol. cold AcOH.Aq. Spar. sol. EtOH.

Anhydride: cryst. from EtOH.Aq. M.p. 276–7°. *Diacetyl*: needles from EtOH. M.p. 189–90°.

N-*Benzoyl*: cryst. from H_2O. M.p. 180°.

See first two references above and also Blum, *Chem. Zentr.*, 1908, II, 1946.

Tyrosine (p-*Tyrosine*, 2-p-*hydroxyphenyl-α-alanine*, 1-*amino-2-p-hydroxyphenyl-propionic acid*, 4-*hydroxy-α-aminohydrocinnamic acid*)

$CH_2 \cdot CH(NH_2) \cdot COOH$

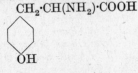

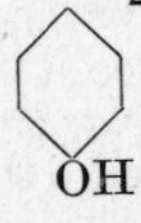

$C_9H_{11}O_3N$ MW, 181

d-.

Cryst. Melts with decomp. $[\alpha]_D^{20}$ + 8·64° in 21% HCl. Aq. sol. + tyrosinase ⟶ red col.

N-*Benzoyl*: m.p. 165·5°. $[\alpha]_D^{20}$ − 19·59° in alk. sol.

l-.

Widely distributed in plant and animal proteins. Needles from H_2O. Decomp. (slow heat.) at 290–5°, (rapid heat.) at 314–18°. Triboluminescent. Sol. 2491 parts H_2O at 17°, 13,500 parts cold 96% EtOH, 700 parts AcOH at 16°. Sol. acids, alkalis, ammonia. Insol. Et_2O. $[\alpha]_D^{20}$ − 8·07° in 21% HCl, − 9·01° in 11·6% KOH. Heat of comb. C_p 1071·2 Cal., C_v 1070·8 Cal. $k = 4 \times 10^{-9}$ at 25°. Heat at 270° ⟶ tyramine. Stable to saturated HCl and HBr at 240°. NaOH fusion ⟶ *p*-hydroxybenzoic acid. Heat with $Ba(OH)_2$.Aq. at 170° ⟶ *dl*-form. Boiling dil. AcOH sol. + $NaNO_2$ ⟶ violet or red col. HCl sol. + Cl water + NH_3 ⟶ red col. Tyrosinase ⟶ red ⟶ black "melanin" pigment. Warm HNO_3 ⟶ yellow col. TiO_2 in H_2SO_4 ⟶ dark orange-yellow col. Paraformaldehyde + pure conc. H_2SO_4 ⟶ green col. Alloxan in H_2O ⟶ murexide col. Forms cryst. salts. Ba and Ag salts spar. sol. cold H_2O.

Cu salt: dark blue needles. Spar. sol. cold H_2O. Sol. hot H_2O.

Picrolonate: decomp. at 260°.

Me ester: $C_{10}H_{13}O_3N$. MW, 195. Prisms from AcOEt. M.p. 135–6°. Very sol. MeOH. Sol. hot H_2O, EtOH, AcOEt, alkalis. Spar. sol. cold H_2O, Et_2O, C_6H_6. $[\alpha]_D^{20}$ + 25·75° in MeOH. N-*Me*: $C_{11}H_{15}O_3N$. MW, 209. Prisms from AcOEt. M.p. 116–17°. Spar. sol. Me_2CO.

Et ester: $C_{11}H_{15}O_3N$. MW, 209. Prisms from AcOEt. M.p. 108–9°. Sol. EtOH, hot C_6H_6, AcOEt. Spar. sol. cold H_2O, Et_2O. $[\alpha]_D^{20}$ + 20·4° in EtOH. *Hydrochloride*: needles from EtOH–Et_2O or AcOEt. M.p. 166°. N-*Chloroacetyl*: needles from $CHCl_3$–pet. ether. M.p. 88–9°. N-*Bromoacetyl*: m.p. 101°. N-*Iodoacetyl*: plates from C_6H_6. M.p. 120°. N-p-*Toluenesulphonyl*: needles from $CHCl_3$–pet. ether. M.p. 114°.

Amide: $C_9H_{12}O_2N_2$. MW, 180. Prisms or plates from EtOH. M.p. 153–4°. Sol. H_2O, EtOH. $[\alpha]_D^{20}$ + 19·47° in H_2O.

Anhydride: $(C_9H_9O_2N)_n$. Two forms. (α-) Needles from EtOH. M.p. 278–9°. Spar. sol. cold H_2O, cold EtOH. Cryst. from EtOH repeatedly ⟶ β-. (β-) Greyish powder. M.p. 279° slight decomp.

Hydrazide: m.p. 195·5°.

N-*Me*: *see* Surinamine.

Me ether: plates. M.p. 264–5°. $[\alpha]^{29}_{5461}$ −5·9° in HCl. *B,H$_2$SO$_4$*: m.p. 191°. *B,HCl*: needles from dil. HCl. M.p. 237–8° decomp. *Picrolonate*: needles. Softens at 145°, m.p. 174° decomp. N-*Acetyl*: plates from H_2O. M.p. 150–1°. N-*Benzoyl*: needles from H_2O. M.p. 136–7°.

N-*Formyl*: prisms or plates + $1H_2O$ from H_2O. Anhyd. in vacuo at 100°. M.p. anhyd. 171–4° decomp. $[\alpha]^{20}_{D}$ + 84·8° in EtOH.

N-*Acetyl*: cryst. from H_2O. Plates from dioxan. M.p. 146–8°.

N-*Chloroacetyl*: prisms from H_2O. M.p. 155–6°.

N-*Benzoyl*: plates from H_2O. M.p. 165–6°.

N-p-*Toluenesulphonyl*: needles or prisms from EtOH.Aq. M.p. 187–8°.

O : N-*Diacetyl*: cryst. M.p. 172°.

O : N-*Dibenzoyl*: needles from AcOH. M.p. 211–12°.

dl-.

Occurs naturally. Plates or needles from H_2O. Decomp. (slow heat.) at 290–5°, (rapid heat.) at 340°. Sol. 2454 parts H_2O at 20°, 154 at 100°. Insol. cold EtOH, Et_2O.

Et ester: *B,HCl*: m.p. 166°. O : N-*Diacetyl*: m.p. 90°. N-*Benzoyl*: needles from EtOH.Aq. or C_6H_6–ligroin. M.p. 122–3°.

Isoamyl ester: $C_{14}H_{21}O_3N$. MW, 251. Yellow needles. M.p. 68–70°. Sol. EtOH, AcOEt, $CHCl_3$, C_6H_6. Spar. sol. H_2O. *B,HCl*: needles from AcOEt–Et_2O. M.p. 181–2°. N-*Benzoyl*: needles. M.p. 106–7°.

Amide: N-*benzoyl*, needles from EtOH.Aq. M.p. 232–3°.

Anhydride: $(C_9H_9O_2N)_n$. Two forms. (α-) Needles from EtOH. M.p. 278–9°. (β-) Amorph. M.p. 279°.

Hydrazide: needles from EtOH. M.p. 171°. N-*Benzoyl*: needles. M.p. 229–30°.

Me ether: plates or prisms. M.p. about 295° decomp. Sol. HCl, NH_3. Spar. sol. H_2O, hot AcOH.

N-*Me*: needles. Decomp. at 318°.

O : N-*Di-Me*: $C_{11}H_{15}O_3N$. MW, 209. Needles from H_2O. Decomp. at 220–55°.

N-*Benzoyl*: needles from AcOH or hot H_2O. M.p. 191–3°. *Anilide*: microcryst. M.p. 212°.

p-*Toluenesulphonyl*: columns. M.p. 224–6°.

Bucherer, Lieb, *J. prakt. Chem.*, 1934, **141**, 37.
Chikano, *Z. physiol. Chem.*, 1929, **180**, 249.
Curtius, Donselt, *J. prakt. Chem.*, 1917, **95**, 349.
Mörner, *Z. physiol. Chem.*, 1913, **88**, 126.
Fischer, *Ber.*, 1901, **34**, 451; 1899, **32**, 3644.

o-Tyrosol (o-β-*Hydroxyethylphenol*, o-*hydroxyphenylethyl alcohol*)

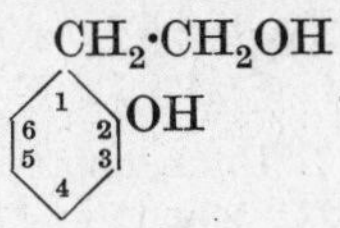

$C_8H_{10}O_2$ MW, 138

Oil. B.p. 168–9°/12 mm. Spar. misc. with cold H_2O. D^{18} 1·1531. n^{18}_{D} 1·5575. $FeCl_3 \longrightarrow$ blue col.

2-*Et ether*: $C_{10}H_{14}O_2$. MW, 166. Oil. B.p. 136–7°.

Mono-acetyl deriv.: cryst. from ligroin. M.p. 64·5°. B.p. 170–80°/30 mm.

Stoermer, Kahlert, *Ber.*, 1901, **34**, 1809.

Tyrosol (p-*Hydroxyphenylethyl alcohol*, p-β-*hydroxyethylphenol*, p-*tyrosol*)

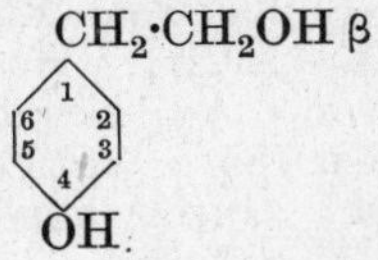

$C_8H_{10}O_2$ MW, 138

Needles from $CHCl_3$. M.p. 93°. B.p. about 310°, 195°/18 mm. Very sol. H_2O, EtOH, Et_2O, Me_2CO, AcOH. Sol. $CHCl_3$, C_6H_6, CS_2. Spar. sol. pet. ether. $FeCl_3 \longrightarrow$ blue col. Hot conc. $H_2SO_4 \longrightarrow$ red col. $H{\cdot}CHO + H_2SO_4 \longrightarrow$ yellowish-green sol. $\longrightarrow$ green ppt. with H_2O.

4-*Me ether*: $C_9H_{12}O_2$. MW, 152. Plates. M.p. 24°. B.p. 143°/13 mm. Insol. ligroin. *Acetyl*: b.p. 277–8°, 156–7°/11 mm. D^0 1·101.

4-*Et ether*: $C_{10}H_{14}O_2$. MW, 166. M.p. about 40°. B.p. 135–40°/7 mm.

β-*Acetyl*: prisms from Et_2O–ligroin. M.p. 59°. B.p. 192°/18 mm.

Diacetyl: oil. B.p. 187°/18 mm.

Dibenzoyl: needles from EtOH. M.p. 111°.

v. Braun, *Ber.*, 1912, **45**, 1283.
Neubauer, Fromherz, *Z. physiol. Chem.*, 1910, **70**, 342.

U

Ulexine.
See Cytisine.

Umbellic Acid (2 : 4-*Dihydroxycinnamic acid*)

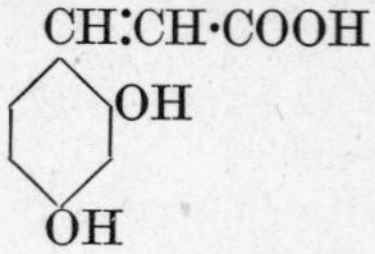

$C_9H_8O_4$ MW, 180

Yellow powder. Darkens at 240°, decomp. at 260°. Sol. EtOH, warm H_2O. Insol. Et_2O, C_6H_6, ligroin. Readily decomp. $k = 1{\cdot}88 \times 10^{-5}$ at 25°. Pb and Cu salts insol. H_2O.

Me ester : $C_{10}H_{10}O_4$. MW, 194. *Di-Me ether* : $C_{12}H_{14}O_4$. MW, 222. Needles from EtOH.Aq. M.p. 87°. Distils above 360°. Sol. EtOH, Et_2O, C_6H_6. Spar. sol. ligroin.

Et ester : $C_{11}H_{12}O_4$. MW, 208. *Di-Me ether* : $C_{13}H_{16}O_4$. MW, 236. Needles from pet. ether. M.p. 61°. B.p. 208–12°/13 mm. Sol. EtOH, Et_2O. Spar. sol. pet. ether.

4-*Me ether* : $C_{10}H_{10}O_4$. MW, 194. Needles from H_2O. M.p. 180–5° decomp.

Di-Me ether : $C_{11}H_{12}O_4$. MW, 208. Two forms. (α-) Needles from EtOH. M.p. 138°. Sol. EtOH, Et_2O, C_6H_6. Heat alone or with HCl ⟶ β-form. (β-). Needles from H_2O or EtOH.Aq. M.p. 186°. Sol. EtOH, Et_2O, C_6H_6. Spar. sol. H_2O. Insol. ligroin. Sol. H_2SO_4 ⟶ yellow col. Sublimes.

Di-Et ether : $C_{13}H_{16}O_4$. MW, 236. Two forms. (α-) Plates from EtOH.Aq. M.p. 106·5°. Sol. EtOH, Et_2O, C_6H_6. Spar. sol. H_2O. Heat ⟶ β-form with part. decomp. (β-) Cryst. from EtOH. M.p. 200°. Sol. Et_2O. Spar. sol. H_2O.

Will, Beck, *Ber.*, 1886, **19**, 1778.
Posen, *Ber.*, 1881, **14**, 2745.

Umbelliferone (7-*Hydroxycoumarin*)

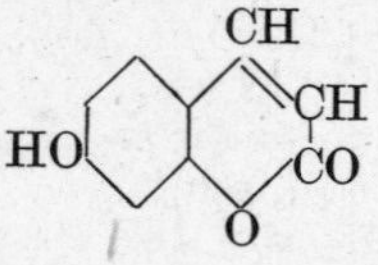

$C_9H_6O_3$ MW, 162

Occurs widely in plants. Needles from H_2O. M.p. 223–4°. Sol. 100 parts boiling H_2O. Very sol. EtOH, $CHCl_3$. Sol. AcOH, HCl. Spar. sol. Et_2O. Sol. alkalis and conc. H_2SO_4 with blue fluor. Sublimes. Forms Na salt. Reduces warm $AgNO_3$.

Me ether : *see* Herniarin.

Et ether : $C_{11}H_{10}O_3$. MW, 190. Plates. M.p. 88°. Very sol. EtOH, AcOH, C_6H_6.

Acetyl : prisms or needles from H_2O. M.p. 140°.

Grimaux, *Bull. soc. chim.*, 1895, **13**, 900.

Umbellulone

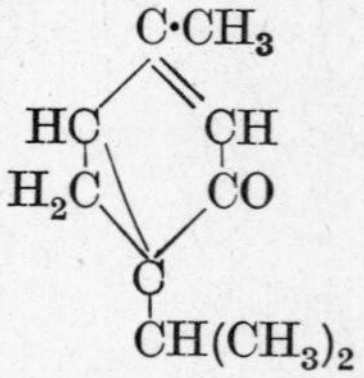

$C_{10}H_{14}O$ MW, 150

Constituent of essential oil from *Umbellularia californica*, Meissn. Colourless oil. B.p. 219–20°/749 mm., 92·5–93°/10 mm. D^{15}_{15} 0·9581. n_D 1·48325. $[\alpha]_D$ — 37°.

Semicarbazone : cryst. from MeOH. Decomp. at 240–3°.

Power, Lees, *J. Chem. Soc.*, 1904, **85**, 636.

Umbilicaric Acid (*Monomethyl ether of gyrophoric acid*)

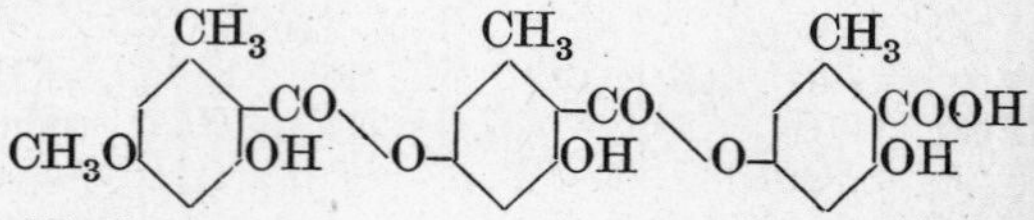

$C_{25}H_{22}O_{10}$ MW, 482

Occurs in numerous lichens. Plates from EtOH. M.p. 185–6°. Sol. EtOH, Et_2O, Me_2CO, $CHCl_3$. Spar. sol. Me_2CO.Aq. Insol. H_2O.

Asahina, Yosioka, *Ber.*, 1937, **70**, 204.
Koller, Pfeiffer, *Monatsh.*, 1933, **62**, 359.

Undecanal.
See Undecyl Aldehyde.

Undecane (*Hendecane*)

$$CH_3{\cdot}[CH_2]_9{\cdot}CH_3$$

$C_{11}H_{24}$ MW, 156

Constituent of natural petroleum. Liq. B.p. 194·5°, 81°/15 mm., 61°/2 mm. D^{20}_{4} 0·7411. $n^{19\cdot5}_{D}$ 1·41862.

Hess, Bappert, *Ann.*, 1925, **441**, 151.
Clemmensen, *Ber.*, 1913, **46**, 1841.

Undecane-1-carboxylic Acid.
See Lauric Acid.

Undecane-1 : 11-dicarboxylic Acid.
See Brassylic Acid.

Undecanol-1.
See Undecyl Alcohol.
Undecanol-2.
See Methylnonylcarbinol.
Undecanol-3.
See Ethyloctylcarbinol.
Undecanone-2.
See Methyl nonyl Ketone.
Undecanone-3.
See Ethyl octyl Ketone.
Undecanone-4.
See Propyl heptyl Ketone.
Undecanone-6.
See *n*-Caprone.

1-Undecenol-10

$CH_2{:}CH{\cdot}[CH_2]_7{\cdot}CH(OH){\cdot}CH_3$

$C_{11}H_{22}O$ MW, 170

Constituent of essential oil of *Litsea odorifera*, Val. B.p. 233°. D^{10} 0·835.

Romburgh, *Chem. Zentr.*, 1911, II, 1863.

1-Undecenol-11.
See Undecenyl Alcohol.

2-Undecenol-11 (*Isoundecylenic alcohol*)

$CH_3{\cdot}CH{:}CH{\cdot}[CH_2]_7{\cdot}CH_2OH$

$C_{11}H_{22}O$ MW, 170

Liq. B.p. 248·5°, 124–5°/8 mm. D^{15} 0·8507. n_D^{19} 1·4535.
Acetyl: b.p. 127–8°/7 mm. D^{15} 0·8841.
Phenylurethane: needles from EtOH.Aq. M.p. 65–6°.

Chuit, Boelsing, Hausser, Malet, *Helv. Chim. Acta*, 1926, **9**, 1085.

Undecenyl Alcohol (1-*Undecenol*-11, *undecylenic alcohol*)

$CH_2{:}CH{\cdot}[CH_2]_8{\cdot}CH_2OH$

$C_{11}H_{22}O$ MW, 170

Liq. solidifying to leaflets on cooling. F.p. — 2°. B.p. 250°, 132–3°/15 mm., 122°/3 mm. D^{15} 0·8495. n_D^{19} 1·4506.
Acetyl: liq. B.p. 125–7°/7 mm. D^{20} 0·8808.
Phenylurethane: needles from EtOH. M.p. 54·5–55°.
Allophanate: m.p. 143°.

Grün, Wirth, *Ber.*, 1922, **55**, 2208.
Bouveault, Blanc, *Bull. soc. chim.*, 1904, **31**, 1210.

Undecenylamine (11-*Amino*-1-*undecylene*, 11-*amino*-1-*undecene*)

$CH_2{:}CH{\cdot}[CH_2]_8{\cdot}CH_2NH_2$

$C_{11}H_{23}N$ MW, 169

Liq. B.p. 238–40°, 123°/16 mm.
N-*Benzoyl*: plates from C_6H_6. M.p. 41–2°.

Krafft, Tritschler, *Ber.*, 1900, **33**, 3581.

1-Undecine.
See Nonylacetylene.
2-Undecine.
See Methyloctylacetylene.
Undecoic Acid.
See Undecylic Acid.

Undecyl Alcohol (*Undecanol*-1, *hendecyl alcohol, hendecanol*-1)

$CH_3{\cdot}[CH_2]_9{\cdot}CH_2OH$

$C_{11}H_{24}O$ MW, 172

F.p. 19° (11°). B.p. 147°/25 mm., 131°/15 mm., 123–5°/6 mm. D_4^{23} 0·8334. n_D^{23} 1·4392.
Phenylurethane: needles from EtOH. M.p. 62°.
o-*Nitrophenylurethane*: m.p. 37°.
m-*Nitrophenylurethane*: plates from EtOH. M.p. 56°.
p-*Nitrophenylurethane*: m.p. 99·5°.
3 : 5-*Dinitrophenylurethane*: m.p. 62°.
Allophanate: cryst. from EtOH. M.p. 155·5–156°.

Ford, Marvel, *Organic Syntheses*, 1930, X, 63.
Levene, West, Allen, Scheer, *J. Biol. Chem.*, 1915, **23**, 72.
Hoeke, *Rec. trav. chim.*, 1935, **54**, 505.

Undecyl Aldehyde (*Undecylic aldehyde, undecanal*)

$CH_3{\cdot}[CH_2]_9{\cdot}CHO$

$C_{11}H_{22}O$ MW, 170

F.p. — 4°. B.p. 116–17°/18 mm. D_4^{23} 0·8251. n_D^{23} 1·4322. Readily polymerises. Oxidises in air to undecylic acid.
Oxime: needles from MeOH.Aq. M.p. 72°.
Semicarbazone: cryst. from MeOH. M.p. 103°.
Azine: cryst. from MeOH. M.p. 57°.
2 : 4-*Dinitrophenylhydrazone*: yellow cryst. from EtOH. M.p. 104°.

Darzens, Levy, *Compt. rend.*, 1933, **196**, 348.
Blaise, Guerin, *Bull. soc. chim.*, 1903, **29**, 1202.
Blaise, *Bull. soc. chim.*, 1904, **31**, 492.

***n*-Undecylamine** (1-*Aminoundecane, hendecylamine*)

$CH_3{\cdot}[CH_2]_9{\cdot}CH_2NH_2$

$C_{11}H_{25}N$ MW, 171

M.p. 15–16°. B.p. 231–2°/727 mm. Sol. hot H_2O, EtOH. Insol. Et_2O. Volatile in steam,

B,HCl : cryst. from conc. HCl. M.p. 190°.

B_2,H_2PtCl_6 : yellow plates from H_2O. Decomp. about 180°.

N-*Acetyl* : needles from pet. ether. M.p. 48°. B.p. 192°/12 mm. *B,HCl* : cryst. M.p. 65–6°.

N-*Benzoyl* : needles from C_6H_6–ligroin. M.p. 60°.

Naegeli, Grüntuch, Lendorff, *Helv. Chim. Acta*, 1929, **12**, 227.

Jeffreys, *Am. Chem. J.*, 1899, **22**, 33.

***sec.-n*-Undecylamine** (2-*Aminoundecane*)

$CH_3\cdot[CH_2]_8\cdot CH(NH_2)\cdot CH_3$

$C_{11}H_{25}N$ MW, 171

B.p. 231°/741 mm., 113°/26 mm. Absorbs CO_2 readily.

B,HCl : needles from ligroin. M.p. 84°.

B_2,H_2PtCl_6 : yellow tablets from EtOH. Darkens at about 240°.

N-*Acetyl* : needles from EtOH.Aq. M.p. 58°.

Picrate : m.p. 111°.

Thoms, Mannich, *Ber.*, 1903, **36**, 2554.

1-Undecylene (*Undecene*-1, *hendecene*-1)

$CH_3\cdot[CH_2]_8\cdot CH{:}CH_2$

$C_{11}H_{22}$ MW, 154

B.p. 192–5°, 84°/18 mm. D_{20}^{20} 0·7787. n_D 1·4440.

Ruhemann, *Z. angew. Chem.*, 1931, **44**, 78.

2-Undecylene (*Undecene*-2, *hendecene*-2)

$CH_3\cdot[CH_2]_7\cdot CH{:}CH\cdot CH_3$

$C_{11}H_{22}$ MW, 154

B.p. 192–3°, 78·5°/14 mm. D_{15}^{15} 0·7735. n_D 1·43325.

Thoms, Mannich, *Ber.*, 1903, **36**, 2548.

1-Undecylenic Acid

$CH_3\cdot[CH_2]_7\cdot CH{:}CH\cdot COOH$

$C_{11}H_{20}O_2$ MW, 184

Nitrile : $C_{11}H_{19}N$. MW, 165. Two stereoisomeric forms. (i) B.p. 119·7–119·9°/10 mm. D_4^{20} 0·83255. n_D^{20} 1·44816. (ii) B.p. 127·9–128·1°/10 mm. D_4^{20} 0·83359. n_D^{20} 1·45146.

Amide : $C_{11}H_{21}ON$. MW, 183. Two stereoisomeric forms corresponding to the above nitriles. (i) Cryst. from C_6H_6. M.p. 76–7°. (ii) Cryst. from C_6H_6. M.p. 114–15°.

Caillie, *Chem. Zentr.*, 1936, I, 4423.

8-Undecylenic Acid

$CH_3\cdot CH{:}CH\cdot[CH_2]_7\cdot COOH$

$C_{11}H_{20}O_2$ MW, 184

M.p. 19°. B.p. 273–5°, 165°/10 mm. D_0^{25} 0·9119. $CrO_3 \longrightarrow$ azelaic acid.

Cu salt : m.p. 229–30°.

Zn salt : m.p. 111–12°.

Pb salt : m.p. 78°.

Et ester : $C_{13}H_{24}O_2$. MW, 212. B.p. 258°, 207–8°/185 mm. D_0^0 0·8966.

Amide : $C_{11}H_{21}ON$. MW, 183. Cryst. from Et_2O. M.p. 77–78·5°.

Krafft, Seldis, *Ber.*, 1900, **33**, 3572.

9-Undecylenic Acid

$CH_2{:}CH\cdot[CH_2]_8\cdot COOH$

$C_{11}H_{20}O_2$ MW, 184

Cryst. M.p. 24·5°. B.p. 275°, 165°/15 mm. D_{25}^{25} 0·9102. n_a^{24} 1·44642.

Cu salt : m.p. 232–4°.

Pb salt : m.p. 80°.

Zn salt : m.p. 115–16°.

Me ester : $C_{12}H_{22}O_2$. MW, 198. M.p. — 27·5°. B.p. 248°, 124°/10 mm. D^{15} 0·889. n_D^{20} 1·43928.

Et ester : $C_{13}H_{24}O_2$. MW, 212. B.p. 263·5–265·5°, 131·5°/16 mm. D_{25}^{25} 0·87658. n_D^{23} 1·4449.

Anhydride : $C_{22}H_{38}O_3$. MW, 350. M.p. 13–13·5°.

Chloride : $C_{11}H_{19}OCl$. MW, 202·5. Liq. B.p. 128·5°/14 mm.

Amide : $C_{11}H_{21}ON$. MW, 183. Plates from EtOH. M.p. 87°.

Nitrile : $C_{11}H_{19}N$. MW, 165. Liq. B.p. 257°, 129–30°/14 mm.

Krafft, Brunner, *Ber.*, 1884, **17**, 2985.

Undecylenic Alcohol.

See Undecenyl Alcohol.

Undecylic Acid (*Undecoic acid, hendecanoic acid*)

$CH_3\cdot[CH_2]_9\cdot COOH$

$C_{11}H_{22}O_2$ MW, 186

Cryst. from Me_2CO. M.p. 29·5–30·5°. B.p. 212·5°/100 mm., 164°/15 mm. Ag salt insol. H_2O. Ba salt spar. sol. H_2O.

Me ester : $C_{12}H_{24}O_2$. MW, 200. B.p. 123°/9–10 mm.

Et ester : $C_{13}H_{26}O_2$. MW, 214. B.p. 140°/20 mm.

p-*Chlorophenacyl ester* : plates from EtOH. M.p. 60·2°.

p-*Bromophenacyl ester* : plates from EtOH. M.p. 68·2°.

p-*Iodophenacyl ester* : plates from EtOH. M.p. 81·8°.

Amide : $C_{11}H_{23}ON$. MW, 185. Cryst. from EtOH. M.p. 103°.

Nitrile : $C_{11}H_{21}N$. MW, 167. Liq. B.p. 253–4°.

Anilide : cryst. from EtOH. M.p. 71°.

o-*Toluidide* : m.p. 78°.
p-*Toluidide* : cryst. from EtOH. M.p. 80°.

Moses, Reid, *J. Am. Chem. Soc.*, 1932, **54**, 2101.
Asano, *Chem. Abstracts*, 1922, **16**, 1931.
Robertson, *J. Chem. Soc.*, 1919, **115**, 1210.
Levene, West, *J. Biol. Chem.*, 1914, **18**, 464.

Undecyl phenyl Ketone.
See Laurophenone.
Ungernine.
See Tazettine.
Uracil (2 : 6-*Dihydroxypyrimidine*, 2 : 6-*pyrimidinedione*)

$$\begin{array}{ccc} HN_1\!-\!_6CO & & N_1\!=\!_6C\cdot OH \\ OC_2 \quad _5CH & or & HO\cdot C_2 \quad _5CH \\ HN^3\!-\!^4CH & & N^3\!-\!^4CH \end{array}$$

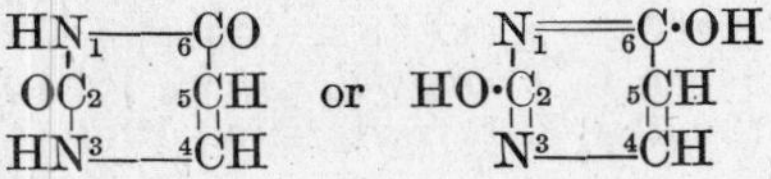

$C_4H_4O_2N_2$ MW, 112

Needles from H_2O. M.p. 335°. Sol. hot H_2O, ammonia. Spar. sol. cold H_2O. Forms K salt.
N-*Me* : *see* Methyluracil.
N-*Di-Me* : *see* Dimethyluracil.
1-N-*Et* : $C_6H_8O_2N_2$. MW, 140. Prisms from C_6H_6. M.p. 173–4°. Sol. hot H_2O, EtOH.
1-N-*Et*-3-N-*Me* : *see* Methylethyluracil.
1 : 3-N-*Di-Et* : $C_8H_{12}O_2N_2$. MW, 168. M.p. 14–15°. B.p. 290–5°, 135°/4 mm.
1-N-*Benzyl* : $C_{11}H_{10}O_2N_2$. MW, 202. Prisms from H_2O. M.p. 175°.
3-N-*Benzyl* : prisms from EtOH. M.p. 173°. Very sol. hot AcOH. Sol. Me_2CO. Spar. sol. H_2O, $CHCl_3$. Insol. Et_2O, cold C_6H_6, dil. min. acids.

Hilbert, Johnson, *J. Am. Chem. Soc.*, 1930, **52**, 2001.
Davidson, Baudisch, *J. Am. Chem. Soc.*, 1926, **48**, 2382.
Gabriel, *Ber.*, 1905, **38**, 1690.

Uracil-4-carboxylic Acid.
See Orotic Acid.
Uradal.
See Adalin.
Uramil (5-*Aminobarbituric acid*)

$$\begin{array}{c} HN_1\!-\!_6CO \\ OC_2 \quad _5CH\cdot NH_2{}^7 \\ HN^3\!-\!^4CO \end{array}$$

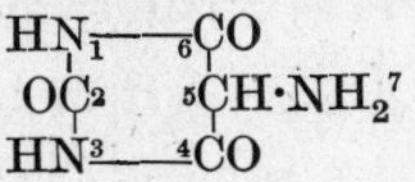

$C_4H_5O_3N_3$ MW, 143

Needles or plates from H_2O. Does not melt below 400°. Mod. sol. hot H_2O. Insol. cold H_2O, Et_2O, $CHCl_3$, CS_2, C_6H_6. Sol. conc. H_2SO_4, dil. aq. KOH, NH_3. Darkens in air.

Forms Na, K, Ba, Pb salts. Pb salt spar. sol. H_2O.
1 : 3-N-*Di-Me* : $C_6H_9O_3N_3$. MW, 171. Needles. M.p. about 200° decomp. Turns red in air. Spar. sol. cold H_2O. Insol. EtOH. Sol. dil. acids. Reduces $AgNO_3$ and Fehling's. Decomp. by alkalis.
1 : 3 : 7-N-*Tri-Me* : $C_7H_{11}O_3N_3$. MW, 185. Needles from H_2O or EtOH. M.p. about 200° decomp. Sol. hot H_2O. Spar. sol. EtOH. Reduces $AgNO_3$.
1 : 3 : 7 : 7-N-*Tetra-Me* : $C_8H_{13}O_3N_3$. MW, 199. Cryst. from EtOH. M.p. 230–2° decomp. Mod. sol. H_2O. Spar. sol. MeOH, EtOH. Very spar. sol. Et_2O, C_6H_6. *Monohydrate* : needles from H_2O. M.p. 225° decomp.
7-N-*Et* : $C_6H_9O_3N_3$. MW, 171. Needles from H_2O. M.p. 297° decomp. Sol. hot H_2O.
1 : 3-N-*Di-Et* : $C_8H_{13}O_3N_3$. MW, 199. Cryst. M.p. about 200° decomp. Spar. sol. H_2O, EtOH, Et_2O, Me_2CO, C_6H_6. Sols decompose on heating.
1 : 3-N-*Diphenyl* : $C_{16}H_{13}O_3N_3$. MW, 295. Needles from EtOH. M.p. 97°. Decomp. in air, becoming red.
7-N-*Benzyl* : $C_{11}H_{11}O_3N_3$. MW, 233. Needles from AcOH. Decomp. about 280°.

Hartmann, Sheppard, *Organic Syntheses*, 1932, XII, 84.

p-Urazine (*Dicarbamide*, *diurea*)

$$\begin{array}{c} CO \\ HN \quad NH \\ HN \quad NH \\ CO \end{array}$$

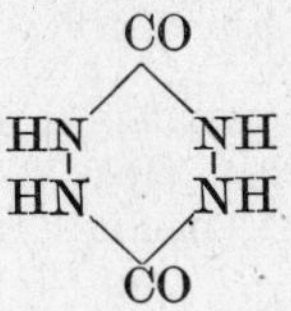

$C_2H_4O_2N_4$ MW, 116

Prisms from H_2O. M.p. about 270° (266°). Spar. sol. EtOH, AcOH, hot H_2O. Reduces $NH_3.AgNO_3$. $FeCl_3 \longrightarrow$ red col. $H_2SO_4 +$ $HNO_3 \longrightarrow$ violet-red col. Acts as monobasic acid.
Hydrazine salt : prisms. M.p. 197°.
N-*Acetyl* : plates. Decomp. at 235°.

Purgotti, Viganò, *Gazz. chim. ital.*, 1901, **31**, ii, 550.
Linch, *J. Chem. Soc.*, 1912, **101**, 1756.

Urazole (3 : 5-*Diketodihydro*-1 : 2 : 4-*triazole*, *hydrazodicarbonimide*, 3 : 5-*diketopyrazolidine*)

$$\begin{array}{c} HN\!-\!-\!NH \\ OC \quad CO \\ NH \end{array}$$

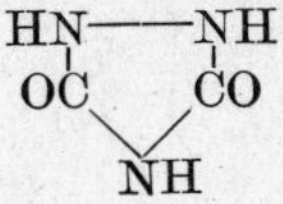

$C_2H_3O_2N_3$ MW, 101

Plates from H_2O. M.p. 244° decomp. Very sol. H_2O. Spar. sol. EtOH. Insol. Et_2O. Reacts acid.

Acetyl deriv.: cryst. from H_2O. M.p. 221·5°.

Diacetyl deriv.: plates from EtOH. M.p. 206°.

Triacetyl deriv.: prisms from C_6H_6. M.p. 138°.

Stollé, Krauch, *J. prakt. Chem.*, 1913, **88**, 314.

Thiele, Stange, *Ann.*, 1894, **283**, 41.

Urea (*Carbamide, isourea*)

$NH_2{\cdot}CO{\cdot}NH_2$ or $NH_2{\cdot}C(OH){:}NH$ Iso-.

CH_4ON_2 MW, 60

Constituent of blood and tissue fluids of all vertebrates and of the urine of all mammals. Also occurs in many invertebrates, Nematodes, Crustaceans, Molluscs, etc., and in many fungi and moulds. Prisms with faint salty taste from H_2O or EtOH. M.p. 132°. Sol. MeOH, EtOH. Insol. Et_2O, $CHCl_3$, C_6H_6. Sol. 1 part H_2O at 17° $\longrightarrow$ neutral sol. Sublimes without decomp. in cathode-ray vacuum. Heat above m.p. $\longrightarrow$ cyanuric acid: at 150–70° $\longrightarrow$ biuret: at 200° $\longrightarrow$ triureide of cyanuric acid. Cold aq. alkalis $\longrightarrow$ NH_3. Hot dil. acids or alkalis $\longrightarrow$ $CO_2 + NH_3$. *p*-Dimethylaminobenzaldehyde + HCl (Ehrlich's reagent) $\longrightarrow$ intense yellow col. After heating $\longrightarrow$ biuret reaction with NaOH and $CuSO_4$. HNO_2 or alk. NaOBr $\longrightarrow$ evolution of N.

B,HCl: plates. Decomp. at 145°.

B,HNO₃: prisms. M.p. 152° decomp.

N : N'-*Diacetyl*: needles from EtOH. M.p. 152–3°.

N : N'-*Dibenzoyl*: needles from EtOH. M.p. 218–22° decomp.

N-*Dibenzoyl*: needles from EtOH. M.p. 197°.

N-*Tri-Me*: $C_4H_{10}ON_2$. MW, 102. Prisms from Et_2O. M.p. 75·5°. B.p. 232·5°/764·5 mm. Very sol. H_2O, EtOH.

N-*Tetra-Me*: $C_5H_{12}ON_2$. MW, 116. B.p. 177·5°/766 mm. Very sol. EtOH, Et_2O.

N-*Tri-Et*: $C_7H_{16}ON_2$. MW, 144. Prisms from pet. ether. M.p. 65°. B.p. 223° (235°).

N-*Tetra-Et*: $C_9H_{20}ON_2$. MW, 172. Liq. with peppermint odour. B.p. 210–15° (205°). Sol. acids, re-ppd. by alkalis. Insol. H_2O.

N-*Triphenyl*: $C_{19}H_{16}ON_2$. MW, 288. Plates. M.p. 136°.

N-*Tetraphenyl*: $C_{25}H_{20}ON_2$. MW, 364. Cryst. from C_6H_6. M.p. 183°. Sol. EtOH.

O-*Me*: $C_2H_6ON_2$. MW, 74. M.p. 44–5°. B.p. 82°/9 mm. $k = 6{\cdot}4 \times 10^{-5}$ at 25°. Volatile in vapours of EtOH, Et_2O. *B,HCl*: m.p. 130° decomp. *B_2,H_2PtCl_6*: m.p. 178° decomp. *Picrate*: m.p. 184° decomp. N-*Acetyl*: cryst. from pet. ether. M.p. 58·5°. N-*Benzoyl*: prisms from MeOH.Aq. M.p. 77–8°.

O-*Et*: $C_3H_8ON_2$. MW, 88. M.p. 42°. B.p. 95–6°/15 mm. Sol. Et_2O. $k = 10{\cdot}4 \times 10^{-5}$ at 25°. *B,HCl*: m.p. 123–4° decomp. *B_2,H_2PtCl_6*: yellow plates from EtOH. M.p. 178·5° decomp. N-*Benzoyl*: cryst. from EtOH.Aq. M.p. 74–5°.

Other urea derivatives are given separately elsewhere.

Foss, *L'Urée* (Paris, 1928).

Werner, *The Chemistry of Urea*, (Monographs on Biochemistry, London, 1923).

Michler, Escherich, *Ber.*, 1879, **12**, 1164.

Wallach, *Ann.*, 1882, **214**, 275.

Schenck, *Z. physiol. Chem.*, 1912, **77**, 383.

Reudler, *Rec. trav. chim.*, 1914, **33**, 64.

Urea chloride.

See under Carbamic Acid.

Ureidoacetic Acid.

See Hydantoic Acid.

5-Ureidobarbituric Acid.

See ψ-Uric Acid.

Ureidoethyl Alcohol.

See *N*-2-Hydroxyethylurea.

Ureidoformamide.

See Biuret.

Ureidoformic Acid.

See Allophanic Acid.

Ureidophenylacetic Acid.

See 1-Phenylhydantoic Acid.

1-Ureidopropionic Acid (N-*Carbamyl-α-alanine*, N-*carbamyl*-1-*aminopropionic acid*)

$$NH_2{\cdot}CO{\cdot}NH{\cdot}\underset{}{\overset{CH_3}{\overset{|}{C}}}H{\cdot}COOH$$

$C_4H_8O_3N_2$ MW, 132

l-.

Prisms from H_2O. M.p. 198–200°. Sol. 70 parts cold H_2O. $[\alpha]_D^{20} - 9{\cdot}6°$ in H_2O. Hot dil. HCl $\longrightarrow$ *l*-5-methylhydantoin.

dl-.

Prisms, needles or plates from H_2O, plates from EtOH. M.p. 185° (161° decomp.). Sol. 100 parts EtOH at 20° and 46 parts H_2O at 20°. Insol. Et_2O. Heat at 140° or with dil. HCl $\longrightarrow$ 5-methylhydantoin.

K salt: needles + $1H_2O$. Decomp. at 200–5°.

Dakin, *J. Chem. Soc.*, 1915, **107**, 439.

2-Ureidopropionic Acid (N-*Carbamyl*-2-*aminopropionic acid*)

$$NH_2{\cdot}CO{\cdot}NH{\cdot}CH_2{\cdot}CH_2{\cdot}COOH$$

$C_4H_8O_3N_2$ MW, 132

Cryst. M.p. 170–1° decomp. Sol. H_2O. Spar. sol. most org. solvents. Heat at 160–70° or with dil. HCl ⟶ 2 : 4-diketohexahydropyrimidine.

K salt: cryst. Sinters at 80°, m.p. 100°.

Lengfeld, Stieglitz, *Am. Chem. J.*, 1893, **15**, 516.

Urethane (*Ethyl carbamate, aminoformic acid ethyl ester*)

$NH_2 \cdot CO \cdot OC_2H_5$

$C_3H_7O_2N$ MW, 89

Prisms from C_6H_6 or toluene. M.p. 49–50°. B.p. 184°. Very sol. H_2O, EtOH, Et_2O, $CHCl_3$, C_6H_6. Spar. sol. ligroin. Heat aq. sol. to 130° ⟶ urea. Heat with NaOH ⟶ NaCNO + Na_2CO_3 + C_2H_5OH.

N-*Nitroso*: $C_3H_6O_3N_2$. MW, 118. Yellow needles from ligroin. M.p. 51–2° decomp. Very sol. MeOH, EtOH, Et_2O, Me_2CO. Sol. H_2O. Spar. sol. ligroin.

N-*Chloroacetyl*: cryst. from EtOH. M.p. 129°.

N-*Bromoacetyl*: cryst. from EtOH. M.p. 119°.

N-*Dichloroacetyl*: needles from H_2O. M.p. 98°.

N-p-*Nitrobenzoyl*: cryst. from C_6H_6. M.p. 152°.

Basterfield, Greig, *Chem. Zentr.*, 1933, II, 1021.

Basterfield, Woods, Wright, *J. Am. Chem. Soc.*, 1926, **48**, 2371.

Guerci, *Chem. Abstracts*, 1922, **16**, 2481.

Urethylan.

Methyl carbamate. *See under* Carbamic Acid.

Uretropine (*Phenylcarbamic tropine ester, anilinoformyltropein*)

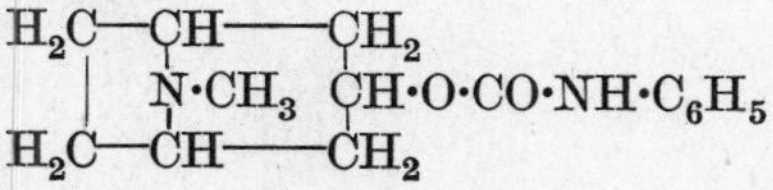

$C_{15}H_{20}O_2N_2$ MW, 260.

Prisms from Et_2O. M.p. 171–2°. Very sol. EtOH, Et_2O. Spar. sol. cold C_6H_6. Has mydriatic action.

B,HCl: prisms from EtOH.Aq. M.p. 289–90°.

B_2,H_2SO_4: needles + $4H_2O$ from H_2O. M.p. 201° decomp.

B,HAuCl$_4$: orange-red cryst. powder. M.p. 188–9°.

Picrate: yellow prisms from EtOH.Aq. M.p. 223–4°.

Jowett, Pyman, *J. Chem. Soc.*, 1909, **95**, 1027.

Uric Acid (2 : 6 : 8-*Trihydroxypurine*)

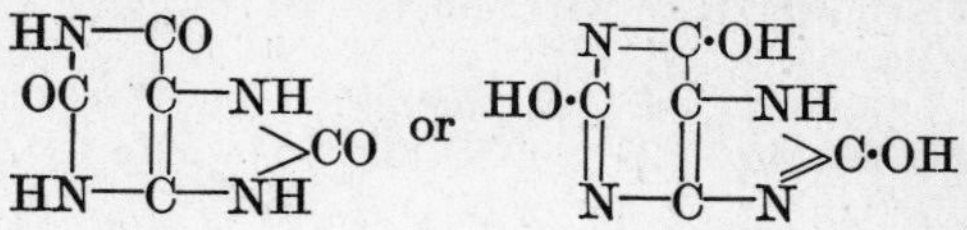

$C_5H_4O_3N_4$ MW, 168

Chief end-product of purine metabolism in man. Constituent of urine of animals, excrement of birds, reptiles, insects, etc. Rhombic prisms or plates. Insol. EtOH, Et_2O. Very spar. sol. H_2O. Sol. glycerol. Spar. sol. min. acids. Readily sol. alkalis. Heat ⟶ urea, cyanuric acid, HCN and NH_3. KOH fusion ⟶ KCN, KCNO, K_2CO_3 and $(COOK)_2$. HNO_3 ⟶ alloxan + urea. $KMnO_4$ ⟶ allantoin. Acts as weak dibasic acid. In alk. sol. reduces Ag and Cu salts, phosphomolybdates and phosphotungstates. Gives murexide reaction.

Traube, *Ber.*, 1900, **33**, 1371, 3035.

Fischer, *Ber.*, 1897, **30**, 559.

ψ-Uric Acid (5-*Ureidobarbituric acid*)

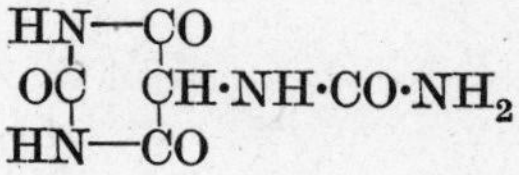

$C_5H_6O_4N_4$ MW, 186

Prisms. Spar. sol. H_2O. Sol. aq. alkalis. Heat of comb. C_v 455·2 Cal. HNO_3 ⟶ alloxan + urea. Alk. $KMnO_4$ ⟶ alloxanic acid. Heat with oxalic acid or with hot dil. HCl ⟶ uric acid.

Biltz, *Ann.*, 1921, **423**, 119.

Fischer, *Ber.*, 1897, **30**, 570, 3091.

Uridine

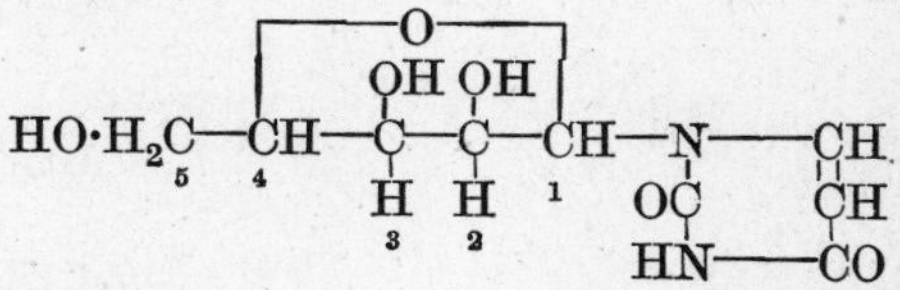

$C_9H_{12}O_6N_2$ MW, 244

Needles from EtOH.Aq. M.p. 165°. $[\alpha]_D^{20}$ + 4·0° in H_2O.

5-*Phosphate*: prisms from MeOH. M.p. 198·5°. $[\alpha]_D^{20}$ + 9·5° in H_2O.

N-*Me*: $C_{10}H_{14}O_6N_2$. MW, 258. Plates. M.p. 108–10°. Sol. MeOH, EtOH, Me_2CO, AcOH, H_2O, Py. Insol. Et_2O, C_6H_6.

2 : 3-*Di-Me ether*: $C_{11}H_{16}O_6N_2$. MW, 272.

Cryst. from AcOEt. M.p. 168–9°. Sol. H_2O, EtOH, MeOH, AcOH, Me_2CO, Py. $[\alpha]_D^{24} + 68{\cdot}0°$ in Me_2CO.

2 : 3-*Di*-p-*toluenesulphonyl* : needles from EtOH. M.p. 199°. $[\alpha]_D^{23} - 26{\cdot}6°$ in Me_2CO.

Levene, Tipson, *J. Biol. Chem.*, 1934, **104**, 385; **105**, 419.
Levene, Jacobs, *Ber.*, 1910, **43**, 3158.

Urobilin (*Stereobilin*)

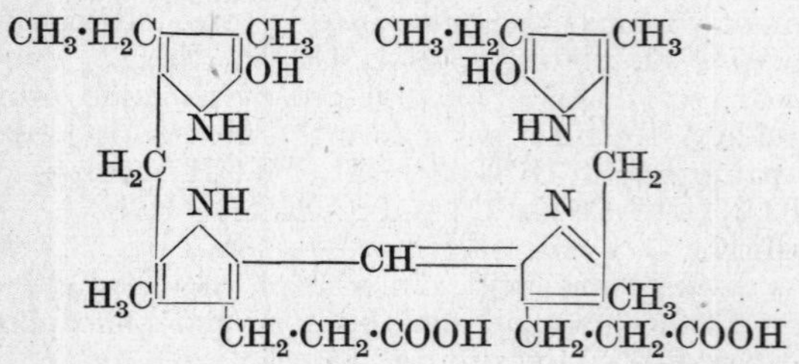

$C_{33}H_{24}O_6N_4$ MW, 572

Also known as Urobilin IX-α. Constituent of urine and fæces. Yellow needles from $CHCl_3$ or MeCO. M.p. 177°. Very sol. MeOH, EtOH, AcOH, Py. Sol. Me_2CO, $CHCl_3$. Spar. sol. H_2O, Et_2O, AcOEt, C_6H_6. Insol. CCl_4, pet. ether. Very sol. amyl alcohol with green fluor. Very sol. conc. HCl and conc. $H_2SO_4 \longrightarrow$ red sols.

B,HCl : prisms from Me_2CO, m.p. 199–200° : prisms from $CHCl_3$, m.p. 147–71°.

B,HBr : prisms from Me_2CO. M.p. 200–1°.

Siedel, Meier, *Z. physiol. Chem.*, 1936, **242**, 101.
Heilmeyer, Krebs, *Z. physiol. Chem.*, 1934, **228**, 33, 46.

Urotropine.
See Hexamethylenetetramine.

Uroxanic Acid (*Diureidomalonic acid*)

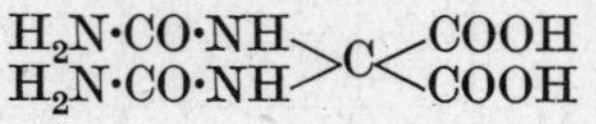

$C_5H_8O_6N_4$ MW, 220

Needles from C_6H_6. Decomp. at 162°. Sol. H_2O, EtOH, Et_2O. Spar. sol. C_6H_6. Insol. pet. ether. Loses CO_2 in H_2O at 60°. Ag salt spar. sol. H_2O.

NH_4 salt : prisms. Decomp. at 182°.

Di-Et ester : $C_9H_{16}O_6N_4$. MW, 276. Cryst. from EtOH. M.p. 170°.

Biltz, Robl, *Ber.*, 1920, **53**, 1950.

Ursol P.
See p-Aminophenol.

Ursolic Acid (*Ursone, prunol, malol, malolic acid*)

$C_{30}H_{48}O_3$ MW, 456

Constituent of leaves and skins of apples and pears, leaves of *Rhododendron hymenanthes*, leaves of *Epigaea asiatica*, Maxim, etc. Prisms from Et_2O. M.p. 285° (291°). Sol. hot AcOH, EtOH. Mod. sol. Et_2O, AcOH, Me_2CO, AcOEt, $CHCl_3$. Insol. H_2O, pet. ether. Liebermann-Salkowski reagent $\longrightarrow$ blue col.

Me ester : $C_{31}H_{50}O_3$. MW, 470. Two forms. (i) Cryst. from EtOH.Aq. M.p. 170·5–171·5° (173°). Sol. cold Me_2CO. (ii) M.p. 230°. Insol. cold Me_2CO. *Benzoyl* : m.p. 215–16°. *Acetyl* : m.p. 246–7°.

Phenacyl ester : m.p. 199–200°.

Drake, Duvall, *J. Am. Chem. Soc.*, 1936, **58**, 1687.
Fujii, Shimada, *J. Pharm. Soc. Japan*, 1935, **55**, 106.
Kuwada, Matsumoto, *Chem. Abstracts*, 1933, **27**, 3925.
Sando, *J. Biol. Chem.*, 1931, **90**, **477**; 1923, **56**, 457.
Haar, *Rec. trav. chim.*, 1924, **43**, 542.
Kuwada, Matsukawa, *Chem. Abstracts*, 1934, **28**, 4739.

Ursone.
See Ursolic acid.

Usnic Acid

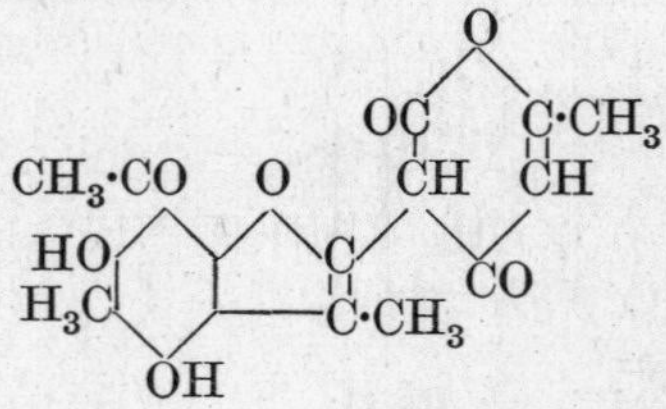

$C_{18}H_{16}O_7$ MW, 344

d-.

Occurs in various species of lichen. Constituent of Chinese drug "Shi-koa." Cryst. from MeOH or C_6H_6. M.p. 202–4° (195–6°). Very sol. $CHCl_3$. Sol. EtOH, Et_2O. Insol. H_2O. $[\alpha]_D^{19} + 508{\cdot}3°$.

Diacetyl : needles from MeOH. M.p. 199–200°. $[\alpha]_D^{16} + 205°$. $FeCl_3 \longrightarrow$ red col.

l-.

M.p. 195–7°. Very sol. $CHCl_3$. Sol. EtOH, Et_2O. Insol. H_2O. $[\alpha]_D^{20} - 495°$.

dl-.
M.p. 193–4°. $FeCl_3 \longrightarrow$ brown col.
Diacetyl : m.p. 199–200°.

Curd, Robertson, *J. Chem. Soc.*, 1937, **894**.
Asahina, Yanagita, *Ber.*, 1937, **70**, 66; 1936, **69**, 1646.
Shöpf, Kraus, Heuck, *Ann.*, 1927, **459**, 263.
Nakao, *Chem. Abstracts*, 1923, **17**, 3184.

Uvaleral.
See 1-Bromoisovalerylurea.
Uvinic Acid.
See Pyrotritaric Acid.
Uvitic Acid.
See 5-Methylisophthalic Acid.

Uvitonic Acid (*α-Picoline*-4 : 6-*dicarboxylic acid*, 6-*methyl-lutidinic acid*)

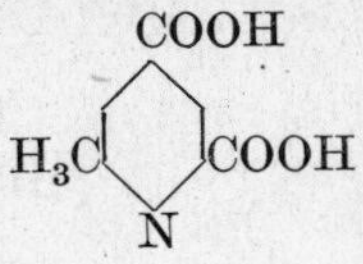

$C_8H_7O_4N$ MW, 181

Cryst. from H_2O. M.p. 282° decomp. Sol. hot AcOH, phenol, aniline. Sol. conc. H_2SO_4, HCl, NH_4OH. Spar. sol. hot $CHCl_3$, amyl alcohol. Very spar. sol. cold H_2O. Insol. CS_2, C_6H_6.

Böttinger, *Ber.*, 1880, **13**, 2032.

V

Vacciniin (6-*Benzoyl*-d-*glucose*)

$\overline{CH(OH)\cdot[CH(OH)]_3\cdot CH}\cdot CH_2O\cdot CO\cdot C_6H_5$ (ring closed through O)

$C_{13}H_{16}O_7$ MW, 284

Amorph. hygroscopic mass with bitter taste. Cryst. from Me_2CO as monohydrate. M.p. 104–6°. Sol. H_2O, MeOH, EtOH, AcOEt, Me_2CO, Py. Spar. sol. $CHCl_3$, C_6H_6. Insol. Et_2O, pet. ether. $[\alpha]_D^{21}$ + 48° in EtOH, $[\alpha]_D^{21}$ (hydrate) + 45·76° in H_2O (after 10 minutes). Reduces Fehling's.

Phenylhydrazone : yellow cryst. from EtOH.Aq. M.p. 146–7° (136°).

Phenylosazone : yellow needles from EtOH.Aq. M.p. 141°.

1 : 2 : 3 : 4-*Tetra-acetyl* : cryst. from EtOH. M.p. 136°.

Brigl, Zerrweck, *Z. physiol. Chem.*, 1934, **229**, 117.
Ohle, *Biochem. Z.*, 1922, **131**, 611.
Fischer, Noth, *Ber.*, 1918, **51**, 326.

***n*-Valeraldehyde** (*Pentanal, valeric aldehyde*)

$CH_3\cdot CH_2\cdot CH_2\cdot CH_2\cdot CHO$

$C_5H_{10}O$ MW, 86

Liq. B.p. 102·5–103·0°. D_4^{20} 0·80952. n_D^{20} 1·39436.

Di-Et acetal : $C_9H_{20}O_2$. MW, 160. B.p. 59°/12 mm. D^{22} 0·829. n_D^{22} 1·4029.

Oxime : m.p. 52°.

Thiosemicarbazone : cryst. from EtOH.Aq., or Et_2O. M.p. 65°.

Phenylsemicarbazone : m.p. 126–7°.

2 : 4-*Dinitrophenylhydrazone* : yellow cryst. M.p. 98°.

o-*Tolylsemicarbazone* : m.p. 131–2°.

p-*Tolylsemicarbazone* : m.p. 157–8°.

Lieben, Rossi, *Ann.*, 1871, **159**, 70.
Bruylants, Ernould, *Chem. Abstracts*, 1932, **26**, 3232.
Blaise, *Compt. rend.*, 1904, **138**, 698.

***n*-Valeric Acid** (*Valereanic acid, butane*-1-*carboxylic acid, propylacetic acid*)

$CH_3\cdot CH_2\cdot CH_2\cdot CH_2\cdot COOH$

$C_5H_{10}O_2$ MW, 102

Liq. with unpleasant odour. M.p. — 34·5°. B.p. 186·35°, 96°/23 mm., 86–8°/15 mm. Sol. 27 parts H_2O at 16°. D_4^{20} 0·9387. n_α^{19} 1·4070. Heat of comb. 681·8 Cal. $k = 1{\cdot}56 \times 10^{-5}$ at 25°.

Me ester : $C_6H_{12}O_2$. MW, 116. B.p. 127·3°. D^0 0·9097.

Et ester : $C_7H_{14}O_2$. MW, 130. B.p. 144·6°/736·5 mm. D^{20} 0·8765.

Propyl ester : $C_8H_{16}O_2$. MW, 144. B.p. 167·5°. D^0 0·8888.

n-*Butyl ester* : $C_9H_{18}O_2$. MW, 158. B.p. 185·8°. D^0 0·8847.

d-sec.-*Butyl ester* : B.p. 67°/18 mm. D_4^{13} 0·8650. n_D^{20} 1·4070. $[\alpha]_D^{20}$ + 20·72°.

n-*Amyl ester* : $C_{10}H_{20}O_2$. MW, 172. B.p. 204°. D^0 0·881.

Isoamyl ester : b.p. 187–90°.

d-sec.-n-*Amyl ester* : b.p. 86°/16 mm. D_4^{17} 0·8631. n_D^{20} 1·4115. $[\alpha]_D^{20}$ + 16·01°.

l-*Menthyl ester*: $C_{15}H_{28}O_2$. MW, 240. B.p. 141°/15 mm. D_4^{20} 0·9074. $[\alpha]_D^{20}$ − 65·55°.

Chloride: C_5H_9OCl. MW, 120·5. B.p. 107–10°/756 mm. D^{15} 1·0155.

Bromide: C_5H_9OBr. MW, 165. B.p. 64°/66 mm.

Amide: *n*-valeramide. $C_5H_{11}ON$. MW, 101. Plates from EtOH. M.p. 106°. Very sol. H_2O, EtOH, Et_2O.

Imide: $C_{10}H_{19}O_2N$. MW, 185. Cryst. M.p. 100°. Very sol. Et_2O. Mod. sol. hot EtOH.

Anhydride: $C_{10}H_{18}O_3$. MW, 186. B.p. 218°/754 mm., 110–11°/15 mm. D_4^{17} 0·9223.

Nitrile: *n*-valeronitrile. C_5H_9N. MW, 83. B.p. 141·1–141·2°/764·7 mm. D_4^{15} 0·80348. n_D^{15} 1·39913.

Anilide: *n*-valeranilide. Prisms from EtOH, cryst. from pet. ether. M.p. 63°.

p-*Bromoanilide*: m.p. 108°.

p-*Toluidide*: cryst. from EtOH. Plates from pet. ether. M.p. 74°.

1-*Naphthalide*: cryst. from EtOH. M.p. 112°.

Ivanoff, *Bull. soc. chim.*, 1925, **37**, 293.
Gilman, Kirby, *Organic Syntheses*, Collective Vol. I, 355.
Wolff, *Ann.*, 1881, **208**, 110.

Valerolactam.
See α-Piperidone.

Valerolactinic Acid.
See 1-Hydroxy-*n*-valeric Acid.

γ-Valerolactone (3-*Methylbutyrolactone*, 3-*valerolactone*)

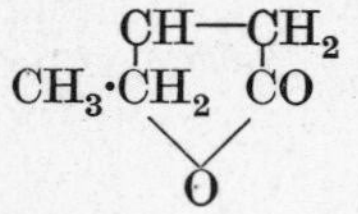

$C_5H_8O_2$ MW, 100

dl-.

Constituent of crude pyroligneous acid. F.p. − 31° to leaflets. B.p. 205–7°, 102–3°/28 mm., 83–4°/13 mm., 78°/4 mm. Misc. in all proportions with H_2O. D^{25} 1·0465. n_D^{25} 1·4303. HI(+ P) ⟶ *n*-valeric acid. HCl ⟶ 3-chloro-*n*-valeric acid. Hyd. by $Ba(OH)_2$, slowly by H_2O. NH_3 ⟶ 3-hydroxy-*n*-valeramide.

d-.

B.p. 86–90°/14 mm. $[\alpha]_D^{20}$ + 13·5°.

Pummerer, Guyot, Birkofer, *Ber.*, 1935, **68**, 490.
Schuette, Thomas, *J. Am. Chem. Soc.*, 1930, **52**, 3011.
Levene, Haller, Walti, *J. Biol. Chem.*, 1927, **72**, 591.
Losanitsch, *Monatsh.*, 1914, **35**, 302, 311.
Boorman, Linstead, *J. Chem. Soc.*, 1933, 578.

δ-Valerolactone (4-*Valerolactone*, *tetrahydro-α-pyrone*, *tetrahydrocoumalin*)

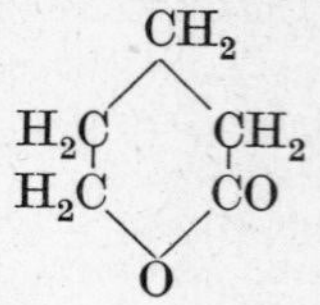

$C_5H_8O_2$ MW, 100

Oil. Solidifies on cooling. M.p. − 12·5°. B.p. 218–20°, 113–14°/13–14 mm., 88°/4 mm. Misc. with EtOH, Et_2O. Spar. misc. with H_2O. D_4^{20} 1·0794. n_D^{20} 1·4503. Readily polymerises on standing to several high MW polymers. $Ba(OH)_2$ ⟶ Ba salt of 4-hydroxy-*n*-valeric acid. HBr ⟶ 4-bromo-*n*-valeric acid.

Coffmann, *J. Am. Chem. Soc.*, 1935, **57**, 1984.
Linstead, Rydon, *J. Chem. Soc.*, 1933, 583.
Fichter, Beisswenger, *Ber.*, 1903, **36**, 1200.

Valerone.
See Di-isobutyl Ketone.

Valerophenone (n-*Butyl phenyl ketone*)

$$C_6H_5{\cdot}CO{\cdot}CH_2{\cdot}CH_2{\cdot}CH_2{\cdot}CH_3$$

$C_{11}H_{14}O$ MW, 162

Liq. B.p. 235–42°, 135–40°/25 mm. D_{20}^{20} 0·988. n_D^{20} 1·532.

Oxime: needles from EtOH.Aq. or pet. ether. M.p. 52·0–52·5°. B.p. 163–5°/13 mm. Sol. EtOH, C_6H_6. Spar. sol. pet. ether.

Semicarbazone: needles from EtOH. M.p. 166° (157–157·5°).

Shriner, Turner, *J. Am. Chem. Soc.*, 1930, **52**, 1269.
Pfeiffer, Oberlin, *J. prakt. Chem.*, 1924, **108**, 347.

***n*-Valerylacetic Acid.**
See 2-Keto-*n*-heptylic Acid.

Valerylanisole.
See under *p*-Hydroxyvalerophenone.

Valerylcarbinol.
See 1-Hexanolone-2.

Valerylphenetole.
See under *p*-Hydroxyvalerophenone.

***p*-Valerylphenol.**
See *p*-Hydroxyvalerophenone.

2-*n*-Valerylpropionic Acid.
See 3-Keto-*n*-caprylic Acid.

Validol.
See under Menthol.

Valine (1-*Aminoisovaleric acid*)

$(CH_3)_2CH{\cdot}CH(NH_2){\cdot}COOH$

$C_5H_{11}O_2N$ MW, 117

d-.

Plates from EtOH.Aq. M.p. 156–157·5° (293° decomp., sealed tube). Sol. 18·4 parts H_2O at 20°. $[\alpha]_D^{20}$ − 29·04° in 20% HCl, $[\alpha]_D^{25}$ − 39·1° in Me_2CO.

Et ester: $C_7H_{15}O_2N$. MW, 145. N-p-*Nitrobenzoyl*: cryst. from ligroin. M.p. 88°. $[\alpha]_D^{20}$ − 3·5° in EtOH.

N-*Formyl*: prisms from hot H_2O. Sinters at 150°, m.p. 156°. $[\alpha]_D^{20}$ − 13·07° in EtOH, + 16·9° in H_2O.

l-.

Occurs in pancreas of oxen, in yellow boletus, in seeds of *Lupinus luteus* L., *Vicia sativa* L., *Lupinus angustifolius* L., etc. Plates from EtOH.Aq. M.p. 93–6° (315°, sealed tube). Sol. H_2O. Spar. sol. EtOH. $[\alpha]_D^{20}$ + 6·42° in H_2O, $[\alpha]_{5461}^{21}$ + 32·77° in HCl. $Ba(OH)_2$.Aq. at 180° ⟶ *dl*-form.

Et ester: b.p. 63·5°/8 mm. N-*Acetyl*: viscous liq. B.p. 158°/21 mm. Cryst. in plates on standing. D_4^{18} 1·028. n_D^{18} 1·4517. $[\alpha]_{5461}^{18}$ − 20·1°. N-*Benzoyl*: needles from pet. ether. M.p. 82°. $[\alpha]_D^{20}$ − 3·44° in EtOH. N-p-*Nitrobenzoyl*: needles from pet. ether. M.p. 88°. $[\alpha]_D^{20}$ + 4·12° in EtOH. N-*Benzenesulphonyl*: cryst. from pet. ether. M.p. 56°. $[\alpha]_D^{20}$ − 1·04° in EtOH. N-p-*Toluenesulphonyl*: cryst. from pet. ether. M.p. 59°. $[\alpha]_D^{20}$ + 3·99° in EtOH.

N-*Formyl*: prisms from hot H_2O. Sinters at 150°, m.p. 156°. $[\alpha]_D^{20}$ + 13·07° in EtOH.

N-*Benzoyl*: needles from H_2O. M.p. 127°. $[\alpha]_D^{20}$ + 17·18°.

N-*Benzenesulphonyl*: needles from EtOH.Aq. M.p. 153°. $[\alpha]_D^{20}$ + 19·5° in EtOH.

N-p-*Toluenesulphonyl*: needles from EtOH.Aq. M.p. 147°. $[\alpha]_D^{20}$ + 25·0° in EtOH.

Picrolonate: m.p. 170–80°.

dl-.

Plates from EtOH. Sublimes. M.p. about 298° decomp., (sealed tube). Sol. 11·7 parts H_2O at 15°. Insol. cold EtOH, Et_2O. Cu and Ag salts spar. sol. H_2O.

B,HCl: cryst. from hot H_2O, leaflets from dil. HCl. M.p. 189°.

Et ester: b.p. 174° part. decomp., 82·5°/23 mm., 63·5°/8 mm. D_4^{15} 0·9617. Very sol. H_2O. *B,HCl*: hygroscopic cryst. M.p. 76°. N-*Acetyl*: b.p. 99°/2 mm. *Picrate*: cryst. M.p. 139·5°.

Butyl ester: $C_9H_{19}O_2N$. MW, 173. Syrup. B.p. 98–98·5°/17 mm. D^{14} 0·9266. Sol. H_2O, EtOH, Et_2O, $CHCl_3$. *B,HCl*: needles from AcOEt. M.p. 59–60°. *Picrate*: yellow needles. M.p. 91–2°.

Amide: $C_5H_{12}ON_2$. MW, 116. Prisms from C_6H_6. M.p. 78–80°. Very sol. H_2O, EtOH, AcOEt, hot C_6H_6. Spar. sol. Et_2O, ligroin. Alk. Cu sol. ⟶ violet col. *B,HBr*: cryst. Decomp. at 200°.

Anhydride: $C_{10}H_{20}O_3N_2$. MW, 216. Does not melt below 300°.

Nitrile: $C_5H_{10}N_2$. MW, 98. Unstable yellow oil. Very sol. H_2O, EtOH, Et_2O.

N-*Me*: $C_6H_{13}O_2N$. MW, 131. Powder. Very sol. H_2O. Spar. sol. hot EtOH. Insol. Et_2O. Sublimes.

N-*Formyl*: plates from H_2O. Sinters at 137°, m.p. 140–5°.

N-*Benzoyl*: m.p. 132·5°.

N-p-*Toluenesulphonyl*: m.p. 110–11°.

Barrow, Ferguson, *J. Chem. Soc.*, 1935, 415.
Holmes, Adams, *J. Am. Chem. Soc.*, 1934, **56**, 2093.
Karrer, Sluys Veer, *Helv. Chim. Acta*, 1932, **15**, 746.
Levene, Bass, Rothen, Steiger, *J. Biol. Chem.*, 1929, **81**, 687.
Abderhalden, Landau, *Z. physiol. Chem.*, 1911, **71**, 458.
Fischer, Scheibler, *Ber.*, 1908, **41**, 2891.
Fischer, *Ber.*, 1906, **39**, 2322.
Slimmer, *Ber.*, 1902, **35**, 401.

Valinol (2-*Aminoisoamyl alcohol*)

$(CH_3)_2CH{\cdot}CH(NH_2){\cdot}CH_2OH$

$C_5H_{13}ON$ MW, 103

d-.

B,HCl: plates from Me_2CO. M.p. 113°. $[\alpha]_{5461}^{20}$ − 16·5° in H_2O.

Dibenzoyl deriv.: needles from EtOH.Aq. M.p. 117°. $[\alpha]_{5461}^{21}$ + 20·2° in Py.

Tribenzoyl: needles. M.p. 119°. $[\alpha]_{5461}^{20}$ − 133·8° in Py.

l-.

B,HCl: plates from Me_2CO. M.p. 112–14°. $[\alpha]_{5461}^{20}$ + 16·4° in H_2O.

Dibenzoyl deriv.: needles. M.p. 117°. $[\alpha]_{5461}^{20}$ − 20·1° in Py.

Tribenzoyl: needles. M.p. 119°. $[\alpha]_{5461}^{19}$ + 133·1° in Py.

dl-.

Oil. B.p. 181–6°/720 mm. Sol. H_2O, EtOH. Mod. sol. Et_2O. Slowly volatile in steam.

B,HCl: plates from Me_2CO. M.p. 118–19°.

N-*Benzoyl* : needles from pet. ether. M.p. 81–2°.
Dibenzoyl deriv. : prisms from Me_2CO.Aq. M.p. 114°.
Tribenzoyl : plates from EtOH.Aq. M.p. 135°.

Barrow, Ferguson, *J. Chem. Soc.*, 1935, 410.
Karrer *et al.*, *Helv. Chim. Acta*, 1922, **5**, 478.

Vanillic Acid (*Protocatechuic acid* 3-*methyl ether*, 4-*hydroxy*-3-*methoxybenzoic acid*)

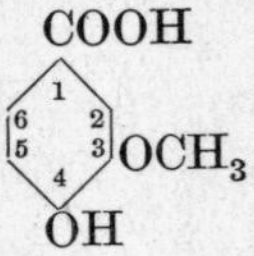

$C_8H_8O_4$ MW, 168

Needles from H_2O. M.p. 210°. Sublimes. Sol. 850 parts H_2O at 14°, 62 parts at 75°, 40 parts at 95°. Sol. Et_2O. Very sol. EtOH. $k = 3{\cdot}0 \times 10^{-5}$ at 25°. Salts all very sol. H_2O. No col. with $FeCl_3$. HCl at 150° or KOH fusion ⟶ protocatechuic acid. Dist. Ca salt + Ca formate ⟶ guaiacol. Loses CO_2 with aniline at 240°.
Me ester : $C_9H_{10}O_4$. MW, 182. Needles from EtOH.Aq. M.p. 62–3°. B.p. 285–7°. *Benzoyl* : needles from MeOH. M.p. 104°.
Et ester : $C_{10}H_{12}O_4$. MW, 196. Needles. M.p. 44°. B.p. 291–3°.
Propyl ester : $C_{11}H_{14}O_4$. MW, 210. M.p. 43°.
Isopropyl ester : m.p. 113·5°.
Butyl ester : $C_{12}H_{16}O_4$. MW, 224. M.p. 48–9°.
p-*Nitrobenzyl ester* : $C_{15}H_{13}O_6N$. MW, 303. Cryst. from EtOH.Aq. M.p. 140–1° decomp.
Chloride : $C_8H_7O_3Cl$. MW, 186·5. *Benzoyl* : needles from pet. ether. M.p. 96–8°.
Nitrile : $C_8H_7O_2N$. MW, 149. Needles from H_2O. M.p. 89–90°. Very sol. hot H_2O, EtOH, Et_2O, C_6H_6. *Acetyl* : needles from H_2O. M.p. 110°.
Me ether : *see* Veratric Acid.
Et ether : 3-methoxy-4-ethoxybenzoic acid. $C_{10}H_{12}O_4$. MW, 196. Needles from H_2O or C_6H_6. M.p. 195–6°. Sublimes. Very sol. EtOH, Et_2O. Spar. sol. hot H_2O, insol. cold.
Acetyl : needles from EtOH.Aq. M.p. 145–6°.
Benzoyl : plates from EtOH.Aq. M.p. 178°.

Sabalitsehka, Tietz, *Chem. Zentr.*, 1932, I, 1110.
Zeltner, Landau, D.R.P., 258,887, (*Chem. Zentr.*, 1913, I, 1641).

Vanillin (*Protocatechuic aldehyde* 3-*methyl ether*, 4-*hydroxy*-3-*methoxybenzaldehyde*)

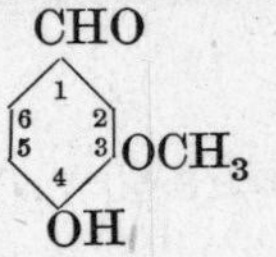

$C_8H_8O_3$ MW, 152

Widely occurring in plant world. Constituent of fruit of *Vanilla planifolia*, etc. Needles with characteristic odour from H_2O or ligroin. M.p. 80–1°. B.p. 170°/15 mm., 140–5°/6 mm. Very sol. EtOH, Et_2O, $CHCl_3$, CS_2, AcOH, Py. Mod. sol. hot ligroin, C_6H_6. Insol. cold ligroin. Sol. 90 parts H_2O at 14°, 20 parts at 75°. Sublimes. Heat of comb. C_p 9147 Cal., C_v 9144 Cal. Reacts in sol. as monobasic acid. Slowly oxidises in moist air ⟶ vanillic acid. KOH fusion ⟶ protocatechuic acid. NaHg or catalytic reduction ⟶ vanillyl alcohol. Electrolytic reduction ⟶ 4-hydroxy-3-methoxytoluene. $FeCl_3$ ⟶ bluish-violet col. Conc. H_2SO_4 + 1-naphthol ⟶ bluish-red col. Conc. H_2SO_4 + 2-naphthol ⟶ emerald-green col. Bromine ⟶ red col. or red ppt. Zn and Mg salts spar. sol. H_2O. Used for flavouring and in perfumery.
Me ether : *see* Veratric Aldehyde.
Et ether : $C_{10}H_{12}O_3$. MW, 180. Prisms. M.p. 64–5°. Sublimes. Sol. EtOH, Et_2O. Spar. sol. hot H_2O.
Propyl ether : $C_{11}H_{14}O_3$. MW, 194. Cryst. from EtOH.Aq. M.p. 59–60°. *Semicarbazone* : needles from EtOH. M.p. 156°.
Isopropyl ether : pale yellow viscous liq. B.p. 150–2°/13 mm. *Semicarbazone* : needles from EtOH. M.p. 151–2°.
2 : 4-*Dinitrophenyl ether* : $C_{14}H_{10}O_7N_2$. MW, 318. Needles from AcOH.Aq. M.p. 131°.
Picryl ether : $C_{14}H_9O_9N_3$. MW, 363. Plates from Et_2O–ligroin. M.p. 114–16°.
Benzyl ether : $C_{15}H_{14}O_3$. MW, 242. Needles or plates from EtOH. M.p. 64–5°.
p-*Nitrobenzyl ether* : $C_{15}H_{13}O_5N$. MW, 287. Cryst. from EtOH.Aq. M.p. 124·5°.
Acetyl : needles from Et_2O. M.p. 102–3°.
Benzoyl : needles from EtOH.Aq. M.p. 78°.
p-*Toluenesulphonyl* : needles from EtOH. M.p. about 115°.
2-*Naphthalenesulphonyl* : m.p. 98°.
Phenylurethane : m.p. 116–17°.
Oxime : plates or needles from H_2O. M.p. 121–2°. Very sol. hot H_2O, EtOH, Et_2O. Insol. C_6H_6, ligroin. *B,HCl* : m.p. 139°. N-*Acetyl* : needles from EtOH.Aq. M.p. 114°. O : N-*Diacetyl* : pale red needles. M.p. 95°.

Azine: yellow prisms from EtOH. M.p. 195–7°, solidifies and remelts at 230–5°.

Anil: slightly yellow needles from EtOH. M.p. 152–3°.

Semicarbazone: needles. M.p. 230°.

Thiosemicarbazone: needles. Sinters at 194°, m.p. 196–7°.

Phenylhydrazone: plates from C_6H_6–ligroin. M.p. 105°.

p-*Bromophenylhydrazone*: yellow plates from EtOH. M.p. 146°.

p-*Nitrophenylhydrazone*: red plates from AcOH. M.p. 227°.

2 : 4-*Dinitrophenylhydrazone*: orange-red micro-prisms from AcOH. M.p. 267–8°.

Mottern, *J. Am. Chem. Soc.*, 1934, **56**, 2107.

Hoffmann-La Roche, E.P., 399,723, (*Chem. Zentr.*, 1934, I, 127), D.R.P., 580,981, (*Chem. Zentr.*, 1933, II, 1763).

Vanillyl Alcohol (4-*Hydroxy*-3-*methoxybenzyl alcohol*)

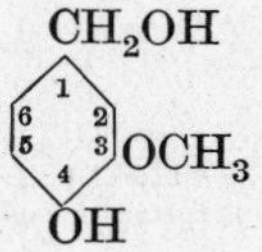

$C_8H_{10}O_3$ MW, 154

Prisms from H_2O. M.p. 115°. Not distillable at ord. press. Sol. warm H_2O, EtOH, Et_2O.

4-*Me ether*: *see* Veratryl Alcohol.

4-*Et ether*: $C_{10}H_{14}O_3$. MW, 182. Needles from EtOH. M.p. 56–7°. B.p. 185–7°/8 mm. Sol. Et_2O, EtOH, AcOEt, C_6H_6. *Allophanate*: m.p. 173°. *Acetyl*: m.p. 22–3°. B.p. 170–3°/13 mm. *Benzoyl*: m.p. 49°.

4-*Acetyl*: m.p. 51°. B.p. 194–6°/13 mm.

Diacetyl: plates from C_6H_6–ligroin. M.p. 48°. B.p. 185°/12 mm.

4-*Benzoyl*: cryst. from AcOEt–EtOH. M.p. 90° (99°).

Dibenzoyl: m.p. 121°.

Goethals, *Chem. Zentr.*, 1937, I, 580.

Carothers, Adams, *J. Am. Chem. Soc.*, 1924, **46**, 1675.

Vavon, *Ann. chim.*, 1914, **1**, 159.

Vanillylamine (4-*Hydroxy*-3-*methoxybenzylamine*)

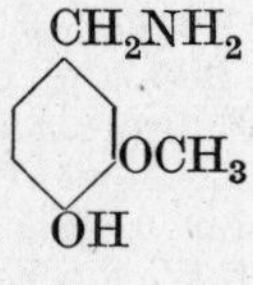

$C_8H_{11}O_2N$ MW, 153

Needles + $2H_2O$. M.p. anhyd. 137° (145–6°). Becomes yellow in daylight. Easily decomp. with boiling H_2O or alkalis.

B,HCl: m.p. 227°.

N-*Acetyl*: cryst. from AcOEt. M.p. 109–109·5°.

N-*Propionyl*: cryst. from C_6H_6. M.p. 111·5°.

N-*Butyryl*: cryst. from C_6H_6. M.p. 75·5 76·5°.

N-*Valeryl*: cryst. from C_6H_6–pet. ether. M.p. 60–60·5°.

Ford-Moore, Phillips, *Rec. trav. chim.*, 1934, **53**, 854.

I.G., D.R.P., 442,774, F.P., 610,830, (*Chem. Zentr.*, 1927, II, 506); U.S.P., 1,873,402, (*Chem. Abstracts*, 1932, **26**, 5965).

Jones, Pyman, *J. Chem. Soc.*, 1925, 2592.

Nelson, *J. Am. Chem. Soc.*, 1919, **41**, 1118.

Varianose

$(C_6H_{10}O_5)_n$ MW, $(162)_n$

White amorph. powder. Mod. sol. H_2O. $[\alpha]_D^{20}$ + 15° in H_2O. Reduces hot Fehling's slightly. Gives no col. with I sol. Hyd. by min. acids ⟶ *d*-galactose (70%) + *d*-glucose (14%) + either *d*-idose or *l*-altrose (14%).

Fully acetylated deriv. ("*triacetyl*"): white powder. M.p. 148–55°. Sol. Me_2CO, $CHCl_3$, hot EtOH. Does not reduce Fehling's. $[\alpha]_D^{20}$ + 30° in $CHCl_3$, + 38·2° in Me_2CO.

Fully methylated deriv. ("*trimethyl*"): white powder. M.p. 90–100°. Sol. cold, insol. hot H_2O. Sol. $CHCl_3$, Me_2CO. $[\alpha]_D^{22}$ + 15° in H_2O, + 20° in $CHCl_3$, + 23° in C_6H_6.

Haworth, Raistrick, Stacey, *Biochem. J.*, 1935, **29**, 2668.

Vasicine.

See Peganine.

Vellosine

$C_{23}H_{28}O_4N_2$ MW, 396

Constituent of bark of *Geissospermum Vellosii*. Prisms from EtOH. M.p. 189°. Sol. common org. solvents. Insol. H_2O. $[\alpha]_D$ + 22·8° in $CHCl_3$.

B,HCl: cryst. + H_2O. M.p. 180° decomp., anhyd. 245–8°.

B,HBr: needles + H_2O. M.p. 194–5°.

B,HI: plates + H_2O from EtOH.Aq. M.p. 217–18°.

B,HNO₃: plates + H_2O from EtOH.Aq. Decomp. at 225°.

B,H₂SO₄: cryst. + H_2O from EtOH.Aq. M.p. 210°.

B_2,H_2PtCl_6 : cryst. M.p. about 80°.
Methiodide : cryst. from H_2O. M.p. 264°.

Freund, Fauvet, *Ann.*, 1894, **282**, 247.

Veratric Acid (*Protocatechuic acid dimethyl ether*, 3 : 4-*dimethoxybenzoic acid*)

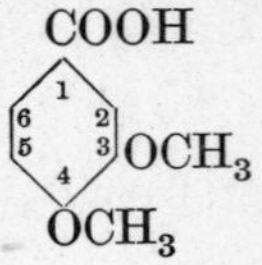

$C_9H_{10}O_4$ MW, 182

Cryst. from H_2O. M.p. anhyd. 181°. Sublimes in rhombic cryst. Sol. 2,100 parts H_2O at 14°, 160 parts at 100°. Very sol. EtOH, Et_2O. $k = 3{\cdot}6 \times 10^{-5}$ at 25°. Ba salt spar. sol. H_2O.

Me ester : $C_{10}H_{12}O_4$. MW, 196. Needles from EtOH.Aq. M.p. 59–60°. B.p. 300° (283°). Sol. EtOH, Et_2O. Spar. sol. H_2O.

Et ester : $C_{11}H_{14}O_4$. MW, 210. Needles from EtOH. M.p. 43–4°. B.p. 295–6°. Sol. EtOH, Et_2O. Insol. H_2O.

Chloride : $C_9H_9O_3Cl$. MW, 200·5. Cryst. M.p. 70°. B.p. about 290°.

Amide : $C_9H_{11}O_3N$. MW, 181. Cryst. M.p. 164°. Sol. hot H_2O. N-*Di-Me* : $C_{11}H_{15}O_3N$. MW, 209. M.p. 103°. B.p. 203°/12 mm. N-*Di-Et* : $C_{13}H_{19}O_3N$. MW, 237. B.p. 205°/12 mm.

Nitrile : $C_9H_9O_2N$. MW, 163. Needles from H_2O. M.p. 67–8°.

Anhydride : $C_{18}H_{18}O_7$. MW, 346. Prisms from AcOEt or C_6H_6. M.p. 124–5°.

Anilide : needles from EtOH. M.p. 154°.

Buck, Ide, *Organic Syntheses*, 1935, XV, 85.
Grignard, *Compt. rend.*, 1934, **198**, 625.
Rodionov, Fedorova, *Arch. Pharm.*, 1933, **271**, 287.
Tiemann, Matsmoto, *Ber.*, 1876, **9**, 937.

***o*-Veratric Acid.**
See 2 : 3-Dimethoxybenzoic Acid.

Veratric Aldehyde (3 : 4-*Dimethoxybenzaldehyde, protocatechuic aldehyde dimethyl ether, vanillin methyl ether, veratraldehyde*)

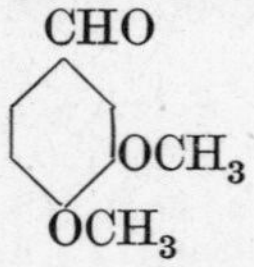

$C_9H_{10}O_3$ MW, 166

Needles from Et_2O, ligroin, CCl_4 or toluene. M.p. 58° (42°). B.p. 285°, 154–5°/10 mm. Sol. EtOH, Et_2O. Insol. cold H_2O. Readily oxidises in air.

Oxime : cryst. from ligroin. M.p. 94–5°. Sol. common org. solvents. *B,HCl* : dark red solid. M.p. 151°.

Anil : cryst. from EtOH. M.p. 81°.

Azine : yellow plates from EtOH–$CHCl_3$. M.p. 169–70°.

Semicarbazone : m.p. 177°.

Phenylhydrazone : yellow plates from EtOH. M.p. 121°.

2 : 4-*Dinitrophenylhydrazone* : orange prisms from AcOEt. M.p. 264–5°.

Johnson, Stevenson, *Organic Syntheses*, 1936, XVI, 91.
Briner, Tscharner, Paillard, *Helv. Chim. Acta*, 1925, **8**, 406.
Gatterman, *Ann.*, 1907, **357**, 367.

Veratrine.
See Cevadine.

Veratrol (*Catechol dimethyl ether*, 1 : 2-*dimethoxybenzene*)

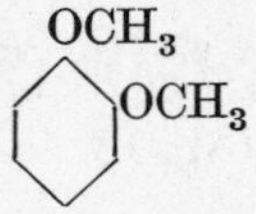

$C_8H_{10}O_2$ MW, 138

Cryst. from pet. ether. M.p. 22·5°. B.p. 206°/759 mm. D_{25}^{25} 1·0842. $n_\alpha^{21\cdot2}$ 1·52870.

Picrate : red plates. M.p. 56–7°.

Voss, Blaneke, *Ann.*, 1931, **485**, 279.
Perkin, Weizmann, *J. Chem. Soc.*, 1906, **89**, 1649.

2-Veratroylcinchomeronic Acid.
See Papaveric Acid.

Veratryl Alcohol (3 : 4-*Dimethoxybenzyl alcohol*)

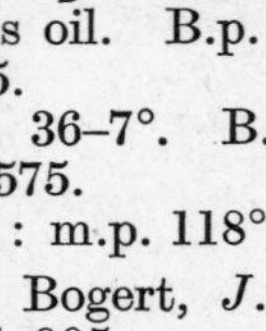

$C_9H_{12}O_3$ MW, 168

Viscous oil. B.p. 296–7°/732 mm., 172°/12 mm. D_{17}^{17} 1·179. n_D^{17} 1·555. Sol. H_2O, EtOH.

Acetyl : viscous oil. B.p. 170°/12 mm. D_4^{17} 1·157. n_D^{17} 1·5245.

Benzoyl : m.p. 36–7°. B.p. 233–6°/12 mm. D^{13} 1·193. n_D^{13} 1·575.

Phenylurethane : m.p. 118°.

Davidson, Bogert, *J. Am. Chem. Soc.*, 1935, **57**, 905.
Tiffeneau, Fuhrer, *Bull. soc. chim.*, 1914, **15**, 171.
Vavon, *Compt. rend.*, 1912, **154**, 360.
Tiffeneau, *Bull. soc. chim.*, 1911, **9**, 929.

Veratrylamine (3 : 4-*Dimethoxybenzylamine*)

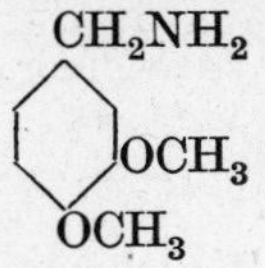

$C_9H_{13}O_2N$ MW, 167

Liq. B.p. 154–8°/12 mm. D^0 1·143. Slowly volatile in steam.
B,HCl : cryst. from EtOH. M.p. 257–8°.
Picrate : m.p. 169°.
Methiodide : m.p. 228°.

Juliusberg, *Ber.*, 1907, **40**, 120.
Nelson, *J. Am. Chem. Soc.*, 1919, **41**, 1117.
Douetteau, *Bull. soc. chim.*, 1911, **9**, 937.

Verbanol

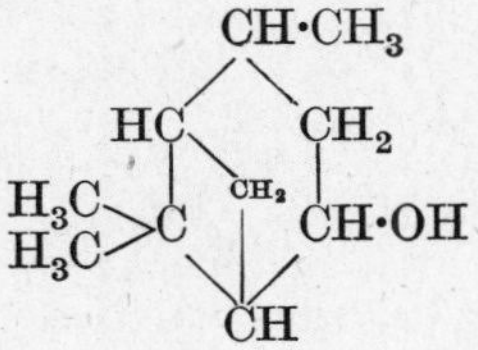

$C_{10}H_{18}O$ MW, 154

Needles from EtOH.Aq. or ligroin. M.p. 58°. B.p. 218°, 102°/20 mm. D^{20} 0·940. n_D^{20} 1·47018. $[\alpha]_D$ + 24·4°.

Blumann, Zeitschel, *Ber.*, 1913, **46**, 1191.

Verbanone

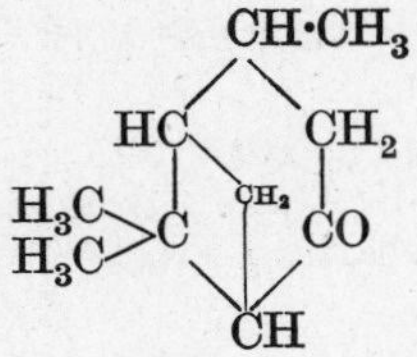

$C_{10}H_{16}O$ MW, 152

B.p. 222°, 117°/32 mm. D^{20} 0·961. n_D^{20} 1·47518. $[\alpha]_D$ + 52·5°.
Oxime : plates from ligroin. M.p. 88° (77–8°). B.p. 148–60°/35 mm. $[\alpha]_D$ − 30·5°. *B,HCl* : prisms. M.p. 142° (rapid heat.).
Semicarbazone : cryst. from EtOH.Aq. Decomp. at 230°.
Hydrazone : m.p. 27°. B.p. 146°/22 mm. D_4^{27} 0·986. n_D^{27} 1·51734. $[\alpha]_D^{27}$ − 29·2°.

Wienhaus, Schumm, *Ann.*, 1924, **439**, 35.
Blumann, Zeitschel, *Ber.*, 1913, **46**, 1192.

Verbascose

$C_{36}H_{62}O_{31}$ MW, 990

Occurs in roots of mullein (*Verbascum thapsus*). Needles. M.p. 219–20°. $[\alpha]_D$ + 169·9° in H_2O. Does not reduce Fehling's. Hyd. ⟶ glucose + fructose + galactose.

Bourquelot, Bridel, *Compt. rend.*, 1910, **151**, 760.

Verbenol

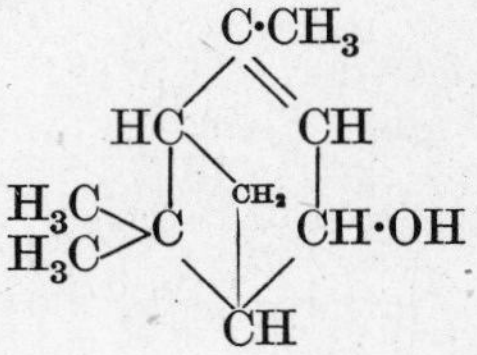

$C_{10}H_{16}O$ MW, 152

d-.
Liq. Cryst. in plates on cooling. M.p. 8°. B.p. 216–18° (with dehydration), 95°/9 mm. D^{20} 0·9702. n_D^{20} 1·4890. $[\alpha]_D^{18}$ + 132·3°.

l-.
Liq. B.p. 100–4°/12 mm.

Blumann, Schmidt, *Ann.*, 1927, **453**, 48.
Blumann, Zeitschel, *Ber.*, 1913, **46**, 1195.

Verbenone

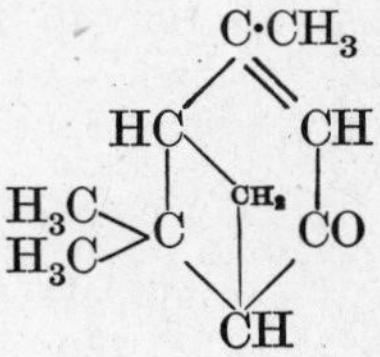

$C_{10}H_{14}O$ MW, 150

d-.
Constituent of Spanish verbena oil. M.p. 6·5°. B.p. 227–8°, 103–4°/16 mm. Sol. H_2O. D^{20} 0·9976. n_D^{18} 1·49928. $[\alpha]_D^{18}$ + 249·6°.
Oxime : cryst. from ligroin. M.p. 119–20°. B.p. 140–2°/17 mm. $[\alpha]_D$ + 80° in Et_2O.
Semicarbazone : plates from EtOH. M.p. 208–9°. $[\alpha]_D$ + 77·6°.

l-.
Liq. D^{15} 0·982. n_D 1·4994. $[\alpha]_D$ − 144°.
Semicarbazone : m.p. 185–90°.

dl-.
Semicarbazone : m.p. 180–1°.

Dupont, Zacharewicz, *Bull. soc. chim.*, 1935, 2, 533.
Wienhaus, Schumm, *Ann.*, 1924, **439**, 20.
Blumann, Zeitschel, *Ber.*, 1913, **46**, 1188.
Kerschbaum, *Ber.*, 1900, **33**, 885.

Vernine.
See Guanosine.

Veronal (5 : 5-*Diethylbarbituric acid, diethylmalonylurea, Barbitone*)

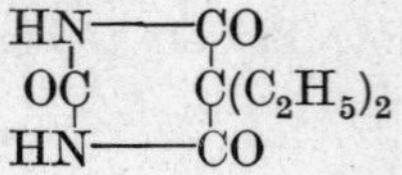

$C_8H_{12}O_3N_2$ MW, 184

White cryst. powder. M.p. 191°. Sol. EtOH, Et_2O, aq. alkalis. Spar. sol. $CHCl_3$. Prac. insol. H_2O. $k = 3{\cdot}7 \times 10^{-8}$ at 25°. Powerful hypnotic.

Fischer, Dilthey, *Ann.*, 1904, **335**, 338.

Vicianin

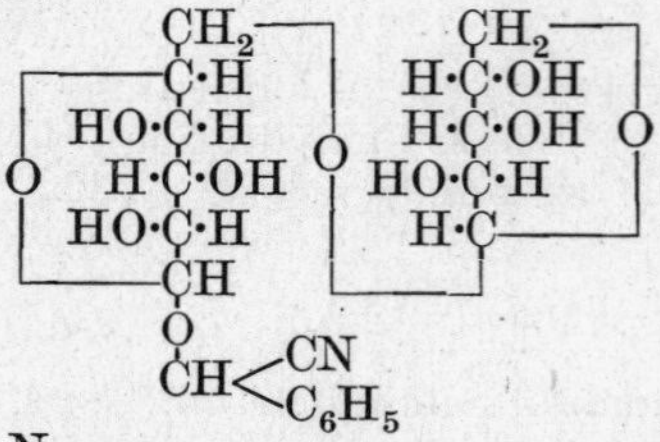

$C_{19}H_{25}O_{10}N$ MW, 427

Occurs in seeds of *Vicia angustifolia*. Needles. M.p. 147–8°. Sol. hot H_2O. Spar. sol. EtOH. Insol. $CHCl_3$, C_6H_6, CS_2, pet. ether. $[\alpha]_D -20{\cdot}7°$ in H_2O. Hyd. by vicianase $\longrightarrow$ vicianose + HCN + $C_6H_5{\cdot}CHO$.

Bertrand, *Compt. rend.*, 1906, **143**, 832.
Bertrand, Weisweiller, *Compt. rend.*, 1908, **147**, 252; 1910, **151**, 884; *Bull. soc. chim.*, 1911, **9**, 147.

Vicianose

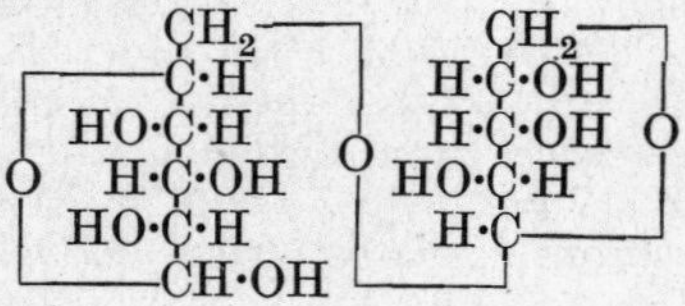

$C_{11}H_{20}O_{10}$ MW, 312

Does not occur in free state but in various glucosides, *e.g.* gein from *Geum urbanum*, vicianin from *Vicia angustifolia*, violutin from *Viola cornuta*. Needles from dil. EtOH. M.p. 210° decomp. Sinters at 190°. Sol. H_2O, dil. EtOH. Sweet taste. $[\alpha]_D^{20} + 56{\cdot}5° \longrightarrow + 39{\cdot}72°$ in H_2O. Does not ferment. Hyd. by dil. acids $\longrightarrow$ *d*-glucose + *l*-arabinose.

β-*Hepta-acetyl* : needles from EtOH. M.p. 158–60°. $[\alpha]_D^{14} + 7{\cdot}5°$ in $CHCl_3$. Sol. $CHCl_3$, Et_2O, Me_2CO. Spar. sol. EtOH. Prac. insol. H_2O.

Bertrand, Weisweiller, *Bull. soc. chim.*, 1911, **9**, 38, 84, 147.
Herissey, Cheymol, *Compt. rend.*, 1925, **181**, 565.
Helferich, Bredereck, *Ann.*, 1928, **465**, 166.

Vinaconic Acid.
See Cyclopropane-1 : 1-dicarboxylic Acid.

Vinopyrin.
See under p-Phenetidine.

Vinylacetic Acid (*Propylene-3-carboxylic acid, 2-methylenepropionic acid*)

$$CH_2{:}CH{\cdot}CH_2{\cdot}COOH$$

$C_4H_6O_2$ MW, 86

M.p. − 39°. B.p. 163°, 71°/12–14 mm. D_{15}^{15} 1·013. n_D^{15} 1·42572. $k = 3{\cdot}83 \times 10^{-5}$ at 25°.

Et ester : $C_6H_{10}O_2$. MW, 114. B.p. 119°. D_4^{20} 0·91224. n_D^{20} 1·41054.

Amide : C_4H_7ON. MW, 85. Plates from pet. ether. M.p. 72–3°.

Nitrile : *see* Allyl cyanide.

Anilide : needles from EtOH.Aq. M.p. 58°.

Mannich, *Arch. Pharm.*, 1935, **273**, 415.
Linstead, Noble, Boorman, *J. Chem. Soc.*, 1933, 560.
Houben, *Ber.*, 1903, **36**, 2897.

Vinylacetone.
See Methyl allyl Ketone.

Vinylacetylene (3-*Butenine*-1)

$$CH_2{:}CH{\cdot}C{:}CH$$

C_4H_4 MW, 52

Gas with odour resembling acetylene. Sets to cryst. in liq. air. B.p. 2–3°. Decomp. violently on heating. Explodes with fuming HNO_3.

Shaworonkow, *Chem. Zentr.*, 1937, I, 1668.
du Pont, F.P., 43,351, addn. to F.P., 733,663, and 41,454, (*Chem. Abstracts*, 1934, **28**, 6727).
Willstätter, Wirth, *Ber.*, 1913, **46**, 538.
Nieuwland, *Ind. Eng. Chem.*, 1935, **27**, 850 (*Review*).

2-Vinylacrylic Acid (1 : 3-*Butadiene*-1-*carboxylic acid, erythrene*-1-*carboxylic acid*)

$$CH_2{:}CH{\cdot}CH{:}CH{\cdot}COOH$$

$C_5H_6O_2$ MW, 98

Prisms from Et_2O. M.p. 80°. Very hygroscopic. Very sol. Et_2O, EtOH, hot H_2O, C_6H_6. Sol. pet. ether.

Et ester : $C_7H_{10}O_2$. MW, 126. B.p. 70–1°/31 mm., 57·2–57·5°/13 mm. $D_4^{23\cdot3}$ 0·9348. $n_a^{19\cdot8}$ 1·49306.

Nitrile : C_5H_5N. MW, 79. B.p. 135–8° (with polymerisation), 48–50°/28 mm. D_4^{20} 0·8644. n_D^{20} 1·4880.

Coffmann, *J. Am. Chem. Soc.*, 1935, **57**, 1982.
Muskat, Becker, Lowenstein, *J. Am. Chem. Soc.*, 1930, **52**, 329.
Burton, Ingold, *J. Chem. Soc.*, 1929, 2028.
Noffbohm, *Ann.*, 1917, **412**, 73.

Vinyl Alcohol (*Ethenol*)

$CH_2{:}CHOH$

C_2H_4O MW, 44

Does not exist in free state. Polymers of the alcohol and its esters used in synthetic resins.

Acetyl : vinyl acetate. Polymerises in air to transparent mass, polyvinyl acetate. Used in lacquers and resins.

Benzoyl : b.p. 203°. D^{20} 1·065. Polymers used in lacquers.

Et ether : *see* Ethyl vinyl Ether.

Vinyl ether : *see* Divinyl Ether.

Phenyl ether : C_8H_8O. MW, 120. B.p. 158–60°.

I.G., D.R.P., 604,640, (*Chem. Zentr.*, 1935, II, 2125).
Evans, Looker, *J. Am. Chem. Soc.*, 1921, **43**, 1925.
Chem. Fabr. Griesheim-Elektron, D.R.P., 271,381, (*Chem. Zentr.*, 1914, I, 1316).

Vinylallylcarbinol (1 : 5-*Hexadienol*-3)

$CH_2{:}CH{\cdot}CH_2{\cdot}CH(OH){\cdot}CH{:}CH_2$

$C_6H_{10}O$ MW, 98

Liq. B.p. 133–4°. D_4^{25} 0·8596. n_D^{25} 1·4464.

Levene, Haller, *J. Biol. Chem.*, 1929, **83**, 185.

***sym*.-Vinylallylethylene.**
See 1 : 3 : 6-Heptatriene.

Vinylamine.
See Ethyleneimine.

Vinylanisole.
See under Hydroxystyrene.

Vinylbenzene.
See Styrene.

Vinyl bromide (*Bromoethylene*)

$CH_2{:}CHBr$

C_2H_3Br MW, 107

F.p. − 137·8°. B.p. 15·8°. D^{11} 1·5286. n_D 1·4462. $H_2O + PbO \longrightarrow$ acetylene. $KMnO_4$ $\longrightarrow$ H·COOH. Polymerises rapidly in sunlight $\longrightarrow$ mixture of polymers.

Staudinger, Brunner, Feisst, *Helv. Chim. Acta*, 1930, **13**, 805.
Juvala, *Ber.*, 1930, **63**, 1991.
Bauer, U.S.P., 1,414,852, (*Chem. Abstracts*, 1922, **16**, 2150).

2-Vinylbutane.
See 3-Methyl-1-pentene.

Vinyl-*n*-butyl Alcohol.
See 1-Hexenol-6.

Vinylbutylene.
See 1 : 3-Hexadiene *and* 3-Methyl-1 : 3-pentadiene.

Vinyl chloride (*Chloroethylene*)

$CH_2{:}CHCl$

C_2H_3Cl MW, 62·5

Gas. Liquefies on cooling. F.p. − 159·7°. B.p. − 14°. Heat of comb. C_p 286·2 Cal. Polymerises in light or in absence of light in presence of catalysts.

Carbide and Carbon Chem. Corp., U.S.P., 1,934,824, (*Chem. Abstracts*, 1934, **28**, 488); U.S.P., 1,926,638, (*Chem. Abstracts*, 1933, **27**, 5756).
Dana, Burdick, Jenkins, *J. Am. Chem. Soc.*, 1927, **49**, 2801.

Vinyl cyanide.
See under Acrylic Acid.

Vinylcyclohexane (*Cyclohexylethylene*)

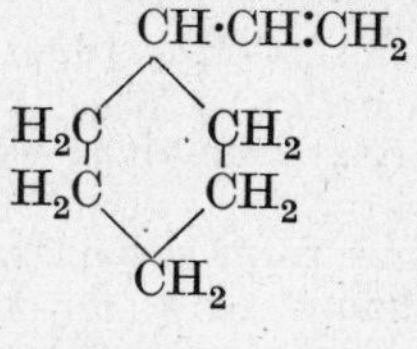

C_8H_{14} MW, 110

Liq. B.p. 130–1°/749 mm. D_4^{19} 0·8166. n_D^{19} 1·455.

Lewina, Zurikow, *Chem. Zentr.*, 1936, I, 4289.

Vinyldiacetonalkamine (4-*Hydroxy*-2 : 2 : 6-*trimethylpiperidine*)

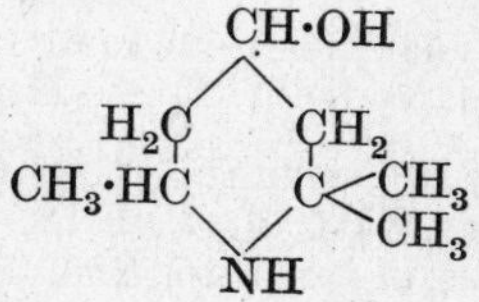

$C_8H_{17}ON$ MW, 143

α-Form :

d-.

B,HCl : does not melt below 300°. $[\alpha]_D$ + 13·3° in H_2O.

l-.

Prisms from C_6H_6. M.p. 79–81°.

B,HCl : does not melt below 300°. $[\alpha]_{5461}$ − 18·5° in H_2O.

Picrate : needles. M.p. 242–4°.

dl-.

Cryst. from C_6H_6. M.p. 137–8°. B.p. 209–11°. Sol. 9 parts boiling H_2O. Spar. sol. pet. ether.

B,HCl : prisms from EtOH.Aq.

N-*Me* : $C_9H_{19}ON$. MW, 157. Pale yellow oil. B.p. 218–20°. Very sol. H_2O. *Dihydrate* : plates from C_6H_6–pet. ether. M.p. 39–40°. *B,HCl* : m.p. 192°. *B_2,H_2PtCl_6* : cryst. M.p. 208° decomp. O-*Benzoyl* : pale yellow oil. B.p. 194–5°/16 mm. *Picrate* : cryst. from EtOH.Aq. M.p. 180–1°.

N-*Nitroso* : $C_8H_{16}O_2N_2$. MW, 172. Cryst. from C_6H_6–pet. ether. M.p. 92°.

O-*Benzoyl* : *see* β-Eucaine.

Picrate : plates from H_2O. M.p. 171–2°.

β-Form :

d-.

Plates from C_6H_6. M.p. 121–3°.

B,HCl : plates. M.p. 217–19°. $[\alpha]_{5461}$ + 22·85°.

Picrate : needles from H_2O. M.p. 181–2°.

dl-.

Prisms from C_6H_6. M.p. 160–1°. B.p. 204–5°. Sol. 30 parts boiling C_6H_6. Spar. sol. H_2O, Et_2O. Na amylate in amyl alcohol ⟶ *dl*-*α*-form.

N-*Me* : prisms from pet. ether. M.p. 70–2°. B.p. 220°/744 mm. Very sol. H_2O. Na amylate in amyl alcohol ⟶ *dl*-*α*-*N*-Me. *B,HCl* : m.p. 58°. *Nitrate* : prisms. M.p. 163° decomp. *B_2,H_2PtCl_6* : cryst. M.p. 218° decomp. *Methiodide* : prisms from EtOH. Decomp. at 270°. O-*Benzoyl* : pale yellow oil. B.p. 195°/15 mm. *Picrate* : yellow cryst. from EtOH.Aq. M.p. 213°.

N-*Nitroso* : yellow needles from C_6H_6–pet. ether. M.p. 60°.

O-*Benzoyl* : *see* Iso-β-eucaine.

Picrate : plates from H_2O. M.p. 171–2°.

King, *J. Chem. Soc.*, 1924, **125**, 41.
Harries, Zart, *Ann.*, 1918, **417**, 176.
Harries, *Ann.*, 1897, **294**, 372; 1897, **296**, 334.

Vinyldiacetonamine (4-*Keto*-2 : 2 : 6-*trimethylpiperidine*, 2 : 2 : 6-*trimethyl*-*γ*-*piperidone*)

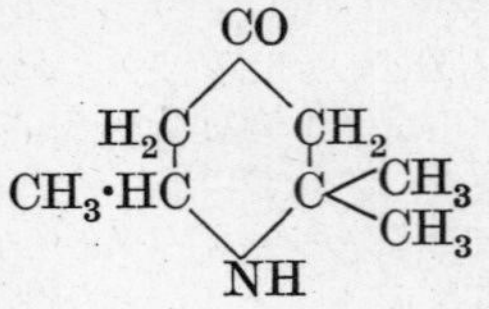

$C_8H_{15}ON$ MW, 141

Hygroscopic plates and prisms. M.p. 27°. B.p. 199–200°. NaHg ⟶ vinyldiacetonalkamine.

B_2,H_2SO_4 : needles from EtOH.Aq. M.p. above 105° decomp.

Nitrate : needles from Me_2CO–pet. ether. M.p. 160–1°.

B,$(COOH)_2$: m.p. 184–5° decomp.

N-*Me* : $C_9H_{17}ON$. MW, 155. Oil. B.p. 96–7°/14 mm. *Oxime* : prisms from pet. ether. M.p. 93°.

N-*Nitroso* : $C_8H_{14}O_2N_2$. MW, 170. Pale yellow plates from MeOH.Aq. M.p. 61°. *Oxime* : cryst. from H_2O. M.p. 195°.

N-*Acetyl* : prisms from Et_2O. M.p. 92°.

N-m-*Nitrobenzoyl* : needles from Me_2CO. M.p. 159–60°.

N-p-*Nitrobenzoyl* : needles from Me_2CO. M.p. 170°.

Oxime : plates from EtOH. M.p. 151°. Sol. 5 parts boiling H_2O. N-*Acetyl* : cryst. from EtOH. M.p. 130°.

Semicarbazone : cryst. from EtOH–C_6H_6. M.p. 196–7°.

Picrate : prisms from H_2O. M.p. 198–9°.

Harries, Schellhorn, *Ann.*, 1918, **417**, 131.
Harries, *Ber.*, 1896, **29**, 522.

α-Vinyldiphenylmethane.

See 3 : 3-Diphenylpropylene.

Vinyl fluoride (*Fluoroethylene*)

CH_2:CHF

C_2H_3F MW, 46

Gas at ord. temps. B.p. − 51°. Burns with green flame. Sol. EtOH, Me_2CO. Insol. H_2O.

Swarts, *Bull. soc. chim.*, 1919, **25**, 163; *Chem. Zentr.*, 1909, II, 1414; 1901, II, 804.

Vinylformic Acid.

See Acrylic Acid.

Vinylfuran.

See α-Furylethylene.

Vinylglycollic Acid (1-*Hydroxyvinylacetic acid*)

CH_2:CH·CH(OH)·COOH

$C_4H_6O_3$ MW, 102

Hygroscopic needles. M.p. 42–4°. B.p. 128·6–130·2°/12–13 mm. Very sol. H_2O. Sol. EtOH, Et_2O, $CHCl_3$. Insol. CS_2. Volatile in steam. $k = 4{\cdot}6 \times 10^{-4}$. Min. acids ⟶ 1-ketobutyric acid.

Et ester: $C_6H_{10}O_3$. MW, 130. Liq. with pleasant odour. B.p. 173° slight decomp., 68°/15 mm. D_4^{15} 1·0470. n_D^{13} 1·436. *Acetyl*: b.p. 89°/15 mm. D^{16} 1·055. n_D^{16} 1·429.

Amide: $C_4H_7O_2N$. MW, 101. Plates from Et_2O. M.p. 80·8°. B.p. 155–8°/20–1 mm. slight decomp. Sol. H_2O, EtOH. Spar. sol. Et_2O.

Nitrile: *see under* Acrolein.

Glattfield, Hoen, *J. Am. Chem. Soc.*, 1935, **57**, 1406.
Kirrmann, Rambaud, *Compt. rend.*, 1932, **194**, 1169.
Sleen, *Rec. trav. chim.*, 1902, **21**, 222.

Vinylidene bromide.
See unsym.-Dibromoethylene.
Vinylidene chloride.
See unsym.-Dichloroethylene.
Vinylidene-ethyl Alcohol.
See 4-Hydroxy-1 : 2-butadiene.
Vinyl iodide (*Iodoethylene*)

$CH_2{:}CHI$

C_2H_3I MW, 154

B.p. 56–56·5°. D^{20} 2·037. n_D 1·53845. Decomp. on exposure to ultra-violet light ⟶ C_2H_2, C_2H_4 and I.

Spence, *J. Am. Chem. Soc.*, 1933, **55**, 1290.

Vinylisoamylcarbinol.
See 6-Methyl-1-heptenol-3.
1-Vinylisobutylene.
See 4-Methyl-1 : 3-pentadiene.
Vinylisobutyric Acid.
See Dimethylvinylacetic Acid.
1-Vinylisopentane.
See 4-Methyl-1-hexene.
***sym*.-Vinylisopropenylethane.**
See 2-Methyl-1 : 5-hexadiene.
Vinylnaphthalene.
See Naphthylethylene.
Vinyl-1-naphthylcarbinol (*1-α-Naphthylallyl alcohol, 1-α-hydroxyallylnaphthalene*)

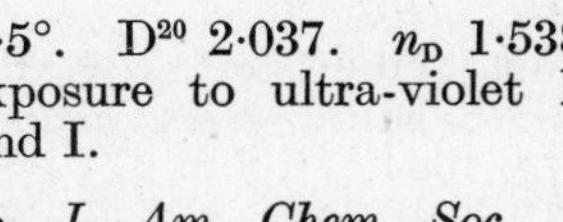

$C_{13}H_{12}O$ MW, 184

Viscous oil. B.p. 186–7°/19 mm.

Phenylurethane: needles from pet. ether. M.p. 108–9°.

p-*Nitrobenzoyl*: prisms from EtOH. M.p. 79–80°.

Burton, *J. Chem. Soc.*, 1931, 761.

Vinyl-2-naphthylcarbinol (*1-β-Naphthylallyl alcohol, 2-α-hydroxyallylnaphthalene*).

Viscous oil. B.p. 195–8°/21 mm.

Phenylurethane: prisms from C_6H_6–pet. ether. M.p. 134–5°.

See previous reference.

2-Vinylpentane.
See 3-Methyl-1-hexene.
1-Vinyl-2-pentene.
See 1 : 4-Heptadiene.
Vinylphenetole.
See under p-Hydroxystyrene.
Vinylphenol.
See Hydroxystyrene.
Vinylphenylcarbinol.
See 1-Phenylallyl Alcohol.
3-Vinylpiperidine (*β-Vinylpiperidine, 3-piperidylethylene*)

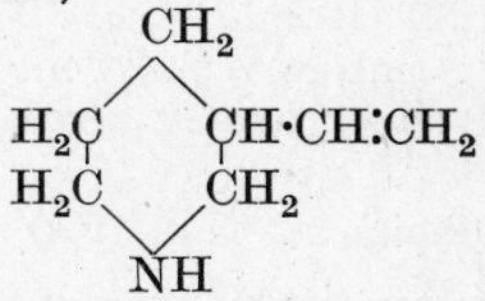

$C_7H_{13}N$ MW, 111

Liq. B.p. 152–5°. D_4^{25} 0·9274. n_D^{25} 1·4731.

B_2,H_2PtCl_6: cryst. + $2H_2O$ from EtOH.Aq. M.p. 223–4° decomp.

N-*Me*: $C_8H_{15}N$. MW, 125. Liq. B.p. 161–2°/724 mm. Sol. 30 parts cold H_2O. Spar. sol. hot H_2O. Decolorises acid $KMnO_4$. Zn + HCl ⟶ 1-methyl-3-ethylpiperidine. *$B,HAuCl_4$*: prisms from H_2O. M.p. 58–9°. *B_2,H_2PtCl_6*: orange-red plates or prisms. M.p. 185–6° decomp. *Picrate*: yellow prisms or needles. M.p. 193–4°.

N-*Et*: $C_9H_{17}N$. MW, 139. Liq. B.p. 185–90°/721 mm. Spar. sol. H_2O. *$B,HAuCl_4$*: cryst. M.p. 44–5°. *B_2,H_2PtCl_6*: cryst. from H_2O. M.p. 175–6° decomp.

Merchant, Marvel, *J. Am. Chem. Soc.*, 1928, **50**, 1201.
Lipp, Widmann, *Ann.*, 1915, **409**, 92; *Ber.*, 1905, **38**, 2481.

4-[3-Vinylpiperidyl]-acetic Acid.
See Meroquinene.
2-Vinylpropane.
See 3-Methylbutylene-1.

***sym.*-Vinylpropenylethylene.**
See 1 : 3 : 5-Heptatriene.

2-Vinylpropionic Acid.
See Allylacetic Acid.

1-Vinyl-3-propylidene-propylene.
See 1 : 3 : 5-Heptatriene.

2-Vinylpyridine (*α-Vinylpyridine, 2-pyridylethylene*)

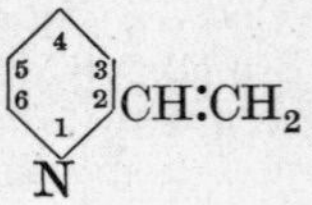

C_7H_7N MW, 105

Liq. B.p. 79–82°/29 mm. D^0 0·9985. Very sol. EtOH, Et_2O, $CHCl_3$. Spar. sol. H_2O. Volatile in steam. $KMnO_4$ ⟶ picolinic acid. Na + EtOH ⟶ 2-ethylpiperidine.

$B,HAuCl_4$: yellow needles from H_2O. M.p. 144°.

B_2,H_2PtCl_6 : needles or plates. M.p. 174° decomp.

Löffler, Grosse, *Ber.*, 1907, **40**, 1326.

4-Vinylpyridine (*γ-Vinylpyridine, 4-pyridylethylene*).
Liq. B.p. 59°/12 mm.

B,H_2PtCl_3 : sinters at 200°, m.p. above 350°.

Picrate : yellow leaflets from C_6H_6. M.p. 197–8°.

Meisenheimer, *Ann.*, 1920, **420**, 208.

Vinylpyridinium hydroxide.
See Pyridine-neurine.

2-Vinylquinoline (*α-Vinylquinoline, 2-quinolylethylene*)

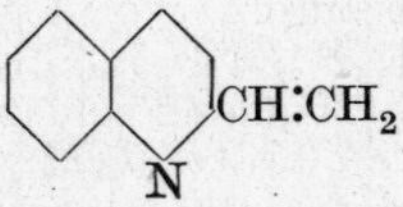

$C_{11}H_9N$ MW, 155

Pale yellow oil. Decomp. on dist. at 10 mm. Volatile in steam.

$B,HgCl_2,HCl$: needles from H_2O. M.p. 151–2° decomp.

$B,HAuCl_4$: yellowish-red needles from dil. min. acids. M.p. 158–9°.

B_2,H_2PtCl_6 : orange-red needles. Decomp. at 182°.

$B_2,H_2PtCl_6,4H_2O$: orange needles from dil. min. acids. M.p. 186–7°.

Methner, *Ber.*, 1894, **27**, 2691.

Vinyltoluene.
See Methylstyrene.

4-Vinylvaleric Acid.
See 5-Heptenic Acid.

Violanin (*Rhamnoglucoside of delphinidin*)

$C_{27}H_{28}O_{15}$ MW, 592

Constituent of *Viola tricolor*, Linn.

Chloride : bluish-violet plates with green metallic lustre. Sol. alkalis and alk. carbonates ⟶ blue sols. Alc. $FeCl_3$ ⟶ blue col. Boiling dil. HCl ⟶ delphinidin + rhamnose + glucose.

Willstätter, Weil, *Ann.*, 1916, **412**, 178.

Violanthrone.
See Dibenzanthrone.

Violaquercitrin.
See Rutin.

Violaxanthin

$C_{40}H_{56}O_4$ MW, 600

Constituent of *Viola tricoloris*, etc. Red prisms from MeOH, EtOH–Et_2O, or CS_2. M.p. 208° (198–9°). $[\alpha]^{20}_{Cd}$ + 35° (+ 38°) in $CHCl_3$. Optical maxima in CS_2 at 500·5, 469 and 440 mμ, in $CHCl_3$ at 482, 451·5 and 424 mμ. Sol. conc. H_2SO_4 ⟶ indigo-blue col. Sol. H·COOH ⟶ blue col. Sol. cold AcOH ⟶ green col. $SbCl_3$ + $CHCl_3$ ⟶ deep blue col. Conc. HCl in AcOH ⟶ greenish-blue col.

Zechmeister, Tuzson, *Ber.*, 1934, **67**, 824.
Kuhn, Grundmann, *ibid.*, 596.
Zechmeister, Cholnoky, *Z. physiol. Chem.*, 1932, **208**, 26.
Kuhn, Winterstein, *Ber.*, 1931, **64**, 326.
Karrer, Morf, *Helv. Chim. Acta*, 1931, **14**, 1044.

Violuric Acid (*5-Isonitrosobarbituric acid, alloxan-5-oxime*)

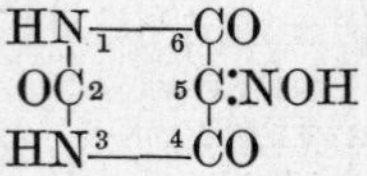

$C_4H_3O_4N_3$ MW, 157

Rhombic cryst. Mod. sol. H_2O ⟶ violet sol. Sol. EtOH. $k = 2{\cdot}7 \times 10^{-5}$ at 25°. $FeCl_3$ ⟶ blue col. Warm with HCl ⟶ NH_2OH. Red. ⟶ uramil. Forms series of variously coloured metallic salts.

5-O-*Me ether* : $C_5H_5O_4N_3$. MW, 171. Plates from ligroin. M.p. 268°. Sol. H_2O, alkalis and org. solvents ⟶ yellow sols. $k = 1{\cdot}8 \times 10^{-7}$ at 25°.

5-O-*Benzyl ether* : $C_{11}H_9O_4N_3$. MW, 247. Plates from C_6H_6. M.p. 226° decomp. Sol. H_2O, EtOH.

Andreasch, *Monatsh.*, 1900, **21**, 286.
Hantzsch, Isherwood, *Ber.*, 1909, **42**, 986.

Violutin (*Violutoside*)

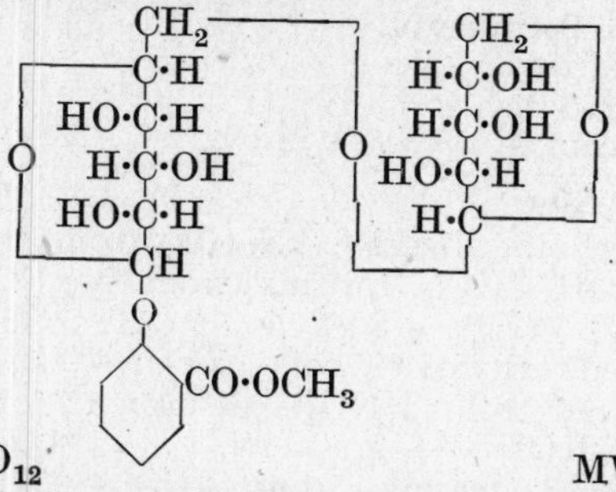

$C_{19}H_{26}O_{12}$ MW, 446

Occurs in *Viola cornuta*. M.p. 168·5° (173°). $[\alpha]_D$ − 36·20° in H_2O, $[\alpha]^{21}_{5461}$ − 39·72° in H_2O, $[\alpha]^{21}_{5790}$ − 36·21° in H_2O. Sol. H_2O. Prac. insol. dry Me_2CO or AcOEt. Hyd. ⟶ methyl salicylate + *d*-glucose + *l*-arabinose.

Hexa-acetyl: m.p. 158°. $[\alpha]^{21}_{5461}$ − 42·94° in Me_2CO.

Picard, *Compt. rend.*, 1926, **182**, 1167.
Robertson, Waters, *J. Chem. Soc.*, 1932, 2770.

Violutoside.
See Violutin.

Viscol

$C_{30}H_{50}O$ MW, 426

Isolated in two forms from mistletoe or cloves.

α-.
Needles from MeOH or Me_2CO.Aq. M.p. 200°. $[\alpha]^{20}_D$ + 85·3° in $CHCl_3$.
Acetyl deriv.: needles from EtOH. M.p. 241°. $[\alpha]^{20}_D$ + 80·2° in $CHCl_3$.
Benzoyl deriv.: plates from EtOH or Me_2CO. M.p. 240°.

β-.
Needles from Me_2CO.Aq. or EtOH.Aq. M.p. 217°. $[\alpha]^{20}_D$ + 55·7° in $CHCl_3$.
Acetyl deriv.: needles from EtOH or AcOEt–MeOH. M.p. 213°. $[\alpha]^{20}_D$ + 42·8° in $CHCl_3$.
Benzoyl deriv.: plates from EtOH or Me_2CO. M.p. 257°.

Bauer, Gerloff, *Arch. Pharm.*, 1936, **274**, 473.

Vitamin A (*Antixerophthalmic, anti-infective and growth-promoting vitamin*)

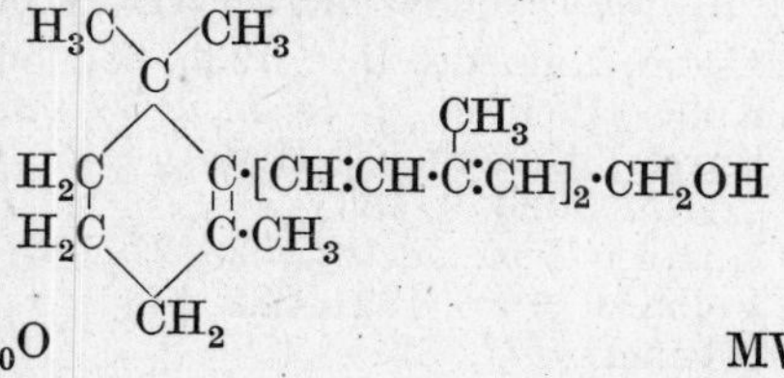

$C_{20}H_{30}O$ MW, 286

Constituent of many fish-liver oils, milk, egg-yolk, seed embryos, etc. Pale yellow viscous liq. B.p. 137–8°/10^{-6} mm. Sol. all org. solvents. Insol. H_2O. Unstable in air. Characteristic absorption band at 328 mμ. $SbCl_3$ in $CHCl_3$ ⟶ blue sol. with absorption bands at 583 and 617 mμ. Conc. H_2SO_4 ⟶ violet col. Physiological activity destroyed on reduction.

Karrer, Morf, Schöpp, *Helv. Chim. Acta*, 1931, **14**, 1431.
Heilbron *et al.*, *Biochem. J.*, 1932, **26**, 1178.
Hamano, *Sci. Papers Inst. Phys. Chem. Research, Tokyo*, 1937, **32**, 44.
Terada, *Chem. Abstracts*, 1934, **28**, 5182.

Vitamin B.

Numerous factors, in addition to B_1 and B_2, are described in the literature, but no chemically pure substances, other than those described as B_1 and B_2, have been isolated. The following are representative references:

O'Brien, *Biochem. J.*, 1934, **28**, 926.
Kinnersley *et al.*, *Biochem. J.*, 1933, **27**, 225.
Keenan *et al.*, *J. Biol. Chem.*, 1933, **103**, 671.
Eddy, Gurin, Keresztesy, *J. Biol. Chem.*, 1930, **87**, 729.
Carter, Kinnersley, Peters, *Biochem. J.*, 1930, **24**, 1832.
Reader, *Biochem. J.*, 1930, **24**, 77; 1929, **23**, 689.
Peters, *Nature*, 1929, **124**, 411.
Smith, *Chem. Abstracts*, 1928, **22**, 2399.

Vitamin B_1 (*Anti-beri-beri or antineuritic vitamin, aneurin, torulin, oryzanin, vitamin F, vitamin P*)

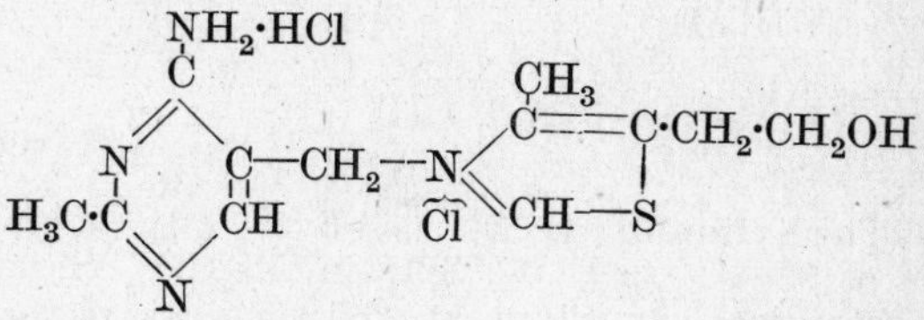

$C_{12}H_{18}ON_4Cl_2S$ MW, 337

Rice husks are chief source. Variable constituent of yeast, milk, green leaves, roots and tubers. Cryst. from MeOH–Et_2O. M.p. 233–4°. Plates from MeOH–EtOH or H_2O–EtOH. M.p. 250°. Very sol. H_2O. Spar. sol. EtOH, Me_2CO. Insol. Et_2O, C_6H_6. Generally more sol. than B_2. Thermolabile and more readily decomp. by alkalis than B_2. Sol. in H_2O or

EtOH shows absorption bands at 235 mμ and 267 mμ.

Nitrate : m.p. 164–5°.

Sulphate : two forms. (i) M.p. 203°. (ii) M.p. 276–8°.

Todd, Bergel, *J. Chem. Soc.*, 1937, **364**.
Williams *et al.*, *J. Am. Chem. Soc.*, 1937, **59**, 216 ; 1936, **58**, 1063 ; 1935, **57**, 517, 536, 1093, 1751, 1849, 1856.
Itter, Orent, McCollum, *J. Biol. Chem.*, 1935, **108**, 571.
Kinnersley, O'Brien, Peters, *Biochem. J.*, 1935, **29**, 701, 716.
Kakefuda, *Chem. Abstracts*, 1935, **29**, 6278.
Ohdake, *Chem. Zentr.*, 1935, I, 3677.
Windaus *et al.*, *Z. physiol. Chem.*, 1932, **204**, 123.
Veen, *Z. physiol. Chem.*, 1932, **208**, 125.

Vitamin B$_2$.
See Lactoflavine.

Vitamin C.
See Ascorbic Acid.

Vitamin D$_1$.
Has been shown to be a mixture of Vitamin D$_2$ and lumisterol.

Vitamin D$_2$.
See Calciferol.

Vitamin D$_3$ (*Anti-rachitic vitamin*)

$$(CH_3)_2CH \cdot CH_2 \cdot CH_2 \cdot CH_2 \cdot CH \cdot CH_3$$

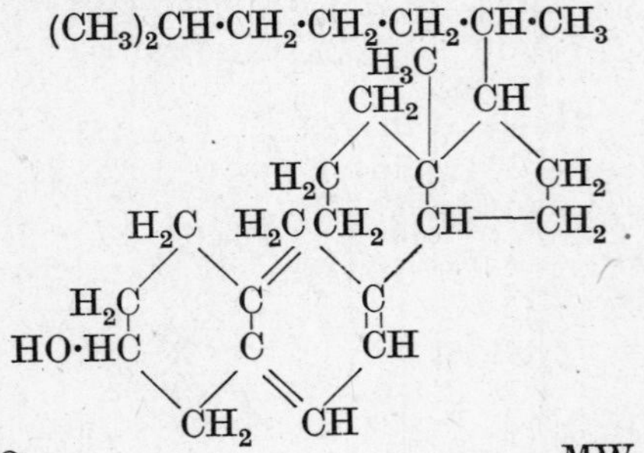

$C_{27}H_{44}O$ MW, 384

The vitamin D of fish-liver oils. Cryst. M.p. 82–4°. $[\alpha]_D^{20}$ + 83·3° in Me$_2$CO. Shows absorption maximum at 265 mμ. As physiologically active as calciferol on rat test.

3 : 5-Dinitrobenzoyl : yellow needles. M.p. 129°.

Allophanate : cryst. from Me$_2$CO. M.p. 173–4°.

Schenck, *Naturwissenschaften*, 1937, **10**, 159.
Windaus, Schenck, Werder, *Z. physiol. Chem.*, 1936, **241**, 100.

Vitamin E.
See α-Tocopherol.

Volemitol.
See Sedoheptitol.

Vomicine

$C_{22}H_{24}O_4N_2$ MW, 380

Strychnine alkaloid. Needles from EtOH.Aq. or EtOH–CHCl$_3$, prisms from Me$_2$CO. M.p. 278–80°. $[\alpha]_D^{22}$ + 80·4° in EtOH. Acid FeCl$_3$ ⟶ reddish-violet col. CrO$_3$ + H$_2$SO$_4$ ⟶ deep red sol. HNO$_3$ ⟶ brown col. Hot MeOH–KOH ⟶ green sol.

B,HCl : prisms from H$_2$O. M.p. 245° decomp.

Methosulphate : cryst. from MeOH.Aq. M.p. 264° decomp.

Me ether : $C_{23}H_{26}O_4N_2$. MW, 394. Needles from EtOH. M.p. 286–90° decomp. $[\alpha]_D^{20}$ + 16·4° in EtOH.

Benzylidene deriv. : yellow plates from EtOH–CHCl$_3$. M.p. 280° decomp.

Wieland, Horner, *Ann.*, 1937, **528**, 73.
Wieland, Calvet, *Ann.*, 1931, **491**, 124.
Wieland, Oertel, *Ann.*, 1929, **469**, 193.

Vulpinic Acid (*Vulpic acid, pulvinic acid methyl ester*)

$$C_6H_5 \cdot HC \!-\! CO \!-\! C{:}C \!\!<^{C_6H_5}_{CO \cdot OCH_3}$$
$$\qquad OC \!-\!\!-\! O$$

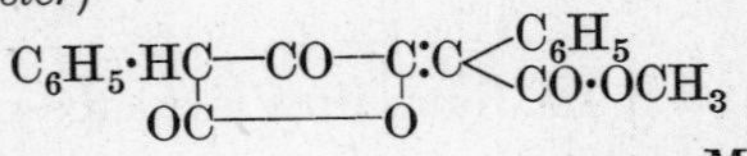

$C_{19}H_{14}O_5$ MW, 322

Occurs in many lichens. Exists in keto-form but can react as enol. Yellow plates from EtOH, needles or prisms from Et$_2$O. M.p. 148–9°. Very sol. CHCl$_3$. Mod. sol. Et$_2$O. Spar. sol. boiling EtOH. Insol. boiling H$_2$O. Hyd. ⟶ pulvinic acid. Reacts strongly acid and forms water stable salts. Poisonous.

Me ether : $C_{20}H_{16}O_5$. MW, 336. Needles from EtOH. M.p. 143–4°.

Et ether : $C_{21}H_{18}O_5$. MW, 350. Plates from EtOH. M.p. 138–9°.

Acetate : needles from EtOH or AcOH. M.p. 148° (156°).

Phenylacetate : needles from AcOH. M.p. 172°.

Benzoate : cryst. from AcOH. M.p. 176°.

Phenylurethane : yellow needles from EtOH. M.p. 237°.

Semicarbazone : yellow microcryst. M.p. 175°.

Asano, Kameda, *Ber.*, 1935, **68**, 1569.
Koller, Pfeiffer, *Monatsh.*, 1933, **62**, 164.
Karrer, Gehrckens, Heuss, *Helv. Chim. Acta*, 1926, **9**, 456.
Mazza, *Chem. Zentr.*, 1926, II, 1037.
Volhard, *Ann.*, 1894, **282**, 14.
Schenck, *ibid.*, 39.

W

Wogonin (5 : 7-*Dihydroxy-8-methoxyflavone*)

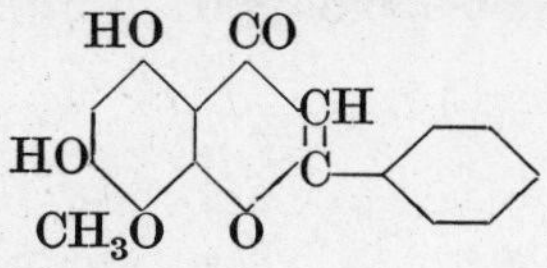

$C_{16}H_{12}O_5$ MW, 284

Present in small amount in roots of *Scutellaria baicalensis*, Georgi. Yellow needles from EtOH.Aq. M.p. 203°. Very sol. MeOH, EtOH. Sol. Et_2O, AcOH, $CHCl_3$, Me_2CO, C_6H_6. Spar. sol. H_2O. Insol. CS_2, ligroin.

Mono-Me ether: $C_{17}H_{14}O_5$. MW, 298. M.p. 183°.

Di-Me ether: $C_{18}H_{16}O_5$. MW, 312. Needles from H_2O. M.p. 167–8°.

Acetyl: m.p. 152–3°.

Benzoyl: m.p. 170°.

Hattori, Hayashi, *J. Chem. Soc. Japan*, 1933, **54**, 919.
Hattori, *Acta Phytochimica*, 1930, **5**, 99.

Wood sugar.
See Xylose.

X

Xanthaline.
See Papaveraldine.

Xanthanoic Acid.
See Xanthene-5-carboxylic Acid.

Xanthene (*Dibenzpyran, xanthane*)

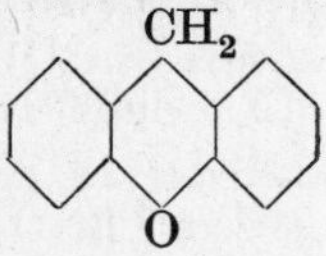

$C_{13}H_{10}O$ MW, 182

Leaflets from EtOH. M.p. 100·5° (98·5°). B.p. 310–12°. Sol. Et_2O, $CHCl_3$, C_6H_6, ligroin. Spar. sol. EtOH, AcOH, pet. ether. Insol. H_2O. Sublimes slowly below m.p. Volatile in steam. Ox. ⟶ xanthone.

Ipatiev, Orlov, Petrov, *Ber.*, 1927, **60**, 130.
Heller, v. Kostanecki, *Ber.*, 1908, **41**, 1325.

Xanthene-5-carboxylic Acid (*Xanthanoic acid*)

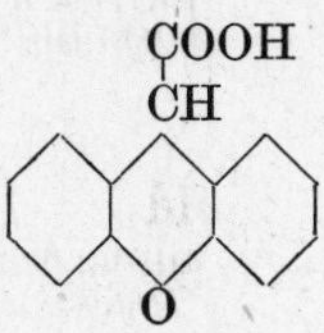

$C_{14}H_{10}O_3$ MW, 226

Needles from 50% EtOH. M.p. 223–4°.

Me ester: $C_{15}H_{12}O_3$. MW, 240. Cryst. from MeOH. M.p. 85–6°.

Conant, Garvey, *J. Am. Chem. Soc.*, 1927, **49**, 2085.

Xanthenol-5.
See Xanthydrol.

Xanthic Acid.
See Xanthogenic Acid.

Xanthine (2 : 6-*Dihydroxypurine*)

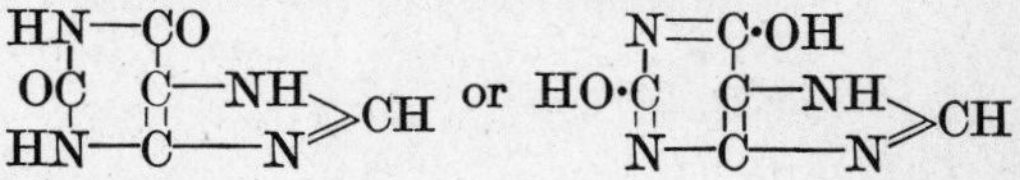

$C_5H_4O_2N_4$ MW, 152

Found in potatoes, coffee beans, etc. Cryst. powder. Sol. 1400 parts H_2O at 100°, 14,400 parts at 16°. Sol. 3000 parts EtOH at 17°. Very sol. KOH. Decomp. on heating. Very weak base. Conc. HCl at 220° ⟶ CO_2 + NH_3 + formic acid + glycine.

Perchlorate: cryst. + H_2O. Sinters at 255°, m.p. 262–4° decomp.

Frèrejacque, *Compt. rend.*, 1930, **191**, 950.
Biltz, Beck, *J. prakt. Chem.*, 1928, **118**, 166.

Xanthione

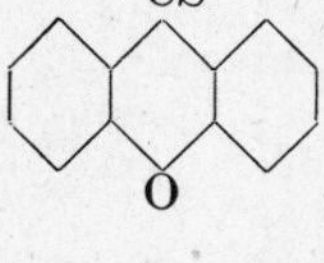

$C_{13}H_8OS$ MW, 212

Red needles from C_6H_6. M.p. 156°. Sol. Et_2O, C_6H_6. Spar. sol. EtOH. Insol. H_2O. Conc. H_2SO_4 ⟶ yellow sol. with green fluor.

Schönberg, Schütz, Nickel, *Ber.*, 1928, **61**, 1382.
Meyer, Szanecki, *Ber.*, 1900, **33**, 2580.

Xanthochelidonic Acid.

See 1 : 3 : 5-Triketopimelic Acid.

Xanthogenic Acid (*Dithiocarbonic O-ethyl ester, ethoxydithioformic acid, ethylxanthogenic acid, xanthic acid*)

$C_2H_5O{\cdot}CSSH$

$C_3H_6OS_2$ MW, 122

Unstable oily liq. F.p. about − 53°. Decomp. at 25° ⟶ $CS_2 + C_2H_5OH$.

NH_4 salt : unstable powder.

K salt : cryst. Sol. H_2O, EtOH. Prac. insol. Et_2O. D^{21} 1·558. Decomp. by boiling H_2O or by heat. Used as soil fumigant.

Me ester : $C_4H_8OS_2$. MW, 136. B.p. 182–3°. D_4^{25} 1·1189. Sol. EtOH, Et_2O. Insol. H_2O.

Et ester : $C_5H_{10}OS_2$. MW, 150. B.p. 199–200°, 76°/10 mm. Sol. EtOH, Et_2O. Insol. H_2O. D^{19} 1·085. n_D^{18} 1·5370.

Anhydride : golden-yellow needles from EtOH. M.p. 55°. Very sol. EtOH. Sol. Et_2O. Insol. H_2O.

Willcox, *J. Am. Chem. Soc.*, 1906, **28**, 1032.
Raag, *Chem.-Ztg.*, 1910, **34**, 83.
Reillen, Elben, Everet, *Ann.*, 1931, **485**, 50.
Great Western Electro-Chemical Co., U.S.P., 1,753,787, (*Chem. Abstracts*, 1930, **24**, 2471).

Xanthone (*Dibenz-γ-pyrone*)

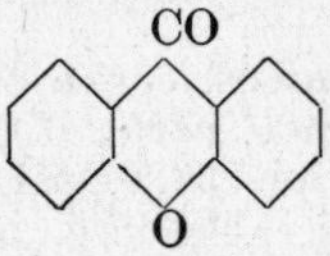

$C_{13}H_8O_2$ MW, 196

Needles from EtOH. M.p. 174°. B.p. 349–50°/730 mm. Sol. $CHCl_3$, C_6H_6. Less sol. EtOH, Et_2O. Spar. sol. ligroin. Insol. cold H_2O. Spar. volatile in steam. Conc. H_2SO_4 ⟶ yellow sol. with intense light blue fluor. Zn dust + NaOH ⟶ xanthydrol. Zn dust dist. ⟶ xanthene.

Oxime : cryst. M.p. 161°. Conc. H_2SO_4 ⟶ yellow sol. with blue fluor.

Phenylhydrazone : golden-yellow needles from EtOH. M.p. 152°. Conc. H_2SO_4 ⟶ yellow sol. with green fluor.

Anil : golden-yellow cryst. from EtOH. M.p. 134·5°. Insol. alkalis. Conc. H_2SO_4 ⟶ yellow sol. with green fluor.

Perkin, *Ber.*, 1883, **16**, 339.
Graebe, *Ann.*, 1899, **254**, 280.
Graebe, Röder, *Ber.*, 1899, **32**, 1690.
Simon, *Bull. soc. chim. biol.*, 1926, **8**, 203.
Spektor, *Chem. Abstracts*, 1934, **28**, 575.
Holleman, *Organic Syntheses*, Collective Vol. I, 537.

Xanthone-1-carboxylic Acid

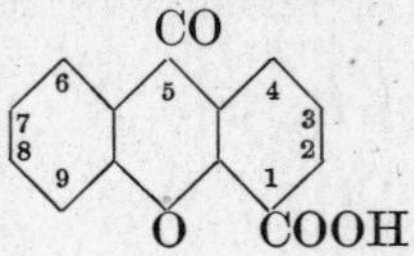

$C_{14}H_8O_4$ MW, 240

Needles from $PhNO_2$. M.p. 289° (275°). Sol. boiling AcOH, $PhNO_2$, anisole, phenetole. Mod. sol. boiling EtOH. Insol. $CHCl_3$, CCl_4, C_6H_6. Cold conc. H_2SO_4 ⟶ yellowish-green sol. Distils undecomp. Sublimes in needles. KOH fusion ⟶ salicylic acid.

Me ester : $C_{15}H_{10}O_4$. MW, 254. Yellowish needles from MeOH. M.p. 146·5°. Sol. MeOH. Insol. H_2O.

Et ester : $C_{16}H_{12}O_4$. MW, 268. Yellowish microneedles from EtOH. M.p. 123°.

Chloride : $C_{14}H_7O_3Cl$. MW, 258·5. Cryst. from *sym.*-tetrachloroethane. M.p. 165°.

Amide : $C_{14}H_9O_3N$. MW, 239. Powder. M.p. 320°.

Anilide : needles from EtOH. M.p. 252°.

Perkin, *J. Chem. Soc.*, 1883, **43**, 188.
Anschütz, Claasen, *Ber.*, 1922, **55**, 686.

Xanthone-3-carboxylic Acid.

Cryst. from AcOH or $PhNO_2$. M.p. 305°.

Me ester : needles from MeOH. M.p. 185°.

Et ester : needles from EtOH. M.p. 152°.

Chloride : pale yellowish needles from $CHCl_3$. M.p. 173°.

Amide : powder. M.p. 324° decomp.

Anilide : needles from EtOH. M.p. 271°.

Anschütz, Stoltenhoff, Voeller, *Ber.*, 1925, **58**, 1740.

Xanthophyll.

This name is now employed as a generic term for hydroxylated carotenoids, *e.g.* lutein, zeazanthin, etc.

Xanthopurpurin.

See Purpuroxanthin.

Xanthoquininic Acid.

See 6-Hydroxycinchoninic Acid.

Xanthorhamnin (*α-Rhamnegin*)

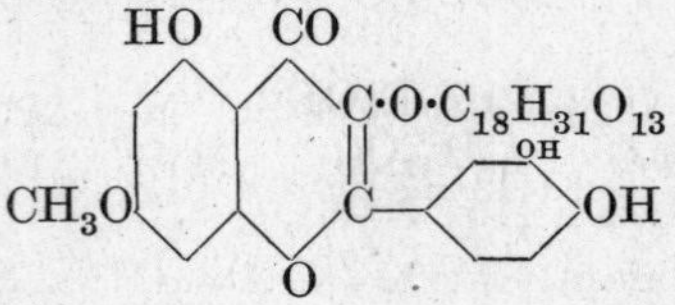

$C_{34}H_{42}O_{20}$ MW, 770

Yellow glucoside from Persian berries, *Rhamnus tinctoria*. Needles from EtOH–Et_2O. $[\alpha]_D + 3{\cdot}75°$. Sol. EtOH. Insol. Et_2O, $CHCl_3$, C_6H_6. Decomp. by H_2O. $FeCl_3$ ⟶ dark brown col. Hyd. ⟶ rhamnetin + rhamnose.

Tri-Me ether: $C_{37}H_{48}O_{20}$. MW, 812. Needles + $3H_2O$ from H_2O. M.p. 175–8°. Sol. H_2O. $FeCl_3$ ⟶ brown col.

Attree, Perkin, *J. Chem. Soc.*, 1927, 238.
Tanret, Tanret, *Bull. soc. chim.*, 1899, **21**, 1073.

Xanthosine (*Xanthine 9-ribofuranoside*)

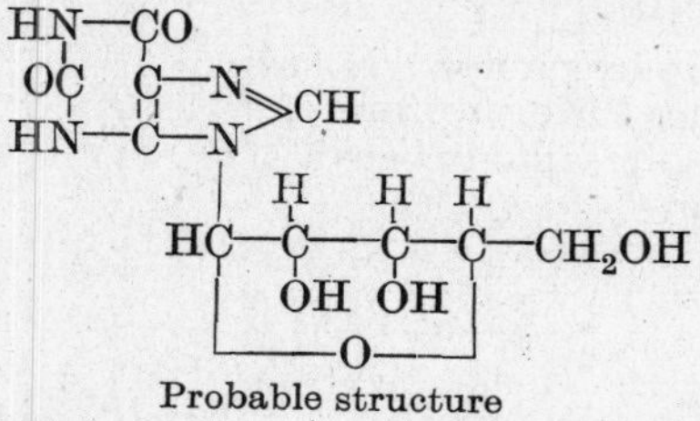

Probable structure

$C_{10}H_{12}O_6N_4$ MW, 284

A typical nucleoside. Prismatic rods + $2H_2O$ from H_2O. Decomp. on heating without melting. Sol. hot H_2O, EtOH.Aq. Spar. sol. cold H_2O. Hyd. by min. acids ⟶ xanthine + ribose.

Phosphoric ester: *see* Xanthylic Acid.

Levene, Jacobs, *Ber.*, 1910, **43**, 3163.
Gulland, Macrae, *J. Chem. Soc.*, 1933, 667.
Gulland, Holiday, Macrae, *J. Chem. Soc.*, 1934, 1640.

Xanthotoxin (*Zanthotoxin*)

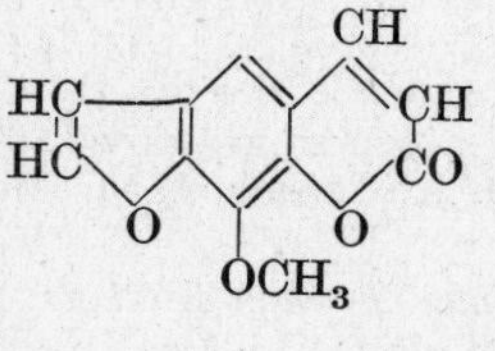

$C_{12}H_8O_4$ MW, 216

Constituent of fruit of *Fagara xanthoxyloides*, Linn. Prisms from 80% EtOH, needles from C_6H_6–pet. ether. M.p. 146° (144–5°). Very sol. boiling EtOH. Mod. sol. Me_2CO, AcOH. Spar. sol. H_2O, Et_2O, pet. ether. Spar. volatile in steam. Cold conc. H_2SO_4 ⟶ yellow sol. ⟶ brown on warming. Poisonous to fish.

Thoms, *Ber.*, 1911, **44**, 3325.
Späth, Pailer, *Ber.*, 1936, **69**, 767.

Xanthotoxol

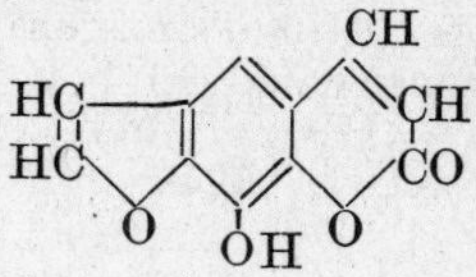

$C_{11}H_6O_4$ MW, 202

Present in seeds of *Angelica archangelica*. M.p. 251–2° (in evacuated tube). Diazomethane ⟶ xanthotoxin.

Späth, Vierhapper, *Ber.*, 1937, **70**, 248.

Xanthoxyletin (*Xanthoxylin-N*)

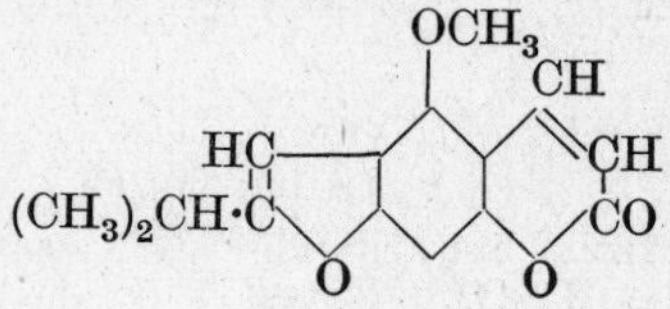

or

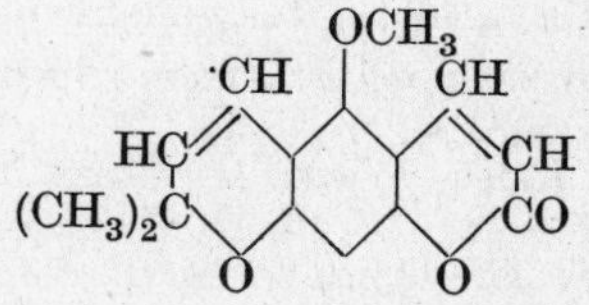

$C_{15}H_{14}O_4$ MW, 258

Constituent of bark of *Zanthoxylum americanum*, M. Prisms from pet. ether. M.p. 133°. Very sol. hot EtOH, $CHCl_3$, C_6H_6. Less sol. Me_2CO. Spar. sol. Et_2O. Sol. 49 parts cold EtOH, 25,000 parts cold H_2O. Cold conc. H_2SO_4 ⟶ red sol. Tasteless.

Dieterle, Kruta, *Chem. Zentr.*, 1937, **I**, 4243.
Gordin, *J. Am. Chem. Soc.*, 1906, **28**, 1650.
Bell, Robertson, Subramaniam, *J. Chem. Soc.*, 1936, 627.

Xanthoxylin-N.
See Xanthoxyletin.

Xanthurenic Acid (*Xanthuric acid, 3 : 4-dihydroxyquinoline-2-carboxylic acid, 3 : 4-dihydroxyquinaldinic acid*)

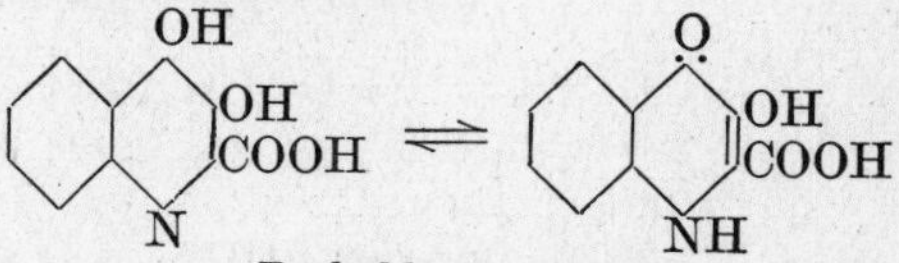

Probable structure

$C_{10}H_7O_4N$ MW, 205

Yellow micro-cryst. from H_2O. M.p. 286°. Sol. HCl, EtOH, AcOH + HCl. Spar. sol.

usual solvents. Caustic alkalis and carbonates ⟶ yellow sols. Millon's reagent ⟶ red col. $FeSO_4$ ⟶ intense green col.

Me ester: $C_{11}H_9O_4N$. MW, 219. Yellow cryst. from MeOH. M.p. 262°. *Dibenzoyl*: m.p. 171°.

Musajo, *Chem. Zentr.*, 1935, II, 2079; 1936, II, 3540.

Xanthydrol (*Dibenz-γ-pyranol, 5-hydroxy-xanthene, xanthenol-5*)

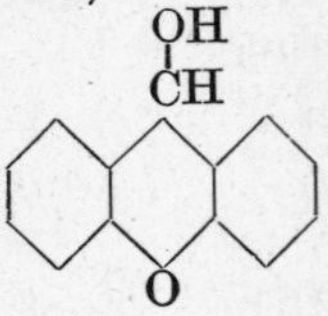

$C_{13}H_{10}O_2$ MW, 198

Needles from hot EtOH–H_2O. M.p. about 123°. Conc. H_2SO_4 ⟶ yellow sol. with green fluor. Warm in air ⟶ xanthone. Forms salts with min. acids. Reagent for urea.

Kirkhgof, Spektor, *Chem. Abstracts*, 1934, **28**, 5451.
Kyn-Jones, Ward, *J. Chem. Soc.*, 1930, 535.
Holleman, *Organic Syntheses*, Collective Vol. I, 539.

Xanthyletin

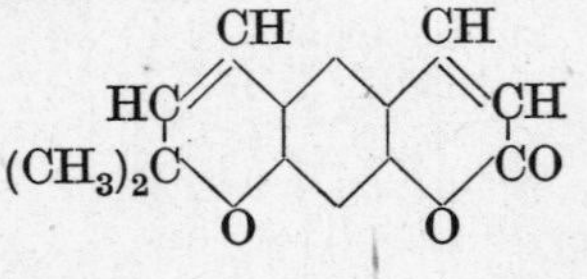

$C_{14}H_{12}O_3$ MW, 228

Constituent of bark of *Zanthoxylum americanum*, M. Prisms from petrol. M.p. 128–128·5°. Conc. H_2SO_4 ⟶ orange-red sol. NaOH ⟶ acetone + resorcinol.

Bell, Robertson, *J. Chem. Soc.*, 1936, 1828.

Xanthylic Acid (*Xanthine 9-ribosephosphoric acid*)

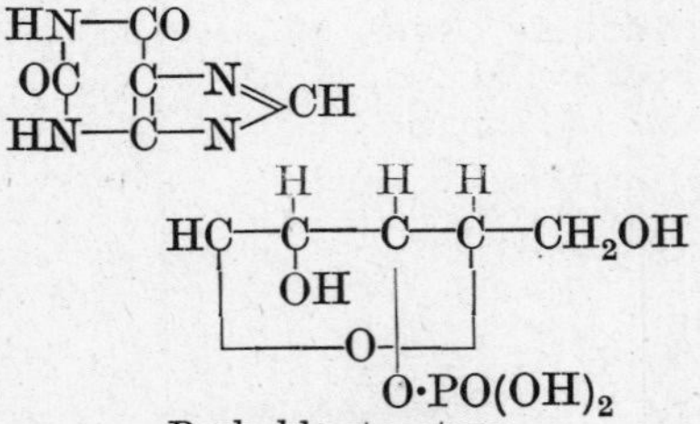

Probable structure

$C_{10}H_{15}O_9N_4P$ MW, 366

A typical nucleic acid. Powder from H_2O. $[\alpha]_D^{20}$ − 61·66° in 5% NaOH. Aq. sol. at 50° decomp. with formation of *d*-ribose-phosphoric acid.

Brucine salt: needles from 30% EtOH. M.p. 200°.

Knopf, *Z. physiol. Chem.*, 1914, **92**, 160.
Levene, Dmochowski, *J. Biol. Chem.*, 1931, **93**, 565.
Levene, Harris, *J. Biol. Chem.*, 1932, **95**, 757.

Xaxaquin.
See under Quinine.

Xenylamine.
See Aminodiphenyl.

Xenylcarbinol.
See Hydroxymethyldiphenyl.

***p*-Xenyl Mercaptan.**
See 4-Mercaptodiphenyl.

Xylan

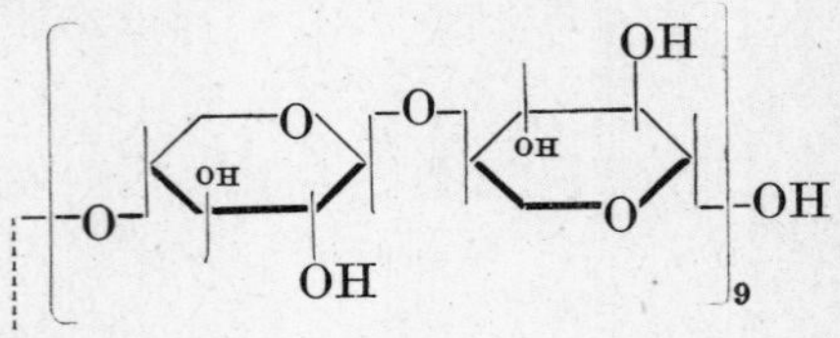

Arabo-furanose unit

Probable structure

$(C_5H_8O_4)_n$ MW, $(132)_n$

Occurs in wood gum, straw, esparto grass, maize cobs, oat hulls, hemp stalk, and is one of the hemicelluloses present in wood. White powder. M.p. 198°. $[\alpha]_D^{22}$ − 109·5° in 2·5% aq. NaOH (for xylan containing 10% H_2O). Does not reduce Fehling's. Hyd. by 3% HNO_3 ⟶ xylose (93%) + arabinose.

"*Dimethyl ether*": m.p. 194–6° (198°). B.p. about 80°/0·04 mm. n_D^{17} 1·4581. $[\alpha]_D^{21}$ + 61·8° in MeOH, $[\alpha]_D^{20}$ − 98·3° in $CHCl_3$. Sol. AcOH, Me_2CO, $CHCl_3$. Spar. sol. Et_2O.

"*Diacetyl*": amorph. powder. Sol. Py. Spar. sol. $CHCl_3$. Insol. H_2O, MeOH, EtOH, Et_2O.

Salkowski, *Z. physiol. Chem.*, 1901, **34**, 162.
Hurd, Currie, *J. Am. Chem. Soc.*, 1933, **55**, 1521.
Heuser, *J. prakt. Chem.*, 1921, **103**, 69.
Heuser, Schlosser, *Ber.*, 1923, **56**, 392.
Hibino, *J. Chem. Soc. Japan*, 1930, **51**, 417.
Hampton, Haworth, Hirst, *J. Chem. Soc.*, 1929, 1739.
Haworth, Percival, *J. Chem. Soc.*, 1931, 2850.
Haworth, Hirst, Oliver, *J. Chem. Soc.*, 1934, 1917.

***o*-Xylene** (1 : 2-*Dimethylbenzene*)

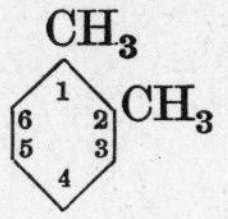

C_8H_{10} MW, 106

Colourless mobile liq. M.p. — 25·0°. B.p. 143·95–144·15° (142·3°). Vap. press.: 4·5 mm. at 0°, 10 mm. at 20°, 34·5 mm. at 50°, 199·5 mm. at 100°. D_4^{20} 0·89679. $n_D^{16\cdot57}$ 1·50712. Sol. EtOH, Et_2O. $CrO_2Cl_2 \longrightarrow$ *o*-toluic aldehyde. $KMnO_4 \longrightarrow$ phthalic acid + *o*-toluic acid. CO + HCl in presence of $AlCl_3 + Cu_2Cl_2 \longrightarrow$ 3 : 4-dimethylbenzaldehyde.

Picrate: lemon-yellow cryst. from EtOH. M.p. 88·5°.

I.G., D.R.P., 567,331, (*Chem. Abstracts*, 1933, **27**, 1366); F.P., 639,252, (*Chem. Abstracts*, 1929, **23**, 611).
General Aniline Works, U.S.P., 1,727,682, (*Chem. Abstracts*, 1929, **23**, 5196).

***m*-Xylene** (1 : 3-*Dimethylbenzene*).

Colourless, mobile liq. M.p. — 47·4°. B.p. 139·30°. Vap. press.: 2 mm. at 0°, 6 mm. at 20°, 31 mm. at 50°, 218 mm. at 100°. D_4^0 0·88113, D_4^{15} 0·86835. $n_{\text{He yellow}}^{15}$ 1·49989. Sol. EtOH, Et_2O. $CrO_3 \longrightarrow$ isophthalic acid.

Picrate: lemon-yellow cryst. from EtOH. M.p. 90–91·5°.

I.G., D.R.P., 567,331, (*Chem. Abstracts*, 1933, **27**, 1366).

***p*-Xylene** (1 : 4-*Dimethylbenzene*).

Plates or prisms. M.p. 13–14°. B.p. 137·5–138·0°. Vap. press.: 2 mm. at 0°, 6 mm. at 20°, 32 mm. at 50°, 230 mm. at 100°. D_4^{28} 0·8541. n_D^{21} 1·5004. Sol. EtOH, Et_2O. Dil. $HNO_3 \longrightarrow$ *p*-toluic acid. $CrO_3 \longrightarrow$ terephthalic acid.

Picrate: lemon-yellow cryst. from EtOH. M.p. 90·5°.

Jannasch, *Ber.*, 1877, **10**, 1356.
I.G., D.R.P., 567,331, (*Chem. Abstracts*, 1933, **27**, 1366); F.P., 639,252, (*Chem. Abstracts*, 1929, **23**, 611).
General Aniline Works, U.S.P., 1,727,682, (*Chem. Abstracts*, 1929, **23**, 5196).

Xyleneazocresol.

See 6-Hydroxy-3 : 2′ : 4′-trimethylazobenzene *and* 6-Hydroxy-3 : 3′ : 4′-trimethylazobenzene.

Xyleneazophenetole.

See under 4′-Hydroxy-2 : 4-dimethylazobenzene.

Xyleneazophenol.

See 4′-Hydroxy-2 : 4-dimethylazobenzene.

***m*-Xyleneazo-*m*-5-xylenol.**

See 4-Hydroxy-2 : 6 : 2′ : 4′-tetramethylazobenzene.

Xyleneazoxylidine.

See Aminotetramethylazobenzene.

Xylene-carboxylic Acid.

See Dimethylbenzoic Acid.

Xylene-dicarboxylic Acid.

See Dimethylphthalic Acid, Dimethylisophthalic Acid, Dimethylterephthalic Acid, *and* Phenylenediacetic Acid.

***o*-Xylene-3 : 5-disulphonic Acid** (4 : 5-*Dimethylbenzene*-1 : 3-*disulphonic acid*)

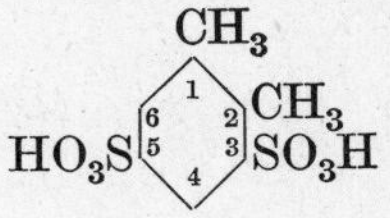

$C_8H_{10}O_6S_2$ MW, 266

Dichloride: $C_8H_8O_4Cl_2S_2$. MW, 303. Yellow prisms from Et_2O. M.p. 79°. Sol. Et_2O, $CHCl_3$, CS_2.

Diamide: $C_8H_{12}O_4N_2S_2$. MW, 264. Cryst. M.p. 239°. Mod. sol. H_2O.

Dianilide: cryst. from EtOH. M.p. 199–200°. Very sol. Me_2CO. Sol. EtOH. Spar. sol. H_2O.

Pollak, Heimberg-Krauss, Katscher, Lustig, *Monatsh.*, 1930, **55**, 365.

***o*-Xylene-3 : 6-disulphonic Acid** (2 : 3-*Dimethylbenzene*-1 : 4-*disulphonic acid*).

Diamide: cryst. from EtOH.Aq. M.p. 251°.

Holleman, Choufoer, *Chem. Abstracts*, 1924, **18**, 3183.

***m*-Xylene-2 : 4-disulphonic Acid** (2 : 4-*Dimethylbenzene*-1 : 3-*disulphonic acid*)

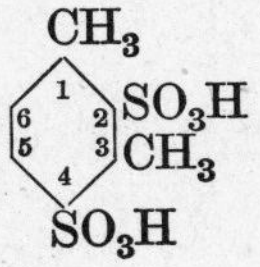

$C_8H_{10}O_6S_2$ MW, 266

Dichloride: $C_8H_8O_4Cl_2S_2$. MW, 303. Viscous oil.

Diamide: $C_8H_{12}O_4N_2S_2$. MW, 264. Needles from H_2O. M.p. 223–4° (235°).

Pollak, v. Meissner, *Monatsh.*, 1928, **50**, 247.
Choufoer, *Chem. Abstracts*, 1925, **19**, 2195.

***m*-Xylene-4 : 6-disulphonic Acid** (4 : 6-*Dimethylbenzene*-1 : 3-*disulphonic acid*).

Needles. Decomp. very readily.

Di-Et ester: $C_{12}H_{18}O_6S_2$. MW, 322. Leaflets. Sol. EtOH. Insol. H_2O.

Difluoride: $C_8H_8O_4F_2S_2$. MW, 270. Cryst. M.p. 116–18°.

Dichloride: cryst. from pet. ether. M.p. 130°. Mod. sol. Et_2O, $CHCl_3$, CS_2.

Diamide: needles from H_2O. M.p. 249°. Spar. sol. H_2O. N : N′-*Di-Et*: needles from H_2O. M.p. 135°.

Dianilide: cryst. from 50% EtOH. M.p. 196°.

Pollak, v. Meissner, *Monatsh.*, 1928, **50**, 244.
Davies, Dick, *J. Chem. Soc.*, 1931, 2107.
Holleman, Choufoer, *Rec. trav. chim.*, 1929, **48**, 1076.

***p*-Xylene-2 : 3-disulphonic Acid** (3 : 6-*Dimethylbenzene*-1 : 2-*disulphonic acid*)

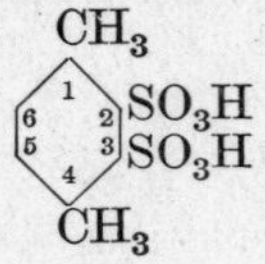

$C_8H_{10}O_6S_2$ MW, 266

Anhydride: $C_8H_8O_5S_2$. MW, 248. Leaflets from pet. ether. M.p. 189–90°.

Holleman, Choufoer, *Rec. trav. chim.*, 1929, **48**, 1082.

***p*-Xylene-2 : 6-disulphonic Acid** (2 : 5-*Dimethylbenzene*-1 : 3-*disulphonic acid*).

Needles. Very sol. H_2O.

Dichloride: $C_8H_8O_4Cl_2S_2$. MW, 303. Cryst. from ligroin. M.p. 81°. Sol. Et_2O, AcOEt, $CHCl_3$, C_6H_6. Spar. sol. CS_2, pet. ether, ligroin.

Diamide: $C_8H_{12}O_4N_2S_2$. MW, 264. Cryst. from EtOH.Aq. M.p. 294–5° decomp. Sol. Me_2CO. Spar. sol. Et_2O, AcOH, $CHCl_3$. Very spar. sol. H_2O.

Dianilide: cryst. from EtOH. M.p. 174°.

Holmes, *Am. Chem. J.*, 1891, **13**, 372.
Pollak, Schadler, *Monatsh.*, 1918, **39**, 144.
Pollak, Heimberg-Krauss, Katscher, Lustig, *Monatsh.*, 1930, **55**, 366.

***p*-Xylene-3 : 6-disulphonic Acid** (2 : 5-*Dimethylbenzene*-1 : 4-*disulphonic acid*).

Dichloride: cryst. from pet. ether. M.p. 164°.

Diamide: m.p. about 310° (297°).

Dianilide: cryst. from EtOH. M.p. 223°.

See last reference above.

Xylene Musk.

See 2 : 4 : 6-Trinitro-5-*tert.*-butyl-*m*-xylene.

***o*-Xylene-3-sulphinic Acid** (2 : 3-*Dimethylbenzenesulphinic acid*)

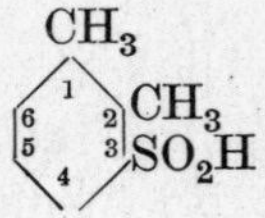

$C_8H_{10}O_2S$ MW, 170

Cryst. M.p. 105°. Sol. Et_2O.

Moschner, *Ber.*, 1901, **34**, 1260.

***o*-Xylene-4-sulphinic Acid** (3 : 4-*Dimethylbenzenesulphinic acid*).

Plates from H_2O. M.p. 83°.

Jacobsen, *Ber.*, 1877, **10**, 1010.
Knoevenagel, Kenner, *Ber.*, 1908, **41**, 3319.

***m*-Xylene-4-sulphinic Acid** (2 : 4-*Dimethylbenzenesulphinic acid*)

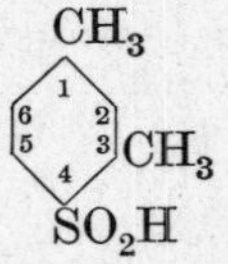

$C_8H_{10}O_2S$ MW, 170

Needles from H_2O. M.p. 77–8°.

Gattermann, *Ber.*, 1899, **32**, 1141.
Knoevenagel, Kenner, *Ber.*, 1908, **41**, 3318.

***m*-Xylene-5-sulphinic Acid** (3 : 5-*Dimethylbenzenesulphinic acid*).

Reddish cryst. mass. M.p. 75–6°.

Moschner, *Ber.*, 1901, **34**, 1260.

***p*-Xylene-2-sulphinic Acid** (2 : 5-*Dimethylbenzenesulphinic acid*)

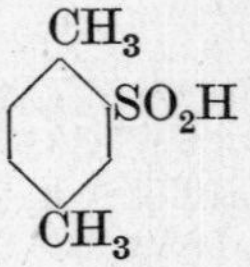

$C_8H_{10}O_2S$ MW, 170

Needles from H_2O. M.p. 85°. Sol. EtOH, Et_2O. Spar. sol. H_2O.

Anhydride: m.p. 68–9°.

Hilditch, *J. Chem. Soc.*, 1908, **93**, 1527.
Gattermann, *Ber.*, 1899, **32**, 1141.
Knoevenagel, Polack, *Ber.*, 1908, **41**, 3327.

o-Xylene-3-sulphonic Acid (2 : 3-*Dimethylbenzenesulphonic acid*)

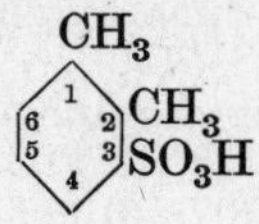

$C_8H_{10}O_3S$ MW, 186

Cryst. from H_2O. Heat in air at 115–20° ⟶ 4-sulphonic acid.

Chloride: $C_8H_9O_2ClS$. MW, 204·5. Prisms from pet. ether. M.p. 47°.

Amide: $C_8H_{11}O_2NS$. MW, 185. Needles from H_2O. M.p. 167° (165°). Spar. sol. H_2O.

Moody, *Chem. News*, 1893, **67**, 34.
Moschner, *Ber.*, 1901, **34**, 1260.

o-Xylene-4-sulphonic Acid (3 : 4-*Dimethylbenzenesulphonic acid*).

Plates or prisms + $2H_2O$ from $CHCl_3$. M.p. 63–4° (55°). Very hygroscopic.

Chloride: prisms from Et_2O. M.p. 51–2°.

Amide: prisms from EtOH. M.p. 143–4°.

Patterson, McMillan, Somerville, *J. Chem. Soc.*, 1924, **125**, 2489.
Jacobsen, *Ber.*, 1877, **10**, 1010.

m-Xylene-2-sulphonic Acid (2:6-*Dimethylbenzenesulphonic acid*)

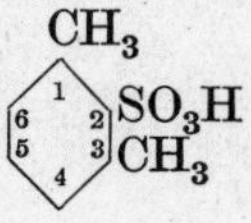

$C_8H_{10}O_3S$ MW, 186

Cryst. Heat at 100° ⟶ 4-sulphonic acid.

Chloride: $C_8H_9O_2ClS$. MW, 204·5. Prisms. M.p. 39°.

Amide: $C_8H_{11}O_2NS$. MW, 185. Needles. M.p. 113°.

Pollak, v. Meissner, *Monatsh.*, 1928, **50**, 246.
Moody, *Chem. News*, 1888, **58**, 21.

m-Xylene-4-sulphonic Acid (2:4-*Dimethylbenzenesulphonic acid*).

Plates or prisms + $2H_2O$ from H_2O. M.p. 61–2°.

Fluoride: $C_8H_9O_2FS$. MW, 188. B.p. 246° (239–40°), 149–50°/15 mm. n_D^{20} 1·5086.

Chloride: cryst. M.p. 34°.

Amide: needles from H_2O. M.p. 138–9° (137°). N-*Benzoyl*: needles from EtOH. M.p. 149–51°.

Methylamide: $C_9H_{13}O_2NS$. MW, 199. Cryst. from EtOH. M.p. 43°. Sol. EtOH, Et_2O.

Dimethylamide: $C_{10}H_{15}O_2NS$. MW, 213. Cryst. from EtOH.Aq. M.p. 35°.

Anilide: cryst. from EtOH. M.p. 109–10°. N-*Me*: m.p. 55°.

p-*Nitroanilide*: cryst. + C_6H_6 from C_6H_6. M.p. 91–3°, solvent free 117–19°.

Anhydride: m.p. 139°. Decomp. on standing.

Crafts, *Ber.*, 1901, **34**, 1352.
Pollak, v. Meissner, *Monatsh.*, 1928, **50**, 246.
Davies, Dick, *J. Chem. Soc.*, 1931, 2107.
Patterson, McMillan, Somerville, *J. Chem. Soc.*, 1924, **125**, 2489.

m-Xylene-5-sulphonic Acid (3:5-*Dimethylbenzenesulphonic acid*).

Needles from H_2O.

Chloride: needles from pet. ether or C_6H_6. M.p. 94° (89–90°).

Bromide: $C_8H_9O_2BrS$. MW, 249. M.p. 92–3°.

Amide: prisms from boiling EtOH. M.p. 135°. Sol. EtOH. Less sol. Et_2O. Mod. sol. hot H_2O. Insol. ligroin.

Anilide: cryst. from EtOH. M.p. 119°.

p-*Toluidide*: prisms from EtOH. M.p. 121–2°.

Moschner, *Ber.*, 1901, **34**, 1260.
Jungahn, *Ber.*, 1902, **35**, 3756.
Armstrong, Wilson, *Chem. News*, 1901, **83**, 46.

p-Xylene-2-sulphonic Acid (2 : 5-*Dimethylbenzenesulphonic acid*)

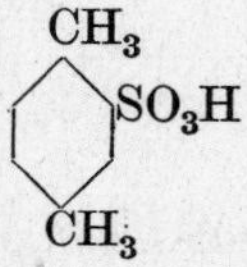

$C_8H_{10}O_3S$ MW, 186

Leaflets or prisms + $2H_2O$ from H_2O. M.p. 86°. Sol. $CHCl_3$.

Fluoride: $C_8H_9O_2FS$. MW, 188. M.p. 24·5°. B.p. 124–5°/21 mm.

Chloride: $C_8H_9O_2ClS$. MW, 204·5. Prisms. M.p. 24–6°.

Amide: $C_8H_{11}O_2NS$. MW, 185. Needles. M.p. 147–8°. Sol. EtOH. Mod. sol. hot H_2O.

Jacobsen, *Ber.*, 1877, **10**, 1009; 1878, **11**, 22.
Steinkopf *et al.*, *J. prakt. Chem.*, 1927, **117**, 39.

o-3-Xylenol (2 : 3-*Dimethylphenol*, 3-*hydroxy*-o-*xylene*)

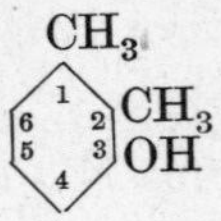

$C_8H_{10}O$ MW, 122

Needles from EtOH.Aq. M.p. 75° (73·5°). B.p. 218°. $FeCl_3 \longrightarrow$ blue col.

Me ether: 2 : 3-dimethylanisole. $C_9H_{12}O$. MW, 136. Cryst. M.p. 29°. B.p. 199°. Sol. EtOH, Et_2O, C_6H_6.

Et ether: 2 : 3-dimethylphenetole. $C_{10}H_{14}O$. MW, 150. M.p. 10°. B.p. 212·5°.

Moschner, *Ber.*, 1900, **33**, 742.
Short, Stromberg, Wiles, *J. Chem. Soc.*, 1936, 322.
Kruber, Schmitt, *Ber.*, 1931, **64**, 2270.

o-4-Xylenol (3 : 4-*Dimethylphenol*, 4-*hydroxy*-o-*xylene*).

Needles from H_2O. M.p. 62·5°. B.p. 225°/757 mm. Heat of comb. C_p 1035·4 Cal. $k = 5{\cdot}2 \times 10^{-11}$ at 25°.

Me ether: 3 : 4-dimethylanisole. B.p. 204–5°.

Et ether: 3 : 4-dimethylphenetole. B.p. 218°.

3 : 5-*Dinitrobenzoyl*: needles from 95% EtOH. M.p. 181·6°.

1-*Naphthylurethane*: m.p. 141–2°.

Picrate: chrome yellow. M.p. 83·8°.

Jacobsen, *Ber.*, 1878, **11**, 28; 1884, **17**, 161.
Moschner, *Ber.*, 1900, **33**, 743.

m-2-Xylenol (2 : 6-*Dimethylphenol*, 2-*hydroxy*-m-*xylene*)

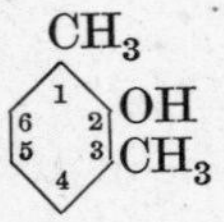

$C_8H_{10}O$ MW, 122

Leaflets or flat needles. M.p. 49°. B.p. 203°.

Me ether: 2 : 6-dimethylanisole. $C_9H_{12}O$. MW, 136. B.p. 182–3°.

Et ether: 2 : 6-dimethylphenetole. $C_{10}H_{14}O$. MW, 150. B.p. 195·5–196·5°. $D_4^{13\cdot9}$ 0·9420. $n_D^{13\cdot9}$ 1·497.

3 : 5-*Dinitrobenzoyl*: plates from 95% EtOH. M.p. 158·8°.

Picrate: orange-yellow. M.p. 50–3°.

Bamberger, *Ber.*, 1903, **36**, 2036.
Gattermann, *Ann.*, 1907, **357**, 363.

m-4-Xylenol (2 : 4-*Dimethylphenol*, 4-*hydroxy*-m-*xylene*).

Needles. M.p. 27–8°. B.p. 211·5°/766 mm., 97–8°/14 mm. D_4^{14} 1·0276. n_D^{14} 1·5420. Misc. with EtOH, Et_2O. Spar. sol. H_2O. Heat of comb. C_p 1037·5 Cal.

Me ether: 2 : 4-dimethylanisole. B.p. 192°. $D_4^{13\cdot45}$ 0·9691. $n_D^{12\cdot85}$ 1·517.

Et ether: 2 : 4-dimethylphenetole. B.p. 202–3°. $D_4^{13\cdot8}$ 0·9488. $n_D^{13\cdot95}$ 1·507.

Acetyl: b.p. 107·5–108·5°/13 mm. $D_4^{15\cdot5}$ 1·0298. $n_D^{15\cdot5}$ 1·4990.

Propionyl: b.p. 121·5°/15 mm. D^{17} 1·0104. n_D^{17} 1·4944.

Benzoyl: cryst. from AcOH. M.p. **37–8°**. B.p. 110·5–111°/15 mm.

3 : 5-*Dinitrobenzoyl*: plates from 95% EtOH. M.p. 164·6°.

Phenylurethane: m.p. 102°.

1-*Naphthylurethane*: m.p. 134–5°.

Sabatier, Mailhe, *Compt. rend.*, 1910, **151**, 361.
Palfray, Duboc, *Compt. rend.*, 1927, **185**, 1479.

m-5-Xylenol (3 : 5-*Dimethylphenol*, 5-*hydroxy*-m-*xylene*).

Needles from H_2O. M.p. 68° (64°). B.p. 219·5°. Sublimes.

Me ether: 3 : 5-dimethylanisole. B.p. 193°.

Et ether: 3 : 5-dimethylphenetole. B.p. 208°.

Isopropyl ether: $C_{11}H_{16}O$. MW, 164. B.p. 208–10°.

Allyl ether: $C_{11}H_{14}O$. MW, 162. B.p. 109°/11 mm.

Acetyl: b.p. 130°/26 mm., 120°/11 mm.

Chloroacetyl: b.p. 175–7°/48 mm., 146–7°/12 mm.

3 : 5-*Dinitrobenzoyl*: rods from 95% EtOH. M.p. 195·4°.

Phenylurethane: m.p. 151°.

Raschig, D.R.P., 254,716, (*Chem. Zentr.*, 1913, I, 353).
Auwers, Borsche, *Ber.*, 1915, **48**, 1708, 1722.

p-2-Xylenol (2 : 5-*Dimethylphenol*, *hydroxy*-p-*xylene*)

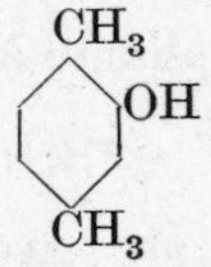

$C_8H_{10}O$ MW, 122

Prisms from EtOH–Et_2O. M.p. 75°. B.p. 211·5°/762 mm. Sol. EtOH, Et_2O. Heat of comb. C_p 1035·6 Cal. $k = 4{\cdot}8 \times 10^{-11}$ at 25°. No col. with $FeCl_3$. Sublimes. Volatile in steam.

Me ether: 2 : 5-dimethylanisole. $C_9H_{12}O$. MW, 136. B.p. 194°/772 mm.

Et ether : 2 : 5-dimethylphenetole. $C_{10}H_{14}O$. MW, 150. B.p. 198·8°/748 mm. Heat of comb. C_p 1368·85 Cal.

Acetyl : b.p. 237°/768 mm.

3 : 5-*Dinitrobenzoyl* : needles from 95% EtOH. M.p. 137·2°.

Phenylurethane : m.p. 162° (160–1°).

1-*Naphthylurethane* : m.p. 172–3°.

Picrate : orange. M.p. 81–2°.

Morgan, Pettet, E.P., 397,148, (*Chem. Abstracts*, 1934, **28**, 784).
Jacobsen, *Ber.*, 1878, **11**, 26.
Noelting, Witt, Forel, *Ber.*, 1885, **18**, 2665.

Xylenol-carboxylic Acid.

See Hydroxydimethylbenzoic Acid.

***m*-5-Xylenol-2 : 4-disulphonic Acid** (3 : 5-*Dimethylphenol*-2 : 4-*disulphonic acid*, 6-*hydroxy*-2 : 4-*dimethylbenzene*-1 : 3-*disulphonic acid*)

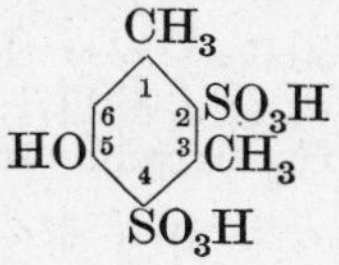

$C_8H_{10}O_7S_2$ MW, 282

Dichloride : $C_8H_8O_5Cl_2S_2$. MW, 319. M.p. 117–19°.

Diamide : $C_8H_{12}O_5N_2S_2$. MW, 280. Leaflets from H_2O. M.p. 206–8°.

Dianilide : cryst. from C_6H_6. M.p. 205–7°.

Katscher, Lehr, *Monatsh.*, 1934, **64**, 238.
Ler, *Chem. Abstracts*, 1934, **28**, 4714.

***m*-5-Xylenol-4 : 6-disulphonic Acid** (3 : 5-*Dimethylphenol*-2 : 6-*disulphonic acid*, 2-*hydroxy*-4 : 6-*dimethylbenzene*-1 : 3-*disulphonic acid*).

Dichloride : cryst. from pet. ether. M.p. 89–91°.

Dianilide : m.p. 160–1°.

See last reference above.

***o*-4-Xylenol-5-sulphonic Acid** (3 : 4-*Dimethylphenol*-6-*sulphonic acid*, 2-*hydroxy*-4 : 5-*dimethylbenzenesulphonic acid*)

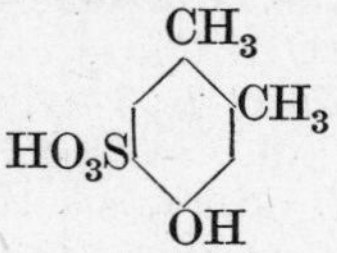

$C_8H_{10}O_4S$ MW, 202

Cryst. Steam at 107–10° ⟶ *o*-4-xylenol.

Na salt : prisms.

Ba salt : rhombic plates. Spar. sol. cold H_2O.

Jacobsen, *Ber.*, 1878, **11**, 28.

***m*-4-Xylenol-2-sulphonic Acid** (2 : 4-*Dimethylphenol*-3-*sulphonic acid*, 3-*hydroxy*-2 : 6-*dimethylbenzenesulphonic acid*)

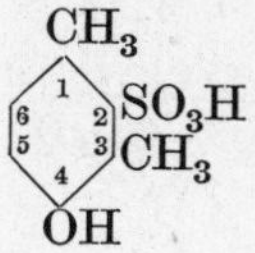

$C_8H_{10}O_4S$ MW, 202

Cryst.

Ba salt : needles.

Jacobsen, *Ann.*, 1879, **195**, 283.

***m*-4-Xylenol-5-sulphonic Acid** (2 : 4-*Dimethylphenol*-6-*sulphonic acid*, 2-*hydroxy*-3 : 5-*dimethylbenzenesulphonic acid*).

Needles. Very sol. H_2O, EtOH. $FeCl_3$ ⟶ blue col. ⟶ green on adding EtOH. Decomp. with steam at 121–5°.

Fluoride : $C_8H_9O_3FS$. MW, 204. B.p. 71–3° in high vacuum.

Chloride : $C_8H_9O_3ClS$. MW, 220·5. *Acetyl* : cryst. from pet. ether. M.p. 62°.

Anilide : leaflets from EtOH.Aq. M.p. 142–3°. N-*Me* : prisms from pet. ether. M.p. 111–12°. N-*Acetyl* : cryst. from pet. ether. M.p. 105°.

Katscher, Lehr, *Monatsh.*, 1934, **64**, 242.
Ler, *Chem. Abstracts*, 1934, **28**, 4715.

***m*-4-Xylenol-6-sulphonic Acid** (2 : 4-*Dimethylphenol*-5-*sulphonic acid*, 3-*hydroxy*-4 : 6-*dimethylbenzenesulphonic acid*).

Needles. Very sol. H_2O, EtOH. $FeCl_3$ ⟶ bluish-violet col.

Me ether : $C_9H_{12}O_4S$. MW, 216. Needles. Sol. H_2O, EtOH, Et_2O. Spar. sol. C_6H_6. Decomp. on heating. *Amide* : $C_9H_{13}O_3NS$. MW, 215. Needles. M.p. 190°. Sol. EtOH. Spar. sol. H_2O.

Et ether : $C_{10}H_{14}O_4S$. MW, 230. Plates. Sol. EtOH. *Chloride* : $C_{10}H_{13}O_3ClS$. MW, 248·5. Rhombic plates from ligroin. M.p. 56°. *Amide* : $C_{10}H_{15}O_3NS$. Needles from EtOH. M.p. 169–70°.

Propyl ether : $C_{11}H_{16}O_4S$. MW, 244. Plates or needles. Mod. sol. H_2O, EtOH. *Amide* : $C_{11}H_{17}O_3NS$. Needles. M.p. 146°. Sol. EtOH. Spar. sol. H_2O.

Sartig, *Ann.*, 1885, **230**, 336.
Shober, Kiffer, *Am. Chem. J.*, 1897, **19**, 386.
Moody, *Chem. News*, 1892, **65**, 60.

***p*-2-Xylenol-3-sulphonic Acid** (2 : 5-*Dimethylphenol*-6-*sulphonic acid*, 2-*hydroxy*-3 : 6-*dimethylbenzenesulphonic acid*)

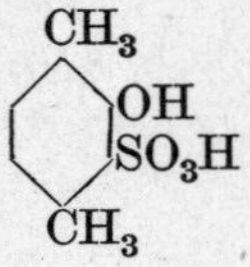

$C_8H_{10}O_4S$ MW, 202

Cryst. from H_2O. Decomp. with steam at 115–18°.

Ba salt : needles.

Morgan, Pettet, E.P., 397,148, (*Chem. Abstracts*, 1934, **28**, 784).
Jacobsen, *Ber.*, 1878, **11**, 27.

***o*-3-Xylidine** (3-*Amino*-o-*xylene*)

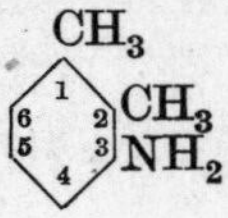

$C_8H_{11}N$ MW, 121

Liq. B.p. 221–2°. D^{15} 0·991.

B,HCl : m.p. 254°.

N-*Me* : *see* *N*-Methyl-*o*-3-xylidine.

N-*Di-Me* : *see* *N*-Dimethyl-*o*-3-xylidine.

N-*Et* : $C_{10}H_{15}N$. MW, 149. B.p. 227–8°.

N-*Acetyl* : 3-acet-1 : 2-xylidide. Needles from EtOH or H_2O. M.p. 135° (131°). Sol. EtOH, Et_2O. Mod. sol. C_6H_6.

Hodgkinson, Limpach, *J. Chem. Soc.*, 1900, **77**, 68.
Menton, *Ann.*, 1891, **263**, 321.

***o*-4-Xylidine** (4-*Amino*-o-*xylene*).

Plates or prisms from ligroin. M.p. 51° (47–8°). B.p. 226°. Mod. sol. pet. ether. Spar. sol. cold H_2O.

B,HCl : m.p. 256°.

N-*Formyl* : m.p. 52°.

N-*Di-Me* : *see* *N*-Dimethyl-*o*-4-xylidine.

N-*Acetyl* : 4-acet-1 : 2-xylidide. Prisms or needles from EtOH.Aq. M.p. 99°. Very sol. EtOH.

N-*Chloroacetyl* : needles from EtOH.Aq. M.p. 109°. Sol. EtOH, Et_2O, AcOH.

N-*Cinnamoyl* : m.p. 175–6°.

Bamberger, Blangey, *Ann.*, 1911, **384**, 318, *Note* 2.
Jacobsen, *Ber.*, 1884, **17**, 160.
Graebe, *Ber.*, 1901, **34**, 1779.
Limpach, *Ber.*, 1888, **21**, 646.

***m*-2-Xylidine** (2-*Amino*-m-*xylene*)

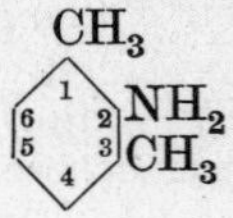

$C_8H_{11}N$ MW, 121

Liq. B.p. 214°/739 mm. Ox. ⟶ *m*-xyloquinone.

N-*Me* : *see* *N*-Methyl-*m*-2-xylidine.

N-*Di-Me* : *see* *N*-Dimethyl-*m*-2-xylidine.

N-*Et* : $C_{10}H_{15}N$. MW, 149. Oil. B.p. 217–18°.

N-*Di-Et* : $C_{12}H_{19}N$. MW, 177. B.p. 220–21°. Volatile in steam.

N-*Formyl* : needles from EtOH. M.p. 176–7° (rapid heat.). Mod. sol. EtOH.

N-*Acetyl* : 2-acet-1 : 3-xylidide. Needles. M.p. 177°. N-*Nitroso* : plates from pet. ether. M.p. 62–3°. Heat in C_6H_6 ⟶ 7-methylindazole.

N-*Benzoyl* : needles from EtOH.Aq. M.p. 168–168·5°. Very sol. EtOH, Et_2O, $CHCl_3$. Spar. sol. cold C_6H_6, ligroin.

Friedländer, Brand, *Monatsh.*, 1898, **19**, 639.
Busch, *Ber.*, 1899, **32**, 1008.
I.C.I., U.S.P., 1,867,962, (*Chem. Abstracts*, 1932, **26**, 5106) ; E.P., **328**,418, (*Chem. Abstracts*, 1930, **24**, 5309).

***m*-4-Xylidine** (4-*Amino*-m-*xylene*).

B.p. 215·8–216·0°/728 mm. $D_4^{19·6}$ 0·9783. $n_D^{19·6}$ 1·56066. Heat of comb. C_v 1111·42 Cal. $k = 6·3 \times 10^{-10}$ at 15°.

B,HCl : prisms from H_2O. M.p. 235–6°.

Oxalate : m.p. 167°.

Picrate : yellow cryst. powder. M.p. 209° decomp.

N-*Me* : *see* *N*-Methyl-*m*-4-xylidine.

N-*Di-Me* : *see* *N*-Dimethyl-*m*-4-xylidine.

N-*Butyl* : $C_{12}H_{19}N$. MW, 177. Pale yellow oil. B.p. 267–70°/765 mm., 162–4°/29 mm. *Acetyl* : b.p. 290–3°/765 mm. *Benzoyl* : m.p. 193°.

N-*Formyl* : plates or needles from H_2O. M.p. 113–14°. Sol. EtOH, Et_2O.

N-*Acetyl* : 4-acet-1 : 3-xylidide. Needles from EtOH.Aq. M.p. 129–30°. B.p. 170°/10 mm. Sol. EtOH. Spar. sol. H_2O.

N-*Chloroacetyl* : needles from C_6H_6 or EtOH. M.p. 151–2°. Sol. EtOH. Spar. sol. C_6H_6.

N-*Benzoyl* : needles from EtOH. M.p. 192°. Sol. EtOH. Insol. H_2O.

N-p-*Nitrobenzoyl* : prisms from EtOH.Aq. M.p. 166°.

N-p-*Toluenesulphonyl*: m.p. 180·4–181·3°.

Pinnow, Oesterreich, *Ber.*, 1898, **31**, 2930.
Hodgkinson, Limpach, *J. Chem. Soc.*, 1900, **77**, 66.
Willgerodt, Schmierer, *Ber.*, 1905, **38**, 1473.
Reilly, O'Neill, *J. Soc. Chem. Ind.*, 1927, **46**, 226T.
Silesia Verein, F.P., 691,911, (*Chem. Abstracts*, 1931, **25**, 1265).

***m*-5-Xylidine** (5-*Amino*-m-*xylene*).
B.p. 220–1°. D^0 0·9935.
B,HCl: needles. Sublimes.
N-*Di-Me*: *see N*-Dimethyl-*m*-5-xylidine.
N-*Formyl*: prisms from EtOH.Aq. M.p. 76·5°.
N-*Acetyl*: 5-acet-1 : 3-xylidide. Needles from EtOH. M.p. 140·5° (144·5°).

Wroblewski, *Ann.*, 1881, **207**, 95.
Haller, Adams, Wherry, *J. Am. Chem. Soc.*, 1920, **42**, 184.

***p*-Xylidine** (2-*Amino*-p-*xylene*)

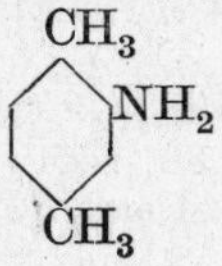

$C_8H_{11}N$ MW, 121

Pale yellow leaflets. M.p. 15·5°. B.p. 213·5°. D_4^{21} 0·9790. $n_D^{21\cdot3}$ 1·55914. Mod. sol. H_2O. $k = 9{\cdot}63 \times 10^{-10}$ at 20°. Turns deep yellow in air. $CrO_3 \longrightarrow$ *p*-xyloquinone.
B,HCl: m.p. 228°.
Picrate: greenish-yellow. M.p. 171° decomp.
N-*Me*: *see N*-Methyl-*p*-xylidine.
N-*Di-Me*: *see N*-Dimethyl-*p*-xylidine.
N-*Et*: $C_{10}H_{15}N$. MW, 149. Oil. B.p. 222–3°/748 mm.
N-*Benzyl*: $C_{15}H_{17}N$. MW, 211. B.p. 320–5°.
N-*Formyl*: needles from H_2O. M.p. 116–17°.
N-*Acetyl*: 2-acet-1 : 4-xylidide. Needles from H_2O or toluene. M.p. 139°.
N-*Chloroacetyl*: needles from EtOH.Aq. M.p. 153°.
N-*Benzoyl*: needles from EtOH. M.p. 140°.
N-p-*Toluenesulphonyl*: m.p. 232–3°.

Pflug, *Ann.*, 1889, **255**, 172.
Noelting, Witt, Forel, *Ber.*, 1885, **18**, 2664.
Jannasch, *Ann.*, 1875, **176**, 55.
Schmidt, E.P., 252,460, (*Chem. Abstracts*, 1927, **21**, 2273).

β-Xylidinic Acid.
See 4-Methylisophthalic Acid.

Xylitol

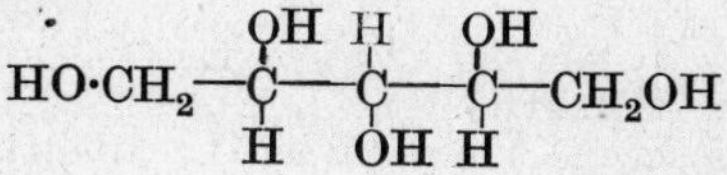

$C_5H_{12}O_5$ MW, 152

Syrup. Sweet taste. HI $\longrightarrow$ *sec.-n*-amyl iodide. PbO_2 + HCl $\longrightarrow$ xyloketose. Not oxidised by sorbose bacterium.
Dibenzylidene deriv.: cryst. M.p. 175°. Sol. $CHCl_3$. Prac. insol. H_2O, EtOH.
Penta-acetyl: m.p. 61·5–62·5°.

Fischer, *Ber.*, 1894, **27**, 2487.
Bertrand, *Bull. soc. chim.*, 1891, **5**, 555.
de Bruyn, v. Ekenstein, *Rec. trav. chim.*, 1899, **18**, 151.
Bertrand, *Compt. rend.*, 1936, **203**, 143.

2-Xylodesose

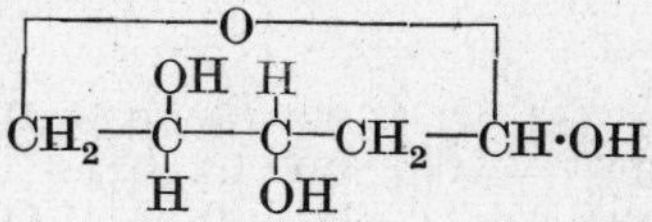

$C_5H_{10}O_4$ MW, 134

d-.
Plates. M.p. 92–6°. $[\alpha]_D^{22}$ $-$ 40·25° $\longrightarrow$ + 50·75° in Py, $-$ 22·5° $\longrightarrow$ $-$ 2·0° in H_2O. Sol. H_2O, EtOH, Py. Spar. sol. Me_2CO. Insol. Et_2O, $CHCl_3$, CCl_4, C_6H_6. Reduces Fehling's.
Benzylphenylhydrazone: prisms or plates. M.p. 116–18°. $[\alpha]_D^{25}$ + 13·5° in Py. Sol. EtOH, Me_2CO, Py. Spar. sol. Et_2O. Insol. H_2O.

Levene, Mori, *J. Biol. Chem.*, 1929, **83**, 803.

***p*-Xylohydroquinone.**
See 2 : 5-Dihydroxy-*p*-xylene.

Xyloketose

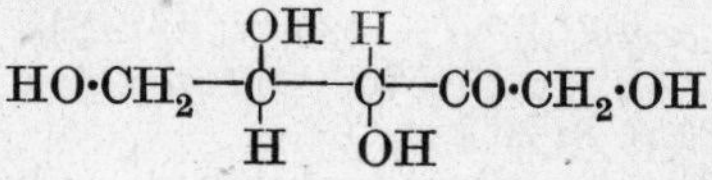

$C_5H_{10}O_5$ MW, 150

d-.
Syrup. Hygroscopic. $[\alpha]_D^{18}$ $-$ 33·2°. Reduces Fehling's. p-*Bromophenylhydrazone*: m.p. 128–9°. $[\alpha]_D^{20}$ + 23·7° $\longrightarrow$ $-$ 31·2° in Py.

l-.
Free sugar not isolated. Reduces Fehling's. $[\alpha]_D^{20}$ + 33·1°.
Phenylosazone: m.p. 160–3°. $[\alpha]_D$ + 0° 15′ in Py–EtOH. Identical with *l*-xylosazone and *l*-lyxosazone.

p-Bromophenylhydrazone : yellow plates from dil. EtOH. M.p. 130–1° (128°). $[\alpha]^{20} - 25\cdot8°$ $\longrightarrow + 31\cdot5°$ in Py. $[\alpha]_D - 1°$ in EtOH.

dl-.

Syrup. Sol. H_2O.

Phenylosazone : m.p. 210–15°. Identical with *dl-*xylosazone.

Methylphenylosazone : yellow needles. M.p. 173°.

Neuberg, *Ber.*, 1902, **35**, 2628.
Levene, La Forge, *J. Biol. Chem.*, 1914, **18**, 319.
v. Vargha, *Ber.*, 1935, **68**, 24.
Schmidt, Treiber, *Ber.*, 1933, **66**, 1765.

Xylonic Acid

$$\text{HO·CH}_2\overset{\overset{\text{OH}}{|}}{\underset{\underset{\text{H}}{|}}{\text{C}}}\overset{\overset{\text{H}}{|}}{\underset{\underset{\text{OH}}{|}}{\text{C}}}\overset{\overset{\text{OH}}{|}}{\underset{\underset{\text{H}}{|}}{\text{C}}}\text{COOH}$$

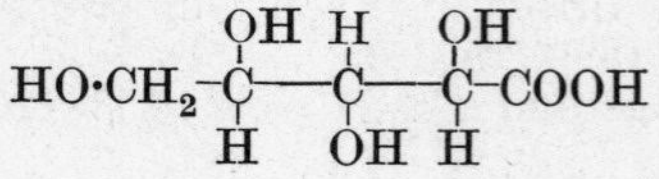

$C_5H_{10}O_6$ MW, 166

d-.

Syrup. $[\alpha]_D + 17\cdot98°$ (final) in H_2O, $- 1\cdot9°$ $\longrightarrow - 3\cdot6° \longrightarrow + 20\cdot2°$ in H_2O.

Cinchonine salt : plates from H_2O or needles from EtOH. M.p. 180° decomp. (170°). $[\alpha]_D^{17} + 125\cdot0°$ in H_2O.

Brucine salt : cryst. from EtOH. M.p. 176° (172–4°). $[\alpha]_D^{20} - 18\cdot7°$ in H_2O.

Morphine salt : needles from dil. EtOH. M.p. 153°.

Amide : $C_5H_{11}O_5N$. MW, 165. Plates. M.p. 81–2°. $[\alpha]_D^{16} + 44\cdot5° \longrightarrow + 23\cdot8°$ in H_2O. Sol. H_2O. Spar. sol. EtOH.

Phenylhydrazide : needles from AcOEt. M.p. 129° decomp.

γ-*Lactone* : $C_5H_8O_5$. MW, 148. Cryst. from Me_2CO. M.p. 99–103° (98–101°, 90–2°). $[\alpha]_D + 91\cdot8° \longrightarrow + 86\cdot7°$ in H_2O. *Triacetyl* : m.p. 99°. $[\alpha]_D^{16} + 62\cdot4°$ in EtOH.

Tetra-acetyl : m.p. 86–8°. $[\alpha]_D^{20} + 5°$ in EtOH, $- 2°$ in $CHCl_3$. *Nitrile* : laminæ from H_2O. M.p. 81·5°.

2 : 3-Di-Me ether : obtained only in sol. $[\alpha]_D^{22} + 30\cdot4° \longrightarrow + 63°$ in H_2O. *Phenylhydrazide* : needles. M.p. 107–8°. $[\alpha]_D^{23} + 30°$ in EtOH. p-*Bromophenylhydrazide* : needles. M.p. 150–1°. γ-*Lactone* : syrup. B.p. about 115°/0·02 mm. $[\alpha]_D^{23} + 97° \longrightarrow + 69°$ in H_2O. $n_D^{16\cdot5}$ 1·4640.

3 : 5-Di-Me ether : obtained only in sol. *Phenylhydrazide* : needles from C_6H_6. M.p. 94–5°. γ-*Lactone* : syrup. B.p. 105–6°/0·08 mm. $[\alpha]_{5780}^{21\cdot5} + 81\cdot5° \longrightarrow + 85\cdot1° \longrightarrow + 39°$ in H_2O. n_D^{15} 1·4643.

2 : 3 : 5-Tri-Me ether : obtained only in sol. $[\alpha]_{5780}^{17} + 42\cdot5° \longrightarrow + 40° \longrightarrow + 62\cdot5°$ in H_2O. *Phenylhydrazide* : needles from C_6H_6. M.p. 89–90°. γ-*Lactone* : syrup. B.p. 82°/0·06 mm. $[\alpha]_{5780}^{17} + 108° \longrightarrow + 110° \longrightarrow + 67\cdot5°$ in H_2O. n_D^{17} 1·4464.

2 : 3 : 4-Tri-Me ether : obtained only in sol. $[\alpha]_{5461}^{16} + 32\cdot7° \longrightarrow + 21\cdot5°$ in H_2O. *Phenylhydrazide* : m.p. 137–138·5°. δ-*Lactone* : needles from pet. ether. M.p. 56°. $[\alpha]_{5461}^{20} 0° \longrightarrow 21\cdot5°$ in H_2O, $[\alpha]_D^{15} - 3\cdot8° \longrightarrow + 20\cdot8°$ in H_2O.

l-.

Free acid not isolated.

Tetra-acetyl : m.p. 86–8°. $[\alpha]_D^{20} - 4\cdot5°$ in EtOH. *Nitrile* : cryst. from EtOH. M.p. 82°. Sol. EtOH, Et_2O, $CHCl_3$. Prac. insol. H_2O.

dl-.

Free acid not isolated.

Tetra-acetyl : m.p. 134–5°.

Allen, Tollens, *Ann.*, 1890, **260**, 306.
Bertrand, *Bull. soc. chim.*, 1891, **5**, 556; 1896, **15**, 593.
Clowes, Tollens, *Ann.*, 1900, **310**, 175.
Maquenne, *Ann. chim. phys.*, 1901, **24**, 403.
Nef, Hedenburg, Glattfeld, *J. Am. Chem. Soc.*, 1917, **39**, 1650.
Haworth, Westgarth, *J. Chem. Soc.*, 1926, 880.
Haworth, Porter, *J. Chem. Soc.*, 1928, 616.
Hampton, Haworth, Hirst, *J. Chem. Soc.*, 1929, 1748.
Deulofeu, *J. Chem. Soc.*, 1929, 2459.
Isbell, Frush, *Chem. Abstracts*, 1934, **28**, 1667.
Major, Cook, *J. Am. Chem. Soc.*, 1936, **58**, 2476.

Xylopicric Acid.

*See 2 : 4 : 6-*Trinitro-*m-5-*xylenol.

***sym.-o-*Xylo-*o-*quinone** (*4 : 5-*Dimethyl-*o-*benzoquinone)

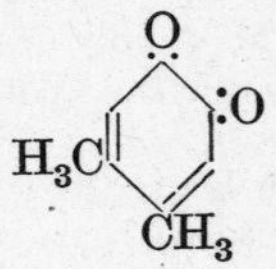

$C_8H_8O_2$ MW, 136

Exist in two forms. (i) Red cryst. from Et_2O. M.p. 102°. Spar. sol. C_6H_6, pet. ether. Sol. EtOH. (ii) Yellow plates.

Diepolder, *Ber.*, 1909, **42**, 2921.

m-Xylo-o-quinone (3 : 5-*Dimethyl*-o-*benzoquinone*)

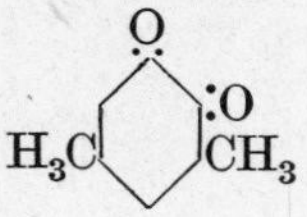

$C_8H_8O_2$ MW, 136

Dioxime: yellow needles from H_2O. M.p. 142° decomp. Sol. EtOH, AcOH, $CHCl_3$. Spar. sol. H_2O, petrol, C_6H_6.

Zincke, Schwarz, *Ann.*, 1899, **307**, 48.

o-Xylo-p-quinone (2 : 3-*Dimethyl*-p-*benzoquinone*)

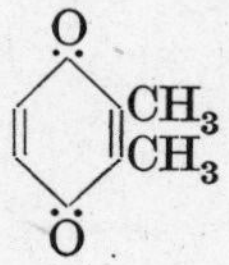

$C_8H_8O_2$ MW, 136

Yellow needles. M.p. 55°. Sublimes. Mod. sol. EtOH, Et_2O. Spar. sol. H_2O.

Monoxime: yellow needles. M.p. 166°. Very sol. MeOH, EtOH, C_6H_6, NH_3. Spar. sol. H_2O.

Noelting, Forel, *Ber.*, 1885, **18**, 2673.

m-Xylo-p-quinone (2 : 6-*Dimethyl*-p-*benzoquinone*)

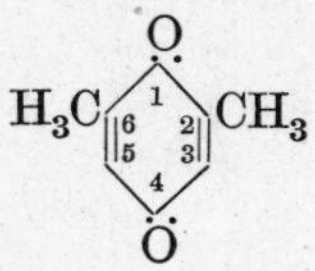

$C_8H_8O_2$ MW, 136

Yellow needles. M.p. 72–3°. Sublimes.

1-*Oxime*: yellow prisms from EtOH.Aq. M.p. 175°. Very sol. EtOH, Et_2O, C_6H_6, NH_3.

4-*Oxime*: yellow prisms from C_6H_6. M.p. 170–1°. Sol. EtOH, AcOH. Spar. sol. ligroin, C_6H_6. *Acetyl*: yellow cryst. from ligroin.

Noelting, Forel, *Ber.*, 1885, **18**, 2679.

p-Xylo-p-quinone (2 : 5-*Dimethyl*-p-*benzoquinone*, *phlorone*)

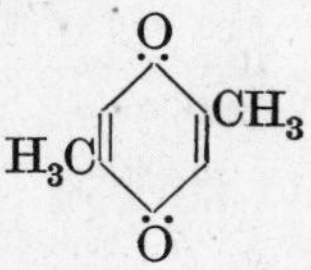

$C_8H_8O_2$ MW, 136

Yellow needles from EtOH. M.p. 125°. Sol. Et_2O, $CHCl_3$, C_6H_6. Mod. sol. EtOH. Spar. sol. H_2O. Sublimes. Zn + AcOH ⟶ 2 : 5-dihydroxy-*p*-xylene.

Monoxime: yellow needles from H_2O. M.p. 168°. Sol. EtOH, Et_2O, C_6H_6. Very spar. sol. H_2O. *Me ether*: yellow cryst. M.p. 70·5–71°.

Dioxime: yellow needles from EtOH. M.p. about 272° (254°). Spar. sol. EtOH, AcOH, C_6H_6. Insol. H_2O. Sol. alkalis. *Diacetyl*: yellow prisms from AcOH. M.p. 170°.

Monobenzoylphenylhydrazone: yellow prisms from ligroin. M.p. 122–4°; solidifies to orange cryst., m.p. 154–5°.

Veibel, Simesen, *Ber.*, 1930, **63**, 2480.
Auwers, Michaelis, *Ber.*, 1914, **47**, 1289.
Carstanjen, *J. prakt. Chem.*, 1881, **23**, 423.

m-Xylorcinol.
See 4 : 6-Dihydroxy-*m*-xylene.

p-Xylorcinol.
See 2 : 6-Dihydroxy-*p*-xylene.

Xylose (*Wood sugar*)

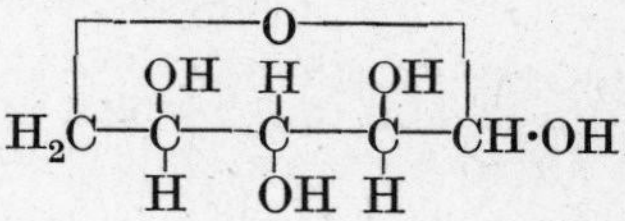

$C_5H_{10}O_5$ MW, 150

d-.

Needles. M.p. 144–5° (145–50°, 153–4°, 143°). Sweet taste. $[\alpha]_D^{20}$ + 92·0° ⟶ + 19·0° in H_2O. Sol. H_2O, hot EtOH. D^0 1·535. Heat of comb. C_v 3735 Cal. Reduces warm Fehling's. Does not ferment. Br water ⟶ *d*-xylonic acid. HNO_3 ⟶ xylotrihydroxyglutaric acid. Boil with dil. H_2SO_4 ⟶ furfural.

Semicarbazone: m.p. 202–4°. $[\alpha]_D^{20}$ − 38·8° ⟶ − 24·4° in H_2O. *Tetra-acetyl*: m.p. 232–3°. $[\alpha]_D^{20}$ + 21° in MeOH.

Phenylosazone: m.p. 159° (167° decomp., 164°, 161°). $[\alpha]_D$ − 40·9° in EtOH. Sol. Et_2O, Me_2CO. Spar. sol. H_2O. Identical with *d*-lyxosazone.

p-*Bromophenylosazone*: yellow needles. M.p. 208° (204°). Insol. Me_2CO.

o-*Tolylosazone*: m.p. 98–9°.

m-*Tolylosazone*: m.p. 137–8°.

p-*Tolylosazone*: m.p. 175–6°.

Phenylhydrazone: yellow cryst.

p-*Bromophenylhydrazone*: yellow cryst. M.p. 128°. $[\alpha]_D$ − 20·49° in H_2O.

2 : 4-*Dibromophenylhydrazone*: m.p. 127–8°.

p-*Nitrophenylhydrazone*: deep yellow cryst. M.p. 156° (154–5°). Sol. EtOH.

Methylphenylhydrazone: laminæ from AcOEt. M.p. 108–10° (103–5°). Sol. H_2O. Insol. C_6H_6.

Benzylphenylhydrazone: needles. M.p. 99° (95–100°). $[\alpha]_D$ − 33° in EtOH. Sol. EtOH, Et_2O. Spar. sol. H_2O.

Diphenylhydrazone: yellow plates from dil.

EtOH or white needles from ligroin–Py. M.p. 128° (107–8°). Sol. hot H_2O, EtOH, Me_2CO, $CHCl_3$. Insol. Et_2O, ligroin.

2-*Naphthylhydrazone*: brown needles from MeOH. M.p. 123–4° (70°). $[\alpha]_D + 18{\cdot}6°$ in MeOH, $+ 15{\cdot}8°$ in AcOH. Sol. EtOH. Prac. insol. Et_2O, $CHCl_3$, C_6H_6.

α-*Methylglucoside*: α-methylxyloside. Cryst. M.p. 90–2°. $[\alpha]^{20}_D + 153{\cdot}2°$ in H_2O ($+ 153{\cdot}9°$). *Triacetyl*: m.p. 86°. $[\alpha]^{20}_D + 119{\cdot}6°$ in $CHCl_3$. 2 : 3 : 4-*Tri-Me ether*: b.p. 110°/10 mm. n^{23}_D 1·4397. $[\alpha]^{20}_D + 121{\cdot}5°$ in $CHCl_3$, $+ 112{\cdot}7°$ in H_2O, $+ 122{\cdot}2°$ in MeOH.

β-*Methylglucoside*: β-methylxyloside. Cryst. from AcOEt. M.p. 157° (155–6°). $[\alpha]^{20}_D - 65{\cdot}9°$ in H_2O. *Triacetyl*: m.p. 115°. $[\alpha]^{20}_D - 60{\cdot}8°$ in $CHCl_3$. 2 : 3 : 4-*Tri-Me ether*: m.p. 51°. B.p. 69–72°/0·5 mm. $[\alpha]^{20}_D - 69{\cdot}5°$ in $CHCl_3$, $- 81{\cdot}7°$ in H_2O.

γ-*Methylglucoside*: γ-methylxyloside. Syrup. B.p. 161·5°/0·03 mm. $[\alpha]_D + 62{\cdot}8°$ in EtOH.

2 : 3-*Di-Me ether*: syrup. $[\alpha]^{20}_D + 22{\cdot}6° \longrightarrow + 24°$ in H_2O. n^{20}_D 1·4783.

2 : 3 : 4-*Tri-Me ether*: prisms from AcOEt. M.p. 91–2°. $[\alpha]^{20}_D + 64{\cdot}5° \longrightarrow + 17{\cdot}7°$ in H_2O, $+ 55{\cdot}8° \longrightarrow + 24{\cdot}2°$ in $CHCl_3$, $+ 74° \longrightarrow + 21°$ in EtOH.

2 : 3 : 5-*Tri-Me ether*: liq. B.p. 110°/0·04 mm. $[\alpha]_D + 24{\cdot}7° \longrightarrow + 31{\cdot}2°$ in H_2O.

Triacetyl: cryst. from Et_2O. M.p. 138–41°. $[\alpha]^{23}_D + 70{\cdot}11° \longrightarrow + 40{\cdot}8°$ in $CHCl_3$.

Tetra-acetyl: β-*form*. M.p. 126–8°. $[\alpha]^{21}_D - 24{\cdot}4°$ in $CHCl_3$.

Tetrabenzoyl: m.p. 178°. $[\alpha]^{22}_D - 47{\cdot}45°$ in Me_2CO.

Acetone deriv.: m.p. 41–3°. $[\alpha]^{18}_D - 19{\cdot}0°$.

Diacetone deriv.: m.p. 44–5°. B.p. 85–7°/0·5 mm. $[\alpha]^{22}_D + 13{\cdot}0°$ in H_2O, $+ 6{\cdot}0°$ in $CHCl_3$.

l-.

Needles or prisms. M.p. 144° (141–3°). $[\alpha]^{20}_D - 79{\cdot}3° \longrightarrow - 18{\cdot}6°$ in H_2O.

Tetra-acetyl: β-*form*. M.p. 126°. $[\alpha]^{25}_D + 25{\cdot}7°$ in $CHCl_3$. *Aldehydo form*: m.p. 90–1°. $[\alpha]^{20}_D + 22{\cdot}5°$ in $CHCl_3$.

Phenylosazone: m.p. 159–61°.

dl-.

Prisms. M.p. 129–31°.

Phenylosazone: yellow needles. M.p. 210–15° decomp. Identical with *dl*-lyxosazone.

Wheeler, Tollens, *Ann.*, 1889, **254**, 304.
Fischer, Stahel, *Ber.*, 1891, **24**, 528.
Schulze, Tollens, *Ann.*, 1892, **271**, 40.
Hudson, Harding, *J. Am. Chem. Soc.*, 1918, **40**, 1601.
Ling, Nanji, *J. Chem. Soc.*, 1923, **123**, 620.
Harding, *Sugar*, 1923, **25**, 124.
Carruthers, Hirst, *J. Chem. Soc.*, 1922, **121**, 2299.
Hirst, Purves, *J. Chem. Soc.*, 1923, **123**, 1352.
Haworth, Westgarth, *J. Chem. Soc.*, 1926, 880.
Hampton, Haworth, Hirst, *J. Chem. Soc.*, 1929, 1747.
Robertson, Speedie, *J. Chem. Soc.*, 1934, 824.
von Vargha, *Ber.*, 1935, **68**, 18.
Appel, *J. Chem. Soc.*, 1935, 425.
Sokolov, *Chem. Abstracts*, 1936, **30**, 5563.

Xylosimine

$C_5H_{11}O_4N$ MW, 149

Cryst. M.p. 130° decomp. $[\alpha]_D - 18°\ 3' \longrightarrow - 0°\ 46'$ in H_2O.

de Bruyn, van Leent, *Rec. trav. chim.*, 1895, **14**, 144.
Levene, *J. Biol. Chem.*, 1916, **24**, 61.

Xylo-trihydroxyglutaric Acid.
See Trihydroxyglutaric Acid.

***o*-Xylylamine** (o-*Methylbenzylamine*, ω-*amino*-o-*xylene*)

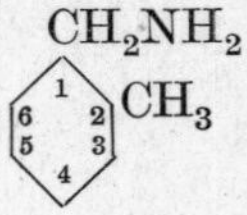

$C_8H_{11}N$ MW, 121

Oil. Cryst. in needles at − 20°. B.p. 205·5–206°/745 mm., 125°/105 mm. D^{19}_0 0·9768. n^{19}_D 1·5436.

B,HCl: plates from H_2O. M.p. 219–20°.
B,HBr: m.p. about 209°.
Sulphate: m.p. 176–9°.
B,HNO_3: m.p. 130°.
Oxalate: m.p. 94–5°.
$B,HAuCl_4$: m.p. about 180°.
B_2,H_2PtCl_6: yellow needles. M.p. 220–3° decomp.
N-*Acetyl*: needles from EtOH. M.p. 69°.
N-*Benzoyl*: needles from EtOH.Aq. M.p. 88°.
Picrate: yellow needles. M.p. 214–215·5°.

Konowalow, *J. Russ. Phys.-Chem. Soc.*, 1905, **37**, 536.
Strassmann, *Ber.*, 1888, **21**, 577.

***m*-Xylylamine** (m-*Methylbenzylamine*, ω-*amino*-m-*xylene*).

Liq. B.p. 205–205·5°/750·5 mm., 96°/20 mm. Sol. EtOH, Et_2O. Insol. H_2O. D^{20}_0 0·9654.

B,HCl: needles from EtOH. M.p. 208°.
Sulphate: m.p. 248° decomp.
$B_2,(COOH)_2$: plates. M.p. 172°.
B_2,H_2PtCl_6: yellow plates. M.p. 214°.
N-*Acetyl*: liq. B.p. 235–40°.
N-*Benzoyl*: needles from $CHCl_3$–ligroin. M.p. 150–150·5° (70°).
Picrate: cryst from MeOH. M.p. 198° decomp. (156°).

Shoppee, *J. Chem. Soc.*, 1932, 701.
Rupe, Bernstein, *Helv. Chim. Acta*, 1930, **13**, 462.
Sommer, *Ber.*, 1900, **33**, 1074.
Brömme, *Ber.*, 1888, **21**, 2701.

p-Xylylamine (p-*Methylbenzylamine*, ω-*amino*-p-*xylene*).
M.p. 12·6–13·2°. B.p. 204°/739 mm. D_0^{20} 0·9520. n_D^{20} 1·53639. Spar. sol. H_2O.
B,HCl: needles. M.p. 234·5–235°.
Sulphate: plates from H_2O. M.p. about 130°.
$B,HAuCl_4$: yellow needles from H_2O. M.p. 169–71°.
B_2,H_2PtCl_6: plates from H_2O.
$B,HSnCl_3$: m.p. 107°.
N-*Acetyl*: cryst. from EtOH. M.p. 107–8°.
N-*Benzoyl*: needles from EtOH. M.p. 137°.
Picrate: cryst. from H_2O. M.p. 204° decomp.

Druce, *J. Chem. Soc.*, 1918, **113**, 718.
Curtius, Darapsky, *Ber.*, 1902, **35**, 3232.
Lustig, *Ber.*, 1895, **28**, 2988.

o-Xylyl bromide (o-*Methylbenzyl bromide*, ω-*bromo*-o-*xylene*)

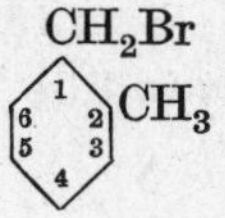

C_8H_9Br MW, 185

Prisms. M.p. 21°. B.p. 216–17°/742 mm., 108°/16 mm. D^{23} 1·3811.

Atkinson, Thorpe, *J. Chem. Soc.*, 1907, **91**, 1695.

m-Xylyl bromide (m-*Methylbenzyl bromide*, ω-*bromo*-m-*xylene*).
Liq. B.p. 212·5° (slight decomp.), 185°/340 mm., 100–1°/14 mm. D^{23} 1·3711.

Titley, *J. Chem. Soc.*, 1926, 514.
Haller, Bauer, *Compt. rend.*, 1911, **153**, 22.
Atkinson, Thorpe, *J. Chem. Soc.*, 1907, **91**, 1696.

p-Xylyl bromide (p-*Methylbenzyl bromide*, ω-*bromo*-p-*xylene*).
Needles from EtOH. M.p. 35°. B.p. 218–20°/740 mm. Sol. Et_2O, $CHCl_3$.

Atkinson, Thorpe, *J. Chem. Soc.*, 1907, **91**, 1697.

o-Xylyl chloride (o-*Methylbenzyl chloride*, ω-*chloro*-o-*xylene*)

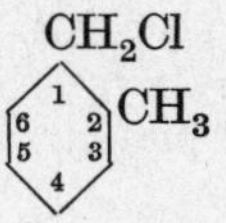

C_8H_9Cl MW, 140·5

Liq. B.p. 197–9° (195–203°).

Reyman, *Bull. soc. chim.*, 1876, **26**, 534.

m-Xylyl chloride (m-*Methylbenzyl chloride*, ω-*chloro*-m-*xylene*).
Liq. B.p. 195–6°. D^{20} 1·064. n_D^{25} 1·5327.

King, Merriam, *Chem. Zentr.*, 1935, II, 2359.
Gundelach, *Bull. soc. chim.*, 1876, **26**, 43.

p-Xylyl chloride (p-*Methylbenzyl chloride*, ω-*chloro*-p-*xylene*).
Fuming liq. B.p. 200–2°, 90°/20 mm.

Curtius, Sprenger, *J. prakt. Chem.*, 1900, **62**, 111.

Xylyl cyanide.
See under Tolylacetic Acid.

o-Xylylenediamine (ω-*Diamino*-o-*xylene*)

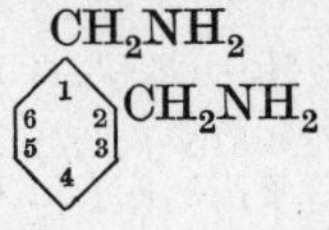

$C_8H_{12}N_2$ MW, 136

Liq. with ammoniacal odour. Absorbs CO_2 from the air.
N-*Tetra-Me*: $C_{12}H_{20}N_2$. MW, 192. Liq. B.p. 105–6°/14 mm. *Dimethiodide*: m.p. 219° decomp. *Dimethobromide*: prisms from EtOH–Et_2O. M.p. 207–8°. *Picrate*: yellow cryst. M.p. 187–8°.
N-*Tetra-Et*: $C_{16}H_{28}N_2$. MW, 248. Liq. B.p. 170–5°/20 mm.
N : N′-*Diphenyl*: $C_{20}H_{20}N_2$. MW, 288. Plates from EtOH. M.p. 114°. Sol. EtOH, C_6H_6. Insol. H_2O, ligroin. N : N′-*Di-Me*: $C_{22}H_{24}N_2$. MW, 316. Plates from EtOH. M.p. 110°.
N-*Tetraphenyl*: $C_{32}H_{28}N_2$. MW, 440. Needles from Me_2CO.Aq. M.p. 179°. Sol. Me_2CO, $CHCl_3$. Spar. sol. EtOH.

N : N'-*Diacetyl* : cryst. from Et_2O. M.p. 146°.
N : N'-*Dibenzoyl* : needles from EtOH. M.p. 184°.
Picrate : yellow needles. Decomp. at 170°.

Gabriel, Pinkus, *Ber.*, 1893, **26**, 2212.
Strassmann, *Ber.*, 1888, **21**, 579.

***m*-Xylylenediamine** (ω-*Diamino*-m-*xylene*).
Liq. B.p. 245–8°. Misc. with EtOH, Et_2O.
N : N'-*Diacetyl* : cryst. M.p. 118–19°.
Picrate : yellow plates. Decomp. at 185–90°.

Brömme, *Ber.*, 1888, **21**, 2705.

***p*-Xylylenediamine** (ω-*Diamino*-p-*xylene*).
Cryst. M.p. 35°.
B,H_2PtCl_6 : cryst. Decomp. at 250°.
N-*Tetraphenyl* : $C_{32}H_{28}N_2$. MW, 440. Needles from AcOH. M.p. 186°. Sol. AcOH. Mod. sol. Me_2CO. Spar. sol. EtOH.
N-*Tetra-acetyl* : needles from EtOH. M.p. 194°.
N : N'-*Dibenzoyl* : needles. M.p. 193–4°.
Picrate : orange needles. Decomp. at 232°.

Lustig, *Ber.*, 1895, **28**, 2992.

***o*-Xylylene dibromide** (o-*Xylylene bromide*, ω-*dibromo*-o-*xylene*)

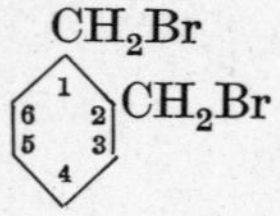

$C_8H_8Br_2$ MW, 264

Cryst. from $CHCl_3$. M.p. 95°. Decomp. on dist. Sol. EtOH, Et_2O, $CHCl_3$. Mod. sol. pet. ether.

Atkinson, Thorpe, *J. Chem. Soc.*, 1907, **91**, 1696.

***m*-Xylylene dibromide** (m-*Xylylene bromide*, ω-*dibromo*-m-*xylene*).
Prisms from Me_2CO. M.p. 77°. B.p. 158–60°/12 mm. Sol. Et_2O, $CHCl_3$, ligroin. D^0 1·959.

Titley, *J. Chem. Soc.*, 1926, 514.
Braun, Karpf, Garn, *Ber.*, 1920, **53**, 101.

***p*-Xylylene dibromide** (p-*Xylylene bromide*, ω-*dibromo*-p-*xylene*).
Cryst. from $CHCl_3$ or C_6H_6. M.p. 145–7°. B.p. 245°. D^0 2·012. Sol. $CHCl_3$. Spar. sol. Et_2O.

Atkinson, Thorpe, *J. Chem. Soc.*, 1907, **91**, 1698.

***o*-Xylylene dichloride** (o-*Xylylene chloride*, ω-*dichloro*-o-*xylene*)

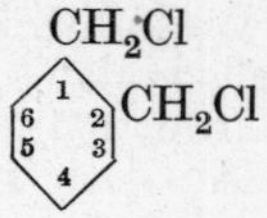

$C_8H_8Cl_2$ MW, 175

Cryst. from pet. ether. M.p. 55°. B.p. 239–41°, 130–5°/19 mm. Sol. EtOH, Et_2O, $CHCl_3$, ligroin. D^0 1·393.

Quelet, *Bull. soc. chim.*, 1933, **53**, 222.

***m*-Xylylene dichloride** (m-*Xylylene chloride*, ω-*dichloro*-m-*xylene*).
Cryst. M.p. 34·2°. B.p. 250–5°. D^{20} 1·302.

Colson, Gautier, *Ann. chim.*, 1887, **11**, 23.

***p*-Xylylene dichloride** (p-*Xylylene chloride*, ω-*dichloro*-p-*xylene*).
Plates from EtOH. M.p. 100°. B.p. 240–5° decomp., 135°/16 mm. D^0 1·417.

Quelet, *Bull. soc. chim.*, 1933, **53**, 222.
Sabetay, *Compt. rend.*, 1931, **192**, 1109.
Grimaux, *Ann.*, 1870, **155**, 340.

Xylylene dicyanide.
See under Phenylenediacetic Acid.

***o*-Xylylene di-iodide** (o-*Xylylene iodide*, ω-*di-iodo*-o-*xylene*)

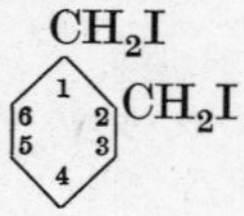

$C_8H_8I_2$ MW, 358

Yellow prisms from Et_2O. M.p. 109–10°.

Finkelstein, *Ber.*, 1910, **43**, 1532.

***m*-Xylylene di-iodide** (m-*Xylylene iodide*, ω-*di-iodo*-m-*xylene*).
M.p. 106°.

See previous reference.

***p*-Xylylene di-iodide** (p-*Xylylene iodide*, ω-*di-iodo*-p-*xylene*).
M.p. 175° decomp. Sol. hot EtOH, $CHCl_3$. Spar. sol. Et_2O.

Knoll, D.R.P., 230,172, (*Chem. Zentr.*, 1911, I, 359).
Finkelstein, *Ber.*, 1910, **43**, 1532.

***o*-Xylylene Dimercaptan** (*Dithio*-o-*xylylene glycol*, ω-*dimercapto*-o-*xylene*)

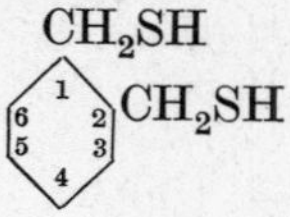

$C_8H_{10}S_2$ MW, 170

Prisms. M.p. 45–6°. B.p. 160°/20 mm. Sol. EtOH, Et_2O. Spar. sol. pet. ether.

Autenrieth, Hennings, *Ber.*, 1901, **34**, 1774.

***m*-Xylylene Dimercaptan** (*Dithio*-m-*xylylene glycol, ω-dimercapto*-m-*xylene*).
Liq. with characteristic odour. B.p. 157–8°/15 mm.
Dibenzoyl: prisms. M.p. 52·5°.

Autenrieth, Beuttel, *Ber.*, 1909, **42**, 4358.

***p*-Xylylene Dimercaptan** (*Dithio*-p-*xylylene glycol, ω-dimercapto*-p-*xylene*).
Cryst. M.p. 46–7°. B.p. 156°/12 mm.
Dibenzoyl: needles. M.p. 135°.

Autenrieth, Beuttel, *Ber.*, 1909, **42**, 4349.

***o*-Xylylene oxide.**
See Phthalan.

Xylylic Acid.
See Dimethylbenzoic Acid.

Xylylidene chloride.
See Methylbenzylidene chloride.

***o*-Xylyl iodide** (o-*Methylbenzyl iodide, ω-iodo*-o-*xylene*)

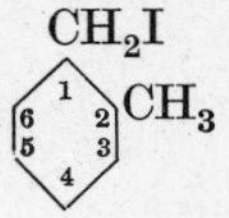

C_8H_9I MW, 232

Needles from Et_2O. M.p. 34°. Decomp. on dist.

Zeltner, Tarassow, *Ber.*, 1910, **43**, 945.

***p*-Xylyl iodide** (p-*Methylbenzyl iodide, ω-iodo*-p-*xylene*).
Needles from Et_2O. M.p. 45·5–46·5°.

Zeltner, Tarassow, *Ber.*, 1910, **43**, 944.

Y

Yangonalactone

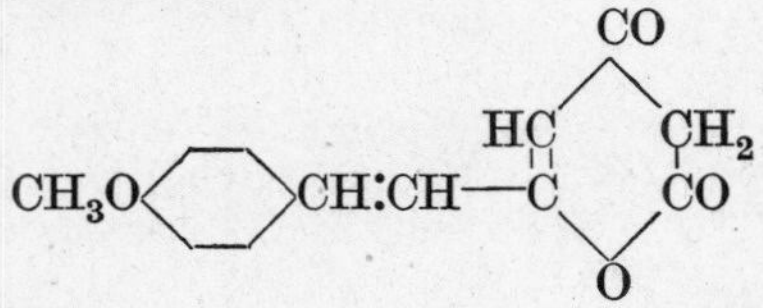

$C_{14}H_{12}O_4$ MW, 244

Yellow prisms from MeOH or EtOH. M.p. 238°. Sol. Et_2O, AcOEt, AcOH, C_6H_6. Forms derivs. of enolic form.
Me ether: *see* Yangonin.
O-*Acetyl*: red prisms from AcOEt. M.p. 133°.
O-*Benzoyl*: yellow leaflets from EtOH. M.p. 147°.

Borsche, Blount, *Ber.*, 1932, **65**, 820.
Borsche, Bodenstein, *Ber.*, 1929, **62**, 2519.

Yangonin

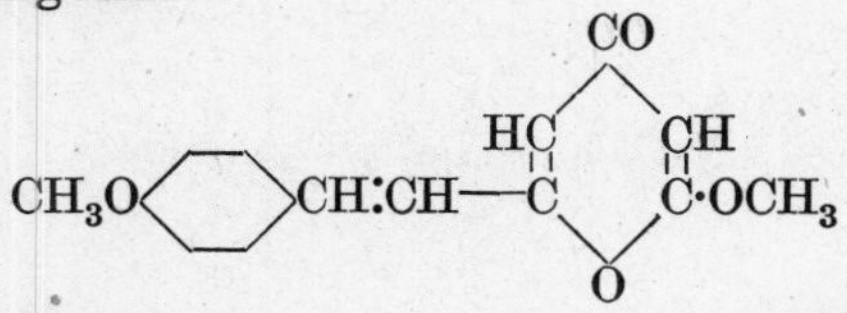

$C_{15}H_{14}O_4$ MW, 258

Constituent of Kawa root. Greenish-yellow cryst. with blue fluor. from MeOH or Me_2CO. M.p. 153–4°. Sol. Me_2CO, AcOH. Spar. sol. Et_2O, CS_2. Sol. conc. $H_2SO_4 \longrightarrow$ yellow sol. with green fluor.

Jablonski, *Chem. Abstracts*, 1935, **29**, 7982.
Borsche, Bodenstein, *Ber.*, 1929, **62**, 2519.
Murakami, *Chem. Abstracts*, 1918, **12**, 2547.

Yatren (*Loretin, quinoxyl, 7-iodo-8-hydroxyquinoline-5-sulphonic acid*)

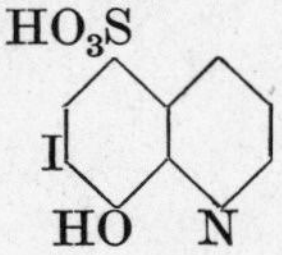

$C_9H_6O_4NIS$ MW, 351

Yellow prisms or laminæ. Decomp. at about 260°. Very spar. sol. H_2O, EtOH. Prac. insol. Et_2O, $CHCl_3$, C_6H_6. Sol. conc. H_2SO_4. HNO_3 (D 1·52) $\longrightarrow$ 5 : 7-dinitro-8-hydroxyquinoline. Forms cryst. salts with Na, K, Mg, Ca, Ba, Sr. Used as disinfectant in treatment of amœbic dysentery, etc.

I.G., D.R.P., 545,915, (*Chem. Abstracts*, 1933, **27**, 566).
Claus, *Arch. Pharm.*, 1893, **231**, 706.

Yobyrine

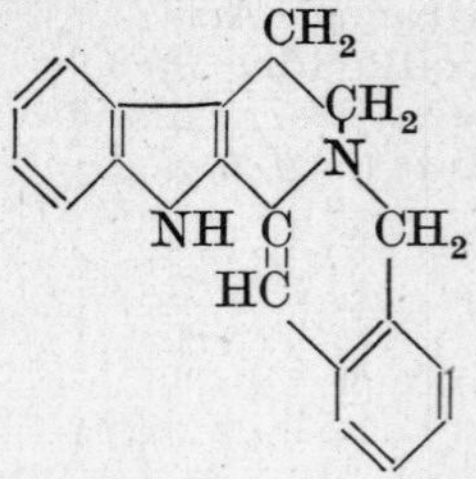

$C_{19}H_{16}N_2$ MW, 272

Cryst. from C_6H_6 or EtOH. M.p. 218–19°.

Wibaut, Gastel, *Rec. trav. chim.*, 1935, **54**, 85.

Barger, Scholz, *Helv. Chim. Acta*, 1933, **16**, 1346.

Yohimbene

$C_{21}H_{26}O_3N_2$ MW, 354

Isomeric with yohimbine. Leaflets from MeOH. M.p. 278° decomp. Sol. MeOH, EtOH. Spar. sol. Me_2CO, $CHCl_3$, Et_2O. Insol. AcOEt, petrol, C_6H_6, toluene. [α] + 43·7° in Py. Hyd. with loss of CO_2 ⟶ yohimbol. Extremely poisonous.

B,HCl: needles + $3H_2O$ from MeOH.Aq. M.p. 234°. [α] − 8·8° in H_2O.

B,MeI: needles + $4H_2O$ from Et_2O–EtOH. Decomp. at 288°.

Hahn, Stenner, *Ber.*, 1928, **61**, 282.

Hahn, Brandenberg, *Ber.*, 1926, **59**, 2189.

Yohimbic Acid

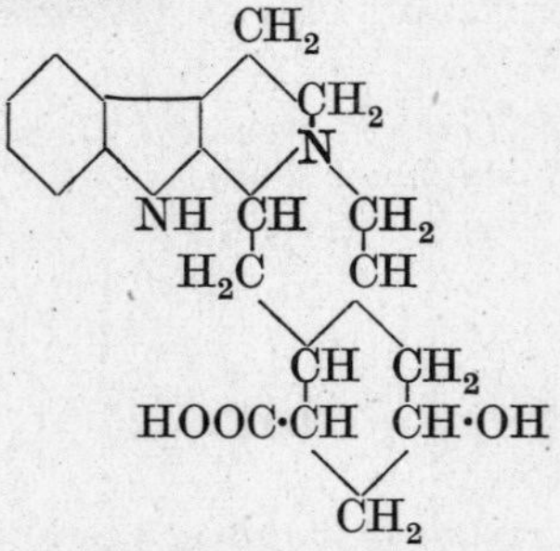

Suggested formula

$C_{20}H_{24}O_3N_2$ MW, 340

Cryst. + $1H_2O$ from H_2O. M.p. 256° (265–9°). $[\alpha]_D^{20}$ + 138·8° in Py. Loss of CO_2 ⟶ yohimbol.

Me ester: *see* Yohimbine.

Et ester: $C_{22}H_{28}O_3N_2$. MW, 368. Cryst. M.p. 190°.

Propyl ester: $C_{23}H_{30}O_3N_2$. MW, 382. Cryst. + $1H_2O$. M.p. 137°.

Butyl ester: $C_{24}H_{32}O_3N_2$. MW, 396. Cryst. + $1H_2O$. M.p. 119–22°, anhyd. 127°.

Benzyl ester: $C_{27}H_{30}O_3N_2$. MW, 430. Amorp. powder from EtOH.Aq. M.p. 77–8°. *B,HCl*: cryst. powder from EtOH–Me_2CO. M.p. 253–4°.

Worrall, *J. Am. Chem. Soc.*, 1935, **57**, 900; 1933, **55**, 3715.

Field, *J. Chem. Soc.*, 1923, **123**, 3003.

Yohimbine (*Quebrachine, hydroergotocin, aphrodine, corynine, methyl ester of yohimbic acid*)

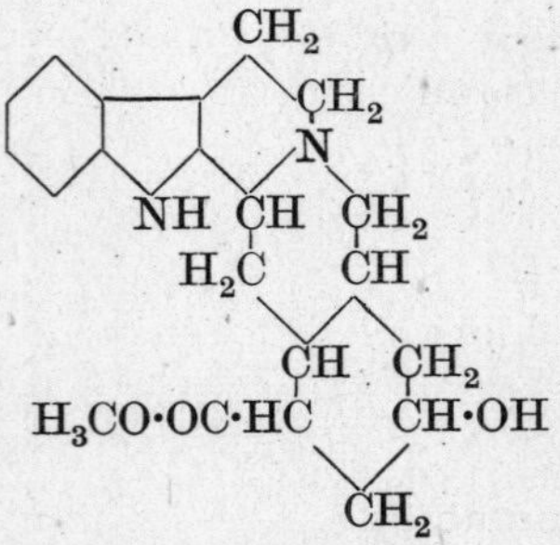

Suggested formula

$C_{21}H_{26}O_3N_2$ MW, 354

Chief alkaloid of *Corynanthe Johimbe*. Needles from EtOH.Aq. M.p. 235°. Sol. EtOH, $CHCl_3$, hot C_6H_6. Mod. sol. Et_2O. Spar. sol. H_2O. $[\alpha]_D^{20}$ + 107·9° in Py.

B,HCl: plates. M.p. 302°. $[\alpha]_D^{22}$ + 103·3° in H_2O.

Nitrate: m.p. 276°.

Mono-acetyl: m.p. 150°. Sol. EtOH, Et_2O, $CHCl_3$ with green fluor.

O : N-*Diacetyl*: m.p. 183°.

Methiodide: plates from Me_2CO. M.p. 249–50°.

Robinson, *Annual Reviews on Biochemistry*, 1935, **4**, 504.

Warnat, *Ber.*, 1930, **63**, 2959.

Schomer, *Chem. Zentr.*, 1927, II, 2309.

Field, *J. Chem. Soc.*, 1923, **123**, 3003.

Isomeric forms of yohimbine are described in Heinemann, *Ber.*, 1934, **67**, 18.

Yperite.

See 2 : 2′-Dichlorodiethyl sulphide.

Z

Zanthotoxin.
See Xanthotoxin.

Zeaxanthin

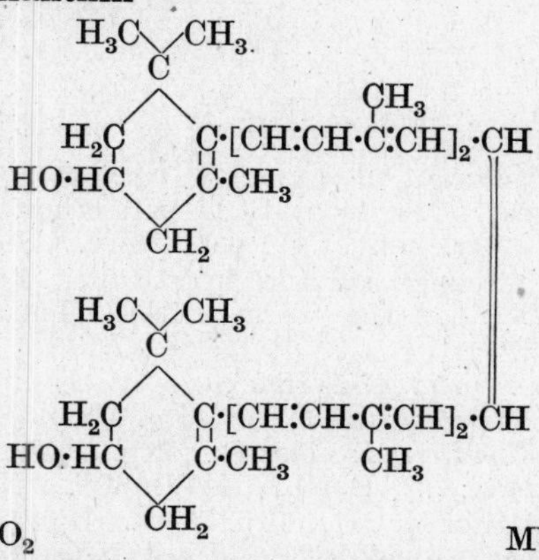

$C_{40}H_{56}O_2$ MW, 568

Constituent of lipochrome of *Fucus vesiculosus*, *Physalis*, egg yolk and spindle-tree maize. Yellow prisms from MeOH, cryst. + $\frac{1}{2}$MeOH from MeOH–C_6H_6. M.p. 206·5° (215·5° corr.). Mod. sol. Et_2O, CS_2, C_6H_6, $CHCl_3$, CCl_4, Py, AcOEt. Spar. sol. pet. ether, MeOH. Absorption maxima at 515 mμ and 485 mμ in CS_2.

Mono-Me ether: $C_{41}H_{58}O_2$. MW, 582. Needles from MeOH. M.p. 153°.

Di-Me ether: $C_{42}H_{60}O_2$. MW, 596. Cryst. from MeOH. M.p. 176°.

Diacetyl: m.p. 154°.

Dipropionyl: cryst. from C_6H_6–MeOH. M.p. 142°.

Dibutyryl: cryst. from C_6H_6–MeOH. M.p. 132°.

Divaleryl: cryst. from C_6H_6–MeOH. M.p. 125°.

Dicaproyl: cryst. from C_6H_6–MeOH. M.p. 117–18°.

Dicaprylyl: cryst. from C_6H_6. M.p. 107°.

Dilauryl: m.p. 104°.

Monopalmityl: plates from C_6H_6–EtOH. M.p. 148°.

Dipalmityl: cryst. from C_6H_6–MeOH. M.p. 99·5°.

Distearyl: m.p. 95°.

Karrer, Solmssen, *Helv. Chim. Acta*, 1935, **18**, 477.
Heilbron, Phipers, *Biochem. J.*, 1935, **29**, 1369.
Gillam, *ibid.*, 1831.
Kuhn, Grundmann, *Ber.*, 1934, **67**, 596.
Karrer, Wehrli, Helfenstein, *Helv. Chim. Acta*, 1930, **13**, 271.

Zebromal (*Ethyl ester of* trans-α : β-*dibromocinnamic acid*)

$C_6H_5\cdot CHBr\cdot CHBr\cdot CO\cdot OC_2H_5$

$C_{11}H_{12}O_2Br_2$ MW, 336

Plates. M.p. 75–6°. Sol. Et_2O, $CHCl_3$. Spar. sol. EtOH. Insol. H_2O. Boiling alc. KOH ⟶ phenylpropiolic acid. Used in treatment of epilepsy.

Merck, D.R.P., 271,434, (*Chem. Zentr.*, 1914, I, 1235).
Merck, *Pharmazeutische Zentralhalle*, 1912, **53**, 591.
Anschütz, Kinnicutt, *Ber.*, 1878, **11**, 1220.

Zierin (*Glucoside of cyanhydrin of* m-*hydroxybenzaldehyde*)

$C_{14}H_{17}O_7N$ MW, 311

Obtained from aerial parts of *Zieria lævigata*. Needles from AcOEt–$CHCl_3$. Softens at 153°, m.p. 156°. Sol. H_2O, EtOH, Me_2CO, MeCOEt. Very spar. sol. Et_2O, $CHCl_3$, pet. ether, C_6H_6. $[\alpha]_D^{20\cdot 2}$ − 29·5°. $FeCl_3$ ⟶ faint blue col. Hyd- ⟶ glucose + HCN + *m*-hydroxybenzaldehyde.

Acetyl: cryst. from EtOH.Aq. M.p. 115–18°.

Finnemore, Cooper, *J. Proc. Roy. Soc. New South Wales*, 1936, **70**, 175. (*Chem. Zentr.*, 1937, I, 878).

Zierone

$C_{15}H_{22}O$ MW, 218

Constituent of volatile oil of *Zieria macrophylla*, Bonpland. Sesquiterpene ketone, isomeric with eremophilone. Viscous colourless oil. B.p. 147–9°/18 mm.

Semicarbazone: prisms from MeOH. M.p. 182°.

2 : 4-*Dinitrophenylhydrazone*: needles from EtOH. M.p. 95–7°.

Bradfield, Penfold, Simonsen, *J. Proc. Roy. Soc. New South Wales*, 1933, **67**, 200, (*Chem. Zentr.*, 1934, I, 1982).

Zinc dibutyl

$Zn(CH_2\cdot CH_2\cdot CH_2\cdot CH_3)_2$

$C_8H_{18}Zn$ MW, 179·5

Liq. B.p. 81–2°/9 mm.

Noller, *Organic Syntheses*, 1932, XII, 86.

Zinc diethyl (*Zinc ethyl*)

$Zn(C_2H_5)_2$

$C_4H_{10}Zn$ MW, 123·5

M.p. — 28°. B.p. 118°. D^{18} 1·1826. Spontaneously inflammable in air. $H_2O \longrightarrow C_2H_6 + Zn(OH)_2$. $NH_3 \longrightarrow Zn(NH_2)_2$. Hydroxy compounds ⟶ ethane.

See previous reference.

Zinc di-isobutyl

$Zn[CH_2{\cdot}CH(CH_3)_2]_2$

$C_8H_{18}Zn$ MW, 179·5

Liq. B.p. 185° (165–7°).

Ponzio, *Gazz. chim. ital.*, 1900, **30**, ii, 25.

Zinc di-isopropyl

$Zn[CH(CH_3)_2]_2$

$C_6H_{14}Zn$ MW, 151·5

Liq. B.p. 135°, 94–8°/40 mm. Fumes in air. Inflammable with difficulty in air and oxidised to $Zn(OC_3H_7)_2$.

Bohm, *Chem. Zentr.*, 1899, I, 1067.

Zinc dimethyl (*Zinc methyl*)

$Zn(CH_3)_2$

C_2H_6Zn MW, 95·5

M.p. — 42·5°. B.p. 46°. $D^{10·5}$ 1·386. Ignites spontaneously in air. $H_2O \longrightarrow CH_4 + Zn(OH)_2$.

Renshaw, Greenlaw, *J. Am. Chem. Soc.*, 1920, **42**, 1472.

Zinc diphenyl

$Zn(C_6H_5)_2$

$C_{12}H_{10}Zn$ MW, 219·5

Needles from C_6H_6. M.p. 105–6°. B.p. 280–5° slight decomp. Sol. Et_2O, C_6H_6. Spar. sol. pet. ether. Decomp. in dry air ⟶ ZnO + diphenyl. $H_2O \longrightarrow Zn(OH)_2 + C_6H_6$. $CHCl_3$ ⟶ triphenylmethane.

Hilpert, Grüttner, *Ber.*, 1913, **46**, 1680.

Zinc dipropyl (*Zinc propyl*)

$Zn(CH_2{\cdot}CH_2{\cdot}CH_3)_2$

$C_6H_{14}Zn$ MW, 151·5

Liq. B.p. 146°, 39–40°/9 mm. $H_2O \longrightarrow$ propane + $Zn(OH)_2$.

Noller, *Organic Syntheses*, 1932, XII, 86.

Zingerone (*Zingiberone, 4-hydroxy-3-methoxybenzylacetone*)

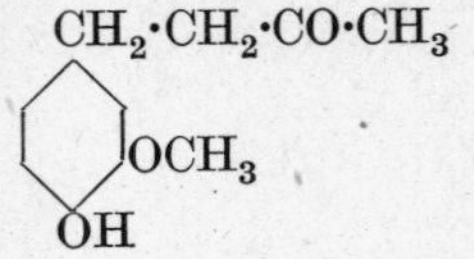

$C_{11}H_{14}O_3$ MW, 294

Constituent of oil of ginger. Needles or plates with sweet odour from Et_2O–pet. ether. M.p. 40–1°. Spar. sol. H_2O, pet. ether. Sol. dil. alkalis. Slowly volatile in steam. Reduces $NH_3.AgNO_3$ in the warm. Alc. $FeCl_3 \longrightarrow$ green col.

Oxime: m.p. 87·5–88·5°.

Semicarbazone: needles. M.p. about 133°.

Phenylhydrazone: plates. M.p. about 143°.

Me ether: $C_{12}H_{16}O_3$. MW, 308. Needles from EtOH or MeOH. M.p. 55–6°. B.p. 186°/16 mm. Spar. sol. pet. ether. Insol. H_2O. *Oxime*: needles from Et_2O–pet. ether or MeOH.Aq. M.p. 93–4°.

Et ether: $C_{13}H_{18}O_3$. MW, 322. Cryst. from EtOH.Aq. or pet. ether. M.p. 66°. Insol. H_2O.

Acetyl: cryst. M.p. 40–2°. B.p. 204–5°/14 mm.

Benzoyl: cryst. from EtOH. M.p. 126–7°.

Mannich, Merz, *Chem. Abstracts*, 1927, **21**, 1449.

Nomura, Canadian P., 203,512 (*Chem. Abstracts*, 1920, **14**, 2936).

Lapworth, Pearson, Royle, *J. Chem. Soc.*, 1917, **111**, 777.

Zingiberene

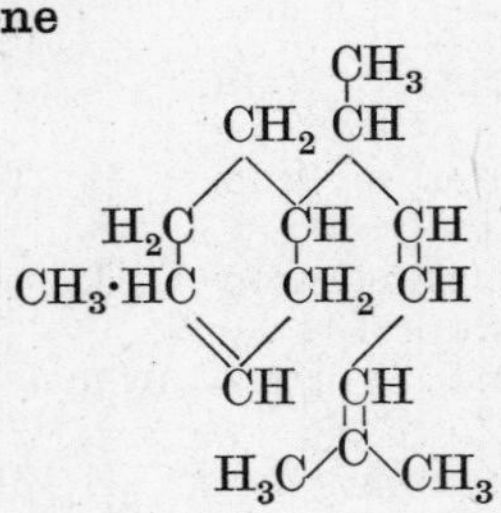

$C_{15}H_{24}$ MW, 204

Constituent of ginger oil. Natural oil is always contaminated with bisabolene. B.p. 134°/14 mm. D^{20} 0·8684. n_D^{20} 1·4956. $[\alpha]_D^{20}$ — 73·38°. Resinifies on standing. HBr ⟶ dihydrobromide of isozingiberene. AcOH + H_2SO_4 ⟶ isozingiberene. AcOH (+ Pt) ⟶ hexahydrozingiberene. Heat with S ⟶ cadalene.

Nitrosochloride: m.p. 93–4°.

Nitrosite: (i) M.p. 120–1°. (ii) M.p. 105°.
Nitrosate: m.p. 86–8°.

Ruzicka, van Veen, *Ann.*, 1929, **468**, 143.
Moudgill, *J. Indian Chem. Soc.*, 1928, **5**, 255.

Zingiberol

$C_{15}H_{26}O$ MW, 222

Constituent of ginger oil. Liq. B.p. 154–7°/14·5 mm. HCl in AcOH ⟶ isozingiberene dihydrochloride.

Brooks, *J. Am. Chem. Soc.*, 1916, **38**, 431.

Zingiberone.
See Zingerone.

Zoomaric Acid.
See Palmitoleic Acid.

Zygadenine

$C_{39}H_{63}O_{10}N$ MW, 705

Alkaloid from leaves of *Zygadenus intermedius* (Death camas). Cryst. from Et_2O, needles from C_6H_6, prisms + 2EtOH from EtOH. M.p. 200–1°. [α] − 48·2° in $CHCl_3$. Conc. H_2SO_4 ⟶ orange to red col. Physiological action resembles that of cevadine.

Heyl, Hepner, Loy, *J. Am. Chem. Soc.*, 1913, **35**, 258.

DICTIONARY OF ORGANIC COMPOUNDS

1943 SUPPLEMENT TO VOLUME III

Editors

I. M. HEILBRON, D.S.O., D.Sc., LL.D., F.I.C., F.R.S.

Professor of Organic Chemistry at the Imperial College of Science and Technology, London

and

H. M. BUNBURY, M.Sc., F.I.C., *Barrister-at-Law*

Imperial Chemical Industries Ltd.

Assistant Editors

E. R. H. JONES, D.Sc., F.I.C.

and

W. E. JONES, Ph.D., A.I.C.

Authors

D. H. R. BARTON, Ph.D., A.R.C.S., H. COATES, Ph.D., A.R.C.S., J. H. GORVIN, Ph.D., A.I.C., A. W. JOHNSON, Ph.D., A.R.C.S., A. LAMBERT, Ph.D., A.R.C.S., J. T. McCOMBIE, B.Sc., A.R.C.S., R. A. RAPHAEL, B.Sc., A.R.C.S., A. SPINKS, Ph.D.

1943 SUPPLEMENT TO VOLUME III

N

Napelline

$C_{22}H_{33}O_3N$ MW, 359

Alkaloid of *Aconitum napellus*. Plates from Et_2O–pet. ether or Me_2CO.Aq.

B,HCl: m.p. 220–2° decomp. $[\alpha]_D^{22}$ − 93·9° in H_2O.

B,HBr: needles from MeOH–Et_2O. M.p. 229° decomp. $[\alpha]_D^{22}$ − 42·7° in H_2O.

B,HI: cryst. from MeOH–Et_2O. M.p. 181–5° decomp.

Freudenberg, Rogers, *J. Am. Chem. Soc.*, 1937, **59**, 2572.

Naphthacene.
See 2 : 3-Benzanthracene.

Naphthacenequinone.
See 2 : 3-Benzanthraquinone.

Naphthaflavone.
See Benzflavone.

Naphthaflavonol.
See Benzflavonol.

Naphthalepidine.
See Methylbenzquinoline.

Naphthanthracene.
See 1 : 2-Benzanthracene.

Naphthanthraquinone.
See 1 : 2-Benzanthraquinone.

Naphthaphenazine.
See Benzphenazine.

Naphthapyridine.
See Benzquinoline *and* Anthrapyridine.

Naphthaquinaldine.
See Methylbenzquinoline.

Naphthaquinoline.
See Benzquinoline.

Naphthazine.
See α-Anthrapyridine.

Naphthylbutane.
See Butylnaphthalene.

1-Naphthylcarbinol (α-*Menaphthyl alcohol*, 1-*hydroxymethylnaphthalene*)

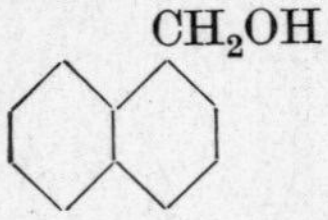

$C_{11}H_{10}O$ MW, 158

Needles from H_2O. M.p. 59·5–60°. B.p. 301°/715 mm., 163–6°/15 mm.

Acetyl: b.p. 172–3°/13 mm.

Ziegler, *Ber.*, 1921, **54**, 739.

2-Naphthylcarbinol (β-*Menaphthyl alcohol*, 2-*hydroxymethylnaphthalene*).

Leaflets. M.p. 80–80·5°. Spar. sol. cold H_2O. Volatile in steam.

Acetyl: cryst. M.p. 51–3°.

Bamberger, Bökmann, *Ber.*, 1887, **20**, 1118.

Naphthylenediamine.
N:N-*Diphenyl*: *see* Diphenylnaphthylenediamine.

Naphthylisobutane.
See tert.-Butylnaphthalene.

Naphthylmethyl bromide.
See Bromomethyl-naphthalene.

Naphthylmethyl chloride.
See Chloromethyl-naphthalene.

Naphthylpropylene.
See Allylnaphthalene.

3-α-Naphthylvaleric Acid.
See 3-Methyl-3-α-naphthylbutyric Acid.

Narcotoline

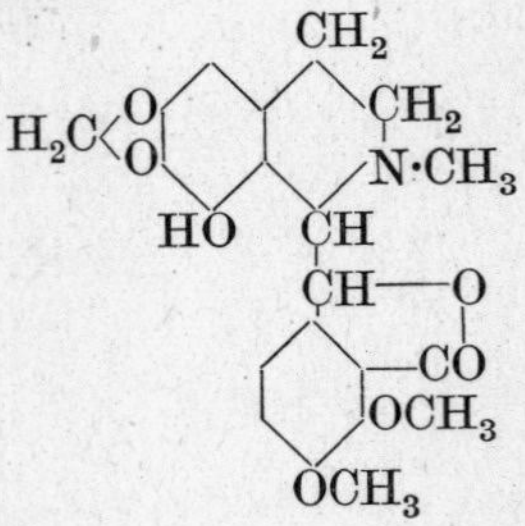

$C_{21}H_{21}O_7N$ MW, 399

Alkaloid from poppy, *Papaver somniferum*. Rectangular rods from MeOH.Aq. M.p. 202°. $[\alpha]_D^{20}$ − 189° in $CHCl_3$, + 5·8° in 0·1*N*/HCl. $CH_2N_2 \longrightarrow$ narcotine.

Bitartrate: needles. Decomp. at about 200°.

Wrede, *Chem. Zentr.*, 1938, II, 863; 1937, I, 2611.

Neocholestene.
See Δ^2-Cholestene.

Neoline

$C_{24}H_{41}O_6N$ MW, 439

Alkaloid from *Aconitum napellus*. Prisms from Et_2O–pet. ether. M.p. 153–4°. $[\alpha]_D^{23}$ +9·7° in EtOH.

B,HCl: cryst. from MeOH–Et_2O. Decomp. at 178–80°.

B,HBr : needles from MeOH–Et_2O. M.p. 215° decomp. $[\alpha]_D^{23}$ + 2·1° in H_2O.

Freudenberg, Rogers, *J. Am. Chem. Soc.*, 1937, **59**, 2572.

Neopentyl Alcohol.
See tert.-Butylcarbinol.

Neoprene.
See Chloroprene.

Neoquassin

$C_{22}H_{30}O_6$ MW, 390

Occurs together with quassin in wood of *Quassia amara*. Prisms and plates from MeOH.Aq. M.p. 225–6°. $[\alpha]_D^{20}$ + 46·6° in $CHCl_3$. Contains two CH_3O groups and one active H atom. 3·5% HCl ⟶ semidemethoxyquassin, $C_{21}H_{28}O_6$, m.p. 213°.

Clark, *J. Am. Chem. Soc.*, 1937, **59**, 927, 2511; 1938, **60**, 1146.

Niacin.
See Nicotinic Acid.

Ninhydrin (*Triketohydrindene hydrate*)

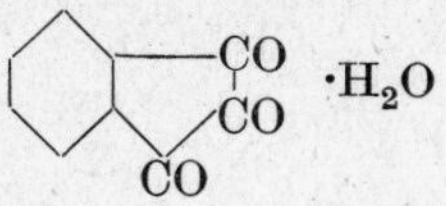

$C_9H_6O_4$ MW, 178

Prisms from H_2O. Anhyd. at 125–30°. M.p. 241–3° decomp. Alkalis ⟶ yellow ⟶ blue ⟶ colourless sols. Reagent for the detection of uncombined amino and carboxyl groups in proteins, etc. Warm with amino acid ⟶ blue col.

Di-phenylhydrazone : cryst. from EtOH. M.p. 180°.

Phenazine deriv. : cryst. from EtOH. M.p. 219–20°.

Vanags, Lode, *Ber.*, 1938, **71**, 1267.
Teeters, Shriner, *J. Am. Chem. Soc.*, 1933, **55**, 3026.
Ruhemann, *J. Chem. Soc.*, 1910, **97**, 2025.

Niquidine

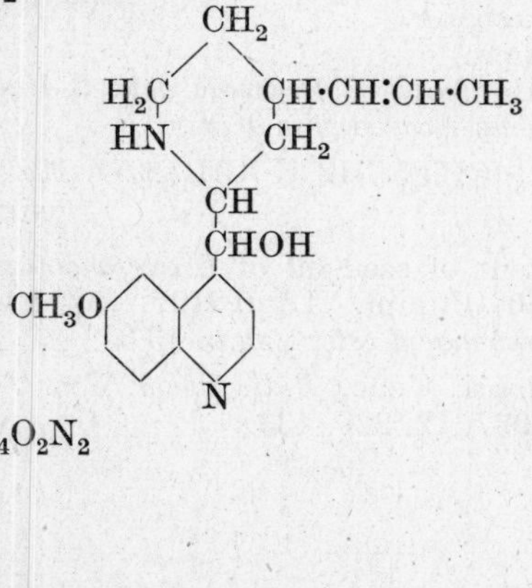

$C_{19}H_{24}O_2N_2$ MW, 312

Needles from moist Et_2O. M.p. 172°. $[\alpha]_D^{18}$ + 301·5° in 0·1N/H_2SO_4, + 186° in EtOH. H_2O_2 ⟶ quininic acid.

B,HBr : prisms. M.p. 217°. $[\alpha]_D^{18}$ + 240° in 0·1N/H_2SO_4.

B,2HBr : prisms from H_2O. M.p. 230° decomp. $[\alpha]_D^{18}$ + 199° in H_2O.

Hydrogen oxalyl : needles. M.p. 215°.

Gibbs, Henry, *J. Chem. Soc.*, 1939, 240, 1294.

Nitrohydroxyethylbenzene.
See Nitromethylphenylcarbinol *and* Methylnitrophenyl-carbinol.

Nitromethylbenzyl chloride.
See Nitroxylyl chloride.

Nitromethylphenylcarbinol (*2-Nitro-1-phenylethyl alcohol*, *β-nitro-α-hydroxyethylbenzene*)

C_6H_5·CH(OH)·CH_2NO_2

$C_8H_9O_3N$ MW, 167

Yellow liq. B.p. 163–5°/15 mm. decomp. Mod. sol. H_2O. CrO_3 ⟶ ω-nitroacetophenone.

Me ether : $C_9H_{11}O_3N$. MW, 181. B.p. 135–6°/12 mm.

Et ether : $C_{10}H_{13}O_3N$. MW, 195. Yellowish oil. B.p. 136–7°/12 mm. Volatile in steam.

Hollemann, *Rec. trav. chim.*, 1904, **23**, 299.
Rosenmund, *Ber.*, 1913, **46**, 1038.
Meisenheimer, Heim, *Ber.*, 1905, **38**, 469.

Nitrophenylethyl Alcohol.
See Methylnitrophenylcarbinol.

***p*-Nitrosobenzylaniline.**
See Benzyl-*p*-nitrosoaniline.

5-Nitro-*o*-xylyl chloride (*ω-Chloro-5-nitro-o-xylene*, *5-nitro-2-methylbenzyl chloride*)

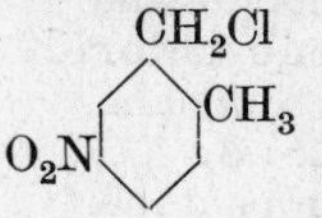

$C_8H_8O_2NCl$ MW, 185·5

Needles from MeOH. M.p. 50°. Sol. EtOH, Et_2O, C_6H_6. Spar. sol. Me_2CO, ligroin. Irritates skin and mucous membrane. $KMnO_4$ ⟶ 4-nitrophthalic acid.

Stephen, Short, Gladding. *J. Chem. Soc.*, 1920, **117**, 526.

3-Nitro-*p*-xylyl chloride (*ω-Chloro-3-nitro-p-xylene*, *3-nitro-4-methylbenzyl chloride*)

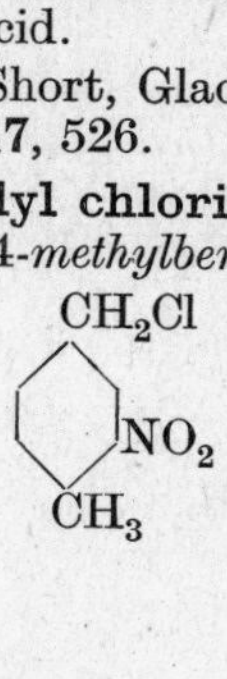

$C_8H_8O_2NC$ MW, 185·5

Cryst. from MeOH. M.p. 45°. Sol. EtOH, Me_2CO, C_6H_6, $CHCl_3$. Irritates skin and mucous membrane. $KMnO_4 \longrightarrow$ 2-nitroterephthalic acid.

Stephen, Short, Gladding, *J. Chem. Soc.*, 1920, **117**, 525.

Nobiletin (5 : 6 : 7 : 8 : 3′ : 4′-*Hexamethoxy-flavone*)

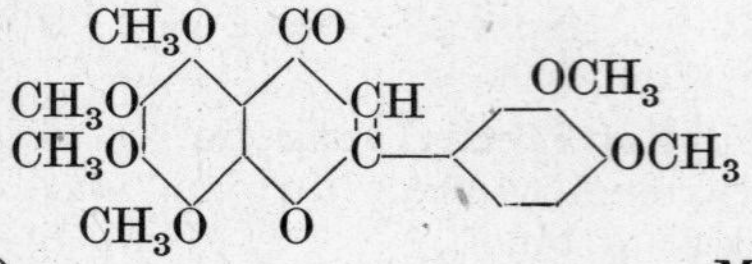

$C_{21}H_{22}O_8$ MW, 402

Constituent of peel of fruits of *Citrus nobilis*, Lour. Pale yellow cryst. from MeOH. M.p. 134°. Spar. sol. H_2O, Et_2O. EtOH–KOH $\longrightarrow$ veratric acid + acetoveratrone.

Tseng, *J. Chem. Soc.*, 1938, 1003.
Robinson, Tseng, *ibid.*, 1004.

Nonadecanone-10.
See Caprinone.

Nonalupine

$C_{15}H_{24}ON_2$ MW, 248

Alkaloid from *Lupinus sericeus*, Pursh. Leaflets from methyl isobutyl ketone. M.p. 91·5–92·5°. When anhydrous, softens at 219°, m.p. 235°. B.p. 260–70°/18 mm. $[\alpha]_D^{25}$ − 21·3° in EtOH.

Chloroaurate: yellow needles from H_2O. M.p. 177·5–178° decomp.

Picrate: cryst. from 50% EtOH. M.p. 185–6°.

Couch, *J. Am. Chem. Soc.*, 1940, **62**, 554.

Nonamethylene bromide.
See 1 : 9-Dibromononane.

Nonamethylene chloride.
See 1 : 9-Dichlorononane.

Nonandione-2 : 8.
See 1 : 5-Diacetopentane.

3-Nonene-1-carboxylic Acid.
See Obtusilic Acid.

***sec.-n*-Nonylamine.**
See 2-Amino-*n*-nonane.

Nonylone.
See Di-*n*-octyl Ketone.

Norlupinane-A (*Octahydropyridocoline, bicyclo*-[0 : 4 : 4]-*aza-1-decane*)

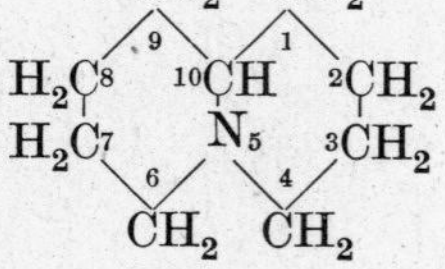

$C_9H_{17}N$ MW, 139

B.p. 74–6°/14 mm., 69–70°/11 mm.

B,HBr: prisms from $CHCl_3$–AcOEt. M.p. 265–6°.

B,HAuCl₄: golden yellow leaflets or prisms from EtOH. M.p. 168°.

Picrate: yellow needles from EtOH. M.p. 194°.

Picrolonate: yellow rods from AcOH. M.p. 245°.

Methiodide: plates from Me_2CO. M.p. 333–5° decomp.

Clemo, Morgan, Raper, *J. Chem. Soc.*, 1935, 1743.
Clemo, Ramage, *J. Chem. Soc.*, 1931, **437**, 3190.
Clemo, Metcalfe, Raper, *J. Chem. Soc.*, 1936, 1430.
Prelog, Bozicevic, *Ber.*, 1939, **72**, 1103.
Winterfield, Holschneider, *Ann.*, 1932, **499**, 109.
Sugasawa, Lee, *J. Pharm. Soc. Japan*, 1939, **59**, 326.

Norlupinane-B (*Bicyclo*-[0 : 3 : 5]-*aza*-1-*decane*)

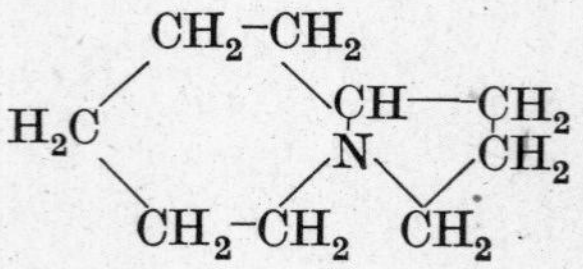

$C_9H_{17}N$ MW, 139

B.p. 80°/14 mm.

Picrate: yellow needles from EtOH. M.p. 213–14° corr.

Picrolonate: yellow tablets from EtOH. M.p. 191·5° corr.

Methiodide: needles from Me_2CO. M.p. 282·5–283° corr.

Clemo, Ramage, *J. Chem. Soc.*, 1931, 437.
Prelog, Seiwerth, *Ber.*, 1939, **72**, 1638.

Norvaline.
N-*Phenyl*: *see* 1-Anilinovaleric Acid.

O

Obaculactone.
See Limonin.

Obtusilic Acid (3-*Decenoic acid*, 3-*decylenic acid*, 3-*nonene-1-carboxylic acid*)

$CH_3\cdot[CH_2]_4\cdot CH{:}CH\cdot[CH_2]_2\cdot COOH$

$C_{10}H_{18}O_2$ MW, 170

Constituent of seed oil of *Lindera obtusiloba*. B.p. 148–50°/13 mm. D_4^{20} 0·9197. n_D^{20} 1·4497.

p-*Bromophenacyl ester*: m.p. 43·3°.

Komori, Ueno, *Bull. Chem. Soc. Japan*, 1937, **12**, 226, 433.

Ochotensine

$C_{21}H_{21}O_4N$ MW, 351

Alkaloid of *Corydalis ochotensis*, Turcz. M.p. 252°. $[\alpha]_D^{23} + 63·9°$ in $0·1N$/HCl, $[\alpha]_D^{24} + 51·7°$ in $CHCl_3$. Spar. sol. Et_2O. Phenolic.

Manske, *Chem. Abstracts*, 1940, **34**, 4070.

Ochrobirine

$C_{20}H_{19}O_6N$ MW, 369

Alkaloid of *Corydalis lutea*. M.p. 138–9°. $[\alpha]_D^{21} + 35·9°$ in $CHCl_3$.

Acetyl deriv.: m.p. 177°.

Manske, *Chem. Abstracts*, 1939, **33**, 6323.

9 : 12-Octadecadienol-1.
See Linoleyl Alcohol.

Octadecylhydroquinone (*Octadecylquinol, 2 : 5-dihydroxyoctadecylbenzene*)

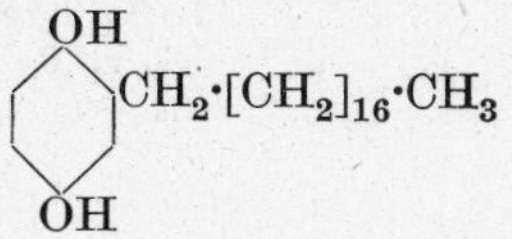

$C_{24}H_{42}O_2$ MW, 362

Cryst. from pet. ether. M.p. 100·5°. Ag_2O ⟶ octadecylbenzoquinone. M.p. 76°.

Di-Me ether: 2 : 5-dimethoxyoctadecylbenzene. B.p. 188°/0·2 mm.

Di-Et ether: 2 : 5-diethoxyoctadecylbenzene. B.p. 201°/0·06 mm.

Cook, Heilbron, Lewis, *J. Chem. Soc.*, 1942, 660.

Octahydropyridocoline.
See Norlupinane-A.

Octamethylene bromide.
See 1 : 8-Dibromo-octane.

Octamethylene chloride.
See 1 : 8-Dichloro-octane.

5-Octanolone-4.
See Butyroin.

2 : 4 : 6-Octatrienal

$CH_3·[CH{:}CH]_3·CHO$

$C_8H_{10}O$ MW, 122

Needles from pet. ether. M.p. 55°. B.p. 57–68°/0·5 mm. Sol. org. solvents. Absorption maximum at 3160 Å in EtOH.

Oxime: yellow. M.p. 186–7° decomp.

Hydrazone: yellow needles from EtOH. Sinters at 153–4°.

Azine: orange cryst. from butyl or amyl alcohol. Decomp. at 220–5°.

Fischer, Hultzsch, Flaig, *Ber.*, 1937, **70**, 370.

Kuhn, Hoffer, *Ber.*, 1930, **63**, 2164; 1931, **64**, 1977.
Kuhn, *Angew. Chem.*, 1937, **50**, 703.
Gödde, *Chem. Abstracts*, 1940, **34**, 1970.

2 : 4 : 6-Octatrienol

$CH_3·[CH{:}CH]·CH_2OH$

$C_8H_{12}O$ MW, 124

Needles. M.p. 99·5–100·5°. B.p. 95°/12 mm.

Reichstein, Ammann, Trivelli, *Helv. Chim. Acta*, 1932, **15**, 261, 502.

Octopin (*Pectenin*, l-*arginine*-l-α-*propionic acid*)

$$\begin{matrix}H_3C\\HOOC\end{matrix}>CH·NH·CH<\begin{matrix}COOH\\CH_2·[CH_2]_2·NH·C\ll\begin{matrix}NH\\NH_2\end{matrix}\end{matrix}$$

$C_9H_{18}O_4N_4$ MW, 246

Isolated from aq. extracts of tentacle muscles of *Loligo pealii* and *Octopus vulgaris*, the adductor muscles of the scallop *Pecten magellanicus* and the muscles of the octopod *Eledone moschata*. Needles from H_2O or EtOH.Aq. M.p. 281–2° (261–4°). Odourless and tasteless. Readily sol. hot H_2O. Spar. sol. MeOH, EtOH, Et_2O. $[\alpha]_D^{17} + 20·94°$ in H_2O.

Cu salt: m.p. 223–7° decomp.
Ni salt: m.p. above 290°.
Picrate: m.p. 226–30° corr. decomp.
Picrolonate: m.p. 237–9° corr. decomp.

Akashi, *Chem. Abstracts*, 1937, **31**, 5766.
Knoop, Martius, *Z. physiol. Chem.*, 1938, **254**, 1; 1939, **258**, 238.
Irvin, Wilson, *J. Biol. Chem.*, 1939, **127**, 555, 565, 575.
Karrer, Koenig, Legler, *Helv. Chim. Acta*, 1941, **24**, 127.

***sec.-n*-Octylamine.**
See 2-Amino-*n*-octane.

Oenanthylidene.
See 1-Heptine.

α-Oestradiol (trans-*Oestradiol*, trans-*dihydro-œstrone*)

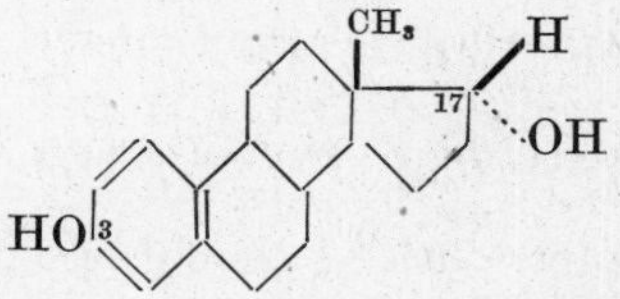

$C_{18}H_{24}O_2$ MW, 272

Isolated from ovaries and pregnancy urine. Leaflets or needles from EtOH.Aq. Cryst. from Me_2CO. M.p. 174°. $[\alpha]_D^{18} +78°$ in EtOH. Digitonide is insol. 80% EtOH. The most potent of the natural œstrogens.

3-*Me ether*: needles from MeOH.Aq. M.p. 97–8°.

3-*Acetyl*: m.p. 137°.

17-*Acetyl*: m.p. 215–17°.

Diacetyl: leaflets from MeOH.Aq. M.p. 125–6°.

3-*Propionyl*: m.p. 125°.

17-*Propionyl*: m.p. 199–200°.

Dipropionyl: m.p. 104–5°.

17-n-*Butyryl*: m.p. 166–7°.

Di-n-butyryl: m.p. 64–5°.

3-*Trimethylacetyl*: needles from MeOH.Aq. M.p. 178–80°.

Di-trimethylacetyl: needles from Me_2CO–MeOH. M.p. 174–6°.

3-*Palmityl*: m.p. 69–71°.

3-*Benzoyl*: needles from EtOH.Aq. M.p. 192–3°.

3 : 17-*Dibenzoyl*: leaflets from EtOH. M.p. 168–9°.

Butenandt, *Z. physiol. Chem.*, 1937, **248**, 129.
Doisy, *J. Biol. Chem.*, 1936, **115**, 435.
Wintersteiner, *J. Biol. Chem.*, 1937, **118**, 789; *J. Am. Chem. Soc.*, 1937, **59**, 765.
Marker, *J. Am. Chem. Soc.*, 1938, **60**, 2927.

β-Oestradiol (cis-*Oestradiol*, cis-*dihydrocestrone*)

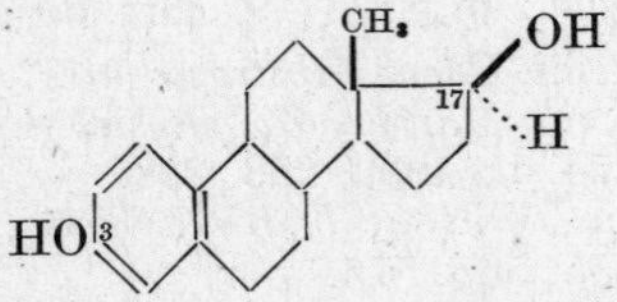

$C_{18}H_{24}O_2$ MW, 272

Isolated from pregnancy urine. Needles from EtOH.Aq. Cryst. from Me_2CO. M.p. 223°. $[\alpha]_D^{18}$ +56·7° in EtOH. Much less potent than the α-isomer.

3-*Me ether*: leaflets from MeOH. M.p. 109–10°.

3 : 17-*Diacetyl*: needles from EtOH.Aq. M.p. 139–40°.

3-*Benzoyl*: leaflets from MeOH.Aq. M.p. 156–7°.

Butenandt, *Z. physiol. Chem.*, 1937, **248**, 129.
Wintersteiner, *J. Biol. Chem.*, 1938, **122**, 303; *J. Am. Chem. Soc.*, 1937, **59**, 765.
Marker, *J. Am. Chem. Soc.*, 1938, **60**, 2927.

Oleic Acid.

Dibromide: *see* 8 : 9-Dibromostearic Acid.
Dichloride: *see* 8 : 9-Dichlorostearic Acid.

Oöcyan.

See Biliverdin.

Ophiocarpine

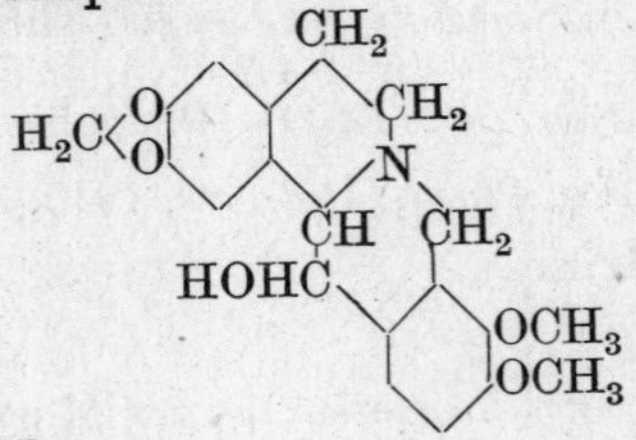

$C_{20}H_{21}O_5N$ MW, 355

Principal alkaloidal constituent (0·25%) of *Corydalis ophiocarpa*. M.p. 188°. $[\alpha]_D^{24}$ − 284° in $CHCl_3$.

Manske, *Chem. Abstracts*, 1939, **33**, 6321.

Orcacetophenone.

See 4 : 6-Dihydroxy-2-methylacetophenone.

Orobol (5 : 7 : 3′ : 4′-*Tetrahydroxyisoflavone*)

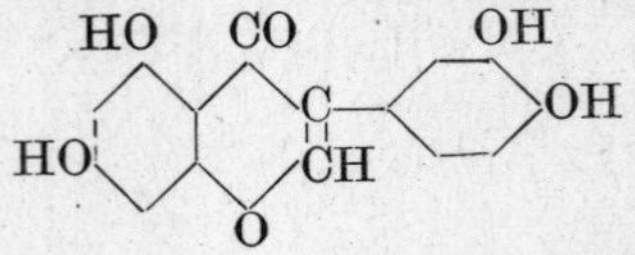

$C_{15}H_{10}O_6$ MW, 286

Occurs as glucoside, oroboside, in *Orobus tuberosus*, L. Pale yellow needles from AcOH. M.p. 270·5°. 30% KOH ⟶ phloroglucinol + homoprotocatechuic acid.

Tetra-acetyl: cryst. from AcOH. M.p. 210–12°.

Bridel, Charaux, *Compt. rend.*, 1930, **190**, 387; *Bull. soc. chim. biol.*, 1930, **12**, 615.
Charaux, Rabaté, *Bull. soc. chim. biol.*, 1939, **21**, 1330.

Oroboside

$C_{21}H_{20}O_{11}$ MW, 448

Occurs in *Orobus tuberosus*, L. Yellow prisms from 40% EtOH.Aq. M.p. 220–1°. $[\alpha]_D$ − 61·3° in Py. Acid hyd. ⟶ orobol + glucose.

Bridel, Charaux, *Compt. rend.*, 1930, **190**, 387; *Bull. soc. chim. biol.*, 1930, **12**, 615.

***p*-Orsellinaldehyde.**

See Atranol.

Oryzanin.

See Aneurin.

Osajin

$C_{25}H_{24}O_5$ MW, 404

Isolated from fruit of osage orange tree (*Maclura pomifera*, Raf.). Lemon yellow cryst.

from xylene or 95% EtOH. M.p. 189° (193° corr.). Very sol. $CHCl_3$, Et_2O, Me_2CO, Py. Mod. sol. C_6H_6, warm CCl_4. Prac. insol. H_2O, pet. ether. Reduces Fehling's, and Tollen's in Py. Alc. sol. + aq. $FeCl_3 \longrightarrow$ dark green col. $\longrightarrow$ reddish violet on addn. of a few drops of NH_4OH.

Monoacetyl deriv.: yellow cryst. from EtOH. M.p. 159°.

Diacetyl deriv.: cryst. from EtOH.Aq. Two forms. M.ps. 162° and 152°.

*Mono-*p*-toluenesulphonyl*: yellow plates from EtOH. M.p. 152°.

Me ether: $C_{26}H_{26}O_5$. MW, 418. Yellow needles from 95% EtOH. M.p. 134–5°. *Monoacetyl*: prisms from 95% EtOH. M.p. 140–140·5°.

Di-Me ether: $C_{27}H_{28}O_5$. MW, 432. Needles from 95% EtOH. M.p. 118·5°.

Wolfrom, Gregory, *J. Am. Chem. Soc.*, 1940, **62**, 651.

Wolfrom, Benton, Gregory, Hess, Mahan, Morgan, *J. Am. Chem. Soc.*, 1939, **61**, 2833.

Walter, Wolfrom, Hess, *J. Am. Chem. Soc.*, 1938, **60**, 575.

P

Palustrin

$C_{12}H_{24}O_2N_2$ MW, 228

Alkaloid isolated from swamp horsetail (*Equisetum palustre*). Pale yellow oil with amine-like odour. B.p. 205–10°/0·1 mm.

B,HCl: cubes. M.p. 181°.

Glet, Gutschmidt, Glet, *Z. physiol. Chem.*, 1936, **244**, 229.

Pamaquin.

See Plasmoquin.

Pantocaine.

See Decicaine.

Pantothenic Acid

$$HOCH_2{\cdot}\overset{\displaystyle CH_3}{\underset{\displaystyle CH_3}{C}}{\cdot}CH(OH){\cdot}CO{\cdot}NH{\cdot}CH_2{\cdot}CH_2{\cdot}COOH$$

$C_9H_{17}O_5N$ MW, 219

d-.

Growth-promoting and antidermatitic factor ("Filtrate factor") of vitamin B complex, present in living cells particularly of the liver. Viscous oil. $[\alpha]_D^{25}$ + 37·5° in H_2O. Acid or alk. hyd. $\longrightarrow$ β-alanine + *l*-α-hydroxy-ββ-dimethyl-γ-butyrolactone (or salt of corresponding acid).

Na salt: cryst. from EtOH. M.p. 122–4° (121–2°). $[\alpha]_D^{12\cdot5}$ + 29·5° in H_2O, $[\alpha]_D^{25}$ + 27·04° in H_2O.

Ca salt: cryst. from MeOH. M.p. 195–6°. $[\alpha]_D^{26}$ + 28·2° in H_2O. Anisotropic.

Benzylthiuronium salt: m.p. 148–9°.

Cinchonidine salt: m.p. 178–9° (176–7°). $[\alpha]_D^{28\cdot4}$ − 60·6° in MeOH, $[\alpha]_D^{18}$ − 62·8° in H_2O.

Quinine salt: m.p. 136–7°. $[\alpha]_D^{19}$ − 95° in H_2O.

Me ester: $C_{10}H_{19}O_5N$. MW, 233. Oil. $[\alpha]_D^{15}$ + 37·1° in Me_2CO.

Et ester: $C_{11}H_{21}O_5N$. MW, 247. Oil. $[\alpha]_D^{18}$ + 36·8° in EtOH.

l-.

Little or no biological activity (conflicting results). Viscous oil. $[\alpha]_D^{21}$ − 26·7° in H_2O, − 56·3° in MeOH.

Na salt: m.p. 120–2°. $[\alpha]_D^{15}$ − 27·4° in H_2O.

Ca salt: cryst. from MeOH. M.p. 187·5–189°. $[\alpha]_D^{26}$ − 27·8° in H_2O.

Benzylthiuronium salt: m.p. 150–1° (145–6°).

Quinine salt: needles from Me_2CO–MeOH. M.p. 183·0° (167–8°). $[\alpha]_D^{19}$ − 121° in H_2O.

Et ester: oil. $[\alpha]_D^{19}$ − 37·3° in EtOH.

dl-.

Viscous oil. Possesses half biological activity of *d*- form.

Benzylthiuronium salt: needles from Me_2CO. M.p. 135–6°.

Woolley *et al.*, *J. Biol. Chem.*, 1939, **129**, 673.

Williams *et al.*, *J. Am. Chem. Soc.*, 1940, **62**, 1776, 1784.

Stiller *et al.*, *J. Am. Chem. Soc.*, 1940, **62**, 1779, 1785; 1941, **63**, 1237, 2846.

Woolley, *J. Am. Chem. Soc.*, 1940, **62**, 2251.

Reichstein *et al.*, *Helv. Chim. Acta*, 1940, **23**, 650, 1276; 1941, **24**, 185.

Kuhn *et al.*, *Ber.*, 1940, **73**, 971, 1134; 1941, **74**, 218.

Parke, Lawson, *J. Am. Chem. Soc.*, 1941, **63**, 2869.

Harris, Boyack, Folkers, *J. Am. Chem. Soc.*, 1941, **63**, 2662.

Paracasein.

See Caseinogen.

Parachloralose.

See β-Glucochloralose.

Paracyanoformic Acid.

See Triazine-tricarboxylic Acid.

Paredrine (1 - p - *Hydroxyphenylisopropylamine*, p-β-*aminopropylphenol*)

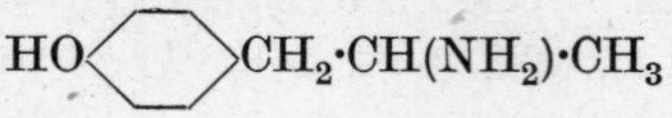

$C_9H_{13}ON$ MW, 151

Exerts marked pressor activity similar to that of benzedrine.

B,HCl : cryst. from EtOH–Et_2O. M.p. 171–2°. Sol. H_2O, Et_2O.

Alles, *J. Am. Chem. Soc.*, 1932, **54**, 271.
Woodruff, Conger, *J. Am. Chem. Soc.*, 1938, **60**, 465.
Iglauer, Altschule, *American Journal of Medical Sciences*, 1940, **199**, 359, (*Chem. Abstracts*, 1940, **34**, 3821).

Parinaric Acid

$CH_3 \cdot CH_2 \cdot [CH{:}CH]_4 \cdot [CH_2]_7 \cdot COOH$

$C_{18}H_{28}O_2$ MW, 276

Acid of the kernel fat of *Parinarium laurinum*. Faintly yellow plates from pet. ether. M.p. 85–6°. Isomerised by I or light to acid, m.p. 95–6°. Absorption maxima: 3200, 3070 and 2920 Å. in EtOH.

Farmer, Sunderland, *J. Chem. Soc.*, 1935, 759.
Kaufmann, Baltes, Funke, *Chem. Zentr.*, 1938, II, 4143.

Patuletin

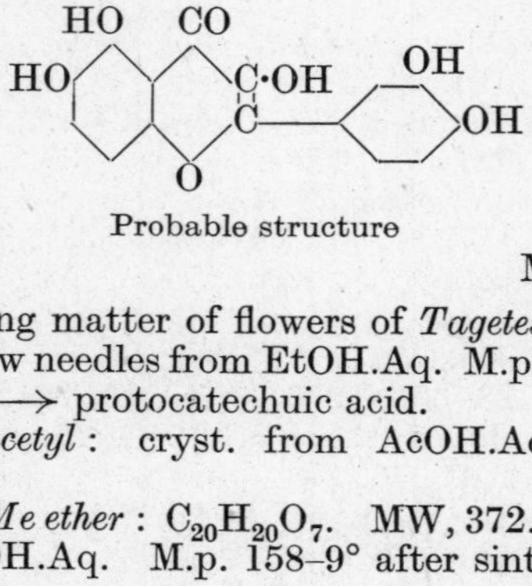

Probable structure

$C_{15}H_{10}O_7$ MW, 302

Colouring matter of flowers of *Tagetes patula*. Pale yellow needles from EtOH.Aq. M.p. 262–4°. Alk. ox. ⟶ protocatechuic acid.

Penta-acetyl : cryst. from AcOH.Aq. M.p. 170–2°.

Penta-Me ether : $C_{20}H_{20}O_7$. MW, 372. Cryst. from AcOH.Aq. M.p. 158–9° after sintering at 143°.

Rao, Seshadri, *Proceedings of the Indian Academy of Sciences*, 1941, **14**, 643, (*Brit. Chem. Abstracts*, 1942, A II, 202).

Pectenin.
See Octopin.

Pectenine.
See Carnegine.

Pedicellin

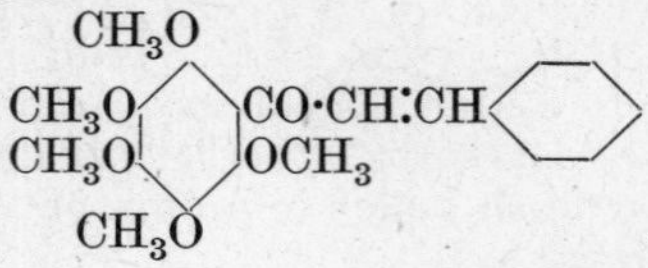

$C_{20}H_{22}O_6$ MW, 358

Isolated from dried leaves of *Didymocarpus pedicellata*. Cryst. from Et_2O. M.p. 93°. HNO_3 ⟶ methylpedicinin ($C_{17}H_{14}O_6$), m.p. 110°.

Phenylhydrazone : rods from AcOEt. M.p. 133–5°.

Sharma, Siddiqui, *J. Indian Chem. Soc.*, 1939, **16**, 1.
Bose, Dutt, *J. Indian Chem. Soc.*, 1940, **17**, 499.
Baker, *J. Chem. Soc.*, 1941, 662.

Pedicin

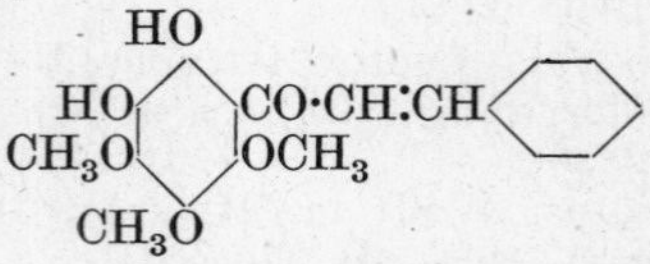

Suggested structure

$C_{18}H_{18}O_6$ MW, 330

Isolated from coarsely powdered leaves of *Didymocarpus pedicellata*. Orange red plates. M.p. 145°. Br in $CHCl_3$ or $KMnO_4$ ⟶ pedicinin. Methylation ⟶ pedicellin.

Dibenzoyl : rods from C_6H_6. M.p. 181–3°.

Phenylhydrazone : needles from EtOH. M.p. 165–7°.

Siddiqui *et al.*, *J. Indian Chem. Soc.*, 1937, **14**, 703; 1939, **16**, 1, 423.

Pedicinin

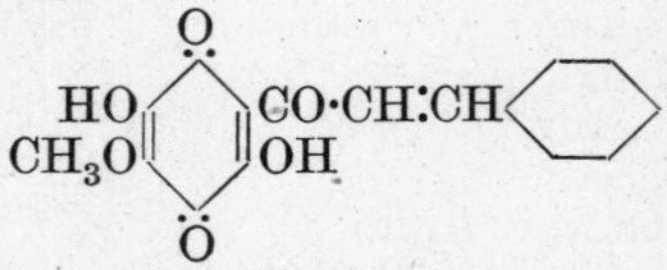

Probable structure

$C_{16}H_{12}O_6$ MW, 300

Isolated from dried leaves of *Didymocarpus pedicellata*. Red rods or needles from C_6H_6. M.p. 203°. Alkalis ⟶ benzaldehyde.

Monoacetyl : prisms from AcOEt. M.p. 175°.

Siddiqui, *J. Indian Chem. Soc.*, 1937, **14**, 703.
Bose, Dutt, *J. Indian Chem. Soc.*, 1940, **17**, 499.

Peiminine

$C_{26}H_{43}O_3N$ MW, 417

Alkaloid of Chinese drug Pei-Mu from corms of *Fritillaria Roylei*, Stuart. Needles from EtOH–pet. ether. Sinters at 140°, melts at 147–8°, solidifies at 157°, finally melts at 212–13°. $[\alpha]_D^{13} - 65.8°$.

Hydrochloride : m.p. 292°.
Hydrobromide : m.p. 295°.

Chi, Kao, Chang, *J. Am. Chem. Soc.*, 1940, **62**, 2896; 1936, **58**, 1306.

Penicillic Acid

$$CH_3 \atop CH_2 \Big\rangle C \cdot CO \cdot \overset{OCH_3}{C} : CH \cdot COOH \rightleftharpoons {CH_3 \atop CH_2} \Big\rangle C \cdot \overset{HO}{C} \cdot \overset{OCH_3}{C} : CH \cdot CO$$

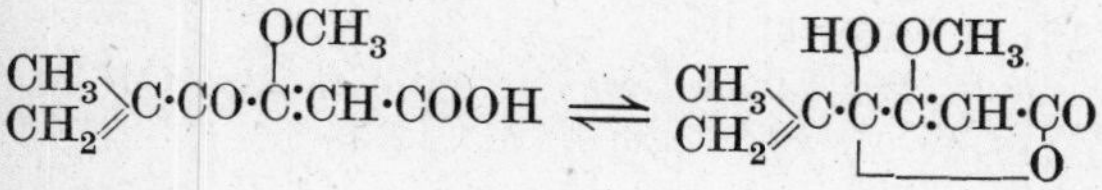

$C_8H_{10}O_4$ MW, 170

Metabolic product of *Penicillium puberulum* Bainier, and *Penicillium cyclopium* Westling. Rhombic or hexagonal plates $+ 1H_2O$ from H_2O. M.p. 64–5°, anhyd. 87°. Sol. to 2% in cold H_2O. Readily sol. hot H_2O, EtOH, Et_2O, C_6H_6, $CHCl_3$. Insol. pet. ether. $NH_4OH \longrightarrow$ reddish purple col.

Acetyl : prisms from pet. ether. M.p. 72°.
Dimedone deriv. : $C_8H_{10}O_4$, $C_8H_{12}O_2$. Cryst. from EtOH.Aq. M.p. 201–3°.
Dihydro-comp. : needles $+ 1H_2O$ from H_2O. M.p. 62–4°, anhyd. 83–5°.
Dibromide : needles from CCl_4. M.p. 154–5°.

Birkinshaw, Oxford, Raistrick, *Biochem. J.*, 1936, **30**, 394.

Pentadecanol-8.
See Di-*n*-heptylcarbinol.
Pentadecanone-8.
See Caprylone.
Pentahydroxy-1-aminohexane.
See Glucamine.
Pentahydroxycyclohexane.
See Viburnitol.
3 : 5 : 7 : 3′ : 4′-Pentahydroxyflavan.
See Catechin.
3 : 5 : 7 : 8 : 4′-Pentahydroxyflavone.
See Herbacetin.
Pentahydroxyhexylamine.
See Glucamine.
3 : 5 : 6 : 7 : 8 - Pentahydroxy - 2 - ethyl - 1 : 4-naphthoquinone.
See Echinochrome A.
Pentamethylene-tetrazole.
See Cardiazole.
Pentane-3-carboxylic Acid.
See Diethylacetic Acid.

Pentane-1 : 3-dicarboxylic Acid.
See 1-Ethylglutaric Acid.
Pentanolamine.
See Aminopentanol.
p-Pentaphenyl (p-*Quinquiphenyl*)

$C_{30}H_{22}$ MW, 382

Needles from quinoline. M.p. 388·5°. Sublimes.

Gerngross, Dunkel, *Ber.*, 1924, **57**, 739.
Bursch, Weber, *J. prakt. Chem.*, 1936, **146**, 29.
Müller, Töpel, *Ber.*, 1939, **72**, 290.

3-Pentenic Acid.
See Allylacetic Acid.
1-Pentinol-3.
See Ethylethinylcarbinol.
Perbenzoic Acid.
Benzoyl : *see* Benzoyl peroxide.

Periflanthene

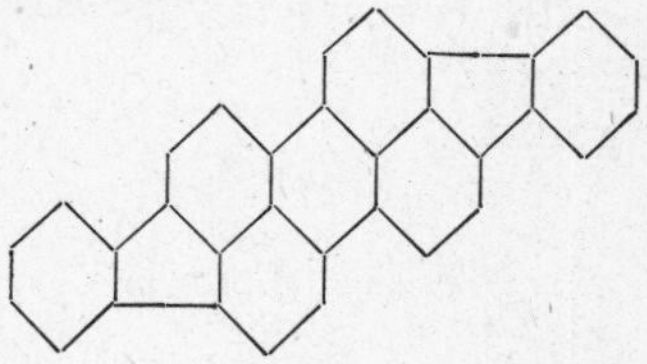

$C_{32}H_{16}$ MW, 400

Dark red solid. M.p. above 360°. Spar. sol. chlorobenzene, bromobenzene, phenol. Insol. Et_2O, xylene. Sublimes. Very stable and very resistant to oxidising agents. Sol. conc. H_2SO_4 at 100° with blue col.

Braun, Manz, *Ber.*, 1937, **70**, 1603.

Periplocin

$C_{13}H_{23}O_8 \cdot O$

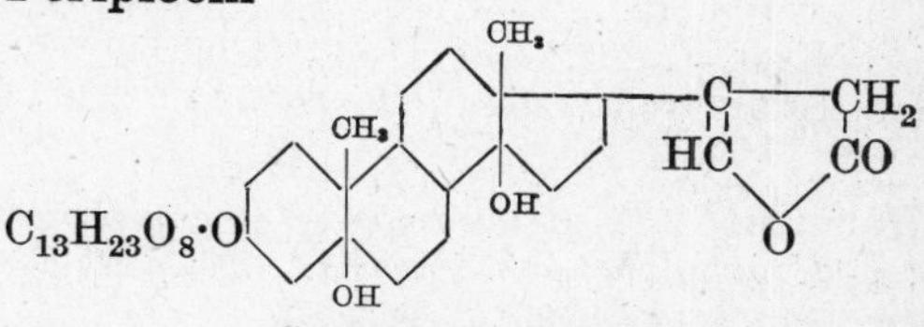

Suggested structure

$C_{36}H_{56}O_{13}$ MW, 696

Cardiac glycoside from *Periploca graeca*, L. Needles from H_2O. M.p. 224° decomp. Sol. EtOH. Spar. sol. H_2O. Prac. insol. Et_2O, $CHCl_3$. $[\alpha]_D^{20} + 22.9°$ in MeOH. Hyd. $\longrightarrow$ periplogenin + periplobiose. Enzyme hyd. $\longrightarrow$ periplocymarin.

Tetra-acetyl : prisms from EtOH. M.p. 195°.

Sol. EtOH, $CHCl_3$. Spar. sol. H_2O. $[\alpha]_D^{20}$ + 20·0° in EtOH.

Lehmann, *Arch. Pharm.*, 1897, **235**, 157.
Jacobs, Hoffmann, *J. Biol. Chem.*, 1928, **79**, 519.
Stoll, Renz, *Helv. Chim. Acta*, 1939, 22, 1193.

Periplocymarin

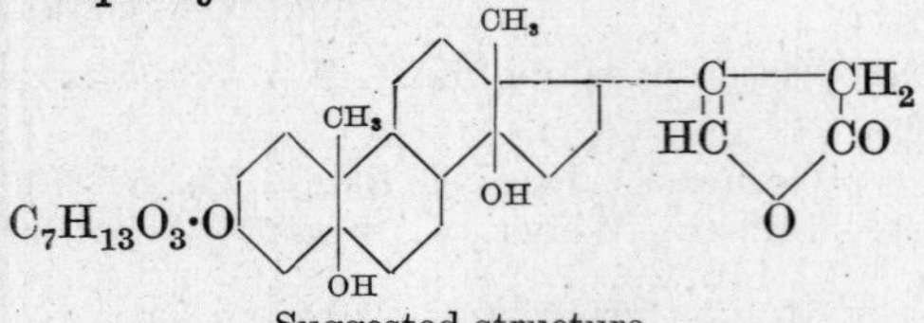

Suggested structure

$C_{30}H_{46}O_8$ MW, 534

Prisms from MeOH.Aq. M.p. 148–51°. $[\alpha]_D^{20}$ + 27·6° in MeOH. HCl ⟶ periplogenin.

Jacobs, Hoffmann, *J. Biol. Chem.*, 1928, **79**, 519.
Stoll, Renz, *Helv. Chim. Acta*, 1939, **22**, 1207.
Solacolu, Herrmann, *Compt. rend. soc. biol.*, 1934, **117**, 1138.

Periplogenin

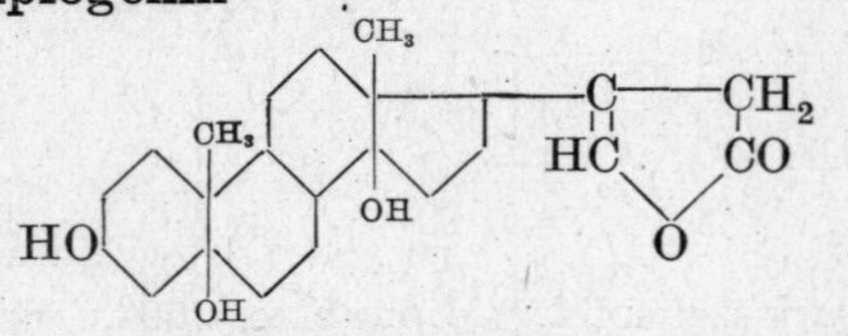

Suggested structure

$C_{23}H_{34}O_5$ MW, 390

Aglucone of periplocin. Prisms from MeOH.Aq. M.p. 232°. $[\alpha]_D^{27}$ + 31·5° in EtOH.

Lehmann, *Arch. Pharm.*, 1897, **235**, 157.
Jacobs, Elderfield, *J. Biol. Chem.*, 1935, **108**, 497.
Kon, *J. Soc. Chem. Ind.*, 1934, **53**, 593.
Stoll, Renz, *Helv. Chim. Acta*, 1939, **22**, 1193.

Pervitin (2-*Methylamino*-1-*phenylpropane*, N ; α - *dimethylphenylethylamine*, N - *methyl* - 1 - *phenylisopropylamine*)

$$C_6H_5 \cdot CH_2 \cdot CH(CH_3) \cdot NHCH_3$$

$C_{10}H_{15}N$ MW, 149

B.p. 78–80°/6 mm. Exhibits analeptic action. Excitatory and peripheral action similar to that of benzedrine.

B,HCl : cryst. from EtOH–Et_2O. M.p. 135–6°.

Woodruff, Lambooy, Burt, *J. Am. Chem. Soc.*, 1940, **62**, 922.

Phellandric Acid (3 : 4 : 5 : 6-*Tetrahydro*-p-*isopropylbenzoic acid*, 3 : 4 : 5 : 6-*tetrahydrocuminic acid*)

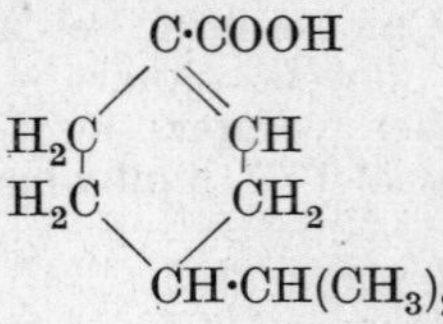

$C_{10}H_{16}O_2$ MW, 168

d-.

Cryst. from EtOH.Aq. M.p. 144–5°. $[\alpha]_D^{20}$ + 112·8° in MeOH.

p-*Chlorophenacyl ester* : needles from EtOH.Aq. M.p. 78–78·5°. $[\alpha]_D^{20}$ + 71° in $CHCl_3$.

p-*Bromophenacyl ester* : needles from EtOH.Aq. M.p. 86°. $[\alpha]_D^{20}$ + 68·1° in $CHCl_3$.

l-.

M.p. 144–5°. $[\alpha]_D^{20}$ − 112·6° in MeOH.

p-*Chlorophenacyl ester* : needles from EtOH.Aq. M.p. 78–78·5°. $[\alpha]_D^{20}$ − 57° in $CHCl_3$.

p-*Bromophenacyl ester* : needles from EtOH.Aq. M.p. 86°. $[\alpha]_D^{20}$ − 52·2° in $CHCl_3$.

p-*Nitrobenzyl ester* : pale yellow needles from MeOH. M.p. 56–7°.

dl-.

Cryst. from MeOH.Aq. M.p. 143–4°.

p-*Bromophenacyl ester* : m.p. 86–86·5°.

Cooke, Macbeth, Swanson, *J. Chem. Soc.*, 1940, 808.

Phemitone.
See Prominal.

Phenacyl Aldehyde.
See Benzoylacetaldehyde.

Phenacylformaldehyde.
See Benzoylacetaldehyde.

1-Phenacylpropionic Acid.
See 2-Benzoylisobutyric Acid.

Phenanthracridine.
See 1 : 2 : 3 : 4-Dibenzacridine.

" Phenarsazine chloride."
See 10-Chloro-5 : 10-dihydrophenarsazine.

Phenmorpholone.
See under 2-Aminophenoxyacetic Acid.

Phenothiazine.
See Thiodiphenylamine.

***p*-Phenylacetophenone.**
See 4-Acetodiphenyl.

Phenylacetylene.
Dibromide : *see* α : β-Dibromostyrene.
Dichloride : *see* α : β-Dichlorostyrene.

Phenylallylamine.
See Cinnamylamine *and under* Aniline.

Phenyl aminotolyl Ketone.
See Amino-methylbenzophenone.

4-Phenylazulene

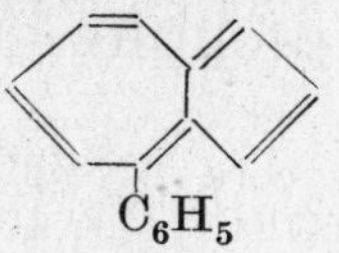

$C_{16}H_{12}$ MW, 204

Blue oil.

Picrate: black needles from EtOH. M.p. 80–1°.

sym.-*Trinitrobenzene add. comp.*: black needles from EtOH. M.p. 86–7°.

St. Pfau, Plattner, *Helv. Chim. Acta*, 1936, **19**, 878.

Phenylbenzylcarbinol (1 : 2-*Diphenylethyl alcohol*, *α-hydroxydiphenylethane*)

$C_6H_5 \cdot CH(OH) \cdot CH_2 \cdot C_6H_5$

$C_{14}H_{14}O$ MW, 198

dl-.

Needles from pet. ether–benzene. M.p. 67°. B.p. 177°/15 mm.

Acetyl: b.p. 202–5°/10 mm.

Benzoyl: needles. M.p. 70°.

Hydrogen phthaloyl: needles from pet. ether–Et_2O. M.p. 131°.

Phenylurethane: m.p. 94–5°.

d-.

Needles from Et_2O–pet. ether. M.p. 67°. D_4^{70} 1·0358. $[\alpha]_D^{25}$ − 8·5° in $CHCl_3$, + 53° in EtOH.

Hydrogen phthaloyl: needles from Et_2O–pet. ether. M.p. 131°. $[\alpha]_D^{25}$ + 33° in EtOH. *Quinine salt*: needles from EtOH. M.p. 205°.

l-.

Needles from Et_2O–pet. ether. M.p. 67°.

Acetyl: b.p. 182°/15 mm. D_4^{17} 1·0831. $[\alpha]_D^{17}$ + 23·5°.

Hydrogen phthaloyl: needles from Et_2O–pet. ether. M.p. 131°. $[\alpha]_{5461}^{25}$ − 39° in EtOH. *Cinchonine salt*: cryst. from MeOH–Me_2CO. M.p. 110°.

Gerrard, Kenyon, *J. Chem. Soc.*, 1928, 2564.

Phenylbenzylideneacetone.
See Benzyl styryl Ketone.

Phenylbenzylidenebutyric Acid.
See Diphenylbutylene-carboxylic Acid.

Phenylbenzylsuccinic Acid.
See 1 : 3-Diphenylpropane-1 : 2-dicarboxylic Acid.

Phenylbenzylvinylacetic Acid.
See 1 : 4-Diphenyl-2-butylene-1-carboxylic Acid.

2-Phenyl-2-butylene (*αβ-Dimethylstyrene*)

$CH_3 \cdot CH{:}C(C_6H_5) \cdot CH_3$

$C_{10}H_{12}$ MW, 132

B.p. 187–9°, 80–1°/20 mm., 73°/14 mm. D_4^{25} 0·8911, D_4^{20} 0·9088. n_D^{20} 1·5339.

Haller, Bauer, *Ann. chim.*, 1918, **9**, 12.
Klages, *Ber.*, 1902, 35, 2641, 3508.

Phenyl-chlorobenzylamine.
See under Chlorobenzylamine.

Phenyl chlorobenzyl Ketone.
See Chlorodeoxybenzoin.

1-Phenylcyclohexene (3 : 4 : 5 : 6-*Tetrahydrodiphenyl*)

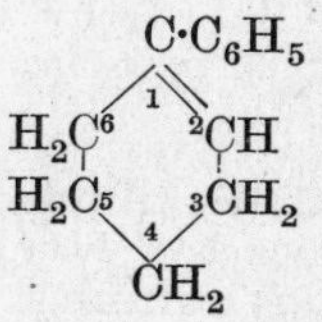

$C_{12}H_{14}$ MW, 158

Mobile liq. B.p. 250°, 133°/20 mm., 125–6°/14 mm. $D_4^{14 \cdot 9}$ 0·9930, D_4^{20} 0·9931, $D_4^{25 \cdot 2}$ 0·9871. n_D^{20} 1·5718 (1·5670), $n_D^{25 \cdot 2}$ 1·5669. $KMnO_4 \longrightarrow$ 4-benzoylvaleric acid.

Price, Karabinos, *J. Am. Chem. Soc.*, 1940, **62**, 1160.
Sabatier, Mailhe, *Compt. rend.*, 1904, **138**, 1323.

3-Phenylcyclohexene (1 : 2 : 3 : 4-*Tetrahydrodiphenyl*).

B.p. 115–17°/16 mm. D_4^{20} 0·9800. n_D^{20} 1·5530. Reflux with 5% $HNO_3 \longrightarrow$ 2-phenyladipic acid.

Price, Karabinos, *J. Am. Chem. Soc.*, 1940, **62**, 1160.

4-Phenylcyclohexene (1 : 2 : 5 : 6-*Tetrahydrodiphenyl*).

B.p. 88–90°/16 mm. D_4^{20} 0·9715. n_D^{20} 1·5420. $KMnO_4 \longrightarrow$ 2-phenyladipic acid.

Price, Karabinos, *J. Am. Chem. Soc.*, 1940, **62**, 2243.

Phenyldichloroacetic Acid.
See α : α-Dichlorophenylacetic Acid.

Phenyl 3 : 4-dihydroxystyryl Ketone.
See 3 : 4-Dihydroxychalkone.

Phenyl dihydroxytolyl Ketone.
See Dihydroxy-methylbenzophenone.

***N*-Phenyl-dinitrobenzylamine.**
See Dinitrobenzylaniline.

Phenyldodecane.
See Dodecylbenzene.

Phenylenediamine.
Carbethoxyl : *see* Aminophenylurethane.

***o*-Phenyleneurea.**
See Benziminazolone.

Phenylethanolamine.
See Hydroxyaminoethylbenzene.

Phenyliminodeoxybenzoin.
See under Benzil.

1-Phenylisobutylene (ββ-*Dimethylstyrene*)

$$C_6H_5{\cdot}CH{:}C{<}^{CH_3}_{CH_3}$$

$C_{10}H_{12}$ MW, 132

M.p. – 52°. B.p. 183–5°, 76–7°/11 mm. D_4^{20} 0·8980. n_D^{20} 1·5273.

Nitrosite : needles from C_6H_6. M.p. 122° decomp. (154° decomp.).

Lévy, Tabart, *Bull. soc. chim.*, 1931, **49**, 1776.

Phenylisophthalic Acid.
See Diphenyl-dicarboxylic Acid.

Phenylisopropylamine.
Benzedrine is 2-amino-1-phenylpropane. See p. 426, where the compound is incorrectly numbered as 2-Phenylisopropylamine.

2-Phenylisovaleric Acid.
See β : β-Dimethylhydrocinnamic Acid.

Phenylphthalic Acid.
See Diphenyl-dicarboxylic Acid.

Phenylpivalic Acid.
See α : α-Dimethylhydrocinnamic Acid.

1-Phenylpropinol-1.
See Ethinylphenylcarbinol.

1-Phenylpropionaldehyde.
See Hydratropic Aldehyde.

2-Phenylpropyl chloride.
See β-Chlorocumene.

Phenylpyromellitic Acid.
See Diphenyl-2 : 3 : 5 : 6-tetracarboxylic Acid.

Phenylsuccinic Acid.
Nitrile : *see* β-Cyanohydrocinnamic Acid.

Phloionic Acid

$$HOOC{\cdot}[CH_2]_7{\cdot}[CHOH]_2{\cdot}[CH_2]_7{\cdot}COOH$$

$C_{18}H_{34}O_6$ MW, 346

Isolated from cork. Cryst. from MeOH or EtOH. M.p. 124°. Spar. sol. Et_2O, cold $CHCl_3$. Insol. cold H_2O.

Di-Me ester : $C_{20}H_{38}O_6$. MW, 374. Plates from 70% MeOH. M.p. 77–8°.

p : p′-*Dimethylcarbanilide* : needles from EtOH. M.p. 179–80°.

Zetsche *et al.*, *J. prakt. Chem.*, 1938, **150**, 140; *Helv. Chim. Acta*, 1931, **14**, 632, 846.

Phloionolic Acid

$$HOOC{\cdot}[CH_2]_7{\cdot}[CHOH]_2{\cdot}[CH_2]_7{\cdot}CH_2OH$$

$C_{18}H_{36}O_5$ MW, 332

Isolated from cork. Needles from MeOH, 80% EtOH or AcOEt. M.p. 104°. An enantiomorph, with m.p. 95°, is gradually converted to stable form on standing.

Me ester : cryst. from 70% MeOH. M.p. 77°.

p : p′-*Dimethylcarbanilide* : needles from EtOH. M.p. 155–6°.

Zetsche *et al.*, *J. prakt. Chem.*, 1938, **150**, 140; *Helv. Chim. Acta*, 1931, **14**, 849.

Phœnicine (2 : 2′-*Dihydroxy*-4 : 4′-*ditoluquinone*)

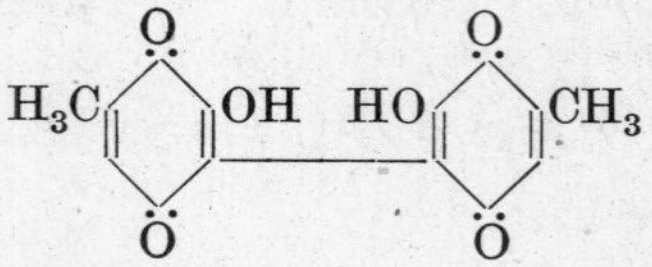

$C_{14}H_{10}O_6$ MW, 274

Pigment from *Penicillium phoeniceum* and *P. rubrum*. Yellowish brown plates from EtOH, prisms from C_6H_6. M.p. 231–2°. $FeCl_3 \longrightarrow$ violet col. Yellowish red sols. at p_H 1·8–3·5, reddish violet at p_H 5·4–6·4.

Diacetyl : yellow plates from EtOH.Aq. M.p. 117–18°.

Cyclopentadiene add. comp. : $C_{24}H_{22}O_6$. Colourless needles from EtOH. M.p. 181° decomp.

Hydroquinone add. comp. : $C_{14}H_{10}O_6$, $2C_6H_6O_2$. Red plates from H_2O. M.p. 198–200°.

Tetrahydro deriv. : leucophoenicin. Colourless needles from H_2O. M.p. 247° decomp.

Posternak, *Helv. Chim. Acta*, 1938, **21**, 1326.
Friedheim, *ibid.*, 1464.
Curtin, Fitzgerald, Reilly, *Biochem. J.*, 1940, **34**, 1605.

Phthalamic Acid.
Nitrile : *see under o*-Cyanobenzoic Acid.

Picoline-dicarboxylic Acid.
See Methyldinicotinic Acid *and* Methylquinolinic Acid.

Picolylamine.
See Aminopicoline.

Picrasmin

$C_{22}H_{30}O_6$ MW, 390

Bitter constituent of *Picrasma* or *Picraena, excelsa*. Colourless rectangular plates and rods from MeOH.Aq. M.p. 218°. $[\alpha]_D^{20}$ + 45·4° in $CHCl_3$. Contains two methoxy groups. AcOH–HCl $\longrightarrow$ quassinol, $C_{20}H_{24}O_6$, m.p. 263°. CrO_3–AcOH $\longrightarrow$ isoquassin, $C_{22}H_{30}O_6$, m.p. 221°.

3·5% HCl ⟶ semidemethoxyquassin, $C_{21}H_{28}O_6$, m.p. 213°.

Clark, *J. Am. Chem. Soc.*, 1938, **60**, 1146.

Pilosine

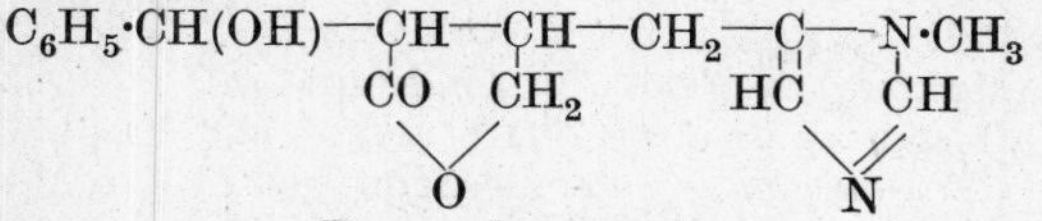

Proposed structure

$C_{16}H_{18}O_3N_2$ MW, 286

Alkaloid from *Pilocarpus microphyllus*. Plates from EtOH. M.p. 187°. Sol. hot H_2O. Very spar. sol. Et_2O, $CHCl_3$, AcOEt, Me_2CO, C_6H_6. $[\alpha]_D$ + 40·2° in $CHCl_3$.

Sulphate: plates from EtOH. M.p. 194–5°. $[\alpha]_D$ + 21·0° in H_2O.

Chloroaurate: golden plates from AcOH. M.p. 143–4°.

Polyakova, Preobrazhenskiĭ, Preobrazhenskiĭ, *J. Gen. Chem. U.S.S.R.*, 1939, **9**, 1402.

Pyman, *J. Chem. Soc.*, 1912, 2260.

***d*-Pinoresinol**

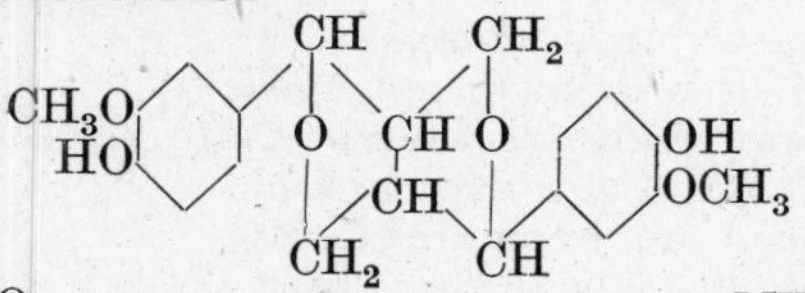

$C_{20}H_{22}O_6$ MW, 358

Constituent of fir resin. Cryst. from EtOH.Aq. M.p. 122°. $[\alpha]_D^{21}$ + 84·4° in Me_2CO.

Diacetyl: m.p. 166–167·5°. $[\alpha]_D^{20}$ + 50·9° in Me_2CO, + 49·1° in $CHCl_3$.

Dibenzoyl: m.p. 163–4°. $[\alpha]_D^{20}$ + 42·8° in Me_2CO, + 46·9° in $CHCl_3$.

Di-Me ether: $C_{22}H_{26}O_6$. MW, 386. M.p. 107–8°. $[\alpha]_D^{20}$ + 64·5° in $CHCl_3$.

Di-Et ether: $C_{24}H_{30}O_6$. MW, 414. M.p. 122°. $[\alpha]_D^{20}$ + 62° in $CHCl_3$.

Bamberger, Landsiedl, *Monatsh.*, 1897, **18**, 481.

Kaku, Ri, *J. Pharm. Soc. Japan*, 1937, **57**, 1015.

Erdtmann, *Ann.*, 1935, **516**, 162.

Haworth, *J. Chem. Soc.*, 1942, 448.

Pinosylvin.

See 3 : 5-Dihydroxystilbene.

Piperidine-2 : 6-dicarboxylic Acid.

See Hexahydrodipicolinic Acid.

4-[ω-4-Piperidylpropyl]-quinoline.

See Rubatoxan.

Polyporenic Acid A

$C_{30}H_{48}O_4$ MW, 472

Isolated from the fungus, *Polyporus betulinus*, Fr. Needles from MeOH.Aq., Me_2CO.Aq. or dil. AcOH. M.p. 194°. Spar. sol. Et_2O, C_6H_6, $CHCl_3$. $[\alpha]_D^{20}$ + 69° in Py. Tetranitromethane in $CHCl_3$ ⟶ yellow col. H_2SO_4–$CHCl_3$ ⟶ red col. Liebermann–Burchard reagent ⟶ red col. with green fluor.

Me ester: $C_{31}H_{50}O_4$. MW, 486. Needles from MeOH. M.p. 142°. $[\alpha]_D^{20}$ + 77° in $CHCl_3$. Contains 2 active H atoms and 2 ethylenic linkages. *Monoformyl*: plates from MeOH. M.p. 148°. $[\alpha]_D^{20}$ + 84° in $CHCl_3$. *Monoacetyl*: needles from MeOH. M.p. 112°. $[\alpha]_D^{20}$ + 88° in $CHCl_3$.

Cross, Eliot, Heilbron, Jones, *J. Chem. Soc.*, 1940, 632.

Cross, Jones, *ibid.*, 1491.

Polyporenic Acid B

$C_{30}H_{48}O_4$ MW, 472

Constituent of the fungus, *Polyporus betulinus*, Fr. Asbestos-like mass from Me_2CO or AcOH. M.p. 300–10° decomp. Spar. sol. cold Py. Prac. insol. Et_2O, C_6H_6, $CHCl_3$. Tetranitromethane in $CHCl_3$ ⟶ yellow col. H_2SO_4–$CHCl_3$ ⟶ orange col. Liebermann–Burchard reagent ⟶ violet col.

Me ester: $C_{31}H_{50}O_4$. MW, 486. Needles from MeOH.Aq. Softens at 155°, m.p. 160°. Contains 2 active H atoms and 2 ethylenic linkages.

Cross, Eliot, Heilbron, Jones, *J. Chem. Soc.*, 1940, 632.

Pomiferin

$C_{25}H_{24}O_6$ MW, 420

Pigment from the fruit of the osage orange tree (*Maclura pomifera*, Raf.). Yellow cryst. from xylene, C_6H_6 or EtOH. M.p. 200·5°.

Di-Me ether: $C_{27}H_{28}O_6$. MW, 448. Yellow needles from EtOH. M.p. 132°. *Monoacetyl*: needles from EtOH. M.p. 128–9°.

Tri-Me ether: $C_{28}H_{30}O_6$. MW, 462. Cryst. from EtOH. M.p. 139·5°.

Diacetyl: yellow plates from MeOH.Aq. M.p. 134·5°.

Triacetyl: needles from EtOH or C_6H_6–pet. ether. M.p. 154°.

Di-p-toluenesulphonyl: cryst. from EtOH. M.p. 148°.

Wolfrom, Benton, Gregory, Hess, Mahan, Morgan, *J. Am. Chem. Soc.*, 1939, **61**, 2833.

Wolfrom, Gregory, *J. Am. Chem. Soc.*, 1940, **62**, 651.

Wolfrom, Mahan, *J. Am. Chem. Soc.*, 1941, **63**, 1253.

Populnetin

$C_{14}H_8O_6$ MW, 272

Aglucone of populnin. M.p. 270–5°. $FeCl_3$ $\longrightarrow$ pale green col.

Tetra-acetyl deriv.: m.p. 127–9°.

Neelakantam, Seshadri, *Current Science*, 1938, **7**, 16, (*Chem. Abstracts*, 1938, **32**, 8486).

Populnin

$C_{20}H_{18}O_{11}$ MW, 434

Pigment isolated from Indian tulip flowers. M.p. 228–30° decomp. Hyd. $\longrightarrow$ glucose + populnetin. $FeCl_3$ $\longrightarrow$ pale green col.

See previous reference.

Pregneninolone (17-*Ethinyltestosterone*)

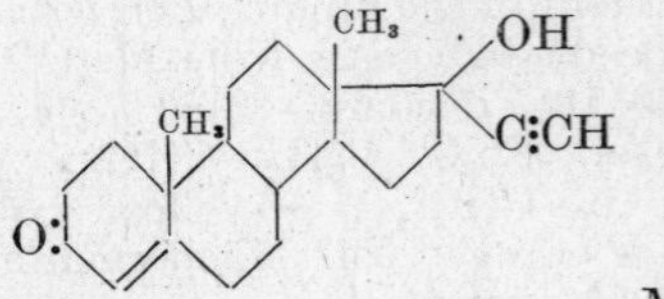

$C_{21}H_{28}O_2$ MW, 312

Cryst. from $CHCl_3$-Me_2CO or AcOEt. M.p. 270–2° corr. $[\alpha]_D^{20}$ + 22·5° in dioxan. Absorption maximum at 2385 Å. More effective than progesterone for oral administration.

Oxime: cryst. from EtOH.Aq. M.p. 234–5° decomp.

Semicarbazone: cryst. from Me_2CO. M.p. 230–1° decomp.

Inhoffen, *Ber.*, 1939, **72**, 595.
Ruzicka, Hofmann, Meldahl, *Helv. Chim. Acta*, 1938, **21**, 371.
Ruzicka, Hofmann, *Helv. Chim. Acta*, 1937, **20**, 1280.

Primetin.
See 5 : 8-Dihydroxyflavone.

Prontosil.
See also Sulphanilamide.

Propenylacetylene (4-*Methylvinylacetylene*)

$CH_3{\cdot}CH{:}CH{\cdot}C{:}CH$

C_5H_6 MW, 66

B.p. 62°. D^{20} 0·759. n_D^{20} 1·438.

Lespieau, Journaud, *Bull. soc. chim.*, 1931, **49**, 1423.

Propenyl-*tert*.-butylcarbinol.
See 5 : 5-Dimethyl-2-hexenol-4.

Propenylcarbinol.
See Crotyl Alcohol.

Propenylethinylcarbinol

$CH_3{\cdot}CH{:}CH{\cdot}CH(OH){\cdot}C{:}CH$

C_6H_8O MW, 96

B.p. 154–6°, 102–3°/111 mm., 75°/24 mm. n_D^{23} 1·4651.

Hg comp.: prisms. M.p. above 360°.

Acetyl: b.p. 110–12°/100 mm. $n_D^{20\cdot5}$ 1·4463.

Phenylurethane: needles from pet. ether. M.p. 65°.

β-*Naphthylurethane*: needles from pet. ether or MeOH.Aq. M.p. 89°.

Jones, McCombie, *J. Chem. Soc.*, 1942, 734.
Lespieau, Lombard, *Bull. soc. chim.*, 1935, **2**, 369.

2-Propenylpiperidine.
See β-Coniceine.

Propionylcatechol.
See Dihydroxypropiophenone.

Propionylhydroquinone.
See Dihydroxypropiophenone.

2-Propionylpiperidine.
See Conhydrinone.

Propionylresorcinol.
See Dihydroxypropiophenone.

Propiophenone-β-carboxylic Acid.
See 1-Benzoylpropionic Acid.

Propylene bromohydrin.
See 1-Bromoisopropyl Alcohol.

***n*-Propylethinylcarbinol** (1-*Hexinol*-3)

$CH_3{\cdot}CH_2{\cdot}CH_2{\cdot}CH(OH){\cdot}C{:}CH$

$C_6H_{10}O$ MW, 98

B.p. 55–60°/10 mm.

I.G., E.P. 508,062 (*Chem. Abstracts*, 1940, **34**, 447).

3-Propylindole

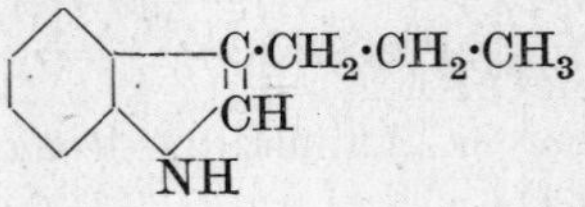

$C_{11}H_{13}N$ MW, 159

B.p. 162–4°/20 mm.

Picrate: red needles from pet. ether–C_6H_6. M.p. 113–14°.

Cornforth, Robinson, *J. Chem. Soc.*, 1942, 681.

Propyl naphthyl Ketone.
See Butyronaphthone.

Propylresorcinol.
See 2 : 4- *and* 2 : 6-Dihydroxypropylbenzene, *and* Divarinol.

1-Propylvaleraldehyde.
See Di-*n*-propylacetaldehyde.

Protokosin

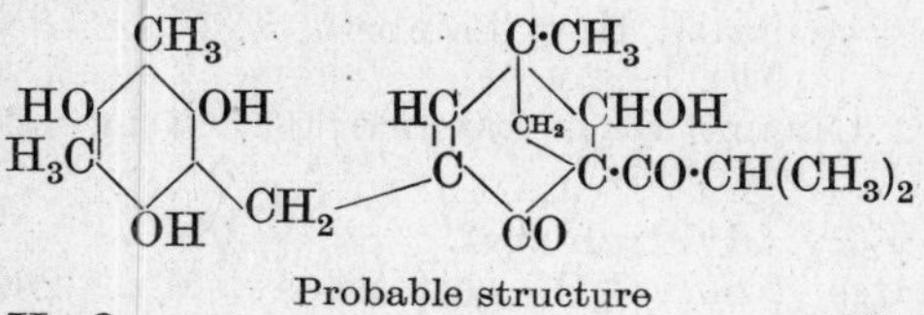

Probable structure

$C_{22}H_{28}O_7$ MW, 404

Isolated from the dried female flowers of *Hagenia abyssinica* (= *Brayera anthelmintica*). Needles from $CHCl_3$–EtOH. M.p. 182°. Sol. Et_2O, $CHCl_3$, Me_2CO, AcOEt. Spar. sol. EtOH, pet. ether. Insol. H_2O. $[\alpha]_D$ + 8·0° in $CHCl_3$. Possesses no vermicidal properties. Sol. conc. H_2SO_4 with pale green col. ⟶ deep red on warming. Alc. $FeCl_3$ ⟶ reddish brown col.

Hems, Todd, *J. Chem. Soc.*, 1937, 562.

Protostephanine

$C_{21}H_{25}O_4N$ MW, 355

Alkaloid from *Stephnia japonica*, Miers. Prisms + $1\frac{1}{2}$MeOH from MeOH. M.p. 75°, 90–5° solvent free. Optically inactive. Contains 1 $N{\cdot}CH_3$ and 4 OCH_3 groups.

B,HCl: decomp. at 150°.

B_2,H_2PtCl_6: orange prisms. Decomp. at 223°.

Methiodide: prisms from H_2O. M.p. 220–1°.

Methomethylsulphate: prisms from H_2O. Sinters at 227°. M.p. 235°.

Kondo, Watanabe, *J. Pharm. Soc. Japan*, 1938, **58**, 46.

Protoveratridine

$C_{31}H_{49}O_9N$ MW, 579

Alkaloid from *Veratrum album*. Cryst. M.p. 266–7° corr. Spar. sol. all org. solvents.

B,HCl: cryst. from EtOH. M.p. 243–5° corr. decomp.

Methylethylglycollic ester: *see* Germerine.

Picrate: yellow needles from Me_2CO–Et_2O. Decomp. at 244–6° corr.

Chloroplatinate: cryst. from EtOH.Aq. Decomp. at 195–200° corr.

Poethke, *Arch. Pharm.*, 1937, **275**, 571.

Protoveratrine

$C_{40}H_{63}O_{14}N$ MW, 781

Alkaloid from *Veratrum album*. Cryst. from EtOH. M.p. 255–6° corr. decomp. $[\alpha]_D^{20}$ − 9·1° in $CHCl_3$.

B,HCl: plates. M.p. 234–6° corr. decomp.

B,HBr: prisms. M.p. 230–2° corr. decomp.

B,HI: prisms. M.p. 247–8° corr. decomp.

B,HSCN: prisms. M.p. 221–3° corr. decomp.

$B,HAuCl_4$: yellow cryst. Decomp. at 199° corr.

Picrate: yellow needles. M.p. 216–20° corr. decomp.

Poethke, *Arch. Pharm.*, 1937, **275**, 571.

Pterobilin

$C_{33}H_{34}O_6N_4$ MW, 582

Wing pigment of butterflies *Pteris brassicae*, *P. rapae*, *P. napi*, *Catopsilia rurina* and *C. statira*. Dark blue rods from AcOEt. Does not melt or decomp. at 310°. Conc. HNO_3 on $CHCl_3$ sol. ⟶ blue col. eventually becoming colourless after passing through green, orange, yellow, etc.

Di-Me ester: $C_{35}H_{38}O_6N_4$. MW, 610. M.p. 234°. *Zn salt*: green needles. Decomp. above 300°.

Wieland, Tartter, *Ann.*, 1940, **545**, 197.

Punicic Acid

$CH_3{\cdot}[CH_2]_3{\cdot}[CH{:}CH]_3{\cdot}[CH_2]_7{\cdot}COOH$

$C_{18}H_{30}O_2$ MW, 278

Geometrical isomer of elæostearic acid isolated from oil of pomegranate seeds. Cryst. from pet. ether. M.p. 44°. D_4^{50} 0·9027. n_D^{50} 1·5114. Readily absorbs atmospheric oxygen. Irradiation of xylene sol. for 4 hours ⟶ β-elæostearic acid. H(+ Pt) ⟶ stearic acid. $KMnO_4$ ⟶ azelaic, oxalic and valeric acids.

Toyama, Tsuchiya, *Chem. Abstracts*, 1935, **29**, 5294.

Farmer, van den Heuvel, *J. Chem. Soc.*, 1936, 1809.

Toyama, Uozaki, *Chem. Abstracts*, 1937, **31**, 249.

Purapurine.
See Solasonine.

Pyridoxin.
See Adermin.

4 : 5-[α : β′-Pyridino]-acenaphthene (*Acenaphthapyridine, acenaphthaquinoline*)

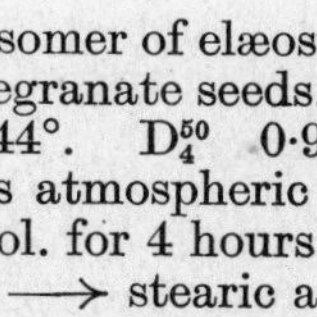

$C_{15}H_{11}N$ MW, 205

Needles from Et_2O. M.p. 67°. Sol. EtOH, Et_2O, AcOH, $CHCl_3$, C_6H_6. Sol. dil. AcOH with blue fluor. Sol. conc. H_2SO_4 with yellowish green col.

B,HCl: yellow needles from EtOH. M.p. 305°.

B,H_2SO_4: yellow needles from EtOH. M.p. 238°.

Methiodide: yellow needles from MeOH. M.p. above 315°.

Picrate: m.p. 234°.

Zinke, Raith, *Monatsh.*, 1919, **40**, 273.
Stewart, *J. Chem. Soc.*, 1925, **127**, 1331.

3-α-Pyridyldiphenyl

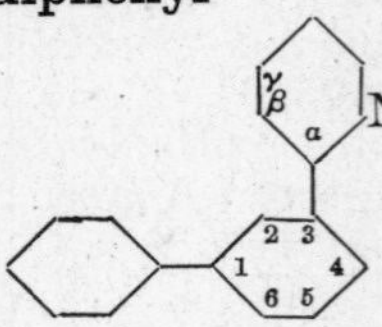

$C_{17}H_{13}N$ MW, 231

Viscous oil. B.p. 75–85°/0·002 mm. Absorption maximum: 2480 Å. in hexane.

Picrate: yellow prisms from Me_2CO. M.p. 169°.

Heilbron, Hey, Lambert, *J. Chem. Soc.*, 1940, 1281.
Gillam, Hey, Lambert, *J. Chem. Soc.*, 1941, 364.

3-β-Pyridyldiphenyl.

Viscous oil. B.p. 75–85°/0·002 mm. Absorption maximum: 2455 Å. in hexane.

Picrate: needles from Me_2CO. M.p. 178–9°.

Heilbron, Hey, Lambert, *J. Chem. Soc.*, 1940, 1281.
Gillam, Hey, Lambert, *J. Chem. Soc.*, 1941, 364.

3-γ-Pyridyldiphenyl.

Plates from pet. ether. M.p. 81–2°. Absorption maximum: 2480 Å. in hexane.

Picrate: needles from Me_2CO. M.p. 231°.

Heilbron, Hey, Lambert, *J. Chem. Soc.*, 1940, 1282.
Gillam, Hey, Lambert, *J. Chem. Soc.*, 1941, 364.

4-α-Pyridyldiphenyl.

Plates from EtOH. M.p. 141–2°. Absorption maximum: 2920 Å. in hexane.

Picrate: needles from Me_2CO. M.p. 186–7°.

Heilbron, Hey, Lambert, *J. Chem. Soc.*, 1940, 1282.
Gillam, Hey, Lambert, *J. Chem. Soc.*, 1941, 364.

4-β-Pyridyldiphenyl.

Plates from C_6H_6–pet. ether. M.p. 151–2°. Absorption maximum: 2790 Å. in hexane.

Picrate: needles from Me_2CO. M.p. 208–10°.

Heilbron, Hey, Lambert, *J. Chem. Soc.*, 1940, 1282.
Gillam, Hey, Lambert, *J. Chem. Soc.*, 1941, 364.

4-γ-Pyridyldiphenyl.

Plates from C_6H_6–pet. ether. M.p. 209°. Absorption maximum: 2790 Å. in hexane.

Picrate: needles from Me_2CO. M.p. 215°.

Heilbron, Hey, Lambert, *J. Chem. Soc.*, 1940, 1283.
Gillam, Hey, Lambert, *J. Chem. Soc.*, 1941, 364.

Pyridylmethylamine.
See Aminopicoline.

Pyridylsulphanilamide.
See Sulphapyridine.

Pyrimidone-imide.
See Aminopyrimidine.

Pyrimidylsulphanilamide.
See Sulphadiazine.

Pyrocinchonic Acid.
See Dimethylmaleic Acid.

Q

Quassin

$C_{22}H_{30}O_6$ MW, 390

Bitter constituent of quassia or Surinam wood (*Quassia amara*). Rods and plates from MeOH.Aq. M.p. 205–6°. $[\alpha]_D^{20}$ + 39·8° in $CHCl_3$. Contains one active H atom and two CH_3O groups. Conc. HBr or HCl ⟶ quassinol, $C_{20}H_{24}O_6$, m.p. 263°. CrO_3 ⟶ isoquassin, $C_{22}H_{30}O_6$, m.p. 221°.

Clark, *J. Am. Chem. Soc.*, 1937, **59**, 927, 2511; 1938, **60**, 1146.

Quillaic Acid

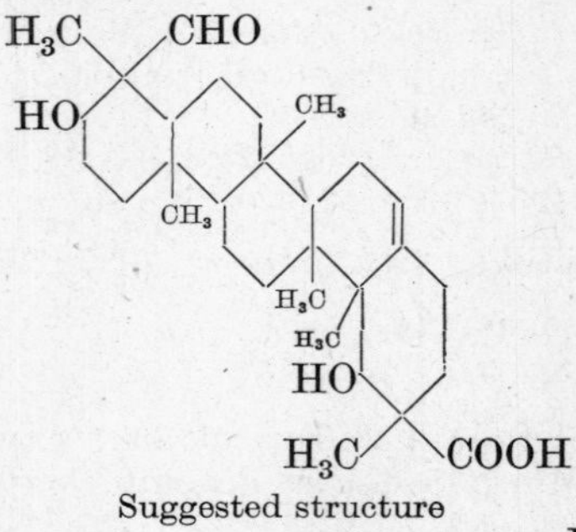

Suggested structure

$C_{30}H_{46}O_5$ MW, 48

Sapogenin obtained on hydrolysis of quillaia saponin. Needles from EtOH. M.p. 294°. $[\alpha]_D$

+ 56·1° in Py. Tetranitromethane $\longrightarrow$ yellow col.

Me ester : $C_{31}H_{48}O_5$. MW, 500. Needles from MeOH. M.p. 225°. $[\alpha]_D$ + 40·5° in Py.
Oxime : needles. M.p. 238°.
Diacetyl : needles from AcOH. M.p. 250°.
Oxime : needles from MeOH. M.p. 282°.
Semicarbazone : needles. M.p. 288°.

Windaus, Hampe, Rabe, *Z. physiol. Chem.*, 1926, **160**, 301.
Elliott, Kon, *J. Chem. Soc.*, 1939, 1130.
Bilham, Kon, *J. Chem. Soc.*, 1940, 1471 ; 1941, 552.
Bilham, Kon, Ross, *J. Chem. Soc.*, 1942, 532.

Quinaldine-sulphonic Acid.
See Methylquinoline-sulphonic Acid.
Quinaldylamine.
See Aminomethylquinoline.
Quinethyline.
See under Cupreine.
Quinisoamyline.
See under Cupreine.
Quinisopropyline.
See under Cupreine.
Quinizarin-5-carboxylic Acid (5 : 8-*Di-hydroxyanthraquinone-1-carboxylic acid*, 1 : 4-*di-hydroxyanthraquinone-5-carboxylic acid*).
Red needles from *p*-xylene. Decomp. at 250°. Sol. EtOH, Et_2O, C_6H_6. Spar. sol. H_2O.

Kögl, Deijs, *Ann.*, 1935, **515**, 31.

Quinizarin-6-carboxylic Acid (5 : 8-*Di-hydroxyanthraquinone-2-carboxylic acid*, 1 : 4-*di-hydroxyanthraquinone-6-carboxylic acid*).
Orange brown needles from AcOH. Sol. $Na_2CO_3 \longrightarrow$ violet red col. Sol. NaOH $\longrightarrow$ blue col.

Bayer, D.R.P. 84,505.

Quinpropyline.
See under Cupreine.
p-Quinquiphenyl.
See p-Pentaphenyl.

R

2-R Acid.
See 2-Amino-8-naphthol-3 : 6-disulphonic Acid.
Renghol (*Dihydrourushiol*; 15-[2 : 3-*dihydroxy-phenyl*]-5-*pentadecylene*)

$$CH_2 \cdot [CH_2]_8 \cdot CH{:}CH \cdot [CH_2]_3 \cdot CH_3$$

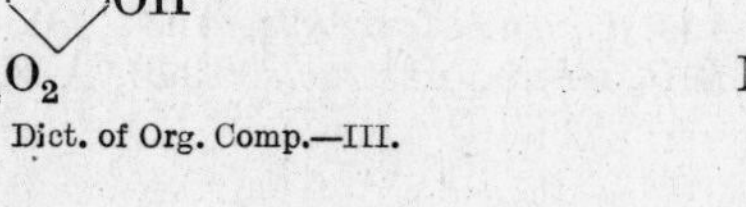

$C_{21}H_{34}O_2$ MW, 318

Toxic constituent of renghas fruit (*Semecarpus heterophylla*, Bl.). M.p. 14–15°. B.p. 170–2°/ 0·0001 mm. Ozonolysis $\longrightarrow$ valeraldehyde. Vesicant.

Me ether : $C_{22}H_{36}O_2$. MW, 332. B.p. 160°/ 0·0001 mm.
Di-Me ether : $C_{23}H_{38}O_2$. MW, 346. B.p. 226°/5 mm., 155–7°/0·0001 mm.

Backer, Haack, *Rec. trav. chim.*, 1938, **57**, 225.

Resorcitol.
See Hexahydroresorcinol.
Resveratrol (3 : 5 : 4′-*Trihydroxystilbene*)

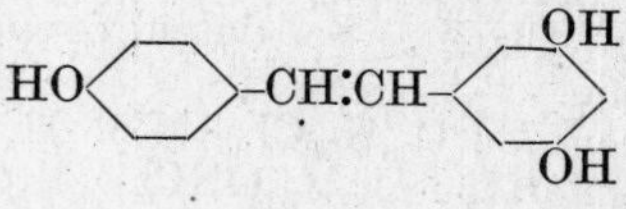

$C_{14}H_{12}O_3$ MW, 228

Obtained from roots of white hellebore (*Veratrum grandiflorum*, Loes. fil.). Cryst. from EtOH.Aq. M.p. 261° decomp. Absorption maxima at 3610, 3350, 3020, 2900 and 2480 Å. $FeCl_3 \longrightarrow$ dark green col.
Triacetyl : needles from EtOH. M.p. 114–16°.
Tri-Me ether : cryst. from MeOH. M.p. 56–7°. B.p. 140–60°/0·01 mm.

Takaoka, *Chem. Abstracts*, 1940, **34**, 7887 ; 1941, **35**, 1398.
Späth, Kromp, *Ber.*, 1941, **74**, 867.

Rhapontigenin (3 : 4 : 3′ : 5′-*Tetrahydroxy-stilbene* 4-*methyl ether*)

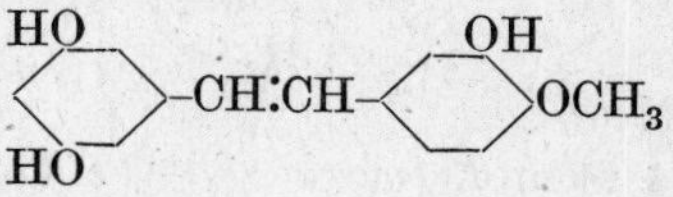

$C_{15}H_{14}O_4$ MW, 258

Aglucone from rhapontin from rhapontic spice. M.p. 186–7°.
Triacetyl : (1) M.p. 114°. (2) M.p. 128°.
Tribenzoyl : m.p. 142°.

Kawamura, *J. Pharm. Soc. Japan*, 1938, **58**, 405.
Takaoka, *Proc. Imper. Acad., Tokyo*, 1940, **16**, 408.

Rhapontin
$C_{21}H_{24}O_9$ MW, 420

Glycoside from rhapontic spice. Decomp. at 236–7°. $[\alpha]_D^{32}$ − 59·5° in Me_2CO. Hyd. $\longrightarrow$ glucose + rhapontigenin.
Acetyl deriv. : m.p. 135–6°.

Kawamura, *J. Pharm. Soc. Japan*, 1938, **58**, 405.

Riboflavine.
See Lactoflavine.

Rimuene

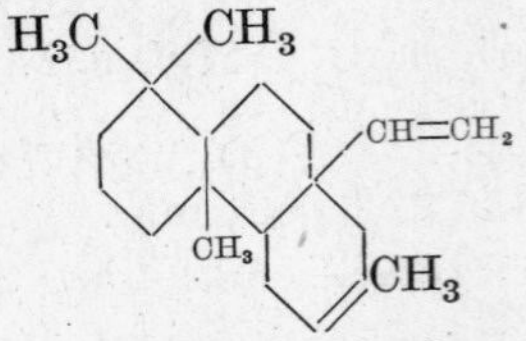

Suggested formula

$C_{20}H_{32}$ MW, 272

From leaves of *Dacrydium cupressinum* (Salander), etc. Cryst. from EtOH. M.p. 55°. $[\alpha]_D$ + 44·7° in $CHCl_3$. Se dehydrogenation ⟶ pimanthrene.

Hydrochloride: $C_{20}H_{33}Cl$. M.p. 63°.
Nitroso-chloride: $C_{20}H_{32}ONCl$. M.p. 86–8°.
Tetrabromide: m.p. 55–60°.

McDowall, Finlay, *J. Soc. Chem. Ind.*, 1925, **44**, 42T.
Beath, *J. Soc. Chem. Ind.*, 1933, **52**, 338T.
Brandt, *Chem. Abstracts*, 1939, **33**, 551.

Rivanol.
See under 7-Hydroxy-2 : 5-diaminoacridine.

Roemerine

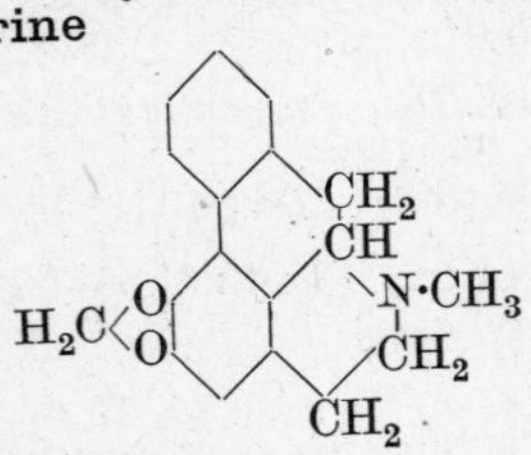

$C_{18}H_{17}O_2N$ MW, 279

Alkaloid from *Roemaria refracta*, D.C. M.p. 102–3°. $[\alpha]_D$ − 77·18° in EtOH.

B,HCl: m.p. 262–3°.
Methiodide: m.p. 215–16°.
Picrate: m.p. 195–6°.

Konovalova, Junusov, Orékhov, *J. Gen. Chem. U.S.S.R.*, 1939, **9**, 1868; *Bull. soc. chim.*, 1939, **6**, 1479; 1940, **7**, 70.

Rottlerin

$C_{30}H_{28}O_8$ MW, 516

Isolated from "kamala," an Indian colouring matter and anthelmintic drug, also from *Rottlera tinctoria*, Roxb. Yellowish brown cryst. from toluene or AcOEt. M.p. 212° (201–2°). O_3 or heating with dil. alkali ⟶ $C_6H_5{\cdot}CHO$. H_2O_2 ⟶ cinnamic acid. Heat with EtOH or AcOH ⟶ isorottlerin, m.p. 180°.

Di-Me ether: pale yellow leaflets from $CHCl_3$–MeOH or AcOEt–Me_2CO. M.p. 245–6° decomp.

Penta-Me ether: cryst. from pet. ether. M.p. 144°.

Penta-acetyl deriv.: plates from C_6H_6–EtOH or Me_2CO–EtOH. M.p. 214°.

Dutt, *J. Chem. Soc.*, 1925, **127**, 2044.
Brockmann, Maier, *Ann.*, 1938, **535**, 149.
Rojahn, *Chem. Abstracts*, 1937, **31**, 6816.

Rotundifoline

$C_{22}H_{26}O_5N_2$ MW, 398

Alkaloid from *Mitragyna rotundifolia*. Prisms from MeOH. M.p. 233–4°. Sol. $CHCl_3$. Mod. sol. Me_2CO, EtOH, C_6H_6. Spar. sol. Et_2O, AcOEt. $[\alpha]_D^{15}$ + 124° in $CHCl_3$. $FeCl_3$ ⟶ red col. Hyd. ⟶ rotundifolic acid, decomp. about 165°.

Barger, Dyer, Sargent, *J. Org. Chem.*, 1939, **4**, 418.

Rubatoxan (1-[4-*Piperidyl*]-3-[4-*quinolyl*]-*propane*, 4-[ω-4-*piperidylpropyl*]-*quinoline*)

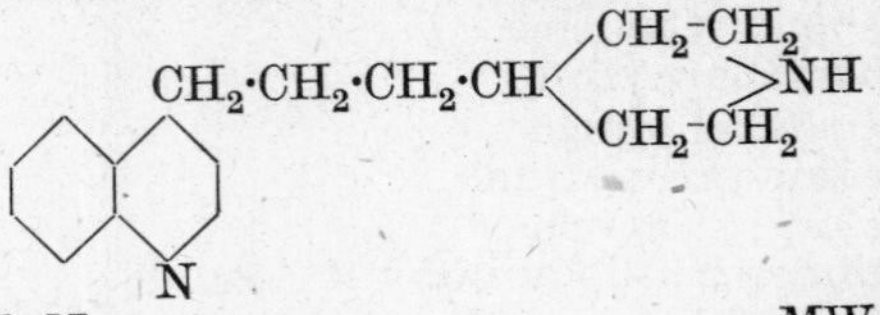

$C_{17}H_{22}N_2$ MW, 254

Yellowish liq. B.p. 185°/0·02 mm.

B,2HCl: cryst. from EtOH–AcOEt. M.p. 197°.
Chloroplatinate: orange cryst. from EtOH. M.p. above 360°.
Dipicrate: cryst. from EtOH. M.p. 203–5°.

Prelog, Seiwerth, Hahn, Cerkovnikov, *Ber.*, 1939, **72**, 1325.

Rubijervine

$C_{26}H_{43}O_2N$ MW, 401

Alkaloid from *Veratrum album*. Cryst. + $1H_2O$ from EtOH or Me_2CO. M.p. 239–40° decomp. Conc. H_2SO_4 ⟶ green col.

B,HI: needles from Me_2CO–Et_2O. M.p. 261–2° decomp.
p-*Bromobenzoyl*: cryst. from EtOH–C_6H_6. M.p. 254–6° decomp.

Poethke, *Arch. Pharm.*, 1938, **276**, 170.

Rubradinine (*Mitraphyline*)

$C_{24}H_{28}O_4N_2$ MW, 408

Alkaloid from *Adina rubrostipulata*, K. Schum. Needles from 95% EtOH. M.p. 306°. $[\alpha]_D$ − 22·3° in $CHCl_3$.

B,H_2SO_4,$5H_2O$: m.p. 245°.
Picrate: m.p. 166°.

Denis, *Chem. Abstracts*, 1937, **31**, 3928; *Brit. Chem. Abstracts*, 1940, A II, 262.

Rubrofusarin

$C_{15}H_{12}O_5$ MW, 272

Pigment of *Fusarium culmorum* Sacc., and related forms. Orange red needles from pet. ether, C_6H_6 or EtOH. M.p. 210–11°. Insol. H_2O. Spar. sol. aq. alkalis. $FeCl_3 \longrightarrow$ greenish brown col.

Monoacetyl deriv.: golden yellow hexagonal prisms from C_6H_6 or AcOH. M.p. 211°.

Diacetyl deriv.: prac. colourless rods. M.p. 260°.

Me ether: m.p. 203–4°.

Di-Me ether: m.p. 187–8°. *Ferrichloride*: maroon prisms from AcOH. M.p. 183–4° decomp.

Ashley, Hobbs, Raistrick, *Biochem. J.*, 1937, **31**, 385.

S

Salsolidine (O-*Methylsalsoline*, 6 : 7-*dimethoxy*-1-*methyl*-1 : 2 : 3 : 4-*tetrahydroisoquinoline*)

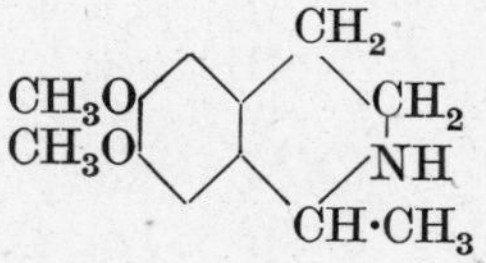

$C_{12}H_{17}O_2N$ MW, 207

l-.

Alkaloid from *Salsola richteri*. Plates from H_2O. M.p. 47·5–48·5° (60–2°, anhyd. 71–3°). B.p. about 120°/0·01 mm. $[\alpha]_D^{16}$ − 59·7° in EtOH.

B,HCl: plates from H_2O. M.p. 235–6°. $[\alpha]_D^{18}$ − 24·8° in H_2O.

N-*Benzoyl*: needles from Me_2CO. M.p. 124–5°.

Picrate: yellow cryst. from EtOH. M.p. 194–5°.

Picrolonate: cryst. from EtOH. M.p. 235·5–236° (220–1°).

d-.

M.p. 47·5–48·5°. $[\alpha]_D^{16}$ + 59·9° in EtOH.

B,HCl: m.p. 235–6°. $[\alpha]_D^{18}$ + 25·3° in H_2O.

Picrate: m.p. 193–4°.

Picrolonate: m.p. 235·5–236°.

dl-.

M.p. 53–53·5°. B.p. about 140°/1 mm.

B,HCl: m.p. 196–7°.

N-*Benzoyl*: cryst. from EtOH.Aq. M.p. 127–8°.

Picrate: cryst. from MeOH. M.p. 201–201·5° decomp.

Picrolonate: cryst. from MeOH. M.p. 241° decomp.

Späth, Dengel, *Ber.*, 1938, **71**, 114.

Proskurnina, Orekhov, *Bull. soc. chim.*, 1937, **4**, 1265.

Salsoline (6-*Hydroxy*-7-*methoxy*-1-*methyl* 1 : 2 : 3 : 4-*tetrahydroisoquinoline*)

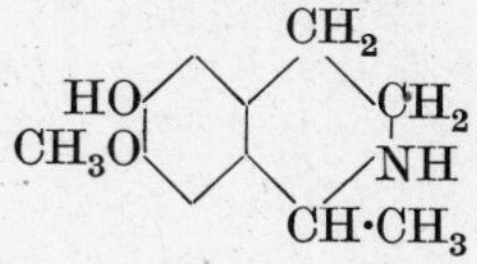

$C_{11}H_{15}O_2N$ MW, 193

Alkaloid from *Salsola richteri*. Micro-cryst. powder. M.p. 218–21°. Sol. EtOH, $CHCl_3$. Spar. sol. H_2O, C_6H_6. Insol. pet. ether. Sol. aq. alkalis.

B,HCl: needles + $1\frac{1}{2}H_2O$. M.p. 141–52°.

Benzoyl deriv.: cryst. from EtOH. M.p. 172–4°.

Dibenzoyl: cryst. from EtOH. M.p. 166–8°.

Me ether: *see* Salsolidine.

Orekhov, Proskurnina, *Ber.*, 1933, **66**, 841; 1934, **67**, 878.

Späth, Orekhov, Kuffner, *Ber.*, 1934, **67**, 1214.

Sarmentogenin

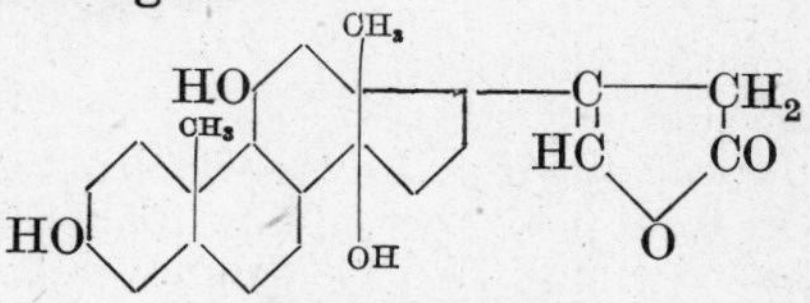

Suggested structure

$C_{23}H_{34}O_5$ MW, 390

Isolated from seeds of *Strophanthus sarmentosus*. Needles from EtOH. M.p. 270°. $[\alpha]_D$ + 21·3° in EtOH.

Dibenzoyl deriv.: hexagonal prisms from Me_2CO.Aq. M.p. 281°. $[\alpha]_D^{20}$ + 14° in Me_2CO.

Jacobs, Heidelberger, *J. Biol. Chem.*, 1929, **81**, 765.

Mason, Hoehn, *J. Am. Chem. Soc.*, 1938, **60**, 2824.

Tschesche, Bohle, *Ber.*, 1936, **69**, 2497.

ψ-Sarsapogenin

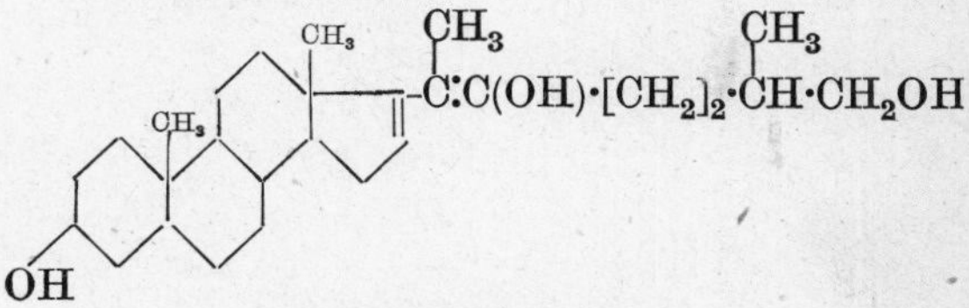

Suggested structure

$C_{27}H_{44}O_3$ MW, 416

Needles from AcOEt. M.p. 171–3°. Sol. Et_2O.

Di-p-nitrobenzoyl: pale yellow cryst. from Me_2CO. M.p. 156·5–159°.

Marker, Rohrmann, *J. Am. Chem. Soc.*, 1940, **62**, 518, 521.
Marker, Jones, Krueger, *ibid.*, 2532.

Satisterol

$C_{27}H_{46}O$ MW, 386

Phytosterol from rice embryo. M.p. 156°. $[\alpha]_D^{23}$ − 14·5°.

Acetyl: m.p. 111°. $[\alpha]_D^{23}$ − 9·7°.
Propionyl: m.p. 106°. $[\alpha]_D^{23}$ − 6·8°.
Benzoyl: m.p. 129°. $[\alpha]_D^{20}$ − 14·5°.

Kimm, *Sci. Papers Inst. Phys. Chem. Research, Tokyo*, 1938, **34**, 637.

Sclareol

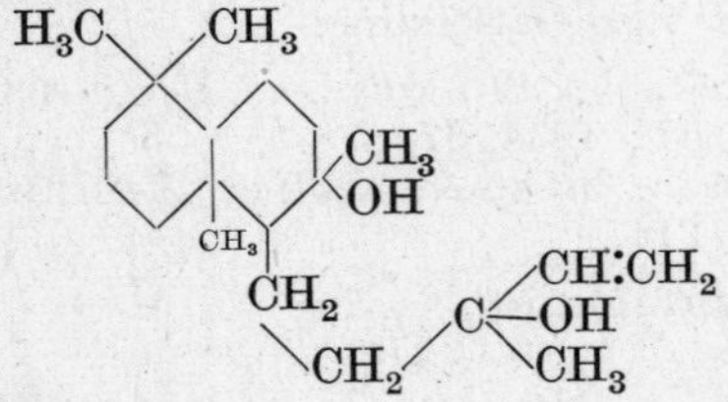

$C_{20}H_{36}O_2$ MW, 308

Diterpene diol from leaves of *Salvia sclarea*, L. Needles from pet. ether. M.p. 105·5–106° corr. B.p. 182°/1 mm., 163–5°/0·25 mm. $[\alpha]_D^{18}$ − 6·25° in EtOH.

Ruzicka, Engel, Fischer, *Helv. Chim. Acta*, 1938, **21**, 364.
Ruzicka, Janot, *Helv. Chim. Acta*, 1931, **14**, 645.
Hosking, Brandt, *Ber.*, 1935, **68**, 37.
Janot, *Ann. chim.*, 1932, **17**, 5.
Ruzicka, Seidel, Engel, *Helv. Chim. Acta*, 1942, **25**, 621.

Senecioaldehyde.

See 2 : 2-Dimethylacrolein.

***p*-Septiphenyl.**

See *p*-Heptaphenyl.

Seselin

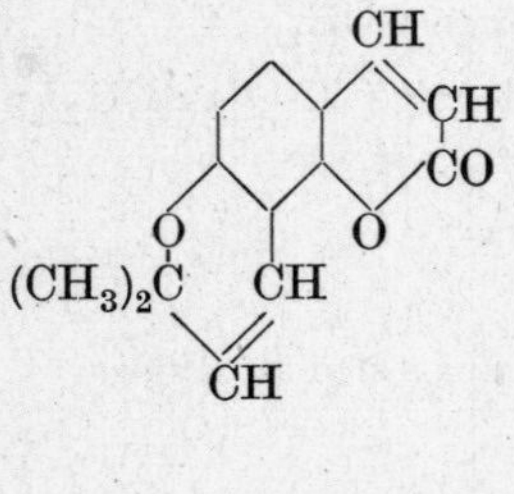

$C_{14}H_{12}O_3$ MW, 228

Constituent of fruit of *Selesi indicum* (Wall.) W. and A. Cryst. from MeOH–Et_2O. M.p. 119–20°. AcOH–H_2SO_4 ⟶ umbelliferone.

Bose, Guha, *Chem. Zentr.*, 1937, II, 238.
Späth, Bose, Matzke, Guha, *Ber.*, 1939, **72**, 821.
Späth, Hillel, *ibid.*, **963**, 2093.

Sesquigoyol

$C_{15}H_{26}O$ MW, 222

Sesquiterpene alcohol from oil of *Pinus formosama*, Hayata. M.p. 137–137·5°. B.p. 285–9°, 160–5°/8 mm. $[\alpha]_D^{33}$ + 93·4°.

Acetyl: b.p. 152–5°/4 mm. n_D^{32} 1·4902. $[\alpha]_D^{32}$ + 22·2°.

Yeigai, Sabe, *J. Chem. Soc. Japan*, 1935, **56**, 1118.

***p*-Sexiphenyl.**

See *p*-Hexaphenyl.

Shellolic Acid

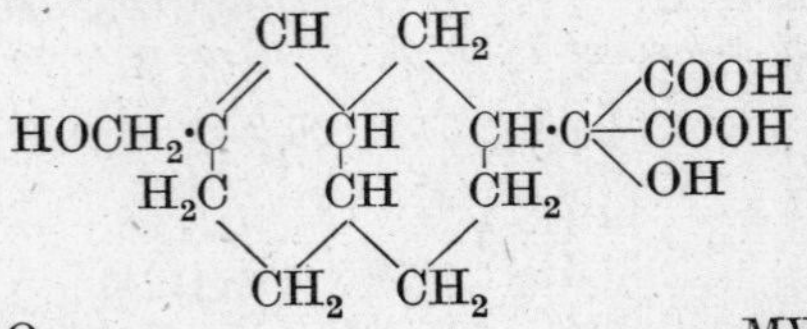

$C_{15}H_{20}O_6$ MW, 296

Isolated from shellac. Plates from H_2O. M.p. 206°. Sol. EtOH. Spar. sol. Et_2O, AcOEt, C_6H_6, $CHCl_3$. Insol. petrol.

Di-Me ester: $C_{17}H_{24}O_6$. MW, 224. Prisms from EtOH. M.p. 156°. $[\alpha]_D^{20}$ + 36°.

Di-hydrazide: prisms from H_2O. M.p. 246° decomp.

Di-phenylurethane: cryst. from CCl_4. M.p. about 92–4°.

Kirk, Spoerri, Gardner, *J. Am. Chem. Soc.*, 1941, **63**, 1243.
Nagel, Martens, *Ber.*, 1937, **70**, 2173.
Harries, Nagel, *Ber.*, 1922, **55**, 3833.

Shikimic Acid

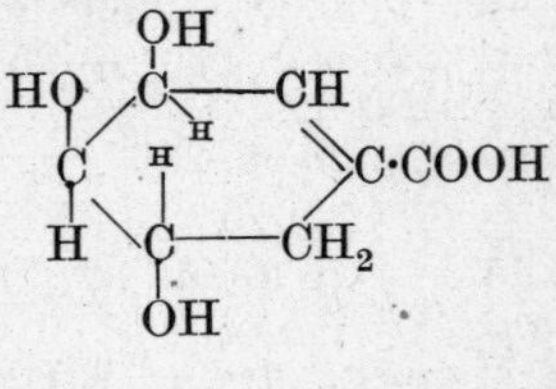

$C_7H_{10}O_5$ MW, 174

Constituent of fruits of *Illicium religiosum*, Siebold. Cryst. from H_2O. M.p. 178–80°. Insol. EtOH, Et_2O, $CHCl_3$.

A,CH_3NH_2: m.p. 163–4°.
A,$NH_2{\cdot}NH_2$: m.p. 147–8°.

A,$C_6H_5NH_2$: m.p. 194–5°.
A,Py : micro-plates. M.p. 184–5°.
A,Quinine : needles from EtOH. M.p. 221–2°.
A,Strychnine : plates. Sinters at 154°. M.p. 234–6°.
Me ester : needles from AcOH–petrol. M.p. 113–14°.
Triacetyl : b.p. 200–10°/1 mm.
Me_2CO comp. : cryst. from AcOH–petrol. M.p. 184°.

Fischer, Dangschat, *Naturwissenschaften*, 1938, **26**, 562; *Helv. Chim. Acta*, 1937, **20**, 705; 1935, **18**, 1206; 1934, **17**, 1200.

Siaresinolic Acid

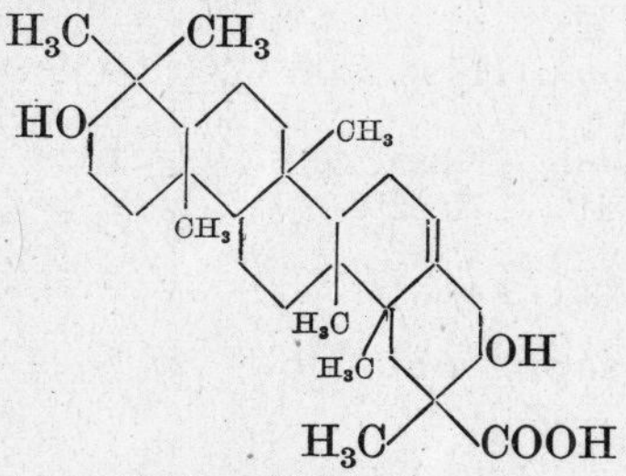

Suggested structure

$C_{30}H_{48}O_4$ MW, 472

Isolated from Siam benzoin (Siamese gum). Plates from MeOH–Et_2O. M.p. 274–5°. $[\alpha]_D^{24}$ + 98·5° in $CHCl_3$.

Me ester : prismatic plates from petrol. M.p. 180–1°. $[\alpha]_D^{24}$ + 48·4° in $CHCl_3$. *Acetyl* : needles from MeOH. M.p. 110–20°.

Et ester : needles or plates from petrol. M.p. 108°.

Bromolactone : m.p. 178–80°. $[\alpha]_D^{24}$ + 151·8° in $CHCl_3$.

Winterstein, Egli, *Z. physiol. Chem.*, 1931, **202**, 207.
Zinke, Lieb, *Monatsh.*, 1918, **39**, 95, 627.
Bilham, Kon, Ross, *J. Chem. Soc.*, 1942, 540.

Skimmin (7-*Hydroxycoumarin* d-*glucoside*, *umbelliferone* d-*glucoside*)

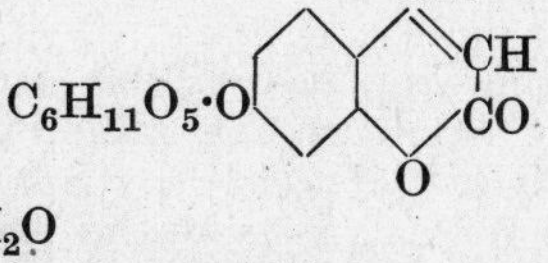

$C_{15}H_{16}O_8 \cdot H_2O$ MW, 342

Isolated from wood of *Skimmia Japonica*. M.p. 219–21°. $[\alpha]_D^{18}$ – 79·8° in Py. 4% H_2SO_4 ⟶ umbelliferone + glucose.

Tetra-acetyl : cryst. from MeOH. M.p. 183–4°. $[\alpha]_D^{16}$ – 63·3° in Py.

Späth, Neuefeld, *Rec. trav. chim.*, 1938, **57**, 535.

Solancarpidine.
See Solasodine.

Solanine-S.
See Solasonine.

Solasodine (*Solancarpidine*)

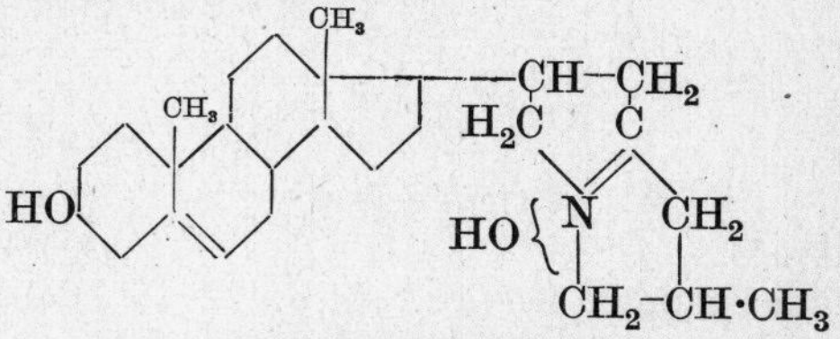

Suggested structure

$C_{27}H_{43}O_2N$ MW, 413

Occurs as glucoside in *Solanum xanthocarpum* and *S. aviculare*. M.p. 197–8°. $[\alpha]_D^{20}$ – 92·4° in C_6H_6. Gives usual sterol colour reactions.

Monoacetyl : plates from EtOH–AcOEt. M.p. 195°.

Monobenzoyl : m.p. 216–17°.

3 : 5-*Dinitrobenzoyl* : yellowish needles from EtOH. M.p. 191·5–193°.

Hydriodide : prisms from MeOH–Et_2O. M.p. 286° decomp.

Rochelmeyer, Chen, *Arch. Pharm.*, 1939, **277**, 329.
Briggs, *J. Chem. Soc.*, 1942, 3.

Solasonine (*Solanine-S*, *purapurine*)

$C_{45}H_{73}O_{16}N$ MW, 883

Glycoside isolated from *Solanum aviculare*. Sol. hot alcohols ⟶ gels on cooling. $[\alpha]_D$ about – 87° in EtOH. Hyd. ⟶ solasodine, glucose, galactose and rhamnose. Conc. H_2SO_4 finally ⟶ crimson col. with brown fluor.

Briggs, *Nature*, 1939, **144**, 247; *J. Chem. Soc.*, 1942, 3.
Levi, *J. Soc. Chem. Ind.*, 1930, **49**, 395T.

Sophoraflavanoloside

$C_{27}H_{30}O_{16}$ MW, 610

Glycoside from green fruits of *Sophora japonica*. Yellow needles. M.p. 207–8°. $[\alpha]_D^{20}$ –61° in EtOH. Hyd. ⟶ kæmpferol + sophorose, m.p. 195–6°. Emulsin ⟶ *d*-glucose.

Rabaté, Dussy, *Bull. soc. chim. biol.*, 1938, **20**, 459.

Sophoricoside (*Genistein* β-*glucoside*)

$C_{21}H_{20}O_{10}$ MW, 432

Isolated from green pods of *Sophora japonica*. Prisms from EtOH. M.p. 297°. $[\alpha]_D^{20} - 46{\cdot}7°$. Acid hyd. ⟶ genistein + glucose.

Hexa-acetyl: cryst. from AcOH or EtOH. M.p. 230°.

Charaux, Rabaté, *Bull. soc. chim. biol.*, 1938, **20**, 454; *J. pharm. chim.*, 1935, **21**, 546.

α-Sorigenin

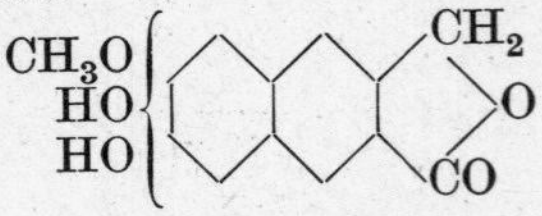

Proposed structure

$C_{13}H_{10}O_5$ MW, 246

Pale yellow needles. M.p. 227–9° decomp. Monobasic.

Di-Me ether: m.p. 183·5–184·5°.

Diacetyl: m.p. 255–9°.

Nikuni, *Chem. Abstracts*, 1940, **34**, 3259; 1939, **33**, 6301; 1938, **32**, 7469.

α-Sorinin

$C_{24}H_{28}O_{14}$ MW, 540

Isolated from bark of *Rhamnus japonica*, Max. Needles from MeOH.Aq. M.p. 159°. Boiling H_2O ⟶ α-sorigenin + primeverose.

Nikuni, *Chem. Abstracts*, 1939, **33**, 6301; 1938, **32**, 7469.

Soya-sapogenol A

$C_{30}H_{50}O_4$ MW, 474

Triterpene alcohol from soya bean saponin. Leaflets from MeOH. M.p. 308–12°. $[\alpha]_D^{21}$ + 102·3° in $CHCl_3$.

Tetra-acetyl: m.p. 232°. $[\alpha]_D^{15}$ + 86·1° in $CHCl_3$.

Tribenzoyl: m.p. 255°.

Tsuda, Kitewaga, *Ber.*, 1938, **71**, 790; 1937, **70**, 2083.

Miyasaka, *J. Pharm. Soc. Japan*, 1937, **57**, 464.

Soya-sapogenol B

$C_{30}H_{50}O_3$ MW, 458

Triterpene alcohol from soya bean saponin. Needles from MeOH. M.p. 258–9°. $[\alpha]_D^{30\cdot5}$ + 92·4° in $CHCl_3$.

Triformyl: prisms from Me_2CO–Et_2O. M.p. 218°.

Triacetyl: plates from MeOH. M.p. 175–6°. $[\alpha]_D^{16}$ + 83° in $CHCl_3$. *Dibromide*: needles from Me_2CO–MeOH. M.p. 225–7°.

Tribenzoyl: m.p. 133°.

Tri-p-*bromobenzoyl*: cryst. from Me_2CO. M.p. 255–7°.

Tsuda, Kitewaga, *Ber.*, 1938, **71**, 790; 1937, **70**, 2083.

Miyasaka, *J. Pharm. Soc. Japan*, 1937, **57**, 464.

Soya-sapogenol C

$C_{30}H_{50}O_2$ MW, 442

Triterpene alcohol from soya bean saponin. Needles from MeOH. M.p. 238–9°. $[\alpha]_D^{31}$ + 70·7° in $CHCl_3$.

Diformyl: prisms from Me_2CO–Et_2O. M.p. 265°.

Diacetyl: plates from MeOH–EtOH. M.p. 198°. *Dibromide*: needles from Me_2CO–Et_2O. M.p. 225–7°.

Dibenzoyl: cryst. from Me_2CO–MeOH. M.p. 188°.

Tsuda, Kitewaga, *Ber.*, 1938, **71**, 790; 1937, **70**, 2083.

Miyasaka, *J. Pharm. Soc. Japan*, 1937, **57**, 464.

Soya-sapogenol D

$C_{30}H_{50}O_3$ MW, 458

Triterpene alcohol from soya bean saponin. Prisms from Me_2CO–MeOH. M.p. 298–9°. $[\alpha]_D^{31}$ — 60·8° in $CHCl_3$.

Diformyl: needles from Me_2CO–Et_2O. M.p. 231°.

Diacetyl: prisms from MeOH. M.p. 192°.

Dibenzoyl: needles from Me_2CO. M.p. 240°.

Tsuda, Kitewaga, *Ber.*, 1938, **71**, 790; 1937, **70**, 2083.

Miyasaka, *J. Pharm. Soc. Japan*, 1937, **57**, 464.

Spartioidine

$C_{18}H_{23}O_5N$ MW, 333

Alkaloid from *Senecio spartioides*. Prisms from MeOH. M.p. 178°.

Methiodide: plates from $CHCl_3$. M.p. 239° decomp.

Manske, *Can. J. Research.*, 1939, **17**, 1.

Spathulatine

$C_{33}H_{64}O_5N_4$ MW, 596

Alkaloid from *Lupinus sericeus* and *L. spathulatus*. Cryst. from Me_2CO. M.p. 233–4° corr. Sol. H_2O, EtOH, C_6H_6, $CHCl_3$. Spar. sol. Et_2O, pet. ether. Sols. are slightly lævorotatory. Sensitive to strong min. acids.

B,3KI: prisms from H_2O. M.p. 260–1°.

Picrate: yellow needles. M.p. 182–4°.

Methiodide : cryst. M.p. 250–2°.

Couch, *J. Am. Chem. Soc.*, 1940, **62**, 554; 1924, **46**, 2507.

Spinulosin (3 : 6-*Dihydroxy-5-methoxytoluquinone*)

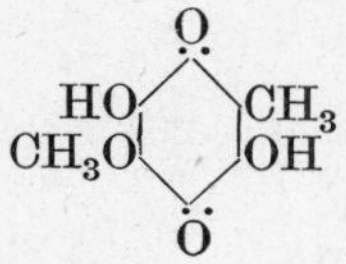

$C_8H_8O_5$ MW, 184

Metabolic product of *Penicillium spinulosum*, Tham. Sublimes at 120°/1 mm. in black metallic plates, m.p. 202–3°.

Di-Me ether : $C_{10}H_{12}O_5$. MW, 212. Reddish orange needles from EtOH. M.p. 80°.

Diacetyl : needles from EtOH. M.p. 139·5°.

Anslow, Raistrick, *Biochem. J.*, 1938, **32**, 803; *J. Chem. Soc.*, 1939, 1446.

Sphærophorin

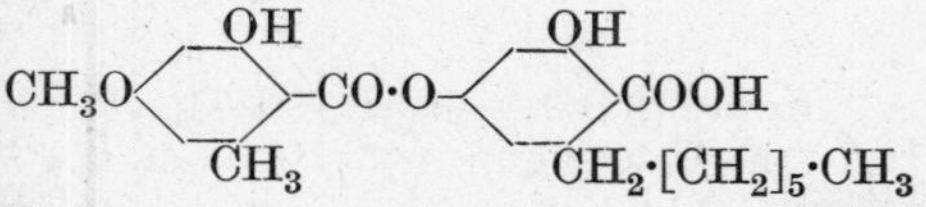

$C_{23}H_{27}O_7$ MW, 415

Depside from the lichen *Sphærophorus melanocarpus*. Plates or needles from C_6H_6. M.p. 140°. Alc. KOH ⟶ everninic acid + 5-heptylresorcinol, m.p. 57–8°.

Diacetyl : needles from 80% EtOH. M.p 133–4°.

Di-Me ether–Me ester : prisms from 80% EtOH. M.p. 85–6°.

Asahina, Hashimoto, *Ber.*, 1934, **67**, 416.

Stemonidine

$C_{19}H_{31}O_5N$ MW, 353

Alkaloid isolated from roots of *Stemona japonica*. M.p. 116°. $[\alpha]_D^{12}$ − 7·65°. Tertiary base.

B,HCl : decomp. at 260°.

Methiodide : decomp. at 248°.

Suzuki, *J. Pharm. Soc. Japan*, 1929, **49**, 457; 1939, **59**, 184.

Stilboestrol.

See Diethylstilboestrol.

See also 4 : 4′-Dihydroxystilbene, *and* Dodds, Goldberg, Lawson, Robinson, *Nature*, 1938, **141**, 247 : Dodds, Lawson, *Nature*, 1937, **139**, 627.

Styrylamine.

See Cinnamylamine.

6-Styryl-α : γ-lutidine.

See 4 : 6-Dimethyl-α-stilbazole.

Suberoxime.

See under Cycloheptanone.

Succinodiformic Acid.

See 1 : 4-Diketoadipic Acid.

Sulochrin

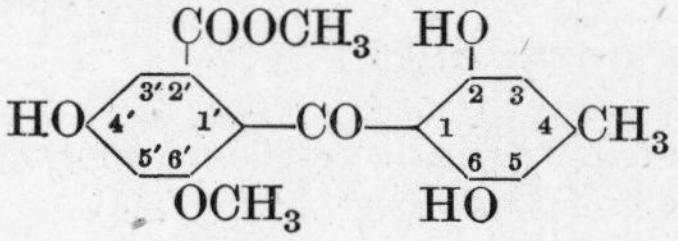

$C_{17}H_{16}O_7$ MW, 332

Mycelial constituent of *Oospora sulphureaochracea*. M.p. 262°.

2 : 4′-*Di-Me ether* : m.p. 158°.

Tri-Me ether : plates. M.p. 157°.

Triacetyl : m.p. 164°.

Nishikawa, *Acta Phytochim.*, 1939, **11**, 167; *Bulletin of the Agricultural Chemical Society Japan*, 1940, **16**, 97.

Sulphadiazine (*Sulphapyrimidine, sulphanilamidopyrimidine, N_1-2-pyrimidylsulphanilamide*)

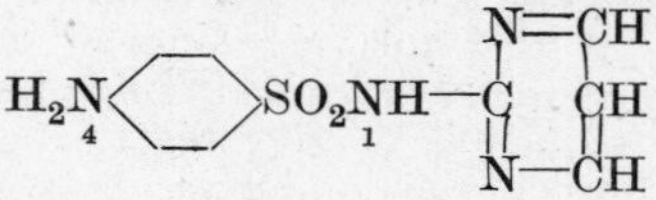

$C_{10}H_{10}O_2N_4S$ MW, 250

Cryst. from H_2O. M.p. 255–6° corr. decomp. Sol. H_2O to 12·3 mgm. per c.c. at 37°. Sol. acids and alkalis. Na deriv. sol. H_2O (sol. p_H 9·6). Used in medicine as bactericide of the sulphanilamide class.

N_4-*Acetyl* : m.p. 258–9° corr. Sol. H_2O to 15 mgm. per c.c. at 37°.

Roblin, Williams, Winnek, English, *J. Am. Chem. Soc.*, 1940, **62**, 2002.

Roblin, Winnek, English, *J. Am. Chem. Soc.*, 1942, **64**, 568.

Sulphaguanidine.

See Sulphanilylguanidine.

Sulphamethazine (2-*Sulphanilamido*-4 : 6-*dimethylpyrimidine*, N_1-2-[4 : 6-*dimethylpyrimidyl*]-*sulphanilamide, Sulphamezathine*)

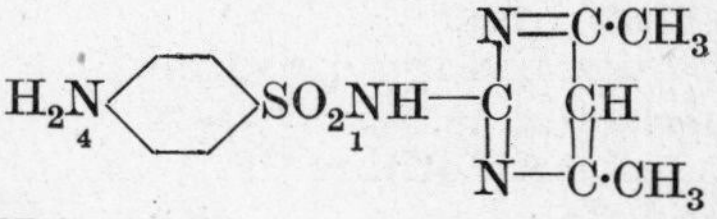

$C_{12}H_{14}O_2N_4S$ MW, 278

M.p. 198–9° corr. Sol. H_2O to 75 mgm. per c.c. at 37°. Sol. acids and alkalis. Used in medicine as bactericide of the sulphanilamide class.

N_4-*Acetyl*: m.p. 249–50° corr.

Roblin, Winnek, English, *J. Am. Chem. Soc.*, 1942, **64**, 568.
Caldwell, Kornfeld, Donnell, *J. Am. Chem. Soc.*, 1941, **63**, 2188.

Sulphamezathine.
See Sulphamethazine.

Sulphanilamide (p-*Aminobenzenesulphonamide*, *Prontosil album*)

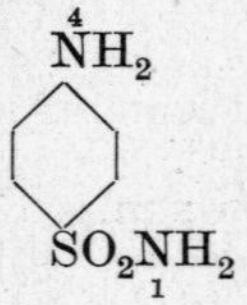

$C_6H_8O_2N_2S$ MW, 172

Leaflets from EtOH.Aq. M.p. 165–6° (163°). Sol. MeOH, EtOH, Et_2O, Me_2CO, dil. HCl, hot H_2O. Sol. 632 parts H_2O at 0°, 240 parts at 15°, 47·4 parts at 100°. Spar. sol. pet. ether, $CHCl_3$. Boil with water, acids or alkalis ⟶ sulphanilic acid. Can be diazotised. Extensively employed in medicine in the treatment of streptococcal infections, of meningococcal meningitis, etc., and in the treatment of open wounds to prevent gas gangrene.

N_1-*Acetyl*: prisms from H_2O. M.p. 182–4°.

N_4-*Acetyl*: needles from EtOH.Aq. M.p. 219°.

N_1 : N_4-*Diacetyl*: prisms from EtOH. M.p. 253·5–255°.

N_4-*Benzoyl*: cryst. from Py. M.p. 284°.

N_1 : N_4-*Dibenzoyl*: cryst. from EtOH. M.p. 268–70°.

Carranza, Márques, *Chem. Abstracts*, 1940, **34**, 5422.
Gelmo, *J. prakt. Chem.*, 1908, **77**, 372.
Northey, *Chem. Reviews*, 1940, **27**, 85 (*Bibl.*).
Dewing, Gray, Platt, Stephenson, *J. Chem. Soc.*, 1942, 239.

Sulphanilamidodimethylpyrimidine.
See Sulphamethazine.

Sulphanilamidopyridine.
See Sulphapyridine.

Sulphanilamidopyrimidine.
See Sulphadiazine.

Sulphanilamidothiazole.
See Sulphathiazole.

Sulphanilylguanidine (*Sulphaguanidine*)

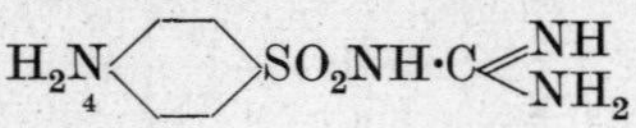

$C_7H_{10}O_2N_4S$ MW, 214

Cryst. + $1H_2O$ from H_2O. M.p. 142·5–143·5° (sealed tube). M.p. anhyd. 189–90°. Sol. to 10% in boiling H_2O, 5% in boiling 95% EtOH, 1·5% in boiling acetone. Spar. sol. cold H_2O, cold EtOH. Sol. dil. min. acids; insol. dil. aq. alkalis. Insol. Et_2O, C_6H_6. Used in medicine as bactericide particularly for bacillary dysentery.

Hydrochloride: m.p. 205–6°.

N_4-*Acetyl*: m.p. 262–6°.

Marshall *et al.*, Bulletin of the Johns Hopkins Hospital, 1940, **67**, 163, (*Chem. Abstracts*, 1940, **34**, 7405).
Dewing, Smith, *Nature*, 1941, **148**, 24.

Sulphapyridine (p-*Amino*-N-2-*pyridylbenzenesulphonamide*, 2-*sulphanilamidopyridine*, *M. & B.* 693, *Dagenan*, ω-N-2-*pyridylsulphanilamide*)

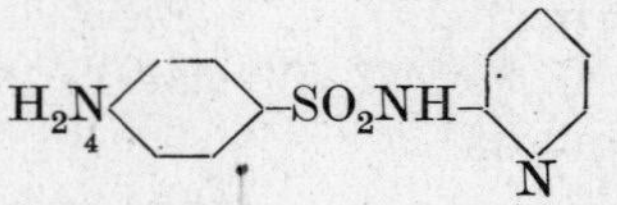

$C_{11}H_{11}O_2N_3S$ MW, 249

Cryst. from EtOH. M.p. 190–1° (191–2°). Sol. H_2O to 49·5 mgm. per 100 c.c. at 37°. Extensively employed in medicine in the treatment of bacterial infections, especially pneumonia.

N_4-*Acetyl*: needles from Me_2CO. M.p. 226–7° (225°).

Márques, *Chem. Abstracts*, 1940, **34**, 5422.
Winterbottom, *J. Am. Chem. Soc.*, 1940, **62**, 160.
Roblin, Winnek, *J. Am. Chem. Soc.*, *ibid.*, 1999.

Sulphapyrimidine.
See Sulphadiazine.

Sulphathiazole (2-*Sulphanilamidothiazole*)

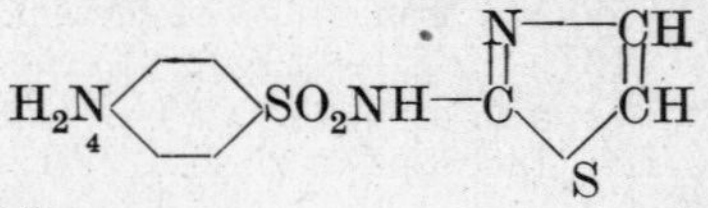

$C_9H_9O_2N_3S_2$ MW, 255

Cryst. powder from 45% EtOH. M.p. 202–202·5°. Sol. H_2O to 60 mgm. per 100 c.c. at 26° (p_H 6·03), 94 mgm. at 37°. Sol. EtOH to 525 mgm. per 100 c.c. at 26°. Used in medicine as a bactericide particularly in treatment of streptococcal and staphylococcal infections, pneumonia and gonorrhea.

Hydrochloride: m.p. 193–7°.

Na deriv.: m.p. 264·5–265°. p_H of 2% aq. sol. 9·57.

N_4-*Acetyl*: m.p. 256–7°.

Lott, Bergheim, *J. Am. Chem. Soc.*, 1939, **61**, 3592.
Fosbinder, Walter, *ibid.*, 2032.

Sulphido-α-alanine.
See Lanthionine.

Sumaresinolic Acid

$C_{31}H_{50}O_4$ MW, 486

Isolated from Sumatra benzoin. Needles from EtOH.Aq. M.p. 298–9°. $[\alpha]_D^{24}$ + 102·2° in $CHCl_3$.

Me ester: cryst. from MeOH.Aq. M.p. 220–1°. $[\alpha]_D^{24}$ + 53·6° in $CHCl_3$.

Et ester: needles from EtOH.Aq. M.p. 207–8°.

Bromolactone: needles. M.p. 252°. $[\alpha]_D^{24}$ + 60·2° in $CHCl_3$.

Winterstein, Egli, *Z. physiol. Chem.*, 1931, **202**, 207.
Zinke, Liebe, *Monatsh.*, 1918, **39**, 219.

Sympathol (1-[p-*Hydroxyphenyl*]-N-*methylaminoethyl alcohol*, *synephrine*, p-[α-*hydroxy*-β-*methylaminoethyl*]-*phenol*)

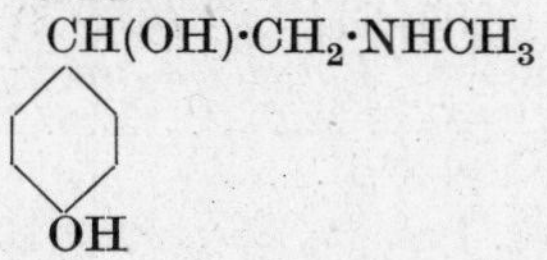

$C_9H_{13}O_2N$ MW, 167

M.p. 184–5° decomp. Spar. sol. org. solvents.

B,HCl: cryst. powder. M.p. 149·5–151°. $FeCl_3$ ⟶ violet col. Phosphotungstic acid ⟶ blue col. Vasoconstrictor. Substitute for epinephrine.

Dibenzoyl: m.p. 176°.

Priestley, Moness, *J. Org. Chem.*, 1940, **5**, 355.
Gordon, *Chem. Zentr.*, 1931, II, 3016.

Synephrine.
See Sympathol.

T

Tachysterol

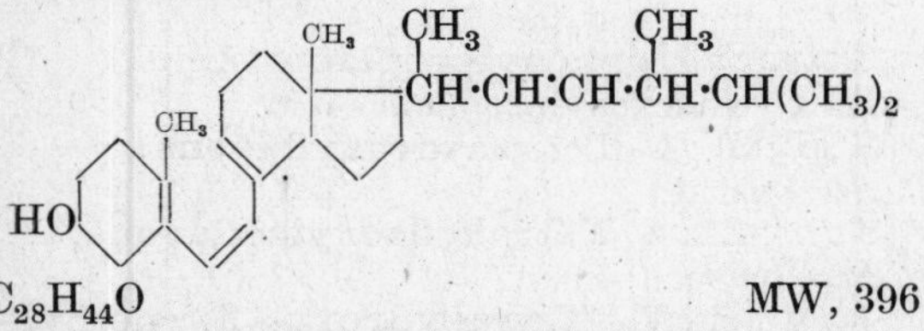

$C_{28}H_{44}O$ MW, 396

B.p. 220°/high vac. Sol. most org. solvents. $[\alpha]_D^{18}$ − 70° (− 11·5°) in C_6H_6. Absorption maximum at 2800 Å. with inflexions at 2940 and 2680 Å. Irradiation ⟶ calciferol (vitamin D_2).

3 : 5-*Dinitro*-p-*toluyl*: cryst. from Me_2CO–MeOH or Et_2O–MeOH. M.p. 154·5°. $[\alpha]_D^{16}$ + 40·4° in $CHCl_3$.

Citraconic anhydride adduct of acetyl: needles from AcOH.Aq. M.p. 161–2°. $[\alpha]_D^{20}$ + 75·2° in $CHCl_3$.

Windaus, Deppe, Wunderlich, *Ann.*, 1938, **533**, 118.
Windaus, Werder, Luttringhaus, Fernholz, *Ann.*, 1932, **499**, 188.
Lettré, *Ann.*, 1934, **511**, 280.
Grundmann, *Z. physiol. Chem.*, 1938, **252**, 151.

Taraxasterol

$C_{30}H_{50}O$ MW, 426

Triterpene alcohol from roots of *Taraxacum officinale* and flowers of *Anthemis nobilis*. Needles from EtOH. M.p. 221–2°. $[\alpha]_D^{17}$ + 95·9° in $CHCl_3$.

Acetyl: plates from AcOEt. M.p. 251–2°. $[\alpha]_D^{18}$ + 100·5° in $CHCl_3$.

Bromoacetyl: needles from AcOEt. M.p. 233–4°.

Benzoyl: needles from Me_2CO or C_6H_6–EtOH. M.p. 240–1°. $[\alpha]_D^{12}$ + 106·8° in $CHCl_3$.

p-*Nitrobenzoyl*: needles from $CHCl_3$–EtOH. M.p. 277–8°. $[\alpha]_D^{17}$ + 98·3° in $CHCl_3$.

Burrows, Simpson, *J. Chem. Soc.*, 1938, 2042.
Power, Browning, *J. Chem. Soc.*, 1912, **101**, 2411.

Taraxerol

$C_{30}H_{50}O$ MW, 426

Triterpene alcohol from rhizomes of *Taraxacum officinale*. Plates from $CHCl_3$–EtOH. M.p. 269–71°. $[\alpha]_D^{18}$ + 8·4° in $CHCl_3$.

Acetyl: needles from C_6H_6–EtOH. M.p. 296–7°. $[\alpha]_D^{18}$ + 8·4°.

Benzoyl: needles from $CHCl_3$–EtOH. M.p. 282–4°. $[\alpha]_D^{11}$ + 35·0° in $CHCl_3$.

Burrows, Simpson, *J. Chem. Soc.*, 1938, 2042.

Taraxol

$C_{30}H_{46}O_3$ MW, 454

Triterpene alcohol from rhizomes of *Taraxacum officinale*. Needles from C_6H_6–EtOH. M.p. above 360°. $[\alpha]_D^{14}$ + 78·6° in $CHCl_3$.

Monoacetyl: plates from C_6H_6. M.p. 299–301° decomp. $[\alpha]_D^{14}$ + 93·9° in $CHCl_3$.

Oxide: needles from MeOH.Aq. M.p. 261–261·5°. *Acetyl*: plates from C_6H_6. M.p. 294–7°.

Burrows, Simpson, *J. Chem. Soc.*, 1938, 2042.

Tectorigenin (5 : 7 : 4′-*Trihydroxy*-6-*methoxy-isoflavone*)

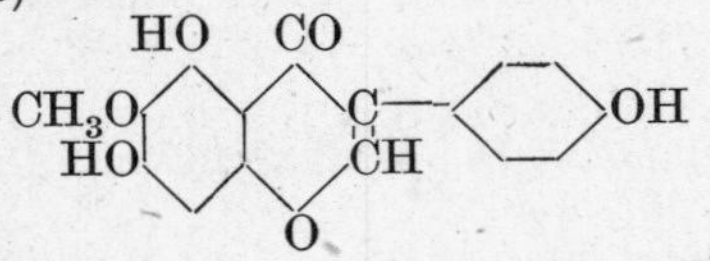

$C_{16}H_{12}O_6$ MW, 300

Occurs as glycoside, tectoridin, in the rhizomes of *Balameanda chinensis* and *Iris tectorum*, Maxim. Yellow plates from EtOH. M.p. 227° decomp.

Triacetyl: prisms. M.p. 187°.

Tribenzoyl: plates. M.p. 238°.

Di-Me ether: $C_{18}H_{16}O_6$. MW, 328. M.p. 188°. *Acetyl*: m.p. 213–14°.

Asahina, Shibata, Ogawa, *J. Pharm. Soc. Japan*, 1928, **48**, 1087.
Shibata, *Chem. Zentr.*, 1927, II, 839.

Tenulin

$C_{15}H_{18}O\begin{cases}—OH\\ =O\\ —OOC{\cdot}CH_3\end{cases}$

$C_{17}H_{22}O_5$ MW, 306

Constituent of *Helenium tenuifolium*, *H. elegans*, etc. Cryst. from H_2O. M.p. 193–5°. $[\alpha]_D^{20}$ − 21·7° in EtOH. Fish poison. Mild sternutatory action. H(+ Pt) ⟶ dihydrotenulin, m.p. 182°. Br ⟶ dibromotenulin, m.p. 124–5°. Alkalis ⟶ isotenulin, m.p. 162°.

Clark, *J. Am. Chem. Soc.*, 1940, **62**, 597; 1939, **61**, 1836.

Testosterone.
See Δ^4-Androstene-17-*cis*-ol-3-one *and* Δ^5-Androstene-17-*trans*-ol-3-one.

Tetradecanone-2.
See Methyl dodecyl Ketone.

4-Tetradecylenic Acid.
See Tsuzuic Acid.

Tetradecylhydroquinone (*Myristylquinol*, 2 : 5-*dihydroxytetradecylbenzene*)

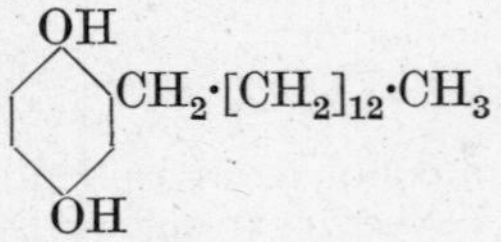

$C_{20}H_{34}O_2$ MW, 306

Cryst. from pet. ether. M.p. 110°. Ag_2O ⟶ tetradecylbenzoquinone, m.p. 77·5°.

Di-Me ether: 2 : 5-dimethoxytetradecylbenzene. B.p. 165°/0·5 mm.

Di-Et ether: 2 : 5-diethoxytetradecylbenzene. B.p. 183°/0·1 mm.

Cook, Heilbron, Lewis, *J. Chem. Soc.*, 1942, 660.

Tetrahydroanisole.
See under Cyclohexenol.

Tetrahydrocoptisine

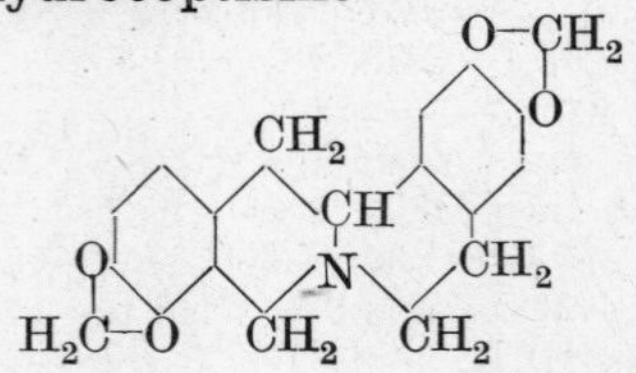

$C_{19}H_{17}O_4N$ MW, 323

l-. Corydalis-D.

Occurs in Chinese *Corydalis ambigua*. Prisms. M.p. 204°. $[\alpha]_D^{25}$ − 295°.

B,HCl: m.p. about 250°.

B,HBr: m.p. about 260°.

dl-. Corydalis-E.

From Chinese *Corydalis ambigua*. Needles from $CHCl_3$. M.p. 222–3°. B.p. 260°/0·01 mm.

B,HCl: m.p. 246°.

Späth, Posega, *Ber.*, 1929, **62**, 1032.
Huang-Minlon, *Ber.*, 1936, **69**, 1737.
Chou, *Chinese Journal of Physiology*, 1936, **10**, 507, (*Chem. Abstracts*, 1937, **31**, 1161).

Tetrahydrocuminic Acid.
See Phellandric Acid.

Tetrahydrodiphenyl.
See Phenylcyclohexene.

Tetrahydrogeraniol.
See 3 : 7-Dimethyloctanol-1.

Tetrahydrolinalool.
See 3 : 7-Dimethyloctanol-3.

Tetrahydrophenetole.
See under Cyclohexenol.

Tetrahydrophenylacetaldehyde.
See Cyclohexenylacetaldehyde.

Tetrahydrophenylacetone.
See Cyclohexenylacetone.

Tetrahydrophenylpropionic Acid.
See Cyclohexenylpropionic Acid.

3 : 7 : 3′ : 4′-Tetrahydroxyflavone.
See Fustin.

5 : 7 : 3′ : 4′-Tetrahydroxyisoflavone.
See Orobol.

1 : 4 : 5 : 7 - Tetrahydroxy - 2 - methyl - anthraquinone.
See Catenarin.

1 : 4 : 5 : 8 - Tetrahydroxy - 2 - methyl - anthraquinone.
See Cynodontin.

3 : 4 : 3′ : 5′ - Tetrahydroxystilbene 4 - methyl Ether.
See Rhapontigenin.

Tetramethyldiaminobenzaldehyde.
See under 2 : 4-Diaminobenzaldehyde.

Tetramethylphenol.
See Durenol *and* Prehnitenol.

Tetramethyltetraethylporphin.
See Aetioporphyrin.

Thiamin.
See Aneurin.

Thioamyl Alcohol.
See Amyl Mercaptan.

Thiocarbanilic Acid.
See Phenylthiocarbamic Acid.

Thiodiphenylamine.
S-*Dioxide* : *see* Diphenylamine sulphone.

Thiododecyl Alcohol.
See Dodecyl Mercaptan.

Thioethylene Glycol.
See Ethylene Thioglycol.

Thioglycol.
See Ethylene Thioglycol.

Thiophenetidine.
See under *p*-Aminothiophenol.

Thiotoluidine.
See Diaminoditolyl sulphide.

Toluylcatechol.
See Dihydroxymethylbenzophenone.

Toluylresorcinol.
See Dihydroxymethylbenzophenone.

3-*o*-Tolylbutyric Acid

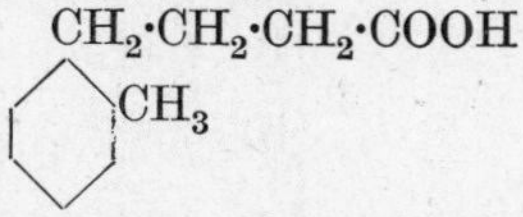

$C_{11}H_{14}O_2$ MW, 178

M.p. 70·5°.

Et ester : $C_{13}H_{18}O_2$. MW, 206. B.p. 140–50°/9 mm.

Wessely, Wang, *Ber.*, 1940, **73**, 19.

2-*p*-Tolylbutyric Acid.
See Curcumic Acid.

2 : 4-Tolylenediamine.
2-N-*Phenyl* : *see* 5-Amino-2-methyldiphenylamine.
4-N-*Phenyl* : *see* 3-Amino-4-methyldiphenylamine.

2 : 5-Tolylenediamine.
2-N-*Phenyl* : *see* 4-Amino-2-methyldiphenylamine.
5-N-*Phenyl* : *see* 4-Amino-3-methyldiphenylamine.

3 : 4-Tolylenediamine.
3-N-*Phenyl* : *see* 6-Amino-3-methyldiphenylamine.
4-N-*Phenyl* : *see* 2-Amino-4-methyldiphenylamine.

2-*p*-Tolylisobutyric Acid (α : 4-*Dimethylhydrocinnamic acid*)

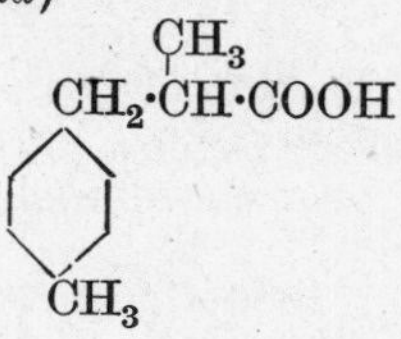

$C_{11}H_{14}O_2$ MW, 178

Plates from H_2O. M.p. 85°. B.p. 168–9°/9 mm.

Et ester : $C_{13}H_{18}O_2$. MW, 206. B.p. 130–2°/10 mm.

Amide : $C_{11}H_{15}ON$. MW, 177. Needles from H_2O. M.p. 130°.

Ruzicka, Ehmann, Delbes, *Helv. Chim. Acta*, 1932, **15**, 162.

***m*-Tolylisopropyl Alcohol.**
See Methyl-*m*-xylylcarbinol.

3-*o*-Tolylpropyl Alcohol (γ-*Hydroxy*-o-*propyltoluene*)

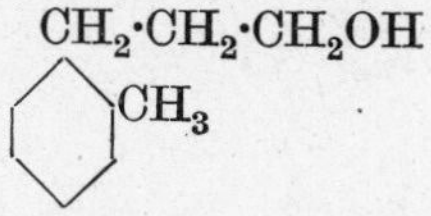

$C_{10}H_{14}O$ MW, 150

B.p. 136°/15 mm.

Phenylurethane : needles from pet. ether. M.p. 58°.

Harvey, Heilbron, Wilkinson, *J. Chem. Soc.*, 1930, 428.

3-*m*-Tolylpropyl Alcohol (γ-*Hydroxy*-m-*propyltoluene*).

B.p. 140°/14 mm. D_4^{20} 0·9609.

Acetyl : b.p. 136°/10 mm.

v. Braun, Grabowski, Kirschbaum, *Ber.*, 1913, **46**, 1274.

1-*p*-Tolylpropylene (1-*Methyl*-4-*propenylbenzene*, β : 4-*dimethylstyrene*)

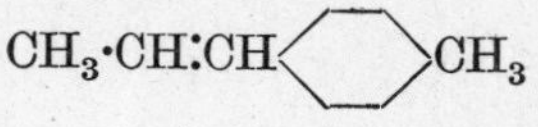

$C_{10}H_{12}$ MW, 132

B.p. 195–7°, 92–3°/20 mm., 83–5°/10 mm. D^{13} 0·9057.

Nitrosochloride : needles. M.p. 135°.

Klages, *Ber.*, 1902, **35**, 2254.

2-*o*-Tolylpropylene (1-*Methyl*-2-*isopropenylbenzene*, o-*isopropenyltoluene*, α : 2-*dimethylstyrene*)

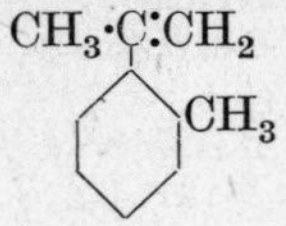

$C_{10}H_{12}$ MW, 132

B.p. 172–3°. D^0 0·9076. Oxidises in air.

Tiffeneau, *Ann. chim.*, 1907, **10**, 194.

2-*m*-Tolylpropylene (1-*Methyl*-3-*isopropenylbenzene*, m-*isopropenyltoluene*, α : 3-*dimethylstyrene*).

B.p. 185–6°. D^0 0·9115. Oxidises in air.

See previous reference.

2-*p*-Tolylpropylene (1-*Methyl*-4-*isopropenylbenzene*, p-*isopropenyltoluene*, α : 4-*dimethylstyrene*).

M.p. — 20°. B.p. 184–5°. D^0 0·9122. Oxidises in air. Slowly polymerises.

Nitrosochloride : cryst. from MeOH. M.p. 100–2°.

Tiffeneau, *Ann. chim.*, 1907, **10**, 194.
Perkin, Pickles, *J. Chem. Soc.*, 1905, **87**, 653.

Torulin.

See Aneurin.

Totarol

$C_{20}H_{30}O$ MW, 286

Diterpene alcohol occurring in *Podocarpus totara*. Tricylic and containing 3 ethylenic linkages. Needles from ligroin. M.p. 132°. $[\alpha]_D^{20}$ + 41·3° in EtOH. Heat with Se ⟶ 7-hydroxy-1-methylphenanthrene and 1-methylphenanthrene.

Formyl : hexagonal prisms from EtOH. M.p. 125·5°.

Acetyl : rectangular plates from EtOH. M.p. 121·5°. $[\alpha]_D^{18}$ + 44·6° in Et_2O.

Hydrogen phthaloyl : prisms from EtOH. M.p. 161–3°.

Me ether : cryst. from $CHCl_3$–EtOH. M.p. 92–92·5°. $[\alpha]_D^{18}$ + 41·95° in Et_2O.

Short, Stromberg, *J. Chem. Soc.*, 1937, 516.

T. P. N.

See Coenzyme II.

Trasentin (*Hydrochloride of* 2-*diethylaminoethyl diphenylacetate*)

$(C_6H_5)_2CH·COO·CH_2·CH_2N(C_2H_5)_2,HCl$

$C_{20}H_{26}O_2NCl$ MW, 347·5

Cryst. M.p. 113–14°. Sol. H_2O. Parasympathetic antispasmodic.

Ciba, Swiss Ps., 190,541, 192,070, 192,697, (*Chem. Abstracts*, 1938, **32**, 589, 4174, 4284).

Traumatic Acid (1-*Decylene*-1 : 10-*dicarboxylic acid*)

$HOOC·CH_2·[CH_2]_7·CH:CH·COOH$

$C_{12}H_{20}O_4$ MW, 228

Plant wound hormone isolated from string bean pods. Cryst. from EtOH or Me_2CO. M.p. 165–6°.

English, Benner, Haagen-Smit, *J. Am. Chem. Soc.*, 1939, **61**, 3434.

Triazine-tricarboxylic Acid (*Cyanuric tricarboxylic acid, paracyanoformic acid*)

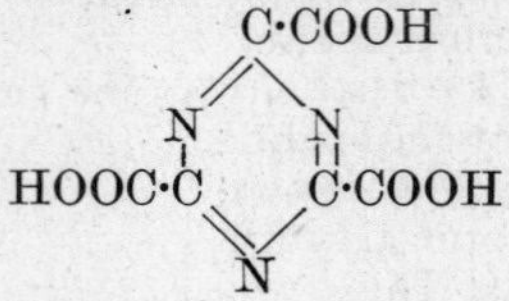

$C_6H_3O_6N_3$ MW, 213

Cryst. powder. M.p. above 250° decomp. Spar. sol. H_2O. Insol. EtOH, Et_2O. Boiling H_2O ⟶ NH_3 + oxalic acid.

Tri-Me ester : $C_9H_9O_6N_3$. MW, 252. Needles from EtOH. M.p. 154°.

Tri-Et ester : $C_{12}H_{15}O_6N_3$. MW, 297. Needles from EtOH. M.p. 165°.

Tri-isobutyl ester : needles from EtOH. M.p. 158°.

Tri-Me-amide : needles from EtOH or H_2O. M.p. above 250° with decomp.

Trinitrile : C_6N_6. MW, 156. M.p. 119° with sublimation. B.p. 262°.

Weddige, *J. prakt. Chem.*, 1874, **10**, 212.

α : β : 4-Tribromodiphenylethane.

See under p-Bromostilbene.

Tricetylamine.

See under Cetylamine.

1 : 1 : 1-Trichloro-*tert*.-butyl Alcohol.

See Chloretone.

ψ-Trichloro-γ-hydroxybutyrophenone.

See Chloralacetophenone.

5 : 5 : 5-Trichloro-4-hydroxy-2-ketopentane.

See Chloralacetophenone.

2 : 2′ : 2″-Trichlorotriethylamine.

See under 2-Chloroethylamine.

Tridecanol.

See Di-*n*-hexylcarbinol.

Tridecanone-7.

See Di-*n*-hexyl Ketone.

4-Tridecylene-1-carboxylic Acid.
See Tsuzuic Acid.

Triethylenetetramine (N:N′-*Di*-[2-*amino-ethyl*]-*ethylenediamine*, 1 : 2-*di*-[*aminoethylamino*]-*ethane*)

$NH_2CH_2 \cdot CH_2 \cdot NH \cdot CH_2 \cdot CH_2 \cdot NH \cdot CH_2 \cdot CH_2NH_2$

$C_6H_{18}N_4$ MW, 146

B.p. 174°/31 mm., 157°/20 mm.

B,4HCl : needles from EtOH–HCl. M.p. 266–70°.

Hydrogen oxalyl : needles from H_2O. Decomp. at 243° corr.

Tetrabenzoyl : micro-cryst. from $CHCl_3$–EtOH. M.p. 238°.

Tetrapicrate : prisms from H_2O. Decomp. at 240° corr.

Peacock, *J. Chem. Soc.*, 1936, 1518.
van Alphen, *Rec. trav. chim.*, 1936, **55**, 412.
Fargher, *J. Chem. Soc.*, 1920, **117**, 1351.

Triglycine.
See Diglycylglycine.

α : 3 : 4-Trihydroxyacetophenone.
See 3 : 4-Dihydroxyphenacyl Alcohol.

4 : 5 : 7 - Trihydroxyanthraquinone - 2 - carboxylic Acid.
See Emodic Acid.

Trihydroxybutyric Acid.
See Erythronic Acid *and* Threonic Acid.

7 : 3′ : 4′-Trihydroxyflavanol.
See Fustin.

1 : 6 : 8 - Trihydroxy - 3 - hydroxymethyl - anthraquinone.
Me ether : *see* Carviolin.

5 : 7 : 4′ - Trihydroxy - 6 - methoxyiso - flavone.
See Tectorigenin.

8 : 9 : 15-Trihydroxypalmitic Acid.
See Aleuritic Acid.

3 : 5 : 4′-Trihydroxystilbene.
See Resveratrol.

Triketohydrindene Hydrate.
See Ninhydrin.

Trillin (3-α-*Glucoside of diosgenin*)

$C_{33}H_{52}O_8$ MW, 576

Occurs in *Trillium erectum* as the diglucoside, trillarin, m.p. 197–200°. Cryst. + $\frac{1}{2}H_2O$ from MeOH. M.p. 275–80°. EtOH–HCl ⟶ diosgenin.

Tetra-acetyl : cryst. from MeOH. M.p. 197°.

Marker, Krueger, *J. Am. Chem. Soc.*, 1940, **62**, 2548, 3349.

2 : 4 : 6-Trimethoxyisobutyrophenone.
See Conglomerone.

Trimethylallantoin.
See Caffoline.

1 : 1 : 1-Trimethylbutane.
See 2 : 2-Dimethylpentane.

Trimethylbutylene.
See Dimethylpentene.

Trimethylcaffolide.
See under Caffolide.

4 : 5 : 5 - Trimethylcyclopentene - 1 - carboxylic Acid.
See Δ^5-Campholytic Acid.

Trimethylene chloroiodide.
See 3-Chloro-1-iodopropane.

Trimethylhydroquinone.
See ψ-Cumohydroquinone.

Trimethylresorcinol.
See Dihydroxy-ψ-cumene *and* Dihydroxyhemimellitene.

Trimethyltetrolic Acid.
See tert.-Butylpropiolic Acid.

Trinitrotrimethylenetriamine.
See Cyclonite.

Triphenylchloroethylene.
See Chlorotriphenylethylene.

Triphenylmethylamine.
See α-Aminotriphenylmethane.

α-Tritisterol

$C_{30}H_{50}O$ MW, 426

Occurs in unsaponifiable portion of wheat germ oil. Needles from Me_2CO–MeOH. M.p. 114–15°. $[\alpha]_D^{20}$ + 54·3° in EtOH.

Acetyl : leaflets from EtOH. M.p. 107–8°. $[\alpha]_D$ + 70·4° in $CHCl_3$.

3 : 5-*Dinitrobenzoyl* : cryst. from AcOEt. M.p. 182°.

β-*Naphthoyl* : needles. M.p. 158–9°.

Karrer, Salomon, *Helv. Chim. Acta*, 1937, **20**, 424.
Karrer, Salomon, Fritzsche, *ibid.*, 1422.
Todd, Bergel, Waldmann, Work, *Biochem. J.*, 1937, **31**, 2247.
Drummond, Hoover, *ibid.*, 1852.

β-Tritisterol

$C_{30}H_{50}O$ MW, 426

Occurs in unsaponifiable portion of wheat germ oil. Needles from MeOH. M.p. 97°. $[\alpha]_D^{20}$ + 49·2° in EtOH.

Acetyl : needles from MeOH–EtOH. $[\alpha]_D^{20}$ + 55·5° in $CHCl_3$.

Acetyl-dibromide : cryst. from Me_2CO. M.p. 160–2°.

See previous references.

Trypaflavine.
See Acriflavine.

Tryptamine (3-[ω-*Aminoethyl*]-*indole*, 2-[3-*indolyl*]-*ethylamine*)

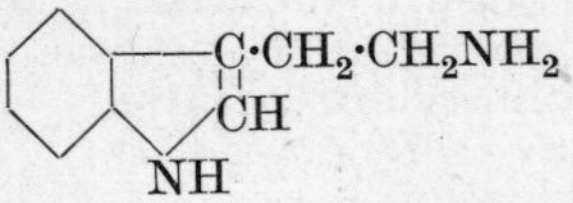

$C_{10}H_{12}N_2$ MW, 160

Needles from ligroin. M.p. 146° (115°). Sol. EtOH, Me_2CO. Prac. insol. H_2O, Et_2O, $CHCl_3$, C_6H_6.

B,HCl : prisms. M.p. 248–9°.

B_2,$CH_2(COOH)_2$: needles from AcOEt. M.p. 162° decomp.

B_2,$(CH_2{\cdot}COOH)_2$: m.p. 201°.

B_2,$(CH_2{\cdot}CH_2{\cdot}COOH)_2$: needles from AcOEt. M.p. 203° decomp.

N-*Thioformyl* : plates from $CHCl_3$–pet. ether. M.p. 82°.

N-*Acetyl* : cryst. from pet. ether. M.p. 77°.

N-*Benzoyl* : prisms. M.p. 137–8°.

N-*Me* : *see* 3-[ω-Methylaminoethyl]-indole.

Picrate : dark red prisms from Et_2O. M.p. 247° decomp.

Majima, Hoskins, *Ber.*, 1925, **58**, 2045.
Manske, *J. Am. Chem. Soc.*, 1929, **51**, 1202.
Späth, Lederer, *Ber.*, 1930, **63**, 123.

Tsuzuic Acid (4-*Tetradecenoic acid*, 4-*tetradecylenic acid*, 4-*tridecylene*-1-*carboxylic acid*)

$CH_3{\cdot}[CH_2]_7{\cdot}CH{:}CH{\cdot}[CH_2]_3{\cdot}COOH$

$C_{14}H_{26}O_2$ MW, 226

Occurs in tohaku oil (seed oil of *Lindera obtusiloba*) and in seed oil of "tsuzu" (*Tetradenia glauca*). M.p. 18–18·5°. B.p. 185–8°/13 mm. D_4^{20} 0·9024. n_D^{20} 1·4559.

Me ester : $C_{15}H_{28}O_2$. MW, 240. B.p. 158–60°/15 mm. D^{15} 0·8857. n_D^{15} 1·4489.

Et ester : $C_{16}H_{30}O_2$. MW, 254. B.p. 168–70°/15 mm. D^{15} 0·8783. n_D^{15} 1·4479.

p-*Bromophenacyl ester* : m.p. 61·3°.

p-*Phenylphenacyl ester* : m.p. 54·5°.

Toyama, *J. Soc. Chem. Ind. Japan*, 1937, **40**, 285.
Komori, Ueno, *Bull. Chem. Soc. Japan*, 1937, **12**, 433.
Tsujimoto, *Chem. Abstracts*, 1928, **22**, 4470.

U

Umbelliferone.

d-*Glucoside* : *see* Skimmin.

Umbelliprenin (*Umbelliferone farnesyl ether*)

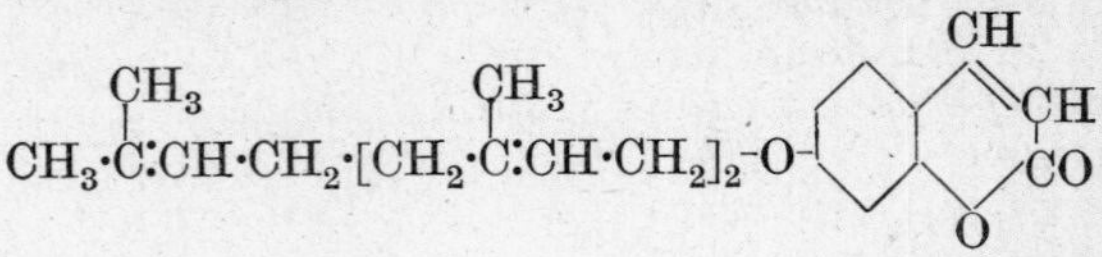

$C_{24}H_{30}O_3$ MW, 246

Occurs in angelica seed (*Angelica archangelica*). Cryst. from Et_2O–pet. ether. M.p. 61–3°. Cold AcOH–H_2SO_4 ⟶ umbelliferone.

Späth, Vierhapper, *Ber.*, 1938, **71**, 1667; *Monatsh.*, 1938, **72**, 179.

Umbellularic Acid (1-*Isopropylcyclopropane*-1: 2-*dicarboxylic acid*)

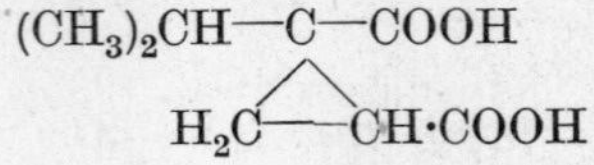

$C_8H_{12}O_4$ MW, 172

Cis-.

dl-.

Needles from C_6H_6–pet. ether. M.p. 126–7°. Also labile form, m.p. 117–18°.

p-*Phenylphenacyl ester* : needles from AcOH. M.p. 116–17°.

Anhydride : b.p. 140°/20 mm.

d-.

Needles + $1H_2O$ from H_2O, m.p. 78–9°. Prisms from C_6H_6–pet. ether, m.p. 119–20°. $[\alpha]_D^{16}$ + 86·9° in $CHCl_3$.

Acid brucine salt : plates from H_2O. M.p. 110–20°. $[\alpha]_{5461}^{20}$ + 6·2° in Me_2CO.

l-.

Needles + $1H_2O$ from H_2O, m.p. 78–9°. Prisms from C_6H_6–pet. ether, m.p. 119–20°. $[\alpha]_D^{13}$ − 88·8° in $CHCl_3$.

Acid brucine salt : needles from H_2O. $[\alpha]_{5461}^{16}$ − 29·5° in Me_2CO.

Trans-.

dl-.

Prisms from H_2O. M.p. 197°. Sol. Me_2CO, AcOEt. Spar. sol. C_6H_6, $CHCl_3$. Heat alone or with CH_3COCl or Ac_2O ⟶ *cis*-anhydride.

p-*Phenylphenacyl ester* : needles from AcOEt or Me_2CO. M.p. 175–6°.

Di-Et ester : b.p. 130–5°/20 mm.

d-.

Needles from H_2O. M.p. 155°. $[\alpha]_{5461}^{21}$ + 232·1° in Me_2CO.

Brucine salt : needles from H_2O. $[\alpha]_{5461}^{22}$ − 15·4° in $CHCl_3$.

l-.

Needles from H_2O. M.p. 153°. $[\alpha]_{5461}^{21}$ − 236·2° in Me_2CO.

Brucine salt: prisms from H_2O. M.p. 149–51° decomp. $[\alpha]_{5261}^{25}$ − 98·8° in $CHCl_3$.

Phillips, Ramage, Simonsen, *J. Chem. Soc.*, 1936, 828.
Rydon, *ibid.*, 829.
Guha, Muthanna, *Ber.*, 1938, **71**, 2668.

Undecanol-5.
See Butyl-*n*-hexylcarbinol.

Undecanol-6.
See Di-*n*-amylcarbinol.

Undecanone-5.
See Butyl *n*-hexyl Ketone.

5-Undecine.
See Butylamylacetylene.

4-Undecylene-1-carboxylic Acid.
See Linderic Acid.

***p*-Ureidophenetole.**
See Dulcin.

Uteroverdin.
See Biliverdin.

V

Vanguerigenin

$C_{30}H_{46}O_3$ MW, 454

Needles + ½EtOH from EtOH. M.p. 266°. $[\alpha]_D^{22}$ + 191·3° in $CHCl_3$. Heat at 300° ⟶ vanguerol, m.p. 207°.

Me ester: cryst. from EtOH. M.p. 195°.
Acetyl: prisms from EtOH. M.p. 248°.
Acetyl: needles + 1EtOH from EtOH. M.p. 295°.
Lactone: needles from EtOH.Aq. M.p. 281°.

Merz, Tschubel, *Ber.*, 1939, **72**, 1017.

Vanguerin

$C_{41}H_{64}O_{11}$ MW, 732

From *Vangueria tomentosa*. Powder. Sinters at 255–60°. M.p. about 275–80° decomp. Sol. hot EtOH, Py. $[\alpha]_D^{22}$ − 10·1° in dioxan. Ac_2O–H_2SO_4 ⟶ yellow ⟶ red ⟶ bluish violet ⟶ brown col. Hyd. ⟶ vanguerigenin + rhamnose + arabinose.

Penta-acetyl: powder. Decomp. at 184°.

Merz, Tschubel, *Ber.*, 1939, **72**, 1017.

***o*-Vanillic Acid.**
See under 2 : 3-Dihydroxybenzoic Acid.

***o*-Vanillin.**
See under 2 : 3-Dihydroxybenazaldehyde.

Veratramine

$C_{26}H_{35}O_2N$ MW, 393

Alkaloid of white hellebore (*Veratrum grandiflorum*, Loes). Monohydrate, m.p. 209·5–210·5°. $[\alpha]_D^{19}$ anhyd. − 70° in MeOH. H(+ Pt) ⟶ dihydroveratramine, m.p. 197–8°.

B,HCl: plates from EtOH. M.p. 201–2°.
Monoacetyl: prisms from EtOH.Aq. M.p. 201–2°.
Diacetyl: needles. M.p. 205·5–206°.
Picrate: yellow plates from EtOH.Aq. M.p. 217·5–218°.

Saito, *Bull. Chem. Soc. Japan*, 1940, **15**, 22.

***o*-Veratric Aldehyde.**
See under 2 : 3-Dihydroxybenzaldehyde.

2-Veratroylbenzoic Acid.
See under 3′ : 4′-Dihydroxybenzophenone-2-carboxylic Acid.

Veratroylcarbinol.
See under 3 : 4-Dihydroxyphenacyl Alcohol.

Veratroylformic Acid.
See under 3 : 4-Dihydroxybenzoylformic Acid.

Vetivazulene (4 : 8-*Dimethyl-2-isopropylazulene*)

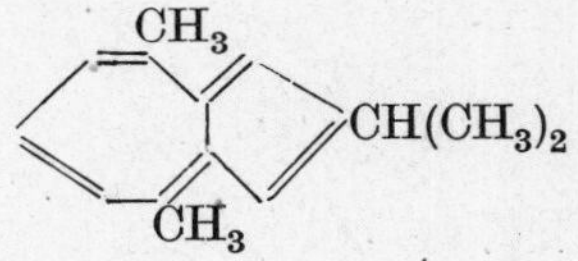

$C_{15}H_{18}$ MW, 198

B.p. 140–60°/2 mm.

Picrate: black needles from EtOH. M.p. 121·5–122°.
sym-Trinitrobenzene add. comp.: black needles with copper reflex from EtOH. M.p. 151·5–152°.
2 : 4 : 6-*Trinitrotoluene add. comp.*: copper coloured needles. M.p. 80·5–81°.

Pfau, Plattner, *Helv. Chim. Acta*, 1939, **22**, 202; 1936, **19**, 858.
Coates, Cook, *J. Chem. Soc.*, 1942, 559.

β-Vetivone

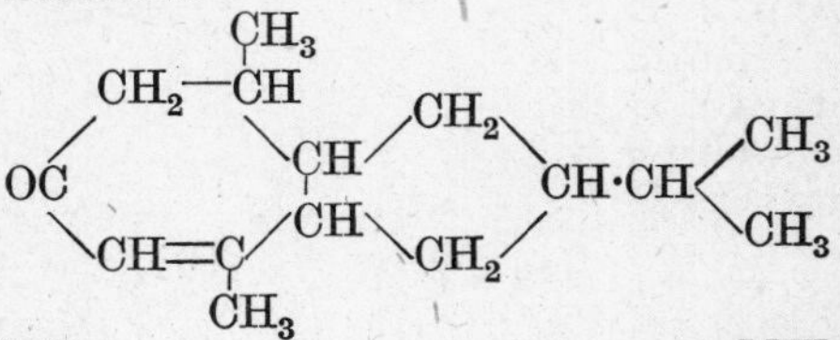

$C_{15}H_{22}O$ MW, 218

Isolated from vetiver oil. M.p. 44–44·5°. B.p. 141–2°/2 mm. D_4^{20} 1·0001. n_D^{20} 1·5309. $[\alpha]_D$ − 38·9° in EtOH.

Semicarbazone: leaflets from Py. M.p. 288–9°. $[\alpha]_D$ − 71·1° in AcOH.
2 : 4-*Dinitrophenylhydrazone*: m.p. 190·5–191°.

Naves, Perrotet, *Helv. Chim. Acta*, 1941, **24**, 3.
Pfau, Plattner, *Helv. Chim. Acta*, 1940, **23**, 768; 1939, **22**, 640.

Viburnitol (*Pentahydroxycyclohexane*)

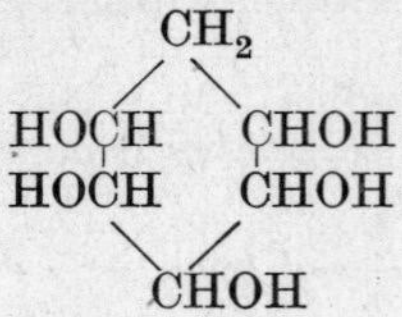

$C_6H_{12}O_5$ MW, 164

Isolated from *Viburnum tinus*, L. Needles + $1H_2O$ from H_2O. M.p. anhyd. 180–1° corr. Very sol. H_2O. Spar. sol. EtOH. $[\alpha]_D - 49{\cdot}5°$ in H_2O.

Penta-acetyl : needles. M.p. 125–6°.

Hérissey, Poirot, *J. pharm. chim.*, 1937, **26**, 385 (*Chem. Abstracts*, 1938, **32**, 7024).

Vinylethinylcarbinol

$H_2C{:}CH{\cdot}CH(OH){\cdot}C{:}CH$

C_5H_6O MW, 82

B.p. 128·5–129·5°, 83·5–84·5°/150 mm. n_D^{16} 1·4545.

Acetyl : b.p. 87–8°/100 mm. n_D^{23} 1·4319.

Phenylurethane : needles from pet. ether. M.p. 37°.

α-Naphthylurethane : needles from pet. ether. M.p. 127·5–128·5°.

Jones, McCombie, *J. Chem. Soc.*, 1942, 735.

Lespieau, Lombard, *Bull. Soc. chim.*, 1935, **2**, 369.

Vinylidene fluoride.
See Difluoroethylene.

Vinylxylene.
See Dimethylstyrene.

Vitamin B_1.
See Aneurin.

Vitamin B_6.
See Adermin.

Vitamin D_4

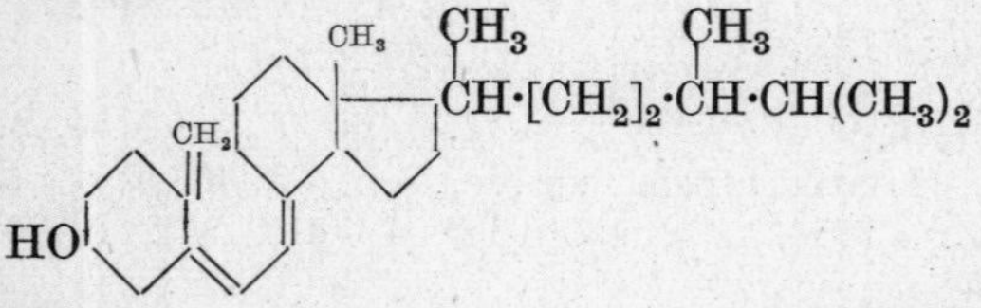

$C_{28}H_{46}O$ MW, 398

Plates from Me_2CO.Aq. M.p. 107–8°. $[\alpha]_D^{18}$ + 89·3° in Me_2CO. Shows absorption maximum at 2650 Å. Antirachitic activity about one-half that of calciferol on rat tests.

3 : 5-*Dinitrobenzoyl* : yellow needles. M.p. 135–6°. $[\alpha]_D^{18}$ + 94·5° in Me_2CO.

Windaus, Langer, *Ann.*, 1933, **508**, 105.

Windaus, Trautmann, *Z. physiol. Chem.*, 1937, **247**, 185.

Windaus, Güntzel, *Ann.*, 1939, **538**, 120.

Vitamin K_1 (2-*Methyl*-3-*phytyl*-1 : 4-*naphthoquinone*)

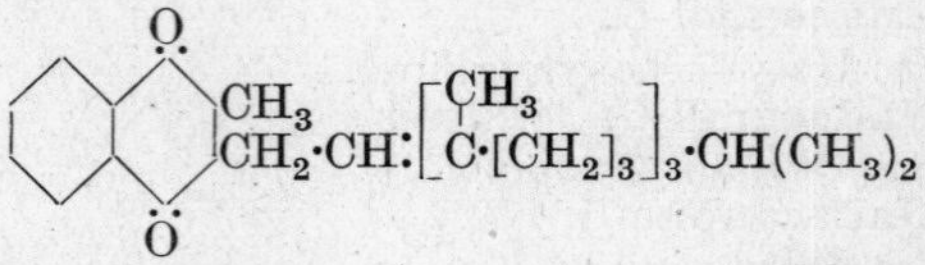

$C_{31}H_{46}O_2$ MW, 450

Fat soluble dietary factor essential for blood coagulation. Widely distributed in green leaves and vegetables, especially chestnut leaves and alfalfa. Lemon yellow oil which separates from Me_2CO or EtOH at − 70° in pale yellow rosettes, m.p. − 20°. Sol. EtOH, Me_2CO, hexane, C_6H_6, $CHCl_3$. Spar. sol. MeOH. Insol. H_2O. NaOEt ⟶ blue col. Absorption maxima at 2400, 2480 (main), 2610, 2700 and 3230 Å. Reductive acetylation ⟶ diacetyl-dihydro-comp., m.p. 62–3°. Reductive benzoylation ⟶ dibenzoyl-dihydro-comp., m.p. 85–6°. CrO_3 ⟶ phthalic acid + 2-methyl-1 : 4-naphthoquinone-3-acetic acid.

Doisy, Binkley, Thayer, *Chemical Reviews*, 1941, **28**, 477, (*Review and Bibl.*).

Fieser, *J. Am. Chem. Soc.*, 1939, **61**, 3467.

Vitamin K_2

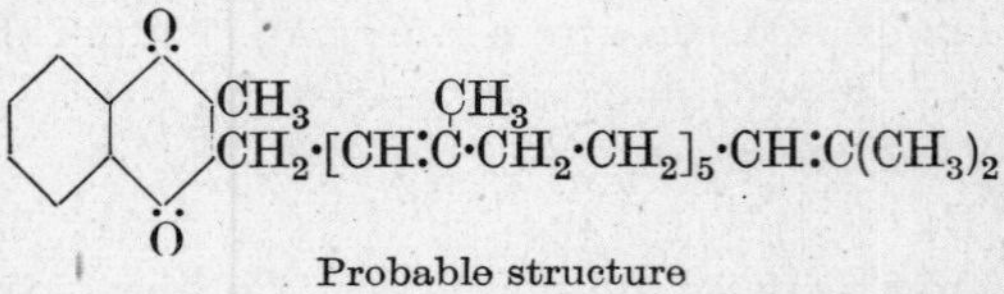

Probable structure

$C_{41}H_{56}O_2$ MW, 580

Fat soluble dietary factor effective in controlling blood coagulation. Widely distributed in green leaves and vegetables. Isolated most readily from chestnut leaves and putrefied fish meal. Yellow cryst. from Me_2CO–EtOH or MeOH–$CHCl_3$. M.p. 51–2°. Slightly less sol. in org. solvents than vitamin K_1. Absorption spectrum similar to that of K_1. Reductive acetylation ⟶ diacetyl-dihydro-comp., m.p. 59·5–60°.

Binkley, McKee, Thayer, Doisy, *J. Biol. Chem.*, 1940, **133**, 721.

Doisy, Binkley, Thayer, *Chemical Reviews*, 1941, **28**, 477 (*Review and Bibl.*).

Vitexin

$C_{15}H_{14}O_7$ MW, 306

Pigment from wood of *Vitex littoralis* or *Saponaria officinalis*. Yellow micro-plates from 40% Py. M.p. 263°.

Acetyl deriv.: colourless prismatic needles from AcOH. M.p. 257–8°.

Perkin, *J. Chem. Soc.*, 1898, **73**, 1019.
Barger, *J. Chem. Soc.*, 1906, **89**, 1210.
Péteri, *J. Chem. Soc.*, 1939, 1635.

Voluntal.
See under Carbamic Acid.

X

Xanthopterin

$$\begin{array}{c} NH-CO \\ HN{:}C \quad C-NH-CO \\ NH-C-N{=\!=\!=}CH \end{array}$$

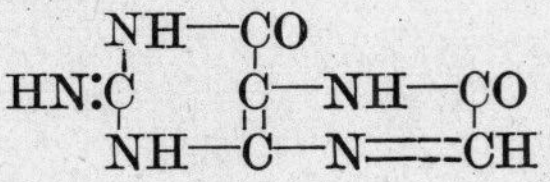

$C_6H_5O_2N_5$ MW, 179

Yellow wing pigment of butterflies, e.g. *Gonepteryx rhamni*, *Appias nero*, *Colias edusa*, etc. Amorph. hygroscopic mass. M.p. above 410° but carbonises above 360°. Prac. insol.

H_2O. Readily sol. dil. NH_4OH and $NaOH$ to yellow sols., and in $2N/HCl$ to colourless sol. $H_2O_2 \longrightarrow$ leucopterin.

Wieland, Purrmann, *Ann.*, 1940, **544**, 163.
Schöpf, Kottler, *Ann.*, 1939, **539**, 128.
Schöpf, Becker, *Ann.*, 1936, **524**, 55, 126; 1933, **507**, 266.
Purrmann, *Ann.*, 1941, **548**, 284.

Xeronic Acid.
See Diethylmaleic Acid.

Z

Zeorin
$C_{30}H_{52}O_2$ MW, 444

Triterpene from various lichens, e.g. *Anaptychia speciosa*, *A. hypoleuca*, *A. heterochroa*. Hexagonal pyramids from MeOH. M.p. 253°. $[\alpha]_D^{24} + 101\cdot4°$ in Py.

Acetyl deriv.: cryst. powder from AcOH.Aq. M.p. 178°.

Asahina, Yosioka, *Ber.*, 1940, **73**, 742.
Asahina, Akagi, *Ber.*, 1938, **71**, 980.

Printed in England for
Eyre and Spottiswoode (Publishers) Ltd.
15, *Bedford Street, Strand, London, W.C.2*